VOLUME 1

# Teacher's Edition

Prentice Hall

# Algebra 2

Randall I. Charles
Basia Hall
Dan Kennedy
Allan E. Bellman
Sadie Chavis Bragg
William G. Handlin
Stuart J. Murphy
Grant Wiggins

PEARSON

Boston, Massachusetts • Chandler, Arizona • Glenview, Illinois • Upper Saddle River, New Jersey

Acknowledgments appear on page T574, which constitutes an extension of this copyright page.

ISBN-13: 978-0-13-369705-6
ISBN-10: 0-13-369705-3
6 7 8 9 10  VOUD  19 18 17 16 15

# Algebra 2 *Teacher's Edition Contents*

## Teacher Handbook

Authors................................................................ T4
Reviewers.............................................................. T6
Contents in Brief...................................................... T7
Program Overview...................................................... T8
Achieve ADP Standards................................................. T24
Leveled Pacing Chart.................................................. T78
Big Ideas............................................................. T32
Student Edition Table of Contents..................................... T32
Entry-Level Assessment................................................ T42

### VOLUME 1

| | | |
|---|---|---|
| Chapter 1 | Expressions, Equations, and Inequalities.......................... | 1 |
| Chapter 2 | Functions, Equations, and Graphs................................. | 57 |
| Chapter 3 | Linear Systems................................................... | 131 |
| Chapter 4 | Quadratic Functions and Equations................................ | 191 |
| Chapter 5 | Polynomials and Polynomial Functions............................. | 277 |
| Chapter 6 | Radical Functions and Rational Exponents......................... | 357 |
| Chapter 7 | Exponential and Logarithmic Functions............................ | 431 |

### VOLUME 2

| | | |
|---|---|---|
| Chapter 8 | Rational Functions............................................... | 495 |
| Chapter 9 | Sequences and Series............................................. | 561 |
| Chapter 10 | Quadratic Relations and Conic Sections.......................... | 611 |
| Chapter 11 | Probability and Statistics...................................... | 671 |
| Chapter 12 | Matrices........................................................ | 753 |
| Chapter 13 | Periodic Functions and Trigonometry............................. | 817 |
| Chapter 14 | Trigonometric Identities and Equations.......................... | 893 |

**End-of-Course Assessment** ........................................ 956
**Skills Handbook** ................................................. T495
**Tables and Properties** ........................................... T509
**Visual Glossary** ................................................. T512
**Selected Answers** ................................................ T526
**Additional Answers** .............................................. T549
**Index** ........................................................... T554
**Acknowledgments** ................................................. T574

# Series *Authors*

**Randall I. Charles, Ph.D.,** is Professor Emeritus in the Department of Mathematics and Computer Science at San Jose State University, San Jose, California. He began his career as a high school mathematics teacher, and he was a mathematics supervisor for five years. Dr. Charles has been a member of several NCTM committees and is the former Vice President of the National Council of Supervisors of Mathematics. Much of his writing and research has been in the area of problem solving. He has authored more than 75 mathematics textbooks for kindergarten through college.

**Dan Kennedy, Ph.D.,** is a classroom teacher and the Lupton Distinguished Professor of Mathematics at the Baylor School in Chattanooga, Tennessee. A frequent speaker at professional meetings on the subject of mathematics education reform, Dr. Kennedy has conducted more than 50 workshops and institutes for high school teachers. He is coauthor of textbooks in calculus and precalculus, and from 1990 to 1994 he chaired the College Board's AP Calculus Development Committee. He is a 1992 Tandy Technology Scholar and a 1995 Presidential Award winner.

**Basia Hall** currently serves as Manager of Instructional Programs for the Houston Independent School District. With 33 years of teaching experience, Ms. Hall has served as a department chair, instructional supervisor, school improvement facilitator, and professional development trainer. She has developed curricula for Algebra 1, Geometry, and Algebra 2 and co-developed the Texas state mathematics standards. A 1992 Presidential Awardee, Ms. Hall is past president of the Texas Association of Supervisors of Mathematics and is a state representative for the National Council of Supervisors of Mathematics (NCSM).

# Consulting *Authors*

**Stuart J. Murphy** is a visual learning author and consultant. He is a champion of developing visual learning skills and using related strategies to help children become more successful students. He is the author of MathStart, a series of children's books that presents mathematical concepts in the context of stories. A graduate of the Rhode Island School of Design, he has worked extensively in educational publishing and has been on the authorship teams of a number of elementary and high school mathematics programs. He is a frequent presenter at meetings of the National Council of Teachers of Mathematics, the International Reading Association, and other professional organizations.

**Grant Wiggins, Ed.D.,** is the President of Authentic Education in Hopewell, New Jersey. He earned his Ed.D. from Harvard University and his B.A. from St. John's College in Annapolis. Dr. Wiggins consults with schools, districts, and state education departments on a variety of reform matters; organizes conferences and workshops; and develops print materials and Web resources on curricular change. He is perhaps best known for being the coauthor, with Jay McTighe, of *Understanding by Design* and *The Understanding by Design Handbook*, the award-winning and highly successful materials on curriculum published by ASCD. His work has been supported by the Pew Charitable Trusts, the Geraldine R. Dodge Foundation, and the National Science Foundation.

# **Program** *Authors*

## *Algebra 1 and Algebra 2*

**Allan E. Bellman, Ph.D.,** is a Lecturer/Supervisor in the School of Education at the University of California, Davis. Before coming to Davis, he was a mathematics teacher for 31 years in Montgomery County, Maryland. He has been an instructor for both the Woodrow Wilson National Fellowship Foundation and the $T^3$ program. He has been involved in the development of many products from Texas Instruments. Dr. Bellman has a particular expertise in the use of technology in education and speaks frequently on this topic. He was a 1992 Tandy Technology Scholar and has twice been listed in Who's Who Among America's Teachers.

**Sadie Chavis Bragg, Ed.D.,** is Senior Vice President of Academic Affairs at the Borough of Manhattan Community College of the City University of New York. A former professor of mathematics, she is a past president of the American Mathematical Association of Two-Year Colleges (AMATYC), co-director of the AMATYC project to revise the standards for introductory college mathematics before calculus, and an active member of the Benjamin Banneker Association. Dr. Bragg has coauthored more than 50 mathematics textbooks for kindergarten through college.

**William G. Handlin, Sr.,** is a classroom teacher and Department Chairman of Technology Applications at Spring Woods High School in Houston, Texas. Awarded Life Membership in the Texas Congress of Parents and Teachers for his contributions to the well-being of children, Mr. Handlin is also a frequent workshop and seminar leader in professional meetings throughout the world.

## *Geometry*

**Laurie E. Bass** is a classroom teacher at the 9–12 division of the Ethical Culture Fieldston School in Riverdale, New York. A classroom teacher for more than 30 years, Ms. Bass has a wide base of teaching experience, ranging from Grade 6 through Advanced Placement Calculus. She was the recipient of a 2000 Honorable Mention for the Radio Shack National Teacher Awards. She has been a contributing writer for a number of publications, including software-based activities for the Algebra 1 classroom. Among her areas of special interest are cooperative learning for high school students and geometry exploration on the computer. Ms. Bass is a frequent presenter at local, regional, and national conferences.

**Art Johnson, Ed.D.,** is a professor of mathematics education at Boston University. He is a mathematics educator with 32 years of public school teaching experience, a frequent speaker and workshop leader, and the recipient of a number of awards: the Tandy Prize for Teaching Excellence, the Presidential Award for Excellence in Mathematics Teaching, and New Hampshire Teacher of the Year. He was also profiled by the Disney Corporation in the American Teacher of the Year Program. Dr. Johnson has contributed 18 articles to NCTM journals and has authored over 50 books on various aspects of mathematics.

# Reviewers *National*

**Tammy Baumann**
K-12 Mathematics Coordinator
School District of the City
 of Erie
Erie, Pennsylvania

**Sandy Cowgill**
Mathematics Department Chair
Muncie Central High School
Muncie, Indiana

**Kari Egnot**
Mathematics Teacher
Newport News High School
Newport News, Virginia

**Sheryl Ezze**
Mathematics Chairperson
DeWitt High School
Lansing, Michigan

**Dennis Griebel**
Mathematics Coordinator
Cherry Creek School District
Aurora, Colorado

**Bill Harrington**
Secondary Mathematics
 Coordinator
State College School District
State College, Pennsylvania

**Michael Herzog**
Mathematics Teacher
Tucson Small School Project
Tucson, Arizona

**Camilla Horton**
Secondary Instruction Support
Memphis School District
Memphis, Tennessee

**Gary Kubina**
Mathematics Consultant
Mobile County School System
Mobile, Alabama

**Sharon Liston**
Mathematics Department Chair
Moore Public Schools
Oklahoma City, Oklahoma

**Ann Marie Palmeri Monahan**
Mathematics Supervisor
Bayonne Public Schools
Bayonne, New Jersey

**Indika Morris**
Mathematics Department Chair
Queen Creek School District
Queen Creek, Arizona

**Jennifer Petersen**
K-12 Mathematics Curriculum
 Facilitator
Springfield Public Schools
Springfield, Missouri

**Tammy Popp**
Mathematics Teacher
Mehlville School District
St. Louis, Missouri

**Mickey Porter**
Mathematics Teacher
Dayton Public Schools
Dayton, Ohio

**Steven Sachs**
Mathematics Department Chair
Lawrence North High School
Indianapolis, Indiana

**John Staley**
Secondary Mathematics
 Coordinator
Office of Mathematics, PK-12
Baltimore, Maryland

**Robert Thomas, Ph.D.**
Mathematics Teacher
Yuma Union High School
 District #70
Yuma, Arizona

**Linda Ussery**
Mathematics Consultant
Alabama Department of
 Education
Tuscumbia, Alabama

**Denise Vizzini**
Mathematics Teacher
Clarksburg High School
Montgomery County,
 Maryland

**Marcia White**
Mathematics Specialist
Academic Operations,
 Technology and Innovations
Memphis City Schools
Memphis, Tennessee

**Merrie Wolf**
Mathematics Department Chair
Tulsa Public Schools
Tulsa, Oklahoma

# Contents *in Brief*

Welcome to Pearson's *Prentice Hall Algebra 2* student book. Throughout this textbook, you will find content that has been developed to cover all of the American Diploma Project's (ADP) math benchmarks. The End-of-Course Assessment is modeled after the ADP Algebra 2 test and can serve as practice before taking the actual ADP test.

**Using Your Book for Success** . . . . . . . . . . . . . . . . . . . . . . . . . . . . . . . . . . . . . . . . . . viii

**Contents** . . . . . . . . . . . . . . . . . . . . . . . . . . . . . . . . . . . . . . . . . . . . . . . . . . . . . . . . . . xxii

**Entry-Level Assessment** . . . . . . . . . . . . . . . . . . . . . . . . . . . . . . . . . . . . . . . . . . . . . xxxvi

Chapter 1     Expressions, Equations, and Inequalities . . . . . . . . . . . . . . . . . . . . . . . 1

Chapter 2     Functions, Equations, and Graphs . . . . . . . . . . . . . . . . . . . . . . . . . . . . 57

Chapter 3     Linear Systems . . . . . . . . . . . . . . . . . . . . . . . . . . . . . . . . . . . . . . . . . . 131

Chapter 4     Quadratic Functions and Equations . . . . . . . . . . . . . . . . . . . . . . . . . . 191

Chapter 5     Polynomials and Polynomial Functions . . . . . . . . . . . . . . . . . . . . . . . 277

Chapter 6     Radical Functions and Rational Exponents . . . . . . . . . . . . . . . . . . . . 357

Chapter 7     Exponential and Logarithmic Functions . . . . . . . . . . . . . . . . . . . . . . 431

Chapter 8     Rational Functions . . . . . . . . . . . . . . . . . . . . . . . . . . . . . . . . . . . . . . 495

Chapter 9     Sequences and Series . . . . . . . . . . . . . . . . . . . . . . . . . . . . . . . . . . . . 561

Chapter 10    Quadratic Relations and Conic Sections . . . . . . . . . . . . . . . . . . . . . . 611

Chapter 11    Probability and Statistics . . . . . . . . . . . . . . . . . . . . . . . . . . . . . . . . . 671

Chapter 12    Matrices . . . . . . . . . . . . . . . . . . . . . . . . . . . . . . . . . . . . . . . . . . . . . . 753

Chapter 13    Periodic Functions and Trigonometry . . . . . . . . . . . . . . . . . . . . . . . 817

Chapter 14    Trigonometric Identities and Equations . . . . . . . . . . . . . . . . . . . . . . 893

**End-of-Course Assessment** . . . . . . . . . . . . . . . . . . . . . . . . . . . . . . . . . . . . . . . . . . . . 956

**Skills Handbook** . . . . . . . . . . . . . . . . . . . . . . . . . . . . . . . . . . . . . . . . . . . . . . . 964–976

Percents and Percent Application, 964; Operations With Fractions, 965; Ratios and Proportions, 966; Simplifying Expressions With Integers, 967; Area and Volume, 968; The Coordinate Plane, Slope, and Midpoint, 969; Operations With Exponents, 970; Factoring and Operations With Polynomials, 971; Scientific Notation and Significant Digits, 972; The Pythagorean Theorem and the Distance Formula, 973; Bar and Circle Graphs, 974; Descriptive Statistics and Histograms, 975; Operations With Rational Expressions, 976

**Reference** . . . . . . . . . . . . . . . . . . . . . . . . . . . . . . . . . . . . . . . . . . . . . . . . . . . . . 977–985

Measures, 977; Symbols, 978; Properties and Formulas, 979; Formulas From Geometry, 985

**Visual Glossary** . . . . . . . . . . . . . . . . . . . . . . . . . . . . . . . . . . . . . . . . . . . . . . . . . . . . . 986

**Selected Answers** . . . . . . . . . . . . . . . . . . . . . . . . . . . . . . . . . . . . . . . . . . . . . . . . . . 1039

**Index** . . . . . . . . . . . . . . . . . . . . . . . . . . . . . . . . . . . . . . . . . . . . . . . . . . . . . . . . . . . . 1122

**Acknowledgments** . . . . . . . . . . . . . . . . . . . . . . . . . . . . . . . . . . . . . . . . . . . . . . . . . . 1144

TEACH
ME

INSPIRE
ME

PREPARE
ME

**ENGAGE ME**

**HELP ME**

**ENCOURAGE ME**

# Change
## the way students see math.

*Prentice Hall Algebra 2* helps students see math like never before. This blended print and digital curriculum provides an environment where you can engage students, teach for understanding, and promote mastery—for success today and through life. It's a whole new way to look at math. See for yourself.

Algebra 1

Geometry

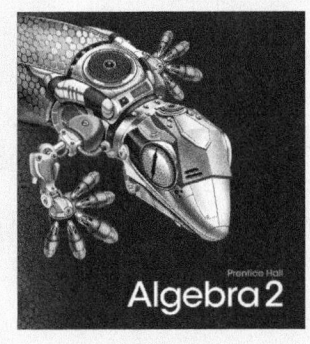
Algebra 2

# PowerAlgebra.com

Using the latest in digital instructional technology, PowerAlgebra.com provides a pedagogically relevant interface to support your math classroom. PowerAlgebra.com can be used as a stand-alone digital course or integrated with print materials to provide a balanced classroom environment for you and your students to engage in the study of math. This online learning environment is designed to enable you to easily access resources, plan lessons, incorporate presentation tools, assign student work and support student understanding.

Today's students—digital natives—approach their lives differently, seamlessly integrating technology throughout their daily activities.

PowerAlgebra.com is the gateway for students and teachers to all digital components for Algebra 2. This includes access to the complete Student Edition and Teacher's Edition, editable worksheets, presentation tools and a sophisticated classroom management system.

"Today's students are digital natives. These students are not merely technology-savvy; they are approaching their lives differently as they integrate digital technologies seamlessly throughout their daily activities. Let's not have them power-down when they get to math class."

—Laurie Bass

My Math Video

PEARSON

# video ▶ challenge

My Math Videos are student-produced videos that engage students in math concepts and are relevant to their lives. Through the Pearson Video Challenge, students can generate and submit their own videos to be included on PowerAlgebra.com.

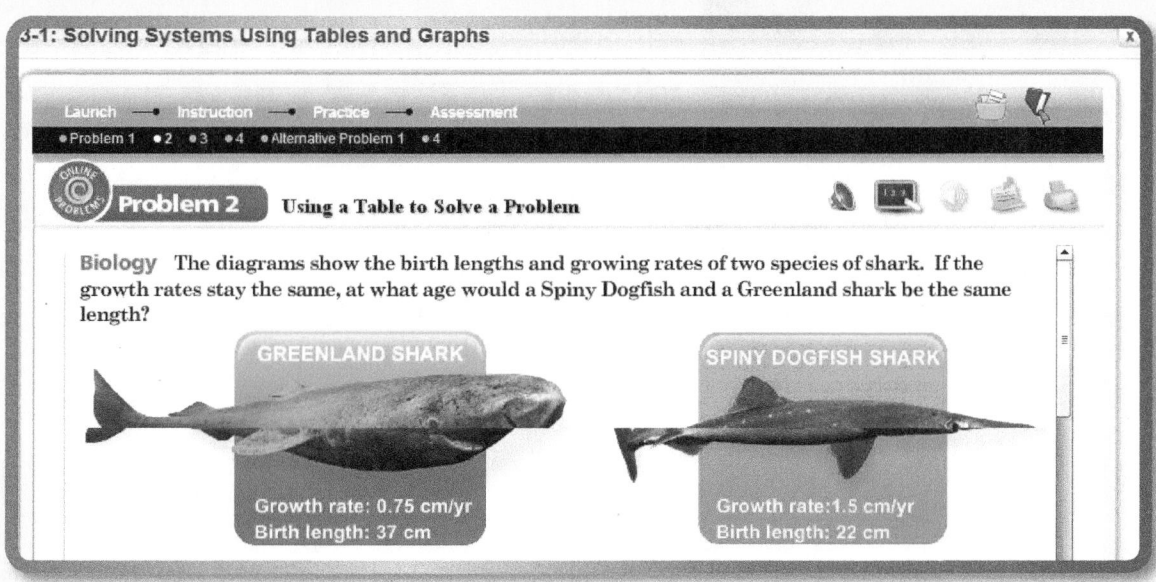

3-1: Solving Systems Using Tables and Graphs

Launch ⟶ Instruction ⟶ Practice ⟶ Assessment
● Problem 1   ● 2   ● 3   ● 4   ● Alternative Problem 1   ● 4

**Problem 2**  Using a Table to Solve a Problem

**Biology**  The diagrams show the birth lengths and growing rates of two species of shark. If the growth rates stay the same, at what age would a Spiny Dogfish and a Greenland shark be the same length?

GREENLAND SHARK

SPINY DOGFISH SHARK

Growth rate: 0.75 cm/yr
Birth length: 37 cm

Growth rate: 1.5 cm/yr
Birth length: 22 cm

The Portable Study Center provides access to and control over the learning process. Students can download audio, video and animations to support their own personal learning.

# Visual *Learning*

Visual learning is about acquiring and communicating information. By presenting concepts visually, and through different media, students can understand the importance of a mathematical idea and the context in which it is useful.

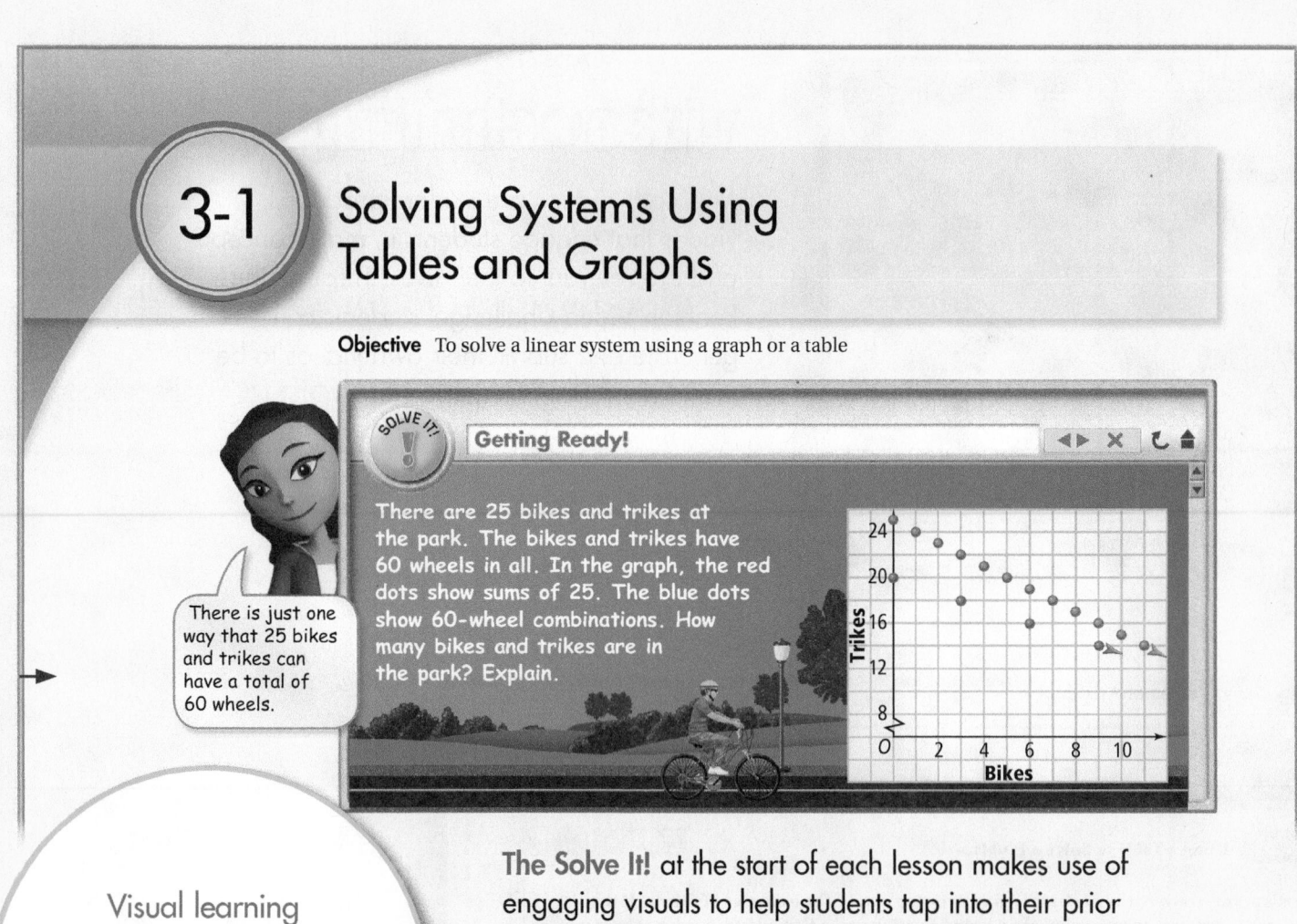

**3-1**

## Solving Systems Using Tables and Graphs

**Objective** To solve a linear system using a graph or a table

**Getting Ready!**

There are 25 bikes and trikes at the park. The bikes and trikes have 60 wheels in all. In the graph, the red dots show sums of 25. The blue dots show 60-wheel combinations. How many bikes and trikes are in the park? Explain.

There is just one way that 25 bikes and trikes can have a total of 60 wheels.

**The Solve It!** at the start of each lesson makes use of engaging visuals to help students tap into their prior knowledge and connect it to important concepts in the lesson.

Visual learning strategies increase the learning potential of all students.

"Through visual models, students interact with mathematical concepts, process information, observe change, reflect on their experiences, modify their thinking, and draw conclusions. They learn."

—Stuart Murphy

**Got It? 1.** What is the solution of the system of equations? $\begin{cases} x + 3y = 5 \\ -2x - 4y = -5 \end{cases}$

**Problem 2** Using Substitution to Solve a Problem

**Dynamic Activity**
Special Types of Solutions to Linear Systems

**Music** A music store offers piano lessons at a discount for customers buying new pianos. The costs for lessons and a one-time fee for materials (including music books, CDs, software, etc.) are shown in the advertisement. What is the cost of each lesson and the one-time fee for materials?

**Piano Lessons**

| Controls | Table |
|---|---|

$y = a \cdot b^x$

$y = 3^x$

a       1.00
b       3.00

☑ Show trace

| x | $3^x$ |
|---|---|
| 2 | 9 |

☑ Show y-value calculation
$y = a \cdot b^x$
$y = 1 \cdot 3^2$
$y = 1 \cdot 9$
$y = 9$

| Domain | -9.00 | 9.00 | Range | -9.00 | 9.00 |
|---|---|---|---|---|---|
| | Min | Max | | Min | Max |

Dynamic Activities at PowerAlgebra.com provide an interactive way for students to explore lesson concepts. Additionally, Math Tools enable students and teachers to utilize the functionality of tools such as a graphing calculator, algebra tiles, and geometry software.

# Big *Ideas*

Big Ideas are the organizing ideas for all of the lessons in the program. They appear in every lesson and throughout the chapters and courses. These Big Ideas help students focus on the key mathematical concepts they will be studying.

**BIG** ideas focus student learning.

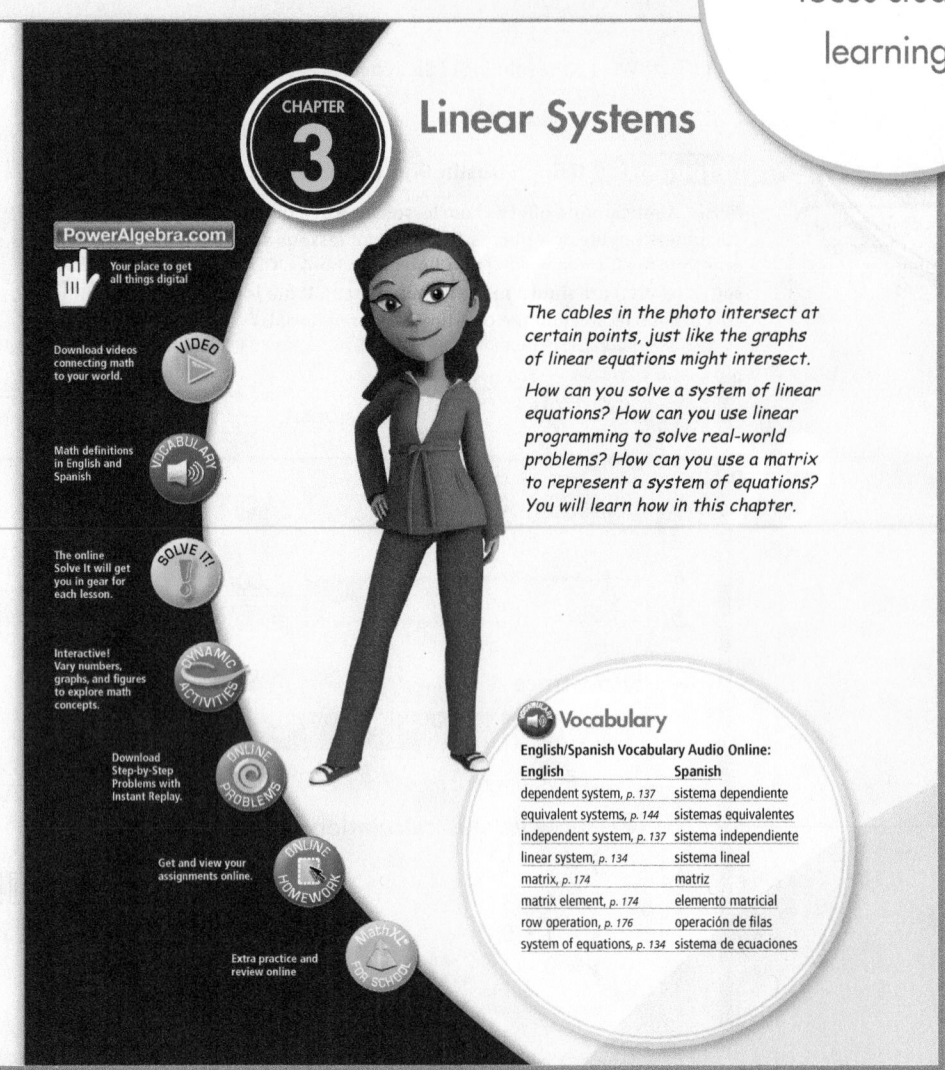

## Chapter 3 Overview

**UbD** Understanding by Design

Chapter 3 expands on students' understandings and skills related to functions, equations, and graphs. In this chapter, students will develop the answers to the Essential Questions posed on the opposite page as they learn the concepts and skills bulleted below.

**BIG** idea **Function**

**ESSENTIAL QUESTION** How does representing functions graphically help you solve a system of equations?
- Students will solve a system of linear equations by graphing the equations to find the point(s) of intersection.

**BIG** idea **Equivalence**

**ESSENTIAL QUESTION** How does writing equivalent equations help you solve a system of equations?
- Students will use substitution and elimination methods to write equivalent equations until they get an equation with only one variable.

**BIG** idea **Solving Equations and Inequalities**

**ESSENTIAL QUESTION** How are the properties of equality used in the matrix solution of a system of equations?
- Students will use the Addition Property of Equality to add rows of matrices and the Multiplication Property of Equality to multiply rows by a constant.
- Students will use row operations to get reduced row echelon form, which gives the solution.

**CHAPTER 3** **Linear Systems**

**PowerAlgebra.com**
Your place to get all things digital

Download videos connecting math to your world.

Math definitions in English and Spanish

The online Solve It will get you in gear for each lesson.

Interactive! Vary numbers, graphs, and figures to explore math concepts.

Download Step-by-Step Problems with Instant Replay.

Get and view your assignments online.

Extra practice and review online

*The cables in the photo intersect at certain points, just like the graphs of linear equations might intersect.*

*How can you solve a system of linear equations? How can you use linear programming to solve real-world problems? How can you use a matrix to represent a system of equations? You will learn how in this chapter.*

### Vocabulary

English/Spanish Vocabulary Audio Online:

| English | Spanish |
| --- | --- |
| dependent system, p. 137 | sistema dependiente |
| equivalent systems, p. 144 | sistemas equivalentes |
| independent system, p. 137 | sistema independiente |
| linear system, p. 134 | sistema lineal |
| matrix, p. 174 | matriz |
| matrix element, p. 174 | elemento matricial |
| row operation, p. 176 | operación de filas |
| system of equations, p. 134 | sistema de ecuaciones |

**Understanding by Design** uses backward design to create a comprehensive curriculum. By starting with the end results in mind, instruction can be planned more effectively.

**Essential Questions** help students think about the Big Ideas presented in the lesson.

"A Big Idea is a way of seeing better and working smarter, not just another piece of knowledge."

—*Grant Wiggins*

# 3 Chapter Review

## Connecting **BIG** ideas and Answering the Essential Questions

**1 Functions**
Find a point of intersection $(x, y)$ of the graphs of functions $f$ and $g$ and you have found a solution of the system $y = f(x)$, $y = g(x)$.

**Solving Systems Using Tables and Graphs** (Lesson 3-1)

$$\begin{cases} y = -2x + 3 \\ y = 2x - 1 \end{cases}$$

(1, 1)

The solution is (1, 1).

**Systems of Inequalities and Linear Programming** (Lessons 3-3 and 3-4)

$$\begin{cases} y > -2x + 3 \\ y \le 2x - 1 \end{cases}$$

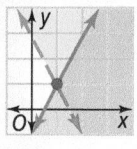

**2 Equivalence**
If the equations of two systems are equivalent, then a solution of the system that is easier to solve is also a solution of the more difficult system.

**Solving Systems Algebraically** (Lesson 3-2)

$$\begin{cases} -y = -x + 2 \\ 3y = 2x - 2 \end{cases} \rightarrow \begin{aligned} -2y &= -2x + 4 \\ 3y &= 2x - 2 \\ \hline y &= 2 \end{aligned}$$

$$3(2) = 2x - 2 \quad \rightarrow \quad x = 4$$

The solution is $x = 4$, $y = 2$.

**Systems With Three Variables** (Lesson 3-5)

$$\begin{cases} -2x + y + z = -3 \\ 2x - y + z = -1 \\ -2x, -y - z = -1 \end{cases}$$

$x = 1$, $y = 1$, $z = -2$

**3 Solving Equations and Inequalities**
The matrix row operations of adding rows and multiplying a row by a constant are equivalent to addition and multiplication properties of equality.

**Solving Systems Using Matrices** (Lesson 3-6)

$$\begin{bmatrix} -2 & 3 & | & 1 \\ 2 & -1 & | & 1 \end{bmatrix}$$
$$\begin{bmatrix} 1 & 0 & | & 1 \\ 0 & 1 & | & 1 \end{bmatrix} \rightarrow x = 1, y = 1$$

In the Chapter Review, students will find answers to the Essential Questions for the Big Ideas. The Chapter Review also provides a comprehensive set of notes for student reference.

# Problem *Solving*

Problem solving strategies are an integral part of the program and are embedded throughout each lesson. The worked-out problems model effective thinking and reasoning strategies and can help foster students' mathematical reasoning. These important skills can help students score well on the Algebra 2 End-of-Course exam.

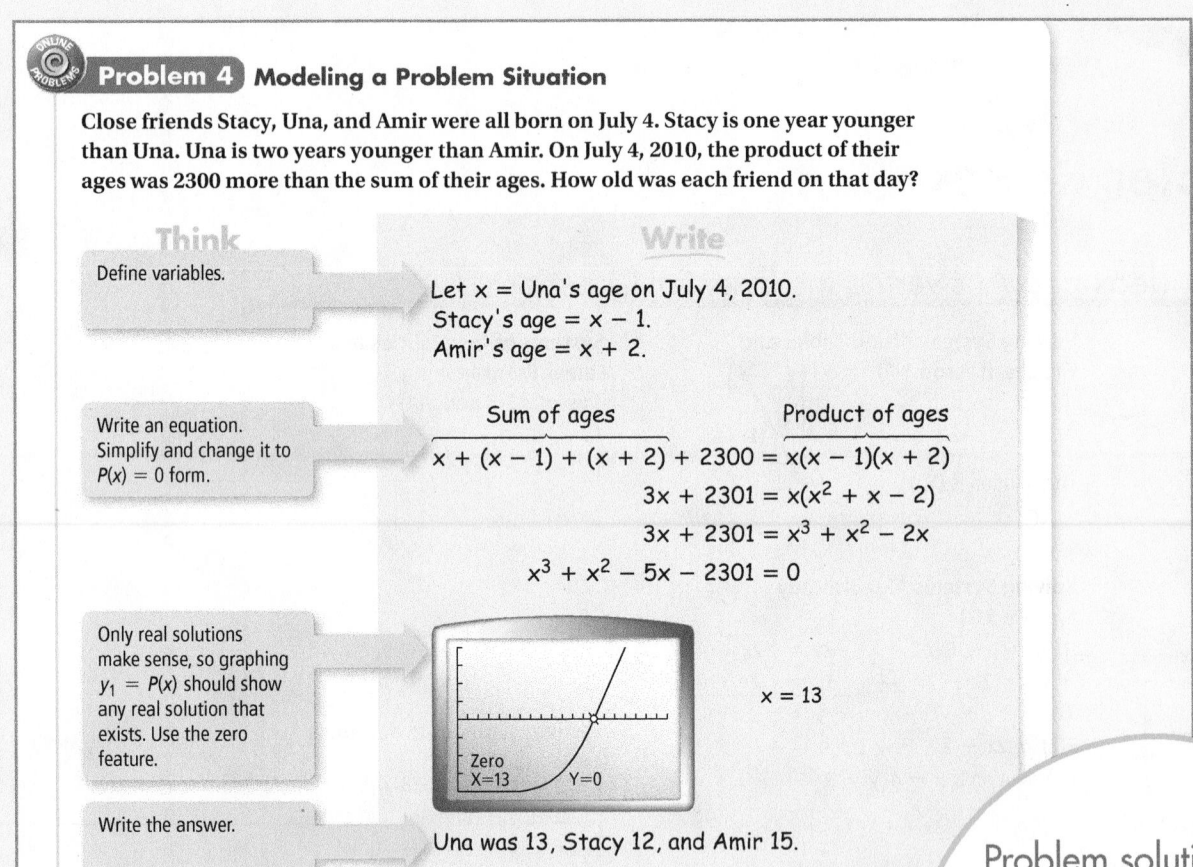

**Problem 4** **Modeling a Problem Situation**

Close friends Stacy, Una, and Amir were all born on July 4. Stacy is one year younger than Una. Una is two years younger than Amir. On July 4, 2010, the product of their ages was 2300 more than the sum of their ages. How old was each friend on that day?

**Think**

**Write**

Define variables.

Let x = Una's age on July 4, 2010.
Stacy's age = x − 1.
Amir's age = x + 2.

Write an equation.
Simplify and change it to
P(x) = 0 form.

Sum of ages      Product of ages

$x + (x - 1) + (x + 2) + 2300 = x(x - 1)(x + 2)$

$3x + 2301 = x(x^2 + x - 2)$

$3x + 2301 = x^3 + x^2 - 2x$

$x^3 + x^2 - 5x - 2301 = 0$

Only real solutions
make sense, so graphing
$y_1 = P(x)$ should show
any real solution that
exists. Use the zero
feature.

Zero
X=13     Y=0

x = 13

Write the answer.

Una was 13, Stacy 12, and Amir 15.

**Think-Write Boxes** guide students' thinking and reasoning by modeling the problem solving process. Students gain a deeper understanding of the problem and learn how to arrive at the solution.

Problem solutions are stepped out to help students develop mathematical thinking and reasoning skills.

"Research shows that understanding develops during the process of solving problems in which important math concepts and skills are embedded."

—*Randy Charles*

**3-1: Solving Systems Using Tables and Graphs**

Launch → Instruction → Practice → Assessment

● Problem 1   ● 2   ● 3   ● 4   ● Alternative Problem 1   ● 4

**Problem 3**   Using Linear Regression

will the populations of these regions be equal? What will that population be?

Populations of New York City and Los Angeles (1950–2000)

|  | 1950 | 1960 | 1970 | 1980 | 1990 | 2000 |
|---|---|---|---|---|---|---|
| **New York City** | 12,911,994 | 14,759,429 | 16,178,700 | 16,121,297 | 18,087,251 | 21,199,865 |
| **Los Angeles** | 4,367,911 | 6,742,696 | 7,032,075 | 11,497,568 | 14,531,529 | 16,373,645 |

Source: US Census Bureau

**Know**
Population data for two cities

**Need**
The point in time when their populations will

**Plan**
• Use a calculator to find linear regression models.
• Find the point of intersection.

Enter all the numbers as millions, rounded to the nearest hundred thousand.

**Step 1**   Enter the data into lists on your

| L1 | L2 | L3 | 1 |

◀ 2 of 4 ▶

**Online Problems** at PowerAlgebra.com provide students with step-by-step instruction at their own pace—and include guided support from an avatar. These problems can be used for in-class presentation or assigned to students on their own.

# Differentiated *Instruction*

Differentiating instruction helps all students develop conceptual understanding, fosters mathematical reasoning, and refines problem solving strategies. The program offers options for differentiating instruction at the start of each chapter and throughout the lessons.

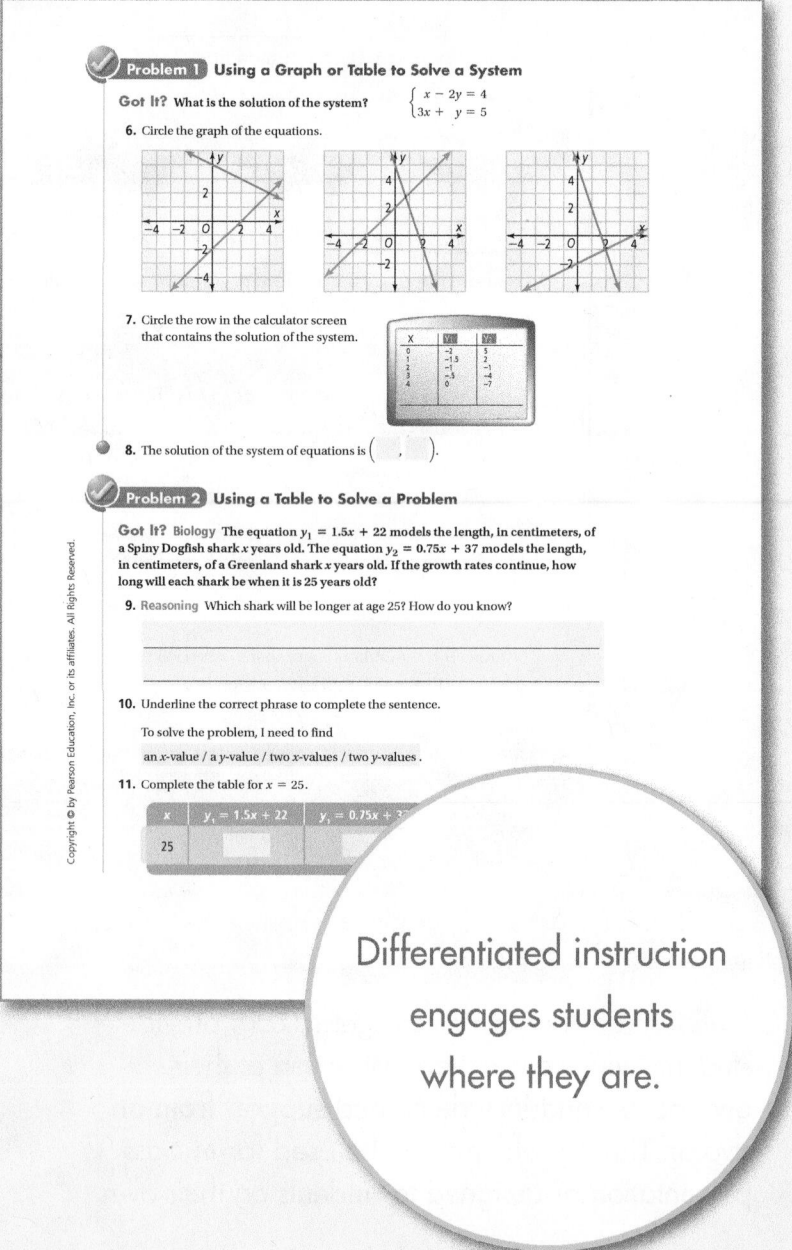

**The Student Companion,** a student worktext, has graphic organizers and other tools, such as Vocabulary Builder and Think-Write Boxes, that allow for differentiated instruction.

Differentiated instruction engages students where they are.

> "Differentiated instruction does not change what is taught; it changes how it is taught."
>
> —*Basia Hall*

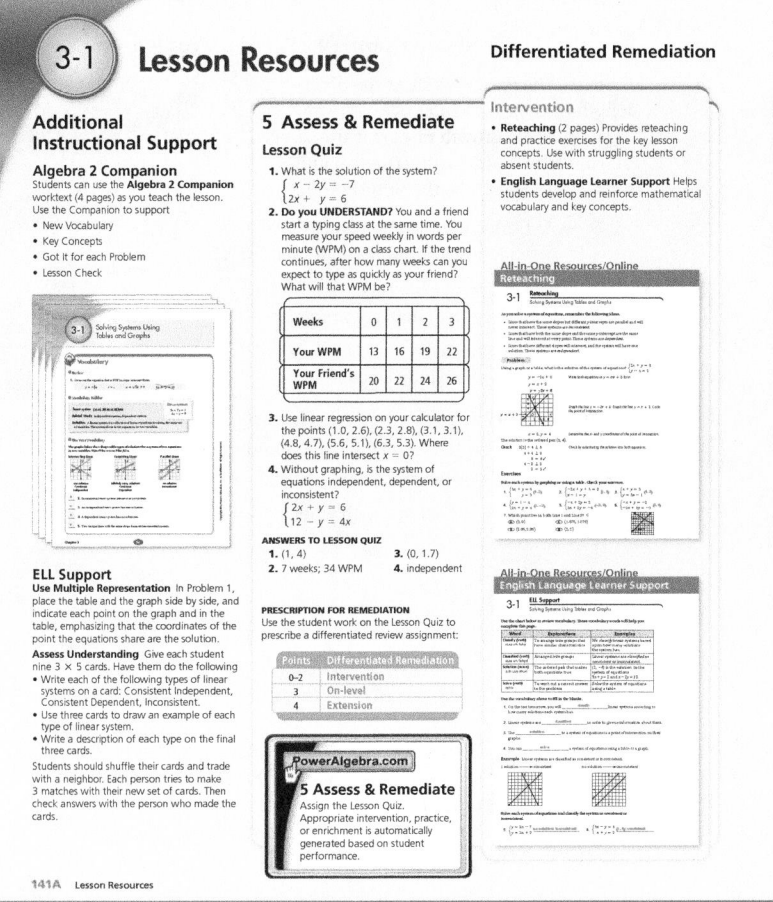

**Math Background** provides ongoing professional development in key content for each chapter and lesson, enabling teachers to adapt and respond to the needs of each individual learner.

**Lesson Resources** provide a detailed blueprint for instruction, assessment, and remediation that includes prescriptions for all levels of students from intervention to extension.

# Assessment

Effective and useful assessments are frequent and varied. The program includes formative assessment, such as Got It?, that allows teachers to evaluate students' understanding of concepts and informs instruction. The summative assessments at the end of each lesson and chapter are more structured and give students valuable practice for the Algebra 2 End-of-Course exam.

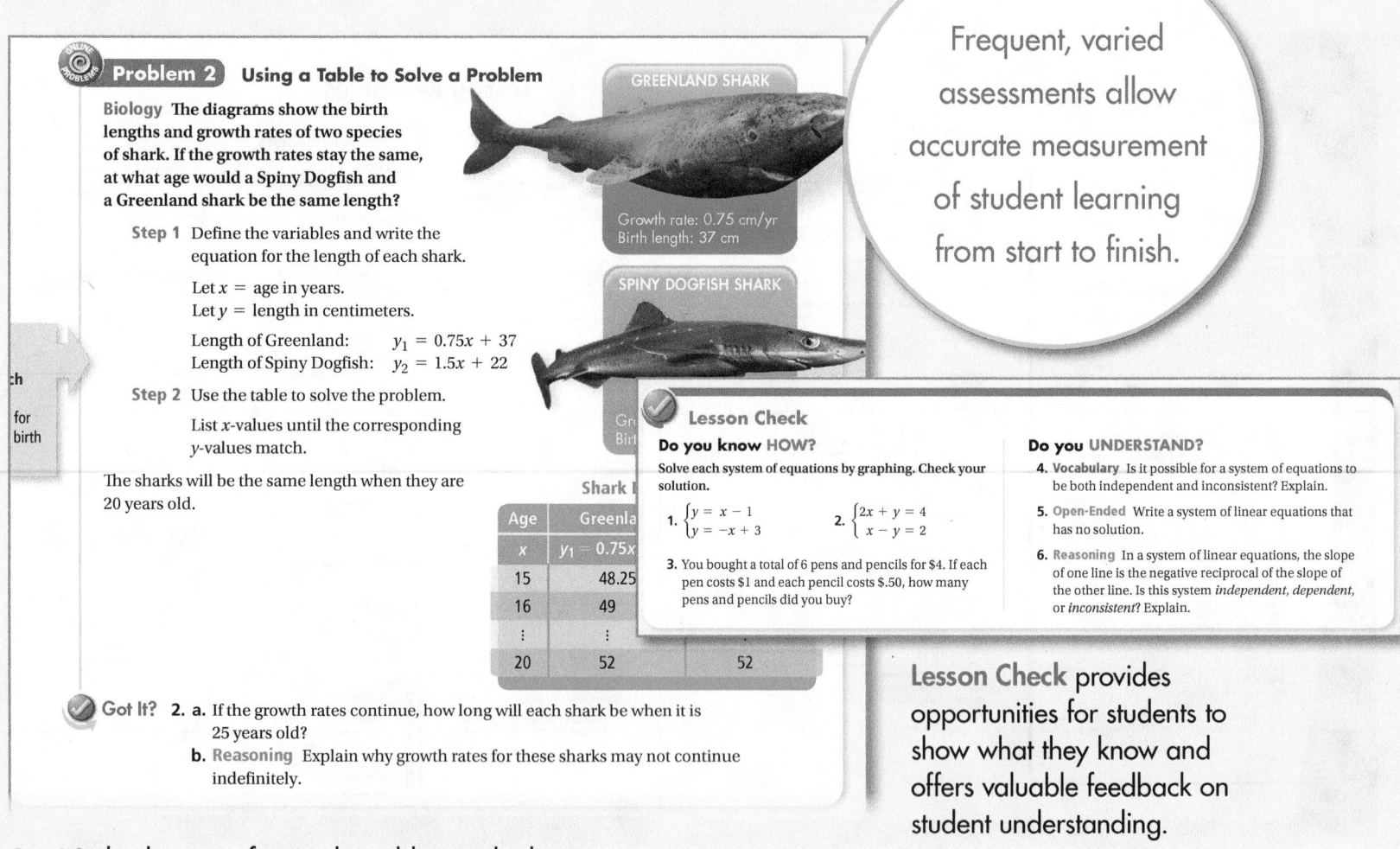

**Frequent, varied assessments allow accurate measurement of student learning from start to finish.**

**Problem 2**  **Using a Table to Solve a Problem**

**Biology** The diagrams show the birth lengths and growth rates of two species of shark. If the growth rates stay the same, at what age would a Spiny Dogfish and a Greenland shark be the same length?

**GREENLAND SHARK**

Growth rate: 0.75 cm/yr
Birth length: 37 cm

**SPINY DOGFISH SHARK**

**Step 1** Define the variables and write the equation for the length of each shark.

Let $x$ = age in years.
Let $y$ = length in centimeters.

Length of Greenland:  $y_1 = 0.75x + 37$
Length of Spiny Dogfish:  $y_2 = 1.5x + 22$

**Step 2** Use the table to solve the problem.

List $x$-values until the corresponding $y$-values match.

The sharks will be the same length when they are 20 years old.

**Shark**

| Age | Greenla... | |
|-----|------------|--|
| $x$ | $y_1 = 0.75x$ | |
| 15 | 48.25 | |
| 16 | 49 | |
| ⋮ | ⋮ | |
| 20 | 52 | 52 |

**Got It?**  **2. a.** If the growth rates continue, how long will each shark be when it is 25 years old?
**b. Reasoning** Explain why growth rates for these sharks may not continue indefinitely.

**Lesson Check**

**Do you know HOW?**

Solve each system of equations by graphing. Check your solution.

**1.** $\begin{cases} y = x - 1 \\ y = -x + 3 \end{cases}$  **2.** $\begin{cases} 2x + y = 4 \\ x - y = 2 \end{cases}$

**3.** You bought a total of 6 pens and pencils for $4. If each pen costs $1 and each pencil costs $.50, how many pens and pencils did you buy?

**Do you UNDERSTAND?**

**4. Vocabulary** Is it possible for a system of equations to be both independent and inconsistent? Explain.

**5. Open-Ended** Write a system of linear equations that has no solution.

**6. Reasoning** In a system of linear equations, the slope of one line is the negative reciprocal of the slope of the other line. Is this system *independent, dependent,* or *inconsistent*? Explain.

**Lesson Check** provides opportunities for students to show what they know and offers valuable feedback on student understanding.

**Got It?** checkpoints after each problem in the lesson constantly monitor student understanding. These quick assessments keep instruction on track for all students and allow teachers to make informed instructional decisions.

"The key to education is to be fair and consistent. The same is true for assessment. Fair, consistent, quality assessment is the only way to ensure that students are learning what you are teaching."

—*Bill Handlin*

## Success ⚙ Tracker™

**The Success Tracker** online assessment system provides instant analysis of student performance. Success Tracker includes built-in diagnostic and benchmark tests, diagnoses student mastery, prescribes automatically assigned remediation for every standard not mastered, and reports on student and class progress.

# MathXL® for School

MathXL® for School is a powerful online homework, tutorial, and assessment system for *Prentice Hall Algebra 2*. It provides students with a personalized, interactive learning environment where they can learn at their own pace. MathXL for School assigns students homework problems, automatically grades their work, and then provides immediate feedback and tutorial assistance to ensure mastery before high-stakes tests.

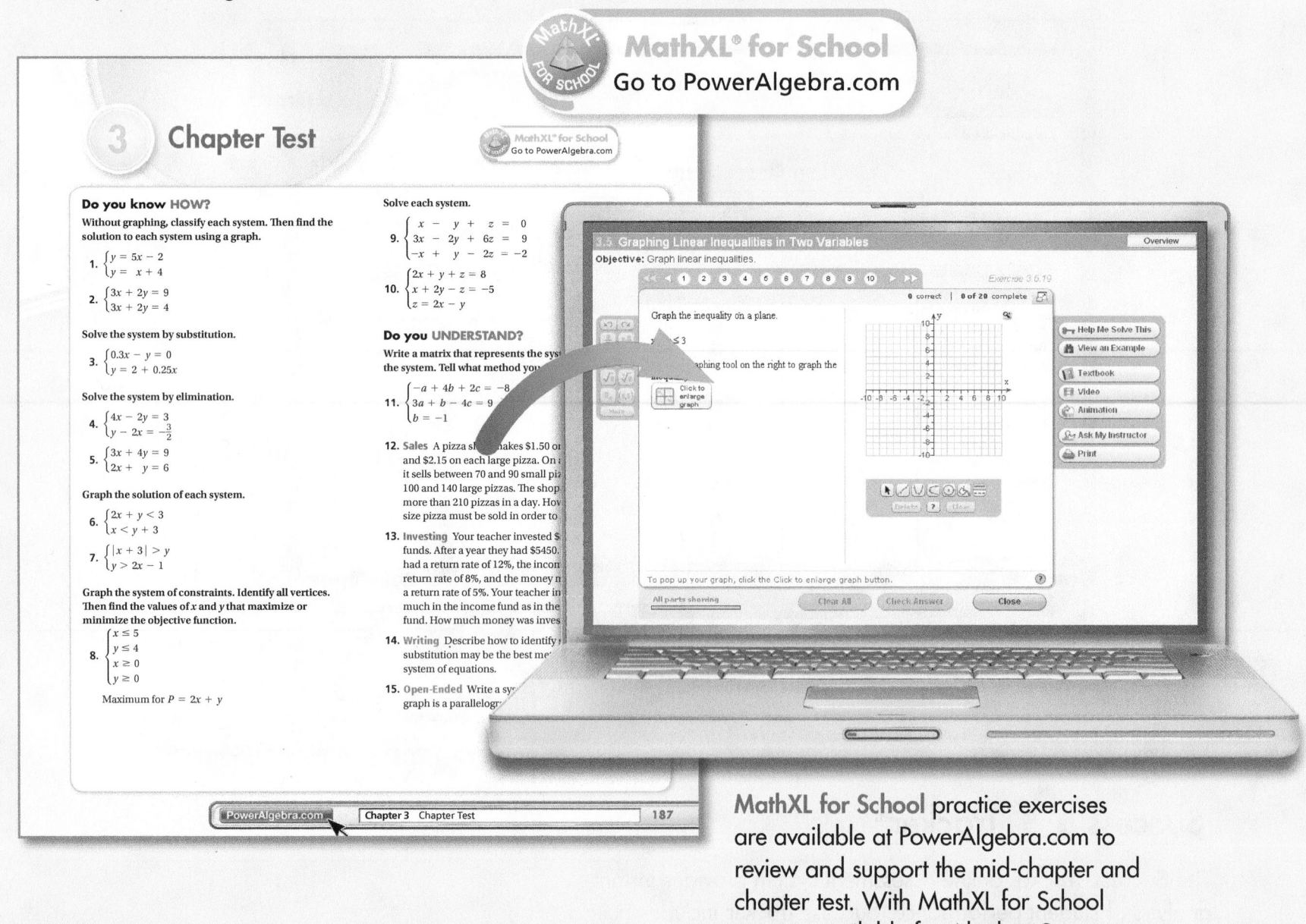

MathXL® for School
Go to PowerAlgebra.com

MathXL for School practice exercises are available at PowerAlgebra.com to review and support the mid-chapter and chapter test. With MathXL for School courses available for Algebra 2, you can prepare students for high-stakes tests with their own personalized study plans based on quiz and test results.

# Success for All Students

Success in mathematics is essential for students facing rigorous coursework in college, career challenges, and global competitiveness. But success can no longer be determined solely by a student's performance on a math assessment. Students need to develop the thinking and reasoning habits that will empower them to reach full potential in their lives at school and in their career paths. While only some students will pursue further math education or careers in math and science, all students will benefit from learning to analyze problems independently and solve them in different applications. They will need those abilities to lead successful lives as citizens and leaders of the 21st century.

### Engage Students

- Blended environment of print and digital motivates students.
- Different approaches make learning accessible to more students.
- Visual approach makes math more interesting.

### Teach for Understanding

- Comprehensive coverage ensures strong grasp of algebra (or geometry) skills.
- Stepped-out instruction reduces cognitive load.
- Emphasis on math reasoning helps students make sense of math.

### Promote Mastery

- Ongoing formative assessment cements skills.
- Teacher and students ask and answer questions to reinforce understanding.
- Development of math reasoning results in transferability of skills.

## SUCCESS
School • Career • Life

# ADP END-OF-COURSE EXAM CONTENT STANDARDS
# for Algebra 2

The following chart shows the alignment of the ADP Core and Module Content to the lessons and features in Pearson's *Prentice Hall Algebra 2 Honors* text.

| Content Standards | | Where to Find |
|---|---|---|
| **Operations on Numbers and Expressions** | | |
| **O1.a** | Convert between and among radical and exponential forms of numerical expressions. | Lessons: 6-1, 6-4 |
| **O1.b** | Simplify and perform operations on numerical expressions containing radicals. | Lesson: 6-2 |
| **O1.c** | Apply the laws of exponents to numerical expressions with rational and negative exponents to order and rewrite them in alternative forms. | Lesson: 6-2 Concept Byte: p. 360 |
| **O2.a** | Represent complex numbers in the form $a + bi$, where $a$ and $b$ are real; simplify powers of pure imaginary numbers. | Lesson: 4-8 Concept Byte: p. 265 |
| **O2.b** | Perform operations on the set of complex numbers. | Lesson: 4-8 Concept Byte: p. 265 |
| **O3.a** | Convert between and among radical and exponential forms of algebraic expressions. | Lesson: 6-4 |
| **O3.b** | Simplify and perform operations on radical algebraic expressions. | Lessons: 6-1, 6-2, 6-3, 6-4, 6-5, 6-7 |
| **O3.c** | Apply the laws of exponents to algebraic expressions, including those involving rational and negative exponents, to order and rewrite them in alternative forms. | Lesson: 6-4 Concept Byte: p. 360 |
| **O3.d** | Perform operations on polynomial expressions. | Lessons: 5-2, 5-4, 5-5 |
| **O3.e** | Perform operations on rational expressions, including complex fractions. | Lessons: 8-4, 8-5, 8-6 |
| **O3.f** | Identify or write equivalent algebraic expressions in one or more variables to extract information. | Lessons: 4-7, 8-5, 10-2, 10-4, 10-5, 10-6 |
| **Equations and Inequalities** | | |
| **E1.a** | Solve equations and inequalities involving the absolute value of a linear expression. | Lesson: 1-6 |
| **E1.b** | Express and solve systems of linear equations in three variables with and without the use of technology. | Lessons: 3-5, 3-6, 4-3 |
| **E1.c** | Solve systems of linear inequalities in two variables and graph the solution set. | Lessons: 3-3, 3-4 Concept Byte: p. 163 |
| **E1.d** | Recognize and solve problems that can be represented by single variable linear equations or inequalities or systems of linear equations or inequalities involving two or more variables. Interpret the solution(s) in terms of the context of the problem. | Lessons: 1-4, 1-5, 3-1, 3-2, 3-3, 3-6 |
| **E2.a** | Solve single-variable quadratic, exponential, rational, radical, and factorable higher-order polynomial equations over the set of real numbers, including quadratic equations involving absolute value. | Lessons: 4-5, 4-6, 4-7, 5-2, 5-5, 5-6, 7-5, 8-6 |
| **E2.b** | Solve single variable quadratic equations and inequalities over the complex numbers; graph real solution sets on a number line. | Lessons: 4-5, 4-6, 4-7, 4-8 Concept Byte: p. 256 |
| **E2.c** | Use the discriminant, $D = b^2 - 4ac$, to determine the nature of the solutions of the equation $ax^2 + bx + c = 0$. | Lesson: 4-7 |
| **E2.d** | Graph the solution set of a two-variable quadratic inequality in the coordinate plane. | Lesson: 4-9 |
| **E2.e** | Rewrite nonlinear equations and inequalities to express them in multiple forms in order to facilitate finding a solution set or to extract information about the relationships or graphs indicated. | Lessons: 4-1, 4-2, 5-3 |
| **Polynomial and Rational Equations** | | |
| **P1.a** | Determine key characteristics of quadratic functions and their graphs. | Lessons: 4-1, 4-2, 4-8 |
| **P1.b** | Describe and represent the effect that changes in the parameters of a quadratic function have on the shape and position of its graph. | Lessons: 4-1, 4-2, 4-3 |

| Content Standards | | Where to Find |
|---|---|---|
| **P1.c** | Describe the effect that changes in the parameters of a quadratic function have on the shape and position of its graph. | Lesson: 4-1 |
| **P1.d** | Recognize, express, and solve problems that can be modeled using quadratic functions. Interpret their solutions in terms of the context. | Lessons: 4-3, 4-5, 4-6, 4-7 |
| **P2.a** | Determine key characteristics of power functions in the form $f(x) = zx^n$, $a \neq 0$, for positive integral values of $n$ and their graphs. | Lessons: 5-1, 5-9 |
| **P2.b** | Determine key characteristics of polynomial functions and their graphs | Lessons: 5-1, 5-2, 5-3 |
| **P2.c** | Represent polynomial functions using tables, graphs, verbal statements, and equations Translate among these representations. | Lessons: 5-1, 5-2, 5-8, 5-9 |
| **P2.d** | Determine key characteristics of simple rational functions and their graphs. | Lessons: 8-2, 8-3, 8-2, 8-3 |
| **P2.e** | Represent simple rational functions using tables, graphs, verbal statements, and equations. Translate among these representations. | Lessons: 8-2, 8-3 |
| **P2.f** | Recognize, express, and solve problems that can be modeled using polynomial and simple rational functions. Interpret their solutions in terms of the context. | Lessons: 5-8, 8-3 |

| Exponential Functions | | |
|---|---|---|
| **X1.a** | Determine key characteristics of exponential functions and their graphs. | Lessons: 7-1, 7-2 |
| **X1.b** | Represent exponential functions using tables, graphs, verbal statements, and equations. Represent exponential expressions in multiple forms. Translate among these representations. | Lessons: 7-1, 7-2, 7-5 |
| **X1.c** | Describe and represent the effect that changes in the parameters of an exponential function have on the shape and position of its graph. | Lesson: 7-2 |
| **X1.d** | Recognize, express, and solve problems that can be modeled using exponential functions, including those where logarithms provide an efficient method of solution. Interpret their solutions in terms of the context. | Lessons: 7-2, 7-6, 7-6 |

| Function Operations and Inverses | | |
|---|---|---|
| **F1.a** | Combine functions by addition, subtraction, multiplication, and division. | Lesson: 6-6 |
| **F1.b** | Determine the composition of two functions, including any necessary restrictions on the domain. | Lessons: 6-6, 6-7 |
| **F2.a** | Describe the conditions under which an inverse relation is a function. | Lessons: 6-7, 14-2 |
| **F2.b** | Determine and graph the inverse relation of a function. | Lessons: 6-7, 14-2 |
| **F3.a** | Determine key characteristics of absolute value, step, and other piecewise-defined functions. | Lesson: 1-6 Concept Byte: p.90 |
| **F3.b** | Represent piecewise-defined functions using tables, graphs, verbal statements, and equations. Translate among these representations. | Lesson: 1-6 Concept Byte: p.90 |
| **F3.c** | Recognize, express, and solve problems that can be modeled using absolute value, step, and other piecewise-defined functions. Interpret their solutions in terms of the context. | Lesson: 1-6 Concept Byte: p.90 |

| Data and Statistics | | |
|---|---|---|
| **S1.a** | Summarize and compare data sets using statistical methods. | Lessons: 11-5, 11-6, 11-7 |
| **S1.b** | Determine, use, and identify potential misuses of weighted averages. | Lesson: 11-5 |
| **S1.c** | Use a computer or calculator to find a linear regression equation (least squares line) as a model for data that suggest a linear trend, and determine the correlation coefficient. | Lesson: 2-5 |
| **S2.a** | Analyze the strength of the linear relationship indicated by the regression line. | Lesson: 2-5 |
| **S2.b** | Interpret data and communicate conclusions effectively. | Lesson: 11-7 Concept Byte: p. 724 |
| **S2.c** | Make judgments regarding accuracy, reasonableness, and bias in the use of data. | Lesson: 11-7 |
| **S2.d** | Critique and justify various methods of sampling and data collection used in real world problems. | Lesson: 11-7 |

| Content Standards | | Where to Find |
|---|---|---|
| **Probability** | | |
| R1.a | Determine the number of ways events can occur using permutations, combinations, and other systematic counting methods. | Lessons: 11-1, 11-2 |
| R1.b | Relate the expansion of $(x + y)^n$ (i.e., the binomial theorem) with the possible outcomes of a binomial experiment and/or the $n$th row of Pascal's triangle. | Lesson: 11-8 |
| R1.c | Apply probability concepts to calculate the probability of events and to make informed decisions in practical situations. | Lessons: 11-2, 11-3, 11-4 |
| R1.d | Analyze and interpret actual data to estimate probabilities and predict outcomes, including those involving relative frequency. | Lessons: 11-2, 11-3, 11-4 |
| R1.e | Compare theoretical probabilities with the results of simple experiments (e.g., tossing number cubes, flipping coins, spinning spinners). | Concept Byte: p. 694 |
| R1.f | Compute and graph cumulative frequencies. | Concept Byte: p. 694 |
| R2.a | Identify and distinguish between discrete and continuous probability distributions. | Lesson: 11-9 Concept Byte: p. 740 |
| R2.b | Identify the principal characteristics of the normal distribution and use them to estimate probabilities. | Lesson: 11-9 |
| R2.c | Identify and describe the key characteristics of and create frequency distributions of both discrete and continuous data. | Lessons: 11-8, 11-9 Concept Byte: p. 694 |
| **Logarithmic Functions** | | |
| L1.a | Apply the properties of logarithms and use them to manipulate logarithmic expressions. | Lessons: 7-4, 7-5, 7-6 |
| L1.b | Solve logarithmic equations, paying attention to the possibility of extraneous roots. | Lessons: 7-5, 7-6 |
| L2.a | Determine key characteristics of logarithmic functions. | Lesson: 7-3 |
| L2.b | Represent logarithmic functions using tables, graphs, verbal statements, and equations. Translate among these representations. | Lesson: 7-3 |
| L2.c | Describe the effect that changes in the parameters of a logarithmic function have on the shape and position of its graph. | Lesson: 7-3 |
| L2.d | Recognize, express, and solve problems that can be modeled using logarithmic functions. Interpret their solutions in terms of the context of the problem. | Lessons: 7-3, 7-5, 7-6 |
| **Trigonometric Functions** | | |
| T1.a | Recognize periodic phenomena and determine key characteristics of such phenomena. | Lessons: 13-1, 13-4, 13-5 |
| T1.b | Use the relationship of the sine and cosine functions to a central angle of the unit circle to determine the exact trigonometric ratio of angles on the unit circle. ($0°$ to $360°$, $0$ to $2\pi$) | Lessons: 13-2, 14-2 |
| T1.c | Explain and use both degree and radian measure for angles. | Lessons: 13-2, 13-3 Concept Byte: p. 835 |
| T1.d | Represent trigonometric functions using tables, graphs, verbal statements, and equations. Translate among these representations. | Lessons: 13-4, 13-5, 13-6, 13-7, 13-8, 14-2 |
| T1.e | Determine key characteristics of trigonometric functions and their graphs. | Lessons: 13-4, 13-5, 13-6, 13-7, 13-8 |
| T1.f | Describe the effect that changes in the parameters of an equation of a trigonometric function in the form $f(x) = A \sin B(x - C) + D$ (or the similar cosine function) have on the shape and position of its graph. | Lesson: 13-7 |
| T1.g | Recognize, express, and solve problems that can be modeled using trigonometric or other periodic functions. | Lessons: 13-4, 13-5, 13-6, 14-2, 14-3, 14-4, 14-5 |
| **Matrices** | | |
| M1.a | Perform addition, subtraction, and scalar multiplication of matrices. | Lesson: 12-2 |
| M1.b | Perform matrix multiplication. | Lessons: 12-3, 12-5 |
| M2.a | Find the determinant of a $2 \times 2$ or $3 \times 3$ matrix. | Lessons: 12-3, 12-4 |

| Content Standards | | Where to Find |
|---|---|---|
| **M2.b** | Determine the inverse of a $2 \times 2$ or $3 \times 3$ matrix or indicate that no inverse exists. | Lessons: 12-3, 12-4 |
| **M2.c** | Represent 2-variable and 3-variable systems of linear equations using matrices and use them to solve the system. | Lessons: 3-6, 12-4 |
| **M2.d** | Solve a matrix equation. | Lessons: 12-1, 12-4 |
| **M3.a** | Use matrix tools to represent and transform geometric objects in the coordinate plane. | Lesson: 12-5 |
| **M4.b** | Add, subtract, and compute the dot product of two-dimensional vectors; multiply a two-dimensional vector by a scalar. | Lesson: 12-6 |
| **Conic Sections** | | |
| **C1.a** | Identify a parabola, circle, ellipse, or hyperbola from its equation, description, or key characteristics. | Lessons: 10-1, 10-2, 10-3, 10-4, 10-5, 10-6 |
| **C1.b** | Represent conic sections whose axes are parallel to the *x*- and *y*-axes using graphs, verbal statements and equations. Translate among these representations. Represent the equations of conic sections in multiple forms to extract information about the parabola, circle, ellipse, or hyperbola. | Lessons: 10-2, 10-3, 10-4, 10-5, 10-6 |
| **C1.c** | Describe the effect that changes in the parameters of a particular conic section have on its shape and position. | Lessons: 10-2, 10-3, 10-4, 10-5, 10-6 |
| **C1.d** | Recognize, express, and solve problems that can be modeled using conic sections. Interpret their solutions in terms of the context of the problem. | Lessons: 10-2, 10-3, 10-4, 10-5 |
| **Sequences and Series** | | |
| **I1.a** | Represent the general term of an arithmetic or geometric sequence and use it to generate the sequence or determine the value of any particular term. | Lessons: 9-2, 9-3, 9-4, 9-5 |
| **I1.b** | Represent partial sums of an arithmetic or geometric sequence and determine the value of a particular partial sum or sum of a finite sequence. | Lessons: 9-4, 9-5 |
| **I1.c** | Recognize when an infinite geometric sum can be determined and determine the sum when possible. | Lesson: 9-5 Concept Byte: p. 594 |
| **I1.d** | Convert the recursive model for linear growth ($a_1 = a$, $a_{n+1} = a_n + d$, where $a$ is the first term and $d$ is the constant difference) to a closed linear form ($a_n = a(n - 1)d$). | Lesson: 9-1 |
| **I1.e** | Convert the recursive model of geometric growth ($p_1 = a$, $p_{n+1}rp_n$ where $a$ is the first term and $r$ is the constant growth rate) to a closed exponential form ($p_n = ar^{n-1}$). | Lesson: 9-5 |
| **I1.f** | Recognize, express, and solve problems that can be modeled using a finite geometric series. Interpret their solutions in terms of the context of the problem. | Lesson: 9-5 |
| **I2.a** | Use recursion to generate and describe, analyze, and interpret patterned relationships other than arithmetic or geometric sequences. | Lesson: 9-1 Concept Byte: p. 578 |
| **I2.b** | Use iterative methods to solve problems. | Lessons: 7-1, 9-1 |

# Algebra 2 Leveled Pacing Chart

This Leveled Pacing Chart will help you customize your course to include topics in discrete math or trigonometry and to provide for differentiated instruction.

The suggested number of days for each chapter is based on a traditional 45-minute class period and on a 90-minute block period. The suggested number of days for instruction leaves time for assessments, projects, assemblies, or other special days that vary from school to school. The chapter pacing guides will need to be adjusted for courses taught with Discrete Math or Trigonometry and for the Comprehensive Course.

**KEY**

✓ = Content to prepare for Sunshine State Standards testing

○ = Reviews the previous year

| | Regular Course | Course with Trigonometry | Comprehensive Course |
|---|---|---|---|
| **Chapter 1 Expressions, Equations, and Inequalities** | **T = 10  B = 5** | **T = 10  B = 5** | **T = 4  B = 2** |
| 1-1  Patterns and Expressions | ✓ | ✓ | |
| 1-2  Properties of Real Numbers | ✓ | ✓ | |
| 1-3  Algebraic Expressions | ✓ | ✓ | |
| 1-4  Solving Equations | ✓ | ✓ | |
| 1-5  Solving Inequalities | ✓ | ✓ | ✓ |
| 1-6  Absolute Value Equations and Inequalities | ✓ | ✓ | ✓ |
| **Chapter 2 Functions, Equations, and Graphs** | **T = 14  B = 7** | **T = 14  B = 7** | **T = 12  B = 6** |
| 2-1  Relations and Functions | ✓ | ✓ | ✓ |
| 2-2  Direct Variation | ✓ | ✓ | ✓ |
| 2-3  Linear Functions and Slope-Intercept Form | ✓ | ✓ | ✓ |
| 2-4  More About Linear Equations | ✓ | ✓ | ✓ |
| **Concept Byte:** Piecewise Functions | | | ✓ |
| 2-5  Using Linear Models | ✓ | ✓ | ✓ |
| 2-6  Families of Functions | ✓ | ✓ | ✓ |
| 2-7  Absolute Value Functions and Graphs | ✓ | ✓ | ✓ |
| 2-8  Two-Variable Inequalities | ✓ | ✓ | ✓ |
| **Chapter 3 Linear Systems** | **T = 12  B = 6** | **T = 12  B = 6** | **T = 10  B = 5** |
| 3-1  Solving Systems Using Tables and Graphs | ✓ | ✓ | ✓ |
| 3-2  Solving Systems Algebraically | ✓ | ✓ | ✓ |
| 3-3  Systems of Inequalities | ✓ | ✓ | ✓ |
| 3-4  Linear Programming | ✓ | ✓ | ✓ |
| **Concept Byte:** Linear Programming | | | ✓ |
| **Concept Byte:** Graphs in Three Dimensions | ✓ | ✓ | ✓ |
| 3-5  Systems With Three Variables | ✓ | ✓ | ✓ |
| 3-6  Solving Systems Using Matrices | ✓ | ✓ | ✓ |
| **Chapter 4 Quadratic Functions and Equations** | **T = 20  B = 10** | **T = 20  B = 10** | **T = 16  B = 8** |
| 4-1  Quadratic Functions and Transformations | ✓ | ✓ | ✓ |
| 4-2  Standard Form of a Quadratic Function | ✓ | ✓ | ✓ |
| 4-3  Modeling With Quadratic Functions | ✓ | ✓ | ✓ |
| **Concept Byte:** Identifying Quadratic Data | ✓ | ✓ | ✓ |

| | Regular Course | Course with Trigonometry | Comprehensive Course |
|---|---|---|---|
| **Chapter 4 (continued) Quadratic Functions and Equations** | T = 20   B = 10 | T = 20   B = 10 | T = 16   B = 8 |
| 4-4   Factoring Quadratic Expressions | ✓ | ✓ | ✓ |
| **Algebra Review:** Square Roots and Radicals | ✓ | ✓ | |
| 4-5   Quadratic Equations | ✓ | ✓ | ✓ |
| **Concept Byte:** Writing Equations From Roots | ✓ | ✓ | ✓ |
| 4-6   Completing the Square | ✓ | ✓ | ✓ |
| 4-7   The Quadratic Formula | ✓ | ✓ | ✓ |
| 4-8   Complex Numbers | ✓ | ✓ | ✓ |
| **Concept Byte:** Quadratic Inequalities | | | ✓ |
| 4-9   Quadratic Systems | ✓ | ✓ | ✓ |
| **Concept Byte:** Powers of Complex Numbers | ✓ | ✓ | ✓ |
| **Chapter 5 Polynomials and Polynomial Functions** | T = 16   B = 8 | T = 16   B = 8 | T = 14   B = 7 |
| 5-1   Polynomial Functions | ✓ | ✓ | ✓ |
| 5-2   Polynomials, Linear Factors, and Zeros | ✓ | ✓ | ✓ |
| 5-3   Solving Polynomial Equations | ✓ | ✓ | ✓ |
| 5-4   Dividing Polynomials | ✓ | ✓ | ✓ |
| 5-5   Theorems About Roots of Polynomial Equations | ✓ | ✓ | ✓ |
| **Concept Byte:** Solving Polynomial Inequalities | ✓ | | ✓ |
| 5-6   The Fundamental Theorem of Algebra | ✓ | ✓ | ✓ |
| **Concept Byte:** Pascal's Triangle | | | ✓ |
| 5-7   The Binomial Theorem | ✓ | ✓ | ✓ |
| 5-8   Polynomial Models in the Real World | ✓ | ✓ | ✓ |
| 5-9   Transforming Polynomial Functions | ✓ | ✓ | ✓ |
| **Chapter 6 Radical Functions and Rational Exponents** | T = 16   B = 8 | T = 16   B = 8 | T = 14   B = 7 |
| **Algebra Review:** Properties of Exponents | ✓ | ✓ | |
| 6-1   Roots and Radical Expressions | ✓ | ✓ | ✓ |
| 6-2   Multiplying and Dividing Radical Expressions | ✓ | ✓ | ✓ |
| 6-3   Binomial Radical Expressions | ✓ | ✓ | ✓ |
| 6-4   Rational Exponents | ✓ | ✓ | ✓ |
| 6-5   Solving Square Root and Other Radical Equations | ✓ | ✓ | ✓ |
| 6-6   Function Operations | ✓ | ✓ | ✓ |
| 6-7   Inverse Relations and Functions | ✓ | ✓ | ✓ |
| **Concept Byte:** Graphing Inverses | | ✓ | ✓ |
| 6-8   Graphing Radical Functions | ✓ | ✓ | ✓ |
| **Chapter 7 Exponential and Logarithmic Functions** | T = 12   B = 6 | T = 12   B = 6 | T = 10   B = 5 |
| 7-1   Exploring Exponential Models | ✓ | ✓ | ✓ |
| 7-2   Properties of Exponential Functions | ✓ | ✓ | ✓ |
| 7-3   Logarithmic Functions as Inverses | ✓ | ✓ | ✓ |
| **Concept Byte:** Fitting Curves to Data | ✓ | ✓ | ✓ |
| 7-4   Properties of Logarithms | ✓ | ✓ | ✓ |

| | Regular Course | Course with Trigonometry | Comprehensive Course |
|---|:---:|:---:|:---:|
| **Chapter 7 (continued) Exponential and Logarithmic Functions** | T = 12  B = 6 | T = 12  B = 6 | T = 10  B = 5 |
| 7-5   Exponential and Logarithmic Equations | ✓ | ✓ | ✓ |
| **Concept Byte:** Using Logarithms for Exponential Models | ✓ | | ✓ |
| 7-6   Natural Logarithms | ✓ | ✓ | ✓ |
| **Concept Byte:** Exponential and Logarithmic Inequalities | | | ✓ |
| **Chapter 8 Rational Functions** | T = 12  B = 6 | T = 12  B = 6 | T = 10  B = 5 |
| 8-1   Inverse Variation | ✓ | ✓ | ✓ |
| **Concept Byte:** Graphing Rational Functions | ✓ | ✓ | ✓ |
| 8-2   The Reciprocal Function Family | ✓ | ✓ | ✓ |
| 8-3   Rational Functions and Their Graphs | ✓ | ✓ | ✓ |
| **Concept Byte:** Oblique Asymptotes | | ✓ | ✓ |
| 8-4   Rational Expressions | ✓ | ✓ | ✓ |
| 8-5   Adding and Subtracting Rational Expressions | ✓ | ✓ | ✓ |
| 8-6   Solving Rational Equations | ✓ | ✓ | ✓ |
| **Concept Byte:** Systems with Rational Equations | | | ✓ |
| **Concept Byte:** Rational Inequalities | | | ✓ |
| **Chapter 9 Sequences and Series** | T = 10  B = 5 | | T = 10  B = 5 |
| 9-1   Mathematical Patterns | ✓ | | ✓ |
| 9-2   Arithmetic Sequences | ✓ | | ✓ |
| **Concept Byte:** The Fibonacci Sequence | ✓ | | ✓ |
| 9-3   Geometric Sequences | ✓ | | ✓ |
| 9-4   Arithmetic Series | ✓ | | ✓ |
| **Concept Byte:** Geometry and Infinite Series | | | ✓ |
| 9-5   Geometric Series | ✓ | | ✓ |
| **Chapter 10 Quadratic Relations and Conic Sections** | T = 12  B = 6 | T = 12  B = 6 | T = 10  B = 5 |
| 10-1   Exploring Conic Sections | ✓ | ✓ | ✓ |
| **Concept Byte:** Graphing Conic Sections | ✓ | ✓ | ✓ |
| 10-2   Parabolas | ✓ | ✓ | ✓ |
| 10-3   Circles | ✓ | ✓ | ✓ |
| 10-4   Ellipses | ✓ | ✓ | ✓ |
| 10-5   Hyperbolas | ✓ | ✓ | ✓ |
| 10-6   Translating Conic Sections | ✓ | ✓ | ✓ |
| **Concept Byte:** Solving Quadratic Systems | | | ✓ |
| **Chapter 11 Probability and Statistics** | T = 14  B = 7 | | T = 14  B = 7 |
| 11-1   Permutations and Combinations | ✓ | | ✓ |
| 11-2   Probability | ✓ | | ✓ |
| 11-3   Probability of Multiple Events | ✓ | | ✓ |
| **Concept Byte:** Probability Distributions | | | ✓ |
| 11-4   Conditional Probability | ✓ | | ✓ |

| | Regular Course | Course with Trigonometry | Comprehensive Course |
|---|---|---|---|
| **Chapter 11 (continued) Probability and Statistics** | T = 14   B = 7 | | T = 14   B = 7 |
| 11-5    Analyzing Data | ✓ | | ✓ |
| 11-6    Standard Deviation | ✓ | | ✓ |
| 11-7    Samples and Surveys | ✓ | | ✓ |
| **Concept Byte:** Describing Data | ✓ | | ✓ |
| 11-8    Binomial Distributions | ✓ | | ✓ |
| 11-9    Normal Distributions | ✓ | | ✓ |
| **Concept Byte:** Approximating a Binomial Distribution | | | ✓ |
| **Chapter 12 Matrices** | T = 12   B = 6 | | T = 10   B = 5 |
| 12-1    Adding and Subtracting Matrices | ✓ | | ✓ |
| **Concept Byte:** Working With Matrices | ✓ | | ✓ |
| 12-2    Matrix Multiplication | ✓ | | ✓ |
| **Concept Byte:** Networks | | | ✓ |
| 12-3    Determinants and Inverses | ✓ | | ✓ |
| 12-4    Inverse Matrices and Systems | ✓ | | ✓ |
| 12-5    Geometric Transformations | ✓ | | ✓ |
| 12-6    Vectors | ✓ | | ✓ |
| **Chapter 13 Periodic Functions and Trigonometry** | | T = 18   B = 9 | T = 14   B = 7 |
| 13-1    Exploring Periodic Data | | ✓ | ✓ |
| **Geometry Review:** Special Right Triangles | | ✓ | ✓ |
| 13-2    Angles and the Unit Circle | | ✓ | ✓ |
| **Activity Lab:** Measuring Radians | | ✓ | ✓ |
| 13-3    Radian Measure | | ✓ | ✓ |
| 13-4    The Sine Function | | ✓ | ✓ |
| **Concept Byte:** Graphing Trigonometric Functions | | ✓ | ✓ |
| 13-5    The Cosine Function | | ✓ | ✓ |
| 13-6    The Tangent Function | | ✓ | ✓ |
| 13-7    Translating Sine and Cosine Functions | | ✓ | ✓ |
| 13-8    Reciprocal Trigonometric Functions | | ✓ | ✓ |
| **Chapter 14 Trigonometric Identities and Equations** | | T = 16   B = 8 | T = 12   B = 6 |
| 14-1    Trigonometric Identities | | ✓ | ✓ |
| 14-2    Solving Trigonometric Equations Using Inverses | | ✓ | ✓ |
| 14-3    Right Triangles and Trigonometric Ratios | | ✓ | ✓ |
| 14-4    Area and the Law of Sines | | ✓ | ✓ |
| **Activity Lab:** The Ambiguous Case | | ✓ | ✓ |
| 14-5    The Law of Cosines | | ✓ | ✓ |
| 14-6    Angle Identities | | ✓ | ✓ |
| 14-7    Double-Angle and Half-Angle Identities | | ✓ | ✓ |
| **Total Number of Days** | **160** | **158** | **160** |

# **BIG**ideas

These Big Ideas are the organizing ideas for the study of important areas of mathematics: algebra, geometry, and statistics.

## Algebra

### Properties

- In the transition from arithmetic to algebra, attention shifts from arithmetic operations (addition, subtraction, multiplication, and division) to use of the *properties* of these operations.
- All of the facts of arithmetic and algebra follow from certain properties.

### Variable

- Quantities are used to form expressions, equations, and inequalities.
- An expression refers to a quantity but does not make a statement about it. An equation (or an inequality) is a statement about the quantities it mentions.
- Using variables in place of numbers in equations (or inequalities) allows the statement of relationships among numbers that are unknown or unspecified.

### Equivalence

- A single quantity may be represented by many different expressions.
- The facts about a quantity may be expressed by many different equations (or inequalities).

### Solving Equations & Inequalities

- Solving an equation is the process of rewriting the equation to make what it says about its variable(s) as simple as possible.
- Properties of numbers and equality can be used to transform an equation (or inequality) into equivalent, simpler equations (or inequalities) in order to find solutions.
- Useful information about equations and inequalities (including solutions) can be found by analyzing graphs or tables.
- The numbers and types of solutions vary predictably, based on the type of equation.

### Proportionality

- Two quantities are *proportional* if they have the same ratio in each instance where they are measured together.
- Two quantities are *inversely proportional* if they have the same product in each instance where they are measured together.

### Function

- A function is a relationship between variables in which each value of the input variable is associated with a unique value of the output variable.
- Functions can be represented in a variety of ways, such as graphs, tables, equations, or words. Each representation is particularly useful in certain situations.
- Some important families of functions are developed through transformations of the simplest form of the function.
- New functions can be made from other functions by applying arithmetic operations or by applying one function to the output of another.

### Modeling

- Many real-world mathematical problems can be represented algebraically. These representations can lead to algebraic solutions.
- A function that models a real-world situation can be used to make estimates or predictions about future occurrences.

xx

# Statistics and Probability

### Data Collection and Analysis

- Sampling techniques are used to gather data from real-world situations. If the data are representative of the larger population, inferences can be made about that population.
- Biased sampling techniques yield data unlikely to be representative of the larger population.
- Sets of numerical data are described using measures of central tendency and dispersion.

### Data Representation

- The most appropriate data representations depend on the type of data—quantitative or qualitative, and univariate or bivariate.
- Line plots, box plots, and histograms are different ways to show distribution of data over a possible range of values.

### Probability

- Probability expresses the likelihood that a particular event will occur.
- Data can be used to calculate an experimental probability, and mathematical properties can be used to determine a theoretical probability.
- Either experimental or theoretical probability can be used to make predictions or decisions about future events.
- Various counting methods can be used to develop theoretical probabilities.

# Geometry

### Visualization

- Visualization can help you see the relationships between two figures and help you connect properties of real objects with two-dimensional drawings of these objects.

### Transformations

- Transformations are mathematical functions that model relationships with figures.
- Transformations may be described geometrically or by coordinates.
- Symmetries of figures may be defined and classified by transformations.

### Measurement

- Some attributes of geometric figures, such as length, area, volume, and angle measure, are measurable. Units are used to describe these attributes.

### Reasoning & Proof

- Definitions establish meanings and remove possible misunderstanding.
- Other truths are more complex and difficult to see. It is often possible to verify complex truths by reasoning from simpler ones using deductive reasoning.

### Similarity

- Two geometric figures are similar when corresponding lengths are proportional and corresponding angles are congruent.
- Areas of similar figures are proportional to the squares of their corresponding lengths.
- Volumes of similar figures are proportional to the cubes of their corresponding lengths.

### Coordinate Geometry

- A coordinate system on a line is a number line on which points are labeled, corresponding to the real numbers.
- A coordinate system in a plane is formed by two perpendicular number lines, called the $x$- and $y$-axes, and the quadrants they form. The coordinate plane can be used to graph many functions.
- It is possible to verify some complex truths using deductive reasoning in combination with the Distance, Midpoint, and Slope formulas.

**Using Your Book for Success**

# Expressions, Equations, and Inequalities

**Get Ready!**                                                    **1**

My Math Video                                                      3

1-1    Patterns and Expressions                                    4
1-2    Properties of Real Numbers                                  11
1-3    Algebraic Expressions                                       18

**Mid-Chapter Quiz**                                               **25**

1-4    Solving Equations                                           26
1-5    Solving Inequalities                                        33
1-6    Absolute Value Equations and Inequalities                   41

**Assessment and Test Prep**

        Pull It All Together                                       49
        Chapter Review                                             50
        Chapter Test                                               53
        Cumulative Test Prep                                       54

# 2 Functions, Equations, and Graphs

**Get Ready!**     **57**

My Math Video     59

2-1    Relations and Functions     60
2-2    Direct Variation     68
2-3    Linear Functions and Slope-Intercept Form     74
2-4    More About Linear Equations     81

**Mid-Chapter Quiz**     **89**

     **Concept Byte:** Piecewise Functions     90
2-5    Using Linear Models     92
2-6    Families of Functions     99
2-7    Absolute Value Functions and Graphs     107
2-8    Two-Variable Inequalities     114

**Assessment and Test Prep**

     Pull It All Together     121
     Chapter Review     122
     Chapter Test     127
     Cumulative Test Prep     128

## Visual See It!

My Math Video     3
Solve It!     11
Connecting BIG IDEAS     50

## Reasoning Try It!

Essential Understanding     60
Think-Write     108
Know → Need → Plan     20

## Practice Do It!

Practice by Example     22
Think About a Plan     105
Error Analysis/Reasoning     78

# 3 Linear Systems

**Get Ready!**     **131**

My Math Video     133
3-1   Solving Systems Using Tables and Graphs     134
3-2   Solving Systems Algebraically     142
3-3   Systems of Inequalities     149

**Mid-Chapter Quiz**     **156**

3-4   Linear Programming     157
    **Concept Byte:** Linear Programming     163
    **Concept Byte:** Graphs in Three Dimensions     164
3-5   Systems With Three Variables     166
3-6   Solving Systems Using Matrices     174

**Assessment and Test Prep**

    Pull It All Together     182
    Chapter Review     183
    Chapter Test     187
    Cumulative Test Prep     188

# 4 Quadratic Functions and Equations

**Get Ready!**     **191**

My Math Video     193

4-1   Quadratic Functions and Transformations     194
4-2   Standard Form of a Quadratic Function     202
4-3   Modeling With Quadratic Functions     209
      Concept Byte: Identifying Quadratic Data     215
4-4   Factoring Quadratic Expressions     216

**Mid-Chapter Quiz**     **224**

      Algebra Review: Square Roots and Radicals     225
4-5   Quadratic Equations     226
      Concept Byte: Writing Equations From Roots     232
4-6   Completing the Square     233
4-7   The Quadratic Formula     240
4-8   Complex Numbers     248
      Concept Byte: Quadratic Inequalities     256
4-9   Quadratic Systems     258
      Concept Byte: Powers of Complex Numbers     265

**Assessment and Test Prep**

      Pull It All Together     266
      Chapter Review     267
      Chapter Test     273
      Cumulative Test Prep     274

## *Visual* See It!

My Math Video     133
Solve It!     166
Connecting BIG IDEAS     267

## *Reasoning* Try It!

Essential Understanding     226
Think-Write     144
Know → Need → Plan     205

## *Practice* Do It!

Practice by Example     221
Think About a Plan     199
Error Analysis/Reasoning     152

# 5

# Polynomials and Polynomial Functions

**Get Ready!** **277**

My Math Video 279

5-1 Polynomial Functions 280
5-2 Polynomials, Linear Factors, and Zeros 288
5-3 Solving Polynomial Equations 296
5-4 Dividing Polynomials 303

**Mid-Chapter Quiz** **311**

5-5 Theorems About Roots of Polynomial Equations 312
 Concept Byte: Solving Polynomial Inequalities 318
5-6 The Fundamental Theorem of Algebra 319
 Concept Byte: Pascal's Triangle 325
5-7 The Binomial Theorem 326
5-8 Polynomial Models in the Real World 331
5-9 Transforming Polynomial Functions 339

**Assessment and Test Prep**

 Pull It All Together 346
 Chapter Review 347
 Chapter Test 353
 Cumulative Test Prep 354

# 6 Radical Functions and Rational Exponents

**Get Ready!** **357**

My Math Video 359

    **Concept Byte:** Properties of Exponents 360
6-1 Roots and Radical Expressions 361
6-2 Multiplying and Dividing Radical Expressions 367
6-3 Binomial Radical Expressions 374
6-4 Rational Exponents 381

**Mid-Chapter Quiz** **389**

6-5 Solving Square Root and Other Radical Equations 390
6-6 Function Operations 398
6-7 Inverse Relations and Functions 405
    **Concept Byte:** Graphing Inverses 413
6-8 Graphing Radical Functions 414

**Assessment and Test Prep**

    Pull It All Together 421
    Chapter Review 422
    Chapter Test 427
    Cumulative Test Prep 428

## *Visual* See It!

My Math Video 359
Solve It! 296
Connecting BIG IDEAS 422

## *Reasoning* Try It!

Essential Understanding 288
Think-Write 300
Know → Need → Plan 391

## *Practice* Do It!

Practice by Example 322
Think About a Plan 402
Error Analysis/Reasoning 379

Contents    **xxvii**

# Exponential and Logarithmic Functions

| | | |
|---|---|---|
| **Get Ready!** | | **431** |
| My Math Video | | 433 |
| 7-1 | Exploring Exponential Models | 434 |
| 7-2 | Properties of Exponential Functions | 442 |
| 7-3 | Logarithmic Functions as Inverses | 451 |
| | **Concept Byte:** Fitting Curves to Data | 459 |
| **Mid-Chapter Quiz** | | **461** |
| 7-4 | Properties of Logarithms | 462 |
| 7-5 | Exponential and Logarithmic Equations | 469 |
| | **Concept Byte:** Using Logarithms for Exponential Models | 477 |
| 7-6 | Natural Logarithms | 478 |
| | **Concept Byte:** Exponential and Logarithmic Inequalities | 484 |
| **Assessment and Test Prep** | | |
| | Pull It All Together | 486 |
| | Chapter Review | 487 |
| | Chapter Test | 491 |
| | Cumulative Test Prep | 492 |

# 8  Rational Functions

**Get Ready!**                                                        495

My Math Video                                                         497

8-1   Inverse Variation                                              498
      **Concept Byte:** Graphing Rational Functions                  506
8-2   The Reciprocal Function Family                                 507
8-3   Rational Functions and Their Graphs                            515
      **Concept Byte:** Oblique Asymptotes                           524

**Mid-Chapter Quiz**                                                 **526**

8-4   Rational Expressions                                           527
8-5   Adding and Subtracting Rational Expressions                    534
8-6   Solving Rational Equations                                     542
      **Concept Byte:** Systems With Rational Equations              549
      **Concept Byte:** Rational Inequalities                        550

**Assessment and Test Prep**

      Pull It All Together                                           552
      Chapter Review                                                 553
      Chapter Test                                                   557
      Cumulative Test Prep                                           558

## *Visual* See It!

My Math Video                 497
Solve It!                     434
Connecting BIG IDEAS          553

## *Reasoning* Try It!

Essential Understanding       451
Think-Write                   529
Know → Need → Plan            445

## *Practice* Do It!

Practice by Example           473
Think About a Plan            546
Error Analysis/Reasoning      522

# 9 Sequences and Series

**Get Ready!**                                               561

My Math Video                                                563

9-1   Mathematical Patterns                                  564
9-2   Arithmetic Sequences                                   572
      **Concept Byte:** The Fibonacci Sequence               578

**Mid-Chapter Quiz**                                         579

9-3   Geometric Sequences                                    580
9-4   Arithmetic Series                                      587
      **Concept Byte:** Geometry and Infinite Series         594
9-5   Geometric Series                                       595

**Assessment and Test Prep**

      Pull It All Together                                   602
      Chapter Review                                         603
      Chapter Test                                           607
      Cumulative Test Prep                                   608

# 10 Quadratic Relations and Conic Sections

| | | |
|---|---|---|
| **Get Ready!** | | **611** |
| My Math Video | | 613 |
| 10-1 | Exploring Conic Sections | 614 |
| | **Concept Byte:** Graphing Conic Sections | 621 |
| 10-2 | Parabolas | 622 |
| 10-3 | Circles | 630 |
| **Mid-Chapter Quiz** | | **637** |
| 10-4 | Ellipses | 638 |
| 10-5 | Hyperbolas | 645 |
| 10-6 | Translating Conic Sections | 653 |
| | **Concept Byte:** Solving Quadratic Systems | 661 |
| **Assessment and Test Prep** | | |
| | Pull It All Together | 662 |
| | Chapter Review | 663 |
| | Chapter Test | 667 |
| | Cumulative Test Prep | 668 |

## Visual See It!

| | |
|---|---|
| **My Math Video** | 613 |
| **Solve It!** | 564 |
| **Connecting BIG IDEAS** | 663 |

## Reasoning Try It!

| | |
|---|---|
| **Essential Understanding** | 614 |
| **Think-Write** | 566 |
| **Know → Need → Plan** | 631 |

## Practice Do It!

| | |
|---|---|
| **Practice by Example** | 599 |
| **Think About a Plan** | 585 |
| **Error Analysis/Reasoning** | 634 |

# 11 Probability and Statistics

**Get Ready!**                                                                 **671**

My Math Video                                                                  673

11-1   Permutations and Combinations                                          674
11-2   Probability                                                            681
11-3   Probability of Multiple Events                                         688
       **Concept Byte:** Probability Distributions                            694
11-4   Conditional Probability                                                696

**Mid-Chapter Quiz**                                                          **703**

11-5   Analyzing Data                                                         704
11-6   Standard Deviation                                                     712
11-7   Samples and Surveys                                                    718
       **Concept Byte:** Describing Data                                      724
11-8   Binomial Distributions                                                 725
11-9   Normal Distributions                                                   733
       **Concept Byte:** Approximating a
       Binomial Distribution                                                  740

**Assessment and Test Prep**

       Pull It All Together                                                   742
       Chapter Review                                                         743
       Chapter Test                                                           749
       Cumulative Test Prep                                                   750

# 12 Matrices

**Get Ready!**     753

My Math Video     755

12-1   Adding and Subtracting Matrices     756
    **Concept Byte:** Working With Matrices     763
12-2   Matrix Multiplication     764
    **Concept Byte:** Networks     772
12-3   Determinants and Inverses     774

**Mid-Chapter Quiz**     783

12-4   Inverse Matrices and Systems     784
12-5   Geometric Transformations     793
12-6   Vectors     801

**Assessment and Test Prep**

    Pull It All Together     808
    Chapter Review     809
    Chapter Test     813
    Cumulative Test Prep     814

## Visual See It!

My Math Video     673
Solve It!     696
Connecting BIG IDEAS     809

## Reasoning Try It!

Essential Understanding     688
Think-Write     778
Know → Need → Plan     726

## Practice Do It!

Practice by Example     780
Think About a Plan     692
Error Analysis/Reasoning     716

# 13

# Periodic Functions and Trigonometry

**Get Ready!**                                                          **817**

My Math Video                                                           819

13-1   Exploring Periodic Data                                          820
       **Geometry Review:** Special Right Triangles                     827
13-2   Angles and the Unit Circle                                       828
       **Activity Lab:** Measuring Radians                              835
13-3   Radian Measure                                                   836
13-4   The Sine Function                                                843

**Mid-Chapter Quiz**                                                    **851**

       **Concept Byte:** Graphing Trigonometric Functions              852
13-5   The Cosine Function                                              853
13-6   The Tangent Function                                             860
13-7   Translating Sine and Cosine Functions                           867
13-8   Reciprocal Trigonometric Functions                              875

**Assessment and Test Prep**

       Pull It All Together                                             883
       Chapter Review                                                   884
       Chapter Test                                                     889
       Cumulative Test Prep                                             890

# 14 Trigonometric Identities and Equations

**Get Ready!**                                                                893

My Math Video                                                                 895

14-1    Trigonometric Identities                                             896
14-2    Solving Trigonometric Equations Using Inverses                      903
14-3    Right Triangles and Trigonometric Ratios                            911

**Mid-Chapter Quiz**                                                          **919**

14-4    Area and the Law of Sines                                            920
        **Activity Lab:** The Ambiguous Case                                 927
14-5    The Law of Cosines                                                   928
14-6    Angle Identities                                                     935
14-7    Double-Angle and Half-Angle Identities                              943

**Assessment and Test Prep**

        Pull It All Together                                                 950
        Chapter Review                                                       951
        Chapter Test                                                         955
        End-of-Course Assessment                                            956

## *Visual* **See It!**

My Math Video            895
Solve It!                843
Connecting BIG IDEAS     884

## *Reasoning* **Try It!**

Essential Understanding    903
Think-Write                876
Know → Need → Plan         831

## *Practice* **Do It!**

Practice by Example        824
Think About a Plan         917
Error Analysis/Reasoning   872

# Answers

1. B
2. F
3. A
4. F
5. D
6. G
7. B
8. G
9. A
10. H

# Entry-Level Assessment

## Multiple Choice

**Read each question. Then write the letter of the correct answer on your paper.**

1. Let $A = \{1, 2, 3, 4\}$ be a set in the universe $U = \{1, 2, 3, 4, 5, 6, 7, 8\}$. What is the complement of $A$?

   (A) $\{2, 3\}$      (C) $\{1, 2, 3, 4\}$

   (B) $\{5, 6, 7, 8\}$      (D) $\{2, 3, 7, 8\}$

2. Solve $x^2 + 2x - 3 = 0$ by factoring.

   (F) $x = -3$ and $x = 1$

   (G) $x = -1$ and $x = 3$

   (H) $x = 0$

   (I) $x = -3$ and $x = 0$

3. Simplify $\dfrac{3a^2b^3 - 12a^4b^3 + 6a^4b^2}{3a^2b}$.

   (A) $b^2 - 4a^2b^2 + 2a^2b$

   (B) $a^2b - 4a^2b^2 + 2a^2b$

   (C) $3b^2 - 12a^2b + 6b^2$

   (D) $3ab^2 - 4a^2b + 2ab^2$

4. Which relation is not a function?

   (F) $\{(1, -5), (2, 4), (1, -4)\}$

   (G) $\{(1, -5), (2, 4), (3, -3)\}$

   (H) $\{(1, -5), (2, 4), (3, 2)\}$

   (I) $\{(1, -5), (2, 4), (3, -4)\}$

5. In the diagram, $m$ and $n$ are parallel.

   What is the value of $x$?

   (A) $36°$      (C) $120°$

   (B) $60°$      (D) $144°$

6. Solve $2(1 - 2w) = 4w + 18$.

   (F) $-4$      (H) $8$

   (G) $-2$      (I) $16$

7. Which of the following lines is perpendicular to the line $3x + y = 2$?

   (A) $y = 3x + 4$

   (B) $y = \frac{1}{3}x - 2$

   (C) $y = -3x + 3$

   (D) $y = -\frac{1}{3}x + 1$

8. If $y = 1$, then $(x + 5) \cdot y = x + 5$. Which property supports this statement?

   (F) Inverse Property of Multiplication

   (G) Identity Property of Multiplication

   (H) Associative Property of Addition

   (I) Commutative Property of Addition

9.

   Which inequality does the graph represent?

   (A) $y < 2x - 4$

   (B) $y > -4x + 2$

   (C) $y > 2x - 4$

   (D) $y < -4x + 2$

10. The area of a trapezoid is $A = \frac{1}{2}h(b_1 + b_2)$. Solve for $b_1$.

    (F) $b_1 = \dfrac{2A - b_2}{h}$

    (G) $b_1 = \dfrac{2A - h}{b_2}$

    (H) $b_1 = \dfrac{2A}{h} - b_2$

    (I) $b_1 = 2A - b_2$

**11.** Let $\overleftrightarrow{AB}$ be parallel to $\overleftrightarrow{CD}$, with $A(-2, 3)$, $B(1, 4)$, and $C(1, 2)$. Which of the following could be the coordinates of point $D$?

   Ⓐ $(4, 1)$        Ⓒ $(-2, 3)$

   Ⓑ $(-2, -1)$     Ⓓ $(4, 3)$

**12.** Solve $3 \geq 4g - 5 \geq -1$.

   Ⓕ $-\frac{3}{2} \leq g \leq 2$       Ⓗ $-4 \leq g \leq 8$

   Ⓖ $-1 \leq g \leq \frac{3}{4}$      Ⓘ $1 \leq g \leq 2$

**13.** Which is *not* a solution of $5(2x + 4) \geq 2(x + 34)$?

   Ⓐ 48           Ⓒ 6

   Ⓑ 8            Ⓓ 3

**14.** Factor $6x^2 - 216$.

   Ⓕ $6(x - 6)(x + 6)$

   Ⓖ $(6x - 36)(6x + 36)$

   Ⓗ $6(x - 6)$

   Ⓘ $6(x - 36)(x + 6)$

**15.** Mike and Jane leave their home on bikes traveling in opposite directions on a straight road. Mike rides 5 mi/h faster than Jane. After 4 h they are 124 mi apart. At what rate does Mike ride his bike?

   Ⓐ 5 mi/h       Ⓒ 18 mi/h

   Ⓑ 13 mi/h     Ⓓ 31 mi/h

**16.** What is the point-slope form for the equation of the line in the graph?

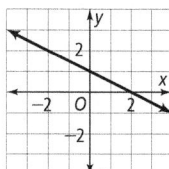

   Ⓕ $y - 2 = \frac{3}{2}(x + 2)$

   Ⓖ $y - 2 = \frac{1}{2}(x + 2)$

   Ⓗ $y - 2 = -\frac{1}{2}(x + 2)$

   Ⓘ $y - 2 = -\frac{2}{3}(x + 2)$

**17.** A rectangular photograph is being enlarged to poster size by making both the length and width six times larger than the original. How many times larger is the area of the poster than the area of the original photograph?

   Ⓐ $\frac{1}{6}$         Ⓒ 12

   Ⓑ 6           Ⓓ 36

**18.** A rectangle has a length of $2x + 3$ and a width of $x - 4$. Find the area of the rectangle.

   Ⓕ $2x^2 - 12$

   Ⓖ $2x^2 - 8x$

   Ⓗ $2x^2 - 5x - 12$

   Ⓘ $2x^2 - 11x - 12$

**19.** What is the $y$-intercept of the line that passes through the points $(-4, 4)$ and $(2, -5)$?

   Ⓐ $-2$        Ⓒ $\frac{3}{2}$

   Ⓑ $-\frac{3}{2}$      Ⓓ 2

**20.** Which of the following is equivalent to $\sqrt{2}(\sqrt{6} - 4)$?

   Ⓕ $\sqrt{12} - 4$       Ⓗ $\sqrt{12} - 8$

   Ⓖ $2\sqrt{3} - 2\sqrt{2}$    Ⓘ $2\sqrt{3} - 4\sqrt{2}$

**21.** Which of the following represents the system shown in the graph?

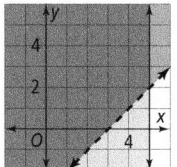

   Ⓐ $\begin{cases} y = x - 3 \\ x \geq 5 \end{cases}$     Ⓒ $\begin{cases} y < x - 3 \\ x = 5 \end{cases}$

   Ⓑ $\begin{cases} y \leq x - 3 \\ x > 5 \end{cases}$     Ⓓ $\begin{cases} y > x - 3 \\ x \leq 5 \end{cases}$

**22.** Which of the following equations represents the line that is parallel to the line $y = 5x + 2$ and that passes through the point $(1, -3)$?

   Ⓕ $y = -5x + 2$     Ⓗ $y = \frac{1}{5}x - 8$

   Ⓖ $y = 5x + 8$      Ⓘ $y = 5x - 8$

**11.** D

**12.** I

**13.** D

**14.** F

**15.** C

**16.** H

**17.** D

**18.** H

**19.** A

**20.** I

**21.** D

**22.** I

# Answers

23. A
24. G
25. A
26. G
27. D
28. H
29. A
30. F
31. A
32. I
33. A
34. H

---

23. Which equation represents a line that would be perpendicular to a second line with a slope of $\frac{1}{5}$?

    (A) $y = -5x + 2$

    (B) $y = -\frac{1}{5}x + 3$

    (C) $y = 5x - 2$

    (D) $5y + x = 2$

24. $\triangle ABC$ is similar to $\triangle DEF$.

    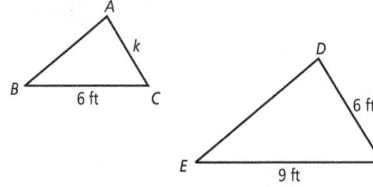

    What is the value of $k$?

    (F) 3 ft          (H) 6 ft

    (G) 4 ft          (I) 9 ft

25. Solve the equation using the Quadratic Formula.

    $6x^2 - 10x + 3 = 0$

    (A) $\frac{5 \pm \sqrt{7}}{6}$

    (B) $\frac{3 \pm \sqrt{5}}{6}$

    (C) $-2$ and $5$

    (D) $\frac{3}{4}$ and $\frac{2}{3}$

26. A rectangle in the coordinate plane has vertices $(3, 2)$, $(8, 2), (3, 6),$ and $(8, 6)$. Which of the following sets of vertices describes a rectangle that is congruent to this one?

    (F) $(3, -2), (3, -8), (5, -8), (5, -2)$

    (G) $(-2, -4), (-2, -8), (3, -8), (3, -4)$

    (H) $(0, 0), (5, 0), (5, 5), (0, 5)$

    (I) $(-3, 2), (1, 2), (1, 6), (-3, 6)$

27. Simplify the expression below.

    $(-6y^{-4})^5$

    (A) $7776y^{20}$          (C) $-7776y^{20}$

    (B) $\frac{7776}{y^{20}}$          (D) $-\frac{7776}{y^{20}}$

28. What is the solution to $\frac{2n + 8}{3} = \frac{n + 7}{2}$?

    (F) $-9$          (H) $5$

    (G) $-1$          (I) $13$

29. Solve the system of equations below.

    $\begin{cases} 3x + y = -7 \\ 4x - y = -14 \end{cases}$

    (A) $(-3, 2)$          (C) $(-3, -2)$

    (B) $(3, 2)$          (D) no solution

30. Which of the following is equivalent to $\frac{2x - 12}{x^2 - 2x - 24}$?

    (F) $\frac{2}{x + 4}$          (H) $\frac{1}{x^2 - 2}$

    (G) $\frac{1}{x + 2}$          (I) $\frac{2x - 3}{x - 6}$

31. What is (are) the solution(s) of the graphed function when the value of the function is 0?

    (A) $-1$ and $2$          (C) $2$

    (B) $1$ and $-2$          (D) $2.2$

32. Which of the following is true?

    (F) $\sqrt{85} < 9$          (H) $\sqrt{\frac{16}{25}} > \sqrt{\frac{16}{4}}$

    (G) $8 < \sqrt{62}$          (I) $\sqrt{121} < \sqrt{144}$

33. A firefighter leans a 30-ft ladder against a building in order to reach a window that is 24 ft high. How far away from the building is the base of the ladder?

    (A) 18 ft          (C) 24 ft

    (B) 20 ft          (D) 30 ft

34. What is the number of $x$-intercepts of the parabola with equation $y = 6x^2 - 4x - 3$?

    (F) 0          (H) 2

    (G) 1          (I) 3

# Get Ready!

## Adding Rational Numbers

**Find each sum.**

**1.** $6 + (-6)$    **2.** $-8 + 6$    **3.** $5.31 + (-7.40)$    **4.** $-1.95 + 10$

**5.** $7\frac{3}{4} + \left(-8\frac{1}{2}\right)$    **6.** $-2\frac{1}{3} + 3\frac{1}{4}$    **7.** $6\frac{2}{5} + 4\frac{3}{10}$    **8.** $-1\frac{5}{6} + 5\frac{1}{3}$

## Subtracting Rational Numbers

**Find each difference.**

**9.** $-28 - 14$    **10.** $61 - (-11)$    **11.** $-16 - (-25)$    **12.** $-6.2 - 3.6$

**13.** $-5\frac{2}{3} - \left(-2\frac{1}{3}\right)$    **14.** $-2\frac{1}{4} - 3\frac{1}{4}$    **15.** $2\frac{2}{3} - 7\frac{1}{3}$    **16.** $\frac{5}{2} - \frac{13}{4}$

## Multiplying and Dividing Rational Numbers

**Find each product or quotient.**

**17.** $-3 \cdot 7$    **18.** $-2.1 \cdot (-3.5)$    **19.** $-\frac{2}{3} \div 4$    **20.** $-\frac{3}{8} \div \frac{5}{8}$

## Using the Order of Operations

**Simplify each expression.**

**21.** $8 \cdot (-3) + 4$    **22.** $3 \cdot 4 - 8 \div 2$    **23.** $1 \div 2^2 - 0.54 + 1.26$

**24.** $9 \div (-3) - 2$    **25.** $5(3 \cdot 5 - 4)$    **26.** $1 - (1 - 5)^2 \div (-8)$

**27. Reasoning** Why don't the expressions $3 + 5^2 \cdot 3 \div 15$ and $(3 + 5^2) \cdot 3 \div 15$ yield the same answer?

 **Looking Ahead Vocabulary**

**28.** The current of a river flows north at a *constant* rate. What is the constant in the mathematical expression $3x + 5y + 3$?

**29.** Before signing a contract, you must review the *terms* and conditions of the contract. How many terms are there in the surface area formula below?

$$2(\ell w + wh + h\ell)$$

**30.** Engineers *evaluate* the efficiency of the memory and speed of a computer. What does evaluate mean in mathematics?

**31.** Smiling is a facial *expression* of happiness or contentment. In math, what is the expression that represents the quotient of 3 and 3 less than a number?

---

# Answers

## Get Ready!

**1.** 0    **2.** $-2$

**3.** $-2.09$    **4.** $8.05$

**5.** $-\frac{3}{4}$    **6.** $\frac{11}{12}$

**7.** $10\frac{7}{10}$    **8.** $3\frac{1}{2}$

**9.** $-42$    **10.** 72

**11.** 9    **12.** $-9.8$

**13.** $-3\frac{1}{3}$    **14.** $-5\frac{1}{2}$

**15.** $-4\frac{2}{3}$    **16.** $-\frac{3}{4}$

**17.** $-21$    **18.** 7.35

**19.** $-\frac{1}{6}$    **20.** $-\frac{3}{5}$

**21.** $-20$    **22.** 8

**23.** 0.97    **24.** $-5$

**25.** 55    **26.** 3

**27.** because the placement of the parentheses changes the order of operations

**28.** 3

**29.** 3 terms

**30.** Calculate the answer numerically.

**31.** $\frac{3}{n - 3}$

---

# Get Ready!

Assign this diagnostic assessment to determine if students have the prerequisite skills for Chapter 1.

| Lesson | Skill |
|---|---|
| Skills Handbook, p. T497 | Add Rational Numbers |
| Skills Handbook, p. T497 | Subtract Rational Numbers |
| Skills Handbook, p. T497 | Multiply and Divide Rational Numbers |
| Skills Handbook, p. T499 | Use the Order of Operations |

To remediate students, select from these resources (available for every lesson).
- Online Problems (PowerAlgebra.com)
- Reteaching (All-in-One Teaching Resources)
- Practice (All-in-One Teaching Resources)

## Why Students Need These Skills

**ADDING RATIONAL NUMBERS**
The addition of rational numbers is essential to the application of the Addition Property of Equality.

**SUBTRACTING RATIONAL NUMBERS**
The subtraction of rational numbers is essential to the application of the Subtraction Property of Equality.

**MULTIPLYING AND DIVIDING RATIONAL NUMBERS**
The multiplication and division of rational numbers is essential to the application of the Multiplication and Division Properties of Equality.

**USING THE ORDER OF OPERATIONS**
The order of operations is necessary when simplifying expressions with exponents.

## Looking Ahead Vocabulary

**CONSTANT** Tell students that a constant friend is someone who remains your friend no matter what. Ask them how a constant is different from a variable.

**TERMS** If students do not understand how a legal provision of a contract relates to a mathematical formula, explain that a term can also refer to a component of a mathematical expression.

**EVALUATE** Tell students that real estate agents evaluate properties to determine the worth or value. Ask them how they would evaluate the expression $2x + 3$ if they knew that $x$ is 5.

**EXPRESSION** Tell students that an idiomatic expression is a phrase with a meaning that is different from the individual meanings of the words. Ask for an example. Ask students how the value of an expression is different from the value of each number and operation by itself.

# Chapter 1 Overview

## UbD Understanding by Design

Chapter 1 expands on students' understandings and skills related to expressions, equations, and inequalities. In this chapter, students will develop the answers to the Essential Questions posed on the opposite page as they learn the concepts and skills bulleted below.

### BIG idea Variable

**ESSENTIAL QUESTION** How do variables help you model real-world situations?
- Students will use an expression to model the $n$th term of a pattern.
- Students will use variables to represent unknown quantities in real-world situations.

### BIG idea Properties

**ESSENTIAL QUESTION** How can you use the properties of real numbers to simplify algebraic expressions?
- Students will apply properties of real numbers to simplify algebraic expressions.

### BIG idea Solving Equations and Inequalities

**ESSENTIAL QUESTION** How do you solve an equation or inequality?
- Students will apply the Properties of Equality to solve an equation.
- Students will apply the Properties of Inequality to solve an inequality.
- Students will find all of the values of a variable that make an equation or inequality true.

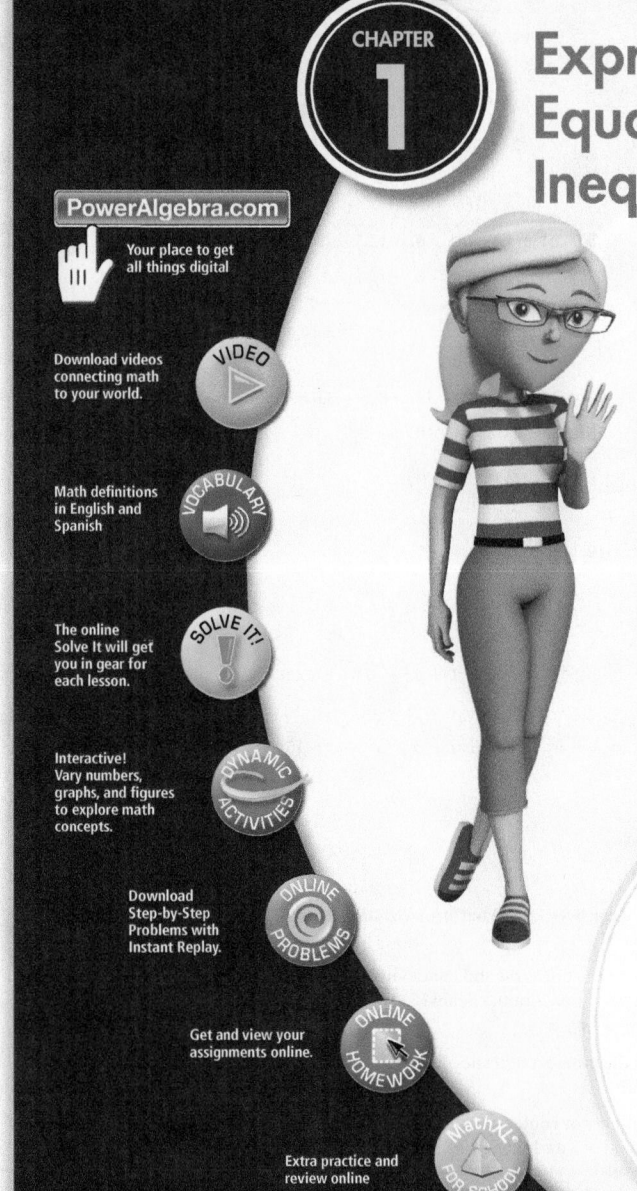

# Expressions, Equations, and Inequalities

**PowerAlgebra.com**

Your place to get all things digital

**VIDEO** Download videos connecting math to your world.

**VOCABULARY** Math definitions in English and Spanish

**SOLVE IT!** The online Solve It will get you in gear for each lesson.

**DYNAMIC ACTIVITIES** Interactive! Vary numbers, graphs, and figures to explore math concepts.

**ONLINE PROBLEMS** Download Step-by-Step Problems with Instant Replay.

**ONLINE HOMEWORK** Get and view your assignments online.

**MathXL FOR SCHOOL** Extra practice and review online

*You can use variables to represent the distance or time of the swimmer in the video.*

*How can you use algebraic expressions to represent patterns? How can you solve equations and inequalities? How can you solve absolute value equations? You will learn how in this chapter.*

## Vocabulary

**English/Spanish Vocabulary Audio Online:**

| English | Spanish |
| --- | --- |
| absolute value, p. 41 | valor absoluto |
| algebraic expression, p. 5 | expresión algebraica |
| compound inequality, p. 36 | desigualdad compuesta |
| like terms, p. 21 | términos semejantes |
| literal equation, p. 29 | ecuación literal |
| term, p. 20 | término |
| variable, p. 5 | variable |

**PowerAlgebra.com**

## Chapter 1 Overview

Use these online assets to engage your students. These include support for the Solve It and step-by-step solutions for Problems.

 Show the student-produced video demonstrating relevant and engaging applications of the new concepts in the chapter.

 Find online definitions for new terms in English and Spanish.

 Start each lesson with an attention-getting Problem. View the Problem online with helpful hints.

## BIG ideas

1 **Variable**

**Essential Question** How do variables help you model real-world situations?

2 **Properties**

**Essential Question** How can you use the properties of real numbers to simplify algebraic expressions?

3 **Solving Equations and Inequalities**

**Essential Question** How do you solve an equation or inequality?

## Chapter Preview

1-1 Patterns and Expressions
1-2 Properties of Real Numbers
1-3 Algebraic Expressions
1-4 Solving Equations
1-5 Solving Inequalities
1-6 Absolute Value Equations and Inequalities

PowerAlgebra.com | Chapter 1 Expressions, Equations, and Inequalities | 3

## My Math Video

**FACILITATE** Use this photo to introduce algebraic expressions. The distance the swimmer goes can be expressed with respect to the rate he swims.

**Q** What is the relationship between rate, distance and time? **[distance = rate · time]**

**Q** Suppose this swimmer is maintaining a constant rate of 1.2 m/s. How far will he swim in a minute? **[1.2 m/s · 60 s = 72 m]**

**Q** Let $n$ represent the number of seconds the swimmer swam before stopping for a breath. What expression represents the distance he went? **[1.2$n$]**

**Q** Suppose the swimmer took off his flippers and is now swimming only 0.8 m/s. What expression represents the distance he now swims in $n$ seconds? **[0.8$n$]**

**ERROR PREVENTION**

Watch for students who may not understand which unit the variable represents. Show that multiplying m/s by s gives meters, which is the correct unit of the distance.

**EXTENSION**

Have students identify some other sports or activities that have a distance dependent on a rate. Suggest students research the activity to find typical rates and model the distance with an expression.

 Increase students' depth of knowledge with interactive online activities.

 Show Problems from each lesson solved step by step. Instant replay allows students to go at their own pace when studying online.

 Assign homework to individual students or to an entire class.

 Prepare students for the Mid-Chapter Quiz and Chapter Test with online practice and review.

# Math Background

**UbD**

## Variable

**BIG** idea Quantities are used to form expressions, equations, and inequalities. An expression refers to a quantity but does not make a statement about it. An equation (or an inequality) is a statement about the quantities it mentions. Using variables in place of numbers in equations (or inequalities) allows the statement of relationships among numbers that are unknown or unspecified.

### ESSENTIAL UNDERSTANDINGS

**1-1**   You can represent some patterns using diagrams, words, numbers, or algebraic expressions.

**1-3**   You can represent some mathematical phrases and real-world quantities using algebraic expressions.

## Properties

**BIG** idea All of the facts of arithmetic and algebra follow from certain properties.

### ESSENTIAL UNDERSTANDINGS

**1-2**   The set of real numbers has several special subsets related in particular ways.

**1-3**   You can represent some mathematical phrases and real-world quantities using algebraic expressions.

## Solving Equations and Inequalities

**BIG** idea Solving an equation is the process of rewriting the equation to make what it says about its variable(s) as simple as possible. Properties of numbers and equality can be used to transform an equation (or inequality) into equivalent, simpler equations (or inequalities) in order to find solutions. Useful information about equations and inequalities (including solutions) can be found by analyzing graphs or tables. The numbers and types of solutions vary predictably, based on the type of equation.

### ESSENTIAL UNDERSTANDINGS

**1-4**   You can use the properties of equality and inverse operations to solve equations.

  Sometimes, no value of the variable makes an equation true. For identities, all values of the variable make the equation true.

**1-5**   Just as you use properties of equality to solve equations, you can use properties of inequality to solve inequalities.

**1-6**   An absolute value quantity is nonnegative. Since opposites have the same absolute value, an absolute value equation can have two solutions.

  You can write an absolute value inequality as a compound inequality without absolute value signs.

## Variable

A variable is a symbol, usually a letter, which represents one or more numbers.

The context of a problem will determine the set of values for which a variable is defined. If $p$ represents the number of people that use a certain airport each day, then $p$ must take on whole number values. If $t$ is the lifetime of a light bulb, then it can be any positive real number.

Variables allow scientists and mathematicians to summarize data as a general rule. For example, you could write the following table to with columns for the side length and the perimeter of a square.

| Length of a side | Perimeter of square |
|---|---|
| 1 | 4 |
| 2 | 8 |
| 3 | 12 |
| 4 | 16 |
| 5 | 20 |
| 6 | 24 |

It is much easier, however, to summarize the relationship between side length and perimeter with the equation $p = 4s$, where $p$ represents perimeter, and $s$ represents side length. Because we discover general laws from observations, the use of variables to state relationships is important.

An *open sentence* is an equation that contains one or more variables. To solve the equation is to find the value of the variable that makes the equation true. For example, $x = 2$ is a solution to the open sentence $x^2 = 4$ ($x = -2$ is also a solution).

### Common Errors With Variables

Many different letters and symbols can represent variables. Students may be confused when confronted with the symbols $e$ and $\pi$. They conventionally stand for specific irrational numbers and not variables.

## Solving Equations and Inequalities

**An equation** is a statement that two expressions are equal. Solving an algebraic equation means finding all of the values of the variable that make the equation true. The Properties of Equality and inverse operations are used to solve equations.

**The Properties of Equality** for real numbers include the following:

| Reflexive | Symmetric |
|---|---|
| $a = a$ | $a = b \longrightarrow b = a$ |
| **Transitive** | **Substitution** |
| $a = b, b = c \longrightarrow a = c$ | $a = b \longrightarrow 2a + 3 = 2b + 3$ |

**Inverse operations** are operations that "undo" each other.
• Addition and subtraction are inverse operations.
• Multiplication and division are inverse operations.

Some equations are never true (no solutions):

$x + 1 = x + 2$

Some equations are always true (Identities):

$x + 2 = x + 2$

**Solving an inequality** means finding the range of values of the variable. The properties of inequalities are similar to the properties used for solving equations, with an important difference: when you multiply or divide each side of an inequality by a negative number, you must reverse the inequality symbol.

**A compound inequality** is two inequalities joined by the word *and* or *or*.

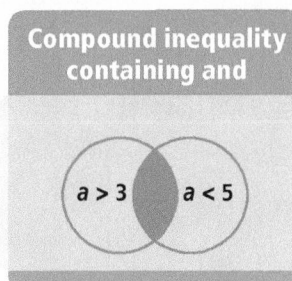

**Compound inequality containing and**
$a > 3$   $a < 5$

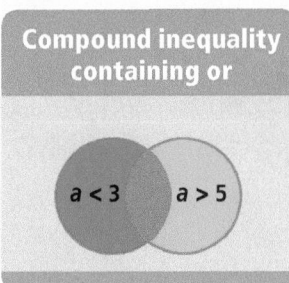

**Compound inequality containing or**
$a < 3$   $a > 5$

### Common Errors With Solving Equations and Inequalities

Some common errors students make when solving equations and inequalities include
• performing an operation on one side of an equation or inequality but not the other.
• not checking the solution to an equation or inequality in the *original* equation or inequality.
• failing to reverse the direction of the inequality sign when multiplying or dividing both sides of an inequality by a negative number.

## Absolute Value

The absolute value of a number $x$, written $|x|$, represents the distance from any number $x$ to 0 on the number line. As the diagram makes clear, for example, $|4| = |-4| = 4$.

4 units    4 units

$-5\ -4\ -3\ -2\ -1\quad 0\quad 1\quad 2\quad 3\quad 4\quad 5$

With this in mind, the following properties are reasonable:

(1) $|x| \geq 0$

(2) $|x| = 0$ if and only if $x = 0$

(3) $|x - y| \leq |x| + |y|$

(1) just says that all distances are nonnegative. (2) says that only zero is a distance of zero from zero on the number line. (3) tells you that it is not farther to go directly from $x$ to $y$ than it is to go from zero to $x$ and then from zero to $y$. In three-dimensions, this is the triangle inequality. In popular speech, we say that it is faster to go "as the crow flies."

In more advanced math courses, students will see that the absolute value function is generalized as the *distance function*, $d(x, y)$. Compare the following properties of $d(x, y)$ to the properties of the absolute value function:

(1') $d(x, y) \geq 0$

(2') $d(x, y) = 0$ if and only if $x = y$

(3') $d(x, y) \leq d(x, y) + d(x, z)$

(1') again says that distances are nonnegative. (2) states that two different points cannot be located in exactly the same place. (3') is the triangle inequality.

Absolute values have many applications.

### Common Errors With Absolute Value

**A definition error** occurs when students assume an absolute value is always positive. The absolute value of zero is zero, which is neither positive nor negative. The value of an absolute value is always *nonnegative*. Also, students sometimes confuse absolute value with *opposite*. Point out that the opposite of a positive number is not the same as its absolute value.

# EXPRESSIONS, EQUATIONS, AND INEQUALITIES
# Pacing and Assignment Guide

| | | TRADITIONAL | | | BLOCK |
|---|---|---|---|---|---|
| **Lesson** | **Teaching Day(s)** | **Basic** | **Average** | **Advanced** | **Block** |
| **1-1** | 1 | Problems 1–3<br>Exs. 8–24, 26–32 even, 33, 34–38 even, 43–57 | Problems 1–3<br>Exs. 9–23 odd, 25–39, 43–57 | Problems 1–3<br>Exs. 9–23 odd, 25–42, 43–57 | **Day 1**<br>Problems 1–3<br>Exs. 9–23 odd, 25–39, 43–57 |
| **1-2** | 1 | Problems 1–4<br>Exs. 10–40, 42–48 even, 49, 58–66 even, 72–83 | Problems 1–4<br>Exs. 11–39 odd, 41–67, 72–83 | Problems 1–4<br>Exs. 11–39 odd, 41–83 | Problems 1–4<br>Exs. 11–39 odd, 41–67, 72–83 |
| **1-3** | 1 | Problems 1–5<br>Exs. 10–38, 41–49 odd, 52–55, 63–74 | Problems 1–5<br>Exs. 11–37 odd, 39–60, 63–74 | Problems 1–5<br>Exs. 11–37 odd, 39–74 | **Day 2**<br>Problems 1–5<br>Exs. 11–37 odd, 39–60, 63–74 |
| **1-4** | 1 | Problems 1–5<br>Exs. 10–40, 43–45, 52, 53, 58–62 even, 66–79 | Problems 1–5<br>Exs. 11–39 odd, 41–63, 66–79 | Problems 1–5<br>Exs. 11–39 odd, 41–79 | Problems 1–5<br>Exs. 11–39 odd, 41–63, 66–79 |
| **1-5** | 1 | Problems 1–4<br>Exs. 10–35, 44–50 even, 51 | Problems 1–4<br>Exs. 11–35 odd, 44–53 | Problems 1–4<br>Exs. 11–35 odd, 44–53 | **Day 3**<br>Problems 1–6<br>Exs. 11–43 odd, 44–61, 67–78 |
| | 2 | Problems 5–6<br>Exs. 36–43, 57, 60, 67–78 | Problems 5–6<br>Exs. 37–43 odd, 54–61, 67–78 | Problems 5–6<br>Exs. 37–43 odd, 54–66, 67–78 | |
| **1-6** | 1 | Problems 1–3<br>Exs. 10–24 all, 48–52 even | Problems 1–3<br>Exs. 11–23 odd, 43–52 | Problems 1–3<br>Exs. 11–23 odd, 43–52 | **Day 4**<br>Problems 1–5<br>Exs. 11–41 odd, 43–81, 90–102 |
| | 2 | Problems 4–6<br>Exs. 25–42 all, 53, 58–66 even, 69, 81, 90–102 | Problems 4–6<br>Exs. 25–41 odd, 53–81, 90–102 | Problems 4–6<br>Exs. 25–41 odd, 53–89, 90–102 | |
| **Review** | 1 | Chapter 1 Review | Chapter 1 Review | Chapter 1 Review | **Day 5**<br>Chapter 1 Review<br>Chapter 1 Test |
| **Assess** | 1 | Chapter 1 Test | Chapter 1 Test | Chapter 1 Test | |
| **Total** | | **10 Days** | **10 Days** | **10 Days** | **5 Days** |

Note: Pacing does not include Concept Bytes and other feature pages.

# Resources

| | For the Chapter | 1-1 | 1-2 | 1-3 | 1-4 | 1-5 | 1-6 |
|---|---|---|---|---|---|---|---|
| **Planning** | | | | | | | |
| Teacher Center Online Planner & Grade Book | I | I | I | I | I | I | I |
| **Interactive Learning & Guided Instruction** | | | | | | | |
| My Math Video | I | | | | | | |
| Solve It! | | I   TM | I   TM | I   TM | I   TM | I   TM | I   TM |
| Student Companion (SP)* | | P M | P M | P M | P M | P M | |
|   *Vocabulary Support* | | I  P M | I  P M | I  P M | I  P M | I  P M | I  P M |
|   *Got It? Support* | | I  P | I  P | I  P | I  P | I  P | I  P |
| Dynamic Activity | | | I | | | I | |
| Online Problems | | I | I | I | I | I | I |
| Additional Problems | | M | M | M | M | M | M |
| English Language Learner Support (TR) | | E P M | E P M | E P M | E P M | E P M | E P M |
| Activities, Games, and Puzzles | | E   M | E   M | E   M | E   M | E   M | E   M |
| Teaching With TI Technology With CD-ROM | | | | | | | |
| TI-Nspire™ Support CD-ROM | | ✓ | ✓ | ✓ | ✓ | ✓ | ✓ |
| **Lesson Check & Practice** | | | | | | | |
| Student Companion (SP)* | | P M | P M | P M | P M | P M | P M |
|   *Lesson Check Support* | | I  P | I  P | I  P | I  P | I  P | I  P |
| Practice and Problem Solving Workbook (SP) | | P | P | P | P | P | P |
|   *Think About a Plan* (TR)* | | E P M | E P M | E P M | E P M | E P M | E P M |
|   *Practice Form G* (TR)* | | E P M | E P M | E P M | E P M | E P M | E P M |
|   *Standardized Test Prep* (TR)* | | P M | P M | P M | P M | P M | P M |
| Practice *Form K* (TR)* | | E P M | E P M | E P M | E P M | E P M | E P M |
| Extra Practice | E   M | | | | | | |
| Find the Errors! | M | | | | | | |
| Enrichment (TR) | | E P M | E P M | E P M | E P M | E P M | E P M |
| Answers and Solutions CD-ROM | ✓ | ✓ | ✓ | ✓ | ✓ | ✓ | ✓ |
| **Assess & Remediate** | | | | | | | |
| ExamView CD-ROM | ✓ | ✓ | ✓ | ✓ | ✓ | ✓ | ✓ |
| Lesson Quiz | | I   TM | I   TM | I   TM | I   TM | I   TM | I   TM |
| Quizzes and Tests *Form G* (TR)* | E P M | | | E P M | | | E P M |
| Quizzes and Tests *Form K* (TR)* | E P M | | | E P M | | | E P M |
| Reteaching (TR)* | | E P M | E P M | E P M | E P M | E P M | E P M |
| Performance Tasks (TR)* | P M | | | | | | |
| Cumulative Review (TR)* | P M | | | | | | |
| Progress Monitoring Assessments | I  P M | | | | | | |

(TR) Available in All-In-One Teaching Resources    * Spanish available

# 1 Interactive Learning

## Solve It!

**PURPOSE** To describe a geometric pattern and extend it to find the eighth term

**PROCESS** Students may
- trace the first pattern of squares and then rotate it clockwise 90° to see the next image.
- realize the 4th and 8th figures are the same.

### FACILITATE
**Q** Why is the middle square always the same? **[It is at the center of the rotation.]**

**Q** How do the 5th and 1st figures compare? **[They are identical.]**

**Q** Must you draw 8 figures to solve the problem? Explain. **[No; the 4th and 8th figures match.]**

**ANSWER** See Solve It in Answers on next page.
**CONNECT THE MATH** In the Solve It, students find a pattern in a video game. In this lesson, they continue to discover patterns and express them mathematically.

# 2 Guided Instruction

## Problem 1

**Q** Number the figures 1, 2, 3, and 4. How does the figure number relate to the number of sides? **[The figure number is 2 less the number of sides.]**

## Got It?                    VISUAL LEARNERS

**Q** What changes in each figure? **[The length of each arm increases by 1 block.]**

**Q** What remains the same? **[the center]**

---

**Objective** To identify and describe patterns

**Getting Ready!**

Some video games really make you think! This one can turn your head round and round.

You are playing a video game. You reach a locked gate. The lock is a square with 9 sections. You can make a key by placing a red or yellow block in each section. Near the gate is a carving of a pattern of squares.

1st        2nd        3rd

The key to the gate is the eighth image in the pattern. Draw the key to the gate. How do you know it will work?

### Lesson Vocabulary
- constant
- variable quantity
- variable
- numerical expression
- algebraic expression

In the Solve It, you identified and used a geometric pattern. In this lesson, you will identify patterns in pictures, tables, and graphs and describe them using numbers and variables.

**Essential Understanding** You can represent some patterns using diagrams, words, numbers, or algebraic expressions.

**Problem 1** Identifying a Pattern

**Think**

**How can you identify a pattern?** Look for the same type of change between consecutive figures.

Look at the figures from left to right. What is the pattern? What would the next figure in the pattern look like?

The pattern shows regular polygons with the number of sides increasing by one.

The last figure shown above has six sides, so the next figure would have seven sides. This is a heptagon: ◯.

**Got It? 1.** Look at the figures from left to right. What is the pattern? Draw the next figure in the pattern.

4    Chapter 1   Expressions, Equations, and Inequalities

---

**BIG idea** Variable    UbD

**ESSENTIAL UNDERSTANDINGS**
- Some patterns can be represented using diagrams, words, numbers, or algebraic expressions.
- Variables can represent variable quantities in real world situations and in patterns.

## Math Background
This lesson illustrates that searching for patterns underlies much of mathematical knowledge. The lesson builds on students' previous experience with patterns by discussing both geometric and numeric patterns. Most of the patterns are arithmetic in nature, having the form $an$, $n + a$, or $an + b$. Patterns of this type are linear functions.

This lesson uses the three-column tables to organize information. The input and output values in the tables represent the independent and dependent variables.

## Support Student Learning
Use the **Algebra 2 Companion** to engage and support students during instruction. See Lesson Resources at the end of this lesson for details.

## PowerAlgebra.com

### 1 Interactive Learning

**Solve It!**
Step out how to solve the Problem with helpful hints and an online question. Other questions are listed above in Interactive Learning.

A mathematical *quantity* is anything that can be measured or counted. The *value* of the quantity is its measure or the number of items that are counted. Quantities whose values do not change are called **constants**. In other situations, the value of a quantity can change. Quantities whose values change or vary are called **variable quantities**.

### Key Concepts   Variables and Expressions

| Definition | Examples | |
|---|---|---|
| A **variable** is a symbol, usually a letter, that represents one or more numbers. | $n$ | $x$ |
| A **numerical expression** is a mathematical phrase that contains numbers and operation symbols. | $3 + 5$ | $(8 - 2) + 5$ |
| An **algebraic expression** is a mathematical phrase that contains one or more variables. | $3n + 5$ | $(8x - 2) + 5n$ |

Tables are a convenient way to organize data and discover patterns. They work much like an "input/output" machine: a machine that takes one value as an input, processes it, and gives a value as an output. A process column in the table provides a way to understand what happens to the input values.

### Problem 2   Expressing a Pattern With Algebra

**Use a pattern to answer each question.**

**A** How many toothpicks are in the 20th figure?

Use a table. Look for a pattern that relates the figure number to the number of toothpicks.

| Figure Number (Input) | Process Column | Number of Toothpicks (Output) |
|---|---|---|
| 1 | 1(4) | 4 |
| 2 | 2(4) | 8 |
| 3 | 3(4) | 12 |
| ⋮ | ⋮ | ⋮ |
| $n$ | ■ | ■ |

To get the output, multiply the input by 4.

Pattern: Multiply the figure number by 4 to get the number of toothpicks. So, there are $20(4) = 80$ toothpicks in the 20th figure.

**B** What is an expression that describes the number of toothpicks in the *n*th figure?

Use the pattern from part (A). There are $4n$ toothpicks in the *n*th figure.

**Think**

What would the process look like for the *n*th row?
Multiply the figure number, *n*, by 4.

**Got It?  2.** How many tiles are in the 25th figure in this pattern? Show a table of values with a process column.

**Take Note**

**Q** What is the only difference between algebraic expressions and numerical expressions? **[An algebraic expression contains one or more variables while a numerical expression contains no variables.]**

## Problem 2
In analyzing the process, students may look at the pattern and think of it as adding 4 each time. Remind them that multiplication is repeated addition.

Have volunteers come to the board and draw the next two or three figures in the pattern to make sure all students see how it works.

**Q** The numbers of toothpicks form the pattern 4, 8, 12, and so on. Describe this pattern. **[multiples of 4]**

**Q** How does the Process Column relate the numbers in the Input and Output columns? **[The Process Column shows that the input number is always multiplied by 4.]**

**Q** A student described this pattern as "add 4." Why is this not as useful as "multiply by 4"? **["Add 4" tells how the output numbers are increasing, but it does not relate the output numbers to the input numbers.]**

### Got It?

**Q** What is the total number of squares in each figure? **[4, 6, 8]**

**Q** How is the 2nd figure different from the first? **[It has two more yellow squares on the right.]**

**Q** How is the 3rd figure different from the second? **[The 3rd figure has two more yellow squares on the right.]**

## 2  Guided Instruction

Each Problem is worked out and supported online.

**Problem 1**
Identifying a Pattern
*Animated*

**Problem 2**
Expressing a Pattern with Algebra
*Animated*

**Problem 3**
Using a Graph
*Animated*

**Support in Algebra 2 Companion**
- Vocabulary
- Key Concepts
- Got It?

# Answers

### Solve It!

You can get each image in the pattern by turning the image before it clockwise 90°. Notice that the pattern begins to repeat with the fifth image. So, the 4th and 8th images will be the same.

### Got It?

**1.** The pattern shows a center square and a yellow square added to each side with the number of squares per side increasing by one.

**2.** 52 tiles

## Problem 3

Many mathematical patterns can be shown with graphs. Make sure all students know how to use ordered pairs to describe the coordinates of points on Cartesian grids.

**Q** Use an ordered pair to describe a point on the line. What do the coordinates of the ordered pair represent? **[Answers may vary. Sample: (6, 8); if the total of all the fish lengths is 6 inches, you need an 8 gallon tank.]**

**Q** The line rises from left to right, so the relationship is increasing. Why? **[As you get more fish, you need a bigger tank.]**

**Q** You can use the variables $L$ and $G$ for the quantities in this relationship. What equation relates $L$ and $G$? **[$G = L + 2$]**

**Q** If a tank held 12 gallons, what would that mean in terms of fish length? **[The tank could hold 10 inches of fish.]**

### Got It?

**Q** Using the graph, what is the cost of one platy? Explain. **[$2; when $x = 1$, $y = 2$.]**

**Q** If you continue the graph, what figure would contain all of the points? **[a line]**

**Q** Do you need the entire graph to determine the cost of 40 platys? Explain. **[No; if you know the cost of one you can calculate the cost for 40.]**

### Problem 3 Using a Graph

**Aquarium** You want to set up an aquarium and need to determine what size tank to buy. The graph shows tank sizes using a rule that relates the capacity of the tank to the combined lengths of the fish it can hold.

If you want five 2-in. platys, four 1-in. guppies, and a 3-in. loach, which is the smallest capacity tank you can buy: 15-gallon, 20-gallon, or 25-gallon? Use a table to find the answer.

Tank Sizes

**Plan**

How can you use the given graph?
You can use the graph to make a table and find a pattern relating capacity and combined fish length.

**Think**

Choose some points on the graph.

Make a table using the input and output values shown in the ordered pairs.
Find a pattern in the process column. Each output is 2 more than the corresponding input.

You want 5 platys, 4 guppies, and 1 loach. So, you will have a total of 17 in. of fish. Find the output when the input is 17.

Write the answer in words.

**Write**

(0, 2), (5, 7), (10, 12)

| Input | Process Column | Output |
|-------|----------------|--------|
| 0 | 0 + 2 | 2 |
| 5 | 5 + 2 | 7 |
| 10 | 10 + 2 | 12 |

$$\text{output} = \text{input} + 2$$
$$= 17 + 2$$
$$= 19$$

You need to buy the 20-gal tank.

**Got It?** **3.** The graph at the right shows the total cost of platys at the aquarium shop. Use a table to answer the questions.
  **a.** How much do six platys cost?
  **b.** How much do ten platys cost?
  **c.** Reasoning Why is the graph in Problem 3 a line while the graph at the right is a set of points?

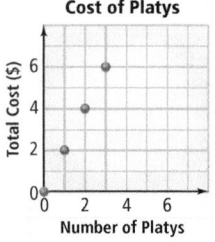

Cost of Platys

---

# Additional Problems

**1.** Describe the pattern. What would the next figure in the pattern look like?

**ANSWER** Answers may vary. Sample: Each figure has one more equilateral triangle. The next figure will have 5 triangles, arranged like this:

**2.** These figures are made with toothpicks.

**a.** How many toothpicks are in the 20th figure? Use a table of values with a process column to justify your answer.

**b.** What expression describes the number of toothpicks in the $n$th figure?

**ANSWERS** 100; $5n$

**3.** You buy a bag of fish food and some goldfish. The graph shows the total cost depending on how many goldfish you buy.

What is your total cost if you buy the food plus 9 goldfish? Use a table to find the answer.

**ANSWER** $19

# Answers

**Got It?** (continued)

**3. a.** $12

**b.** $20

**c.** The number of platys must be a whole number whereas the lengths of fish can be a fraction or decimal.

**Lesson Check**

**Do you know HOW?**

Describe a rule for each pattern.

**1.** 35, 70, 105, 140, . . .

**2.**

Make a table to represent each pattern. Use a process column.

**3.** 2, 4, 6, 8, . . .

**4.** ‖‖ ‖‖‖‖ ‖‖‖‖‖‖ ‖‖‖‖‖‖‖‖

**Do you UNDERSTAND?**

**5.** Explain the strategy you use to identify a pattern.

**6. Compare and Contrast** How are tables of values like pictorial representations? How are they different?

**7. Error Analysis** Your friend looks for a pattern in the table below and claims that the output equals the input divided by 2. Is your friend correct? Explain.

| Input | 3 | 6.8 | 8 | 10 | 25 |
|---|---|---|---|---|---|
| Output | 2 | 3.4 | 4 | 5 | 12.5 |

## Practice and Problem-Solving Exercises

Ⓐ **Practice**   Describe each pattern using words. Draw the next likely figure in each pattern.   ◀ **See Problem 1.**

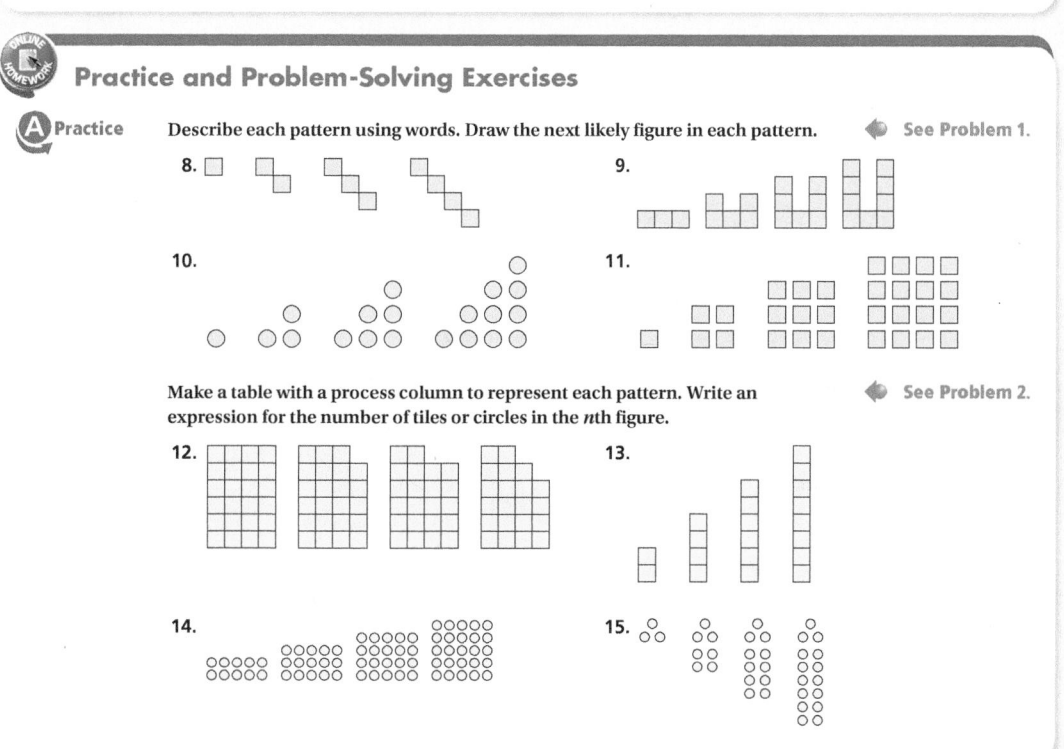

**8.**

**9.**

**10.**

**11.**

Make a table with a process column to represent each pattern. Write an expression for the number of tiles or circles in the *n*th figure.   ◀ **See Problem 2.**

**12.**

**13.**

**14.**

**15.**

---

# 3 Lesson Check

## Do you know HOW?

- For Exercise 1, compare the rules "add 35" and "multiply the term number by 35." Only the second type can be used to find the value of the *n*th term.
- For Exercises 3–4, students may need to be told to use the term numbers 1, 2, 3, and 4 as the input numbers in the chart. Most students should recognize these patterns as the even numbers and the doubling pattern. For students who do not recognize patterns, help them make a list of patterns they have seen in this lesson. They can use this list for ideas on future problems.

## Do you UNDERSTAND?

- For Exercise 5, ask how patterns can be represented. Ask students if the representation of the pattern affects the solution strategy.
- For Exercise 6, "pictorial representation" could be a graph or a series of figures. Have students discuss both interpretations of the question.

## Close

> **Q** Why is it useful to be able to describe patterns?
> **[Answers may vary. Sample: If you can describe a pattern, you can use the description to make predictions.]**

---

# Answers

## Lesson Check

**1.** add 35

**2.** rotate 90° clockwise

**3.**

| Input | Process Column | Output |
|---|---|---|
| 1 | 2(1) | 2 |
| 2 | 2(2) | 4 |
| 3 | 2(3) | 6 |
| 4 | 2(4) | 8 |
| ⋮ | ⋮ | ⋮ |
| *n* | 2(*n*) | 2*n* |

**4.**

| Input | Process Column | Output |
|---|---|---|
| 1 | 3(1) | 3 |
| 2 | 3(2) | 6 |
| 3 | 3(3) | 9 |
| 4 | 3(4) | 12 |
| ⋮ | ⋮ | ⋮ |
| *n* | 3(*n*) | 3*n* |

**5.** Check students' work.

**6.** Answers may vary. Sample: Tables of values and pictorial representations are both convenient ways to organize data and discover patterns. Tables give more detail. Pictorial representations are visual.

**7.** No; the output is $\frac{1}{2}$ the input for all values except the first (Input: 3; Output: 2).

**8–15.** See next page.

**PowerAlgebra.com**

## 3 Lesson Check

For a digital lesson check, use the Got It questions.

**Support in Algebra 2 Companion**
- Lesson Check

## 4 Practice

Assign homework to individual students or to an entire class.

# 4 Practice

**ASSIGNMENT GUIDE**

Basic: 8–24 all, 24–32 even, 33, 34, 36, 38

Average: 9–23 odd, 25–39

Advanced: 9–23 odd, 25–42

Standardized Test Prep: 43–45

Mixed Review: 46–57

Reasoning exercises have blue headings.

Applications exercises have red headings.

**EXERCISE 34:** Use the Think About a Plan worksheet in the Practice and Problem Solving Workbook (also available in the Teaching Resources in print and online) to further support students' development in becoming independent learners.

**HOMEWORK QUICK CHECK**
To check students' understanding of key skills and concepts, go over Exercises 13, 21, 33, 34, and 38.

---

**Copy and complete each table. Include a process column.**

**16.**

| Input | Output |
|-------|--------|
| 1 | 0 |
| 2 | 1 |
| 3 | 2 |
| 4 | 3 |
| 5 | ■ |
| 6 | ■ |
| ⋮ | ⋮ |
| $n$ | ■ |

**17.**

| Input | Output |
|-------|--------|
| 1 | 3 |
| 2 | 4 |
| 3 | 5 |
| 4 | 6 |
| 5 | ■ |
| 6 | ■ |
| ⋮ | ⋮ |
| $n$ | ■ |

**18.**

| Input | Output |
|-------|--------|
| 1 | −3 |
| 2 | −6 |
| 3 | −9 |
| 4 | −12 |
| 5 | ■ |
| 6 | ■ |
| ⋮ | ⋮ |
| $n$ | ■ |

**Identify a pattern by making a table. Include a process column.**

◄ **See Problem 3.**

**19.**

**20.**

**21.**

The graph shows the number of bottles of water needed for students going on a field trip.

**22.** How many bottles of water are needed if 5 students attend?

**23.** How many bottles of water are needed if 20 students attend?

**24.** How many bottles of water are needed if $n$ students attend?

**Class Field Trip**

**Ⓑ Apply**  **Identify a pattern and find the next three numbers in the pattern.**

**25.** 6, 12, 18, 24, . . .

**26.** 1, 4, 3, 6, 5, . . .

**27.** 3, 6, 10, 15, . . .

**28.** 2, 6, 10, 14, . . .

**29.** 1, 3, 9, 27, 81, . . .

**30.** 4, 20, 100, 500, . . .

**31.** Identify a pattern and draw the next three figures in the pattern.

**32. Open-Ended** Write a rule so that for every input, the output is an even number.

---

# Answers

## Practice and Problem-Solving Exercises
(continued)

**8.** One square, with the number of squares increasing by one. The top left vertex of the added square is the same as the bottom right vertex of the previous square.

**9.** Base of 3 squares with the number of squares increasing vertically by one on each of the outer squares of the base.

**10.** One circle, then 1 + 2 or 3 circles, then 1 + 2 + 3 or 6 circles. In general, the number is increasing vertically by $n$ to the right of the previous figure.

**11.** One square, then $2^2$ or 4 squares, then $3^2$ or 9 squares, then $4^2$ or 16 squares. In general, the number of squares is $n \times n$ or $n^2$.

**12.** $25 - n$

| Input | Process Column | Output |
|-------|----------------|--------|
| 1 | 24 | 24 |
| 2 | 24 − 1 | 23 |
| 3 | 24 − 2 | 22 |
| 4 | 24 − 3 | 21 |
| ⋮ | ⋮ | ⋮ |
| $n$ | $24 - (n - 1)$ | $25 - n$ |

**13.** $2n$

| Input | Process Column | Output |
|-------|----------------|--------|
| 1 | 2(1) | 2 |
| 2 | 2(2) | 4 |
| 3 | 2(3) | 6 |
| 4 | 2(4) | 8 |
| ⋮ | ⋮ | ⋮ |
| $n$ | 2($n$) | $2n$ |

**14.** $5 + 5n$

| Input | Process Column | Output |
|-------|----------------|--------|
| 1 | 5 + 5(1) | 10 |
| 2 | 5 + 5(2) | 15 |
| 3 | 5 + 5(3) | 20 |
| 4 | 5 + 5(4) | 25 |
| ⋮ | ⋮ | ⋮ |
| $n$ | 5 + 5($n$) | $5 + 5n$ |

**15.** $4n - 1$

| Input | Process Column | Output |
|-------|----------------|--------|
| 1 | 4(1) − 1 | 3 |
| 2 | 4(2) − 1 | 7 |
| 3 | 4(3) − 1 | 11 |
| 4 | 4(4) − 1 | 15 |
| ⋮ | ⋮ | ⋮ |
| $n$ | 4($n$) − 1 | $4n - 1$ |

**16–32.** See next page.

**33. Think About a Plan** A moving company sells different sizes of boxes as shown. The extra-large box is one size larger than the third box shown. What is its volume?
- Identify a pattern of the dimension changes.
- What is the formula for the volume of a rectangular prism?

12 in. 16 in. 12 in.  16 in. 16 in. 16 in.  20 in. 16 in. 20 in.

**34.** Use the graph shown.
- **a.** Identify a pattern of the graph by making a table of the inputs and outputs.
- **b.** What are the outputs for inputs 6, 7, and 8?

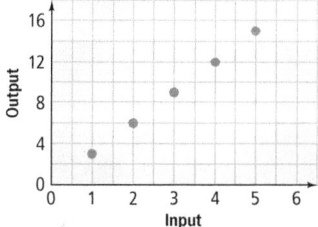

**35. Collecting** Jay has a rare baseball card collection. He currently owns 10 baseball cards. Each month, he purchases a new card for his collection. Write a model to represent the number of cards in Jay's collection after $n$ months.

**36.** Use the figures below.

- **a.** Draw the next two figures.
- **b.** Copy and complete the table to find the number of squares in each figure.
- **c.** What is the number of squares in the $n$th figure? Explain your reasoning.

| Figure (Input) | Process Column | Number of Squares (Output) |
|---|---|---|
| 1 | ■ | ■ |
| 2 | ■ | ■ |
| 3 | ■ | ■ |
| 4 | ■ | ■ |
| 5 | ■ | ■ |

**Copy and complete each table.**

**37.**

| Input | Output |
|---|---|
| 1 | 5 |
| 2 | 9 |
| 3 | 13 |
| 4 | 17 |
| 5 | ■ |
| ⋮ | ⋮ |
| $n$ | ■ |

**38.**

| Input | Output |
|---|---|
| 1 | 2 |
| 2 | −3 |
| 3 | −8 |
| 4 | −13 |
| 5 | ■ |
| ⋮ | ⋮ |
| $n$ | ■ |

**39.**

| Input | Output |
|---|---|
| 1 | 3 |
| 2 | −1 |
| 3 | −5 |
| 4 | −9 |
| 5 | ■ |
| ⋮ | ⋮ |
| $n$ | ■ |

 **Challenge**

**40. Open-Ended** Write the first five numbers of two different patterns in which 12 is the third number.

**41. Reasoning** For the past 4 years, Jesse has grown 3 inches each year. He is now 15 years old and is 5 feet 6 inches tall. He predicts that when he is 20 years old, he will be 6 feet 9 inches tall. What would you tell Jesse about his prediction?

**16.** 4; 5; $n − 1$

**17.** 7; 8; $n + 2$

**18.** −15; −18; −3n

**19.** Output = Input + 1

| Input | Process Column | Output |
|---|---|---|
| 1 | (1) + 1 | 2 |
| 2 | (2) + 1 | 3 |
| 3 | (3) + 1 | 4 |
| 4 | (4) + 1 | 5 |
| 5 | (5) + 1 | 6 |
| ⋮ | ⋮ | ⋮ |
| $n$ | $(n) + 1$ | $n + 1$ |

**20.** Output = $\frac{1}{2}$ Input

| Input | Process Column | Output |
|---|---|---|
| 1 | $(1) \cdot \frac{1}{2}$ | $\frac{1}{2}$ |
| 2 | $(2) \cdot \frac{1}{2}$ | 1 |
| 3 | $(3) \cdot \frac{1}{2}$ | $1\frac{1}{2}$ |
| 4 | $(4) \cdot \frac{1}{2}$ | 2 |
| 5 | $(5) \cdot \frac{1}{2}$ | $2\frac{1}{2}$ |
| ⋮ | ⋮ | ⋮ |
| $n$ | $(n) \cdot \frac{1}{2}$ | $\frac{1}{2}n$ |

**21.** Output = Input − 1

| Input | Process Column | Output |
|---|---|---|
| 1 | (1) − 1 | 0 |
| 2 | (2) − 1 | 1 |
| 3 | (3) − 1 | 2 |
| 4 | (4) − 1 | 3 |
| 5 | (5) − 1 | 4 |
| ⋮ | ⋮ | ⋮ |
| $n$ | $(n) − 1$ | $n − 1$ |

**22.** 10  **23.** 40  **24.** 2n

**25.** add 6 or 6$n$; 30, 36, 42

**26.** add 3; subtract 1; 8, 7, 10

**27.** add 3, then add 4, then add 5, and so on; 21, 28, 36

**28.** add 4; 18, 22, 26

**29.** multiply by 3; 243, 729, 2187

**30.** multiply by 5; 2500, 12,500, 62,500

**31.** The black square and dot each move clockwise one block.

**32.** Answers may vary. Sample: multiply each input by 4

**33.** 9216 in.$^3$

**34. a.**

| Input | Output |
|---|---|
| 1 | 3 |
| 2 | 6 |
| 3 | 9 |
| 4 | 12 |
| 5 | 15 |
| ⋮ | ⋮ |
| $n$ | 3n |

**b.** 18; 21; 24

**35.** $n + 10$, where $n$ is the number of months

**36. a.**

**b.** Process Column: (1), 2(2), 3(3), 4(4), 5(5); Number of squares: 1, 4, 9, 16, 25

**c.** $n^2$; Since the number of squares for each figure is the square of the figure number, the number of squares for the $n$th figure is $n(n)$ or $n^2$.

**37.** 21; 4n + 1

**38.** −18; 7 − 5$n$; or −5$n$ + 7

**39.** −13; 7 − 4$n$; or −4$n$ + 7

**40.** Check students' work.

**41.** Answers may vary. Sample: Jesse will not grow at the same rate between the ages of 15 and 20 as he has during the 4 years prior to age 15.

# Lesson Resources

## Additional Instructional Support

### Algebra 2 Companion

Students can use the **Algebra 2 Companion** worktext (4 pages) as you teach the lesson. Use the Companion to support

- New Vocabulary
- Key Concepts
- Got It for each Problem
- Lesson Check

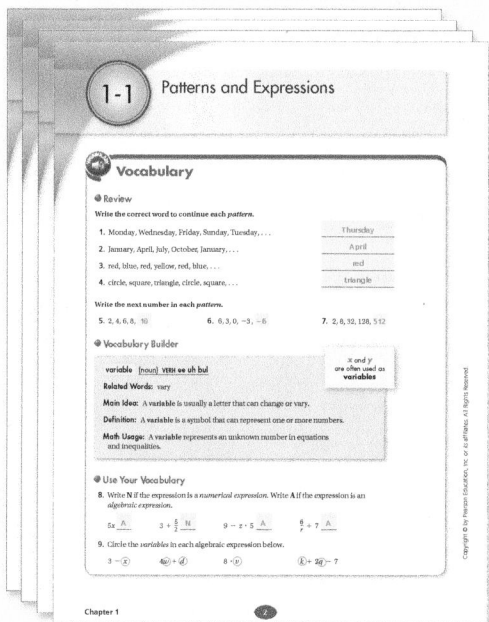

### ELL Support

**Use Manipulatives** Have students work in pairs. One student makes a pattern with available materials, such as one pencil, one eraser, two pencils, two erasers. The other student describes the pattern in words and builds the next part of the pattern. Students reverse roles and repeat with a different set of materials, such as coins.

**Use Graphic Organizers** Have groups of students make a graphic organizer covering the mathematics they already know. Students might include numbers, operations, fractions, decimals, and percents. Congratulate students on the great amount of mathematics they have already learned.

## 5 Assess & Remediate

### Lesson Quiz

**1.** Describe the pattern. Sketch the next figure in the pattern.

**2.** How many tiles are in the *n*th figure?

**3. Do you UNDERSTAND?** The graph shows the cost of bowling for one person. What is the total cost if four people each bowl four games? Explain your answer.

**Bowling**

Cost per Person

Total Games

### ANSWERS TO LESSON QUIZ

**1.** The pattern shows groups of squares with the number of squares increasing by 2. The next figure has 12 squares.

**2.** 3*n*

**3.** $48; each game cost $3 per person, so 16 total games costs $48.

### PRESCRIPTION FOR REMEDIATION

Use the student work on the Lesson Quiz to prescribe a differentiated review assignment:

| Points | Differentiated Remediation |
|--------|---------------------------|
| 0–1 | Intervention |
| 2 | On-level |
| 3 | Extension |

**PowerAlgebra.com**

## 5 Assess & Remediate

Assign the Lesson Quiz. Appropriate intervention, practice, or enrichment is automatically generated based on student performance.

## Differentiated Remediation

Available in editable format online.

### Intervention

- **Reteaching** (2 pages) Provides reteaching and practice exercises for the key lesson concepts. Use with struggling students or absent students.
- **English Language Learner Support** Helps students develop and reinforce mathematical vocabulary and key concepts.

### All-in-One Resources/Online
**Reteaching**

### All-in-One Resources/Online
**English Language Learner Support**

# Differentiated Remediation *continued*

Available in editable format online.

## On-Level

- **Practice** (2 pages) Provides extra practice for each lesson. For simpler practice exercises, use the Form K Practice pages found in the All-in-One Teaching Resources and online.

- **Think About a Plan** Helps students develop specific problem-solving skills and strategies by providing scaffolded guiding questions.

- **Standardized Test Prep** Focuses on all major exercises, all major question types, and helps students prepare for the high-stakes assessments.

## Extension

- **Enrichment** Provides students with interesting problems and activities that extend the concepts of the lesson.

- **Activities, Games, and Puzzles** Worksheets that can be used for concepts development, enrichment, and for fun!

### Practice and Problem Solving Wkbk/ All-in-One Resources/Online
**Practice page 1**

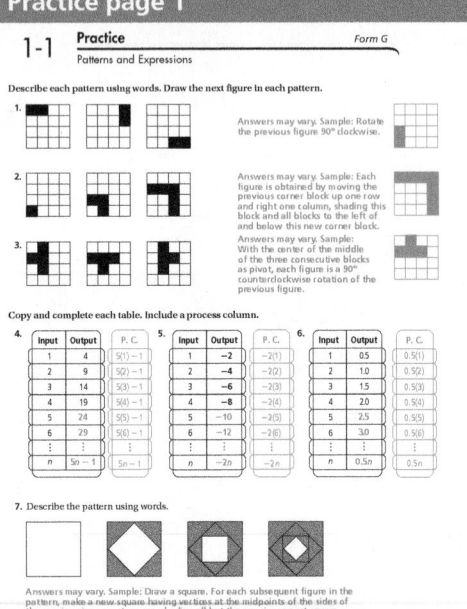

### Practice and Problem Solving Wkbk/ All-in-One Resources/Online
**Practice page 2**

### All-in-One Resources/Online
**Enrichment**

### Practice and Problem Solving Wkbk/ All-in-One Resources/Online
**Think About a Plan**

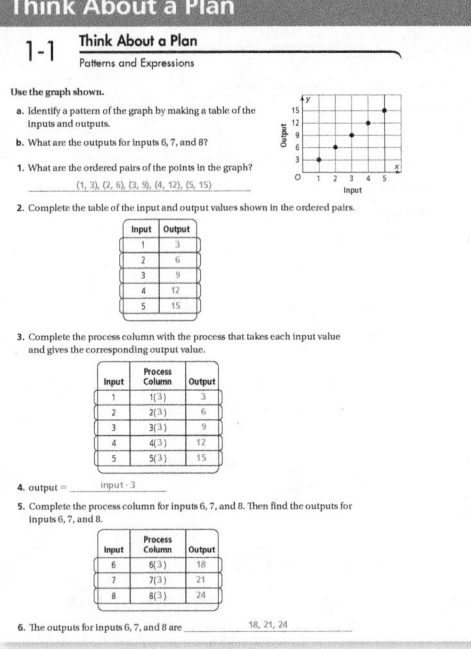

### Practice and Problem Solving Wkbk/ All-in-One Resources/Online
**Standardized Test Prep**

### Online Teacher Resource Center
**Activities, Games, and Puzzles**

# 1-2 Properties of Real Numbers

**Objectives** To graph and order real numbers
To identify properties of real numbers

Getting Ready!

You use emoticons in text messages to help you communicate. Here are six emoticons. How can you describe a set that includes five of the emoticons but not the sixth?

In the Solve It, you classified sets of emoticons. In this lesson, you will classify real numbers into special subsets.

**Essential Understanding** The set of real numbers has several special subsets related in particular ways.

Algebra involves operations on and relations among numbers, including real numbers and imaginary numbers. (You will learn about imaginary numbers in Chapter 4.) Rational numbers and irrational numbers form the set of real numbers.

You can graph every real number as a point on the number line.

---

# 1 Interactive Learning

**Solve It!**

**PURPOSE** To classify objects according to common features

**PROCESS** Students may
• identify a feature that only five of the emoticons have in common.
• look for an emoticon with a unique feature and exclude that emoticon from the set.

**FACILITATE**

**Q** What are some features that only one emoticon has? **[glasses, wink, tongue, frown, toothy smile, round mouth]**

**Q** What sets could you define that include only five emoticons? **[Samples: both eyes open, no glasses, not unhappy]**

**ANSWER** See Solve It in Answers on next page.

**CONNECT THE MATH** In the Solve It, students group emoticons into subsets by common characteristics. In the lesson, students classify numbers into subsets.

---

# 1-2 Preparing to Teach

**BIG idea Properties** UbD

**ESSENTIAL UNDERSTANDINGS**

• The set of real numbers has several subsets related in particular ways.
• Algebra involves operations on and relations among numbers, including real and imaginary numbers.
• The properties of real numbers are relationships that are true for all real numbers (except, in one case, zero).

## Math Background

Students may take the properties of real numbers for granted. It seems clear, for example, that $3 + 5 = 5 + 3$, and that the sum of two real numbers is a real number. Point out that some sets of mathematical objects do not obey these rules.

For example, the set of real-valued functions is not commutative. In other words, it matters in what order functions are applied

to a number. For example, let $f(x) = |x|$ and $g(x) = -x$. If we first apply $g$ to a positive number $a$, and then apply $f$, the result is again $a$. However, if we first apply $f$ and then $g$, we get $-a$. You can summarize this by saying that the set of real-valued functions is not commutative.

A more familiar mathematical example is that the set of integers is not closed under division. A not mathematical example is that the putting on shoes and putting on socks are not commutative actions. Can students think of other examples from math or every day life that do not follow these rules?

On the other hand, the set of real numbers is not the only set that has these properties. For example, the set of all even integers is closed under addition and multiplication. It may be helpful for students to think of other sets that have these properties.

**PowerAlgebra.com**

# 1 Interactive Learning

**Solve It!**
Step out how to solve the Problem with helpful hints and an online question. Other questions are listed above in Interactive Learning.

**Dynamic Activity** This interactive real number line allows students to plot and compare numbers, their opposites, and their absolute values. Students who have trouble understanding absolute value should use this tool.

# 2 Guided Instruction

The diagram shows how subsets of the real numbers are related.

**Real Numbers**

Use **natural numbers** to count.

1, 2, 3, ...

The **whole numbers** are the natural numbers and zero.

0, 1, 2, 3, ...

**Integers** are the natural numbers, their opposites, and zero.

... −1, −2, −3, 0, 1, 2, 3, ...

$... -\frac{1}{2}, 0.222, 1, 2, \frac{2}{3}, \frac{5}{4}, 6.1, ...$

**Rational numbers**

$\sqrt{2}$

$\pi$

Irrational numbers

**Rational numbers**
- are all numbers you can write as a quotient of integers $\frac{a}{b}$, $b \neq 0$.
- include terminating decimals. For example, $\frac{1}{8} = 0.125$.
- include repeating decimals. For example, $\frac{1}{3} = 0.\overline{3}$.

**Irrational numbers**
- have decimal representations that neither terminate nor repeat. For example, $\sqrt{2} = 1.414213\ldots$.
- cannot be written as quotients of integers.

## Problem 1

**Q** Would it make sense to use the set of integers to describe the number of people who participated in the race? The set of rational numbers? Explain. **[No; that would indicate a negative number of participants in the race. No; that would indicate a fractional number of participants in the race.]**

## Got It?

**Q** Would the answer change if you were referring to the amount of money in pennies rather than in dollars? Explain. **[Yes; $15.50 in dollars is best described by the set of rational numbers but in pennies is best described by the set of natural numbers.]**

You classify a variable by naming the subset that gives you the most information about the numbers the variable represents.

**Problem 1** Classifying a Variable

**Multiple Choice** Your school is sponsoring a charity race. Which set of numbers best describes the number of people *p* who participate in the race?

Ⓐ natural numbers     Ⓒ rational numbers

Ⓑ integers     Ⓓ irrational numbers

The number of people *p* is a natural number. The correct answer is A.

**Think**

**Can you eliminate any answer choices?** You can't have part of a person, so you can eliminate the rational and irrational numbers. The number of people can't be negative, so you can eliminate the integers.

**Got It?** **1.** In Problem 1, if each participant made a donation *d* of $15.50 to a local charity, which subset of real numbers best describes the amount of money raised?

# Answers

**Solve It!**

Answers may vary. Sample: the set of the emoticons not wearing glasses

**Got It?**

**1.** rational numbers

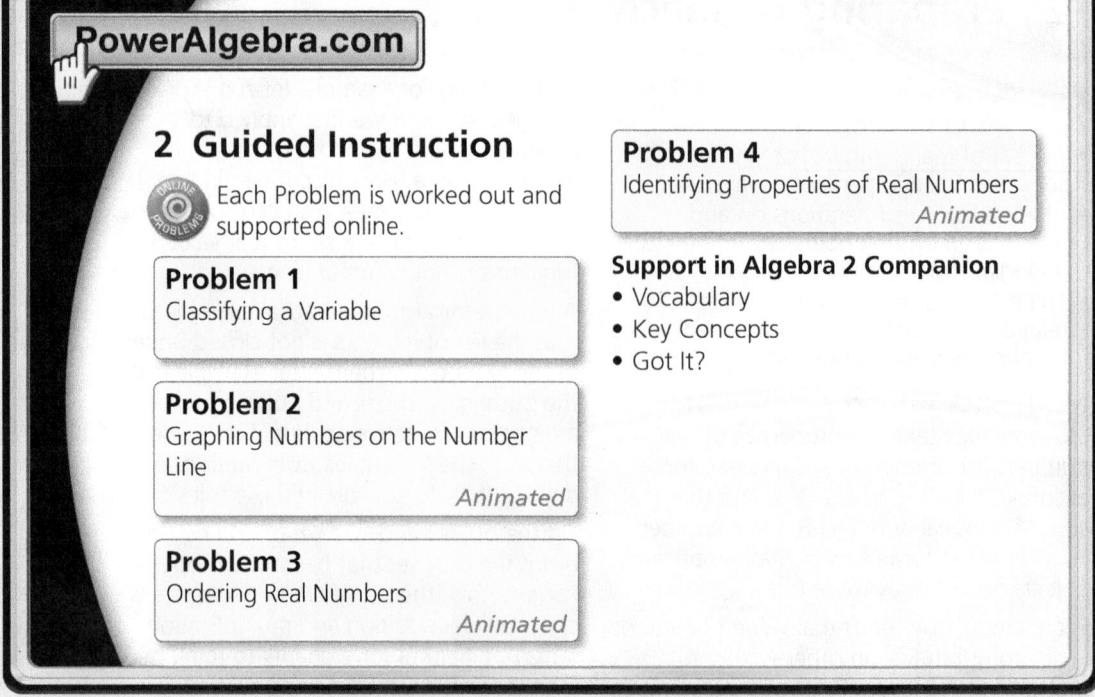

**PowerAlgebra.com**

## 2 Guided Instruction

Each Problem is worked out and supported online.

**Problem 1**
Classifying a Variable

**Problem 2**
Graphing Numbers on the Number Line
*Animated*

**Problem 3**
Ordering Real Numbers
*Animated*

**Problem 4**
Identifying Properties of Real Numbers
*Animated*

**Support in Algebra 2 Companion**
- Vocabulary
- Key Concepts
- Got It?

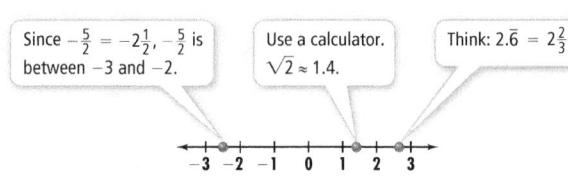 **Problem 2** Graphing Numbers on the Number Line

What is the graph of the numbers $-\frac{5}{2}$, $\sqrt{2}$, and $2.\overline{6}$?

| Since $-\frac{5}{2} = -2\frac{1}{2}$, $-\frac{5}{2}$ is between $-3$ and $-2$. | Use a calculator. $\sqrt{2} \approx 1.4$. | Think: $2.\overline{6} = 2\frac{2}{3}$. |

**Got It?** **2.** What is the graph of the numbers $\sqrt{3}$, $-1.\overline{4}$, and $\frac{1}{3}$?

The number line is helpful for ordering several real numbers. For two numbers, however, it is easier to show order, or compare, using one of the inequality symbols $>$ or $<$.

 **Problem 3** Ordering Real Numbers

How do $\sqrt{17}$ and $3.8$ compare? Use $>$ or $<$.

Compare both numbers to $\sqrt{16}$.

$\sqrt{16} < \sqrt{17}$     16 is less than 17.

$3.8 < \sqrt{16}$     $\sqrt{16} = 4$ and $3.8 < 4$.

Therefore, $3.8 < \sqrt{17}$, or $\sqrt{17} > 3.8$.

**Check** Use a calculator.

$\sqrt{17} \approx 4.123$

$3.8 < 4.123$ ✔

**Got It?** **3. a.** How do $\sqrt{26}$ and $6.25$ compare? Use $>$ or $<$.
  **b.** Reasoning Let $a$, $b$, and $c$ be real numbers such that $a < b$ and $b < c$. How do $a$ and $c$ compare? Explain.

**Essential Understanding** The properties of real numbers are relationships that are true for all real numbers (except, in one case, zero).

One property of real numbers excludes a single number, zero. Zero is the *additive identity* for the real numbers, and zero is the one real number that has no *multiplicative inverse*.

**Plan**

**How do you graph a number on the number line?**
If the number is an integer, determine whether it is positive or negative. If it's not an integer, determine which integer it's closest to.

**Think**

**Why compare $\sqrt{17}$ to the square root of a perfect square?**
It makes it easier to determine which two integers $\sqrt{17}$ is between.

**Problem 2**

Review how to find square roots and how to convert fractions to decimals and decimals to fractions on a calculator.

**Q** Which two integers is $\sqrt{2}$ between? **[1 and 2]**

**Got It?**

**Q** What decimal equals $\frac{1}{3}$? **[$0.\overline{3}$]**

**Problem 3**

**Q** What two square roots of perfect squares is $\sqrt{17}$ between? **[$\sqrt{16}$ and $\sqrt{25}$]**

**Got It?**

**Q** The square root of what perfect square is between 6.25 and $\sqrt{26}$? **[36]**

**Q** How does $\sqrt{36}$ compare to 6.25? **[$\sqrt{36} = 6 < 6.25$]**

**Q** How does $\sqrt{36}$ compare to $\sqrt{26}$? **[$\sqrt{26} < \sqrt{36}$]**

# Additional Problems

**1.** Bankers and investors use "The rule of 72," which is modeled by $y = \frac{72}{x}$, where $x$ is the percent interest rate and $y$ is the years it takes an investment to double. Which set of numbers best describes the number of years $y$ it takes for an investment to double when $x$ is a natural number?

**ANSWER** Rational numbers

**2.** What is the graph of the numbers $-\frac{5}{3}$, $-\sqrt{8}$, and $-2.\overline{3}$?

**ANSWER**

**3.** How do $\sqrt{85}$ and 8.9 compare? Use $>$ or $<$.

**ANSWER** $\sqrt{85} > 8.9$

**4.** What property is illustrated by each of the following equations?

**a.** $xyz = xzy$

**b.** $(fg)h = f(gh)$

**c.** $(p + q)r = (q + p)r$

**d.** $(5 + y)x = x(5 + y)$

**e.** $8 + 0 = 0 + 8$

**f.** $v + 0 + w = v + w$

**ANSWER** 'a,' and 'd' show the Commutative Property of Multiplication; 'b' shows the Associative Property of Multiplication; 'c' and 'e' show the Commutative Property of Addition; 'f' shows the Identity Property of Addition.

# Answers

**Got It?** (continued)

**2.**

**3. a.** $\sqrt{26} < 6.25$ or $6.25 > \sqrt{26}$
  **b.** $a < c$; $a$ will be to the left of $c$ on the number line.

Remind students that a set is closed with respect to an operation if the operation can always be completed with elements in the set.

**Q** Why are subtraction and division not included in the table? [**Answers may vary. Sample: Subtraction and division both lack the commutative property; division also lacks closure because a denominator of 0 yields a non–real number as a quotient.**]

**Q** Is the set of whole numbers closed under subtraction? Explain. [**No; $2 - 5 = -3$, which is not a whole number.**]

## Problem 4

**Q** Is the reciprocal of a negative number positive or negative? Explain. [**Negative; answers may vary. Sample: The product of a number and its reciprocal is 1; the product of two negative numbers is positive.**]

**Q** How are the expressions on each side of the equation in 4B the same or different? [**Sample: 3 and 4 are reversed and the other parts are identical.**]

## Got It?                    ERROR PREVENTION

Students may be confused by the role of $2g$. It is not affected when the Distributive Property is applied to $3(g + h)$.

**Q** In 4b what property allows you to move the like terms next to each other so that they can be combined? [**Commutative Property of Addition**]

---

The **opposite** or **additive inverse** of any number $a$ is $-a$.
The sum of a number and its opposite is 0, the additive identity.

**Examples**    $12 + (-12) = 0$        $-7 + 7 = 0$

The **reciprocal** or **multiplicative inverse** of any nonzero number $a$ is $\frac{1}{a}$.
The product of a number and its reciprocal is 1, the multiplicative identity.

**Examples**    $8\left(\frac{1}{8}\right) = 1$        $-5\left(-\frac{1}{5}\right) = 1$

### Properties    Properties of Real Numbers

Let $a$, $b$, and $c$ represent real numbers.

| Property | Addition | Multiplication |
|---|---|---|
| **Closure** | $a + b$ is a real number. | $ab$ is a real number. |
| **Commutative** | $a + b = b + a$ | $ab = ba$ |
| **Associative** | $(a + b) + c = a + (b + c)$ | $(ab)c = a(bc)$ |
| **Identity** | $a + 0 = a, 0 + a = a$<br>0 is the additive identity. | $a \cdot 1 = a, 1 \cdot a = a$<br>1 is the multiplicative identity. |
| **Inverse** | $a + (-a) = 0$ | $a \cdot \frac{1}{a} = 1, a \neq 0$ |
| **Distributive** | $a(b + c) = ab + ac$ | |

### Problem 4    Identifying Properties of Real Numbers

Which property does the equation illustrate?

**A** $\left(-\frac{2}{3}\right)\left(-\frac{3}{2}\right) = 1$

The product of the numbers is 1.

Inverse Property of Multiplication

**B** $(3 \cdot 4) \cdot 5 = (4 \cdot 3) \cdot 5$

The equation reorders 3 and 4.

Commutative Property of Multiplication

**Got It?** 4. **a.** Which property does the equation $3(g + h) + 2g = (3g + 3h) + 2g$ illustrate?
   **b.** **Reasoning** Use properties of real numbers to show that $a + [3 + (-a)] = 3$. Justify each step of your solution.

**Plan**

How can you analyze an equation?
Determine whether it
• uses addition or multiplication
• reorders or regroups the numbers
• uses an identity

---

# Answers

## Got It? (continued)

**4. a.** Distributive Property

   **b.** $a + [3 + (-a)] = a + [(-a) + 3]$    Comm.
   $= [a + (-a)] + 3$    Assoc.
   $= 0 + 3$        Inverse Identity
   $= 3$

**Lesson Check**

**Do you know HOW?**

Write an example from daily life that uses each type of real number.

1. whole numbers

2. integers

3. rational numbers

Identify the property illustrated by the equation.

4. $5 + (-5) = 0$

5. $2 \cdot (4 \cdot 5) = (2 \cdot 4) \cdot 5$

**Do you UNDERSTAND?**

6. **Vocabulary** Identify another name for a reciprocal.

7. **Compare and Contrast** How is the Additive Identity Property similar to the Multiplicative Identity Property? How is it different?

8. **Reasoning** There are grouping symbols in the equation $(5 + w) + 8 = (w + 5) + 8$, but it does not illustrate the Associative Property of Addition. Explain.

9. Give an example of a number that is not a rational number. Explain why it is not rational.

  **Practice and Problem-Solving Exercises**

**A Practice** Classify each variable according to the set of numbers that best describes its values. *See Problem 1.*

10. the number of times $n$ a ball bounces; the height $h$ from which the ball is dropped

11. the year $y$; the median selling price $p$ for a house that year

12. the circumference $C$ of a circle found by using the formula $C = 2\pi r$

Graph each number on a number line. *See Problem 2.*

13. 0    14. $-\sqrt{24}$    15. $-2$    16. $2\frac{1}{2}$    17. $-4\frac{2}{3}$

18. 3.5    19. $-1.4$    20. $\sqrt{10}$    21. $-2\frac{1}{5}$    22. 4.8

Compare the two numbers. Use > or <. *See Problem 3.*

23. $16, \sqrt{16}$    24. $-4, -\sqrt{4}$    25. $\sqrt{5}, \sqrt{7}$

26. $-\sqrt{3}, -\sqrt{5}$    27. $5, \sqrt{22}$    28. $-\sqrt{38}, 6$

29. $4, \sqrt{12}$    30. $-8, \sqrt{70}$    31. $\sqrt{63}, 7.5$

32. $4.7, \sqrt{26}$    33. $\sqrt{75}, 9$    34. $12, -\sqrt{150}$

Name the property of real numbers illustrated by each equation. *See Problem 4.*

35. $\pi(a + b) = \pi a + \pi b$    36. $-10 + 4 = 4 + (-10)$

37. $(2\sqrt{7}) \cdot \sqrt{3} = 2(\sqrt{7} \cdot \sqrt{3})$    38. $29 \cdot \pi = \pi \cdot 29$

39. $-\sqrt{5} + 0 = -\sqrt{5}$    40. $\frac{4}{7} \cdot \frac{7}{4} = 1$

---

# 3 Lesson Check

## Do you know HOW?  ERROR INTERVENTION

- For Exercise 5, if students confuse the Associative Property with the Distributive Property, explain that the difference between them is that the Associative Property can be applied to an expression involving either multiplication or addition, while the Distributive Property can be applied to an expression involving both addition and multiplication.

## Do you UNDERSTAND? ERROR INTERVENTION

- Exercise 8 may be difficult for students unless they ask: How are the expressions on each side of the equation different? Students will answer correctly if they ignore the term that is not contained in grouping symbols.

## Close

**Q** Why is it important to know the properties of real numbers? **[Answers may vary. Sample: They are needed to solve equations.]**

---

## Lesson Check

1. Answers may vary. Sample: the number of times a cricket chirps

2. Answers may vary. Sample: the change in number of people on a bus after a stop

3. Answers may vary. Sample: the outdoor temperature in tenths of a degree

4. Inverse Prop. of Add.

5. Assoc. Prop. of Mult.

6. multiplicative inverse

7. Both properties result in the original term; 0 is the additive identity, whereas 1 is the multiplicative identity.

8. The equation illustrates the Comm. Prop. of Add.

9. Answers may vary. Sample: $\sqrt{2}$ is not a rational number because it cannot be written as a quotient of integers.

### Practice and Problem-Solving Exercises

10. $n$, whole numbers; $h$, rational numbers

11. $y$, natural numbers; $p$, rational numbers

12. $C$, irrational numbers; $r$, rational numbers

13. [number line: point at 1, marks −3 −2 −1 0 1 2]

14. [number line: point at −5, marks −6 −5 −4 −3 −2 −1 0 1]

15. [number line: point at −2, marks −4 −3 −2 −1 0 1 2]

16. [number line: point between 2 and 3, marks −1 0 1 2 3 4]

17. [number line: point near −4.67, marks −6 −5 −4 −3 −2 −1 0 1]

18. [number line: point at 3.5, marks −1 0 1 2 3 4 5]

19. [number line: point at −1.4, marks −3 −2 −1 0 1]

20. [number line: point near 3.16, marks −1 0 1 2 3 4 5]

21. [number line: point near −2.2, marks −4 −3 −2 −1 0 1]

22. [number line: point at 4.8, marks −1 0 1 2 3 4 5 6]

23. >    24. <    25. <

26. >    27. >    28. <

29. >    30. <    31. >

32. <    33. <    34. >

35. Distr. Prop.

36. Comm. Prop. of Add.

37–40. See next page.

**PowerAlgebra.com**

## 3 Lesson Check

For a digital lesson check, use the Got It questions.

**Support in Algebra 2 Companion**
- Lesson Check

## 4 Practice

Assign homework to individual students or to an entire class.

# 4 Practice

## ASSIGNMENT GUIDE

Basic: 10–40 all, 42–48 even, 49, 58–66 even

Average: 11–39 odd, 41–67

Advanced: 11–39 odd, 41–71

Standardized Test Prep: 72–74

Mixed Review: 75–83

**Reasoning** exercises have blue headings.

**Applications** exercises have red headings.

**EXERCISE 66:** Use the Think About a Plan worksheet in the **Practice and Problem Solving Workbook** (also available in the Teaching Resources in print and online) to further support students' development in becoming independent learners.

## HOMEWORK QUICK CHECK

To check students' understanding of key skills and concepts, go over Exercises 21, 39, 49, 58, and 66.

---

 **Apply**    Estimate the numbers graphed at the labeled points.

**41.** point $A$     **42.** point $B$     **43.** point $C$     **44.** point $D$

**45.** point $E$     **46.** point $F$     **47.** point $G$     **48.** point $H$

**49. Think About a Plan** A cube-shaped jewelry box has a surface area of 300 square inches. What are the dimensions of the jewelry box?
- Write an algebraic expression to find the total surface area of a cube. What is the surface area of one side of a cube?
- How is the side length of a square related to its area?

**50. Error Analysis** A student labeled the points on the number line as shown. Explain the student's error.

**Science** The formula $I = \sqrt{\dfrac{W}{R}}$ gives the electric current $I$ in amperes that flows through an appliance, where $W$ is the power in watts and $R$ is the resistance in ohms. Which set of numbers best describes the value of $I$ for the given values of $W$ and $R$?

**51.** $W = 100, R = 25$     **52.** $W = 100, R = 5$     **53.** $W = 500, R = 100$

**54.** $W = 50, R = 200$     **55.** $W = 250, R = 100$     **56.** $W = 240, R = 100$

**Write the numbers in decreasing order.**

**57.** $1, -3, -\sqrt{2}, 8, \dfrac{1}{3}$     **58.** $\sqrt{14}, \dfrac{5}{2}, -\dfrac{9}{16}, 1, 11$     **59.** $-17, -0.06, -3\sqrt{3}, 5.73, \dfrac{1}{4}$

**Reasoning** An example is a *counterexample* to a general statement if it makes the statement false. Show that each of the following statements is false by finding a counterexample.

**60.** The reciprocal of each natural number is a natural number.

**61.** The opposite of each whole number is a whole number.

**62.** There is no integer that has a reciprocal that is an integer.

**63.** The product of two irrational numbers is an irrational number.

**64.** All square roots are irrational numbers.

**65. Writing** Write an example of each of the 11 properties of real numbers shown on page 14.

**66. Restaurant** Five friends each ordered a sandwich and a drink at a restaurant. Each sandwich costs the same amount and each drink costs the same amount. What are two ways to compute the bill? What property of real numbers is illustrated by the two methods?

**67. Open-Ended** Write an algebraic problem that requires the use of the real-number properties to solve. Then solve the problem.

---

# Answers

## Practice and Problem-Solving Exercises
## (continued)

**37.** Assoc. Prop. of Mult.

**38.** Comm. Prop. of Mult.

**39.** Ident. Prop. of Add.

**40.** Inv. Prop. of Mult.

**41–48.** Answers may vary. Samples are given.

**41.** $-5$

**42.** $-3\dfrac{1}{2}$

**43.** $-1\dfrac{1}{4}$

**44.** $\dfrac{1}{2}$

**45.** $1\dfrac{2}{3}$

**46.** $3\dfrac{1}{3}$

**47.** $4$

**48.** $4.8$

**49.** $\sqrt{50}$ in. $\times$ $\sqrt{50}$ in. $\times$ $\sqrt{50}$ in.

**50.** The point for $\sqrt{5}$ is not at the correct position on the number line; $\sqrt{5} \approx 2.24$.

**51.** natural numbers

**52.** irrational numbers

**53.** irrational numbers

**54.** irrational numbers

**55.** irrational numbers

**56.** irrational numbers

**57.** $8, 1, \dfrac{1}{3}, -\sqrt{2}, -3$

**58.** $11, \sqrt{14}, \dfrac{5}{2}, 1, -\dfrac{9}{16}$

**59.** $5.73, \dfrac{1}{4}, -0.06, -3\sqrt{3}, -17$

**60.** Answers may vary. Sample: 4

**61.** Answers may vary. Sample: 7

**62.** Answers may vary. Sample: $-1$

**63.** Answers may vary. Sample: $\sqrt{2}$ and $\sqrt{2}$

**64.** Answers may vary. Sample: $\sqrt{4}$

**65.** Check students' work.

**66.** Multiply the cost of a drink by 5 and multiply the cost of a sandwich by 5, then add, or add the cost for one drink and one sandwich, then multiply by 5; Distr. Prop., $5s + 5d = 5(s + d)$

**67.** Check students' work.

**68. Writing** Are there two integers with a product of $-12$ and a sum of $-3$? Explain.

**69.** Your friend used the Distributive Property and got the expression $5x + 10y - 35$. What algebraic expression could your friend have started with?

**70. Geometry** $\pi$ is an irrational number you can use to calculate the circumference or area of a circle.
   **a.** Find the value of $\pi$ on your calculator. Can you obtain an exact representation? Explain.
   **b.** The value of $\pi$ is often represented as $\frac{22}{7}$. How does this representation compare to the decimal representation your calculator gives using the $\pi$ key?

**71.** Does zero have a multiplicative inverse? Explain.

## Standardized Test Prep

**SAT/ACT**

**72.** Which of the following shows the numbers $\pi$, $\sqrt{8}$, and 3.5 in the correct order from greatest to least?
   Ⓐ $\pi$, $\sqrt{8}$, 3.5   Ⓑ 3.5, $\pi$, $\sqrt{8}$   Ⓒ $\sqrt{8}$, $\pi$, 3.5   Ⓓ $\sqrt{8}$, 3.5, $\pi$

**73.** Which of the following is the best statement about the graph?
   Ⓕ A 400-minute plan costs $40.
   Ⓖ A 100-minute plan costs $10.
   Ⓗ A 1000-minute plan costs $110.
   Ⓘ A 200-minute plan costs $35.

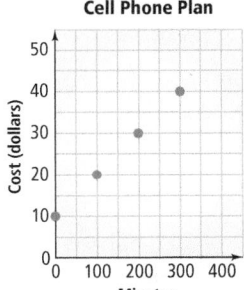

**Cell Phone Plan**

**Short Response**

**74.** Why is the opposite of the reciprocal of 5 the same as the reciprocal of the opposite of 5?

## Mixed Review

Identify a pattern and find the next three terms in the pattern.       *See Lesson 1-1.*

**75.** 4, 8, 12, 16, . . .      **76.** 8, 9, 10, 11, . . .      **77.** $-4, -3, -2, -1, . . .$

**Get Ready!** To prepare for Lesson 1-3, do Exercises 78–83.

Use the order of operations to simplify each expression.      *See p. 967.*

**78.** $3 \div 4 + 6 \div 4$

**79.** $5[(2 + 5) \div 3]$

**80.** $\frac{8 + 5 \times 2}{12}$

**81.** $(40 + 24) \div 8 - (2^2 - 1)$

**82.** $40 + 24 \div 8 - 2^2 - 1$

**83.** $(40 + 24) \div (8 - 2^2) - 1$

# Answers

**68.** No; answers may vary. Sample: The only pairs of integers that have a product of $-12$ are $-1$ and 12, $-2$ and 6, $-3$ and 4, $-4$ and 3, $-6$ and 2, and $-12$ and 1. None of these pairs has a sum of $-3$.

**69.** $5(x + 2y - 7)$

**70. a.** 3.141592654... ; No, $\pi$ is an irrational number.
   **b.** $\frac{22}{7} \approx 3.142857143...$ ; $\frac{22}{7} > \pi$

**71.** No; $\frac{1}{0}$ is undefined.

## Standardized Test Prep

**72.** B

**73.** H

**74. [2]** To find the opposite of the reciprocal of 5, divide 1 by 5 and then multiply the quotient by $-1$. To find the reciprocal of the opposite of 5, multiply 5 by $-1$ and then divide 1 by the product. Both methods result in the same answer $\left(-\frac{1}{5}\right)$ because the order of operations does not matter for mult. and div.

**[1]** incomplete explanation

## Mixed Review

**75.** add 4; 20, 24, 28

**76.** add 1; 12, 13, 14

**77.** add 1; 0, 1, 2

**78.** $2\frac{1}{4}$      **79.** $11\frac{2}{3}$

**80.** $1\frac{1}{2}$      **81.** 5

**82.** 38      **83.** 15

## Differentiated Remediation

Available in editable format online.

## Additional Instructional Support

### Algebra 2 Companion

Students can use the **Algebra 2 Companion** worktext (4 pages) as you teach the lesson. Use the Companion to support

- New Vocabulary
- Key Concepts
- Got It for each Problem
- Lesson Check

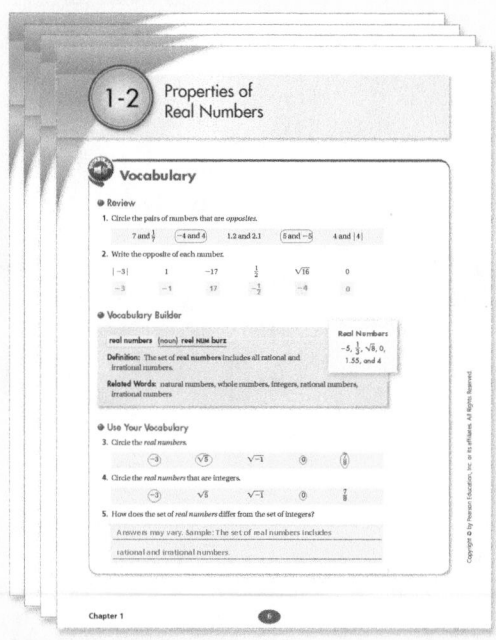

### ELL Support

**Use Graphic Organizers** Have groups of students make a graphic organizer showing different subsets of real numbers. Students may refer to the organizer on page 12 to help them get started. Have students illustrate their graphic organizers. They might use countable objects with whole numbers, a pie with a slice cut out for rational numbers, or a number line for integers. Have students label their graphic organizers with correct terminology and with familiar words that will remind them of the meanings. When they are finished, have students compare and discuss their diagrams with another group.

## 5 Assess & Remediate

### Lesson Quiz

1. **Do you UNDERSTAND?** The height of an equilateral triangle $h$ equals $\frac{\sqrt{3}}{2}s$ where $s$ is the length of a side. Suppose an equilateral triangle is made with 2-inch toothpicks.

   **a.** Which set of numbers best describes the value of $s$ in inches?

   **b.** Which set of numbers best describes the value of $h$ in inches?

2. What is the graph of the numbers $\frac{9}{4}$, $-\sqrt{7}$, and $1.\overline{2}$?

3. Compare $\sqrt{37}$ and 5.9.

4. Which property does the equation illustrate? $1 \cdot \frac{4}{5} = \frac{4}{5}$

**ANSWERS TO LESSON QUIZ**

1. **a.** natural numbers

   **b.** irrational numbers

2.

3. $\sqrt{37} > 5.9$

4. Identity Property of Multiplication

**PRESCRIPTION FOR REMEDIATION**

Use the student work on the Lesson Quiz to prescribe a differentiated review assignment:

| Points | Differentiated Remediation |
|--------|---------------------------|
| 0–2 | Intervention |
| 3 | On-level |
| 4 | Extension |

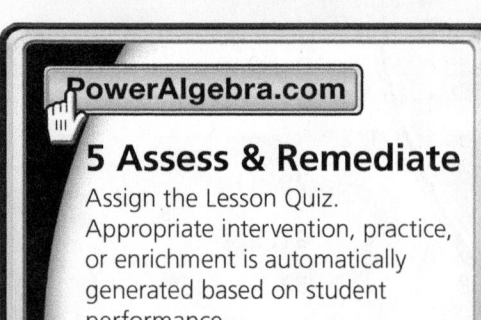

### PowerAlgebra.com

### 5 Assess & Remediate

Assign the Lesson Quiz. Appropriate intervention, practice, or enrichment is automatically generated based on student performance.

## Intervention

- **Reteaching** (2 pages) Provides reteaching and practice exercises for the key lesson concepts. Use with struggling students or absent students.

- **English Language Learner Support** Helps students develop and reinforce mathematical vocabulary and key concepts.

All-in-One Resources/Online
**Reteaching**

All-in-One Resources/Online
**English Language Learner Support**

# Differentiated Remediation *continued*

Available in editable format online.

## On-Level

- **Practice** (2 pages) Provides extra practice for each lesson. For simpler practice exercises, use the Form K Practice pages found in the All-in-One Teaching Resources and online.

- **Think About a Plan** Helps students develop specific problem-solving skills and strategies by providing scaffolded guiding questions.
- **Standardized Test Prep** Focuses on all major exercises, all major question types, and helps students prepare for the high-stakes assessments.

## Extension

- **Enrichment** Provides students with interesting problems and activities that extend the concepts of the lesson.
- **Activities, Games, and Puzzles** Worksheets that can be used for concepts development, enrichment, and for fun!

---

### Practice and Problem Solving Wkbk/All-in-One Resources/Online
#### Practice page 1

**1-2 Practice** — Form G
Properties of Real Numbers

Classify each variable according to the set of numbers that best describes its values.

1. the area of the circle $A$ found by using the formula $\pi r^2$ irrational number

2. the number $n$ of equal slices in a pizza; the portion $p$ of the pizza in one slice
natural number; rational number

3. the air temperature $t$ in Saint Paul, MN, measured to the nearest degree Fahrenheit integer

4. the last four digits $s$ of a Social Security number natural (or whole) number

Graph each number on a number line.

5. −1    6. $\sqrt{3}$    7. 2.8    8. $-2\frac{1}{2}$

Compare the two numbers. Use > or <.

9. $-\sqrt{2}, -2$ >    10. $4, \sqrt{17}$ <

11. $\sqrt{29}, 5$ >    12. $\sqrt{50}, 6.8$ >

13. $11, \sqrt{130}$ <    14. $-6, -\sqrt{30}$ <

15. $7\frac{1}{2}, \sqrt{67}$ >    16. $-\sqrt{10}, -\sqrt{12}$ >

Name the property of real numbers illustrated by each equation.

17. $2(3 + \sqrt{5}) = 2 \cdot 3 + 2 \cdot \sqrt{5}$ Distributive Property

18. $16 + (-13) = -13 + 16$ Commutative Property of Addition

19. $-7 \cdot -\frac{1}{7} = 1$ Inverse Property of Multiplication

20. $5(0.2 \cdot 7) = (5 \cdot 0.2) \cdot 7$ Associative Property of Multiplication

---

### Practice and Problem Solving Wkbk/All-in-One Resources/Online
#### Practice page 2

**1-2 Practice (continued)** — Form G
Properties of Real Numbers

Estimate the numbers graphed at the labeled points.

21. point A −2.7    22. point B −1.2

23. point C 0.9    24. point D 3.0

**Geometry** To find the length of side $b$ of a rectangular prism with a square base, use the formula $b = \sqrt{\frac{V}{h}}$, where $V$ is the volume of the prism and $h$ is the height. Which set of numbers best describes the value of $b$ for the given values of $V$ and $h$?

25. $V = 100, h = 5$ irrational numbers

26. $V = 100, h = 25$ natural numbers

27. $V = 100, h = 20$ irrational numbers

28. $V = 5, h = 20$ rational numbers

Write the numbers in increasing order.

29. $2\sqrt{2}, \frac{4}{5}, -\frac{9}{4}, 0.9, -1$
$-\frac{9}{4}, -1, \frac{4}{5}, 0.9, 2\sqrt{2}$

30. $\frac{5}{8}, -6, \frac{2}{3}, -\pi, -0.5$
$-6, -\pi, -0.5, \frac{5}{8}, \frac{2}{3}$

Justify the equation by stating one of the properties of real numbers.

31. $(x + 37) + (-37) = x + (37 + (-37))$ Associative Property of Addition

32. $x \cdot 1 = x$ Identity Property of Multiplication

33. $x + (37 + (-37)) = x + 0$ Inverse Property of Addition

34. $x + 0 = x$ Identity Property of Addition

---

### All-in-One Resources/Online
#### Enrichment

**1-2 Enrichment**
Properties of Real Numbers

There are four words beginning with the letter "I" that describe certain types of operations:

a. **Identity:** an operation that does not change anything. For example, adding 0 to a number is an identity operation, because adding 0 does not change the original number.

b. **Inverse:** an operation that can be undone by another operation. For instance, the operation of adding 2 to a number can be undone by subtracting 2 from the number. However, the operation of multiplying a number by 0 cannot be undone.

c. **Idempotent:** an operation that, when done twice, is the same as doing it once. For example, multiplying a number by 1 and then multiplying the result by 1 again has exactly the same effect as multiplying the number by 1 only once.

d. **Involutory:** an operation that, when done twice, leaves a number unchanged. For instance, multiplying a number by −1 and then multiplying the result by −1 again returns the original number.

For each of the following operations, state which of the "I" words apply. If none apply, write *none*.

1. finding the absolute value of a number idempotent

2. dividing a number by 1 identity, inverse, idempotent, involutory

3. multiplying the absolute value of a number by −1 idempotent

4. finding the reciprocal of a nonzero number inverse, involutory

5. dividing a number by −1 inverse, involutory

6. multiplying a number by 0 idempotent

7. adding 0 to the reciprocal of a nonzero number inverse, involutory

8. multiplying the reciprocal of a nonzero number by 2 inverse, involutory

9. adding the absolute value of a nonzero number to the absolute value of its reciprocal none

10. finding the reciprocal of the absolute value of the reciprocal of a nonzero number idempotent

11. finding the absolute value of −1 times a nonzero number, then taking the reciprocal none

---

### Practice and Problem Solving Wkbk/All-in-One Resources/Online
#### Think About a Plan

**1-2 Think About a Plan**
Properties of Real Numbers

Five friends each ordered a sandwich and a drink at a restaurant. Each sandwich costs the same amount, and each drink costs the same amount. What are two ways to compute the bill? What property of real numbers is illustrated by the two methods?

**Understanding the Problem**

1. There are 5 sandwiches and 5 drinks on the bill.

2. What is the problem asking you to determine?
two ways to represent the cost of 5 sandwiches and 5 drinks, and the property of real numbers illustrated by the two representations

**Planning the Solution**

3. How can you represent the cost of five sandwiches?
Answers may vary. Sample: 5s

4. How can you represent the cost of five drinks?
Answers may vary. Sample: 5d

5. How can you represent the cost of the items ordered by one friend?
Answers may vary. Sample: d + s

**Getting an Answer**

6. Write an expression that represents the cost of five drinks and the cost of five sandwiches.
Answers may vary. Sample: 5d + 5s

7. Write an expression that represents the cost of the items ordered by five friends.
Answers may vary. Sample: 5(d + s)

8. What property of real numbers tells you that these two expressions are equal? Explain.
Distributive Property; the Distributive Property states a(b + c) = ab + ac.

---

### Practice and Problem Solving Wkbk/All-in-One Resources/Online
#### Standardized Test Prep

**1-2 Standardized Test Prep**
Properties of Real Numbers

**Multiple Choice**

For Exercises 1–5, choose the correct letter.

1. Which letter on the graph corresponds to $\sqrt{5}$? C

2. Which letter on the graph corresponds to −1.5? F

What property of real numbers is illustrated by the equation?

3. $-6 + (6 + 5) = (-6 + 6) + 5$ D
   Ⓐ Identity Property of Addition
   Ⓒ Commutative Property of Addition
   Ⓑ Inverse Property of Addition
   Ⓓ Associative Property of Addition

4. $2(-4 + x) = 2(-4) + 2 \cdot x$ G
   Ⓕ Associative Property of Multiplication
   Ⓗ Associative Property of Addition
   Ⓖ Distributive Property
   Ⓘ Closure Property of Multiplication

5. Which of the following shows the numbers 13, 1.3, $1\frac{2}{3}$, −4, and $-\sqrt{10}$ in order from greatest to least? B
   Ⓐ 13, 1.3, $1\frac{2}{3}$, −4, $-\sqrt{10}$
   Ⓒ 13, $1\frac{2}{3}$, 1.3, $-\sqrt{10}$, −4
   Ⓑ 13, 1.3, $1\frac{2}{3}$, $-\sqrt{10}$, −4
   Ⓓ −4, $-\sqrt{10}$, $1\frac{2}{3}$, 1.3, 13

**Short Response**

**Geometry** The length $c$ of the hypotenuse of a right triangle with legs having lengths $a$ and $b$ is found by using the formula $c = \sqrt{a^2 + b^2}$. Which set of numbers best describes the value of $c$ for the given values of $a$ and $b$?

6. $a = 3, b = 4$ [2] natural numbers [1] incorrect set of numbers [0] no answer given

7. $a = \frac{1}{3}, b = \frac{1}{4}$ [2] rational numbers [1] incorrect set of numbers [0] no answer given

8. $a = \sqrt{3}, b = \sqrt{4}$ [2] irrational numbers [1] incorrect set of numbers [0] no answer given

---

### Online Teacher Resource Center
#### Activities, Games, and Puzzles

**1-2 Activity: Property Patterns**
Properties of Real Numbers

Examples of the properties of real numbers with addition and multiplication follow patterns. These patterns can be identifiable even if numbers and symbols are not used. For example, consider the following phrase. It does not make any sense, but it illustrates a property of real numbers.

*peanuts bake apples inside apples*

This word structure follows the pattern for the Identity Property of Addition.

*peanuts bake apples inside apples*
0 + a = a

Likewise, you can designate a word to indicate grouping.

*twisted apples bake bananas bake coconuts inside apples bake twisted bananas bake coconuts*
( a + b ) + c = a + ( b + c )

The equation above illustrates the Associative Property of Addition. The word "twisted" is used for grouping. In translating the two phrases above, "bake" represents addition, "inside" represents equal to, "twisted" represents grouping, and "peanuts" represents the additive identity. A word can also be used to designate an additive inverse. For example, "sour" can be used to make "sour apples," the additive inverse of "apples."

Determine which properties are illustrated using the phrases below, and which words represent *addition, multiplication, equal to, grouping, the additive identity, the additive inverse, the multiplicative identity,* and *the multiplicative inverse.* Record these at the bottom of the page.

1. *lizards slap frogs over frogs slap lizards* Commutative Property of Addition

2. *lizards jump crickets over lizards* Identity Property of Multiplication

3. *frogs slap green frogs over toads* Additive Inverse Property

4. *crickets over yellow snakes jump snakes* Multiplicative Inverse Property

5. *snakes jump slimy frogs jump lizards over slimy snakes jump frogs jump frogs* Associative Property of Multiplication

6. *lizards jump slimy frogs slap snakes over lizards jump slimy frogs slap lizards jump snakes* Distributive Property

| | | |
|---|---|---|
| additive identity toads | multiplicative identity crickets |
| additive inverse green | multiplicative inverse yellow |
| addition slap | multiplication jump |
| grouping slimy | equal to over |

# 1 Interactive Learning

## Solve It!

**PURPOSE** To find a value by applying the correct operations to given values in an appropriate order

**PROCESS** Students may

- find weekly amounts earned, add them, and multiply the sum by number of weeks.
- add each ten-week amount earned.

### FACILITATE

**Q** How much do you earn each week by walking dogs? Explain. **[$60; 3 dogs × $20 per week per dog = $60]**

**Q** How much do you earn each week working in the studio? Explain. **[$160; you work 5 days, 4 hours each day, at $8 per hour. 5 × 4 × $8 = $160]**

**ANSWER** See Solve It in Answers on next page.

**CONNECT THE MATH** Students perform operations in the Solve It that can be represented by an expression. One focus of the lesson will be on writing and evaluating expressions.

# 2 Guided Instruction

## Problem 1

**Q** Is subtraction commutative? Explain. **[No. Answers may vary. Sample: Let $t = 9$; $9 - 7 = 2$ and $7 - 9 = -2$.]**

## Got It?                    EXTENSION

**Q** If you distribute the answer, what word phrase represents the new but equivalent expression? **[the sum of two $a$ and two $b$]**

## 1-3  Algebraic Expressions

**Objectives** To evaluate algebraic expressions
To simplify algebraic expressions

**Getting Ready!**

During summer vacation, you work two jobs. You walk three dogs several times a week, and you work part-time as a receptionist at a hair studio. You earn $8 per hour as a receptionist and $20 per week per dog. Your weekly schedule (shown below) is the same each week. How much will you earn in 10 weeks? Explain.

| Monday | Tuesday | Wednesday | Thursday | Friday | Saturday |
|--------|---------|-----------|----------|--------|----------|
| Walk dogs: 8-9 a.m. | | Walk dogs: 8-9 a.m. | | Walk dogs: 8-9 a.m. | |
| Studio: 1-5 p.m. | Studio: 1-5 p.m. | Studio: 1-5 p.m. | Studio: 1-5 p.m. | | Studio: Noon-4 p.m. |

Ten weeks is a long time! Perhaps you can solve a simpler problem first.

### Lesson Vocabulary
- evaluate
- term
- coefficient
- constant term
- like terms

**Essential Understanding** You can represent some mathematical phrases and real-world quantities using algebraic expressions.

**Think**

What does "seven fewer than $t$" mean? "Seven fewer than $t$" means your answer will be less than $t$.

### Problem 1  Modeling Words With an Algebraic Expression

**Multiple Choice** Which algebraic expression models the word phrase *seven fewer than a number t*?

(A) $t + 7$        (B) $-7t$        (C) $t - 7$        (D) $7 - t$

"Seven fewer than" suggests subtraction. Begin with the number $t$ and subtract 7. This can be represented by the expression $t - 7$. The correct answer is C.

**Got It?** **1.** Which algebraic expression models the word phrase *two times the sum of a and b*?

(F) $a + b$           (H) $2(a + b)$
(G) $2a + b$          (I) $a + 2b$

18    **Chapter 1**  Expressions, Equations, and Inequalities

---

**BIG** ideas **Variables**
                 **Properties**                    **UbD**

**ESSENTIAL UNDERSTANDINGS**

- Some mathematical phrases and real-world quantities can be represented using algebraic expressions.
- Variables can represent variable quantities in real world situations and in patterns.
- The properties that apply to real numbers also apply to variables that represent them.

## Math Background

The difference between a numeric expression and an algebraic expression is that an algebraic expression contains one or more variables.

These variables model a changing or unknown number, and the expression may have different values depending on this quantity. Algebraic expressions can be mathematical models for the real-world situations.

Algebraic expressions can be simplified, forming equivalent expressions, or evaluated for given values of the variables.

Review the order of operations with students as needed. You may also have students study their calculator manuals or experiment to see how their calculators handle the order of operations.

### Support Student Learning

Use the **Algebra 2 Companion** to engage and support students during instruction. See Lesson Resources at the end of this lesson for details.

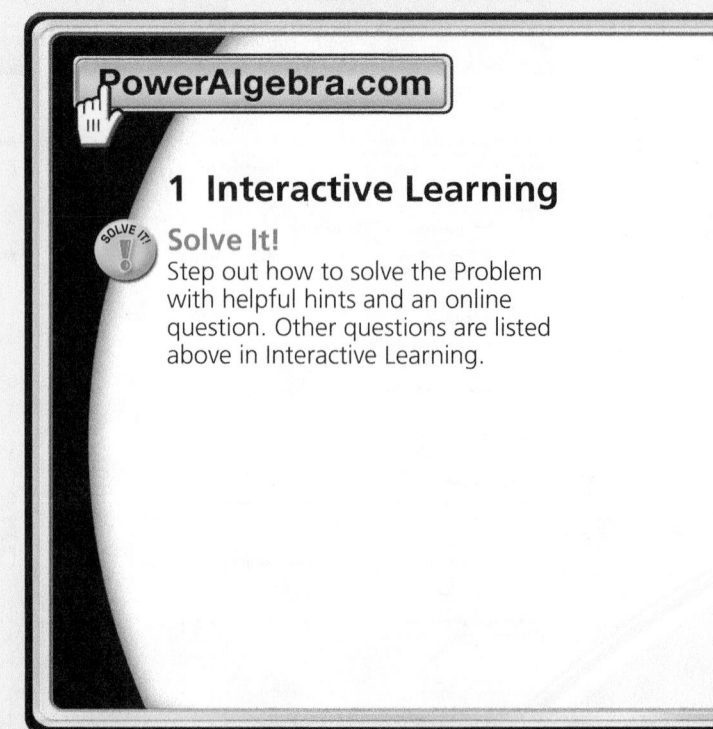

## PowerAlgebra.com

### 1 Interactive Learning

**Solve It!**
Step out how to solve the Problem with helpful hints and an online question. Other questions are listed above in Interactive Learning.

To model a situation with an algebraic expression, do the following:
- Identify the actions that suggest operations.
- Define one or more variables to represent the unknown(s).
- Represent the actions using the variables and the operations.

 **Problem 2** Modeling a Situation

**Plan**

**How can you identify the variable?**
Determine which quantity is unknown.

**Savings** You start with $20 and save $6 each week. What algebraic expression models the total amount you save?

| **Relate** | starting amount | plus | amount saved | times | number of weeks |
|---|---|---|---|---|---|

**Define** Let $w$ = the number of weeks.

| **Write** | 20 | + | 6 | · | $w$ |
|---|---|---|---|---|---|

The expression $20 + 6w$ models the situation.

 **Got It? 2.** You had $150, but you are spending $2 each day. What algebraic expression models this situation?

To **evaluate** an algebraic expression, substitute a number for each variable in the expression. Then simplify using the order of operations.

 **Problem 3** Evaluating Algebraic Expressions

**Plan**

**What operations should you start with?**
Do operations that occur in grouping symbols first. Parentheses are grouping symbols.

What is the value of the expression for the given values of the variables?

**A** $7(a + 4) + 3b - 8$ for $a = -4$ and $b = 5$

| $7(-4 + 4) + 3(5) - 8$ | Substitute the value for each variable. |
|---|---|
| $= 7(0) + 3(5) - 8$ | Perform operations within grouping symbols. |
| $= 0 + 15 - 8$ | Multiply. |
| $= 15 - 8$ | Add and subtract from left to right. |
| $= 7$ | |

**B** $\frac{x}{2} + y^2$ for $x = 1$ and $y = \frac{1}{2}$

| $\frac{1}{2} + \left(\frac{1}{2}\right)^2$ | Substitute the value for each variable. |
|---|---|
| $= \frac{1}{2} + \frac{1}{4}$ | Simplify the power. |
| $= \frac{3}{4}$ | Add. |

 **Got It? 3. a.** What is the value of the expression $\frac{2(x^2 - y^2)}{3}$ for $x = 6$ and $y = -3$?
**b. Reasoning** Will the value of the expression change if the parentheses are removed? Explain.

## Problem 2

**Q** What is the action in this situation? **[saving]**

**Q** What operation represents saving? Explain. **[Addition; by saving, you are accumulating, or adding to your starting amount.]**

**Q** By convention, the term containing the variable is usually written first. What expression is equivalent to $20 + 6w$ and has the variable term written first? Justify your answer. **[$6w + 20$; the expressions are equivalent because of the Commutative Property of Addition.]**

**Got It?**    ERROR PREVENTION

Make sure students realize that they need to model the *remaining* amount.

## Problem 3

**Q** In 3A, $7(-4 + 4)$ is evaluated by adding within grouping symbols and then multiplying. What is an alternate way of evaluating the expression? **[Use the Distributive Property: $7(-4 + 4) = -28 + 28 = 0$]**

**Q** In 3B, what is meant by "Simplify the power"? **[Evaluate the power term to remove the exponent.]**

**Got It?**

**Q** What role do parentheses have in an expression? **[Answers may vary. Sample: Parentheses change the order of operation.]**

## 2 Guided Instruction

 Each Problem is worked out and supported online.

**Problem 1**
Modeling Words With an Algebraic Expression

**Problem 2**
Modeling a Situation
*Animated*

**Problem 3**
Evaluating Algebraic Expressions

**Alternative Problem 3**
Evaluating Algebraic Expressions
*Animated*

**Problem 4**
Writing and Evaluating an Expression

**Problem 5**
Simplifying Algebraic Expressions
*Animated*

**Support in Algebra 2 Companion**
- Vocabulary
- Key Concepts
- Got It?

# Answers

### Solve It!
You earn $20 × 3 = $60 per week for dog walking. You work five 4-hour-shifts at the studio: 5 × 4 × $8 = $160 per week for receptionist work. In 10 weeks you will earn 10($60 + $160) = 10($220) = $2200.

### Got It?
**1.** H

**2.** $150 - 2d$; with $d$ = the number of days

**3. a.** 18
   **b.** Yes; the numerator will become $2x^2 - y^2$; not $2x^2 - 2y^2$.

## Problem 4 — VISUAL LEARNERS

This problem presents two tasks. Organize the information by completing the tables below.

### Writing the expression

| Type of scoring play | Number of points the play is Worth | Number of scoring plays |
|---|---|---|
| TD | 6 | $t$ |
| EPK | 1 | $k$ |
| FG | 3 | $f$ |

### Finding the number of points scored (Evaluating the expression)

| Type of scoring play | Number of points the play is Worth | Number of scoring plays |
|---|---|---|
| TD | 6 | 3 |
| EPK | 1 | 2 |
| FG | 3 | 4 |

### Got It?

**Q** What information do you know? **[the number of points each scoring play is worth and the number of each type of score]**

**Q** Determine what you need and how you will plan for this problem. How does this problem compare to Problem 4? **[You need the same things and have the same plan.]**

---

 **Problem 4** Writing and Evaluating an Expression

**Sports** In football, a touchdown (TD) is worth six points, an extra-point kick (EPK) one point, and a field goal (FG) three points. What algebraic expression models the total number of points that a football team scores in a game, assuming each scoring play is one of the three given types? Suppose a football team scores 3 touchdowns, 2 extra-point kicks, and 4 field goals. How many points did the team score?

| Know | Need | Plan |
|---|---|---|
| • Number of points each scoring play is worth<br>• Number of each type of score | • Algebraic expression to model points scored<br>• Total number of points scored | • Determine the variables.<br>• Write an expression.<br>• Evaluate the expression. |

**Think**

How many points come from touchdowns?
The number of points from touchdowns is six times the number of touchdowns.

**Relate**  $\dfrac{\text{points}}{\text{per TD}} \cdot \dfrac{\text{number}}{\text{of TDs}} + \dfrac{\text{points}}{\text{per EPK}} \cdot \dfrac{\text{number}}{\text{of EPKs}} + \dfrac{\text{points}}{\text{per FG}} \cdot \dfrac{\text{number}}{\text{of FGs}}$

**Define**  Let $t$ = the number of touchdowns.
Let $k$ = the number of extra-point kicks.
Let $f$ = the number of field goals.

**Write**  $6 \cdot t + 1 \cdot k + 3 \cdot f$

The expression $6t + 1k + 3f$ models the team's total score.

The football team scores 3 touchdowns, 2 extra-point kicks, and 4 field goals, so $t = 3$, $k = 2$, and $f = 4$.

$6(3) + 1(2) + 3(4)$   Substitute the value for each variable.
$= 18 + 2 + 12$   Multiply.
$= 32$   Add.

The team scored 32 points.

**Got It?  4.** In basketball, teams can score by making two-point shots, three-point shots, and one-point free throws. What algebraic expression models the total number of points that a basketball team scores in a game? If a team makes 10 two-point shots, 5 three-point shots, and 7 free throws, how many points does it score in all?

---

An expression that is a number, a variable, or the product of a number and one or more variables is a **term**. A **coefficient** is the numerical factor of a term. A **constant term** is a term with no variables. You can add terms to form longer expressions. The expression below has three terms.

$$-4ax + 7w - 6$$

- coefficients
- constant term — Think of $7w - 6$ as $7w + (-6)$. The constant term is $-6$.

---

# Additional Problems

**1.** Which algebraic expression models the word phrase *one less than the product of six and w*?

**A.** $1 - 6 \cdot w$   **B.** $6 \cdot w - 1$
**C.** $w \cdot 1 - 6$   **D.** $1 \cdot 6 - w$

**ANSWER** B

**2.** You are on a bicycle trip. You traveled 52 miles the first day. Since then, your average rate has been 12 miles per hour. What algebraic expression models the distance you traveled so far?

**ANSWER** $52 + 12h$; $h$ represents the number of hours since the first day.

**3.** What is the value of the expression for the given values of the variables?

**a.** $2r + 5(s + 6) - 1$ for $r = 3$ and $s = -9$

**b.** $c^3 - \dfrac{d}{8}$ for $c = \dfrac{1}{4}$ and $d = 1$

**ANSWERS**
**a.** $-10$
**b.** $-\dfrac{7}{64}$

**4.** Ticket prices for admission to a museum are $8 for adults, $5 for children, and $6 for seniors.

**a.** What algebraic expression models the total number of dollars collected in ticket sales?

**b.** If 20 adult tickets, 16 children's tickets, and 10 senior tickets are sold one morning, how much money is collected in all?

**ANSWERS**
**a.** The expression $8a + 5c + 6s$ models the total number of dollars collected; $a$ is the number of adult tickets; $c$ is the number of children's tickets; and $s$ is the number of senior tickets.

**b.** The total amount collected is $300.

**5.** What is the simplified form of each expression?

**a.** $2a^2 + 3b^2 + 6b^2 + 5a^2$
**b.** $-(x + 4y) + 5(3x - y)$

**ANSWERS**
**a.** $7a^2 + 9b^2$
**b.** $14x - 9y$

# Answers

**Got It?** (continued)

**4.** Let $x$ = the number of two-point shots, $y$ = the number of three-point shots, $z$ = the number of one-point free throws, $2x + 3y + 1z$; 42 points

**Like terms** have the same variables raised to the same powers.

like terms    like terms

$$3x^2 + 5x^2 + 9y^3z + 2yz - 4y^3z$$

You can simplify an algebraic expression that has like terms. You combine like terms using the properties of real numbers (Lesson 1-2). An expression and its simplified form are equivalent. Their values are equal for all values of their variables.

---

**take note**

### Concept Summary   Properties for Simplifying Algebraic Expressions

Let $a$, $b$, and $c$ represent real numbers.

| | |
|---|---|
| **Definition of Subtraction** | $a - b = a + (-b)$ |
| **Definition of Division** | $a \div b = \dfrac{a}{b} = a \cdot \dfrac{1}{b}, b \neq 0$ |
| **Distributive Property for Subtraction** | $a(b - c) = ab - ac$ |
| **Multiplication by 0** | $0 \cdot a = 0$ |
| **Multiplication by $-1$** | $-1 \cdot a = -a$ |
| **Opposite of a Sum** | $-(a + b) = -a + (-b) = -a - b$ |
| **Opposite of a Difference** | $-(a - b) = -a + b = b - a$ |
| **Opposite of a Product** | $-(ab) = -a \cdot b = a \cdot (-b)$ |
| **Opposite of an Opposite** | $-(-a) = a$ |

---

**Problem 5**   **Simplifying Algebraic Expressions**

**Combine like terms. What is a simpler form of each expression?**

 **A** $7x^2 + 3y^2 + 2y^2 - 4x^2$

| | |
|---|---|
| $7x^2 + 3y^2 + 2y^2 - 4x^2$ | Identify like terms. |
| $= 7x^2 - 4x^2 + 3y^2 + 2y^2$ | Commutative Property of Addition |
| $= (7 - 4)x^2 + (3 + 2)y^2$ | Distributive Property |
| $= 3x^2 + 5y^2$ | Combine like terms. |

**B** $-(3k + m) + 2(k - 4m)$

| | |
|---|---|
| $-3k - m + 2k - 8m$ | Opposite of a Sum and Distributive Property |
| $= -k - 9m$ | Combine like terms. |

 **Got It?**  **5.** Combine like terms. What is a simpler form of each expression?

 **a.** $-4j^2 - 7k + 5j + j^2$          **b.** $-(8a + 3b) + 10(2a - 5b)$

**Think**

Are $7x^2$ and $3y^2$ like terms?
No; they have different variables.

---

---

## Answers

**5. a.** $-3j^2 - 7k + 5j$

 **b.** $12a - 53b$

## 3 Lesson Check

**Do you know HOW?** ERROR INTERVENTION

- If students have trouble substituting in Exercises 3–6, suggest they rewrite the problem, replacing the variables with parentheses and writing the variable above it. For example: $\dfrac{x \qquad y}{2(\ ) - 3(\ )}$.

**Do you UNDERSTAND?**

- If students have trouble with Exercise 9, look at Problem 4. An algebraic expression becomes a numeric expression when values are substituted for the variables.

### Close

> **Q** How do you evaluate an algebraic expression? **[Substitute values for the variables, then find the value of the resulting numeric expression.]**
>
> **Q** What does it mean to simplify an algebraic expression of the type in this lesson? **[Combine like terms.]**
>
> **Q** To model a situation with an expression, what are some tasks you might need to do? **[Answers may vary. Sample: identify the action(s), choose the correct operation(s), identify how quantities are related, define variables to represent unknown quantities]**

---

 **Lesson Check**

**Do you know HOW?**

Write an algebraic expression that models each word phrase.

**1.** the quotient of the sum of 2 and a number $b$, and 3

**2.** the sum of the product of a number $k$ and 4, and a number $m$

Evaluate each algebraic expression for $x = 3$ and $y = -2$.

**3.** $2x - 3y$  **4.** $5x + y$

**5.** $y - x$  **6.** $x + 4y$

**Do you UNDERSTAND?**

**7. Error Analysis** A student simplified the expression as shown.

$$3p^2q + 2p - (5q + p - 2p^2q) = q^2p + 3p - 5q$$

Identify the errors and correct them.

**8. Vocabulary** Explain the difference between a constant and a coefficient.

**9. Compare and Contrast** How are algebraic expressions and numerical expressions alike? How are they different? Include examples to justify your reasoning.

---

 **Practice and Problem-Solving Exercises**

**Ⓐ Practice**

Write an algebraic expression that models each word phrase.  ◀ See Problem 1.

**10.** four more than a number $b$

**11.** the product of 8 and the sum of a number $x$ and 3

**12.** the quotient of the difference between 5 and a number $n$, and 2

Write an algebraic expression that models each situation.  ◀ See Problem 2.

**13.** Jenny had $130, but she is spending $10 per week.

**14.** The piggy bank contained $25, and $1.50 is added each day.

**15.** You had 250 minutes left on your cell phone, and you talk an hour a week.

Evaluate each expression for the given values of the variables.  ◀ See Problem 3.

**16.** $4a + 7b + 3a - 2b + 2a$; $a = -5$ and $b = 3$

**17.** $-k^2 - (3k - 5n) + 4n$; $k = -1$ and $n = -2$

**18.** $-5(x + 2y) + 15(x + 2y)$; $x = 7$ and $y = -7$

**19.** $4(2m - n) - 3(2m - n)$; $m = -15$ and $n = -18$

**Physics** The expression $16t^2$ models the distance in feet that an object falls during the first $t$ seconds after being dropped. What is the distance the object falls during each time?

**20.** 0.25 second  **21.** 0.5 second  **22.** 2 seconds  **23.** 10 seconds

---

## 3 Lesson Check

For a digital lesson check, use the Got It questions.

**Support in Algebra 2 Companion**
- Lesson Check

## 4 Practice

Assign homework to individual students or to an entire class.

---

## Answers

### Lesson Check

**1.** $\dfrac{2 + b}{3}$

**2.** $4k + m$

**3.** 12

**4.** 13

**5.** $-5$

**6.** $-5$

**7.** The student did not distribute the $-1$.
$3p^2q + 2p - (5q + p - 2p^2q) = 3p^2q + 2p - 5q - p + 2p^2q = 5p^2q + p - 5q$

**8.** A constant is a term with no variables, whereas a coefficient is the numerical factor in a term.

**9.** Answers may vary. Sample: Both algebraic expressions and numerical expressions represent a quantity using numbers, operations and grouping symbols. An algebraic expression includes variables when representing a quantity. Examples: numerical expression: $3 + 6(5 - 2)$; algebraic expression: $2z + 3z(6 + 5z)$.

### Practice and Problem-Solving Exercises

**10.** $b + 4$

**11.** $8(x + 3)$

**12.** $\dfrac{5 - n}{2}$

**13.** $130 - 10w$; with $w = $ number of weeks

**14.** $25 + 1.5d$; with $d = $ number of days

**15.** $250 - 60w$; with $w = $ number of weeks

**16.** $-30$  **17.** $-16$

**18.** $-70$  **19.** $-12$

**20.** 1 ft

**21.** 4 ft

**22.** 64 ft

**23.** 1600 ft

**Investing** The expression $1000(1.1)^t$ represents the value of a $1000 investment that earns 10% interest per year, compounded annually for $t$ years. What is the value of a $1000 investment at the end of each period?

**24.** 2 years      **25.** 3 years      **26.** 4 years      **27.** 5 years

Write an algebraic expression to model the total score in each situation. Then evaluate the expression to find the total score.    ◄ **See Problem 4.**

**28.** In the first set, the volleyball team made only 8 shots worth one point each.

**29.** In the last baseball game, there were two 3-run home runs and 4 hits that each scored 2 runs.

Simplify by combining like terms.    ◄ **See Problem 5.**

**30.** $5a - a$      **31.** $5 + 10s - 8s$      **32.** $-5a - 4a + b$

**33.** $2a + 3b + 4a$      **34.** $6r + 3s + 2s + 4r$      **35.** $0.5x - x$

**36.** $7b - (3a - 8b)$      **37.** $5 + (4g - 7)$      **38.** $-(3x - 4y) + x$

 **Apply**

Evaluate each expression for the given value of the variable.

**39.** $x + 2x - x - 1; x = 2$      **40.** $2z + 3 + 5 - 3z; z = -3$      **41.** $3(2a + 5) + 2(3 - a); a = 4$

**42.** $\frac{5(2k - 3) - 3(k + 4)}{3k + 2}; k = -2$      **43.** $y^2 + 3; y = \sqrt{7}$      **44.** $5c^3 - 6c^2 - 2c; c = -5$

**45. Think About a Plan** Tran's truck gets very poor gas mileage. If Tran pays $84 to fill his truck with gas and is able to drive $m$ miles on a full tank, what expression shows his gas cost per mile?
- What operation does "per" indicate?
- Check your expression by substituting 200 miles for $m$. Does your answer make sense?

Simplify by combining like terms.

**46.** $-a^2 + 2b^2 + \frac{1}{4}a^2$      **47.** $x + \frac{x^2}{2} + 2x^2 - x$      **48.** $\frac{y^2}{4} + \frac{y}{3} + \frac{y^2}{3} - \frac{y}{5}$

**49.** $-(2x + y) - 2(-x - y)$      **50.** $x(3 - y) + y(x + 6)$      **51.** $\frac{1}{2}(x^2 - y^2) - \frac{5}{2}(x^2 - y^2)$

Write an algebraic expression to model each situation.

**52. Class Project** The freshman class will be selling carnations as a class project. What is the class's income after it pays the florist a flat fee of $200 and sells $x$ carnations for $2 each?

**53. Jobs** You have a summer job at a car wash. You earn $8.50 per hour and are expected to pay a one-time fee of $15 for the uniform. If you work $x$ hours per week, how much will you make during the first week?

**54. Reasoning** Suppose you need to subtract $a$ from $b$ but mistakenly subtract $b$ from $a$ instead. How is the answer you get related to the correct answer? Explain.

**ASSIGNMENT GUIDE**
Basic: 10–38 all, 39–46 even, 51
Average: 11–37 odd, 39–60
Advanced: 11–37 odd, 39–62
Standardized Test Prep: 63–66
Mixed Review: 67–74

**Reasoning** exercises have blue headings.
**Applications** exercises have red headings.

**EXERCISE 51:** Use the Think About a Plan worksheet in the **Practice and Problem Solving Workbook** (also available in the Teaching Resources in print and online) to further support students' development in becoming independent learners.

**HOMEWORK QUICK CHECK**
To check students' understanding of key skills and concepts, go over Exercises 21, 31, 40, 44, and 51.

---

**24.** $1210

**25.** $1331

**26.** $1464.10

**27.** $1610.51

**28.** Let $s$ = number of shots, $1s$; 8

**29.** Let $x$ = 3-run home runs and $y$ = 2-run hits; $3x + 2y$; 14

**30.** $4a$

**31.** $2s + 5$

**32.** $-9a + b$

**33.** $6a + 3b$

**34.** $10r + 5s$

**35.** $-0.5x$

**36.** $-3a + 15b$

**37.** $4g - 2$

**38.** $-2x + 4y$

**39.** 3

**40.** 11

**41.** 37

**42.** $\frac{41}{4}$

**43.** 10

**44.** $-765$

**45.** $\frac{\$84}{m}$

**46.** $-\frac{3}{4}a^2 + 2b^2$

**47.** $\frac{5x^2}{2}$

**48.** $\frac{7y^2}{12} + \frac{2y}{15}$

**49.** $y$

**50.** $3x + 6y$

**51.** $-2x^2 + 2y^2$

**52.** $2x - 200$

**53.** $8.5x - 15$

**54.** It is the correct answer's opposite; $a - b = -b + a = -(b - a)$

# Answers

## Practice and Problem-Solving Exercises (continued)

**55.** No; John did not use the Distr. Prop. correctly.
$-(x + y) + 3(x - 4y)$
$-x - y + 3x - 12y$
$2x - 13y$

**56.** Answers may vary. Sample: $x^2$

**57.** Distr. Prop.

**58.** Opposite of an Opposite or Opposite of a Difference used twice

**59.** Opposite of a Difference

**60.** Mult. by $-1$

**61.** Answers may vary. Sample:
$2(b - a) + 5(b - a)$
$\quad = (2 + 5)(b - a) \quad$ Distr. Prop.
$\quad = 7(b - a) \qquad$ Add.
$\quad = 7b - 7a \qquad$ Distr. Prop.

**62. a.** 18
   **b.** $2x^2$; 18
   **c.** Properties of operations were used to simplify the original expression into an equivalent expression. Equivalent expressions have equal values for all values of their variables.

## Standardized Test Prep

**63.** A

**64.** F

**65.** C

**66.** [2] $\sqrt{26} > \sqrt{25}$ and $\sqrt{25} = 5$. So $\sqrt{26} > 5 > 4.9$ therefore, $\sqrt{26} > 4.9$.
   [1] Correct comparison with no explanation OR incorrect explanation

## Mixed Review

**67.** $-1.5, -\sqrt{2}, -1.4, -0.5$

**68.** $-\frac{5}{6}, -\frac{3}{4}, -\frac{3}{8}, \frac{1}{2}$

**69.** $-20, 0.2, \frac{1}{2}, \sqrt{2}$

**70.** $-3, -0.5, -\frac{1}{4}, \frac{3}{4}$

**71.** $7x - 4$

**72.** $-p - \frac{2q}{3}$

**73.** $2b - 28$

**74.** $2k - 2m$

---

**55. Error Analysis** John simplified the expression as shown. Describe and correct his error.

**56. Open-Ended** Write an example of an algebraic expression that has a nonnegative value regardless of the value of the variable.

**Name the property of real numbers illustrated by the equation.**

**57.** $2(s - t) = 2s - 2t$

**58.** $-[-(x - 10)] = x - 10$

**59.** $-(2t - 11) = 11 - 2t$

**60.** $-(a - b) = (-1)(a - b)$

 **Challenge**

**61.** Simplify $2(b - a) + 5(b - a)$ and justify each step in your simplification.

**62. a.** Evaluate the expression $2(2x^2 - x) - 3(x^2 - x) + x^2 - x$ for $x = 3$. Do *not* simplify the expression before evaluating it.
   **b.** Simplify the expression in part (a) and then evaluate your answer for $x = 3$.
   **c. Writing** Explain why the values in parts (a) and (b) should be the same.

### Standardized Test Prep

**SAT/ACT**

**63.** Which expression best represents a simpler form of $4m + 3(m + n)$?
   Ⓐ $7m + 3n$    Ⓑ $4m + 3mn$    Ⓒ $3m + 4n$    Ⓓ $7m^2 + 3n$

**64.** A driver drove 12 miles and made a pit stop. After that, the driver continued driving at a constant speed of 65 miles per hour for $t$ hours. Which of the following represents the total distance driven?
   Ⓕ $12 + 65t$    Ⓖ $65t$    Ⓗ $12t + 65$    Ⓘ $12(t + 65)$

**65.** What is the value of $r$ when $s = -1$, $t = 4$, and $u = \frac{1}{5}$?
$$r = 3s^2 + 5(t - 2u)$$
   Ⓐ 7    Ⓑ 15    Ⓒ 21    Ⓓ $22\frac{1}{5}$

**Short Response**

**66.** Compare $\sqrt{26}$ and 4.9. Explain your answer.

### Mixed Review

**Order the numbers from least to greatest.**
◀ See Lesson 1-2.

**67.** $-1.5, -0.5, -\sqrt{2}, -1.4$

**68.** $-\frac{3}{8}, \frac{1}{2}, -\frac{3}{4}, -\frac{5}{6}$

**69.** $\sqrt{2}, -20, 0.2, \frac{1}{2}$

**70.** $\frac{3}{4}, -3, -0.5, -\frac{1}{4}$

**Get Ready!** **To prepare for Lesson 1-4, do Exercises 71–74.**

**Simplify each expression.**
◀ See Lesson 1-3.

**71.** $4x + 3x - 4$

**72.** $-\frac{p}{3} + \frac{q}{3} - \frac{2p}{3} - q$

**73.** $-2(4 + b) + 4(b - 5)$

**74.** $(k - m) - (m - k)$

# Differentiated Remediation

Available in editable format online.

## Additional Instructional Support

### Algebra 2 Companion

Students can use the **Algebra 2 Companion** worktext (4 pages) as you teach the lesson. Use the Companion to support

- New Vocabulary
- Key Concepts
- Got It for each Problem
- Lesson Check

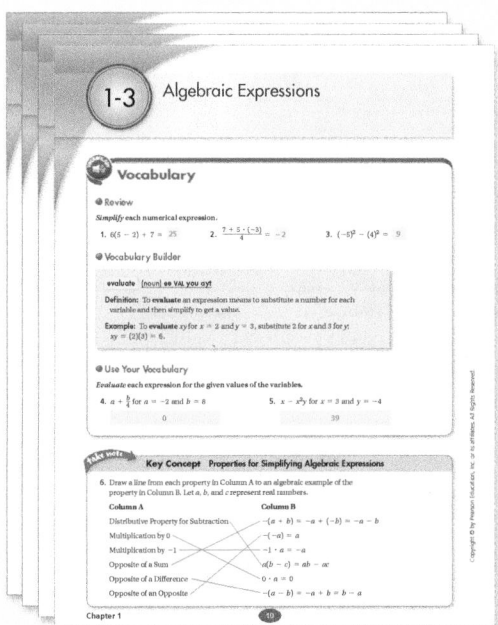

### ELL Support

**Focus on Language** After students have studied the information about terms, coefficients, and constant terms, reinforce the vocabulary. Have students work in pairs. One student writes an expression and the other student answers the following questions: What are the terms? What is the constant term? What are the coefficients?

## 5 Assess & Remediate

### Lesson Quiz

**1.** Which algebraic expression models the word phrase *three fewer than the sum of c and d*?

  (a) $3 - c + d$       (b) $(c + d) - 3$

  (c) $c + 3 - d$       (d) $d + 3 - c$

**2.** You have 128 ounces of milk and drink 16 ounces per day. What algebraic expression models the amount of milk you have?

**3.** Evaluate the expression for the given variables.

  $-a^2 - (2a - 7b) + b$ for $a = -2$ and $b = 3$

**4. Do you UNDERSTAND?** You have a summer job detailing cars. You charge $5 to wash a car, $25 to wax a car, and $2 to vacuum a car. What algebraic expression models the total amount you earn? If you wash 8 cars, wax 2 cars, and vacuum 6 cars, how much will you earn in all?

**5.** What is the simplified form of the expression $-(2a + 5s) + 10(a - 3s)$?

### ANSWERS TO LESSON QUIZ

**1.** (b)

**2.** $128 - 16d$; $d$ is the number of days

**3.** 24

**4.** $5w + 25x + 2v$; $w$ is number of washes; $x$ is number of waxes; and $v$ is number of vacuums; $102

**5.** $8a - 35s$

### PRESCRIPTION FOR REMEDIATION

Use the student work on the Lesson Quiz to prescribe a differentiated review assignment:

| Points | Differentiated Remediation |
|--------|----------------------------|
| 0–2 | Intervention |
| 3–4 | On-level |
| 5 | Extension |

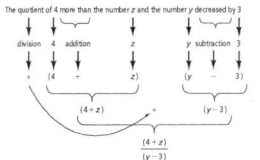

### 5 Assess & Remediate

Assign the Lesson Quiz. Appropriate intervention, practice, or enrichment is automatically generated based on student performance.

## Intervention

- **Reteaching** (2 pages) Provides reteaching and practice exercises for the key lesson concepts. Use with struggling students or absent students.

- **English Language Learner Support** Helps students develop and reinforce mathematical vocabulary and key concepts.

### All-in-One Resources/Online
**Reteaching**

#### 1-3 Reteaching
Algebraic Expressions

You can model words with algebraic expressions. In a word problem, look for words and word phrases that indicate mathematical operations.

| Addition | Subtraction | Multiplication | Division |
|----------|-------------|----------------|----------|
| added to | subtracted from | multiplied by | divided by |
| plus | minus | product | quotient |
| sum | difference | times | fraction of |
| more than | less than | of | per |
| longer than | shorter than | | |
| increased by | decreased by | | |
| total | fewer than | | |
| in all | | | |

**Problem**

What is an algebraic expression that models the given word phrase?

The quotient of 4 more than the number $z$ and the number $y$ decreased by 3

**Exercises**

Write an algebraic expression that models each word phrase.

**1.** nine less than 5 multiplied by the number $p$   $5p - 9$

**2.** the product of 2 divided by the number $h$ and 8 more than the number $k$   $\left(\frac{2}{h}\right)(k + 8)$

**3.** two decreased by the quotient of the number $a$ and 7 and increased by $a$ multiplied by 3   $2 - \frac{a}{7} + 3a$

### All-in-One Resources/Online
**English Language Learner Support**

#### 1-3 ELL Support
Algebraic Expressions

Use the chart below to review vocabulary. These vocabulary words will help you complete this page.

| Addition (+) | Subtraction (−) | Multiplication (×) | Division (÷) |
|--------------|-----------------|--------------------|--------------|
| sum | difference | product | quotient |
| more than | less than | times | divided by |
| increased by | fewer than | | |
| total | subtracted from | | |
| added to | | | |

Circle the word or words in each word phrase that tell you what operations to use. Write the operation symbol word (+, −, ×, ÷) next to the algebraic expression.

**1.** the sum of a number $m$ and $-12$   +

**2.** the product of $b$ and $c$   ×

**3.** 14 less than $p$   −

**4.** the total of $-75$ and $t$   +

**5.** the quotient of $d$ and 28   ÷

Match each word phrase in Column A with the matching algebraic expression in Column B. The first one is done for you.

| Column A | Column B |
|----------|----------|
| **6.** the difference of a number $p$ and 36 | A. $y + 9$ |
| **7.** 15 more than the number $q$   C | B. $10(r)$ |
| **8.** the product of 10 and a number $r$   B | C. $q + 15$ |
| **9.** the total of a number $y$ and 9   A | D. $p - 36$ |

Match each algebraic expression in Column A with the matching word phrase in Column B.

| Column A | Column B |
|----------|----------|
| **10.** $m + 45$   C | A. 45 less than a number $m$ |
| **11.** $\frac{m}{45}$   D | B. 45 times the sum of a number $m$ and 1 |
| **12.** $m - 45$   A | C. a number $m$ increased by 45 |
| **13.** $45(m + 1)$   B | D. a number $m$ divided by 45 |

# Differentiated Remediation *continued*

Available in editable format online.

## On-Level

- **Practice** (2 pages) Provides extra practice for each lesson. For simpler practice exercises, use the Form K Practice pages found in the All-in-One Teaching Resources and online.

- **Think About a Plan** Helps students develop specific problem-solving skills and strategies by providing scaffolded guiding questions.
- **Standardized Test Prep** Focuses on all major exercises, all major question types, and helps students prepare for the high-stakes assessments.

## Extension

- **Enrichment** Provides students with interesting problems and activities that extend the concepts of the lesson.
- **Activities, Games, and Puzzles** Worksheets that can be used for concepts development, enrichment, and for fun!

---

### Practice and Problem Solving Wkbk/All-in-One Resources/Online
#### Practice page 1

**1-3 Practice** Form G
Algebraic Expressions

Write an algebraic expression that models each word phrase.

1. seven less than the number $t$   $t - 7$

2. the sum of 11 and the product of 2 and a number $r$   $11 + 2r$

Write an algebraic expression that models each situation.

3. Arin has $520 and is earning $75 each week babysitting.   $520 + 75w$

4. You have 50 boxes of raisins and are eating 12 boxes each month.   $50 - 12m$

Evaluate each expression for the given values of the variables.

5. $-4v + 3(w + 2v) - 5w$; $v = -2$ and $w = 4$   $-12$

6. $c(3 - a) - c^2$; $a = 4$ and $c = -1$   $0$

7. $2(3e - 5f) + 3(e^2 + 4f)$; $e = 3$ and $f = -5$   $35$

**Surface Area** The expression $6z^2$ represents the surface area of a cube with edges of length $s$. What is the surface area of a cube with each edge length?

8. 3 inches   54 in.$^2$

9. 1.5 meters   13.5 m$^2$

The expression $4.95 + 0.07x$ models a household's monthly long-distance charges, where $x$ represents the number of minutes of long-distance calls during the month. What are the monthly charges for each number of long-distance minutes?

10. 73 minutes   $10.06

11. 29 minutes   $6.98

Simplify by combining like terms.

12. $5x - 3x^2 + 16x^2$   $13x^2 + 5x$

13. $\frac{3(a - b)}{9} + \frac{4}{9}b$   $\frac{1}{3}a + \frac{1}{9}b$

14. $t + \frac{t^2}{2} + t^2 + t$   $\frac{3}{2}t^2 + 2t$

15. $4a - 5(a + 1)$   $-a - 5$

16. $-2(j^2 - k) - 6(j^2 + 3k)$   $-8j^2 - 16k$

17. $x(x - y) + y(y - x)$   $x^2 - 2xy + y^2$

---

### Practice and Problem Solving Wkbk/All-in-One Resources/Online
#### Practice page 2

**1-3 Practice** (continued) Form G
Algebraic Expressions

18. In a soccer tournament, teams receive 6 points for winning a game, 3 points for tying a game, and 1 point for each goal they score. What algebraic expression models the total number of points that a soccer team receives in a tournament? Suppose one team wins two games and ties one game, scoring a total of five goals. How many points does the team receive?   $6w + 3t + 1g$; 20 points

Evaluate each expression for the given value of the variable.

19. $-t^2 - (3t + 2)$; $t = 5$   $-42$

20. $t^2 - 5(t^2 - t^2)$; $t = 4$   $-224$

21. **Perimeter** Write an expression for the perimeter of the figure at the right as the sum of the lengths of its sides. What is the simplified form of this expression?
$a + (a - b) + c + b + (a - 2c) + (a - b)$; $4a$

22. **Simplify** $-(2x - 5y) + 3(4x + 2y)$ and justify each step in your simplification.   $-2x + 5y + 12x + 6y$; Opposite of a Difference and Distributive Property; $10x + 11y$; Combine like terms using the Distributive Property

23. **Error Analysis** Alana simplified the expression as shown. Do you agree with her work? Explain.   No; Dist. Prop. and Opp. of a Diff. incorrectly applied. Correct simplification: $2x + 8 - 5x + 7 = -3x + 15$

24. **Open-Ended** Write an example of an algebraic expression that always has the same value regardless of the value of the variable.   Answers may vary. Sample: any expression that results in the variable having a coefficient of 0; sample: $x - x$

Match the property name with the appropriate expression.

25. Opposite of a Difference   E

26. Opposite of a Sum   A

27. Opposite of an Opposite   F

28. Multiplication by 0   B

29. Multiplication by $-1$   D

30. Distributive Property   C

A. $-[(-r) + 2p] = -(-r) - 2p$

B. $16d - (3d + 2)(0) = 16d - 0$

C. $5(2 - x) = 10 - 5x$

D. $-(4r + 3s) + t = (-1)(4r + 3s) + t$

E. $-(8 - 3m) = 3m - 8$

F. $-[-(9 - 2w)] = 9 - 2w$

---

### Practice and Problem Solving Wkbk/All-in-One Resources/Online
#### Think About a Plan

**1-3 Think About a Plan**
Algebraic Expressions

Write an algebraic expression to model the situation.

The freshman class will be selling carnations as a class project. What is the class's income after it pays the florist a flat fee of $200 and sells $x$ carnations for $2 each?

1. What does the variable represent?
   the number of carnations sold

2. How will the class's income change for each carnation sold?
   It will increase by $2.

3. Will paying the florist increase or decrease their income? By how much?
   decrease; $200

4. Will the expression include both the income for each carnation and the florist's fee? Explain.
   Yes; the class's profit is a function of the proceeds from carnation sales and the florist's fee.

5. Write the expression in words.
   The [ income ] is [ -200 ] and [ 2 ] times [ x ]

6. Write the expression using symbols.
   income = [ -200 ] + [ 2 ] [ • ] [ x ]

7. Check your expression by substituting 300 for the number of carnations. Does your answer make sense? Explain.
   $-200 + 2(300) = -200 + 600 = 400$; yes; the class has an income of $400 after they make $600 and pay the florist $200.

8. The algebraic expression [ -200 + 2x ] models the freshman class income.

---

### Practice and Problem Solving Wkbk/All-in-One Resources/Online
#### Standardized Test Prep

**1-3 Standardized Test Prep**
Algebraic Expressions

**Multiple Choice**

For Exercises 1–3, choose the correct letter.

1. The expression $2\pi(rh + r^2)$ represents the total surface area of a cylinder with height $h$ and radius $r$. What is the surface area of a cylinder with height 6 centimeters and radius 2 centimeters?   C
   A. $16\pi$ cm$^2$
   C. $32\pi$ cm$^2$
   B. $28\pi$ cm$^2$
   D. $96\pi$ cm$^2$

2. Which expression best represents the simplified form of $3(m - 3) + m(5 - m) - m^2$?   F
   F. $-2m^2 + 8m - 9$
   H. $-2m^2 - 2m - 9$
   G. $8m - 9$
   I. $-2m - 9$

3. The price of a discount airline ticket starts at $150 and increases by $30 each week. Which algebraic expression models this situation?   D
   A. $30 + 150w$
   C. $30 - 150w$
   B. $150 - 30w$
   D. $150 + 30w$

**Extended Response**

4. Members of a club are selling calendars as a fundraiser. The club pays $100 for a box of wall and desk calendars. They sell wall calendars for $12 and desk calendars for $8.
   a. Write an algebraic expression to model the club's profit from selling $w$ wall calendars and $d$ desk calendars. Explain in words or show your work for how you determined the expression.
   b. What is the club's profit from selling 9 wall calendars and 7 desk calendars? Show your work.

[4] a. The income from wall calendars is $12w$. The income from desk calendars is $8d$. The total income is $12w + 8d$. The club must pay $100 from the total income, so the profit is $12w + 8d - 100$. (OR equivalent explanation)
   b. $12w + 8d - 100 = 12(9) + 8(7) - 100 = 108 + 56 - 100 = 64$; $64

[3] appropriate methods and correct expression, but minor computational error

[2] incorrect expression or multiple computational errors

[1] correct expression and profit, without work shown

[0] no answer or no attempt made.

---

### All-in-One Resources/Online
#### Enrichment

**1-3 Enrichment**
Algebraic Expressions

**Math Puzzle**

Algebraic expressions can help reveal the secret behind number puzzles that appear to be magic. Start by trying the puzzle below. Complete the puzzle two times and record each step in the table.

| Directions | First Guess | Second Guess |
|---|---|---|
| Think of a number. | | |
| Add 1 to your number. | | |
| Multiply your answer by 2. | | |
| Subtract 2 from your answer. | | |
| Finally, subtract your original number. | | |

What did you notice about your final answer each time?
Answers may vary. Sample: The final number is the same as the original number.

By writing and simplifying algebraic expressions, you can explain the puzzle.

Let $n$ represent your number. Write an algebraic expression for each of the steps in the puzzle above.

1. Add 1 to your number.   $n + 1$

2. Multiply your answer by 2.   $2n + 2$

3. Subtract 2 from your answer.   $2n$

4. Subtract your original number.   $n$

5. Explain how your algebraic expressions show why the puzzle always ends with the original number.
   Answers may vary. Sample: The final expression is the same as the original expression.

Write and simplify algebraic expressions for the puzzle below.

6. Think of a number.   $n$

7. Multiply your number by 4.   $4n$

8. Subtract 2.   $4n - 2$

9. Divide your number by 2.   $2n - 1$

10. Add 1.   $2n$

11. Subtract your original number.   $n$

---

### Online Teacher Resource Center
#### Activities, Games, and Puzzles

**1-3 Game: Number-Cube Substitution**
Algebraic Expressions

**Material**
- 1 six-sided number cube

**Game Play**

Play this game in pairs. Each player takes a turn and rolls the number cube. Whoever rolls the lowest number goes first.

On your turn, roll the number cube. This number is the value of $x$ for the first expression shown, $x + 32$. Substitute the value of $x$ in the expression to calculate your score for the first roll. Record your roll and score on the scorecard.

Players take turns evaluating each expression. Then each player totals up his or her score, and the player with the higher total wins.

**Scorecard**   Check students' work.

| | Player 1 | | Player 2 | |
|---|---|---|---|---|
| | Number rolled, $x$ | Score | Number rolled, $x$ | Score |
| $x + 32$ | | | | |
| $x^2 - 3x$ | | | | |
| $\frac{120}{x}$ | | | | |
| $6x - 10$ | | | | |
| $-x^2$ | | | | |
| $-2 - x$ | | | | |
| $(x - 3)(x + 2)$ | | | | |
| $x^2 - 5x - 3$ | | | | |
| $(x + 3)^2 - 7$ | | | | |
| $-3x + 5$ | | | | |
| $\frac{60}{x - 7}$ | | | | |
| | | Total | | Total |

---

## Do you know HOW?

**1.** Draw the next figure in the pattern.

Identify a pattern and find the next number in the pattern.

**2.** $-405, -135, -45, -15, \ldots$

**3.** $\frac{2x}{3}, \frac{x}{3}, \frac{x}{6}, \frac{x}{12}, \ldots$

**4.** $101, 92, 83, 74, \ldots$

**5.** $0.4, 1.2, 3.6, 10.8, \ldots$

Name the property of real numbers illustrated by the equation.

**6.** $7(x - y) = 7x - 7y$

**7.** $\sqrt{7} \cdot 1 = \sqrt{7}$

**8.** $-2 \cdot \left(-\frac{1}{2}\right) = 1$

**9.** $2.3(3.4 \cdot 12.9) = (2.3 \cdot 3.4)(12.9)$

Write an algebraic expression to model each word phrase.

**10.** eight times the sum of $a$ and $b$

**11.** four more than the product of $x$ and $y$

**12.** six less than the quotient of $d$ and $g$

**13.** ten less than twice the product of $s$ and $t$

Simplify each expression.

**14.** $-x^2 + 2y - 3x^2 + 10$

**15.** $-2(d + 2e) + 5(3d - 8e)$

**16.** $-(a + 2b) + 4(a + 2b) - 2(a + 2b)$

**17.** $-3x + 14x + 7x^2 - 3x + 4x(x + 1)$

---

Identify a pattern by making a table of the inputs and outputs. Include a process column.

**18.**

**19.**
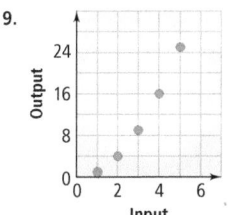

Evaluate each expression for $a = 4$, $b = -3$, and $c = 10$.

**20.** $7a - 5b$

**21.** $4a + b - |2c|$

**22.** $|a - b - c^2|$

Write an algebraic expression to model each situation.

**23.** You have 16 tomatoes, and your tomato plants produce 5 tomatoes each day.

**24.** Your car's gas tank holds 25 gallons, and you use 1.5 gallons of gas each day.

## Do you UNDERSTAND?

**25. Writing** Explain why every integer is also a rational number.

**26. Reasoning** What expression describes the number of squares in the $n$th figure?

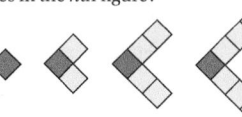

**27. Reasoning** Is there a Closure Property of Subtraction that applies to whole numbers? Explain.

---

**19.** Output = Input²

| Input | Process Column | Output |
|-------|----------------|--------|
| 1 | $(1) \times (1)$ | 1 |
| 2 | $(2) \times (2)$ | 4 |
| 3 | $(3) \times (3)$ | 9 |
| 4 | $(4) \times (4)$ | 16 |
| 5 | $(5) \times (5)$ | 25 |
| ⋮ | ⋮ | ⋮ |
| $n$ | $(n) \times (n)$ | $n^2$ |

**20.** 43

**21.** $-7$

**22.** 93

**23.** $16 + 5d$; Let $d$ = number of days

**24.** $25 - 1.5d$; Let $d$ = number of days

**25.** Every integer can be written as a quotient of integers.

**26.** $2n - 1$

**27.** No; the subtraction of a larger number from a smaller number results in a negative number, which is not a whole number.

---

# Answers

## Mid-Chapter Quiz

**1.**

**2.** div. by 3; $-5$

**3.** mult. by $\frac{1}{2}$; $\frac{x}{24}$

**4.** subtr. 9; 65

**5.** mult. by 3; 32.4

**6.** Distr. Prop.

**7.** Ident. Prop. of Mult.

**8.** Inv. Prop. of Mult.

**9.** Assoc. Prop. of Mult.

**10.** $8(a + b)$

**11.** $xy + 4$

**12.** $\frac{d}{g} - 6$

**13.** $2st - 10$

**14.** $-4x^2 + 2y + 10$

**15.** $13d - 44e$

**16.** $a + 2b$

**17.** $12x + 11x^2$

**18.** Output = Input $- 0.5$

| Input | Process Column | Output |
|-------|----------------|--------|
| 1 | $(1) - 0.5$ | 0.5 |
| 2 | $(2) - 0.5$ | 1.5 |
| 3 | $(3) - 0.5$ | 2.5 |
| 4 | $(4) - 0.5$ | 3.5 |
| 5 | $(5) - 0.5$ | 4.5 |
| 6 | $(6) - 0.5$ | 5.5 |
| ⋮ | ⋮ | ⋮ |
| $n$ | $(n) - 0.5$ | $n - 0.5$ |

**PowerAlgebra.com**

## MathXL for School

Prepare students for the Mid-Chapter Quiz and Chapter Test with online practice and review.

# 1 Interactive Learning

## Solve It!

**PURPOSE** Find unknown quantities by relating them to known quantities

**PROCESS** Students may

- first solve for the figure on the left.
- write and solve equations that use the idea of balance.

### FACILITATE

**Q** What does half the mobile weigh? **[20 oz]**

**Q** What is the weight of the crossbar on the left side? How do you know? **[4 oz; each inch weighs 1 oz.]**

**Q** How much does the figure on the left weigh? **[16 oz]**

**Q** What is the total weight of all objects on the right side below the 4-oz crossbar? Explain. **[16 oz; their total weight must equal the weight of the figure on the left.]**

**Q** What does the figure on the right weigh? **[6 oz]**

**Q** How much does each of the middle figures weigh? Explain. **[2 oz; 8 − 2 − 1 − 1 = 4 and 4 ÷ 2 = 2]**

**ANSWER** See Solve It in Answers on next page.

**CONNECT THE MATH** In the Solve It, students implicitly use the Properties of Equality to find unknown quantities. The properties are formally introduced in this lesson and used to solve equations.

# 2 Guided Instruction

## Take Note

The Properties of Equality hold for all real numbers, even though the examples shown are rational numbers. Challenge students to give some examples using other numbers.

---

# Solving Equations

**Objectives** To solve equations
To solve problems by writing equations

 **Getting Ready!**

You bought a mobile kit. You read on the package that the weight of the entire mobile is 40 oz. Each inch of crossbar weighs 1 oz. What is the weight of each shape? Justify your reasoning.

An **equation** is a statement that two expressions are equal. In this lesson you will use equations to model and solve problems.

**Essential Understanding** You can use the properties of equality and inverse operations to solve equations.

### Lesson Vocabulary
- equation
- solution of an equation
- inverse operations
- identity
- literal equation

 **Properties** Properties of Equality

Assume $a$, $b$, and $c$ represent real numbers.

| Property | Definition | Example |
|----------|-----------|---------|
| Reflexive | $a = a$ | $5 = 5$ |
| Symmetric | If $a = b$, then $b = a$. | If $\frac{1}{2} = 0.5$, then $0.5 = \frac{1}{2}$. |
| Transitive | If $a = b$ and $b = c$, then $a = c$. | If $2.5 = 2\frac{1}{2}$ and $2\frac{1}{2} = \frac{5}{2}$, then $2.5 = \frac{5}{2}$. |
| Substitution | If $a = b$, then you can replace $a$ with $b$ and vice versa. | If $a = b$ and $9 + a = 15$, then $9 + b = 15$. |

---

# Preparing to Teach

**BIG** idea Solving Equations and Inequalities **UbD**

### ESSENTIAL UNDERSTANDINGS

- Properties of numbers and equality and inverse operations can be used to solve an equation by finding increasingly simpler equations that have the same solution as the original equation.
- Important properties of equality include reflexive, symmetric, transitive, substitution, addition, subtraction, multiplication and division.

## Math Background

All of the one-variable equations in this lesson are linear (first degree) equations. Usually if a one-variable linear equation has a solution, then it has exactly one real solution. One-variable equations of higher degrees can have more than one real solution.

An identity is an equation that is true for all permissible values of the variable(s). Consider:

1. $x + 5 = x + 8 - 3$
2. $x + \dfrac{x}{x - 3} = \dfrac{x^2 - 2x}{x - 3}$
3. $(x + y)(x - y) = x^2 - y^2$

The first and third statements are identities, but the second is not. The second statement is true for all values of $x$ except 3. Three is not in the domain since it makes the equation undefined.

## Support Student Learning

Use the **Algebra 2 Companion** to engage and support students during instruction. See Lesson Resources at the end of this lesson for details.

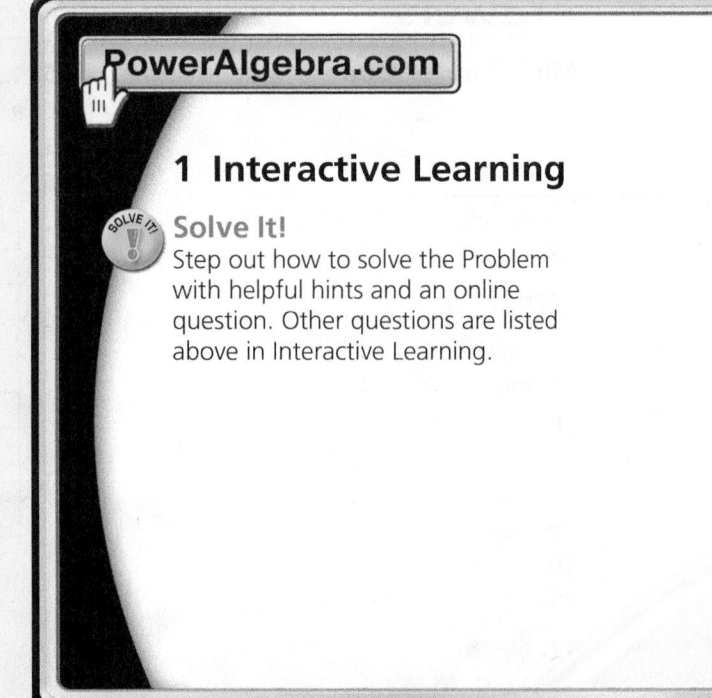

**PowerAlgebra.com**

## 1 Interactive Learning

### Solve It!

Step out how to solve the Problem with helpful hints and an online question. Other questions are listed above in Interactive Learning.

## Properties   Properties of Equality, Continued

Assume $a$, $b$, and $c$ represent real numbers.

| Property | Definition | Example |
|---|---|---|
| Addition | If $a = b$, then $a + c = b + c$. | If $x = 12$, then $x + 3 = 12 + 3$. |
| Subtraction | If $a = b$, then $a - c = b - c$. | If $x = 12$, then $x - 3 = 12 - 3$. |
| Multiplication | If $a = b$, then $a \cdot c = b \cdot c$. | If $x = 12$, then $x \cdot 3 = 12 \cdot 3$. |
| Division | If $a = b$, then $a \div c = b \div c$ (with $c \neq 0$). | If $x = 12$, then $x \div 3 = 12 \div 3$. |

Solving an equation that contains a variable means finding all values of the variable that make the equation true. Such a value is a **solution of the equation**. To find a solution, isolate the variable on one side of the equation using *inverse operations*.

**Inverse operations** are operations that "undo" each other. Addition and subtraction have this inverse relationship, as do multiplication and division.

 **Problem 1**   Solving a One-Step Equation

**Plan**

**How can you isolate the variable?**
To isolate the variable, you have to remove the $+4$ from the left side of the equation.

**What is the solution of $x + 4 = -12$?**

$$x + 4 = -12$$

> Subtraction is the inverse operation of addition, so subtract 4 from each side.

$x + 4 - 4 = -12 - 4$    Subtraction Property of Equality

$x = -16$    Simplify.

**Check**    $-16 + 4 \stackrel{?}{=} -12$

$-12 = -12$ ✔

 **Got It?   1.** What is the solution of $12b = 18$?

 **Problem 2**   Solving a Multi-Step Equation     GRIDDED RESPONSE

**Plan**

**How do you solve an equation with the variable on both sides?**
Choose a side for the variable and remove it from the other side.

**What is the solution of $-27 + 6y = 3(y - 3)$?**

$-27 + 6y = 3(y - 3)$

$-27 + 6y = 3y - 9$    Distributive Property

$6y = 3y + 18$    Add 27 to each side.

$3y = 18$    Subtract $3y$ from each side.

$y = 6$    Divide each side by 3.

 **Got It?   2.** What is the solution of $3(2x - 1) - 2(3x + 4) = 11x$?

---

## Problem 1

**Q** Why do you subtract 4 from the left and right sides of the equation? **[The left side indicates that 4 is added to *x*. The inverse operation of addition is subtraction, so subtract 4 to undo the addition, isolating *x* on the left side. Subtract 4 from the right side by the Subtraction Property of Equality.]**

**Got It?**    ERROR PREVENTION

Watch for $18 - 12$. Accept the answer in simplified fraction form, simplified mixed number form, or decimal form.

**Q** How do you isolate the variable? **[Divide both sides by 12.]**

## Problem 2

Students use the Distributive Property to remove parentheses before isolating the variable on one side.

**Q** What property do you apply when you add 27 to each side? **[Addition Property of Equality]**

**Q** What property do you apply when you subtract $3y$ from each side? **[Subtraction Property of Equality]**

**Q** What property do you apply when you divide each side by 3? **[Division Property of Equality]**

**Got It?**    ERROR PREVENTION

Watch for the incorrect distribution of $-2$ on the left side of the equation.

---

# 2 Guided Instruction

 Each Problem is worked out and supported online.

**Problem 1**
Solving a One-Step Equation

**Problem 2**
Solving a Multi-Step Equation
*Animated*

**Problem 3**
Using an Equation to Solve a Problem
*Animated*

**Problem 4**
Equations with No Solutions and Identities

**Problem 5**
Solving a Literal Equation
*Animated*

**Support in Algebra 2 Companion**
• Vocabulary
• Key Concepts
• Got It?

# Answers

### Solve It!

The orange shape weighs 16 oz, yellow shape weighs 6 oz, and each green shape weighs 2 oz. When you add the weight of the shapes and the crossbars, you have 20 oz on each side of the mobile.

### Got It?

**1.** $\frac{3}{2}$

**2.** $-1$

## Problem 3

> **Q** What does the picture tell you about the ratio of length to width of the flower carpet? **[The carpet is three times as long as it is wide; the ratio of length to width is 3:1.]**
>
> **Q** Could you determine the dimensions if you did not know this ratio? Explain. **[No; answers may vary. Sample: There are many different possible lengths and widths of a rectangle whose perimeter is 200.]**
>
> **Q** How can you check that the final answer is correct? **[Answers may vary. Sample: Two times the width plus two times the length equals the perimeter: 2(25) + 2(75) = 200.]**

## Got It?

> **Q** What is the only difference between this question and the one in Problem 3? **[The perimeter is 320 meters instead of 200 meters.]**
>
> **Q** How does that difference affect the answer? How will it still be the same? **[The length and width of this carpet are greater than the carpet in Problem 3. The ratio of length to width is still 3:1.]**

---

**Problem 3** Using an Equation to Solve a Problem

**Flowers** "Flower carpets" incorporate hundreds of thousands of brightly-colored flowers as well as grass, tree bark, and sometimes fountains to form intricate designs and motifs. The flower carpet shown here, from Grand Place in Brussels, Belgium, has a perimeter of 200 meters. What are the dimensions of the flower carpet?

**Plan**

**How can you relate the dimensions to the perimeter?**
Use the formula for the perimeter of a rectangle.

**Relate**   2 ·  width   plus 2 ·  length   equals   perimeter

**Define**   Let  $x$  = the width.

Then  $3x$  = the length.

**Write**   2 ·  $x$   + 2 ·  $3x$   =   200

$2x + 2 \cdot 3x = 200$

$2x + 6x = 200$   Multiply.

$8x = 200$   Combine like terms.

$\dfrac{8x}{8} = \dfrac{200}{8}$   Divide each side by 8.

$x = 25$   Simplify.

Find the length: $3x = 3 \cdot 25 = 75$.

The width is 25 meters. The length is 75 meters.

**Got It?**  **3.** Suppose the flower carpet from Problem 3 had a perimeter of 320 meters. What would the dimensions of the flower carpet be?

An equation does not always have one solution. An equation has no solution if no value of the variable makes the equation true. An equation that is true for every value of the variable is an **identity**.

---

# Additional Problems

**1.** What is the solution of $x - 8 = -10$?

**ANSWER** $x = -2$

**2.** What does $y$ equal in $-2(y - 1) = -16 + y$?

**ANSWER** $y = 6$

**3.** The map shows distances between towns in miles. You and your friend drive together from Newtown to Essex. You drive first, for a total of 40 miles. Then your friend drives 1.5 hours, reaching Essex. What is your friend's average rate?

**ANSWER** 58 miles per hour

**4.** Is the equation *sometimes*, *always*, or *never* true?

**a.** $1 + 5x - 6 = 6x - 5 - x$

**b.** $-x + 2(5x - 1) = 2(3x + 4) + x$

**ANSWER**

**a.** always true

**b.** sometimes true

**5.** If $1000 is in a bank account earning 5% simple interest, the dollar value of the account $A$ in $t$ years is given by $A = 1000(1 + 0.05t)$. What is $t$ in terms of $A$?

**ANSWER** $t = \dfrac{1}{50} A - 20$

# Answers

**Got It?** (continued)

**3.** 40 m × 120 m

PowerAlgebra.com

## 3 Lesson Check

For a digital lesson check, use the Got It questions.

**Support in Algebra 2 Companion**
• Lesson Check

## 4 Practice

Assign homework to individual students or to an entire class.

# 3 Lesson Check

## Do you know HOW?     ERROR INTERVENTION

- Exercises 4–6 are literal equations. Ask students to restate the direction line to match the style in Problem 5. For example, for Exercise 4, ask: What is $k$ in terms of $r$?
- If students have trouble with Exercise 6, remind them that to undo multiplication by $-2$, divide by $-2$, which is the same as multiplying by $-\frac{1}{2}$. Distribute $-\frac{1}{2}$ on the right side.

## Do you UNDERSTAND?

- In Exercise 8, if students do not understand what 4.3 buses means, ask them whether 4 buses is enough. It is not, so you need 5 buses; the .3 means that the fifth bus would only be partly filled.

## Close

> **Q** How is solving a literal equation like solving an equation containing one variable? **[Answers may vary. Sample: In both cases, you need to isolate a variable on one side of the equation.]**

---

 **Lesson Check**

**Do you know HOW?**

Solve each equation.

1. $w - 15 = 8.2$

2. $\frac{x}{3} = -30$

3. $2y - 1 = y + 11$

Solve each equation for $k$.

4. $r - 2k = 15$

5. $6k - 2z = 12$

6. $4k + h = -2k - 14$

**Do you UNDERSTAND?**

7. **Vocabulary** Explain what it means to find a solution of an equation.

8. **Reasoning** Suppose you solve an equation and find that your school needs 4.3 buses for a class trip. Explain how to interpret this solution.

9. **Error Analysis** Find the error(s) in the steps shown.

---

## Practice and Problem-Solving Exercises

**A** Practice   Solve each equation.   *See Problem 1.*

10. $h - 12 = 6$      11. $-\frac{x}{3} = 27$      12. $4t = 48$      13. $22 + r = 36$

Solve each equation. Check your answer.   *See Problem 2.*

14. $7w + 2 = 3w + 94$      15. $15 - g = 23 - 2g$      16. $43 - 3d = d + 9$

17. $5y + 1.8 = 4y - 3.2$      18. $6a - 5 = 4a + 2$      19. $7y + 4 = 3 - 2y$

20. $5c - 9 = 8 - 2c$      21. $4y - 8 - 2y + 5 = 0$      22. $6(n - 4) = 3n$

23. $2 - 3(x + 4) = 8$      24. $5(2 - g) = 0$      25. $2(x + 4) = 8$

Write an equation to solve each problem.   *See Problem 3.*

26. **Bus Travel** Two buses leave Houston at the same time and travel in opposite directions. One bus averages 55 mi/h and the other bus averages 45 mi/h. When will they be 400 mi apart?

27. **Aviation** Two planes left an airport at noon. One flew east and the other flew west at twice the speed. After 3 hours the planes were 2700 mi apart. How fast was each plane flying?

28. **Geometry** The length of a rectangle is 3 cm greater than its width. The perimeter is 24 cm. What are the dimensions of the rectangle?

Determine whether the equation is *always*, *sometimes*, or *never* true.   *See Problem 4.*

29. $5x + 3 - 2x = 7x + 3$      30. $2(5x + 4) = 10x + 6$

31. $\frac{2}{3}x + 4 = 2x$      32. $6x - 12 + 2x = 3 + 8x - 15$

---

# Answers

## Lesson Check

1. 23.2

2. −90

3. 12

4. $K = \frac{1}{2}(r - 15)$

5. $K = \frac{1}{3}(z + 6)$

6. $K = -\left(\frac{1}{6}\right)(h + 14)$

7. To find a solution of an equation means to find the value of the variable that makes the equation true.

8. Four buses are not enough. The number of buses must be a whole number, so round the number of buses to 5.

9. The second line is incorrect; subtract 10 from both sides:
$12x = -12$
$x = -1$

## Practice and Problem-Solving Exercises

10. 18

11. −81

12. 12

13. 14

14. 23

15. 8

16. $\frac{17}{2}$

17. −5

18. $\frac{7}{2}$

19. $-\frac{1}{9}$

20. $\frac{17}{7}$

21. $\frac{3}{2}$

22. 8

23. −6

24. 2

25. 0

26. 4 h

27. 300 mi/h; 600 mi/h

28. width = 4.5 cm, length = 7.5 cm

29. sometimes

30. never

31. sometimes

32. always

Solve each formula for the indicated variable.

**See Problem 5.**

**33.** $A = \frac{1}{2}bh$, for $h$    **34.** $s = \frac{1}{2}gt^2$, for $g$    **35.** $V = lwh$, for $w$    **36.** $I = prt$, for $r$

Solve each equation for $x$.

**37.** $ax + bx = c$    **38.** $\frac{x}{a} - 5 = b$    **39.** $\frac{x-2}{2} = m + n$    **40.** $\frac{2}{5}(x + 1) = g$

**B Apply**

Solve each equation.

**41.** $0.2(x + 3) - 4(2x - 3) = 0.9$    **42.** $12 - 3(2w + 1) = 7w - 3(7 + w)$

**43.** $(m - 2) - 5 = 8 - 2(m - 4)$    **44.** $7(a + 1) - 3a = 5 + 4(2a - 1)$

**45. Think About a Plan** The measures of an angle and its complement differ by 22°. What are the measures of the angles?
- What is true about the sum of the measures of an angle and its complement?
- When modeling the problem with an equation, how can you algebraically represent that the two angle measures differ by 22°?

Solve each formula for the indicated variable.

**46.** $R(r_1 + r_2) = r_1 r_2$, for $R$    **47.** $A = \frac{1}{2}h(b_1 + b_2)$, for $b_2$    **48.** $S = 2\pi r^2 + 2\pi rh$, for $h$

**49.** $h = vt - 5t^2$, for $v$    **50.** $v = s^2 + \frac{1}{2}sh$, for $h$    **51.** $R(r_1 + r_2) = r_1 r_2$, for $r_2$

**52. Writing** Suppose you write and solve an equation to determine the amount of money $m$ you have in your bank account after several weeks. You find that $m = -36$. What does this solution mean?

**53. Geometry** The measure of the supplement of an angle is 20° more than three times the measure of the original angle. Find the measures of the angles.

**54.** Find 4 consecutive odd integers with a sum of 184.

Solve each equation for $x$.

**55.** $c(x + 2) - 5 = b(x - 3)$    **56.** $a(3tx - 2b) = c(dx - 2)$    **57.** $b(5px - 3c) = a(qx - 4)$

**58.** $\frac{a}{b}(2x - 12) = \frac{c}{d}$    **59.** $\frac{3ax}{5} - 4c = \frac{ax}{5}$    **60.** $\frac{a-c}{x-a} = m$

Write an equation to solve each problem.

**61. Swimming** A city park is opening a new swimming pool. You can pay a daily entrance fee of $3 or purchase a membership for the 12-week summer season for $82 and pay only $1 per day to swim. How many days would you have to swim to make the membership worthwhile?

**62. Rocket** The first stage of a rocket burns 28 s longer than the second stage. If the total burning time for both stages is 152 s, how long does each stage burn?

**63. Error Analysis** Your friend says that the equations shown are two ways to write the same formula. Is your friend correct? Explain your answer.

$$s = \frac{n}{n+1} \quad \frac{s}{s-1} = n$$

# 4 Practice

**ASSIGNMENT GUIDE**
Basic: 10–40 all, 43–45, 52, 53, 58–62 even
Average: 11–39 odd, 41–63
Advanced: 11–39 odd, 41–65
Standardized Test Prep: 66–69
Mixed Review: 70–79

**Reasoning** exercises have blue headings.

**Applications** exercises have red headings.

**EXERCISE 53:** Use the Think About a Plan worksheet in the **Practice and Problem Solving Workbook** (also available in the Teaching Resources in print and online) to further support students' development in becoming independent learners.

**HOMEWORK QUICK CHECK**
To check students' understanding of key skills and concepts, go over Exercises 27, 37, 45, 53, and 62.

**33.** $h = \frac{2A}{b}$

**34.** $g = \frac{2s}{t^2}$

**35.** $w = \frac{V}{\ell h}$

**36.** $r = \frac{I}{pt}$

**37.** $x = \frac{c}{a + b}$, $a \neq -b$

**38.** $x = a(b + 5)$, $a \neq 0$

**39.** $x = 2(m + n) + 2$

**40.** $x = \frac{5g}{2} - 1$

**41.** 1.5

**42.** 3

**43.** $\frac{23}{3}$, or $7\frac{2}{3}$

**44.** $\frac{3}{2}$

**45.** 34° and 56°

**46.** $R = \frac{r_1 r_2}{r_1 + r_2}$

**47.** $b_2 = \frac{2A}{h} - b_1$

**48.** $h = \frac{S - 2\pi r^2}{2\pi r}$

**49.** $v = \frac{h + 5t^2}{t}$

**50.** $h = \frac{2(v - s^2)}{s}$

**51.** $r_2 = \frac{Rr_1}{r_1 - R}$

**52.** The account has a balance less than $0, or you overdrew on the account by $36.

**53.** 40°, 140°

**54.** 43, 45, 47, and 49

**55.** $x = \frac{3b + 2c - 5}{b - c}$, $b \neq c$

**56.** $x = \frac{2ab - 2c}{3at - cd}$, $3at \neq cd$

**57.** $x = \frac{4a - 3bc}{aq - 5bp}$, $5bp \neq aq$

**58.** $x = \frac{cb}{2da} + 6$, $a, b, d \neq 0$

**59.** $x = \frac{10c}{a}$, $a \neq 0$

**60.** $x = \frac{a - c}{m} + a$, $m \neq 0$, $x \neq a$

**61.** Let $c$ = number of swim days; $3c = 82 + c$; 41 days

**62.** Let $s$ = burning time for second stage; $s + 28 + s = 152$; first stage, 90 s; second stage, 62 s

**63.** No; $n = \frac{s}{1 - s}$ not $\frac{s}{s - 1}$.

# Answers

## Practice and Problem-Solving Exercises
(continued)

**64. a.** Check students' work. Sample: If you solve $ax - b = c$ for $x$, you get $x = \frac{b + c}{a}$. Since $b$ and $c$ are integers, $b + c$ is an integer. But $a$ is a nonzero integer. So $\frac{b + c}{a}$ is the quotient of two integers and hence, by the definition of a rational number, $\frac{b + c}{a}$ is a rational number.

**b.** Solutions are rational when $\frac{c - b}{a} \geq 0$, $a \neq 0$, and $\frac{c - b}{a}$ is a square of a rational number.

**65.** 264 ft

## Standardized Test Prep

**66.** 350 tiles

**67.** 3200

**68.** 17.9

**69.** 7 ft.

## Mixed Review

**70.** $-7$

**71.** $-\frac{16}{3}$

**72.** $-20$

**73.** $-\frac{11}{2}$

**74.** $x + 5$

**75.** $16x$

**76.** $3(12 - x)$

**77.** true

**78.** false

**79.** true

---

 **Challenge**

**64.** Assume that $a$, $b$, and $c$ are integers and $a \neq 0$.

    **a. Proof** Prove that the solution of the linear equation $ax - b = c$ must be a rational number.

    **b. Writing** Describe the values of $a$, $b$, and $c$ for which the solutions of $ax^2 + b = c$ are rational.

**65.** A tortoise crawling at a rate of 0.1 mi/h passes a resting hare. The hare wants to rest another 30 min before chasing the tortoise at a rate of 5 mi/h. How many feet must the hare run to catch the tortoise?

## Standardized Test Prep
                                     GRIDDED RESPONSE

 **SAT/ACT**

**66.** A mural made of triangular tiles has an area of 1750 square centimeters. Each triangle has a height that is 3 centimeters longer than its base of 2 centimeters. How many triangular tiles are there?

**67.** The table shows the population of bacteria in a petri dish at various times. If the pattern continues, what will the bacteria population be at 6:00 P.M.?

| Bacteria Population | | | | |
|---|---|---|---|---|
| **Time** | 8:00 A.M. | 10:00 A.M. | 12:00 P.M. | 2:00 P.M. |
| **Population** | 100 | 200 | 400 | 800 |

**68.** To the nearest tenth, what is the value of $t$ in the following equation?

$$4(t - 30) = 5 - 3t$$

**69.** A 10-foot-tall basketball hoop is 4 feet shorter than twice the height of a flag pole. What is the height in feet of the flag pole?

## Mixed Review

Evaluate each expression for $x = -4$ and $y = 3$.         ◀ See Lesson 1-3.

**70.** $x - 2y + 3$      **71.** $x + x \div y$      **72.** $3x - 4y - x$      **73.** $x + 2y \div x$

Write an algebraic expression for each phrase.        ◀ See Lesson 1-3.

**74.** 5 more than a number $x$

**75.** the product of 16 and a number $x$

**76.** 3 times the difference of 12 and a number $x$

**Get Ready!** To prepare for Lesson 1-5, do Exercises 77–79.

State whether each inequality is *true* or *false*.      ◀ See Lesson 1-2.

**77.** $5 < 12$               **78.** $5 < -12$          **79.** $5 \geq 5$

# Lesson Resources

## Additional Instructional Support

### Algebra 2 Companion

Students can use the **Algebra 2 Companion** worktext (4 pages) as you teach the lesson. Use the Companion to support

- New Vocabulary
- Key Concepts
- Got It for each Problem
- Lesson Check

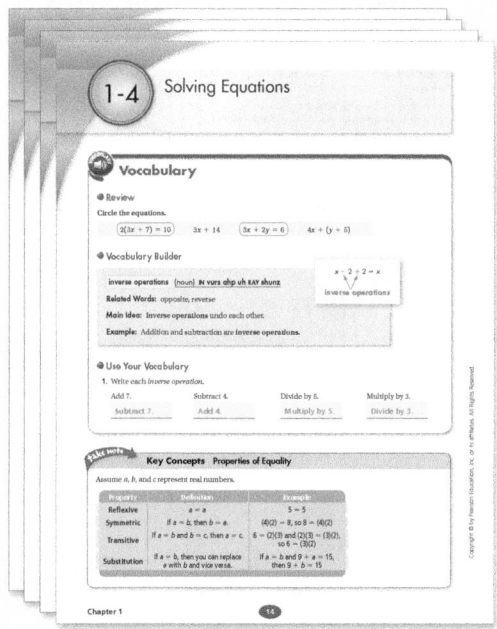

### ELL Support

**Use Role Playing** Have groups of eight to ten students play the roles of the parts of an expression. Students can play the role of a coefficient, variable, exponent, or operator. For instance, a student might be the coefficient 8 in the expression $3x - 8y^2$. Have students first act out their expression by standing in the correct order and saying their parts and then explain how their role as a coefficient, variable, exponent, or operator changes the expression.

Next, have students keep the same roles but form new groups acting out new expressions.

## 5 Assess & Remediate

### Lesson Quiz

1. What is the solution of $6x = 15$?
2. What does $n$ equal in $6(2n - 3) - 2(6n + 1) = 10n$?
3. **Do you UNDERSTAND?** You manage a coffee shop. You begin the day with 25 pounds of coffee beans. You use 4 pounds of beans to brew coffee and sell 20 equal-weight bags of beans. At the end of the day you have 6 pounds of beans left. What is the weight of each bag of beans you sell?
4. Is the equation *sometimes*, *always*, or *never* true?

    **a.** $15 + 2x - 4 = 9x + 11 - 7x$

    **b.** $2x + 3(4x - 1) = 2(5x + 3) + 4x$
5. The equation $V = \frac{1}{3}\pi r^2 h$ relates the volume $V$, the radius $r$, and the height $h$ of a cone. Write $h$ in terms of $V$ and $r$.

### ANSWERS TO LESSON QUIZ

1. $x = 2.5$
2. $n = -2$
3. 0.75 pound
4. **a.** always true　　**b.** never true
5. $h = \dfrac{3V}{\pi r^2}$

### PRESCRIPTION FOR REMEDIATION

Use the student work on the Lesson Quiz to prescribe a differentiated review assignment:

| Points | Differentiated Remediation |
|--------|---------------------------|
| 0–2 | Intervention |
| 3–4 | On-level |
| 5 | Extension |

### PowerAlgebra.com

#### 5 Assess & Remediate

Assign the Lesson Quiz. Appropriate intervention, practice, or enrichment is automatically generated based on student performance.

## Differentiated Remediation

Available in editable format online.

### Intervention

- **Reteaching** (2 pages) Provides reteaching and practice exercises for the key lesson concepts. Use with struggling students or absent students.
- **English Language Learner Support** Helps students develop and reinforce mathematical vocabulary and key concepts.

**All-in-One Resources/Online**
**Reteaching**

**1-4 Reteaching**
Solving Equations

To solve an equation that contains a variable, find all of the values of the variable that make the equation true. Use the equality properties of real numbers and inverse operations to rewrite the equation until the variable is alone on one side of the equation. Whatever remains on the other side of the equation is the solution.

**All-in-One Resources/Online**
**English Language Learner Support**

**1-4 ELL Support**
Solving Equations

# Differentiated Remediation *continued*

Available in editable format online.

## On-Level

- **Practice** (2 pages) Provides extra practice for each lesson. For simpler practice exercises, use the Form K Practice pages found in the All-in-One Teaching Resources and online.

- **Think About a Plan** Helps students develop specific problem-solving skills and strategies by providing scaffolded guiding questions.

- **Standardized Test Prep** Focuses on all major exercises, all major question types, and helps students prepare for the high-stakes assessments.

## Extension

- **Enrichment** Provides students with interesting problems and activities that extend the concepts of the lesson.

- **Activities, Games, and Puzzles** Worksheets that can be used for concepts development, enrichment, and for fun!

---

### Practice and Problem Solving Wkbk/ All-in-One Resources/Online
#### Practice page 1

### Practice and Problem Solving Wkbk/ All-in-One Resources/Online
#### Practice page 2

Practice page 2 content (1-4 Practice continued, Solving Equations, Form G)

### All-in-One Resources/Online
#### Enrichment

1-4 Enrichment — Solving Equations

### Practice and Problem Solving Wkbk/ All-in-One Resources/Online
#### Think About a Plan

### Practice and Problem Solving Wkbk/ All-in-One Resources/Online
#### Standardized Test Prep

1-4 Standardized Test Prep — Solving Equations

### Online Teacher Resource Center
#### Activities, Games, and Puzzles

1-4 Game: Solve That Equation — Solving Equations

---

**Objectives**  To solve and graph inequalities
To write and solve compound inequalities

This is like solving an equation, but with a twist!

**Getting Ready!**

You want to download some new songs on your MP3 player. Each song will use about 4.3 MB of space. The amount of storage space on your MP3 player is shown at the right. At most how many songs can you download? Explain. (Hint: 1 GB = 1000 MB)

7.8 GB free of 19.5 GB

**Dynamic Activity**
Solving Inequalities
Compound Inequalities

**Lesson Vocabulary**
• compound inequality

Words like "at most" and "at least" suggest a relationship in which two quantities may not be equal. You can represent such a relationship with a mathematical inequality.

**Essential Understanding**  Just as you use properties of equality to solve equations, you can use properties of inequality to solve inequalities.

### Key Concept   Writing and Graphing Inequalities

| Inequality | Word Sentence | Graph |
|---|---|---|
| $x > 4$ | $x$ is greater than 4. | −1 0 1 2 3 4 5 |
| $x \geq 4$ | $x$ is greater than or equal to 4. | −1 0 1 2 3 4 5 |
| $x < 4$ | $x$ is less than 4. | −1 0 1 2 3 4 5 |
| $x \leq 4$ | $x$ is less than or equal to 4. | −1 0 1 2 3 4 5 |

In the graphs above, the point at 4 is a boundary point because it separates the graph of the inequality from the rest of the number line. An open dot at 4 means that 4 *is not* a solution. A closed dot at 4 means that 4 *is* a solution.

# 1 Interactive Learning

## Solve It!
**PURPOSE**  To distinguish between situations that involve equations and those that involve inequalities
**PROCESS**  Students may
• multiply 7.8 by 1000 to find the number of available MB and then divide by 4.3.
• solve $4.3x = 7800$ and then use context to round to the nearest whole number.

**FACILITATE**
**Q** Why is it necessary to know 1 GB = 1000 MB? **[The songs are given in MB; the space is given in GB.]**
**Q** How many MB of space are available? **[7800]**
**Q** Does $\frac{7800}{4.3}$ give you the answer? Why or why not? **[No; it is not a whole number, and you cannot download part of a song.]**
**Q** What is the greatest number of songs that can still be downloaded? **[1813 songs]**

**ANSWER**  See Solve It in Answers on next page.
**CONNECT THE MATH**  The context of the Solve It requires students to use the concept of an inequality. The lesson formally introduces writing, solving, and graphing inequalities.

# 2 Guided Instruction

## Take Note                              VISUAL LEARNERS
When the variable is on the left of the inequality, the arrow on the graph points the same way as the pointed end of the inequality symbol.

---

## 1-5  Preparing to Teach

**BIG idea**  **Solving Equations and Inequalities**  **UbD**
**ESSENTIAL UNDERSTANDINGS**
• Just as properties of equality can be used to solve equations, properties of inequality can be used to solve inequalities.
• Properties of numbers and inequality can be used to solve an inequality by finding increasingly simpler inequalities that have the same solution as the original inequality.

### Math Background
Students are familiar with the Properties of Equality. In this lesson, they will learn the Properties of Inequality. These properties are closely related.

For example, the Addition Property of Equality states that if $a = b$, then $a + c = b + c$. In the Addition Property of Inequality, the difference is that the equality symbol is replaced with an inequality symbol: If $a < b$, then $a + c < b + c$.

The Multiplication and Division Properties of Equality and the corresponding Properties of Inequality are also related, provided that students multiply or divide by a positive number. When multiplying or dividing by a negative number, students must remember to change the direction of the inequality symbol.

### Support Student Learning
Use the **Algebra 2 Companion** to engage and support students during instruction. See Lesson Resources at the end of this lesson for details.

**PowerAlgebra.com**

## 1 Interactive Learning

**Solve It!**
Step out how to solve the Problem with helpful hints and an online question. Other questions are listed above in Interactive Learning.

**Dynamic Activity**  Students who have trouble differentiating *and* and *or* in compound inequalities will benefit from this activity. The activity also displays algebraic solutions of inequalities.

## Problem 1

ERROR PREVENTION

Students may use the symbol > instead of ≥. Use the sentence, "You must be at least 18 to vote" to show that 18 is included in the allowable age range.

> **Q** Explain why $5 - x \geq 12$ is incorrect. **[5 fewer than a number means 5 is being subtracted from the number; the expression $5 - x$ means a number is being subtracted from 5.]**

## Got It?

ERROR PREVENTION

If students write $\frac{3}{x} \leq 15$, remind them that, as with subtraction, the order of division matters: $\frac{3}{45}$ is not the same as $\frac{45}{3}$. The first value stated after the phrase "the quotient of" is the numerator; the second is the denominator.

## Take Note

When reading the chart, you may need to remind students that $c < 0$ is just a symbolic way of writing that $c$ is negative.

## Here's Why It Works

Sketch a number line with $-2$, $-1$, $0$, $1$, and $2$ on it. Remind students that the number to the right of another number is always greater. Therefore, $2 > 1$. Also, $-1 > -2$. If we say the number to the left of another number is the lesser number, then $-2 < -1$. Have students compare this inequality to the first inequality.

---

Plan

**How can you translate a sentence into an inequality?** Look for key words, such as "at least" or "greater than."

**Problem 1** Writing an Inequality From a Sentence

**What inequality represents the sentence, "5 fewer than a number is at least 12."?**

5 fewer than a number is at least 12.

| "Fewer" indicates subtraction. | "At least" indicates greater than or equal to. |

$x - 5 \geq 12$

**Got It?** **1.** What inequality represents the sentence, "The quotient of a number and 3 is no more than 15."?

---

The solutions of an inequality are the numbers that make it true. The properties you use for solving inequalities are similar to the properties you use for solving equations. However, when you multiply or divide each side of an inequality by a negative number, you must reverse the inequality symbol.

### take note  Properties  Properties of Inequalities

Let $a$, $b$, $c$, and $d$ represent real numbers.

| Property | Definition | Example |
|---|---|---|
| Transitive | If $a > b$ and $b > c$, then $a > c$. | $5 > 3$ and $3 > 1$, so $5 > 1$ |
| Addition | If $a > b$, then $a + c > b + c$. | $4 > 2$, so $4 + 1 > 2 + 1$ |
| Subtraction | If $a > b$, then $a - c > b - c$. | $7 > 4$, so $7 - 3 > 4 - 3$ |
| Multiplication | If $a > b$ and $c > 0$, then $ac > bc$. | $6 > 5$ and $3 > 0$, so $6(3) > 5(3)$ |
| | If $a > b$ and $c < 0$, then $ac < bc$. | $3 > 2$ and $-4 < 0$, so $3(-4) < 2(-4)$ |
| Division | If $a > b$ and $c > 0$, then $\frac{a}{c} > \frac{b}{c}$. | $9 > 3$ and $3 > 0$, so $\frac{9}{3} > \frac{3}{3}$ |
| | If $a > b$ and $c < 0$, then $\frac{a}{c} < \frac{b}{c}$. | $12 > 6$ and $-6 < 0$, so $\frac{12}{-6} < \frac{6}{-6}$ |

**Here's Why It Works** The steps below show that if $a > b$, then $-a < -b$. Therefore, you need to reverse the inequality symbol when multiplying each side of the inequality $a > b$ by $-1$.

$$a > b$$
$$a - b > 0 \qquad \text{Subtract } b \text{ from each side.}$$
$$-b - (-a) > 0 \qquad a - b = -b + a = -b - (-a).$$
$$-b > -a \qquad \text{Add } -a \text{ to each side.}$$
$$-a < -b \qquad \text{Rewrite the inequality with } -a \text{ on the left side.}$$

---

# Answers

## Solve It!

You have 7.8 GB = 7800 MB of free space. $7800 \div 4.3 = 1813.95$ is the greatest number of songs you can download. Round down to 1813 songs because you can only download a whole number of songs.

## Got It?

**1.** $\frac{x}{3} \leq 15$

---

**PowerAlgebra.com**

## 2 Guided Instruction

Each Problem is worked out and supported online.

**Problem 1**
Writing an Inequality From a Sentence

**Problem 2**
Solving and Graphing an Inequality

**Problem 3**
Using an Inequality
*Animated*

**Problem 4**
No Solution or All Real Numbers as Solution
*Animated*

**Problem 5**
Solving an *And* Inequality
*Animated*

**Problem 6**
Solving an *Or* Inequality

**Support in Algebra 2 Companion**
• Vocabulary
• Key Concepts
• Got It?

**Problem 2** Solving and Graphing an Inequality

**Plan**

**How is solving an inequality like solving an equation?**
You isolate the variable by doing the same things to each side of the inequality.

What is the solution of $-3(2x - 5) + 1 \geq 4$? Graph the solution.

$$-3(2x - 5) + 1 \geq 4$$
$$-6x + 15 + 1 \geq 4 \qquad \text{Distributive Property}$$
$$-6x + 16 \geq 4 \qquad \text{Simplify.}$$
$$-6x \geq -12 \qquad \text{Subtraction Property of Inequality}$$
$$x \leq 2 \qquad \text{Divide each side by } -6. \text{ Reverse the inequality symbol.}$$

$$\overset{\longleftarrow}{\underset{-3 \quad -2 \quad -1 \quad 0 \quad 1 \quad 2 \quad 3}{\rule{4cm}{0.4pt}}}$$

**Got It? 2.** What is the solution of $-2(x + 9) + 5 \geq 3$? Graph the solution.

 **Problem 3** Using an Inequality

**Plan**

**How will an inequality help answer this question?**
The cost of the first plan must be less than the cost of the second plan, so an inequality can be used to determine the number of movies.

**Movie Rentals** A movie rental company offers two subscription plans. You can pay $36 a month and rent as many movies as desired, or you can pay $15 a month and $1.50 to rent each movie. How many movies must you rent in a month for the first plan to cost less than the second plan?

| Think | Write |
|---|---|
| Assign a variable. | Let n = the number of movie rentals in one month. |
| Write an expression for the cost of each plan for a month. | first plan: 36 <br> second plan: 15 + 1.5n |
| The first plan must cost less than the second plan. | 36 < 15 + 1.5n |
| Solve. | 21 < 1.5n <br> 14 < n |
| Write the answer in words. | You must rent more than 14 movies in a month for the first plan to cost less. |

**Got It? 3.** A digital music service offers two subscription plans. The first has a $9 membership fee and charges $1 per download. The second has a $25 membership fee and charges $.50 per download. How many songs must you download for the second plan to cost less than the first plan?

 **PowerAlgebra.com** | Lesson 1-5 Solving Inequalities | 35

---

## Problem 2

When the solution of an inequality is a range of numbers, it is impossible to list them all. There are an infinite number of solutions to $x \leq 2$.

**Q** Up to which point is the process of finding the solution the same as it would be if the inequality were an equation instead? **[up to the point of dividing both sides by −6]**

**Q** How can you check that you drew the arrow in the correct direction? **[Substitute any point that is shaded, such as 0, for x in the original inequality to see if the statement is true.]**

### Got It?

**Q** Did you have to reverse the direction of the inequality symbol? Why or why not? **[Yes; both sides are divided by a negative number.]**

## Problem 3

**Q** How do you determine whether to use < or ≤ in the inequality? **[The problem asks for the number of rentals that make the first plan less than the second, not less than or equal to.]**

### Got It?

If a student says 32 downloads, show them that the cost is the same for both plans ($41). For the second plan to cost less, you must download *more* than 32 songs or *at least* 33.

---

# Additional Problems

**1.** What inequality represents the sentence, "The product of 7 and a number is no more than 50"?

**ANSWER** $7n \leq 50$

**2.** What is the solution of $4(x - 7) > -20$? Graph the solution.

**ANSWER** $x > 2$

$$\overset{\longleftarrow}{\underset{-3 \quad -2 \quad -1 \quad 0 \quad 1 \quad 2 \quad 3}{\rule{3cm}{0.4pt}}}$$

**3.** Plumber A charges $75 for a service charge and $40 per hour. Plumber B charges $50 per hour but no service charge. How many hours must a plumbing job last for Plumber A to cost less than Plumber B?

**ANSWER** greater than 7.5 hours

**4.** Is the inequality sometimes, always, or never true?

**a.** $3(x + 3) \geq 3(2 + x)$

**b.** $9 - x - 5 < -x + 4$

**ANSWERS**

**a.** always true

**b.** never true

**5.** What is the solution of $\frac{a}{2} < 3$ and $-3a + 5 < 8$? Graph the solution.

**ANSWER** $a < 6$ and $a > -1$

$$\overset{\longleftarrow}{\underset{-3 \; -2 \; -1 \; 0 \; 1 \; 2 \; 3 \; 4 \; 5 \; 6 \; 7}{\rule{4cm}{0.4pt}}}$$

**6.** What is the solution of $5 - 2m \geq 21$ or $4m - 1 \geq -21$? Graph the solution.

**ANSWER** $m \leq -8$ or $m \geq -5$

$$\overset{\longleftarrow}{\underset{-9 \; -8 \; -7 \; -6 \; -5 \; -4 \; -3}{\rule{4cm}{0.4pt}}}$$

# Answers

**Got It?** (continued)

**2.** $x \leq -8$

$$\overset{\longleftarrow}{\underset{-11 \; -10 \; -9 \; -8 \; -7 \; -6 \; -5}{\rule{4cm}{0.4pt}}}$$

**3.** more than 32 songs

Lesson 1-5 **35**

## Problem 4

> **Q** How would you graph the result of 4A? **[Draw a number line. Graph nothing on it.]**
>
> **Q** How do the last inequalities in 4A and 4B compare? **[Answers may vary. Sample: In simplified form neither inequality contains variables. In both cases, the variable was divided out, leaving either a false (for no solutions) or a true (for all real numbers as solution) numerical statement.]**

### Got It?                          AUDITORY LEARNERS

After distributing, tell students that $8x$ represents some number, so the statement can be read as "twelve less than some number is less than eight more than the number."

## Problem 5

Any solution to a compound inequality joined by *and* must make both inequalities true. Because $7 < 9$ and $12 \le 18$, 4 makes both inequalities true. However, 7 only makes the first inequality true.

> **Q** Does the fact that there are no arrows on the graph of the solution indicate that there are a finite number of solutions? Explain. **[No; there are an infinite number of rational numbers between 3 and 6, such as 3.1, 3.11, 3.111, etc.]**

### Got It?

> **Q** What does the graph of an inequality that is sometimes true look like? **[The solution covers part but not all of a number line.]**

---

### Problem 4  No Solution or All Real Numbers as Solutions

**Is the inequality *always*, *sometimes*, or *never* true?**

**A** $-2(3x + 1) > -6x + 7$

$$-6x - 2 > -6x + 7 \qquad \text{Distributive Property}$$
$$-2 > 7 \qquad \text{Add } 6x \text{ to each side.}$$

The last inequality $-2 > 7$ is false, so $-2(3x + 1) > -6x + 7$ is always false. It has no solution, so it is never true.

**B** $5(2x - 3) - 7x \le 3x + 8$

$$10x - 15 - 7x \le 3x + 8 \qquad \text{Distributive Property}$$
$$3x - 15 \le 3x + 8 \qquad \text{Combine like terms.}$$
$$-15 \le 8 \qquad \text{Subtract } 3x \text{ from each side.}$$

The inequality $-15 \le 8$ is true, so $5(2x - 3) - 7x \le 3x + 8$ is always true. All real numbers are solutions.

**Got It?** **4.** Is $4(2x - 3) < 8(x + 1)$ *always*, *sometimes*, or *never* true?

---

**Think**

**How did you determine that an *equation* has no solution?**
If you solve an equation and obtain a false statement, then the equation has no solution.

---

You can join two inequalities with the word *and* or the word *or* to form a **compound inequality.** To solve a compound inequality containing *and*, find all values of the variable that make both inequalities true.

### Problem 5  Solving an *And* Inequality

**What is the solution of $7 < 2x + 1$ and $3x \le 18$? Graph the solution.**

$$7 < 2x + 1 \quad \text{and} \quad 3x \le 18$$
$$3 < x \quad \text{and} \quad x \le 6 \qquad \text{Solve each inequality.}$$

AND means that a solution makes BOTH inequalities true.

**Think**

**How do you graph a compound inequality with *and*?**
Find the intersection of the solutions of the two inequalities.

**Got It?** **5. a.** What is the solution of $5 \le 3x - 1$ and $2x < 12$? Graph the solution.
  **b.** Reasoning  Is the compound inequality in Problem 5 *always*, *sometimes*, or *never* true? Explain your reasoning.

---

## Answers

### Got It? (continued)

**4.** always

**5. a.** $x \ge 2$ and $x < 6$

**b.** sometimes; The compound inequality is true when $x = 5$ and not true when $x = 7$.

You can collapse a compound *and* inequality, like $5 < x + 1$ and $x + 1 < 13$, into a simpler form, $5 < x + 1 < 13$. You read $5 < x + 1 < 13$ as "$x + 1$ is greater than 5 and less than 13."

To solve a compound inequality containing *or*, find all values of the variable that make at least one of the inequalities true.

Think

**How does the solution to an *or* inequality differ from the solution to an *and* inequality?**
The solution to an *or* inequality includes all of the solutions of each inequality, not just the solutions of both inequalities.

### Problem 6 Solving an *Or* Inequality

**What is the solution of $7 + k \geq 6$ or $8 + k < 3$? Graph the solution.**

$$7 + k \geq 6 \quad \text{or} \quad 8 + k < 3$$

$$k \geq -1 \quad \text{or} \quad k < -5 \qquad \text{Subtraction Property of Inequality}$$

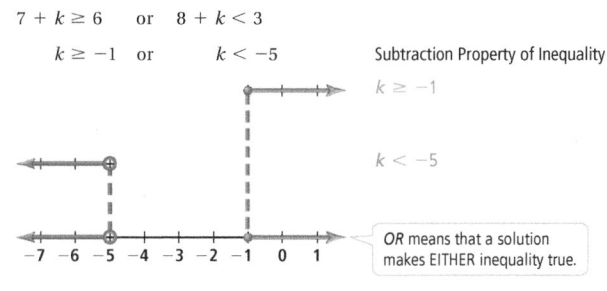

$k \geq -1$

$k < -5$

OR means that a solution makes EITHER inequality true.

**Got It? 6.** What is the solution of each compound inequality? Graph the solution.
**a.** $7w + 3 > 11$ or $4w - 1 < -13$ **b.** $16 < 5x + 1$ or $3x + 9 < 6$

## Lesson Check

### Do you know HOW?

**Write an inequality that represents each sentence.**

1. Rachel's hair is at least as long as Julia's.

2. The wind speeds of tropical storms are at least 40 mi/h, but less than 74 mi/h.

**Solve each inequality. Graph the solution.**

3. $-4(3x + 2) \geq 16$

4. $3 < 5x - 2 < 7$

5. $7x - 3 > 18$ or $3x - 2 \leq -2$

### Do you UNDERSTAND?

6. **Reasoning** Make up an example to help explain why you must reverse the inequality symbol when you multiply or divide by a negative number.

7. **Compare and Contrast** Describe how the properties of inequality are similar to the properties of equality and how they differ.

8. Write an inequality for which the solution is the set of all real numbers.

9. **Error Analysis** Your classmate says that you cannot write a compound inequality that has no solution. Do you agree? If so, explain why. If not, give a counterexample.

---

### Problem 6

Any solution to a compound inequality joined by *or* will make one or both of the inequalities true. If it makes *neither* inequality true, it is not a solution.

### Got It?

Zero is not a solution in either question because it is in the region between the two rays and it makes both equations false.

## 3 Lesson Check

### Do you know HOW?

• In Exercise 2, if students use the wrong inequality symbols, ask them questions such as: Can the wind speeds be 39 mi/h? 40 mi/h? Can the wind speeds be 74 mi/h? 75 mi/h?

### Do you UNDERSTAND?

• For Exercise 9, refer to the solutions shown for Problem 6. The region between $-5$ and $-1$ does not make either solution true, so changing the *or* to an *and* for the two separate inequalities will result in a compound inequality with no solutions.

### Close

Q How are the solutions to a compound inequality joined by *and* different from those joined by *or*?
[Answers may vary. Sample: Solutions to the former must make both individual inequalities true; solutions to the latter must only make at least one of the inequalities true.]

---

**6. a.** $w < -3$ or $w > \dfrac{8}{7}$

**b.** $x < -1$ or $x > 3$

### Lesson Check

**1.** $R \geq J$

**2.** $w \geq 40$ and $w < 74$

**3.** $x \leq -2$

**4.** $1 < x < \dfrac{9}{5}$

**5.** $x \leq 0$ or $x > 3$

6. Answers may vary. Sample: $5 < 6$, but $-5 > -6$.

7. The transitive, addition and subtraction properties of inequality are similar to the properties of equality. The multiplication and division properties differ. Multiplying or dividing each side of an inequality by a negative number reverses the direction of the inequality symbol.

8. Answers may vary. Sample: $3x + 5 < 3(x + 5)$

9. No; Answers may vary. Sample: $2x < x + 1$ and $x + 1 > 3$

### 3 Lesson Check

For a digital lesson check, use the Got It questions.

**Support in Algebra 2 Companion**
• Lesson Check

### 4 Practice

Assign homework to individual students or to an entire class.

# 4 Practice

## ASSIGNMENT GUIDE

Basic: 10–43 all, 44–50 even, 51, 57, 60

Average: 11–43 odd, 44–61

Advanced: 11–43 odd, 44–66

Standardized Test Prep: 67–70

Mixed Review: 71–78

**Reasoning** exercises have blue headings.

**Applications** exercises have red headings.

**EXERCISE 51:** Use the Think About a Plan worksheet in the **Practice and Problem Solving Workbook** (also available in the Teaching Resources in print and online) to further support students' development in becoming independent learners.

## HOMEWORK QUICK CHECK

To check students' understanding of key skills and concepts, go over Exercises 23, 39, 44, 51, and 57.

---

## Practice and Problem-Solving Exercises

**A Practice**

Write the inequality that represents the sentence.  ◆ See Problem 1.

**10.** The sum of a number and 5 is less than $-7$.

**11.** The product of a number and 8 is at least 25.

**12.** Six less than a number is greater than 54.

**13.** The quotient of a number and 12 is no more than 6.

Solve each inequality. Graph the solution.  ◆ See Problem 2.

**14.** $-12 \geq 24x$

**15.** $-7k < 63$

**16.** $8a - 15 > 73$

**17.** $57 - 4t \geq 13$

**18.** $-18 - 5y \geq 52$

**19.** $14 - 4y \geq 38$

**20.** $4(x + 3) \leq 44$

**21.** $2(m - 3) + 7 < 21$

**22.** $4(n - 2) - 6 > 18$

**23.** $-2(w + 4) + 9 < -11$

Solve each problem by writing an inequality.  ◆ See Problem 3.

**24.** The length of a picture frame is 3 in. greater than the width. The perimeter is less than 52 in. Describe the dimensions of the frame.

**25.** The lengths of the sides of a triangle are in the ratio 5 : 6 : 7. Describe the length of the longest side if the perimeter is less than 54 cm.

**26.** Find the lesser of two consecutive integers with a sum greater than 16.

**27.** The cost of a field trip is $220 plus $7 per student. If the school can spend at most $500, how many students can go on the field trip?

Is the inequality *always, sometimes,* or *never* true?  ◆ See Problem 4.

**28.** $9(x + 2) > 9(x - 3)$

**29.** $6x - 13 < 6(x - 2)$

**30.** $-6(2x - 10) + 12x \leq 180$

**31.** $-7(3x - 7) + 21x \geq 50$

**32.** $3 + 5x < 5(x + 1)$

**33.** $2(x + 6) < 30$

**34.** $4x - 8 > 1 + 4(x + 3)$

**35.** $9x + 2(2 + x) < 5 + 9x$

Solve each compound inequality. Graph the solution.  ◆ See Problems 5 and 6.

**36.** $2x > -10$ and $9x < 18$

**37.** $3x \geq -12$ and $8x \leq 16$

**38.** $6x \geq -24$ and $9x < 54$

**39.** $7x > -35$ and $5x \leq 30$

**40.** $4x < 16$ or $12x > 144$

**41.** $3x \geq 3$ or $9x < 54$

**42.** $8x > -32$ or $-6x \geq 48$

**43.** $9x \leq -27$ or $4x \geq 36$

---

# Answers

## Practice and Problem-Solving Exercises

**10.** $x + 5 < -7$  **11.** $8x \geq 25$

**12.** $x - 6 > 54$  **13.** $\frac{x}{12} \leq 6$

**14.** $x \leq -\frac{1}{2}$

**15.** $k > -9$

**16.** $a > 11$

**17.** $t \leq 11$

**18.** $y \leq -14$

**19.** $y \leq -6$

**20.** $x \leq 8$

**21.** $m < 10$

**22.** $n > 8$

**23.** $w > 6$

**24.** The width is less than 11.5 in., and the length is 3 in. greater than the width.

**25.** The longest side is less than 21 cm.

**26.** The smaller number is an integer greater than or equal to 8.

**27.** at most 40 students

**28.** always  **29.** always  **30.** always

**31.** never  **32.** always  **33.** sometimes

**34.** never  **35.** sometimes

**36.** $-5 < x < 2$

**37.** $-4 \leq x \leq 2$

**38.** $-4 \leq x < 6$

**39.** $-5 < x \leq 6$

**40.** $x < 4$ or $x > 12$

**41.** all real numbers

**42.** $x \leq -8$ or $x > -4$

**43.** $x \leq -3$ or $x \geq 9$

**44. Think About a Plan** The diagram shows the scores in seconds of a skater's first three trials in a speed-skating event. What is the maximum time she can score on her last trial so that her average time on all four trials is under 36 seconds?

- What do you need to find an average?
- What inequality can you use to model the situation?

**Solve each inequality. Graph the solution.**

**45.** $2 - 3z \geq 7(8 - 2z) + 12$

**46.** $6(x - 2.5) \geq 8 - 6(3.5 + x)$

**47.** $\frac{2}{3}(x - 12) \leq x + 8$

**48.** $\frac{3}{5}(x - 12) > x - 24$

**49.** $3[4x - (2x - 7)] < 2(3x - 5)$

**50.** $6[5y - (3y - 1)] \geq 4(3y - 7)$

**51. Grades** Your math test scores are 68, 78, 90, and 91. What is the lowest score you can earn on the next test and still achieve an average of at least 85?

**52. Chemistry** The pH level of a popular shampoo is between 6.0 and 6.5 inclusive. What compound inequality shows the pH levels of this shampoo? Graph the solution.

**53. Geometry** The sum of the lengths of any two sides of a triangle is greater than the length of the third side. In $\triangle ABC$, $BC = 4$ and $AC = 8 - AB$. What can you conclude about $AB$?

**54. Writing** Write a word problem that can be solved using $25 + 0.5x \leq 60$.

**55. Error Analysis** A classmate solved the inequality $\frac{1}{2}(y - 16) \geq y + 2$ as shown. Prove that his answer is incorrect by checking a number that is less than $-20$. (Select a number that makes the computation easy.) What was his error?

**56. Construction** A contractor estimated that her expenses for a construction project would be between \$700,000 and \$750,000. She has already spent \$496,000. How much more can she spend and remain within her estimate?

**Justifying Steps** Justify each step by identifying the property used.

**57.** $3x \leq 4(x - 1) - 8$

$3x \leq 4x - 4 - 8$

$3x \leq 4x - 12$

$-x \leq -12$

$x \geq 12$

**58.** $\frac{1}{2}(y + 3) > \frac{1}{3}(4 - y)$

$3(y + 3) > 2(4 - y)$

$3y + 9 > 8 - 2y$

$5y + 9 > 8$

$5y > -1$

$y > -0.2$

**Solve each compound inequality. Graph the solution.**

**59.** $-6 < 2x - 4 < 12$

**60.** $4x \leq 12$ and $-7x \leq 21$

**61.** $15x > 30$ or $18x < -36$

---

**44.** less than 36.57 seconds

**45.** $z \geq 6$

**46.** $x \geq \frac{1}{6}$

**47.** $x \geq -48$

**48.** $x < 42$

**49.** no solution

**50.** all real numbers

**51.** 98

**52.** $6.0 \leq x \leq 6.5$

**53.** $2 < AB < 6$

**54.** Check students' work.

**55.** The classmate reversed the direction of the $\geq$ symbol to $\leq$ incorrectly. The correct answer is $y \leq -20$.

**56.** between \$204,000 and \$254,000

**57.** Distr. Prop.; arithmetic; Subtr. Prop. of Inequality; Mult. Prop. of Inequality

**58.** Mult. Prop. of Inequality; Distr. Prop.; Add. Prop. of Inequality; Subtr. Prop. of Inequality; Div. Prop. of Inequality

**59.** $-1 < x < 8$

**60.** $-3 \leq x \leq 3$

**61.** $x < -2$ or $x > 2$

# Answers

## Practice and Problem-Solving Exercises
(continued)

**62.** Answers may vary. Sample: $2x - 7 \geq -11$

**63.** Answers may vary. Sample: $-3x + 1 > 4$

**64.** Answers may vary. Sample: $-9 < 5x + 1 < 6$

**65.** Answers may vary. Sample: $2x + 4 \leq 0$ or $-3x - 3 \leq 0$

**66. a.** no

    **b.** yes; values of $a$ that are 8 or greater

    **c.** (a) yes; values of $a$ that are less than 8

        (b) no

## Standardized Test Prep

**67.** D

**68.** I

**69.** D

**70. [4]** $3(x - 2) + 8 = 12$

    $3x - 6 + 8 = 12$    Distr. Prop.

       $3x + 2 = 12$    Simplify.

          $3x = 10$    Subtr. Prop. of Eq.

           $x = \frac{10}{3}$    Div. Prop. of Eq.

  **[3]** all steps and properties, but with one computational error

  **[2]** two computational errors OR an incorrect property

  **[1]** correct solution, without properties identified

## Mixed Review

**71.** $7a + 5$

**72.** $-2x + 14y$

**73.** $\frac{b}{12} + 1$

**74.** $1.61 - 0.1k$

**75.** 4

**76.** no solution

**77.** $\frac{9}{10}$

**78.** $-20$

---

 **Challenge**

**Open-Ended** Write an inequality with a solution that matches the graph. At least two steps should be needed to solve your inequality.

**62.**
$$\begin{array}{c} \text{-4 \ -3 \ -2 \ -1 \ \ 0 \ \ 1 \ \ 2 \ \ 3 \ \ 4} \end{array}$$

**63.**
$$\begin{array}{c} \text{-4 \ -3 \ -2 \ -1 \ \ 0 \ \ 1 \ \ 2 \ \ 3 \ \ 4} \end{array}$$

**64.**
$$\begin{array}{c} \text{-4 \ -3 \ -2 \ -1 \ \ 0 \ \ 1 \ \ 2 \ \ 3 \ \ 4} \end{array}$$

**65.**
$$\begin{array}{c} \text{-4 \ -3 \ -2 \ -1 \ \ 0 \ \ 1 \ \ 2 \ \ 3 \ \ 4} \end{array}$$

**66. Reasoning** Consider the compound inequality $x < 8$ and $x > a$.

    **a.** Are there any values of $a$ such that all real numbers are solutions of the compound inequality? If so, what are they?

    **b.** Are there any values of $a$ such that no real numbers are solutions of the compound inequality? If so, what are they?

    **c.** Repeat parts (a) and (b) for the compound inequality $x < 8$ or $x > a$.

### Standardized Test Prep

**SAT/ACT**

**67.** What is the solution of $1 < 2x + 3 < 9$?

    Ⓐ $-1 > x < 2$    Ⓑ $2 < x < 3$    Ⓒ $-1 < x < 2$    Ⓓ $-1 < x < 3$

**68.** Which expression best represents the value of $x$ in $y = mx + b$?

    Ⓕ $\frac{b - y}{m}$    Ⓖ $\frac{y + b}{m}$    Ⓗ $m(y - b)$    Ⓘ $\frac{y - b}{m}$

**69.** The hourly rate of a waiter is \$4 plus tips. On a particular day, the waiter worked 8 hours and received more than \$150 in pay. Which could be the amount of tips the waiter received?

    Ⓐ \$18.75    Ⓑ \$32    Ⓒ \$118    Ⓓ \$120.75

**Extended Response**

**70.** Solve $3(x - 2) + 8 = 12$. Identify each property of real numbers or equality you use.

### Mixed Review

Simplify each expression.    ◀ **See Lesson 1-3.**

**71.** $(2a - 4) + (5a + 9)$    **72.** $3(x + 3y) - 5(x - y)$

**73.** $\frac{1}{3}(b + 12) - \frac{1}{4}(b + 12)$    **74.** $0.4(k - 0.1) + 0.5(3.3 - k)$

**Get Ready!**  **To prepare for Lesson 1-6, do Exercises 75–78.**

Solve each equation. Check your answers.    ◀ **See Lesson 1-4.**

**75.** $7x - 6(11 - 2x) = 10$    **76.** $10x - 7 = 2(13 + 5x)$

**77.** $4y - \frac{1}{10} = 3y + \frac{4}{5}$    **78.** $0.4x + 1.18 = -3.1(2 - 0.01x)$

## Differentiated Remediation
Available in editable format online.

## Additional Instructional Support

### Algebra 2 Companion
Students can use the **Algebra 2 Companion** worktext (4 pages) as you teach the lesson. Use the Companion to support
- New Vocabulary
- Key Concepts
- Got It for each Problem
- Lesson Check

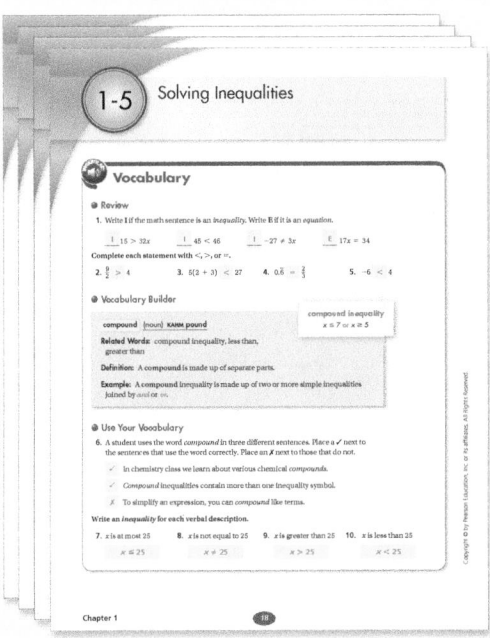

### ELL Support
**Use Graphic Organizers** To assist students in understanding inequality word problems, help them make a graphic organizer including words for each symbol, such as the following: $<$ less than, less, fewer; $>$ more than, more, greater; $\leq$ less than or equal to, no more than, at most; $\geq$ greater than or equal to, no less than, at least. Then have students rewrite an inequality in English several different ways. For example, $2x - 5 \geq 4$ could be "five less than the product of 2 and $x$ is at least 4" or "five fewer than the product of $x$ and 2 is greater than or equal to 4."

Encourage students to illustrate their graphic organizer and to add any familiar words which will help them to understand each concept.

Next have students compare their graphic organizer with a partner's and add any new ideas to their organizer.

## 5 Assess & Remediate

### Lesson Quiz
1. What inequality represents the sentence, "The product of 6 and a number is less than 20"?
2. What is the solution of $-5(2x - 1) + 3 \leq -2$? Graph the solution.
3. **Do you UNDERSTAND?** Eastside Gym charges a $60 initial fee and $28.50 per month. Valley Gym charges $36 per month, and no initial fee. After how many months of use would Eastside cost less than Valley?
4. Is the inequality *sometimes, always,* or *never* true?
   $3(4x + 2) + x \leq 1 + 13x$
5. What is the solution of $2 \leq 3x + 8$ and $20 > 4x$? Graph the solution.

### ANSWERS TO LESSON QUIZ
1. $6x < 20$
2. $x \geq 1$

3. More than 8 months.
4. never true
5. $-2 \leq x < 5$

### PRESCRIPTION FOR REMEDIATION
Use the student work on the Lesson Quiz to prescribe a differentiated review assignment:

| Points | Differentiated Remediation |
|---|---|
| 0–2 | Intervention |
| 3–4 | On-level |
| 5 | Extension |

**PowerAlgebra.com**

### 5 Assess & Remediate
Assign the Lesson Quiz. Appropriate intervention, practice, or enrichment is automatically generated based on student performance.

## Intervention
- **Reteaching** (2 pages) Provides reteaching and practice exercises for the key lesson concepts. Use with struggling students or absent students.
- **English Language Learner Support** Helps students develop and reinforce mathematical vocabulary and key concepts.

### All-in-One Resources/Online
**Reteaching**

1-5 Reteaching
Solving Inequalities

As with an equation, the solutions of an inequality are numbers that make it true. The procedure for solving a linear inequality is much like the one for solving linear equations. To isolate the variable on one side of the inequality, perform the same algebraic operation on each side of the inequality symbol.

The **Addition and Subtraction Properties of Inequality** state that adding or subtracting the same number from both sides of the inequality does not change the inequality.

If $a < b$, then $a + c < b + c$.     If $a < b$, then $a - c < b - c$.

The **Multiplication and Division Properties of Inequality** state that multiplying or dividing both sides of the inequality by the same *positive* number does not change the inequality.

If $a < b$ and $c > 0$, then $ac < bc$.     If $a < b$ and $c > 0$, then $\frac{a}{c} < \frac{b}{c}$.

**Problem**

What is the solution of $3(x + 2) - 5 \leq 21 - x$? Graph the solution.

Justify each line in the solution by naming one of the properties of inequalities.

$3x + 6 - 5 \leq 21 - x$   Distributive Property
$3x + 1 \leq 21 - x$   Simplify.
$4x + 1 \leq 21$   Addition Property of Inequality
$4x \leq 20$   Subtraction Property of Inequality
$x \leq 5$   Division Property of Inequality

To graph the solution, locate the boundary point. Plot a point at $x = 5$. Because the inequality is "*less than or equal to,*" the boundary point is part of the solution set. Therefore, use a closed dot to graph the boundary point. Shade the number line to the left of the boundary point because the inequality is "*less than.*"

Graph the solution on a number line.

**Exercises**

Solve each inequality. Graph the solution.

1. $2x + 4(x - 2) > 4$, $x > 2$
2. $4 - (2x - 4) \geq 5 - (4x + 3)$, $x \geq -3$

### All-in-One Resources/Online
**English Language Learner Support**

1-5 ELL Support
Solving Inequalities

| is greater than | is greater than or equal to | is less than | is less than or equal to |
|---|---|---|---|
| $>$ | $\geq$ | $<$ | $\leq$ |

To write an inequality from a sentence, first identify the operation and then identify the inequality.

**Example** What inequality represents the sentence "6 more than a number is at least 20"?

"more than" means addition    "is at least" means is greater than or equal to

6 more than a number is at least 20
$6 + x \geq 20$

Underline the word or words that indicate an operation.

1. the product of 12 and a number
2. 8 less than a number
3. the difference between a number and 24
4. the sum of a number and 7

Circle the word phrase that identifies the inequality to use. Then write the inequality that represents the sentence.

5. The product of 12 and a number is more than 190.   $12x > 190$
6. 8 less than a number is at least 34.   $x - 8 \geq 34$
7. The difference between a number and 24 is no more than 4.   $x - 24 \leq 4$
8. The sum of twice a number and 7 is less than 25.   $2x + 7 < 25$

Some word phrases are very similar, but have different meanings.

**Example** Does the sentence indicate an operation or an inequality?

A number is four greater than 15.     Four is greater than a number.
$x = 4 + 15$     $4 > x$
operation     inequality

Does the sentence indicate an *operation* or an *inequality*?

9. 22 is 7 greater than a number.   operation
10. A number is greater than 99.   inequality
11. A number is 8 less than another number.   operation
12. 50 is less than a number.   inequality

# Differentiated Remediation _continued_

Available in editable format online.

## On-Level

- **Practice** (2 pages) Provides extra practice for each lesson. For simpler practice exercises, use the Form K Practice pages found in the All-in-One Teaching Resources and online.

- **Think About a Plan** Helps students develop specific problem-solving skills and strategies by providing scaffolded guiding questions.

- **Standardized Test Prep** Focuses on all major exercises, all major question types, and helps students prepare for the high-stakes assessments.

## Extension

- **Enrichment** Provides students with interesting problems and activities that extend the concepts of the lesson.

- **Activities, Games, and Puzzles** Worksheets that can be used for concepts development, enrichment, and for fun!

---

### Practice and Problem Solving Wkbk/ All-in-One Resources/Online

#### Practice page 1

**1-5 Practice**     Form G
Solving Inequalities

Write the inequality that represents the sentence.

1. Four less than a number is greater than −28.   $x - 4 > -28$

2. Twice a number is at least 15.   $2x \geq 15$

3. A number increased by 7 is less than 5.   $x + 7 < 5$

4. The quotient of a number and 8 is at most −6.   $\frac{x}{8} \leq -6$

Solve each inequality. Graph the solution.

5. $3(x + 1) + 2 < 11$   $x < 2$

6. $5t - 2(t + 2) \geq 8$   $t \geq 4$

7. $2[(2y - 1) + y] \leq 5(y + 3)$   $y \leq 17$

8. $\frac{1}{3}(7a - 1) \leq 2a + 7$   $a \leq 22$

9. $5 - 2(n + 2) \leq 4 + n$   $n \geq -1$

10. $-2(w - 7) + 3 > w - 1$   $w < 6$

Solve each problem by writing an inequality.

11. **Geometry** The length of a rectangular yard is 30 meters. The perimeter is at most 90 meters. Describe the width of the yard.   at most 15 m

12. **Geometry** A piece of rope 20 feet long is cut from a longer piece that is at least 32 feet long. The remainder is cut into four pieces of equal length. Describe the length of each of the four pieces.   at least 3 ft

13. A school principal estimates that no more than 6% of this year's senior class will graduate with honors. If 350 students graduate this year, how many will graduate with honors?   no more than 21 students

14. Two sisters drove 144 miles on a camping trip. They averaged at least 32 miles per gallon on the trip. Describe the number of gallons of gas they used.   at most 4.5 gal

---

### Practice and Problem Solving Wkbk/ All-in-One Resources/Online

#### Practice page 2

**1-5 Practice** (continued)     Form G
Solving Inequalities

Is the inequality _always_, _sometimes_, or _never_ true?

15. $3(2x + 1) > 5x - (2 - x)$   always true

16. $2(x - 1) \geq x + 7$   sometimes true

17. $7x + 2 \leq 2(2x - 4) + 3x$   never true

18. $5(x - 3) < 2(x - 9)$   sometimes true

Solve each compound inequality. Graph the solution.

19. $3x > -6$ and $2x < 6$   $x > -2$ and $x < 3$

20. $4x \geq -12$ and $7x \leq 7$   $x \geq -3$ and $x \leq 1$

21. $5x > -20$ and $8x \leq 32$   $x > -4$ and $x \leq 4$

22. $6x < -12$ or $5x > 5$   $x < -2$ or $x > 1$

23. $6x \leq -18$ or $2x > 18$   $x \leq -3$ or $x > 9$

24. $2x > 3 - x$ or $2x < x - 3$   $x > 1$ or $x < -3$

Solve each problem by writing and solving a compound inequality.

25. A student believes she can earn between $5200 and $6250 from her summer job. She knows that she will have to buy four new tires for her car at $90 each. She estimates her other expenses while she is working at $660. How much can the student save from her summer wages?   between $4180 and $5230

26. Before a chemist can combine a solution with other liquids in a laboratory, the temperature of the solution must be between 39°C and 52°C. The chemist places the solution in a warmer that raises the temperature 6.5°C per hour. If the temperature is originally 0°C, how long will it take to raise the temperature to the necessary range of values?   between 6 and 8 h

27. The Science Club advisor expects that between 42 and 49 students will attend the next Science Club field trip. The school allows $5.50 per student for sandwiches and drinks. What is the advisor's budget for food for the trip?   between $231 and $269.50

---

### All-in-One Resources/Online

#### Enrichment

**1-5 Enrichment**
Solving Inequalities

| F | R | I | E | D | R | I | C | H | B | E | S | S | E | L |
|---|---|---|---|---|---|---|---|---|---|---|---|---|---|---|
| 1 | 2 | 3 | 4 | 5 | 6 | 7 | 8 | 9 | 10 | 11 | 12 | 13 | 14 | 15 | 16 |

He was the first person to measure the distance to a star successfully. He also discovered that certain mathematical functions play a key role in models of physical phenomena. These functions were named after him.

To find his name, solve each of the following inequalities. Then use the solutions and the table below to determine the position in which to write the associated letter.

| Solutions | Position | Solutions | Position | Solutions | Position |
|---|---|---|---|---|---|
| $x > 1$ | 1 | $x > \frac{1}{2}$ | 6 | $x < 4$ | 11 |
| $x < 2$ | 2 | $x > 5$ | 7 | $x < 0$ | 12 |
| $x > -1$ | 3 | $x < -\frac{5}{2}$ | 8 | $x > -\frac{4}{3}$ | 13 |
| $x > -2$ | 4 | $x > 0$ | 9 | $x > -\frac{1}{2}$ | 14 |
| all real numbers | 5 | | 10 | $x > 2$ | 15 |
| | | | | $x > 3$ | 16 |

B   $2(x + 1) - (2 - x) < 12$   $x < 4$

C   $3x + 6 < 16 - x$   $x < \frac{5}{2}$

D   $3x + 5 + 3(x + 5) > 6x + 15$   all real numbers

E   $8x - 2 - 6(x - 3) < 16$   $x < 0$

E   $3(x + 2) + 2x > -4$   $x > -2$

E   $(3 + x) + (3 - 3x) < x$   $x > 2$

F   $3x - 5 + (x + 9) > 8$   $x > 1$

H   $5x - 3(x - 1) > 3$   $x > 0$

I   $5x - 3 - 3(x + \frac{1}{4}) > 0$   $x > 5$

I   $2(x + 4) - (5 - x) > x - 1$   $x > -1$

L   $(x + 1) - (1 - x) < (x - 1) - (2 - 2x)$   $x > 3$

R   $7x - 5 - (-1 - x) > 0$   $x > \frac{1}{2}$

R   $2x + 5 + 2(x + 5) < 23$   $x < 2$

S   $2(x - 1) < 2 + 2(1 + 7x)$   $x > -\frac{1}{2}$

S   $3 - x < 5 + 2(x + 1)$   $x > -\frac{4}{3}$

---

### Practice and Problem Solving Wkbk/ All-in-One Resources/Online

#### Think About a Plan

**1-5 Think About a Plan**
Solving Inequalities

Your math test scores are 68, 78, 90, and 91. What is the lowest score you can earn on the next test and still achieve an average of at least 85?

**Understanding the Problem**

1. What information do you need to find an average of scores? How do you find an average?
The sum of the scores and the total number of scores;
divide the sum of the scores by the total number of scores.

2. How many scores should you include in the average?   5

3. You want to achieve an average that is [greater than] or [equal to] what score?   85

**Planning the Solution**

4. Assign a variable, x.
$x =$ the score on the next test

5. Write an expression for the sum of all of the scores, including the next test.
$327 + x$

6. Write an expression for the average of all of the scores.
$\frac{327 + x}{5}$

7. Write an inequality that can be used to determine the lowest score you can earn on the next test and still achieve an average of at least 85.
$\frac{327 + x}{5} \geq 85$

**Getting an Answer**

8. Solve your inequality to find the lowest score you can earn on the next test and still achieve an average of at least 85. What score do you need to earn?   at least 98

---

### Practice and Problem Solving Wkbk/ All-in-One Resources/Online

#### Standardized Test Prep

**1-5 Standardized Test Prep**
Solving Inequalities

**Multiple Choice**

For Exercises 1–5, choose the correct letter.

1. What is the solution of $4t - (3 + t) \leq t + 7$?   B
   - Ⓐ $t \leq \frac{5}{2}$
   - Ⓑ $t \leq 5$
   - Ⓒ $t \leq 2$
   - Ⓓ $t \leq 1$

2. What is the solution of $-17 - 2r < 3(r + 1)$?   I
   - Ⓕ $r > 4$
   - Ⓖ $r > -20$
   - Ⓗ $r < -4$
   - Ⓘ $r > -4$

3. Which graph best represents the solution of $\frac{3}{4}(m + 4) > m + 37$?   A

4. What is the solution of the compound inequality $4x < -8$ or $9x > 18$?   I
   - Ⓕ $x < 2$ or $x > -2$
   - Ⓗ $x > 2$
   - Ⓖ $x < -2$
   - Ⓘ $x < -2$ or $x > 2$

5. What is the solution of the compound inequality $-2x \leq 6$ and $-3x > -27$?   C
   - Ⓐ $x \leq -3$ and $x > 9$
   - Ⓒ $x \geq -3$ and $x < 9$
   - Ⓑ $x \geq 3$ and $x < -9$
   - Ⓓ $x \leq 3$ and $x > -9$

**Short Response**

6. **Geometry** The lengths of the sides of a triangle are in the ratio 3 : 4 : 5. Describe the length of the longest side if the perimeter is not more than 72 in.
[2] Solve the inequality $3x + 4x + 5x \leq 72$ or $12x \leq 72$ or $x \leq 6$. The longest side, $5x$, is not more than $5 \cdot 6 = 30$ in. [1] minor incorrect calculation [0] no answer given

7. Between 8.5% and 9.4% of the city's population uses the municipal transit system daily. According to the latest census, the city's population is 785,000. How many people use the transit system daily?
[2] between 66,725 and 73,790 people [1] minor incorrect miscalculation [0] no answer given

---

### Online Teacher Resource Center

#### Activities, Games, and Puzzles

**1-5 Puzzle: What's the Inequality?**
Solving Inequalities

To solve this puzzle, each box must be filled in with a math symbol $(x, +, -, <, >)$ or a digit from 0 to 9 to complete an inequality. The clues below give the solution to the inequality you complete. 1-Across has been done for you. The boldfaced "4" and ">" complete the inequality $4x > 4$, $x > 1$ (See clue below).

**ACROSS**

1. $x > 1$

3. $x < 7$   $2x < 14$

7. $x \geq -\frac{1}{8}$   $11x - 2 \leq -1$

9. $x > \frac{1}{4}$   $9x > x + 2$

10. $x > 3$   $5x - 5 > 7 + x$

**DOWN**

2. $x < -\frac{3}{7}$   $4x + 3 < -3x$

3. $x < 4$   $2x < 8$

5. $x > 3$   $39 < 13x$

6. $x < 12$   $2x - 10$

8. $x \leq 3$   $x + 2 \leq 5$

# 1-6 Absolute Value Equations and Inequalities

**Objective** To write and solve equations and inequalities involving absolute value

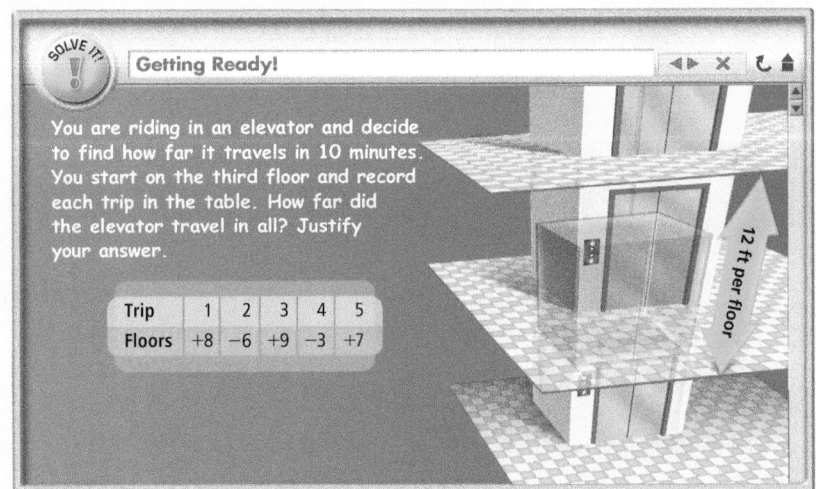

**Getting Ready!**

You are riding in an elevator and decide to find how far it travels in 10 minutes. You start on the third floor and record each trip in the table. How far did the elevator travel in all? Justify your answer.

| Trip | 1 | 2 | 3 | 4 | 5 |
|---|---|---|---|---|---|
| Floors | +8 | −6 | +9 | −3 | +7 |

12 ft per floor

In the Solve It, signed numbers represent distance and direction. Sometimes, only the size of a number (its *absolute value*), not the direction, is important.

**Essential Understanding** An absolute value quantity is nonnegative. Since opposites have the same absolute value, an absolute value equation can have two solutions.

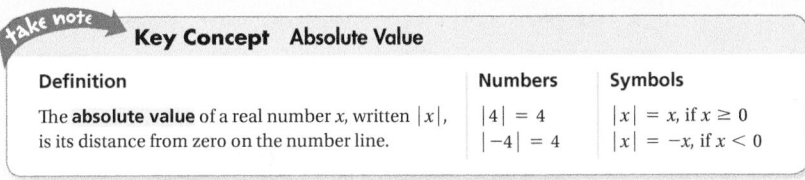

### Key Concept Absolute Value

| Definition | Numbers | Symbols |
|---|---|---|
| The **absolute value** of a real number $x$, written $|x|$, is its distance from zero on the number line. | $\|4\| = 4$ <br> $\|-4\| = 4$ | $\|x\| = x$, if $x \geq 0$ <br> $\|x\| = -x$, if $x < 0$ |

An absolute value equation has a variable within the absolute value sign. For example, $|x| = 5$. Here, the value of $x$ can be 5 or −5 since $|5|$ and $|-5|$ both equal 5.

Both 5 and −5 are 5 units from 0.

$$-6\ -5\ -4\ -3\ -2\ -1\ \ 0\ \ 1\ \ 2\ \ 3\ \ 4\ \ 5\ \ 6$$

# 1 Interactive Learning

**Solve It!**
**PURPOSE** To use a natural understanding of distance to explore absolute value
**PROCESS** Students may
• count the total number of floors traveled without respect to direction and then multiply by the height of each floor.
• find the distance traveled in each direction.

**FACILITATE**
**Q** Is the distance of the trip affected by the number of the floor where you start your trip? Explain. **[No; traveling 8 floors up is the same distance whether you start on the ground floor or third floor.]**
**Q** What is the total number of floors traveled upward? **[24]**
**Q** What is the total number of floors traveled in both directions? **[33]**
**Q** On which floor does your trip end? **[18]**
**Q** How far would the elevator travel if it went up $n$ floors and down $m$ floors? **[$12(n + m)$]**

**ANSWER** See Solve It in Answers on next page.
**CONNECT THE MATH** Since distance is positive, students implicitly use absolute value in the Solve It. In the lesson, absolute value is formally defined, and absolute value equations and inequalities are written, solved, and graphed.

# 2 Guided Instruction

**Take Note**
Point out that when $x < 0$, the quantity $-x > 0$. Show examples with several values for $x$.

# 1-6 Preparing to Teach

**BIG** idea **Solving Equations and Inequalities**  UbD

**ESSENTIAL UNDERSTANDINGS**
• An absolute value quantity is nonnegative.
• Since opposites have the same absolute value, an absolute value equation can have two solutions.
• Absolute value inequalities can be written as compound inequalities without absolute value signs.

## Math Background
To some students, the concept of absolute value may seem artificial. Explain that absolute value is of central importance in mathematics itself, as well as in applied subjects such as statistics.

As a rule, absolute value equations have two solutions, representing two points on a number line that are at the same distance from a certain number. For inequalities, there are two possible situations depending on the sign of the inequality:
• The solution set is a segment, for inequalities of the type $|x| < a$.
• The solution set is two rays, for inequalities of the type $|x| > a$ ($a \geq 0$).

## Support Student Learning
Use the **Algebra 2 Companion** to engage and support students during instruction. See Lesson Resources at the end of this lesson for details.

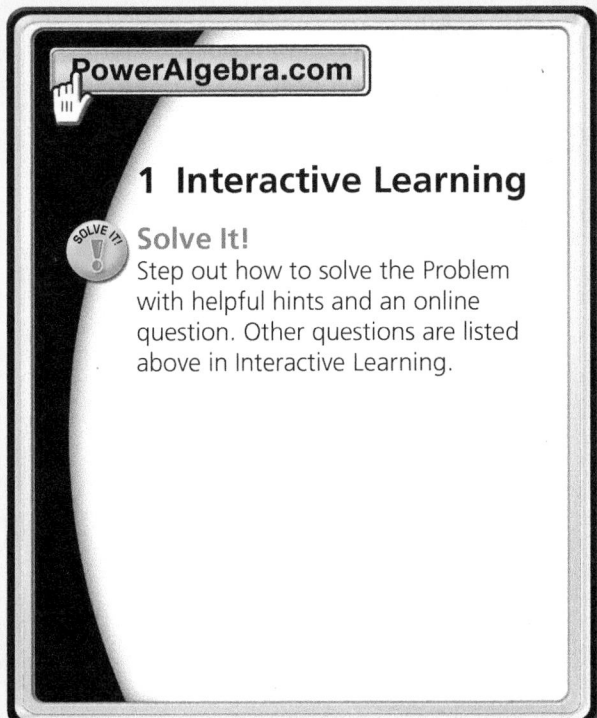

**PowerAlgebra.com**

## 1 Interactive Learning

**Solve It!**
Step out how to solve the Problem with helpful hints and an online question. Other questions are listed above in Interactive Learning.

## Problem 1

**Q** Why is the equation written as 2 separate equations *without* absolute value signs? **[Answers may vary. Sample: There are two values that have absolute value of 5: 5 and −5.]**

## Got It?

**Q** What is the process for checking your answer? **[Substitute the values you found for *x* in the original equation.]**

## Problem 2

In this problem, it is necessary to isolate the absolute value expression first before rewriting the equation as two linear equations.

**Q** What happens if you set the original expression on the left side equal to 8 and to −8? **[The solutions might not check because you need to isolate the absolute value expression first.]**

## Got It?

**Q** What is the first goal in your solution process? **[Isolate the quantity $|x + 9|$.]**

**Q** Can you solve $|x| = -5$? Why? **[No; absolute value expressions are never negative.]**

---

**Think**

**How is solving this equation different from solving a linear equation?**
In the absolute value equation, $2x - 1$ can represent two opposite quantities.

**Problem 1** Solving an Absolute Value Equation

**What is the solution of $|2x - 1| = 5$? Graph the solution.**

$$|2x - 1| = 5$$

$2x - 1 = 5$  or  $2x - 1 = -5$    Rewrite as two equations. $2x - 1$ could be 5 or −5.

$2x = 6$      $2x = -4$    Add 1 to each side of both equations.

$x = 3$  or  $x = -2$    Divide each side of both equations by 2.

**Check** $|2(3) - 1| \stackrel{?}{=} 5$      $|2(-2) - 1| \stackrel{?}{=} 5$

        $|6 - 1| \stackrel{?}{=} 5$          $|-4 - 1| \stackrel{?}{=} 5$

           $|5| = 5$ ✔             $|-5| = 5$ ✔

**Got It?** **1.** What is the solution of $|3x + 2| = 4$? Graph the solution.

**Plan**

**Is there a simpler way to think of this problem?**
Solving
$3|x + 2| - 1 = 8$
is similar to solving
$3y - 1 = 8$.

**Problem 2** Solving a Multi-Step Absolute Value Equation

**What is the solution of $3|x + 2| - 1 = 8$? Graph the solution.**

$$3|x + 2| - 1 = 8$$

$3|x + 2| = 9$                  Add 1 to each side.

$|x + 2| = 3$                  Divide each side by 3.

$x + 2 = 3$  or  $x + 2 = -3$    Rewrite as two equations.

$x = 1$  or  $x = -5$    Subtract 2 from each side of both equations.

**Check** $3|(1) + 2| - 1 \stackrel{?}{=} 8$      $3|(-5) + 2| - 1 \stackrel{?}{=} 8$

        $3|3| - 1 \stackrel{?}{=} 8$          $3|-3| - 1 \stackrel{?}{=} 8$

           $8 = 8$ ✔              $8 = 8$ ✔

**Got It?** **2.** What is the solution of $2|x + 9| + 3 = 7$? Graph the solution.

Distance from 0 on the number line cannot be negative. Therefore, some absolute value equations, such as $|x| = -5$, have no solution. It is important to check the possible solutions of an absolute value equation. One or more of the possible solutions may be *extraneous*.

An **extraneous solution** is a solution derived from an original equation that is *not* a solution of the original equation.

---

# Answers

## Solve It!

$(8 - 6 + 9 - 3 + 7) \times 12$ ft $=$
    $15 \times 12$ ft $= 180$ ft

## Got It?

**1.** $\frac{2}{3}, -2$

**2.** $-7, -11$

**PowerAlgebra.com**

# 2 Guided Instruction

Each Problem is worked out and supported online.

**Problem 1**
Solving an Absolute Value Equation

**Problem 2**
Solving a Multi-Step Absolute Value Equation
*Animated*

**Problem 3**
Checking for Extraneous Solutions
*Animated*

**Problem 4**
Solving the Absolute Value Inequality $|A| < b$
*Animated*

**Problem 5**
Solving the Absolute Value Inequality $|A| \geq b$

**Problem 6**
Using an Absolute Value Inequality

**Support in Algebra 2 Companion**
• Vocabulary
• Key Concepts
• Got It?

**Problem 3** Checking for Extraneous Solutions

**Think**

Can you solve this the same way as you solved Problem 1?
Yes, let $3x + 2$ equal $4x + 5$ and $-(4x + 5)$.

**What is the solution of $|3x + 2| = 4x + 5$? Check for extraneous solutions.**

$$|3x + 2| = 4x + 5$$

$3x + 2 = 4x + 5$  or  $3x + 2 = -(4x + 5)$    Rewrite as two equations.

$-x = 3$  |  $3x + 2 = -4x - 5$    Solve each equation.

  |  $7x = -7$

$x = -3$  or  $x = -1$

**Check** $|3(-3) + 2| \stackrel{?}{=} 4(-3) + 5$    $|3(-1) + 2| \stackrel{?}{=} 4(-1) + 5$

$|-9 + 2| \stackrel{?}{=} -12 + 5$    $|-3 + 2| \stackrel{?}{=} -4 + 5$

$|-7| \neq -7$ ✗    $|-1| = 1$ ✔

Since $x = -3$ does not satisfy the orginal equation, $-3$ is an extraneous solution. The only solution to the equation is $x = -1$.

 **Got It? 3.** What is the solution of $|5x - 2| = 7x + 14$? Check for extraneous solutions.

The solutions of the absolute value inequality $|x| < 5$ include values greater than $-5$ *and* less than 5. This is the compound inequality $x > -5$ and $x < 5$, which you can write as $-5 < x < 5$. So, $|x| < 5$ means $x$ is between $-5$ and 5.

The graph of $|x| < 5$ is all values of $x$ between $-5$ and 5.

$$-6\,-5\,-4\,-3\,-2\,-1\ \ 0\ \ 1\ \ 2\ \ 3\ \ 4\ \ 5\ \ 6$$

**Essential Understanding** You can write an absolute value inequality as a compound inequality without absolute value symbols.

**Plan**

Is this an *and* problem or an *or* problem?
$2x - 1$ is less than 5 and greater than $-5$. It is an *and* problem.

 **Problem 4** Solving the Absolute Value Inequality $|A| < b$

**What is the solution of $|2x - 1| < 5$? Graph the solution.**

$$|2x - 1| < 5$$

$-5 < 2x - 1 < 5$    $2x - 1$ is between $-5$ and 5.

$-4 < 2x < 6$    Add 1 to each part.

$-2 < x < 3$    Divide each part by 2.

$$-3\,-2\,-1\ \ 0\ \ 1\ \ 2\ \ 3$$

 **Got It? 4.** What is the solution of $|3x - 4| \leq 8$? Graph the solution.

PowerAlgebra.com | **Lesson 1-6** Absolute Value Equations and Inequalities | 43

---

**Problem 3**

**Q** How is the expression outside of the absolute value signs in this problem different from Problem 1 and Problem 2? **[There is an $x$ outside of the absolute value signs.]**

**Q** If the expression outside the absolute value signs was negative, what would the solutions be? **[There would be no solutions because the absolute value is never negative.]**

**Got It?**    ERROR PREVENTION
Make sure students use the Opposite of a Sum Property when simplifying
$-(7x + 14) = -7x - 14$.

**Problem 4**    ERROR PREVENTION
Be aware of the placement of the inequality signs. If a student sets up the inequalities as $2x - 1 < 5$ and $2x - 1 < -5$, remind the student that the inequality sign must be flipped in the second example. Review multiplication of inequalities by negative numbers.

VISUAL LEARNERS

**Q** Read $-2 < x < 3$ as $x$ is between $-2$ and 3. How does the graph confirm this? **[The graph is the segment from $-2$ to 3, not inclusive of endpoints, so the values of $x$ are between $-2$ and 3.]**

**Got It?**

**Q** How does this inequality compare to the one in Problem 4? **[The solution is like the one in Problem 4, except the boundary points are included in the set of solutions.]**

---

# Additional Problems

**1.** What is the solution of $|2x + 5| = 9$? Graph the solution.

ANSWER $-7, 2$

$$-8\,-7\,-6\,-5\,-4\,-3\,-2\,-1\ \ 0\ \ 1\ \ 2\ \ 3\ \ 4$$

**2.** What is the solution of $\frac{1}{3}|3x - 6| - 2 = 5$?

ANSWER $-5, 9$

**3.** What is the solution of $|-2x + 9| = 3x + 10$?

ANSWER $-\frac{1}{5}$

**4.** What is the solution of $|4x + 3| < 5$? Graph the solution.

ANSWER

$$-3\,-2\,-1\ \ 0\ \ 1\ \ 2\ \ 3$$

**5.** What is the solution of $|2x + 6| \geq 10$? Graph the solution.

ANSWER

$$-8\ \ \ -6\ \ \ -4\ \ \ -2\ \ \ 0\ \ \ 2$$

**6.** You are cutting pieces of wood to make a table. Each piece should be 4.75 ft, but you will use a piece if it is greater than 4.7 ft. and less than 4.8 ft. What absolute value inequality describes the tolerance of the length of wood?

ANSWER $|x - 4.75| < 0.05$

---

# Answers

**Got It?** (continued)

**3.** $-1$

**4.** $-\frac{4}{3} \leq x \leq 4$

$$-3\,-2\,-1\ \ 0\ \ 1\ \ 2\ \ 3\ \ 4\ \ 5\ \ 6$$

**Lesson 1-6** 43

When an absolute value is *less than* a number, the solutions are *between* the number and its opposite. When an absolute value is *more than* a number, the solutions are *outside* of the number and its opposite.

## Problem 5

**Q** What is the smallest positive value in the solution set? The largest negative value? **[1; −5]**

## Got It?

**Q** In 5a, will the graph be two rays or a line segment? **[two rays pointing in opposite directions]**

**Q** In 5b, how is this inequality different from the one in 5a? How does this affect the graph? **[In 5b the end points are included. The graph will have solid dots.]**

## Take Note

**Q** When $|x| \le a$ or $|x| \ge a$, how does the graph change? **[For $|x| \le a$, the graph is a segment. For $|x| \ge a$, the graph is 2 rays.]**

Draw each of the three graphs on the board. Have students describe each graph in words. Reverse the activity by describing a graph in words and having students draw it.

---

$|x| < 5$ means $x$ is between $-5$ and $5$. So, $|x| > 5$ means $x$ is outside the interval from $-5$ to $5$. You can say $x < -5$ *or* $x > 5$.

**Problem 5** Solving the Absolute Value Inequality $|A| \ge b$

**What is the solution of $|2x + 4| \ge 6$? Graph the solution.**

$|2x + 4| \ge 6$

$2x + 4 \le -6$ or $2x + 4 \ge 6$    Rewrite as a compound inequality.

$2x \le -10$      $2x \ge 2$    Subtract 4 from each side of both inequalities.

$x \le -5$ or      $x \ge 1$    Divide each side of both inequalities by 2.

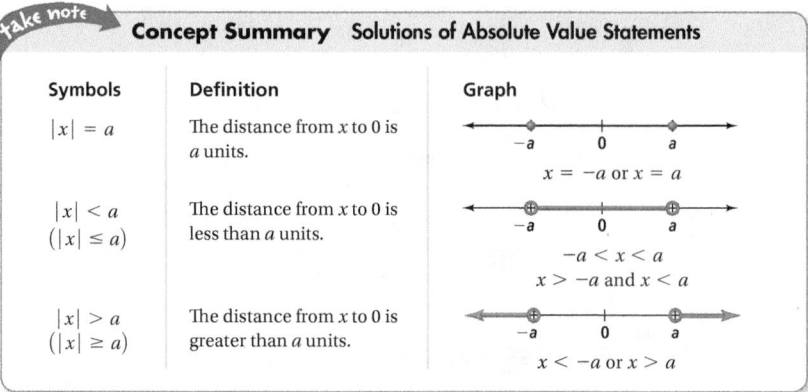

**Think**

**How do you determine the boundary points?**
To find the boundary points, find the solutions of the related equation.

**Got It? 5. a.** What is the solution of $|5x + 10| > 15$? Graph the solution.
    **b. Reasoning** Without solving $|x - 3| \ge 2$, describe the graph of its solution.

---

**take note**

### Concept Summary    Solutions of Absolute Value Statements

| Symbols | Definition | Graph |
|---|---|---|
| $|x| = a$ | The distance from $x$ to 0 is $a$ units. | $x = -a$ or $x = a$ |
| $|x| < a$ ($|x| \le a$) | The distance from $x$ to 0 is less than $a$ units. | $-a < x < a$    $x > -a$ and $x < a$ |
| $|x| > a$ ($|x| \ge a$) | The distance from $x$ to 0 is greater than $a$ units. | $x < -a$ or $x > a$ |

---

A manufactured item's actual measurements and its target measurements can differ by a certain amount, called *tolerance*. Tolerance is one half the difference of the maximum and minimum acceptable values. You can use absolute value inequalities to describe tolerance.

---

# Answers

## Got It? (continued)

**5. a.** $x < -5$ or $x > 1$

-8 -7 -6 -5 -4 -3 -2 -1 0 1 2 3

    **b.** The graph will have two closed circles with an arrow extending to the left of one and to the right of the other.

## Problem 6 Using an Absolute Value Inequality

**Car Racing** In car racing, a car must meet specific dimensions to enter a race. Officials use a template to ensure these specifications are met. What absolute value inequality describes heights of the model of race car shown within the indicated tolerance?

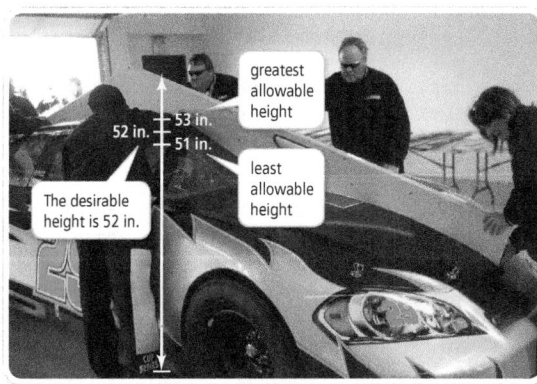

53 in.
52 in.
51 in.

greatest allowable height

least allowable height

The desirable height is 52 in.

$\frac{53 - 51}{2} = \frac{2}{2} = 1$   Find the tolerance.

$-1 \le h - 52 \le 1$   Use $h$ for the height of the race car. Write a compound inequality.

$|h - 52| \le 1$   Rewrite as an absolute value inequality.

**Got It? 6.** Suppose the least allowable height of the race car in Problem 6 was 52 in. and the desirable height was 52.5 in. What absolute value inequality describes heights of the model of race car shown within the indicated tolerance?

### Lesson Check

**Do you know HOW?**

Solve each equation. Check your answers.

**1.** $|-6x| = 24$

**2.** $|2x + 8| - 4 = 12$

**3.** $|x - 2| = 4x + 8$

Solve each inequality. Graph the solution.

**4.** $|2x + 2| - 5 < 15$

**5.** $|4x - 6| \ge 10$

**Do you UNDERSTAND?**

**6. Vocabulary** Explain what it means for a solution of an equation to be extraneous.

**7. Reasoning** When is the absolute value of a number equal to the number itself?

**8.** Give an example of a compound inequality that has no solution.

**9. Compare and Contrast** Describe how absolute value equations and inequalities are like linear equations and inequalities and how they differ.

---

---

**6.** $|h - 52.5| \le 0.5$

**Lesson Check**

**1.** $-4, 4$

**2.** $-12, 4$

**3.** $-\frac{6}{5}$

**4.** $-11 < x < 9$

-12 -10 -8 -6 -4 -2  0  2  4  6  8  10

**5.** $x \le -1$ or $x \ge 4$

-3 -2 -1  0  1  2  3  4  5  6

**6.** A solution of an eq. is extraneous if it is a solution to a derived eq., but is not a solution to the original eq.

**7.** when the number is positive or 0

**8.** Answers may vary. Sample: $d < -5$ and $5d > 25$

**9.** Answers may vary. Sample: An absolute value equation or inequality represents two equations or inequalities; each equation or inequality is solved in the same manner as a linear equation or inequality.

# 4 Practice

**ASSIGNMENT GUIDE**

Basic: 10–42 all, 48–52 even, 53, 58–66 even, 69, 81

Average: 11–41 odd, 43–81

Advanced: 11–41 odd, 43–89

Standardized Test Prep: 90–93

Mixed Review: 94–102

**Reasoning** exercises have blue headings.

**Applications** exercises have red headings.

**EXERCISE 69:** Use the Think About a Plan worksheet in the **Practice and Problem Solving Workbook** (also available in the Teaching Resources in print and online) to further support students' development in becoming independent learners.

**HOMEWORK QUICK CHECK**

To check students' understanding of key skills and concepts, go over Exercises 29, 39, 53, 58, and 69.

---

## Practice and Problem-Solving Exercises

**A Practice**     Solve each equation. Check your answers.     ← *See Problems 1 and 2.*

**10.** $|3x| = 18$     **11.** $|-4x| = 32$     **12.** $|x - 3| = 9$

**13.** $2|3x - 2| = 14$     **14.** $|3x + 4| = -3$     **15.** $|2x - 3| = -1$

**16.** $|x + 4| + 3 = 17$     **17.** $|y - 5| - 2 = 10$     **18.** $|4 - z| - 10 = 1$

Solve each equation. Check for extraneous solutions.     ← *See Problem 3.*

**19.** $|x - 1| = 5x + 10$     **20.** $|2z - 3| = 4z - 1$     **21.** $|3x + 5| = 5x + 2$

**22.** $|2y - 4| = 12$     **23.** $3|4w - 1| - 5 = 10$     **24.** $|2x + 5| = 3x + 4$

Solve each inequality. Graph the solution.     ← *See Problem 4.*

**25.** $3|y - 9| < 27$     **26.** $|6y - 2| + 4 < 22$     **27.** $|3x - 6| + 3 < 15$

**28.** $\frac{1}{4}|x - 3| + 2 < 1$     **29.** $4|2w + 3| - 7 \le 9$     **30.** $3|5t - 1| + 9 \le 23$

Solve each inequality. Graph the solution.     ← *See Problem 5.*

**31.** $|x + 3| > 9$     **32.** $|x - 5| \ge 8$     **33.** $|y - 3| \ge 12$

**34.** $|2x + 1| \ge -9$     **35.** $3|2x - 1| \ge 21$     **36.** $|3z| - 4 > 8$

Write each compound inequality as an absolute value inequality.     ← *See Problem 6.*

**37.** $1.3 \le h \le 1.5$     **38.** $50 \le k \le 51$     **39.** $27.25 \le C \le 27.75$

**40.** $50 \le b \le 55$     **41.** $1200 \le m \le 1300$     **42.** $0.1187 \le d \le 0.1190$

**B Apply**     Solve each equation.

**43.** $-|4 - 8b| = 12$     **44.** $4|3x + 4| = 4x + 8$

**45.** $|3x - 1| + 10 = 25$     **46.** $\frac{1}{2}|3c + 5| = 6c + 4$

**47.** $5|6 - 5x| = 15x - 35$     **48.** $7|8 - 3h| = 21h - 49$

**49.** $2|3x - 7| = 10x - 8$     **50.** $6|2x + 5| = 6x + 24$

**51.** $\frac{1}{4}|4x + 7| = 8x + 16$     **52.** $\frac{2}{3}|3x - 6| = 4(x - 2)$

**53. Think About a Plan** The circumference of a basketball for college women must be from 28.5 in. to 29.0 in. What absolute value inequality represents the circumference of the ball?
- What is the tolerance?
- What is the inequality without using absolute value?

Write an absolute value equation or inequality to describe each graph.

**54.**      **55.**     **56.**

---

# Answers

## Practice and Problem-Solving Exercises (continued)

**10.** $-6, 6$    **11.** $-8, 8$    **12.** $-6, 12$

**13.** $-\frac{5}{3}, 3$    **14.** no solution    **15.** no solution

**16.** $-18, 10$    **17.** $-7, 17$    **18.** $-7, 15$

**19.** $-\frac{3}{2}$    **20.** $\frac{2}{3}$    **21.** $\frac{3}{2}$

**22.** $-4, 8$    **23.** $-1, \frac{3}{2}$    **24.** $1$

**25.** $0 < y < 18$

**26.** $-2\frac{2}{3} < y < 3\frac{1}{3}$

**27.** $-2 < x < 6$

**28.** no solution

**29.** $-3\frac{1}{2} \le w \le \frac{1}{2}$

**30.** $-\frac{11}{15} \le t \le \frac{17}{15}$

**31.** $x < -12$ or $x > 6$

**32.** $x \le -3$ or $x \ge 13$

**33.** $y \le -9$ or $y \ge 15$

**34.** all real numbers

**35.** $x \le -3$ or $x \ge 4$

**36.** $z < -4$ or $z > 4$

**37.** $|h - 1.4| \le 0.1$

**38.** $|k - 50.5| \le 0.5$

**39.** $|C - 27.5| \le 0.25$

**40.** $|b - 52.5| \le 2.5$

**41.** $|m - 1250| \le 50$

**42.** $|d - 0.11885| \le 0.00015$

**43.** no solution    **44.** $-\frac{3}{2}, -1$

**45.** $-\frac{14}{3}, \frac{16}{3}$    **46.** $-\frac{1}{3}$

**47.** no solution    **48.** $\frac{5}{2}$

**49.** $\frac{11}{8}$    **50.** $-1, -3$

**51.** $-\frac{71}{36}$    **52.** $2$

**53.** $|c - 28.75| \le 0.25$; 0.25; $28.50 \le c \le 29.00$

**54.** $|x| = 3$    **55.** $|x| < 4$

**56.** $|x| \ge 1.5$

**Solve each inequality. Graph the solutions.**

**57.** $|3x - 4| + 5 \leq 27$

**58.** $|2x + 3| - 6 \geq 7$

**59.** $-2|x + 4| < 22$

**60.** $2|4t - 1| + 6 > 20$

**61.** $|3z + 15| \geq 0$

**62.** $|-2x + 1| > 2$

**63.** $\frac{1}{9}|5x - 3| - 3 \geq 2$

**64.** $\frac{1}{11}|2x - 4| + 10 \leq 11$

**65.** $\left|\frac{x - 3}{2}\right| + 2 < 6$

**66.** $\left|\frac{x + 5}{3}\right| - 3 > 6$

**67. Writing** Describe the differences in the graphs of $|x| < a$ and $|x| > a$, where $a$ is a positive real number.

**68. Open-Ended** Write an absolute value inequality for which every real number is a solution. Write an absolute value inequality that has no solution.

**Write an absolute value inequality to represent each situation.**

**69. Cooking** Suppose you used an oven thermometer while baking and discovered that the oven temperature varied between +5 and −5 degrees from the setting. If your oven is set to 350°, let $t$ be the actual temperature.

**70. Time** Workers at a hardware store take their morning break no earlier than 10 A.M. and no later than noon. Let $c$ represent the time the workers take their break.

**71. Climate** A friend is planning a trip to Alaska. He purchased a coat that is recommended for outdoor temperatures from −15°F to 45°F. Let $t$ represent the temperature for which the coat is intended.

**Write an absolute value inequality and a compound inequality for each length $x$ with the given tolerance.**

**72.** a length of 36.80 mm with a tolerance of 0.05 mm

**73.** a length of 9.55 mm with a tolerance of 0.02 mm

**74.** a length of 100 yd with a tolerance of 4 in.

**Is the absolute value inequality or equation *always*, *sometimes*, or *never* true? Explain.**

**75.** $|x| = -6$

**76.** $-8 > |x|$

**77.** $|x| = x$

**78.** $|x| + |x| = 2x$

**79.** $|x + 2| = x + 2$

**80.** $(|x|)^2 < x^2$

**81. Error Analysis** A classmate wrote the solution to the inequality $|-4x + 1| > 3$ as shown. Describe and correct the error.

**74.** $x$ is in inches,
$|x - 3600| \leq 4$; $3596 \leq x \leq 3604$

**75.** never; absolute value is nonnegative

**76.** never; absolute value is nonnegative

**77.** sometimes; $|5| = 5$ but $|-5| \neq -5$

**78.** sometimes; $|-3| + |-3| \neq 2(-3)$

**79.** sometimes; $|-4 + 2| \neq -4 + 2$

**80.** never; squaring any number results in a positive result so the two sides will always equal.

**81.** The "3" in the second set of equations should be "−3."
$$-4x + 1 < -3$$
$$-4x < -4$$
$$x > 1 \; not \; x > -\frac{1}{2}$$

**57.** $-6 \leq x \leq 8\frac{2}{3}$

**58.** $x \leq -8$ or $x \geq 5$

**59.** all real numbers

**60.** $t < -\frac{3}{2}$ or $t > 2$

**61.** all real numbers

**62.** $x < -\frac{1}{2}$ or $x > \frac{3}{2}$

**63.** $x \leq -8.4$ or $x \geq 9.6$

**64.** $-3.5 \leq x \leq 7.5$

**65.** $-5 < x < 11$

**66.** $x < -32$ or $x > 22$

**67.** The graph of $|x| < a$ is the set of all points on the number line that lie between $a$ and $-a$. The graph of $|x| > a$ has two parts; the left part consists of the points to the left of $-a$, and the right part consists of the points to the right of $a$.

**68.** Answers may vary. Sample:
$|x - 1| \geq 0$; $|x| < -5$

**69.** $|t - 350| \leq 5$

**70.** $|c - 11| \leq 1$

**71.** $|t - 15| \leq 30$

**72.** $|x - 36.80| \leq 0.05$;
$36.75 \leq x \leq 36.85$

**73.** $|x - 9.55| \leq 0.02$; $9.53 \leq x \leq 9.57$

# Answers

## Practice and Problem-Solving Exercises
(continued)

**82.** $-\frac{b+c}{a}, \frac{b+c}{a}, a \neq 0, b + c \geq 0$

**83.** $\frac{ab+d}{c}, \frac{-ab+d}{c}, c \neq 0, ab \geq 0$

**84.** $\frac{ac+d}{ab}, \frac{ac-d}{ab}, ab \neq 0, \frac{d}{a} \geq 0$

**85.** $(-6 \leq x \leq -5)$ or $(5 \leq x \leq 6)$

**86.** $(x \leq -6)$ or $(-5 < x < 5)$ or $(x \geq 6)$

**87.** $x \geq \frac{5}{2}$

**88.** $|x + 3| > 4$ becomes $x + 3 > 4$ or $x + 4 < -4$. $x + 3$ is outside the interval from $-4$ to $4$ so the solution is an *or* solution. $|x + 3| < 4$ becomes $-4 < x + 3 < 4$ so the solution is an *and* solution.

**89.** Use *and* if the absolute value is less than a value and use *or* if the absolute value is greater than a value.

## Standardized Test Prep

**90.** $\frac{11}{3}$

**91.** 0

**92.** 1.875

**93.** 0.04

## Mixed Review

**94.** $y < 6$

**95.** $s < \frac{2}{15}$

**96.** $a > 4$

**97.** Each figure has 4 more squares than the previous figure.

**98.** Each figure $n$ has $n$ more circles than the previous figure.

**99.**

---

**82.** $|ax| - b = c$

**83.** $|cx - d| = ab$

**84.** $a|bx - c| = d$

**Graph each solution.**

**85.** $|x| \geq 5$ and $|x| \leq 6$

**86.** $|x| \geq 6$ or $|x| < 5$

**87.** $|x - 5| \leq x$

**88. Writing** Describe the difference between solving $|x + 3| > 4$ and $|x + 3| < 4$.

**89. Reasoning** How can you determine whether an absolute value inequality is equivalent to a compound inequality joined by the word *and* or one joined by the word *or*?

### Standardized Test Prep

GRIDDED RESPONSE

SAT/ACT

**90.** What is the positive solution of $|3x + 8| = 19$?

**91.** If $p$ is an integer, what is the least possible value of $p$ in the following inequality?

$$|3p - 5| \leq 7$$

**92.** In wood shop, you have to drill a hole that is 2 inches deep into a wood panel. The tolerance for drilling a hole is described by the inequality $|t - 2| \leq 0.125$. What is the shallowest hole allowed?

**93.** The normal thickness of a metal structure is shown. It expands to 6.54 centimeters when heated and shrinks to 6.46 centimeters when cooled down. What is the maximum amount in cm that the thickness of the structure can deviate from its normal thickness?

6.5 cm

### Mixed Review

Solve each inequality. Graph the solution.

See Lesson 1-5.

**94.** $5y - 10 < 20$

**95.** $15(4s + 1) < 23$

**96.** $4a + 6 > 2a + 14$

Describe each pattern using words. Draw the next figure in each pattern.

See Lesson 1-1.

**97.**

**98.**

**Get Ready!**  To prepare for Lesson 2-1, do Exercises 99–102.

See p. 969.

Graph each ordered pair on the coordinate plane.

**99.** $(-4, -8)$

**100.** $(3, 6)$

**101.** $(0, 0)$

**102.** $(-1, 3)$

**100.**

**101.**

**102.**

# Additional Instructional Support

## Algebra 2 Companion

Students can use the **Algebra 2 Companion** worktext (4 pages) as you teach the lesson. Use the Companion to support

- New Vocabulary
- Key Concepts
- Got It for each Problem
- Lesson Check

## ELL Support

**Connect to Prior Knowledge** When learning the word *extraneous* highlight *extra*. Since an extraneous solution is not a solution in the original equation, it is *extra*.

**Connect to Prior Knowledge** Illustrate the difference between a real-life situation where the sign of an answer matters, such as temperature, and a real-life situation where the absolute value is more important, such as distance. Then have small groups of students list more real-life situations modeled either by absolute values or by signed numbers. Have the groups share some of their examples with the class.

# 5 Assess & Remediate

## Lesson Quiz

1. Solve and graph $|3x + 1| = 8$.
2. What is the solution of $3|x - 7| - 2 = 4$?
3. What is the solution of $|2x + 1| = 3x + 4$?
4. Solve and graph $|4x + 1| < 5$.
5. Solve and graph $|3x - 2| \geq 7$.
6. **Do you UNDERSTAND?** You order 1.5 pounds of turkey at a deli. You will accept the turkey if its weight is between 1.54 and 1.46. What absolute value inequality describes the tolerance of the weight of the turkey?

### ANSWERS TO LESSON QUIZ

1. $-3, \dfrac{7}{3}$

$$-5\ -4\ -3\ -2\ -1\ \ 0\ \ 1\ \ 2\ \ 3\ \ 4\ \ 5$$

2. 5, 9

3. $-1$

4. $-\dfrac{3}{2} < x < 1$

$$-3\quad -2\quad -1\quad\ 0\quad\ 1\quad\ 2\quad\ 3$$

5. $x \leq -\dfrac{5}{3}$ or $x \geq 3$

$$-4\quad -3\quad -2\quad -1\quad 0\quad 1\quad 2\quad 3\quad 4$$

6. $|x - 1.5| \leq 0.04$

### PRESCRIPTION FOR REMEDIATION

Use the student work on the Lesson Quiz to prescribe a differentiated review assignment:

| Points | Differentiated Remediation |
|--------|---------------------------|
| 0–3 | Intervention |
| 4–5 | On-level |
| 6 | Extension |

**PowerAlgebra.com**

## 5 Assess & Remediate

Assign the Lesson Quiz. Appropriate intervention, practice, or enrichment is automatically generated based on student performance.

# Differentiated Remediation

Available in editable format online.

## Intervention

- **Reteaching** (2 pages) Provides reteaching and practice exercises for the key lesson concepts. Use with struggling students or absent students.
- **English Language Learner Support** Helps students develop and reinforce mathematical vocabulary and key concepts.

### All-in-One Resources/Online
**Reteaching**

**1-6 Reteaching**
Absolute Value Equations and Inequalities

Solving absolute value equations require solving two equations separately. Recall that for a real number $x$, $|x|$ is the distance from zero to $x$ on the number line. The equation $|x| = p$ means that either $x = p$ or $x = -p$ because both are $p$ units from 0.

**Problem**

What is the solution set for the equation $|5x + 1| - 3 = 4$?

The first step in solving an absolute value equation is to isolate the absolute value on one side of the equal sign.

$$|5x + 1| - 3 = 4$$
$$|5x + 1| - 3 + 3 = 4 + 3 \quad \text{Add 3 to each side.}$$
$$|5x + 1| = 7 \quad \text{Simplify.}$$

Next, rewrite the absolute value as two equations and solve each of them separately.

$5x + 1 = 7$ or $5x + 1 = -7$    Definition of absolute value
$5x = 6$ or $5x = -8$    Addition Property of Equality
$x = \dfrac{6}{5}$ or $x = -\dfrac{8}{5}$    Division Property of Equality

Notice that the same operations are performed in the same order on each of the two equations. However, do not try to "simplify" the process by solving a single equation. This leads to errors.

The solutions are $x = \dfrac{6}{5}$ or $x = -\dfrac{8}{5}$. Check each solution in the original equation:

Check

$$\left|5 \cdot \dfrac{6}{5} + 1\right| - 3 = 4 \qquad \left|5 \cdot \left(-\dfrac{8}{5}\right) + 1\right| - 3 = 4$$
$$|6 + 1| - 3 = 4 \qquad |-8 + 1| - 3 = 4$$
$$4 = 4 \checkmark \qquad 4 = 4 \checkmark$$

**Exercises**

Solve each absolute value equation. Check your work.

1. $|2x - 3| - 4 = 3$ $x = -2$ or $x = 5$    2. $|3x - 6| + 1 = 13$ $x = 6$ or $x = -2$

### All-in-One Resources/Online
**English Language Learner Support**

**1-6 ELL Support**
Absolute Value Equations and Inequalities

**Concept List**

| $|x| < 3$ | $|x| > 3$ | $|x| \leq 3$ | $|x| \geq 3$ | $|x| = 3$ |

Choose the concept from the list below that best represents the item in each box.

| 1. numbers more than 3 units away from zero $|x| > 3$ | 2. numbers three units away from zero or more than three units away from 0 $|x| \geq 3$ | 3. $|x| > 3$ |
| 4. numbers less than 3 units away from zero $|x| < 3$ | 5. $|x| > 3$ | 6. numbers 3 units away from zero $|x| = 3$ |
| 7. $|x| \leq 3$ | 8. numbers three units away from zero or less than three units away from 0 $|x| \leq 3$ | 9. $|x| \leq 3$ |

# Differentiated Remediation *continued*

Available in editable format online.

## On-Level

- **Practice** (2 pages) Provides extra practice for each lesson. For simpler practice exercises, use the Form K Practice pages found in the All-in-One Teaching Resources and online.

- **Think About a Plan** Helps students develop specific problem-solving skills and strategies by providing scaffolded guiding questions.

- **Standardized Test Prep** Focuses on all major exercises, all major question types, and helps students prepare for the high-stakes assessments.

## Extension

- **Enrichment** Provides students with interesting problems and activities that extend the concepts of the lesson.

- **Activities, Games, and Puzzles** Worksheets that can be used for concepts development, enrichment, and for fun!

### Practice and Problem Solving Wkbk/ All-in-One Resources/Online
#### Practice page 1

### Practice and Problem Solving Wkbk/ All-in-One Resources/Online
#### Practice page 2

### All-in-One Resources/Online
#### Enrichment

### Practice and Problem Solving Wkbk/ All-in-One Resources/Online
#### Think About a Plan

### Practice and Problem Solving Wkbk/ All-in-One Resources/Online
#### Standardized Test Prep

### Online Teacher Resource Center
#### Activities, Games, and Puzzles

# Pull It All Together

These problems will challenge you to pull together many concepts and skills of algebra that you have learned.

**BIG idea** Variable

You can use variables to represent variable quantities in real-world situations and in patterns.

**BIG idea** Properties

You can use the properties of real numbers to simplify algebraic expressions.

## Task 1

The tables below show the same set of inputs and outputs using two different process columns.

| Input | Process Column | Output |
|---|---|---|
| 1 | $2(1-1)+5$ | 5 |
| 2 | $2(2-1)+5$ | 7 |
| 3 | $2(3-1)+5$ | 9 |
| 4 | ▪ | ▪ |
| ⋮ | ⋮ | ⋮ |
| $n$ | ▪ | ▪ |

| Input | Process Column | Output |
|---|---|---|
| 1 | $2(1+1)+1$ | 5 |
| 2 | $2(2+1)+1$ | 7 |
| 3 | $2(3+1)+1$ | 9 |
| 4 | ▪ | ▪ |
| ⋮ | ⋮ | ⋮ |
| $n$ | ▪ | ▪ |

a. Copy and complete each table. Write an algebraic expression for each rule using $n$.
b. Show that the two algebraic expressions are equivalent.
c. Describe a pattern using a third rule.

**BIG idea** Solving Equations and Inequalities

You can use properties of numbers and equality to solve an equation by finding increasingly simpler equations that have the same solution as the original equation.

## Task 2

Find all possible values of $a$ and $b$ in the figures below, given the following conditions.
• The perimeters are equal.
• The rectangle has an area between 80 and 100 square units.
• The values of $a$ and $b$ are integers.

# Performance Task

## Pull It All Together

The concepts and skills required to solve these problems are from several lessons within this chapter. As students solve these problems, they will demonstrate their reasoning strategies and their growth as independent problem solvers.

The following questions are designed for you to
• help support students as they do the Tasks.
• gauge the amount of support a student needs as they progress to becoming an independent problem solver.

### Task 1

Use properties of real numbers to simplify algebraic expressions and write algebraic expressions to describe patterns.
• How can the process column help you write an algebraic expression?
• What does it mean for algebraic expressions to be equivalent?

### Task 2

Simplify equivalent algebraic expressions and apply conditions to find solutions.
• How does simplifying the equation that represents the equivalent perimeters restrict the possible solutions?
• How does the condition on the area of the rectangle restrict the possible solutions?
• Without the condition that the values of $a$ and $b$ are integers, could there be more than one solution?

# Assess Performance UbD

## Analytic Holistic Scoring

Holistic scoring provides feedback to students to help them become autonomous, confident problem solvers. Holistic scoring considers the entire solution to evaluate students' strategies, process, and answers. Use the rubric below to evaluate students' work for Pull It All Together and for Performance Tasks found in the Teaching Resources.

### Understanding the Problem

| | |
|---|---|
| 2 | complete understanding of the problem |
| 1 | part of the problem misunderstood or misinterpreted |
| 0 | complete misunderstanding of the problem |

### Planning a Solution

| | |
|---|---|
| 2 | plan could lead to a correct solution if implemented properly |
| 1 | partially correct plan based on part of the problem interpreted correctly |
| 0 | no attempt or totally inappropriate plan |

### Getting an Answer

| | |
|---|---|
| 2 | correct answer and correct label for the answer |
| 1 | copying error; computational error; partial answer for a problem with multiple answers |
| 0 | no answer or wrong answer based on an inappropriate plan |

### Developing Autonomy

| | |
|---|---|
| 2 | completed the problem without help |
| 1 | needed one or two hints |
| 0 | could not work the problem without extensive guidance |

**SOLUTION OUTLINES**

**1. a.** First step: Copy and complete the tables.

| Input | Process Column | Output |
|---|---|---|
| 1 | $2(1-1)+5$ | 5 |
| 2 | $2(2-1)+5$ | 7 |
| 3 | $2(3-1)+5$ | 9 |
| 4 | $2(4-1)+5$ | 11 |
| ⋮ | ⋮ | ⋮ |
| $n$ | $2(n-1)+5$ | $2n+3$ |

| Input | Process Column | Output |
|---|---|---|
| 1 | $2(1+1)+1$ | 5 |
| 2 | $2(2+1)+1$ | 7 |
| 3 | $2(3+1)+1$ | 9 |
| 4 | $2(4+1)+1$ | 11 |
| ⋮ | ⋮ | ⋮ |
| $n$ | $2(n+1)+1$ | $2n+3$ |

**1.b–2.** See next page.

**Pull It All Together** 49

# Essential Questions

**BIG** idea **Variable**

**ESSENTIAL QUESTION** How do variables help you model real-world situations?

**ANSWER** You can use variables to represent variable quantities in real-world situations and in patterns.

**BIG** idea **Properties**

**ESSENTIAL QUESTION** How can you use the properties of real numbers to simplify algebraic expressions?

**ANSWER** The properties that apply to real numbers also apply to variables that represent them.

**BIG** idea **Solving Equations and Inequalities**

**ESSENTIAL QUESTION** How do you solve an equation or inequality?

**ANSWER** You can use properties of numbers and equality (or inequality) to solve an equation (or inequality) by finding increasingly simpler equations (or inequalities) which have the same solution as the original equation (or inequality).

---

# ① Chapter Review

## Connecting BIG ideas and Answering Essential Questions

**1 Variable**
You can use variables to represent variable quantities in real-world situations and in patterns.

**Patterns and Expressions (Lesson 1-1)**
$6, 12, 18, 24, \ldots 6n$
$8, 9, 10, 11, \ldots (n + 7)$

**Algebraic Expressions (Lesson 1-3)**
$6n$
$n + 7$
$5x - x = (5 - 1)x$
$a + 0 = a$
$h + k = k + h$

**2 Properties**
The properties that apply to real numbers also apply to variables that represent them.

**Properties of Real Numbers (Lesson 1-2)**
$4(6 - 1) = 4(6) - 4(1)$
$23 + 0 = 23$
$5 + 12 = 12 + 5$

**3 Solving Equations and Inequalities**
You can use properties of numbers and equality (or inequality) to solve an equation (or inequality) by finding increasingly simpler equations (or inequalities) which have the same solution as the original equation (or inequality).

**Solving Equations and Inequalities (Lessons 1-4 and 1-5)**
$$4x - 1 = 5 \qquad 7 > -3h - 2$$
$$4x = 6 \qquad 9 > -3h$$
$$x = \frac{3}{2} \qquad -3 < h$$

**Absolute Value Equations and Inequalities (Lesson 1-6)**
$$|2b + 7| = 15$$
$$2b + 7 = 15 \text{ or } 2b + 7 = -15$$
$$2b = 8 \qquad 2b = -22$$
$$b = 4 \quad \text{or} \quad b = -11$$

---

###  Chapter Vocabulary

- absolute value (p. 41)
- additive inverse (p. 14)
- algebraic expression (p. 5)
- coefficient (p. 20)
- compound inequality (p. 36)
- constant (p. 5)
- constant term (p. 20)
- equation (p. 26)
- evaluate (p. 19)
- extraneous solution (p. 42)
- identity (p. 28)
- inverse operations (p. 27)
- like terms (p. 21)
- literal equation (p. 29)
- multiplicative inverse (p. 14)
- numerical expression (p. 5)
- opposite (p. 14)
- reciprocal (p. 14)
- solution of an equation (p. 27)
- term (p. 20)
- variable (p. 5)
- variable quantity (p. 5)

**Choose the correct term to complete each sentence.**

**1.** The _?_ makes an equation true.

**2.** A number's distance from zero on the number line is its _?_ .

**3.** _?_ is another name for the multiplicative inverse of a number.

**4.** A pair of inequalities joined by *and* or *or* are called a _?_ .

---

# Summative Questions

Use the following prompts as you review this chapter with your students. The prompts are designed to assess your students' understanding of the BIG Ideas they have studied.

- The expression $\frac{2}{3}n + 3$ describes a pattern of numbers. To which set of real numbers do the numbers in this pattern belong?
- Which property would you use to start the solution of $3|x + 4| - 2 = 7$?
- Describe the graph of $5 < 2x + 1$. How would the graph change if you reversed the inequality sign?

**SOLUTION OUTLINES** (continued)

**b.** First step: Simplify each expression.
$$2(n - 1) + 5 = 2n - 2 + 5$$
$$= 2n + 3$$
$$2(n + 1) + 1 = 2n + 2 + 1$$
$$= 2n + 3$$
$$2n + 3 = 2n + 3$$
Therefore, $2(n - 1) + 5$
$$= 2(n + 1) + 1.$$

**c.** Possible Plan: Modify either pattern you found in part (a). (Another pattern that uses the same input and results in the same output is $2n + 3$.)

**2.** First step: Write an equation to represent the perimeter of each figure. (Perimeter of the rectangle $= 2a + 2b$, perimeter of the triangle $= 4a + b$.)

Second step: Use the condition, the perimeters are equal, to find a relationship between $a$ and $b$. ($b = 2a$)

Third step: Since the area of the rectangle has an area between 80 and 100 and the values of $a$ and $b$ are integers, use trial and error to find the values of $a$ and $b$. ($a = 7$ and $b = 14$)

## 1-1 Patterns and Expressions

### Quick Review

You can represent patterns using words, diagrams, numbers, and **algebraic expressions**. You can identify a pattern by looking for the same type of change between consecutive figures or numbers. It often helps to make a table.

### Example

Identify a pattern by making a table of inputs and outputs. Include a process column. $7, 14, 21, 28, 35, \ldots$

| Input | Process Column | Output |
|-------|---------------|--------|
| 1 | $1 \cdot 7$ | 7 |
| 2 | $2 \cdot 7$ | 14 |
| 3 | $3 \cdot 7$ | 21 |
| $\vdots$ | $\vdots$ | $\vdots$ |
| $n$ | $n \cdot 7$ | $7n$ |

The $n$th output is $7n$.

### Exercises

Identify a pattern and find the next three numbers in the pattern.

**5.** $5, 10, 15, 20, \ldots$       **6.** $3, 4, 5, 6, \ldots$

Copy and complete the table. Then find the output when the input is $n$.

**7.**
| Input | Output |
|-------|--------|
| 1 | 9 |
| 2 | 10 |
| 3 | 11 |
| 4 | ■ |
| $\vdots$ | $\vdots$ |
| $n$ | ■ |

**8.**
| Input | Output |
|-------|--------|
| 1 | 19 |
| 2 | 38 |
| 3 | 57 |
| 4 | ■ |
| $\vdots$ | $\vdots$ |
| $n$ | ■ |

**9. Finance** If you put $20 in your savings account each week, how much have you saved after $n$ weeks?

## 1-2 Properties of Real Numbers

### Quick Review

The natural numbers, whole numbers, integers, rational numbers, and irrational numbers are all subsets of the real numbers.

You can use properties such as the ones listed below to simplify and evaluate expressions.

| | |
|---|---|
| **Commutative Properties** | $-3 + 5 = 5 + (-3)$ |
| | $2 \times 9 = 9 \times 2$ |
| **Associative Properties** | $3 + (5 + 7) = (3 + 5) + 7$ |
| | $4 \times (8 \times 11) = (4 \times 8) \times 11$ |
| **Distributive Property** | $5(7 + 9) = 5(7) + 5(9)$ |

### Example

Identify the property illustrated by the equation.

$4 \cdot x = x \cdot 4$       Commutative Property of Multiplication

### Exercises

Name the subset(s) of real numbers to which each number belongs.

**10.** $8.1\pi$       **11.** $-79$

**12.** $\sqrt{121}$       **13.** $12\frac{7}{8}$

Compare the two numbers. Use $<$ or $>$.

**14.** $-\sqrt{60}, -8$       **15.** $5, \sqrt{32}$

Name the property of real numbers illustrated by each equation.

**16.** $\frac{9}{4} \cdot \frac{4}{9} = 1$

**17.** $\left(8 \cdot \frac{1}{3}\right) \cdot 12 = 8 \cdot \left(\frac{1}{3} \cdot 12\right)$

## Answers

### Chapter Review

**1.** solution of the equation

**2.** absolute value

**3.** reciprocal

**4.** compound inequality

**5.** add 5; 25, 30, 35

**6.** add 1; 7, 8, 9

**7.** 12; $n + 8$

**8.** 76; $19n$       **9.** $20n$

**10.** irrational numbers

**11.** rational numbers, integers

**12.** rational numbers, integers, whole numbers, natural numbers

**13.** rational numbers

**14.** $-\sqrt{60} > -8$, or $-8 < -\sqrt{60}$

**15.** $5 < \sqrt{32}$, or $\sqrt{32} > 5$

**16.** Inv. Prop. of Mult.

**17.** Assoc. Prop. of Mult.

# Answers

## Chapter Review (continued)

**18.** 114

**19.** $5b$

**20.** 11

**21.** 6

**22.** $z \le \dfrac{2}{5}$

**23.** $x > 2$

**24.** no solution

**25.** $x \le \dfrac{3}{2}$ or $x > 6$

**26.** 10 cm, 6 cm

**27.** 1

**28.** no solution

**29.** $x = -8$ or $x = -12$

**30.** no solution

**31.** $-\dfrac{1}{3} \le x \le \dfrac{5}{3}$

**32.** $y < 0$ or $y > 18$

**33.** $-\dfrac{18}{7} \le x \le \dfrac{18}{7}$

**34.** $x < -14$ or $x > 10$

**35.** $|x - 43.6| \le 0.1$

---

## 1-3, 1-4, and 1-5 Expressions, Equations, and Inequalities

### Quick Review

You **evaluate** an algebraic expression by substituting numbers for the variables. You simplify an algebraic expression by combining **like terms**. To find the **solution of an equation** or inequality, use the properties of equality or inequality. Some **equations** and inequalities are true for all real numbers, and some have no solution.

### Example

Evaluate $3(x - 4) + 2x - x^2$ for $x = 6$.

$3(6 - 4) + 2(6) - 6^2$    Substitute.

$= 3(2) + 2(6) - 6^2$    Simplify inside parentheses.

$= 6 + 12 - 36$    Multiply.

$= 18 - 36$    Add.

$= -18$    Subtract.

### Exercises

**18.** Evaluate $3t(t + 2) - 3t^2$ for $t = 19$.

**19.** Simplify $-(3a - 2b) - 3(-a - b)$.

Solve each equation. Check your answer.

**20.** $2x - 5 = 17$      **21.** $3(x + 1) = 9 + 2x$

Solve each inequality. Graph the solution.

**22.** $4 - 5z \ge 2$

**23.** $2(5 - 3x) < x - 4(3 - x)$

Solve each compound inequality. Graph the solution.

**24.** $10 \ge 7 + 3x$ and     **25.** $3 \ge 2x$ or
       $9 - 4x \le 1$             $x - 4 > 2$

Write an equation to solve the problem.

**26.** **Geometry** The length and width of a rectangle are in the ratio $5 : 3$. The perimeter of the rectangle is 32 cm. Find the length and width.

## 1-6 Absolute Value Equations and Inequalities

### Quick Review

To rewrite an equation or inequality that involves the **absolute value** of an algebraic expression, you must consider both cases of the definition of absolute value.

### Example

Solve $|3x - 5| = 4 + 2x$. Check for extraneous solutions.

$3x - 5 = 4 + 2x$ or $3x - 5 = -(4 + 2x)$

$\qquad\qquad\qquad\qquad\quad 3x - 5 = -4 - 2x$

$\qquad\qquad\qquad\qquad\qquad\quad 5x = 1$

$x = 9 \qquad$ or $\qquad x = \dfrac{1}{5}$

**Check** $|3(9) - 5| \stackrel{?}{=} 4 + 2(9)$    $\left|3\left(\frac{1}{5}\right) - 5\right| \stackrel{?}{=} 4 + 2\left(\frac{1}{5}\right)$

$\qquad\qquad |27 - 5| \stackrel{?}{=} 22$        $\left|\frac{3}{5} - 5\right| \stackrel{?}{=} 4 + \frac{2}{5}$

$\qquad\qquad\quad |22| = 22$ ✔       $\left|-\frac{22}{5}\right| = \frac{22}{5}$ ✔

### Exercises

Solve each equation. Check for extraneous solutions.

**27.** $|2x + 8| = 3x + 7$    **28.** $|x - 4| + 3 = 1$

**29.** $3|x + 10| = 6$      **30.** $2|x - 7| = x - 8$

Solve each inequality. Graph the solution.

**31.** $|3x - 2| + 4 \le 7$    **32.** $4|y - 9| > 36$

**33.** $|7x| + 3 \le 21$      **34.** $\frac{1}{2}|x + 2| > 6$

**35.** The specification for a length $x$ is 43.6 cm with a tolerance of 0.1 cm. Write the specification as an absolute value inequality.

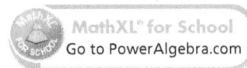

## Do you know HOW?

Evaluate each expression for $x = 5$.

1. $\frac{5}{3}(3x - 6) - (6 - 4x)$

2. $3(x^2 - 4) + 7(x - 2)$

3. $x - 2x + 3x - 4x + 5x$

Simplify each expression.

4. $a^2 + a + a^2$

5. $2x + 3y - 5x + 2y$

6. $5(a - 2b) - 3(a - 2b)$

7. $3[2(x - 3) + 2] + 5(x - 3)$

Solve each equation.

8. $4y - 6 = 2y + 8$

9. $3(2z + 1) = 35$

10. $5(3w - 2) - 7 = 23$

11. $t - 2(3 - 2t) = 2t + 9$

12. $5(s - 12) - 24 = 3(s + 2)$

13. The lateral surface area of a cylinder is given by the formula $S = 2\pi rh$. Solve the equation for $r$.

14. **Savings** Briana and her sister Molly both want to buy the same model bicycle. Briana needs $73 more before she can afford the bike. Molly needs $65 more. If they combine their money, they will have just enough to buy one bicycle that they could share. What is the cost of the bicycle?

15. **Musical** There is only one freshman in the cast of a high school musical. There are 6 sophomores and 11 juniors. One third of the cast are seniors. How many seniors are in the musical?

Determine whether each equation is *always*, *sometimes*, or *never* true.

16. $2x + 7 - x = 3 + x + 4$

17. $5a - 1 - 3a = 2a + 1$

Solve each equation or inequality. Graph the solution.

18. $3x + 17 \geq 5$

19. $25 - 2x < 11$

20. $\frac{3}{8}x < -6$ or $5x > 2$

21. $2 < 10 - 4d < 6$

22. $4 - x = |2 - 3x|$

23. $5|3w + 2| - 3 > 7$

## Do you UNDERSTAND?

24. **Writing** Describe the relationships among these sets of numbers: natural numbers, whole numbers, integers, rational numbers, irrational numbers, and real numbers.

25. **Reasoning** Justify each step by identifying the property used.

$$t + 5(t + 1) = t + (5t + 5)$$
$$= (t + 5t) + 5$$
$$= (1t + 5t) + 5$$
$$= (1 + 5)t + 5$$
$$= 6t + 5$$

26. **Reasoning** The first four figures of a pattern are shown.

Describe the tenth figure in the pattern.

24. Answers may vary. Sample: The natural numbers are the counting numbers (1, 2, 3, . . .); the whole numbers are the natural numbers and zero (0, 1, 2, 3, . . .); the integers are the whole numbers and their opposites (. . . , −3, −2, −1, 0, 1, 2, 3, . . .); the rational numbers are all numbers you can write as a quotient of integers $\frac{a}{b}$, $b \neq 0$; the irrational numbers are decimal representations that neither terminate nor repeat; and the real numbers include all rational numbers and irrational numbers.

25. Distr. Prop.; Assoc. Prop. of Add.; Ident. Prop. of Mult.; Distr. Prop.; add.

26. A triangle formed from 100 smaller triangles arranged in 10 rows.

## Chapter Test

**1.** 29

**2.** 84

**3.** 15

**4.** $2a^2 + a$

**5.** $-3x + 5y$

**6.** $2a - 4b$

**7.** $11x - 27$

**8.** 7

**9.** $\frac{16}{3}$

**10.** $\frac{8}{3}$

**11.** 5

**12.** 45

**13.** $r = \frac{S}{2\pi h}$

**14.** $138

**15.** 9 seniors

**16.** always

**17.** never

**18.** $x \geq -4$

**19.** $x > 7$

**20.** $x < -16$ or $x > \frac{2}{5}$

**21.** $1 < d < 2$

**22.** $-1, \frac{3}{2}$

**23.** $w < -\frac{4}{3}$ or $w > 0$

PowerAlgebra.com

**MathXL for School**

Prepare students for the Mid-Chapter Quiz and Chapter Test with online practice and review.

| Item Number | Lesson |
|:---:|:---:|
| 1 | 1-3 |
| 2 | 6-5 |
| 3 | 1-6 |
| 4 | 1-6 |
| 5 | 1-3 |
| 6 | 1-3 |
| 7 | 1-6 |
| 8 | 1-6 |
| 9 | 2-2 |
| 10 | 2-2 |
| 11 | 1-4 |
| 12 | 1-4 |
| 13 | 2-2 |
| 14 | 2-2 |
| 15 | 1-6 |
| 16 | 1-6 |
| 17 | 2-2 |
| 18 | 1-1 |
| 19 | 1-6 |
| 20 | 1-3 |
| 21 | 1-3 |
| 22 | 1-6 |
| 23 | 1-2 |

# ① Cumulative Test Prep

## TIPS FOR SUCCESS

Some questions on tests ask you to write a short response. To get full credit for an answer, you must give the correct answer (including appropriate units, if applicable) and justify your reasoning or show your work. Read the sample question at the right. Then follow the tips to answer it.

**Short Response** Your school is having a bake sale to raise money for a field trip. The ingredients for each batch of bran muffins cost $3.25, and the cost for the energy to bake them is $.50. You plan to sell each batch for $5.

Write an expression to represent the total amount of money your school will have after selling $n$ batches of muffins. Evaluate your expression for 25 batches. Show your work.

### TIP 2

You need to make a profit in the bake sale in order to raise money. Consider the total sales and the cost to make the muffins. What operation do you use to find the profit?

### Think It Through

It costs $3.25 + $.50 = $3.75 to bake each batch. The school makes $5 − ($3.75) = $1.25 after selling one batch. So, it makes $1.25n$ after selling $n$ batches. It earns $1.25(25) = $31.25 after selling 25 batches. This answer is complete and earns full credit.

### TIP 1

Think about the total cost to make a batch of muffins.

## Vocabulary Builder

As you solve test items, you must understand the meanings of mathematical terms. Match each term with its mathematical meaning.

A. inequality

B. compound inequality

C. extraneous solution

D. expression

E. equation

I. a mathematical sentence that contains $>$, $<$, $\geq$, $\leq$, or $\neq$

II. a solution of an equation derived from an original equation but not a solution of the original equation

III. a pair of inequalities joined by *and* or *or*

IV. a mathematical sentence that contains an equals sign

V. a mathematical phrase that uses numbers, variables, and operational symbols

## Multiple Choice

Read each question. Then write the letter of the correct answer on your paper.

**1.** Which equation represents the data in the table?

| x | −2 | −1 | 1 | 3 | 5 |
|:---:|:---:|:---:|:---:|:---:|:---:|
| y | 2 | 0 | 0 | 4 | 8 |

Ⓐ $y = -2x - 2$

Ⓑ $y = |x| + 2$

Ⓒ $y = |x| - 1$

Ⓓ $y = 2|x| - 2$

**2.** A model of a suspension bridge is built as shown.

Which of the following is closest to the length of the cable?

Ⓕ 2 inches

Ⓖ 4 inches

Ⓗ 10 inches

Ⓘ 20 inches

# Answers

## Vocabulary Builder

**A** I

**B** III

**C** II

**D** V

**E** IV

## Multiple Choice

**1.** D

**2.** G

**3.** Which is the graph of the inequality
$|x - 2| - 3 > -2$?

**4.** A worker is taking boxes of nails on an elevator. Each box weighs 54 lb, and the worker weighs 170 lb. The elevator has a weight limit of 2500 lb. Which inequality describes the number of boxes $b$ that he can safely take on each trip?

Ⓕ $54b - 170 \le 2500$   Ⓗ $54(b - 170) \le 2500$

Ⓖ $54b + 170 \le 2500$   Ⓘ $54(b + 170) \le 2500$

**5.** Which expression is equivalent to
$-8(a - 3b) + 2(-a + 4b + 1)$?

Ⓐ $-10a - 16b + 2$   Ⓒ $-10a + 5b + 2$

Ⓑ $-10a + 32b + 2$   Ⓓ $-10a + b + 1$

**6.** An electrical circuit is connected in series as shown. The total voltage $V$ can be calculated by using the equation shown, where $I$ is the total current and $R$ is the resistance across the circuit. $\left(\textit{Hint: } 1\text{A} = 1\frac{\text{volt}}{\text{ohm}}\right)$

$V = I(R_1 + R_2 + R_3)$

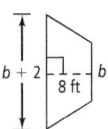

$R_1 = 10\ \Omega$   $R_2$

$I = 2\ \text{A}$       A = amperes
$V = 120\ \text{V}$     V = volts
               $\Omega$ = ohms
$R_3 = 35\ \Omega$

What is the value of $R_2$?

Ⓕ $15\ \Omega$   Ⓖ $45\ \Omega$   Ⓗ $60\ \Omega$   Ⓘ $75\ \Omega$

**7.** Which value is a solution to $2|3x - 6| \le 6$?

Ⓐ $-3$   Ⓑ $-2$   Ⓒ $-1$   Ⓓ $2$

**8.** For which value of $a$ does $4 = a + |x - 4|$ have no solution?

Ⓕ $-6$   Ⓖ $0$   Ⓗ $4$   Ⓘ $6$

**9.** A rectangular solid has a volume of 81 cubic feet. If the length, width, and height are all changed to $\frac{1}{3}$ of their original size, what will be the volume of the new rectangular solid?

Ⓐ 54 cubic feet   Ⓒ 9 cubic feet

Ⓑ 27 cubic feet   Ⓓ 3 cubic feet

**10.** Two rectangular boxes are each 9 inches tall. Both boxes have square bases. The base edge of the larger box is 1.5 times as long as the base edge of the smaller box. Which statement is true?

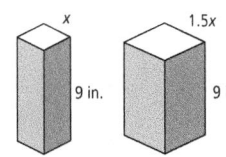

Ⓕ The larger box holds 10.5 cubic inches more than the smaller box.

Ⓖ The larger box holds 13.5 cubic inches more than the smaller box.

Ⓗ The larger box holds 1.5 times as much as the smaller box.

Ⓘ The larger box holds 2.25 times as much as the smaller box.

**11.** Solve $3(x - 2) + 4 \ge -3x + 1$.

Ⓐ $x \ge -3$       Ⓒ $x \ge \frac{3}{2}$

Ⓑ $x \ge \frac{1}{2}$       Ⓓ $x \le 3$

**12.** A trapezoidal deck has dimensions as shown.

$b + 2$  $b$
   $8\ \text{ft}$

What is the longer base length if the area is 88 square feet ($\text{ft}^2$)?

Ⓕ 20 ft   Ⓖ 12 ft   Ⓗ 10 ft   Ⓘ 9 ft

**3.** A
**4.** G
**5.** B
**6.** F
**7.** D
**8.** I
**9.** D
**10.** I
**11.** B
**12.** G

# Answers

**13.** B
**14.** H
**15.** D
**16.** G
**17.** 7.5
**18.** 25
**19.** −4
**20.** 2.75
**21.** [2] $1.80 + .10(8n) = 1.8 + .8n$
   $1.8 + .8(4.5) = 1.8 + 3.6$
   $= 5.4$
   $1.8 + .8n$; $5.40

   [1] a computational error

**22.** [2] $\dfrac{10.05 - 9.95}{2} = \dfrac{0.1}{2} = .05$

   $-.05 \le d - 10 \le .05$
   $|d - 10| \le .05$
   $.05; |d - 10| \le .05$

   [1] correct tolerance, but incorrect inequality
   OR a computational error

**23.** [2] 56 is between $7^2$ and $8^2$, so $\sqrt{56} > 7$.
   (OR equivalent explanation)

   [1] correct comparison, without an
   explanation.

---

**13.** Each dimension of a rectangular prism is tripled. How does the surface area of the new rectangular prism compare to the original surface area?

Ⓐ The new surface area is 12 times as great.

Ⓑ The new surface area is 9 times as great.

Ⓒ The new surface area is 6 times as great.

Ⓓ The new surface area is 3 times as great.

**14.** The two cylinders below have identical bases. Which statement is true?

Ⓕ The shorter cylinder has one-half the surface area of the taller cylinder for all values of $x$.

Ⓖ The shorter cylinder has the same surface area as the taller cylinder for some values of $x$.

Ⓗ The shorter cylinder has one-half the volume of the taller cylinder for all values of $x$.

Ⓘ The shorter cylinder has the same volume as the taller cylinder for some values of $x$.

**15.** You used an oven thermometer while baking and found out that the oven temperature varied between $+7$ degrees and $-7$ degrees from the setting. If your oven is set to 325°F, let $t$ be the actual temperature. What is the absolute value inequality that represents this situation?

Ⓐ $|t - 325| \ge 7$

Ⓑ $|t - 325| < 7$

Ⓒ $|t - 7| \le 325$

Ⓓ $|t - 325| \le 7$

**16.** A designer is designing a handbag. The height of the handbag must be between 16 in. and 18 in. The desirable height is 17 in. Which absolute value inequality represents the height of the handbag?

Ⓕ $|h - 16| \le 1$    Ⓗ $|h - 17| \ge 2$

Ⓖ $|h - 17| \le 1$    Ⓘ $|h - 18| \ge 2$

**GRIDDED RESPONSE**

**17.** The graph shows the amount of paint needed (in gallons) to paint the walls (in square feet) of an office building.

**Amount of Paint**

If the pattern continues, how many gallons of paint will be needed to paint 900 square feet?

**18.** What is the next term?  1, 4, 9, 16, . . .

**19.** What is the sum of the solutions of $|2x + 4| - 6 = 8$?

**20.** What is the value of $4x^2 + 2x - 1$ when $x = \frac{3}{4}$? Express the answer as a decimal.

## Short Response

**21.** The cost for taking a taxi is $1.80 plus $.10 per eighth of a mile. Write an expression for the cost of a taxi ride that is $n$ miles long. Evaluate your expression to find the cost of a ride that is 4.5 miles long. Show all work.

**22.** A new 10-lb dumbbell will pass inspection if it is between 9.95 lb and 10.05 lb. What is the tolerance of the weight of the dumbbell? What absolute value inequality describes acceptable weights of the dumbbell within an indicated tolerance? Show all work.

**23.** Without calculating $\sqrt{56}$, compare $\sqrt{56}$ and 7. Explain your answer.

# Get Ready!

**Lesson 1-3** ➡️ Simplifying Expressions

**Simplify by combining like terms.**

**1.** $7s - s$      **2.** $3a + b + a$      **3.** $xy - y + x$

**4.** $0.5g + g$      **5.** $4t - (t + 3t)$      **6.** $b - 2(1 + c - b)$

**7.** $5f - (5d - f)$      **8.** $2(h + 2g) - (g - h)$      **9.** $-(3z - 5) + z$

**10.** $(2 - d)g - 3d(4 + g)$      **11.** $5v - 3(2 - v)$      **12.** $7t - 3s(2 + t) + s$

**Lesson 1-4** ➡️ Solving Equations

**Solve each equation.**

**13.** $4 + x = -52$      **14.** $-y + 13 = -67$      **15.** $12 = 2 - k$

**16.** $3x = -72$      **17.** $\frac{h}{5} = 215$      **18.** $64 = 4 + 12g$

**19.** $5 - 4t = 12$      **20.** $7x - 9 = x$      **21.** $3(w - 8) = 36$

**22.** $-10p = 2(p - 12)$      **23.** $3(2 - c) = -(c + 4)$      **24.** $7 + b = 11(b - 3)$

**Lesson 1-6** ➡️ Solving Absolute Value Inequalities

**Solve each absolute value inequality. Graph the solution.**

**25.** $|x - 3| < 5$      **26.** $|2a - 1| \geq 2a + 1$      **27.** $|3x + 4| > -4x - 3$

**28.** $|3x + 1| + 1 > 12$      **29.** $3|d - 4| \leq 13 - d$      **30.** $-\frac{1}{3}|f + 3| + 2 \geq -5$

## Looking Ahead Vocabulary

**31.** A person's field of study is often called that person's *domain*. If your domain is American history, what topics might you be interested in?

**32.** When is a person's height likely to show a greater *rate of change*, from 1 to 2 years of age or from 30 to 31 years of age? Explain.

**33.** When you look in the mirror, you see your *reflection*. How does the image in the mirror differ from the way other people see you? How is it the same?

**34.** The boundaries of a country determine the limit of the country's land. How does an inequality form a *boundary* on a number line?

---

# Get Ready!

Assign this diagnostic assessment to determine if students have the prerequisite skills for Chapter 2.

| Lesson | Skill |
|--------|-------|
| 1-3 | Simplify Expressions |
| 1-4 | Solve Equations |
| 1-6 | Solve Absolute Value Inequalities |

To remediate students, select from these resources (available for every lesson).
- Online Problems (PowerAlgebra.com)
- Reteaching (All-in-One Teaching Resources)
- Practice (All-in-One Teaching Resources)

## Why Students Need These Skills

### SIMPLIFYING EXPRESSIONS
Students will simplify equivalent expressions when converting an equation from one form to another.

### SOLVING EQUATIONS
Solving equations for one variable prepares students to solve an equation for one variable in terms of another variable. The resulting expression is the function rule for finding the value of one variable given the value of the second.

### SOLVING ABSOLUTE VALUE INEQUALITIES
Solving absolute value inequalities in one variable prepares students to solve and graph absolute value inequalities in two variables.

## Looking Ahead Vocabulary

**DOMAIN** Ask students how a person's domain affects their range of interests.

**RATE OF CHANGE** Ask students to name other common examples of rate of change.

**REFLECTION** To better understand this, have students sketch a simple figure and its reflection. Have them identify a line of symmetry.

**BOUNDARY** Ask students how an inequality limits the possible solutions. Ask how they could form a boundary on a plane.

---

# Answers

## Get Ready!

**1.** $6s$      **2.** $4a + b$

**3.** $xy - y + x$      **4.** $1.5g$

**5.** $0$      **6.** $3b - 2c - 2$

**7.** $6f - 5d$      **8.** $3h + 3g$

**9.** $-2z + 5$

**10.** $2g - 4dg - 12d$

**11.** $8v - 6$      **12.** $7t - 3st - 5s$

**13.** $-56$      **14.** $80$

**15.** $-10$      **16.** $-24$

**17.** $1075$      **18.** $5$

**19.** $-1.75$      **20.** $1.5$

**21.** $20$      **22.** $2$

**23.** $5$      **24.** $4$

**25.** $-2 < x < 8$

**26.** $a \leq 0$

**27.** $x > -1$

**28.** $x < -4$ or $x > \frac{10}{3}$

**29.** $-\frac{1}{2} \leq d \leq \frac{25}{4}$

**30.** $-24 \leq f \leq 18$

**31.** Answers may vary. Sample: the Civil War, the Great Depression, the Louisiana Purchase

**32.** Answers may vary. Sample: From 1 to 2 years of age; a person has usually stopped growing by age 30, but a baby is still growing at age 1.

**33.** Answers may vary. Sample: The image is a reflection, left to right, of what other people see; the size is the same.

**34.** Answers may vary. Sample: An inequality determines the limit of a value, or a boundary, for the solution on the number line.

# Chapter 2 Overview

## UbD Understanding by Design

Chapter 2 expands on students' understandings and skills related to functions, equations, and graphs. In this chapter, students will develop the answers to the Essential Questions posed on the opposite page as they learn the concepts and skills bulleted below.

### BIG idea Equivalence

**ESSENTIAL QUESTION** Does it matter which form of a linear equation you use?

- Students will identify different forms of linear equations.
- Students will determine which form of a linear equation is most easily found with the given information.
- Students will convert between various forms of linear equations.

### BIG idea Functions

**ESSENTIAL QUESTION** How do you use transformations to help graph absolute value functions?

- Students will identify the different kinds of transformations.
- Students will determine whether a transformation changes the location or shape of a graph or both.

### BIG idea Modeling

**ESSENTIAL QUESTION** How can you model data with a linear function?

- Students will make a scatter plot of linear data.
- Students will determine the correlation of linear data.
- Students will use linear regression to find the line of best fit of linear data with a graphing calculator.
- Students will use the correlation coefficient to analyze linear data with a graphing calculator.

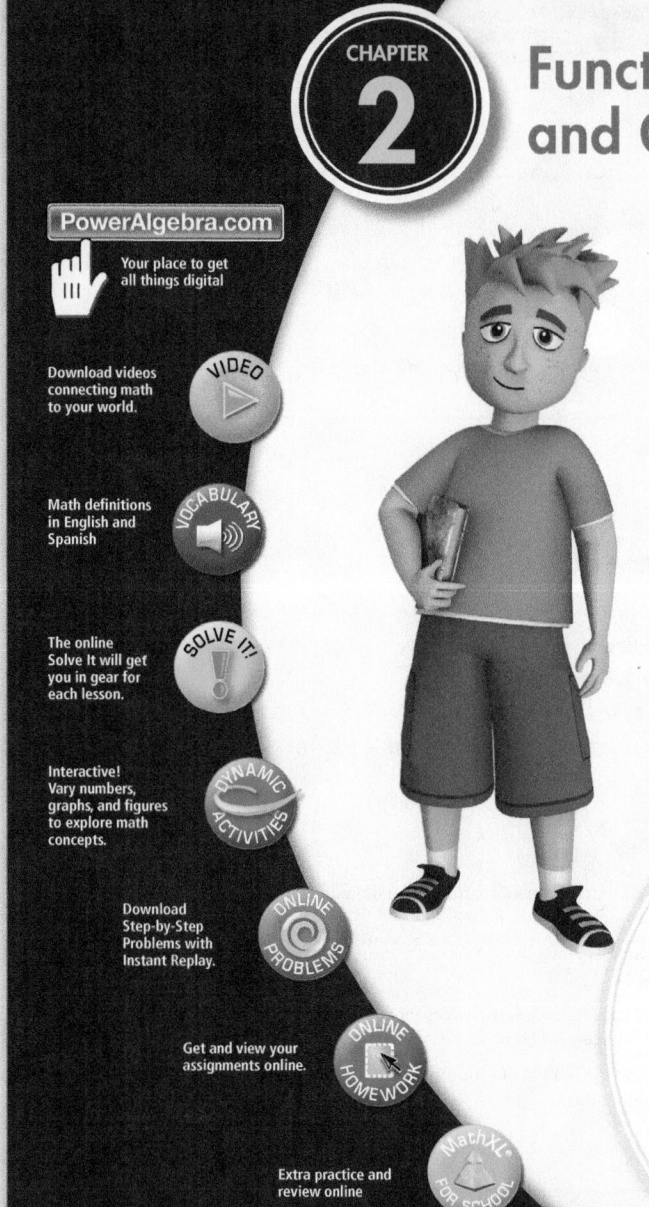

# CHAPTER 2
# Functions, Equations, and Graphs

## PowerAlgebra.com

Your place to get all things digital

**Download videos** connecting math to your world.

**Math definitions** in English and Spanish

The online **Solve It** will get you in gear for each lesson.

**Interactive!** Vary numbers, graphs, and figures to explore math concepts.

**Download** Step-by-Step Problems with Instant Replay.

**Get and view your** assignments online.

**Extra practice and** review online

*You can use functions to model all kinds of real-world situations. A function can model something as simple as a line between two points or as complex as the curves of a roller coaster. You will learn how to work with functions in this chapter.*

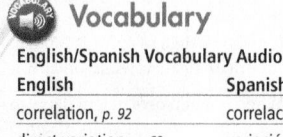
## Vocabulary

**English/Spanish Vocabulary Audio Online:**

| English | Spanish |
| --- | --- |
| correlation, p. 92 | correlación |
| direct variation, p. 68 | variación directa |
| domain, p. 61 | dominio |
| function, p. 62 | función |
| linear equation, p. 75 | ecuación lineal |
| range, p. 61 | rango |
| relation, p. 60 | relación |
| slope, p. 74 | pendiente |

## PowerAlgebra.com

## Chapter 2 Overview

Use these online assets to engage your students. These include support for the Solve It and step-by-step solutions for Problems.

 Show the student-produced video demonstrating relevant and engaging applications of the new concepts in the chapter.

 Find online definitions for new terms in English and Spanish.

 Start each lesson with an attention-getting Problem. View the Problem online with helpful hints.

My Math Video

## My Math Video

Use this photo to introduce the connection between a graph and the function that models the graph. This chapter defines and explores linear and absolute value functions and how to model data with a linear function.

**Q** Picture a roller coaster. Geometrically, how is it shaped? **[Sample: curves going up and down]**

**Q** Many roller coasters follow a complex, three-dimensional path, while some curve up and down above and below a straight path. Sketch a roller coaster curving above and below a horizontal path on a coordinate grid. What does the sketch look like? **[Sample: A graph of a curve that starts at the origin curves up and down and eventually reaches the *x*-axis again.]**

**Q** How do the *y*-values change with respect to *x*-values along your graph? Look at small sections. For example, for the first section, the *y*-values increase as the *x*-values increase. What do you observe? **[The *x*-values are always increasing. As the roller coaster goes up, the *y*-values increase, and as the roller coaster goes down, the *y*-values decrease.]**

**ERROR PREVENTION**

This activity may be confusing if students sketch graphs that are not functions. This may happen if the roller coaster dips backwards.

**EXTENSION**

Ask students to sketch another graph modeling a different situation.

## BIG ideas

**1 Equivalence**
**Essential Question** Does it matter which form of a linear equation you use?

**2 Function**
**Essential Question** How do you use transformations to help graph absolute value functions?

**3. Modeling**
**Essential Question** How can you model data with a linear function?

## Chapter Preview

2-1 Relations and Functions
2-2 Direct Variation
2-3 Linear Functions and Slope-Intercept Form
2-4 More About Linear Equations
2-5 Using Linear Models
2-6 Families of Functions
2-7 Absolute Value Functions and Graphs
2-8 Two-Variable Inequalities

 Increase students' depth of knowledge with interactive online activities.

 Show Problems from each lesson solved step by step. Instant replay allows students to go at their own pace when studying online.

 Assign homework to individual students or to an entire class.

 Prepare students for the Mid-Chapter Quiz and Chapter Test with online practice and review.

# FUNCTIONS, EQUATIONS, AND GRAPHS
# Math Background

## UbD

## Equivalence

**BIG** idea A single quantity may be represented by many different expressions. The facts about a quantity may be expressed by many different equations (or inequalities).

**ESSENTIAL UNDERSTANDINGS**

**2-3**   Consider a line in the coordinate plane. If you move from any point on the line to any other point on the line, the ratio of the vertical change to the horizontal change is constant. That constant ratio describes the slope of the line.

**2-4**   The slopes of two lines in the same plane indicate how the lines are related.

## Functions

**BIG** idea A function is a relationship between variables in which each value of the input variable is associated with a unique value of the output variable. Functions can be represented in a variety of ways, such as graphs, tables, equations, or words. Each representation is particularly useful in certain situations. Some important families of functions are developed through transformations of the simplest form of the function.

**ESSENTIAL UNDERSTANDINGS**

**2-1**   A pairing of items from two sets is special if each item from one set pairs with exactly one item from the second set.

**2-2**   Some quantities are in a relationship where the ratio of corresponding values is constant.

**2-6**   There are sets of functions, called families, in which each function is a transformation of a special function called the parent.

**2-7**   Just as the absolute value of $x$ is its distance from 0, the absolute value of $f(x)$, or $|f(x)|$, gives the distance from the line $y = 0$ for each value of $f(x)$.

## Modeling

**BIG** idea Many real-world mathematical problems can be represented algebraically. These representations can lead to algebraic solutions. A function that models a real-world situation can then be used to make estimates or predictions about future occurrences.

**ESSENTIAL UNDERSTANDINGS**

**2-5**   Sometimes it is possible to model data from a real-world situation with a linear equation. You can then use the equation to draw conclusions about the situation.

**2-8**   Graphing an inequality in two variables is similar to graphing a line. The graph of a linear inequality contains all points on one side of the line and may or may not include the points on the line.

## Functions

A function is a relation that assigns to every element in one set, called the *domain*, exactly one element in another set, called the *range*.

There are several ways to represent a function.

| Ordered Pairs | Graph | Mapping | Table |
|---|---|---|---|

Ordered Pairs: (−2, 4), (−1, 1), (0, 0)

Mapping — Domain: −2, −1, 1, 2 → Range: 4, 1

| x | y |
|---|---|
| −2 | 4 |
| −1 | 1 |
| 0 | 0 |
| 1 | 1 |
| 2 | 4 |

**The domain and range** of a relation can be determined by examining each representation. For ordered pairs, graphs, and tables, the domain is the set of $x$-values, and the range is the set of $y$-values. For mapping diagrams, the domain is the set of input values, and the range is the set of output values.

If any value in the domain corresponds to more than one value in the range, the relation is not a function.

**The Vertical Line Test** is one way to determine whether a relation is a function. If any vertical line intersects the graph of a relation in more than one point, the relation is not a function.

**Function notation** represents an output value in terms of an input value. In the examples, $x$ is the independent variable, and $y$ is the dependent variable. Using function notation,

$y = 3x + 2$ is written as $f(x) = 3x + 2$.

In the notation $f(x)$, $x$ is the argument of function $f$, and $y$ is a function of $x$.

## Common Errors With Functions

**Errors in determining whether a relation is a function** can occur when students do not fully understand the definition of a function as well as the meaning of domain and range.

Multiple representations of the same example may help students. Show that an equation can be graphed and that the graph is made up of ordered pairs. Make a mapping diagram and table of some of the ordered pairs. Ask students to find the domain and range of each representation. Then ask them to determine whether the relation is a function.

**Errors in evaluating functions** are common when $f(x)$ notation is first introduced. Some students can evaluate $y = 4x + 1$ for $x = 2$ but struggle when asked to find $f(2)$ if $f(x) = 4x + 1$.

Provide multiple examples. Write $y = 4x + 1$ and $f(x) = 4x + 1$ and evaluate both side-by-side.

## Linear Models

It is often useful to model data sets with a linear equation.

To model a set of data with a linear equation, it is sometimes helpful to plot the data on a coordinate grid. Then a line can be drawn through the midst of the data passing as close to all of the data points as possible. Such a line is called a trend line. Many trend lines can be drawn, and it may not be possible for a line to pass through all or any of the points.

**A line of best fit** is the trend line that gives the most accurate model of the data. It is calculated by adding the squares of all vertical distances from the data points to the trend line. The line of best fit is the trend line whose sum of squares is minimum. For example, the line of best fit for the data points $P_1$, $P_2$, and $P_3$ is the line for which $d_1^2 + d_2^2 + d_3^2$ is a minimum.

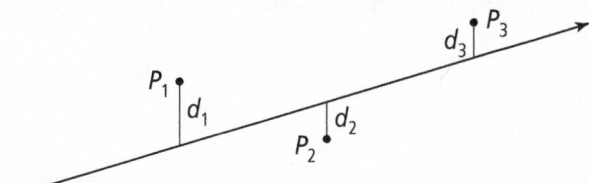

**Graphing calculators** contain a least-squares function to calculate the line of best fit. Once the line is found, it can be used to make predictions about the data.

### Common Errors With Linear Regression

**Graphing calculator errors** can happen when students do not remember the steps involved. Make a sheet of instructions available until students are comfortable with the steps. Indicate that the calculator will always give the line of best fit, which may be different from any trend line they draw.

## Transformations

Transformations are changes to a function that produce another related function. A family of functions consists of a parent function and all the possible transformations of that function.

**A translation** is a vertical and/or horizontal displacement. This transformation shifts the graph without changing the graph's orientation or shape.

**Translations**

| Parent function | Vertical | Horizontal |
|---|---|---|
| $f(x) = x^2$ | $f(x) = x^2 + k$ | $f(x) = (x - k)^2$ |

**A reflection** flips the graph of the parent function over a line.

Parent function     Reflection in $x$-axis

**A vertical stretch or compression** changes the shape of the graph by multiplying all of the $y$-values by a factor.

$y = x^2$ **parent function**

$y = \frac{1}{2}x^2$ **vertical compression**

$y = 2x^2$ **vertical stretch**

### Common Errors With Transformations

**Translation errors** occur when students do not know in what direction to translate a graph. Vertical translations are relatively intuitive: $-k$ translates a graph down $k$ units while $k$ translates the graph up $k$ units. However, horizontal translations may confuse students because they are the opposite of what might be expected: $-h$ translates the graph right $h$ units while $h$ translates the graph left $h$ units.

FUNCTIONS, EQUATIONS, AND GRAPHS
# Pacing and Assignment Guide

| | | TRADITIONAL | | | BLOCK |
|---|---|---|---|---|---|
| **Lesson** | **Teaching Day(s)** | **Basic** | **Average** | **Advanced** | **Block** |
| **2-1** | 1 | Problems 1–4<br>Exs. 8–16, 40–52 | Problems 1–4<br>Exs. 9–15 odd, 40–52 | Problems 1–6<br>Exs. 9–25 odd, 27–39, 40–52 | **Day 1**<br>Problems 1–6<br>Exs. 9–25 odd, 27–34, 40–52 |
| | 2 | Problems 5–6<br>Exs. 17–32 | Problems 5–6<br>Exs. 17–25 odd, 27–34 | | |
| **2-2** | 1 | Problems 1–5<br>Exs. 7–29, 32–36 even, 46–48, 52, 57–73 | Problems 1–5<br>Exs. 7–29 odd, 30–53, 57–73 | Problems 1–5<br>Exs. 7–29 odd, 30–73 | **Day 2**<br>Problems 1–5<br>Exs. 7–29 odd, 30–53, 57–73 |
| **2-3** | 1 | Problems 1–4<br>Exs. 8–36, 44–56 even, 57–59, 63–72 | Problems 1–4<br>Exs. 9–35 odd, 37–61, 63–72 | Problems 1–4<br>Exs. 9–35 odd, 37–72 | Problems 1–4<br>Exs. 9–35 odd, 37–61, 63–72 |
| **2-4** | 1 | Problems 1–3<br>Exs. 10–25, 63–75 | Problems 1–6<br>Exs. 11–35 odd, 36–58, 63–75 | Problems 1–6<br>Exs. 11–35 odd, 36–75 | **Day 3**<br>Problems 1–6<br>Exs. 11–35 odd, 36–58, 63–75 |
| | 2 | Problems 4–6<br>Exs. 26–35, 38–44 even, 45, 46–56 even | | | |
| **2-5** | 1 | Problems 1–3<br>Exs. 7–18, 20–28 | Problems 1–3<br>Exs. 7–11 odd, 13–18, 20–28 | Problems 1–3<br>Exs. 7–11 odd, 13–28 | Problems 1–3<br>Exs. 7–11 odd, 13–18, 20–28 |
| **2-6** | 1 | Problems 1–3<br>Exs. 10–25, 37–39, 51–58 | Problems 1–3<br>Exs. 11–25 odd, 37–39, 51–58 | Problems 1–3<br>Exs. 11–25 odd, 37–39, 51–58 | **Day 4**<br>Problems 1–5<br>Exs. 11–33 odd, 34–45, 51–58 |
| | 2 | Problems 4–5<br>Exs. 26–36, 44, 45 | Problems 4–5<br>Exs. 27–33 odd, 34–36, 40–45 | Problems 4–5<br>Exs. 27–33 odd, 34–36, 40–50 | |
| **2-7** | 1 | Problems 1–3<br>Exs. 8–22, 51–64 | Problems 1–3<br>Exs. 9–21 odd, 51–64 | Problems 1–3<br>Exs. 9–21 odd, 51–64 | **Day 5**<br>Problems 1–5<br>Exs. 9–29 odd, 31–45, 51–64 |
| | 2 | Problems 4–5<br>Exs. 23–33, 40–44 even, 45 | Problems 4–5<br>Exs. 23–29 odd, 31–45 | Problems 4–5<br>Exs. 23–29 odd, 31–50 | |
| **2-8** | 1 | Problems 1–2<br>Exs. 8–17, 52–74 | Problems 1–2<br>Exs. 9–17 odd, 52–74 | Problems 1–2<br>Exs. 9–17 odd, 52–74 | **Day 6**<br>Problems 1–4<br>Exs. 9–29 odd, 30–46, 52–74 |
| | 2 | Problems 3–4<br>Exs. 18–29, 36–46 even | Problems 3–4<br>Exs. 19–29 odd, 30–46 | Problems 3–4<br>Exs. 19–29 odd, 30–51 | |
| **Review** | 1 | Chapter 2 Review | Chapter 2 Review | Chapter 2 Review | **Day 7**<br>Chapter 2 Review<br>Chapter 2 Test |
| **Assess** | 1 | Chapter 2 Test | Chapter 2 Test | Chapter 2 Test | |
| **Total** | | **15 Days** | **14 Days** | **13 Days** | **7 Days** |

Note: Pacing does not include Concept Bytes and other feature pages.

# Resources

| | For the Chapter | 2-1 | 2-2 | 2-3 | 2-4 | 2-5 | 2-6 | 2-7 | 2-8 |
|---|---|---|---|---|---|---|---|---|---|
| **Planning** | | | | | | | | | |
| Teacher Center Online Planner & Grade Book | I | I | I | I | I | I | I | I | I |
| **Interactive Learning & Guided Instruction** | | | | | | | | | |
| My Math Video | I | | | | | | | | |
| Solve It! | | I TM | I TM | I TM | I TM | I TM | I TM | I TM | I TM |
| Student Companion (SP)* | | P M | P M | P M | P M | P M | P M | P M | P M |
| Vocabulary Support | | I P M | I P M | I P M | I P M | I P M | I P M | I P M | I P M |
| Got It? Support | | I P | I P | I P | I P | I P | I P | I P | I P |
| Dynamic Activity | I | | | | | | I | I | I |
| Online Problems | | I | I | I | I | I | I | I | I |
| Additional Problems | | M | M | M | M | M | M | M | M |
| English Language Learner Support (TR) | | E P M | E P M | E P M | E P M | E P M | E P M | E P M | E P M |
| Activities, Games, and Puzzles | | E M | E M | E M | E M | E M | E M | E M | E M |
| Teaching With TI Technology With CD-ROM | | | | ✓ P | | ✓ P | ✓ P | ✓ P | ✓ P |
| TI-Nspire™ Support CD-ROM | | ✓ | ✓ | ✓ | ✓ | ✓ | ✓ | ✓ | ✓ |
| **Lesson Check & Practice** | | | | | | | | | |
| Student Companion (SP)* | | P M | P M | P M | P M | P M | P M | P M | P M |
| Lesson Check Support | | I P | I P | I P | I P | I P | I P | I P | I P |
| Practice and Problem Solving Workbook (SP) | | P | P | P | P | P | P | P | P |
| Think About a Plan (TR)* | | E P M | E P M | E P M | E P M | E P M | E P M | E P M | E P M |
| Practice Form G (TR)* | | E P M | E P M | E P M | E P M | E P M | E P M | E P M | E P M |
| Standardized Test Prep (TR)* | | P M | P M | P M | P M | P M | P M | P M | P M |
| Practice Form K (TR)* | | E P M | E P M | E P M | E P M | E P M | E P M | E P M | E P M |
| Extra Practice | E M | | | | | | | | |
| Find the Errors! | M | | | | | | | | |
| Enrichment (TR) | | E P M | E P M | E P M | E P M | E P M | E P M | E P M | E P M |
| Answers and Solutions CD-ROM | ✓ | ✓ | ✓ | ✓ | ✓ | ✓ | ✓ | ✓ | ✓ |
| **Assess & Remediate** | | | | | | | | | |
| ExamView CD-ROM | ✓ | ✓ | ✓ | ✓ | ✓ | ✓ | ✓ | ✓ | ✓ |
| Lesson Quiz | | I TM | I TM | I TM | I TM | I TM | I TM | I TM | I TM |
| Quizzes and Tests Form G (TR)* | E P M | | | | E P M | | | | E P M |
| Quizzes and Tests Form K (TR)* | E P M | | | | E P M | | | | E P M |
| Reteaching (TR)* | | E P M | E P M | E P M | E P M | E P M | E P M | E P M | E P M |
| Performance Tasks (TR)* | P M | | | | | | | | |
| Cumulative Review (TR)* | P M | | | | | | | | |
| Progress Monitoring Assessments | I P M | | | | | | | | |

(TR) Available in All-In-One Teaching Resources    * Spanish available

# 1 Interactive Learning

## Solve It!

**PURPOSE** Determine the mapping between the first 12 digits of a bar code and the check digit

**PROCESS** Students may try various strings of 12 numbers to get the same check digit or change the order of the first 12 digits to get a different check digit.

**FACILITATE** In a bar code, two digits identify a region, five digits identify the manufacturer, and five digits indicate the product. Digit 13 is a check that the scanner read the first 12 digits correctly.

> **Q** Study the diagram. What calculations are used on the first 12 digits to determine the check digit? **[Multiply the first digit and every other one after that by 1. Multiply the second digit and every other one by 3. Add all these products. Subtract the sum from the next greater multiple of 10.]**
>
> **Q** Could a different set of 12 numbers generate the same check digit, 9? Explain. **[Yes; any set whose sum is 9 less than a multiple of 10 would have 9 as the check digit.]**

**ANSWER** See Solve It in Answers on next page.
**CONNECT THE MATH** In the Solve It, students form correspondences between the set of strings of the first 12 digits and the set of possible check digits. After studying relations in the lesson, students will recognize that they can use these two sets to form a function.

# 2 Guided Instruction

## Take Note

Written in set notation, the relation in this Key Concept is $\{(-3, 4), (3, -1), (4, -1), (4, 3)\}$.

---

## 2-1 Relations and Functions

**Objectives** To graph relations
To identify functions

**Dynamic Activity** Function Explorer

**Lesson Vocabulary**
- relation
- domain
- range
- function
- vertical-line test
- function rule
- function notation
- independent variable
- dependent variable

You can use mappings to describe relationships between sets of numbers.

**Essential Understanding** A pairing of items from two sets is special if each item from one set pairs with exactly one item from the second set.

A **relation** is a set of pairs of input and output values. You can represent a relation in four different ways as shown below.

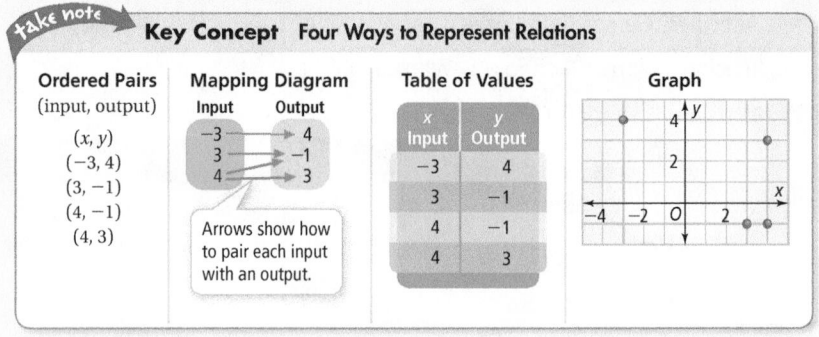

**take note**

**Key Concept** Four Ways to Represent Relations

60    Chapter 2   Functions, Equations, and Graphs

---

## 2-1 Preparing to Teach

### BIG idea Functions    UbD

**ESSENTIAL UNDERSTANDINGS**

- A pairing of items from two sets is special if each item from one set pairs with exactly one item from the second set.
- A relation is a set of pairs of input and output values.
- Relations can be represented with ordered pairs, mapping diagrams, tables of values, and graphs.

### Math Background

A relation is a set of ordered pairs. Some relations meet a special condition that makes them functions. In a function each item from the domain pairs with exactly one item from the range.
A relation is identified as a function if
- its graph passes the vertical line test,
- its domain values appear only once (in a list of ordered pairs, in a table, or on a mapping diagram), or

- its mapping diagram maps each input to only one output. (This means only one arrow can be drawn from each input value.)

### Support Student Learning

Use the **Algebra 2 Companion** to engage and support students during instruction. See Lesson Resources at the end of this lesson for details.

---

**PowerAlgebra.com**

## 1 Interactive Learning

### Solve It!

Step out how to solve the Problem with helpful hints and an online question. Other questions are listed above in Interactive Learning.

**Dynamic Activity** This activity allows students to create relations between two sets of data and then test those relations to determine if they are functions. They can view the output of their relation as ordered pairs and also as plotted points.

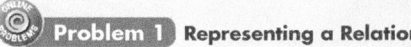 **Problem 1** Representing a Relation

**Skydiving** When skydivers jump out of an airplane, they experience free fall. The photos show various heights of a skydiver at different times during free fall, ignoring air resistance. How can you represent this relation in four different ways?

**Think**

What is the input? The output?
The input is the time. The output is the height above the ground.

(0 seconds, 10,000 ft)

(8 seconds, 8976 feet)

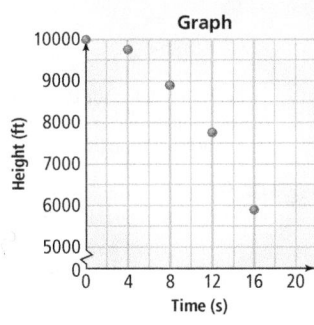

(12 seconds, 7696 feet)

(4 seconds, 9744 ft)

(16 seconds, 5904 feet)

**Mapping Diagram**

| Input | | Output |
|---|---|---|
| 0 | → | 10,000 |
| 4 | → | 9744 |
| 8 | → | 8976 |
| 12 | → | 7696 |
| 16 | → | 5904 |

**Ordered Pairs**

{(0, 10,000),
(4, 9744),
(8, 8976),
(12, 7696),
(16, 5904)}

**Table of Values**

| Time (s) | Height (ft) |
|---|---|
| 0 | 10,000 |
| 4 | 9744 |
| 8 | 8976 |
| 12 | 7696 |
| 16 | 5904 |

Each time value represents an input, which is paired with its corresponding output value (height).

**Graph**

 **Got It?** **1.** The monthly average water temperature of the Gulf of Mexico in Key West, Florida varies during the year. In January, the average water temperature is 69°F, in February, 70°F, in March, 75°F, and in April, 78°F. How can you represent this relation in four different ways?

The **domain** of a relation is the set of inputs, also called *x*-coordinates, of the ordered pairs. The **range** is the set of outputs, also called *y*-coordinates, of the ordered pairs.

---

**Problem 1**    VISUAL LEARNERS

**Q** What does each point in the graph represent? Explain. **[An ordered pair; the first coordinate is the number of seconds in the air; the second coordinate is the height in feet at that time.]**

**Q** Suppose you are given a relation only in table form and you need to graph the relation. How would you do it? **[Answers may vary. Sample: Use the values in the table to form ordered pairs and then graph them.]**

Insert parentheses and commas in a table to show an easy way to see the ordered pairs.

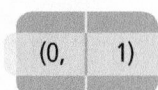

**ERROR PREVENTION**

Students sometimes misinterpret graphs that show elapsed time versus height, inferring that the graph shows a trajectory, or path of an object. Explain that the points do not show the path of the skydiver.

**Got It?**

**Q** What is the first fact given in the problem that contains a value? **[In January, the average water temperature is 69°F.]**

**Q** What is one way to form ordered pairs of numbers that represent months and temperatures? **[Answers may vary. Sample: Number the months of the year from 1 to 12. Use numbered months and temperature readings to form ordered pairs.]**

**Q** What are the domain and range for the Got It problem you just solved? **[domain: {1, 2, 3, 4}; range: {69, 70, 75, 78}]**

---

## 2 Guided Instruction

 Each Problem is worked out and supported online.

**Problem 1**
Representing a Relation

**Problem 2**
Finding Domain and Range

**Alternative Problem 2**
Finding Domain and Range
*Animated*

**Problem 3**
Identifying Functions

**Problem 4**
Using the Vertical-Line Test

**Problem 5**
Using Function Notation
*Animated*

**Problem 6**
Writing and Evaluating a Function
*Animated*

**Support in Algebra 2 Companion**
• Vocabulary
• Key Concepts
• Got It?

## Answers

### Solve It!

Sample: Yes, if the 12 digits are arranged in a different order by switching an even-placed digit and an odd-placed digit, they may generate two different check digits; yes, the sums of the products of the 12 digits can be equal even if the digits and/or products are not the same. This will generate the same check digit.

### Got It?

**1.** Let Jan = 1, Feb = 2, Mar = 3, and Apr = 4.

| Input | | Output |
|---|---|---|
| 1 | → | 69 |
| 2 | → | 70 |
| 3 | → | 75 |
| 4 | → | 78 |

{(1, 69), (2, 70),
(3, 75), (4, 78)}

| *x* Month | *y* Temperature (°F) |
|---|---|
| 1 | 69 |
| 2 | 70 |
| 3 | 75 |
| 4 | 78 |

**Lesson 2-1    61**

## Problem 2 — ERROR PREVENTION

Students may mistakenly omit parentheses when writing a relation as ordered pairs or include them when writing a domain or range. Parentheses are used in a relation to indicate ordered pairs but are not used in a domain or range because there are no ordered pairs in a domain or range.

### Got It?

**Q** If you graph these points, will any two of them fall directly above one another? Why? **[No; the x-values of each point are different.]**

### Problem 3

**Q** How many ordered pairs are represented in the relation in 3A? Explain. **[3; there are 3 arrows in the mapping diagram.]**

**Q** If you represent this relation with a mapping diagram, how many arrows would point *from* the domain element 4 in 3B? Explain. **[2; there are 2 ordered pairs that have 4 as the x-coordinate.]**

### Got It?

Ask the following after solving the problem.

**Q** What would you change in 3a to make the relation a function? **[Remove either arrow from 2.]**

**Q** What change would make 3b only a relation, not a function? **[Sample: Change 9 to 14.]**

### Here's Why It Works

**Q** Does the diagram show a relation that is a function? Explain. **[No; two different range elements, $y_1$ and $y_2$, correspond to the single domain element $x$.]**

---

**Think**

**How could you use the mapping diagram in Problem 1 to find the domain and range?**
The *input* corresponds to the domain of the relation. The *output* corresponds to the range.

**Plan**

**How can you use a mapping diagram to determine whether a relation is a function?**
A function has only one arrow from each element of the domain.

---

**Problem 2** Finding Domain and Range

**Use the relation from Problem 1. What are the domain and range of the relation?**

The relation is $\{(0, 10{,}000), (4, 9744), (8, 8976), (12, 7696), (16, 5904)\}$.

The domain is the set of $x$-coordinates.　　$\{0, 4, 8, 12, 16\}$

The range is the set of $y$-coordinates.　　$\{10{,}000, 9744, 8976, 7696, 5904\}$

**Got It? 2.** What are the domain and range of this relation?
$\{(-3, 14), (0, 7), (2, 0), (9, -18), (23, -99)\}$

A **function** is a relation in which each element of the domain corresponds with exactly one element of the range.

**Problem 3** Identifying Functions

**Is the relation a function?**

**A**

Each element in the domain corresponds with exactly one element in the range. This relation is a function.

**B** $\{(4, -1), (8, 6), (1, -1), (6, 6), (4, 1)\}$

Each $x$-coordinate must correspond to only one $y$-coordinate. The $x$-coordinate 4 corresponds to $-1$ and 1. The relation is *not* a function.

**Got It? 3.** Is the relation a function?

**a.** Domain　Range

**b.** $\{(-7, 14), (9, -7), (14, 7), (7, 14)\}$

**c. Reasoning** How does a mapping diagram of a relation that is not a function differ from a mapping diagram of a function?

You can use the *vertical-line test* to determine whether a relation is a function. The **vertical-line test** states that if a vertical line passes through more than one point on the graph of a relation, then the relation is *not* a function.

**Here's Why It Works** If a vertical line passes through a graph at more than one point, there is more than one value in the range that corresponds to one value in the domain.

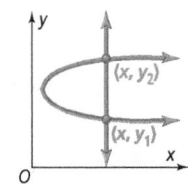

---

## Additional Problems

**1.** In 2000, the 4 most populous states (in millions), were CA (32), TX (21), NY (19), and FL (16). The numbers of U.S. Representatives were CA (53), TX (32), NY (29), and FL (25). How can you represent a relation for these data in 4 different ways?

**ANSWERS**

$\{(32, 53), (21, 32), (19, 29), (16, 25)\}$

| Pop. in Millions | No. of Reps |
|---|---|
| 32 | 53 |
| 21 | 32 |
| 19 | 29 |
| 16 | 25 |

**2.** What are the domain and range of the relation in Additional Problem 1?

**ANSWER**
domain: {32, 21, 19, 16}
range: {53, 32, 29, 25}

**3.** Is the relation a function?

**a.** Domain　Range

**b.** $\{(0, 0), (2, 4), (-2, 4), (3, 9), (-3, 9)\}$

**ANSWERS a.** no **b.** yes

**4.** Use the vertical-line test. Which graph(s) represent functions?

**A.** 　　**B.**

**ANSWER** graph **A**

**5.** For $f(x) = -3x + 2$, what is the output for the input $-4$, 0, and 0.2?

**ANSWERS** 14, 2, and 1.4

**6.** A pizza costs $14; the flat delivery fee is $1.50. What function rule models the total cost of the number of pizzas delivered? Evaluate for 5 pizzas.

**ANSWER** $C(p) = 14p + 1.50$; $p$ is number of pizzas; $C(p)$ is total cost; $71.50.

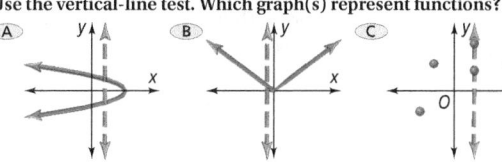

**Problem 4** Using the Vertical-Line Test

Use the vertical-line test. Which graph(s) represent functions?

**Think**

Is a relation a function if it passes through the y-axis twice?
No; the y-axis is a vertical line so the relation fails the vertical-line test.

Graphs A and C fail the vertical-line test because for each graph, a vertical line passes through more than one point. They do not represent functions. Graph B does not fail the vertical-line test so it represents a function.

 **Got It?** **4.** Use the vertical-line test. Which graph(s) represent functions?

A **function rule** is an equation that represents an output value in terms of an input value. You can write a function rule in **function notation**. Shown below are examples of function rules.

$$y = 3x + 2 \qquad f(x) = 3x + 2 \qquad f(1) = 3(1) + 2$$

Output | Input | Read as "*f* of *x*" or "function *f* of *x*." | "*f* of 1" is the output when 1 is the input.

The **independent variable**, $x$, represents the input of the function. The **dependent variable**, $f(x)$, represents the output of the function. It is called the dependent variable because its value depends on the input value.

 **Problem 5** Using Function Notation

**Plan**

How do you find the output?
Substitute the input into the function rule and simplify.

For $f(x) = -2x + 5$, what is the output for the inputs, $-3, 0,$ and $\frac{1}{4}$?

| x Input | Function Rule $f(x) = -2x + 5$ | f(x) Output |
|---|---|---|
| $-3$ | $f(-3) = -2(-3) + 5$ | 11 |
| 0 | $f(0) = -2(0) + 5$ | 5 |
| $\frac{1}{4}$ | $f\left(\frac{1}{4}\right) = -2\left(\frac{1}{4}\right) + 5$ | $4\frac{1}{2}$ |

**Got It?** **5.** For $f(x) = -4x + 1$, what is the output for the given input?
**a.** $-2$      **b.** 0      **c.** 5

PowerAlgebra.com      Lesson 2-1   Relations and Functions      63

---

**Problem 4**

**Q** How many vertical lines does it take to make a graph fail the vertical line test? **[one]**

**Q** In 4A, is the dashed vertical line the only line that makes the graph fail the test? Explain. **[No; a vertical line through any point of the graph except the rightmost point on the *x*-axis would pass through two points.]**

**Q** In 4B, the dashed vertical line intersects the graph in only one point. Could you conclude the graph represents a function? Explain. **[No; if another vertical line intersected the graph in more than one point, the graph would not represent a function.]**

**Got It?**      **ERROR PREVENTION**

Students may think 4b is not a function because its graph consists of only a few ordered pairs. Whether or not a relation is a function has nothing to do with how many ordered pairs are in the relation.

**Problem 5**      **ERROR PREVENTION**

Students sometimes think that $f(x)$ means the variable $f$ times the variable $x$. $f(x)$ is function notation and does not indicate multiplication.

**Got It?**

**Q** How do you write *f of negative two*? **[f(−2)]**

**Q** What does *f of negative two* equal? Explain. **[9; it is the output of the function *f* for the input −2.]**

---

# Answers

### Got It? (continued)

**2.** domain: $\{-3, 0, 2, 9, 23\}$, range: $\{-99, -18, 0, 7, 14\}$

**3. a.** no

  **b.** yes

  **c.** In a mapping diagram for a relation that is not a function, there is at least one element in the domain that has more than one arrow originating from it. In a mapping diagram for a function, each element in the domain has one arrow originating from it.

**4.** b and c

**5. a.** 9

  **b.** 1

  **c.** −19

**Lesson 2-1**   63

## Problem 6

**Q** What are the input and output? **[input: tickets bought; output: total cost]**

**Q** What does it mean to evaluate the function for 4 tickets? **[Use 4 as an input and find the numerical value of the expression equal to C(4).]**

### Got It?

**Q** How are the operations in this function different from the function in Problem 6? Explain. **[Sample: The function in Problem 6 contains multiplication and addition. This function has no addition since there is no other fee.]**

# 3 Lesson Check

### Do you know HOW?   ERROR INTERVENTION

- In Exercise 1, if students list 3 and 4 twice in the domain and −2 twice in the range, remind them to list each element once, no matter how many times it occurs in the ordered pairs.

### Do you UNDERSTAND?

- For Exercise 7, draw a horizontal line intersecting a graph in 2 points. Explain that this represents 2 inputs with the same output, which does *not* invalidate a function.

### Close

**Q** What are three methods you can use to determine whether a relation is a function? **[Mapping diagram: only one arrow from each domain element. List of ordered pairs and table of values: no repeated first coordinate. Graph: no vertical line that intersects the graph in more than one point.]**

---

To model a real-world situation using a function rule, you need to identify the dependent and independent quantities. One way to describe the dependence of a variable quantity is to use a phrase such as, "distance is a function of time." This means that distance *depends* on time.

 **Problem 6** Writing and Evaluating a Function

**Ticket Price** Tickets to a concert are available online for $35 each plus a handling fee of $2.50. The total cost is a function of the number of tickets bought. What function rule models the cost of the concert tickets? Evaluate the function for 4 tickets.

 **Think**

**Why is cost the dependent quantity?**
Cost is dependent because the cost depends on the number of tickets bought.

Cost is the dependent quantity and the number of tickets is the independent quantity.

| **Relate** | Total cost | is | cost per ticket | times | number of tickets bought | plus | handling fee |
|---|---|---|---|---|---|---|---|

**Define**   Let $t$ = number of tickets bought.
Let $C(t)$ = the total cost.

| **Write** | $C(t)$ | = | 35 | · | $t$ | + | 2.50 |
|---|---|---|---|---|---|---|---|

$C(t) = 35t + 2.50$

$C(4) = 35 \cdot 4 + 2.50$   Substitute 4 for $t$.

$= 142.50$   Simplify.

The cost of 4 tickets is $142.50.

**Got It?  6.** You are buying bottles of a sports drink for a softball team. Each bottle costs $1.19. What function rule models the total cost of a purchase? Evaluate the function for 15 bottles.

### Lesson Check

**Do you know HOW?**

List the domain and range of each relation.

**1.** $\{(3, -2), (4, 4), (0, -2), (4, 1), (3, 2)\}$

**2.** $\{(0, 4), (4, 0), (-3, -4), (-4, -3)\}$

Determine whether each relation is a function.

**3.** $\{(3, -8), (-9, 1), (3, 2), (-4, 1), (-11, -2)\}$

**4.** $\{(1, 1), (2, 0), (3, 1), (4, 3), (0, 2)\}$

**Do you UNDERSTAND?**

**5. Vocabulary** Can you have a relation that is not a function? Can you have a function that is not a relation? Explain.

**6. Error Analysis** Your friend writes, "In a function, every vertical line must intersect the graph in exactly one point." Explain your friend's error and rewrite the statement so that it is correct.

**7. Reasoning** Why is there no horizontal-line test for functions?

---

## 3 Lesson Check

For a digital lesson check, use the Got It questions.

**Support in Algebra 2 Companion**
- Lesson Check

## 4 Practice

Assign homework to individual students or to an entire class.

---

## Answers

### Got It? (continued)

**6.** Let $x$ = number of bottles purchased and $C$ = total cost; $C(x) = 1.19x$; $17.85

### Lesson Check

**1.** domain: $\{0, 3, 4\}$, range: $\{-2, 1, 2, 4\}$

**2.** domain: $\{-4, -3, 0, 4\}$, range: $\{-4, -3, 0, 4\}$

**3.** no

**4.** yes

**5.** Yes; a relation is any set of pairs of input and output values. No; a function is a relation in which each element of the domain is paired with exactly one element of the range.

**6.** *Every* vertical line does not need to intersect a function. Rewrite as: "In a function, every vertical line must intersect the graph in *at most* one point."

**7.** A horizontal-line test checks the pairing of one element of the range with one or more elements of the domain. A function can have a pairing of one element of the range with *one or more* elements of the domain. A horizontal-line test cannot determine whether a relation is a function.

## Practice and Problem-Solving Exercises

**Ⓐ Practice**

Every year, the Rock and Roll Hall of Fame and Museum inducts legendary musicians and musical acts to the Hall. The table shows the number of inductees for each year.

◀ See Problems 1 and 2.

**8.** Represent the data using each of the following:
   **a.** a mapping diagram
   **b.** ordered pairs
   **c.** a graph on the coordinate plane

**9.** What are the domain and range of this relation?

**Rock and Roll Hall of Fame Inductees**

| Year | Number of Inductees | Year | Number of Inductees |
|------|------|------|------|
| 2001 | 11 | 2004 | 8 |
| 2002 | 8 | 2005 | 7 |
| 2003 | 9 | 2006 | 6 |

Source: Rock and Roll Hall of Fame

Determine whether each relation is a function.

◀ See Problem 3.

**10.**    **11.**    **12.**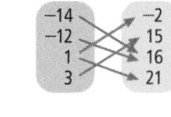

**13.** $\{(3, -9), (11, 21), (121, 34), (34, 1), (23, 45)\}$

Use the vertical-line test to determine whether each graph represents a function.

◀ See Problem 4.

**14.**    **15.**    **16.**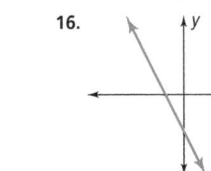

Evaluate each function for the given value of $x$, and write the input $x$ and output $f(x)$ as an ordered pair.

◀ See Problem 5.

**17.** $f(x) = 17x + 3$ for $x = 4$

**18.** $f(x) = -\frac{2x + 1}{3}$ for $x = -5$

**19.** $f(x) = 2x - 33$ for $x = 9$

**20.** $f(x) = -9x - 2$ for $x = 7$

**21.** $f(x) = \frac{7}{3}x - 9$ for $x = 3$

**22.** $f(x) = -\frac{12x}{5}$ for $x = -1$

**23.** $f(x) = 11x - 11$ for $x = -11$

**24.** $f(x) = \frac{2}{9}x - \frac{9}{2}$ for $x = 9$

Write a function rule to model the cost per month of a long-distance cell phone calling plan. Then evaluate the function for the given number of minutes.

◀ See Problem 6.

**25.** Monthly service fee: $4.52
   Rate: $.12 per minute
   Minutes used: 250

**26.** Monthly service fee: $3.12
   Rate: $.18 per minute
   Minutes used: 175

---

**ASSIGNMENT GUIDE**

Basic: 8–26, 27–32

Average: 9–25 odd, 27–34

Advanced: 9–25 odd, 27–39

Standardized Test Prep: 40–43

Mixed Review: 44–52

**Reasoning** exercises have blue headings.

**Applications** exercises have red headings.

**EXERCISE 28:** Use the Think About a Plan worksheet in the **Practice and Problem Solving Workbook** (also available in the Teaching Resources in print and online) to further support students' development in becoming independent learners.

**HOMEWORK QUICK CHECK**

To check students' understanding of key skills and concepts, go over Exercises 9, 11, 27, 28, and 32.

---

## Practice and Problem-Solving Exercises

**8.** Let 1 represent 2001, 2 represent 2002, and so forth.

  **a.**

  **b.** $\{(1, 11), (2, 8), (3, 9), (4, 8), (5, 7), (6, 6)\}$

  **c.**

**Rock and Roll Hall of Fame Inductees**

**9.** domain: $\{1, 2, 3, 4, 5, 6\}$,
   range: $\{6, 7, 8, 9, 11\}$

**10.** no

**11.** yes

**12.** no

**13.** yes

**14.** no

**15.** yes

**16.** yes

**17.** 71; (4, 71)

**18.** 3; (−5, 3)

**19.** −15; (9, −15)

**20.** −65; (7, −65)

**21.** −2; (3, −2)

**22.** $\frac{12}{5}$; $\left(-1, \frac{12}{5}\right)$

**23.** −132; (−11, −132)

**24.** $-\frac{5}{2}$; $\left(9, -\frac{5}{2}\right)$

**25.** $C(m) = 4.52 + 0.12m$; $34.52

**26.** $C(m) = 3.12 + 0.18m$; $34.62

# Answers

## Practice and Problem-Solving
## Exercises (continued)

**27.** 13.5 cm$^2$

**28.** $S(h) = 32 + 16h$; 136 in.$^2$

**29.** domain: all real numbers, range: $y \geq 0$; yes

**30.** domain: $-3 \leq x \leq 3$, range: $-1 \leq y \leq 1$; no

**31.** $\approx 4849$ cm$^3$

**32. a.** $C(m) = 18 + 0.32m$

  **b.** $C(m) = 12 + 0.36m$

  **c.** Proxy

**33. a.** 109.4

  **b.** 10.4

  **c.** $-11.\overline{1}$

  **d.** $-7.\overline{2}$

**34. a.** into

  **b.** into

  **c.** onto

  **d.** into

**35.** $f(x) - g(x) = (3x - 21) - (3x + 21)$
        $= 3x - 21 - 3x - 21 = -42$

**36.** Yes; each nonzero $x$ is paired with a unique $y$.

**37.** No; each $x > \frac{7}{3}$ is paired with two $y$ values.

**38.** Yes; each $x$ is paired with a unique $y$.

---

 **Apply**

**27. Think About a Plan** A cube is a solid figure with six square faces. If the edges of a cube have length 1.5 cm, what is the surface area of the cube?
  • What is the relationship between the length of the edges and the area of each face?
  • What is the relationship between the area of one face and the surface area of the whole cube?

**28. Geometry** Suppose you have a box with a $4 \times 4$-in. square base and variable height $h$. The surface area of this box is a function of its height. Write a function to represent the surface area. Evaluate the function for $h = 6.5$ in.

**Find the domain and range of each relation, and determine whether it is a function.**

**29.**

**30.**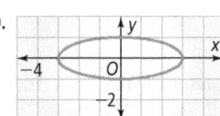

**31. Geometry** The volume of a sphere is a function of its radius, $V = \frac{4}{3}\pi r^3$. Evaluate the function for the volume of a volleyball with radius 10.5 cm.

**32. Car Rental** You are considering renting a car from two different rental companies. Proxy car rental company charges $.32 per mile plus an $18 surcharge. YourPal rental company charges $.36 per mile plus a $12 surcharge.
  **a.** Write a function that shows the cost of renting a car from Proxy.
  **b.** Write a function that shows the cost of renting a car from YourPal.
  **c.** Which company offers the better deal for an 820-mile trip?

**33. Temperature** The relation between degrees Fahrenheit $F$ and degrees Celsius $C$ is described by the function $F = \frac{9}{5}C + 32$. In the following ordered pairs, the first element is degrees Celsius and the second element is its equivalent in degrees Fahrenheit. Find the unknown measure in each ordered pair.

  **a.** $(43, m)$      **b.** $(-12, n)$      **c.** $(p, 12)$      **d.** $(q, 19)$

**34. Reasoning** Suppose a function pairs items from set $A$ with items from set $B$. You can say that the function maps *into* set $B$. If the function uses every item from set $B$, the function maps *onto* set $B$. Does each function below map the set of whole numbers *into* or *onto* the set of whole numbers?
  **a.** Function $f$ doubles every number.
  **b.** Function $g$ maps every number to 1 greater than that number.
  **c.** Function $h$ maps every number to itself.
  **d.** Function $j$ maps every number to its square.

 **Challenge**

**35. Reasoning** Given the functions $f(x) = 3x - 21$ and $g(x) = 3x + 21$, show that the function $f(x) - g(x)$ is a constant for all the values of $x$.

**Determine whether $y$ is a function of $x$. Explain.**

**36.** $y = \frac{3}{x} - 11$      **37.** $y^2 = 3x - 7$      **38.** $x^2 = 3y + y$

**39. Chemistry** The time required for a certain chemical reaction is related to the amount of catalyst present during the reaction. The domain of the relation is the number of grains of catalyst, and the range is the number of seconds required for a fixed amount of the chemical to react. The table shows the data from several reactions.
**a.** Is the relation a function?
**b.** If the domain and range were interchanged, would the relation be a function? Explain.

### Catalyst and Reaction Time

| Number of Grains | Number of Seconds |
|---|---|
| 2.0 | 180 |
| 2.5 | 6 |
| 2.7 | 0.05 |
| 2.9 | 0.001 |
| 3.0 | 6 |
| 3.1 | 15 |
| 3.2 | 37 |
| 3.3 | 176 |

## Standardized Test Prep

 SAT/ACT

**40.** If $f(x) = -3x + 7$ and $g(x) = -7x + 3$, what is the value of $f(-3) - g(3)$?

Ⓐ 40          Ⓑ 34          Ⓒ 8          Ⓓ -8

**41.** What is the formula for the volume of a cylinder, $V = \pi r^2 h$, solved for $h$?

Ⓕ $h = \frac{r^2}{\pi V}$          Ⓖ $h = \frac{\pi V}{r^2}$          Ⓗ $h = \frac{V}{\pi r^2}$          Ⓘ $h = \frac{\pi r^2}{V}$

**42.** Which of the following statements are true?

I. $-(-6) = 6$ and $-(-4) > -4$          III. $5 + 6 = 11$ or $9 - 2 = 11$

II. $-(-4) < 4$ or $-10 > 10 - 10$          IV. $17 > 2$ or $6 < 9$

Ⓐ I and II only          Ⓑ I, II, and III only          Ⓒ I, III, and IV only          Ⓓ III and IV only

**Short Response**

**43.** What are the numbers $1.9$, $\frac{5}{4}$, $-1.2$, and $\sqrt{3}$ in order from greatest to least?

## Mixed Review

Solve each equation or inequality.                     **See Lessons 1-5 and 1-6.**

**44.** $|3x + 9| = 11$          **45.** $19 + |x - 1| = 33$          **46.** $2 - 3x < 11$

**47.** $5x - 3 \leq 12 - 5x$          **48.** $|2x| + 4 < 7$          **49.** $4x + 6 \geq -6$

**Get Ready!**   To prepare for Lesson 2-2, do Exercises 50–52.          **See Lesson 1-4.**

Solve each equation for $y$.

**50.** $12y = 3x$          **51.** $-10y = 5x$          **52.** $\frac{3}{4}y = 15x$

---

**39. a.** yes
**b.** No; 6 would be paired with both 2.5 and 3.

## Standardized Test Prep
**40.** B
**41.** H
**42.** C

**43.** [2] $1.9$, $\sqrt{3}$, $\frac{5}{4}$, $-1.2$

[1] incorrect placement of one number

## Mixed Review
**44.** $\frac{2}{3}$, $-\frac{20}{3}$

**45.** $-13$, $15$

**46.** $x > -3$

**47.** $x \leq \frac{3}{2}$

**48.** $-\frac{3}{2} < x < \frac{3}{2}$

**49.** $x \geq -3$

**50.** $\frac{1}{4}x$

**51.** $-\frac{1}{2}x$

**52.** $20x$

# Lesson Resources

# Differentiated Remediation
Available in editable format online.

## Additional Instructional Support

### Algebra 2 Companion
Students can use the **Algebra 2 Companion** worktext (4 pages) as you teach the lesson. Use the Companion to support

- New Vocabulary
- Key Concepts
- Got It for each Problem
- Lesson Check

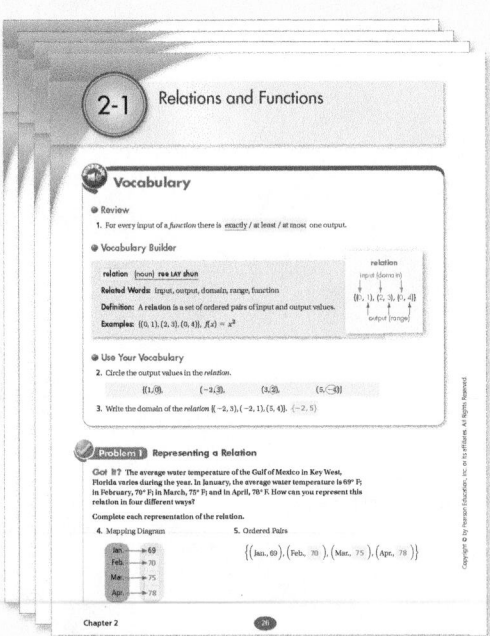

### ELL Support
**Use Graphic Organizers** Have students make a graphic organizer for the bulletin board such as the one shown below to show the domain and range in different situations.

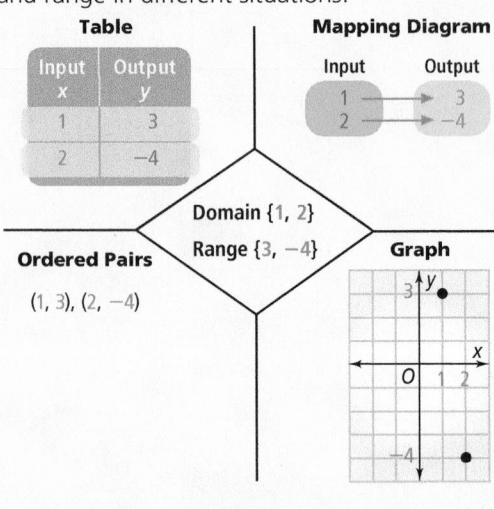

## 5 Assess & Remediate

### Lesson Quiz

1. **Do you UNDERSTAND?** The numbers of tickets sold for a talent show were grade 9: 22; grade 10: 32; grade 11: 41; and grade 12: 30. How can you represent this relation as a mapping diagram?

2. What are the domain and range in Problem 1?

3. **Do you UNDERSTAND?** Is the relation a function? Explain.
$\{(-2, 3), (-1, 2), (0, 2), (-2, 9)\}$

4. Which graph(s) represent a function?

a.    b.

5. Bowling costs $4.50 per game. Shoe rental costs $3.75. The total cost is a function of the number of games. What function rule models the total cost of games and shoe rental? Evaluate the function for 3 games.

### ANSWERS TO LESSON QUIZ

1.
| Input | Output |
|-------|--------|
| 9 | 22 |
| 10 | 32 |
| 11 | 41 |
| 12 | 30 |

2. domain: {9, 10, 11, 12}
range: {22, 32, 41, 30}

3. No; $-2$ is paired with two numbers.

4. graph a

5. $C(g) = 4.50g + 3.75$; $g$ is number of games; $C(g)$ is total cost; for 3 games, the cost is $17.25.

### PRESCRIPTION FOR REMEDIATION
Use the student work on the Lesson Quiz to prescribe a differentiated review assignment:

| Points | Differentiated Remediation |
|--------|---------------------------|
| 0–2 | Intervention |
| 3–4 | On-level |
| 5 | Extension |

**PowerAlgebra.com**

**5 Assess & Remediate**
Assign the Lesson Quiz. Appropriate intervention, practice, or enrichment is automatically generated based on student performance.

## Intervention

- **Reteaching** (2 pages) Provides reteaching and practice exercises for the key lesson concepts. Use with struggling students or absent students.

- **English Language Learner Support** Helps students develop and reinforce mathematical vocabulary and key concepts.

### All-in-One Resources/Online
**Reteaching**

**2-1 Reteaching**
Relations and Functions

- A **relation** is a set of ordered pairs.
- The **domain** is the set of the first numbers in each pair, or the *x*-values.
- The **range** is the set of the second numbers in each pair, or the *y*-values.
- A relation is a **function** if each input value *x* corresponds to exactly one output value *y*. In a set of ordered pairs for a function, an *x*-value cannot be repeated with two or more different *y*-values.

**Problem**
Roll a number cube to find six ordered pairs. Determine whether the set of ordered pairs is a function. Find the domain and range.

Roll a number cube six times to get the *x*-values of the six ordered pairs. Roll it six more times to get the *y*-values of the ordered pairs.

{(6, 1), (2, 1), (5, 4), (2, 2), (1, 4), (4, 2)}   Write the ordered pairs.

{(6, 1), (2, 1), (5, 4), (2, 2), (1, 4), (4, 2)}   Circle any *x*-values that repeat with different *y*-values to determine whether the relation is a function.

The *x*-value 2 is repeated with two different *y*-values so the relation is not a function.

The domain is the set of first numbers in each pair: {1, 2, 4, 5, 6}.
The range is the set of second numbers in each pair: {1, 2, 4}.

**Exercises**
Roll a number cube to find the indicated number of ordered pairs. Determine whether each set of ordered pairs is a function. Find the domain and range of each relation.

1. 5 ordered pairs   2. 4 ordered pairs   3. 6 ordered pairs   4. 8 ordered pairs
Check students' work.

Determine whether each relation is a function. Explain your answer. Find the domain and range of each relation.

5. {(1, 2), (1, 3), (1, 4), (1, 5), (1, 6)}
No; the *x*-value 1 is repeated with different *y*-values; domain: {1}; range: {2, 3, 4, 5, 6}

6. {(0, −1), (1, 2), (−1, −1), (−2, 5), (2, 9)}
Yes; no *x*-value is repeated; domain: {−2, −1, 0, 1, 2}; range: {−1, 2, 5, 9}

7. {(A, B), (C, D), (E, F), (G, H)}
Yes; no *x*-value is repeated; domain: {A, C, E, G}; range: {B, D, F, H}

8. {(L, M), (N, P), (L, T), (L, P)}
No; the *x*-value L is repeated with different *y*-values; domain: {L, N}; range: {M, P, T}

9. {(0, 0)}
Yes; no *x*-value is repeated; domain: {0}; range: {0}

10. {(½, 3), (0.5, 4), (2, 1)}
No; the *x*-value ½ = 0.5 is repeated with different *y*-values; domain: {½, 2}; range: {1, 3, 4}

### All-in-One Resources/Online
**English Language Learner Support**

**2-1 ELL Support**
Relations and Functions

Complete the vocabulary chart by filling in the missing information.

| Word or Word Phrase | Definition | Picture or Example |
|---------------------|------------|--------------------|
| relation | A relation is a set of ordered pairs of input and output values. | (table) (0, 2), (−4, 2), (−2, −9) |
| function | A function is a relation where each *x*-coordinate corresponds to only one *y*-coordinate. | 2. Answers may vary. Sample: {(−3, 1), (5, 9), (3, −3)} |
| domain | 3. Answers may vary. Sample: The domain is the set of inputs, also called the *x*-coordinates, of the ordered pairs. | (table) The domain is {−2, −1, 0, 1, 2}. |
| range | The range is the set of outputs, also called the *y*-coordinates, of the ordered pairs. | (table) Answers may vary. Sample: The range is {−3, −2, −1, 0, 1}. |
| function notation | Function notation is a way to write a function rule. | 4. Answers may vary. Sample: $f(x) = -2x + 5$, read as "*f* of *x*" |

# Differentiated Remediation *continued*

Available in editable format online.

---

## On-Level

- **Practice** (2 pages) Provides extra practice for each lesson. For simpler practice exercises, use the Form K Practice pages found in the All-in-One Teaching Resources and online.

- **Think About a Plan** Helps students develop specific problem-solving skills and strategies by providing scaffolded guiding questions.

- **Standardized Test Prep** Focuses on all major exercises, all major question types, and helps students prepare for the high-stakes assessments.

## Extension

- **Enrichment** Provides students with interesting problems and activities that extend the concepts of the lesson.

- **Activities, Games, and Puzzles** Worksheets that can be used for concepts development, enrichment, and for fun!

---

### Practice and Problem Solving Wkbk/All-in-One Resources/Online
#### Practice page 1

### Practice and Problem Solving Wkbk/All-in-One Resources/Online
#### Practice page 2

### All-in-One Resources/Online
#### Enrichment

**2-1 Enrichment**
Relations and Functions

Although relations can be defined on arbitrary sets, we shall confine our attention to relations in the xy-plane. A relation is said to be reflexive if for any real number x in the domain of the relation, the point (x, x) belongs to the relation.

1. How can you tell geometrically whether a relation is reflexive?
   The graph of the relation must contain the line y = x.

A relation is said to be symmetric if whenever (x, y) belongs to the relation, (y, x) also belongs to the relation. A relation is asymmetric if whenever (x, y) belongs to the relation (y, x) does not belong to the relation.

2. What can you say about a relation that is both symmetric and asymmetric?
   The relation is empty.

A relation is said to be transitive if whenever both (x, y) and (y, z) belong to the relation, (x, z) also belongs to the relation. If a relation is reflexive, symmetric, and transitive, it is said to be an equivalence relation.

Decide whether each of the following relations is reflexive, symmetric, asymmetric, transitive, or an equivalence relation.

3. the set of all pairs of real numbers (x, y) such that x = y  equivalence relation
4. the set of all pairs of real numbers (x, y) such that x ≥ y  reflexive, transitive
5. the set of all pairs of real numbers (x, y) such that x > y  asymmetric, transitive
6. the set of all pairs of real numbers (x, y) such that y = 2x  none
7. the set of all pairs of real numbers (x, y) such that xy is positive  symmetric, transitive
8. the set of all pairs of real numbers (x, y) such that x is an integer  transitive
9. the set of all pairs of real numbers (x, y) such that xy = 0  symmetric
10. the set of all pairs of real numbers (x, y) such that x + y = 1  symmetric
11. the set of all pairs of real numbers (x, y) such that x ≤ y + 1  reflexive
12. the set of all pairs of real numbers (x, y) such that y ≠ 0 when x = 0  symmetric
13. the set of all pairs of real numbers (x, y) such that xy ≠ 0  symmetric, transitive
14. the set of all pairs of real numbers (x, y) such that x < 0  symmetric
15. the set of all pairs of real numbers (x, y) such that x is an integer and y is not an integer  asymmetric

---

### Practice and Problem Solving Wkbk/All-in-One Resources/Online
#### Think About a Plan

**2-1 Think About a Plan**
Relations and Functions

**Geometry** Suppose you have a box with a 4 × 4-in. square base and variable height h. The surface area of this box is a function of its height. Write a function to represent the surface area. Evaluate the function for h = 6.5 in.

**Understanding the Problem**

1. The width of the box is [4] inches. The length of the box is [4] inches. The height of the box is [h] inches.

2. What is the problem asking you to determine?
   A function that gives the surface area of a box with dimensions 4 in. × 4 in. × h in., and the surface area when h = 6.5 in.

**Planning the Solution**

3. What is the area of the top of the box? What is the area of the bottom of the box?
   16 in.²; 16 in.²

4. What is the total area of the top and the bottom of the box?
   32 in.²

5. What is the area of each side of the box?
   4h in.²

6. What is the total area of the sides of the box?
   16h in.²

**Getting an Answer**

7. Write a function to represent the surface area of the box.
   s(h) = 16h + 32

8. Evaluate your function for h = 6.5 inches.
   136 in.²

### Practice and Problem Solving Wkbk/All-in-One Resources/Online
#### Standardized Test Prep

**2-1 Standardized Test Prep**
Relations and Functions

**Multiple Choice**

For Exercises 1–4, choose the correct letter.

1. Which relations are functions? A

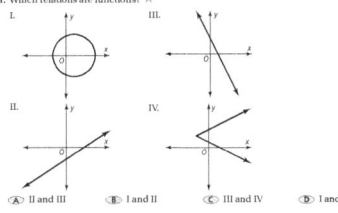

   Ⓐ II and III    Ⓑ I and II    Ⓒ III and IV    Ⓓ I and IV

2. Which point could not be part of a function that includes (3, −1), (4, 2), (5, 4), (−2, 0), and (8, −3)? G
   Ⓕ (6, −7)    Ⓖ (3, −2)    Ⓗ (7, 4)    Ⓘ (2, 2)

3. For the function f(x) = −4x − 3, which of the following is f(−2)? C
   Ⓐ −11    Ⓑ −2    Ⓒ 5    Ⓓ 11

4. What is the domain of the relation given by the ordered pairs G
   (2, −1), (−4, 1), (−2, −1), (3, −3), (2, 3)
   Ⓕ {−3, −2, 1, 3}    Ⓖ {−4, −2, 2, 3}    Ⓗ {−3, −1, 1, 3}    Ⓘ {−4, −1, 1, 3}

**Short Response**

5. A phone store employee earns a salary of $450 per week plus 10% commission on her weekly sales.
   a. What function rule models the employee's weekly earnings?
   b. If the employee earned $570 in a week, what was the amount of her sales for that week?
   [2] a. f(x) = 0.1x + 450  b. $1200
   [1] incorrect function rule OR incorrect sales amount
   [0] no answers given

### Online Teacher Resource Center
#### Activities, Games, and Puzzles

**2-1 Activity: Real-Life Relations and Functions**
Relations and Functions

This activity should be done in groups of 3 to 5 students, with each group completing the entire sheet.

**Relations That Are Not Functions**

Here is an ad for a roofing company from a telephone book. Discuss why this is not a function if:
- domain: roofing companies;
- range: telephone numbers.
  Check students' work.

**Acme Roofing Co.**
(555) 314-1592
(555) 271-8281

Use the spaces below to explain why the following are not functions:
- **Domain:** teachers; **range:** students assigned to each teacher
  Answers may vary. Sample: Any teacher will have more than one student in class.
- **Domain:** all students; **range:** each student's biological parents
  Answers may vary. Sample: Any student has two biological parents.

Find two more relations that are not functions, including one that you encountered today. Think about sports, music, science, art, employment, and so on. Discuss how you could express these relations using ordered pairs, a mapping diagram, a table of values, and a graph.

1. Check students' work.    2. Check students' work.

**Relations That Are Functions**

Here is the cost for mailing a first-class letter at the post office. Discuss why this is a function if:
- domain: letter weight;
- range: mailing cost.
  Check students' work.

**First-Class Mail Letter Prices**

| Weight Up To | Price | Weight Up To | Price |
|---|---|---|---|
| 1 oz | $0.42 | 3 oz | $0.76 |
| 2 oz | $0.59 | 3.5 oz | $0.93 |

Use the spaces below to explain why the following are functions:
- **Domain:** students; **range:** algebra teacher assigned to each student
  Answers may vary. Sample: Each student will have exactly one algebra teacher.
- **Domain:** all students; **range:** each student's biological mother
  Answers may vary. Sample: Each student will have exactly one biological mother.

Find two more relations that are functions, including one that you encountered today. Think about sports, music, science, art, employment, and so on. Discuss how you could express these functions using ordered pairs, a mapping diagram, a table of values, and a graph.

3. Check students' work.    4. Check students' work.

# 1 Interactive Learning

## Solve It!

**PURPOSE** To recognize direct variation in a set of nested similar triangles

**PROCESS** Students may
- see the heights increase in a linear pattern.
- recognize four similar triangles.

### FACILITATE

**Q** What is the length between each pair of adjacent posts along the bottom of the triangle? How do you know? **[2 ft; 8 ft divided into 4 equal intervals equals 2 ft.]**

**Q** How are the base and height of the large triangle related? **[The height is $\frac{3}{4}$ of the base.]**

**Q** The base of the smallest triangle is 2 ft. How can you find the height of this triangle? **[2 ft × $\frac{3}{4}$]**

**Q** When you find the height of a post, will you include the thickness of the wood at the top and bottom of each post? **[Answers may vary.]**

**ANSWER** See Solve It in Answers on next page.

**CONNECT THE MATH** The Solve It uses the direct variation principles behind geometric similarity. The lesson formally defines direct variation and prepares students for linear functions.

# 2 Guided Instruction

## Problem 1

**Q** What is the ratio of $y$ to $x$ in the first row? Is the ratio for the other rows the same? **[2:1; yes]**

**Q** How is the table in 1B different from the one in 1A? **[Sample: The ratio of $y$ to $x$ in table 1B is not constant for every row.]**

---

**Objective** To write and interpret direct variation equations

*These triangles look similar to me!*

**Getting Ready!**

You are building a roof. You mark off four equal intervals from point $A$ to point $B$ and you place vertical posts as shown in the diagram. What are the heights of the four vertical posts? Explain.

6 ft

$A$    8 ft    $B$

### Lesson Vocabulary
- direct variation
- constant of variation

The post heights in the Solve It satisfy a relationship called *direct variation*.

**Essential Understanding** Some quantities are in a relationship where the ratio of corresponding values is constant.

You can write a formula for a **direct variation** function as $y = kx$, or $\frac{y}{x} = k$, where $k \neq 0$. $x$ represents input values, and $y$ represents output values. The formula $\frac{y}{x} = k$ says that, except for $(0, 0)$, the ratio of all output-input pairs equals the constant $k$, the **constant of variation**.

### Problem 1   Identifying Direct Variation From Tables

For each function, determine whether $y$ varies directly with $x$. If so, what is the constant of variation and the function rule?

**A**

| x | y |
|---|---|
| 1 | 2 |
| 3 | 6 |
| 4 | 8 |

**B**

| x | y |
|---|---|
| 1 | 4 |
| 2 | 8 |
| 3 | 11 |

**Think**

**How do you find the constant of variation?**
The constant of variation is the ratio of any $y$-value to the corresponding $x$-value.

$\frac{y}{x} = \frac{2}{1} = \frac{6}{3} = \frac{8}{4} = 2$,

so $y$ varies directly with $x$.

The constant of variation is 2.
The function rule is $y = 2x$.

$\frac{y}{x} = \frac{4}{1} = \frac{8}{2} \neq \frac{11}{3}$

so $\frac{y}{x}$ is *not* constant.

$y$ does *not* vary directly with $x$.

---

**BIG idea** Functions     **UbD**

**ESSENTIAL UNDERSTANDINGS**
- Some quantities are in a relationship where the ratio of corresponding values is constant.
- The formula $\frac{y}{x} = k$ says that the ratio of all output-input pairs equals the constant $k$, the constant of variation.

## Math Background

Direct variation functions have equations of the form $y = kx$, where $k$ is the constant of variation. These functions are a subset of the more general linear function $y = ax + b$. The graphs of direct variation functions always pass through the origin. Many types of physical phenomena exhibit direct variation. Examples include rates such as miles per hour, miles per gallon, cost per pound, and so on.

Students will encounter many types of variation relationships in future lessons. Joint variation is briefly touched upon here in the C exercises. Another type is inverse variation. These equations have the form $y = \frac{k}{x}$. One variable varies directly with the reciprocal of the other. Variation does not have to be linear. In fact, examples of direct and inverse quadratic variation are relatively common.

## Support Student Learning

Use the **Algebra 2 Companion** to engage and support students during instruction. See Lesson Resources at the end of this lesson for details.

### PowerAlgebra.com

## 1 Interactive Learning

### Solve It!
Step out how to solve the Problem with helpful hints and an online question. Other questions are listed above in Interactive Learning.

**Got It? 1.** For each function, determine whether $y$ varies directly with $x$. If so, what are the constant of variation and the function rule?

a.

| x | 3 | 2 | 1 |
|---|---|---|---|
| y | −21 | −14 | −7 |

b.

| x | 2 | 3 | 6 |
|---|---|---|---|
| y | 5 | 7 | 13 |

**Problem 2** Identifying Direct Variation From Equations

For each function, determine whether $y$ varies directly with $x$. If so, what is the constant of variation?

**A** $3y = 7x$

Divide each side of the equation $3y = 7x$ by 3 to get $y = \frac{7}{3}x$. Since you can write the equation in the form $y = kx$, $y$ varies directly with $x$. The constant of variation is $\frac{7}{3}$.

**B** $7y = 14x + 7$

Divide each side of the equation $7y = 14x + 7$ by 7 to get $y = 2x + 1$. Since you cannot write the equation in the form $y = kx$, $y$ does not vary directly with $x$.

**Think**
How is the form of this function different from the function in part (A)? This function includes a nonzero constant term.

 **Got It? 2.** For each function, determine whether $y$ varies directly with $x$. If so, what is the constant of variation?

a. $5x + 3y = 0$

b. $y = \frac{x}{9}$

In a direct variation, $\frac{y}{x}$ is the same for all pairs of data where $x \neq 0$. So, $\frac{y_1}{x_1} = \frac{y_2}{x_2}$ is true for the ordered pairs $(x_1, y_1)$ and $(x_2, y_2)$, where neither $x_1$ nor $x_2$ is zero.

**Problem 3** Using a Proportion to Solve a Direct Variation

Suppose $y$ varies directly with $x$, and $y = 9$ when $x = -15$. What is $y$ when $x = 21$?

**Know**
$y$ varies directly with $x$.
$\frac{y}{x}$ is constant.

**Need**
The value of $y$ when $x$ is 21.

**Plan**
Use two forms of $\frac{y}{x}$ in a proportion.

$\frac{9}{-15} = \frac{y}{21}$   In a direct variation, $\frac{y}{x}$ is constant.

$9(21) = -15(y)$   Write the cross products.

$\frac{9(21)}{-15} = \frac{-15y}{-15}$   Divide each side by −15.

$-12.6 = y$   Simplify.

So $y$ is −12.6 when $x$ is 21.

 **Got It? 3.** Suppose $y$ varies directly with $x$, and $y = 15$ when $x = 3$. What is $y$ when $x = 12$?

PowerAlgebra.com   Lesson 2-2  Direct Variation   69

---

**Got It?**   ERROR PREVENTION
Students must check *every* ordered pair given in a table to be sure it shows direct variation. In a direct variation, if the *x*-values form an arithmetic sequence, so must the *y*-values.

**Problem 2**

Q How does the equation in 2B differ from the equation in 2A? **[Answers may vary. Sample: The equation in 2B has the constant 7 added to the right side.]**

Q Can a direct variation function have a nonzero constant term? Explain. **[No; if it did, the ratio of *y* to *x* would not be constant.]**

Q How can you use graphing to solve problems of this type? **[Answers may vary. Sample: *y* varies directly with *x* if the graph is a line through the origin. The slope equals the constant of variation.]**

**Got It?**

Q How can you find the constant of variation in a function like $5x + 3y = 0$? **[Solve for *y*.]**

EXTENSION

Q Two ordered pairs in a direct variation are (2, 8) and (5, 20). How can you use these to write a proportion? **[The ratio of *y* to *x* is constant, so $\frac{8}{20} = \frac{2}{5}$.]**

**Problem 3**

Q How can you find a missing term in a proportion? **[Find the cross products. Solve for the missing term.]**

**Got It?**   ERROR PREVENTION
If students confuse *x*- and *y*-values, have them organize the values in a table.

---

# Answers

### Solve It!
1.5 ft, 3 ft, 4.5 ft, 6 ft; The vertical posts form similar triangles, so you can use proportions to find their lengths.

### Got It?
**1. a.** yes; $-7$, $y = -7x$
   **b.** no

**2. a.** yes; $-\frac{5}{3}$
   **b.** yes; $\frac{1}{9}$

**3.** 60

---

## 2 Guided Instruction

Each Problem is worked out and supported online.

**Problem 1**
Identifying Direct Variation From Tables
*Animated*

**Problem 2**
Identifying Direct Variation From Equations
*Animated*

**Problem 3**
Using a Proportion to Solve a Direct Variation

**Problem 4**
Using Direct Variation to Solve a Problem
*Animated*

**Problem 5**
Graphing Direct Variation Equations

**Support in Algebra 2 Companion**
• Vocabulary
• Key Concepts
• Got It?

## Problem 4

**Q** How do you know commission varies directly with sales? **[Answers may vary. Sample: because the ratio of $\frac{c}{s}$ is constant.]**

## Got It?

**Q** What are two different ways to solve 4a? **[Answers may vary. Sample: Solve the proportion $\frac{200}{50} = \frac{y}{70}$; or solve $200 = k(50)$ for $k$, write the equation $y = kx$, substitute $x = 70$, and solve for $y$.]**

## Problem 5

**Q** Why is every point on the line in each graph part of a direct variation function? **[For every point, the ratio of $y$ to $x$ equals the constant of variation $k$.]**

**Q** Suppose a student graphs a set of points from a table, and they do not lie on a line. What can the student conclude? **[The points are not part of a direct variation function.]**

**Q** Suppose the data points in a table form the line $y = \frac{1}{2}x + 2$. Is the function a direct variation? Explain. **[No; answers may vary. Sample: A direct variation must go through the origin. This equation has a $y$-intercept of 2.]**

## Got It?

**Q** What point do all graphs of direct variation have in common? **[(0, 0)]**

**Think**

Could you use the method in Problem 3 to solve this problem? Yes; you could solve this problem by using the proportion $\frac{c_1}{s_1} = \frac{c_2}{s_2}$.

 **Problem 4** Using Direct Variation to Solve a Problem

A salesperson's commission varies directly with sales. For $1000 in sales, the commission is $85. What is the commission for $2300 in sales?

**Step 1** Use $y = kx$ to find $k$.

Let $c =$ commission.
Let $s =$ sales.

$c = k(s)$ — Commission varies directly with sales, so it is the dependent variable.

$85 = k(1000)$

$0.085 = k$

**Step 2** Write the direct variation for the situation and find the commission when sales = $2300.

$c = k(s)$

$c = 0.085(s)$    Write the direct variation using $k$.

$c = 0.085(2300)$    Substitute 2300 for $s$.

$c = 195.5$    Simplify.

The commission for $2300 in sales is $195.50.

**Got It?** **4. a.** The number of Calories varies directly with the mass of cheese. If 50 grams of cheese contain 200 Calories, how many Calories are in 70 grams of cheese?

**b. Reasoning** If $y^2$ varies directly with $x^2$, does that mean $y$ must vary directly with $x$? Explain.

The graph of a direct variation function is always a line through the origin.

**Think**

What $x$-values should you use to make a table of values? The constant of variation is a fraction. Use multiples of the denominator for $x$. This ensures integer values for $y$.

**Problem 5** Graphing Direct Variation Equations

What is the graph of each direct variation equation?

**A** $y = \frac{3}{4}x$

| x | y |
|---|---|
| 4 | 3 |
| 8 | 6 |
| 12 | 9 |

**B** $y = -2x$

| x | y |
|---|---|
| -2 | 4 |
| -1 | 2 |
| 1 | -2 |

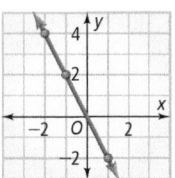

**Got It?** **5.** What is the graph of each direct variation equation?

**a.** $y = -\frac{2}{3}x$      **b.** $y = 3x$

# Additional Problems

**1.** For each function, determine whether $y$ varies directly with $x$. If so, what is the constant of variation and the function rule?

**a.**

| x | y |
|---|---|
| 1 | 0.5 |
| 2 | 1 |
| 3 | 1.5 |

**b.**

| x | y |
|---|---|
| 1 | 10 |
| 2 | 22 |
| 3 | 33 |

**ANSWERS**

**a.** yes; $k = 0.5$; $y = 0.5x$

**b.** no; $\frac{y}{x}$ is not constant

**2.** For each function, determine whether $y$ varies directly with $x$. If so, what is the constant of variation?

**a.** $y + 2 = x - 2$

**b.** $\frac{y}{6} = x$

**ANSWERS**

**a.** no; $\frac{y}{x}$ is not constant

**b.** yes; $k = 6$

**3.** Suppose $y$ varies directly with $x$, and $y = -4$ when $x = 25$. What is $x$ when $y = 10$?

**ANSWER** $-62.5$

**4.** The cost of buying fancy nuts varies directly with the weight. If 8.5 kg of nuts cost $47.60, how much do 20 kg cost?

**ANSWER** $112

**5.** What is the graph of each direct variation equation?

**a.** $y = \frac{x}{5}$

**b.** $y = -4x$

**ANSWERS**

**a.**

**b.**

## Lesson Check

### Do you know HOW?

**1.** Write a function rule for the direct variation in the table.

| x | y |
|---|---|
| 2 | −1 |
| 4 | −2 |
| 6 | −3 |

Identify the constant of variation.

**2.** $y = \frac{3}{2}x$

**3.** $4y - 5x = 0$

### Do you UNDERSTAND?

**4. Vocabulary** Explain what it means for two variables to be directly related.

**5. Reasoning** Explain why the graph of a direct variation function always passes through the origin.

**6.** Give an example of a function that represents a direct variation.

## Practice and Problem-Solving Exercises

**A Practice**

For each function, determine whether y varies directly with x. If so, find the constant of variation and write the function rule.

◀ **See Problem 1.**

**7.**

| x | y |
|---|---|
| 2 | 14 |
| 3 | 21 |
| 5 | 35 |

**8.**

| x | y |
|---|---|
| 27 | 9 |
| 30 | 10 |
| 60 | 20 |

**9.**

| x | y |
|---|---|
| 11 | 22 |
| 16 | 32 |
| 7 | 42 |

**10.**

| x | y |
|---|---|
| 3 | 9 |
| 4 | 10 |
| 5 | 11 |

Determine whether y varies directly with x. If so, find the constant of variation.

◀ **See Problem 2.**

**11.** $y = 12x$    **12.** $y = 6x$    **13.** $y = -2x$    **14.** $y = 4x + 1$

**15.** $y = 4x - 3$    **16.** $y = -5x$    **17.** $y - 6x = 0$    **18.** $y + 3 = -3x$

For Exercises 19–24, y varies directly with x.

◀ **See Problem 3.**

**19.** If $y = 4$ when $x = -2$, find $x$ when $y = 6$.

**20.** If $y = 6$ when $x = 2$, find $x$ when $y = 12$.

**21.** If $y = 7$ when $x = 2$, find $x$ when $y = 3$.

**22.** If $y = 5$ when $x = -3$, find $x$ when $y = -1$.

**23.** If $y = -7$ when $x = -3$, find $y$ when $x = 9$.

**24.** If $y = 25$ when $x = 15$, find $y$ when $x = 6$.

**25. Distance** For a given speed, the distance traveled varies directly with the time. Kate's school is 5 miles away from her home and it takes her 10 minutes to reach the school. If Josh lives 2 miles from school and travels at the same speed as Kate, how long will it take him to reach the school?

◀ **See Problem 4.**

**26. Conservation** A dripping faucet wastes a cup of water if it drips for three minutes. The amount of water wasted varies directly with the amount of time the faucet drips. How long will it take for the faucet to waste $4\frac{1}{2}$ cups of water?

---

# 3 Lesson Check

## Do you know HOW?

• In Exercise 1, students may name the ratio of $y$ to $x$ or write the direct variation function.

## Do you UNDERSTAND?

• For Exercise 5, discuss what students can conclude if the graph of a line does not pass through the origin. **[For $y = ax + b$, $b \neq 0$, the ratio of $y$ and $x$ cannot be constant.]**

## Close

**Q** What are some different ways of representing a direct variation function? **[as a table of ordered pairs, as an equation, by stating the constant of variation]**

**Q** What does it mean for the ratio of two variables to be constant? **[If you divide one variable by the other, you will always get a nonzero constant.]**

**Q** What must be true of $Ax + By + C = 0$ for the equation to represent a direct variation? What would the constant of variation be? **[C must equal 0, and A and B must be nonzero; $k = \frac{A}{B}$.]**

---

# Answers

### Got It? (continued)

**4. a.** 280

**b.** No; if $y^2 = kx^2$ then $y = \pm\sqrt{k}x$. So $\frac{y}{x}$ could be $+\sqrt{k}$ for one pair of values and $-\sqrt{k}$ for another pair. Then $y$ would not vary directly with $x$.

**5. a.**

**b.**

### Lesson Check

**1.** $y = -\frac{1}{2}x$    **2.** $\frac{3}{2}$    **3.** $\frac{5}{4}$

**4.** Answers may vary. Sample: Two variables are directly related when the ratio of the output to the input is a constant value.

**5.** For a direct variation, $y = kx$ where $k$ is the constant of variation. If $x = 0$, then $y = 0$ and the graph of $y = kx$ passes through the origin.

**6.** Check students' work.

### Practice and Problem-Solving Exercises

**7.** yes; 7, $y = 7x$    **8.** yes; $\frac{1}{3}$, $y = \frac{1}{3}x$

**9.** no    **10.** no    **11.** yes; 12

**12.** yes; 6    **13.** yes; −2    **14.** no

**15.** no    **16.** yes; −5    **17.** yes; 6

**18.** no    **19.** −3    **20.** 4

**21.** $\frac{6}{7}$    **22.** $\frac{3}{5}$    **23.** 21

**24.** 10    **25.** 4 min    **26.** 13.5 min

---

# 4 Practice

## ASSIGNMENT GUIDE

Basic: 7–29 all, 32–36 even, 46–48, 52

Average: 7–29 odd, 30–53

Advanced: 7–29 odd, 30–56

Standardized Test Prep: 57–61

Mixed Review: 62–73

**Reasoning** exercises have blue headings.

**Applications** exercises have red headings.

**EXERCISE 52:** Use the Think About a Plan worksheet in the **Practice and Problem Solving Workbook** (also available in the Teaching Resources in print and online) to further support students' development in becoming independent learners.

### HOMEWORK QUICK CHECK

To check students' understanding of key skills and concepts, go over Exercises 7, 19, 34, 47, and 52.

---

Make a table of $x$- and $y$-values and use it to graph the direct variation equation.

◀ See Problem 5.

**27.** $x = \left(-\frac{1}{3}\right)y$      **28.** $y = -9x$      **29.** $x = y$

**B Apply**   Determine whether $y$ varies directly with $x$. If so, find the constant of variation and write the function rule.

**30.**

| x | y |
|---|---|
| 1 | -2 |
| 3 | -8 |
| 5 | 14 |

**31.**

| x | y |
|---|---|
| 9 | 6 |
| 12 | 8 |
| 15 | 10 |

**32.**

| x | y |
|---|---|
| 4 | 1 |
| 6 | 2 |
| 8 | 3 |

**33.**

| x | y |
|---|---|
| 23 | 24 |
| 55 | 56 |
| 66 | 67 |

**34. Think About a Plan** Suppose you make a 4-minute local call using a calling card and are charged 7.6 cents. The cost of a local call varies directly with the length of the call. How much more will it cost to make a 30-minute local call?
- Which quantity is the dependent quantity?
- How does the word "more" affect the method needed to solve the problem?

Write and graph a direct variation equation that passes through each point.

**35.** $(1, 2)$    **36.** $(-3, -7)$    **37.** $(2, -9)$    **38.** $(-0.1, 50)$

**39.** $(-5, -3)$    **40.** $(9, -1)$    **41.** $(7, 2)$    **42.** $(-3, 14)$

For Exercises 43–46, $y$ varies directly with $x$.

**43.** If $y = \frac{1}{2}$ when $x = 4$, find $y$ when $x = 5$.    **44.** If $y = \frac{3}{4}$ when $x = \frac{1}{2}$, find $y$ when $x = 3$.

**45.** If $y = \frac{5}{3}$ when $x = \frac{3}{4}$, find $x$ when $y = \frac{1}{2}$.    **46.** If $y = -\frac{5}{8}$ when $x = \frac{3}{2}$, find $x$ when $y = \frac{2}{5}$.

**47. Reasoning** Explain why you cannot answer the following question.
If $y = 0$ when $x = 0$, what is $x$ when $y = 13$?

**Open-Ended** Choose a value of $k$ within the given range. Then write and graph a direct variation function using your value for $k$.

**48.** $0 < k < 1$    **49.** $3 < k < 4.5$    **50.** $-1 < k < -\frac{1}{2}$

**51. Error Analysis** Identify the error in the statement shown at the right.

> If $y$ varies directly with $x^2$, and $y = 2$ when $x = 4$, then $y = 3$ when $x = 9$.

**52. Sports** The number of rotations of a bicycle wheel varies directly with the number of pedal strokes. Suppose that in the bicycle's lowest gear, 6 pedal strokes move the cyclist about 357 in. In the same gear, how many pedal strokes are needed to move 100 ft?

**53. Writing** Suppose you use the origin to test whether a linear equation is a direct variation function. Does this method work? Support your answer with an example.

---

# Answers

## Practice and Problem-Solving Exercises
(continued)

**27.**

| x | y |
|---|---|
| -1 | 3 |
| 1 | -3 |
| 2 | -6 |

**28.**

| x | y |
|---|---|
| -1 | 9 |
| 1 | -9 |
| 2 | -18 |

**29.**

| x | y |
|---|---|
| -1 | -1 |
| 1 | 1 |
| 2 | 2 |

**30.** no

**32.** no

**34.** 49.4 cents

**35.** $y = 2x$

**36.** $y = \frac{7}{3}x$

**37.** $y = -4.5x$

**38.** $y = -500x$

**31.** yes; $k = \frac{2}{3}$, $y = \frac{2}{3}x$

**33.** no

**39.** $y = \frac{3}{5}x$

**40.** $y = -\frac{x}{9}$

**41.** $y = \frac{2}{7}x$

**42.** $y = -\frac{14}{3}x$

**43.** 0.625

**44.** 4.5

**45.** 0.225

**46.** −0.96

**47.** Every direct variation includes the point (0, 0), so $x$ cannot be determined because $k$ could be any value.

**48.** Answers may vary. Sample: $y = 0.5x$

**49–53.** See next page.

**Challenge**   In Exercises 54–55, *y* varies directly with *x*. Explain your answer.

**54.** If *x* is doubled, what happens to *y*?   **55.** If *x* is divided by 7, what happens to *y*?

**56.** If *z* varies directly with the product of *x* and *y* ($z = kxy$), then *z* is said to vary jointly with *x* and *y*.
- **a. Geometry** The area of a triangle varies jointly with its base and height. What is the constant of variation?
- **b.** Suppose *q* varies jointly with *v* and *s*, and *q* = 24 when *v* = 2 and *s* = 3. Find *q* when *v* = 4 and *s* = 2.
- **c. Reasoning** Suppose *z* varies jointly with *x* and *y*, and *x* varies directly with *w*. Show that *z* varies jointly with *w* and *y*.

## Standardized Test Prep

GRIDDED RESPONSE

**SAT/ACT**

**57.** A speed of 75 mi/h is equal to a speed of 110 ft/s. To the nearest mile per hour, what is the speed of an aircraft traveling at a speed of 1600 ft/s?

**58.** What number is a solution to both $|x - 3| = 2$ and $|9 - x| = 8$?

**59.** If $f(x) = 7 - 3x$ and $g(x) = 3x - 7$, what is the value of $f(1) + g(1)$?

**60.** Look at the pattern. How many circles are in the 6th figure of this pattern?

**61.** What is the solution of $4(x - 5) + x = 8x - 10 - x$?

## Mixed Review

Graph each relation. Find the domain and range.    See Lesson 2-1.

**62.** {(0, 1), (1, −3), (−2, −3), (3, −3)}   **63.** {(4, 0), (7, 0), (4, −1), (7, −1)}

**64.** {(1, −2), (2, −1), (4, 1), (5, 2)}   **65.** {(1, 7), (2, 8), (3, 9), (4, 10)}

Identify a pattern and find the next three numbers in the pattern.   See Lesson 1-1.

**66.** 8, 16, 24, 32, …   **67.** 5, 3, 1, −1, …

**68.** 144, 132, 120, 108, …   **69.** 30, 45, 60, 75, …

**Get Ready!**   To prepare for Lesson 2-3, do Exercises 70–73.

Evaluate each expression for *x* = −2, 0, 1, and 4.   See Lesson 1-3.

**70.** $\frac{2}{3}x + 7$   **71.** $\frac{3}{5}x - 2$   **72.** $3x + 1$   **73.** $\frac{1}{2}x - 8$

PowerAlgebra.com   Lesson 2-2   Direct Variation   73

---

**49.** Answers may vary. Sample: $y = 3.2x$

**50.** Answers may vary. Sample: $y = -\frac{3}{4}x$

**51.** Answers may vary. Sample: If *y* varies directly with $x^2$, and *y* = 2 when *x* = 4, then $y = \frac{81}{8}$ when *x* = 9.

**52.** about 20 strokes

**53.** Answers may vary. Sample: No; the line *y* = 0 passes through the origin, but is not a direct variation.

**54.** *y* is doubled; $y = kx$, so if *x* is doubled, $y = k(2x)$ or twice the original value of *y*.

**55.** *y* is divided by 7; $y = kx$, so if *x* is divided by 7, $y = k\left(\frac{x}{7}\right)$ or $\frac{1}{7}$ the original value of *y*.

**56. a.** $\frac{1}{2}$
**b.** 32
**c.** $z = kxy$, and $x = k_1w$, so $z = kk_1wy$, and *z* varies jointly with *w* and *y*.

## Standardized Test Prep
**57.** 1091
**58.** 1
**59.** 0
**60.** 21
**61.** −5

## Mixed Review
**62.**
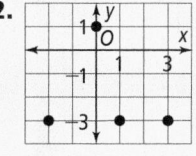
domain: {−2, 0, 1, 3}; range: {−3, 1}

**63.**
domain: {4, 7}; range: {0, −1}

**64.**
domain: {1, 2, 4, 5}; range: {−2, −1, 1, 2}

**65.**
domain: {1, 2, 3, 4}; range: {7, 8, 9, 10}

**66.** 8*n*; 40, 48, 56
**67.** 7 − 2*n*; −3, −5, −7
**68.** 12(13 − *n*); 96, 84, 72
**69.** 15(*n* + 1); 90, 105, 120
**70.** $\frac{17}{3}$; 7; $\frac{23}{3}$; $\frac{29}{3}$
**71.** −3.2; −2; −1.4; 0.4
**72.** −5; 1; 4; 13
**73.** −9; −8; −7.5; −6

Lesson 2-2   73

## Additional Instructional Support

### Algebra 2 Companion

Students can use the **Algebra 2 Companion** worktext (4 pages) as you teach the lesson. Use the Companion to support

- New Vocabulary
- Key Concepts
- Got It for each Problem
- Lesson Check

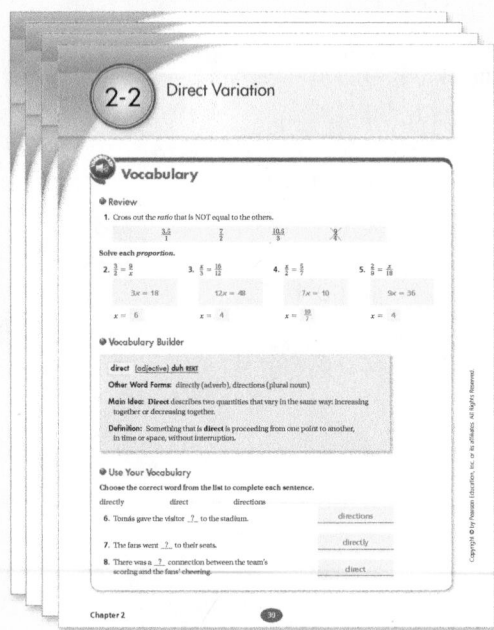

### ELL Support

**Connect to Prior Knowledge** Have groups of students graph a linear equation such as $y = 2x + 1$ and write a step-by-step description of how they make the graph. Next, have the groups graph a related inequality such as $y > 2x + 1$ and write a step-by-step description of that process. Ask each group to contrast the processes of graphing an equation and graphing an inequality.

Next have students make a poster which explains the process of graphing inequalities. Students should include illustrations, examples, and familiar phrases and expressions in their poster.

## 5 Assess & Remediate

### Lesson Quiz

**1.** Does $y$ vary directly with $x$? If so, what is the constant of variation and the function rule?

| x | y |
|---|---|
| 2 | 5 |
| 5 | 12.5 |
| 10 | 25 |

**2.** Determine whether $y$ varies directly with $x$ in $6x - 3 = 2y - 3$. If so, what is the constant of variation?

**3.** $y$ varies directly with $x$, and $y = 24$ when $x = -15$. What is $x$ when $y = 16$?

**4. Do you UNDERSTAND?** You have a set of nested boxes whose lengths vary directly with their widths. One box is 2.5 in. wide and 5.5 in. long. A second box is 3 in. wide. How long is it?

**5.** What is the graph of $y = -1.5x$?

**ANSWERS TO LESSON QUIZ**

**1.** yes; $k = 2.5$; $y = 2.5x$

**2.** yes; $k = 3$

**3.** $-10$

**4.** 6.6 in.

**5.**

**PRESCRIPTION FOR REMEDIATION**

Use the student work on the Lesson Quiz to prescribe a differentiated review assignment:

| Points | Differentiated Remediation |
|--------|---------------------------|
| 0–2 | Intervention |
| 3–4 | On-level |
| 5 | Extension |

**PowerAlgebra.com**

### 5 Assess & Remediate

Assign the Lesson Quiz. Appropriate intervention, practice, or enrichment is automatically generated based on student performance.

## Differentiated Remediation

### Intervention

- **Reteaching** (2 pages) Provides reteaching and practice exercises for the key lesson concepts. Use with struggling students or absent students.

- **English Language Learner Support** Helps students develop and reinforce mathematical vocabulary and key concepts.

#### All-in-One Resources/Online
**Reteaching**

##### 2-2 Reteaching
Direct Variation

A direct variation is a function of the form,

$$y = kx \text{ or } \frac{y}{x} = k, \text{ where } k \neq 0.$$

Represent the input values as $x$ and represent the output values as $y$. The ratio of any output-input pair is equal to $k$, the constant of variation.

**Problem**

For each function, determine whether $y$ varies directly with $x$. If so, what is the constant of variation?

#### All-in-One Resources/Online
**English Language Learner Support**

##### 2-2 ELL Support
Direct Variation

A clerk's weekly salary varies directly with the number of hours he works. For 12 h of work, the clerk earns \$114. How much will he earn for 19 h of work? The steps to solve this problem were written on the note cards below, but they got mixed up.

# Differentiated Remediation *continued*

Available in editable format online.

## On-Level

- **Practice** (2 pages) Provides extra practice for each lesson. For simpler practice exercises, use the Form K Practice pages found in the All-in-One Teaching Resources and online.

- **Think About a Plan** Helps students develop specific problem-solving skills and strategies by providing scaffolded guiding questions.
- **Standardized Test Prep** Focuses on all major exercises, all major question types, and helps students prepare for the high-stakes assessments.

## Extension

- **Enrichment** Provides students with interesting problems and activities that extend the concepts of the lesson.
- **Activities, Games, and Puzzles** Worksheets that can be used for concepts development, enrichment, and for fun!

---

### Practice and Problem Solving Wkbk/ All-in-One Resources/Online
**Practice page 1**

### Practice and Problem Solving Wkbk/ All-in-One Resources/Online
**Practice page 2**

### All-in-One Resources/Online
**Enrichment**

### Practice and Problem Solving Wkbk/ All-in-One Resources/Online
**Think About a Plan**

### Practice and Problem Solving Wkbk/ All-in-One Resources/Online
**Standardized Test Prep**

### Online Teacher Resource Center
**Activities, Games, and Puzzles**

# 1 Interactive Learning

## Solve It!

**PURPOSE** To recognize that in moving along a line, the vertical change is proportional to the horizontal change

**PROCESS** Students may recognize two similar triangles and find the ratios to solve for $H$ in terms of $h$ or replace the variables with numerical values and find the ratio.

---

**FACILITATE**

**Q** Notice that $H$ and $h$ each represent the side of a different triangle. How are these triangles related? **[They are similar.]**

**Q** What proportion do these similar triangles give you? $[\frac{h}{OB} = \frac{H}{OA}]$

**Q** So, what is $H$ in terms of $h$? $[H = h\frac{OA}{OB}]$

**Q** How does rotating the line change the triangles? **[They are larger but still similar.]**

**Q** What is the new $H$ in terms of the new $h$? **[The heights change but the proportion stays the same; $H = h\frac{OA}{OB}$]**

---

**ANSWER** See Solve It in Answers on next page.

**CONNECT THE MATH** In the Solve It, students show that the vertical change is proportional to horizontal change. In the lesson, they will find the slope of a line, which is the ratio of vertical change to horizontal change.

# 2 Guided Instruction

## Take Note

If students find the subscripted variables confusing or intimidating, present the slope formula using $(a, b)$ and $(c, d)$ as the two given points.

---

## 2-3  Linear Functions and Slope-Intercept Form

**Objectives** To graph linear equations
To write equations of lines

You can use proportions to help you solve this.

**Getting Ready!**

By what value do you multiply height h to get height H? Suppose you rotate the line about the origin so that the line passes through point P. By what value do you multiply the new height h to get the new height H?

**Lesson Vocabulary**
• slope
• linear function
• linear equation
• $y$-intercept
• $x$-intercept
• slope-intercept form

You can describe movement in a coordinate plane by describing how far you need to move vertically and how far you need to move horizontally to get from one point to another point.

**Essential Understanding** Consider a nonvertical line in the coordinate plane. If you move from any point on the line to any other point on the line, the ratio of the vertical change to the horizontal change is constant. That constant ratio is the slope of the line.

The **slope** of a nonvertical line is the ratio of the vertical change to the horizontal change between two points. You can calculate slope by finding the ratio of the difference in the $y$-coordinates to the difference in the $x$-coordinates for any two points on the line.

**take note**    **Key Concept   Slope**

The slope of a nonvertical line through points $(x_1, y_1)$ and $(x_2, y_2)$ is the ratio of the vertical change to the corresponding horizontal change.

$$\text{slope} = \frac{\text{vertical change (rise)}}{\text{horizontal change (run)}} = \frac{y_2 - y_1}{x_2 - x_1}, \text{ where } x_2 - x_1 \neq 0$$

---

## 2-3  Preparing to Teach

**BIG idea  Equivalence**            **UbD**

**ESSENTIAL UNDERSTANDINGS**

• Moving from any point on a nonvertical line in the coordinate plane to any other point on the line, the ratio of the vertical change to the horizontal change is constant. That constant ratio describes the slope of the line.

• Slope can be calculated by finding the ratio of the difference in the $y$-coordinates to the difference in the $x$-coordinates for any two points on the line.

## Math Background

Although any two-variable equation can be graphed on a coordinate grid by plotting ordered pairs, there are often more efficient ways. The first step is to recognize the general shape of a graph from its equation. For example, the graph of $y = 3x^2 - 2$ is a parabola and $y = |x - 2|$ is V-shaped. Graphs of linear equations are straight lines. There are various forms for these equations:

standard forms: $Ax + By + C = 0$
$$Ax + By = C$$

slope-intercept form: $y = mx + b$

point-slope form: $y - y_1 = m(x - x_1)$

two-point form:
$$y - y_1 = \frac{y_2 - y_1}{x_2 - x_1}(x - x_1)$$

intercept form: $\frac{x}{a} + \frac{y}{b} = 1$

## Support Student Learning

Use the **Algebra 2 Companion** to engage and support students during instruction. See Lesson Resources at the end of this lesson for details.

---

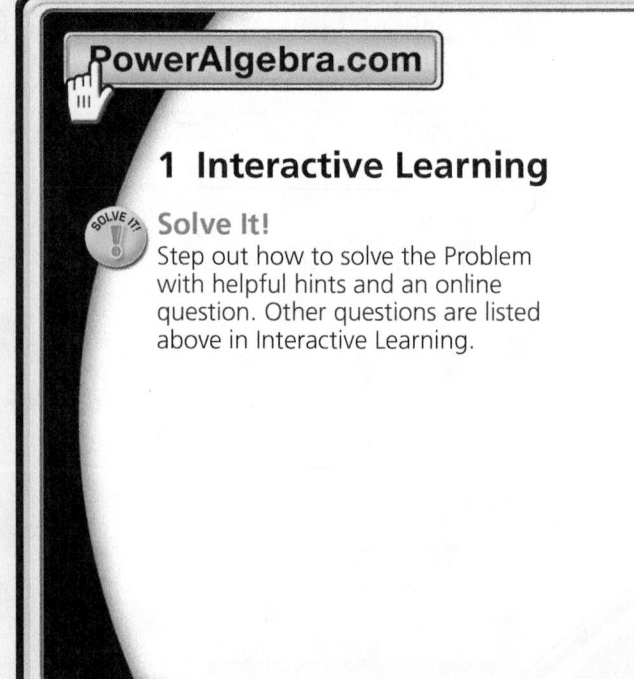

**PowerAlgebra.com**

## 1 Interactive Learning

### Solve It!

Step out how to solve the Problem with helpful hints and an online question. Other questions are listed above in Interactive Learning.

---

## Problem 1 Finding Slope

**What is the slope of the line that passes through the given points?**

**Ⓐ** $(-3, 7)$ and $(-2, 4)$

$$m = \frac{y_2 - y_1}{x_2 - x_1} = \frac{4 - 7}{-2 - (-3)} = \frac{-3}{1}$$

The slope of the line that passes through $(-3, 7)$ and $(-2, 4)$ is $\frac{-3}{1}$ or $-3$.

**Ⓑ** $(3, 1)$ and $(-4, 1)$

$$m = \frac{y_2 - y_1}{x_2 - x_1} = \frac{1 - 1}{-4 - 3} = \frac{0}{-7} = 0$$

The slope of the line that passes through $(3, 1)$ and $(-4, 1)$ is $\frac{0}{-7}$ or 0.

**Ⓒ** $(7, -3)$ and $(7, 1)$

$$m = \frac{y_2 - y_1}{x_2 - x_1} = \frac{1 - (-3)}{7 - 7} = \frac{4}{0}$$

Division by zero is undefined, so slope is undefined for the line that passes through $(7, -3)$ and $(7, 1)$.

**Got It? 1.** What is the slope of the line that passes through the given points?
  **a.** $(5, 4)$ and $(8, 1)$    **b.** $(2, 2)$ and $(-2, -2)$    **c.** $(9, 3)$ and $(9, -4)$
  **d. Reasoning** Use the slope formula to show in part (a) that it does not matter which point you choose for $(x_1, y_1)$.

### Concept Summary  Slope of a Line

| Positive Slope | Negative Slope | Zero Slope | Undefined Slope |
| --- | --- | --- | --- |
| Line rises from left to right | Line falls from left to right | Horizontal line | Vertical line |

A function whose graph is a line is a **linear function**. You can represent a linear function with a **linear equation**, such as $y = 6x - 4$. A solution of a linear equation is any ordered pair $(x, y)$ that makes the equation true.

---

## Problem 1

Sometimes $\frac{y_1 - y_2}{x_1 - x_2}$ is easier to compute than $\frac{y_2 - y_1}{x_2 - x_1}$. Either order of the coordinates will give the correct answer.

**Q** What values do you use in the numerator of the slope fraction? in the denominator? **[y-coordinates; x-coordinates]**

**Q** How can you use graphing to check your answers? **[Plot the two points and draw the line connecting them. Find the slope by counting the squares for the vertical change and horizontal change.]**

### Got It?

Make sure all students can find slope from two points. If necessary, provide remedial practice finding slope using $(0, 0)$ and one other point.

### Take Note

**Q** Why should you look at graphs from left to right? **[If you look at a graph from right to left, it will appear to have the opposite slope than when you look at it from left to right.]**

**Q** Why is the slope of a vertical line undefined? **[Every point on a vertical line has the same x-coordinate, so the slope ratio results in division by a horizontal change of zero.]**

---

## 2 Guided Instruction

 Each Problem is worked out and supported online.

**Problem 1**
Finding Slope

**Problem 2**
Writing Linear Equations
*Animated*

**Problem 3**
Writing Equations in Slope-Intercept Form

**Alternative Problem 3**
Writing Equations in Slope-Intercept Form
*Animated*

**Problem 4**
Graphing a Linear Equation
*Animated*

**Support in Algebra 2 Companion**
• Vocabulary
• Key Concepts
• Got It?

## Answers

### Solve It!
$\frac{A}{B}, \frac{A}{B}$

### Got It?
**1. a.** $-1$
  **b.** $1$
  **c.** undefined
  **d.** $\frac{1 - 4}{8 - 5} = \frac{-3}{3} = -1 = \frac{3}{-3} = \frac{4 - 1}{5 - 8}$

## Take Note

Why is the letter $m$ used to indicate the slope? It may be from the word *modulas,* but nobody knows for sure.

**Q** Why is a direct variation a special form of a linear function? **[Answers may vary. Sample: The general form of a direct variation $y = kx$ is a special case of slope-intercept form $y = mx + b$ where the slope is the constant of variation and the $y$-intercept is (0, 0).]**

## Problem 2

Students write equations for lines using either the slope and $y$-intercept or a line in the coordinate plane.

**Q** In 2A, how do you know what to substitute for $b$? **[The $y$-intercept is (0, $b$) in slope-intercept form. Here, the $y$-intercept is (0, −3), so $b = -3$.]**

**Q** In 2B, how can you find the slope between (0, 4) and (1, 1) without using the slope formula? **[Count the units from (0, 4) to (1, 1). The vertical change is −3; the horizontal change is 1.]**

## Got It?

Have a volunteer explain how to use a graphing calculator to check the answer to 2a.

---

A special form of a linear equation is called *slope-intercept form.*

An *intercept* of a line is a point where a line crosses an axis. The **$y$-intercept** of a nonvertical line is the point at which the line crosses the $y$-axis. The **$x$-intercept** of a nonhorizontal line is the point at which the line crosses the $x$-axis.

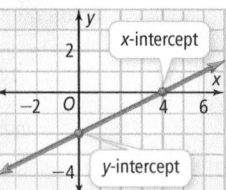

**take note** **Key Concept** **Slope-Intercept Form**

The **slope-intercept form** of an equation of a line is $y = mx + b$, where $m$ is the slope of the line and (0, $b$) is the $y$-intercept.

**Problem 2** **Writing Linear Equations**

**What is an equation of each line?**

**A** $m = \frac{1}{5}$ and the $y$-intercept is (0, −3)

$y = mx + b$  Use the slope-intercept form.

$y = \frac{1}{5}x + (-3)$  Substitute $m = \frac{1}{5}$ and $b = -3$.

$y = \frac{1}{5}x - 3$  Simplify.

**B**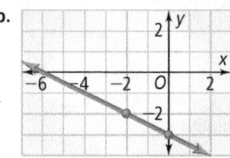

Look at the line shown in the graph. The $y$-intercept is the point where the line crosses the $y$-axis, (0, 4), so $b = 4$.

Use the second point (1, 1) to find the slope.

$m = \frac{y_2 - y_1}{x_2 - x_1} = \frac{1 - 4}{1 - 0} = -3.$

So, $y = -3x + 4$.

**Got It? 2.** What is an equation of each line?

**a.** $m = 6$, $y$-intercept is (0, 5)

**b.**

**c. Reasoning** Using the graph from part (b), do you get a different equation if you use (−6, 0) and the $y$-intercept to find the slope of the line? Explain.

### Plan

**What information do you need from the graph?**
You need the $y$-intercept and another point to find the slope.

76    Chapter 2   Functions, Equations, and Graphs

---

# Additional Problems

**1.** What is the slope of the line that passes through the given points?

**a.** (−10, 2) and (4, −5)

**b.** (6, −1) and (5, −1)

**c.** (−2, 5) and (−2, −3)

**ANSWERS**

**a.** $-\frac{1}{2}$

**b.** 0

**c.** undefined

**2.** What is an equation of each line?

**a.** slope = −3, $y$-intercept is (0, 5)

**b.**

**ANSWERS**

**a.** $y = -3x + 5$

**b.** $y = \frac{2}{3}x - 1$

**3.** Write the equation in slope-intercept form. What are the slope and $y$-intercept?

**a.** $2x + 3y - 15 = 0$

**b.** $12 = 10y - 3x$

**ANSWERS**

**a.** $y = -\frac{2}{3}x + 5$, slope $= -\frac{2}{3}$, $y$-intercept is (0, 5)

**b.** $y = \frac{3}{10}x + \frac{6}{5}$, slope $= \frac{3}{10}$, $y$-intercept is $\left(0, \frac{6}{5}\right)$

**4.** What is the graph of $24 = 4x - 3y$?

**ANSWER**

You can rewrite a linear equation in slope–intercept form by solving for $y$.

 **Problem 3** Writing Equations in Slope-Intercept Form

**Write the equation in slope-intercept form. What are the slope and $y$-intercept?**

Ⓐ $5x - 4y = 16$

$\quad -4y = -5x + 16$     Subtract $5x$ from each side.

$\quad \dfrac{-4y}{-4} = \dfrac{-5x}{-4} + \dfrac{16}{-4}$     Divide each side by $-4$.

$\quad y = \dfrac{5}{4}x - 4$     Compare the equation with $y = mx + b$

The slope $m = \dfrac{5}{4}$. The $y$-intercept is $(0, -4)$.

Ⓑ $-\dfrac{3}{4}x + \dfrac{1}{2}y = -1$

$\quad \dfrac{1}{2}y = \dfrac{3}{4}x - 1$     Add $\dfrac{3}{4}x$ to each side.

$\quad y = \dfrac{3}{2}x - 2$     Multiply each side by 2.

The slope $m = \dfrac{3}{2}$. The $y$-intercept is $(0, -2)$.

**Think**

**Is there another way to solve this problem?**
Yes; clear the fractions by multiplying all terms by 4, the LCM of the denominators.

 **Got It?** **3.** Write the equation in slope-intercept form. What are the slope and $y$-intercept?

   **a.** $3x + 2y = 18$          **b.** $-7x - 5y = 35$

---

 **Problem 4** Graphing a Linear Equation

**What is the graph of $-2x + y = 1$?**

| Know | Need | Plan |
|---|---|---|
| • The equation of a line | Two points to draw the line | • Write the equation in slope-intercept form.<br>• Plot the $y$-intercept.<br>• Use the slope to find a second point.<br>• Draw a line through the two points. |

Write the equation in slope-intercept form.

$\quad -2x + y = 1$

$\quad\quad\quad\quad y = 2x + 1$

The slope is 2 and the $y$-intercept is $(0, 1)$.

Step 1   Plot the $y$-intercept.

Step 2   Use the slope $\dfrac{2}{1}$. Go up 2 units and right 1 unit.

Step 3   Draw a line through the two points.

 **Got It?** **4.** What is the graph of $4x - 7y = 14$?

---

## Problem 3

**Q** In 3A, suppose a student got the answer $y = \dfrac{5}{4}x + 16$. What mistake was made? **[The student did not divide 16 by $-4$.]**

**Q** In 3A, suppose a student got the answer $y = \dfrac{5}{4}x + 4$. What mistake was made? **[16 divided by $-4$ is $-4$, not 4.]**

### Got It?     ERROR PREVENTION

**Q** When you rewrite an equation in slope-intercept form, you are solving for a variable. Which variable? **[$y$]**

## Problem 4

**Q** What is another ratio equivalent to the slope 2? **[Answers may vary. Samples: $\dfrac{4}{2}$ or $\dfrac{-2}{-1}$]**

**Q** What happens if you use your alternative ratio to measure the vertical and horizontal change from $(0, 1)$? **[You end up at another point on the same line.]**

### Got It?     EXTENSION

Write $4x - 7y = 14$. Cover the $y$-term.
**Q** When $y = 0$, what is $x$? **[$\dfrac{7}{2}$]**
Then cover the $x$-term.
**Q** When $x = 0$, what is $y$? **[$-2$]**
**Q** What two points on the line does this give you? **[$(\dfrac{7}{2}, 0)$ and $(0, -2)$]**
**Q** What are these points called? **[$x$-intercept, $y$-intercept]**

---

# Answers

### Got It? (continued)

**2. a.** $y = 6x + 5$

  **b.** $y = -\dfrac{1}{2}x - 3$

  **c.** No; any two points on a line can be used to calculate the slope.

**3. a.** $y = -\dfrac{3}{2}x + 9;\ -\dfrac{3}{2};\ (0, 9)$

  **b.** $y = -\dfrac{7}{5}x - 7;\ -\dfrac{7}{5};\ (0, -7)$

**4.** $y = \dfrac{4}{7}x - 2$

# 3 Lesson Check

## Do you know HOW?

• For Exercises 1 and 2, remind students to first isolate the $y$-term and then divide both sides by the coefficient of that term.

## Do you UNDERSTAND?

• For Exercise 5, write the words *intercept* and *interception* on the board. Have students use dictionaries or online sources to find definitions for each word. As a class, brainstorm a list of usages.

## Close

> **Q** If you have 3 points, how can you use the slope formula to determine whether the points are collinear? **[Calculate the slope between any 2 pairs. If the slope between both pairs is the same, all 3 points are collinear; otherwise they are not.]**

---

 **Lesson Check**

### Do you know HOW?

Write each equation in slope-intercept form.

**1.** $x - 2y + 3 = 1$

**2.** $-4x + 3y = 1$

What is the slope of the line passing through the following points?

**3.** $(2, 4)$ and $(4, 2)$

**4.** $(-1, -3)$ and $(3, 1)$

### Do you UNDERSTAND?

**5. Vocabulary** What is a $y$-intercept? How is a $y$-intercept different from an $x$-intercept?

**6.** Explain why the slope of a vertical line is called "undefined."

**7. Error Analysis** A classmate found the slope between two points. What error did she make?

---

## Practice and Problem-Solving Exercises

 **Practice**  Find the slope of the line through each pair of points.  ◀ See Problem 1.

**8.** $(1, 6)$ and $(8, -1)$   **9.** $(-3, 9)$ and $(0, 3)$   **10.** $(0, 0)$ and $(2, 6)$

**11.** $(-4, -3)$ and $(7, 1)$   **12.** $(-2, -1)$ and $(8, -3)$   **13.** $(1, 2)$ and $(2, 3)$

**14.** $(2, 7)$ and $(-3, 11)$   **15.** $(-3, 5)$ and $(4, 5)$   **16.** $(-5, -7)$ and $(0, 10)$

Write an equation for each line.  ◀ See Problem 2.

**17.** $m = 3$ and the $y$-intercept is $(0, 2)$.

**19.** $m = \frac{5}{6}$ and the $y$-intercept is $(0, 12)$.

**20.** $m = 0$ and the $y$-intercept is $(0, -2)$.

**21.** $m = -5$ and the $y$-intercept is $(0, -7)$.

**18.**

Write each equation in slope-intercept form. Then find the slope and $y$-intercept of each line.  ◀ See Problem 3.

**22.** $5x + y = 4$   **23.** $-3x + 2y = 7$   **24.** $-\frac{1}{2}x - y = \frac{3}{4}$

**25.** $8x + 6y = 5$   **26.** $9x - 2y = 10$   **27.** $y = 7$

Graph each equation.  ◀ See Problem 4.

**28.** $y = 2x$   **29.** $y = -3x - 1$   **30.** $y = 3x - 2$

**31.** $y = -4x + 5$   **32.** $5x - 2y = -4$   **33.** $-2x + 5y = -10$

**34.** $y - 3 = -2x$   **35.** $y + 4 = -3x$   **36.** $-y + 5 = -2x$

---

### PowerAlgebra.com

## 3 Lesson Check

For a digital lesson check, use the Got It questions.

**Support in Algebra 2 Companion**
• Lesson Check

## 4 Practice

Assign homework to individual students or to an entire class.

---

# Answers

## Lesson Check

**1.** $y = \frac{1}{2}x + 1$

**2.** $y = \frac{4}{3}x + \frac{1}{3}$

**3.** $-1$

**4.** $1$

**5.** The $y$-intercept of a line is the point at which the line crosses the $y$-axis. The $x$-intercept is the point at which the line crosses the $x$-axis.

**6.** Since division by zero is undefined, the slope of a vertical line that passes through $(a, b)$ and $(a, c)$, $\frac{c - b}{0}$, is undefined.

**7.** She subtracted the $x$-coordinates in the wrong order. The $x$- and $y$-coordinates of each point must be subtracted consistently.

## Practice and Problem-Solving Exercises

**8.** $-1$   **9.** $-2$   **10.** $3$   **11.** $\frac{4}{11}$

**12.** $-\frac{1}{5}$   **13.** $1$   **14.** $-\frac{4}{5}$   **15.** $0$

**16.** $\frac{17}{5}$   **17.** $y = 3x + 2$

**18.** $y = -\frac{x}{3} - 2$   **19.** $y = \frac{5}{6}x + 12$

**20.** $y = -2$

**21.** $y = -5x - 7$

**22.** $y = -5x + 4$; $-5$, $(0, 4)$

**23.** $y = \frac{3}{2}x + \frac{7}{2}$; $\frac{3}{2}$, $\left(0, \frac{7}{2}\right)$

**24.** $y = -\frac{1}{2}x - \frac{3}{4}$; $-\frac{1}{2}$, $\left(0, -\frac{3}{4}\right)$

**25.** $y = -\frac{4}{3}x + \frac{5}{6}$; $-\frac{4}{3}$, $\left(0, \frac{5}{6}\right)$

**26.** $y = \frac{9}{2}x - 5$; $\frac{9}{2}$, $(0, -5)$

**27.** $y = 7$; $0$, $(0, 7)$

**28–36.** See next page.

**Apply**

Graph each equation.

**37.** $y = -\frac{1}{2}x - \frac{3}{2}$

**38.** $y = -2x + 3$

**39.** $y = -x + 7$

**40.** $3y - 2x = -12$

**41.** $4x + 5y = 20$

**42.** $4x - 3y = -6$

**43.** $\frac{2}{3}x + \frac{y}{3} = -\frac{1}{3}$

**44.** $x = 5$

**45.** $2.4 = -3.6x - 0.4y$

**46. Think About a Plan** Suppose the equation $y = 12 + 10x$ models the amount of money in your wallet, where $y$ is the total in dollars and $x$ is the number of weeks from today. If you graphed this equation, what would the slope represent in the situation? Explain.
• Is the equation in slope-intercept form?
• What units make sense for the slope?

Find the slope and $y$-intercept of each line.

**47.**  **48.**  **49.**

Find the slope and $y$-intercept of each line.

**50.** $y = 0.4 - 0.8x$

**51.** $x = -3$

**52.** $y = 0$

**53.** $-\frac{1}{3}x - \frac{2}{3}y = \frac{5}{3}$

**54.** $-Ax + By = -C$

**55.** $\frac{A}{D}x + \frac{B}{D}y = \frac{C}{D}$

**56.** The equation $d = 4 - \frac{1}{15}t$ represents your distance from home $d$ for each minute you walk $t$.
**a.** If you graphed this equation, what would the slope represent? Explain.
**b.** Are you walking towards or away from your home? Explain.

**57. Reasoning** Use the graph to find the slope between the following points on the line.
**a.** $P$ and $Q$  **b.** $Q$ and $S$
**c.** $S$ and $P$  **d.** $R$ and $Q$
**e.** Make a conjecture based on your answers to parts (a)-(d).

**58. Error Analysis** A classmate says that the graph of $3y - 2x = 5$ has a slope of 2. What mistake did he make?

Find the slope of the line through each pair of points.

**59.** $\left(\frac{3}{2}, -\frac{1}{2}\right)$ and $\left(-\frac{2}{3}, \frac{1}{3}\right)$

**60.** $\left(-\frac{1}{2}, -\frac{1}{2}\right)$ and $(-3, -4)$

**61.** $\left(0, -\frac{1}{2}\right)$ and $\left(\frac{7}{5}, 10\right)$

**ASSIGNMENT GUIDE**
Basic: 8–36 all, 44–56 even, 57–59
Average: 9–35 odd, 37–61
Advanced: 9–35 odd, 37–62
Standardized Test Prep: 63–66
Mixed Review: 67–72

**Reasoning** exercises have blue headings.

**Applications** exercises have red headings.

**EXERCISE 56:** Use the Think About a Plan worksheet in the **Practice and Problem Solving Workbook** (also available in the Teaching Resources in print and online) to further support students' development in becoming independent learners.

**HOMEWORK QUICK CHECK**
To check students' understanding of key skills and concepts, go over Exercises 23, 29, 46, 56, and 57.

**28.**  **29.**  **34.**  **35.**  **40.**  **41.**

**30.**  **31.**  **36.**  **37.** **42.**  **43.**

**38.** **44.**

**32.**  **33.**  **39.** **45.**

**46–61.** See next page.

# Answers

## Practice and Problem-Solving Exercises (continued)

**46.** The slope represents the amount of money you put in your wallet each week.

**47.** 0; (0, 3)  **48.** $\frac{2}{3}$; (0, 2)

**49.** $-\frac{1}{4}$; (0, 3)  **50.** $-0.8$; (0, 0.4)

**51.** undefined slope; no $y$-intercept

**52.** 0; (0, 0)  **53.** $-\frac{1}{2}$; $\left(0, -\frac{5}{2}\right)$

**54.** $\frac{A}{B}$; $\left(0, -\frac{C}{B}\right)$  **55.** $-\frac{A}{B}$; $\left(0, \frac{C}{B}\right)$

**56. a.** the rate at which you walk; the slope is the same as the change in distance divided by the change in time, which is the rate at which you walk.

**b.** towards your home; the slope is negative and the distance ($y$-value) decreases as the time ($x$-value) increases.

**57. a.** 1  **b.** 1  **c.** 1  **d.** 1

**e.** Any two points on a line can be used to find the slope of the line.

**58.** He did not isolate $y$ first and then find the coefficient of $x$. The slope is $\frac{2}{3}$.

**59.** $-\frac{5}{13}$  **60.** $\frac{7}{5}$  **61.** $\frac{15}{2}$

**62. a.** $y = \frac{1}{2}x + 4$

**b.** $y = -3x + 4$

**c.** $y = -4x + 9$

## Standardized Test Prep

**63.** B  **64.** G  **65.** C

**66. [2]**

domain: $\{-2, -1, 0\}$,
range: $\{-2, -1, 1, 2\}$

**[1]** incorrect statement of domain or range

## Mixed Review

**67.** domain: $\{-2, 1, 2, 3, 4\}$,
range: $\{-2, -1, 2, 3\}$; no

**68.** domain: all real numbers, range: $y \geq -2$; no

**69.** domain: $\{-5, 0, 2, 9\}$, range: $\{-3, -1, 5, 15\}$; no

**70.** 2  **71.** 8  **72.** 13

---

**62.** You can find the equation of a line through two points even if one point is not the $y$-intercept.
- Find the slope $m$ of the line passing through the two points.
- Using either point, substitute for $x$, $y$, and $m$ into $y = mx + b$.
- Solve for $b$ and rewrite $y = mx + b$ for the values of $m$ and $b$.

Write an equation in slope-intercept form for the line passing through each pair of points.

**a.** (2, 5) and (6, 7)  **b.** (−4, 16) and (3, −5)  **c.** (−2, 17) and (2, 1)

## Standardized Test Prep

**SAT/ACT**

**63.** Which equation does NOT represent a direct variation?

Ⓐ $y - 3x = 0$  Ⓑ $y + 2 = \frac{1}{2}x$  Ⓒ $\frac{y}{x} = \frac{2}{3}$  Ⓓ $y = \frac{x}{17}$

**64.** Which equation models the data in the table?

Ⓕ $y = x^2 - 1$  Ⓗ $y = -x^2 + 3$
Ⓖ $y = x^2 + 3$  Ⓘ $y = x^2 + 1$

| x | y |
|---|---|
| 1 | 4 |
| 2 | 7 |
| 3 | 12 |
| 4 | 19 |

**65.** In the formula $V = \frac{1}{3}\pi r^2 h$, which expression is equal to $h$?

Ⓐ $\frac{V}{3\pi r^2}$  Ⓒ $\frac{3V}{\pi r^2}$

Ⓑ $V - \frac{1}{3}\pi r^2$  Ⓓ $\frac{3V\pi}{r^2}$

**Short Response**

**66.** Graph the relation $\{(-2, 1), (0, 2), (-1, -1), (-2, -2)\}$. What are the domain and range?

## Mixed Review

Find the domain and range of each relation, and determine whether it is a function.  ◆ See Lesson 2-1.

**67.**

**68.**

**69.**

| Domain | Range |
|--------|-------|
| −5 | −3 |
| 0 | −1 |
| 2 | 5 |
| 9 | 15 |

**Get Ready!** To prepare for Lesson 2-4, do Exercises 70–72.

Evaluate each expression for $x = 0$.  ◆ See Lesson 1-3.

**70.** $5x + 2$  **71.** $(x - 4) + 12$  **72.** $13 - 6.5x$

# Lesson Resources

## Differentiated Remediation
Available in editable format online.

## Additional Instructional Support

### Algebra 2 Companion
Students can use the **Algebra 2 Companion** worktext (4 pages) as you teach the lesson. Use the Companion to support

- New Vocabulary
- Key Concepts
- Got It for each Problem
- Lesson Check

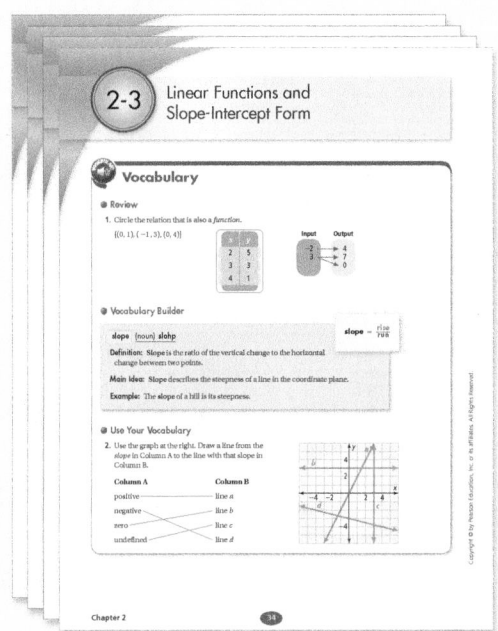

### ELL Support
**Focus on Communication** Divide the class into groups of three. Each student draws a line in a labeled coordinate plane and passes it to the second student. The second student writes the coordinates of the x- and y-intercepts and passes the graph to the third student, who determines whether the slope is positive, negative, zero, or undefined, and labels the line. The students discuss whether they agree with the labels and then switch groups to play again.

## 5 Assess & Remediate

### Lesson Quiz

1. What is the slope of the line that passes through $(-2, 3)$ and $(4, -5)$?
2. What is an equation of the line with slope 4 and y-intercept at $(0, -3)$?
3. Write the equation $12 - y = 2x - 5$ in slope-intercept form. What are the slope and y-intercept?
4. What is the graph of $5x = 2y - 20$?
5. **Do you UNDERSTAND?** Can a horizontal line have an x-intercept? What if the line passes through the origin? Explain.

### ANSWERS TO LESSON QUIZ
1. $-\dfrac{4}{3}$
2. $y = 4x - 3$
3. $y = -2x + 17$, $m = -2$, y-intercept $(0, 17)$
4.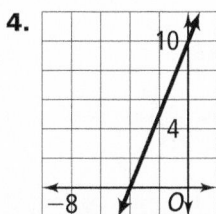
5. A horizontal line cannot have an x-intercept. Even if the horizontal line is the x-axis itself, it will not have an x-intercept, because the x-intercept is defined as the point at which a line *crosses* the x-axis.

**PRESCRIPTION FOR REMEDIATION**
Use the student work on the Lesson Quiz to prescribe a differentiated review assignment:

| Points | Differentiated Remediation |
|--------|---------------------------|
| 0–2 | Intervention |
| 3–4 | On-level |
| 5 | Extension |

**PowerAlgebra.com**

### 5 Assess & Remediate
Assign the Lesson Quiz. Appropriate intervention, practice, or enrichment is automatically generated based on student performance.

## Intervention

- **Reteaching** (2 pages) Provides reteaching and practice exercises for the key lesson concepts. Use with struggling students or absent students.
- **English Language Learner Support** Helps students develop and reinforce mathematical vocabulary and key concepts.

### All-in-One Resources/Online
**Reteaching**

### All-in-One Resources/Online
**English Language Learner Support**

# Differentiated Remediation continued

Available in editable format online.

## On-Level

- **Practice** (2 pages) Provides extra practice for each lesson. For simpler practice exercises, use the Form K Practice pages found in the All-in-One Teaching Resources and online.

- **Think About a Plan** Helps students develop specific problem-solving skills and strategies by providing scaffolded guiding questions.

- **Standardized Test Prep** Focuses on all major exercises, all major question types, and helps students prepare for the high-stakes assessments.

## Extension

- **Enrichment** Provides students with interesting problems and activities that extend the concepts of the lesson.

- **Activities, Games, and Puzzles** Worksheets that can be used for concepts development, enrichment, and for fun!

---

### Practice and Problem Solving Wkbk/All-in-One Resources/Online
#### Practice page 1

### Practice and Problem Solving Wkbk/All-in-One Resources/Online
#### Practice page 2

### All-in-One Resources/Online
#### Enrichment

---

### Practice and Problem Solving Wkbk/All-in-One Resources/Online
#### Think About a Plan

### Practice and Problem Solving Wkbk/All-in-One Resources/Online
#### Standardized Test Prep

### Online Teacher Resource Center
#### Activities, Games, and Puzzles

## 2-4 More About Linear Equations

**Objective** To write an equation of a line given its slope and a point on the line

**SOLVE IT!**

**Getting Ready!**

A contractor needs to build two straight roads, each passing through point A. One road must be parallel to Pine Street and the other road must be perpendicular to Pine Street. Find the coordinates of a second point the parallel road will pass through and the coordinates of a third point the perpendicular road will pass through.

**Lesson Vocabulary**
• point-slope form
• standard form of a linear equation
• parallel lines
• perpendicular lines

If you travel along a line that is parallel to a given line, you will stay the same distance from the given line. If you travel along a line that is perpendicular to a given line, you will travel either toward or away from the given line along the most direct path.

**Essential Understanding** The slopes of two lines in the same plane indicate how the lines are related.

Given the slope and y-intercept, you can write the equation of a line in slope-intercept form. You can also write the equation of a line in *point-slope form*.

### Key Concept   Point-Slope Form

The equation of a line in **point-slope form** through point $(x_1, y_1)$ with slope $m$:
$$y - y_1 = m(x - x_1)$$

**Here's Why It Works** By substituting the general point $(x, y)$, for $(x_2, y_2)$ in the slope formula, you can rewrite the slope formula in point-slope form.

$$m = \frac{y_2 - y_1}{x_2 - x_1} = \frac{y - y_1}{x - x_1}$$

$$m(x - x_1) = \frac{y - y_1}{x - x_1}(x - x_1)$$

$$m(x - x_1) = y - y_1$$

$$y - y_1 = m(x - x_1)$$

---

**Solve It!**

**PURPOSE** Find the coordinates of points that satisfy conditions of parallel and perpendicular lines

**PROCESS** Students may
• sketch lines parallel or perpendicular and choose a point on that line.
• count the units vertically and horizontally from A to find a point on the parallel line.

### FACILITATE

**Q** How could you draw the one line through A that is parallel to Pine Street? **[Answers may vary. Sample: From A, count up and to the right the same as the distance between any two points on Pine Street and plot a point. Draw the line through A and that point.]**

**Q** How could you use the corner of a sheet of paper to find the coordinates of a point on the perpendicular line? [Use the corner to approximate a right angle, and follow the side of the page to find a point.]

**ANSWER** See Solve It in Answers on next page.
**CONNECT THE MATH** In the Solve It, students apply previous knowledge about perpendicular and parallel lines. The lesson compares the slopes of perpendicular and parallel lines.

# 2 Guided Instruction

## Take Note
Show that if $m$ represents the slope, then $m = \frac{y - y_1}{x - x_1}$, so $y - y_1 = m(x - x_1)$.

## Here's Why it Works
In the equation, $x_1$ and $y_1$ represent the coordinates of a given point on the line.

### PowerAlgebra.com

## 1 Interactive Learning

**SOLVE IT!**

**Solve It!**
Step out how to solve the Problem with helpful hints and an online question. Other questions are listed above in Interactive Learning.

---

## 2-4 Preparing to Teach

**BIG idea** Equivalence   **UbD**

**ESSENTIAL UNDERSTANDINGS**
• The slopes of two lines in the same plane indicate how the lines are related.
• Linear functions can be represented by either the slope-intercept, point-slope, or standard form. One version can be transformed to another as needed.

• The shortest distance between a point and a line is the perpendicular distance.
• The slopes of perpendicular lines are negative reciprocals of each other.

## Support Student Learning
Use the **Algebra 2 Companion** to engage and support students during instruction. See Lesson Resources at the end of this lesson for details.

## Math Background
Students know how to compare lines with different slopes: a line of slope 2 is steeper than one with slope $\frac{1}{2}$.

In this lesson, students compare the slopes of parallel and perpendicular lines. Important properties of these lines include:
• Parallel lines are equidistant.
• Parallel lines have the same slope but different y-intercepts.

## Problem 1

Sketch a graph of a line through $(-5, 2)$. Label any other point on the line $(x, y)$ using a magnet or tape. Move $(x, y)$ to a different location on the line to reinforce the idea that it represents *any* point on the line.

### Got It?
**ERROR PREVENTION**

Remind students to be careful with signs.

$$y - y_1 = m(x - x_1)$$
$$y - (-1) = -3(x - 7)$$
$$y + 1 = -3x + 21$$

## Problem 2

When calculating slope, either point can be selected for $(x_1, y_1)$ or $(x_2, y_2)$.

---

**Q** If $(x_1, y_1) = (5, 8)$ and $(x_2, y_2) = (3, 2)$, how would you calculate the slope?
$[m = \dfrac{y_2 - y_1}{x_2 - x_1} = \dfrac{2 - 8}{3 - 5} = \dfrac{-6}{-2} = 3]$

---

The **Think** note refers to substituting for $(x_1, y_1)$ later in the solution process.

### Got It?

---

**Q** Write the equation for 2a in slope-intercept form. Then do the same for 2b. How do the equations compare? **[They are equivalent: $y = \frac{7}{5}x + 7$.]**

---

### Take Note

---

**Q** What variable is used for the coefficient of $x$? for $y$? for the constant term? **[A; B; C]**

**Q** What types of numbers are $A$, $B$, and $C$? **[They must be real numbers.]**

---

Is slope-intercept or point-slope form more helpful for writing this equation?
Since the slope and a point (not the y-intercept) are given, point-slope form is more helpful.

 **Problem 1** Writing an Equation Given a Point and the Slope

A line passes through $(-5, 2)$ with slope $\frac{3}{5}$. What is an equation of the line?

$$y - y_1 = m(x - x_1)$$ Use point-slope form.
$$y - 2 = \frac{3}{5}[x - (-5)]$$ Substitute $m = \frac{3}{5}$ and $(x_1, y_1) = (-5, 2)$.
$$y - 2 = \frac{3}{5}(x + 5)$$ Simplify.

An equation for the line is $y - 2 = \frac{3}{5}(x + 5)$.

✓ **Got It?** **1.** What is an equation of the line through $(7, -1)$ with slope $-3$?

 **Problem 2** Writing an Equation Given Two Points

A line passes through $(3, 2)$ and $(5, 8)$. What is an equation of the line in point-slope form?

| Know | Need | Plan |
|---|---|---|
| Two points | An equation written in point-slope form | Substitute the slope and either point in the point-slope form. |

**Think**

Does it matter which point you substitute into point-slope form?
No; you can choose either point as $(x_1, y_1)$.

Let $(x_1, y_1) = (3, 2)$ and $(x_2, y_2) = (5, 8)$.

$$m = \frac{8 - 2}{5 - 3} = \frac{6}{2} = 3$$ Substitute into the slope formula and simplify.
$$y - 2 = 3(x - 3)$$ Substitute into point-slope form.

✓ **Got It?** **2. a.** A line passes through $(-5, 0)$ and $(0, 7)$. What is an equation of the line in point-slope form?
**b. Reasoning** What is another equation in point-slope form of the line through the points $(-5, 0)$ and $(0, 7)$? Explain.

Another form of the equation of a line is *standard form*, in which the sum of the $x$ and $y$ terms are set equal to a constant. When possible, you write the coefficients of $x$ and $y$ and the constant term as integers.

 **Key Concept** Standard Form of a Linear Equation

A **standard form of a linear equation** is $Ax + By = C$, where $A$, $B$, and $C$ are real numbers and $A$ and $B$ are not *both* zero.

**Chapter 2** Functions, Equations, and Graphs

---

# Answers

### Solve It!
Answers may vary. Sample: (60, 60); (50, 10)

### Got It?
**1.** $y + 1 = -3(x - 7)$

**2. a.** $y - 7 = \frac{7}{5}x$

  **b.** $y = \frac{7}{5}(x + 5)$; either point can be used to put the equation of the line in point-slope form.

**3.** $-91x + 10y = 36$

**4.** $(0, -2)$, $(4, 0)$;

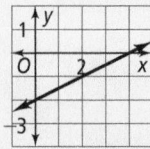

---

**PowerAlgebra.com**

## 2 Guided Instruction

Each Problem is worked out and supported online.

**Problem 1**
Writing an Equation Given a Point and the Slope

**Problem 2**
Writing an Equation Given Two Points
*Animated*

**Problem 3**
Writing an Equation in Standard Form

**Alternative Problem 3**
Writing an Equation in Standard Form
*Animated*

**Problem 4**
Graphing an Equation Using Intercepts

**Problem 5**
Drawing and Interpreting a Linear Graph

**Problem 6**
Writing Equations of Parallel and Perpendicular Lines
*Animated*

**Support in Algebra 2 Companion**
• Vocabulary
• Key Concepts
• Got It?

**82**  **Chapter 2**

### Problem 3 · Writing an Equation in Standard Form

**Think**

How can you rewrite the equation using only integer values?
Multiply each side of the equation by the least common denominator of all fraction coefficients.

What is an equation of the line $y = \frac{3}{4}x - 5$ in standard form? Use integer coefficients.

$$y = \frac{3}{4}x - 5$$

$$-\frac{3}{4}x + y = -5 \qquad \text{Subtract } \frac{3}{4}x \text{ from each side.}$$

$$-3x + 4y = -20 \qquad \text{Multiply each side by 4.}$$

**Got It?** **3.** What is an equation of the line $y = 9.1x + 3.6$ in standard form?

**take note**

### Concept Summary · Writing Equations of Lines

| Slope-Intercept Form | Point-Slope Form | Standard Form |
|---|---|---|
| $y = mx + b$ | $y - y_1 = m(x - x_1)$ | $Ax + By = C$ |
| Use this form when you know the slope and the $y$-intercept. | Use this form when you know the slope and a point, or when you know two points. | $A$, $B$, and $C$ are real numbers. $A$ and $B$ cannot both be zero. |

You can graph an equation in standard form quickly by determining the $x$- and $y$-intercepts and then drawing the line through them.

### Problem 4 · Graphing an Equation Using Intercepts

**Think**

Why set $x = 0$ to find the $y$-intercept?
The $x$-coordinate of any point on the $y$-axis is zero.

What are the intercepts of $3x + 5y = 15$? Graph the equation.

Set $x = 0$ to find the $y$-intercept.

$$3(0) + 5y = 15$$
$$5y = 15$$
$$y = 3$$

Set $y = 0$ to find the $x$-intercept.

$$3x + 5(0) = 15$$
$$3x = 15$$
$$x = 5$$

Step 1 Plot the $y$-intercept: (0, 3).

Step 2 Plot the $x$-intercept: (5, 0).

Step 3 Draw a line through the intercepts.

**Got It?** **4.** What are the intercepts of $2x - 4y = 8$? Graph the equation.

### Problem 3

**Q** Is it necessary to subtract $\frac{3}{4}x$ as the first step? Explain. **[No; you could multiply each side by 4 first and then subtract 3x.]**

### Got It? · ERROR PREVENTION

**Q** How could you write this in standard form with integer coefficients? **[Multiply each side by 10.]**

### Take Note

**Q** In standard form, what kind of line do you get if either $A$ or $B$ is zero? **[If $A = 0$, the line is horizontal; if $B = 0$, the line is vertical.]**

### Problem 4 · TACTILE LEARNERS

Because substituting $x = 0$ or $y = 0$ eliminates a term of the equation, tactile learners may prefer to cover the term with their finger and write the resulting equation with one variable.

### Got It? · SYNTHESIZING

**Q** In Problem 4, the standard form of the equation is $3x + 5y = 15$. Do the coefficients have the same sign or opposite signs? Is the graph's slope positive or negative? **[the same sign; negative]**

**Q** In this problem the standard equation is $2x - 4y = 8$. Do the coefficients have the same sign or opposite signs? Is the graph's slope positive or negative? **[opposite signs; positive]**

**Q** What generalization can you make about a graph's slope? **[Answers may vary. Sample: In standard form, if the coefficients have the same sign, the slope of the graph is negative. If opposite, the slope is positive.]**

## Additional Problems

**1.** A line passes through $(-1, 3)$ with slope $-\frac{2}{3}$. What is an equation of the line?

**ANSWER** $y - 3 = -\frac{2}{3}(x + 1)$

**2.** A line passes through $(5, 1)$ and $(7, 9)$. What is an equation of the line in point-slope form?

**ANSWER** $y - 1 = 4(x - 5)$ or $y - 9 = 4(x - 7)$

**3.** What is an equation of the line $y = \frac{2}{5}x - 3$ in standard form? Use integer coefficients.

**ANSWER** $-2x + 5y = -15$ or $2x - 5y = 15$

**4.** What are the intercepts of $4x + 3y = 12$? Graph the equation.

**ANSWERS** (3, 0) and (0, 4)

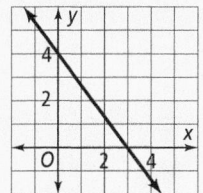

**5.** The cost of a taxi ride depends on the distance traveled. You paid $8.50 for a 3-mile ride, while your friend paid $18.50 for an 8-mile ride.

**a.** What graph models the situation?

**b.** What is an equation of the line in standard form?

**ANSWERS**

**a.**

Taxicab Costs

**b.** $2x - y = -2.50$ or $-2x + y = 2.50$, where $x$ is distance in miles and $y$ is cost in dollars

**6.** What is the equation of each line in slope-intercept form?

**a.** the line parallel to $y = 5x - 4$ through $(-2, 1)$

**b.** the line perpendicular to $y = -2x + \frac{3}{4}$ with the same $y$-intercept as $x + 3y = 12$.

**ANSWERS**

**a.** $y = 5x + 11$

**b.** $y = \frac{1}{2}x + 4$

# Problem 5

> **Q** Which of the equations is in slope-intercept form in 5B? **[$y = 4.5x - 180$]**
>
> **Q** What is the slope? What does it represent in this problem? **[4.5; the change in the number of chirps per 1°F]**

Note that the domain only includes temperatures at or above 40°F since crickets do not chirp at temperatures lower than 40°F.

> **Q** For 5C, does it matter which equation you use? Explain. **[No; answers may vary. Sample: You could use either the standard form or slope-intercept form since they are equivalent.]**

## Got It?

Students may graph the function of packs *used* per number of days, plotting (0, 0) and (80, 140). In order to answer 5c, it makes more sense to find the function of packs *left* per number of days, plotting (0, 140) and (80, 0)

> **Q** What do the *x*-values represent? *y*-values? **[number of days; packs left]**
>
> **Q** The office manager ordered 140 packs of paper. What point represents this situation? Why? **[(0, 140); before any days have passed, the office has 140 packs of paper.]**
>
> **Q** When the office runs out of paper, what point represents this situation? Explain. **[(80, 0); after 80 days pass, there will be 0 packs of paper left.]**

**Think**

How can you find the number of chirps in a minute given the number of chirps in 2 seconds?

There are 60 seconds in 1 minute. Multiply the number of chirps in 2 seconds by $\frac{60}{2}$ or 30.

---

**Problem 5** Drawing and Interpreting a Linear Graph

**Biology** The number of times a cricket chirps per minute depends on the temperature. The number of chirps in 2 seconds for two temperatures are shown at the bottom right.

**Ⓐ** What graph models the situation?

First, find the number of chirps per minute.

$$40°F: 30(0) = 0$$
$$93°F: 30(8) = 240$$

Let $x$ = temperature in degrees Fahrenheit.
Let $y$ = number of times a cricket chirps.

Plot (40,0) and (93, 240).
Draw a line through the points.

**Cricket Chirping**

**Ⓑ** What is an equation of the line in standard form?

$$m = \frac{240 - 0}{93 - 40}$$  Use the slope formula $m = \frac{y_2 - y_1}{x_2 - x_1}$.

$$= \frac{240}{53} \approx 4.5$$  Subtract and simplify.

$$y - y_1 = m(x - x_1)$$  Use point-slope form.

$$y - 0 = 4.5(x - 40)$$  Substitute one of the points: (40, 0).

$$y = 4.5x - 180$$  Simplify.

$$4.5x - y = 180$$  Write in standard form.

**Ⓒ** If the temperature is 70°F, how many times would a cricket be expected to chirp in one minute?

Let $x = 70$.

$$y = 4.5x - 180$$  Use an equation from part (b).

$$y = 4.5(70) - 180$$  Substitute.

$$y = 135$$  Simplify.

If the temperature is 70°F, the cricket would be expected to chirp 135 times in one minute.

 40.0F — 0 chirps
 93.0F — 2 seconds — 8 chirps

✅ **Got It? 5.** The office manager of a small office ordered 140 packs of printer paper. Based on average daily use, she knows that the paper will last about 80 days.
  **a.** What graph represents this situation?
  **b.** What is the equation of the line in standard form?
  **c.** How many packs of printer paper should the manager expect to have after 30 days?

84    Chapter 2   Functions, Equations, and Graphs

---

# Answers

## Got It? (continued)

**5. a.**

**Packs of Paper Left**

**b.** $7x + 4y = 560$

**c.** 87.5

84    **Chapter 2**

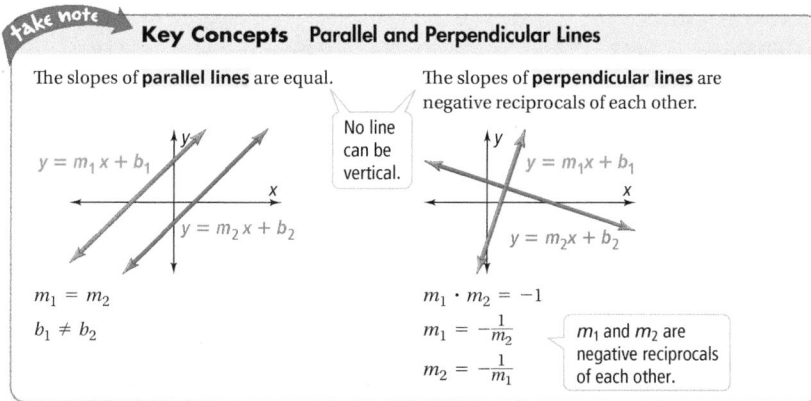

## Key Concepts  Parallel and Perpendicular Lines

The slopes of **parallel lines** are equal.

$y = m_1 x + b_1$

$y = m_2 x + b_2$

No line can be vertical.

$m_1 = m_2$

$b_1 \neq b_2$

The slopes of **perpendicular lines** are negative reciprocals of each other.

$y = m_1 x + b_1$

$y = m_2 x + b_2$

$m_1 \cdot m_2 = -1$

$m_1 = -\frac{1}{m_2}$

$m_2 = -\frac{1}{m_1}$

$m_1$ and $m_2$ are negative reciprocals of each other.

---

**Problem 6**  Writing Equations of Parallel and Perpendicular Lines

**What is the equation of each line in slope-intercept form?**

Ⓐ the line parallel to $y = 6x - 2$ through $(1, -3)$

Identify the slope, use point-slope form, and rewrite in slope-intercept form.

| | |
|---|---|
| $m = 6$ | Parallel lines have the same slope. The slope of the line with equation $y = 6x - 2$ is 6. |
| $y - y_1 = m(x - x_1)$ | Point-slope form |
| $y - (-3) = 6(x - 1)$ | Substitute 6 for $m$ and $(1, -3)$ for $(x_1, y_1)$. |
| $y + 3 = 6x - 6$ | Distributive Property |
| $y = 6x - 9$ | Write in slope-intercept form. |

Ⓑ the line perpendicular to $y = -4x + \frac{2}{3}$ through $(8, 5)$

Identify the slope, use point-slope form, and rewrite in slope-intercept form.

| | |
|---|---|
| $m = -\frac{1}{-4} = \frac{1}{4}$ | The slopes of perpendicular lines are negative reciprocals. |
| $y - y_1 = m(x - x_1)$ | Point-slope form |
| $y - 5 = \frac{1}{4}(x - 8)$ | Substitute $\frac{1}{4}$ for $m$ and $(8, 5)$ for $(x_1, y_1)$. |
| $y - 5 = \frac{1}{4}x - 2$ | Distributive Property |
| $y = \frac{1}{4}x + 3$ | Write in slope-intercept form. |

**Plan**

**How can you find the slope of a perpendicular line?**
Slopes of perpendicular lines are negative reciprocals, so use the equation $m_1 = -\frac{1}{m_2}$.

**Got It?**  **6.** What is the equation of each line in slope-intercept form?
  **a.** the line parallel to $4x + 2y = 7$ through $(4, -2)$
  **b.** the line perpendicular to $y = \frac{2}{3}x - 1$ through $(0, 6)$

---

### Take Note

**Q** When would you start with point-slope form rather than slope-intercept form? **[when the information given is a point and a slope]**

**Q** Notice that the $y$-intercepts of two parallel lines must be different. Can the $y$-intercepts of two perpendicular lines be the same? Explain your answer. **[Yes; the lines can intersect on the $y$-axis.]**

Draw a sketch to illustrate this point, having a student (or students) working at the board.

### Problem 6    ERROR PREVENTION

Have students graph $y = 6x - 2$ and $y = 6x - 9$ to visually check that the lines are parallel.

If students have difficulty with 6B because there are 3 equations involved, have them graph the 3 equations.

### Got It?

**Q** Do you have to use point-slope form to solve these types of problems? Explain. **[No; you could use slope-intercept form $y = mx + b$; substitute the slope and one point for $x$ and $y$, and solve for $b$; then write the equation $y = mx + b$ with the values of $m$ and $b$ substituted.]**

---

**6. a.** $y = -2x + 6$

  **b.** $y = -\frac{3}{2}x + 6$

# 3 Lesson Check

## Do you know HOW?  ERROR INTERVENTION

- For Exercises 4–5, if students are confused about which form to use, have them review Problem 6. They are now being asked to find equations in standard form, which they can derive from slope-intercept form.

## Do you UNDERSTAND?

- For Exercise 6, have students list the differences between the various forms of the linear equation.

## Close

> **Q** How does the format of the equation identify its form? **[Standard form has both variables on one side of the equation, slope-intercept form has $y$ alone on one side of the equation, and point-slope form has $y$ and a $y$-value on one side of the equation.]**

---

 **Lesson Check**

### Do you know HOW?

Write an equation of each line in slope-intercept form.

1. slope $-3$; through $(1, -4)$

2. slope $\frac{1}{2}$; through $(2, 3)$

3. What are the intercepts of $3x + y = 6$? Graph the equation.

Write an equation of each line in standard form.

4. the line parallel to $y = -3x + 4$ through $(0, -1)$

5. the line perpendicular to $-2x + 3y = 9$ through $(-1, -3)$

### Do you UNDERSTAND?

6. **Vocabulary** Tell whether each equation is in slope-intercept, point-slope, or standard form.
   a. $y + 2 = -2(x - 1)$    b. $y = -\frac{1}{4}x + 9$
   c. $-x - 2y = 1$    d. $y - 3 = 4x$

7. Which form would you use to write the equation of a line if you knew its slope and $x$-intercept? Explain.

8. If the intercepts of a line are $(a, 0)$ and $(0, b)$, what is the slope of the line?

9. **Error Analysis** Your friend says the line $y = -2x + 3$ is perpendicular to the line $x + 2y = 8$. Do you agree? Explain.

---

## Practice and Problem-Solving Exercises

**A** Practice

Write an equation of each line.    *See Problem 1.*

10. slope $= 3$; through $(1, 5)$    11. slope $= \frac{5}{6}$; through $(22, 12)$    12. slope $= -\frac{3}{5}$; through $(-4, 0)$

13. slope $= 0$; through $(4, -2)$    14. slope $= -1$; through $(-3, 5)$    15. slope $= 5$; through $(0, 2)$

Write in point-slope form an equation of the line through each pair of points.    *See Problem 2.*

16. $(-10, 3)$ and $(-2, -5)$    17. $(1, 0)$ and $(5, 5)$    18. $(-4, 10)$ and $(-6, 15)$

19. $(0, -1)$ and $(3, -5)$    20. $(7, 11)$ and $(13, 17)$    21. $(1, 9)$ and $(6, 2)$

Write an equation of each line in standard form with integer coefficients.    *See Problem 3.*

22. $y = \frac{1}{2}x - 2$    23. $y = -7x - 9$    24. $y = -\frac{3}{5}x + 3$    25. $y = 4.2x + 7.9$

Find the intercepts and graph each line.    *See Problem 4.*

26. $x - 4y = -4$    27. $2x + 5y = -10$    28. $-3x + 2y = 6$    29. $5x + 7y = 14$

Write and graph an equation to represent each situation.    *See Problem 5.*

30. You put 15 gallons of gasoline in your car. You know that this amount of gasoline will allow you to drive about 450 miles.

31. A meal plan lets students buy $20 meal cards. Each meal card lasts about 8 days.

Write the equation of the line through each point. Use slope-intercept form.    *See Problem 6.*

32. $(1, -1)$; parallel to $y = \frac{2}{5}x - 3$    33. $(-3, 1)$; perpendicular to $y = -\frac{2}{5}x - 4$

34. $(-7, 10)$; parallel to $2x - 3y = -3$    35. $(-2, 1)$; perpendicular to $3x + y = 1$

---

## 3 Lesson Check

For a digital lesson check, use the Got It questions.

**Support in Algebra 2 Companion**
- Lesson Check

## 4 Practice

Assign homework to individual students or to an entire class.

---

# Answers

## Lesson Check

1. $y = -3x - 1$    2. $y = \frac{1}{2}x + 2$

3. $(0, 6), (2, 0)$

4. $3x + y = -1$    5. $3x + 2y = -9$

6. a. point-slope    b. slope-intercept
   c. standard    d. point-slope

7. Point-slope form; since the $x$-intercept is the point where $y$ is zero, you know the point on the line, $(x, 0)$, and you know the slope.

8. $-\frac{b}{a}$

9. No; one line has a slope of $-2$ and the other line has a slope of $-\frac{1}{2}$. $-\frac{1}{2}$ is the reciprocal of $-2$, not the *negative* reciprocal.

## Practice and Problem-Solving Exercises

10. $y - 5 = 3(x - 1)$

11. $y - 12 = \frac{5}{6}(x - 22)$

12. $y = -\frac{3}{5}(x + 4)$

13. $y + 2 = 0$

14. $y - 5 = -(x + 3)$

15. $y - 2 = 5x$

16. Sample: $y - 3 = -(x + 10)$ or $y + 5 = -(x + 2)$

17. Sample: $y = \frac{5}{4}(x - 1)$ or $y - 5 = \frac{5}{4}(x - 5)$

18. Sample: $y - 10 = -\frac{5}{2}(x + 4)$ or $y - 15 = -\frac{5}{2}(x + 6)$

19. Sample: $y + 1 = -\frac{4}{3}x$ or $y + 5 = -\frac{4}{3}(x - 3)$

20. Sample: $y - 11 = x - 7$ or $y - 17 = x - 13$

21–35. See next page.

Graph each equation.

**36.** $3x + 5y = 12$   **37.** $2x + y = 3$   **38.** $6y - 4x = -24$

**39.** $3y - x = -6$   **40.** $-20x - 45y = 48$   **41.** $2x - \frac{3}{2}y = -3$

Write an equation of the line through each pair of points. Use point-slope form.

**42.** $\left(\frac{3}{2}, -\frac{1}{2}\right)$ and $\left(-\frac{2}{3}, \frac{1}{3}\right)$   **43.** $\left(-\frac{1}{2}, -\frac{1}{2}\right)$ and $(-3, -4)$   **44.** $\left(0, \frac{1}{2}\right)$ and $\left(\frac{5}{7}, 0\right)$

**45. Think About a Plan** Write an equation for the line shown here. Each interval is 1 unit.
  • What do you know from the graph?
  • Which form of the equation of a line could you use with the information you have?

Write an equation for each line. Each interval is 1 unit.

**46.**    **47.**

Find the slope, if any, and the intercepts, if any, of each line.

**48.** $f(x) = \frac{2}{3}x + 4$   **49.** $y = -x + 1000$   **50.** $y + 0.8x = 0.4$

**51.** $g(x) = 54x - 1$   **52.** $x + 3 = 0$   **53.** $y + 3 = 3$

**54. a.** Write the point-slope form of the line that passes through $A(-3, 12)$ and $B(9, -4)$. Use point $A$ in the equation.
  **b.** Write the point-slope form of the same line using point $B$ in the equation.
  **c.** Rewrite each equation in standard form. What do you notice?

Write an equation for each line. Then graph the line.

**55.** $m = 0$, through $(5, -1)$   **56.** $m = \frac{5}{6}$, through $(-4, 0)$   **57.** $m = -\frac{3}{2}$, through $(0, -1)$

**58. Reasoning** Suppose lines $\ell_1$ and $\ell_2$ intersect at the origin. Also, $\ell_1$ has slope $\frac{y}{x}$ ($x > 0, y > 0$) and $\ell_2$ has slope $-\frac{x}{y}$. Then $\ell_1$ contains $(x, y)$ and $\ell_2$ contains $(-y, x)$.
  **a.** Explain why the two right triangles are congruent.
  **b.** Complete each equation about the angle measures $a$, $b$, $c$, and $d$.

$a = \blacksquare$   $c = \blacksquare$
$a + c = \blacksquare$   $b + d = \blacksquare$

  **c.** What must be true about $a + b$? Why?
  **d.** What must be true about $\ell_1$ and $\ell_2$? Why?

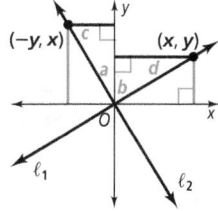

# 4 Practice

## ASSIGNMENT GUIDE
Basic: 10–35 all, 38–44 even, 45, 46–56 even

Average: 11–35 odd, 36–58

Advanced: 11–35 odd, 36–62

Standardized Test Prep: 63–65

Mixed Review: 66–75

**Reasoning** exercises have blue headings.

**Applications** exercises have red headings.

**EXERCISE 54:** Use the Think About a Plan worksheet in the **Practice and Problem Solving Workbook** (also available in the Teaching Resources in print and online) to further support students' development in becoming independent learners.

## HOMEWORK QUICK CHECK
To check students' understanding of key skills and concepts, go over Exercises 27, 31, 33, 45, and 54.

---

**21.** Sample: $y - 9 = -\frac{7}{5}(x - 1)$ or $y - 2 = -\frac{7}{5}(x - 6)$

**22.** $-x + 2y = -4$

**23.** $7x + y = -9$

**24.** $3x + 5y = 15$

**25.** $-42x + 10y = 79$

**26.** $(0, 1), (-4, 0)$

**27.** $(0, -2), (-5, 0)$

**28.** $(0, 3), (-2, 0)$   **29.** $(0, 2), \left(\frac{14}{5}, 0\right)$

   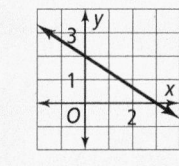

**30.** $y = -\frac{1}{30}x + 15$

**Gas Mileage**

**31.** $y = -2.5x + 20$

**Meal Cards**

**32.** $y = \frac{2}{5}x - \frac{7}{5}$

**33.** $y = \frac{5}{2}x + \frac{17}{2}$

**34.** $y = \frac{2}{3}x + \frac{44}{3}$

**35.** $y = \frac{1}{3}x + \frac{5}{3}$

**36.**     **37.**

**38.**    **39.**

**40–58.** See next page.

# Answers

## Practice and Problem-Solving Exercises (continued)

**40.**  **41.**

**42.** $y - \frac{1}{3} = -\frac{5}{13}\left(x + \frac{2}{3}\right)$ or
$y + \frac{1}{2} = -\frac{5}{13}\left(x - \frac{3}{2}\right)$

**43.** $y + 4 = \frac{7}{5}(x + 3)$ or
$y + \frac{1}{2} = \frac{7}{5}\left(x + \frac{1}{2}\right)$

**44.** $y - \frac{1}{2} = -\frac{7}{10}x$ or $y = -\frac{7}{10}\left(x - \frac{5}{7}\right)$

**45.** $y = \frac{3}{4}x + 3$  **46.** $y = 3x + 2$

**47.** $y = -\frac{3}{2}x - \frac{1}{2}$  **48.** $\frac{2}{3}$; $(0, 4)$, $(-6, 0)$

**49.** $-1$; $(0, 1000)$, $(1000, 0)$

**50.** $-0.8$; $(0, 0.4)$, $(0.5, 0)$

**51.** $54$; $(0, -1)$, $\left(\frac{1}{54}, 0\right)$

**52.** undefined slope; no $y$-intercept, $(-3, 0)$

**53.** $0$; $(0, 0)$, all points on $x$-axis

**54. a.** $y - 12 = -\frac{4}{3}(x + 3)$

    **b.** $y + 4 = -\frac{4}{3}(x - 9)$

    **c.** They have the same standard form:
$4x + 3y = 24$.

**55.** $y = -1$  **56.** $y = \frac{5}{6}x + \frac{10}{3}$

**57.** $y = -\frac{3}{2}x - 1$

**58. a.** The rt. triangles have the same length
legs ($x$ and $y$) as the congruent rt. angle,
so by SAS congruence the triangles are
congruent.

    **b.** $a = d$; $c = b$; $a + c = 90°$; $b + d = 90°$

    **c.** $a + c = 90°$, and $c = b$, therefore
$a + b = 90°$

    **d.** $\ell_1$ and $\ell_2$ must be perpendicular because
they intersect at a rt. angle.

**59.** yes  **60.** no

**61.** The eq. of the line connecting $(1, 3)$ to $(-2, 6)$
is $y = -x + 4$. The eq. of the line connecting
$(1, 3)$ to $(3, 5)$ is $y = x + 2$. The slopes are
neg. reciprocals so the lines are perpendicular.

---

**Challenge** Points that are on the same line are *collinear.* Use the definition of slope to
determine whether the given points are collinear.

**59.** $(-2, 6)$, $(0, 2)$, $(1, 0)$        **60.** $(3, -5)$, $(-3, 3)$, $(0, 2)$

**61. Geometry** Prove that the triangle with vertices $(3, 5)$, $(-2, 6)$, and $(1, 3)$ is a right
triangle.

**62. Geometry** Prove that the quadrilateral with vertices $(2, 5)$, $(4, 8)$, $(7, 6)$, and $(5, 3)$ is
a rectangle.

### Standardized Test Prep

**SAT/ACT**

**63.** Which line is perpendicular to the line shown in the graph?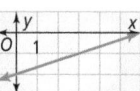

    (A) $-3x + y = 5$      (C) $x - 3y = 0$

    (B) $3x + y = -1$      (D) $x + 3y = -3$

**64.** Which line is parallel to the line $5x + 6y = 30$?

    (F) $5x + 9y = 30$    (G) $9x + 6y = 30$    (H) $5x + 6y = 9$    (I) $6x + 5y = 30$

**Short Response**

**65.** What is the solution of the inequality $|x - 3| \geq 5$? Graph the solution.

### Mixed Review

Find the domain and range of each relation and determine whether it is a
function.     ◆ **See Lesson 2-1.**

**66.** $\{(-3, 4), (-1, 2), (0, -2), (1, 0), (2, 2)\}$    **67.**     **68.**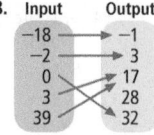

Name the property of real numbers illustrated by each equation.     ◆ **See Lesson 1-2.**

**69.** $\frac{2}{5} + \frac{27}{5} \cdot \frac{5}{27} = \frac{2}{5} + 1$      **70.** $97(7) = 100(7) - 3(7)$      **71.** $21 + 19.7 - 19.7 = 21$

**Get Ready!** To prepare for Lesson 2-5, do Exercises 72–75.

Write the equation for each line. Use slope-intercept form.     ◆ **See Lesson 2-3.**

**72.** $m = 3$ and the $y$-intercept is $(0, -5)$.      **73.** $m = \frac{1}{2}$ and the $y$-intercept is $(0, 0)$.

**74.** $m = \frac{4}{5}$ and the $y$-intercept is $(0, 7)$.      **75.** $m = -\frac{3}{8}$ and the $y$-intercept is $(0, 12)$.

**88**    Chapter 2   Functions, Equations, and Graphs

---

Therefore, by def. of a rt. triangle, it is
a rt. triangle.

**62.** The slope of the line connecting
$(2, 5)$ to $(4, 8)$ is $\frac{3}{2}$, $(2, 5)$ to $(5, 3)$ is
$-\frac{2}{3}$, $(4, 8)$ to $(7, 6)$ is $-\frac{2}{3}$, and $(5, 3)$
to $(7, 6)$ is $\frac{3}{2}$. Since the adjacent
sides' slopes are neg. reciprocals, they
are perpendicular. By the def. of a
rectangle, it is a rectangle.

### Standardized Test Prep

**63.** B            **64.** H

**65.** [2] $|x - 3| \geq 5$
         $x - 3 \geq 5$ or $x - 3 \leq -5$
         $x \geq 8$ or $x \leq -2$

    [1] open circles on graph or a
computational error

### Mixed Review

**66.** domain: $\{-3, -1, 0, 1, 2\}$, range:
$\{-2, 0, 2, 4\}$; yes

**67.** domain: all real numbers, range:
$\{-2\}$; yes

**68.** domain: $\{-18, -2, 0, 3, 39\}$,
range: $\{-1, 3, 17, 28, 32\}$; yes

**69.** Multiplicative Inv.

**70.** Distr. Prop.      **71.** Add. Inv., Add.
                            Ident.

**72.** $y = 3x - 5$      **73.** $y = \frac{1}{2}x$

**74.** $y = \frac{4}{5}x + 7$      **75.** $y = -\frac{3}{8}x + 12$

# Lesson Resources

## Differentiated Remediation
Available in editable format online.

## Additional Instructional Support

### Algebra 2 Companion

Students can use the **Algebra 2 Companion** worktext (4 pages) as you teach the lesson. Use the Companion to support

- New Vocabulary
- Key Concepts
- Got It for each Problem
- Lesson Check

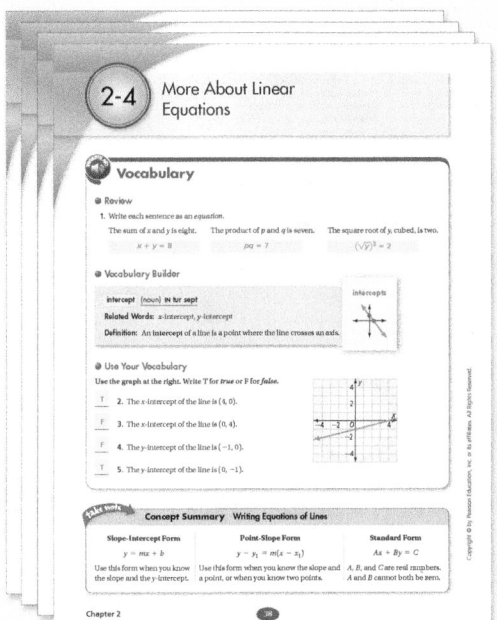

### ELL Support

**Use Graphic Organizers** Sketch and have students copy the following graphic organizer. Students should finish filling out the table by rewriting each equation in the two other forms.

| Point-Slope | Standard | Slope-Intercept |
|---|---|---|
| $y - 1 = 2(x + 5)$ | | |
| | $2x - 5y = 18$ | |
| | | $y = mx + b$ |

## 5 Assess & Remediate

### Lesson Quiz

1. A line passes through $(2, -1)$ with slope 3. What is the equation of the line in point-slope form?
2. A line passes through $(3, 5)$ and $(6, 14)$. What is the equation of the line in point-slope form?
3. What is the equation of the line $y = -0.25x + 1$ in standard form? Use integer coefficients.
4. What are the intercepts of $4x - 5y = -20$?
5. **Do you UNDERSTAND?** You sell sporting goods. Your wages depend on the value of your sales. One week you sold \$3,500 in sporting goods, earning \$950. Another week you sold \$2,800 in sporting goods, earning \$810. Write an equation of the line in standard form.
6. What is the equation of each line in slope-intercept form?
   a. parallel to $y = 3x + 1$ through $(4, -1)$
   b. perpendicular to $y = 3x - 4$ with the same $y$-intercept as $-x + 5y = 10$.

### ANSWERS TO LESSON QUIZ

1. $y + 1 = 3(x - 2)$
2. $y - 5 = 3(x - 3)$ or $y - 14 = 3(x - 6)$
3. Answers may vary. Sample: $x + 4y = 4$
4. $(-5, 0)$ and $(0, 4)$
5. $-x + 5y = 1250$ or $x - 5y = -1250$, where $x$ is sales and $y$ is wages
6. a. $y = 3x - 13$
   b. $y = -\frac{1}{3}x + 2$

### PRESCRIPTION FOR REMEDIATION

Use the student work on the Lesson Quiz to prescribe a differentiated review assignment:

| Points | Differentiated Remediation |
|---|---|
| 0–3 | Intervention |
| 4–5 | On-level |
| 6 | Extension |

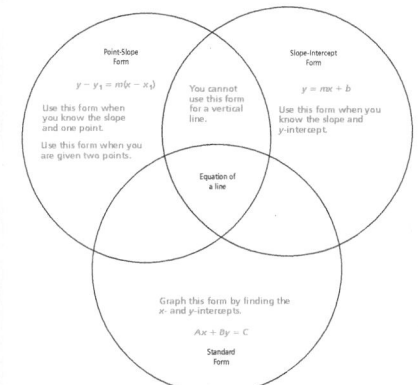

## 5 Assess & Remediate

Assign the Lesson Quiz. Appropriate intervention, practice, or enrichment is automatically generated based on student performance.

## Intervention

- **Reteaching** (2 pages) Provides reteaching and practice exercises for the key lesson concepts. Use with struggling students or absent students.
- **English Language Learner Support** Helps students develop and reinforce mathematical vocabulary and key concepts.

### All-in-One Resources/Online
**Reteaching**

**2-4 Reteaching**
More About Linear Equations

You can use the point-slope form to write equations of lines if you are given two points on the line. The point-slope form of a linear equation is:

$$y - y_1 = m(x - x_1)$$

**Problem**

What is the point-slope form of an equation of the line through $(3, 4)$ and $(5, -2)$?

Find the slope. Substitute for each variable using the coordinates of the given points.

Let $(x_1, y_1) = (3, 4)$ and $(x_2, y_2) = (5, -2)$.  Identify each point.

So $x_1 = 3$, $y_1 = 4$, $x_2 = 5$, and $y_2 = -2$.  Identify $x_1$, $x_2$, $y_1$, and $y_2$.

$m = \frac{y_2 - y_1}{x_2 - x_1} = \frac{-2 - 4}{5 - 3} = \frac{-6}{2} = -3$  Substitute the $x$- and $y$-values and simplify.

The slope is $-3$.

Write the equation of the line in point-slope form. Substitute one point and the slope into the point-slope formula. It does not matter which point is substituted into the point-slope formula.

Let $(x_1, y_1) = (3, 4)$.  Use either of the points as $(x_1, y_1)$.

So $x_1 = 3$, $y_1 = 4$, and $m = -3$.  Identify the values of $x_1$, $y_1$, and $m$.

$y - y_1 = m(x - x_1)$  Write the point-slope form.

$y - 4 = -3(x - 3)$  Substitute the values of $x_1$, $y_1$, and $m$.

An equation for the line in point-slope form is $y - 4 = -3(x - 3)$.

**Exercises**

Using point-slope form, write an equation of the line through each pair of points.

1. $(6, -7)$ and $(4, -1)$  $y + 7 = -3(x - 6)$
2. $(3, 5)$ and $(0, 7)$  $y - 5 = -\frac{2}{3}(x - 3)$
3. $(-1, 3)$ and $(2, 6)$  $y - 3 = x + 1$
4. $(-1, -2)$ and $(0, -1)$  $y + 2 = x + 1$
5. $(-2, -5)$ and $(8, -3)$  $y + 5 = \frac{1}{5}(x + 2)$
6. $(-1, 3)$ and $(-7, -6)$  $y - 3 = \frac{3}{2}(x + 1)$
7. $(-3, 8)$ and $(-2, 4)$  $y - 8 = -4(x + 3)$
8. $(0, -2)$ and $(9, 3)$  $y + 2 = \frac{5}{9}x$

### All-in-One Resources/Online
**English Language Learner Support**

**2-4 ELL Support**
More About Linear Equations

1. Write each equation in the correct location in the circles below.
$y = mx + b$   $y - y_1 = m(x - x_1)$   $Ax + By = C$

2. Each sentence below describes one or more of the equations. Write each sentence in the correct location in the circles below.
   - Use this form when you know the slope and one point.
   - Graph this form by finding the $x$- and $y$-intercepts.
   - You cannot use this form for a vertical line.
   - Use this form when you know the slope and $y$-intercept.
   - Use this form when you are given two points.

# Differentiated Remediation _continued_

Available in editable format online.

## On-Level

- **Practice** (2 pages) Provides extra practice for each lesson. For simpler practice exercises, use the Form K Practice pages found in the All-in-One Teaching Resources and online.

- **Think About a Plan** Helps students develop specific problem-solving skills and strategies by providing scaffolded guiding questions.

- **Standardized Test Prep** Focuses on all major exercises, all major question types, and helps students prepare for the high-stakes assessments.

## Extension

- **Enrichment** Provides students with interesting problems and activities that extend the concepts of the lesson.

- **Activities, Games, and Puzzles** Worksheets that can be used for concepts development, enrichment, and for fun!

### Practice and Problem Solving Wkbk/ All-in-One Resources/Online
#### Practice page 1

### Practice and Problem Solving Wkbk/ All-in-One Resources/Online
#### Practice page 2

### All-in-One Resources/Online
#### Enrichment

### Practice and Problem Solving Wkbk/ All-in-One Resources/Online
#### Think About a Plan

### Practice and Problem Solving Wkbk/ All-in-One Resources/Online
#### Standardized Test Prep

### Online Teacher Resource Center
#### Activities, Games, and Puzzles

MathXL® for School
Go to PowerAlgebra.com

## Do you know HOW?

**Determine whether each relation is a function.**

**1.**

| x | y |
|---|---|
| 3 | 7 |
| 4 | 2 |
| 3 | 2 |
| 5 | 1 |

**2.**

| x | y |
|---|---|
| 1 | 4 |
| 2 | 3 |
| 3 | 3 |
| 4 | 4 |

**Find the *x*- and *y*-intercepts of each line.**

**3.** $x - 3y = 9$

**4.** $y = 7x + 5$

**5.** $y = 6x$

**6.** $-4x + y = 10$

**Write the equation of each line in slope-intercept form and identify the slope.**

**7.** $2x - y = 9$

**8.** $4x = 2 + y$

**9.** $5y = -3x - 10$

**10.** $4x + 6y = 12$

**Write an equation of each line in standard form with integer coefficients.**

**11.** the line through $(2, 3)$ and $(4, 5)$

**12.** the line through $(-4, 6)$ and $(2, -2)$

**13.** the line through $(-4, 2)$ with slope 3

**14.** the line through $(1, 2)$ with slope $\frac{4}{5}$

**15.** a line through $(3, 1)$ with slope 0

**16.** a line with slope of $\frac{2}{3}$ and *y*-intercept $(0, 5)$

**17.** $2y = -4x - 12$

**18.** $\frac{2}{3}x + 3 = 6y - 15$

**Write an equation of each line in point-slope form.**

**19.** $(-4, 2)$ and $(-3, 5)$

**20.** $(0, 0)$ and $(-4, -5)$

**21.** $(-4, -3)$ and $(2, 7)$

**Graph each equation.**

**22.** $2y = 4x + 8$

**23.** $2x - 3y = 6$

**24.** $4y - x = 16$

**For each function, determine whether *y* varies directly with *x*. If so, identify the constant of variation.**

**25.** $2y = 3x$

**26.** $4y - 7x = 0$

**27.** $y + \frac{3}{4}x = 12$

## Do you UNDERSTAND?

**28. a.** A group of friends is going to the movies. Each ticket costs $8.00. Write an equation to model the total cost of the group's tickets.
**b.** Graph the equation. Explain what the *x*- and *y*-intercepts represent.
**c.** What would be the cost for 12 tickets?
**d.** Writing Could the domain include fractions? Explain.

**29.** Which line is perpendicular to $3x + 2y = 6$?
Ⓐ $4x - 6y = 3$   Ⓒ $2x + 3y = 12$
Ⓑ $y = -\frac{3}{2}x + 4$   Ⓓ $y = \frac{3}{2}x + 1$

**30.** Reasoning Why is the slope of a vertical line undefined?

**31.** Suppose $m = 25 - 0.15n$ describes the amount of money remaining on a $25 phone card *m*, as a function of the number of minutes of calls you make *n*. What are a reasonable domain and range?

**24.**

**25.** yes; $\frac{3}{2}$

**26.** yes; $\frac{7}{4}$

**27.** no

**28. a.** $y = 8x$ where $x$ = number of tickets
**b.**

Both intercepts are zero when no one has bought any tickets
**c.** $96
**d.** No; the number of tickets must be a whole number.

**29.** A

**30.** The change in $x$ is 0 in a vertical line, so the slope formula has a 0 in the denominator and is undefined.

**31.** domain: all real numbers 0 to $166\frac{2}{3}$; range: all real numbers 0 to 25

# Answers

**1.** no

**2.** yes

**3.** $(9, 0), (0, -3)$

**4.** $\left(-\frac{5}{7}, 0\right), (0, 5)$

**5.** $(0, 0)$

**6.** $\left(-\frac{5}{2}, 0\right), (0, 10)$

**7.** $y = 2x - 9; 2$

**8.** $y = 4x - 2; 4$

**9.** $y = -\frac{3}{5}x - 2; -\frac{3}{5}$

**10.** $y = -\frac{2}{3}x + 2; -\frac{2}{3}$

**11.** $-x + y = 1$

**12.** $4x + 3y = 2$

**13.** $-3x + y = 14$

**14.** $-4x + 5y = 6$

**15.** $y = 1$

**16.** $-2x + 3y = 15$

**17.** $2x + y = -6$

**18.** $x - 9y = -27$

**19.** $y - 2 = 3(x + 4)$ or
$y - 5 = 3(x + 3)$

**20.** $y = \frac{5}{4}x$ or $y + 5 = \frac{5}{4}(x + 4)$

**21.** $y - 7 = \frac{5}{3}(x - 2)$ or
$y + 3 = \frac{5}{3}(x + 4)$

**22.**

**23.**

# Guided Instruction

**PURPOSE** To graph, write, and apply piecewise functions

**PROCESS** Students will
- graph the absolute value function and the greatest integer function.
- write a piecewise function rule for a graph.
- identify characteristics of piecewise functions.
- use a piecewise function to solve a problem.

**DISCUSS** The absolute value function can be written using one rule: $f(x) = |x|$. It can also be written using more than one rule, as a piecewise function.

**ERROR PREVENTION**
Students may think that $-x$ represents a negative number. If $x$ is negative, $-x$ is positive.

## Example 1

**1.** $f(x) = \begin{cases} -x, & \text{if } x \leq 0 \\ x, & \text{if } x > 0 \end{cases}$

**2.** $f(x) = \begin{cases} -x, & \text{if } x < 0 \\ x, & \text{if } x > 0 \end{cases}$

> **Q** Consider the functions above. Which function is identical to the absolute value function? Explain. **[1; it assigns the same function values as the absolute value function to all $x$-values. Function 2 is different, since it does not assign any function value to $x = 0$.]**

## Example 2

> **Q** Is there a gap in the function? Explain. **[No; the second part of the function is directly above the first part where $x = 2$. Also, you can tell that there is no gap in the domain by looking at the function; 2 is included.]**

---

Recall from Lesson 1-6 that $|x|$, the absolute value of $x$, is the distance of $x$ from zero. When $x \geq 0$, $|x| = x$. When $x < 0$, $|x| = -x$. The absolute value function is an example of a *piecewise function*. A **piecewise function** has different rules for different parts of its domain.

### Example 1

Graph the absolute value function $f(x) = \begin{cases} x, & \text{for } x \geq 0 \\ -x, & \text{for } x < 0 \end{cases}$.

Graph each piece separately.

$f(x) = -x$      $f(x) = x$

### Example 2

Use a graphing calculator to graph the function $f(x) = \begin{cases} -2x + 3, & \text{if } x < 2 \\ x - 1, & \text{if } x \geq 2 \end{cases}$.

Define the function $f(x)$. Use the brackets from the math expression templates to enter the piecewise function.

Enter the rules for the two branches. Set $f_1(x) = f(x)$ and graph.

Step functions are piecewise functions. A **step function** pairs every number in an interval with a single value. The graph of a step function can look like the steps of a staircase. One step function is the **greatest integer function** $y = [x]$, where $[x]$ represents the greatest integer less than or equal to $x$.

## Example 3

**What is the graph of the function $f(x) = [x]$?**

Each piece of the graph is a horizontal segment that is missing its right endpoint. The open circle indicates that the right endpoint is not part of the graph.

Given a piecewise function in one form, you can represent it in each of the other forms, including a table, graph, algebraic function, or verbal statement.

## Example 4

**Media Postage** You want to mail a book that weighs 2.5 lb. The table lists postage for a book weighing up to 3 lb. Define and graph the media-postage function. How much will you pay in postage?

$$f(x) = \begin{cases} 2.23, & \text{for } 0 < x \le 1 \\ 2.58, & \text{for } 1 < x \le 2 \\ 2.93, & \text{for } 2 < x \le 3 \end{cases}$$

Since $2 < 2.5 \le 3$, you will pay $2.93.

**Media Postage**

| Weight (lb) | Price ($) |
|---|---|
| $x \le 1$ | 2.23 |
| $1 < x \le 2$ | 2.58 |
| $2 < x \le 3$ | 2.93 |

## Example 5

**What piecewise function represents the graph?**

**Piece 1** When $x \le -2$, the rule is $f(x) = 2x + 6$.

**Piece 2** When $-2 < x \le 0$, the rule is $f(x) = -2x - 2$.

**Piece 3** When $x > 0$, the rule is $f(x) = 3x - 2$.

$$f(x) = \begin{cases} 2x + 6, & \text{for } x \le -2 \\ -2x - 2, & \text{for } -2 < x \le 0 \\ 3x - 2, & \text{for } x > 0 \end{cases}$$

## Exercises

1. Graph the sign function. $f(x) = \begin{cases} -1, & \text{for } x < 0 \\ 0, & \text{for } x = 0 \\ 1, & \text{for } x > 0 \end{cases}$

2. Graph the function $f(x) = $ the least integer greater than $x$.

3. What piecewise function represents the graph at the right?

4. **Postage** In 2008, first-class letter postage was $.42 for up to one ounce and $.17 for each additional ounce up to 3.5 oz. Graph this postage function.

## Example 3    VISUAL LEARNERS

Copy, complete, and extend this table.

| $x$ | $-2$ | $-1.9$ | $-1.1$ | $-1$ | $-0.9$ |
|---|---|---|---|---|---|
| $[x]$ | $-2$ | $-2$ | $-2$ | $-1$ | $-1$ |

## Example 4    ERROR PREVENTION

**Q** Does this graph show the entire function? That is, does it show all function values for its entire domain? Explain. **[Yes; the domain is the set of all *x*-values between 0 and 3, and the graph shows all function values for all those *x*-values.]**

**Q** Does the graph in Example 3 show the entire function? Explain. **[No; the domain is the set of all real numbers, and the graph shows function values for only some *x*-values.]**

## Example 5

**Q** Name two points that appear to be on the leftmost piece. **[(−3, 0) and (−2, 2)]**

**Q** How can you write an equation using two points on the line? **[Use point-slope form.]**

## Exercises

**Q** For Exercise 1, what is the graph of $y = 1$? $y = -1$? **[the horizontal line 1 unit above the x-axis; the horizontal line 1 unit below the x-axis]** Use these lines and (0, 0) to draw the graph.

For Exercise 3, pay close attention to whether the endpoints are solid or not. This determines whether or not the endpoint is included in that part of the function. For Exercise 4, notice that the segments in this piecewise function are not the same length.

# Answers

## Exercises

1.

2.

4.

3.

$$f(x) = \begin{cases} 2x + 2, & -1 < x < 0 \\ 2x, & 0 < x < 1 \\ 2x - 2, & 1 < x < 2 \\ 2x - 4, & 2 < x < 3 \\ 2x - 6, & 3 < x < 4 \\ 2x - 8, & 4 < x < 5 \end{cases}$$

# 1 Interactive Learning

## Solve It!

**PURPOSE** To use a scatter plot to estimate an unknown quantity

**PROCESS** Students may

- estimate the hourly rate modeled by each point, find the mean, and divide $200 by that mean.
- identify (6, 120) as a point in the graph and reason that 6 : 120 = 1 : 20 = 10 : 200.

---

**FACILITATE**

**Q** The leftmost point in the graph is (5, 90). What hourly rate does it represent? Explain. **[$18 per hour; 90 ÷ 5 = 18]**

**Q** Did you earn money at the same rate each day? Explain. **[No; answers may vary. Sample: If you earned the same rate per hour, the data would form a direct variation and the points would be on a line.]**

**Q** How could you use an hourly rate to solve the problem? **[Answers may vary. Sample: Find the mean of the hourly rates in the graph and divide $200 by the mean.]**

---

**ANSWER** See Solve It in Answers on next page.

**CONNECT THE MATH** In the Solve It, students estimate an unknown quantity using rates, means, or proportional reasoning. In the lesson, they will make similar scatter plots and use trend lines to estimate unknown quantities.

---

**Objectives** To write linear equations that model real-world data
To make predictions from linear models

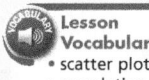

**Lesson Vocabulary**
- scatter plot
- correlation
- line of best fit
- correlation coefficient

Graphs of data pairs for a real-world situation rarely fall in a line. Their arrangement, however, can suggest a relationship that you can model with a linear function.

**Essential Understanding** Sometimes it is possible to model data from a real-world situation with a linear equation. You can then use the equation to draw conclusions about the situation.

A **scatter plot** is a graph that relates two sets of data by plotting the data as ordered pairs. You can use a scatter plot to determine the strength of the relationship, or **correlation**, between data sets. The closer the data points fall along a line with positive slope,

- the stronger the linear relationship and
- the stronger the positive correlation

between the two variables.

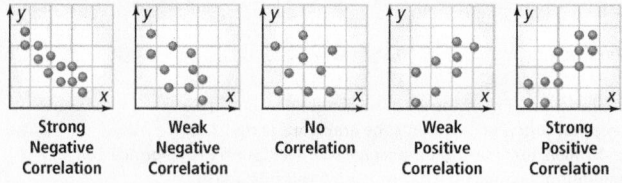

---

# 2-5 Preparing to Teach

**BIG** idea **Modeling** **UbD**

**ESSENTIAL UNDERSTANDINGS**

- Sometimes it is possible to model data from a real-world situation with a linear equation. The equation can then be used to draw conclusions about the situation.
- The equation of a trend line, or line of best fit, can be used to model data that cluster in a linear pattern.
- A scatter plot is a graph that relates two sets of data by plotting the data as ordered pairs. A scatter plot can be used to determine the strength of the relationship, or correlation between data sets.

## Math Background

When data from a real-world situation can be written as a set of ordered pairs, you can use various types of regression equations as models. The idea of correlation is addressed throughout the lesson. It is a common mistake to conclude

that because two events are correlated, one must be the cause of the other. It is possible, however, for two events to be correlated, even strongly correlated, without one event causing the other.

It may be the case that a third event is the common cause of the correlated events. For example, houses and milk do seem to cost more as time goes by. However, time itself does not *cause* these prices to go up; rather, other factors like inflation and demand, which change over time, are the causes.

## Support Student Learning

Use the **Algebra 2 Companion** to engage and support students during instruction. See Lesson Resources at the end of this lesson for details.

## 1 Interactive Learning

**Solve It!**
Step out how to solve the Problem with helpful hints and an online question. Other questions are listed above in Interactive Learning.

**Problem 1** Using a Scatter Plot

**Utilities** The table lists average monthly temperatures and electricity costs for a Texas home in 2008. The table displays the values rounded to the nearest whole number. Make a scatter plot. How would you describe the correlation?

**Average Temperatures and Electricity Costs**

| Month | Average Temp. (°F) | Electricity Bill ($) | Month | Average Temp. (°F) | Electricity Bill ($) |
|-------|-------|-------|-------|-------|-------|
| January | 61 | 150 | July | 84 | 255 |
| February | 58 | 139 | August | 85 | 245 |
| March | 67 | 172 | September | 81 | 210 |
| April | 75 | 205 | October | 76 | 183 |
| May | 79 | 170 | November | 65 | 132 |
| June | 83 | 234 | December | 58 | 110 |

**Plan**

**Which variable is the independent variable?**
Temperature does not depend on the electric bill, so temperature is the independent variable.

**Step 1** Make a scatter plot.

**Step 2** Describe the correlation.

As the temperature increases, the electricity cost also increases. The points are relatively tightly clustered around a line. There is a strong positive correlation between temperature and electricity cost.

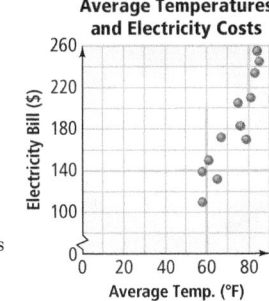

**Average Temperatures and Electricity Costs**

 **Got It? 1. a.** The table shows the numbers of hours students spent online the day before a test and the scores on the test. Make a scatter plot. How would you describe the correlation?

**b. Reasoning** Using the graph from Problem 1, how much would you expect to pay for electricity if the average temperature was 70°F? Explain.

**Computer Use and Test Scores**

| Number of Hours Online | 0 | 0 | 1 | 1 | 1.5 | 1.75 | 2 | 2 | 3 | 4 | 4.5 | 5 |
|---|---|---|---|---|---|---|---|---|---|---|---|---|
| Test score | 100 | 94 | 98 | 88 | 92 | 89 | 75 | 70 | 78 | 72 | 57 | 60 |

A *trend line* is a line that approximates the relationship between the variables, or data sets, of a scatter plot. You can use a trend line to make predictions from the data. In a previous lesson you learned how to use two points to write the equation of a line to model a real-world problem. You can use this method to write the equation of a trend line.

# 2 Guided Instruction

## Problem 1

**Q** What quantities form each ordered pair? **[average temperature and electricity cost]**

**Q** Which quantity should you represent on each axis? Explain. **[Answers may vary. Sample: Represent temperature on the horizontal axis and cost on the vertical axis because the independent quantity is represented on the horizontal axis and the dependent quantity is represented on the vertical axis. In this case, the amount of electricity used probably depends on the temperature.]**

**Q** What ordered pair corresponds to January? **[(61, 150)]**

**Q** How many ordered pairs should be graphed? Explain. **[12; there are 12 months represented by the data.]**

## Got It?

**Q** What scale will you use on the horizontal axis? Explain. **[Answers may vary. Sample: 0 to 5 because the hours range from 0 to 5.]**

**Q** What scale will you use on the vertical axis? Explain. **[Answers may vary. Sample: 0 to 100 because the highest test score is 100.]**

# 2 Guided Instruction

Each Problem is worked out and supported online.

**Problem 1**
Using a Scatter Plot
*Animated*

**Problem 2**
Writing the Equation of a Trend Line
*Animated*

**Problem 3**
Finding the Line of Best Fit
*Animated*

**Support in Algebra 2 Companion**
• Vocabulary
• Key Concepts
• Got It?

# Answers

## Solve It!

about 10; based on the graph, you can assume that you generally earn more money the more hours you work.

## Got It?

**1. a.** strong negative correlation

**Computer Use and Test Scores**

**b.** about $170

## Problem 2

**Q** Why do you think letting the *x*-values represent the number of years since 1940 is a good idea? **[Answers may vary. Sample: Doing so allows you to begin the scale on the *x*-axis at 0 without having a lot of unused distance on the axis.]**

**Q** Look at the graph and table of values. What are the coordinates of the leftmost point, and what do they represent? **[(0, 23,100); the median home price in Florida in 1940 was $23,100.]**

For Step 2, suggest the following way to sketch a trend line: Sketch a line that follows the pattern of the points with approximately the same number of points above it as below it.

In Step 3, two points must be chosen to use in finding an equation of the trend line. Point out that any two points on the line may be chosen; they need not be actual data points.

### Got It?

**Q** How will you define the variable *x*? **[Let *x* = number of years since 1940.]**

**Q** In which year(s) did the median home price vary the most from your trend line? Was the median price higher or lower than the trend? Explain. **[Answers may vary. Sample: On a graphing calculator with a true regression line, the median price in 1970 is the lowest below the trend by almost $40,000, and 1990 is the highest above the trend by almost $50,000.]**

**Problem 2** Writing the Equation of a Trend Line

**Finance** The table shows the median home prices in Florida. What is the equation of a trend line that models a relationship between time and home prices? Use the equation to predict the median home price in 2020.

| Florida Median Home Prices | | | | | | | |
|---|---|---|---|---|---|---|---|
| Year | 1940 | 1950 | 1960 | 1970 | 1980 | 1990 | 2000 |
| Median Price ($) | 23,100 | 40,100 | 58,100 | 57,600 | 89,300 | 98,500 | 105,500 |

**Know**
Seven data points

**Need**
The equation of a trend line

**Plan**
- Plot the given points.
- Find a trend line.
- Write the equation.

**Step 1** Make a scatter plot. Let *x* = 0 correspond to 1940.

**Step 2** Sketch a trend line.

**Step 3** Choose two points on the trend line, (10, 40,000) and (55, 110,000). Use slope-intercept form to write an equation for the line.
$y = 1556x + 24{,}440$

**Step 4** Use the equation to predict the median home price in 2020.
$y = 1556(80) + 24{,}440 = 148{,}920$

Based on the trend line, the median home price in 2020 will be around $149,000.

**Got It? 2.** The table shows median home prices in California. What is an equation for a trend line that models the relationship between time and home prices?

| California Median Home Prices | | | | | | | |
|---|---|---|---|---|---|---|---|
| Year | 1940 | 1950 | 1960 | 1970 | 1980 | 1990 | 2000 |
| Median Price ($) | 36,700 | 57,900 | 74,400 | 88,700 | 167,300 | 249,800 | 211,500 |

The trend line that gives the most accurate model of related data is the **line of best fit**. One method for finding a line of best fit is *linear regression*. You can use the **LinReg** function on your graphing calculator to find the line of best fit. The **correlation coefficient**, *r*, indicates the strength of the correlation. The closer *r* is to 1 or −1, the more closely the data resembles a line and the more accurate your model is likely to be.

---

## Additional Problems

**1.** The table lists the percent of persons 25 years or older with at least a Bachelor's degree and the median household income for 12 states in 2000. Percents are rounded to the nearest whole percent; incomes are rounded to the nearest thousand dollars. Describe the correlation between the percentage of adults with a college degree and median income.

**ANSWER** There is a weak positive correlation between level of education and income.

| State | Adults With at Least BS/BA | Income |
|---|---|---|
| AK | 25% | $52,000 |
| AL | 19% | $34,000 |
| CA | 27% | $47,000 |
| FL | 22% | $39,000 |
| MS | 17% | $31,000 |
| MT | 24% | $33,000 |
| ND | 22% | $35,000 |
| NY | 27% | $43,000 |
| NV | 18% | $45,000 |
| TX | 23% | $40,00 |
| WA | 28% | $46,000 |
| WV | 15% | $30,000 |

**2.** The table shows the median home prices in New Jersey. What is an equation of a trend line that models a relationship between time and home prices? Use that equation to predict the median home price in 2020.

**ANSWERS** Sample:
$y = 2061x + 47{,}100$
$x$ = the years since 1940
$y$ = price;
$211,980$

| Year | Median Price ($) |
|---|---|
| 1940 | 47,100 |
| 1950 | 63,100 |
| 1960 | 76,900 |
| 1970 | 89,900 |
| 1980 | 119,200 |
| 1990 | 207,400 |
| 2000 | 170,800 |

**Problem 3** Finding the Line of Best Fit

**Food** You research the average cost of whole milk for several recent years to look for trends. The table shows your data.

| Cost of Whole Milk | | | | | | |
|---|---|---|---|---|---|---|
| Year | 1998 | 2000 | 2002 | 2004 | 2006 | 2008 |
| Average cost for one gallon ($) | 2.65 | 2.89 | 3.00 | 3.01 | 3.20 | 3.77 |

Source: U.S. Department of Agriculture

**A** What is the equation for the line of best fit? How accurate is your line of best fit?

**Step 1**
Use the **STAT** feature to enter the data in your graphing calculator. Enter the $x$-values (year) in **L1** and the $y$-values (price) in **L2**. Let 1997 = year 0.

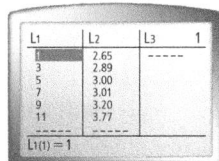

**Step 2**
Use **LinReg** to find the linear regression line of best fit for the data.

$y = 0.09x + 2.53$

The correlation coefficient, $r$, is approximately 0.92. Since $r$ is close to 1, the line of best fit is quite accurate.

**B** Based on your linear model, how much would you expect to pay for a gallon of whole milk in 2020?

$y = 0.09x + 2.53$     Use the line of best fit.
$y = 0.09(23) + 2.53$     Substitute 23 for $x$.
$y = 4.60$

In 2020, you would expect to pay about $4.60 for a gallon of whole milk.

**Think**

**What factors could affect the accuracy of your prediction?**
Predictions based on strongly correlated data are likely to be more reliable than predictions based on weakly correlated data.

✓ **Got It?** 3. The table lists the cost of 2% milk. Use a scatter plot to find the equation of the line of best fit. Based on your linear model, how much would you expect to pay for a gallon of 2% milk in 2025?

| Cost of 2% Milk | | | | | | |
|---|---|---|---|---|---|---|
| Year | 1998 | 2000 | 2002 | 2004 | 2006 | 2008 |
| Average cost for one gallon ($) | 2.57 | 2.83 | 2.93 | 2.93 | 3.10 | 3.71 |

Source: U.S. Department of Agriculture

 **Lesson 2-5** Using Linear Models    **95**

---

**Problem 3**

**Q** Look at Step 2 in 3A. In the context of the problem, what does the value 0.09 in the equation represent? **[It represents an increase of $0.09 per year in the cost of a gallon of milk.]**

**Q** Is this representation exact? Explain. **[No; it is based on the regression equation, which is a model, so it provides only an estimate.]**

**Q** What was the actual average yearly increase in the cost of a gallon of milk from 1998 to 2008? Explain. **[About $0.11: ($3.72 − $2.65) ÷ 10 = $0.107]**

For Step 2 of 3A, if the values for $r$ and $r^2$ do not appear on the TI-83 or TI-84 calculator screen, press **(2nd)** CATALOG, then scroll down to Diagnostic On, press **(enter)** and then press **(enter)** again.

**Got It?**

**Q** Compare this data with Problem 3. How do you expect the equations to compare? Explain. **[Answers may vary. Sample: They will be very similar because the years are the same and the costs are very close.]**

**Q** Why is comparing the equations useful? **[Answers may vary. Sample: It is a way to check the reasonableness of the equation.]**

---

**3.** You research the cost of movie tickets for recent years to look for trends. The table shows your data.

| Year | Average Cost of Movie Ticket |
|---|---|
| 1995 | 4.35 |
| 1997 | 4.59 |
| 1999 | 5.06 |
| 2001 | 5.65 |
| 2003 | 6.03 |
| 2005 | 6.41 |
| 2007 | 6.88 |

**a.** What is the equation for the line of best fit? How accurate is your line of best fit?

**b.** Based on your linear model, how much would you expect to pay for a movie ticket in 2025?

**ANSWERS**

**a.** $y = 0.22x + 4.26$, where $x$ is the years since 1995 and $y$ is the average movie ticket cost. Since $r = 0.997$, which is close to 1, the line of best fit is quite accurate.

**b.** $10.86

**Answers**

**Got It?** (continued)

**2.** $y = 3500x + 25{,}000$

**3.** $y = 0.09x + 2.44$, where 1997 is year 0; $4.96

# 3 Lesson Check

## Do you know HOW?

- For Exercises 1–2, if students have difficulty choosing appropriate scales for the axes or estimating when graphing some of the ordered pairs, ask them to look at the domain and range of the given values.
- For Exercise 3, either make a scatter plot with paper and pencil or do a linear regression on a calculator and use the value of *r*.

## Do you UNDERSTAND?

- For Exercise 5, if students have difficulty understanding the line of best fit, try graphing some points on a coordinate plane and using a piece of spaghetti to help students see the line of best fit.

## Close

> **Q** What is a scatter plot? **[a graph that relates two sets of data by plotting the data as ordered pairs]**
>
> **Q** How is the line of best fit related to a trend line? **[A line of best fit is a special trend line that was calculated by a standard procedure. Trend lines are visual estimates, so not all are accurate enough to be a line of best fit.]**
>
> **Q** How can you write an equation of a trend line? **[Use two points on the trend line along with the point-slope form.]**

---

---

## Lesson Check

### Do you know HOW?

**Make a scatter plot of each set of points and describe the correlation.**

1. {(1.2, 1), (2.5, 6), (2.5, 7.5), (4.1, 11), (7.9, 19)}

2. {(1, 55), (2, 38), (3, 54), (4, 37), (5, 53), (6, 40), (7, 53), (8, 36)}

3. Make a scatter plot for the following set of points. Describe the correlation and sketch a trend line. {(2, 58), (6, 105), (8, 88), (8, 118), (12, 117), (16, 137), (20, 157), (20, 169)}

### Do you UNDERSTAND?

4. **Writing** How can you determine whether two variables *x* and *y* for a real-life situation are correlated?

5. Do you think a trend line on a graph is always the same as the line of best fit? Why or why not?

6. **Compare and Contrast** What is the difference between a positive correlation and a negative correlation? How might you relate positive correlation with direct variation?

---

### Practice and Problem-Solving Exercises

**A** Practice

**Make a scatter plot and describe the correlation.** ⬅ **See Problem 1.**

7. {(0, 11), (2, 8), (3, 7), (7, 2), (8, 0)}

8. **Manufacturing** The table shows the numbering system used in Europe and the United States for shoe sizes.

| Shoe Sizes | | | | | | |
|---|---|---|---|---|---|---|
| U.S. Size | 1 | 3 | 5 | 7 | 9 | 11 |
| European Size | 31 | 34 | 36 | 39 | 41 | 44 |

**Write the equation of a trend line.** ⬅ **See Problem 2.**

9. {(−10, 3), (−5, 1), (−1, −4), (3, −7), (12, −12)}

10. {(−15, 8), (−8, 7), (−3, 0), (0, 0), (7, −3)}

11. The table shows the number of hours you studied before your eight math tests and your percent score on each test.

| Studying Hours and Test Score | | | | | | | | |
|---|---|---|---|---|---|---|---|---|
| Number of Hours | 8 | 5 | 12 | 10 | 2 | 9 | 11 | 14 |
| Score (%) | 75 | 62 | 80 | 85 | 35 | 70 | 82 | 95 |

12. **a. Food Production** The table below shows pork production in China from 2000 to 2007. Use a calculator to find the line of best fit. ⬅ **See Problem 3.**
    **b.** Use your linear model to predict how many metric tons of pork will be produced in 2025.
    **c.** Use your linear model to predict when production is likely to reach 100,000 metric tons.

| Pork Production in China | | | | | | | | |
|---|---|---|---|---|---|---|---|---|
| Year | 2000 | 2001 | 2002 | 2003 | 2004 | 2005 | 2006 | 2007 |
| Production (metric tons) | 40,475 | 42,010 | 43,413 | 45,331 | 47,177 | 50,254 | 52,407 | 54,491 |

Source: USDA Foreign Agricultural Service GAIN Report

---

## 3 Lesson Check

For a digital lesson check, use the Got It questions.

**Support in Algebra 2 Companion**
- Lesson Check

## 4 Practice

Assign homework to individual students or to an entire class.

---

# Answers

## Lesson Check

**1.** strong positive correlation

**2.** no correlation

**3.** strong positive correlation

**4.** Plot the data points in a scatter plot to determine the correlation. The closer the data points fall along a line with a positive or negative slope, the stronger the correlation.

**5.** No; answers may vary. Sample: A trend line is determined by using two pts. close to the line drawn through the data sets of the scatter plot. The line of best fit is the most accurate of the trend lines because it uses all the data pts.

**6.** The slope of the trend line or line of best fit is positive for data pts. with positive correlation and negative for data pts. with negative correlation. The constant of variation for a direct variation is positive for data pts. with positive correlation.

**7–12.** See next page.

**13. Think About a Plan** The table shows the relationship between the production and the export of rice in Vietnam from 1985 to 2005.

| Rice Production and Export | | | | | |
|---|---|---|---|---|---|
| Production (1000 tonnes) | 15,875 | 19,225 | 24,964 | 32,554 | 35,600 |
| Export (1000 tonnes) | 59 | 1624 | 1988 | 3400 | 5100 |

Source: International Rice Research Institute

How much rice would you expect Vietnam to export in 2015 if the production that year is 42,250,000 tonnes?
- How can you use a scatter plot to find a linear model?
- How can you use your model to make a prediction?

**14. Nutrition** The table shows the relationship between Calories and fat in various fast-food hamburgers.

| Fast Food Calories | | | | | | | | | |
|---|---|---|---|---|---|---|---|---|---|
| Restaurant | A | B | C | D | E | F | G | H | I |
| Number of Calories | 720 | 530 | 510 | 500 | 305 | 410 | 440 | 320 | 598 |
| Grams of fat | 46 | 30 | 27 | 26 | 13 | 20 | 25 | 13 | 26 |

**a.** Find the line of best fit for the relationship between Calories and fat.
**b.** How much fat would you expect a 330-Calorie hamburger to have?
**c. Error Analysis** Which estimate is *not* reasonable: 10 g of fat for a 200-Calorie hamburger or 36 g of fat for a 660-Calorie hamburger? Explain.

**Reasoning** For a strong correlation, people often assume that change in one quantity causes change in the second quantity. This is not always true. For each situation, predict the type of correlation you might find. Do you think that change in the first quantity causes change in the second quantity? Explain.

**15.** the number of ice cream cones sold and the temperature

**16.** the size of a car's engine and the number of passengers it is designed for

**17.** a person's age and the number of cassette tapes he or she owns

**18. Data Analysis** The table shows population and licensed driver statistics from a recent year.
**a.** Make a scatter plot.
**b.** Draw a trend line.
**c.** The population of Michigan was approximately 10 million that year. About how many licensed drivers lived in Michigan that year?
**d. Writing** Is the correlation between population and number of licensed drivers strong or weak? Explain.

**Licensed Drivers**

| State | Population (millions) | Number of Drivers (millions) |
|---|---|---|
| Arkansas | 2.8 | 2.0 |
| Illinois | 12.8 | 8.1 |
| Kansas | 2.8 | 2.0 |
| Massachusetts | 6.4 | 4.7 |
| Pennsylvania | 12.4 | 8.5 |
| Texas | 23.5 | 14.9 |

---

## Practice and Problem-Solving Exercises

**7.** strong negative correlation

**8.** strong positive correlation

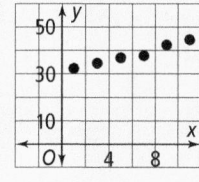

**9.** Sample: $y = -0.7x - 4$

**10.** not possible

**11.** Sample: $y = 4.47x + 33.31$

**12. a.** Sample:
Let 2000 = year 0
$y = 2053.17x + 39,758.67$
**b.** about 91,090 tons
**c.** in the year 2030

**13.** 6,055,359 tonnes

**14. a.** Sample: $y = 0.0714x - 9.2682$
**b.** 14.3 g
**c.** 200 Cal; a 200-Cal hamburger has about 5 g of fat.

**15.** positive correlation; no

**16.** positive correlation; yes

**17.** positive correlation; yes

**18. a.**

**b.**

**c.** about 6.5 million
**d.** Strong; the pts. fall close to a straight line.

---

# 4 Practice

**ASSIGNMENT GUIDE**
Basic: 7–12 all, 13–18
Average: 7–11 odd, 13–18
Advanced: 7–11 odd, 13–19
Standardized Test Prep: 20–23
Mixed Review: 24–32

**Reasoning** exercises have blue headings.

**Applications** exercises have red headings.

**EXERCISE 18:** Use the Think About a Plan worksheet in the **Practice and Problem Solving Workbook** (also available in the Teaching Resources in print and online) to further support students' development in becoming independent learners.

**HOMEWORK QUICK CHECK**
To check students' understanding of key skills and concepts, go over Exercises 7, 11, 13, 14, and 18.

# Answers

## Practice and Problem-Solving Exercises (continued)

**19. a.**

**b.** about $2506   **c.** about $5610

**d.** Answers may vary. Sample: Yes; expenditure would be predicted to be between $5300 and $5400.

## Standardized Test Prep

**20.** C     **21.** G     **22.** B

**23. [2]** $(y - 1) = \frac{2}{3}(x + 1)$

$(-3 - 1) = \frac{2}{3}(a + 1)$

$-4 = \frac{2}{3}a + \frac{2}{3}$

$\frac{-14}{3} = \frac{2}{3}a$

$-7 = a$

**[1]** a computational error

## Mixed Review

**24.**      **25.**

**26.**

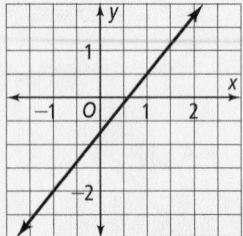

**27.** $-2x + y = 2$   **28.** $x + y = 0$   **29.** $y = 2$

**30.**

**31.**

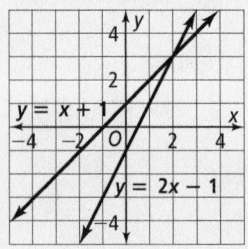

---

---

**C Challenge**

**19. Social Studies** The table shows per capita revenues and expenditures for selected states for a recent year.
  **a.** Show the data on a scatter plot. Draw a trend line.
  **b.** If a state collected revenue of $3000 per capita, how much would you expect it to spend per capita?
  **c.** Ohio spent $5142 per capita during that year. According to your model, how much did it collect in taxes per capita?
  **d.** In that same year, New Jersey collected $5825 per capita in taxes and spent $5348 per capita. Does this information follow the trend? Explain.

**Per Capita Revenue and Expenditure**

| State | Per Capita Revenue ($) | Per Capita Expenditure ($) |
| --- | --- | --- |
| Arizona | 4144 | 3789 |
| Georgia | 3904 | 3834 |
| Maryland | 5109 | 4557 |
| Mississippi | 5292 | 4871 |
| New Mexico | 6205 | 5793 |
| Nevada | 4345 | 3723 |
| New York | 7081 | 6891 |
| Texas | 4030 | 3442 |
| Utah | 5439 | 4459 |

## Standardized Test Prep

**SAT/ACT**

**20.** What is the equation of the line shown in the graph?

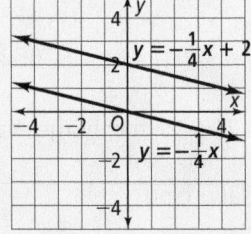

  Ⓐ $y = -2x + 2$      Ⓒ $y = 2x + 1$
  Ⓑ $y = 2x$           Ⓓ $y = 2x + 2$

**21.** Shauna drove 75 miles in 3 hours at a constant speed. How many miles did she drive in 2 hours?

  Ⓕ 25 miles      Ⓖ 50 miles      Ⓗ 75 miles      Ⓘ 100 miles

**22.** Which equation does NOT represent a direct variation?

  Ⓐ $y = x$              Ⓒ $2x - y = 0$
  Ⓑ $2x - y = 5$         Ⓓ $2x - 5y = 0$

**Short Response**

**23.** The line $(y - 1) = \frac{2}{3}(x + 1)$ contains point $(a, -3)$. What is the value of $a$? Show your work.

## Mixed Review

Graph the following linear equations.     ◀ See Lesson 2-3.

**24.** $y = -7.5x + 11$     **25.** $-\frac{2}{9}x - \frac{5}{9}y = 10$     **26.** $5x - 4y = 3$

Write the equation of each line in standard form.     ◀ See Lesson 2-4.

**27.** slope = 2; (2, 6)     **28.** slope = -1; (-3, 3)     **29.** slope = 0; (0, 2)

**Get Ready!   To prepare for Lesson 2-6, do Exercises 30–32.**

Graph each pair of functions on the same coordinate plane.     ◀ See Lesson 2-3.

**30.** $y = -x; y = x$     **31.** $y = x + 1; y = 2x - 1$     **32.** $y = -\frac{1}{4}x; y = -\frac{1}{4}x + 2$

**32.**

# Lesson Resources

## Differentiated Remediation
Available in editable format online.

## Additional Instructional Support

### Algebra 2 Companion
Students can use the **Algebra 2 Companion** worktext (4 pages) as you teach the lesson. Use the Companion to support

- New Vocabulary
- Key Concepts
- Got It for each Problem
- Lesson Check

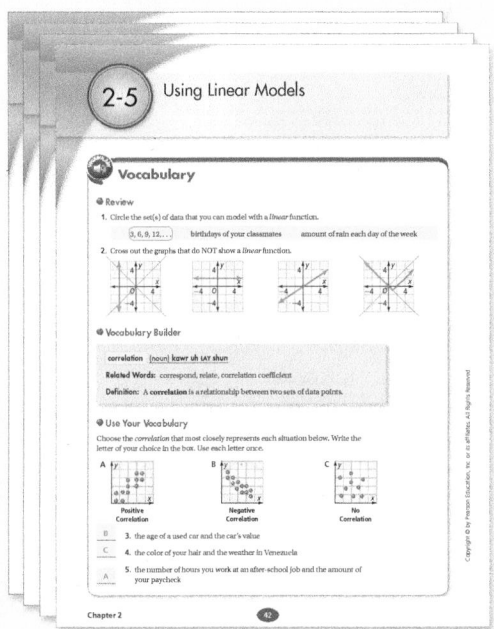

### ELL Support
**Use Manipulatives** Have groups of students select two variables whose relationship can be tested in the classroom. For instance, they might investigate the correlation between the number of pages in a book and its weight or the number of faces and number of edges of polyhedra. The group should predict the correlation they expect to find and explain their reasoning.

Groups should next test as many cases as possible and make a scatter plot of their data. Each group should find a line of best fit for their data and report how the results of their research matches with their predictions.

## 5 Assess & Remediate

### Lesson Quiz
1. The table shows how much Kim earned. What is the equation of a trend line that models a relationship between time and Kim's annual salary?

| Year | Annual Salary ($) |
|------|-------------------|
| 1996 | 42,000 |
| 1998 | 47,500 |
| 2000 | 48,900 |
| 2002 | 55,000 |
| 2004 | 60,000 |

2. Using the table in 1, predict Kim's salary in 2025.

3. **Do you UNDERSTAND?** The table shows the cost of the lunch special for selected years since a diner opened. What is an equation for the line of best fit? How accurate is the line of best fit?

| Year | Cost ($) |
|------|----------|
| 1997 | 6.95 |
| 1999 | 7.95 |
| 2001 | 8.00 |
| 2003 | 8.00 |
| 2005 | 9.25 |
| 2007 | 9.50 |

#### ANSWERS TO LESSON QUIZ
1. $y = 2500x + 40,000$; $x$ is years since 1996; $y$ is annual salary.
2. Kim's salary in 2025 should be $112,500.
3. $y = 0.24x + 6.85$; $x$ is years since 1996; $y$ is cost of the lunch special. Since $r = .94$, which is close to 1, the line of best fit is quite accurate.

#### PRESCRIPTION FOR REMEDIATION
Use the student work on the Lesson Quiz to prescribe a differentiated review assignment:

| Points | Differentiated Remediation |
|--------|----------------------------|
| 0–1 | Intervention |
| 2 | On-level |
| 3 | Extension |

### 5 Assess & Remediate
Assign the Lesson Quiz. Appropriate intervention, practice, or enrichment is automatically generated based on student performance.

## Intervention

- **Reteaching** (2 pages) Provides reteaching and practice exercises for the key lesson concepts. Use with struggling students or absent students.
- **English Language Learner Support** Helps students develop and reinforce mathematical vocabulary and key concepts.

### All-in-One Resources/Online
#### Reteaching

**2-5 Reteaching**
Using Linear Models

The strength of the relationship between data sets is called a *correlation*.

**Positive Correlation:** Data points fall close to a line with a positive slope.
**Negative Correlation:** Data points fall close to a line with a negative slope.
**No Correlation:** Data points are scattered and do not fall close to any line.

**Problem**
The table shows nutritional data for different types of pizza. Make a scatter plot of the data. How would you describe the correlation?

**Nutritional Data for Pizza**

| Type | Cheese | Pepperoni | Veggie | Mexican | Hawaiian | BBQ Chicken | The Works |
|------|--------|-----------|--------|---------|----------|-------------|-----------|
| Calories per Slice | 272 | 298 | 180 | 537 | 160 | 270 | 410 |
| Calories From Fat | 88 | 109 | 63 | 274 | 41 | 81 | 171 |

Plot the points. Use the calories per slice for the independent variable. The data points fall closely along a line with a positive slope. The data sets have a strong positive correlation.

**Exercises**
Make a scatter plot and describe the correlation.
1. {(0, 10), (2, 7), (4, 5), (6, 2), (10, 1)} negative correlation
2.

**Nutritional Data for Juice**

| Cup of Juice | Orange | Passion fruit | Grape | Apple | Cranberry |
|--------------|--------|---------------|-------|-------|-----------|
| Calories | 112 | 148 | 170 | 117 | 268 |
| Vitamin C (mg) | 124 | 45 | 60 | 103 | 121 |

no correlation

### All-in-One Resources/Online
#### English Language Learner Support

**2-5 ELL Support**
Using Linear Models

Use a word or phrase from the list below to complete each sentence. Each word or phrase will be used twice.

| correlation | correlation coefficient | line of best fit | scatter plot |

1. A _scatter plot_ relates two sets of data by plotting the data as ordered pairs.
2. The strength of the relationship between data sets is called the _correlation_.
3. The _correlation coefficient_ is a number between 1 and −1.
4. Data that has a strong linear relationship has a strong _correlation_.
5. The trend line that gives the most accurate linear model for the data is called the _line of best fit_.
6. The _correlation coefficient_ is a number that shows the strength of the correlation.
7. Linear regression is one way to find the _line of best fit_.
8. Use the STAT feature on your graphing calculator to enter data for a _scatter plot_.

Circle the word or phrase in column B that has the same meaning as the word in Column A.

| Column A | | Column B | |
|----------|--|----------|--|
| 9. correlation | relationship | y-intercept | ordered pairs |
| 10. data points | x-intercept | ordered pairs | linear |
| 11. plotting | relationship | graphing | y-intercept |
| 12. best trend line | line of best fit | positive slope | ordered pairs |

13. Describe the difference between a line of best fit that has a positive correlation and a line that has a negative one. Draw an example of each.
Answers may vary. Sample: A line of best fit that has a positive correlation will have a positive slope. A line of best fit that has a negative correlation will have a negative slope.

# Differentiated Remediation *continued*

Available in editable format online.

## On-Level

- **Practice** (2 pages) Provides extra practice for each lesson. For simpler practice exercises, use the Form K Practice pages found in the All-in-One Teaching Resources and online.

- **Think About a Plan** Helps students develop specific problem-solving skills and strategies by providing scaffolded guiding questions.

- **Standardized Test Prep** Focuses on all major exercises, all major question types, and helps students prepare for the high-stakes assessments.

## Extension

- **Enrichment** Provides students with interesting problems and activities that extend the concepts of the lesson.

- **Activities, Games, and Puzzles** Worksheets that can be used for concepts development, enrichment, and for fun!

---

### Practice and Problem Solving Wkbk/All-in-One Resources/Online
**Practice page 1**

### Practice and Problem Solving Wkbk/All-in-One Resources/Online
**Practice page 2**

### All-in-One Resources/Online
**Enrichment**

---

### Practice and Problem Solving Wkbk/All-in-One Resources/Online
**Think About a Plan**

### Practice and Problem Solving Wkbk/All-in-One Resources/Online
**Standardized Test Prep**

### Online Teacher Resource Center
**Activities, Games, and Puzzles**

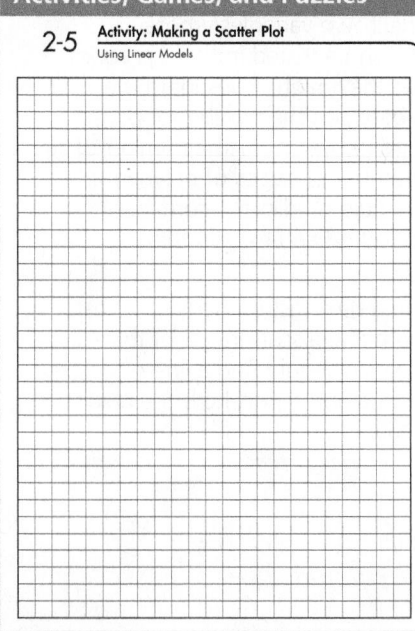

# Families of Functions

**Objective** To analyze transformations of functions

**Dynamic Activity**
Translating
Functions

**Lesson
Vocabulary**
• parent function
• transformation
• translation
• reflection
• vertical stretch
• vertical
  compression

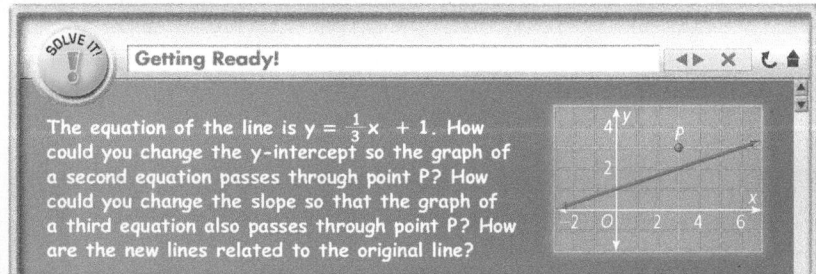

**SOLVE IT!** Getting Ready!

The equation of the line is $y = \frac{1}{3}x + 1$. How could you change the y-intercept so the graph of a second equation passes through point P? How could you change the slope so that the graph of a third equation also passes through point P? How are the new lines related to the original line?

Different nonvertical lines have different slopes, or y-intercepts, or both. They are graphs of different linear functions. For two such lines, you can think of one as a *transformation* of the other.

**Essential Understanding** There are sets of functions, called *families*, in which each function is a transformation of a special function called the *parent*.

The linear functions form a family of functions. Each linear function is a transformation of the function $y = x$. The function $y = x$ is the *parent* linear function.

A **parent function** is the simplest form in a set of functions that form a family. Each function in the family is a **transformation** of the parent function.

One type of transformation is a **translation**. A translation shifts the graph of the parent function horizontally, vertically, or both without changing shape or orientation. For a positive constant $k$ and a parent function $f(x)$, $f(x) \pm k$ is a vertical translation. For a positive constant $h$, $f(x \pm h)$ is a horizontal translation.

Adding k to the outputs shifts the graph up.

**Vertical Translation**

Subtracting h from the inputs shifts the graph right.

**Horizontal Translation**

# 1 Interactive Learning

### Solve It!

**PURPOSE** To determine how changing the y-intercept or slope affects the graph of a line

**PROCESS** Students may

• realize that if you move the line directly up 1 unit, it will go through (3, 3).
• plot a point at (0, 1) and find the slope of the line that connects (0, 1) and (3, 3).

**FACILITATE**

**Q** What happens when you change the y-intercept? **[The line moves up or down.]**

**Q** How must the graph move to pass through P? How does this affect the y-intercept? **[The graph must move up one unit, so the y-intercept will increase by 1.]**

**Q** What happens when you change m? **[The line pivots clockwise or counterclockwise on (0, 1).]**

**Q** What point stays on the line when you change m? **[(0, 1)]**

**Q** How can you find the new slope? **[Find the slope of the line though (0, 1) and P.]**

**ANSWER** See Solve It in Answers on next page.
**CONNECT THE MATH** In the Solve It, students use visual clues to determine how to change a function so that its graph goes through a desired point. The lesson illustrates how changing a function changes the graph of that function and vice versa.

---

## 2-6 Preparing to Teach

**BIG idea Functions**                    **UbD**

**ESSENTIAL UNDERSTANDINGS**

• There are sets of functions, called *families*, in which each function is a transformation of a special function called the *parent*.
• A parent function is the simplest form of a set of functions that form a family. Each function in the family is a transformation of the parent function.

### Math Background

This lesson shows how to sketch families of functions by performing transformations. The basic, or parent, linear function is $y = x$. The parent quadratic function is $y = x^2$. Learning how to transform these simpler functions will help students later when working with logarithmic and trigonometric functions.

Be aware of students who think all transformations are translations. Translations are a type of transformations. Rigid transformations (also called isometries) do not change the shape, only the location. The three types are translations, reflections, and rotations. Non-rigid transformations include stretches, compressions, and dilations. An example of a stretch is the graph $y = 2x^2$ when compared to the parent graph $y = x^2$.

### Support Student Learning

Use the **Algebra 2 Companion** to engage and support students during instruction. See Lesson Resources at the end of this lesson for details.

**PowerAlgebra.com**

## 1 Interactive Learning

**SOLVE IT Solve It!**
Step out how to solve the Problem with helpful hints and an online question. Other questions are listed above in Interactive Learning.

**Dynamic Activity** This activity allows students to create relations between two sets of data and then test those relations to determine if they are functions. They can view the output of their relation as ordered pairs and also as plotted points.

# 2 Guided Instruction

## Problem 1
**TACTILE LEARNERS**

A translation can be thought of as a slide or shift. Have students lay their pencils on the line $y = x$ and then slide their pencils straight down until they align with $y = x - 2$.

> **Q** How can you determine whether the graph of a function is translated up or down? **[It is translated up when a positive value is added to the function and down when a positive value is subtracted.]**

### Got It?

> **Q** How can you tell whether the lines are parallel? **[The slopes are the same.]**
>
> **Q** If you made a table for the functions in 1a, what would you notice? **[Corresponding *y*-values would differ by 3.]**

## Problem 2
**SYNTHESIZING**

> **Q** What would negative *x*-values model in this situation? **[the number of hours before noon]**
>
> **Q** How can you determine whether the graph of a function is translated left or right? **[It is translated left when a positive value is added to the input variable and right when a positive value is subtracted from it.]**

### Got It?

> **Q** Why is $f(x + 30)$ incorrect? **[Since the scale is in hours, 30 min must be converted to 0.5h.]**

---

**Plan**

**What is one way to compare two functions?**
Use a table to compare their values.

### Problem 1  Vertical Translation

**A** How are the functions $y = x$ and $y = x - 2$ related? How are their graphs related?

Make a table of values.

| x | y = x | y = x − 2 |
|----|----|----|
| −2 | −2 | −4 |
| −1 | −1 | −3 |
| 0 | 0 | −2 |
| 1 | 1 | −1 |
| 2 | 2 | 0 |

Draw their graphs.

Each output for $y = x - 2$ is two less than the corresponding output for $y = x$.

The graph of $y = x - 2$ is the graph of $y = x$ translated down two units.

**B** What is the graph of $y = x^2 - 1$ translated up 5 units?

Translate the graph of $y = x^2 - 1$ up 5 units to get the blue parabola. The equation of the blue parabola is $y = x^2 + 4$.

**Check** Every value in the $y = x^2 + 4$ column is 5 greater than the corresponding value in the $y = x^2 - 1$ column.

| x | y = x² − 1 | y = x² + 4 |
|----|----|----|
| −2 | 3 | 8 |
| −1 | 0 | 5 |
| 0 | −1 | 4 |
| 1 | 0 | 5 |
| 2 | 3 | 8 |

**Got It?** **1. a.** How are the functions $y = 2x$ and $y = 2x - 3$ related? How are their graphs related?

**b.** What is the graph of $y = 3x$ translated up 2 units?

---

**Think**

**If the time of the flight is later, why do you subtract rather than add in $f(x - 2)$?**
The *y*-values of the delayed flight correspond to *x*-values 2 hours *earlier* than the delayed flight.

### Problem 2  Horizontal Translation

The graph shows the projected altitude $f(x)$ of an airplane scheduled to depart an airport at noon. If the plane leaves two hours late, what function represents this transformation?

A two-hour delay means the plane leaves at 2 P.M. This shifts the graph to the right 2 units.

The function $f(x - 2)$ represents this transformation.

**Airplane Altitude**

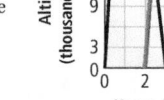

**Got It?** **2.** Suppose the flight leaves 30 minutes early. What function represents this transformation?

---

# Answers

## Solve It!

Change the *y*-intercept to (0, 2); change the slope to $\frac{2}{3}$; the first new line is parallel to the original line. The second new line has the same *y*-intercept as the original line.

## Got It?

**1. a.** Each output for $y = 2x - 3$ is three less than the corresponding output for $y = 2x$. The graph of $y = 2x - 3$ is the graph of $y = 2x$ translated down three units.

**b.**

**2.** $f\left(x + \frac{1}{2}\right)$

**3.** $h(x) = -3x - 3$

---

### PowerAlgebra.com

## 2 Guided Instruction

Each Problem is worked out and supported online.

**Problem 1**
Vertical Translation

**Alternative Problem 1**
Vertical Translation
*Animated*

**Problem 2**
Horizontal Translation

**Problem 3**
Reflecting a Function Algebraically
*Animated*

**Alternative Problem 3**
Reflecting a Function Algebraically

**Problem 4**
Stretching and Compressing a Function
*Animated*

**Problem 5**
Combining Transformations

**Support in Algebra 2 Companion**
• Vocabulary
• Key Concepts
• Got It?

A **reflection** flips the graph of a function across a line, such as the *x*- or *y*-axis. Each point on the graph of the reflected function is the same distance from the line of reflection as its corresponding point on the graph of the original function.

When you reflect a graph in the *y*-axis, the *x*-values change signs and the *y*-values stay the same.

When you reflect a graph in the *x*-axis, the *x*-values stay the same and the *y*-values change signs.

For a function $f(x)$, the reflection in the *y*-axis is $f(-x)$ and the reflection in the *x*-axis is $-f(x)$.

Reflection of $f(x)$ in the *y*-axis

$f(x)$

Reflection of $f(x)$ in the *x*-axis

**Problem 3** Reflecting a Function Algebraically

Let $g(x)$ be the reflection of $f(x) = 3x + 3$ in the *y*-axis. What is a function rule for $g(x)$?

**Think**

For a reflection in the *y*-axis, change the sign of *x*.

Evaluate $f(-x)$ and simplify.

You can check by graphing $f(x)$ and $g(x)$.

**Write**

$g(x) = f(-x)$

$g(x) = f(-x)$
$\quad = 3(-x) + 3$
$g(x) = -3x + 3$

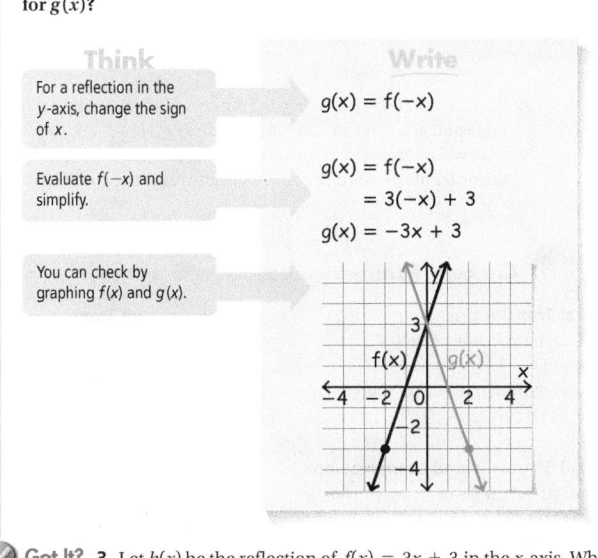

✔ **Got It? 3.** Let $h(x)$ be the reflection of $f(x) = 3x + 3$ in the *x*-axis. What is a function rule for $h(x)$?

---

**TACTILE LEARNERS**
Have students copy or sketch the graphs on patty paper or very thin notebook paper. They can fold the paper in half along the *x*-axis or *y*-axis and confirm that the reflected images coincide.

**EXTENSION**
The transformation that transforms each point $(x, y)$ into $(-x, -y)$ is called a reflection in the origin. It is a composition of a reflection in the *x*-axis and a reflection in the *y*-axis.

**Problem 3**          **ERROR PREVENTION**
$f(-x)$ means to replace every instance of *x* with $-x$ while $-f(x)$ means to take the opposite of the function. To take the opposite, enclose the function rule in parentheses and multiply by $-1$.

**Q** How does the graph show that $g(x)$ is correct? **[It is a reflection of $f(x)$ in the *y*-axis. Opposite *x*-values have the same *y*-value.]**

**Q** What is true about the slopes of the lines? **[The slopes are opposites.]**

**Q** What is true about the *y*-intercepts? **[The *y*-intercepts are the same.]**

**Got It?**          **EXTENSION**

**Q** Graph the functions $f(x)$ and $h(x)$. How do the slopes and *y*-intercepts compare? **[Both the slopes and the *y*-intercepts are opposites.]**

---

# Additional Problems

**1. a.** How are the functions $y = x$ and $y = x + 4$ related? How are their graphs related?

**b.** What is the graph of $y = -x^2$ translated down 3 units?

**ANSWER**

**a.** Each output for $y = x + 4$ is 4 more than the corresponding output for $y = x$. The graph of $y = x + 4$ is the graph of $y = x$ translated up four units.

**b.**

$y = -x^2 - 3$

**2.** The graph shows the distance $f(x)$ you will hike if you leave at 8 A.M. If you leave at 10 A.M., what function represents the transformation?

**Hiking Plan**

Hours After 8 AM

**ANSWER** $f(x - 2)$

**3.** Let $g(x)$ be the reflection of $f(x) = 2x - 7$ in the *x*-axis. What is the function rule for $g(x)$?

**ANSWER** $g(x) = -2x + 7$

**4.** The function $f(x)$ is shown below. What is the graph of $h(x) = 0.5\ f(x)$?

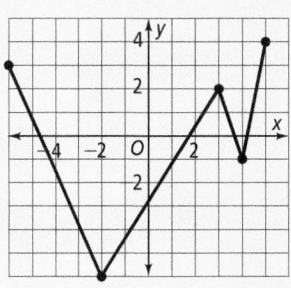

**ANSWER**

**5. a.** The function $f(x) = 8x$. The graph of $g(x)$ is $f(x)$ vertically compressed by a factor of .5 and reflected in the *x*-axis. What is the function rule for $g(x)$?

**b.** What transformations change the graph of $f(x)$ to the graph of $g(x)$?
$f(x) = x^3$
$g(x) = (x + 4)^3 - 1$

**ANSWER**

**a.** $g(x) = -4x$

**b.** a horizontal translation left 4 units and a vertical translation down one unit

A vertical stretch pulls away from the *x*-axis. A vertical compression pushes towards the *x*-axis.

## Problem 4

**Q** For which points will the output values for both functions be the same? Why? **[The points that are on the *x*-axis, because the *y*-values are 0, and anything multiplied by 0 is 0.]**

**Q** How many such points are in this graph? **[3]**

**Q** Why can you see these points in the graph but not in the table? **[because the table does not include those specific input values]**

## Got It?

**Q** How you could you sketch the graph of *h*(*x*) without making a table of values? **[Draw the same graph $\frac{1}{3}$ the distance from either side of the *x*-axis.]**

## Take Note

The option $a < 0$ is not listed for vertical stretches and compressions. This would be the same as a vertical stretch of the absolute value of *a*, followed by a reflection in the *x*-axis.

---

A **vertical stretch** multiplies all *y*-values of a function by the same factor greater than 1. A **vertical compression** reduces all *y*-values of a function by the same factor between 0 and 1. For a function $f(x)$ and a constant *a*, $y = af(x)$ is a vertical stretch when $a > 1$ and a vertical compression when $0 < \frac{1}{a} < 1$.

### Problem 4  Stretching and Compressing a Function

The table at the right represents the function $f(x)$. What are corresponding values of $g(x)$ and possible graphs for the transformation $g(x) = 3f(x)$?

| *x* | *f(x)* |
|---|---|
| −5 | 2 |
| −2 | 2 |
| 0 | −3 |
| 3 | 1 |
| 5 | −2 |

**Think**

Is this a vertical stretch or compression?
3 is greater than 1, so this is a vertical stretch.

**Step 1** Multiply each value of $f(x)$ by 3 to find each corresponding value of $g(x)$.

| *x* | *f(x)* | *3f(x)* | *g(x)* |
|---|---|---|---|
| −5 | 2 | 3(2) | 6 |
| −2 | 2 | 3(2) | 6 |
| 0 | −3 | 3(−3) | −9 |
| 3 | 1 | 3(1) | 3 |
| 5 | −2 | 3(−2) | −6 |

**Step 2** Use the values from the table in Step 1. Draw simple graphs for $f(x)$ and $g(x)$.

**Got It?** **4. a.** For the function $f(x)$ shown in Problem 4, what are the corresponding table and graph for the transformation $h(x) = \frac{1}{3}f(x)$?

**b. Reasoning** If several transformations are applied to a graph, will changing the order of transformations change the resulting graph? Explain.

---

**take note**

### Concept Summary  Transformations of *f(x)*

**Vertical Translations**
Translation up *k* units, $k > 0$
$$y = f(x) + k$$
Translation down *k* units, $k > 0$
$$y = f(x) - k$$

**Horizontal Translations**
Translation right *h* units, $h > 0$
$$y = f(x - h)$$
Translation left *h* units, $h > 0$
$$y = f(x + h)$$

**Vertical Stretches and Compressions**
Vertical stretch, $a > 1$
$$y = af(x)$$
Vertical compression, $0 < a < 1$
$$y = af(x)$$

**Reflections**
In the *x*-axis
$$y = -f(x)$$
In the *y*-axis
$$y = f(-x)$$

---

# Answers

### Got It? (continued)

**4. a.**

| *x* | *y* |
|---|---|
| −5 | $\frac{2}{3}$ |
| −2 | $\frac{2}{3}$ |
| 0 | −1 |
| 3 | $\frac{1}{3}$ |
| 5 | $-\frac{2}{3}$ |

**b.** Sometimes; answers may vary. Sample: switching the order of a horizontal translation and a reflection in the *y*-axis will change the resulting graph, but switching the order of a horizontal and vert. translation will not.

**Problem 5** Combining Transformations

**A** The graph of $g(x)$ is the graph of $f(x) = 4x$ compressed vertically by the factor $\frac{1}{2}$ and then reflected in the $y$-axis. What is a function rule for $g(x)$?

$\frac{1}{2}(4x) = 2x$ \qquad Compress $f(x)$.

$2(-x) = -2x$ \quad Reflect the new function in the $y$-axis.

The function rule is $g(x) = -2x$.

**Think**

How can you write $g(x)$ in terms of $f(x)$? Factor out 3 from the $6x^2$ term.

**B** What transformations change the graph of $f(x)$ to the graph of $g(x)$?

$f(x) = 2x^2 \quad g(x) = 6x^2 - 1$

$g(x) = 6x^2 - 1$

$\quad\quad = 3(2x^2) - 1$

$\quad\quad = 3(f(x)) - 1$

The graph of $g(x)$ is the graph of $f(x)$ stretched vertically by a factor of 3 and then translated down 1 unit.

 **Got It? 5. a.** The graph of $g(x)$ is the graph of $f(x) = x$ stretched vertically by a factor of 2 and then translated down 3 units. What is the function rule for $g(x)$?
   **b.** What transformations change the graph of $f(x) = x^2$ to the graph of $g(x) = (x + 4)^2 - 2$?

---

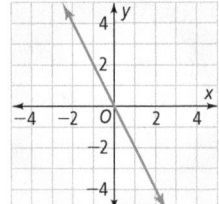 **Lesson Check**

**Do you know HOW?**

Describe the transformation of the parent function $f(x)$.

**1.** $g(x) = f(x) + 6$ \qquad **2.** $h(x) = 0.25f(x)$

**3.** $j(x) = f(x - 4)$ \qquad **4.** $k(x) = f(-x)$

The graph of $f(x) = -2x$ is shown. Describe and graph each transformation.

**5.** $g(x) = f(x + 1) - 2$

**6.** $h(x) = 2f(x) + 1$

**Do you UNDERSTAND?**

**7. Compare and Contrast** The graph shows $f(x) = 0.5x - 1$.

Graph $g(x)$ by translating $f(x)$ up 2 units and then stretching it vertically by the factor 2. Graph $h(x)$ by stretching $f(x)$ vertically by the factor 2 and then translating it up 2 units. Compare the graphs of $g(x)$ and $h(x)$.

**8. Reasoning** Can you give an example of a function for which a horizontal translation gives the same resulting graph as a vertical translation? Explain.

**9.** Find a new function $g(x)$ transformed from $f(x) = -x - 2$ such that $g(x)$ is perpendicular to $f(x)$.

---

**Problem 5**

**Q** What are the values of $a$ and $h$ in the function $g(x)$ in 5A? **[−2 and 0]**

**Got It?**

**Q** Without first finding the function rule, what are the values of $a$ and $k$ in the function $g(x)$ in 3a? **[2, −3]**

# 3 Lesson Check

**Do you know HOW?** \qquad **ERROR INTERVENTION**

• For Exercise 3, if students describe the transformation as a horizontal translation left, show an alternate rule, which fits the mental match of positive/right and negative/left: for $f(x - h)$, $h$ moves left when $h$ is negative (show the double negative becoming a positive) and right when $h$ is positive.

**Do you UNDERSTAND?**

• For Exercise 9, slopes of perpendicular lines are opposite reciprocals. Refer to the Take Note chart to help determine what transformations need to be performed.

**Close**

**Q** In which transformations are you changing the input values? **[horizontal translations and reflections in the $y$-axis]**

**Q** In which transformations are you changing the output values? **[vertical translations, reflections in the $x$-axis, and vertical stretches and compressions]**

---

**5. a.** $g(x) = 2x - 3$
   **b.** $g(x) = f(x + 4) - 2$; translated left 4 units and translated down 2 units

**6.** stretched vertically by a factor of 2 and translated 1 unit up

**Lesson Check**

**1.** translated 6 units up

**2.** compressed vertically by a factor of 0.25

**3.** translated 4 units to the rt.

**4.** reflected over $y$-axis

**5.** translated 1 unit to the left and 2 units down

**7.** $g(x)$ is the graph of $h(x)$ translated 2 units up

**8.** Answers may vary. Sample: $f(x) = x$, $f(x - 2) = f(x) - 2$

**9.** $f(x) = -x - 2$; $g(x) = f(-x) = x - 2$

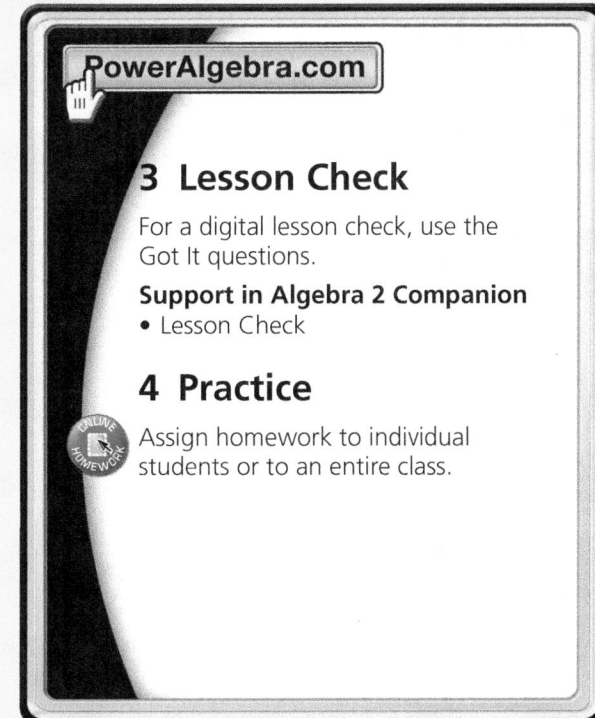

**PowerAlgebra.com**

## 3 Lesson Check

For a digital lesson check, use the Got It questions.

**Support in Algebra 2 Companion**
• Lesson Check

## 4 Practice

Assign homework to individual students or to an entire class.

# 4 Practice

**ASSIGNMENT GUIDE**

Basic: 10–33 all, 34–39, 44, 45

Average: 11–33 odd, 34–45

Advanced: 11–33 odd, 34–50

Standardized Test Prep: 51–54

Mixed Review: 55–58

**Reasoning** exercises have blue headings.

**Applications** exercises have red headings.

**EXERCISE 35:** Use the Think About a Plan worksheet in the **Practice and Problem Solving Workbook** (also available in the Teaching Resources in print and online) to further support students' development in becoming independent learners.

**HOMEWORK QUICK CHECK**

To check students' understanding of key skills and concepts, go over Exercises 17, 33, 34, 35, and 45.

---

## Practice and Problem-Solving Exercises

Ⓐ Practice

How is each function related to $y = x$? Graph the function by translating the parent function. ◆ **See Problem 1.**

**10.** $y = x - 3$      **11.** $y = x + 4.5$      **12.** $y = x + 1.5$

Make a table of values for $f(x)$ after the given translation.

**13.** 3 units up

| x | f(x) |
|----|------|
| −2 | 3 |
| 0 | 1 |
| 1 | −2 |
| 3 | −1 |

**14.** 1 unit down

| x | f(x) |
|----|------|
| −1 | 1 |
| 0 | 0 |
| 2 | −4 |
| 3 | 2 |

**15.** 4 units up

| x | f(x) |
|----|------|
| −3 | 1 |
| −1 | −2 |
| 1 | 0 |
| 4 | 3 |

Write an equation for each vertical translation of $y = f(x)$.

**16.** $\frac{2}{3}$ unit down      **17.** 4 units up      **18.** 2 units up

For each function, identify the horizontal translation of the parent function, $f(x) = x^2$. Then graph the function. ◆ **See Problems 2 and 3.**

**19.** $y = (x - 4)^2$      **20.** $y = (x + 1)^2$      **21.** $y = (x + 3)^2$

**22.** The graph of the function $f(x)$ is shown at the right.
  **a.** Make a table of values for $f(x)$ and $f(x + 3)$.
  **b.** Graph $f(x)$ and $f(x + 3)$ on the same coordinate grid.

Write the function rule for each function reflected in the given axis.

**23.** $f(x) = x + 1$; $x$-axis      **24.** $f(x) = 3x$; $y$-axis      **25.** $f(x) = 2x - 4$; $x$-axis

Write an equation for each transformation of $y = x$. ◆ **See Problem 4.**

**26.** vertical stretch by a factor of 4      **27.** vertical stretch by a factor of 2

**28.** vertical compression by a factor of $\frac{1}{2}$      **29.** vertical compression by a factor of $\frac{1}{4}$

Write the function rule $g(x)$ after the given transformations of the graph of $f(x) = 4x$. ◆ **See Problem 5.**

**30.** translation up 5 units; reflection in the $x$-axis

**31.** reflection in the $y$-axis; vertical compression by a factor of $\frac{1}{8}$

Describe the transformations of $f(x)$ that produce $g(x)$.

**32.** $f(x) = \frac{x}{2}$; $g(x) = -2x + 4$      **33.** $f(x) = 3x$; $g(x) = \left(\frac{3x}{4} - 2\right)$

---

# Answers

## Practice and Problem-Solving Exercises

**10.** The function is $y = x$ translated 3 units down.

**11.** The function is $y = x$ translated 4.5 units up.

**12.** The function is $y = x$ translated 1.5 units up.

**13.**

| x | f(x) + 3 |
|----|------|
| −2 | 6 |
| 0 | 4 |
| 1 | 1 |
| 3 | 2 |

**14.**

| x | f(x) − 1 |
|----|------|
| −1 | 0 |
| 0 | −1 |
| 2 | −5 |
| 3 | 1 |

**15.**

| x | f(x) + 4 |
|----|------|
| −3 | 5 |
| −1 | 2 |
| 1 | 4 |
| 4 | 7 |

**16.** $y = f(x) - \frac{2}{3}$

**17.** $y = f(x) + 4$    **18.** $y = f(x) + 2$

**19.** translated rt. 4 units

**20.** translated left 1 unit

**21–33.** See next page.

**34. Think About a Plan** Suppose you are playing with a yo-yo during a school talent show. The string is 3 ft long and you hold your hand 4 ft above the stage. The stage is 3.5 ft above the floor of the auditorium. Make a graph of the yo-yo's distance from the auditorium floor with respect to time during the show.
- How could you graph the position of the yo-yo with respect to the stage, if you let time $t = 0$ when you start your routine?
- How could you transform this graph to show the position with respect to the auditorium floor?

**35.** If someone started to take a video of your yo-yo routine when you were introduced, 10 seconds before you actually started, what transformation would you have to make to your graph to match their video?

**Write the equations for $f(x)$ and $g(x)$. Then identify the reflection that transforms the graph of $f(x)$ to the graph of $g(x)$.**

**36.**   **37.**   **38.**

**39. Open-Ended** Draw a figure in Quadrant I. Use a translation to move your figure into Quadrant III. Describe your translation.

**40. Writing** The graph of $f(x)$ is shown at the right. Suppose each transformation of $f(x)$ results in the given functions.
  i. vertical translation; $g(x)$
  ii. reflection in the $x$-axis; $h(x)$
  iii. vertical stretch; $k(x)$,
  iv. horizontal translation; $m(x)$
  **a.** Describe how the domain and range of the four new functions compare with the domain and range of $f(x)$.
  **b. Reasoning** Do you think these effects on the domain and range of the original function hold true for all functions? Explain.

**Graph each pair of functions on the same coordinate plane. Describe a transformation that changes $f(x)$ to $g(x)$.**

**41.** $f(x) = x + 1; g(x) = x - 5$

**42.** $f(x) = -x + 3; g(x) = x - 4$

**43.** $f(x) = x - 3; g(x) = x + 1$

**44.** $f(x) = -x - 1; g(x) = -x + 2$

**45. Error Analysis** Your friend wrote the transformations shown to describe how to change the graph of $f(x) = x^2$ to the graph of $g(x) = 2(x + 1)^2 - 3$. Explain the error and give the correct transformations.

- shift vertically 1 unit up
- shift horizontally 2 units right
- shift vertically three units down

**21.** translated left 3 units

**22. a.**

| $x$ | $f(x)$ |   | $x$ | $f(x + 3)$ |
|---|---|---|---|---|
| 2 | 0 |   | −1 | 0 |
| 3 | 2 |   | 0 | 2 |
| 5 | 3.5 |   | 2 | 3.5 |
| 6 | 0 |   | 3 | 0 |

**b.**

**23.** $g(x) = -x - 1$     **24.** $g(x) = -3x$

**25.** $g(x) = -2x + 4$     **26.** $y = 4x$

**27.** $y = 2x$     **28.** $y = \frac{1}{2}x$

**29.** $y = \frac{1}{4}x$     **30.** $g(x) = -4x - 5$

**31.** $g(x) = -0.5x$

**32.** vertically stretched by a factor of 4, reflected over the $x$-axis, and translated up 4 units

**33.** vertically compressed by a factor of $\frac{1}{4}$ and translated down 2 units

**34.**

**35.** translate to the right 10 s

**36.** $f(x) = -2x + 1; g(x) = 2x - 1;$ $g(x) = -f(x)$

**37.** $f(x) = -\frac{1}{3}x - 1; g(x) = \frac{1}{3}x + 1;$ $g(x) = -f(x)$

**38.** $f(x) = -2x + 2; g(x) = 2x + 2; g(x) = f(-x)$

**39.** Check students' work.

**40. a.** The functions $g(x)$, $h(x)$, and $k(x)$ have the same domain as the function $f(x)$, but different ranges, and the function $m(x)$ has the same range as $f(x)$ but a different domain.

  **b.** Yes; the transformations in (i), (ii), and (iii) affect only the vert. position of a function, which determines the range. The transformation in (iv) affects only the horizontal position, which determines the domain.

**41.** translated 6 units down

**42.** translated 7 units down, then reflected over the $y$-axis; or reflected over the $x$-axis, then translated 1 unit down

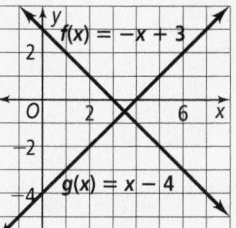

**43.** translated 4 units up

**44.** translated 3 units up

**45.** The first two steps are incorrect; the transformations should be: shift 1 unit left, vertically stretch by a factor of 2, and shift 3 units down.

# Answers

## Practice and Problem-Solving Exercises (continued)

**46.**

**47.**

**48.**

**49.**

**50.**

## Standardized Test Prep

**51.** D

**52.** F

**53.** A

**54.** [2] $y = kx$
$772 = k(40)$
$19.3 = k$
  $y = (19.3)(100)$
  $y = 1930\ g$
[1] appropriate method, with one computational error

## Mixed Review

**55.** $y = -15.82x + 914.59$

**56.** $-2, 8$

**57.** $-12, 11$

**58.** $-3, \frac{21}{5}$

---

**Challenge**  Using the graph of the function $f(x)$ shown, sketch the graph of each transformed function.

**46.** $f(x + 1)$
**47.** $f(x) - 2$
**48.** $f(x + 2) + 1$
**49.** $-2f(x)$

**50.** Graph all of the following functions in the same viewing window. After you enter each new function, view its graph.
  i. $y = x^2$     ii. $y = x^2 + 2$     iii. $y = (x + 2)^2$     iv. $y = (x - 1)^2 - 4$     v. $y = -x^2 - 2$

Based on your results, make a sketch of the graph of $f(x) = -(x + 2)^2 + 1$ and check your prediction on your calculator.

## Standardized Test Prep

**SAT/ACT**  What is an equation for each vertical translation of $y = 2x - 1$?

**51.** 3 units down
  Ⓐ $y = 2x - 7$     Ⓑ $y = 2x + 2$     Ⓒ $y = 2x + 5$     Ⓓ $y = 2x - 4$

**52.** $\frac{3}{5}$ units up
  Ⓕ $y = 2x - \frac{2}{5}$     Ⓖ $y = 2x - \frac{11}{5}$     Ⓗ $y = 2x - \frac{8}{5}$     Ⓘ $y = 2x + \frac{1}{5}$

**53.** What is the slope of the line in the graph at the right?
  Ⓐ $-\frac{5}{2}$     Ⓒ $\frac{2}{5}$
  Ⓑ $-\frac{2}{5}$     Ⓓ $\frac{5}{2}$

**Short Response**  **54.** The weight of a gold bar varies directly with its volume. If a 40 cm³ bar weighs 772 grams, how much will a 100 cm³ bar weigh?

## Mixed Review

**55.** A musician's manager keeps track of the ticket prices and the attendance at recent performances. Use a graphing calculator to determine the equation of the line of best fit for the given data.  ◀ See Lesson 2-5.

| Ticket Prices($) | 41.00 | 41.50 | 42.00 | 43.00 | 43.50 | 44.00 | 44.50 | 45.00 | 45.00 | 47.00 |
|---|---|---|---|---|---|---|---|---|---|---|
| Number Sold | 256 | 276 | 250 | 241 | 210 | 235 | 195 | 194 | 205 | 180 |

**Get Ready!**  To prepare for Lesson 2-7, do Exercises 56–58.

Solve each absolute value equation.  ◀ See Lesson 1-6.

**56.** $|x - 3| + 2 = 7$     **57.** $|2x + 1| - 14 = 9$     **58.** $\frac{1}{3}|5x - 3| = 6$

# Lesson Resources

## Differentiated Remediation
Available in editable format online.

## Additional Instructional Support

### Algebra 2 Companion
Students can use the **Algebra 2 Companion** worktext (4 pages) as you teach the lesson. Use the Companion to support

- New Vocabulary
- Key Concepts
- Got It for each Problem
- Lesson Check

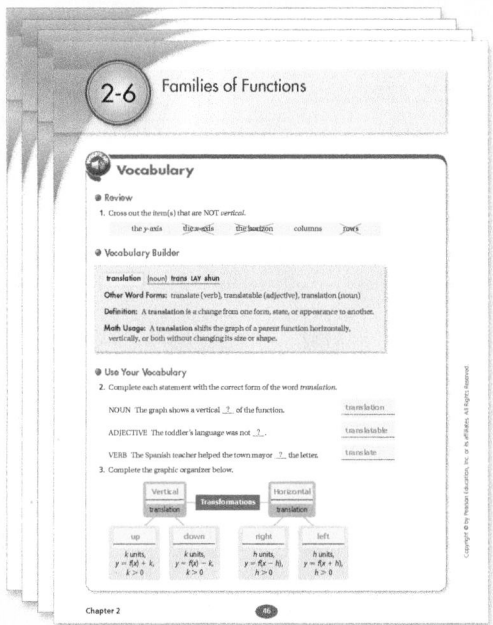

### ELL Support
**Use Graphic Organizers** Make a table that connects the different ways of describing transformations. Headings could be Words, Geometry, Graphs, and Functions. Students can identify a transformation in words and then describe it the remaining three ways. For example,

- Words: translate right 2 units
- Geometry: graph of the points $(x, y)$ and $(x + 2, y)$
- Graph: graph of two parabolas, one 2 units to the right of the other
- Function: $f(x) = x^2$ and $g(x) = (x - 2)^2$

## 5 Assess & Remediate

### Lesson Quiz

**1.** How are the functions $y = 2x^2$ and $y = 2x^2 + 7$ related? How are their graphs related?

**2. Do you UNDERSTAND?** The graph shows how many words you have written for a paper. What function models the progress if you had begun an hour earlier?

Words (100)

Hours After Noon

**3.** Let $g(x)$ be the reflection of $f(x) = -4x - 1$ in the $x$-axis. What is a function rule for $g(x)$?

**4.** What transformations change the graph of $f(x) = -x$ to the graph of $g(x) = -0.1(x - 6)$?

### ANSWERS TO LESSON QUIZ

**1.** Each output for $y = 2x^2 + 7$ is 7 greater than the corresponding output of $y = 2x^2$. The graph of $y = 2x^2 + 7$ is the graph of $y = 2x^2$ translated up 7 units.

**2.** $f(x + 1)$

**3.** $g(x) = 4x + 1$

**4.** vertical compression by a factor of 0.1 and a horizontal translation 6 units right

### PRESCRIPTION FOR REMEDIATION
Use the student work on the Lesson Quiz to prescribe a differentiated review assignment:

| Points | Differentiated Remediation |
|--------|---------------------------|
| 0–2 | Intervention |
| 3 | On-level |
| 4 | Extension |

**PowerAlgebra.com**

## 5 Assess & Remediate
Assign the Lesson Quiz. Appropriate intervention, practice, or enrichment is automatically generated based on student performance.

## Intervention

- **Reteaching** (2 pages) Provides reteaching and practice exercises for the key lesson concepts. Use with struggling students or absent students.

- **English Language Learner Support** Helps students develop and reinforce mathematical vocabulary and key concepts.

### All-in-One Resources/Online
**Reteaching**

### All-in-One Resources/Online
**English Language Learner Support**

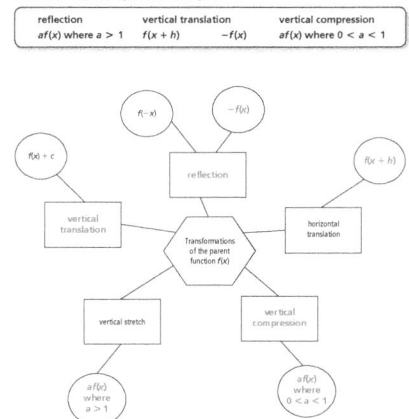

# Differentiated Remediation *continued*

Available in editable format online.

## On-Level

- **Practice** (2 pages) Provides extra practice for each lesson. For simpler practice exercises, use the Form K Practice pages found in the All-in-One Teaching Resources and online.

- **Think About a Plan** Helps students develop specific problem-solving skills and strategies by providing scaffolded guiding questions.

- **Standardized Test Prep** Focuses on all major exercises, all major question types, and helps students prepare for the high-stakes assessments.

## Extension

- **Enrichment** Provides students with interesting problems and activities that extend the concepts of the lesson.

- **Activities, Games, and Puzzles** Worksheets that can be used for concepts development, enrichment, and for fun!

---

### Practice and Problem Solving Wkbk/ All-in-One Resources/Online
#### Practice page 1

### Practice and Problem Solving Wkbk/ All-in-One Resources/Online
#### Practice page 2

### All-in-One Resources/Online
#### Enrichment

---

### Practice and Problem Solving Wkbk/ All-in-One Resources/Online
#### Think About a Plan

### Practice and Problem Solving Wkbk/ All-in-One Resources/Online
#### Standardized Test Prep

### Online Teacher Resource Center
#### Activities, Games, and Puzzles

## 2-7 Absolute Value Functions and Graphs

**Objective** To graph absolute value functions

**SOLVE IT** Getting Ready!

You jog at a constant speed. Your jogging route takes you across the county line. Suppose you graph your distance from the county line with respect to time. What would the graph look like? Explain.

ENTERING Jefferson County

You'll study more graphs like this one in the lesson.

There is a family of functions related to the one you represented in the Solve It.

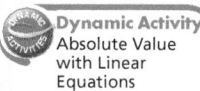

**Dynamic Activity** Absolute Value with Linear Equations

**Essential Understanding** Just as the absolute value of $x$ is its distance from 0, the absolute value of $f(x)$, or $|f(x)|$, gives the distance from the line $y = 0$ for each value of $f(x)$.

**Lesson Vocabulary**
• absolute value function
• axis of symmetry
• vertex

The simplest example of an **absolute value function** is $f(x) = |x|$. The graph of the absolute value of a linear function in two variables is V-shaped and symmetric about a vertical line called the **axis of symmetry**. Such a graph has either a single maximum point or a single minimum point, called the **vertex**.

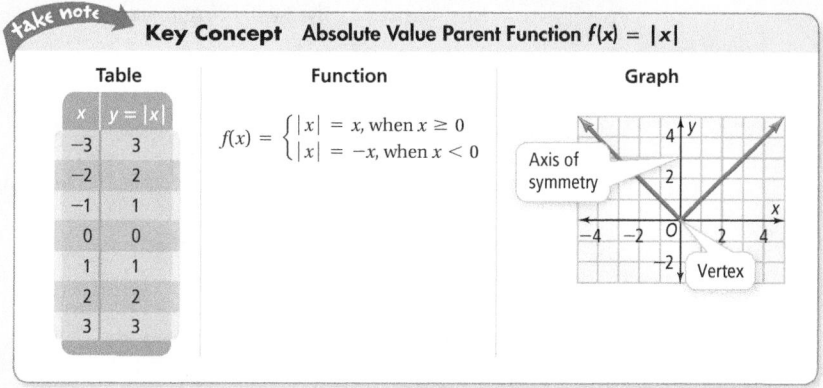

**take note**

**Key Concept** Absolute Value Parent Function $f(x) = |x|$

| Table | Function | Graph |
|---|---|---|

| $x$ | $y = |x|$ |
|---|---|
| −3 | 3 |
| −2 | 2 |
| −1 | 1 |
| 0 | 0 |
| 1 | 1 |
| 2 | 2 |
| 3 | 3 |

$f(x) = \begin{cases} |x| = x, \text{ when } x \geq 0 \\ |x| = -x, \text{ when } x < 0 \end{cases}$

Axis of symmetry

Vertex

PowerAlgebra.com   **Lesson 2-7** Absolute Value Functions and Graphs   **107**

---

## 2-7 Preparing to Teach

**BIG idea Functions**   **UbD**

**ESSENTIAL UNDERSTANDINGS**

• Just as the absolute value of $x$ is its distance from 0, the absolute value of $f(x)$, or $|f(x)|$, gives the distance from the line $y = 0$ for each value of $f(x)$.

• The simplest example of an absolute value function is $f(x) = |x|$.

• The values of $a$, $b$, and $k$, in the form $y = a|x - h| + k$ determine how the parent function $y = |x|$ can be transformed.

### Math Background

Students can apply translations, stretches, compressions, and reflections to any parent function $f(x)$. The absolute value function is a particularly good parent function to use for these transformations since it has an easily recognizable V shape.

This lesson discusses vertical stretches and compressions (those in which all $y$-coordinates are multiplied by a common factor). You may also wish to have students explore horizontal stretches and compressions (those in which the $x$-coordinates are multiplied by a common factor). Making tables of ordered pairs can help students analyze the effects of the transformations on each coordinate.

### Support Student Learning

Use the **Algebra 2 Companion** to engage and support students during instruction. See Lesson Resources at the end of this lesson for details.

---

# 1 Interactive Learning

**Solve It!**

**PURPOSE** To represent a physical situation with an absolute value graph

**PROCESS** Students may try assigning arbitrary numerical values or realize the graph has two linear parts.

**FACILITATE**

**Q** Where do you start? Explain. **[(0, $p$); the time starts at $x = 0$, when you are a positive distance $p$ from the county line.]**

**Q** Is the slope from (0, $p$) to ($q$, 0) positive or negative? Explain. **[Negative; the distance between you and the county line is decreasing.]**

**Q** Assume the $x$-intercept is ($q$, 0). What does this point mean in terms of the problem situation? **[This is when you reach the county line.]**

**Q** Is the slope from ($q$, 0) rightward positive or negative? Explain. **[Positive; the distance between you and the county line is increasing.]**

**Q** Is this graph symmetric? If so, where is the axis of symmetry? Explain. **[Yes; since you are jogging at a constant speed, $x = q$, where $q$ is the time at which you get to the county line.]**

**ANSWER** See Solve It in Answers on next page.
**CONNECT THE MATH** The Solve It models an absolute value graph in a realistic situation. In the lesson, students will identify different parts of absolute value graphs and graph transformations of the absolute value parent function.

# 2 Guided Instruction

## Take Note

Absolute value graphs are not linear. They are, however, composed of two linear parts.

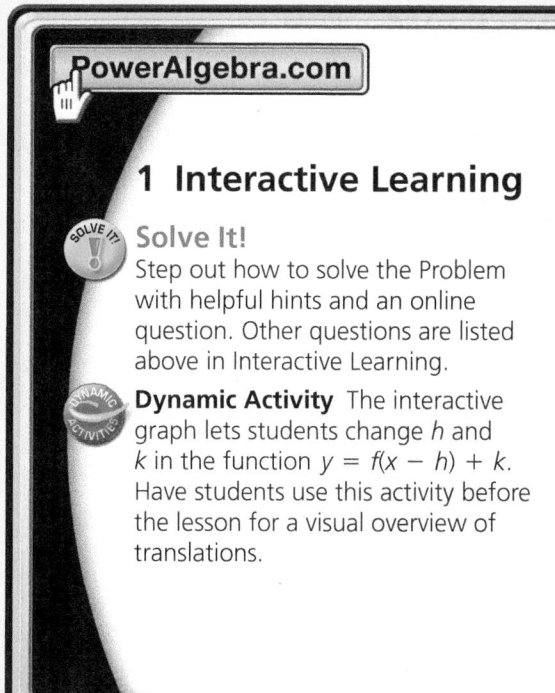

PowerAlgebra.com

## 1 Interactive Learning

**Solve It!**
Step out how to solve the Problem with helpful hints and an online question. Other questions are listed above in Interactive Learning.

**Dynamic Activity** The interactive graph lets students change $h$ and $k$ in the function $y = f(x - h) + k$. Have students use this activity before the lesson for a visual overview of translations.

**Lesson 2-7** **107**

# Problem 1

## Got It?                            VISUAL LEARNERS

Some students may not be able to compare the graph with the parent function unless they draw both graphs on the same grid. Have them use different colors to distinguish the functions clearly.

**Q** What kinds of transformations affect the axis of symmetry? **[Transformations that change the x-value of the vertex, such as a horizontal translation, change the axis of symmetry.]**

## Take Note

Sketch examples of the graphs for $k = 2$ and $-2$, $h = 2$ and $-2$, and $a = 2$, $-2$, $\frac{1}{2}$ and $-\frac{1}{2}$.

---

 **Problem 1** Graphing an Absolute Value Function

What is the graph of the absolute value function $y = |x| - 4$? How is this graph different from the graph of the parent function $f(x) = |x|$?

**Think**

Make a table of values and graph the function.

Use the location of the vertex to see how the graph has been translated. The parent function was not multiplied by a number, so the graph wasn't stretched, compressed, or reflected.

**Write**

| x | y |
|----|----|
| -3 | -1 |
| -1 | -3 |
| 0 | -4 |
| 1 | -3 |
| 3 | -1 |

Since the vertex is at $(0, -4)$, you translated the graph of $y = |x|$ down 4 units.

 **Got It? 1. a.** What is the graph of the function $y = |x| + 2$? How is this graph different from the parent function?

**b. Reasoning** Do transformations of the form $y = |x| + k$ affect the axis of symmetry? Explain.

The transformations you studied in Lesson 2-6 also apply to absolute value functions.

 **Key Concept   The Family of Absolute Value Functions**

**Parent Function $y = |x|$**

| **Vertical Translation** | **Horizontal Translation** |
|---|---|
| Translation up $k$ units, $k > 0$  $y = |x| + k$ | Translation right $h$ units, $h > 0$  $y = |x - h|$ |
| Translation down $k$ units, $k > 0$  $y = |x| - k$ | Translation left $h$ units, $h > 0$  $y = |x + h|$ |
| **Vertical Stretch and Compression** | **Reflection** |
| Vertical stretch, $a > 1$  $y = a|x|$ | In the x-axis  $y = -|x|$ |
| Vertical compression, $0 < a < 1$  $y = a|x|$ | In the y-axis  $y = |-x|$ |

---

# Answers

## Solve It!

The graph would be V-shaped with its vertex on the x-axis: the left branch of the graph will have a neg. slope because the y-values decrease as you approach the county line. The rt. branch of the graph will have a pos. slope because the y-values increase as you pass the county line and continue jogging.

## Got It?

**1. a.** 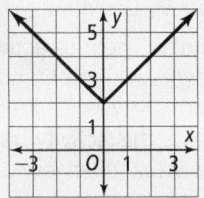 vertex at $(0, 2)$; translated up 2 units from the parent function

**b.** No; transformations of this form move the vertex up or down along the axis of symmetry, so the axis stays the same.

---

 **PowerAlgebra.com**

## 2 Guided Instruction

Each Problem is worked out and supported online.

**Problem 1**
Graphing an Absolute Value Function

**Problem 2**
Combining Translations

**Alternative Problem 2**
Combining Translations Animated
*Animated*

**Problem 3**
Vertical Stretch and Compression
*Animated*

**Problem 4**
Identifying Transformations

**Problem 5**
Writing an Absolute Value Function
*Animated*

**Support in Algebra 2 Companion**
• Vocabulary
• Key Concepts
• Got It?

**Problem 2** Combining Translations

**Multiple Choice** Which of the following is the graph of $y = |x + 2| + 3$?

 **Think**

Can you eliminate any answers after this comparison?
Only choices A and D show translations of $y = |x|$ to the left.

Compare $y = |x + 2| + 3$ to each form, $y = |x + h|$ and $y = |x| + k$.

$y = |x + h|$    The parent function, $y = |x|$, is translated left 2 units.

$y = |x| + k$    The parent function, $y = |x|$, is translated up 3 units.

The parent function $y = |x|$ is translated left 2 units and up 3 units. The vertex will be at $(-2, 3)$. The correct choice is D.

 **Got It?** **2.** What is the graph of the function $y = |x - 2| + 1$?

The right branch of the graph of $y = |x|$ has slope 1. The graph of $y = a|x|, a > 0$, is a stretch or compression of the graph of $y = |x|$. Its right branch has slope $a$. The graph of $y = -a|x|$ is a reflection of $y = a|x|$ in the x-axis and its right branch has slope $-a$.

 **Problem 3** Vertical Stretch and Compression

What is the graph of $y = \frac{1}{2}|x|$?

The graph is a vertical compression of the graph of $f(x) = |x|$ by the factor $\frac{1}{2}$. Graph the right branch and use symmetry to graph the left branch.

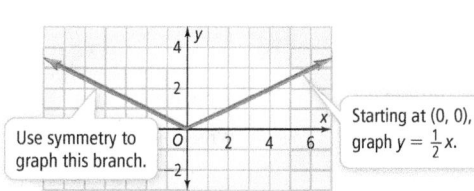

Use symmetry to graph this branch.

Starting at (0, 0), graph $y = \frac{1}{2}x$.

**Got It?** **3.** What is the graph of each function?
     **a.** $y = 2|x|$      **b.** $y = -\frac{2}{3}|x|$

PowerAlgebra.com      Lesson 2-7   Absolute Value Functions and Graphs      **109**

## Problem 2

**Q** What absolute value functions are shown in the other three graphs? [A: $y = |x + 2| - 3$; B: $y = |x - 2| + 3$; C: $y = |x - 2| - 3$]

### Got It?      SYNTHESIZING

**Q** Does the order in which you identify the vertical and horizontal translations matter? Explain. [No; answers may vary. Sample: As long as you correctly identify the vertical change as the *y*-coordinate of the vertex and the horizontal change as the *x*-coordinate, the order in which you identify them is not important.]

## Problem 3

**Q** How are the equations $y = |x|$ and $y = \frac{1}{2}|x|$ different? [In the second equation, the absolute value term is multiplied by $\frac{1}{2}$.]

**Q** What is the difference between a vertical stretch and a vertical compression? [In a stretch, each *y*-coordinate is multiplied by a number whose value is greater than 1. In a compression, the value of the factor is between 0 and 1.]

### Got It?      SYNTHESIZING

**Q** What characteristic of the equation results in the V shape opening downward? [when the sign of the coefficient of the absolute value term is negative]

# Additional Problems

**1.** What is the graph of the absolute value function $y = |x| + 3$? How is this graph different from the parent function $f(x) = |x|$?

**ANSWER** It is translated up 3 units.

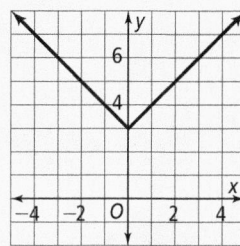

**2.** Which of the following is the graph of $y = |x + 3| - 1$?

   **a.**

   **b.**

   **c.**

   **d.**

   **ANSWER** b

**3.** What is the graph of $y = -\frac{1}{4}|x|$? What are the transformations of the parent function?

**ANSWER** Vertical compression by the factor $\frac{1}{4}$ and reflection in the x-axis.

**4.** Compare $y = -2|x + 2| + 3$ with the parent function. Without graphing, what are the vertex, axis of symmetry, and transformations of the parent function?

**ANSWER** vertex $(-2, 3)$; axis of symmetry $x = -2$; translated 2 units left, vertically stretched by the factor 2, reflected in x-axis and translated 3 units up

**5.** What is the equation of the absolute value function?

**ANSWER** $y = \frac{1}{4}|x - 2| + 1$

**Got It 2–3.** See next page.

**Lesson 2-7**    **109**

## Take Note

An absolute value function of the form $a|x| + k$, with no horizontal translation, is not changed by being reflected in the y-axis.

### Problem 4

**Q** Can the y-value of this function ever be less than 4? Explain. **[No; the minimum value of $3|x - 2|$ is 0 because the absolute value factor can never be negative, so the minimum value of $3|x - 2| + 4$ is 4.]**

**Q** Describe the y-coordinates of two points that are an equal distance from the axis of symmetry. **[The y-coordinates are equal.]**

### Got It?                    ERROR PREVENTION

Make sure students use order of operations when describing order of transformations to avoid unintentionally changing the vertex.

### Problem 5

**Q** What is the slope of the right branch of the graph in terms of the function? **[the stretch or compression factor a]**

**Q** What is the vertex in terms of the function? **[(h, k)]**

**Q** Does it matter in what order you perform the steps of this solution? Explain. **[Sample: No; you could find the slope of the right branch and the coordinates of the vertex in either order since one result does not affect the other. ]**

### Got It?

**Q** What two parts of the graph do you need to identify to write the equation? **[the slope of the right branch a and vertex (h, k)]**

---

You can combine the equations for stretches and compressions with the equations for translations to write a general form for absolute value functions.

 **Key Concept**   General Form of the Absolute Value Function

$$y = a|x - h| + k$$

The stretch or compression factor is $|a|$, the vertex is located at $(h, k)$, and the axis of symmetry is the line $x = h$.

 **Problem 4**  Identifying Transformations

**Without graphing, what are the vertex and axis of symmetry of the graph of $y = 3|x - 2| + 4$? How is the parent function $y = |x|$ transformed?**

Compare $y = 3|x - 2| + 4$ with the general form $y = a|x - h| + k$.

$a = 3, h = 2$, and $k = 4$.

The vertex is $(2, 4)$ and the axis of symmetry is $x = 2$.

The parent function $y = |x|$ is translated 2 units to the right, vertically stretched by the factor 3, and translated 4 units up.

**Check**  Check by graphing the equation on a graphing calculator.

**Got It?  4.** What are the vertex and axis of symmetry of $y = -2|x - 1| - 3$? How is $y = |x|$ transformed?

 **Problem 5**  Writing an Absolute Value Function

**What is the equation of the absolute value function?**

**Step 1**  Identify the vertex.
        The vertex is at $(-1, 4)$, so $h = -1$ and $k = 4$.

**Step 2**  Identify $a$.
        The slope of the branch to the right of the vertex is $-\frac{1}{3}$, so $a = -\frac{1}{3}$.

**Step 3**  Write the equation.
        Substitute the values of $a$, $h$, and $k$ into the general form $y = a|x - h| + k$.
        The equation that describes the graph is $y = -\frac{1}{3}|x + 1| + 4$.

**Got It?  5.** What is the equation of the absolute value function?

---

# Answers

## Got It? (continued)

**2.**

**3. a.**   **b.**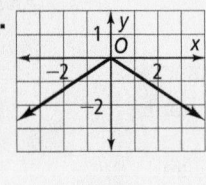

**4.** $(1, -3)$; $x = 1$; translated 1 unit to the rt., vertically stretched by a factor of 2, then reflected over the x-axis and translated down 3 units

**5.** $y = \frac{1}{4}|x - 2| - 1$

## Lesson Check

**1.** $(-4, -3)$; $x = -4$

**2.** $(-3, 9)$; $x = -3$

**3.** vert. stretch       **4.** vert. stretch

**5.** Yes; you can determine the position of a graph of an absolute value function by identifying the vertex, axis of symmetry and the transformation of the absolute value parent function. Answers may vary. Sample: $y = -\frac{1}{2}|x + 3| - 5$; vertex $(-3, -5)$; axis of symmetry, $x = -3$; translated 3 units to the left, vertically compressed by a factor of $\frac{1}{2}$, then reflected over the x-axis and translated down 5 units.

**6.** Sample: $y = |x + 1| - 2$ and $y = -|x + 1| - 2$

**7.** $y = |x|$ is the same as $y = x$ when $x \geq 0$ and is the reflection of $y = x$ across the x-axis when $x < 0$.

## Practice and Problem-Solving Exercises

**8.**

| x | y |
|---|---|
| -2 | 3 |
| -1 | 2 |
| 0 | 1 |
| 1 | 2 |
| 2 | 3 |

**9.**

| x | y |
|---|---|
| -2 | 1 |
| -1 | 0 |
| 0 | -1 |
| 1 | 0 |
| 2 | 1 |

## Lesson Check

**Do you know HOW?**

Find the vertex and the axis of symmetry of the graph of each function.

**1.** $y = 2|x + 4| - 3$     **2.** $y = |-x - 3| + 9$

Determine if each function is a vertical stretch or vertical compression of the parent function $y = |x|$.

**3.** $y = -\frac{7}{2}|x|$      **4.** $y = \frac{3}{2}|x|$

**Do you UNDERSTAND?**

**5.** Is it true that without making a graph of an absolute value function, you can describe its position in the coordinate plane? Explain with an example.

**6.** Write two absolute value functions such that they have a common vertex in Quadrant III and one is the reflection of the other in a horizontal line.

**7. Compare and Contrast** How is the graph of $y = x$ different from the graph of $y = |x|$?

## Practice and Problem-Solving Exercises

**A Practice**

Make a table of values for each equation. Then graph the equation.    🔶 **See Problems 1 and 2.**

**8.** $y = |x| + 1$     **9.** $y = |x| - 1$     **10.** $y = |x| - 3$

**11.** $y = |x + 2|$     **12.** $y = |x + 4|$     **13.** $y = |x + 5|$

**14.** $y = |x - 1| + 3$     **15.** $y = |x + 6| - 1$     **16.** $y = |x - 5| + 4$

Graph each equation. Then describe the transformation from the parent function $f(x) = |x|$.    🔶 **See Problem 3.**

**17.** $y = 3|x|$     **18.** $y = -\frac{1}{2}|x|$     **19.** $y = -2|x|$

**20.** $y = \frac{1}{3}|x|$     **21.** $y = \frac{3}{2}|x|$     **22.** $y = -\frac{3}{4}|x|$

Without graphing, identify the vertex, axis of symmetry, and transformations from the parent function $f(x) = |x|$.    🔶 **See Problem 4.**

**23.** $y = |x + 2| - 4$     **24.** $y = \frac{3}{2}|x - 6|$     **25.** $y = 3|x + 6|$

**26.** $y = 4 - |x + 2|$     **27.** $y = -|x - 5|$     **28.** $y = |x - 2| - 6$

Write an absolute value equation for each graph.    🔶 **See Problem 5.**

**29.**

**30.**

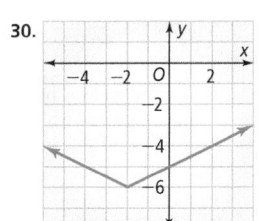

---

**10.**

| x | y |
|----|----|
| -2 | -1 |
| -1 | -2 |
| 0 | -3 |
| 1 | -2 |
| 2 | -1 |

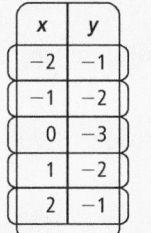

**11.**

| x | y |
|----|----|
| -4 | 2 |
| -3 | 1 |
| -2 | 0 |
| -1 | 1 |
| 0 | 2 |

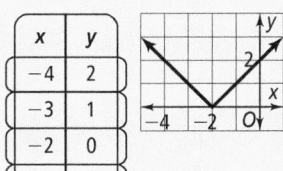

**12.**

| x | y |
|----|----|
| -6 | 2 |
| -5 | 1 |
| -4 | 0 |
| -3 | 1 |
| -2 | 2 |

**13.**

| x | y |
|----|----|
| -7 | 2 |
| -6 | 1 |
| -5 | 0 |
| -4 | 1 |
| -3 | 2 |

**14–30.** See pages 112–113.

---

# 3 Lesson Check

## Do you know HOW?

- For Exercise 1, encourage students to rewrite the equation in the form $y = a|x - h| + k$.
- In Exercises 3–4, point out that just because a number is written as a fraction, it is not necessarily less than 1. The sign of the coefficient of the absolute value expression does not affect the answer because the question asks only if each function is a stretch or compression. If students have difficulty, revisit Problem 2.

## Do you UNDERSTAND?

- For Exercise 5, giving the location of the vertex is not enough to describe the position; you also need to specify the slopes of both sides of the graph.
- For Exercise 6, make sure students know which quadrant is Quadrant III.

## Close

**Q** The absolute value of a quantity is always nonnegative. How can an absolute value graph extend below the x-axis? **[If the absolute value term is multiplied by a negative number, the graph is reflected across the x-axis, or if the graph is translated down $k$ units, the vertex will be below the x-axis.]**

**Q** For what values in its domain is an absolute value function linear? **[for $x \geq$ x-coordinate of the vertex; for $x \leq$ x-coordinate of the vertex]**

**PowerAlgebra.com**

### 3 Lesson Check

For a digital lesson check, use the Got It questions.

**Support in Algebra 2 Companion**
- Lesson Check

### 4 Practice

Assign homework to individual students or to an entire class.

# 4 Practice

## ASSIGNMENT GUIDE

Basic: 8–30 all, 31–33, 40–44 even, 45

Average: 9–29 odd, 31–45

Advanced: 9–29 odd, 31–50

Standardized Test Prep: 51–54

Mixed Review: 55–64

**Reasoning** exercises have blue headings.

**Applications** exercises have red headings.

**EXERCISE 32:** Use the Think About a Plan worksheet in the **Practice and Problem Solving Workbook** (also available in the Teaching Resources in print and online) to further support students' development in becoming independent learners.

## HOMEWORK QUICK CHECK

To check students' understanding of key skills and concepts, go over Exercises 23, 29, 31, 32, and 33.

---

 **Apply**

**31. Think About a Plan** Graph $y = -2|x + 3| + 4$. List the $x$- and $y$-intercepts, if any.
- What is the vertex?
- What does $y$ equal at the $x$-intercept(s)? What does $x$ equal at the $y$-intercept(s)?

**32.** Graph $y = 4|x - 3| + 1$. List the vertex and the $x$- and $y$-intercepts, if any.

**33. Error Analysis** A classmate says that the graphs of $y = -3|x|$ and $y = |-3x|$ are identical. Graph each function and explain why your classmate is not correct.

**34.** Graph each pair of equations on the same coordinate grid.
   **a.** $y = 2|x + 1|; y = |2x + 1|$     **b.** $y = 5|x - 2|; y = |5x - 2|$
   **c. Reasoning** Explain why each pair of graphs in parts (a) and (b) are different.

**35.** The graphs of the absolute value functions $f(x)$ and $g(x)$ are given.
   **a.** Describe a series of transformations that you can use to transform $f(x)$ into $g(x)$.
   **b. Reasoning** If you change the order of the transformations you found in part(a), could you still transform $f(x)$ into $g(x)$? Explain.

**Graph each absolute value equation.**

**36.** $y = \left|-\frac{1}{4}x - 1\right|$     **37.** $y = \left|\frac{5}{2}x - 2\right|$     **38.** $y = \left|\frac{3}{2}x + 2\right|$

**39.** $y = |3x - 6| + 1$     **40.** $y = -|x - 3|$     **41.** $y = |2x + 6|$

**42.** $y = 2|x + 2| - 3$     **43.** $y = 6 - |3x|$     **44.** $y = 6 - |3x + 1|$

**45. a.** Graph the equations $y = |\frac{1}{2}x - 6| + 3$ and $y = -|\frac{1}{2}x + 6| - 3$ on the same set of axes.
   **b. Writing** Describe the similarities and differences in the graphs.

**Challenge**     **Graph each absolute value equation.**

**46.** $y = |3x| - \frac{x}{3}$     **47.** $y = \frac{1}{2}|x| + 4|x - 1|$     **48.** $y = |2x| + |x - 4|$

**49.** The graph at the right models the distance between a roadside stand and a car traveling at a constant speed. The $x$-axis represents time and the $y$-axis represents distance. Which equation best represents the relation shown in the graph?

   Ⓐ $y = |60x|$     Ⓒ $y = |x| + 60$
   Ⓑ $y = |40x|$     Ⓓ $y = |x| + 40$

**50. a. Open-Ended** Find two absolute value equations with graphs that share a vertex.
   **b.** Find two absolute value equations with graphs that share part of a ray.

---

# Answers

## Practice and Problem-Solving Exercises (continued)

**14.**

| x | y |
|---|---|
| −1 | 5 |
| 0 | 4 |
| 1 | 3 |
| 2 | 4 |
| 3 | 5 |

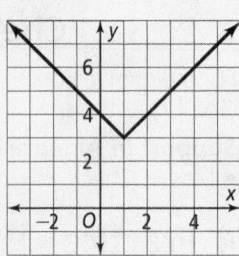

**15.**

| x | y |
|---|---|
| −8 | 1 |
| −7 | 0 |
| −6 | −1 |
| −5 | 0 |
| −4 | 1 |

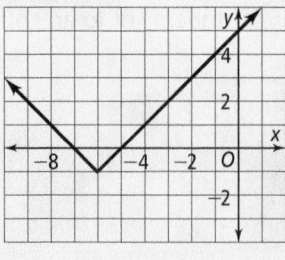

**16.**

| x | y |
|---|---|
| 3 | 6 |
| 4 | 5 |
| 5 | 4 |
| 6 | 5 |
| 7 | 6 |

**17.**

vertically stretched by a factor of 3

**18.**

vertically compressed by a factor of $\frac{1}{2}$ and reflected across the $x$-axis

**19.**

vertically stretched by a factor of 2 and reflected across the $x$-axis

**20.**

vertically compressed by a factor of $\frac{1}{3}$

**21.**

vertically stretched by a factor of $\frac{3}{2}$

**22.**

vertically compressed by a factor of $\frac{3}{4}$, reflected across the $x$-axis

**23–44.** See page 113.

**SAT/ACT**

**51.** The graph shows which equation?

   Ⓐ $y = |3x - 1| + 2$        Ⓒ $y = |x - 1| - 2$

   Ⓑ $y = |x - 1| + 2$        Ⓓ $y = |3x - 3| - 2$

**52.** How are the graphs of $y = 2x$ and $y = 2x + 2$ related?

   Ⓕ The graph of $y = 2x + 2$ is the graph of $y = 2x$ translated down two units.

   Ⓖ The graph of $y = 2x + 2$ is the graph of $y = 2x$ translated up two units.

   Ⓗ The graph of $y = 2x + 2$ is the graph of $y = 2x$ translated to the left two units.

   Ⓘ The graph of $y = 2x + 2$ is the graph of $y = 2x$ translated to the right two units.

**53.** What is the equation of a line parallel to $y = x$ that passes through the point $(0, 1)$?

   Ⓐ $y = x + 1$        Ⓒ $y = x - 1$

   Ⓑ $y = 2x + 2$        Ⓓ $y = -x$

**Short Response**

**54.** Is $|y| = x$ a function? Explain.

## Mixed Review

Write an equation for each transformation of the graph of $y = x + 2$.    ◆ See Lesson 2-6.

**55.** 2 units up, 3 units right

**56.** vertical compression by a factor of $\frac{1}{2}$, reflection in the $y$-axis

Write the function rule for each function reflected in the given axis.

**57.** $f(x) = x - 7$; $y$-axis      **58.** $f(x) = 2x - 6$; $y$-axis      **59.** $f(x) = 4 + x$; $x$-axis

Find a trend line for each scatter plot. Write the equation for each trend line.    ◆ See Lesson 2-5.

**60.**       **61.**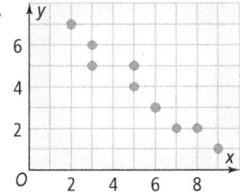

**Get Ready!**   **To prepare for Lesson 2-8, do Exercises 62–64.**

Solve each inequality. Graph the solution on a number line.    ◆ See Lesson 1-5.

**62.** $12p \leq 15$        **63.** $4 + t > 17$        **64.** $5 - 2t \geq 11$

---

**23.** $(-2, -4)$; $x = -2$; translate 2 units to the left and 4 units down

**24.** $(0, 0)$; $x = 0$; vertically stretch by a factor of $\frac{3}{2}$

**25.** $(-6, 0)$; $x = -6$; translate 6 units to the left and vertically stretch by a factor of 3

**26.** $(-2, 4)$; $x = -2$; reflect across the $x$-axis, translate 2 units to the left and 4 units up

**27.** $(5, 0)$; $x = 5$; translate 5 units to the rt. and reflect across the $x$-axis

**28.** $(2, -6)$; $x = 2$; translate 2 units to the rt. and 6 units down

**29.** $y = -2|x - 5| + 1$

**30.** $y = 0.5|x + 2| - 6$

**31.** 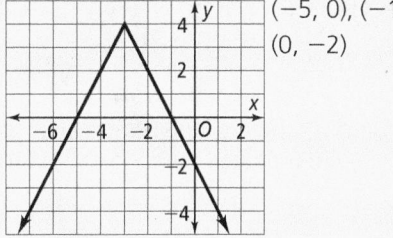   $(-5, 0), (-1, 0),$ $(0, -2)$

**32.**    $(3, 1)$; no $x$-intercept; $(0, 13)$

**33.**  The graphs are not identical; one is the reflection across the $x$-axis of the other.

**34. a.**

   **b.**

   **c.** The absolute value bars act as grouping symbols, like parentheses.

**35. a.** Answers may vary. Sample: reflection across the $x$-axis, vert. compression by a factor of $\frac{1}{2}$, translation down $\frac{1}{2}$ unit, translation rt. 6 units

   **b.** Yes; changing the order of the transformations may or may not change the result.

**36.**

**37.**       **38.**

**39.**       **40.**

**41.**       **42.**

**43.**       **44.**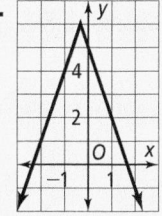

**45–64.** See back of book.

# Differentiated Remediation

Available in editable format online.

## Additional Instructional Support

### Algebra 2 Companion

Students can use the **Algebra 2 Companion** worktext (4 pages) as you teach the lesson. Use the Companion to support

- New Vocabulary
- Key Concepts
- Got It for each Problem
- Lesson Check

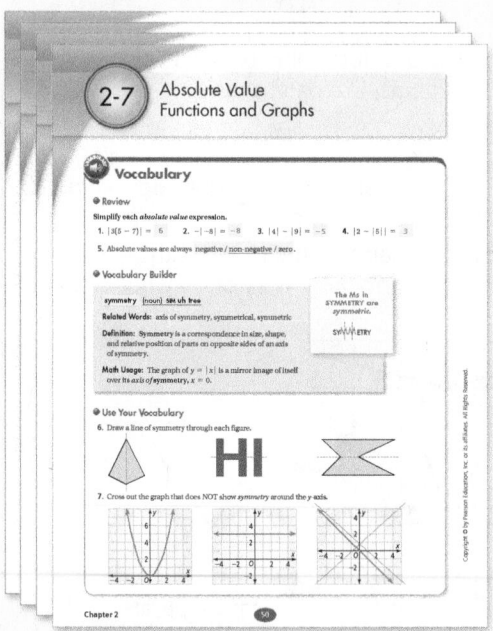

### ELL Support

**Use Role Playing** Use your arms to demonstrate as you verbally describe the transformations of an absolute value function, with your body being the axis of symmetry. Stretch out your arms over your head to make the V shape. To model compression, move arms further apart, and for stretch, closer. Step to one side to model a horizontal translation, and stand on toes or stoop to model a vertical translation. Reverse the activity by writing an equation on the board and having students model it with their bodies and verbally describe their actions.

## 5 Assess & Remediate

### Lesson Quiz

1. How is the graph of $y = |x| - 1$ different from the parent function $f(x) = |x|$?
2. What is the graph of $y = |x - 3| + 1$?
3. What is the graph of $y = 3|x|$?
4. **Do you UNDERSTAND?** Compare $y = \frac{1}{3}|x - 2| - 5$ with the parent function. Without graphing, what are the vertex, axis of symmetry, and transformations of the parent function?
5. What is the equation of the absolute value function?

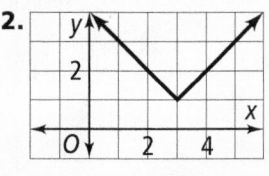

**ANSWERS TO LESSON QUIZ**

1. It is translated down 1 unit.

2.

3.

4. $a = \frac{1}{3}$, $h = 2$, $k = -5$; vertex: $(2, -5)$; axis of symmetry: $x = 2$; translated 2 units right, vertically compressed by the factor $\frac{1}{3}$, and translated 5 units down.

5. $y = \frac{1}{2}|x + 1| + 1$

**PRESCRIPTION FOR REMEDIATION**

Use the student work on the Lesson Quiz to prescribe a differentiated review assignment:

| Points | Differentiated Remediation |
| --- | --- |
| 0–2 | Intervention |
| 3–4 | On-level |
| 5 | Extension |

**PowerAlgebra.com**

### 5 Assess & Remediate

Assign the Lesson Quiz. Appropriate intervention, practice, or enrichment is automatically generated based on student performance.

## Intervention

- **Reteaching** (2 pages) Provides reteaching and practice exercises for the key lesson concepts. Use with struggling students or absent students.
- **English Language Learner Support** Helps students develop and reinforce mathematical vocabulary and key concepts.

**All-in-One Resources/Online**
**Reteaching**

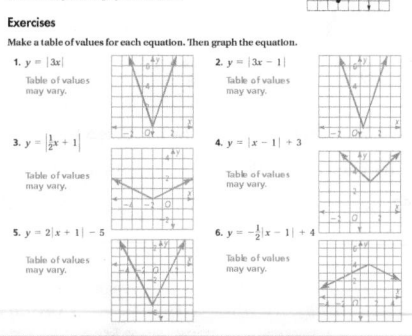

**All-in-One Resources/Online**
**English Language Learner Support**

# Differentiated Remediation *continued*

Available in editable format online.

## On-Level

- **Practice** (2 pages) Provides extra practice for each lesson. For simpler practice exercises, use the Form K Practice pages found in the All-in-One Teaching Resources and online.

- **Think About a Plan** Helps students develop specific problem-solving skills and strategies by providing scaffolded guiding questions.

- **Standardized Test Prep** Focuses on all major exercises, all major question types, and helps students prepare for the high-stakes assessments.

## Extension

- **Enrichment** Provides students with interesting problems and activities that extend the concepts of the lesson.

- **Activities, Games, and Puzzles** Worksheets that can be used for concepts development, enrichment, and for fun!

---

### Practice and Problem Solving Wkbk/ All-in-One Resources/Online
#### Practice page 1

### Practice and Problem Solving Wkbk/ All-in-One Resources/Online
#### Practice page 2

### All-in-One Resources/Online
#### Enrichment

---

### Practice and Problem Solving Wkbk/ All-in-One Resources/Online
#### Think About a Plan

### Practice and Problem Solving Wkbk/ All-in-One Resources/Online
#### Standardized Test Prep

### Online Teacher Resource Center
#### Activities, Games, and Puzzles

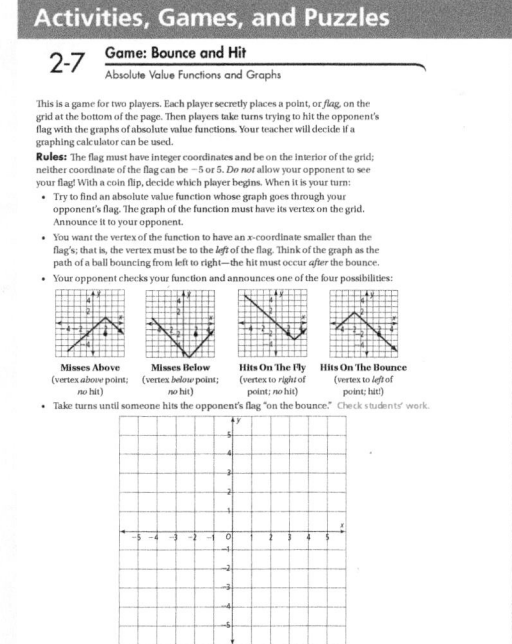

# 1 Interactive Learning

## Solve It!

**PURPOSE** To use prior knowledge to write a two-variable inequality

**PROCESS** Students may
- assign variables and write the inequality.
- use trial and error to generate values of the variables that satisfy the inequality.

### FACILITATE

**Q** What items can be bought with the gift card? **[CDs and books]**

**Q** Assign variables. Let $x$ = number of CDs and $y$ = number of books. What inequality models the situation? **[$5.25x + 3y \leq 50$]**

**Q** What values of $x$ and $y$ make the inequality true? **[Answers may vary. Sample: $x = 8$ and $y = 2$]**

**Q** How do you know whether you chose the combination that uses as much of the card as possible? **[There are many combinations that give a total of less than 50. With trial and error, it can take quite a while to check all the possibilities, unless you find one that costs exactly $50.]**

**ANSWER** See Solve It in Answers on next page.

**CONNECT THE MATH** Students use the Solve It's context to solve a two-variable inequality by trial and error. In this lesson, students will solve two-variable inequalities by graphing.

# 2-8 Two-Variable Inequalities

**Objective** To graph two-variable inequalities

**Getting Ready!**

You have a gift card for a store that sells pre-owned CDs and paperback books. You want to spend as much of the gift card as possible. How many of each item can you buy? Explain.

Gift card
For the gift you really want...
$50

USED Books & CDs

U$ED
Sale!
CD's...$5.25
Books...$3.00

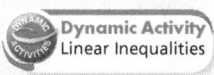

The words "as much... as possible" are important here.

**Dynamic Activity**
Linear Inequalities

In some situations you need to compare quantities. You can use inequalities for situations that involve these relationships: *less than, less than or equal to, greater than,* and *greater than or equal to.*

**Essential Understanding** Graphing an inequality in two variables is similar to graphing a line. The graph of a linear inequality contains all points on one side of the line and may or may not include the points on the line.

A **linear inequality** is an inequality in two variables whose graph is a region of the coordinate plane bounded by a line. This line is the **boundary** of the graph. The boundary separates the coordinate plane into two **half-planes**, one of which consists of solutions of the inequality.

**Lesson Vocabulary**
- linear inequality
- boundary
- half-plane
- test point

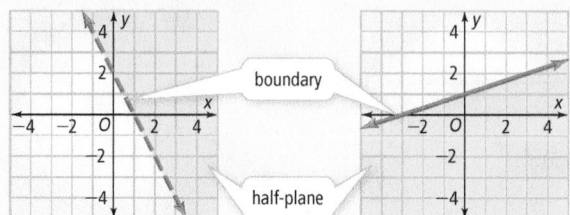

boundary

half-plane

---

# 2-8 Preparing to Teach

## BIG idea Modeling    UbD

**ESSENTIAL UNDERSTANDING**
- The graph of a linear inequality contains all points on one side of a line and may or may not include the points on the line.

## Math Background

While the steps involved in solving a linear inequality may seem straightforward, this knowledge opens the door to many advanced mathematical topics. Students may now extend their investigation into the two-variable coordinate plane by graphing two-variable inequalities. The principles learned in this lesson will also apply to linear programming problems. Solving a linear programming problem consists of maximizing or minimizing a function subject to a list of constraints or inequalities. Advancement in the computer field allows mathematicians to solve linear programming problems subject to hundreds of inequalities. Many

economic, labor, and business problems can be solved using linear programming techniques.

## Support Student Learning

Use the **Algebra 2 Companion** to engage and support students during instruction. See Lesson Resources at the end of this lesson for details.

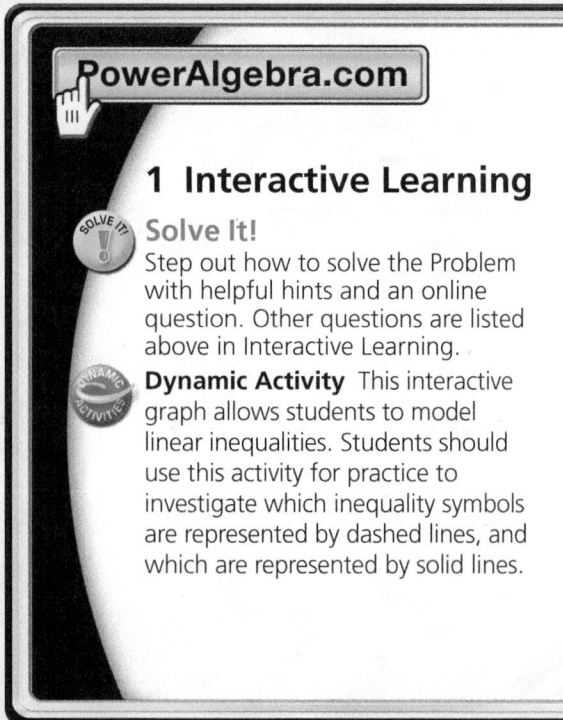

## PowerAlgebra.com

### 1 Interactive Learning

**Solve It!**
Step out how to solve the Problem with helpful hints and an online question. Other questions are listed above in Interactive Learning.

**Dynamic Activity** This interactive graph allows students to model linear inequalities. Students should use this activity for practice to investigate which inequality symbols are represented by dashed lines, and which are represented by solid lines.

To determine which half-plane to shade, pick a **test point** that is *not* on the boundary. Check whether that point satisfies the inequality. If it does, shade the half-plane that includes the test point. If not, shade the other half-plane. The origin, (0, 0), is usually an easy test point as long as it is not on the boundary.

 **Problem 1** Graphing Linear Inequalities

**What is the graph of each inequality?**

**A** $y > 3x - 1$

**Step 1**
Graph the boundary line $y = 3x - 1$. Use a dashed boundary line because the inequality is *greater than*, and the points on the line do not satisfy the inequality.

**Step 2**
Choose a test point, (0, 0). Substitute $x = 0$ and $y = 0$ into $y > 3x - 1$.
$$0 > 3(0) - 1$$
$$0 > -1$$
Since $0 > -1$ is true, shade the half plane that includes (0, 0).

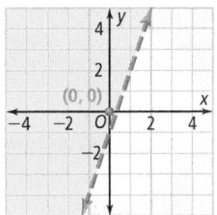

**B** $y \leq 3x - 1$

The boundary line is again $y = 3x - 1$, but it is solid because the inequality is less than or *equal to*.

Shade the region opposite the region shaded above (for $>$) because the inequality is *less than* or equal to.

You can also check the point (0, 0).
$$0 \leq 3(0) - 1$$
$$0 \leq -1$$
Since $0 \leq -1$ is false, (0, 0) is not part of the solution.

 **Got It? 1.** What is the graph of each inequality?
    **a.** $y \geq -2x + 1$         **b.** $y < -2x + 1$

You can also inspect inequalities solved for $y$, such as $y > mx + b$ to determine which half-plane describes the solution. Since $y$ describes vertical position, the solution of $y > mx + b$ will be *above* the boundary line. The solution of $y < mx + b$ will be *below* the boundary line.

**Plan**

**Can you use the graph of $y > 3x - 1$ to help graph $y \leq 3x - 1$?**
If you shaded above the line for $y > 3x - 1$, then shade below the line for $y \leq 3x - 1$.

## 2 Guided Instruction

**Problem 1**      SYNTHESIZING
To obtain the boundary line, write the inequality as an equation. Use a test point to determine which half-plane contains the solutions, and shade that half-plane.

**Q** Can you use $(0, -1)$ as a test point? Explain. **[No; $(0, -1)$ lies on the boundary line $y = 3x - 1$.]**

**Q** Why is it helpful to plot the test point on the graph? **[The test point determines where to shade and where not to shade.]**

### Got It?      ERROR PREVENTION

**Q** What is the difference between 1a and 1b? **[Answers may vary. Sample: The inequality is changed from $\geq$ to $<$.]**

**Q** How will the change affect the graphs? Explain. **[The inequality symbol determines whether the boundary line is included in the solutions and which half-plane contains the solutions, so the boundary line will change from solid to dashed, and the shaded half-plane will change from one side of the boundary line to the other.]**

         EXTENSION

**Q** What would a graph of $y \neq -2x + 1$ look like? **[A dashed boundary line with both half planes shaded; the only excluded solutions are those on the line itself.]**

---

## 2 Guided Instruction

 Each Problem is worked out and supported online.

**Problem 1**
Graphing a Linear Inequality

**Problem 2**
Using a Linear Inequality
         *Animated*

**Problem 3**
Graphing an Absolute Value Inequality

**Problem 4**
Writing an Inequality Based on a Graph
         *Animated*

**Alternative Problem 4**
Writing an Inequality Based on a Graph
         *Animated*

**Support in Algebra 2 Companion**
• Vocabulary
• Key Concepts
• Got It?

## Answers

**Solve It!**
You can buy 6 CDs and 6 books or 2 CDs and 13 books. In both cases you will spend $49.50.

**Got It?**
**1. a.**

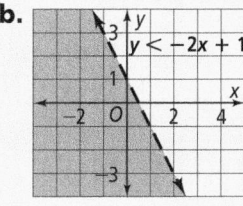

$y \geq -2x + 1$

**b.**

$y < -2x + 1$

## Problem 2

Students may use other techniques to graph the boundary line such as changing the equation to slope-intercept form.

**Q** What words in the paragraph suggest an inequality? **[more than]**

**Q** How is the type of inequality determined? **[The phrase "do not want to spend more than $15" suggests ≤.]**

**Q** Is $3x + 5y \le 60$ the only inequality that could be used to solve this problem? Explain. **[Answers may vary. Samples: No; you could let $x$ = number of large rides and $y$ = number of small rides and use $5x + 3y \le 60$; or you could convert number of tickets per ride to cost per ride and use $0.75x + 1.25y \le 15$.]**

**Q** What is another example of a discrete variable? **[Answers may vary. Sample: number of people at the fair]**

### Got It?

**Q** How is this different from Problem 2? **[The only difference is the amount of money you may spend.]**

**Q** If you double the money you spend, do you double the number of discrete ordered-pair solutions? Explain. **[Answers may vary. Sample: No; doubling the amount doubles both the base and height of the triangular solution region, so the number of solutions increases by a factor greater than 2 (though in most cases less than 4).]**

---

**Problem 2** Using a Linear Inequality

**Entertainment** The map shows the number of tickets needed for small or large rides at the fair. You do not want to spend more than $15 on tickets. How many small or large rides can you ride?

You can buy 60 tickets with $15.

**Think**

*What are the unknowns?*
The unknowns are the number of small rides and the number of large rides you can get on.

**Relate** the number of tickets for small rides **plus** the number of tickets for large rides **is less than or equal to** 60

**Define** Let $x$ = the number of small rides.

Let $y$ = the number of large rides.

**Write** $3x$ + $5y$ ≤ 60

**Step 1**

Find the intercepts of the boundary line. Use the intercepts to graph the boundary line.

When $y = 0$, $3x + 5(0) = 60$.
$3x = 60$
$x = 20$

When $x = 0$, $3(0) + 5y = 60$.
$5y = 60$
$y = 12$

Graph the line that connects the intercepts $(20, 0)$ and $(0, 12)$. Since the inequality is ≤, use a solid boundary line.

**Step 2**

The region above the boundary line represents combinations of rides that require more than 60 tickets. You purchased a *finite* number of tickets, 60, so you will not be able to go on an infinite number of rides. Shade the region below the boundary line.

The number of small rides $x$ and the number of large rides $y$ are whole numbers. In math, such a situation is called *discrete*. All points with whole number coordinates in the shaded region represent possible combinations of small and large rides.

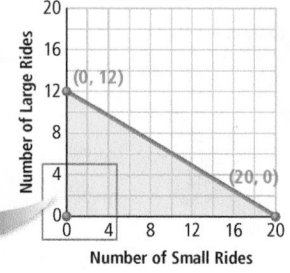

Rides at the Fair

**Got It?** **2. a.** Suppose that you decide to spend no more than $30 for tickets. What are the possible combinations of small and large rides that you can ride now? Use a graph to find your answer.

**b.** **Reasoning** Why did the graph of the solution in Problem 2 only include Quadrant I?

---

# Additional Problems

**1.** What is the graph of $y > 2x - 3$?

**ANSWER**

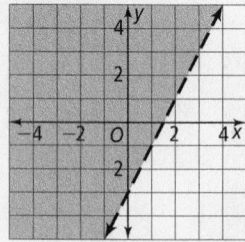

**2.** You put up a new shelf that is 1 ft wide to store some of your books and trophies. Each book takes up 1 inch and each trophy takes up 3 inches. What is a graph showing how many books and how many trophies will fit on the shelf?

**ANSWER**

**3.** What is the graph of $y \le |x - 2| + 1$?

**ANSWER**

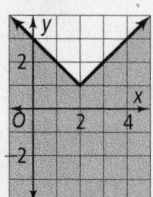

**4.** What inequality does this graph represent?

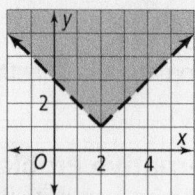

**ANSWER** $y > |x - 2| + 1$

### Got It? (continued)

**2. a.**

Rides at the Fair

**b.** The number of rides cannot be neg.

**3.**

$y \ge 2|x - 1| + 4$

**4. a.** $y > -|x + 4| + 3$

**b.** No; when you solve the ineq. for $y$, you multiply both sides by $-1$. This changes the ineq. sign from $>$ to $<$.

You can graph two-variable absolute value inequalities in the same way that you graph linear inequalities.

 **Problem 3** Graphing an Absolute Value Inequality

**What is the graph of** $1 - y < |x + 2|$?

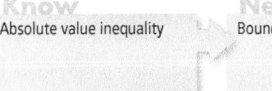
Know — Absolute value inequality
Need — Boundary
Plan — • Solve the inequality for $y$.
• Graph the related equation.
• Shade the solution.

$1 - y < |x + 2|$

$-y < |x + 2| - 1$    Subtract 1 from each side.

$y > -|x + 2| + 1$    Multiply both sides by $-1$.

The graph of $y = -|x + 2| + 1$ is the graph of $y = |x|$, reflected in the $x$-axis and translated left 2 units and up 1 unit.

Since the inequality is solved for $y$ and $y > -|x + 2| + 1$, shade the region above the boundary.

 **Got It? 3.** What is the graph of $y - 4 \geq 2|x - 1|$?

You can use the transformations discussed in previous lessons to help draw the boundary graphs more quickly. You can also use them to write an inequality based on a graph.

 **Problem 4** Writing an Inequality Based on a Graph

**Plan**
How can you tell that the graph is not a stretch or compression of the graph of $y = |x|$?
The slopes of the branches are 1 and $-1$.

**What inequality does this graph represent?**

The boundary is the graph of the absolute value function $y = |x|$, translated. The vertex of $y = |x|$ is translated to $(3, -2)$, so the boundary is the graph of $y = |x - 3| - 2$.

The solution is shaded above the boundary, so the inequality is either $>$ or $\geq$. Since the boundary is a dashed line, the correct inequality is $y > |x - 3| - 2$.

 **Got It? 4. a.** What inequality does this graph represent?
 **b.** Reasoning You can tell from looking at the inequality $y > 5x - 3$ to shade above the boundary line to represent the solution. Can you use the same technique to show the solution of an inequality like $2x - y > 1$? Explain.

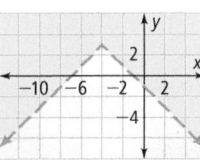

PowerAlgebra.com    Lesson 2-8   Two-Variable Inequalities    **117**

**Problem 3**

**Q** Why did the inequality symbol reverse direction in the solution process? **[To solve for $y$, both sides were multiplied by $-1$.]**

**Q** What does the graph of an absolute value function look like? How can you use this as a check? **[Answers may vary. Sample: It is shaped like a "V." If your graph does not look like a "V," you made a mistake.]**

**Q** How does the coefficient $a = -1$ affect the absolute value graph? **[It reflects the "V" shape in the $x$-axis.]**

**Got It?**

Graph $y = |x|$ first and then use transformations to identify the boundary curve.

**Problem 4**      **ERROR PREVENTION**

**Q** When determining what inequality a graph represents, what do you need to find? **[The vertex, the slope of the branches, whether the boundary line is shaded or dashed, and what region of the graph is shaded.]**

**Got It?**

**Q** How has the boundary line been transformed from the parent function $y = |x|$? **[It was reflected in the $x$-axis, and the vertex of $y = |x|$ was translated to $(-4, 3)$.]**

# Answers

## Practice and Problem-Solving Exercises (continued)

**11.**
**12.**

**13.**
**14.**

**15.**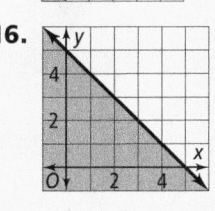
**16.**

**17. a.** $y \geq 20x$ if $x \leq 6$; $y \geq 15x$ if $x > 6$
**b.**

**18.**
**19.**

**20.**
**21.**

**22.**
**23.**

**24.**
**25.**

**26.**

**27.** $y < -x - 2$    **28.** $5x + 3y \leq 9$
**29.** $2y \geq |2x + 6|$

# 3 Lesson Check

## Do you know HOW? ERROR INTERVENTION

• For Exercises 1–4, if students shade the wrong half-planes, remind them that the inequality sign relates to above or below the boundary line, and determines which half-plane to shade.

## Do you UNDERSTAND? ERROR INTERVENTION

• For Exercise 6, suggest students make a list of the steps for graphing a linear inequality in two variables and another list of steps for graphing the linear equation in two variables, and then compare the lists.

## Close

**Q** What are the differences between solving linear equations in two variables and solving linear inequalities in two variables? **[The graph of a linear equation is a line; all solutions are on that line. The graph of a linear inequality includes the linear equation solution (called the boundary line) as well as a set of points that make up a half-plane. The boundary line may or may not be included in the solution of the inequality.]**

---

## Lesson Check

### Do you know HOW?

**What is the graph of each inequality?**

1. $9y \le 12x$

2. $7x + y \ge 8$

**What is the graph of each absolute value inequality?**

3. $y \le |x + 1|$

4. $y \ge |2x - 3|$

### Do you UNDERSTAND?

5. Do the points on the boundary line of the graph of an inequality help determine the shaded area of the graph? Explain.

6. **Compare and Contrast** How is graphing a linear inequality in two variables different from graphing a linear equation in two variables?

7. **Reasoning** Is the ordered pair $\left(\frac{3}{4}, 0\right)$ a solution of $3x + y > 3$? Explain.

## Practice and Problem-Solving Exercises

**Ⓐ Practice**

**Graph each inequality.**                                                        ◀ See Problem 1.

8. $y > 2x + 1$          9. $y < 3$              10. $x \le 0$

11. $y \le x - 5$        12. $2x + 3y \ge 12$    13. $2y \ge 4x - 6$

14. $3x - 2y \le 9$      15. $-y < 2x + 2$       16. $5 - y \ge x$

17. **Cooking** The time needed to roast a chicken depends on its weight. Allow at least 20 min/lb for a chicken weighing as much as 6 lb. Allow at least 15 min/lb for a chicken weighing more than 6 lb.            ◀ See Problem 2.
   a. Write two inequalities to represent the time needed to roast a chicken.
   b. Graph the inequalities.

**Graph each absolute value inequality.**                                         ◀ See Problem 3.

18. $y \ge |2x - 1|$        19. $y \le |3x| + 1$        20. $y \le |4 - x|$

21. $y > |-x + 4| + 1$      22. $y - 7 > |x + 2|$       23. $y + 2 \le \left|\frac{1}{2}x\right|$

24. $3 - y \ge -|x - 4|$    25. $1 - y < |2x - 3|$      26. $y + 3 \le |3x| - 1$

**Write an inequality for each graph. The equation for the boundary line is given.**   ◀ See Problem 4.

27. $y = -x - 2$        28. $5x + 3y = 9$        29. $2y = |2x + 6|$

---

# Answers

## Lesson Check

1.

$y \le \frac{4}{3}x$

2.

$y \ge -7x + 8$

3.
(graph)

4.

$y \ge |2x - 3|$

5. No; points on the boundary line distinguish between shaded and non-shaded areas, but do not give any information as to which side of the boundary line should be shaded.

6. Graphing a linear inequality in two variables includes first graphing the boundary line, which is a linear eq. in two variables, and then shading the half-plane.

7. No; $\left(\frac{3}{4}, 0\right)$ does not satisfy the inequality because $2.25 > 3$ is false.

## Practice and Problem-Solving Exercises

8.    9.     10.

**11–29.** See page 117.

Graph each inequality on a coordinate plane.

**30.** $5x - 2y \geq -10$ **31.** $2x - 5y < -10$ **32.** $\frac{3}{4}x + \frac{2}{3}y > \frac{5}{2}$ **33.** $3(x-2) + 2y \leq 6$

**34.** $|x - 1| > y + 7$ **35.** $y - |2x| \leq 21$ **36.** $\frac{2}{3}x + 2 \leq \frac{2}{9}y$ **37.** $0.25y - 1.5x \geq -4$

**38. Think About a Plan** The graph at the right relates the number of hours you spend on the phone to the number of hours you spend studying per week. Describe the domain for this situation. Write an inequality for the graph.
- What is the least amount of time you can spend on the phone per week? What is the most?
- What is the least amount of time you can spend studying per week? What is the most?
- What is the greatest amount of time you can spend either on the phone or studying per week?

**Time per Week**

Write an inequality for each graph.

**39.**  **40.**  **41.**

**42.**  **43.**  **44.**

**45.** Which graph best represents the solution of the inequality $y \geq 2|x - 1| - 2$?

**46.** The graph at the right relates the amount of gas in the tank of your car to the distance you can drive.
- **a.** Describe the domain for this situation.
- **b.** Why does the graph stop?
- **c.** Why is only the first quadrant shown?
- **d. Reasoning** Would every point in the solution region be a solution?
- **e.** Write an inequality for the graph.
- **f.** What does the coefficient of $x$ represent?

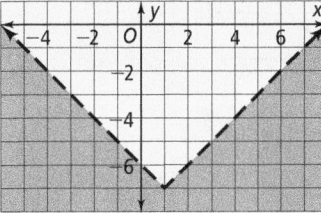
**Miles to Travel**

## 4 Practice

**ASSIGNMENT GUIDE**
Basic: 8–29 all, 36–46 even
Average: 9–29 odd, 30–46
Advanced: 9–29 odd, 30–51
Standardized Test Prep: 52–55
Mixed Review: 56–74

**Reasoning** exercises have blue headings.

**Applications** exercises have red headings.

**EXERCISE 46:** Use the Think About a Plan worksheet in the **Practice and Problem Solving Workbook** (also available in the Teaching Resources in print and online) to further support students' development in becoming independent learners.

**HOMEWORK QUICK CHECK**
To check students' understanding of key skills and concepts, go over Exercises 17, 19, 38, 44, and 46.

**30.**

**31.**

**32.**

**33.**

**34.**

**35.**

**36.**  **37.**

**38.** domain: $0 \leq x \leq 28$; $y \leq -x + 28$
**39.** $x > -3$ **40.** $y \leq \frac{3}{2}x + 2$
**41.** $y \geq -2x + 4$ **42.** $y \leq |x + 2|$

**43.** $y < -|x - 4|$
**44.** $y > |x + 1| - 1$
**45.** C
**46. a.** domain: $0 \leq x \leq 16$
  **b.** There is a limit to the number of gallons in your car's gas tank.
  **c.** You can't have a negative number of gallons of gas in your tank, nor can you drive a negative number of miles.
  **d.** Yes; you can use a fraction of a gallon, and you can drive a fraction of a mile.
  **e.** $y \leq 25x$
  **f.** the number of miles you can drive per gallon

**Lesson 2-8** 119

# Answers

## Practice and Problem-Solving Exercises (continued)

**47.** when the origin lies on the boundary line

**48.**

**49.**

**50.**

**51.**

## Standardized Test Prep

**52.** B

**53.** I

**54.** D

**55.** **[4]** let $c$ = amnt. of a commission,
let $s$ = amnt. of a sale
$c = ks$
$(\$48,000) = k(\$800,000)$
$.06 = k$
$c = .06 (\$650,000) = \$39,000$
(OR sltn. by another appropriate method)
**[3]** appropriate method, with one computational error
**[2]** correct value for $k$
**[1]** no work shown

## Mixed Review

**56.**

**57.**

---

Challenge   **47. Writing** When you graph an inequality, you can often use the point $(0, 0)$ to test which side of the boundary line to shade. Describe a situation in which you could not use $(0, 0)$ as a test point.

Graphing Calculator   **Graph each inequality on a graphing calculator. Then sketch the graph.**

**48.** $y \le |x + 1| - |x - 1|$

**49.** $y > |x| + |x + 3|$

**50.** $y < |x - 3| - |x + 3|$

**51.** $y < 7 - |x - 4| + |x|$

### Standardized Test Prep

SAT/ACT   **52.** Suppose $y$ varies directly with $x$. If $x$ is 30 when $y$ is 10, what is $x$ when $y$ is 9?

Ⓐ 3      Ⓑ 27      Ⓒ 29      Ⓓ $\frac{300}{9}$

**53.** Which equation represents a line with slope $-2$ and $y$-intercept 3?

Ⓕ $3y = x - 2$   Ⓖ $3y = -2x + 1$   Ⓗ $y = 2x - 3$   Ⓘ $y = -2x + 3$

**54.** What is the vertex of $y = |x| - 5$?

Ⓐ $(5, 0)$   Ⓑ $(-5, 0)$   Ⓒ $(0, 5)$   Ⓓ $(0, -5)$

Extended Response   **55.** The amount of a commission is directly proportional to the amount of a sale. A realtor received a commission of $48,000 on the sale of an $800,000 house. How much would the commission be on a $650,000 house?

### Mixed Review

**Graph each function by translating its parent function.**   ◀ See Lesson 2-7.

**56.** $y = |2x + 5|$

**57.** $y = |x| - 3$

**58.** $f(x) = |x + 6|$

**59.** $f(x) = |x| - 2$

**60.** $y = |x + 2|$

**61.** $y = |x - 1| + 5$

**Determine whether $y$ varies directly with $x$. If so, find the constant of variation.**   ◀ See Lesson 2-2.

**62.** $y = x + 1$

**63.** $y = 100x$

**64.** $5x + y = 0$

**65.** $y - 2 = 2x$

**66.** $x = \frac{y}{3}$

**67.** $-4 = y - x$

**68.** $y = -10x$

**69.** $xy = 1$

**Make a scatter plot and describe the correlation.**   ◀ See Lesson 2-5.

**70.** $\{(0, 6), (1, 4), (2, 4), (4, 1), (5, 0)\}$

**71.** $\{(-10, 5), (-5, -5), (-2, 0), (0, 3), (5, -2)\}$

**Get Ready!**   **To prepare for Lesson 3-1, do Exercises 72–74.**

**Graph each equation. Use one coordinate plane for all three graphs.**   ◀ See Lesson 2-3.

**72.** $3x - y = 2$

**73.** $3x - y = -2$

**74.** $x + 3y = -2$

---

**58.**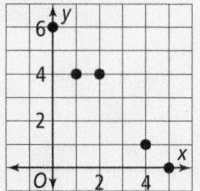

**59.** 

**60.** 

**61.** 

**62.** no

**63.** yes; 100

**64.** yes; $-5$

**65.** no

**66.** yes; 3

**67.** no

**68.** yes; $-10$

**69.** no

**70.** strong neg. correlation

**71.** no correlation

**72–74.**
$y = 3x + 2$
$y = 3x - 2$
$y = -\frac{1}{3}x - \frac{2}{3}$

# Differentiated Remediation
Available in editable format online.

## Additional Instructional Support

### Algebra 2 Companion
Students can use the **Algebra 2 Companion** worktext (4 pages) as you teach the lesson. Use the Companion to support

- New Vocabulary
- Key Concepts
- Got It for each Problem
- Lesson Check

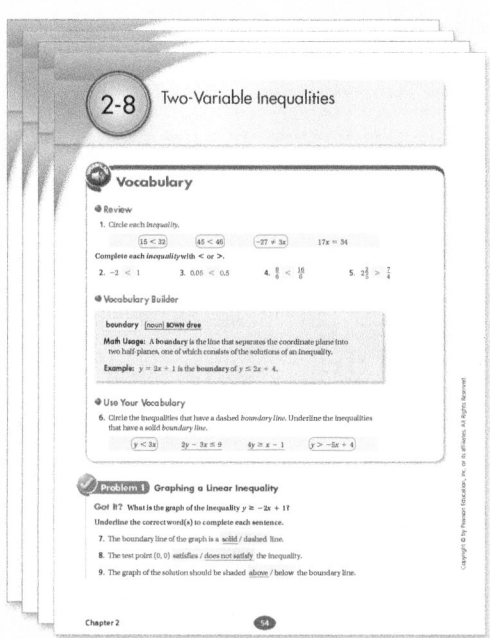

### ELL Support
**Focus on Language** Draw a linear inequality on the board and have students identify each element. Ask students to identify the *boundary*, and a *half-plane*. Ask students if they can think of other examples of boundaries. Ask why it is called a *linear* inequality.

## 5 Assess & Remediate

### Lesson Quiz
1. What is the graph of $y \leq 5x + 2$?
2. **Do you UNDERSTAND?** At a local carnival, a hot dog costs $1.50 and water costs $0.80. You want to buy food and water for yourself and your friends but do not want to spend more than $20. What inequality represents how many hot dogs and how much water you can buy?
3. What is the graph of $-y > |x - 1| + 4$?
4. What inequality does this graph represent?

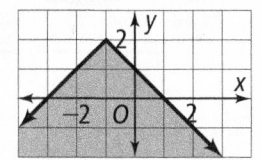

### ANSWERS TO LESSON QUIZ

1.

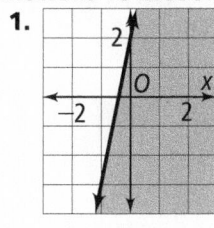

2. $0.8x + 1.5y \leq 20$ or $1.5x + 0.8y \leq 20$

3.

4. $y \leq -|x + 1| + 2$

### PRESCRIPTION FOR REMEDIATION
Use the student work on the Lesson Quiz to prescribe a differentiated review assignment:

| Points | Differentiated Remediation |
|--------|---------------------------|
| 0–1 | Intervention |
| 2–3 | On-level |
| 4 | Extension |

**PowerAlgebra.com**

## 5 Assess & Remediate
Assign the Lesson Quiz. Appropriate intervention, practice, or enrichment is automatically generated based on student performance.

## Intervention

- **Reteaching** (2 pages) Provides reteaching and practice exercises for the key lesson concepts. Use with struggling students or absent students.
- **English Language Learner Support** Helps students develop and reinforce mathematical vocabulary and key concepts.

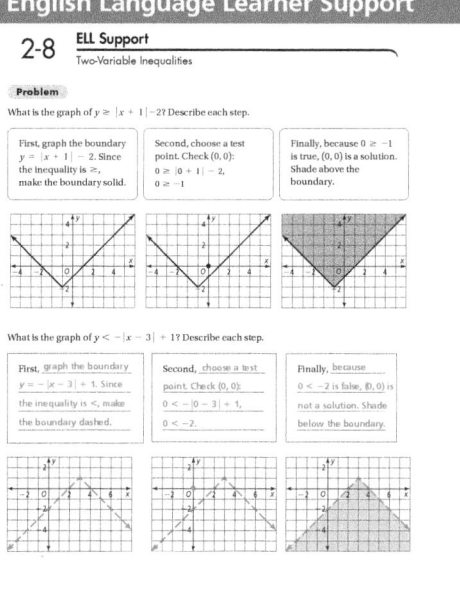

# Differentiated Remediation *continued*

Available in editable format online.

## On-Level

- **Practice** (2 pages) Provides extra practice for each lesson. For simpler practice exercises, use the Form K Practice pages found in the All-in-One Teaching Resources and online.

- **Think About a Plan** Helps students develop specific problem-solving skills and strategies by providing scaffolded guiding questions.

- **Standardized Test Prep** Focuses on all major exercises, all major question types, and helps students prepare for the high-stakes assessments.

## Extension

- **Enrichment** Provides students with interesting problems and activities that extend the concepts of the lesson.

- **Activities, Games, and Puzzles** Worksheets that can be used for concepts development, enrichment, and for fun!

### Practice and Problem Solving Wkbk/ All-in-One Resources/Online
**Practice page 1**

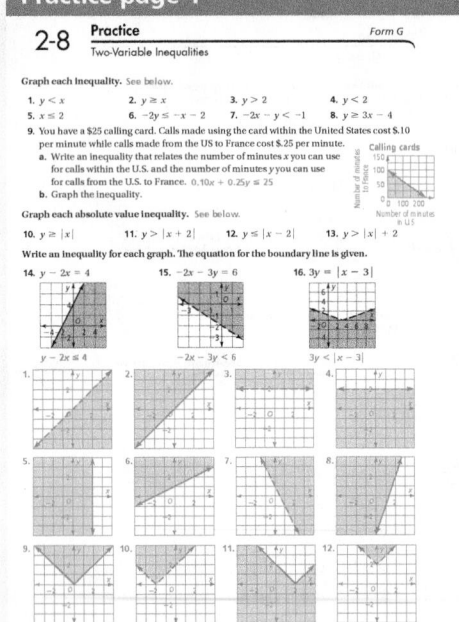

### Practice and Problem Solving Wkbk/ All-in-One Resources/Online
**Practice page 2**

### All-in-One Resources/Online
**Enrichment**

### Practice and Problem Solving Wkbk/ All-in-One Resources/Online
**Think About a Plan**

### Practice and Problem Solving Wkbk/ All-in-One Resources/Online
**Standardized Test Prep**

### Online Teacher Resource Center
**Activities, Games, and Puzzles**

# *Pull It* **All Together**

To solve these problems, you will pull together concepts about equivalence, linear functions and modeling. Show your work and justify your reasoning.

**BIG idea** Equivalence

You can represent a function with many different equivalent equations.

## Task 1

**The graph represents a function.**

**a.** Write the equation for the graph in standard form, point-slope form, and slope-intercept form.

**b.** Which equation is the easiest to write by looking at the graph? Explain why.

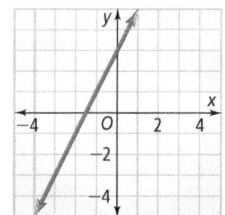

**BIG idea** Modeling

You can use scatter plots to model, analyze, and make predictions about certain kinds of data.

## Task 2

**The table at the right shows the boiling point of water at various elevations.**

**a.** Identify the independent and dependent quantities. Explain your choices.

**b.** Make a scatter plot that models this data.

**c.** Determine what kind of correlation is shown in your plot.

**d.** Write an equation of the line of best fit.

**e.** Use your equation to predict the temperature at which water boils at 8000 feet above sea level.

**f.** At what elevation would you expect water to boil at 207°F?

**Boiling Point of Water**

| Elevation (ft) | Boiling Point (°F) |
|---|---|
| sea level | 212 |
| 1000 | 210.2 |
| 2000 | 208.4 |
| 3000 | 206.6 |
| 4000 | 204.8 |
| 5000 | 203 |

## Task 3

**Consider the following data: (2, 1), (4, 3), (5, 5), (7, 6), (3, 18).**

**a.** Exclude (3, 18) and draw a trend line for the rest of the data.

**b.** Use a graphing calculator to find the line of best fit for all of the points.

**c.** Which linear model does a better job predicting most of the values? Explain.

# Performance Task

## Pull It All Together

The concepts and skills required to solve these problems are from several lessons within this chapter and from earlier chapters. As students solve these problems, they will demonstrate their reasoning strategies and their growth as independent problem solvers.

The following tasks are designed to
- Help support students as they do the Tasks.
- Gauge the amount of support students need as they become independent problem solvers.

## Problem 1

Write several equations of a line using the graph.
- What information do you need from the graph to write each equation?
- Can you use one equation to write the others without using additional information from the graph?

## Problem 2

Apply properties of lines to a scatter plot to model data and make predictions.
- Is the boiling point determined by the elevation, or is the elevation determined by the boiling point?
- What information do you need to write the equation of the line of best fit?
- Are your answers to 2e and 2f reasonable with respect to the data?

## Problem 3

Use algebraic methods and technology to analyze data.
- What window on your calculator will allow you to most easily compare your trend line with the line of best fit?

# Assess Performance

## Pull It All Together

See p. 49 for a holistic scoring rubric to gauge a student's progress on Understanding the Problem, Planning a Solution, Getting an Answer, and Assessing Autonomy.

**SOLUTION OUTLINES**

**1. a.** First step: Find two points from the graph. [(0, 3) and (−3, −3)]

Second step: Find the slope using the two points you found in Step 1. ($m = 2$)

Third step: Use the points and the slope to write the equation in three forms. ($-2x + y = 3$; $y + 3 = 2(x + 3)$; $y = 2x + 3$)

**b.** The slope-intercept equation is the easiest equation to write because you can find the value of $b$ directly from the graph.

**2. a.** The boiling point depends on the elevation so the elevation is the independent variable and the boiling point is the dependent variable.

**b.** Make a scatter plot. Let the $x$-values represent the elevation and the $y$-values the boiling point of water.

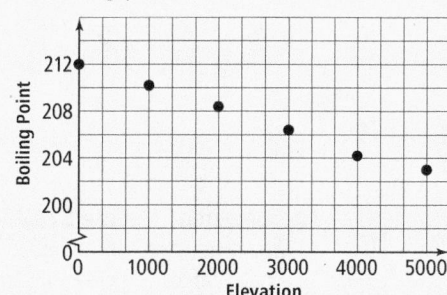

**c.** Describe the correlation. (As the elevation increases the boiling point decreases. The points appear to make a straight line from upper left to lower right. There is a strong negative correlation.)

**d.** First step: Sketch a line that best suggests the trend line given by the data.

Second step: Choose two points on the trend line.
[(1000, 210.2) and (4000, 204.8)]
Third step: Use the point-slope formula to write an equation for the line that passes through the two points. ($y = -0.0018x + 212$)

**e.** First step: Substitute 8000 for $x$ in the equation from part (d) and simplify. (approximately 197.6°)

**f.** Possible Plan: You can use the equation you found in part (d). Substitute 207 for $y$ and solve for $x$. (approximately 2778 feet)

**3a–c.** See next page

# Essential Questions

**BIG** idea  **Equivalence**

**ESSENTIAL QUESTION**  Does it matter which form of a linear equation you use?

**ANSWER**  You can use either slope-intercept, point-slope, or standard form to represent linear functions. (You can transform one version to another as needed.)

**BIG** idea  **Functions**

**ESSENTIAL QUESTION**  How do you use transformations to help graph absolute value functions?

**ANSWER**  You can use the values of $a$, $h$, and $k$ in the form $y = a|x - h| + k$ to determine how the parent function $y = |x|$ has been transformed.

**BIG** idea  **Modeling**

**ESSENTIAL QUESTION**  How can you model data with a linear function?

**ANSWER**  You can use the equation of a trend line or line of best fit to model data that cluster in a linear pattern.

---

## 2  Chapter Review

### Connecting **BIG** ideas and Answering the Essential Questions

**1 Equivalence**
You can use either slope-intercept, point-slope, or standard form to represent linear functions. (You can transform one version to another as needed.)

**Slope-Intercept Form  (Lesson 2-3)**
$y = mx + b$
$y = 2x - 1$

**More Linear Equations (Lesson 2-4)**
$y - y_1 = m(x - x_1)$    $Ax + By = C$
$y - 5 = 2(x - 3)$      $2x - y = 1$

**2 Function**
You can use the values of $a$, $h$, and $k$ in the form $y = a|x - h| + k$ to determine how the parent function $y = |x|$ has been transformed.

**Families of Functions  (Lesson 2-6)**

| | |
|---|---|
| $f(x) + k$ | vertical translation |
| $f(x - h)$ | horizontal translation |
| $af(x)$ | stretch or compression |
| $-f(x)$ | reflection in the $x$-axis |
| $f(-x)$ | reflection in the $y$-axis |

**Absolute Value Functions and Graphs  (Lesson 2-7)**
Parent: $y = |x|$
General form:
$y = a|x - h| + k$
vertex: $(h, k)$

**3 Modeling**
You can use the equation of a trend line or line of best fit to model data that cluster in a linear pattern.

**Using Linear Models  (Lesson 2-5)**
Positive correlation      Trend Line

### Chapter Vocabulary

- absolute value function (p. 107)
- axis of symmetry (p. 107)
- boundary (p. 114)
- constant of variation (p. 68)
- correlation (p. 92)
- correlation coefficient (p. 94)
- dependent variable (p. 63)
- direct variation (p. 68)
- domain (p. 61)
- function (p. 62)
- function notation (p. 63)
- function rule (p. 63)
- half-plane (p. 114)
- independent variable (p. 63)
- line of best fit (p. 94)
- linear equation (p. 75)
- linear function (p. 75)
- linear inequality (p. 114)
- parallel lines (p. 85)
- parent function (p. 99)
- perpendicular lines (p. 85)
- point-slope form (p. 81)
- range (p. 61)
- reflection (p. 101)
- relation (p. 60)
- scatter plot (p. 92)
- slope (p. 74)
- slope-intercept form (p. 76)
- standard form of a linear equation (p. 82)
- test point (p. 115)
- transformation (p. 99)
- translation (p. 99)
- vertex (p. 107)
- vertical compression (p. 102)
- vertical stretch (p. 102)
- vertical-line test (p. 62)
- $x$-intercept (p. 76)
- $y$-intercept (p. 76)

**Choose the correct term to complete each sentence.**

**1.** The graph of a function is (*always*/*sometimes*) a line.

**2.** The equation $y - 5 = 3(x + 2)$ is in (*point-slope*/*slope-intercept*) form.

---

# Summative Questions UbD

Use the following prompts as you review this chapter with your students. The prompts are designed to help you assess your students' understanding of the Big Ideas they have studied.

- A data set can be modeled by a direct variation function. What type of correlation might a scatter plot of this data show?
- What does the slope of the line of best fit of a scatter plot tell you about the correlation?
- How does a translation change a graph? reflection? vertical stretch or compression?
- How does a horizontal translation change the axis of symmetry of the graph of an absolute value function? How does a vertical translation change the axis of symmetry?
- What information does the slope-intercept form of a linear function give you about the graph of the function?

**SOLUTION OUTLINES** (continued)

**3. a.** First step: Make a graph of the given data.

Second step: Draw a trend line.

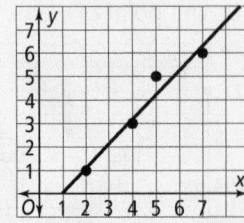

**b.** First step: Use the **STAT** feature to enter the data in your graphing calculator. Enter the $x$-values in **L1** and the $y$-values in **L2**.

Second step: Use **LinReg** to find the linear regression line of best fit for the data. ($y = -0.24x + 7.62$)

**c.** The model using the trend line does a better job predicting most of the data points because the point (3, 18) was excluded from the graph while it was included in the data for part (b).

## 2-1 Relations and Functions

### Quick Review

A **relation** is a set of ordered pairs. The **domain** of a relation is the set of $x$-coordinates. The **range** is the set of $y$-coordinates. When each element of the domain is paired with exactly one element of the range, the relation is a **function**.

### Example

**Determine whether the relation is a function. Find the domain and range.**

$$\{(5, 0), (8, 1), (1, 3), (5, 2), (3, 8)\}$$

In this relation, the $x$-coordinate 5 is paired with both 0 and 2. This relation is not a function.

The domain is the set of $x$-coordinates, which is $\{5, 8, 1, 3\}$.

The range is the set of $y$-coordinates, which is $\{0, 1, 3, 2, 8\}$.

### Exercises

**Determine whether each relation is a function. Find the domain and range.**

**3.** $\{(10, 2), (-10, 2), (6, 4), (5, 3), (-6, 7)\}$

**4.** $\{(4, 5), (1, 5), (3, 8), (4, 6), (10, 12)\}$

**5.**   **6.**

**For each function, find $f(-2)$, $f(-0.5)$, and $f(3)$.**

**7.** $f(x) = -x + 4$  **8.** $f(x) = \frac{3}{8}x - 3$

## 2-2 Direct Variation

### Quick Review

A linear equation of the form $y = kx$, $k \neq 0$, represents **direct variation**. The **constant of variation** is $k$. You can use proportions to solve direct variation problems.

### Example

**In the table, determine whether $y$ varies directly with $x$. If so, what is the constant of variation and the function rule?**

$\frac{6}{2} = \frac{9}{3} = \frac{24}{8} = 3$, so $y$ varies directly with $x$, and the constant of variation is 3.

The function rule is $y = 3x$.

### Exercises

**For each function, determine whether $y$ varies directly with $x$. If so, find the constant of variation and write the function rule.**

**9.**

| x | y |
|---|---|
| -2 | 3 |
| 1 | 4 |
| 2 | 7 |

**10.**

| x | y |
|---|---|
| 4 | 5 |
| 6 | 9 |
| 10 | 17 |

**11.**

| x | y |
|---|---|
| 1 | 1 |
| 2 | 2 |
| 5 | 5 |

**For each function, $y$ varies directly with $x$. Find each constant of variation. Then find the value of $y$ when $x = -0.3$.**

**12.** $y = 2$ when $x = -\frac{1}{2}$  **13.** $y = \frac{2}{3}$ when $x = 0.2$

**14.** $y = 7$ when $x = 2$  **15.** $y = 4$ when $x = -3$

# Answers

## Chapter Review

**1.** sometimes

**2.** point-slope

**3.** yes; domain: $\{-10, -6, 5, 6, 10\}$, range: $\{2, 3, 4, 7\}$

**4.** no; domain: $\{1, 3, 4, 10\}$, range: $\{5, 6, 8, 12\}$

**5.** no; domain:
$$\left\{-2, -\frac{3}{2}, -1, \frac{1}{2}, 1, 2, 3\right\},$$
range: $\left\{-\frac{7}{2}, -\frac{1}{2}, 0, \frac{1}{2}, \frac{3}{2}, 2, \frac{5}{2}\right\}$

**6.** yes; domain:
$\{-2, -1, \frac{1}{2}, 3\}$, range: $\{2\}$

**7.** 6, 4.5, 1

**8.** $-3\frac{3}{4}, -3\frac{3}{16}, -1\frac{7}{8}$

**9.** no

**10.** no

**11.** yes; 1; $y = x$

**12.** $-4$; 1.2

**13.** $\frac{10}{3}$; $-1$

**14.** $\frac{7}{2}$; $-1\frac{1}{20}$

**15.** $-\frac{4}{3}$; 0.4

# Answers

## Chapter Review (continued)

**16.** $-\frac{2}{5}$

**17.** $\frac{7}{6}$

**18.** $\frac{2}{3}$

**19.** $-\frac{4}{9}$

**20.** $y = -3x + 4$

**21.** $y = \frac{1}{2}x + 6$

**22.** $y = 2x - \frac{3}{2}$

**23.** $y = \frac{2}{3}x + 3$

**24.** $y = -x + 5$

**25.** $y = -\frac{1}{3}x + \frac{5}{3}$

**26.** $y = -3(x - 4)$; $3x + y = 12$

**27.** $y + 1 = 5(x - 1)$; $5x - y = 6$

**28.** $y + 7 = -\frac{7}{3}(x - 3)$; $7x + 3y = 0$

**29.** $y - 3 = 2(x - 2)$; $2x - y = 1$

**30. a.** $y = -\frac{1}{2}x + 7$

   **b.** $y = 2x - 13$

   **c.** $y = -\frac{1}{2}x + 7$

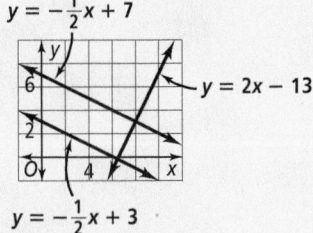

$y = -\frac{1}{2}x + 3$

## 2-3 Linear Functions and Slope-Intercept Form

### Quick Review

The graph of a **linear function** is a line. You can represent a linear function with a **linear equation**. Given two points on a line, the **slope** of the line is the ratio of the change in the $y$-coordinates to the change in the corresponding $x$-coordinates. The slope is the coefficient of $x$ when you write a linear equation in **slope-intercept form**.

### Example

**What is the slope of the line that passes through (3, 5) and (−1, −2)?**

$$m = \frac{y_2 - y_1}{x_2 - x_1} \qquad \text{Find the difference between the coordinates.}$$

$$= \frac{5 - (-2)}{3 - (-1)} = \frac{7}{4} \qquad \text{Simplify.}$$

### Exercises

**Identify the slope of the line that passes through the given points.**

**16.** (1, 3) and (6, 1)      **17.** (4, 4) and (−2, −3)

**18.** (3, 2) and (−3, −2)      **19.** (5, 2) and (−4, 6)

**Write an equation for each line in slope-intercept form.**

**20.** slope = −3 and the $y$-intercept is (0, 4)

**21.** slope = $\frac{1}{2}$ and the $y$-intercept is (0, 6)

**Rewrite each equation in slope-intercept form. Graph each line.**

**22.** $4x - 2y = 3$      **23.** $-4x + 6y = 18$

**24.** $3y + 3x = 15$      **25.** $3y + x = 5$

## 2-4 More About Linear Equations

### Quick Review

You write the equation of a line in **point-slope form** when you have a point and the slope or when you have two points. The **standard form** of an equation has both variables and no constants on the left side.

When two lines have the same slope, they are **parallel**. When two lines have slopes that are negative reciprocals of each other, they are **perpendicular**.

### Example

**Write an equation in standard form for the line with a slope of 2, going through (1, 6).**

$$y - 6 = 2(x - 1) \qquad \text{Write the equation in point-slope form, substituting the given point and slope.}$$

$$y = 2x - 2 + 6 \qquad \text{Simplify.}$$

$$-2x + y = 4 \qquad \text{Write in standard form.}$$

### Exercises

**Write an equation for each line in point-slope form and then convert it to standard form.**

**26.** slope = −3, through (4, 0)

**27.** slope = 5, through (1, −1)

**28.** through (0, 0) and (3, −7)

**29.** through (2, 3) and (3, 5)

**30. a.** Write an equation of the line parallel to $x + 2y = 6$ through (8, 3).

   **b.** Write an equation of the line perpendicular to $x + 2y = 6$ through (8, 3).

   **c.** Graph the three lines on the same coordinate plane.

## 2-5 Using Linear Models

### Quick Review

You can use a **scatter plot** to show relationships between data sets. You can make predictions using a **trend line**, which approximates the relationship between two data sets. The most accurate trend line is a **line of best fit**.

### Example

Draw a scatter plot of the data. Is a linear model reasonable? If so, predict the value of $y$ when $x = 9$.

$\{(0, 6), (1, 7), (2, 5), (3, 4), (4, 2), (5, 1)\}$

The points are close to the line $y = -\frac{4}{3}x + 8$, so a linear model is reasonable. When $x = 9$,

$y = -\frac{4}{3}(9) + 8$

$= -4$

### Exercises

Draw a scatter plot of each set of data. Decide whether a linear model is reasonable. If so, describe the correlation. Then draw a trend line and write its equation. Predict the value of $y$ when $x$ is 15.

**31.** $\{(3, 5), (4, 7), (5, 9), (7, 10), (8, 10), (9, 11), (10, 13)\}$

**32.** $\{(6, 15.5), (7, 14.0), (8, 13.0), (9, 12.5), (10, 12.0), (11, 11.5), (12, 10.0)\}$

**33.**

| x | 0 | 3 | 6 | 9 | 12 |
|---|---|---|---|---|---|
| y | 17.5 | 35.4 | 50.5 | 60.6 | 66.3 |

## 2-6 Families of Functions

### Quick Review

A **parent function** is the simplest form of a function in a family of functions. Each member is a **transformation** of the parent function.

**Translations** shift the graph horizontally, vertically, or both. A **reflection** flips the graph over a line of symmetry. **Vertical stretches** and **compressions** change the shape of the graph by a factor.

### Example

Write the equation of the transformation of the graph of $f(x) = x^2$ translated 3 units up, vertically stretched by a factor of 6, and reflected across the $y$-axis.

| | |
|---|---|
| $y = x^2 + 3$ | Translated 3 units up. |
| $y = 6(x^2 + 3)$ | Vertically stretched. |
| $y = 6(-x)^2 + 18$ | Reflected across the $y$-axis. |
| $y = 6x^2 + 18$ | |

### Exercises

Write the equation for the transformation of the graph of $y = f(x)$.

**34.** translated 2 units left, 7 units down

**35.** translated 5 units right, reflected across the $x$-axis

**36.** translated 3 units up, reflected across the $y$-axis

Describe the transformation(s) of the parent function $f(x)$.

**37.** $g(x) = f(x) - 4$

**38.** $h(x) = 12f(x) + 2$

**39.** $k(x) = -2f(-x)$

**31.**

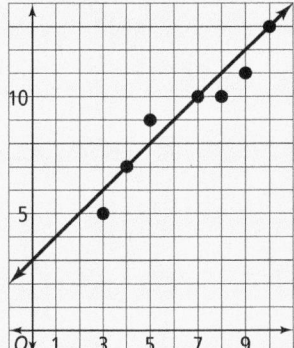

Strong pos. correlation; answers may vary. Sample: $y = x + 3$; 18

**32.**

Strong neg. correlation; answers may vary. Sample: $y = -0.9x + 21$; 7.5

**33.**

Strong pos. correlation; answers may vary. Sample:
$y = 4x + 22$; 82

**34.** $y = f(x + 2) - 7$

**35.** $y = -f(x - 5)$

**36.** $y = f(-x) + 3$

**37.** translated 4 units down

**38.** vertically stretched by a factor of 12, translated 2 units up

**39.** vertically stretched by a factor of 2, reflected across the $y$-axis, reflected across the $x$-axis

# Answers

## Chapter Review (continued)

**40.** $y = |x - 2| + 4$

**41.** $y = |x + 3|$

**42.** $y = |x - 5| + 2$

**43.** $y = |x - 4| + 1$

**44.**

**45.**

**46.**

**47.**

**48.** $(4, 0)$; $x = 4$

**49.** $(0, 2)$; $x = 0$

**50.**

**51.**

**52.**

**53.**

**54. a.** Answers may vary. Sample: $x + 3y \le 15$

**b.** Answers may vary. Sample: domain: {0, 1, 2, 3, 4, 5, 6, 7, 8, 9, 10, 11, 12, 13, 14, 15}, range: {0, 1, 2, 3, 4, 5}

**c.**

**55.** Answers may vary. Sample: $y \le -|x| - 1$

## 2-7 Absolute Value Functions and Graphs

### Quick Review

The **absolute value function** $y = |x|$ is the **parent function** for the family of functions of the form $y = a|x - h| + k$. The maximum or minimum point of the graph is the vertex of the graph.

$y = 2|x + 3| + 1$
$a = 2, h = -3, k = 1$
- Vertex is at $(-3, 1)$
- Translated left 3 units
- Stretched by a factor of 2
- Translated up 1 unit

### Example

Write an equation for the translation of the graph $y = |x|$ **up 5 units.**

Because the graph is translated up, $k$ is positive, so the equation of the translated graph is $y = |x| + 5$.

### Exercises

Write an equation for each translation of the graph of $y = |x|$.

**40.** up 4 units, right 2 units
**41.** vertex $(-3, 0)$
**42.** vertex $(5, 2)$
**43.** vertex $(4, 1)$

Graph each function.

**44.** $f(x) = |x| - 8$
**45.** $f(x) = 2|x - 5|$
**46.** $y = -\frac{1}{4}|x - 2| + 3$
**47.** $y = -2|x + 1| - 1$

Without graphing, identify the vertex and axis of symmetry of each function.

**48.** $y = 2|x - 4|$
**49.** $y = -|x| + 2$

## 2-8 Two Variable Inequalities

### Quick Review

An inequality describes a region of the coordinate plane that has a **boundary**. To graph an inequality involving two variables, first graph the boundary. Then determine which side of the boundary contains the solutions. Points on a dashed boundary are not solutions. Points on a solid boundary are solutions.

### Example

Graph the inequality $y \ge 2x + 3$.

Graph the solid boundary line $y = 2x + 3$.

Since $y$ is *greater than* $2x + 3$, shade above the boundary.

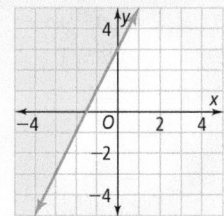

### Exercises

Graph each inequality.

**50.** $y \ge -2$
**51.** $y < 3x + 1$
**52.** $y < -|x - 5|$
**53.** $y > |2x + 1|$

**54. Transportation** An air cargo plane can transport as many as 15 regular shipping containers. One super-size container takes up the space of 3 regular containers.
   **a.** Write an inequality to model the number of regular and super size containers the plane can transport.
   **b.** Describe the domain and range.
   **c.** Graph the inequality you wrote in part (a).

**55. Open-Ended** Write an absolute value inequality with a solid boundary that only has solutions below the x-axis.

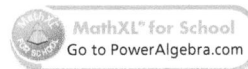

MathXL™ for School
Go to PowerAlgebra.com

### Do you know HOW?

**Find the domain and range. Graph each relation.**

1. $\{(0, 0), (1, -1), (2, -4), (3, -9), (4, -16)\}$

2. $\{(3, 2), (4, 3), (5, 4), (6, 5), (7, 6)\}$

**Determine whether each relation is a function.**

3.

4.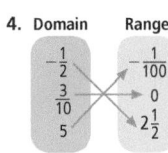

Suppose $f(x) = 2x - 5$ and $g(x) = |-3x - 1|$.
**Find each value.**

5. $f(3)$    6. $f(1) + g(2)$    7. $g(0)$

8. $g(2) - f(0)$    9. $f(-1) - g(3)$    10. $2g(-4)$

**Find the slope of each line.**

11. through $(3, 5)$, parallel to $y = 5x - 1$

12. through $(-0.5, 0.5)$, perpendicular to $y = -2x - 4$

**Write an equation of the line in standard form with the given slope through the given point.**

13. slope $= -3, (0, 0)$    14. slope $= \frac{2}{5}, (6, 7)$

15. slope $= 4, (-2, -5)$    16. slope $= -0.5, (0, 6)$

**Write an equation of the line in point-slope form through each pair of points.**

17. $(0, 0)$ and $(-4, 7)$    18. $(-1, -6)$ and $(-2, 10)$

19. $(3, 0)$ and $(-1, -2)$    20. $(9, 5)$ and $(8, 2)$

**For each direct variation, find the constant of variation. Then find the value of $y$ when $x = -0.5$.**

21. $y = 4$ when $x = 0.5$    22. $y = 2$ when $x = 3$

**Write an equation of the line with the given slope and $y$-intercept. Use slope-intercept form. Then rewrite each equation in standard form.**

23. $m = 3, b = -7$    24. $m = -6, b = 9$

25. $m = \frac{1}{4}, b = 11$    26. $m = -\frac{1}{2}, b = 4$

**Graph each inequality.**

27. $y \geq x + 7$    28. $y > 2|x + 3| - 3$

29. $4x - 3y < 2$    30. $y \leq -\frac{1}{2}|x + 2| - 3$

### Do you UNDERSTAND?

31. **Open-Ended** Graph a relation that is *not* a function. Find its domain and range.

32. **Writing** Explain how point-slope form is related to the formula for slope.

**Describe each transformation of the parent function $y = |x|$. Then, graph each function.**

33. $y = |x| - 4$    34. $y = |x - 1| - 5$

35. $y = -|x + 4| + 3$    36. $y = 2|x + 1|$

37. **Recreation** The table displays the amounts the Jackson family spent on vacations during the years 2000–2009.

**Family Vacations**

| Year | Cost | Year | Cost |
|------|------|------|------|
| 2000 | $1750 | 2005 | $2750 |
| 2001 | $1750 | 2006 | $3200 |
| 2002 | $2000 | 2007 | $2900 |
| 2003 | $2200 | 2008 | $3100 |
| 2004 | $2700 | 2009 | $3300 |

a. Make a scatter plot of the data.
b. Draw a trend line. Write its equation.
c. Estimate the amount the Jackson family will spend on vacations in 2015.
d. **Writing** Explain how to use a trend line to make a prediction.

27.

28.

29.

30.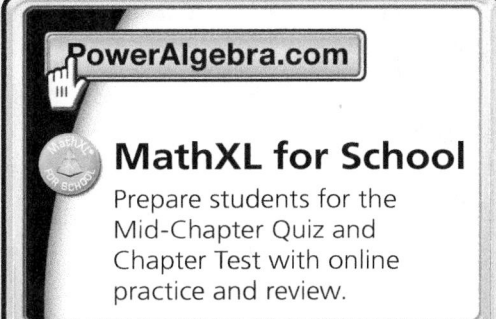

31. Check students' work.

32. The slope $m$ of the line through pts. $(x, y)$ and $(x_1, y_1)$ is given by the formula $m = \frac{y - y_1}{x - x_1}$. Multiplying both sides of this eq. by the denominator $(x - x_1)$ gives the point-slope form of the eq. of a line: $y - y_1 = m(x - x_1)$.

33. translated 4 units down

34–37. See next page

## Answers

### Chapter Test

1. domain: $\{0, 1, 2, 3, 4\}$, range: $\{-16, -9, -4, -1, 0\}$

2. domain: $\{3, 4, 5, 6, 7\}$, range: $\{2, 3, 4, 5, 6\}$

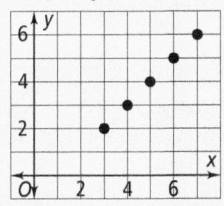

3. no    4. yes    5. 1

6. 4    7. 1    8. 12

9. $-17$    10. 22    11. 5

12. $\frac{1}{2}$    13. $3x + y = 0$

14. $2x - 5y = -23$

15. $4x - y = -3$

16. $x + 2y = 12$

17. $y = -\frac{7x}{4}$ or $y - 7 = \frac{-7}{4}(x + 4)$

18. $y + 6 = -16(x + 1)$ or $y - 10 = -16(x + 2)$

19. $y = \frac{1}{2}(x - 3)$ or $y + 2 = \frac{1}{2}(x + 1)$

20. $y - 2 = 3(x - 8)$ or $y - 5 = 3(x - 9)$

21. $8; -4$    22. $\frac{2}{3}; -\frac{1}{3}$

23. $y = 3x - 7; 3x - y = 7$

24. $y = -6x + 9; 6x + y = 9$

25. $y = \frac{1}{4}x + 11; -x + 4y = 44$

26. $y = -\frac{1}{2}x + 4; x + 2y = 8$

PowerAlgebra.com

MathXL for School

Prepare students for the Mid-Chapter Quiz and Chapter Test with online practice and review.

| Item Number | Lesson |
|:---:|:---:|
| 1 | 2-8 |
| 2 | 1-6 |
| 3 | 1-6 |
| 4 | 1-6 |
| 5 | 2-8 |
| 6 | 2-1 |
| 7 | 1-2 |
| 8 | 2-7 |
| 9 | 2-7 |
| 10 | 2-4 |
| 11 | 3-3 |
| 12 | 2-4 |
| 13 | 2-4 |
| 14 | 2-4 |
| 15 | 2-4 |
| 16 | 2-3 |
| 17 | 1-4 |
| 18 | 1-2 |
| 19 | 2-2 |
| 20 | 2-4 |
| 21 | 2-2 |
| 22 | 2-2 |
| 23 | 2-4 |
| 24 | 2-2 |
| 25 | 1-3 |
| 26 | 2-7 |
| 27 | 2-2 |
| 28 | 2-1 |
| 29 | 2-4 |
| 30 | 1-2 |
| 31 | 2-4 |

# ② Cumulative Test Prep

## Vocabulary Builder

As you solve test items, you must understand the meanings of mathematical terms. Match each term with its mathematical meaning.

**A.** linear function

**B.** direct variation

**C.** range

**D.** translation

**I.** the set of all outputs, or $y$-coordinates, of a relation

**II.** a transformation that shifts a graph horizontally, vertically, or both

**III.** a function that can be written in the form $y = mx + b$

**IV.** a function that can be written in the form $y = kx,\ k \neq 0$

## Multiple Choice

Read each question. Then write the letter of the correct answer on your paper.

**1.** Which of the following absolute value inequalities has no solutions in Quadrant IV?

Ⓐ $y + 2 \geq |x - 3|$    Ⓒ $y - 1 > |2x + 6|$

Ⓑ $y > 3 - |5 - x|$    Ⓓ $y \leq |4x| - 7$

**2.** For which value of $b$ would the equation $3|x - 2| = bx - 6$ have infinitely many solutions?

Ⓕ $-6$      Ⓗ $-3$

Ⓖ $3$      Ⓘ $6$

# Answers

## Chapter Test (continued)

**34.** translated 1 unit to the rt. and 5 units down

**35.** translated 4 units to the left, reflected vertically across the $x$-axis, then translated up 3 units

**36.** translated 1 unit to the left and vertically stretched by a factor of 2

**37. a–b.**

Answers may vary. Sample: $y = 200x + 1700$, where 2000 corresponds to $x = 0$.

**c.** $4700

**d.** Check students' work.

**3.** A meteorologist predicts the daily high and low temperatures as 91°F and 69°F. If $t$ represents the temperature, then this situation can be described with the inequality $69 \leq t \leq 91$. Which of the following absolute value inequalities is an equivalent way of expressing this?

- Ⓐ $69 \leq |t| \leq 91$
- Ⓒ $|t - 69| \leq 91$
- Ⓑ $|t - 80| \leq 11$
- Ⓓ $|t - 11| \leq 80$

**4.** What is the solution of the inequality $|x - 2| - 3 \leq 2$?

**5.** Which inequality best describes the graph?

- Ⓐ $y \leq \frac{1}{2}|x + 1| - 1$
- Ⓑ $y \geq \frac{1}{2}|x - 1| - 1$
- Ⓒ $y \leq \frac{1}{2}|x - 1| - 1$
- Ⓓ $y \geq \frac{1}{2}|x + 1| - 1$

**6.** Which relation is a function?

**7.** Which phrase does NOT describe $\sqrt{625}$?

- Ⓐ whole number
- Ⓒ irrational number
- Ⓑ integer
- Ⓓ rational number

**8.** Which equation is graphed?

- Ⓕ $y = -3|x + 1| + 3$
- Ⓖ $y = 3|x + 1| + 3$
- Ⓗ $y = -3|x - 1| + 3$
- Ⓘ $y = 3|x + 1| - 3$

**9.** Which describes the translation of $y = |x - 3| + 5$?

- Ⓐ $y = |x|$ translated 3 units left and 5 units up
- Ⓑ $y = |x|$ translated 3 units right and 5 units up
- Ⓒ $y = |x|$ translated 5 units left and 3 units up
- Ⓓ $y = |x|$ translated 5 units right and 3 units up

**10.** Which lines are parallel?

I. $y = -2x + 1$     II. $y = x - 4$
III. $y = -x + 5$     IV. $y = 3 - 2x$

- Ⓕ I and II
- Ⓗ I and III
- Ⓖ I and IV
- Ⓘ II and III

**11.** Which value is in the solution set of $4 < -4x - 2 < 8$ and $3 > 4x + 2 > -10$?

- Ⓐ $-2$
- Ⓒ $0$
- Ⓑ $3$
- Ⓓ $4$

**12.** Which function has the graph shown?

- Ⓕ $f(x) = \begin{cases} -x, & x < 0 \\ 3x, & x \geq 0 \end{cases}$
- Ⓖ $f(x) = \begin{cases} x, & x < 0 \\ -3x, & x \geq 0 \end{cases}$
- Ⓗ $f(x) = \begin{cases} x, & x > 0 \\ -3x, & x \leq 0 \end{cases}$
- Ⓘ $f(x) = \begin{cases} -x, & x > 0 \\ 3x, & x \leq 0 \end{cases}$

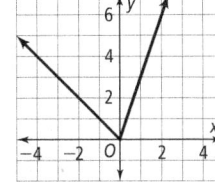

**13.** Which equation has the same graph as

$$f(x) = \begin{cases} \frac{1}{3}x, & x > 6 \\ -\frac{1}{3}x + 4, & x \leq 6 \end{cases}?$$

- Ⓐ $f(x) = -\frac{1}{3}|x - 6| + 4$
- Ⓑ $f(x) = \frac{1}{3}x$
- Ⓒ $f(x) = \frac{1}{3}|x - 6| + 2$
- Ⓓ $f(x) = -\frac{1}{3}x + 10$

# Answers

## Cumulative Test Prep

**A.** III
**B.** IV
**C.** I
**D.** II

## Multiple Choice

**1.** C      **8.** F
**2.** G      **9.** B
**3.** B      **10.** G
**4.** G      **11.** A
**5.** C      **12.** F
**6.** G      **13.** C
**7.** C

# Answers

## Multiple Choice (continued)

**14.** I

**15.** A

**16.** G

**17.** B

**18.** H

**19.** A

**20.** $\frac{2}{25}$

**21.** 2.25

**22.** 0

**23.** $\frac{1}{4}$

**24.** 4

**25.** [2] $f(-3) = \frac{2}{5}(-3) - 2 = -3\frac{1}{5}$

$f(0) = \frac{2}{5}(0) - 2 = -2$

$f(1) = \frac{2}{5}(1) - 2 = -1\frac{3}{5}$

[1] computational error

**26.** [2]

the parent function is $y = |x|$, and $y = |x + 3|$ is $y = |x|$ shifted 3 units to the left.

[1] correct graph, incorrect description of the translation

**27.** [2] $y = kx$

$(2) = k(-2)$

$-1 = k$

$y = (-1)x$

$(3) = (-1)x$

$-3 = x$ (OR another appropriate method)

[1] computational error

**28.** [2]

domain: $\{-3, -1, 0\}$, range: $\{-1, 0, 2, 3\}$

[1] incorrect statement of domain OR incorrect statement of range

**29.** [4] **a.** $y - 6 = 2(x + 2) = 2x + 4$

$y = 2x + 10$ (OR equivalent eq.)

**b.** $y - 1 = -\frac{1}{2}(x - 1) = -\frac{1}{2}x + \frac{1}{2}$

$y = -\frac{1}{2}x + \frac{3}{2}$ (OR equivalent eq.)

**c.**

---

**14.** Which line is perpendicular to $y = 2x - 4$?

(F) $y = -2x + 4$     (H) $y = -4 - 2x$

(G) $y = -x - 2$     (I) $y = -\frac{1}{2}x + 4$

**15.** Which equation is in standard form?

(A) $x - y = 7$     (C) $y = 3x - 1$

(B) $x = 4y + 2$     (D) $10 - 5x = 2y$

**16.** Which ordered pairs are solutions of $y < 2x + 3$?

   I. $(0, 2)$    II. $(-1, 1)$    III. $(2, 0)$

(F) I only     (H) II only

(G) I and III     (I) II and III

**17.** Use the Addition Property of Equality to complete the statement: If $p = q$, then $x + p = $ _____.

(A) $p + x$     (C) $x + 0$

(B) $x + q$     (D) $p + q$

**18.** Which phrase describes $\sqrt{145}$?

(F) whole number     (H) irrational number

(G) integer     (I) rational number

**19.** If a rate of speed $r$ is constant, then distance, rate, and time are related by the direct variation equation $d = rt$, where $d$ represents distance and $t$ represents time. If $r = 30$ miles per hour, which of the following best describes the graph of $d = rt$?

(A) A straight line through the point $(0, 0)$

(B) A straight line through the point $(0, 30)$

(C) A parabola through the point $(0, 0)$

(D) A parabola through the point $(0, 30)$

### GRIDDED RESPONSE

**20.** What is the slope of the line $5y + 3 = \frac{2}{5}x$?

**21.** A recipe for custard sauce calls for 6 egg yolks, $\frac{2}{3}$ cup of sugar, and $1\frac{1}{2}$ cups of hot milk. Chelsea needs more sauce than the recipe yields. She plans to use 1 cup of sugar. How many cups of hot milk should she use?

**22.** What is the $y$-coordinate of the point through which the graph of every direct variation passes?

**23.** The line $(y - 2) = k(x + 1)$ passes through the points $L(3, 3)$ and $M(7, 4)$. Find $k$.

---

**24.** Matt drove at a steady speed during the first morning of his road trip. The table shows data about his driving.

| Time Driving (hours) | Total Distance (miles) |
|---|---|
| 1.5 | 87 |
| 2.25 | 130.5 |
| 3 | 174 |

After lunch, Matt drove an additional 232 miles at the same steady speed. How many hours did he drive after lunch?

### Short Response

**25.** Find $f(-3)$, $f(0)$, and $f(1)$ for the function $f(x) = \frac{2}{5}x - 2$.

**26.** Graph $y < |x + 3|$. Identify the parent function of the boundary and describe the translation.

**27.** Suppose $y$ varies directly with $x$, and $y = 2$ when $x = -2$. Find the constant of variation. Then find the value of $x$ when $y = 3$.

**28.** Graph the relation $\{(-3, 2), (-1, 3), (0, 0), (-1, -1)\}$. Find the domain and range.

### Extended Response

**29. a.** Write an equation of the line through $(-2, 6)$ with slope 2.

**b.** Write an equation of the line through $(1, 1)$ and perpendicular to the line in part (a).

**c.** Graph the two lines on the same set of axes.

**30.** Will the product of an integer and a natural number always be an integer? Why or why not? Justify your answer with two examples.

**31.** Write an equation of the line that passes through $(-1, -1)$ and is perpendicular to $y = -3x + 4$. If you draw another two lines such that all four lines intersect to form a square, what would be the slopes of those two lines? Explain your reasoning.

---

[3] appropriate method, but with one computational error

[2] incorrect eq. of the perpendicular ln., graph drawn correctly given previous results

[1] correct equations, no graph

**30.** [4] Yes; the product of an integer and an integer is always an integer. Since the set of natural numbers is a subset of integers, the product of an integer and a natural number will always be an integer. For example: the number 1 is a natural number. 1 multiplied by any integer will always be that integer because 1 is the mult. ident. Also, 0 is an integer. 0 multiplied by any natural number is always 0. (OR equivalent explanation)

[3] incomplete explanation OR only one example provided

[2] correct explanation, but without examples provided

[1] two examples provided, no explanation

**31.** [4] The slope of the line is $-\frac{1}{(-3)} = \frac{1}{3}$

$y + 1 = \frac{1}{3}(x + 1) = \frac{1}{3}x + \frac{1}{3}$

$y = \frac{1}{3}x - \frac{2}{3}$ (OR equivalent eq.)

The other lines will have slopes $-3$ and $\frac{1}{3}$ because opp. sides of a square are parallel, and parallel lines have equal slopes.

[3] appropriate method and explanation, but with one computational error

[2] incomplete explanation

[1] no explanation given

# Get Ready!

Lesson 1-3  **Evaluating Algebraic Expressions**

Evaluate each expression for the given values of the variables.

**1.** $9t + 6(2v - t) - 7v; t = 1$ and $v = 5$

**2.** $11(a + 2b) + 2(a - 2b); a = -3$ and $b = 4$

**3.** $\frac{3}{5}d + \frac{1}{10}h - \frac{7}{10}d - \frac{4}{5}h; d = 5$ and $h = 10$

**4.** $12\left(\frac{3}{4}x - \frac{1}{2}y\right) - 6\left(\frac{1}{2}x - \frac{3}{4}y\right); x = 2$ and $y = -2$

Lesson 2-3  **Writing Linear Equations in Slope-Intercept Form**

Write the equation of each line in slope-intercept form.

**5.** $2x - 4y = 10$    **6.** $3y + 9 = -6x$    **7.** $y - 5x = 16$    **8.** $-7 - y = -3x$

**9.** $\frac{x}{6} - \frac{5}{12}y = \frac{5}{8}$    **10.** $4x = y - 11$    **11.** $2y = -12x - 16$    **12.** $\frac{y}{9} + \frac{x}{3} = 2$

Lesson 2-3 **Graphing Linear Equations**

Graph each equation.

**13.** $3x = y - 1$    **14.** $x - 5y = 10$    **15.** $12 + 2y = 3x$    **16.** $y = 4x$

Lesson 2-8 **Graphing Inequalities**

Graph each inequality.

**17.** $4y \leq 24x$    **18.** $y \geq 2|x - 1.5|$    **19.** $x + 5y \geq 20$    **20.** $y > |x + 6| - 2$

## Looking Ahead Vocabulary

**21.** A *system* of mountains is a group of mountains that share similar geographic and geological features. What are some mountain systems in the United States?

**22.** Two things are *consistent* if they are in agreement with each other. What does it mean for your actions to be consistent with your words?

**23.** How many books does Jeff own if he has more than 14 books? Describe the number of books that Jeff owns if you add the *constraint* that he owns fewer than his sister, who owns 19 books.

---

# Get Ready!

Assign this diagnostic assessment to determine if students have the prerequisite skills for Chapter 3.

| Lesson | Skill |
|--------|-------|
| 1-3 | Evaluate Algebraic Expressions |
| 2-3 | Write Linear Equations in Slope-Intercept Form |
| 2-3 | Graph Linear Equations |
| 2-8 | Graph Inequalities |

To remediate students, select from these resources (available for every lesson).
- Online Problems (PowerAlgebra.com)
- Reteaching (All-in-One Teaching Resources)
- Practice (All-in-One Teaching Resources)

## Why Students Need These Skills

**EVALUATING ALGEBRAIC EXPRESSIONS**
To check whether a solution is correct, students will need to evaluate the expressions on both sides of the equation for the values of the variables to make sure they are equivalent.

**WRITING LINEAR EQUATIONS IN SLOPE-INTERCEPT FORM**
Students will need to rewrite the equations in a system of linear equations in slope-intercept form when making a table. This form makes it easy to find $y$, given a value of $x$.

**GRAPHING LINEAR EQUATIONS**
Graphing is one way to find the solution to a system of linear equations.

**GRAPHING INEQUALITIES**
To find the feasible region of a linear programming problem, students will need to graph the given constraints, which are inequalities.

## Looking Ahead Vocabulary

**SYSTEM** Ask students what a system of equations might be, based on the mountain definition.
**CONSISTENT** Ask students what it would mean if their actions were *not* consistent with their words.
**CONSTRAINT** Ask students how the constraint affects the possible number of books that Jeff owns. Ask students for some more examples of constraints that act as limitations or restrictions.

---

# Answers

## Get Ready!

**1.** 28    **2.** 33    **3.** $-\frac{15}{2}$    **4.** 15

**5.** $y = \frac{1}{2}x - \frac{5}{2}$    **6.** $y = -2x - 3$

**7.** $y = 5x + 16$    **8.** $y = 3x - 7$

**9.** $y = \frac{2}{5}x - \frac{3}{2}$    **10.** $y = 4x + 11$

**11.** $y = -6x - 8$    **12.** $y = -3x + 18$

**13.**     **14.**

**15.**     **16.**

**17.**     **18.**

**19.**     **20.**

**21.** Answers may vary. Samples: Rocky Mountains, Appalachian Mountains

**22.** Answers may vary. Sample: Your actions are consistent with your words when your actions show what you are saying. For example, if you say you are happy and you are laughing or smiling.

**23.** 15 books or more; 15 books or more but less than 19, i.e., 15, 16, 17, or 18 books

# Chapter 3 Overview

## UbD Understanding by Design

Chapter 3 expands on students' understandings and skills related to functions, equations, and graphs. In this chapter, students will develop the answers to the Essential Questions posed on the opposite page as they learn the concepts and skills bulleted below.

### BIG idea Function

**ESSENTIAL QUESTION** How does representing functions graphically help you solve a system of equations?

- Students will solve a system of linear equations by graphing the equations to find the point(s) of intersection.

### BIG idea Equivalence

**ESSENTIAL QUESTION** How does writing equivalent equations help you solve a system of equations?

- Students will use substitution and elimination methods to write equivalent equations until they get an equation with only one variable.

### BIG idea Solving Equations and Inequalities

**ESSENTIAL QUESTION** How are the properties of equality used in the matrix solution of a system of equations?

- Students will use the Addition Property of Equality to add rows of matrices and the Multiplication Property of Equality to multiply rows by a constant.
- Students will use row operations to get reduced row echelon form, which gives the solution.

---

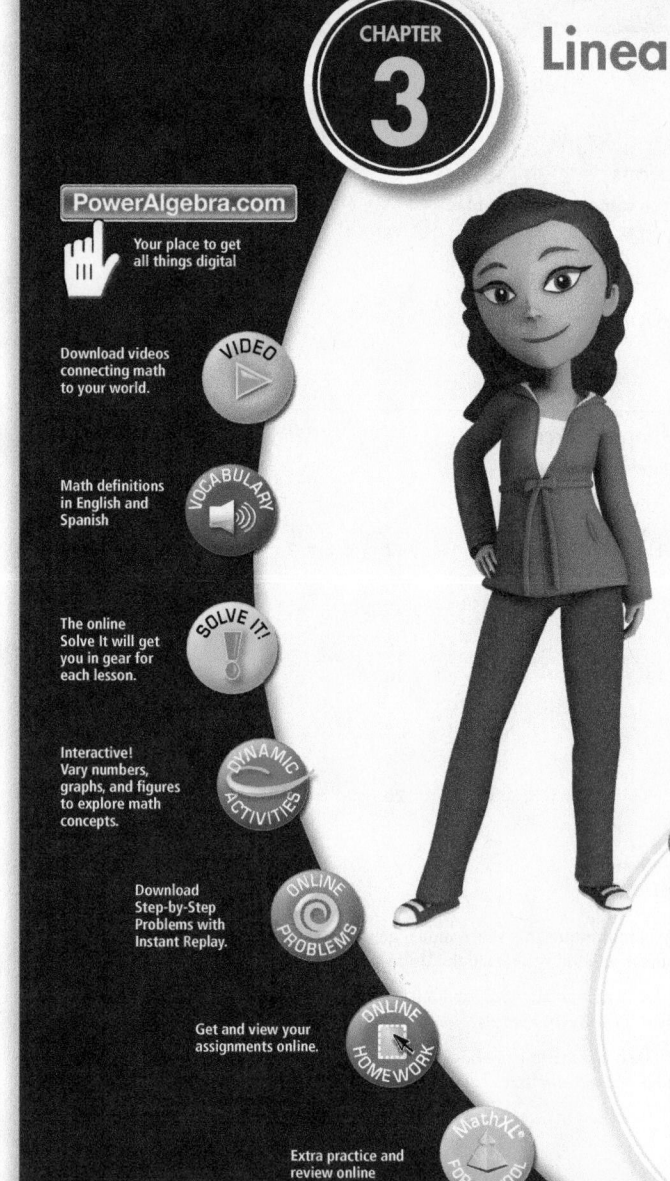

## CHAPTER 3 Linear Systems

**PowerAlgebra.com**
Your place to get all things digital

**VIDEO** Download videos connecting math to your world.

**VOCABULARY** Math definitions in English and Spanish

**SOLVE IT!** The online Solve It will get you in gear for each lesson.

**DYNAMIC ACTIVITIES** Interactive! Vary numbers, graphs, and figures to explore math concepts.

**ONLINE PROBLEMS** Download Step-by-Step Problems with Instant Replay.

**ONLINE HOMEWORK** Get and view your assignments online.

**MathXL® FOR SCHOOL** Extra practice and review online

*The cables in the photo intersect at certain points, just like the graphs of linear equations might intersect.*

*How can you solve a system of linear equations? How can you use linear programming to solve real-world problems? How can you use a matrix to represent a system of equations? You will learn how in this chapter.*

### Vocabulary

**English/Spanish Vocabulary Audio Online:**

| English | Spanish |
|---|---|
| dependent system, p. 137 | sistema dependiente |
| equivalent systems, p. 144 | sistemas equivalentes |
| independent system, p. 137 | sistema independiente |
| linear system, p. 134 | sistema lineal |
| matrix, p. 174 | matriz |
| matrix element, p. 174 | elemento matricial |
| row operation, p. 176 | operación de filas |
| system of equations, p. 134 | sistema de ecuaciones |

---

**PowerAlgebra.com**

## Chapter 3 Overview

Use these online assets to engage your students. These include support for the Solve It and step-by-step solutions for Problems.

**VIDEO** Show the student-produced video demonstrating relevant and engaging applications of the new concepts in the chapter.

**VOCABULARY** Find online definitions for new terms in English and Spanish.

**SOLVE IT!** Start each lesson with an attention-getting Problem. View the Problem online with helpful hints.

My Math Video

00:04:04

## My Math Video

Use this photo to introduce systems of linear equations and their possible solutions. The wires represent the lines and the intersections represent the solutions to the system.

**Q** Look at any two intersecting wires. In how many places do they intersect? **[one]**

**Q** Is it possible for two straight wires to intersect at more than one point? Does it happen in this picture? Explain. **[Yes; if the wires were tied together, one on top of the other, they would intersect at all points along both lines. No; the wires in the picture do not intersect at more than one point.]**

**Q** Are there any wires that do not intersect at all? **[Yes; the vertical wires appear to be parallel and do not intersect each other. The horizontal lines may also be parallel, bit it is difficult to tell in the picture.]**

**ERROR PREVENTION**

Explain that the photo shows depth, and that the wires do not necessarily behave in the way they appear.

## BIGideas

**1 Function**
**Essential Question** How does representing functions graphically help you solve a system of equations?

**2 Equivalence**
**Essential Question** How does writing equivalent equations help you solve a system of equations?

**3 Solving Equations and Inequalities**
**Essential Question** How are the properties of equality used in the matrix solution of a system of equations?

## Chapter Preview

3-1  **Solving Systems Using Tables and Graphs**
3-2  **Solving Systems Algebraically**
3-3  **Systems of Inequalities**
3-4  **Linear Programming**
3-5  **Systems With Three Variables**
3-6  **Solving Systems Using Matrices**

PowerAlgebra.com        Chapter 3   Linear Systems        133

 Increase students' depth of knowledge with interactive online activities.

 Show Problems from each lesson solved step by step. Instant replay allows students to go at their own pace when studying online.

 Assign homework to individual students or to an entire class.

 Prepare students for the Mid-Chapter Quiz and Chapter Test with online practice and review.

# LINEAR SYSTEMS
# Math Background

**UbD**

## Function

**BIG** idea A function is a relationship between variables in which each value of the input variable is associated with a unique value of the output variable. Functions can be represented in a variety of ways, such as graphs, tables, equations, or words. Each representation is particularly useful in certain situations. Some important families of functions are developed through transformations of the simplest form of the function.

**ESSENTIAL UNDERSTANDINGS**

**3–1** To solve a system of equations, find a set of values that replace the variables in the equations and make each equation true.

**3–3** You can solve a system of inequalities in more than one way. Graphing the solution is usually the most appropriate method. The solution is the set of all points that are solutions of each inequality in the system.

**3–4** Some real-world problems involve multiple linear relationships. Linear programming accounts for all of these linear relationships and gives the solution to the problem.

## Equivalence

**BIG** idea A single quantity may be represented by many different expressions. The facts about a quantity may be expressed by many different equations (or inequalities).

**ESSENTIAL UNDERSTANDINGS**

**3–2** You can solve a system of equations by writing equivalent systems until the value on one variable is clear. Then substitute to find the value(s) of the other variable.

**3–5** To solve systems of three equations in three variables, you can use some of the same algebraic methods you used to solve systems of two equations in two variables.

## Solving Equations & Inequalities

**BIG** idea Solving an equation is the process of rewriting the equation to make what it says about its variable(s) as simple as possible. Properties of numbers and equality can be used to transform an equation (or inequality) into equivalent, simpler equations (or inequalities) in order to find solutions. Useful information about equations and inequalities (including solutions) can be found by analyzing graphs or tables. The numbers and types of solutions vary predictably, based on the type of equation.

**ESSENTIAL UNDERSTANDINGS**

**3–1 to 3–3, 3–5** See above.

**3–6** You can use a matrix to represent and solve a system of equations without writing the variables.

## Solving Systems of Linear Equations

A solution to a system of linear equations is an ordered pair that makes all of the equations true. A system of linear equations can be solved by graphing or by algebraic methods.

**Solving by graphing** requires graphing each equation. It gives a visual representation of the solution of the system.
- Parallel lines indicate no solution.
- Intersecting lines indicate one solution—the point of intersection.
- Coinciding lines indicate infinitely many solutions—all the points on the line.

**Solving by algebraic methods** requires writing equivalent systems until the value of one variable is found. Use substitution to find the value(s) of the other variables.

**Substitution** is most often used when it is simple to isolate one of the variables. Solve $\begin{cases} y - x = 3 \\ 3y + 2x = 4 \end{cases}$.

$y = x + 3$          Solve the first equation for $y$.

$3(x + 3) + 2x = 4$    Substitute the expression for $y$ into

$x = -1$            the second equation. Solve for $x$.

Substituting into either equation yields $y = 2$.

**Elimination** uses the Addition Property of Equality to solve systems. Write equivalent systems (if necessary) and use additive inverses to eliminate one of the variables. Solve for the other variable, and then substitute to find a solution.

$$\begin{cases} y - x = 3 \\ 3y + 2x = 4 \end{cases} \rightarrow \begin{array}{l} 2[y - x = 3] \\ 3y + 2x = 4 \end{array} \rightarrow \begin{array}{l} 2y - 2x = 6 \\ \underline{3y + 2x = 4} \end{array}$$

Add the equations to get $5y = 10$ so $y = 2$. Substituting into one of the original equations yields $x = -1$. The solution is $(-1, 2)$.

### Common Errors With Solving Systems of Linear Equations

**Graphing errors** can occur when graphs are not drawn carefully. Errors include
- incorrect sign on the slope
- incorrectly graphed ordered pairs
- straight edge not used to draw lines.

**Algebraic errors** in substitution or elimination include
- solving for a variable and substituting the value back into the same equation rather than in the other equation
- failing to multiply through the entire equation when writing equivalent systems

Remind students to check the ordered pair in both equations to be sure they have solved correctly.

## Solving Systems of Inequalities

**Graphing and tables** can be used to solve systems of inequalities. The lines are boundary lines and may or may not be included in the solution. The shaded area for each inequality is determined, and the overlap area is the solution set of the system. Note that instead of the solution being a single ordered pair, the solution is the area where both inequalities are true.

For the system $\begin{cases} y \geq x + 3 \\ y < -2x - 4 \end{cases}$

(−3, 2) is NOT a solution.

Solution area

$y \geq x + 3$

(−5, −2) is a solution.

$y < -2x - 4$

**Linear programming** is a type of inequality system used for solving many real-world problems. It consists of an objective function that needs to be maximized or minimized as well as several constraints represented by linear inequalities. Most real world problems solved by linear programming contain many variables. The solution area for this type of system is usually closed and is referred to as the feasible region. Like the solution area, the feasible region contains all points that satisfy all constraints. If there is a maximum or minimum value for the objective function, it will occur at one of the vertices of the feasible region.

### Common Errors With Solving Systems of Inequalities

**Graphing errors** with inequalities occur when students are unsure of which area to shade. With steep lines, it is often difficult to tell which area is above or below the line.

**Linear programming errors** might occur due to confusion in writing the constraints and the objective function. Suggest students begin with one constraint and write and graph that inequality. Then select a point in the solution area thus far to make sure it satisfies the constraint. Write and graph the next inequality and check the solution area. Continue until all constraints in the objective function have been graphed.

## Solving Systems With 3 Variables

The graph of a linear equation in three variables is a plane. The graph of a solution of a system of three linear equations in three variables will be
- planes intersecting in one common point (one solution),
- planes intersecting along a common line (infinitely many solutions), or
- no point lying in all three planes (no solution).

Elimination, substitution, and matrix operations are used to solve any linear system if the number of variables is less than or equal to the number of equations in the system. Thus, two equations are needed to solve a system with two variables, three equations are needed to solve a system with three variables, and so on.

**Elimination and substitution** are used to combine any two of the equations into one equation with two variables. Then the unused linear equation is added to either of the original equations to obtain an equation with the same two variables.

To solve $\begin{cases} -6x - y - 3z = 10 \\ -x - y + 4z = 0 \\ x - y - z = -4 \end{cases}$, add the bottom two

equations to eliminate $x$, resulting in $-2y + 3z = -4$. The top equation was not used, so add it to either remaining equation to eliminate $x$. Multiplying the bottom equation by 6 and adding it to the top equation yields $-7y - 9z = -14$. Use substitution or elimination to find $y = 2$. By substitution, $z = 0$ and $x = -2$.

**Matrices** are helpful for representing and solving linear systems because it is not necessary to write the variables. The above system is represented by a matrix as

$A = \begin{bmatrix} -6 & -1 & -3 & | & 10 \\ -1 & -1 & 4 & | & 0 \\ 1 & -1 & -1 & | & -4 \end{bmatrix}$. Using row operations to get

Reduced Row Echelon Form yields $\begin{bmatrix} -2 \\ 2 \\ 0 \end{bmatrix}$ in the last

column, indicating that $x = -2$, $y = 2$, and $z = 0$.

### Common Errors With Solving Systems With 3 or More Variables

**Algebraic errors** occur when students
- forget to eliminate the same variable
- make calculation errors.

**Matrix errors** can occur when students make arithmetic mistakes during row operations.

# Pacing and Assignment Guide

| | | TRADITIONAL | | | BLOCK |
|---|---|---|---|---|---|
| Lesson | Teaching Day(s) | Basic | Average | Advanced | Block |
| 3-1 | 1 | Problems 1–2<br>Exs. 7–14, 55–69 | Problems 1–2<br>Exs. 7–13 odd, 55–69 | Problems 1–2<br>Exs. 7–13 odd, 55–69 | **Day 1**<br>Problems 1–4<br>Exs. 7–27 odd,<br>29–49, 55–68 |
| | 2 | Problems 3–4<br>Exs. 15–31, 41–44 | Problems 3–4<br>Exs. 15–27 odd, 29–49 | Problems 3–4<br>Exs. 15–27 odd, 29–54 | |
| 3-2 | 1 | Problems 1–3<br>Exs. 10–30, 67–80 | Problems 1–3<br>Exs. 11–29 odd, 67–80 | Problems 1–3<br>Exs. 11–29 odd, 67–80 | **Day 2**<br>Problems 1–5<br>Exs. 11–41 odd,<br>43–61, 67–80 |
| | 2 | Problems 4–5<br>Exs. 31–43, 53–57 | Problems 4–5<br>Exs. 31–41 odd, 43–61 | Problems 4–5<br>Exs. 31–41 odd, 43–66 | |
| 3-3 | 1 | Problems 1–4<br>Exs. 8–34, 36–44 even,<br>59–72 | Problems 1–4<br>Exs. 9–31 odd, 32–54, 59–72 | Problems 1–4<br>Exs. 9–31 odd, 32–72 | **Day 3**<br>Problems 1–4<br>Exs. 9–29 odd,<br>31–54, 59–72 |
| 3-4 | 1 | Problems 1–2<br>Exs. 10–19, 25–37 | Problems 1–2<br>Exs. 11–13 odd, 14–22,<br>25–37 | Problems 1–2<br>Exs. 11–13 odd, 14–37 | Problems 1–2<br>Exs. 11–13 odd,<br>14–22, 25–37 |
| 3-5 | 1 | Problems 1–2<br>Exs. 9–20, 46–56 | Problems 1–2<br>Exs. 9–19 odd, 46–56 | Problems 1–2<br>Exs. 9–19 odd, 46–56 | **Day 4**<br>Problems 1–4<br>Exs. 9–29 odd,<br>31–42, 46–56 |
| | 2 | Problems 3–4<br>Exs. 21–33, 38–42 even | Problems 3–4<br>Exs. 21–29 odd, 31–42 | Problems 3–4<br>Exs. 21–29 odd, 31–45 | |
| 3-6 | 1 | Problems 1–3<br>Exs. 8–23, 48–58 | Problems 1–3<br>Exs. 9–23 odd, 48–58 | Problems 1–3<br>Exs. 9–23 odd, 48–58 | **Day 5**<br>Problems 1–5<br>Exs. 9–29 odd,<br>30–41, 48–58 |
| | 2 | Problems 4–5<br>Exs. 24–32, 39–41 | Problems 4–5<br>Exs. 25–29 odd, 30–41 | Problems 4–5<br>Exs. 25–29 odd, 30–47 | |
| Review | 1 | Chapter 3 Review | Chapter 3 Review | Chapter 3 Review | **Day 6**<br>Chapter 3 Review<br>Chapter 3 Test |
| Assess | 1 | Chapter 3 Test | Chapter 3 Test | Chapter 3 Test | |
| **Total** | | **12 Days** | **12 Days** | **12 Days** | **6 Days** |

Note: Pacing does not include Concept Bytes and other feature pages.

# Resources

| | For the Chapter | 3-1 | 3-2 | 3-3 | 3-4 | 3-5 | 3-6 |
|---|---|---|---|---|---|---|---|
| **Planning** | | | | | | | |
| Teacher Center Online Planner & Grade Book | I | I | I | I | I | I | I |
| **Interactive Learning & Guided Instruction** | | | | | | | |
| My Math Video | I | | | | | | |
| Solve It! | | I TM | I TM | I TM | I TM | I TM | I TM |
| Student Companion (SP)* | | P M | P M | P M | P M | P M | |
| *Vocabulary Support* | | I P M | I P M | I P M | I P M | I P M | I P M |
| *Got It? Support* | | I P | I P | I P | I P | I P | I P |
| Dynamic Activity | | I | I | I | I | | |
| Online Problems | | I | I | I | I | I | I |
| Additional Problems | | M | M | M | M | M | M |
| English Language Learner Support (TR) | | E P M | E P M | E P M | E P M | E P M | E P M |
| Activities, Games, and Puzzles | | E M | E M | E M | E M | E M | E M |
| Teaching With TI Technology With CD-ROM | | | | ✓ P | ✓ P | | |
| TI-Nspire™ Support CD-ROM | | ✓ | ✓ | ✓ | ✓ | ✓ | ✓ |
| **Lesson Check & Practice** | | | | | | | |
| Student Companion (SP)* | | P M | P M | P M | P M | P M | P M |
| *Lesson Check Support* | | I P | I P | I P | I P | I P | I P |
| Practice and Problem Solving Workbook (SP) | | P | P | P | P | P | P |
| *Think About a Plan* (TR)* | | E P M | E P M | E P M | E P M | E P M | E P M |
| *Practice Form G* (TR)* | | E P M | E P M | E P M | E P M | E P M | E P M |
| *Standardized Test Prep* (TR)* | | P M | P M | P M | P M | P M | P M |
| Practice *Form K* (TR)* | | E P M | E P M | E P M | E P M | E P M | E P M |
| Extra Practice | E M | | | | | | |
| Find the Errors! | M | | | | | | |
| Enrichment (TR) | | E P M | E P M | E P M | E P M | E P M | E P M |
| Answers and Solutions CD-ROM | ✓ | ✓ | ✓ | ✓ | ✓ | ✓ | ✓ |
| **Assess & Remediate** | | | | | | | |
| ExamView CD-ROM | ✓ | ✓ | ✓ | ✓ | ✓ | ✓ | ✓ |
| Lesson Quiz | | I TM | I TM | I TM | I TM | I TM | I TM |
| Quizzes and Tests *Form G* (TR)* | E P M | | | E P M | | | E P M |
| Quizzes and Tests *Form K* (TR)* | E P M | | | E P M | | | E P M |
| Reteaching (TR)* | | E P M | E P M | E P M | E P M | E P M | E P M |
| Performance Tasks (TR)* | P M | | | | | | |
| Cumulative Review (TR)* | P M | | | | | | |
| Progress Monitoring Assessments | I P M | | | | | | |

(TR) Available in All-In-One Teaching Resources    *Spanish available

# 1 Interactive Learning

## Solve It!

**PURPOSE** To find the intersection of two lines
**PROCESS** Students may
- copy the graph and extend the lines to find the point of intersection.
- write the equations of the lines.

**FACILITATE**

**Q** Copy the graph and draw lines through the red and blue dots. What are the x-intercepts of the lines? **[red: (25, 0); blue: (30, 0)]**

**Q** What is the slope of the red line? Why does it make sense? **[−1; one more bike means one less trike, so the slope is $\frac{-1}{1} = -1$.]**

**Q** What does the point of intersection represent? **[an ordered pair of the number of bikes and trikes that sum to 25 and have 60 wheels]**

**Q** Do you need to know the equations of the lines to answer the question? Explain. **[No; you can find the solution graphically.]**

**ANSWER** See Solve It in Answers on next page.
**CONNECT THE MATH** In the Solve It, students find the intersection of two lines. In the lesson, students will solve systems of linear equations by using tables and graphs.

# 2 Guided Instruction

**Problem 1**                    **ERROR PREVENTION**

**Q** Why should you check the intersection point you read from the graph by trying the values in both equations? **[You may have graphed incorrectly or misread the graph.]**

---

**Objective** To solve a linear system using a graph or a table

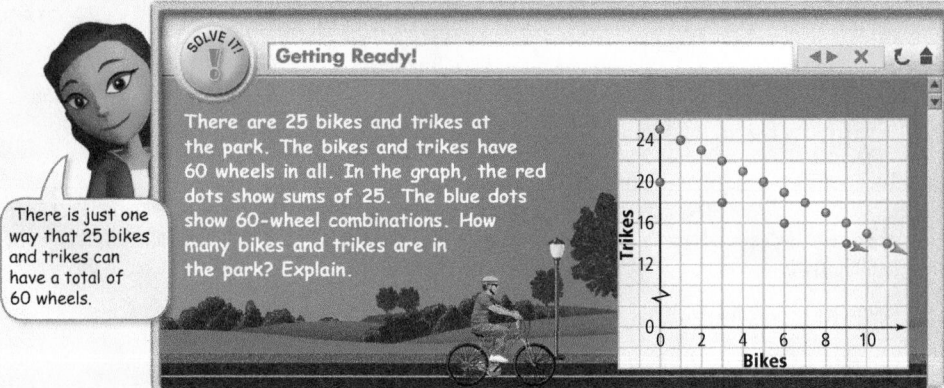

**Getting Ready!**

There are 25 bikes and trikes at the park. The bikes and trikes have 60 wheels in all. In the graph, the red dots show sums of 25. The blue dots show 60-wheel combinations. How many bikes and trikes are in the park? Explain.

There is just one way that 25 bikes and trikes can have a total of 60 wheels.

When you have two or more related unknowns, you may be able to represent their relationship with a **system of equations**—a set of two or more equations.

**Essential Understanding** To solve a system of equations, find a set of values that replace the variables in the equations and make each equation true.

A **linear system** consists of linear equations. A **solution of a system** is a set of values for the variables that makes all the equations true. You can solve a system of equations graphically or by using tables.

### Lesson Vocabulary
- system of equations
- linear system
- solution of a system
- inconsistent system
- consistent system
- independent system
- dependent system

**Think**
How can you use a graph to find the solution of a system?
Find the point where the two lines intersect.

 **Problem 1** Using a Graph or Table to Solve a System

What is the solution of the system? $\begin{cases} -3x + 2y = 8 \\ x + 2y = -8 \end{cases}$

**Method 1** Graph the equations. The point of intersection appears to be $(-4, -2)$.

Check by substituting the values into both equations.

$$-3x + 2y = 8 \qquad x + 2y = -8$$
$$-3(-4) + 2(-2) = 8 \checkmark \qquad -4 + 2(-2) = -8 \checkmark$$

Both equations are true so $(-4, -2)$ is the solution of the system.

---

**BIG idea** Solving Equations and Inequalities    **UbD**

**ESSENTIAL UNDERSTANDINGS**
- A system of equations is solved by finding a set of values that replace the variables in the equations and make each equation true.
- A point of intersection $(x, y)$ of the graphs of the functions $f$ and $g$ is a solution of the system $y = f(x)$, $y = g(x)$.

## Math Background
Linear systems of two equations can be analyzed using the nature of the solutions.

### One solution
- consistent—independent
- 2 lines intersect at one point
- the slopes of the lines are not equal
- the y-intercepts may or may not be equal

### Infinitely many solutions
- consistent—dependent
- 2 lines coincide
- the slopes of the lines are equal
- the y-intercepts are equal

### No solution
- inconsistent
- 2 parallel lines
- the slopes of the lines are equal
- the y-intercepts are not equal

## Support Student Learning
Use the **Algebra 2 Companion** to engage and support students during instruction. See Lesson Resources at the end of this lesson for details.

**PowerAlgebra.com**

## 1 Interactive Learning

**Solve It!**
Step out how to solve the Problem with helpful hints and an online question. Other questions are listed above in Interactive Learning.

**Dynamic Activity** Using sliders and input boxes, students can graph each equation separately to solve systems of linear equations, find their point of intersection, and view ordered pairs in tables and matrices.

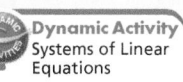

**Method 2** Use a table. Write the equations in slope-intercept form.

$$-3x + 2y = 8 \qquad x + 2y = -8$$
$$2y = 3x + 8 \qquad 2y = -x - 8$$
$$y_1 = \frac{3}{2}x + 4 \qquad y_2 = -\frac{1}{2}x - 4$$

| X | Y₁ | Y₂ |
|---|---|---|
| -5 | -3.5 | -1.5 |
| -4 | -2 | -2 |
| -3 | -.5 | -2.5 |
| -2 | 1 | -3 |
| -1 | 2.5 | -3.5 |
| 0 | 4 | -4 |
| 1 | 5.5 | -4.5 |

X=-4

Enter the equations in the **Y=** screen as **Y1** and **Y2**.
View the table. Adjust the $x$-values until you see $y_1 = y_2$.

When $x = -4$, both $y_1$ and $y_2$ equal $-2$. So, $(-4, -2)$ is the solution of the system.

 **Got It?** **1.** What is the solution of the system? $\begin{cases} x - 2y = 4 \\ 3x + y = 5 \end{cases}$

 **Problem 2** **Using a Table to Solve a Problem**

**Biology** The diagrams show the birth lengths and growth rates of two species of shark. If the growth rates stay the same, at what age would a Spiny Dogfish and a Greenland shark be the same length?

GREENLAND SHARK
Growth rate: 0.75 cm/yr
Birth length: 37 cm

SPINY DOGFISH SHARK
Growth rate: 1.5 cm/yr
Birth length: 22 cm

**Step 1** Define the variables and write the equation for the length of each shark.

Let $x$ = age in years.
Let $y$ = length in centimeters.

Length of Greenland: $y_1 = 0.75x + 37$
Length of Spiny Dogfish: $y_2 = 1.5x + 22$

**Step 2** Use the table to solve the problem.

List $x$-values until the corresponding $y$-values match.

**Think**
How can you use slope-intercept form to write each equation?
Use the growth rate for $m$ and the length at birth for $b$.

The sharks will be the same length when they are 20 years old.

**Shark Length in cm**

| Age | Greenland | Spiny Dogfish |
|---|---|---|
| $x$ | $y_1 = 0.75x + 37$ | $y_2 = 1.5x + 22$ |
| 15 | 48.25 | 44.5 |
| 16 | 49 | 46 |
| ⋮ | ⋮ | ⋮ |
| 20 | 52 | 52 |

 **Got It?** **2. a.** If the growth rates continue, how long will each shark be when it is 25 years old?
**b. Reasoning** Explain why growth rates for these sharks may not continue indefinitely.

**Q** In Method 2, why do you put the equations in slope-intercept form? **[So you can efficiently find $y$-values for each value of $x$.]**

**Got It?**
Have students solve this system by both methods to show that both methods are valid and that the answer will be the same.

**Problem 2**

**Step 1**

**Q** Why is the slope of the linear equation of the Spiny Dogfish's length 1.5? **[Every two years, the spiny dogfish grows 3 cm, which is 1.5 cm per year.]**
**Q** Why is the $y$-intercept of the equation of the Greenland's length 37? **[This is the length of the shark when it is born at age zero.]**

**Step 2**

**Q** How can you choose $x$-values to use in a table when you are looking for a solution? **[As the difference between the $y$-values approaches zero, you get closer to the solution.]**

**ERROR PREVENTION**
Remind students that the slope is a ratio. When it is written as a single number, it is understood that the second value in the ratio is 1. A slope of 1.5 is the ratio 1.5 : 1.

**Got It?**
If students have trouble with 2b, ask them how much they expect to grow in height when they are thirty years old.

## 2 Guided Instruction

 Each Problem is worked out and supported in the Student Online Center.

**Problem 1**
Using a Graph or Table to Solve a System
*Animated*

**Alternative Problem 1**
Using a Graph or Table to Solve a System
*Animated*

**Problem 2**
Using a Table to Solve a Problem

**Problem 3**
Using Linear Regression

**Problem 4**
Classifying a System Without Graphing
*Animated*

**Alternative Problem 4**
Classifying a System Without Graphing

**Support in Algebra 2 Companion**
• Vocabulary
• Key Concepts
• Got It?

## Answers

**Solve It!**
15 bikes and 10 trikes

**Got It?**
**1.** $(2, -1)$
**2. a.** Spiny Dogfish: 59.5 cm; Greenland: 55.75 cm
   **b.** Each species of shark has a maximum total length; growth rates decrease with increase in age.

## Problem 3

Students may prefer to use the actual years, 1950 to 2000, instead of the number of years after 1950, 0 to 50.

**Q** How accurate do you think your prediction is? **[Answers may vary. Sample: Not very accurate because a population grows exponentially, not linearly.]**

**ERROR PREVENTION**

Remind students to add the *x*-value of the point of intersection to 1950 to find the year the populations will be equal. If students are having trouble using the calculator to find the regression equation and are getting a DIM MISMATCH error message, have them check that there are no stray values in any of the columns.

**EXTENSION**

Show students how to do an exponential regression (ExpReg). Graph these exponential models and find the predicted intersection. [about 21.9 million in 2008]

**EXTENSION**

In the problem, students perform *extrapolation* by making a prediction outside the domain and range of the given data. Prediction within the domain and range, or between the given data, is called *interpolation*. The Got It uses interpolation.

## Got It?

**Q** What is different about Detroit's population? How is this reflected in the line of best fit? **[Detroit's population is declining instead of growing. Detroit's line of best fit has a negative slope.]**

---

### Problem 3 Using Linear Regression

**Population** The table shows the populations of the New York City and Los Angeles metropolitan regions from the census reports for 1950 through 2000. Assuming these linear trends continue, when will the populations of these regions be equal? What will that population be?

**Populations of New York City and Los Angeles Metropolitan Regions (1950–2000)**

|  | 1950 | 1960 | 1970 | 1980 | 1990 | 2000 |
|---|---|---|---|---|---|---|
| New York City | 12,911,994 | 14,759,429 | 16,178,700 | 16,121,297 | 18,087,251 | 21,199,865 |
| Los Angeles | 4,367,911 | 6,742,696 | 7,032,075 | 11,497,568 | 14,531,529 | 16,373,645 |

Source: U.S. Census Bureau

| Know | Need | Plan |
|---|---|---|
| Population data for two regions | The point in time when their populations will be the same | • Use a calculator to find linear regression models.<br>• Plot the models.<br>• Find the point of intersection. |

Enter all the numbers as millions, rounded to the nearest hundred thousand. For example, enter 12,911,994 as 12.9.

**Step 1** Enter the data into lists on your calculator.
**L1**: number of years since 1950
**L2**: New York City populations
**L3**: Los Angeles populations

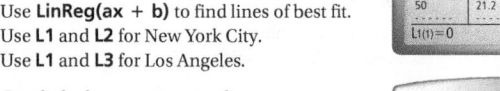

**Step 2** Use **LinReg(ax + b)** to find lines of best fit.
Use **L1** and **L2** for New York City.
Use **L1** and **L3** for Los Angeles.

**Step 3** Graph the linear regression lines.
Use the **Intersect** feature.

**Think**

**What does *x* represent?**
The *x*-value is the number of years *since* the zero year.

The *x*-value of the point of intersection is about 87, which represents the year 2037. The data suggest that the populations of the New York City and Los Angeles metropolitan regions will each be about 25.6 million in 2037.

**Got It?** **3.** The table shows the populations of the San Diego and Detroit metropolitan regions. When were the populations of these regions equal? What was that population?

**Populations of San Diego and Detroit Metropolitan Regions (1950–2000)**

|  | 1950 | 1960 | 1970 | 1980 | 1990 | 2000 |
|---|---|---|---|---|---|---|
| San Diego | 334,387 | 573,224 | 696,769 | 875,538 | 1,110,549 | 1,223,400 |
| Detroit | 1,849,568 | 1,670,144 | 1,511,482 | 1,203,339 | 1,027,974 | 951,270 |

Source: U.S. Census Bureau

---

# Additional Problems

**1.** What is the solution of the system?
$$\begin{cases} 2x - y = -1 \\ \frac{1}{2}x - 2 = y \end{cases}$$
**ANSWER** $(-2, -3)$

**2.** You want to buy a camera. A film camera costs $89.98, and each photo costs $0.24. A digital camera costs $124.48, and each photo costs $0.09. After how many photos will the overall cost of the cameras be the same? What will that cost be?

**ANSWER** 230 photos; $145.18

**3.** The enrollments for two high schools are given in the table. If the trends continue, when can the schools expect to

have the same enrollment? What will the enrollment be?

| Year | School A | School B |
|---|---|---|
| 2005 | 628 | 432 |
| 2006 | 632 | 436 |
| 2007 | 627 | 461 |
| 2008 | 621 | 477 |
| 2009 | 615 | 488 |
| 2010 | 612 | 498 |

**ANSWER** In 2016, the enrollment will be about 589 students.

**4.** Determine without graphing whether the system is independent, dependent, or inconsistent.
$$\begin{cases} 3x - 4y = 6 \\ 6x + 3 = 8y \end{cases}$$
**ANSWER** inconsistent

You can classify a system of two linear equations by the number of solutions.

A **consistent system** has at least one solution.

An **inconsistent system** has no solution.

Consistent system → Independent / Dependent

An **independent system** has one solution.

A **dependent system** has infinitely many solutions.

Inconsistent system

The graphs for an inconsistent system are parallel lines. So, there are no solutions. For a dependent system, the two equations represent the same line.

 **take note**

**Concept Summary   Graphical Solutions of Linear Systems**

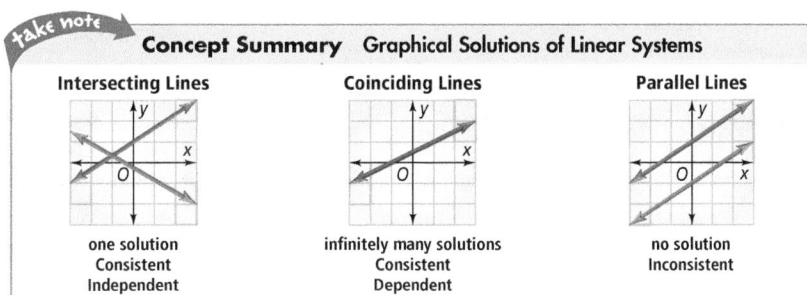

| Intersecting Lines | Coinciding Lines | Parallel Lines |
|---|---|---|
| one solution | infinitely many solutions | no solution |
| Consistent | Consistent | Inconsistent |
| Independent | Dependent | |

 **Problem 4**   **Classifying a System Without Graphing**

Without graphing, is the system *independent*, *dependent*, or *inconsistent*?

$$\begin{cases} 4y - 2x = 6 \\ 8y = 4x - 12 \end{cases}$$

Rewrite each equation in slope-intercept form. Compare slopes and *y*-intercepts.

$4y - 2x = 6$ $\qquad\qquad$ $8y = 4x - 12$

$y = \frac{1}{2}x + \frac{3}{2}$ $\qquad\qquad$ $y = \frac{1}{2}x - \frac{3}{2}$

$m = \frac{1}{2}$; *y*-intercept is $\frac{3}{2}$ $\qquad$ $m = \frac{1}{2}$; *y*-intercept is $-\frac{3}{2}$

The slopes are equal and the *y*-intercepts are different. The lines are different but parallel. The system is inconsistent.

 **Got It?**   **4.** Without graphing, is each system *independent*, *dependent*, or *inconsistent*?

**a.** $\begin{cases} -3x + y = 4 \\ x - \frac{1}{3}y = 1 \end{cases}$
**b.** $\begin{cases} 2x + 3y = 1 \\ 4x + y = -3 \end{cases}$
**c.** $\begin{cases} y = 2x - 3 \\ 6x - 3y = 9 \end{cases}$

PowerAlgebra.com   **Lesson 3-1**  Solving Systems Using Tables and Graphs   137

**Plan**

**What should you compare to classify the system?**
Compare the slopes and *y*-intercepts of each line.

---

**Take Note**

**Q** How do the slopes of parallel lines compare? **[They are the same.]**

**Q** How do the slopes of coinciding lines compare? **[They are the same.]**

**Q** How can you tell whether the graphs of two linear equations with the same slope will be coinciding lines or parallel lines? **[Compute the *y*-intercepts. If the *y*-intercepts are different, the lines are parallel. If the *y*-intercepts are the same, the lines coincide.]**

**EXTENSION**

For linear systems in standard form $ax + by = c$, if the equations are linear multiples of each other, then the system is dependent.

Example: $\begin{cases} 3x - 2y = 5 \\ -6x + 4y = -10 \end{cases}$

If the coefficients are the same linear multiples but the constants are not, then the system is inconsistent. Example: $\begin{cases} 3x - 2y = 5 \\ -6x + 4y = 15 \end{cases}$

If the coefficients are not of the same multiple, then the system is independent.

Example: $\begin{cases} 3x - 2y = 5 \\ -6x - 4y = -10 \end{cases}$

**Problem 4**

**Q** What condition indicates an independent system? **[the equations have different slopes]**

**Q** What conditions indicate a dependent system? **[when the equations have the same slope and the same *y*-intercept]**

**Got It?**

Students can check their answers by graphing.

---

# Answers

**Got It?** (continued)

**3.** in the yr 1990; about 1,100,000

**4. a.** inconsistent

   **b.** independent

   **c.** dependent

# 3 Lesson Check

## Do you know HOW?

- For Exercises 1 and 2, students sometimes accidentally drop the negative sign in front of the *y*. To avoid this, have students put a 1 in front of the *y*.
- For Exercise 3, students may have trouble defining the variables. Have students identify that they are looking for the number of pens and the number of pencils.

## Do you UNDERSTAND? ERROR INTERVENTION

- For Exercise 4, if students have trouble identifying the conditions that make a system of equations independent and inconsistent, refer to Problem 4 and the text preceding it.
- For Exercise 6, suggest writing an example system and graphing the system to illustrate that the negative reciprocal slopes mean that the lines are perpendicular.

## Close

> **Q** What does it mean to find the solution to a system of equations? **[Find the values for the variables that make all equations true.]**
>
> **Q** From this lesson, what two methods can you use to find a solution to a system of equations? **[graphing and making a table]**
>
> **Q** How can you determine whether a system is independent, dependent, or inconsistent? **[Use a graph or the coefficients and constants of the equations to determine the number of solutions.]**

---

 **Lesson Check**

### Do you know HOW?

Solve each system of equations by graphing. Check your solution.

1. $\begin{cases} y = x - 1 \\ y = -x + 3 \end{cases}$

2. $\begin{cases} 2x + y = 4 \\ x - y = 2 \end{cases}$

3. You bought a total of 6 pens and pencils for $4. If each pen costs $1 and each pencil costs $.50, how many pens and pencils did you buy?

### Do you UNDERSTAND?

4. **Vocabulary** Is it possible for a system of equations to be both independent and inconsistent? Explain.

5. **Open-Ended** Write a system of linear equations that has no solution.

6. **Reasoning** In a system of linear equations, the slope of one line is the negative reciprocal of the slope of the other line. Is this system *independent*, *dependent*, or *inconsistent*? Explain.

---

  **Practice and Problem-Solving Exercises**

**Ⓐ Practice**

Solve each system by graphing or using a table. Check your answers.  ◀ See Problem 1.

7. $\begin{cases} y = x - 2 \\ y = -2x + 7 \end{cases}$

8. $\begin{cases} y = -x + 3 \\ y = \frac{3}{2}x - 2 \end{cases}$

9. $\begin{cases} 2x + 4y = 12 \\ x + y = 2 \end{cases}$

10. $\begin{cases} x = -3 \\ y = 5 \end{cases}$

11. $\begin{cases} 2x - 2y = 4 \\ y - x = 6 \end{cases}$

12. $\begin{cases} 3x + y = 5 \\ x - y = 7 \end{cases}$

Write and solve a system of equations for each situation. Check your answers.  ◀ See Problem 2.

13. A store sells small notebooks for $8 and large notebooks for $10. If you buy 6 notebooks and spend $56, how many of each size notebook did you buy?

14. A shop has one-pound bags of peanuts for $2 and three-pound bags of peanuts for $5.50. If you buy 5 bags and spend $17, how many of each size bag did you buy?

**Graphing Calculator** Find linear models for each set of data. In what year will the two quantities be equal?  ◀ See Problem 3.

15. **U.S. Life Expectancy at Birth (1970–2000)**

| Year | 1970 | 1975 | 1980 | 1985 | 1990 | 1995 | 2000 |
|---|---|---|---|---|---|---|---|
| Men (years) | 67.1 | 68.8 | 70.0 | 71.1 | 71.8 | 72.5 | 74.3 |
| Women (years) | 74.7 | 76.6 | 77.4 | 78.2 | 78.8 | 78.9 | 79.7 |

SOURCE: U.S. Census Bureau

16. **Annual U.S. Consumption of Vegetables**

| Year | 1980 | 1985 | 1990 | 1995 | 1998 | 1999 | 2000 |
|---|---|---|---|---|---|---|---|
| Broccoli (lb/person) | 1.5 | 2.6 | 3.4 | 4.3 | 5.1 | 6.5 | 6.1 |
| Cucumbers (lb/person) | 3.9 | 4.4 | 4.7 | 5.6 | 6.5 | 6.8 | 6.4 |

SOURCE: U.S. Census Bureau

---

**PowerAlgebra.com**

## 3 Lesson Check

For a digital lesson check, use the Got It questions.

**Support in Algebra 2 Companion**
- Lesson Check

## 4 Practice

Assign homework to individual students or to an entire class.

---

# Answers

## Lesson Check

1. (2, 1)

2. (2, 0)

3. 2 pens; 4 pencils

4. No; an independent system has a unique solution whereas an inconsistent system has no solution.

5. Answers may vary. Sample:
$\begin{cases} y = 2x + 1 \\ y = 2x - 3 \end{cases}$

6. Independent; if the slope of one equation is the negative reciprocal of the slope of the other equation, the lines are perpendicular and intersect at a unique point.

## Practice and Problem-Solving Exercises

7–12. How solutions are determined may vary (graphing or using a table).

7. (3, 1)

8. (2, 1)

9–16. See next page.

Without graphing, classify each system as *independent*, *dependent*, or *inconsistent*.

◀ See Problem 4.

**17.** $\begin{cases} 7x - y = 6 \\ -7x + y = -6 \end{cases}$

**18.** $\begin{cases} -3x + y = 4 \\ x - \frac{1}{3}y = 1 \end{cases}$

**19.** $\begin{cases} 4x + 8y = 12 \\ x + 2y = -3 \end{cases}$

**20.** $\begin{cases} y = 2x - 1 \\ y = -2x + 5 \end{cases}$

**21.** $\begin{cases} x = 6 \\ y = -2 \end{cases}$

**22.** $\begin{cases} 2y = 5x + 6 \\ -10x + 4y = 8 \end{cases}$

**23.** $\begin{cases} x - 3y = 2 \\ 4x - 12y = 8 \end{cases}$

**24.** $\begin{cases} y - x = 0 \\ y = -x \end{cases}$

**25.** $\begin{cases} 2y - x = 4 \\ \frac{1}{2}x + y = 2 \end{cases}$

**26.** $\begin{cases} x + 4y = 12 \\ 2x - 8y = 4 \end{cases}$

**27.** $\begin{cases} 4x + 8y = -6 \\ 6x + 12y = -9 \end{cases}$

**28.** $\begin{cases} 4y - 2x = 6 \\ 8y = 4x - 12 \end{cases}$

**Ⓑ Apply**

Graph and solve each system.

**29.** $\begin{cases} 3 = 4y + x \\ 4y = -x + 3 \end{cases}$

**30.** $\begin{cases} y = \frac{1}{2}x + \frac{1}{2} \\ y = \frac{1}{4}x + \frac{3}{2} \end{cases}$

**31.** $\begin{cases} 3x + 6y - 12 = 0 \\ x + 2y = 8 \end{cases}$

**32.** $\begin{cases} y = -3x + 3 \\ y = 2x - 7 \end{cases}$

**33.** $\begin{cases} 3x = -5y + 4 \\ 250 + 150x = 300y \end{cases}$

**34.** $\begin{cases} x + 3y = 6 \\ 6y + 2x = 12 \end{cases}$

**35.** $\begin{cases} -x + 3y = 6 \\ 2x - y = 8 \end{cases}$

**36.** $\begin{cases} y = -\frac{1}{2}x + 8 \\ y = 2x - 6 \end{cases}$

**37.** $\begin{cases} y = -2x + 6 \\ x - 3y = -6 \end{cases}$

Without graphing, classify each system as *independent*, *dependent*, or *inconsistent*.

**38.** $\begin{cases} 3x - 2y = 8 \\ 4y = 6x - 5 \end{cases}$

**39.** $\begin{cases} 2x + 8y = 6 \\ x = -4y + 3 \end{cases}$

**40.** $\begin{cases} 3m = -5n + 4 \\ n - \frac{6}{5} = -\frac{3}{5}m \end{cases}$

**41. Think About a Plan** You and a friend are both reading a book. You read 2 pages each minute and have already read 55 pages. Your friend reads 3 pages each minute and has already read 35 pages. Graph and solve a system of equations to find when the two of you will have read the same number of pages. Since the number of pages you have read depends on how long you have been reading, let $x$ represent the number of minutes it takes to read $y$ pages.
  • How can you describe the relationship between $x$ and $y$ for you?
  • How can you describe the relationship between $x$ and $y$ for your friend?
  • How can a graph help you solve this problem?

**42. Sports** You can choose between two tennis courts at two university campuses to learn how to play tennis. One campus charges $25 per hour. The other campus charges $20 per hour plus a one-time registration fee of $10.
  **a.** Write a system of equations to represent the cost $c$ for $h$ hours of court use at each campus.
  📱 **b. Graphing Calculator** Find the number of hours for which the costs are the same.
  📱 **c. Reasoning** If you want to practice for a total of 10 hours, which university campus should you choose? Explain.

**ASSIGNMENT GUIDE**
Basic: 7–31, 41–44
Average: 7–27 odd, 29–49
Advanced: 7–27 odd, 29–54
Standardized Test Prep: 55–58
Mixed Review: 59–69

**Reasoning** exercises have blue headings.

**Applications** exercises have red headings.

**EXERCISE 42:** Use the Think About a Plan worksheet in the **Practice and Problem Solving Workbook** (also available in the Teaching Resources in print and online) to further support students' development in becoming independent learners.

**HOMEWORK QUICK CHECK**
To check students' understanding of key skills and concepts, go over Exercises 13, 23, 41, 42, and 44.

---

**9.** $(-2, 4)$

**10.** $(-3, 5)$

**11.** no solution

**12.** $(3, -4)$

**13.** 2 small; 4 large

**14.** 3 one-pound bags; 2 three-pound bags

**15.** Models may vary. Sample: Use 0 for 1970.
$$\begin{cases} y = 0.22x + 67.5 \\ y = 0.15x + 75.507 \end{cases}$$
Around 2085, the quantities will be equal.

**16.** Models may vary. Sample: Use 0 for 1980.
$$\begin{cases} y = 0.232x + 1.328 \\ y = 0.145x + 3.673 \end{cases}$$
Around 2007; the quantities were equal.

**17.** dependent      **18.** inconsistent

**19.** inconsistent    **20.** independent

**21.** independent    **22.** inconsistent

**23.** dependent      **24.** independent

**25.** independent    **26.** independent

**27.** dependent      **28.** inconsistent

**29.** infinitely many solutions

**30.** $\left(4, \frac{5}{2}\right)$

**31–42.** See next page.

# Answers

## Practice and Problem-Solving Exercises
(continued)

**31.** no solution

**32.** $(2, -3)$

**33.** $\left(-\dfrac{1}{33}, \dfrac{9}{11}\right)$

**34.** infinitely many solutions

**35.** $(6, 4)$

**36.** $\left(\dfrac{28}{5}, \dfrac{26}{5}\right)$

**37.** $\left(\dfrac{12}{7}, \dfrac{18}{7}\right)$

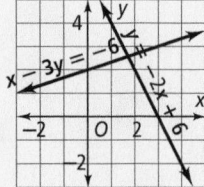

**38.** inconsistent
**39.** dependent
**40.** inconsistent

---

**43. Error Analysis** Your friend used a graphing calculator to solve a system of linear equations, shown below. After using the **TABLE** feature, your friend says that the system has no solution. Explain what your friend did wrong. What is the solution of the system?

$$2x + y = 6 \qquad 3x + 2y = 8$$
$$y = 6 - 2x \qquad y = \dfrac{8 - 3x}{2}$$

**44. Reasoning** Is it possible for an inconsistent linear system to contain two lines with the same $y$-intercept? Explain.

**45. Writing** Summarize the possible relationships for the $y$-intercepts, slopes, and number of solutions in a system of two linear equations in two variables.

**Reasoning** Determine whether each statement is *always*, *sometimes* or *never* true for the following system.

$$\begin{cases} y = x + 3 \\ y = mx + b \end{cases}$$

**46.** If $m = 1$, the system has no solution.

**47.** If $b = 3$, the system has exactly one solution.

**48.** If $m \neq 1$, the system has no solution.

**49.** If $m \neq 1$ and $b = 2$, the system has infinitely many solutions.

**Ⓒ Challenge**  **Open-Ended** Write a second equation for each system so that the system will have the indicated number of solutions.

**50.** infinite number of solutions

$$\begin{cases} \dfrac{x}{4} + \dfrac{y}{3} = 1 \\ \underline{\qquad ?\qquad} \end{cases}$$

**51.** no solutions

$$\begin{cases} 5x + 2y = 10 \\ \underline{\qquad ?\qquad} \end{cases}$$

**52.** Write a system of linear equations with the solution set $\{(x, y) \mid y = 5x + 2\}$.

**53. Reasoning** What relationship exists between the equations in a dependent system?

**54. Economics** Research shows that in a certain market only 2000 widgets can be sold at $8 each, but if the price is reduced to $3, then 10,000 can be sold.
  **a.** Let $p$ represent price and $n$ represent the number of widgets. Identify the independent and dependent variables.
  **b.** Write a linear equation that relates price and the quantity demanded. This type of equation is called a *demand* equation.
  **c.** A shop can make 2000 widgets for $5 each and 20,000 widgets for $2 each. Use this information to write a linear equation that relates price and the quantity supplied. This type of equation is called a *supply* equation.
  **d.** Find the equilibrium point where supply is equal to demand. Explain the meaning of the coordinates of this point within the context of the exercise.

---

**41.**

After 20 min you and your friend will have read the same number of pages.

**42. a.** $\begin{cases} c = 25h \\ c = 20h + 10 \end{cases}$

  **b.**

The cost would be the same for 2 hours of instruction.

  **c.** The campus that charges $20 per hour plus a one-time registration of $10 would be cheaper for 10 hours of practice ($210 versus $250).

**43.** My friend did not extend the table of values far enough. Scrolling down will show that when $x = 4$ then $y_1 = y_2 = -2$, so the system has a solution, $(4, -2)$.

**44.** No; they would be the same line, and the system would be dependent and consistent.

**45.** An independent system has one solution. The slopes are different, but the $y$-intercepts could be the same. An inconsistent system has no solution. The slopes are the same and the $y$-intercepts are different. A dependent system has an infinite number of solutions. The slopes and $y$-intercepts are the same.

**46–54.** See next page.

**55.** Which graph shows the solution of the following system? $\begin{cases} 4x + y = 1 \\ x + 4y = -11 \end{cases}$

 Ⓐ   Ⓑ   Ⓒ   Ⓓ

**56.** Which is the equation of a line that is perpendicular to the line in the graph?

Ⓕ $y = -3x + 2$     Ⓗ $y = -\frac{1}{3}x - 4$

Ⓖ $y = \frac{1}{3}x + 5$     Ⓘ $y = 3x - 1$

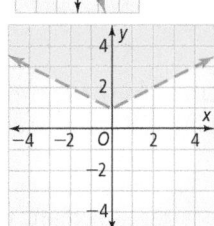

**57.** Which inequality represents the graph at the right?

Ⓐ $y \geq \frac{1}{2}|x| + 1$     Ⓒ $y > \frac{1}{2}|x| + 1$

Ⓑ $y \leq \frac{1}{2}|x| + 1$     Ⓓ $y < \frac{1}{2}|x| + 1$

**58.** Amy ordered prints of a total of 6 photographs in two different sizes, $5 \times 7$ and $4 \times 6$, from an online site. She paid $7.50 for her order. The cost of a $5 \times 7$ print is $1.75 and the cost of a $4 \times 6$ print is $.25. Explain how to solve a system of equations using tables to find the number of $4 \times 6$ prints Amy ordered.

## Mixed Review

Graph each inequality on a coordinate plane.     ◀ See Lesson 2-8.

**59.** $3x - 4y \geq 16$     **60.** $-5x > 8y + 4$     **61.** $x < -4$

Solve each inequality. Check your solution.     ◀ See Lesson 1-5.

**62.** $3n < -4(2 + n)$     **63.** $\frac{x}{3} + 5 \geq \frac{1}{6}$     **64.** $4x - 2 > \frac{1}{2}$

Find the slope of the line through each pair of points.     ◀ See Lesson 2-3.

**65.** $(-2, -4)$ and $(1, 2)$     **66.** $(0, 0)$ and $(5, -3)$     **67.** $(1, 3)$ and $(4, 9)$

**Get Ready!** To prepare for Lesson 3-2, do Exercises 68 and 69.

**68.** What is the value of $a + b - 2c$ for $a = 3$, $b = 1$, and $c = -3$?     ◀ See Lesson 1-3.

**69.** Substitute $-3$ for $x$ in each of the following equations. What is the value of $y$?
a. $y = 2x + 3$
b. $y = -x + 5$
c. $y = 3x - 1$

---

**59.**

**60.**

**61.**

**62.** $n < -\frac{8}{7}$

**63.** $x \geq -\frac{29}{2}$ or $-14.5$

**64.** $x > \frac{5}{8}$

**65.** 2

**66.** $-\frac{3}{5}$

**67.** 2

**68.** 10

**69. a.** $-3$
    **b.** 8
    **c.** $-10$

---

**46.** sometimes

**47.** sometimes

**48.** never

**49.** never

**50.** Answers may vary. Sample: $3x + 4y = 12$

**51.** Answers may vary. Sample: $5x + 2y = 5$

**52.** Answers may vary. Sample:
$\begin{cases} -10x + 2y = 4 \\ 5x - y = -2 \end{cases}$

**53.** They are equivalent eqs.

**54. a.** $p$: independent; $n$: dependent
    **b.** $n = -1600p + 14{,}800$
    **c.** $n = -6000p + 32{,}000$
    **d.** About $(3.91, 8540)$; profits are maximized if about 8540 widgets are sold for about $3.91 each.

**55.** A

**56.** G

**57.** C

**58. [4]** Write the eqs. in slope-intercept form.
Let $x$ = number of $5 \times 7$ prints, let $y$ = number of $4 \times 6$ prints:
$$x + y = 6$$
$$y = -x + 6$$
$$1.75x + 0.25y = 7.5$$
$$y = -7x + 30$$
Enter the eqs. in your calc. and view the table. Adjust the $x$-values until you see $y_1 = y_2$. When $x = 4$, $y_1 = y_2 = 2$. So Amy ordered two $4 \times 6$ prints.

**[3]** error made entering eqs. in calc., OR computational error

**[2]** correct number of $4 \times 6$ prints, incomplete explanation

**[1]** correct number of $4 \times 6$ prints, without an explanation, OR solved by another method

# Additional Instructional Support

## Algebra 2 Companion

Students can use the **Algebra 2 Companion** worktext (4 pages) as you teach the lesson. Use the Companion to support

- New Vocabulary
- Key Concepts
- Got It for each Problem
- Lesson Check

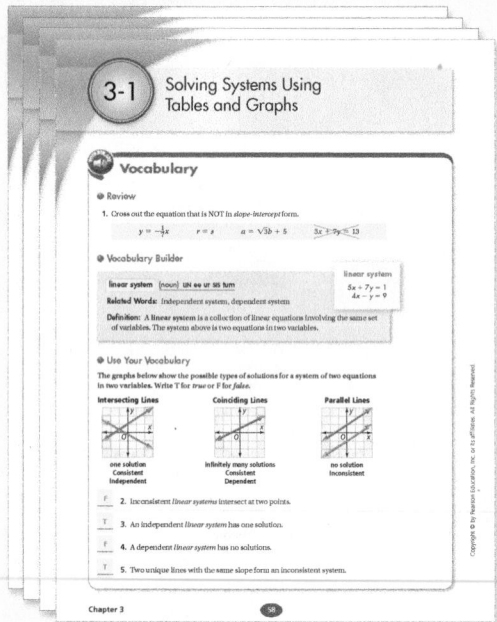

## ELL Support

**Use Multiple Representation** In Problem 1, place the table and the graph side by side, and indicate each point on the graph and in the table, emphasizing that the coordinates of the point the equations share are the solution.

**Assess Understanding** Give each student nine 3 × 5 cards. Have them do the following

- Write each of the following types of linear systems on a card: Consistent Independent, Consistent Dependent, Inconsistent.
- Use three cards to draw an example of each type of linear system.
- Write a description of each type on the final three cards.

Students should shuffle their cards and trade with a neighbor. Each person tries to make 3 matches with their new set of cards. Then check answers with the person who made the cards.

# 5 Assess & Remediate

## Lesson Quiz

1. What is the solution of the system?
$$\begin{cases} x - 2y = -7 \\ 2x + y = 6 \end{cases}$$

2. **Do you UNDERSTAND?** You and a friend start a typing class at the same time. You measure your speed weekly in words per minute (WPM) on a class chart. If the trend continues, after how many weeks can you expect to type as quickly as your friend? What will that WPM be?

| Weeks | 0 | 1 | 2 | 3 |
|---|---|---|---|---|
| Your WPM | 13 | 16 | 19 | 22 |
| Your Friend's WPM | 20 | 22 | 24 | 26 |

3. Use linear regression on your calculator for the points (1.0, 2.6), (2.3, 2.8), (3.1, 3.1), (4.8, 4.7), (5.6, 5.1), (6.3, 5.3). Where does this line intersect $x = 0$?

4. Without graphing, is the system of equations independent, dependent, or inconsistent?
$$\begin{cases} 2x + y = 6 \\ 12 - y = 4x \end{cases}$$

### ANSWERS TO LESSON QUIZ

1. (1, 4)
2. 7 weeks; 34 WPM
3. (0, 1.7)
4. independent

### PRESCRIPTION FOR REMEDIATION

Use the student work on the Lesson Quiz to prescribe a differentiated review assignment:

| Points | Differentiated Remediation |
|---|---|
| 0–2 | Intervention |
| 3 | On-level |
| 4 | Extension |

**PowerAlgebra.com**

## 5 Assess & Remediate

Assign the Lesson Quiz. Appropriate intervention, practice, or enrichment is automatically generated based on student performance.

## Intervention

- **Reteaching** (2 pages) Provides reteaching and practice exercises for the key lesson concepts. Use with struggling students or absent students.

- **English Language Learner Support** Helps students develop and reinforce mathematical vocabulary and key concepts.

### All-in-One Resources/Online
**Reteaching**

### All-in-One Resources/Online
**English Language Learner Support**

# Differentiated Remediation *continued*

## On-Level

- **Practice** (2 pages) Provides extra practice for each lesson. For simpler practice exercises, use the Form K Practice pages found in the All-in-One Teaching Resources and online.

- **Think About a Plan** Helps students develop specific problem-solving skills and strategies by providing scaffolded guiding questions.

- **Standardized Test Prep** Focuses on all major exercises, all major question types, and helps students prepare for the high-stakes assessments.

## Extension

- **Enrichment** Provides students with interesting problems and activities that extend the concepts of the lesson.

- **Activities, Games, and Puzzles** Worksheets that can be used for concepts development, enrichment, and for fun!

---

### Practice and Problem Solving Wkbk/All-in-One Resources/Online
**Practice page 1**

**3-1 Practice**      Form G
Solving Systems Using Tables and Graphs

Solve each system by graphing or using a table. Check your answers.

1. $\begin{cases} y = x - 2 \\ x + y = 10 \end{cases}$ (6, 4)  2. $\begin{cases} y = 7 - x \\ x + 3y = 11 \end{cases}$ (5, 2)  3. $\begin{cases} x - 2y = 10 \\ y = x - 11 \end{cases}$ (12, 1)

4. $\begin{cases} 5x + y = 11 \\ x - y = 1 \end{cases}$ (2, 1)  5. $\begin{cases} x + y = -1 \\ x - y = 3 \end{cases}$ (1, -2)  6. $\begin{cases} x - y = -1 \\ 2x + 2y = 10 \end{cases}$ (2, 3)

7. $\begin{cases} 4x + 3y = -16 \\ -x + y = 4 \end{cases}$ (-4, 0)  8. $\begin{cases} y = -3x \\ x + y = 2 \end{cases}$ (-1, 3)  9. $\begin{cases} y = \frac{3}{2}x - 5 \\ y = -\frac{1}{2}x - 3 \end{cases}$ $\left(\frac{3}{2}, -4\right)$

10. $\begin{cases} y = \frac{1}{2}x + 3 \\ y = -\frac{1}{4}x - 3 \end{cases}$ (-8, -1)  11. $\begin{cases} 2x - 4y = -4 \\ 3x - y = 4 \end{cases}$ (2, 2)  12. $\begin{cases} x + y = 6 \\ x - y = 4 \end{cases}$ (5, 1)

Write and solve a system of equations for each situation. Check your answers.

13. Your school sells tickets for its winter concert. Student tickets are $5 and adult tickets are $10. If your school sells 85 tickets and makes $600, how many of each ticket did they sell?
$5x + 10y = 600, x + y = 85$; 50 student tickets, 35 adult tickets

14. A grocery store has small bags of apples for $5 and large bags of apples for $8. If you buy 6 bags and spend $45, how many of each size bag did you buy?
$5x + 8y = 45, x + y = 6$; 1 small bag, 5 large bags

15. The spreadsheet below shows the monthly income and expenses for a new business.
a. Use your graphing calculator to find linear models for income and expenses as functions of the number of the month. income: $y = 2000x - 8500$; expenses: $y = -2600x + 34,400$
b. In what month will income equal expenses? September

| | A | B | C |
|---|---|---|---|
| | Month | Income | Expenses |
| 1 | May | $1500 | $21,400 |
| 2 | June | $3500 | $18,800 |
| 3 | July | $5500 | $16,200 |
| 4 | August | $7500 | $13,600 |

---

### Practice and Problem Solving Wkbk/All-in-One Resources/Online
**Practice page 2**

**3-1 Practice** *(continued)*      Form G
Solving Systems Using Tables and Graphs

Without graphing, classify each system as *independent*, *dependent*, or *inconsistent*.

16. $\begin{cases} x + y = 3 \\ y = 2x - 3 \end{cases}$ independent  17. $\begin{cases} 2x + y = 3 \\ y = -2x - 1 \end{cases}$ inconsistent  18. $\begin{cases} x + 3y = 9 \\ -2x - 6y = -18 \end{cases}$ dependent

19. $\begin{cases} x + y = 4 \\ y = 2x + 1 \end{cases}$ independent  20. $\begin{cases} x + 3y = 9 \\ 9y + 3x = 27 \end{cases}$ dependent  21. $\begin{cases} 2y = 5 \\ 2x + 3y = 9 \end{cases}$ independent

22. $\begin{cases} 3x + 2y = 7 \\ 3x - 15 = -6y \end{cases}$ independent  23. $\begin{cases} x + y = 6 \\ x + 3y = 3 \end{cases}$ inconsistent  24. $\begin{cases} x + y = 11 \\ y = x - 5 \end{cases}$ independent

25. $\begin{cases} x + 2y = 13 \\ 2y = 7 - x \end{cases}$ inconsistent  26. $\begin{cases} y = 12 - 5x \\ x - 4y = -6 \end{cases}$ independent  27. $\begin{cases} 25x - 10y = 0 \\ y = \frac{5}{2}x \end{cases}$ dependent

28. You and your business partner are mailing advertising flyers to your customers. You address 6 flyers each minute and have already done 80. Your partner addresses 4 flyers each minute and has already done 100. Graph and solve a system of equations to find when the two of you will have addressed equal numbers of flyers.
$y = 6x + 80, y = 4x + 100$; 10 minutes

29. You are going on vacation and leaving your dog in a kennel. Kennel A charges $25 per day which includes a one-time grooming treatment. Kennel B charges $20 per day and a one-time fee of $30 for grooming.
a. Write a system of equations to represent the cost $c$ for $d$ days that your dog will stay at the kennel. $c = 25d, c = 20d + 30$
b. If your vacation is 7 days long, which kennel should you choose? Explain.
Kennel B; it costs $170, while Kennel A costs $175.

**Open-Ended** Write a second equation for each system so that the system will have the indicated number of solutions.

30. one
$\begin{cases} y = 5x - 3 \\ ? \end{cases}$
any equation with a different slope

31. none
$\begin{cases} y = -x + 3 \\ ? \end{cases}$
any equation with the same slope but a different y-intercept

32. an infinite number
$\begin{cases} y = 3x - 2 \\ ? \end{cases}$
any equivalent equation

33. **Multiple Choice** Which ordered pair of numbers is the solution of the system?
$\begin{cases} x + y = -3 \\ x - 2y = 0 \end{cases}$ B
(A) (-6, -3)   (B) (-2, -1)   (C) (6, -3)   (D) (2, 1)

---

### All-in-One Resources/Online
**Enrichment**

**3-1 Enrichment**
Solving Systems Using Tables and Graphs

When navigating their crafts, ship captains might be seen drawing lines on a large map using a straightedge. This procedure is used to plot intercept courses, which help to predict where the craft might meet an oncoming plane or ship.

Air traffic controllers must also plot these intercept courses so that an oncoming plane does *not* meet another plane. To determine whether two ships or planes are on a collision course, it is important to know along which lines they are moving, where they are at a given moment, and how fast they are traveling.

Solve. You might wish to use a drawing to help you solve the problems.

1. Plane A is 40 mi south and 100 mi east of Plane B. Plane A is flying 2 mi north for every mile it flies north, while Plane B is flying 3 mi east for every mile it flies south.
a. Where do their paths cross? 20 mi south and 60 mi east of Plane B's current location
b. Which plane must fly farther? Plane B
c. What ratio of the speed of Plane B to the speed of Plane A would produce a midair collision? $\sqrt{2} : 1$ or $\frac{\sqrt{2}}{1}$

2. A commercial freight carrier is flying at a constant speed of 400 mi/h and is traveling 4 mi east for every 3 mi north. A private plane two planes is observed to be 210 mi due east of the commercial carrier, traveling 12 mi north for every 5 mi west.
a. If it is known that the two planes are on a collision course, how fast is the private plane flying? 260 mi/h
b. When will the collision take place if it is not averted? in $\frac{1}{2}$ hour

3. A cruise ship is traveling in the Atlantic Ocean at a constant rate of 40 mi/h and is traveling 2 mi east for every 5 mi north. An oil tanker is 350 mi due north of the cruise ship and is traveling 1 mi east for every 1 mi south.
a. How far is each ship from the point at which their paths cross? cruise ship: about 269.3 mi; oil tanker: about 141.4 mi
b. What rate of speed for the oil tanker would put it on a collision course with the cruise ship? about 21 mi/h

---

### Practice and Problem Solving Wkbk/All-in-One Resources/Online
**Think About a Plan**

**3-1 Think About a Plan**
Solving Systems Using Tables and Graphs

**Sports** You can choose between two tennis courts at two university campuses to learn how to play tennis. One campus charges $25 per hour. The other campus charges $20 per hour plus a one-time registration fee of $10.

a. Write a system of equations to represent the cost $c$ for $h$ hours of court use at each campus.
b. **Graphing Calculator** Find the number of hours for which the costs are the same.
c. **Reasoning** If you want to practice for a total of 10 hours, which university campus should you choose? Explain.

1. What is an equation that represents the cost $c$ for $h$ hours of court use for the first campus?
$c = 25h$

2. What is an equation that represents the cost $c$ for $h$ hours of court use for the second campus?
$c = 20h + 10$

3. What is one method you can use to find the number of hours for which the costs are the same?
Answers may vary. Sample: Graph both equations and find the point of intersection.

4. What is another method you can use to find the number of hours for which the costs are the same?
Answers may vary. Sample: Use a table to list x-values until the corresponding y-values match each other.

5. Use one of your methods to find the number of hours for which the costs are the same.
2 h

6. What happens to the cost at the two campuses after you have practiced for the number of hours you found in Exercise 5?
The cost at the first campus increases by $25 per hour, while the cost at the second campus increases by $20 per hour.

7. If you want to practice for a total of 10 hours, which university campus should you choose? Explain.
The second campus; after 2 hours, the cost of the first campus will always be greater than the cost of the second campus, because the slope of the equation for the first campus is greater than the slope of the equation for the second campus.

---

### Practice and Problem Solving Wkbk/All-in-One Resources/Online
**Standardized Test Prep**

**3-1 Standardized Test Prep**
Solving Systems Using Tables and Graphs

**Multiple Choice**

For Exercises 1–4, choose the correct letter.

1. Which system of equations is inconsistent? C
(A) $\begin{cases} x + y = 4 \\ x - y = 3 \end{cases}$   (C) $\begin{cases} 6x + 3y = 12 \\ 2y = -4x + 4 \end{cases}$
(B) $\begin{cases} 2y - x = 5 \\ 4y = 2x + 10 \end{cases}$   (D) $\begin{cases} -3x + y = 4 \\ 2y = -6x + 8 \end{cases}$

2. Which ordered pair of numbers is the solution of the system? $\begin{cases} 2x + 3y = 12 \\ 2x - y = 4 \end{cases}$ G
(F) (2, 3)   (G) (3, 2)   (H) (1, -2)   (I) (-3, 6)

3. Which of the following graphs shows the solution of the system? D
$\begin{cases} x + y = -4 \\ 2x - 2y = -8 \end{cases}$
(A) (B) (C) (D)

4. You and your friend are both knitting scarves for charity. You knit 8 rows each minute and already have knitted 10 rows. Your friend knits 5 rows each minute and has already knitted 19 rows. When will you both have knitted the same number of rows? G
(F) 2.6 minutes   (G) 3 minutes   (H) 9.7 minutes   (I) 34 minutes

**Short Response**

5. The sides of an angle are two lines whose equations are $4x + y = 12$ and $y = 3x - 2$. An angle has its vertex at the point where the lines meet. Use a graph to determine the coordinates of the vertex. What are the coordinates of the vertex?
[2] graph to determine the solution; (2, 4)
[1] correct coordinates, without graph

---

### Online Teacher Resource Center
**Activities, Games, and Puzzles**

**3-1 Puzzle: X Marks the Spot**
Solving Systems Using Tables and Graphs

René "Axes" Descartes was a mathematical pirate. He subtracted poor crewmates, added new ones, multiplied his treasure, and divided the goods. Upon arriving at Treasure Island, he would give each of his crewmates a system of equations whose solution, he claimed, was the location of the treasure. Below is a map of the island and the systems he gave to each of his crewmates. Graph each of his crewmates' systems, and list the solution along with the location the crewmates were actually sent.

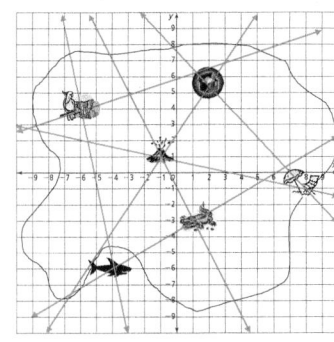

Galois, the dueler: $\begin{cases} y = -5x - 26 \\ 5y = 3x - 18 \end{cases}$
(-4, -6); shark

Poisson, the distributer: $\begin{cases} y = \frac{13}{12}x + \frac{23}{3} \\ y = \frac{3}{2}x - \frac{5}{2} \end{cases}$
(2, 5.5); treasure chest

Fermat, the marginal: $\begin{cases} 2x + y = -1 \\ 3x - 2y = -5 \end{cases}$
(-1, 1); volcano

Lagrange, the multiplier: $\begin{cases} 2x = -y - 1 \\ 5y - 3x = -18 \end{cases}$
(1, -3); alligator

Pascal, the lamb: $\begin{cases} 2x + 9y = 7 \\ 13x + 12y = 92 \end{cases}$
(8, -1); beach

Poincaré, the conjecturer: $\begin{cases} 2y = -10x - 52 \\ 3y - x = 18 \end{cases}$
(-6, 4); waterfall

# 1 Interactive Learning

## Solve It!
**PURPOSE** To use a system of equations to compare two jobs

**PROCESS** Students may
- make a table of sales and wages.
- write two expressions for the wages in terms of sales, set them equal, and solve.
- solve the system by graphing.

### FACILITATE
**Q** What do you want to find? **[the sales that result in equal wages at both stores]**

**Q** Use $x$ for sales made. What expressions model the daily amount you can earn at each store? **[$35 + 0.10x$, $10 + 0.18x$]**

**Q** How can you use these expressions to solve the problem? **[Write an equation setting the expressions equal, and solve for $x$.]**

**Q** Why might it be difficult to solve this problem by graphing? **[Answers may vary. Samples: Decimals in the $x$-terms make graphing difficult. The numbers involved are large.]**

**ANSWERS** See Solve It in Answers on next page.

**CONNECT THE MATH** The Solve It is more easily solved using algebra than graphing. In this lesson students will learn algebraic strategies for solving this type of problem.

# 2 Guided Instruction

## Problem 1

The original system $\begin{cases} 3x + 4y = 12 \\ 2x + y = 10 \end{cases}$ is equivalent

to the system in Step 2: $\begin{cases} 3x + 4y = 12 \\ \quad\quad x = 5.6 \end{cases}$.

**Objective** To solve linear systems algebraically

**Getting Ready!**

What whole-dollar amount of per-day sales would make it more worthwhile to work at Store B? Justify your reasoning.

*Search has yielded two jobs:*

**Store A**
$35 per day plus 10% commission on all sales

**Store B**
$10 per day plus 18% commission on all sales

You can draw graphs of income from each store, but the dollar amounts might be difficult to read.

**Lesson Vocabulary**
- equivalent systems

When you try to solve a system of equations by graphing, the coordinates of the point of intersection may not be obvious.

**Essential Understanding** You can solve a system of equations by writing equivalent systems until the value of one variable is clear. Then substitute to find the value(s) of the other variable(s).

You can use the substitution method to solve a system of equations when it is easy to isolate one of the variables. After isolating the variable, substitute for that variable in the other equation. Then solve for the other variable.

**Problem 1** Solving by Substitution

What is the solution of the system of equations? $\begin{cases} 3x + 4y = 12 \\ 2x + y = 10 \end{cases}$

**Think**

**Which variable should you solve for first?**
In the second equation, the coefficient of $y$ is 1. It is the easiest variable to isolate.

**Step 1**
Solve one equation for one of the variables.
$$2x + y = 10$$
$$y = -2x + 10$$

**Step 2**
Substitute the expression for $y$ in the other equation. Solve for $x$.
$$3x + 4y = 12$$
$$3x + 4(-2x + 10) = 12$$
$$3x - 8x + 40 = 12$$
$$x = 5.6$$

**Step 3**
Substitute the value for $x$ into one of the original equations. Solve for $y$.
$$2x + y = 10$$
$$2(5.6) + y = 10$$
$$11.2 + y = 10$$
$$y = -1.2$$

The solution is $(5.6, -1.2)$.

**BIG idea** Equivalence **UbD**

**ESSENTIAL UNDERSTANDINGS**
- A system of equations can be solved by writing equivalent systems until the value of one variable is clear, then substituting to find the value(s) of the other variable.
- If the equations of two systems are equivalent, then a solution of the system that is easier to solve is also a solution of the more difficult system.

## Math Background

Two algebraic techniques for solving linear systems of equations are substitution and elimination. Both strategies obtain an equation in one variable that can be solved using the Properties of Equality. The resulting value is substituted back into one of the original equations to find the value of the other variable.

For substitution, the equation in one variable is obtained by solving for one variable in terms of the second. Then, substitute the literal expression for the first variable into the other equation and solve for the second variable. Substitution works well when
- one equation is already solved for one variable.
- the coefficient of one or more variables is 1 or −1.

For elimination, the equation in one variable is obtained by adding or subtracting the two equations, eliminating one variable.

Elimination works well when the coefficients of one variable are the same or inverses.

### Support Student Learning
Use the **Algebra 2 Companion** to engage and support students during instruction. See Lesson Resources at the end of this lesson for details.

**PowerAlgebra.com**

## 1 Interactive Learning

**Solve It!**
Step out how to solve the Problem with helpful hints and an online question. Other questions are listed above in Interactive Learning.

**Dynamic Activity** Use this activity with students who have trouble solving systems of linear equations algebraically. Viewing graphs and their algebraic solutions helps students understand the connections.

**Got It?** **1.** What is the solution of the system of equations? $\begin{cases} x + 3y = 5 \\ -2x - 4y = -5 \end{cases}$

 **Problem 2** Using Substitution to Solve a Problem

**Music** A music store offers piano lessons at a discount for customers buying new pianos. The costs for lessons and a one-time fee for materials (including music books, CDs, software, etc.) are shown in the advertisement. What is the cost of each lesson and the one-time fee for materials?

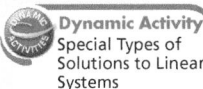
**Dynamic Activity** Special Types of Solutions to Linear Systems

**Relate**    6 · cost of one lesson + one-time fee = $300

          12 · cost of one lesson + one-time fee = $480

**Define**   Let   $c$   = the cost of one lesson.

        Let   $f$   = the one-time fee.

**Write**   $\begin{cases} 6 \cdot c + f = 300 \\ 12 \cdot c + f = 480 \end{cases}$

$6c + f = 300$       Choose one equation. Solve for $f$ in terms of $c$.

    $f = 300 - 6c$

$12c + (300 - 6c) = 480$    Substitute the expression for $f$ into the other equation, $12c + f = 480$. Solve for $c$.

       $c = 30$

**Think**
Which equation should you use to find $f$?
Use the equation with numbers that are easier to work with.

$6(30) + f = 300$    Substitute the value of $c$ into one of the equations. Solve for $f$.

     $f = 120$

**Check**   Substitute $c = 30$ and $f = 120$ in the original equations.

| | |
|---|---|
| $6c + f = 300$ | $12c + f = 480$ |
| $6(30) + 120 \overset{?}{=} 300$ | $12(30) + 120 \overset{?}{=} 480$ |
| $180 + 120 \overset{?}{=} 300$ | $360 + 120 \overset{?}{=} 480$ |
| $300 = 300$ ✔ | $480 = 480$ ✔ |

The cost of each lesson is $30. The one-time fee for materials is $120.

 **Got It?** **2.** An online music company offers 15 downloads for $19.75 and 40 downloads for $43.50. Each price includes the same one-time registration fee. What is the cost of each download and the registration fee?

You can use the Addition Property of Equality to solve a system of equations. If you add a pair of additive inverses or subtract identical terms, you can eliminate a variable.

---

**Got It?**

**Q** Which variable is easier to use in the substitution method? [**Answers may vary. Sample: The $x$ in the first equation is easier to use because its coefficient is 1.**]

## Problem 2
The substitution method is often used when one variable has the coefficient 1 in either equation.

**Q** What ordered pair is the solution to this system? [**(30, 120)**]

**Q** Could you solve this problem by graphing by hand? Explain. [**Answers may vary. Sample: Yes; since 6, 12, 300, and 480 are all multiples of 2, 3, and 6, it would not be too difficult with appropriate scaling.**]

**Q** What is a linear equation for the cost of piano lessons? Let $x$ be the number of lessons and $y$ be the total cost. [**$y = 30x + 120$**]

**Got It?**       **ERROR PREVENTION**
Students may have trouble identifying the variables. Point out that the question at the end of the problem refers to the two variable quantities that you need to find.

**Q** How would the equations be different if there was no registration fee? [**There would be only one variable.**]

---

## 2 Guided Instruction

 Each Problem is worked out and supported in the Student Online Center.

**Problem 1**
Solving by Substitution
         *Animated*

**Problem 2**
Using Substitution to Solve a Problem
         *Animated*

**Problem 3**
Solving by Elimination
         *Animated*

**Problem 4**
Solving an Equivalent System

**Problem 5**
Solving Systems Without Unique Solutions

**Support in Algebra 2 Companion**
• Vocabulary
• Key Concepts
• Got It?

## Answers

**Solve It!**
Per-day sales of $313 or greater;
store A: $35 + 0.1s$
store B: $10 + 0.18s$
$35 + 0.1s < 10 + 0.18s$
$s > 312.5$

**Got It?**
**1.** $(-2.5, 2.5)$
**2.** $.95 per download; $5.50 one-time registration fee

## Problem 3

> **Q** What variable is eliminated when you add the two equations? Why? **[x, because 4x + (−4x) = 0 by the Inverse Property of Addition.]**
>
> **Q** How can you check the solution? **[Answers may vary. Sample: Substitute the values into both of the original equations. Both equations must result in true statements.]**
>
> **Q** How would you solve this problem if both coefficients of x were positive 4? **[Subtract the equations instead of adding them to eliminate x.]**

## Got It?

SYNTHESIZING

> **Q** If you solved the first equation for 8y, how could you use the substitution method to find the solution? **[Substitute that value for 8y in the second equation. Be sure to include the subtraction sign.]**

## Problem 4

> **Q** What happens when you use substitution to solve the system? **[Answers may vary. Sample: The substitution requires fractions or decimals.]**
>
> **Q** Why might graphing also work well to solve this system? **[Answers may vary. Sample: The solution (−5, 2) has integer coordinates.]**

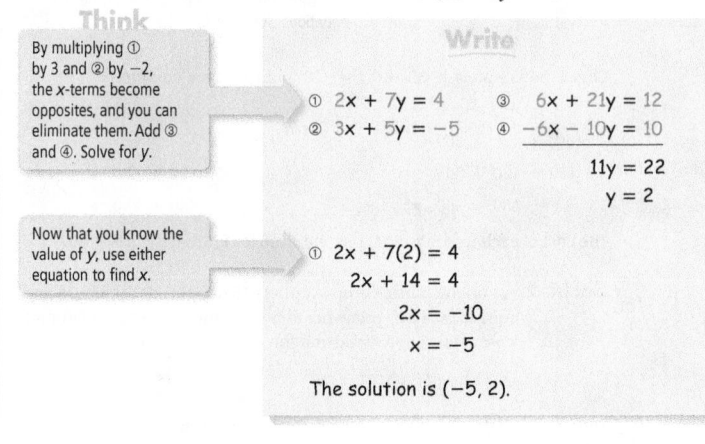

**Problem 3** Solving by Elimination

What is the solution of the system of equations? $\begin{cases} 4x + 2y = 9 \\ -4x + 3y = 16 \end{cases}$

$$4x + 2y = 9$$
$$\underline{-4x + 3y = 16}$$  One equation has 4x and the other has −4x. Add to eliminate the variable x.
$$5y = 25$$
$$y = 5 \quad \text{Solve for } y.$$
$$4x + 2y = 9 \quad \text{Choose one of the original equations.}$$
$$4x + 2(5) = 9 \quad \text{Substitute for } y.$$
$$4x = -1 \quad \text{Solve for } x.$$
$$x = -\frac{1}{4}$$

The solution is $\left(-\frac{1}{4}, 5\right)$.

**Got It?** **3.** What is the solution of the system of equations? $\begin{cases} -2x + 8y = -8 \\ 5x - 8y = 20 \end{cases}$

When you multiply each side of one or both equations in a system by the same nonzero number, the new system and the original system have the same solutions. The two systems are called **equivalent systems**. You can use this method to make additive inverses.

**Problem 4** Solving an Equivalent System

What is the solution of the system of equations? ① $\begin{cases} 2x + 7y = 4 \\ 3x + 5y = -5 \end{cases}$ ②

**Think**

By multiplying ① by 3 and ② by −2, the x-terms become opposites, and you can eliminate them. Add ③ and ④. Solve for y.

**Write**

① $2x + 7y = 4$  ③ $6x + 21y = 12$
② $3x + 5y = -5$  ④ $\underline{-6x - 10y = 10}$
$$11y = 22$$
$$y = 2$$

Now that you know the value of y, use either equation to find x.

① $2x + 7(2) = 4$
$$2x + 14 = 4$$
$$2x = -10$$
$$x = -5$$

The solution is (−5, 2).

# Additional Problems

**1.** What is the solution of the system of equations?
$$\begin{cases} 5x - 3y = -1 \\ x + y = 3 \end{cases}$$
**ANSWER** (1, 2)

**2.** You are in charge of ordering labels for a small business. A company that makes custom labels charges a yearly fee plus a cost per label. You paid $375 last year for 300 labels. This year you ordered 1,000 labels and paid $725. What are the yearly fee and cost per label, assuming the prices did not change?

**ANSWER** $225 yearly fee, $0.50 per label

**3.** What is the solution of the system of equations?
$$\begin{cases} 2x - 3y = 14 \\ 4x + 3y = 46 \end{cases}$$
**ANSWER** (10, 2)

**4.** What is the solution of the system of equations?
$$\begin{cases} 7x + 5y = 2 \\ 8x - 9y = 17 \end{cases}$$
**ANSWER** (1, −1)

**5.** What are the solutions of the following systems?

**a.** $\begin{cases} 6x + 4y = 2 \\ 3x + 2y = -1 \end{cases}$

**ANSWER** no solution

**b.** $\begin{cases} 6x - 3y = 15 \\ -8x + 4y = -20 \end{cases}$

**ANSWER** infinitely many solutions

**Got It?** **4. a.** What is the solution of this system of equations? $\begin{cases} 3x + 7y = 15 \\ 5x + 2y = -4 \end{cases}$

**b.** **Reasoning** In Problem 4, you found that $y = 2$. Substitute this value into equation ② instead of equation ①. Do you still get the same value for $x$? Explain why.

**Got It?**

**Q** Does it matter which variable you solve for first? **[No; either way you get the same solution.]**

Solving a system algebraically does not always provide a unique solution. Sometimes you get infinitely many solutions. Sometimes you get no solutions.

 **Problem 5** **Solving Systems Without Unique Solutions**

What are the solutions of the following systems? Explain.

**Problem 5**

**Q** What are the three possible types of solutions for a system of two equations? **[one solution, no solution, infinitely many solutions]**

 **Think**

How are the two equations in this system related? Multiplying both sides of the first equation by $-1$ results in the second equation.

**Ⓐ** $\begin{cases} -3x + y = -5 \\ 3x - y = 5 \end{cases}$
$\overline{\hspace{2cm} 0 = 0}$

Elimination gives an equation that is always true. The two equations in the system represent the same line. This is a dependent system with infinitely many solutions.

**Ⓑ** $\begin{cases} 4x - 6y = 6 \\ -4x + 6y = 10 \end{cases}$
$\overline{\hspace{2cm} 0 = 16}$

Elimination gives an equation that is always false. The two equations in the system represent parallel lines. This is an inconsistent system. It has no solutions.

**Got It?**
Another way to solve these is to solve each equation for $y$. Compare the slopes and $y$-intercepts to determine whether the lines are parallel, intersecting, or coinciding.

 **Got It?** **5.** What are the solutions of the following systems? Explain.

**a.** $\begin{cases} -x + y = -2 \\ 2x - 2y = 0 \end{cases}$

**b.** $\begin{cases} 4x + y = 6 \\ 12x + 3y = 18 \end{cases}$

## ✓ Lesson Check

### Do you know HOW?

Solve each system by substitution.

**1.** $\begin{cases} 3x + 5y = 13 \\ 2x + y = 4 \end{cases}$
**2.** $\begin{cases} 2x - 3y = 6 \\ x + y = -12 \end{cases}$

Solve each system by elimination.

**3.** $\begin{cases} 2x + 3y = 7 \\ -2x + 5y = 1 \end{cases}$
**4.** $\begin{cases} x + 2y = -1 \\ x - y = 8 \end{cases}$

**5.** $\begin{cases} x - y = -4 \\ 3x + 2y = 7 \end{cases}$
**6.** $\begin{cases} 3x + 4y = 10 \\ 2x + 3y = 7 \end{cases}$

### Do you UNDERSTAND?

**7.** **Vocabulary** Give an example of two equivalent systems.

**8.** **Compare and Contrast** Explain how the substitution method of solving a system of equations differs from the elimination method.

**9.** **Writing** A café sells a regular cup of coffee for $1 and a large cup for $1.50. Melissa and her friends buy 5 cups of coffee and spend a total of $6. Explain how to write and solve a system of equations to find the number of large cups of coffee they bought.

## 3 Lesson Check

### Do you know HOW?
• For Exercises 1 and 2, encourage students to determine which variable is the easiest to use.

### Do you UNDERSTAND?
• In Exercise 7, encourage students to use equations with two variables rather than one.
• For Exercise 9, if students have trouble identifying the variables, review Problem 2.

### Close

**Q** Why might you use different methods for solving a system of equations? **[Answers may vary. Samples: Graphing only works well if the coefficients and constants are small in magnitude and integral. Substitution works best if one of the equations can easily be solved for one of the variables. Elimination is efficient if a variable can be easily eliminated.]**

# Answers

### Got It? (continued)

**3.** $(4, 0)$

**4. a.** $(-2, 3)$

**b.** Yes; the solution $(-5, 2)$ is a solution to both eqs. in the system, so substituting $y = 2$ into either equation will result in $x = -5$.

**5. a.** no solution; The eq. is always false.

**b.** infinite number of solutions; The eq. is always true.

### Lesson Check

**1.** $(1, 2)$
**2.** $(-6, -6)$

**3.** $(2, 1)$
**4.** $(5, -3)$

**5.** $\left(-\frac{1}{5}, \frac{19}{5}\right)$
**6.** $(2, 1)$

**7.** Answers may vary. Sample:
$\begin{cases} 4x - 3y = -2 \\ 3x - 2y = -1 \end{cases}$
$\begin{cases} -8x + 6y = 4 \\ 9x - 6y = -3 \end{cases}$

**8.** In the substitution method of solving a system of equations, you first solve one equation for one of the variables. Then substitute for this variable in the other equation and solve for the other variable. In the elimination method, you create an equivalent system of equations that contain a pair of additive inverses so that you can eliminate one variable and solve for the remaining variable.

**9.** Let $r$ = number of regular cups of coffee and $c$ = number of large cups of coffee. First, $r + c = 5$ because a total of 5 cups of coffee were purchased. Second, $r + 1.5c = 6$ because each regular cup of coffee is $1, each large cup is $1.50, and the total spent is $6. Then, solve the system of equations using elimination by subtracting the first equation from the second to eliminate $r$ and solve for $c$. $c = 2$; 2 large cups

**PowerAlgebra.com**

## 3 Lesson Check

For a digital lesson check, use the Got It questions.

**Support in Algebra 2 Companion**
• Lesson Check

## 4 Practice

Assign homework to individual students or to an entire class.

# 4 Practice

## ASSIGNMENT GUIDE
Basic: 10–43, 53–57

Average: 11–41 odd, 43–61

Advanced: 11–41 odd, 43–66

Standardized Test Prep: 67–71

Mixed Review: 72–80

**Reasoning** exercises have blue headings.

**Applications** exercises have red headings.

**EXERCISE 56:** Use the Think About a Plan worksheet in the **Practice and Problem Solving Workbook** (also available in the Teaching Resources in print and online) to further support students' development in becoming independent learners.

## HOMEWORK QUICK CHECK
To check students' understanding of key skills and concepts, go over Exercises 19, 33, 43, 56, and 57.

---

## Practice and Problem-Solving Exercises

**A** Practice

Solve each system by substitution. Check your answers. ◀ See Problem 1.

10. $\begin{cases} 4x + 2y = 7 \\ y = 5x \end{cases}$

11. $\begin{cases} 3c + 2d = 2 \\ d = 4 \end{cases}$

12. $\begin{cases} x + 12y = 68 \\ x = 8y - 12 \end{cases}$

13. $\begin{cases} 4p + 2q = 8 \\ q = 2p + 1 \end{cases}$

14. $\begin{cases} x + 3y = 7 \\ 2x - 4y = 24 \end{cases}$

15. $\begin{cases} x + 6y = 2 \\ 5x + 4y = 36 \end{cases}$

16. $\begin{cases} t = 2r + 3 \\ 5r - 4t = 6 \end{cases}$

17. $\begin{cases} y = 2x - 1 \\ 3x - y = -1 \end{cases}$

18. $\begin{cases} r + s = -12 \\ 4r - 6s = 12 \end{cases}$

19. **Money** A student has some $1 bills and $5 bills in his wallet. He has a total of 15 bills that are worth $47. How many of each type of bill does he have? ◀ See Problem 2.

20. A student took 60 minutes to answer a combination of 20 multiple-choice and extended-response questions. She took 2 minutes to answer each multiple-choice question and 6 minutes to answer each extended-response question.
   **a.** Write a system of equations to model the relationship between the number of multiple choice questions $m$ and the number of extended-response questions $r$.
   **b.** How many of each type of question was on the test?

21. **Transportation** A youth group with 26 members is going skiing. Each of the five chaperones will drive a van or sedan. The vans can seat seven people, and the sedans can seat five people. Assuming there are no empty seats, how many of each type of vehicle could transport all 31 people to the ski area in one trip?

Solve each system by elimination. ◀ See Problem 3.

22. $\begin{cases} x + y = 12 \\ x - y = 2 \end{cases}$

23. $\begin{cases} x + 2y = 10 \\ x + y = 6 \end{cases}$

24. $\begin{cases} 3a + 4b = 9 \\ -3a - 2b = -3 \end{cases}$

25. $\begin{cases} 4x + 2y = 4 \\ 6x + 2y = 8 \end{cases}$

26. $\begin{cases} 2w + 5y = -24 \\ 3w - 5y = 14 \end{cases}$

27. $\begin{cases} 3u + 3v = 15 \\ -2u + 3v = -5 \end{cases}$

28. $\begin{cases} 3x + 2y = 6 \\ 3x + 3 = y \end{cases}$

29. $\begin{cases} 5x - y = 4 \\ 2x - y = 1 \end{cases}$

30. $\begin{cases} 2r + s = 3 \\ 4r - s = 9 \end{cases}$

Solve each system by elimination. ◀ See Problems 4 and 5.

31. $\begin{cases} 4x - 6y = -26 \\ -2x + 3y = 13 \end{cases}$

32. $\begin{cases} 9a - 3d = 3 \\ -3a + d = -1 \end{cases}$

33. $\begin{cases} 2a + 3b = 12 \\ 5a - b = 13 \end{cases}$

34. $\begin{cases} 2x - 3y = 6 \\ 6x - 9y = 9 \end{cases}$

35. $\begin{cases} 20x + 5y = 120 \\ 10x + 7.5y = 80 \end{cases}$

36. $\begin{cases} 6x - 2y = 11 \\ -9x + 3y = 16 \end{cases}$

37. $\begin{cases} 2x - 3y = -1 \\ 3x + 4y = 8 \end{cases}$

38. $\begin{cases} 5x - 2y = -19 \\ 2x + 3y = 0 \end{cases}$

39. $\begin{cases} r + 3s = 7 \\ 2r - s = 7 \end{cases}$

40. $\begin{cases} y = 4 - x \\ 3x + y = 6 \end{cases}$

41. $\begin{cases} 3x + 2y = 10 \\ 6x + 4y = 15 \end{cases}$

42. $\begin{cases} 3m + 4n = -13 \\ 5m + 6n = -19 \end{cases}$

---

# Answers

## Practice and Problem-Solving Exercises

**10.** (0.5, 2.5)

**11.** (−2, 4)

**12.** (20, 4)

**13.** (0.75, 2.5)

**14.** (10, −1)

**15.** (8, −1)

**16.** (−6, −9)

**17.** (−2, −5)

**18.** (−6, −6)

**19.** seven $1-bills; eight $5-bills

**20. a.** Let $m$ = number of multiple choice and $r$ = number of extended response, then
$\begin{cases} m + r = 20 \\ 2m + 6r = 60 \end{cases}$
   **b.** 15 multiple choice; 5 extended response

**21.** 3 vans and 2 sedans

**22.** (7, 5)

**23.** (2, 4)

**24.** (−1, 3)

**25.** (2, −2)

**26.** (−2, −4)

**27.** (4, 1)

**28.** (0, 3)

**29.** (1, 1)

**30.** (2, −1)

**31.** infinite number of solutions;
$\{(x, y) | -2x + 3y = 13\}$

**32.** infinite number of solutions;
$\{(a, d) | -3a + d = -1\}$

**33.** (3, 2)

**34.** no solution

**35.** (5, 4)

**36.** no solution

**37.** $\left(\dfrac{20}{17}, \dfrac{19}{17}\right)$

**38.** (−3, 2)

**39.** (4, 1)

**40.** (1, 3)

**41.** no solution

**42.** (1, −4)

**43.** Think About a Plan Suppose you have a part-time job delivering packages. Your employer pays you a flat rate of $9.50 per hour. You discover that a competitor pays employees $2 per hour plus $3 per delivery. How many deliveries would the competitor's employees have to make in four hours to earn the same pay you earn in a four-hour shift?
- How can you write a system of equations to model this situation?
- Which method should you use to solve the system?
- How can you interpret the solution in the context of the problem?

**Solve each system.**

**44.** $\begin{cases} 5x + y = 0 \\ 5x + 2y = 30 \end{cases}$

**45.** $\begin{cases} 2m = -4n - 4 \\ 3m + 5n = -3 \end{cases}$

**46.** $\begin{cases} 7x + 2y = -8 \\ 8y = 4x \end{cases}$

**47.** $\begin{cases} 2m + 4n = 10 \\ 3m + 5n = 11 \end{cases}$

**48.** $\begin{cases} -6 = 3x - 6y \\ 4x = 4 + 5y \end{cases}$

**49.** $\begin{cases} \frac{x}{3} + \frac{4y}{3} = 300 \\ 3x - 4y = 300 \end{cases}$

**50.** $\begin{cases} 0.02a - 1.5b = 4 \\ 0.5b - 0.02a = 1.8 \end{cases}$

**51.** $\begin{cases} 4y = 2x \\ 2x + y = \frac{x}{2} + 1 \end{cases}$

**52.** $\begin{cases} \frac{1}{2}x + \frac{2}{3}y = 1 \\ \frac{3}{4}x - \frac{1}{3}y = 2 \end{cases}$

**53.** Error Analysis Identify and correct the error shown in finding the solution of $\begin{cases} 3x - 4y = 14 \\ x + y = -7 \end{cases}$ using substitution.

$x + y = -7$
$y = -7 - x$

$3x - 4y = 14$
$3x - 4(-7 - x) = 14$
$3x - 28 + 4x = 14$
$-x - 28 = 14$
$x = -42$

$y = -7 - (-42)$
$y = 35$

**54.** Break-Even Point Jenny's Bakery sells carrot muffins at $2 each. The electricity to run the oven is $120 per day and the cost of making one carrot muffin is $1.40. How many muffins need to be sold each day to break even?

**55.** Open-Ended Write a system of equations in which both equations must be multiplied by a number other than 1 or −1 before using elimination. Solve the system.

**56.** Chemistry A scientist wants to make 6 milliliters of a 30% sulfuric acid solution. The solution is to be made from a combination of a 20% sulfuric acid solution and a 50% sulfuric acid solution. How many milliliters of each solution must be combined to make the 30% solution?

**57.** Writing Explain how you decide whether to use substitution or elimination to solve a system.

**58.** The equation $3x - 4y = 2$ and which equation below form a system with no solutions?
- Ⓐ $2y = 1.5x - 2$
- Ⓒ $3x + 4y = 2$
- Ⓑ $2y = 1.5x - 1$
- Ⓓ $4y - 3x = -2$

**For each system, choose the method of solving that seems easier to use. Explain why you made each choice. Solve each system.**

**59.** $\begin{cases} 3x - y = 5 \\ y = 4x + 2 \end{cases}$

**60.** $\begin{cases} 2x - 3y = 4 \\ 2x - 5y = -6 \end{cases}$

**61.** $\begin{cases} 6x - 3y = 3 \\ 5x - 5y = 10 \end{cases}$

**43.** 10 deliveries

**44.** (−6, 30)

**45.** (4, −3)

**46.** $\left(-1, -\frac{1}{2}\right)$

**47.** (−3, 4)

**48.** (6, 4)

**49.** (300, 150)

**50.** (−235, −5.8)

**51.** (0.5, 0.25)

**52.** $\left(\frac{5}{2}, -\frac{3}{8}\right)$

**53.** Error in 5th line:
$-4(-7 - x) = 28 + 4x$ **not** $-28 - 4x$; Lines 5–9 should be:
$3x + 28 + 4x = 14$; $7x = -14$; $x = -2$; $y = -7 - (-2)$; $y = -5$

**54.** 200 muffins

**55.** Answers may vary. Sample:
$\begin{cases} -3x + 4y = 12 \\ 5x - 3y = 13 \end{cases}$; (8, 9)

**56.** 4 ml of 20% sulfuric acid solution and 2 ml of 50% sulfuric acid solution

**57.** In determining whether to use substitution or elimination to solve an equation, look at the equations to determine if one is solved or can be easily solved for a particular variable. If that is the case, substitution can easily be used. Otherwise, elimination might be easier.

**58.** A

**59.** Substitution; the second equation is solved for $y$; (−7, −26)

**60.** Elimination; $2x$ would be eliminated from the system if the equations were subtracted; $\left(9\frac{1}{2}, 5\right)$

**61.** Elimination; substitution would be difficult since no coefficient is 1 in the original system. Dividing the first equation by 3 and dividing the second equation by 5 results in an equivalent system where $y$ would be eliminated from the system if the equations were subtracted; (−1, −3)

# Answers

## Practice and Problem-Solving Exercises (continued)

**62.** 2875 votes

**63.** yes; −40 degrees

**64.** −2

**65.** 0

**66.** 8

**67.** 2

**68.** 5

**69.** 6

**70.** 2

**71.** 4

**72.** no solution

**73.** infinite number of solutions, $\{(x, y) | -9x - 3y = 1\}$

**74.** no solution

**75.** function

**76.** function

**77.** not a function

**78.** $x < -1$

**79.** $x > -\dfrac{1}{2}$

**80.** $y < 1$

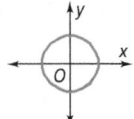

---

**62. Entertainment** In the final round of a singing competition, the audience voted for one of the two finalists, Luke or Sean. Luke received 25% more votes than Sean received. Altogether, the two finalists received 5175 votes. How many votes did Luke receive?

**63. Weather** The equation $F = \frac{9}{5}C + 32$ relates temperatures on the Celsius and Fahrenheit scales. Does any temperature have the same number reading on both scales? If so, what is the number?

**Find the value of $a$ that makes each system a dependent system.**

**64.** $\begin{cases} y = 3x + a \\ 3x - y = 2 \end{cases}$

**65.** $\begin{cases} 3y = 2x \\ 6y - a - 4x = 0 \end{cases}$

**66.** $\begin{cases} y = \frac{x}{2} + 4 \\ 2y - x = a \end{cases}$

### Standardized Test Prep                    GRIDDED RESPONSE

**SAT/ACT**

**67.** What is the slope of the line at the right?

**68.** What is the $x$-value of the solution of $\begin{cases} x + y = 7 \\ 3x - 2y = 11 \end{cases}$?

**69.** Solve $9(x + 7) - 6(x - 3) = 99$. What is the value of $x$?

**70.** Georgia has only dimes and quarters in her bag. She has a total of 18 coins that are worth $3. How many more dimes than quarters does she have?

**71.** The graph of $g(x)$ is a horizontal translation of $f(x) = 2|x + 1| + 3$, 5 units to the right. What is the $x$-value of the vertex of $g(x)$?

### Mixed Review

**Solve each system of equations by graphing.**                    ◀ See Lesson 3-1.

**72.** $\begin{cases} y = 3x + 4 \\ 2y = 6x - 2 \end{cases}$

**73.** $\begin{cases} -3y = 9x + 1 \\ 6y = -18x - 2 \end{cases}$

**74.** $\begin{cases} 4x - y = -5 \\ -8x + 2y = 15 \end{cases}$

**Use the vertical line test to determine whether each graph represents a function.**                    ◀ See Lesson 2-1.

**75.**

**76.**

**77.**

**Get Ready!**    To prepare for Lesson 3-3, do Exercises 78–80.

**Solve each inequality. Graph the solution.**                    ◀ See Lesson 1-5.

**78.** $-3(2x + 1) > 3$

**79.** $4x > -2$

**80.** $8y + 4 < 12$

## Additional Instructional Support

### Algebra 2 Companion

Students can use the **Algebra 2 Companion** worktext (4 pages) as you teach the lesson. Use the Companion to support

- New Vocabulary
- Key Concepts
- Got It for each Problem
- Lesson Check

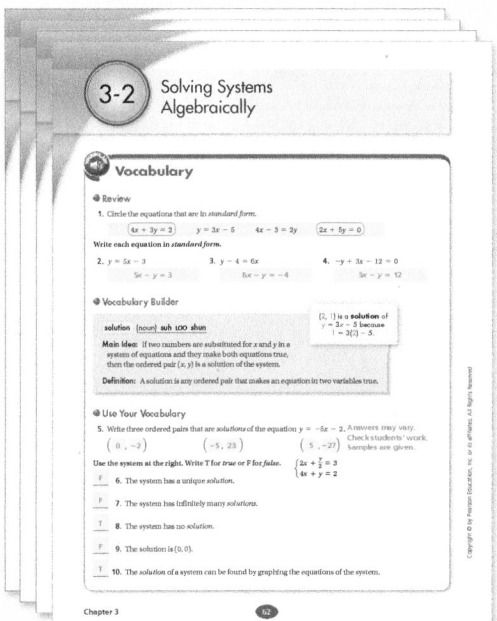

### ELL Support

**Connect to Prior Knowledge** Draw a line on the board. Have a volunteer come up and draw an intersecting line. Have the class identify the relationship between the pair of lines and the number of solutions of the system. Repeat for parallel lines and coinciding lines.

**Focus on Communication** Write a series of systems of equations on the board. Model a statement for students explaining how you would approach the first problem. For example, say: I would use the substitution method because I can quickly solve for the variable $x$. Have each student explain how to do a problem. After each answer, ask if anyone has another idea.

## 5 Assess & Remediate

### Lesson Quiz

1. Solve $\begin{cases} x - 2y = 0 \\ 4x - 3y = 15 \end{cases}$.

2. **Do you UNDERSTAND?** You and your friend are saving for a vacation. You start with the same amount and save for the same number of weeks. You save $75 per week, and your friend saves $50 per week. When the vacation time comes, you have $950, and your friend has $800. How much did you start with, and for how many weeks did you save?

3. Solve $\begin{cases} -3x + 7y = -15 \\ 3x - 7y = 20 \end{cases}$.

4. Solve $\begin{cases} 2x - 3y = -1 \\ 3x + 4y = 24 \end{cases}$.

5. Solve $\begin{cases} 2x + 2y = 4 \\ x + y = 2 \end{cases}$.

### ANSWERS TO LESSON QUIZ

1. $(6, 3)$
2. $500, 6 weeks
3. no solution
4. $(4, 3)$
5. infinitely many solutions

**PRESCRIPTION FOR REMEDIATION**
Use the student work on the Lesson Quiz to prescribe a differentiated review assignment:

| Points | Differentiated Remediation |
|--------|---------------------------|
| 0–2 | Intervention |
| 3–4 | On-level |
| 5 | Extension |

### PowerAlgebra.com

## 5 Assess & Remediate

Assign the Lesson Quiz. Appropriate intervention, practice, or enrichment is automatically generated based on student performance.

## Intervention

- **Reteaching** (2 pages) Provides reteaching and practice exercises for the key lesson concepts. Use with struggling students or absent students.
- **English Language Learner Support** Helps students develop and reinforce mathematical vocabulary and key concepts.

### All-in-One Resources/Online
#### Reteaching

**3-2 Reteaching**
Solving Systems Algebraically

### All-in-One Resources/Online
#### English Language Learner Support

**3-2 ELL Support**
Solving Systems Algebraically

# Differentiated Remediation *continued*

## On-Level

- **Practice** (2 pages) Provides extra practice for each lesson. For simpler practice exercises, use the Form K Practice pages found in the All-in-One Teaching Resources and online.

- **Think About a Plan** Helps students develop specific problem-solving skills and strategies by providing scaffolded guiding questions.

- **Standardized Test Prep** Focuses on all major exercises, all major question types, and helps students prepare for the high-stakes assessments.

## Extension

- **Enrichment** Provides students with interesting problems and activities that extend the concepts of the lesson.

- **Activities, Games, and Puzzles** Worksheets that can be used for concepts development, enrichment, and for fun!

---

### Practice and Problem Solving Wkbk/ All-in-One Resources/Online
**Practice page 1**

**3-2 Practice** Form G
Solving Systems Algebraically

Solve each system by substitution. Check your answers.

1. $\begin{cases} y = x + 1 \\ 2x + y = 7 \end{cases}$ (2, 3)   2. $\begin{cases} x = y - 2 \\ 3x - y = 6 \end{cases}$ (4, 6)   3. $\begin{cases} y = 2x + 3 \\ 5x - y = -3 \end{cases}$ (0, 3)

4. $\begin{cases} 6x - 3y = -33 \\ 2x + y = -1 \end{cases}$ (-3, 5)   5. $\begin{cases} 7x + 2y = 1 \\ 3x - 2y = 10 \end{cases}$ (4, 1)   6. $\begin{cases} 4x = 8y \\ 2x + 5y = 27 \end{cases}$ (6, 3)

7. $\begin{cases} 3x + 3y = -4 \\ y + x = 0 \end{cases}$ (2, -2)   8. $\begin{cases} 3x + 2y = 9 \\ x + y = 3 \end{cases}$ (3, 0)   9. $\begin{cases} 2y - 3x = 4 \\ x = -4 \end{cases}$ (-4, -4)

10. There are a total of 15 apartments in two buildings. The difference of two times the number of apartments in the first building and three times the number of apartments in the second building is 5.
   a. Write a system of equations to model the relationship between the number of apartments in the first building $f$ and the number of apartments in the second building $s$. $f + s = 15, 2f - 3s = 5$
   b. How many apartments are in each building? 10 in the first; 5 in the second

Solve each system by elimination.

11. $\begin{cases} x + y = 10 \\ x - y = 2 \end{cases}$ (6, 4)   12. $\begin{cases} -x + 3y = -1 \\ x - 2y = 2 \end{cases}$ (4, 1)   13. $\begin{cases} x + y = 7 \\ 3x - y = 5 \end{cases}$ (5, 2)

14. $\begin{cases} 4x - 3y = -2 \\ 5x + 3y = 14 \end{cases}$ (1, 2)   15. $\begin{cases} x + 2y = 10 \\ 3x - y = 9 \end{cases}$ (4, 3)   16. $\begin{cases} 2x - 5y = 11 \\ 4x + 10y = 18 \end{cases}$ $(5, -\frac{1}{5})$

17. $\begin{cases} x - y = 0 \\ x + y = 2 \end{cases}$ (1, 1)   18. $\begin{cases} x + 3y = -4 \\ x + y = 0 \end{cases}$ (2, -2)   19. $\begin{cases} 3x - y = 17 \\ 2x + y = 8 \end{cases}$ (5, -2)

20. Suppose you bought eight oranges and one grapefruit for a total of $4.60. Later that day, you bought six oranges and three grapefruits for a total of $4.80. What is the price of each type of fruit? 1 orange costs $.50; 1 grapefruit costs $.60

Solve each system by elimination.

21. $\begin{cases} -x + y = 1 \\ 5x + y = 9 \end{cases}$ (1, 4)   22. $\begin{cases} 5x + 4y = 2 \\ -5x - 2y = 4 \end{cases}$ (-2, 3)   23. $\begin{cases} -2x + y = 3 \\ 5x - y = -3 \end{cases}$ (0, 3)

24. $\begin{cases} 14x + 2y = 10 \\ x - 5y = 11 \end{cases}$ (1, -2)   25. $\begin{cases} x + 5y = 1 \\ 2x + 10y = 2 \end{cases}$ $(x, y); y = -\frac{1}{5}x + \frac{1}{5}$   26. $\begin{cases} 0.3x + 0.4y = 0.8 \\ 0.7x - 0.8y = -6.8 \end{cases}$ (-4, 5)

27. $\begin{cases} 4x + 3y = -6 \\ 5x - 6y = -27 \end{cases}$ (-3, 2)   28. $\begin{cases} 2x + y = 0 \\ 4x + 2y = -11 \end{cases}$ No solution   29. $\begin{cases} 1.2x - 1.4y = 2.7 \\ 0.4x - 0.3y = 0.9 \end{cases}$ (2.25, 0)

---

### Practice and Problem Solving Wkbk/ All-in-One Resources/Online
**Practice page 2**

**3-2 Practice** (continued) Form G
Solving Systems Algebraically

30. **Writing** Explain what it means when elimination results in an equation that is always true.
   When elimination results in an equation that is always true, it means the equations in the system represent the same line.

For each system, choose the solution method that seems easier to use. Explain why you made each choice. Solve each system.

31. $\begin{cases} b = 2a - 5 \\ b = 3 + a \end{cases}$   32. $\begin{cases} 4x - 2y = -1 \\ 4x + 3y = 6 \end{cases}$

33. $\begin{cases} 5p + 2q = 10 \\ 4p + q = 4 \end{cases}$   34. $\begin{cases} f - 3k = 3 \\ f = -k + 15 \end{cases}$

35. **Error Analysis** You and your friend are solving the system $4x - y = 5$ and $4x - y = 3$. Your friend says there is no solution, and you say the solution is (1, -1). Who is correct? Explain.
   You are correct; your friend mistakenly thought both $x$ and $y$ had opposite coefficients, causing both variables to "drop out," giving a system with no solution.

36. You can buy your DVDs at a local store for $15.49 each. You can buy them at an online store for $13.99 each plus $6 for shipping. How many DVDs can you buy for the same amount at the two stores? 4

37. Last year, a baseball team paid $20 per bat and $12 per glove, spending a total of $1040. This year, the prices went up to $25 per bat and $16 per glove. The team spent $1350 to purchase the same amount of equipment as last year. How many bats and gloves did the team purchase each year? 22 bats, 50 gloves

38. If the perimeter of the square at the right is 72 units, what are the values of $x$ and $y$? $x = 9$ units, $y = 6$ units

31. Substitution; one variable is already defined in terms of the other, so it is easy to substitute one equation into the second; $a = 8, b = 11$.
32. Elimination; because both equations have the same $x$-term coefficient, you can multiply one equation by $-1$ and add the equations to eliminate the $x$-term; $x = \frac{3}{8}, y = \frac{5}{4}$.
33. Elimination; you can multiply the second equation by $-2$ and add the equations; OR substitution; you can rewrite the second equation in terms of $q$ and substitute into the first equation; $p = -\frac{2}{3}, q = \frac{20}{3}$.
34. Substitution; one variable is already defined in terms of the other, so it is easy to substitute one equation into the second; $f = 12, k = 3$.

---

### All-in-One Resources/Online
**Enrichment**

**3-2 Enrichment**
Solving Systems Algebraically

Often, two separate items in a restaurant or a store will be made from essentially the same ingredients. The difference between two items may involve different proportions of the same ingredients.

Solve each problem by writing two equations using two variables.

1. Each order of lasagna or ravioli at Casa Italia weighs 1 lb and consists of meat filling wrapped in pasta. On Tuesday evening, the restaurant served 40 orders of ravioli and 60 orders of lasagna and used 60 lb of meat filling. On Wednesday evening, it sold 60 orders of ravioli and 30 orders of lasagna and used 50 lb of meat filling.
   a. How much meat filling is used in an order of ravioli? $\frac{1}{2}$ lb
   b. How much meat filling is used in an order of lasagna? $\frac{2}{3}$ lb

2. Foot Friends uses the same type of leather in their men's and women's hiking boots. During one week the company used 290 ft² of leather to make 40 pairs of size 10 men's hiking boots and 60 pairs of size 7 women's hiking boots. Another week the company used 275 ft² of leather to make 50 pairs of size 10 men's hiking boots and 40 pairs of size 7 women's hiking boots.
   a. How much leather is used to make 1 pair of size 10 men's hiking boots? 3.5 ft²
   b. How much leather is used to make 1 pair of size 7 women's hiking boots? 2.5 ft²

3. The Fruit Emporium sells a dish of two flavors of yogurt with one serving of fruit toppings for $1.40. It also sells a dish of three flavors of yogurt with one serving of fruit toppings for $1.95.
   a. How much is one flavor of yogurt with one serving of fruit toppings? $.85
   b. How much does a customer pay for the one serving of fruit toppings? $.30

4. A health-food store sells trail mix made with granola and dried fruit. The store buys granola at $1.00/lb and dried fruit at $2.00/lb, and it sells these items at a 25% markup. If the trail mix sells for $1.75/lb, what is the recipe for trail mix? $\frac{2}{3}$ lb granola and $\frac{1}{3}$ lb dried fruit make 1 lb of trail mix.

5. The same health-food store sells two special mixtures of granola and dried fruit. One customer buys 6 lb of Mixture A and 4 lb of Mixture B and pays $17.00. Another customer reverses the proportions and pays a dollar more.
   a. What is the cost per lb of Mixture A? $1.50
   b. What is the recipe for Mixture A? $\frac{3}{5}$ lb granola and $\frac{1}{5}$ lb dried fruit make 1 lb of Mixture A.
   c. What is the cost per lb of Mixture B? $2.00
   d. What is the recipe for Mixture B? $\frac{2}{5}$ lb granola and $\frac{3}{5}$ lb dried fruit make 1 lb of Mixture B.

---

### Practice and Problem Solving Wkbk/ All-in-One Resources/Online
**Think About a Plan**

**3-2 Think About a Plan**
Solving Systems Algebraically

**Chemistry** A scientist wants to make 6 milliliters of a 30% sulfuric acid solution. The solution is to be made from a combination of a 20% sulfuric acid solution and a 50% sulfuric acid solution. How many milliliters of each solution must be combined to make the 30% solution?

**Know**

1. The scientist will begin with [20] % and [50] % solutions.

2. The scientist wants to make [6] ml of 30% solution.

**Need**

3. To solve the problem you need to define:
   $x$ = ml of 20% solution
   $y$ = ml of 50% solution

**Plan**

4. What are two equations you can write to model the situation?
   $0.2x + 0.5y = 1.8$ and $x + y = 6$

5. Which method should you use to solve the system of equations? Explain.
   Answers may vary. Sample: Substitution; it is easy to solve one of the equations ($x + y = 6$) and get one of the variables in terms of the other variable.

6. Solve the system of equations.
   $x = 4, y = 2$

7. How can you interpret the solutions in the context of the problem?
   4 ml of the 20% solution and 2 ml of the 50% solution should be combined.

8. Do your solutions check? Explain.
   yes; 4 ml + 2 ml = 6 ml, and
   4 ml · 0.2 + 2 ml · 0.5 = 0.8 ml + 1 ml = 1.8 ml = 6 ml · 0.3

---

### Practice and Problem Solving Wkbk/ All-in-One Resources/Online
**Standardized Test Prep**

**3-2 Standardized Test Prep**
Solving Systems Algebraically

**Multiple Choice**

For Exercises 1–4, choose the correct letter.

Use the system of equations for Exercises 1 and 2. $\begin{cases} 4x - 10y = -3 \\ 12x + 5y = 12 \end{cases}$

1. What is the value of $x$ in the solution? D
   Ⓐ $-\frac{9}{7}$   Ⓑ $-\frac{12}{28}$   Ⓒ $\frac{3}{4}$   Ⓓ $\frac{3}{4}$

2. What is the value of $y$ in the solution? G
   Ⓕ $\frac{9}{35}$   Ⓖ $\frac{3}{5}$   Ⓗ $\frac{3}{4}$   Ⓘ $\frac{24}{35}$

3. Which of the following systems of equations has the solution (4, -1)? A
   Ⓐ $\begin{cases} 3x - 2y = 14 \\ 2x + 2y = 6 \end{cases}$   Ⓒ $\begin{cases} -2x + 4y = 6 \\ -3x + 6y = 8 \end{cases}$
   Ⓑ $\begin{cases} 3x + y = 0 \\ 4x + 3y = 26 \end{cases}$   Ⓓ $\begin{cases} 4x + 9y = 1 \\ 4x + 6y = -2 \end{cases}$

4. At a bookstore, used hardcover books sell for $8 each and used softcover books sell for $2 each. You purchase 36 used books and spend $144. How many softcover books do you buy? I
   Ⓕ 9   Ⓖ 12   Ⓗ 18   Ⓘ 24

**Extended Response**

5. A local cell phone company offers two different calling plans. In the first plan, you pay a monthly fee of $30 and $.35 per minute. In the second plan you pay a monthly fee of $99 and $.05 per minute.
   a. Write a system of equations showing the two calling plans.
   b. When is it better to use the first calling plan?
   c. When is it better to use the second calling plan?
   d. How much does it cost when the calling plans are equal?

[4] $y = 0.35x + 30, y = 0.05x + 99$ where $x$ = number minutes per month and $y$ = total plan cost; the first plan is better when you use less than 230 minutes; the second plan is better when you use more than 230 minutes; $110.50 when plans are equal.
[3] incorrect equation OR multiple computational error
[2] incorrect equation OR multiple computational errors
[1] correct answers, without work shown

---

### Online Teacher Resource Center
**Activities, Games, and Puzzles**

**3-2 Game: Risk and Reward**
Solving Systems Algebraically

Provide the host with the following questions and answers for the given categories and point values.

**Vocabulary**

| Points | Question: What is . . . | Answer |
|---|---|---|
| 10 | a system of equations? | when two or more equations are considered simultaneously |
| 20 | a solution of a system? | an ordered pair that is a solution of all equations in a system |
| 30 | an equivalent system? | systems that have the same solutions |
| 40 | a substitution method? | solving one equation for a variable, substituting it in the other equation, and solving for the remaining variable |
| 50 | an elimination method? | multiplying equations so like terms have opposite coefficients, adding the equations, and solving the result |

**Substitution**

| Points | System | Answer |
|---|---|---|
| 10 | $\begin{cases} y = 3x - 1 \\ -x + y = 7 \end{cases}$ | (2, 5) |
| 20 | $\begin{cases} 3y - 2x = 4 \\ x = 3 - y \end{cases}$ | (1, 2) |
| 30 | $\begin{cases} 2x - y = -8 \\ 3x + 2y = -5 \end{cases}$ | (-3, 2) |
| 40 | $\begin{cases} 3x - 5y = 30 \\ 3y = x + 6 \end{cases}$ | No solution |
| 50 | $\begin{cases} 2a + 4b = -5 \\ 3a - 5b = 9 \end{cases}$ | (0.5, -1.5) |

**Elimination**

| Points | System | Answer |
|---|---|---|
| 10 | $\begin{cases} x + 3y = -9 \\ -x + y = -7 \end{cases}$ | (3, -4) |
| 20 | $\begin{cases} 2x + 6y = -12 \\ 3x - 3y = 4 \end{cases}$ | (0, -1) |
| 30 | $\begin{cases} 2x + y = 2 \\ 3y = -6x + 6 \end{cases}$ | Infinite solutions |
| 40 | $\begin{cases} 5x - 2y = 24 \\ 3x + 5y = 24 \end{cases}$ | (-2, 6) |
| 50 | $\begin{cases} 0.7x - 2y = 1.61 \\ 2x - 0.3y = 0.39 \end{cases}$ | (0.3, 0.7) |

**Application**

| Points | Question | Answer |
|---|---|---|
| 10 | The sum of two numbers is 12, and their difference is 6. What are the two numbers? | 3, 9 |
| 20 | Twice a boy's age is 9 more than his brother's. The average of their ages is 12. How old are they? | 11, 13 |
| 30 | A girl has $6 in 36 coins (all quarters and nickels). How many of each does she have? | 21 quarters, 15 nickels |
| 40 | A girl's cell phone costs $10 per month plus 10¢ per minute. Her friend's costs $3 per month plus 15¢ per minute. For what amount of talking time will the cost of these plans be equal? | 140 min |
| 50 | How many liters of a 60% salt mixture must be added to 2 liters of a 30% salt mixture to yield a 48% mixture? | 3 l |

## 3-3 Systems of Inequalities

**Objective** To solve systems of linear inequalities

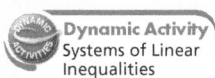
**Dynamic Activity**
Systems of Linear
Inequalities

You get to decide what is "best."

**Getting Ready!**

You want a car that is less than $20,000 after 5% sales tax is added. You want fuel costs under $2,000 for the 10,000 city miles you expect to drive next year. You estimate that the cost of gas will average $4 per gallon. Which car best meets your conditions? Explain.

Model A $19,500 City MPG 29
Model B $19,000 City MPG 19
Model C $19,999 City MPG 25
Model D $19,250 City MPG 22
Model E $22,711 City MPG 17
Model F $18,995 City MPG 14
Model G $16,435 City MPG 27
Model H $18,434 City MPG 21

An inequality and a system of inequalities can each have many solutions. A solution of a system of inequalities is a solution for each inequality in the system.

**Essential Understanding** You can solve a system of inequalities in more than one way. Graphing the solution is usually the most appropriate method. The solution is the set of all points that are solutions of each inequality in the system.

### Plan

**Which inequality should you use to build a table?**
The first inequality has an infinite number of whole number solutions. The second one has a finite number of solutions. Use the second inequality.

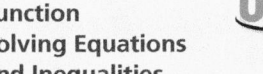 **Problem 1** **Solving a System by Using a Table**

Assume that $g$ and $m$ are whole numbers. What is the solution of the system of inequalities? $\begin{cases} g + m \geq 6 \\ 5g + 2m \leq 20 \end{cases}$

Make a table of values for $g$ and $m$ that satisfy the second inequality. The values for $g$ and $m$ must be whole numbers.

If $g = 0$, then $5(0) + 2m \leq 20$, and $m \leq 10$.
If $m = 0$, then $5g + 2(0) \leq 20$, and $g \leq 4$.

| g | m |
|---|---|
| 0 | 0, 1, 2, 3, 4, 5, 6, 7, 8, 9, 10 |
| 1 | 0, 1, 2, 3, 4, 5, 6, 7 |
| 2 | 0, 1, 2, 3, 4, 5 |
| 3 | 0, 1, 2 |
| 4 | 0 |

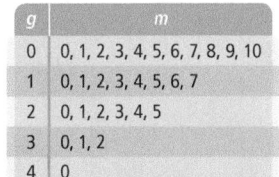

---

PowerAlgebra.com | Lesson 3-3 Systems of Inequalities | 149

# 1 Interactive Learning

**Solve It!**
**PURPOSE** To solve a problem with constraints by using elimination
**PROCESS** Students may determine the cars that satisfy the constraints and then choose the cheapest.

**FACILITATE**

**Q** Which cars cost under $20,000 with tax? **[B, F, G, H]**

**Q** How can you determine the cost of driving 10,000 miles for a car? **[Divide 10,000 by the MPG, and multiply the quotient by the cost of a gallon of gas.]**

**Q** Which remaining cars cost less than $2000 to drive 10,000 miles? **[C, G, H]**

**Q** Which is the cheapest car? **[C]**

**ANSWER** See Solve It in Answers on next page.
**CONNECT THE MATH** The Solve It can be solved using a system of inequalities with the following constraints: total price less than $20,000 and fuel costs less than $2000. Students will use this method to solve similar problems in the lesson.

# 2 Guided Instruction

**Problem 1** **EXTENSION**

**Q** How would the solution be different if the constraint $g + m \geq 6$ was removed? **[All of the pairs of values in the table would be solutions.]**

---

## 3-3 Preparing to Teach

**BIG ideas** Function
Solving Equations and Inequalities **UbD**

**ESSENTIAL UNDERSTANDINGS**
- A system of inequalities can be solved in more than one way. Graphing is usually the most appropriate method to solve a system of inequalities.
- The solution is the set of all points that are solutions of each inequality in the system.

### Math Background
This lesson extends what students know about graphing inequalities and systems of equations to solving systems of inequalities.

A system of two linear inequalities divides the plane into 4 parts:
- points that satisfy one inequality but not the other
- points that satisfy the other inequality but not the first

- points that satisfy both inequalities
- points that satisfy neither of the inequalities

The solution of a system of linear inequalities is the section of the plane where the points satisfy both inequalities: the intersection of each of the corresponding half-plane solutions. The solution may or may not include parts of the boundaries of the graph, depending on the inequality.

If a system has whole number solutions, it can also be solved (with a few more calculations) with a table, as shown in Problem 1.

### Support Student Learning
Use the **Algebra 2 Companion** to engage and support students during instruction. See Lesson Resources at the end of this lesson for details.

### PowerAlgebra.com

## 1 Interactive Learning

**Solve It!**
Step out how to solve the Problem with helpful hints and an online question. Other questions are listed above in Interactive Learning.

**Dynamic Activity** Students explore solving systems of linear inequalities by graphing in this activity. They are guided through graphing boundary lines and noticing their characteristics. They can also view the shared regions and determine which points are part of the solution.

**Lesson 3-3** **149**

## Got It?

**Q** How would the solution be different if $x$ and $y$ were any real numbers? **[There would be infinitely many solutions, since there are infinitely many real numbers that satisfy the constraints.]**

## Problem 2
VISUALIZE

**Q** In the third graph, which inequalities does the blue region satisfy? yellow region? green region? white region? **[first inequality; second inequality; both inequalities; neither inequality]**

## Got It?
EXTENSION

**Q** One way to graph $x + 2y = 4$ is to first solve for $y$. What is another way? **[Answers may vary. Sample: Graph the intercepts (0, 2) and (4, 0).]**

**Q** How is the shading of the graph of $-y \geq -x - 1$ different from the graph of $y \geq x + 1$? **[When you multiply both sides of the inequality by $-1$, the inequality sign flips and the signs change, giving $y \leq x + 1$, so the shading is below the graphed line for the first inequality. For the second inequality, the shading is above the graphed line.]**

---

In the table, highlight each pair of values that satisfies the first inequality. The highlighted pairs are the solutions of both inequalities.

 **Got It?** **1.** Assume that $x$ and $y$ are whole numbers. What is the solution of the system of inequalities?
$$\begin{cases} x + y > 4 \\ 3x + 7y \leq 21 \end{cases}$$

| g | m |
|---|---|
| 0 | 0, 1, 2, 3, 4, 5, 6, 7, 8, 9, 10 |
| 1 | 0, 1, 2, 3, 4, 5, 6, 7 |
| 2 | 0, 1, 2, 3, 4, 5 |
| 3 | 0, 1, 2 |
| 4 | 0 |

You can solve a system of linear inequalities by graphing. Recall that when the variables of a linear inequality represent real numbers, a graphed solution consists of a half-plane and possibly its boundary line. Thus, for two inequalities, the solution is the overlap of the two half-planes.

**Problem 2** Solving a System by Graphing

What is the solution of the system of inequalities? $\begin{cases} 2x - y \geq -3 \\ y \geq -\frac{1}{2}x + 1 \end{cases}$

Graph each inequality. Rewrite $2x - y \geq -3$ in slope-intercept form as $y \leq 2x + 3$. The overlap is the solution of the system.

**Plan**

**How can you be sure to shade the correct half-planes?**
If the inequality is in slope-intercept form, shade above the boundary if $y >$ or $y \geq$ and shade below the boundary if $y <$ or $y \leq$. If not, use a test point.

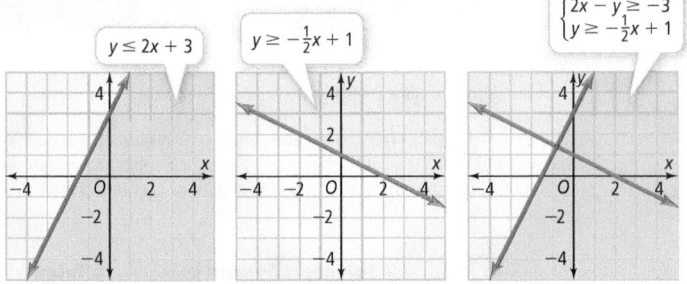

**Check** Pick a point in the overlap region, such as $(0, 2)$, and check it in both inequalities of the system.

$$2x - y \geq -3 \qquad y \geq \frac{1}{2}x + 1$$
$$2(0) - 2 \geq -3 \qquad 2 \geq \frac{1}{2}(0) + 1$$
$$-2 \geq -3 \checkmark \qquad 2 \geq 1 \checkmark$$

 **Got It?** **2.** What is the solution of the system of inequalities? $\begin{cases} x + 2y \leq 4 \\ y \geq -x - 1 \end{cases}$

---

**PowerAlgebra.com**

## 2 Guided Instruction

Each Problem is worked out and supported online.

**Problem 1**
Solving a System by Using a Table
*Animated*

**Problem 2**
Solving a System by Graphing
*Animated*

**Problem 3**
Using a System of Inequalities
*Animated*

**Problem 4**
Solving a Linear/Absolute-Value System

**Support in Algebra 2 Companion**
• Vocabulary
• Key Concepts
• Got It?

## Answers

### Solve It!
Model G; the price after taxes will be about $17,257 and fuel costs for the year will be about $1481.

### Got It?
**1.** (4, 1), (5, 0), (6, 0), (7, 0)

**2.**

**3.** 5 meats and no vegetables; 4 meats and 1 or 2 vegetables; 3 meats and 2, 3, or 4 vegetables; 2 meats and 3, 4, 5, or 6 vegetables; 1 meat and 4–8 vegetables; no meat 5–10 vegetables

Sometimes, you can model a real situation with a system of linear inequalities. Solutions to real-world problems are often whole numbers, so only certain points in the region of overlap will solve the problem.

 **Problem 3** Using a System of Inequalities

**Fundraising** Your city's cultural center is sponsoring a concert to raise at least $30,000 for the city's Youth Services. Tickets are $20 for balcony seats and $30 for orchestra seats. If the center has 500 orchestra seats, how many of each type of seat must they sell?

| Know | Need | Plan |
|---|---|---|
| Must raise at least $30,000. There are at most 500 orchestra seats. | The possible sales of balcony and orchestra seats | • Model the problem with a system of inequalities. • Graph the inequalities on your calculator. |

**Relate**  20 · [balcony seats] + 30 · [orchestra seats] ≥ 30,000

[orchestra seats] ≤ 500

**Define**  Let  $x$  = the number of balcony seats sold.

Let  $y$  = the number of orchestra seats sold.

**Write**  20 · $x$ + 30 · $y$ ≥ 30,000

$y$ ≤ 500

Rewrite $20x + 30y \geq 30,000$ in slope intercept form as $y \geq -\frac{2}{3}x + 1000$.

The system of inequalities is $\begin{cases} y \geq -\frac{2}{3}x + 1000 \\ y \leq 500 \end{cases}$.

**Think**

**What do points in the overlap represent?**
The points represent combinations of balcony and orchestra seats that have a total value of at least $30,000.

Use your graphing calculator to graph the inequalities. The solution is the overlap.

Test a point. If the cultural center sells 900 balcony and 450 orchestra tickets, will the Youth Services meet its goal?

$20(900) + 30(450) \overset{?}{\geq} 30,000$   $450 \overset{?}{\leq} 500$

$18,000 + 13,250 \overset{?}{\geq} 30,000$   $450 \leq 500$ ✔

$31,250 \geq 30,000$ ✔

Because the number of seats must be a whole number, only the points in the overlap that represent whole numbers are solutions.

**Got It? 3.** A pizza parlor charges $1 for each vegetable topping and $2 for each meat topping. You want at least five toppings on your pizza. You have $10 to spend on toppings. How many of each type of topping can you get on your pizza?

**Problem 3**

**Q** Why might this problem be difficult to solve by hand? How could you make it easier? **[Answers may vary. Sample: The numbers are large. To make it easier, you could graph the dollars by thousands and seats by hundreds.]**

**Q** Are all of the points on the boundary solutions? Explain your answer. **[No; only the points with whole-number values are solutions.]**

**Q** Generally speaking, what values of x will result in whole numbers? **[multiples of 3]**

**Q** If 600 balcony seats were sold, would the Cultural Center meet their goal? Explain. **[No; even if they sell all 500 orchestra seats, they will make only $27,000 and not reach their $30,000 goal.]**

**Got It?**

**Q** What will the variables represent? **[the number of vegetable toppings and the number of meat toppings]**

**Q** What is the system of inequalities? **[Let $v$ = vegetable toppings and $m$ = meat toppings. $\begin{cases} v + 2m \leq 10 \\ v + m \geq 5 \end{cases}$]**

# Additional Problems

**1.** Assume that x and y are whole numbers. What is the solution of the system of inequalities?
$\begin{cases} x + y \geq 5 \\ 2x + 3y \leq 15 \end{cases}$
**ANSWER** (0, 5), (1, 4), (2, 3), (3, 2), (3, 3), (4, 1), (4, 2), (5, 0), (5, 1), (6, 0), (6, 1), (7, 0)

**2.** What is the solution of the system of inequalities?
$\begin{cases} y - 3x \leq -4 \\ y \geq x - 3 \end{cases}$
**ANSWER**

**3.** Tickets to a concert cost $70, or $20 with a student discount. Ticket sales must exceed $500,000 for the group to perform. If 20,000 seats are available, how many of each type must be sold? Show the solution on your calculator.
**ANSWER**

**4.** What is the solution of the system of inequalities?
$\begin{cases} y < -3|x + 3| + 1 \\ y \geq -x - 5 \end{cases}$
**ANSWER**

## Problem 4

**Q** Why do two rays and one line bound the overlap when there are only two inequalities? **[The absolute value inequality is equivalent to two linear inequalities.]**

**Q** How would the graph be different if the inequalities were $y < 3$ and $y > |x - 1|$? **[The line and the absolute value graph would be dashed and would not be included in the solutions.]**

### Got It? ERROR PREVENTION

If students have trouble graphing the transformations of the absolute value function, review Lesson 2-7. Some students may benefit from rewriting the inequality as $y > 2|x - 1| + 0$.

## 3 Lesson Check

### Do you know HOW?
• For Exercises 1–2, if students are unsure how to graph the solution, review Problem 2.

### Do you UNDERSTAND? ERROR INTERVENTION
• For Exercise 6, if students talk about the number of solutions, encourage them to also compare the *graphs* of the solutions.

### Close

**Q** How does graphing a system of inequalities on the same coordinate plane help you see which points satisfy both inequalities? **[You can see the overlap, as well as the regions that satisfy only one or neither inequality.]**

---

A system of inequalities can include nonlinear inequalities. You can also solve these systems graphically.

 **Problem 4** Solving a Linear/Absolute-Value System

**What is the solution of the system of inequalities?** $\begin{cases} y \le 3 \\ y \ge |x - 1| \end{cases}$

Graph each inequality.

**Think**

Why is the shape of the overlap different from that of a system of linear inequalities? The overlap is not formed by 2 half-planes so it is more varied in shape.

 The region of overlap represents the solution.

**Got It? 4.** What is the solution of the system of inequalities? $\begin{cases} y < -\frac{1}{3}x + 1 \\ y > 2|x - 1| \end{cases}$

### Lesson Check

**Do you know HOW?**

Solve each system of inequalities by graphing.

1. $\begin{cases} x + y \ge 2 \\ 2x + y \le 5 \end{cases}$

2. $\begin{cases} y > x \\ y < x + 1 \end{cases}$

3. $\begin{cases} y \ge -3x - 1 \\ y < x + 2 \end{cases}$

4. You spend no more than 3 hours each day watching TV and playing football. You play football for at least 1 hour each day. What are the possible numbers of hours you can spend on each activity in one day?

**Do you UNDERSTAND?**

5. **Reasoning** Is the solution of a system of linear inequalities the union or intersection of the solutions of the two inequalities? Justify your answer.

6. **Compare and Contrast** Explain how the graphical solution of a system of inequalities is different from the graphical solution of a system of equations.

7. **Error Analysis** Describe and correct the error made in solving this system of inequalities.

$\begin{cases} y < \frac{1}{2}x - 1 \\ y > -3x + 3 \end{cases}$

---

## Answers

### Got It? (continued)

4. $y > 2|x - 1|$

$y < -\frac{1}{3}x + 1$

### Lesson Check

1. 

$2x + y \le 5$
$x + y \ge 2$

2. 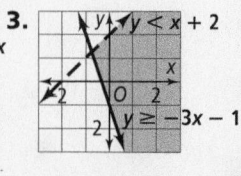 $y < x + 1$

3. $y < x + 2$, $y \ge -3x - 1$, $y > x$

---

4. 0 h TV and 1, 2, or 3 h football; 1 h TV and 1 or 2 h football; or 2 h TV and 1 h football

5. Intersection; the solution of two inequalities is the over-lap or the intersection of the graphs of the individual inequalities.

6. The graphical solution of a system of inequalities consists of the overlap or intersection of the individual half-planes and corresponding boundary lines (either dotted or solid). The graphical solution of a system of equations includes only the intersection of the lines, not the half-planes.

7. For each inequality, the wrong half-plane has been shaded. The half-plane below $y = \frac{1}{2}x - 1$ should be shaded and the half-plane above $y = -3x + 3$ should be shaded. Also, both boundary lines should be dashed because the inequalities are $<$ and $>$.

## Practice and Problem-Solving Exercises

See Problem 1.

**A Practice**   Find all whole number solutions of each system using a table.

8. $\begin{cases} y + 3x \le 8 \\ y - 3 > 2x \end{cases}$

9. $\begin{cases} x + y < 8 \\ 3x \le y + 6 \end{cases}$

10. $\begin{cases} y \ge x + 2 \\ 3y < -6x + 6 \end{cases}$

Solve each system of inequalities by graphing.
See Problem 2.

11. $\begin{cases} y \le 2x + 2 \\ y < -x + 1 \end{cases}$

12. $\begin{cases} y > -2 \\ x < 1 \end{cases}$

13. $\begin{cases} y \le 3 \\ y \le \frac{1}{2}x + 1 \end{cases}$

14. $\begin{cases} y \le 3x + 1 \\ -6x + 2y > 5 \end{cases}$

15. $\begin{cases} x + 2y \le 10 \\ x + y \le 3 \end{cases}$

16. $\begin{cases} -x - y \le 2 \\ y - 2x > 1 \end{cases}$

17. $\begin{cases} y > -2x \\ 2x - y \ge 2 \end{cases}$

18. $\begin{cases} c \ge d - 3 \\ c < \frac{1}{2}d + 3 \end{cases}$

19. $\begin{cases} 2x + y < 1 \\ y > -2x + 3 \end{cases}$

See Problem 3.

20. You want to decorate a party hall with a total of at least 40 red and yellow balloons, with a minimum of 25 yellow balloons. Write and graph a system of inequalities to model the situation.

21. A gardener wants to plant at least 50 tulips and rose plants in a garden, but no more than 20 rose plants. Write and graph a system of inequalities to model the situation.

Solve each system of inequalities by graphing.
See Problem 4.

22. $\begin{cases} y > 4 \\ y < |x - 1| \end{cases}$

23. $\begin{cases} y < -\frac{1}{3}x + 1 \\ y > |2x - 1| \end{cases}$

24. $\begin{cases} y > x - 2 \\ y \ge |x + 2| \end{cases}$

25. $\begin{cases} y \le -\frac{4}{3}x \\ y \ge -|x| \end{cases}$

26. $\begin{cases} 3y < -x - 1 \\ y \le |x + 1| \end{cases}$

27. $\begin{cases} y > -2 \\ y \le -|x - 3| \end{cases}$

28. $\begin{cases} -2y < 4x + 2 \\ y > |2x + 1| \end{cases}$

29. $\begin{cases} -x \ge 4 - y \\ y \ge |3x - 6| \end{cases}$

30. $\begin{cases} y \le x - 4 \\ y > |x - 6| \end{cases}$

 **B Apply**

31. **Think About a Plan** The food pyramid suggests that you eat 4–6 servings of fruits and vegetables a day for a healthy diet. It also says that the number of servings of vegetables should be greater than the number of servings of fruits. Find the number of servings of fruits and vegetables that could make a healthy diet. Use whole numbers only.
    - How can you write two inequalities that model the information in the problem?
    - How can you use a graph to find combinations of fruits and vegetable servings that may help in having a healthy diet?

32. **College Admissions** An entrance exam has two sections, a verbal section and a mathematics section. You can score a maximum of 1600 points. For admission, the school of your choice requires a math score of at least 600. Write a system of inequalities to model scores that meet the school's requirements. Then solve the system by graphing.

**ASSIGNMENT GUIDE**

Basic: 8–34, 36–44 even

Average: 9–31 odd, 32–54

Advanced: 9–31 odd, 32–58

Standardized Test Prep: 59–62

Mixed Review: 63–72

**Reasoning** exercises have blue headings.

**Applications** exercises have red headings.

**EXERCISE 32:** Use the Think About a Plan worksheet in the **Practice and Problem Solving Workbook** (also available in the Teaching Resources in print and online) to further support students' development in becoming independent learners.

**HOMEWORK QUICK CHECK**

To check students' understanding of key skills and concepts, go over Exercises 21, 27, 31, 32, and 34.

---

### Practice and Problem-Solving Exercises

8. (0, 4), (0, 5), (0, 6), (0, 7), (0, 8)

9. (0, 0), (0, 1), (0, 2), (0, 3), (0, 4), (0, 5), (0, 6), (0, 7), (1, 0), (1, 1), (1, 2), (1, 3), (1, 4), (1,5), (1, 6), (2, 0), (2, 1), (2, 2), (2, 3), (2, 4), (2, 5), (3, 3), (3, 4)

10. no solution

11.

12.

13.

14. no solution

15.

16. $-x - y \le 2$   $y - 2x > 1$

17.

18.

19. no solution

20. Let $y$ = number of yellow balloons and $r$ = number of red balloons.
    $r + y \ge 40$
    $y \ge 25$
    Because the number of balloons must be a whole number, only the points in the overlap that represent whole numbers are solutions of the problem; i.e., (0, 40), (0, 41), (1, 39), (1, 40), (2, 38), etc.

21–32. See next page.

# Answers

## Practice and Problem-Solving Exercises (continued)

**21.** Let $r$ = number of rose plants and
$t$ = number of tulip plants.
$t + r \geq 50$
$r \leq 80$
Because the number of plants must be a whole number, only the points in the overlap that represent whole numbers are solutions of the problem.

**22.**

$y > 4$
$y < |x - 1|$

**23.**

$y < -\frac{1}{3}x + 1$
$y < |2x - 1|$

**24.** $y \geq |x + 2|$
$y > x - 2$

**25.**

$y \leq -\frac{4}{3}x$
$y \geq -|x|$

**26.**

$y \leq |x + 1|$
$3y < -x - 1$

**27.**

$y \leq -|x - 3|$
$y > -2$

**28.**

$y > |2x + 1|$
$-2y < 4x + 2$

**29.**

$y \geq |3x - 6|$
$-x \geq 4 - y$

**30.**

$y > |x - 6|$
$y \leq x - 4$

---

**33. Open-Ended** Write and graph a system of inequalities for which the solution is bounded by a dashed vertical line and a solid horizontal line.

**34. Writing** Explain how you determine where to shade when solving a system of inequalities.

**35.** Given a system of two linear inequalities, explain how you can pick test points in the plane to determine where to shade the solution set.

**In Exercises 36–45, identify the inequalities A, B, and C for which the given ordered pair is a solution.**

**A.** $x + y \leq 2$

**B.** $y \leq \frac{3}{2}x - 1$

**C.** $y > -\frac{1}{3}x - 2$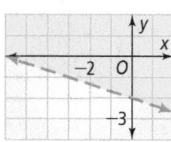

**36.** $(0, 0)$ **37.** $(-2, -5)$ **38.** $(-2, 0)$ **39.** $(0, -2)$ **40.** $(-15, 15)$

**41.** $(3, 2)$ **42.** $(2, 0)$ **43.** $(-6, 0)$ **44.** $(4, -1)$ **45.** $(-8, -11)$

**Solve each system of inequalities by graphing.**

**46.** $\begin{cases} x + y < 8 \\ x \geq 0 \\ y \geq 0 \end{cases}$ **47.** $\begin{cases} 2y - 4x \leq 0 \\ x \geq 0 \\ y \geq 0 \end{cases}$ **48.** $\begin{cases} y \geq -2x + 4 \\ x > -3 \\ y \geq 1 \end{cases}$

**49.** $\begin{cases} y \leq \frac{2}{3}x + 2 \\ y \geq |x| + 2 \end{cases}$ **50.** $\begin{cases} y < x - 1 \\ y > -|x - 2| + 1 \end{cases}$ **51.** $\begin{cases} 2x + y \leq 3 \\ y > |x + 3| - 2 \end{cases}$

**52.** $\begin{cases} y < |x - 1| + 2 \\ x \geq 0 \end{cases}$ **53.** $\begin{cases} y > |x - 1| + 1 \\ y \leq -|x - 3| + 4 \end{cases}$ **54.** $\begin{cases} y \leq |x| - 2 \\ y \leq |x| + 2 \end{cases}$

**Challenge** **Geometry** Write a system of inequalities to describe each shaded figure.

**55.**

**56.**

**57.**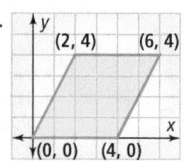

**58. a.** Graph the "bowtie" inequality, $|y| \leq |x|$.
**b.** Write a system of inequalities to describe the graph shown at the right.

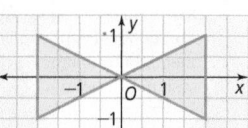

---

**31.** $(0, 4)$, $(0, 5)$, $(0, 6)$, $(1, 3)$, $(1, 4)$, $(1, 5)$, $(2, 3,)$, $(2, 4)$; The sum of the servings must be greater than or equal to 4 and less than or equal to 6.

**32.** $\begin{cases} x + y \leq 1600 \\ y \geq 600 \end{cases}$

$y \geq 600$
$y \leq 1600 - x$

**33.** Answers may vary. Sample: $\begin{cases} x < 5 \\ y \geq 1 \end{cases}$

**34.** Answers may vary. Sample: If the isolated variable, $y$, is greater than the remaining expression, the half-plane above the boundary is shaded. If the variable is less than the remaining expression, then the half-plane below the line is shaded.

**35.** Use test pts. that are not on either of the boundary lines and that make the calculations as easy as possible (e.g., the origin).

**36.** A, C **37.** A, B

**38.** A, C **39.** A, B

**40.** A, C **41.** B, C

**42.** A, B, C **43.** A

**44.** B, C **45.** A

**46–58.** See next page.

## Standardized Test Prep

**59.** Which system of inequalities is shown in the graph?

Ⓐ $\begin{cases} x \geq 4 \\ 3x - 2y > 5 \end{cases}$

Ⓒ $\begin{cases} x < 4 \\ 3x - 2y \geq 5 \end{cases}$

Ⓑ $\begin{cases} x > 4 \\ 3x - 2y \leq 5 \end{cases}$

Ⓓ $\begin{cases} x \leq 4 \\ 3x - 2y < 5 \end{cases}$

**60.** What is the equation of the line that passes through the point $(4, -3)$ and has slope $\frac{1}{2}$?

Ⓕ $y = \frac{1}{2}x + 3$

Ⓗ $y = \frac{1}{2}x - 5$

Ⓖ $y = \frac{1}{2}x - 1$

Ⓘ $y = x - \frac{1}{2}$

**61.** Which equation is a vertical translation of $y = -5x$?

Ⓐ $y = -\frac{5}{2}x$

Ⓒ $y = -10x$

Ⓑ $y = -5x + 2$

Ⓓ $y = 5x - 2$

**Short Response**

**62.** The cost of renting a pool at an aquatic center is either $30 per hour or $20 per hour with a $40 non-refundable deposit. For how many hours is the cost of renting a pool the same for both plans?

## Mixed Review

Solve each system by elimination or substitution.                    ◀ **See Lesson 3-2.**

**63.** $\begin{cases} y = 3x + 1 \\ 2x - y = 8 \end{cases}$

**64.** $\begin{cases} 3x + y = 4 \\ 2x - 4y = 7 \end{cases}$

**65.** $\begin{cases} -x + 5y = 3 \\ 2x - 10y = 4 \end{cases}$

**66.** $\begin{cases} 2x + 4y = -8 \\ -5x + 4y = 6 \end{cases}$

**67.** $\begin{cases} y - 3 = x \\ 4x + y = -2 \end{cases}$

**68.** $\begin{cases} 2 = 4y - 3x \\ 5x = 2y - 3 \end{cases}$

**Get Ready!**   **To prepare for Lesson 3-4, do Exercises 69–72.**

Write an ordered pair that is a solution of each system of inequalities.                    ◀ **See Lesson 3-3.**

**69.** $\begin{cases} x + y > 2 \\ 3x + 2y \leq 6 \end{cases}$

**70.** $\begin{cases} 2y > 4 \\ 3x + 4y \leq 14 \end{cases}$

**71.** $\begin{cases} x \geq 2 \\ 5x + 2y \leq 9 \end{cases}$

**72.** $\begin{cases} x + 3y < 6 \\ y < x \end{cases}$

**46.**

**47.**

**48.**

$x > -3$
$y \geq -2x + 4$
$y \geq 1$

**49.**

$(0, 2)$

**50.**

**51.**

**52.**

**53.** $y > |x - 1| + 1$

$y \leq -|x - 3| + 4$

---

**54.**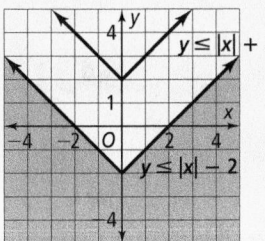

$y \leq |x| + 2$

$y \leq |x| - 2$

**55.** $\begin{cases} y \geq |x| - 2 \\ y \leq -|x| + 2 \end{cases}$

**56.** $\begin{cases} y \leq 3 \\ y \geq 0 \\ y \leq 3x + 9 \\ y \leq -3x + 9 \end{cases}$

**57.** $\begin{cases} y \leq 4 \\ y \geq 0 \\ y \leq 2x \\ y \geq 2x - 8 \end{cases}$

**58. a.**

**b.** Answers may vary. Sample:
$\begin{cases} |y| \leq \frac{1}{2}|x| \\ |x| \leq 2 \end{cases}$

**59.** C

**60.** H

**61.** B

**62.** **[2]** let $x$ = number of hours
$$30x = 20x + 40$$
$$-20x = -20x$$
$$10x = 40$$
$$x = 4$$
**[1]** one computational error, OR correct answer, without work shown

**63.** $(-9, -26)$

**64.** $\left( \frac{23}{14}, -\frac{13}{14} \right)$

**65.** no solution

**66.** $(-2, -1)$

**67.** $(-1, 2)$

**68.** $\left( -\frac{4}{7}, \frac{1}{14} \right)$

**69–72.** Answers may vary. Samples are given for each exercise.

**69.** $(0, 3)$

**70.** $(0, 3)$

**71.** $(2, -1)$

**72.** $(1, -1)$

# Differentiated Remediation

Available in editable format online.

## Additional Instructional Support

### Algebra 2 Companion

Students can use the **Algebra 2 Companion** worktext (4 pages) as you teach the lesson. Use the Companion to support

- New Vocabulary
- Key Concepts
- Got It for each Problem
- Lesson Check

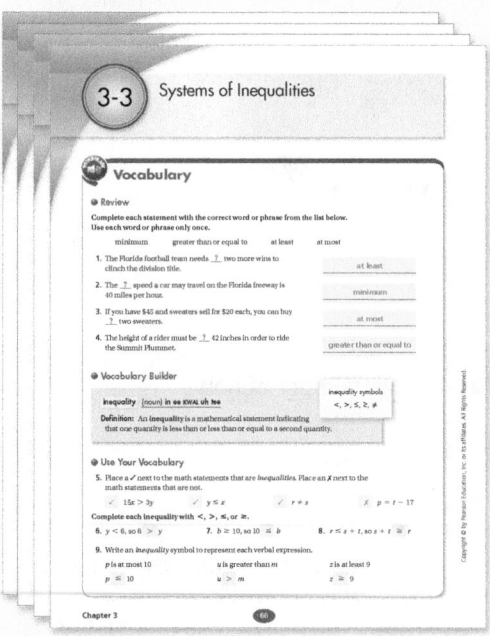

### ELL Support

**Use Graphic Organizers** Match terms and phrases with inequality symbols by making a table of each symbol, words that describe it, and descriptions of the corresponding graph. For example,

Symbol: $<$
Words: less than, up to
Graph: dashed boundary with shading below

**Assess Understanding** Give pairs of students a real-world problem. Have them use the Know/Need/Plan method modeled on page 151. Before they graph their equations, check that they have properly defined the variables and written the correct inequalities.

## 5 Assess & Remediate

### Lesson Quiz

1. Graph the solution of the system of inequalities. $\begin{cases} x + 2y \geq -6 \\ y \geq x + 5 \end{cases}$

2. **Do you UNDERSTAND?** Tickets for a dance are sold for \$5 to seniors and \$7 to juniors. The dance hall can hold 560 students. How many of each type of ticket must be sold to raise at least \$3,500?

3. Graph the solution of the system of inequalities. $\begin{cases} y \leq |x + 2| \\ y \geq 1 \end{cases}$

### ANSWERS TO LESSON QUIZ

1.

2. Let $x$ = number of juniors
   $y$ = number of seniors
   $x$ and $y$ are integers greater than or equal to 0.
   The system of inequalities is
   $x + y \leq 560$
   $7x + 5y \geq 3500$
   At least 350 juniors and at most 210 seniors must attend. Samples: (350, 210), (400, 140), (400, 160), (430, 130), (430, 100), (430, 98). Check that the sales equal or exceed \$3500.

3.

### PRESCRIPTION FOR REMEDIATION

Use the student work on the Lesson Quiz to prescribe a differentiated review assignment:

| Points | Differentiated Remediation |
|--------|----------------------------|
| 0–1 | Intervention |
| 2 | On-level |
| 3 | Extension |

**PowerAlgebra.com**

### 5 Assess & Remediate

Assign the Lesson Quiz. Appropriate intervention, practice, or enrichment is automatically generated based on student performance.

## Intervention

- **Reteaching** (2 pages) Provides reteaching and practice exercises for the key lesson concepts. Use with struggling students or absent students.

- **English Language Learner Support** Helps students develop and reinforce mathematical vocabulary and key concepts.

### All-in-One Resources/Online
#### Reteaching

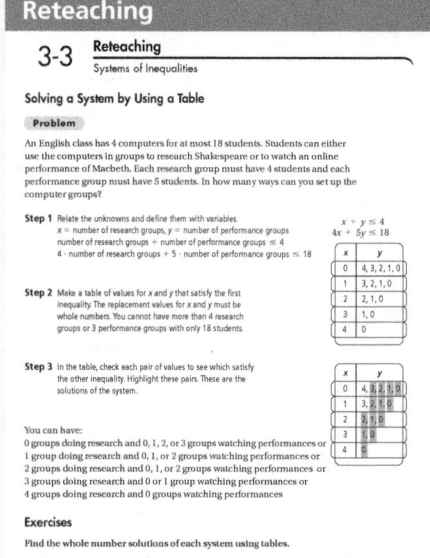

### All-in-One Resources/Online
#### English Language Learner Support

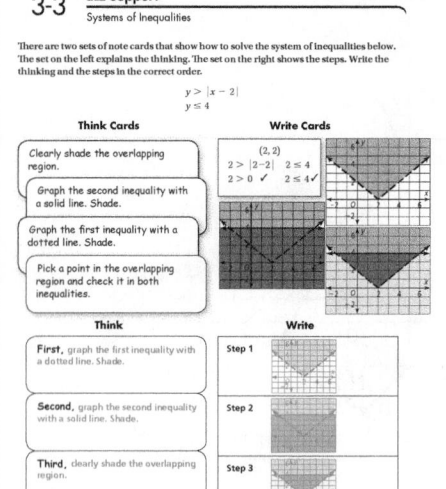

# Differentiated Remediation *continued*

Available in editable format online.

## On-Level

- **Practice** (2 pages) Provides extra practice for each lesson. For simpler practice exercises, use the Form K Practice pages found in the All-in-One Teaching Resources and online.

- **Think About a Plan** Helps students develop specific problem-solving skills and strategies by providing scaffolded guiding questions.

- **Standardized Test Prep** Focuses on all major exercises, all major question types, and helps students prepare for the high-stakes assessments.

## Extension

- **Enrichment** Provides students with interesting problems and activities that extend the concepts of the lesson.

- **Activities, Games, and Puzzles** Worksheets that can be used for concepts development, enrichment, and for fun!

---

### Practice and Problem Solving Wkbk/ All-in-One Resources/Online
**Practice page 1**

### Practice and Problem Solving Wkbk/ All-in-One Resources/Online
**Practice page 2**

### All-in-One Resources/Online
**Enrichment**

---

### Practice and Problem Solving Wkbk/ All-in-One Resources/Online
**Think About a Plan**

### Practice and Problem Solving Wkbk/ All-in-One Resources/Online
**Standardized Test Prep**

### Online Teacher Resource Center
**Activities, Games, and Puzzles**

# Answers

**1.** $(3, 1)$

**2.** $(1, -3)$

**3.** $(1, 4)$

**4.** independent
**5.** independent
**6.** inconsistent
**7.** $(2, 3)$
**8.** $(-3, 0)$
**9.** $\left(-2, \dfrac{1}{2}\right)$
**10.** $\left(-3, -\dfrac{23}{4}\right)$
**11.** $(-1, -2)$
**12.** $\left(\dfrac{5}{2}, 2\right)$

**13.**

**14.**

**15.** D

**16.** $\begin{cases} y \geq -2x + 1 \\ y \geq 1.5x - 6 \end{cases}$

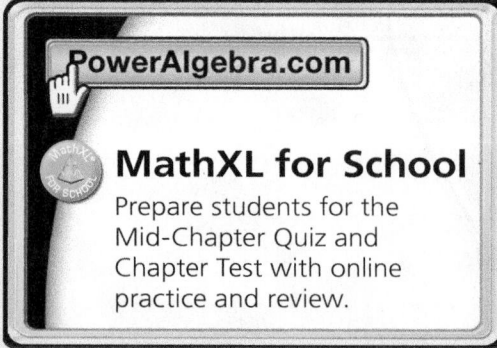
---

## 3  Mid-Chapter Quiz

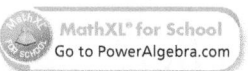
### Do you know HOW?

Solve each system by graphing.

**1.** $\begin{cases} 3x - y = 8 \\ 10 + 2y = 4x \end{cases}$

**2.** $\begin{cases} y + 5 = 2x \\ 3y + 6x = -3 \end{cases}$

**3.** $\begin{cases} 14x - 2y = 6 \\ 6y - 9x = 15 \end{cases}$

Without graphing, classify each system as *independent, dependent,* or *inconsistent.*

**4.** $\begin{cases} 3y + 2x = 12 \\ 36 - 9y = -6x \end{cases}$

**5.** $\begin{cases} -2y = 20 - 2x \\ 3y - 6x = -30 \end{cases}$

**6.** $\begin{cases} 15x = 10y - 20 \\ 18 + 9x = 6y \end{cases}$

Solve each system by substitution.

**7.** $\begin{cases} 5m - n = 7 \\ 3 + 3n = 6m \end{cases}$

**8.** $\begin{cases} 4y - 6 = 2x \\ y - 3x = 9 \end{cases}$

**9.** $\begin{cases} 3u + 8 = 4v \\ 24v = 6 - 3u \end{cases}$

Solve each system by elimination.

**10.** $\begin{cases} 5c - 4t = 8 \\ 14 + 4t = 3c \end{cases}$

**11.** $\begin{cases} 8y + 10 = 6x \\ 8y - 4x = -12 \end{cases}$

**12.** $\begin{cases} 11 - 2c = 3d \\ 2c - 7d = -9 \end{cases}$

Graph the solutions to each of the following systems.

**13.** $\begin{cases} y < 2 + 3x \\ y \geq |x - 3| \end{cases}$

**14.** $\begin{cases} 2x + y > 7 \\ x < 4 \\ y \leq 5 \end{cases}$

### Do you UNDERSTAND?

**15.** Which equation below combines with the equation $-4x + 6y = 3$ to form a system with an infinite number of solutions?

Ⓐ $0.5 + x = 1.5y$

Ⓑ $0.75 + 2x = 1.5y$

Ⓒ $0.5 + 2x = 1.5y$

Ⓓ $0.75 + x = 1.5y$

**16.** Write a system of inequalities to describe the shaded region.

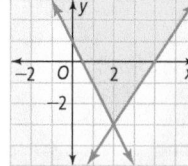

**17.** An ordinary refrigerator costs \$503 and has an estimated annual operating cost of \$92. An energy-efficient model costs \$615 with an estimated annual operating cost of \$64. Write a system of equations to represent this situation.
   **a.** What is the solution of the system?
   **b.** What does the solution mean?
   **c.** Which model would you choose for your family? Why?

**18. Writing** Explain how to classify a linear system as independent, dependent, or inconsistent without graphing.

**17. a.** $(4, 871)$

   **b.** The solution means that in four years the costs to own and operate the refrigerators are the same for both models.

   **c.** Answers may vary. Sample: I would choose the energy-efficient model if I didn't plan on moving within 4 years.

**18.** Use $y$-intercepts, slopes, and the number of solutions to classify a linear system as independent, dependent, or inconsistent without graphing. An independent system has one solution. The slopes are different, but the $y$-intercepts could be the same. An inconsistent system has no solution. The slopes are the same and the $y$-intercepts are different. A dependent system has an infinite number of solutions. The slopes and $y$-intercepts are the same.

## 3-4 Linear Programming

**Objective** To solve problems using linear programming

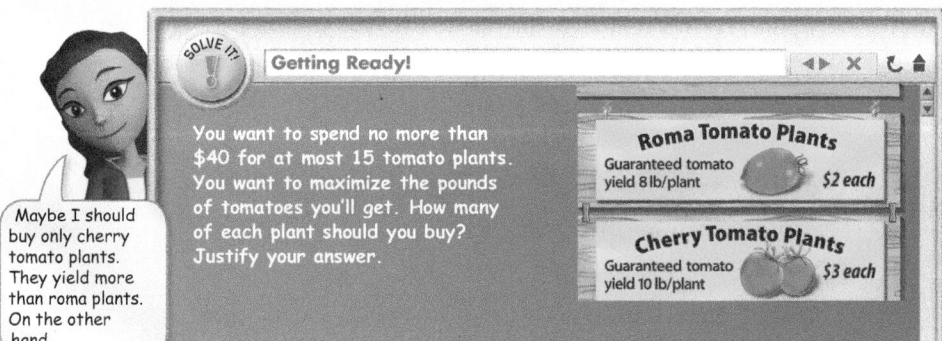

Maybe I should buy only cherry tomato plants. They yield more than roma plants. On the other hand . . .

**Getting Ready!**

You want to spend no more than $40 for at most 15 tomato plants. You want to maximize the pounds of tomatoes you'll get. How many of each plant should you buy? Justify your answer.

**Roma Tomato Plants**
Guaranteed tomato yield 8 lb/plant — $2 each

**Cherry Tomato Plants**
Guaranteed tomato yield 10 lb/plant — $3 each

**Lesson Vocabulary**
• constraint
• linear programming
• feasible region
• objective function

In the Solve It, you maximized your tomato production given some limits, or **constraints**. **Linear programming** is a method for finding a minimum or maximum value of some quantity, given a set of constraints.

**Essential Understanding** Some real-world problems involve multiple linear relationships. Linear programming accounts for all of these linear relationships and gives the solution to the problem.

The constraints in a linear programming situation form a system of inequalities, like the one at the right. The graph of the system is the **feasible region**. It contains all the points that satisfy all the constraints.

$$\begin{cases} x \geq 2 \\ y \geq 3 \\ y \leq 6 \\ x + y \leq 10 \end{cases}$$

The quantity you are trying to maximize or minimize is modeled with an **objective function**. Often this quantity is cost or profit. Suppose the objective function is $C = 2x + y$.

Graphs of the objective function for various values of $C$ are parallel lines. Lines closer to the origin represent smaller values of $C$.

The graphs of the equations $7 = 2x + y$ and $17 = 2x + y$ intersect the feasible region at (2, 3) and (7, 3). These vertices of the feasible represent the least and the greatest values for the objective function.

---

## 1 Interactive Learning

**Solve It!**
**PURPOSE** To introduce the concept of linear programming in a real-world situation with intuitive constraints
**PROCESS** Students may
• write and graph each inequality and the function to maximize.
• compare the number of plants versus the yield of tomatoes.

**FACILITATE**
**Q** What quantities do the variables represent in this problem? **[number of roma tomato plants and number of cherry tomato plants]**

**Q** What inequality symbolizes what you can afford to spend? **[$2x + 3y \leq 40$ where $x$ is the number of roma plants and $y$ is the number of cherry plants]**

**Q** What happens if you buy only one type of plant? **[If you buy all roma you get 15 plants and 120 pounds of tomatoes, and if you buy all cherry you get 13 plants and 130 pounds of tomatoes.]**

**ANSWER** See Solve It in Answers on next page.
**CONNECT THE MATH** In the Solve It, students find the feasible region and maximize a quantity given constraints on the variables. In this lesson, the formal technique of linear programming is introduced.

---

## 3-4 Preparing to Teach

**BIG idea Function**      UbD

**ESSENTIAL UNDERSTANDINGS**
• Some real-world problems involve multiple linear relationships. Linear programming accounts for all of these linear relationships and gives the solution to the problem.
• The feasible region contains all the points that satisfy all the constraints.

### Math Background

This lesson extends students' ability to solve systems of linear inequalities and introduces them to optimization (finding the maximum or minimum value of a function).

An objective function is used in linear programming to model some quantity that we wish to maximize or minimize. An objective function may be used to *maximize* quantities such as profit or items produced

or to *minimize* quantities such as cost or time.

While the objective functions in the lesson would not generally have a maximum or minimum value, they may when the region given by the inequalities restricts the domain. An example of a restriction on a domain is as follows. If one variable represented a number of people, that variable could not be negative.

As in the previous lesson, the most reasonable method to determine the common solutions of a set of inequalities is graphing.

### Support Student Learning

Use the **Algebra 2 Companion** to engage and support students during instruction. See Lesson Resources at the end of this lesson for details.

**PowerAlgebra.com**

### 1 Interactive Learning

**Solve It!**
Step out how to solve the Problem with helpful hints and an online question. Other questions are listed above in Interactive Learning.

**Dynamic Activity** This activity allows students to display up to five constraining inequalities of an objective function. This is useful for quickly modeling or getting extra practice with linear programming situations.

# 2 Guided Instruction

## Take Note
ERROR PREVENTION

Not every objective function has a maximum and/or minimum on a feasible region. This occurs if the region is not bounded.

## Problem 1

To find the vertices of the feasible region, the constraints must all be graphed on the same grid.

> **Q** After graphing in Step 1, what do you notice about the multiple-choice answers? Explain. **[They are vertices of the feasible region, so they can maximize the objective function.]**
>
> **Q** Is there another way to solve this problem? Explain. **[Answers may vary. Sample: Yes; without graphing, you could substitute each given pair into $P = 2x + y$ and see which gives the greatest value of P. Then you would have to make sure it is a vertex of the feasible region.]**
>
> **Q** If this were not a multiple-choice question, could you solve it without graphing? **[No; if you are not given the answers to choose from, you would have to graph to find the vertices.]**

## Got It?
VISUAL LEARNERS

> **Q** What is the maximum value of $P$ in the feasible region? **[7.5]**

---

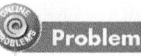

**Dynamic Activity**
Linear Programming

### Key Concept  Vertex Principle of Linear Programming

If there is a maximum or a minimum value of the linear objective function, it occurs at one or more vertices of the feasible region.

You can solve a problem using linear programming by testing in the objective function all of the vertices of the feasible region.

### Problem 1  Testing Vertices

**Multiple Choice** What point in the feasible region maximizes $P$ for the objective function $P = 2x + y$?

Constraints $\begin{cases} x + 2y \le 5 \\ x - y \le 2 \\ x \ge 0 \\ y \ge 0 \end{cases}$

Ⓐ $(2, 0)$  Ⓑ $(0, 0)$  Ⓒ $(3, 1)$  Ⓓ $(0, 2.5)$

**Think**

What quadrant will the feasible region be in?
The constraints $x \ge 0$ and $y \ge 0$ indicate the first quadrant.

**Step 1**
Graph the inequalities.

**Step 2**
Form the feasible region.

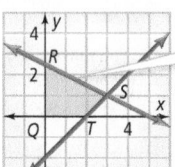

The intersections of the boundaries are the vertices of the feasible region.

**Step 3**
Find the coordinates of each vertex.

$Q\,(0, 0)$
$R\,(0, 2.5)$
$S\,(3, 1)$
$T\,(2, 0)$

**Step 4**
Evaluate $P$ at each vertex.

$P = 2(0) + 0 = 0$
$P = 2(0) + 2.5 = 2.5$
$P = 2(3) + 1 = 7$  ⟵ Maximum Value
$P = 2(2) + 0 = 4$

$P$ has a maximum value of 7 when $x = 3$ and $y = 1$. The correct choice is C.

**Got It?** **1. a.** Use the constraints in Problem 1 with the objective function $P = x + 3y$. What values of $x$ and $y$ maximize $P$?

**b. Reasoning** Can an objective function $P = ax + by + c$ have (the same) maximum value at all four vertex points $Q$, $R$, $S$, and $T$? At points $R$ and $S$ only? Explain using examples.

---

## PowerAlgebra.com

## 2 Guided Instruction

Each Problem is worked out and supported online.

**Problem 1**
Testing Vertices
*Animated*

**Problem 2**
Using Linear Programming to Maximize Profit
*Animated*

**Support in Algebra 2 Companion**
• Vocabulary
• Key Concepts
• Got It?

## Answers

### Solve It!
10 cherry tomato plants, 5 roma tomato plants

### Got It?
**1. a.** $P$ has a maximum value of 7.5 at (0, 2.5).

**b.** Answers may vary. Sample: $P = 5$ has same (maximum) value at all four vertex points. $P = x + 2y$ has maximum value 5 at $R$ and $S$.

**2.** 100 T-shirts and 10 sweatshirts

**Problem 2** Using Linear Programming to Maximize Profit

**Business** You are screen-printing T-shirts and sweatshirts to sell at the Polk County Blues Festival and are working with the following constraints.

- You have at most 20 hours to make shirts.
- You want to spend no more than $600 on supplies.
- You want to have at least 50 items to sell.

**1-Color T-shirt**
Takes 10 minutes to make
Supplies cost $4
Profit $6

**3-Color Sweatshirt**
Takes 30 minutes to make
Supplies cost $20
Profit $20

How many T-shirts and how many sweatshirts should you make to maximize your profit? How much is the maximum profit?

Organize the information in a table.

Write the constraints and the objective function.

Constraints: $\begin{cases} 10x + 30y \le 1200 \\ x + y \ge 50 \\ 4x + 20y \le 600 \\ x \ge 0 \\ y \ge 0 \end{cases}$

|  | T-Shirts, $x$ | Sweatshirts, $y$ | Total |
|---|---|---|---|
| **Minutes** | $10x$ | $30y$ | $1200$ |
| **Number** | $x$ | $y$ | $50$ |
| **Cost** | $4x$ | $20y$ | $600$ |
| **Profit** | $6x$ | $20y$ | $6x + 20y$ |

Objective Function: $P = 6x + 20y$

**Step 1**

Graph the constraints to form the feasible region.

**Think**

How do you find the coordinates of the vertices if they are hard to read off the graph?

Solve the system of equations related to the lines that intersect to form the vertex.

**Step 2**

Find the coordinates of each vertex.

$A(50, 0)$
$B(25, 25)$
$C(75, 15)$
$D(120, 0)$

**Step 3**

Evaluate $P$.

$P = 6(50) + 20(0) = 300$
$P = 6(25) + 20(25) = 650$
$P = 6(75) + 20(15) = 750$
$P = 6(120) + 20(0) = 720$

You can maximize your profit by selling 75 T-shirts and 15 sweatshirts. The maximum profit is $750.

✓ **Got It?** **2.** If it took you 20 minutes to make a sweatshirt, how many of each type of shirt should you make to maximize your profit?

**Q** What does the 1200 in the constraint $10x + 30y \le 1200$ represent? **[It represents the 20 hours you have to make shirts; 20 hours equals 1200 minutes.]**

**Q** Why are $x \ge 0$ and $y \ge 0$ included as constraints? **[Since $x$ represents the number of T-shirts and $y$ represents the number of sweatshirts, they cannot be negative.]**

**Q** Where does the objective function $P = 6x + 20y$ come from? **[Your goal is to maximize the profit, so the objective function is the total profit as a function of the number of T-shirts and the number of sweatshirts made.]**

**Q** The number of T-shirts $x$ and the number of sweatshirts $y$ can only be whole numbers. What type of function is the objective function $P = 6x + 20y$? **[a discrete function]**

**Got It?**

**Q** Which constraint is different from one in Problem 2? What is the new constraint? Explain. **[The constraint $10x + 30y \le 1200$ must change to $10x + 20y \le 1200$ because the time needed to make a sweatshirt changed from 30 minutes to 20 minutes.]**

**Q** How does the new constraint affect the feasible region? **[The intersection with the constraint $4x + 20y \le 600$ changes so vertex C changes from (75, 15) to (100, 10).]**

# Additional Problems

**1.** What point in the feasible region minimizes $P$ for the objective function $P = 5x - y$?

Constraints $\begin{cases} x + y \le 1 \\ 4x + y \ge -2 \\ x \le 0 \end{cases}$

a. $(-1, 2)$    c. $(0, 1)$
b. $(0, -2)$    d. $(-0.5, 0)$

**ANSWER** a

**2.** You are making your summer movie plans and are working with the following constraints:

- It costs $8 to go to the movies at night.
- It costs $5 to go to a matinee.
- You want to go to at least as many night shows as matinees.
- You want to spend at most $42.

What is the greatest number of movies you can see?

**ANSWER** 6; 3 night movies and 3 matinees or 4 night movies and 2 matinees

# 3 Lesson Check

## Do you know HOW? ERROR INTERVENTION

- For Exercises 1–4, if students have trouble graphing the inequalities, revisit Problem 1 or Additional Problem 1, or review Lesson 2-8.

## Do you UNDERSTAND? ERROR INTERVENTION

- For Exercises 7–9, if students have difficulty with the definition of *feasible region*, relate the graphical definition to the set of solutions common to each inequality given by the constraints. Explain that the feasible region is the overlap, and the constraints are the linear inequalities.

## Close

**Q** If the feasible region is a triangle, how can you find the minimum value of the objective function? **[Evaluate the objective function at the three vertices, and choose the point that gives the least value.]**

**Q** If the maximum of an objective function occurs at $(-2, 3)$, can $x \geq 0$ be one of the constraints? Explain. **[No; since $(-2, 3)$ is a vertex, the feasible region is not restricted to nonnegative $x$-values.]**

---

 Lesson Check

### Do you know HOW?

Graph each system of inequalities.

1. $\begin{cases} x + y \leq 6 \\ x \geq 0 \\ y \geq 0 \end{cases}$

2. $\begin{cases} 2x - y \leq 4 \\ x \geq 0 \\ y \geq 0 \end{cases}$

3. $\begin{cases} x + 2y \leq 10 \\ x \geq 1 \\ y \geq 2 \end{cases}$

4. $\begin{cases} 2x + 3y \leq 18 \\ 0 \leq x \leq 5 \\ 0 \leq y \leq 4 \end{cases}$

Graph each system of constraints. Then name the vertices of the feasible region.

5. $\begin{cases} x \leq 5 \\ y \leq 4 \\ x \geq 0 \\ y \geq 0 \end{cases}$

6. $\begin{cases} x + y \leq 8 \\ y \geq 5 \\ x \geq 0 \end{cases}$

### Do you UNDERSTAND?

7. **Vocabulary** Explain why the inequalities of a linear programming problem are called constraints. *Hint:* Use the definition of *constraint* as part of your answer.

8. **Compare and Contrast** What are some similarities between solving a linear programming problem and solving a system of linear inequalities? What are some differences?

9. **Open-Ended** Write a system of constraints whose graphs determine a trapezoid. Write an objective function and evaluate it at each vertex.

---

 **Practice and Problem-Solving Exercises**

 **Practice** Graph each system of constraints. Name all vertices. Then find the values of $x$ and $y$ that maximize or minimize the objective function. ◆ **See Problem 1.**

10. $\begin{cases} x + y \leq 8 \\ 2x + y \leq 10 \\ x \geq 0 \\ y \geq 0 \end{cases}$

Maximum for
$N = 100x + 40y$

11. $\begin{cases} x + 2y \geq 8 \\ x \geq 2 \\ y \geq 0 \end{cases}$

Minimum for
$C = x + 3y$

12. $\begin{cases} 2 \leq x \leq 6 \\ 1 \leq y \leq 5 \\ x + y \leq 8 \end{cases}$

Maximum for
$P = 3x + 2y$

13. **Air Quality** A city wants to plant maple and spruce trees to absorb carbon dioxide. It has $2100 to spend on planting spruce and maple trees. The city has 45,000 ft² available for planting. ◆ **See Problem 2.**
   a. Use the data from the table. Write the constraints for the situation.
   b. Write the objective function.
   c. Graph the feasible region and find the vertices.
   d. How many of each tree should the city plant to maximize carbon dioxide absorption?

**Spruce and Maple Tree Data**

| | Spruce | Maple |
|---|---|---|
| Planting Cost | $30 | $40 |
| Area Required | 600 ft² | 900 ft² |
| Carbon Dioxide Absorption | 650 lb/yr | 300 lb/yr |

Source: Auburn University and Anderson Associates

---

PowerAlgebra.com

## 3 Lesson Check

For a digital lesson check, use the Got It questions.

**Support in Algebra 2 Companion**
- Lesson Check

## 4 Practice

Assign homework to individual students or to an entire class.

---

# Answers

## Lesson Check

1.

2.

3.

4.

5.

$(0, 0), (0, 4), (5, 0), (5, 4)$

6.  $(0, 8), (3, 5), (0, 5)$

7. Constraints are limits or restrictions on the variables in the objective function in a linear programming problem. These constraints are written as linear inequalities.

8. Linear programming is an extension of solving linear inequalities. For each, you are given constraints represented by linear inequalities that are graphed. All the points in the overlapping region are solutions, but linear programming problems are usually looking for maximum or minimum values of some quantity modeled with an objective function.

**9–13.** See next page.

**B** Apply

**14. Think About a Plan** A biologist is developing two new strains of bacteria. Each sample of Type I bacteria produces four new viable bacteria, and each sample of Type II produces three new viable bacteria. Altogether, at least 240 new viable bacteria must be produced. At least 30, but not more than 60, of the original samples must be Type I. Not more than 70 of the original samples can be Type II. A sample of Type I costs $5 and a sample of Type II costs $7. How many samples of Type II bacteria should the biologist use to minimize the cost?
  • What are the unknowns?
  • What constraints do you get from each condition in the problem?
  • Are there any implicit constraints?

**15. Error Analysis** Your friend is trying to find the maximum value of $P = -x + 3y$ subject to the following constraints.
$$\begin{cases} y \le -2x + 6 \\ y \le x + 3 \\ x \ge 0, y \ge 0 \end{cases}$$
What error did your friend make? What is the correct solution?

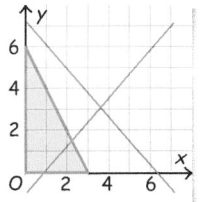

**16. Cooking** Baking a tray of corn muffins takes 4 cups of milk and 3 cups of wheat flour. Baking a tray of bran muffins takes 2 cups of milk and 3 cups of wheat flour. A baker has 16 cups of milk and 15 cups of wheat flour. He makes $3 profit per tray of corn muffins and $2 profit per tray of bran muffins. How many trays of each type of muffin should the baker make to maximize his profit?

**Graph each system of constraints. Name all vertices. Then find the values of $x$ and $y$ that maximize or minimize the objective function. Find the maximum or minimum value.**

**17.** $\begin{cases} 3x + y \le 7 \\ x + 2y \le 9 \\ x \ge 0, y \ge 0 \end{cases}$
Maximum for
$P = 2x + y$

**18.** $\begin{cases} 25 \le x \le 75 \\ y \le 110 \\ 8x + 6y \ge 720 \end{cases}$
Minimum for
$C = 8x + 5y$

**19.** $\begin{cases} x + y \le 11 \\ 2y \ge x \\ x \ge 0, y \ge 0 \end{cases}$
Maximum for
$P = 3x + 2y$

**20.** $\begin{cases} 2x + y \le 300 \\ x + y \le 200 \\ x \ge 0, y \ge 0 \end{cases}$
Maximum for
$P = x + 2y$

**21.** $\begin{cases} 5x + y \ge 10 \\ x + y \le 6 \\ x + 4y \ge 12 \\ x \ge 0, y \ge 0 \end{cases}$
Minimum for
$C = 10{,}000x + 20{,}000y$

**22.** $\begin{cases} 6 \le x + y \le 13 \\ x \ge 3 \\ y \ge 1 \end{cases}$
Maximum for
$P = 4x + 3y$

# 4 Practice

**ASSIGNMENT GUIDE**
Basic: 10–19
Average: 11–13 odd, 14–22
Advanced: 11–13 odd, 14–24
Standardized Test Prep: 25–27
Mixed Review: 28–37
**Reasoning** exercises have blue headings.
**Applications** exercises have red headings.

**EXERCISE 16:** Use the Think About a Plan worksheet in the **Practice and Problem Solving Workbook** (also available in the Teaching Resources in print and online) to further support students' development in becoming independent learners.

**HOMEWORK QUICK CHECK**
To check students' understanding of key skills and concepts, go over Exercises 11, 13, 14, 15, and 16.

---

**9.** Answers may vary. Sample:
$$\begin{cases} y \le x \\ y \le -x + 4 \\ 0 \le y \le 1 \end{cases}$$
$P = 2x + 3y$, $P(0, 0) = 0$, $P(1, 1) = 5$, $P(3, 1) = 9$, $P(4, 0) = 8$; maximum value of $P$ is 9 at $(3, 1)$

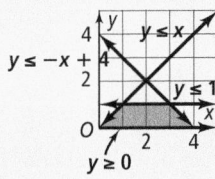

**Practice and Problem-Solving Exercises**

**10.**  vertices: (0, 0), (5, 0), (2, 6), (0, 8); maximized at (5, 0)

**11.** 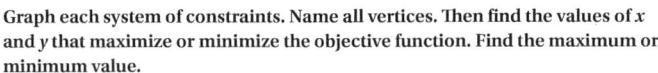 vertices: (8, 0), (2, 3); minimized at (8, 0)

**12.**  vertices: (2, 1), (6, 1), (6, 2), (2, 5), (3, 5); maximized at (6, 2)

**13.** Let $s$ = number of spruce trees and $m$ = number of maple trees.

**a.** $\begin{cases} 30s + 40m \le 2100 \\ 600s + 900m \le 45{,}000 \\ s \ge 0, m \ge 0 \end{cases}$

**b.** $P = 650s + 300m$

**c.**  vertices: (0, 0), (0, 50), (30, 30), (70, 0)

**d.** 70 spruce trees and 0 maple trees

**14.** Let $x$ = number of Type I samples and $y$ = number of Type II samples;
$$\begin{cases} 4x + 3y \ge 240 \\ 30 \le x \le 60 \\ y \le 70 \\ x \ge 0 \\ y \ge 0 \end{cases}$$
$C = 5x + 7y$
The implicit constraints are $x \ge 0, y \ge 0$; $C = 300$ and is minimized at (60, 0); the biologist should use 0 Type II bacteria.

**15–22.** See next page.

# Answers

## Practice and Problem-Solving Exercises
(continued)

**15.** He is not considering the constraint $y \le x + 3$; maximized when $P = 11$ at $(1, 4)$.

**16.** 3 trays of corn muffins and 2 trays of bran muffins

**17.** vertices: $(0, 0)$, $(1, 4)$, $(0, 4.5)$, $\left(\frac{7}{3}, 0\right)$; maximized when $P = 6$ at $(1, 4)$

**18.** vertices: $(75, 20)$, $(75, 110)$, $(25, 110)$; $\left(25, 86\frac{2}{3}\right)$, minimized when $C = 633\frac{1}{3}$ at $\left(25, 86\frac{2}{3}\right)$.

**19.** vertices: $(0, 0)$, $\left(7\frac{1}{3}, 3\frac{2}{3}\right)$, $(0, 11)$; maximized when $P = 29\frac{1}{3}$ at $\left(7\frac{1}{3}, 3\frac{2}{3}\right)$.

**20.** vertices: $(0, 0)$, $(150, 0)$, $(100, 100)$, $(0, 200)$; maximized when $P = 400$ at $(0, 200)$.

**21.** vertices: $\left(\frac{28}{19}, \frac{50}{19}\right)$, $(4, 2)$, $(1, 5)$; minimized when $C = 67,370$ at $\left(\frac{28}{19}, \frac{50}{19}\right)$

**22.** vertices: $(3, 3)$, $(3, 10)$, $(5, 1)$, $(12, 1)$; maximized when $P = 51$ at $(12, 1)$

---

**Challenge**

**23.** A vertex of a feasible region does not always have whole-number coordinates. Sometimes you may need to round coordinates to find the solution. Using the objective function and the constraints at the right, find the whole-number values of $x$ and $y$ that minimize $C$. Then find $C$ for those values of $x$ and $y$.

$C = 6x + 9y$
$\begin{cases} x + 2y \ge 50 \\ 2x + y \ge 60 \\ x \ge 0, y \ge 0 \end{cases}$

**24.** **Reasoning** Sometimes two corners of a graph both yield the maximum profit. In this case, many other points may also yield the maximum profit. Evaluate the profit formula $P = x + 2y$ for the graph shown. Find four points that yield the maximum profit.

### Standardized Test Prep

**SAT/ACT**

**25.** Solve the equation $\frac{1}{2}(a + b) = c$ for $b$.

ⓐ $b = \frac{1}{2}c - a$   Ⓑ $b = 2a - c$   Ⓒ $b = 2c - a$   Ⓓ $b = 2ca$

**26.** Which is the graph of $y \le |x - 3|$?

**Short Response**

**27.** What are the vertices of the feasible region bounded by the constraints at the right?

$\begin{cases} x + y \le 3 \\ 2x + y \le 4 \\ x \ge 0, y \ge 0 \end{cases}$

### Mixed Review

Solve each system of inequalities by graphing.   ◆ **See Lesson 3-3.**

**28.** $\begin{cases} y < -2x + 8 \\ 3y \ge 4x - 6 \end{cases}$   **29.** $\begin{cases} x - 2y \ge 11 \\ 5x + 4y < 27 \end{cases}$   **30.** $\begin{cases} 2x + 6y > 12 \\ 3x + 9y \le 27 \end{cases}$

Evaluate each expression for $a = 3$ and $b = -5$.   ◆ **See Lesson 1-3.**

**31.** $2a + b$   **32.** $-4 + 2ab$   **33.** $3(a - b)$   **34.** $b(2b - a)$

**Get Ready!**   **To prepare for Lesson 3-5, do Exercises 35–37.**

Find the $x$- and $y$-intercepts of the graph of each linear equation.   ◆ **See Lesson 2-4.**

**35.** $y = 2x + 6$   **36.** $2x + 9y = 36$   **37.** $y = x - 1$

---

**23.**

vertices: $(0, 60)$, $\left(23\frac{1}{3}, 13\frac{1}{3}\right)$, $(50, 0)$; minimized when $x = 23\frac{1}{3}$ and $y = 13\frac{1}{3}$; Round to $(23, 14)$ and $(24, 13)$; $(24, 13)$ gives a minimum cost of $261

**24.** Answers may vary. Sample: $(4, 6)$, $(6, 5)$, $(9, 3.5)$, $(10, 3)$

**25.** C          **26.** I

**27.** [2]

vertices: $(0, 0)$, $(2, 0)$, $(0, 3)$, $(1, 2)$

[1] correct vertices, without graph drawn

**28.**

**29.**

**30.**

**31.** 1          **32.** $-34$
**33.** 24          **34.** 65
**35.** $(0, 6)$, $(-3, 0)$
**36.** $(0, 4)$, $(18, 0)$
**37.** $(0, -1)$, $(1, 0)$

## Additional Instructional Support

### Algebra 2 Companion

Students can use the **Algebra 2 Companion** worktext (4 pages) as you teach the lesson. Use the Companion to support

- New Vocabulary
- Key Concepts
- Got It for each Problem
- Lesson Check

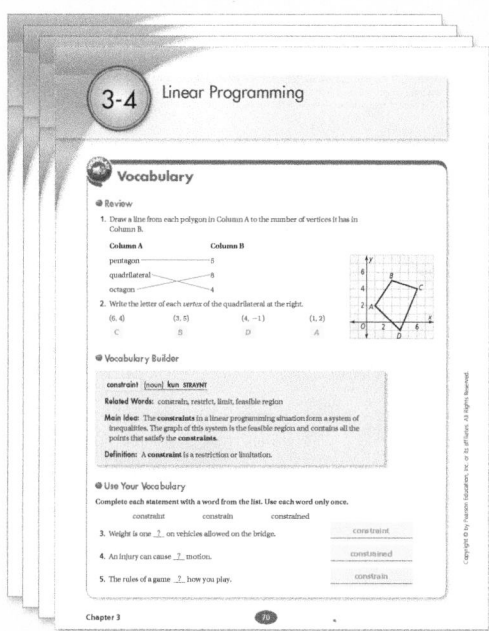

### ELL Support

**Focus on Communication** State the steps you would take to solve a linear programming problem. In Problem 2, state that you are looking for information about the two types of shirts to describe inequalities. Write the variables that you define and the objective function. Have students plan and solve one of the practice word problems with you.

**Focus on Language** Copy the feasible region at the top of page 162 on the board. Give each student a different objective function. Have them find the maximum and minimum values. Then they should say the following sentence and fill in the blanks: For the objective function _____, the minimum value is _____ and the maximum value is _____. Draw another polygonal feasible region and repeat.

## 5 Assess & Remediate

### Lesson Quiz

**1.** What point in the feasible region maximizes *P* for the objective function $P = 2x + 3y$?

Constraints $\begin{cases} 2x + y \le 15 \\ x + 3y \le 20 \\ x \ge 0,\ y \ge 0 \end{cases}$

**a.** $(0, 6\frac{2}{3})$    **b.** $(5, 5)$

**c.** $(0, 0)$    **d.** $(7.5, 0)$

**2. Do you UNDERSTAND?** You are painting pictures to sell and are working with the following constraints:

- It takes 3 h to paint a small picture.
- It takes 5 h to paint a large picture.
- You want to spend no more than 48 h painting.
- You sell the small pictures for $12.
- You sell large pictures for $22.
- You want to sell at least one picture of each size.

How many of each picture size should you paint to maximize your earnings?

### ANSWERS TO LESSON QUIZ

**1.** b

**2.** 1 small picture, 9 large pictures

### PRESCRIPTION FOR REMEDIATION

Use the student work on the Lesson Quiz to prescribe a differentiated review assignment:

| Points | Differentiated Remediation |
|--------|----------------------------|
| 0 | Intervention |
| 1 | On-level |
| 2 | Extension |

**PowerAlgebra.com**

## 5 Assess & Remediate

Assign the Lesson Quiz. Appropriate intervention, practice, or enrichment is automatically generated based on student performance.

## Intervention

- **Reteaching** (2 pages) Provides reteaching and practice exercises for the key lesson concepts. Use with struggling students or absent students.

- **English Language Learner Support** Helps students develop and reinforce mathematical vocabulary and key concepts.

### All-in-One Resources/Online
**Reteaching**

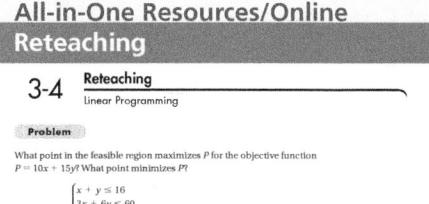

### All-in-One Resources/Online
**English Language Learner Support**

# Differentiated Remediation *continued*

## On-Level

- **Practice** (2 pages) Provides extra practice for each lesson. For simpler practice exercises, use the Form K Practice pages found in the All-in-One Teaching Resources and online.

- **Think About a Plan** Helps students develop specific problem-solving skills and strategies by providing scaffolded guiding questions.

- **Standardized Test Prep** Focuses on all major exercises, all major question types, and helps students prepare for the high-stakes assessments.

## Extension

- **Enrichment** Provides students with interesting problems and activities that extend the concepts of the lesson.

- **Activities, Games, and Puzzles** Worksheets that can be used for concepts development, enrichment, and for fun!

---

### Practice and Problem Solving Wkbk/All-in-One Resources/Online
**Practice page 1**

### Practice and Problem Solving Wkbk/All-in-One Resources/Online
**Practice page 2**

### All-in-One Resources/Online
**Enrichment**

---

### Practice and Problem Solving Wkbk/All-in-One Resources/Online
**Think About a Plan**

### Practice and Problem Solving Wkbk/All-in-One Resources/Online
**Standardized Test Prep**

### Online Teacher Resource Center
**Activities, Games, and Puzzles**

---

# Concept Byte

**Linear Programming**

For Use With Lesson 3-4

TECHNOLOGY

You can solve linear programming problems using your graphing calculator.

## Activity

Find the values of $x$ and $y$ that will maximize the objective function $P = 13x + 2y$ for the constraints at the right. What is the value of $P$ at this maximum point?

$$\begin{cases} -3x + 2y \le 8 \\ -8x + y \ge -48 \\ x \ge 0, y \ge 0 \end{cases}$$

**Step 1** Rewrite the first two inequalities to isolate $y$. Enter the inequalities.

**Step 2** Use the **VALUE** option of **CALC** to find the upper left vertex. Press 0 ⟨enter⟩.

**Step 3** Enter the objective function on the home screen. Press ⟨enter⟩ for the value of $P$ at the vertex.

**Step 4** Use the **INTERSECT** option of **CALC** to find the upper right vertex. Go to the home screen and press ⟨enter⟩ for the value of $P$.

**Step 5** Use the **ZERO** option of **CALC** to find the lower right vertex. Go to the home screen and press ⟨enter⟩ for the value of $P$. The objective function has a value of 0 when the vertex is at the origin. The maximum value of $P$ is 136.

## Exercises

Find the values of $x$ and $y$ that maximize or minimize the objective function.

1. $\begin{cases} 4x + 3y \ge 30 \\ x + 3y \ge 21 \\ x \ge 0, y \ge 0 \end{cases}$
   Minimum for
   $C = 5x + 8y$

2. $\begin{cases} 3x + 5y \ge 35 \\ 2x + y \le 14 \\ x \ge 0, y \ge 0 \end{cases}$
   Maximum for
   $P = 3x + 2y$

3. $\begin{cases} x + y \ge 8 \\ x + 5y \ge 20 \\ x \ge 0, y \ge 2 \end{cases}$
   Minimum for
   $C = 3x + 4y$

4. $\begin{cases} x + 2y \le 24 \\ 3x + 2y \le 34 \\ 3x + y \le 29 \\ x \ge 0 \end{cases}$
   Maximum for
   $P = 2x + 3y$

 PowerAlgebra.com

Concept Byte   Linear Programming

163

---

## Answers

**1.** $x = 3, y = 6; C = 63$
**2.** $x = 5, y = 4; P = 23$
**3.** $x = 5, y = 3; C = 27$
**4.** $x = 5, y = 9.5; P = 38.5$

# Guided Instruction

**PURPOSE** To graph in coordinate space
**PROCESS** Students will

- identify coordinates of points in coordinate space.
- graph three-variable equations in coordinate space.
- graph pairs of three-variable equations in coordinate space and describe their intersections.

**DISCUSS** This Concept Byte prepares students to visualize geometric representations of systems of equations with three variables, the topic of the next lesson. Draw the familiar two-dimensional coordinate system on the board, labeling the axes *x* and *y*. Make a transparency of Quadrant I and place it over Quadrant I on the board. Then erase the *x* and *y* on the board. Turn the transparency so that its *x*-axis and *y*-axis look like the second diagram. The *x*-axis protrudes from the board. Label the vertical axis *z*, the third label in a three-dimensional coordinate system. Next, use a yard stick or similar object to show the position of the *x*-axis through the origin and perpendicular to the plane of the board. Another model that the students can make is a sheet of paper with a pencil sticking through it.

## Activity 1
Students will need a yardstick, meter stick, or tape measure for this activity.

> **Q** What represents the *xy* plane in the picture? **[the floor]** What plane is represented by the wall that contains the board? **[the *yz* plane]**
>
> **Q** Suppose distance is measured in centimeters and the corner of a desk has coordinates (220, 183, 72). Describe how to get to that desk corner from the origin. **[Travel 220 cm along the *x*-axis, then 183 cm parallel to the *y*-axis, then 72 cm up.]**

---

## Concept Byte
For Use With Lesson 3-5

# Graphs in Three Dimensions

To describe positions in space, you need a three-dimensional coordinate system. You have learned to graph on an *xy*-coordinate plane using ordered pairs. Adding a third axis, the *z*-axis, to the *xy*-coordinate plane creates **coordinate space**. In coordinate space you graph points using **ordered triples** of the form $(x, y, z)$.

**Points in a Plane** ● (2, 3) ← ordered pair — 3 units up — 2 units right — origin — *y*-axis — *x*-axis

**Points in Space** (2, 3, 4) ← ordered triple — 4 units up — 2 units forward — 3 units right — origin — *z*-axis — *y*-axis — *x*-axis

A two-dimensional coordinate system allows you to graph points in a plane.

A three-dimensional coordinate system allows you to graph points in space.

In the coordinate plane, point (2, 3) is two units right and three units up from the origin. In coordinate space, point (2, 3, 4) is two units forward, three units right, and four units up.

### Activity 1

Define one corner of your classroom as the origin of a three-dimensional coordinate system like the classroom shown. Write the coordinates of each item in your coordinate system.

1. each corner of your classroom
2. each corner of your desk
3. one corner of the blackboard
4. the clock
5. the waste-paper basket
6. Pick 3 items in your classroom and write the coordinates of each.

---

# Answers

**1–6.** Check students' work.

## Activity 2

**7.**

**8.**

**9.**

## Activity 3

**10.**

**11.** The intersection is a line.

An equation in two variables represents a line in a plane. An equation in three variables represents a plane in space.

### Activity 2

Given the following equation in three variables, draw the plane in a coordinate space. $x + 2y - z = 6$

7. Let $x = 0$. Graph the resulting equation in the $yz$ plane.

8. Let $y = 0$. Graph the resulting equation in the $xz$ plane.

**From geometry you know that two lines determine a plane.**

9. Sketch the plane $x + 2y - z = 6$.
   (If you need help, find a third line by letting $z = 0$ and then graph the resulting equation in the $xy$ plane.)

### Activity 3

**Two equations in three variables represent two planes in space.**

10. Draw the two planes determined by the following equations:
    $2x + 3y - z = 12$
    $2x - 4y + z = 8$

11. Describe the intersection of the two planes above.

### Exercises

**Find the coordinates of each point in the diagram.**

12. $A$        13. $B$        14. $C$

15. $D$        16. $E$        17. $F$

**Sketch the graph of each equation.**

18. $x - y - 4z = 8$                   19. $x + y + z = 2$

20. $-3x + 5y + 10z = 15$        21. $6x + 6y - 12z = 36$

**Graph the following pairs of equations in the same coordinate space and describe their intersection, if any.**

22. $-x + 3y + z = 6$            23. $-2x - 3y + 5z = 7$
    $-3x + 5y - 2z = 60$            $2x - 3y - 4z = -4$

## Activity 2

**Q** In Problem 7, you let $x = 0$. What equation will you graph? **[$2y - z = 6$]**

**Q** What is a method to graph this equation? **[Answers may vary. Sample: Graph the $y$- and $z$-intercepts, and draw the line through them.]**

**Q** What is the $y$-intercept, expressed as an ordered pair in the form $(y, z)$? **[(3, 0)]**

**Q** What is the $z$-intercept, expressed as an ordered pair in the form $(y, z)$? **[(0, −6)]**

**Q** Now, recall that $x = 0$. What are the $y$- and $z$-intercepts, expressed as ordered triples in the form $(x, y, z)$? **[(0, 3, 0) and (0, 0, −6)]**

Students can use the same method to draw the line in Problem 8 and the third line mentioned in the hint for Problem 9.

## Activity 3

For Problem 11, show a model of two intersecting planes, such as two books, two index cards, two walls coming together in the room, or the flat palms of your two hands.

**Q** If two planes intersect, what does the intersection form? **[a line]**

## Exercises

**Q** For Exercise 1, what are the coordinates of point $A$? Explain. **[(0, 0, 0); $A$ is the origin.]**

**Q** For Exercises 2–6, what number is a coordinate of every point? Explain. **[0; $B$ is on the $z$-axis, $C$ is on the $y$-axis, $D$ is in the $xz$-plane, $E$ is in the $yz$-plane, and $F$ is in the $xz$-plane.]**

## Exercises

**12.** (0, 0, 0)        **13.** (0, 0, 50)

**14.** (0, 40, 0)      **15.** (60, 0, 50)

**16.** (0, 80, 100)   **17.** (60, 30, 100)

**18.**

**19.**

**20.**

**21.**

**22.**

The intersection is a line.

**23.**

The intersection is a line.

# 1 Interactive Learning

## Solve It!

**PURPOSE** To find unknown weights by relating them to each other and to a known weight

**PROCESS** Students may
- write two-variable equations and solve using substitution.
- use guess-and-check.

### FACILITATE

**Q** Let $A$, $B$, and $C$ represent the weights. What equation can you write that contains a known weight? **[$B + C = 10$]**

**Q** What equation does the first diagram suggest? **[$2A = B$]**

**Q** What equation does the second diagram suggest? **[$3A = C$]**

**Q** How can you write an equation that you can solve to get an answer? **[Answers may vary. Sample: Rewrite the equation $B + C = 10$, substituting $2A$ for $B$ and $3A$ for $C$.]**

**Q** If you rewrite the equation, substituting $2A$ for $B$ and $3A$ for $C$, what equation do you get? **[$2A + 3A = 10$]**

**ANSWER** See Solve It in Answers on next page.

**CONNECT THE MATH** In the Solve It, students use relationships that can be represented by three equations, each containing two variables. In the lesson, they will solve systems of three equations, each containing as many as three variables.

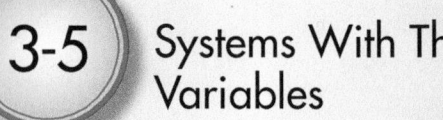
**Objectives** To solve systems in three variables using elimination
To solve systems in three variables using substitution

You can represent three relationships involving three unknowns with a system of equations.

**Essential Understanding** To solve systems of three equations in three variables, you can use some of the same algebraic methods you used to solve systems of two equations in two variables.

You can represent systems of equations in three variables as graphs in three dimensions. The graph of an equation of the form $Ax + By + Cz = D$, where $A$, $B$, and $C$ are not all zero, is a plane. You can show the solutions of a three-variable system graphically as the intersection of planes.

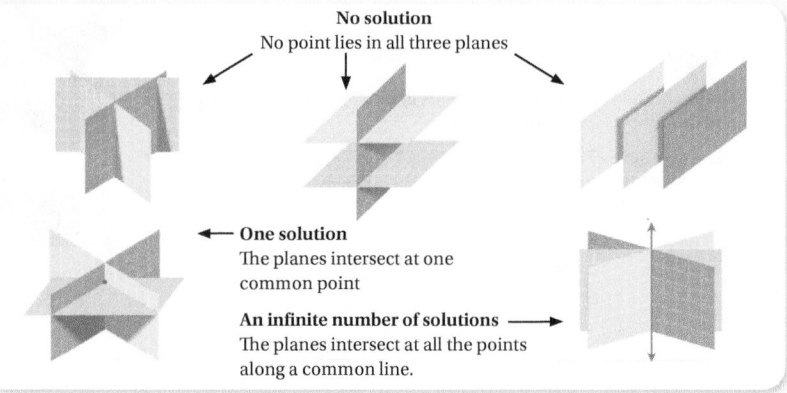

**No solution**
No point lies in all three planes

**One solution**
The planes intersect at one common point

**An infinite number of solutions**
The planes intersect at all the points along a common line.

---

# 3-5 Preparing to Teach

**BIG** ideas **Equivalence**
**Solving Equations and Inequalities** **UbD**

### ESSENTIAL UNDERSTANDINGS

- Systems of three equations in three variables can be solved using some of the same algebraic methods used to solve systems of two equations in two variables.
- If the equations of two systems are equivalent, then a solution of the system that is easier to solve is also a solution of the more difficult system.

## Math Background

Two methods for solving two-variable systems apply to solving three-variable systems: elimination and substitution.

The methods are essentially the same for two or three variables; a few more steps are required to solve for three variables.

For elimination, use two equations at a time to eliminate one variable. This will result in two

equations in two variables, which are solved like any other two-variable system.

Similarly for substitution: solve for one variable in terms of the other two. Substitute that value into the remaining two equations, yielding two equations in two variables.

The solution of a two-variable system can be represented as the intersection of lines in a coordinate plane. Similarly, the solution of a three-variable system can be represented as the intersection of *planes* in a coordinate space.

Although three-variable equations can be graphed as planes (as shown in the preceding Concept Byte), graphing is not an easy or practical method of solving three-variable systems.

## Support Student Learning

Use the **Algebra 2 Companion** to engage and support students during instruction. See Lesson Resources at the end of this lesson for details.

### PowerAlgebra.com

# 1 Interactive Learning

## Solve It!

Step out how to solve the Problem with helpful hints and an online question. Other questions are listed above in Interactive Learning.

You can use the elimination and substitution methods to solve a system of three equations in three variables by working with the equations in pairs. You will use one of the equations *twice*. When one point represents the solution of a system of equations in three variables, write it as an ordered triple $(x, y, z)$.

 **Problem 1** Solving a System Using Elimination

**What is the solution of the system? Use elimination.**
The equations are numbered to make the procedure easy to follow.

① $\begin{cases} 2x - y + z = 4 \\ x + 3y - z = 11 \\ 4x + y - z = 14 \end{cases}$
②
③

**Think**

**Which variable do you eliminate first?**
Eliminate the variable for which the process requires the fewest steps.

**Step 1** Pair the equations to eliminate $z$. Then you will have two equations in $x$ and $y$.

Add.

① $\begin{cases} 2x - y + z = 4 \\ x + 3y - z = 11 \end{cases}$
②
④ $\quad 3x + 2y \quad = 15$

Subtract.

② $\begin{cases} x + 3y - z = 11 \\ 4x + y - z = 14 \end{cases}$
③
⑤ $-3x + 2y \quad = -3$

**Think**

**Does it matter which equation you substitute into to find $z$?**
No, you can substitute into any of the original three equations.

**Step 2** Write the two new equations as a system. Solve for $x$ and $y$.

Add and solve for $y$.

④ $\begin{cases} 3x + 2y = 15 \\ -3x + 2y = -3 \end{cases}$
⑤
$\quad\quad 4y = 12$
$\quad\quad\ y = 3$

Substitute $y = 3$ and solve for $x$.

④ $\quad 3x + 2y = 15$
$\quad 3x + 2(3) = 15$
$\quad 3x = 9$
$\quad x = 3$

**Step 3** Solve for $z$. Substitute the values of $x$ and $y$ into one of the original equations.

① $\quad 2x - y + z = 4$    Use equation ①.
$\quad 2(3) - 3 + z = 4$    Substitute.
$\quad 6 - 3 + z = 4$    Simplify.
$\quad z = 1$    Solve for $z$.

**Step 4** Write the solution as an ordered triple. The solution is $(3, 3, 1)$.

 **Got It?** **1.** What is the solution of the system? Use elimination. Check your answer in all three original equations.

$\begin{cases} x - y + z = -1 \\ x + y + 3z = -3 \\ 2x - y + 2z = 0 \end{cases}$

You can apply the method in Problem 1 to most systems of three equations in three variables. You may need to multiply in one, two, or all three equations by one, two, or three nonzero numbers. Your goal is to obtain a system—equivalent to the original system—with coefficients that allow for the easy elimination of variables.

---

# 2 Guided Instruction

## Problem 1

**Q** Why do you think $z$ was chosen as the variable to eliminate? **[The only $z$-coefficients are 1 and −1, so it is easy to eliminate $z$ by adding or subtracting.]**

**Q** Look at the subtraction in Step 1. What would be the result if equations 2 and 3 were reversed? **[All the signs in equation 5 would be opposite; $z$ would still be eliminated.]**

**Q** In Step 2, the value of $y$ is substituted into equation 4. Could the value of $y$ be substituted into a different equation to solve for $x$? Explain. **[Yes; it could be substituted into equation 5 because it also has $x$ and $y$.]**

**EXTENSION**

Students can substitute the values of $x$ and $y$ into the original equations 2 or 3 to verify that they get the same result for $z$. They can check the solution by substituting the values of $x$, $y$, and $z$ into all three equations in the original system.

### Got It?

**Q** What variable will you eliminate first? Explain. **[Answers may vary. Sample: $y$ because the only $y$-coefficients are 1 and −1.]**

---

# 2 Guided Instruction

 Each Problem is worked out and supported in the Student Online Center.

**Problem 1**
Solving a System Using Elimination
*Animated*

**Problem 2**
Solving an Equivalent System
*Animated*

**Problem 3**
Solving a System Using Substitution
*Animated*

**Problem 4**
Solving a Real-World Problem

**Support in Algebra 2 Companion**
• Vocabulary
• Key Concepts
• Got It?

# Answers

**Solve It!**
A: 2 lb, B: 4 lb, C: 6 lb
$B + C = 10$
$\quad\quad C = 3A$
$\quad\quad B = 2A$
Therefore, $2A + 3A = 10$ and $A = 2$.
Use substitution to find the weights of each box.

**Got It?**
**1.** $(4, 2, -3)$

## Problem 2

**Q** Look at the given system. Does it seem that there is clearly one best choice of a variable that should be eliminated first? Explain your reasoning. **[Answers may vary. Sample: No; $x$ and $y$ seem to be equally good choices because the process to eliminate $x$ would have about the same number of steps as the process to eliminate $y$. The $x$-coefficients are 1, 2, and −1. The $y$-coefficients are 1, 1, and −2.]**

**Q** Which variable *is* eliminated first, and how is it accomplished? **[$y$; both sides of equation 1 are multiplied by −1, and then addition is used on the resulting equation and equation 2.]**

**Q** Can you think of another method that would eliminate $y$ just as quickly? **[Answers may vary. Sample: Use subtraction on equations 1 and 2.]**

### Got It?

**Q** For 2a, which variable will you eliminate first, and how will you start? **[Answers may vary. Sample: $x$; use equations 1 and 2. Multiply equation 1 by −2. Then add.]**

**Problem 2** Solving an Equivalent System

**What is the solution of the system? Use elimination.**

① $\begin{cases} x + y + 2z = 3 \\ ② \quad 2x + y + 3z = 7 \\ ③ \quad -x - 2y + z = 10 \end{cases}$

**Think**

You are trying to get two equations in $x$ and $z$. Multiply ① so you can add it to ② and eliminate $y$. Do the same with ② and ③.

**Write**

①$\begin{cases} x + y + 2z = 3 \\ ② \quad 2x + y + 3z = 7 \end{cases}$ → $\begin{aligned} -x - y - 2z &= -3 \\ 2x + y + 3z &= 7 \\ \hline ④ \quad x \quad\quad + z &= 4 \end{aligned}$

②$\begin{cases} 2x + y + 3z = 7 \\ ③ \quad -x - 2y + z = 10 \end{cases}$ → $\begin{aligned} 4x + 2y + 6z &= 14 \\ -x - 2y + z &= 10 \\ \hline ⑤ \quad 3x \quad\quad + 7z &= 24 \end{aligned}$

Multiply ④ so you can add it to ⑤ and eliminate $x$.

④$\begin{cases} x + z = 4 \\ ⑤ \quad 3x + 7z = 24 \end{cases}$ → $\begin{aligned} -3x - 3z &= -12 \\ 3x + 7z &= 24 \\ \hline 4z &= 12 \\ z &= 3 \end{aligned}$

Substitute $z = 3$ into ④. Solve for $x$.

$\begin{aligned} x + 3 &= 4 \\ x &= 1 \end{aligned}$

Substitute the values for $x$ and $z$ into ① to find $y$. Check the answer in the three original equations.

$\begin{aligned} x + y + 2z &= 3 \\ 1 + y + 2(3) &= 3 \\ y &= -4 \end{aligned}$

**Check**

$\begin{aligned} 1 + (-4) + 2(3) &= 3 \quad ✔ \\ 2(1) + (-4) + 3(3) &= 7 \quad ✔ \\ -(1) - 2(-4) + 3 &= 10 \quad ✔ \end{aligned}$

The solution is $(1, -4, 3)$.

**Got It?** **2. a.** What is the solution of the system? Use elimination.
**b.** **Reasoning** Could you have used elimination in another way? Explain.

$\begin{cases} x - 2y + 3z = 12 \\ 2x - y - 2z = 5 \\ 2x + 2y - z = 4 \end{cases}$

Here is a graphical representation of the solution of Problem 2. The graphs are enclosed in a 10-by-10-by-10 cube with the origin of the coordinate axes at the center.

The graphs of equations ①, ②, and ③, are planes ①, ②, and ③, respectively.

Each pair of planes intersects in a line. The three lines intersect in $(1, -4, 3)$, the solution of the system.

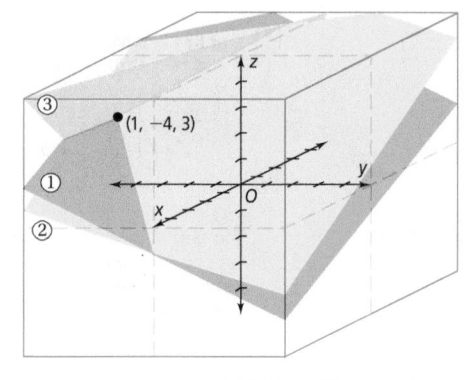

## Additional Problems

**1.** What is the solution of the system? Use elimination.

$\begin{cases} 3x + y - z = 1 \\ x + 2y + z = 4 \\ 3x - y - z = 3 \end{cases}$

**ANSWER** $(2, -1, 4)$

**2.** What is the solution of the system? Use elimination.

$\begin{cases} x + y + 2z = -7 \\ 3x + y - 2z = 7 \\ -x - 3y + z = -9 \end{cases}$

**ANSWER** $(-1, 2, -4)$

**3.** What is the $x$-value of the solution of the system?

$\begin{cases} x - 2y + z = 1 \\ 2x + z = 9 \\ -3x + y = -3 \end{cases}$

**ANSWER** 2

**4.** You are an office supply distributor and budget $7200 for 80 office chairs. You can buy leather chairs for $125 each, mesh chairs for $100 each, and fabric chairs for $75 each. If you want to have 3 times as many fabric chairs as leather chairs, how many of each type should you buy?

**ANSWER** 16 leather chairs, 16 mesh chairs, 48 fabric chairs

You can also use substitution to solve a system of three equations. Substitution is the best method to use when you can easily solve one of the equations for a single variable.

 **Problem 3** Solving a System Using Substitution

**Multiple Choice** What is the $x$-value in the solution of the system?

$$\begin{array}{l} ① \\ ② \\ ③ \end{array} \begin{cases} 2x + 3y - 2z = -1 \\ x + 5y = 9 \\ 4z - 5x = 4 \end{cases}$$

Ⓐ 1      Ⓒ 6
Ⓑ 4      Ⓓ 10

**Think**

**Which equation should you solve for one of its variables?**
Look for an equation that has a variable with coefficient 1.

**Step 1** Choose equation ②. Solve for $x$.

②   $x + 5y = 9$
     $x = 9 - 5y$

**Step 2** Substitute the expression for $x$ into equations ① and ③ and simplify.

①      $2x + 3y - 2z = -1$
     $2(9 - 5y) + 3y - 2z = -1$
     $18 - 10y + 3y - 2z = -1$
         $18 - 7y - 2z = -1$
④          $-7y - 2z = -19$

③      $4z - 5x = 4$
     $4z - 5(9 - 5y) = 4$
     $4z - 45 + 25y = 4$
         $4z + 25y = 49$
⑤          $25y + 4z = 49$

**Step 3** Write the two new equations as a system. Solve for $y$ and $z$.

④ $\begin{cases} -7y - 2z = -19 \\ 25y + 4z = 49 \end{cases}$

$\begin{array}{l} -14y - 4z = -38 \\ \underline{25y + 4z = 49} \\ 11y = 11 \\ y = 1 \end{array}$   Multiply by 2.
     Then add.

④   $-7y - 2z = -19$
     $-7(1) - 2z = -19$    Substitute the value of $y$ into ④.
       $-2z = -12$
         $z = 6$

**Step 4** Use one of the original equations to solve for $x$.

②   $x + 5y = 9$
     $x + 5(1) = 9$    Substitute the value of $y$ into ②.
       $x = 4$

The solution of the system is $(4, 1, 6)$, and $x = 4$.

The correct answer is B.

**Got It?** **3. a.** What is the solution of the system?
Use substitution.

$\begin{cases} x - 2y + z = -4 \\ -4x + y - 2z = 1 \\ 2x + 2y - z = 10 \end{cases}$

     **b. Reasoning** In Problem 3, was it necessary to find the value of $z$ to solve the problem? Explain.

---

**Problem 3**

**Q** Problems 1 and 2 on the previous pages both used a method called elimination. Was the Substitution Property of Equality used in those problems? Explain. **[Yes; answers may vary. Sample: In Problem 2, the value of $z$ was substituted into equation 4, and then the values of $x$ and $z$ were substituted into equation 1.]**

**Q** Look at equations 4 and 5 in Step 3. Would you use substitution to solve for $y$? **[Answers may vary. Sample: No; you could not easily solve for $z$ in terms of $y$ in either equation.]**

**Q** Could you have solved this problem using elimination? Would it have been a better method? Explain. **[Answers may vary. Samples: Yes; this problem could be solved using elimination. No; since none of variables have the same or inverse coefficients in at least two of the three equations, you would have to multiply the equations by constants in order to eliminate a variable.]**

**Got It?**      SYNTHESIS

**Q** What process could you use to solve this system of equations? **[Answers may vary. Sample: Solve equation 2 for $y$ and equation 3 for $z$ and substitute both into equation 1 and solve for $x$.]**

---

# Answers

**Got It?** (continued)

**2. a.** $(4, -1, 2)$

     **b.** Answers may vary. Sample: Yes; you can choose to eliminate either $x$, $y$, or $z$ resulting in a system of equations in 2 variables.

**3. a.** $(2, 1, -4)$

     **b.** No; in Step 1 we solved for $x$ in terms of $y$ only. Therefore, once we found the value of $y$ we could have substituted that value into the equation we wrote in Step 1 and solved for $x$ without ever finding the $z$-value.

## Problem 4      ELL SUPPORT

**Q** You will *budget* $6000 to restock 200 shirts. What does it mean to *budget* an amount of money in this situation? **[Answers may vary. Samples: plan to spend, set aside]**

**Q** You will budget $6000 to *restock* 200 shirts. What does it mean to *restock* a number of shirts in this situation? **[Answers may vary. Samples: replace, buy]**

**Q** Look at the system of equations in the Write section. Which method do you think is best to solve this system: elimination or substitution? Explain your choice. **[Answers may vary. Sample: A combination of substitution and elimination. Use $z = 2y$ to substitute for $z$ in both equation 1 and equation 3, but then use elimination to solve the resulting equations in $x$ and $y$.]**

### Got It?

Make sure students use the following system.

$$\begin{cases} x + y + z = 200 \\ x = y \\ 12x + 24y + 36z = 5400 \end{cases}$$

**Q** Why is equation 1 the same in Problem 4 and the Got It? **[You are still buying a total of 200 shirts.]**

---

 **Problem 4** Solving a Real-World Problem

**Business** You manage a clothing store and budget $6000 to restock 200 shirts. You can buy T-shirts for $12 each, polo shirts for $24 each, and rugby shirts for $36 each. If you want to have twice as many rugby shirts as polo shirts, how many of each type of shirt should you buy?

**Relate**  T-shirts + polo shirts + rugby shirts = 200

rugby shirts = 2 · polo shirts

12 · T-shirts + 24 · polo shirts + 36 · rugby shirts = 6000

**Think**

How many unknowns are there?
There are three unknowns: the number of each type of shirt.

**Define**  Let $x$ = the number of T-shirts.

Let $y$ = the number of polo shirts.

Let $z$ = the number of rugby shirts.

**Write**
$$\begin{cases} ① \quad x + y + z = 200 \\ ② \quad z = 2 \cdot y \\ ③ \quad 12 \cdot x + 24 \cdot y + 36 \cdot z = 6000 \end{cases}$$

**Step 1** Since 12 is a common factor of all the terms in equation ③, write a simpler equivalent equation.

③ $\begin{cases} 12x + 24y + 36z = 6000 \\ ④ \quad x + 2y + 3z = 500 \qquad \text{Divide by 12.} \end{cases}$

**Step 2** Substitute $2y$ for $z$ in equations ① and ④. Simplify to find equations ⑤ and ⑥.

①    $x + y + z = 200$       ④    $x + 2y + 3z = 500$

    $x + y + (2y) = 200$         $x + 2y + 3(2y) = 500$

⑤      $x + 3y = 200$         ⑥      $x + 8y = 500$

**Step 3** Write ⑤ and ⑥ as a system. Solve for $x$ and $y$.

⑤ $\begin{cases} x + 3y = 200 \\ ⑥ \quad x + 8y = 500 \end{cases}$    $\begin{aligned} -x - 3y &= -200 \quad \text{Multiply by } -1. \\ x + 8y &= 500 \quad \text{Then add.} \\ \hline 5y &= 300 \\ y &= 60 \end{aligned}$

⑤      $x + 3y = 200$

       $x + 3(60) = 200$    Substitute the value of $y$ into ⑤.

          $x = 20$

**Step 4** Substitute the value of $y$ in ② and solve for $z$.

② $z = 2y$

   $z = 2(60) = 120$

You should buy 20 T-shirts, 60 polo shirts, and 120 rugby shirts.

 **Got It?**  **4.** Suppose you want to have the same number of T-shirts as polo shirts. Buying 200 shirts with a budget of $5400, how many of each shirt should you buy?

---

# Answers

**Got It?** (continued)

**4.** 50 T-shirts, 50 polo shirts, and 100 rugby shirts

**Lesson Check**

**Do you know HOW?**

Solve each system.

1. $\begin{cases} 2y - 3z = 0 \\ x + 3y = -4 \\ 3x + 4y = 3 \end{cases}$

2. $\begin{cases} 3x + y - 2z = 22 \\ x + 5y + z = 4 \\ x = -3z \end{cases}$

3. $\begin{cases} 2x + 3y - 2z = 1 \\ -x - y + 2z = 5 \\ 3x + 2y - 3z = -6 \end{cases}$

4. $\begin{cases} 2x - y + z = -2 \\ x + 3y - z = 10 \\ x + 2z = -8 \end{cases}$

**Do you UNDERSTAND?**

5. **Reasoning** How do you decide whether substitution is the best method to solve a system in three variables?

6. **Error Analysis** A classmate says that the system consisting of $x = 0$, $y = 0$, and $z = 0$ has no solution. Explain the student's error.

7. **Writing** How many solutions does this system have? Explain your answer in terms of intersecting planes. (*Hint:* Is the system dependent? inconsistent?)

① $\begin{cases} 2x - 3y + z = 5 \\ 2x - 3y + z = -2 \\ -4x + 6y - 2z = 10 \end{cases}$

8. The graph of a system is shown. How many solutions does this system have? Explain.

  **Practice and Problem-Solving Exercises**

Ⓐ **Practice**    Solve each system by elimination. Check your answers.     ◀ **See Problems 1 and 2.**

9. $\begin{cases} x - y + z = -1 \\ x + y + 3z = -3 \\ 2x - y + 2z = 0 \end{cases}$

10. $\begin{cases} x - y - 2z = 4 \\ -x + 2y + z = 1 \\ -x + y - 3z = 11 \end{cases}$

11. $\begin{cases} -2x + y - z = 2 \\ -x - 3y + z = -10 \\ 3x + 6z = -24 \end{cases}$

12. $\begin{cases} a + b + c = -3 \\ 3b - c = 4 \\ 2a - b - 2c = -5 \end{cases}$

13. $\begin{cases} 6q - r + 2s = 8 \\ 2q + 3r - s = -9 \\ 4q + 2r + 5s = 1 \end{cases}$

14. $\begin{cases} x - y + 2z = -7 \\ y + z = 1 \\ x = 2y + 3z \end{cases}$

15. $\begin{cases} 3x + 3y + 6z = 9 \\ 2x + y + 3z = 7 \\ x + 2y - z = -10 \end{cases}$

16. $\begin{cases} 3x - y + z = 3 \\ x + y + 2z = 4 \\ x + 2y + z = 4 \end{cases}$

17. $\begin{cases} x - 2y + 3z = 12 \\ 2x - y - 2z = 5 \\ 2x + 2y - z = 4 \end{cases}$

18. $\begin{cases} x + 2y = 2 \\ 2x + 3y - z = -9 \\ 4x + 2y + 5z = 1 \end{cases}$

19. $\begin{cases} 3x + 2y + 2z = -2 \\ 2x + y - z = -2 \\ x - 3y + z = 0 \end{cases}$

20. $\begin{cases} x + 4y - 5z = -7 \\ 3x + 2y + 3z = 7 \\ 2x + y + 5z = 8 \end{cases}$

---

## Lesson Check

**1.** $(5, -3, -2)$

**2.** $(6, 0, -2)$

**3.** $(0, 3, 4)$

**4.** $(2, 1, -5)$

**5.** Answers may vary. Sample: Substitution is the best method to use when one of the equations can be solved easily for one variable.

**6.** Answers may vary. Sample: $(0, 0, 0)$ is a unique solution to a system of three variables. The planes intersect at one common point. When a system has no solution, no point lies in all three planes.

**7.** No solution since no point lies in all three planes. The three planes are parallel.

**8.** infinitely many solutions

## Practice and Problem-Solving Exercises

**9.** $(4, 2, -3)$

**10.** $(0, 2, -3)$

**11.** $(2, 1, -5)$

**12.** $(-3, 1, -1)$

**13.** $\left(\frac{1}{2}, -3, 1\right)$

**14.** $(0, 3, -2)$

**15.** $(1, -4, 3)$

**16.** $(1, 1, 1)$

**17.** $(4, -1, 2)$

**18.** $\left(-\frac{122}{11}, \frac{72}{11}, \frac{71}{11}\right)$

**19.** $\left(-\frac{10}{13}, -\frac{2}{13}, \frac{4}{13}\right)$

**20.** $(2, -1, 1)$

---

# 3 Lesson Check

## Do you know HOW?

- For Exercise 1, if students have trouble choosing a method, explain that either will work. If they choose elimination, they may want to multiply equation 2 by $-3$. If they choose substitution, they may want to solve equation 2 for $x$.

## Do you UNDERSTAND?

- For Exercise 5, if students have trouble coming up with ideas, suggest that students reread the paragraph preceding Problem 3.

## Close

**Q** How can you represent the solutions of a three-variable system of equations graphically? **[as the intersection of planes]**

**Q** How can you decide whether to use elimination or substitution to solve a three-variable system? **[Choose whichever makes it easier to reduce the system to two equations with two variables and then to find the value of one of the variables.]**

**PowerAlgebra.com**

## 3 Lesson Check

For a digital lesson check, use the Got It questions.

**Support in Algebra 2 Companion**
- Lesson Check

## 4 Practice

Assign homework to individual students or to an entire class.

# 4 Practice

## ASSIGNMENT GUIDE

Basic: 9–33, 38–42 even

Average: 9–29 odd, 31–42

Advanced: 9–29 odd, 31–45

Standardized Test Prep: 46–49

Mixed Review: 50–56

**Reasoning** exercises have blue headings.

**Applications** exercises have red headings.

**EXERCISE 32:** Use the Think About a Plan worksheet in the **Practice and Problem Solving Workbook** (also available in the Teaching Resources in print and online) to further support students' development in becoming independent learners.

## HOMEWORK QUICK CHECK

To check students' understanding of key skills and concepts, go over Exercises 9, 23, 31, 32, and 38.

---

Solve each system by substitution. Check your answers.  See Problems 3 and 4.

**21.** $\begin{cases} x + 2y + 3z = 6 \\ y + 2z = 0 \\ z = 2 \end{cases}$

**22.** $\begin{cases} 3a + b + c = 7 \\ a + 3b - c = 13 \\ b = 2a - 1 \end{cases}$

**23.** $\begin{cases} 5r - 4s - 3t = 3 \\ t = s + r \\ r = 3s + 1 \end{cases}$

**24.** $\begin{cases} 13 = 3x - y \\ 4y - 3x + 2z = -3 \\ z = 2x - 4y \end{cases}$

**25.** $\begin{cases} x + 3y - z = -4 \\ 2x - y + 2z = 13 \\ 3x - 2y - z = -9 \end{cases}$

**26.** $\begin{cases} x - 4y + z = 6 \\ 2x + 5y - z = 7 \\ 2x - y - z = 1 \end{cases}$

**27.** $\begin{cases} x - y + 2z = 7 \\ 2x + y + z = 8 \\ x - z = 5 \end{cases}$

**28.** $\begin{cases} x + y + z = 2 \\ x + 2z = 5 \\ 2x + y - z = -1 \end{cases}$

**29.** $\begin{cases} 5x - y + z = 4 \\ x + 2y - z = 5 \\ 2x + 3y - 3z = 5 \end{cases}$

**30.** **Manufacturing** In a factory there are three machines, *A*, *B*, and *C*. When all three machines are working, they produce 287 bolts per hour. When only machines *A* and *C* are working, they produce 197 bolts per hour. When only machines *A* and *B* are working, they produce 202 bolts per hour. How many bolts can each machine produce per hour?

 **Apply**

**31.** **Think About a Plan** In triangle *PQR*, the measure of angle *Q* is three times the measure of angle *P*. The measure of angle *R* is 20° more than the measure of angle *P*. Find the measure of each angle.
- What are the unknowns in this problem?
- What system of equations represents this situation?
- Which method of solving looks easier for this problem?

**32.** **Sports** A stadium has 49,000 seats. Seats sell for $25 in Section A, $20 in Section B, and $15 in Section C. The number of seats in Section A equals the total number of seats in Sections B and C. Suppose the stadium takes in $1,052,000 from each sold-out event. How many seats does each section hold?

Solve each system using any method.

**33.** $\begin{cases} x - 3y + 2z = 11 \\ -x + 4y + 3z = 5 \\ 2x - 2y - 4z = 2 \end{cases}$

**34.** $\begin{cases} x + 2y + z = 4 \\ 2x - y + 4z = -8 \\ -3x + y - 2z = -1 \end{cases}$

**35.** $\begin{cases} 4x - y + 2z = -6 \\ -2x + 3y - z = 8 \\ 2y + 3z = -5 \end{cases}$

**36.** $\begin{cases} 4a + 2b + c = 2 \\ 5a - 3b + 2c = 17 \\ a - 5b = 3 \end{cases}$

**37.** $\begin{cases} 4x - 2y + 5z = 6 \\ 3x + 3y + 8z = 4 \\ x - 5y - 3z = 5 \end{cases}$

**38.** $\begin{cases} 2\ell + 2w + h = 72 \\ \ell = 3w \\ h = 2w \end{cases}$

**39.** $\begin{cases} 6x + y - 4z = -8 \\ \frac{y}{4} - \frac{z}{6} = 0 \\ 2x - z = -2 \end{cases}$

**40.** $\begin{cases} 4y + 2x = 6 - 3z \\ x + z - 2y = -5 \\ x - 2z = 3y - 7 \end{cases}$

**41.** $\begin{cases} 4x - y + z = -5 \\ -x + y - z = 5 \\ 2x - z - 1 = y \end{cases}$

**42.** **Finance** A worker received a $10,000 bonus and decided to split it among three different accounts. He placed part in a savings account paying 4.5% per year, twice as much in government bonds paying 5%, and the rest in a mutual fund that returned 4%. His income from these investments after one year was $455. How much did the worker place in each account?

---

# Answers

## Practice and Problem-Solving Exercises (continued)

**21.** $(8, -4, 2)$

**22.** $(2, 3, -2)$

**23.** $(-2, -1, -3)$

**24.** $(5, 2, 2)$

**25.** $(0, 1, 7)$

**26.** $(4, 1, 6)$

**27.** $(5, -2, 0)$

**28.** $(1, -1, 2)$

**29.** $(1, 3, 2)$

**30.** Machine A: 112 bolts per hour; Machine B: 90 bolts per hour; Machine C: 85 bolts per hour

**31.** $m\angle P = 32°$; $m\angle Q = 96°$; $m\angle R = 52°$

**32.** Section A has 24,500 seats; Section B has 14,400 seats; and Section C has 10,100 seats.

**33.** $(8, 1, 3)$

**34.** $(3, 2, -3)$

**35.** $\left(\frac{1}{2}, 2, -3\right)$

**36.** $(-2, -1, 12)$

**37.** no solution

**38.** $(21.6, 7.2, 14.4)$

**39.** $(2, 4, 6)$

**40.** $(-1, 2, 0)$

**41.** $(0, 2, -3)$

**42.** He placed $2200 in the savings account, $4400 in government bonds, and $3400 in the mutual fund.

**43. Open-Ended** Write your own system with three variables. Begin by choosing the solution. Then write three equations that are true for your solution. Use elimination to solve the system.

**44. Geometry** Refer to the regular five-pointed star at the right. Write and solve a system of three equations to find the measure of each labeled angle.

**45. Geometry** In the regular polyhedron described below, all faces are congruent polygons. Use a system of three linear equations to find the numbers of vertices, edges, and faces.

Every face has five edges and every edge is shared by two faces. Every face has five vertices and every vertex is shared by three faces. The sum of the number of vertices and faces is two more than the number of edges.

## Standardized Test Prep

GRIDDED RESPONSE

SAT/ACT

**46.** What is the value of $z$ in the solution of the system? $\begin{cases} y = -2x + 10 \\ -x + y - 2z = -2 \\ 3x - 2y + 4z = 7 \end{cases}$

**47.** What is the $x$-intercept of the line at the right after it is translated up 3 units?

**48.** Suppose $y$ varies directly with $x$, and $y = 15$ when $x = 10$. What is $y$ when $x = 22$?

**49.** A theater has 490 seats. Seats sell for $25 on the floor, $20 in the mezzanine, and $15 in the balcony. The number of seats on the floor equals the total number of seats in the mezzanine and balcony. Suppose the theater takes in $10,520 from each sold-out event. How many seats does the mezzanine section hold?

## Mixed Review

**50.** Maximize the objective function $P = x + 3y$ under the given constraints. At what vertex does this maximum value occur?

$\begin{cases} x + y \le 5 \\ x + 2y \le 8 \\ x \ge 0, y \ge 0 \end{cases}$

◆ See Lesson 3-4.

Solve each inequality. Graph the solution on a number line. ◆ See Lesson 1-5.

**51.** $-4x + 3 \le 9$     **52.** $-(x + 4) - 3 \ge 11$     **53.** $2(3x - 1) < x - 7$

**Get Ready!** To prepare for Lesson 3-6, do Exercises 54–56.

Solve each system using elimination. ◆ See Lesson 3-2.

**54.** $\begin{cases} x + 4y = 12 \\ 2x - 8y = 4 \end{cases}$     **55.** $\begin{cases} 4x + 8y = -6 \\ 6x + 12y = -9 \end{cases}$     **56.** $\begin{cases} 4y - 2x = 6 \\ 8y = 4x - 12 \end{cases}$

 PowerAlgebra.com    Lesson 3-5   Systems With Three Variables     173

---

**43.** Answers may vary. Sample: Solution is (1, 2, 3).

$\begin{cases} x + y + z = 6 \\ 2x - y + 2z = 6 \\ 3x + 3y + z = 12 \end{cases}$

**44.** $\begin{cases} x + 2y = 180 \\ y + z = 180 \\ 5z = 540 \end{cases}$

Solution is $x = 36$, $y = 72$, $z = 108$

**45.** Let $E$, $F$, and $V$ represent the number of edges, faces, and vertices, respectively. From the first statement, $E = \frac{5}{2}F$. From the second statement, $V = \frac{5}{3}F$. From the third statement, $V + F = E + 2$. Solving this system of 3 equations yields $E = 30$, $F = 12$, and $V = 20$.

**46.** $\frac{3}{2}$

**47.** $\frac{3}{2}$

**48.** 33

**49.** 144 mezzanine seats

**50.** $P = 12$ is maximized at $(0, 4)$.

**51.** $x \ge -\frac{3}{2}$;

**52.** $x \le -18$;

**53.** $x < -1$;

**54.** $\left(7, \frac{5}{4}\right)$

**55.** dependent system; infinite number of solutions,

$\left\{ (x, y) \mid y = -\frac{1}{2}x - \frac{3}{4} \right\}$

**56.** inconsistent system; no solution

# Additional Instructional Support

## Algebra 2 Companion

Students can use the **Algebra 2 Companion** worktext (4 pages) as you teach the lesson. Use the Companion to support

- New Vocabulary
- Key Concepts
- Got It for each Problem
- Lesson Check

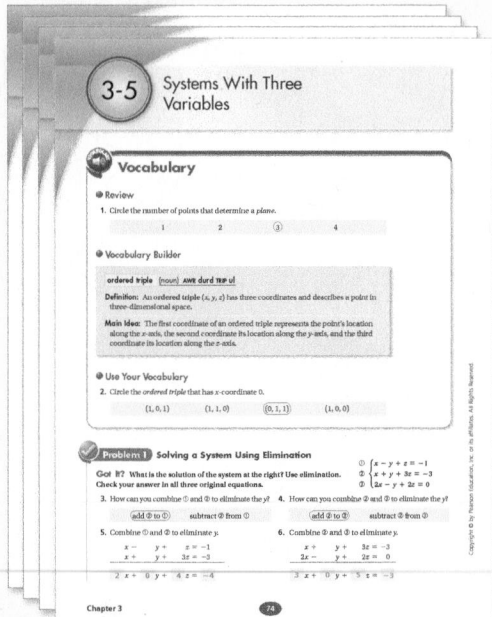

## ELL Support

**Focus on Communication** Write the system below on a transparency including 1s for "missing" coefficients. Place another transparency on top to write on. Draw an oval to enclose the x-column and state the numbers. Move the oval from column to column, stating the coefficients in each column. Ask which coefficients add up to zero. Keep the oval on the z-column and say: 1 and −1 are opposites. I will eliminate z.

$$2x - 1y + 1z = 4$$
$$1x + 3y - 1z = 11$$
$$4x + 2y - 1z = 14$$

---

# 5 Assess & Remediate

## Lesson Quiz

**1.** What is the solution of the system? Use elimination.

$$\begin{cases} x + y - 3z = -8 \\ -x - 2y + z = 4 \\ -x + y + 4z = 7 \end{cases}$$

**2.** What is the solution of the system? Use elimination.

$$\begin{cases} 2x + 2y + z = 7 \\ -x - y + z = -5 \\ x + 3y - 4z = 12 \end{cases}$$

**3.** What is the x-value in the solution of the system?

$$\begin{cases} x - 3y + 2z = 14 \\ 3x - 2z = 7 \\ 2x - y = 9 \end{cases}$$

**4. Do you UNDERSTAND?** You manage a health food store and budget $80 to buy ingredients to make 30 pounds of trail mix. Peanuts cost $2.50 per pound, raisins cost $2.00 per pound, and granola costs $4.00 per pound. If you use twice as many pounds of peanuts as raisins, how many pounds of each ingredient should you buy?

### ANSWERS TO LESSON QUIZ

**1.** $(3, -2, 3)$

**2.** $(2, 2, -1)$

**3.** 3

**4.** 16 lb of peanuts, 8 lb of raisins, 6 lb of granola

### PRESCRIPTION FOR REMEDIATION

Use the student work on the Lesson Quiz to prescribe a differentiated review assignment:

| Points | Differentiated Remediation |
|--------|---------------------------|
| 0–2 | Intervention |
| 3 | On-level |
| 4 | Extension |

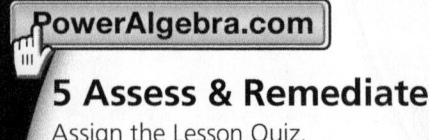

## 5 Assess & Remediate

Assign the Lesson Quiz. Appropriate intervention, practice, or enrichment is automatically generated based on student performance.

---

## Intervention

- **Reteaching** (2 pages) Provides reteaching and practice exercises for the key lesson concepts. Use with struggling students or absent students.

- **English Language Learner Support** Helps students develop and reinforce mathematical vocabulary and key concepts.

### All-in-One Resources/Online
### Reteaching

### All-in-One Resources/Online
### English Language Learner Support

# Differentiated Remediation *continued*

## On-Level

- **Practice** (2 pages) Provides extra practice for each lesson. For simpler practice exercises, use the Form K Practice pages found in the All-in-One Teaching Resources and online.

- **Think About a Plan** Helps students develop specific problem-solving skills and strategies by providing scaffolded guiding questions.

- **Standardized Test Prep** Focuses on all major exercises, all major question types, and helps students prepare for the high-stakes assessments.

## Extension

- **Enrichment** Provides students with interesting problems and activities that extend the concepts of the lesson.

- **Activities, Games, and Puzzles** Worksheets that can be used for concepts development, enrichment, and for fun!

---

### Practice and Problem Solving Wkbk/ All-in-One Resources/Online
**Practice page 1**

### Practice and Problem Solving Wkbk/ All-in-One Resources/Online
**Practice page 2**

### All-in-One Resources/Online
**Enrichment**

---

### Practice and Problem Solving Wkbk/ All-in-One Resources/Online
**Think About a Plan**

### Practice and Problem Solving Wkbk/ All-in-One Resources/Online
**Standardized Test Prep**

### Online Teacher Resource Center
**Activities, Games, and Puzzles**

# 1 Interactive Learning

## Solve It!

**PURPOSE** To prepare students to use matrices to solve a system of linear equations

**PROCESS** Students may

- use Rule 1 to obtain a 1 in row 2, column 2.
- replace the eights in column 2 by using the 1 from the previous step and both rules.
- obtain a 1 in row 3, column 3 using Rule 1.
- replace the 2 in column 3 by using the 1 from the previous step and both rules.

### FACILITATE

**Q** Examine the game array. What numbers from Figure 1 must you change to match Figure 2? **[You must change all of the numbers in column 2, and the numbers in rows 1 and 3 of column 3.]**

**Q** Examine column 2. What math operation would be used to change a 4 to a 1? **[Multiply 4 by its reciprocal, $\frac{1}{4}$ (Rule 1).]**

**Q** How would we use that 1 to change the eights to zeros? **[Multiply row 2 by $-8$ and add the result to row 1 and then row 3 (Rule 2).]**

**Q** What steps would you use on column 3 to change it to a 0,0,1? **[Multiply row 3 by $\frac{1}{2}$ (Rule 1), then multiply row 3 by $-2$ and add the result to row 1 (Rule 2).]**

**ANSWER** See Solve It in Answers on next page.
**CONNECT THE MATH** In the Solve It, the "Game Rules" used to solve the puzzle are actually matrix row operations. In the lesson, students use row operations to solve systems of linear equations expressed as matrices.

---

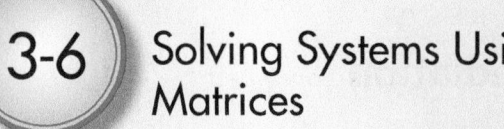
**Objectives** To represent a system of linear equations with a matrix
To solve a system of linear equations using matrices

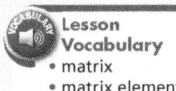

**Lesson Vocabulary**
- matrix
- matrix element
- row operation

An array of numbers, such as each of those suggested by the tile arrangements in the Solve It, is a matrix.

**Essential Understanding** You can use a *matrix* to represent and solve a system of equations without writing the variables.

A **matrix** is a rectangular array of numbers. You usually display the array within brackets. The dimensions of a matrix are the numbers of rows and columns in the array.

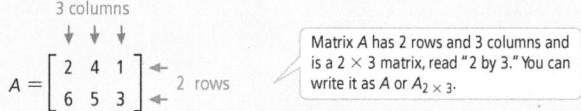

Matrix *A* has 2 rows and 3 columns and is a $2 \times 3$ matrix, read "2 by 3." You can write it as *A* or $A_{2 \times 3}$.

Each number in a matrix is a **matrix element**. You can identify a matrix element by its row and column numbers. In matrix *A*, $a_{12}$ is the element in row 1 and column 2. $a_{12}$ is the element 4.

---

# 3-6 Preparing to Teach

**BIG idea** Solving Equations and Inequalities    **UbD**

### ESSENTIAL UNDERSTANDINGS

- Matrices can be used to represent and solve a system of equations without writing the variables.
- The matrix row operations of adding rows and multiplying by a constant are equivalent to the addition and multiplication properties of equality.

## Math Background

Students have solved systems of linear equations by graphing and by applying the algebraic methods of substitution and elimination. In this lesson, students solve systems of equations using matrices.

Students must recognize that they are solving systems of equations when they use matrix operations. It may help if you relate the row operations to the steps in substitution and elimination.

Matrices have many applications including data storage and computer programming; solving systems of equations is one of these applications.

Emphasize that the order of the elements is important and that every row and column must have an entry. All coefficients are represented in the matrix, including zeros and ones.

## Support Student Learning

Use the **Algebra 2 Companion** to engage and support students during instruction. See Lesson Resources at the end of this lesson for details.

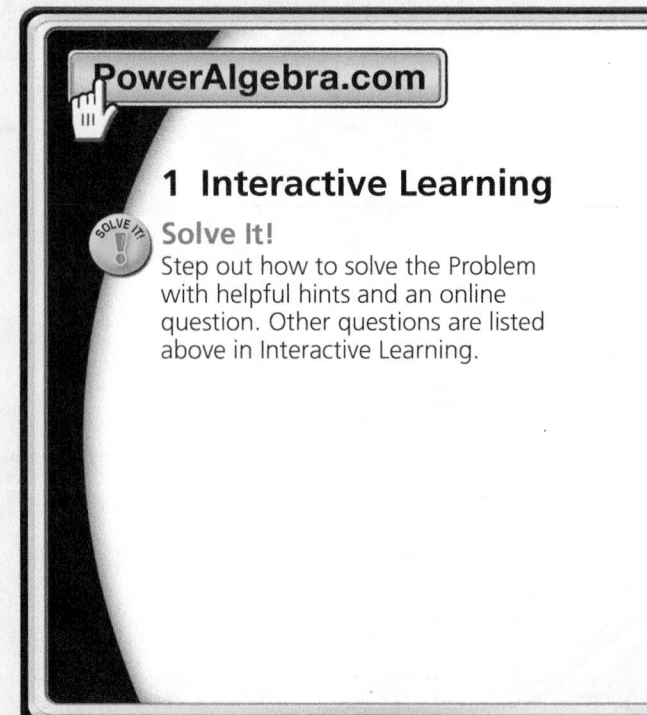

**PowerAlgebra.com**

## 1 Interactive Learning

### Solve It!

Step out how to solve the Problem with helpful hints and an online question. Other questions are listed above in Interactive Learning.

**Problem 1** Identifying a Matrix Element

GRIDDED RESPONSE

Does the order of the subscript in $a_{23}$ matter?
Yes. $a_{23}$ and $a_{32}$ are different elements.

What is element $a_{23}$ in matrix $A$?

$$A = \begin{bmatrix} 4 & -9 & 17 & 1 \\ 0 & 5 & 8 & 6 \\ -3 & -2 & 10 & 0 \end{bmatrix}$$

$A_{23}$ is in Row 2 and Column 3.

$a_{23}$ is 8.

 **Got It? 1.** What is element $a_{13}$ in matrix $A$?

You can represent a system of equations efficiently with a matrix. Each matrix row represents an equation. The last matrix column shows the constants to the right of the equal signs. Each of the other columns shows the coefficients of one of the variables.

**System of Equations**
$$\begin{aligned} x + 3y &= 7 \\ 3x + y &= -8 \end{aligned}$$

x-coefficients  y-coefficients  constants

**Matrix**
$$\begin{bmatrix} 1 & 3 & 7 \\ 3 & 1 & -8 \end{bmatrix}$$

The 1's are coefficients of $x$ and $y$.

Draw a vertical bar to replace the equal signs and separate the coefficients from the constants.

 **Problem 2** Representing Systems With Matrices

Why is the order of elements important in a matrix?
Different orders of elements could correspond to different systems of equations.

How can you represent the system of equations with a matrix?

**A** $\begin{cases} 2x + y = 9 \\ x - 6y = -1 \end{cases}$

The matrix $\begin{bmatrix} 2 & 1 & 9 \\ 1 & -6 & -1 \end{bmatrix}$ represents the system above.

**B** $\begin{cases} x - 3y + z = 6 \\ x + 3z = 12 \\ y = -5x + 1 \end{cases}$

**Step 1** Write each equation in the same variable order. Line up the variables. Leave space where a coefficient is 0.

$$\begin{cases} x - 3y + z = 6 \\ x + 3z = 12 \\ 5x + y = 1 \end{cases}$$

**Step 2** Write the matrix using the coefficients and constants. Notice the 1's and 0's.

$$\begin{bmatrix} 1 & -3 & 1 & 6 \\ 1 & 0 & 3 & 12 \\ 5 & 1 & 0 & 1 \end{bmatrix}$$

---

# 2 Guided Instruction

## Problem 1    SYNTHESIZING
The notation is used to identify a particular element in a matrix.

> **Q** Which is listed first: row or column? **[Row always comes before column.]**

## Got It?    EXTENSION
Ask students to identify all remaining matrix elements by their positions.

## Problem 2    ERROR PREVENTION
Students must be able to write a system of equations in matrix form in order to solve the system by matrices.

> **Q** Why must a zero be included in a matrix that represents an equation that is missing a variable? Explain. **[A zero means that a coefficient is zero. If the zero was not included, the matrix would be missing a number.]**
>
> **Q** Does the matrix $\begin{bmatrix} 1 & -6 & -1 \\ 2 & 1 & 9 \end{bmatrix}$ represent the system in 2A? Why or why not? **[Yes. The rows represent equations. It does not matter which row is first.]**

# Answers

## Solve It!
Yes; multiply row 3 by $-1$ and add it to row 1. Multiply row 2 by 2 and add it to row 3. Divide row 2 by 8 and row 3 by $-2$.

## Got It?
**1.** 17

---

# 2 Guided Instruction

Each Problem is worked out and supported in the Student Online Center.

**Problem 1**
Identifying a Matrix Element

**Problem 2**
Representing a System With a Matrix
*Animated*

**Problem 3**
Writing a System from a Matrix
*Animated*

**Problem 4**
Solving a System Using a Matrix
*Animated*

**Problem 5**
Using a Calculator to Solve a Linear System

**Support in Algebra 2 Companion**
• Vocabulary
• Key Concepts
• Got It?

## Got It?                ERROR PREVENTION

Make sure the students write the third equation in 2b in standard form. A space must be left where a coefficient is zero in the second and third equations. Once the new system is written, represent it as a matrix.

## Problem 3              SYNTHESIZING

Students must be comfortable with representing matrices as systems and understand that matrices can represent many things, such as an inventory of different products at several different retail stores.

> **Q** What does each row represent? **[Each row represents a linear equation.]**
>
> **Q** What does each column represent? **[The columns before the | represent the coefficients of the variables. The column after | represents the constants.]**

## Got It?                ERROR PREVENTION

Before you write the linear system, count the columns to determine the number of variables. Insert variables in alphabetical order, taking note of any zeros.

## Take Note              SYNTHESIZING

The row operations are the only legal operations that can be used to change a matrix to the indicated form.

 **Got It?** **2.** How can you represent the system of equations with a matrix?

a. $\begin{cases} -4x - 2y = 7 \\ 3x + y = -5 \end{cases}$

b. $\begin{cases} 4x - y + 2z = 1 \\ y + 5z = 20 \\ 2x = -y + 7 \end{cases}$

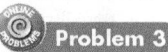 **Problem 3** **Writing a System From a Matrix**

What linear system of equations does this matrix represent? $\begin{bmatrix} 5 & 2 & | & 7 \\ 0 & 1 & | & 9 \end{bmatrix}$

| **Think** | **Write** |
|---|---|
| Each row shows coefficient-coefficient-constant of one equation. | $5x + 2y = 7$ <br> $0x + 1y = 9$ |
| Simplify. Write the system. | $\begin{cases} 5x + 2y = 7 \\ y = 9 \end{cases}$ |

 **Got It?** **3.** What linear system does $\begin{bmatrix} 2 & 0 & | & 6 \\ 5 & -2 & | & 1 \end{bmatrix}$ represent?

You can use a matrix that represents a system of equations to solve the system. In this way, you do not have to write the variables. To solve the system using the matrix, use the steps for solving by elimination. Each step is a **row operation**.

Your goal is to use row operations to get a matrix in the form $\begin{bmatrix} 1 & 0 & | & a \\ 0 & 1 & | & b \end{bmatrix}$ or $\begin{bmatrix} 1 & 0 & 0 & | & a \\ 0 & 1 & 0 & | & b \\ 0 & 0 & 1 & | & c \end{bmatrix}$

Notice that the first matrix represents the system $x = a, y = b$, which then will be the solution of a system of two equations in two unknowns. The second matrix represents the system $x = a, y = b$, and $z = c$.

**take note** **Key Concept** **Row Operations**

| | |
|---|---|
| Switch any two rows. | $\begin{bmatrix} 2 & -1 & 3 \\ 3 & 2 & 5 \end{bmatrix}$ becomes $\begin{bmatrix} 3 & 2 & 5 \\ 2 & -1 & 3 \end{bmatrix}$ |
| Multiply a row by a constant. | $\begin{bmatrix} 3 & 2 & 5 \\ 2 & -1 & 3 \end{bmatrix}$ becomes $\begin{bmatrix} 3 & 2 & 5 \\ 2\cdot2 & -1\cdot2 & 3\cdot2 \end{bmatrix} = \begin{bmatrix} 3 & 2 & 5 \\ 4 & -2 & 6 \end{bmatrix}$ |
| Add one row to another. | $\begin{bmatrix} 3 & 2 & 5 \\ 4 & -2 & 6 \end{bmatrix}$ becomes $\begin{bmatrix} 3+4 & 2-2 & 5+6 \\ 4 & -2 & 6 \end{bmatrix} = \begin{bmatrix} 7 & 0 & 11 \\ 4 & -2 & 6 \end{bmatrix}$ |
| Combine any of these steps. | |

# Additional Problems

**1.** What is $m_{12}$ in matrix $M$?

$M = \begin{bmatrix} 8 & 7 & 4 \\ 2 & 0 & 5 \end{bmatrix}$

**ANSWER** 7

**2.** How do you represent the system of equations $\begin{cases} 6x - y = 12 \\ -x + 10y = 1 \end{cases}$ with a matrix?

**ANSWER** $\begin{bmatrix} 6 & -1 & | & 12 \\ -1 & 10 & | & 1 \end{bmatrix}$

**3.** What linear system of equations does this matrix represent?

$\begin{bmatrix} -2 & 4 & 9 & | & 0 \\ -1 & 3 & 0 & | & 7 \\ 5 & 1 & 9 & | & 8 \end{bmatrix}$

**ANSWER**

$\begin{cases} -2x + 4y + 9z = 0 \\ -x + 3y = 7 \\ 5x + y + 9z = 8 \end{cases}$

**4.** What is the solution of this system?

$\begin{cases} x + 2y = 16 \\ 3x + y = 8 \end{cases}$

**ANSWER** $(0, 8)$

**5.** What is the solution of this system of equations? Use your calculator.

$\begin{cases} 3a + 2b - c = 7 \\ 2a - c = 5 \\ a - 4b + c = -4 \end{cases}$

**ANSWER** $\left(1, \frac{1}{2}, -3\right)$

**Problem 4** Solving a System Using a Matrix

**Think**

How is solving a system using row operations similar to using elimination?
You use the same steps but the variables don't appear in the matrices.

What is the solution of the system? $\begin{cases} x + 4y = -1 \\ 2x + 5y = 4 \end{cases}$

$\begin{bmatrix} 1 & 4 & | & -1 \\ 2 & 5 & | & 4 \end{bmatrix}$ 　　Write the matrix for the system.

$\begin{array}{r} -2 \ \ (1 \quad 4 \quad -1) \\ + \quad \ \ 2 \quad 5 \quad \ \ 4 \\ \hline 0 \quad -3 \quad \ \ 6 \end{array}$ 　Multiply Row 1 by $-2$. Add to Row 2. Replace Row 2 with the sum. Write the new matrix.

$\begin{bmatrix} 1 & 4 & | & -1 \\ 0 & -3 & | & 6 \end{bmatrix}$

$-\frac{1}{3} \ (0 \quad -3 \quad 6) = 0 \quad 1 \quad -2$ 　Multiply Row 2 by $-\frac{1}{3}$. Write the new matrix.

$\begin{bmatrix} 1 & 4 & | & -1 \\ 0 & 1 & | & -2 \end{bmatrix}$

$\begin{array}{r} 1 \quad 4 \quad -1 \\ + \ -4 \ \ (0 \quad 1 \quad -2) \\ \hline 1 \quad 0 \quad \ \ 7 \end{array}$ 　Multiply Row 2 by $-4$. Add to Row 1. Replace Row 1 with the sum. Write the new matrix.

$\begin{bmatrix} 1 & 0 & | & 7 \\ 0 & 1 & | & -2 \end{bmatrix}$

The solution to the system is $(7, -2)$.

**Check** 　　$x + 4y = -1$　　　$2x + 5y = 4$　Use the original equations.

$7 + 4(-2) \stackrel{?}{=} -1$　　$2(7) + 5(-2) \stackrel{?}{=} 4$　Substitute.

$7 + (-8) \stackrel{?}{=} -1$　　$14 + (-10) \stackrel{?}{=} 4$　Multiply.

$-1 = -1$ ✔　　　　$4 = 4$ ✔　Simplify.

**Got It? 4. a.** What is the solution of the system? $\begin{cases} 9x - 2y = 5 \\ 3x + 7y = 17 \end{cases}$

**b. Reasoning** Which method is more similar to solving a system using row operations: *elimination* or *substitution*? Justify your reasoning.

Matrices that represent the solution of a system are in *reduced row echelon form*. Many calculators have a **rref** (reduced row echelon form) function for working with matrices. This function will do all the row operations for you. You can use **rref** to solve a system of equations.

Problem 4 　　　　　　　　　　SYNTHESIZING

**Q** What is the reasoning behind the first row operation? **[The goal is to get a zero in the first column, second row. When you add the rows after multiplying, the $-2$ and 2 cancel, yielding a zero in the right place.]**

**Q** Why can't you multiply a row by 0? **[Multiplying by 0 makes every element in the row 0, eliminating the equation.]**

**Q** When would it be to your advantage to switch rows? Give an example. **[Answers may vary.**

**Sample: Switching rows in** $\begin{bmatrix} 0 & 5 & | & 2 \\ 1 & 0 & | & 3 \end{bmatrix}$ **produces**

$\begin{bmatrix} 1 & 0 & | & 3 \\ 0 & 5 & | & 2 \end{bmatrix}$**. It saves time because the first column now contains 1 and 0 in the correct order.]**

**Got It?**

**Q** What do the matrix row operations have in common with elimination? **[Answers may vary. Sample: In row operations, you can multiply a row by a constant and add rows together. In elimination, you can multiply the coefficients of an equation by a constant and add the coefficients in both equations.]**

# Answers

**Got It?** (continued)

**2. a.** $\begin{bmatrix} -4 & -2 & | & 7 \\ 3 & 1 & | & -5 \end{bmatrix}$

**b.** $\begin{bmatrix} 4 & -1 & 2 & | & 1 \\ 0 & 1 & 5 & | & 20 \\ 2 & 1 & 0 & | & 7 \end{bmatrix}$

**3.** $\begin{cases} 2x = 6 \\ 5x - 2y = 1 \end{cases}$

**4. a.** $(1, 2)$

**b.** elimination; you use the same steps to solve

## Problem 5

Students use the calculator matrix method to solve a system of equations.

**Q** Why is this a 3 × 4 matrix when entered in the calculator? **[The system has 3 equations, which means the matrix has 3 rows. The system has 4 columns because there are 3 variables and 1 column of constants.]**

**Q** What is an example of a system of two linear equations with two variables that has no solution? **[Answers may vary. Sample:** $\begin{cases} x + y = 1 \\ x + y = 2 \end{cases}$**]**

**Q** What happens when you try to solve this as a matrix? **[You get a row that represents a false equation, such as 0 + 0 = 1.]**

**Q** What is an example of a system of two linear equations in two variables that has infinitely many solutions? **[**$\begin{cases} x + y = 1 \\ x + y = 1 \end{cases}$**]**

**Q** What happens when you try to solve this as a matrix? **[You get a row that represents an equation that is always true, such as 0 + 0 = 0.]**

## Got It?

Make a list of all of the calculator matrix steps. Check off each step as it is completed.

---

 **Problem 5** Using a Calculator to Solve a Linear System

What is the solution of the system of equations? $\begin{cases} 2a + 3b - c = 1 \\ -4a + 9b + 2c = 8 \\ -2a + 2c = 3 \end{cases}$

**Think**

How do you enter missing variables into a matrix?
If a variable is not present in an equation, enter its coefficient as 0 in the matrix.

**Step 1** Enter the system into a calculator as a matrix.

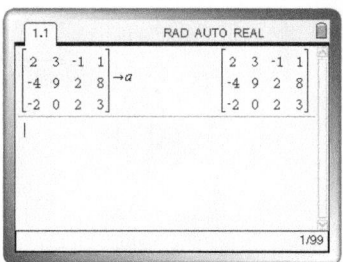

**Step 2** Apply the **rref()** function to the matrix. Put the matrix elements in fraction form if some are not integers.

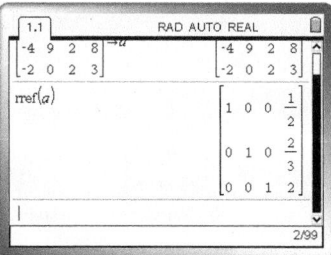

**Step 3** List the solution.

The solution of the system is $a = \frac{1}{2}, b = \frac{2}{3}, c = 2$.

**Check**

$$2a + 3b - c = 1$$
$$2\left(\frac{1}{2}\right) + 3\left(\frac{2}{3}\right) - 2 \stackrel{?}{=} 1$$
$$1 + 2 - 2 \stackrel{?}{=} 1$$
$$1 = 1 \;\checkmark$$

$$-4a + 9b + 2c = 8$$
$$-4\left(\frac{1}{2}\right) + 9\left(\frac{2}{3}\right) + 2(2) \stackrel{?}{=} 8$$
$$-2 + 6 + 4 \stackrel{?}{=} 8$$
$$8 = 8 \;\checkmark$$

$$-2a + 2c = 3$$
$$-2\left(\frac{1}{2}\right) + 2(2) \stackrel{?}{=} 3$$
$$-1 + 4 \stackrel{?}{=} 3$$
$$3 = 3 \;\checkmark$$

 **Got It?** **5.** What is the solution of the system of equations?
$$\begin{cases} a + 4b + 6c = 21 \\ 2a - 2b + c = 4 \\ -8b + c = -1 \end{cases}$$

---

## Answers

**Got It?** (continued)

**5.** $\left(1, \frac{1}{2}, 3\right)$

## Lesson Check

**1.** $2 \times 1$

**2.** $2 \times 4$

**3.** $\begin{bmatrix} 3 & 5 & | & 0 \\ 1 & 1 & | & 2 \end{bmatrix}$

**4.** $\begin{bmatrix} 1 & 3 & -1 & | & 2 \\ 1 & 0 & 2 & | & 8 \\ 0 & 2 & -1 & | & 1 \end{bmatrix}$

**5.** 16

**6.** $a_{21}$ is 0, the element in row 2, column 1. $a_{12}$ is −9, the element in row 1 and column 2.

**7.** Answers may vary. Sample: The entry fee to a school play is $2 for adults. Jamie paid a total of $8 for 4 student entry fees and 2 adult entry fees. What is the student entry fee?

**Do you know HOW?**

State the dimensions of each matrix.

1. $\begin{bmatrix} 2 \\ 5 \end{bmatrix}$

2. $\begin{bmatrix} 6 & 9 & 0 & 3 \\ 4 & 6 & 2 & 7 \end{bmatrix}$

Write a matrix to represent each system.

3. $\begin{cases} 3a + 5b = 0 \\ a + b = 2 \end{cases}$

4. $\begin{cases} x + 3y - z = 2 \\ x + 2z = 8 \\ 2y - z = 1 \end{cases}$

**Do you UNDERSTAND?**

5. How many elements are in a $4 \times 4$ matrix?

6. **Writing** Using Matrix $A$ in Problem 1, describe the difference in identifying element $a_{21}$ and element $a_{12}$.

7. **Open-Ended** Write a situation that can be modeled by the matrix. $\begin{bmatrix} 4 & 2 & 8 \\ 0 & 1 & 2 \end{bmatrix}$

### Practice and Problem-Solving Exercises

**A** Practice

Identify the indicated element. $A = \begin{bmatrix} 3 & 12 & 6 \\ 1 & 0 & 9 \\ 8 & 7 & 4 \end{bmatrix}$

◀ See Problem 1.

8. $a_{32}$  9. $a_{21}$  10. $a_{13}$  11. $a_{31}$

Write a matrix to represent each system.  ◀ See Problem 2.

12. $\begin{cases} x + 2y = 11 \\ 2x + 3y = 18 \end{cases}$

13. $\begin{cases} 3x + 2y = 16 \\ y = 5 \end{cases}$

14. $\begin{cases} 2a - 3b = 6 \\ a + b = 2 \end{cases}$

15. $\begin{cases} r - s + t = 150 \\ 2r + t = 425 \\ s + 3t = 0 \end{cases}$

16. $\begin{cases} y = 3x - 7 \\ x = 2 \end{cases}$

17. $\begin{cases} x - y + z = 0 \\ x - 2y - z = 5 \\ 2x - y + 2z = 8 \end{cases}$

Write the system of equations represented by each matrix.  ◀ See Problem 3.

18. $\begin{bmatrix} 1 & 0 & 4 \\ 0 & 1 & -6 \end{bmatrix}$

19. $\begin{bmatrix} 5 & 1 & -3 \\ -2 & 2 & 4 \end{bmatrix}$

20. $\begin{bmatrix} -1 & 2 & -6 \\ 1 & 1 & 7 \end{bmatrix}$

21. $\begin{bmatrix} 2 & 1 & 1 & 1 \\ 1 & 1 & 1 & 2 \\ 1 & -1 & 1 & -2 \end{bmatrix}$

22. $\begin{bmatrix} 0 & 1 & 2 & 4 \\ -2 & 3 & 6 & 9 \\ 1 & 0 & 1 & 3 \end{bmatrix}$

23. $\begin{bmatrix} 5 & 2 & 1 & 5 \\ 4 & 1 & 2 & 8 \\ 1 & 3 & -6 & 2 \end{bmatrix}$

Solve the system of equations using a matrix.  ◀ See Problems 4 and 5.

24. $\begin{cases} x + 3y = 5 \\ x + 4y = 6 \end{cases}$

25. $\begin{cases} p - 3q = -1 \\ -5p + 16q = 5 \end{cases}$

26. $\begin{cases} 300x - y = 130 \\ 200x + y = 120 \end{cases}$

27. $\begin{cases} x + 3y = 22 \\ 2x - y = 2 \end{cases}$

28. $\begin{cases} x + 3y = 6 \\ 2x + 4y = 12 \end{cases}$

29. $\begin{cases} x + y = 5 \\ -2x + 4y = 8 \end{cases}$

---

## 3 Lesson Check

**Do you know HOW?**  ERROR INTERVENTION

- For Exercise 4, if students forget to place the zeros where the coefficient is zero, review Problem 2B.

**Do you UNDERSTAND?**

- For Exercise 7, if students have trouble coming up with ideas, have them first try writing the matrix as a linear system.

### Close

**Q** Why use matrices to solve systems of equations?
[Answers may vary. Sample: The matrix method can be used for any size system. Row operations can be done quickly. Calculators can be used for large systems.]

---

### Practice and Problem-Solving Exercises

8. 7  9. 1
10. 6  11. 8

12. $\begin{bmatrix} 1 & 2 & 11 \\ 2 & 3 & 18 \end{bmatrix}$

13. $\begin{bmatrix} 3 & 2 & 16 \\ 0 & 1 & 5 \end{bmatrix}$

14. $\begin{bmatrix} 2 & -3 & 6 \\ 1 & 1 & 2 \end{bmatrix}$

15. $\begin{bmatrix} 1 & -1 & 1 & 150 \\ 2 & 0 & 1 & 425 \\ 0 & 1 & 3 & 0 \end{bmatrix}$

16. $\begin{bmatrix} -3 & 1 & -7 \\ 1 & 0 & 2 \end{bmatrix}$

17. $\begin{bmatrix} 1 & -1 & 1 & 0 \\ 1 & -2 & -1 & 5 \\ 2 & -1 & 2 & 8 \end{bmatrix}$

18. $\begin{cases} x = 4 \\ y = -6 \end{cases}$

19. $\begin{cases} 5x + y = -3 \\ -2x + 2y = 4 \end{cases}$

20. $\begin{cases} -x + 2y = -6 \\ x + y = 7 \end{cases}$

21. $\begin{cases} 2x + y + z = 1 \\ x + y + z = 2 \\ x - y + z = -2 \end{cases}$

22. $\begin{cases} y + 2z = 4 \\ -2x + 3y + 6z = 9 \\ x + z = 3 \end{cases}$

23. $\begin{cases} 5x + 2y + z = 5 \\ 4x + y + 2z = 8 \\ x + 3y - 6z = 2 \end{cases}$

24. $(2, 1)$  25. $(-1, 0)$
26. $\left(\frac{1}{2}, 20\right)$  27. $(4, 6)$
28. $(6, 0)$  29. $(2, 3)$

### PowerAlgebra.com

## 3 Lesson Check

For a digital lesson check, use the Got It questions.

**Support in Algebra 2 Companion**
- Lesson Check

## 4 Practice

Assign homework to individual students or to an entire class.

# 4 Practice

## ASSIGNMENT GUIDE

Basic: 8–32, 39–41

Average: 9–29 odd, 30–41

Advanced: 9–29 odd, 30–47

Standardized Test Prep: 48–50

Mixed Review: 51–58

Reasoning exercises have blue headings.

Applications exercises have red headings.

**EXERCISE 41:** Use the Think About a Plan worksheet in the **Practice and Problem Solving Workbook** (also available in the Teaching Resources in print and online) to further support students' development in becoming independent learners.

## HOMEWORK QUICK CHECK

To check students' understanding of key skills and concepts, go over Exercises 15, 25, 31, 40, and 41.

 **Apply**

**30. Business** A manufacturer sells pencils and erasers in packages. The price of a package of five erasers and two pencils is $.23. The price of a package of seven erasers and five pencils is $.41. Write a system of equations to represent this situation. Then write a matrix to represent the system.

**31. Think About a Plan** Last year your town invested a total of $25,000 into two separate funds. The return on one fund was 4% and the return on the other was 6%. If the town earned a total of $1300 in interest, how much money was invested in each fund?
- What variables will you use? What will they represent?
- What equations can you write to model this situation?
- How can you use a matrix to solve this system?

**Graphing Calculator** Solve each system.

**32.** $\begin{cases} x + y + z = 2 \\ 2y - 2z = 2 \\ x - 3z = 1 \end{cases}$
**33.** $\begin{cases} x - y + z = 3 \\ x + 3z = 6 \\ y - 2z = -1 \end{cases}$
**34.** $\begin{cases} x + y + z = -1 \\ 3x + 4y - z = 8 \\ 6x + 8y - 2z = 16 \end{cases}$

**35.** $\begin{cases} x - y + 3z = 9 \\ x + 2z = 3 \\ 2x + 2y + z = 10 \end{cases}$
**36.** $\begin{cases} 2x + 3y + z = 13 \\ 5x - 2y - 4z = 7 \\ 4x + 5y + 3z = 25 \end{cases}$
**37.** $\begin{cases} -2w + x + y = 0 \\ -w + 2x - y + z = 1 \\ -2w + 3x + 3y + 2z = 6 \\ w + x + 2y + z = 5 \end{cases}$

**38. Snacks** Suppose you want to fill nine 1-lb tins with a snack mix. You have $15 and plan to buy almonds for $2.45 per lb, hazelnuts for $1.85 per lb, and raisins for $.80 per lb. You want the mix to contain an equal amount of almonds and hazelnuts and twice as much of the nuts as the raisins by weight.
- **a. Writing** Explain how each equation to the right relates to the problem. What does each variable represent?
- **b.** Solve the system.
- **c.** How many of each ingredient should you buy?

$\begin{cases} x + y + z = 9 \\ 2.45x + 1.85y + 0.8z = 15 \\ x + y = 2z \end{cases}$

**39. Geometry** The coordinates $(x, y)$ of a point in a plane are the solution of the system $\begin{cases} 2x + 3y = 13 \\ 5x + 7y = 31 \end{cases}$. Find the coordinates of the point.

**40. Error Analysis** A classmate writes the matrix at the right to represent a system and says that the solution is $x = 2, y = 0$. Explain your classmate's error and describe how to correct it.

**41. Paint** A hardware store mixes paints in a ratio of two parts red to six parts yellow to make two gallons of pumpkin orange. A ratio of five parts red to three parts yellow makes two gallons of pepper red. A gallon of pumpkin orange sells for $25, and a gallon of pepper red sells for $28. Find the cost of 1 quart of red paint and the cost of 1 quart of yellow paint.

# Answers

**Practice and Problem-Solving Exercises** (continued)

**30.** $\begin{cases} 5e + 2p = 0.23 \\ 7e + 5p = 0.41 \end{cases}$

$\begin{bmatrix} 5 & 2 & | & 0.23 \\ 7 & 5 & | & 0.41 \end{bmatrix}$

**31.** $10,000 at 4% and $15,000 at 6%
Let $x$ = amount invested at 4% and $y$ = amount invested at 6%.

$\begin{cases} x + y = 25{,}000 \\ 0.04x + 0.06y = 1300 \end{cases}$

$\begin{bmatrix} 1 & 1 & | & 25000 \\ 0.04 & 0.06 & | & 1300 \end{bmatrix} = \begin{bmatrix} 1 & 0 & | & 10000 \\ 0 & 1 & | & 15000 \end{bmatrix}$

**32.** (1, 1, 0)

**33.** (3, 1, 1)

**34.** no unique solution

**35.** (35, −22, −16)

**36.** (3, 2, 1)

**37.** (1, 1, 1, 1)

**38. a.** Let $x$ = weight of almonds at $2.45/lb, $y$ = weight of hazelnuts at $1.85/lb and $z$ = weight of raisins at $0.80/lb

$x + y + z = 9$; the total weight of the nuts and raisins is 9 lbs

$2.45x + 1.85y + 0.80z = 15$; the total cost of the nuts and raisins is $15

$x + y = 2z$; twice as much of the nuts as the raisins by weight or the total weight of the nuts is equal to twice the weight of the raisins

**b.** (2.5, 3.5, 3)

**c.** 2.5 lbs almonds, 3.5 lbs hazelnuts, and 3 lbs raisins

**39.** (2, 3)

**40.** Your classmate thinks there is one solution of the system. There are infinitely many solutions since the matrix represents the system $\begin{cases} x + 0y = 2 \\ 0x + 0y = 0 \end{cases}$. Every ordered pair that has 2 as its $x$-coordinate is a solution.

**41.** 1 qt. of red paint: $7.75; 1 qt. of yellow paint: $5.75

**Open-Ended** Complete each system for the given number of solutions.

**42.** infinitely many

$$\begin{cases} x + y = 7 \\ 2x + 2y = \blacksquare \end{cases}$$

**43.** one solution

$$\begin{cases} x + y + z = 7 \\ y + z = \blacksquare \\ z = \blacksquare \end{cases}$$

**44.** no solution

$$\begin{cases} x + y + z = 7 \\ y + z = \blacksquare \\ y + z = \blacksquare \end{cases}$$

Solve the system of equations using a matrix. (Hint: Start by substituting $m = \frac{1}{x}$ and $n = \frac{1}{y}$.)

**45.** $\begin{cases} \frac{4}{x} + \frac{1}{y} = 1 \\ \frac{8}{x} + \frac{4}{y} = 3 \end{cases}$

**46.** $\begin{cases} \frac{4}{x} - \frac{2}{y} = 1 \\ \frac{10}{x} + \frac{20}{y} = 0 \end{cases}$

**47.** $\begin{cases} \frac{7}{x} + \frac{3}{y} = 5 \\ \frac{2}{x} + \frac{1}{y} = -1 \end{cases}$

## Standardized Test Prep

SAT/ACT

**48.** Which equation represents a line with a slope of $\frac{1}{2}$ and a $y$-intercept of $\frac{3}{4}$?

(A) $y = \frac{1}{2}x - \frac{3}{4}$  (B) $y = \frac{3}{4}x - \frac{1}{2}$  (C) $y = \frac{1}{2}x + \frac{3}{4}$  (D) $y = \frac{3}{4}x + \frac{1}{2}$

**49.** Which graph best represents the solution of the inequality $y \le 2|x - 1| - 4$?

   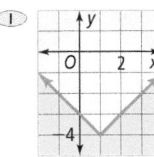

**Short Response**

**50.** At what point do the graphs of the equations $y = 7x - 3$ and $-6x + y = 2$ intersect?

## Mixed Review

Solve each inequality. Graph the solution.                    ◀ **See Lesson 1-5.**

**51.** $12 \ge 2(4x + 1) + 22$     **52.** $2x - (3x + 5) \le 30$     **53.** $4x + 5 - 3x \le 2x + 1$

Solve each equation. Check your answers.                    ◀ **See Lesson 1-6.**

**54.** $|2y - 3| = 12$     **55.** $|4x| = 40$     **56.** $|2y - 4| = 16$

**Get Ready!**  **To prepare for Lesson 4-1, do Exercises 57 and 58.**

Write an equation for each transformation of $y = x$.                    ◀ **See Lesson 2-6.**

**57.** vertical stretch by a factor of 2.     **58.** vertical compression by a factor of $\frac{1}{3}$

**42.** 14

**43.** Answers may vary. Sample: 0; 0

**44.** Answers may vary. Sample: 0; 1

**45.** (8, 2)

**46.** (5, −10)

**47.** $\left(\frac{1}{8}, -\frac{1}{17}\right)$

**48.** C

**49.** G

**50.** [2]     $y = 7x - 3$
         $\underline{-6x + y = 2}$
              $6x = 7x - 5$
              $-x = -5$
                $x = 5$
         $y = 7(5) - 3 = 32$
         (5, 32)

     [1] computational error

**51.** $x \le -\frac{3}{2}$;

**52.** $x \ge -35$;

**53.** $x \ge 4$;

**54.** $\frac{15}{2}, -\frac{9}{2}$

**55.** 10, −10

**56.** 10, −6

**57.** $y = 2x$

**58.** $y = \frac{1}{3}x$

## Additional Instructional Support

### Algebra 2 Companion

Students can use the **Algebra 2 Companion** worktext (4 pages) as you teach the lesson. Use the Companion to support

- New Vocabulary
- Key Concepts
- Got It for each Problem
- Lesson Check

### ELL Support

**Connect to Prior Knowledge** When writing linear systems as matrices, have students assign variables to each column. The last column can be named $c$ to represent the constants. Place an equals sign over the bar separating the constants from the coefficients.

$$\begin{array}{ccc} x & y & z \end{array} = c$$
$$\left[\begin{array}{ccc|c} 1 & 2 & 3 & 4 \\ 5 & 6 & 7 & 8 \\ 9 & 0 & 1 & 2 \end{array}\right]$$

## 5 Assess & Remediate

### Lesson Quiz

**1.** What is $m_{34}$ in matrix $M$?

$$M = \left[\begin{array}{cccc} 3 & 4 & 7 & 1 \\ 0 & 2 & 6 & 8 \\ -9 & 5 & 0 & 16 \end{array}\right]$$

**2.** Represent the system with a matrix.
$$\begin{cases} 2x + 3y + 5z = 9 \\ -x + 4z = 10 \\ -6x + z - 12 = y \end{cases}$$

**3.** What linear system of equations does this matrix represent? $\left[\begin{array}{cc|c} 1 & 4 & 8 \\ -3 & 9 & 0 \end{array}\right]$

**4.** **Do you UNDERSTAND?** You perform row operations and the result is the matrix
$$\left[\begin{array}{ccc|c} 1 & 0 & 0 & 3 \\ 0 & 1 & 0 & 2 \\ 0 & 0 & 0 & 4 \end{array}\right].$$
What is the solution to this system?

**5.** What is the solution of this system of equations? Use your calculator.
$$\begin{cases} a + 2b - c = 9 \\ 3a - b + 5c = -2 \\ -a + c = -3 \end{cases}$$

### ANSWERS TO LESSON QUIZ

**1.** 16

**2.** $\left[\begin{array}{ccc|c} 2 & 3 & 5 & 9 \\ -1 & 0 & 4 & 10 \\ 6 & 1 & -1 & -12 \end{array}\right]$

**3.** $\begin{cases} x + 4y = 8 \\ -3x + 9y = 0 \end{cases}$

**4.** no solution

**5.** $(2, 3, -1)$

### PRESCRIPTION FOR REMEDIATION

Use the student work on the Lesson Quiz to prescribe a differentiated review assignment:

| Points | Differentiated Remediation |
|--------|---------------------------|
| 0–2 | Intervention |
| 3–4 | On-level |
| 5 | Extension |

### PowerAlgebra.com

## 5 Assess & Remediate

Assign the Lesson Quiz. Appropriate intervention, practice, or enrichment is automatically generated based on student performance.

## Intervention

- **Reteaching** (2 pages) Provides reteaching and practice exercises for the key lesson concepts. Use with struggling students or absent students.

- **English Language Learner Support** Helps students develop and reinforce mathematical vocabulary and key concepts.

### All-in-One Resources/Online
### Reteaching

**3-6 Reteaching**
Solving Systems Using Matrices

**Problem**

How can you represent the system of equations with a matrix? $\begin{cases} 4x - 3y + 5z = -13 \\ x + 3y = 3 \\ -2x + 4y + 3z = 17 \end{cases}$

**Step 1** Write each equation in the same variable order. Line up the variables. Write in variables that have 0 coefficients.
$$\begin{cases} 4x - 3y + 5z = -13 \\ x + 3y + 0z = 3 \\ -2x + 4y + 3z = 17 \end{cases}$$

**Step 2** Write the matrix using the coefficients and constants. Remember to enter a 1 for variables with no numeric coefficient.
$$\left[\begin{array}{ccc|c} 4 & -3 & 5 & -13 \\ 1 & 3 & 0 & 3 \\ -2 & 4 & 3 & 17 \end{array}\right]$$

**Exercises**

Write a matrix to represent each system.

**1.** $\begin{cases} 2x + y = -3 \\ 3y = 5 \end{cases}$    **2.** $\begin{cases} 3x - 5y + 2z = 9 \\ 4x + 7y + z = 3 \\ 2x - z = 12 \end{cases}$    **3.** $\begin{cases} 5x - y + 3z = 2 \\ 3y + 2z = 6 \\ 4x + 3y + z = 1 \end{cases}$

**4.** $\begin{cases} 2x - z = 3 \\ 5y + 4z = -5 \\ -x + 2y = 1 \end{cases}$    **5.** $\begin{cases} z = 6 \\ x + y = 2 \\ 3x - 2y - 5z = 10 \end{cases}$    **6.** $\begin{cases} 2x - 5x + 3y = 4 \\ -y + 2x + 4z = -2 \\ 3x + z - 2y = -5 \end{cases}$

### All-in-One Resources/Online
### English Language Learner Support

**3-6 ELL Support**
Solving Systems Using Matrices

Choose the word from the list that best matches each sentence.

| coefficient | column | dimensions | matrix | matrix element | row |

**1.** A rectangular array of numbers is called a _____ matrix _____.

**2.** The numbers that are written horizontally in a matrix form a _____ row _____.

**3.** Each number in a matrix is called a _____ matrix element _____.

**4.** The _____ dimensions _____ of a matrix are the number of rows and columns in the array.

**5.** A _____ column _____ in a matrix is formed by the numbers written vertically.

**6.** You can use a _____ matrix _____ to represent a system of equations.

**7.** Each _____ coefficient _____ and constant from a system of equations are used to represent the system within a matrix.

**8.** Each matrix _____ row _____ represents an equation.

**9.** The last matrix _____ column _____ shows the constants to the right of the equal signs.

The size of a matrix is described by listing the dimensions of the matrix. This means listing the number of rows and columns in the matrix.

3 rows $\left[\begin{array}{cc} -5 & 2 \\ 0 & -1 \\ -9 & -2 \end{array}\right]$ → The size of this matrix is $3 \times 2$.

2 columns

The number of rows is always the first number.
The number of columns is always the second number.

Write the dimensions of each matrix below.

**10.** $\left[\begin{array}{cccc} -1 & 5 & 0 & -6 \\ 3 & -3 & 8 & 2 \end{array}\right]$ $2 \times 4$

**11.** $\left[\begin{array}{cccc} 5 & -2 & 9 & 9 \\ 0 & 6 & -3 & 1 \\ 8 & 8 & 7 & -4 \end{array}\right]$ $3 \times 4$

**12.** $\left[\begin{array}{cccc} -2 & 9 & 0 & -6 \end{array}\right]$ $1 \times 4$

# Differentiated Remediation *continued*

## On-Level

- **Practice** (2 pages) Provides extra practice for each lesson. For simpler practice exercises, use the Form K Practice pages found in the All-in-One Teaching Resources and online.

- **Think About a Plan** Helps students develop specific problem-solving skills and strategies by providing scaffolded guiding questions.
- **Standardized Test Prep** Focuses on all major exercises, all major question types, and helps students prepare for the high-stakes assessments.

## Extension

- **Enrichment** Provides students with interesting problems and activities that extend the concepts of the lesson.
- **Activities, Games, and Puzzles** Worksheets that can be used for concepts development, enrichment, and for fun!

---

### Practice and Problem Solving Wkbk/ All-in-One Resources/Online
#### Practice page 1

**3-6 Practice** — Form G
Solving Systems Using Matrices

Identify the indicated element.

$A = \begin{bmatrix} 3 & 5 & 8 \\ 4 & 1 & 6 \end{bmatrix}$   $B = \begin{bmatrix} 0 & 6 & 3 & 2 \\ 4 & 5 & 1 & 13 \\ 2 & 2 & 0 & -10 \end{bmatrix}$

1. $A_{13}$ 8
2. $B_{24}$ 13
3. $B_{12}$ 6
4. $A_{22}$ 1
5. $B_{31}$ 2
6. $A_{21}$ 4
7. $B_{23}$ 1
8. $A_{11}$ 3

Write a matrix to represent each system.

9. $\begin{cases} 3x + y = -4 \\ -2x + 4y = 7 \end{cases}$   10. $\begin{cases} 6x = 11 \\ -3x + 4y = 9 \end{cases}$   11. $\begin{cases} 4x - y + 2z = 10 \\ 5x + 2y - 3z = 0 \\ x - 3y + z = 6 \end{cases}$

$\begin{bmatrix} 3 & 1 & -4 \\ -2 & 4 & 7 \end{bmatrix}$   $\begin{bmatrix} 6 & 0 & 11 \\ -3 & 4 & 2 \end{bmatrix}$   $\begin{bmatrix} 4 & -1 & 2 & 10 \\ 5 & 2 & -3 & 0 \\ 1 & -3 & 1 & 6 \end{bmatrix}$

Write the system of equations represented by each matrix.

12. $\begin{bmatrix} 2 & 5 & 0 & 13 \\ -3 & 1 & 2 & 6 \\ 4 & 0 & -3 & 5 \end{bmatrix}$   13. $\begin{bmatrix} 2 & 1 & -7 \\ 0 & 4 & 9 \end{bmatrix}$   14. $\begin{bmatrix} 6 & 4 & -2 & 17 \\ 1 & -5 & 2 & -10 \\ 0 & 3 & -1 & 0 \end{bmatrix}$

$\begin{cases} -2x + 5y = 13 \\ -3x + 5y + 2z = 6 \\ -4x - 3z = 5 \end{cases}$   $\begin{cases} 2x + y = -7 \\ 4y = 9 \end{cases}$   $\begin{cases} 6x + 4y - 2z = 17 \\ 6x - 5y + 2z = -10 \\ 3y - z = 0 \end{cases}$

Solve the system of equations using a matrix.

15. $\begin{cases} 4x - y = 10 \\ -2x + 5y = 4 \end{cases}$   16. $\begin{cases} x - 2y + 3z = 18 \\ 9x + 2y - z = -2 \\ -6x + 3y + 2z = 4 \end{cases}$   17. $\begin{cases} 3x - 4y + z = 15 \\ -2x - 6y + 3z = 4 \\ 2x + 2y - 2z = -1 \end{cases}$
$(3, 2)$   $(1, -4, 3)$   $(4, \frac{1}{3}, 5)$

---

### Practice and Problem Solving Wkbk/ All-in-One Resources/Online
#### Practice page 2

**3-6 Practice** *(continued)* — Form G
Solving Systems Using Matrices

**Graphing Calculator** Solve each system.

18. $\begin{cases} 4x + y - 2z = 3 \\ 2y + z = 4 \\ 3x - 3y - z = 9 \end{cases}$   19. $\begin{cases} 5x - 2y + z = -1 \\ -x - y - 2z = 5 \\ 3x + 2y + 2z = 2 \end{cases}$   20. $\begin{cases} 3x + 5z = -4 \\ -2x + y - 3z = 9 \\ -x - 2y + 9z = 0 \end{cases}$

$(4, -1, 1)$   $(2, 3, -5)$   $(-3, 6, 1)$

21. Suppose the movie theater you work at sells popcorn in three different sizes. A small costs $2, a medium costs $5, and a large costs $10. On your shift, you sold 250 total containers of popcorn and brought in $1726. You sold twice as many large containers as small ones.
  a. How many of each popcorn size did you sell? 68 small, 46 medium, 136 large
  b. How much money did you bring in from selling small size containers? $136

22. **Open Ended** Write a matrix for a system of equations that does not have a unique solution. Answers may vary. Sample: $\begin{bmatrix} 4 & -2 & -6 \\ -2 & 1 & 3 \end{bmatrix}$

23. The following matrix shows the prices passengers on a recent airline flight paid for a ticket and how many passengers were on that flight. Some passengers paid full price for their tickets, and some bought their tickets during a half-price sale. How many passengers bought each price of ticket?
$\begin{bmatrix} 1 & 1 & 100 \\ 120 & 240 & 20,160 \end{bmatrix}$
32 people bought $120 tickets; 68 people bought $240 tickets.

24. **Error Analysis** Your friend says that the matrix below represents the system of equations. What error did your friend make? What is the correct system of equations?
$\begin{bmatrix} 4 & 0 & -1 & 4 \\ -3 & 2 & -2 & -2 \\ 1 & -3 & 2 & -6 \end{bmatrix}$   $\begin{cases} 4x + y - z = 4 \\ -3x + 2y - 2z = -2 \\ x - 3y - 2z = -6 \end{cases}$

Your friend incorrectly converted the 0 matrix entry to a coefficient of 1 when writing the first equation; $\begin{cases} 4x - z = 4 \\ -3x + 2y - 2z = -2 \\ x - 3y - 2z = -6 \end{cases}$

---

### All-in-One Resources/Online
#### Enrichment

**3-6 Enrichment**
Solving Systems Using Matrices

**Well-Conditioned Systems of Linear Equations**

A system of linear equations is said to be well-conditioned if a small change in the values of the coefficients produces a small change in the values of the solutions. A system is said to be ill-conditioned if a small change in the values of the coefficients produces a large change in the values of the solutions.

To determine whether a system of linear equations is well-conditioned or ill-conditioned, change each coefficient by one percent. Each time, write and solve the new system, finding the values of x and y to two decimal places by writing and solving a matrix. Then compare the new values of x and y to the solutions of the original system. A change of less than one percent in the values of x and y can be considered small.

1. Determine whether System 1 is well-conditioned or ill-conditioned by completing the following steps.
System 1: $\begin{cases} x + y = 5000 \\ 3x - 2y = 3000 \end{cases}$
  a. Find the values of x and y.
  b. Change the coefficient of x in the first equation by one percent, from 1 to 1.01. Write the new system. Find the values of x and y.
  c. Change the coefficient of y in the first equation by one percent, from 1 to 0.99. Write the new system. Find the values of x and y.
  d. Change the coefficient of x in the second equation by one percent, from 3 to 3.03. Write the new system. Find the values of x and y.
  e. Change the coefficient of y in the second equation by one percent, from −2 to −2.02. Write the new system. Find the values of x and y.
  f. Is the system well-conditioned or ill-conditioned?

2. Determine whether System 2 is well-conditioned or ill-conditioned by completing the same steps as in Exercise 1.
System 2: $\begin{cases} x + y = 5001 \\ 3x - 2y = -9997 \end{cases}$

1a. 2600, 2400
1b. $\begin{cases} 1.01x + y = 5000 \\ 3x - 2y = 3000 \end{cases}$ 2589.64, 2384.46
1c. $\begin{cases} x + 0.99y = 5000 \\ 3x - 2y = 3000 \end{cases}$ 2609.66, 2414.49
1d. $\begin{cases} x + y = 5000 \\ 3.03x - 2y = 3000 \end{cases}$ 2584.49, 2415.51
1e. $\begin{cases} x + y = 5000 \\ 3x - 2.02y = 3000 \end{cases}$ 2609.56, 2390.44
1f. well-conditioned

2a. 1, 5000
2b. $\begin{cases} 1.01x + y = 5001 \\ 3x - 2y = -9997 \end{cases}$ 1.00, 4999.93
2c. $\begin{cases} x + 0.99y = 5001 \\ 3x - 2y = -9997 \end{cases}$ 21.12, 5030.18
2d. $\begin{cases} x + y = 5001 \\ 3.03x - 2y = -9997 \end{cases}$ 0.99, 5000.01
2e. $\begin{cases} x + y = 5001 \\ 3x - 2.02y = -9997 \end{cases}$ 20.92, 4980.08
2f. ill-conditioned

---

### Practice and Problem Solving Wkbk/ All-in-One Resources/Online
#### Think About a Plan

**3-6 Think About a Plan**
Solving Systems Using Matrices

**Paint** A hardware store mixes paints in a ratio of two parts red to six parts yellow to make two gallons of pumpkin orange. A ratio of five parts red to three parts yellow makes two gallons of pepper red. A gallon of pumpkin orange sells for $25, and a gallon of pepper red sells for $28. Find the cost of 1 quart of red paint and the cost of 1 quart of yellow paint.

**Know**

1. There are [4] quarts in 1 gallon.

2. [2] qt red + [6] qt yellow = [8] qt pumpkin orange
   [5] qt red + [3] qt yellow = [8] qt pepper red

3. [4] quarts of pumpkin orange cost [$25]
   [4] quarts of pepper red cost [$28]

**Need**

4. To solve the problem you need to define:
   Variables may vary. Sample: x = cost of 1 qt of red paint, y = cost of 1 qt of yellow paint

5. To solve the problem you need to find:
   a system of two equations

**Plan**

6. What system of equations represents this situation?
   Variables may vary. Sample: $2x + 3y = 25$, $5x + 3y = 56$

7. How can you represent the system of equations with a matrix? $\begin{bmatrix} 1 & 3 & 25 \\ 5 & 3 & 56 \end{bmatrix}$

8. Solve the system of equations using the matrix.
   $(7.75, 5.75)$

9. How can you interpret the solutions in the context of the problem?
   1 qt of red paint costs $7.75 and 1 qt of yellow paint costs $5.75.

---

### Practice and Problem Solving Wkbk/ All-in-One Resources/Online
#### Standardized Test Prep

**3-6 Standardized Test Prep**
Solving Systems Using Matrices

**Multiple Choice**

For Exercises 1–3, choose the correct letter.

1. Which system of equations is equivalent to $\begin{bmatrix} 4 & -1 & 2 & 6 \\ 3 & 0 & 4 & 2 \\ 1 & 5 & 3 & 7 \end{bmatrix}$ ? B

   Ⓐ $\begin{cases} 4x + y + 2z = 6 \\ 3x + 4z = 2 \\ x + 5y + 3z = 7 \end{cases}$   Ⓒ $\begin{cases} 4x + y + 2z = 6 \\ 3x + y + 4z = 2 \\ x + 5y + 3z = 7 \end{cases}$

   Ⓑ $\begin{cases} 4x - y + 2z = 6 \\ 3x + 4z = 2 \\ x + 5y + 3z = 7 \end{cases}$   Ⓓ $\begin{cases} 4x - y + 2z = 6 \\ 3x + y + 4z = 2 \\ x + 5y + 3z = 7 \end{cases}$

2. What is the solution of the system represented by the matrix $\begin{bmatrix} 2 & 3 & -1 & 2 \\ -3 & -4 & 2 & -2 \\ 1 & 2 & -1 & 3 \end{bmatrix}$ ? H

   Ⓕ $(1, 3, 4)$   Ⓖ $(4, -3, 1)$   Ⓗ $(-4, 3, -1)$   Ⓘ $(3, -4, -1)$

3. How many elements are in a 2 × 3 matrix? D
   Ⓐ 2   Ⓑ 4   Ⓒ 5   Ⓓ 6

**Short Response**

4. A clothing store is having a sale. A pair of jeans costs $15 and a shirt costs $8. You spend $131 and buy a total of 12 items. Using a matrix, how many pairs of jeans and shirts do you buy? Show your work.

[2] Matrices may vary. Sample: $\begin{bmatrix} 1 & 1 & 12 \\ 15 & 8 & 131 \end{bmatrix}$; 5 pairs of jeans; 7 shirts
[1] correct solution, without work shown OR correct process with one computational error
[0] incorrect answer and no work shown OR no answer given

---

### Online Teacher Resource Center
#### Activities, Games, and Puzzles

**3-6 Game: Matrix Mania**
Solving Systems Using Matrices

This is a game for two teams of two students.

**Game Play**

There are two rounds in this game. Play each round as follows:
- **Select:** At the beginning of the round each team selects systems, as determined below, that the other team needs to solve.
- **Exchange:** Teams exchange their systems.
- **Solve:** Teams find solutions for each system.
- **Verify:** At end of the game, teams check their opponent's solutions. Your teacher will provide the correct solutions.

**Rules**

- Find systems in the matrices below.
- Determine systems by a matrix element. The matrix element corresponds to the first term in the system. For example, $a_{23}$ from matrix A below corresponds to the following system.
$\begin{cases} 3x + 0y = -6 \\ -1x - 11y = 2 \end{cases}$
- The team that scores the most points wins.

**Scoring**

- Each correct solution is worth 2 points.
- The team that finishes a round first earns 1 point.

**Round 1**

Each team selects four systems of two equations with two unknowns. There are 16 possible systems starting in the first four rows and first four columns.

$A = \begin{bmatrix} 1 & -2 & 4 & 10 & 2 & 0 \\ 2 & 1 & 3 & 0 & -6 & 30 \\ 3 & -4 & -1 & -11 & 2 & 78 \\ 1 & 1 & -1 & -13 & 13 & \\ -2 & 1 & 2 & 5 & -3 & -23 \end{bmatrix}$

$a_{11}$: (2, −1); $a_{12}$: (−1, 3); $a_{13}$: (−2, 1);
$a_{14}$: (−, −5); $a_{21}$: (1, 1); $a_{22}$: (0, −1);
$a_{23}$: (−2, 0); $a_{24}$: (−4, −5); $a_{31}$: (0, 4); $a_{32}$: (2, 3);
$a_{33}$: (−13, 1); $a_{34}$: (−7, 0.5); $a_{41}$: (−3, −4);
$a_{42}$: (1, 2); $a_{43}$: (−14, 12); $a_{44}$: (−1, 1)

**Round 2**

Each team selects two systems of three equations with three unknowns. There are six possible systems starting in the first three rows and first three columns.

$B = \begin{bmatrix} 1 & -2 & -1 & 2 & -17 \\ -2 & 1 & 0 & 1 & 3 \\ -1 & -1 & 2 & 0 & 5 \\ -2 & -2 & 3 & 3 & -1 \\ -2 & 1 & 1 & 3 & 4 \end{bmatrix}$

$b_{11}$: (1, 1); $b_{12}$: (−7, −1, −2); $b_{21}$: (3, −9, −3);
$b_{31}$: (−1, 2, −3); $b_{32}$: (−4, −2, −3); $b_{33}$: (5, 5, −2)

# Performance Task

## Pull It All Together

The concepts and skills required to solve these problems are from several lessons within this chapter and from earlier chapters. As students solve these problems, they will demonstrate their reasoning strategies and their growth as independent problem solvers.

The following questions are designed to:
- help support students as they do the Tasks.
- gauge the amount of support students need as they become independent problem solvers.

### Task 1
Determine the nature of the solution of a system of equations in two unknowns without solving for the unknowns.
- What do you know about the solutions when the system is dependent? inconsistent?

### Task 2
Model and solve a problem as a system of equations in two unknowns.
- What are the unknowns?
- What quantity is represented by each equation in the system?
- What set of numbers can be solutions to the system?

### Task 3
Use row operations on a matrix to find the solution to a system of equations.
- What methods can you use to change a matrix row?
- What does it mean for a matrix to be in reduced row echelon form?

---

To solve these problems, you will pull together concepts and skills related to solving a system of linear equations.

**BIG** idea  Function
The solution of a system of two linear equations corresponds in general to the intersection of the graphs of the corresponding functions.

### Task 1
You are given a linear system of two equations in two unknowns. Before solving, describe how you can mentally check whether the system is independent and consistent. In which order would you do your check? Why?

**BIG** idea  Equivalence
You can solve a system of equations by representing the system in some form that is equivalent to the original form but easier to solve. There are different ways to do this.

### Task 2
During a back-to-school shopping trip, a group of friends spent $245.86 on 14 shirts and pants. Each shirt cost $11.99. Each pair of pants cost $24.99. How many shirts and pairs of pants did the group buy?
a. Write a system of equations to model the information in the problem.
b. Study the system. Explain, without solving, which method you think would be most efficient for solving the system: *substitution, elimination, graphing,* or *making a table.* Explain why the other methods would be less efficient.
c. How could you simplify the numbers used in this system to simplify the system? Does this new system change your answers to part (b)? Explain.

**BIG** idea  Solving Equations and Inequalities
You can represent a system of equations with a matrix. Transforming the matrix to reduced row echelon form gives you an equivalent system for which the solution is obvious.

### Task 3
Solve this system using a matrix. $\begin{cases} 4x + 10y = 3 \\ 7x - 2y = 2 \end{cases}$

Make three columns on your paper. In the first column, show each step, changing one matrix row at a time. In the second column, write the two equations that correspond to each matrix in the first column. In the third column, describe how you could transform each set of equations to the next.

---

# Assess Performance

## Pull It All Together

See p. 49 for a holistic scoring rubric to gauge a student's progress on Understanding the Problem, Planning a Solution, Getting an Answer, and Assessing Autonomy.

### SOLUTION OUTLINES

1. Possible Plan: First check that the system is consistent. Then you can determine if it is independent. Remember, a system that has at least one solution is consistent. If the coefficients for each variable *and* the constant terms are additive inverses, the two equations represent parallel lines and have no solutions. If only the coefficients of the variables are additive inverses, the two equations represent the same line and have infinitely many solutions. If neither of these situations exists, the system is consistent and independent.

2. a. First step: Assign a variable for each item. (Let $x$ = the number of shirts purchased and $y$ = the number of pairs of pants purchased.)
   Second step: Write an equation using the prices and total amount spent. $(11.99x + 24.99y = 245.86)$
   Third step: Write an equation using the total number of items purchased. $(x + y = 14)$
   Fourth step: Write the system.
   $\left( \begin{cases} 11.99x + 24.99y = 245.86 \\ x + y = 14 \end{cases} \right)$

   b. Possible Plan: Since the coefficients of the second equation are both 1, the substitution method will be the most efficient method for solving the system.
   As the first equation has decimal numbers, solving by graphing would not be as accurate and solving by elimination or using a table would be much more work.

   c. Possible Plan: You can simplify the system by multiplying the first equation by 100 to eliminate the decimals. Simplifying the system in this way would not change my answer to part (b) because now the coefficients and the constant term are very large and will be awkward to work with.

3. Possible Plan: Write a matrix to represent the system. Use row operations to get the matrix in the form $\begin{bmatrix} 1 & 0 & | & x \\ 0 & 1 & | & y \end{bmatrix}$. Notice that solving a system using a matrix is similar to the steps for solving the system by elimination. $\left( \text{The solution is } \left( \frac{1}{3}, \frac{1}{6} \right). \right)$

# 3 Chapter Review

Connecting **BIG** ideas and Answering the Essential Questions

**1 Function**
Find a point of intersection $(x, y)$ of the graphs of functions $f$ and $g$ and you have found a solution of the system $y = f(x)$, $y = g(x)$.

**Solving Systems Using Tables and Graphs (Lesson 3-1)**
$$\begin{cases} y = -2x + 3 \\ y = 2x - 1 \end{cases}$$

The solution is (1, 1).

**Systems of Inequalities and Linear Programming (Lessons 3-3 and 3-4)**
$$\begin{cases} y > -2x + 3 \\ y \leq 2x - 1 \end{cases}$$

**2 Equivalence**
If the equations of two systems are equivalent, then a solution of the system that is easier to solve is also a solution of the more difficult system.

**Solving Systems Algebraically (Lesson 3-2)**
$$\begin{cases} -y = -x + 2 \\ 3y = 2x - 2 \end{cases} \rightarrow \begin{array}{r} -2y = -2x + 4 \\ 3y = 2x - 2 \\ \hline y = 2 \end{array}$$
$3(2) = 2x - 2 \rightarrow x = 4$
The solution is $x = 4$, $y = 2$

**Systems With Three Variables (Lesson 3-5)**
$$\begin{cases} -2x + y + z = -3 \\ 2x - y + z = -1 \\ -2x, - y - z = -1 \end{cases}$$
$x = 1, y = 1, z = -2$

**3 Solving Equations and Inequalities**
The matrix row operations of adding rows and multiplying a row by a constant are equivalent to addition and multiplication properties of equality.

**Solving Systems Using Matrices (Lesson 3-6)**
$$\begin{bmatrix} -2 & 3 & | & 1 \\ 2 & -1 & | & 1 \end{bmatrix}$$
$$\begin{bmatrix} 1 & 0 & | & 1 \\ 0 & 1 & | & 1 \end{bmatrix} \rightarrow x = 1, y = 1$$

## Chapter Vocabulary

- consistent system (p. 137)
- constraint (p. 157)
- dependent system (p. 137)
- equivalent systems (p. 144)
- feasible region (p. 157)
- inconsistent system (p. 137)
- independent system (p. 137)
- linear programming (p. 157)
- linear system (p. 134)
- matrix (p. 174)
- matrix element (p. 174)
- objective function (p. 157)
- row operation (p. 176)
- solution of a system (p. 134)
- system of equations (p. 134)

**Fill in the blank.**

**1.** A consistent system with exactly one solution is a(n) _____.

**2.** _____ is a method for finding a minimum or maximum value, given a system of limits called _____.

**BIG** idea **Functions**
**ESSENTIAL QUESTION** How does representing functions graphically help you solve a system of equations?
**ANSWER** Find a point of intersection $(x, y)$ of the graphs of functions $f$ and $g$ and you have found a solution of the system $y = f(x)$, $y = g(x)$

**BIG** idea **Equivalence**
**ESSENTIAL QUESTION** How does writing equivalent equations help you solve a system of equations?
**ANSWER** If the equations of two systems are equivalent, then a solution of the system that is easier to solve is also a solution of the more difficult system.

**BIG** idea **Solving Equations and Inequalities**
**ESSENTIAL QUESTION** How are the properties of equality used in the matrix solution of a system of equations?
**ANSWER** The matrix row operations of adding rows and multiplying a row by a constant are equivalent to addition and multiplication properties of equality.

## Answers

**1.** independent system
**2.** Linear programming; constraints

## Summative Questions

Use the following prompts as you review this chapter with your students. The prompts are designed to help you assess your students' understanding of the Big Ideas they have studied.

- What do you look for to determine whether to use elimination, substitution, or a matrix to solve a linear system?
- In a linear programming problem, what determines the feasible region?
- What are the three different kinds of systems? How many solutions does each have?
- How does the graph of a solution to a system of inequalities compare to the graph of the solutions of a single inequality?
- Are these systems equivalent?
$$\begin{cases} 2x - 2y = 4 \\ 2x + 4y = 7 \end{cases} \text{ and } \begin{cases} 2x - 2y = 4 \\ 2x + 8y = 14 \end{cases}$$
What determines whether two systems are equivalent?

## 3-1 Solving Systems Using Tables and Graphs

### Quick Review

A **system of equations** has two or more equations. Points of intersection are solutions. A **linear system** has linear equations. A **consistent system** can be **dependent**, with infinitely many solutions, or **independent**, with one solution. An **inconsistent system** has no solution.

### Example

Solve the system $\begin{cases} 3x + 2y = 4 \\ 2x - 4y = 8 \end{cases}$

Graph the equations.

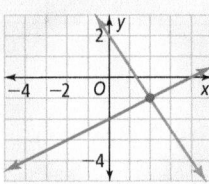

The only solution, where the lines intersect, is $(2, -1)$.

### Exercises

**Without graphing, classify each system of equations as *independent*, *dependent*, or *inconsistent*. Solve independent systems by graphing.**

3. $\begin{cases} 6x - 2y = 2 \\ 2 + 6x = y \end{cases}$    4. $\begin{cases} 5 - y = 2x \\ 6x - 15 = -3y \end{cases}$

5. $\begin{cases} 6y + 2x = 8 \\ 12y + 4x = 4 \end{cases}$    6. $\begin{cases} 1.5 + 3x = 0.5y \\ 6 - 2y = -12x \end{cases}$

7. $\begin{cases} 2 - 0.25x = 0.5y \\ -1.5y = 1.5x - 3 \end{cases}$    8. $\begin{cases} 1 + y = x \\ x + y = 1 \end{cases}$

9. For $7.52, you purchased 8 pens and highlighters from a local bookstore. Each highlighter cost $1.09 and each pen cost $.69. How many pens did you buy?

## 3-2 Solving Systems Algebraically

### Quick Review

To solve an independent system by substitution, solve one equation for a variable. Then substitute that expression into the other equation and solve for the remaining variable. To solve by elimination, add two equations with additive inverses as coefficients to eliminate one variable and solve for the other. In both cases you solve for one of the variables and use substitution to solve for the remaining variable.

### Example

Solve $\begin{cases} 10 - y = 4x \\ x = 4 + 0.5y \end{cases}$ by substitution.

Substitute for $x$: $10 - y = 4(4 + 0.5y) = 16 + 2y$.
Solve for $y$: $y = -2$.
Substitute into the first equation:

$10 - (-2) = 4x$.
Solve for $x$: $x = 3$. The solution is $(3, -2)$.

### Exercises

**Solve each system by substitution.**

10. $\begin{cases} x - 2y = 3 \\ 3x + y = -5 \end{cases}$    11. $\begin{cases} 14x - 35 = 7y \\ -25 - 6x = 5y \end{cases}$

**Solve each system by elimination.**

12. $\begin{cases} 11 - 5y = 2x \\ 5y + 3 = -9x \end{cases}$    13. $\begin{cases} 2x + 3y = 4 \\ 4x + 6y = 9 \end{cases}$

14. Roast beef has 25 g of protein and 11 g of calcium per serving. A serving of mashed potatoes has 2 g of protein and 25 g of calcium. How many servings of each are needed to supply exactly 29 g of protein and 61 g of calcium?

## Answers

3. independent; $(-1, -4)$

4. dependent

5. inconsistent

6. dependent

7. independent; $(-4, 6)$

8. independent; $(1, 0)$

9. 3 pens

10. $(-1, -2)$

11. $(0, -5)$

12. $(-2, 3)$

13. inconsistent; no solution

14. 1 serving of roast beef and 2 servings of mashed potatoes

## 3-3 Systems of Inequalities

### Quick Review

To solve a system of inequalities by graphing, first graph the boundaries for each inequality. Then shade the region(s) of the plane containing solutions valid for both inequalities.

### Example

Solve the system of inequalities by graphing.

$$\begin{cases} y > -3 \\ y \le -|x - 1| \end{cases}$$

Graph both inequalities and shade the region valid for both inequalities.

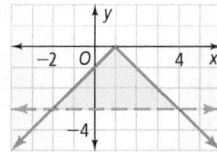

### Exercises

**Solve each system of inequalities by graphing.**

15. $\begin{cases} y < 4x \\ 3x + y \ge 5 \end{cases}$     16. $\begin{cases} y < |2x - 4| \\ x + 5y \ge -1 \end{cases}$

17. $\begin{cases} y \le |x + 2| - 3 \\ y \ge 1 + \frac{1}{4}x \end{cases}$     18. $\begin{cases} 2x + 3y > 6 \\ x \le -1 \\ y \ge 4 \end{cases}$

19. For a community breakfast there should be at least three times as much regular coffee as decaffeinated coffee. A total of ten gallons is sufficient for the breakfast. Write and graph a system of inequalities to model the problem.

## 3-4 Linear Programming

### Quick Review

**Linear programming** is used to find a minimum or maximum of an **objective function**, given **constraints** as linear inequalities. The maximum or minimum occurs at a vertex of the **feasible region**, which contains the solutions to the system of constraints.

### Example

Graph the system of constraints and name the vertices.

$$\begin{cases} x \le 8 \\ y \le 5 \\ x \ge 0, y \ge 0 \end{cases}$$

Objective function: $P = 2x + y$

Graph the inequalities and shade the area satisfying all inequalities.

The vertices of the feasible region are (0, 0), (0, 5), (8, 5), and (8, 0).

Evaluate the objective function at each vertex:

$2(0) + 0 = 0$      $2(0) + 5 = 5$

$2(8) + 5 = 21$      $2(8) + 0 = 16$

The maximum value occurs at (8, 5).

### Exercises

Graph the system of constraints. Name the vertices. Then find the values of $x$ and $y$ that maximize or minimize the objective function.

20. $\begin{cases} x \ge 2 \\ y \ge 0 \\ 3x + 2y \ge 12 \end{cases}$     21. $\begin{cases} 3x + 2y \le 12 \\ x + y \le 5 \\ x \ge 0, y \ge 0 \end{cases}$

Minimum for $\quad\quad$ Maximum for
$C = x + 5y$ $\quad\quad\quad$ $P = 3x + 5y$

22. A lunch stand makes \$.75 profit on each chef's salad and \$1.20 profit on each Caesar salad. On a typical weekday, it sells between 40 and 60 chef's salads and between 35 and 50 Caesar salads. The total number sold has never exceeded 100 salads. How many of each type should be prepared in order to maximize profit?

20. vertices: (4, 0) and (2, 3); $C = 4$ is minimized at (4, 0).

21. vertices: (0, 0), (4, 0), (2, 3), (0, 5); $P = 25$ is maximized at (0, 5).

22. 50 chef's salads and 50 Caesar salads

15.

18.

16.

19. Let $r$ = amount of regular coffee and $d$ = amount of decaffeinated coffee

$$\begin{cases} r + d \le 10 \\ r \ge 3d, r \ge 0, d \ge 0 \end{cases}$$

17.

## 3-5 Systems With Three Variables

### Quick Review

To solve a system of three equations, either pair two equations and eliminate the same variable from both equations, using one equation twice, or choose an equation, solve for one variable, and substitute the expression for that variable into the other two equations. Then, solve the remaining system.

### Example

Solve by elimination.

$$\begin{array}{r}① \quad x + y + z = 10 \\ ② \quad 2x - y + z = 9 \\ ③ \quad -3x + 2y + 2z = 5\end{array}$$

Add equations ① and ② to eliminate $y$.    ④ $3x + 2z = 19$

Add 2 times ② to ③ to eliminate $y$.    ⑤ $x + 4z = 23$

Add $-3$ times ⑤ to ④ to eliminate $x$.    $z = 5$

Substitute $z = 5$ into ⑤.    $x = 3$

Substitute $z = 5$ and $x = 3$ into ① or ②.    $y = 2$

The solution to the system is $(3, 2, 5)$.

### Exercises

**Solve each system by elimination.**

23. $\begin{cases} x + y - 2z = 8 \\ 5x - 3y + z = -6 \\ -2x - y + 4z = -13 \end{cases}$

24. $\begin{cases} -x + y + 2z = -5 \\ 5x + 4y - 4z = 4 \\ x - 3y - 2z = 3 \end{cases}$

**Solve each system by substitution.**

25. $\begin{cases} 3x + y - 2z = 22 \\ x + 5y + z = 4 \\ x = -3z \end{cases}$

26. $\begin{cases} x + 2y + z = 14 \\ y = z + 1 \\ x = -3z + 6 \end{cases}$

## 3-6 Solving Systems Using Matrices

### Quick Review

A **matrix** can represent a system of equations where each row stands for a different equation. The columns contain the coefficients of the variables and the constants.

### Example

Solve using a matrix. $\begin{cases} 6x + 3y = -15 \\ 2x + 4y = 10 \end{cases}$

Enter coefficients as matrix elements $\begin{bmatrix} 6 & 3 & | & -15 \\ 2 & 4 & | & 10 \end{bmatrix}$.

Divide the first row by 3 to get $\begin{bmatrix} 2 & 1 & | & -5 \\ 2 & 4 & | & 10 \end{bmatrix}$. Subtract the first row from the second row to get $\begin{bmatrix} 2 & 1 & | & -5 \\ 0 & 3 & | & 15 \end{bmatrix}$. Multiply the second row by $\frac{1}{3}$ to get $\begin{bmatrix} 2 & 1 & | & -5 \\ 0 & 1 & | & 5 \end{bmatrix}$. Subtract the second row from the first row to get $\begin{bmatrix} 2 & 0 & | & -10 \\ 0 & 1 & | & 5 \end{bmatrix}$. Divide the first row by 2 to get $\begin{bmatrix} 1 & 0 & | & -5 \\ 0 & 1 & | & 5 \end{bmatrix}$. The solution to the system is $(-5, 5)$.

### Exercises

**Solve each system using a matrix.**

27. $\begin{cases} 4x - 12y = -1 \\ 6x + 4y = 4 \end{cases}$

28. $\begin{cases} 7x + 2y = 5 \\ 13x + 14y = -1 \end{cases}$

29. $\begin{cases} -5x + 3y + 4z = 2 \\ 3x - y - z = 4 \\ x - 6y - 5z = -4 \end{cases}$

30. $\begin{cases} x + y + z = 4 \\ 2x - y + z = 5 \\ x + y - 2z = 13 \end{cases}$

# Answers

**23.** $(1, 3, -2)$

**24.** $(-4, 1, -5)$

**25.** $(6, 0, -2)$

**26.** no solution

**27.** $\left(\frac{1}{2}, \frac{1}{4}\right)$

**28.** $(1, -1)$

**29.** $(2, -4, 6)$

**30.** $(5, 2, -3)$

## Do you know HOW?

Without graphing, classify each system. Then find the solution to each system using a graph.

1. $\begin{cases} y = 5x - 2 \\ y = x + 4 \end{cases}$

2. $\begin{cases} 3x + 2y = 9 \\ 3x + 2y = 4 \end{cases}$

Solve the system by substitution.

3. $\begin{cases} 0.3x - y = 0 \\ y = 2 + 0.25x \end{cases}$

Solve the system by elimination.

4. $\begin{cases} 4x - 2y = 3 \\ y - 2x = -\frac{3}{2} \end{cases}$

5. $\begin{cases} 3x + 4y = 9 \\ 2x + y = 6 \end{cases}$

Graph the solution of each system.

6. $\begin{cases} 2x + y < 3 \\ x < y + 3 \end{cases}$

7. $\begin{cases} |x + 3| > y \\ y > 2x - 1 \end{cases}$

Graph the system of constraints. Identify all vertices. Then find the values of x and y that maximize or minimize the objective function.

8. $\begin{cases} x \le 5 \\ y \le 4 \\ x \ge 0 \\ y \ge 0 \end{cases}$

   Maximum for $P = 2x + y$

Solve each system.

9. $\begin{cases} x - y + z = 0 \\ 3x - 2y + 6z = 9 \\ -x + y - 2z = -2 \end{cases}$

10. $\begin{cases} 2x + y + z = 8 \\ x + 2y - z = -5 \\ z = 2x - y \end{cases}$

## Do you UNDERSTAND?

Write a matrix that represents the system. Then solve the system. Tell what method you used and why.

11. $\begin{cases} -a + 4b + 2c = -8 \\ 3a + b - 4c = 9 \\ b = -1 \end{cases}$

12. **Sales** A pizza shop makes $1.50 on each small pizza and $2.15 on each large pizza. On a typical Friday, it sells between 70 and 90 small pizzas and between 100 and 140 large pizzas. The shop can make no more than 210 pizzas in a day. How many of each size pizza must be sold in order to maximize profit?

13. **Investing** Your teacher invested $5000 in three funds. After a year they had $5450. The growth fund had a return rate of 12%, the income fund had a return rate of 8%, and the money market fund had a return rate of 5%. Your teacher invested twice as much in the income fund as in the money market fund. How much money was invested in each fund?

14. **Writing** Describe how to identify situations in which substitution may be the best method for solving a system of equations.

15. **Open-Ended** Write a system of constraints whose graph is a parallelogram.

10. $(2, -1, 5)$

11. $\begin{bmatrix} -1 & 4 & 2 & | & -8 \\ 3 & 1 & -4 & | & 9 \\ 0 & 1 & 0 & | & -1 \end{bmatrix}$;

    $(2, -1, -1)$; Check students' work

12. 70 small; 140 large

13. She invested $2000 in the growth fund, $2000 in the income fund, and $1000 in the money market fund.

14. Substitution is used when an equation is easily solved for one of the variables.

15. Check students' work.

# Answers

1. independent; $\left(\frac{3}{2}, \frac{11}{2}\right)$

2. inconsistent

3. $(40, 12)$

4. infinitely many solutions

5. $(3, 0)$

6.

7.

8.

vertices: $(0, 0)$, $(5, 0)$, $(5, 4)$, $(0, 4)$; maximum $P = 14$ at $(5, 4)$.

9. $(1, 3, 2)$

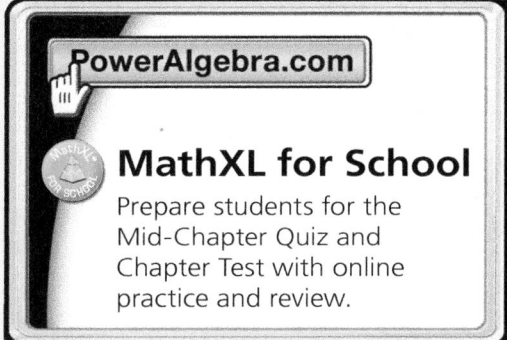
PowerAlgebra.com

**MathXL for School**
Prepare students for the Mid-Chapter Quiz and Chapter Test with online practice and review.

| Item Number | Lesson |
|-------------|--------|
| 1 | 3-2 |
| 2 | 2-7 |
| 3 | 1-6 |
| 4 | 3-2 |
| 5 | 1-6 |
| 6 | 3-1 |
| 7 | 3-5 |
| 8 | 2-8 |
| 9 | 1-4 |
| 10 | 2-4 |
| 11 | 2-4 |
| 12 | 2-2 |
| 13 | 3-2 |
| 14 | 1-6 |
| 15 | 3-5 |
| 16 | 3-3 |
| 17 | 2-4 |
| 18 | 3-1 |
| 19 | 2-5 |

### TIPS FOR SUCCESS

Some problems require the selection of an appropriate representation (concrete, pictorial, graphical, verbal, or symbolic) to find a solution.

**TIP 1**

Make a drawing.

One angle of a right triangle measures 90°. The measure of the second angle is 5 times the measure of the third. What are the measures of these angles?

Ⓐ 30° and 60°

Ⓑ 30° and 150°

Ⓒ 15° and 75°

Ⓓ 20° and 100°

**TIP 2**

Write a system:
$x + y + 90 = 180$
$x = 5y$

**Think It Through**

A triangle can have only one right angle, so the other two angles must each have a measure less than 90°. Use $x$ and $y$ to represent the unknown angles.

$$x = 5y$$
$$5y + y + 90 = 180$$
$$6y + 90 = 180$$
$$6y = 90$$
$$y = 15, x = 75$$

The correct answer is C.

### Vocabulary Builder

As you solve test items, you must understand the meanings of mathematical terms. Match each term with its mathematical meaning.

**A.** equivalent systems

**B.** absolute value

**C.** system of equations

**D.** linear inequality

**I.** a number's distance from zero on a number line

**II.** an inequality in two variables whose graph is a region of the half-plane

**III.** a set of two or more equations that use the same variables

**IV.** systems that have the same solution(s)

### Multiple Choice

Read each question. Then write the letter of the correct answer on your paper.

**1.** Which of the following is true about the given system?
$$\begin{cases} -4y = 12 - 8x \\ y = 2x - 3 \end{cases}$$
The system has

Ⓐ zero solutions.

Ⓑ exactly one solution.

Ⓒ two solutions.

Ⓓ infinitely many solutions.

## Answers

**A.** IV

**B.** I

**C.** III

**D.** II

**1.** D

**2.** Which is the graph of $y = -|x - 2| + 1$?

 F      H

 G      I

**3.** Which graph represents the solution of the inequality $|3x + 12| \geq 3$?

A   $-9 \;\; -7 \;\; -5 \;\; -3 \;\; -1 \;\;\; 1$

B   $-1 \;\;\; 1 \;\;\; 3 \;\;\; 5 \;\;\; 7 \;\;\; 9$

C   $-5 \;\; -3 \;\; -1 \;\;\; 1 \;\;\; 3 \;\;\; 5$

D   $-5 \;\; -3 \;\; -1 \;\;\; 1 \;\;\; 3 \;\;\; 5$

**4.** Josea wants to solve the system using substitution.
$$\begin{cases} x = -2y + 4 \\ 2x - 3y = 5 \end{cases}$$
Which of the following is the best way for Josea to proceed?

F   Solve the first equation for $y$, then substitute into the second equation.

G   Solve the second equation for $y$, then substitute into the first equation.

H   Substitute $-2y + 4$ for $x$ in the second equation.

I   Substitute $-2y + 4$ for $y$ in the second equation.

**5.** A board must be cut so that its length is 40.50 cm. The tolerance is 0.25 cm. Which inequality describes the allowable lengths for the board?

A   $|x - 0.25| \leq 40.50$    C   $|x - 40.50| \leq 0.25$

B   $|x + 0.25| \leq 40.50$    D   $|x - 0.25| \leq 40.75$

**6.** Which graph shows the solution to the given system?
$$\begin{cases} \frac{1}{2}x - y = 1 \\ x = 3 \end{cases}$$

 F      H

 G      I

**7.** Consider the system below.
$$\begin{cases} 4x - 3y - 4z = 17 \\ -2x + 3y - 2z = 1 \\ 4x + 6y + 8z = 2 \end{cases}$$
Which of the following steps would NOT be used to solve the equation by elimination?

A   Add the first row to 2 times the second row.

B   Add the third row to 4 times the second row.

C   Add the first row to the third row.

D   Add the first row to the second row.

**8.** Which of the following inequalities does the graph represent?

F   $y \leq -|x - 3| + 2$    H   $y \leq -|x + 3| + 2$

G   $y \geq -|x - 3| + 2$    I   $y \geq -|x + 3| + 2$

**2.** G

**3.** A

**4.** H

**5.** C

**6.** I

**7.** C

**8.** F

# Answers

**9.** B

**10.** G

**11.** C

**12.** 20

**13.** 5

**14.** 4

**15.** 15

**16.** [2] let $r$ = number of reg. mix-ins, let $p$ = number of premium mix-ins

$r + p \geq 4$     $0.5r + 1p \leq 2.5$

$p \geq 4 - r$     $p \leq -0.5r + 2.5$

you can get 3 reg. and 1 premium mix-in, or 4 reg. mix-ins, or 5 reg. mix-ins.

[1] correct answer, without work shown

**17.** [2] slope of line $m$ = 3, slope of line perpendicular to $m = -\frac{1}{3}$. Write eq. of line in point-slope form:

$y - (-2) = -\frac{1}{3}(x - 3)$

$y + 2 = -\frac{1}{3}x + 1$

$y = -\frac{1}{3}x - 1$

[1] one computational error

**18.** [2] **a.** C

    **b.** A

    **c.** D

    **d.** B

[1] one incorrect answer

**19.** [4] **a.**

$y = 34x + 1$ (OR another reasonable trend line)

    **b.** No; $y = 34(10) + 1 = 341$, Jenna will only do 341 push-ups in 10 min, and the record is 350.

[3] incomplete explanation for part (b)

[2] only part (a) answered correctly

[1] correct answers, without work shown

---

**9.** The formula for the area of a trapezoid is $A = \frac{h}{2}(b_1 + b_2)$. Solve this equation for $b_2$.

Ⓐ $b_2 = \frac{2A}{hb_1}$     Ⓒ $b_2 = \frac{2A}{h - b_1}$

Ⓑ $b_2 = \frac{2A}{h} - b_1$     Ⓓ $b_2 = \frac{2A}{h + b_1}$

**10.** Which line is parallel to the line $2x - 3y = 9$?

Ⓕ $2x + 3y = 9$     Ⓗ $3x + 2y = 9$

Ⓖ $2x - 3y = 6$     Ⓘ $3x - 2y = 6$

**11.** What is the equation of the line that passes through $(-2, 4)$ and $(2, 7)$?

Ⓐ $y - 7 = \frac{3}{4}(x + 2)$     Ⓒ $y - 7 = \frac{3}{4}(x - 2)$

Ⓑ $y + 7 = \frac{3}{4}(x - 2)$     Ⓓ $y - 2 = \frac{3}{4}(x - 7)$

### GRIDDED RESPONSE

**12.** The nutrition label on a package of crackers shows there are 80 Calories in 16 grams of crackers. How many grams are in a package labeled 100 Calories?

**13.** A family with 4 adults and 3 children spends $47 for movie tickets at the theater. Another family with 2 adults and 4 children spends $36. What is the price of a child's ticket in dollars?

**14.** What is the sum of the solutions of $|5 - 3x| = x + 1$?

**15.** Sofia is buying party favors for her birthday party. The candles cost $1 each, the frames are $2 each, and the mugs are $2.50 each. She has $120 to spend on 75 favors. Also, she wants to buy twice as many candles as mugs. How many frames should she buy?

### Short Response

**16.** An ice cream shop has regular mix-ins for $.50 each and premium mix-ins for $1 each. You have $2.50 to spend on mix-ins, and you want at least 4 mix-ins. How many of each type of mix-in can you get in your ice cream?

---

**17.** The equation of line $m$ is $y = 3x - 1$. What is the equation of a line that goes through the point $(3, -2)$ and is perpendicular to line $m$? Show your work.

**18.** The graph below shows the boundaries for the system of linear inequalities.

$\begin{cases} y \leq 0.5x + 5 \\ y \leq -5x - 6 \end{cases}$

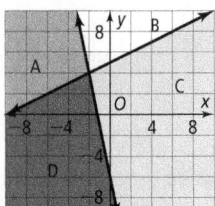

    **a.** Of the shaded areas A, B, C and D, which area represents a solution to the first inequality but not the second?

    **b.** Which represents a solution to the second inequality but not the first?

    **c.** Which represents a solution to both inequalities?

    **d.** Which represents a solution to neither inequality?

### Extended Response

**19.** Jenna is trying to break her school's record for doing the most push-ups in ten minutes. The current record holder did 350 push-ups in ten minutes. The table shows the number of push-ups Jenna completed in the first 6 minutes.

    **a.** Draw a scatter plot and find the line of best fit.

    **b.** Will Jenna beat the current record? Justify your reasoning.

| Time (min) | 1 | 2 | 3 | 4 | 5 | 6 |
|---|---|---|---|---|---|---|
| Number of push-ups | 37 | 70 | 99 | 132 | 169 | 207 |

# Get Ready!

Lesson 1-4 **Solving Linear Equations**

Solve each equation. Check your answer.

**1.** $9x - 16 = 8 + 5x$

**2.** $4(y + 2) + 1 = -5(3 - 2y)$

Lesson 1-6 **Solving Absolute Value Inequalities**

Solve each inequality. Graph the solution.

**3.** $|6x - 12| + 6 < 30$

**4.** $6|4y - 2| \geq 42$

Lesson 2-3 **Writing and Graphing Equations in Slope-Intercept Form**

Graph the line passing through the given points. Then write its equation in slope-intercept form.

**5.** $(1, -1)$ and $(3, 17)$

**6.** $(2, 9)$ and $(6, 11)$

Lesson 2-6 **Identifying Translations**

Identify each horizontal and vertical translation of the parent function $y = |x|$.

**7.** $y = |x - 4| + 2$

**8.** $y = |x + 10| - 3$

Lesson 3-2 **Solving Systems of Equations**

Solve each system of equations by substitution.

**9.** $\begin{cases} 2x + 6y = 14 \\ 4x - 8y = 48 \end{cases}$

**10.** $\begin{cases} x + 2y = -18 \\ 2x - 4y = 12 \end{cases}$

## Looking Ahead Vocabulary

**11.** A *form* is a document with blank spaces to fill in. What types of forms might you use?

**12.** Something is *imaginary* if it has no factual reality. What are some examples of imaginary items?

**13.** Many items have a specific *function*, or purpose for use. What is the function of a pencil?

# Get Ready!

Assign this diagnostic assessment to determine if students have the prerequisite skills for Chapter 4.

| Lesson | Skill |
|--------|-------|
| 1-4 | Solve Linear Equations |
| 1-6 | Solve Absolute Value Inequalities |
| 2-3 | Write and Graph Linear Equations in Slope-Intercept Form |
| 2-6 | Identify Translations |
| 3-2 | Solve Systems of Equations |

To remediate students, select from these resources (available for every lesson).
- Online Problems (PowerAlgebra.com)
- Reteaching (All-in-One Teaching Resources)
- Practice (All-in-One Teaching Resources)

## Why Students Need These Skills

**SOLVING LINEAR EQUATIONS**
Solving linear equations is extended to solving quadratic equations.

**SOLVING ABSOLUTE VALUE INEQUALITIES**
Students will need to solve absolute value equations when solving systems of inequalities.

**WRITING AND GRAPHING EQUATIONS IN SLOPE-INTERCEPT FORM**
Writing and graphing equations in slope-intercept form prepares students for writing and graphing quadratic equations in vertex form.

**IDENTIFYING TRANSLATIONS**
Identifying translations of the absolute value parent functions corresponds to finding translations of the quadratic function.

**SOLVING SYSTEMS OF EQUATIONS**
Solving systems of linear equations prepares students to solve systems of quadratic equations using the same techniques.

## Looking Ahead Vocabulary

**FORM** When comparing the form of an equation to a document, the blank spaces to be filled in correspond to the constant values in the equation.
**IMAGINARY** Ask students why these imaginary items are important regardless of having no factual reality.
**FUNCTION** Students may list several specific functions for a pencil, such as writing and erasing.

# Answers

## Get Ready!

**1.** 6

**2.** 4

**3.** $-2 < x < 6$

**4.** $y \leq -\dfrac{5}{4}$ or $y \geq \dfrac{9}{4}$

**5.** $y = 9x - 10$

**6.** $y = \dfrac{1}{2}x + 8$

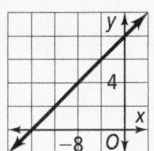

**7.** translated 4 units to the right and 2 units up

**8.** translated 10 units to the left and 3 units down

**9.** $(10, -1)$

**10.** $(-6, -6)$

**11.** Answers may vary. Sample: application forms, registration forms, tests

**12.** Answers may vary. Sample: monsters, ghosts, tooth fairy

**13.** writing

# Chapter 4 Overview

**UbD** **Understanding by Design**

Chapter 4 expands on students' understandings and skills related to functions, equations, and graphs. In this chapter, students will develop the answers to the Essential Questions posed on the opposite page as they learn the concepts and skills bulleted below.

**BIG** idea **Equivalence**

**ESSENTIAL QUESTION** What are the advantages of a quadratic function in vertex form? in standard form?

- Students will identify the vertex, line of symmetry, maximum or minimum, domain, range, and translations of a quadratic function.
- Students will graph quadratic functions with and without graphing calculators.
- Students will use quadratic functions as models.

**BIG** idea **Function**

**ESSENTIAL QUESTION** How is any quadratic function related to the parent quadratic function $y = x^2$?

- Students will graph transformations of the parent quadratic function $y = x^2$.
- Students will compare translations to the parent quadratic function.

**BIG** idea **Solving Equations and Inequalities**

**ESSENTIAL QUESTION** How are the real solutions of a quadratic equation related to the graph of the related quadratic function?

- Students will identify the $x$-intercepts of the graphs of related quadratic functions.

**PowerAlgebra.com**

Your place to get all things digital

Download videos connecting math to your world.

**VIDEO**

Math definitions in English and Spanish

**VOCABULARY**

The online Solve It will get you in gear for each lesson.

**SOLVE IT!**

Interactive! Vary numbers, graphs, and figures to explore math concepts.

**DYNAMIC ACTIVITIES**

Download Step-by-Step Problems with Instant Replay.

**ONLINE PROBLEMS**

Get and view your assignments online.

**ONLINE HOMEWORK**

Extra practice and review online

**MathXL FOR SCHOOL**

*A parabola is the graph of a quadratic function.*

*Parabolas can be seen all over the place. You can find them in the designs of buildings like the one on the next page.*

## Vocabulary

English/Spanish Vocabulary Audio Online:

| English | Spanish |
|---|---|
| axis of symmetry, *p. 194* | eje de simetría |
| complex number, *p. 249* | números complejos |
| discriminant, *p. 242* | discriminante |
| greatest common factor, *p. 218* | máximo factor común de una expresión |
| imaginary number, *p. 249* | número imaginario |
| parabola, *p. 194* | parábola |
| Quadratic Formula, *p. 240* | fórmula cuadrática |
| quadratic function, *p. 194* | función cuadrática |
| standard form, *p. 202* | forma normal |
| vertex form, *p. 194* | forma del vértice |
| zero of a function, *p. 226* | cero de una función |

**PowerAlgebra.com**

## Chapter 4 Overview

Use these online assets to engage your students. These include support for the Solve It and step-by-step solutions for Problems.

 **VIDEO** Show the student-produced video demonstrating relevant and engaging applications of the new concepts in the chapter.

 **VOCABULARY** Find online definitions for new terms in English and Spanish.

 **SOLVE IT!** Start each lesson with an attention-getting Problem. View the Problem online with helpful hints.

## My Math Video

My Math Video

Use this picture to introduce the shape of the graph of a quadratic function, a parabola.

**Q** Look at the glass wall in the center. How would you describe its shape? **[Samples: steep curve, parabolic]**

**Q** What symmetry can you identify? **[The wall is symmetric down the middle from top to bottom.]**

**Q** Where is the highest part of the glass wall? **[on the top, in the very middle]**

**Q** Look at the reflection of the glass wall in the water. How is the shape the same? How is it different? **[The shape of the curve is the same, and the symmetry is the same, but the highest point is now the lowest point.]**

**Q** The shape of the outline of the wall is called a parabola. Can you identify other parabolas in the picture? **[Samples: other walls, the parts that are sticking out]**

**ERROR PREVENTION**

Watch for students who describe the parabolic shape as half of a circle or half of an oval or ellipse. Point out that the glass wall and its reflection do not make up those shapes.

**EXTENSION**

Have students research the parabola and find another example of it occurring in art, construction, or nature. For example, arches, bridges, or path of an animal's jump.

## **BIG** ideas

**1 Equivalence**
**Essential Question** What are the advantages of a quadratic function in vertex form? In standard form?

**2 Function**
**Essential Question** How is any quadratic function related to the parent quadratic function $y = x^2$?

**3 Solving Equations and Inequalities**
**Essential Question** How are the real solutions of a quadratic equation related to the graph of the related quadratic function?

## Chapter Preview

4-1 Quadratic Functions and Transformations
4-2 Standard Form of a Quadratic Function
4-3 Modeling With Quadratic Functions
4-4 Factoring Quadratic Expressions
4-5 Quadratic Equations
4-6 Completing the Square
4-7 The Quadratic Formula
4-8 Complex Numbers
4-9 Quadratic Systems

PowerAlgebra.com | Chapter 4 Quadratic Functions and Equations | 193

 Increase students' depth of knowledge with interactive online activities.

 Show Problems from each lesson solved step by step. Instant replay allows students to go at their own pace when studying online.

 Assign homework to individual students or to an entire class.

 Prepare students for the Mid-Chapter Quiz and Chapter Test with online practice and review.

# QUADRATIC FUNCTIONS AND EQUATIONS
# Math Background

**UbD**

## Equivalence

**BIG idea** A single quantity may be represented by many different expressions. The facts about a quantity may be expressed by many different equations (or inequalities).

**ESSENTIAL UNDERSTANDINGS**

**4-1** The graph of any quadratic function is a transformation of the graph of the parent quadratic function, $y = x^2$.

**4-2** For any quadratic function $f(x) = ax^2 + bx + c$, the values of $a$, $b$, and $c$ provide key information about its graph.

**4-3** Three noncollinear points, no two of which are in line vertically, are on the graph of exactly one quadratic function.

**4-9** You can solve systems involving quadratic equations using methods similar to the ones used to solve systems of linear equations.

## Function

**BIG idea** A function is a relationship between variables in which each value of the input variable is associated with a unique value of the output variable. Functions can be represented in a variety of ways, such as graphs, tables, equations, or words. Each representation is particularly useful in certain situations. Some important families of functions are developed through transformations of the simplest form of the function.

**ESSENTIAL UNDERSTANDINGS**

**4-1 to 4-3 & 4-9** See above.

**4-5** To find the zeros of a quadratic function $y = ax^2 + bx + c$, solve the related quadratic equation $0 = ax^2 + bx + c$.

## Solving Equations & Inequalities

**BIG idea** Solving an equation is the process of rewriting the equation to make what it says about its variable(s) as simple as possible. Properties of numbers and equality can be used to transform an equation (or inequality) into equivalent, simpler equations (or inequalities) in order to find solutions. Useful information about equations and inequalities (including solutions) can be found by analyzing graphs or tables.

**ESSENTIAL UNDERSTANDINGS**

**4-4** You can factor many quadratic trinomials $(ax^2 + bx + c)$ into products of two binomials.

**4-5 & 4-9** See above.

**4-6** Completing a perfect square trinomial allows you to factor the completed trinomial as the square of a binomial.

**4-7** You can solve a quadratic equation $ax^2 + bx + c = 0$ in more than one way. In general, you can find a formula that gives values of $x$ in terms of $a$, $b$, and $c$.

**4-8** A basis for the complex numbers is a number whose square is $-1$. Every quadratic equation has complex number solutions (that sometimes are real numbers).

## Describing and Graphing Quadratic Functions

The features used to describe a quadratic function can be determined by using a graphing calculator or analyzing the function in vertex or standard form.

**Standard Form $y = ax^2 + bx + c$**
- calculator friendly
- features found using simple formulas

**Vertex Form $y = a(x - h)^2 + k$**
- vertex and maximum or minimum can be read directly from equation
- shows how graph is transformed from the parent function

| | Standard Form | Vertex Form |
|---|---|---|
| | $y = ax^2 + bx + c$ | $y = a(x - h)^2 + k$ |
| axis of symmetry | $x = \frac{-b}{2a}$ | $x = h$ |
| vertex | $\left(\frac{-b}{2a}, f\left(\frac{-b}{2a}\right)\right)$ | $(h, k)$ |
| $y$-intercept | $(0, c)$ | $(0, a(x - h)^2 + k)$ |
| maximum or minimum | $f\left(\frac{-b}{2a}\right)$ | $k$ |

### Graphing Calculator

The axis of symmetry, minimum or maximum, vertex, $y$-intercept, domain, and range can be found using the trace key or the table of a graphing calculator.

### Common Errors When Describing and Graphing Quadratic Functions

Many errors occur when students are unfamiliar with the general form, size, and orientation of the quadratic function. Students often rely on graphing calculators and do not use information from the equation to visualize the graph. Suggest that students ask themselves the following before graphing:
- Does the graph open upward or downward?
- In which quadrant is the vertex?
- What is the $y$-intercept?

## Finding Zeros of Quadratic Functions

The zeros of quadratic functions are equivalent to the x-intercepts of the graph of the function or the solutions of the quadratic equation. The zeros can be found by graphing, factoring, completing the square, or using the quadratic formula.

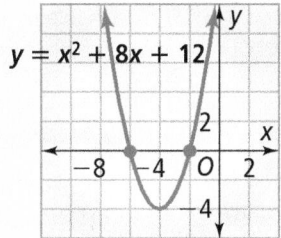

### Factoring

Factor the quadratic function, set the equation equal to zero and solve for x.

$$y = x^2 + 8x + 12$$
$$0 = (x + 6)(x + 2)$$
$$x = -6 \text{ and } x = -2$$

### Completing the Square

Gather the x-terms on one side, and add $\left(\frac{b}{2}\right)^2$ to both sides.

$$x^2 + 8x = -12$$
$$x^2 + 8x + 16 = -12 + 16$$
$$(x + 4)^2 = 4$$
$$x + 4 = \pm 2$$
$$x = -6 \text{ or } -2$$

### Quadratic Formula

The solutions of any quadratic equation can be found using the quadratic formula

$$x = \frac{-b \pm \sqrt{b^2 - 4ac}}{2a}.$$

The discriminant $b^2 - 4ac$ is used to determine the number and types of solutions.

• discriminant $> 0$, then 2 real solutions
• discriminant $= 0$, then 1 real solution (double root)
• discriminant $< 0$, then no real solutions

## Common Errors When Finding Zeros of Quadratic Functions

### Factoring and Completing the Square Errors

Many errors are due to algebraic mistakes. Encourage students to substitute the solutions back into the original equation to check their answers.

### Quadratic Formula Errors

Mistakes occur when students use graphing calculators to solve the quadratic formula because they fail to use parentheses correctly. Encourage students to first find the discriminant to describe and check their solutions.

## Complex Numbers

A complex number has a real part and an imaginary part. Complex numbers can be written in the form $a + bi$ where $a$ and $b$ are real numbers.

• If $a = 0$ and $b \neq 0$, then the number is a pure imaginary number.
• If $b = 0$ and $a \neq 0$, then the number is a real number.
• If $a \neq 0$ and $b \neq 0$, then the number is a complex number with a real and imaginary part.

### Imaginary Numbers

The square root of a negative number is an imaginary number. Imaginary numbers are indicated by $i$. By definition, $i = \sqrt{-1}$ or $i^2 = -1$.

### Operations with Complex Numbers

Complex numbers can be added, subtracted, multiplied, or divided. The rules are similar to the rules for operations with binomials.

### Complex Conjugates

The product of complex conjugates is a real number. Use complex conjugates to simplify quotients of complex numbers and rationalize denominators.

$$\frac{3}{3 + i} = \frac{3}{3 + i}\left(\frac{3 - i}{3 - i}\right)$$
$$= \frac{3(3 - i)}{(3 + i)(3 - i)}$$
$$= \frac{9 - 3i}{10}$$
$$= \frac{9}{10} - \frac{3i}{10}$$

### Graphing Quadratic Functions with No Real Solutions

The graph of a quadratic function with no real solutions has no x-intercepts.

## Common Errors When Using Complex Numbers

**Simplifying** Have students rewrite the problem using $-1$ to help them simplify. For example, $\sqrt{-9} = \sqrt{-1} \cdot \sqrt{9} = i(3)$ or $3i$.

**Operations** Suggest to students that they treat $i$ using the same rules as they do for variables, reminding them that $i^2 = -1$.

**Complex Conjugates** Point out that multiplying complex conjugates is similar to multiplying binomials whose product is a difference of squares. For example,

$$(x + 2)(x - 2) = x^2 - 4$$
$$(2 + i)(2 - i) = 4 - i^2 = 5$$

# QUADRATIC FUNCTIONS AND EQUATIONS
# Pacing and Assignment Guide

| | | TRADITIONAL | | | BLOCK |
|---|---|---|---|---|---|
| **Lesson** | **Teaching Day(s)** | **Basic** | **Average** | **Advanced** | **Block** |
| 4-1 | 1 | Problems 1–3 Exs. 7–28, 70–85 | Problems 1–3 Exs. 7–27 odd, 70–85 | Problems 1–3 Exs. 7–27 odd, 70–85 | **Day 1** Problems 1–5 Exs. 7–37 odd, 38–58, 70–85 |
| | 2 | Problems 4–5; Exs. 29–37, 38–41, 46–48, 51–57 odd | Problems 4–5 Exs. 29–37 odd, 38–58 | Problems 4–5 Exs. 29–37 odd, 38–69 | |
| 4-2 | 1 | Problems 1–2 Exs. 8–25, 54–70 | Problems 1–2 Exs. 9–25 odd, 54–70 | Problems 1–2 Exs. 9–25 odd, 54–70 | **Day 2** Problems 1–4 Exs. 9–31 odd, 33–47, 54–70 |
| | 2 | Problems 3–4 Exs. 26–32, 35–38, 43–46 | Problems 3–4 Exs. 27–31 odd, 33–47 | Problems 3–4 Exs. 27–31 odd, 33–53 | |
| 4-3 | 1 | Problems 1–2 Exs. 7–13, 31–45 | Problems 1–2 Exs. 7–13 odd, 31–45 | Problems 1–2 Exs. 7–13 odd, 31–45 | **Day 3** Problems 1–3 Exs. 7–17 odd, 18–27, 31–45 |
| | 2 | Problem 3 Exs. 14–17, 21–25 | Problem 3 Exs. 15, 18–27 | Problem 3 Exs. 15, 18–30 | |
| 4-4 | 1 | Problems 1–3 Exs. 14–46, 103–110 | Problems 1–3 Exs. 15–45 odd, 103–110 | Problems 1–3 Exs. 15–45 odd, 103–110 | **Day 4** Problems 1–5 Exs. 15–57 odd, 59–90, 103–110 |
| | 2 | Problems 4–5; Exs. 47–58, 59–61, 79–82, 87, 90 | Problems 4–5 Exs. 47–57 odd, 59–90 | Problems 4–5 Exs. 47–57 odd, 59–102 | |
| 4-5 | 1 | Problems 1–2 Exs. 9–26, 60–75 | Problems 1–2 Exs. 9–25 odd, 60–75 | Problems 1–2 Exs. 9–25 odd, 60–75 | **Day 5** Problems 1–4 Exs. 9–35 odd, 37–56, 60–75 |
| | 2 | Problems 3–4 Exs. 27–36, 37–43, 55 | Problems 3–4 Exs. 27–35 odd, 37–56 | Problems 3–4 Exs. 27–35 odd, 37–59 | |
| 4-6 | 1 | Problems 1–3 Exs. 12–27, 86–100 | Problems 1–3 Exs. 13–27 odd, 86–100 | Problems 1–3 Exs. 13–27 odd, 86–100 | **Day 6** Problems 1–6 Exs. 29–51 odd, 52–75, 86–100 |
| | 2 | Problems 4–6; Exs. 28–51, 52, 54, 62, 64, 75 | Problems 4–6 Exs. 29–51 odd, 52–75 | Problems 4–6 Exs. 29–51 odd, 52–85 | |
| 4-7 | 1 | Problems 1–2 Exs. 11–24, 78–90 | Problems 1–2 Exs. 11–23 odd, 78–90 | Problems 1–2 Exs. 11–23 odd, 78–90 | **Day 7** Problems 1–4 Exs. 11–37 odd, 39–69, 78–90 |
| | 2 | Problems 3–4 Exs. 25–42, 57–59, 67 | Problems 3–4 Exs. 25–37 odd, 39–69 | Problems 3–4 Exs. 25–37 odd, 39–77 | |
| 4-8 | 1 | Problems 1–4 Exs. 8–26, 73–89 | Problems 1–4 Exs. 9–25 odd, 73–89 | Problems 1–4 Exs. 9–25 odd, 73–89 | **Day 8** Problems 1–7 Exs. 9–43 odd, 45–69, 73–89 |
| | 2 | Problems 5–7 Exs. 27–46, 48, 50, 56, 57 | Problems 5–7 Exs. 27–43 odd, 45–69 | Problems 5–7 Exs. 27–43 odd, 45–72 | |
| 4-9 | 1 | Problems 1–2 Exs. 8–19, 62–77 | Problems 1–2 Exs. 9–19 odd, 62–77 | Problems 1–2 Exs. 9–19 odd, 62–77 | **Day 9** Problems 1–4 Exs. 9–27 odd, 29–55, 62–77 |
| | 2 | Problems 3–4 Exs. 20–31, 39–41, 47 | Problems 3–4 Exs. 21–27 odd, 29–55 | Problems 3–4 Exs. 21–27 odd, 29–61 | |
| Review | 1 | Chapter 4 Review | Chapter 4 Review | Chapter 4 Review | **Day 10** Chapter 4 Review Chapter 4 Test |
| Assess | 1 | Chapter 4 Test | Chapter 4 Test | Chapter 4 Test | |
| **Total** | | **20 Days** | **20 Days** | **20 Days** | **10 Days** |

Note: Pacing does not include Concept Bytes and other feature pages.

# Resources

| | For the Chapter | 4-1 | 4-2 | 4-3 | 4-4 | 4-5 | 4-6 | 4-7 | 4-8 | 4-9 |
|---|---|---|---|---|---|---|---|---|---|---|
| **Planning** | | | | | | | | | | |
| Teacher Center Online Planner & Grade Book | I | I | I | I | I | I | I | I | I | I |
| **Interactive Learning & Guided Instruction** | | | | | | | | | | |
| My Math Video | I | | | | | | | | | |
| Solve It! | | I TM | I TM | I TM | I TM | I TM | I TM | I TM | I TM | I TM |
| Student Companion (SP)* | | P M | P M | P M | P M | P M | P M | P M | P M | P M |
| Vocabulary Support | | I P M | I P M | I P M | I P M | I P M | I P M | I P M | I P M | I P M |
| Got It? Support | | I P | I P | I P | I P | I P | I P | I P | I P | I P |
| Dynamic Activity | | I | I | | I | I | I | I | | I |
| Online Problems | | I | I | I | I | I | I | I | I | I |
| Additional Problems | | M | M | M | M | M | M | M | M | M |
| English Language Learner Support (TR) | | E P M | E P M | E P M | E P M | E P M | E P M | E P M | E P M | E P M |
| Activities, Games, and Puzzles | | E M | E M | E M | E M | E M | E M | E M | E M | E M |
| Teaching With TI Technology With CD-ROM | | ✓ P | ✓ P | | | ✓ P | | ✓ P | | |
| TI-Nspire™ Support CD-ROM | | ✓ | ✓ | ✓ | ✓ | ✓ | ✓ | ✓ | ✓ | ✓ |
| **Lesson Check & Practice** | | | | | | | | | | |
| Student Companion (SP)* | | P M | P M | P M | P M | P M | P M | P M | P M | P M |
| Lesson Check Support | | I P | I P | I P | I P | I P | I P | I P | I P | I P |
| Practice and Problem Solving Workbook (SP) | | P | P | P | P | P | P | P | P | P |
| Think About a Plan (TR)* | | E P M | E P M | E P M | E P M | E P M | E P M | E P M | E P M | E P M |
| Practice Form G (TR)* | | E P M | E P M | E P M | E P M | E P M | E P M | E P M | E P M | E P M |
| Standardized Test Prep (TR)* | | P M | P M | P M | P M | P M | P M | P M | P M | P M |
| Practice Form K (TR)* | | E P M | E P M | E P M | E P M | E P M | E P M | E P M | E P M | E P M |
| Extra Practice | E M | | | | | | | | | |
| Find the Errors! | M | | | | | | | | | |
| Enrichment (TR) | | E P M | E P M | E P M | E P M | E P M | E P M | E P M | E P M | E P M |
| Answers and Solutions CD-ROM | ✓ | ✓ | ✓ | ✓ | ✓ | ✓ | ✓ | ✓ | ✓ | ✓ |
| **Assess & Remediate** | | | | | | | | | | |
| ExamView CD-ROM | ✓ | ✓ | ✓ | ✓ | ✓ | ✓ | ✓ | ✓ | ✓ | ✓ |
| Lesson Quiz | | I TM | I TM | I TM | I TM | I TM | I TM | I TM | I TM | I TM |
| Quizzes and Tests Form G (TR)* | E P M | | | | | E P M | | | | E P M |
| Quizzes and Tests Form K (TR)* | E P M | | | | | E P M | | | | E P M |
| Reteaching (TR)* | | E P M | E P M | E P M | E P M | E P M | E P M | E P M | E P M | E P M |
| Performance Tasks (TR)* | P M | | | | | | | | | |
| Cumulative Review (TR)* | P M | | | | | | | | | |
| Progress Monitoring Assessments | I P M | | | | | | | | | |

(TR) Available in All-In-One Teaching Resources     * Spanish available

# 1 Interactive Learning

## Solve It!

**PURPOSE** To identify features of a parabola and translate it

**PROCESS** Students may
- sketch the path of the jump onto paper and shift it so the highest part is over the fence.
- count the horizontal distance between the start and highest part of the jump.

---

**FACILITATE**

**Q** How can you calculate the horizontal distance between the start of the jump and the highest part? [$x_2 - x_1 = 2 - 0 = 2$]

**Q** What are the coordinates of the top of the fence? [(4.5, 1)]

**Q** What equation could you solve to find the start of a jump over the fence? [$4.5 - x = 2$]

---

**ANSWER** See Solve It in Answers on next page.

**CONNECT THE MATH** In the Solve It, students find the vertex, axis of symmetry, and points on a parabola and apply a translation. In the lesson, students will use these elements to identify and graph quadratic functions.

# 2 Guided Instruction

## Take Note

**Q** How can you use vertex form to verify the axis of symmetry and vertex of $f(x) = x^2$? [$h = 0$, so the axis of symmetry is $x = h = 0$; $k = 0$, so the vertex is $(h, k) = (0, 0)$.]

**Q** What is $f(x) = x^2$ in vertex form? [$f(x) = 1(x - 0)^2 + 0$]

---

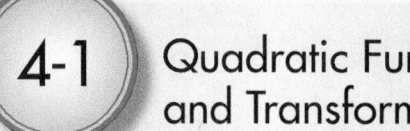

## 4-1 Quadratic Functions and Transformations

**Objective** To identify and graph quadratic functions

The path of the jump is a parabola.

**Dynamic Activity** Quadratics in Vertex Form

**Lesson Vocabulary**
- parabola
- quadratic function
- vertex form
- axis of symmetry
- vertex of the parabola
- minimum value
- maximum value

In the Solve It, you used the *parabolic* shape of the horse's jump. A **parabola** is the graph of a **quadratic function**, which you can write in the form $f(x) = ax^2 + bx + c$, where $a \neq 0$.

**Essential Understanding** The graph of any quadratic function is a transformation of the graph of the parent quadratic function, $y = x^2$.

The **vertex form** of a quadratic function is $f(x) = a(x - h)^2 + k$, where $a \neq 0$. The **axis of symmetry** is a line that divides the parabola into two mirror images. The equation of the axis of symmetry is $x = h$. The **vertex of the parabola** is $(h, k)$, the intersection of the parabola and its axis of symmetry.

### Key Concept The Parent Quadratic Function

The parent quadratic function is $f(x) = x^2$. Its graph is the parabola shown. The axis of symmetry is $x = 0$. The vertex is $(0, 0)$.

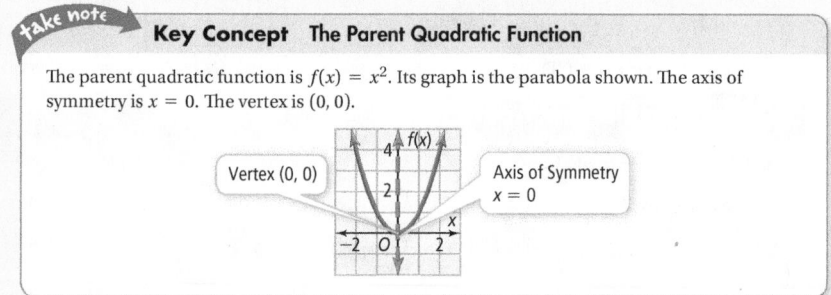

Vertex $(0, 0)$

Axis of Symmetry $x = 0$

---

# 4-1 Preparing to Teach

**BIG** ideas Function
Equivalence
**UbD**

**ESSENTIAL UNDERSTANDINGS**
- The graph of any quadratic function is a transformation of the graph of the parent quadratic function, $y = x^2$.
- The vertex form of a quadratic function is $f(x) = a(x - h)^2 + k$, where $a \neq 0$.
- The axis of symmetry is a line that divides the parabola into two mirror images.
- The vertex of the parabola is $(h, k)$, the intersection of the parabola and its axis of symmetry.

## Math Background

When considering transformations, students may wonder whether they can transform the graph of a quadratic function so that the parabola opens leftward or rightward. The graph can be transformed this way, for example, by a reflection in $y = x$. Suggest that students draw the graph and check to see whether the graph represents

a function. Except for the vertex, two values in the range are paired with each value in the domain. Only parabolas that open upward or downward are functions of $x$.

Note the comparisons between the transformations of the quadratic function $y = x^2$ and the transformations of the absolute value function in Lesson 2-7. However, be aware that students sometimes confuse absolute value graphs with parabolas. If this happens, help them determine the degree of the function. Absolute value functions, like linear functions, have the variable in the first degree.

## Support Student Learning

Use the **Algebra 2 Companion** to engage and support students during instruction. See Lesson Resources at the end of this lesson for details.

---

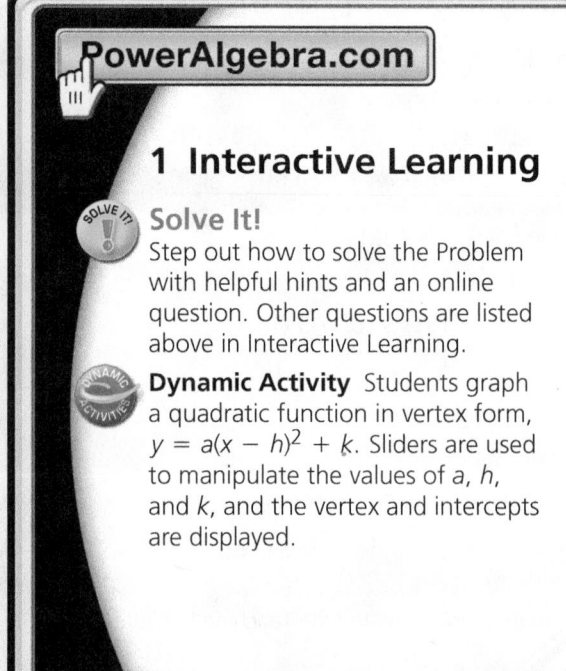

## PowerAlgebra.com

### 1 Interactive Learning

**Solve It!**
Step out how to solve the Problem with helpful hints and an online question. Other questions are listed above in Interactive Learning.

**Dynamic Activity** Students graph a quadratic function in vertex form, $y = a(x - h)^2 + k$. Sliders are used to manipulate the values of $a$, $h$, and $k$, and the vertex and intercepts are displayed.

**Plan**

**How do you choose points to plot?**
Choose the vertex and two points on one side of the axis of symmetry that give integer values of $f(x)$.

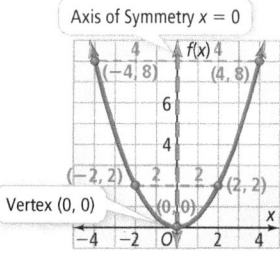 **Problem 1** **Graphing a Function of the Form** $f(x) = ax^2$

**What is the graph of** $f(x) = \frac{1}{2}x^2$?

**Step 1** Plot the vertex $(0, 0)$. Draw the axis of symmetry, $x = 0$.

**Step 2** Find and plot two points on one side of the axis of symmetry.

| x | $f(x) = \frac{1}{2}x^2$ | $(x, f(x))$ |
|---|---|---|
| 0 | $\frac{1}{2}(0)^2 = 0$ | $(0, 0)$ |
| 2 | $\frac{1}{2}(2)^2 = 2$ | $(2, 2)$ |
| 4 | $\frac{1}{2}(4)^2 = 8$ | $(4, 8)$ |

**Step 3** Plot the corresponding points on the other side of the axis of symmetry.

**Step 4** Sketch the curve.

**Got It?** **1. a.** What is the graph of $f(x) = -\frac{1}{3}x^2$?

**b.** **Reasoning** What can you say about the graph of the function $f(x) = ax^2$ if $a$ is a negative number? Explain.

Graphs of $y = ax^2$ and $y = -ax^2$ are reflections of each other across the $x$-axis. Increasing $|a|$ stretches the graph vertically and narrows it horizontally. Decreasing $|a|$ compresses the graph vertically and widens it horizontally.

**Key Concept** **Reflection, Stretch, and Compression**

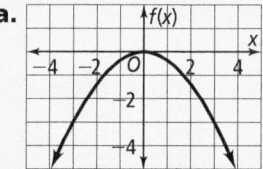

Reflection, $a$ and $-a$

Stretch, $a > 1$

Compression, $0 < a < 1$

If $a > 0$, the parabola opens upward. The $y$-coordinate of the vertex is the **minimum value** of the function. If $a < 0$, the parabola opens downward. The $y$-coordinate of the vertex is the **maximum value** of the function.

Minimum Value    Vertex    Maximum Value

**Problem 1** **EXTENSION**
An alternate strategy is to think of $f(x) = x^2$ as the relation between $x$-values and their squares: $(-1, 1), (0, 0), (1, 1), (2, 4)$. Then $f(x) = \frac{1}{2}x^2$ is the relation between $x$-values and *half* of their squares: $(-1, 0.5), (0, 0), (1, 0.5), (2, 2)$.

**Q** Why is it preferable to use two points on each side of the axis? [**Two points help determine the curvature of the parabola.**]

**Got It?**

**Q** What is the vertex of $f(x) = ax^2$? What is the greatest value of $f(x)$ for $a < 0$? [**(0, 0); 0**]

**Take Note** **ELL SUPPORT**
The terms *stretch*, *compression*, *minimum*, and *maximum* are challenging, since each word can be used in different contexts and has several synonyms. Focus on the mathematical meanings by creating a graphic organizer with several examples of meanings of each term. If time allows, use word webs to raise students' comfort with alternate meanings and synonyms such as *mirror image* for *reflection* or *shrink* for *compression*.

**Q** For the parabola in the Solve It, what can you say about $a$? [**$a < 0$, because the parabola opens downward and has a maximum.**]

**ERROR PREVENTION**
Explain that a stretch moves each $y$-value higher as if the parabola were stretched up. Do not allow students to describe the transformation as the process that makes the parabola thinner.

# Answers

## Solve It!
2 units before the fence, or at 2.5; the horse is at its highest pt. 2 units after beginning the jump.

## Got It?
**1. a.**

**b.** If $a$ is a negative number, the parabola will open downward. There will be a maximum value for $y$ at the vertex of the parabola.

# 2 Guided Instruction

Each Problem is worked out and supported online.

**Problem 1**
Graphing a Function of the Form $f(x) = ax^2$

**Problem 2**
Graphing Translations of $f(x) = x^2$
*Animated*

**Problem 3**
Interpreting Vertex Form

**Problem 4**
Using Vertex Form
*Animated*

**Problem 5**
Writing a Quadratic Function in Vertex Form
*Animated*

**Support in Algebra 2 Companion**
• Vocabulary
• Key Concepts
• Got It?

## Problem 2 — EXTENSION

**Q** What function $p(x)$ translates the graph of $f(x)$ up 5 units? [$p(x) = x^2 + 5$]

**Q** What function $q(x)$ translates the graph of $f(x)$ left 4 units? [$q(x) = (x + 4)^2$]

**Q** What function $n(x)$ translates the graph of $h(x) = (x - 4)^2$ right 5 units? [$n(x) = (x - 9)^2$]

### Got It? — ERROR PREVENTION

Be aware of students who interpret the +1 in 2b as a translation of the vertex one unit to the right on the $x$-axis.

**Q** How can you write 2b in vertex form? [$h(x) = 1[x - (-1)]^2 + 0$]

## Problem 3

This problem is the first to show the combined effects of all three constants, $a$, $h$, and $k$, in a single quadratic function. You may need to briefly review the definitions of domain and range.

**Q** Do all quadratic functions have a domain of all real numbers? [Answers may vary. Sample: No; some real-world quadratic models have restricted domains; for example, the function that models the path of the jump in the Solve It is restricted to $x$-values between 0 and 4.]

### Got It? — EXTENSION

**Q** Assuming $f(x) = a(x - h)^2 + k$ has an unrestricted domain, what is the range in terms of $a$, $h$, and $k$? [If $a > 0$, then the range is all real numbers $\geq k$; if $a < 0$, then the range is all real numbers $\leq k$.]

---

 **Problem 2** Graphing Translations of $f(x) = x^2$

Graph each function. How is each graph a translation of $f(x) = x^2$?

Ⓐ $g(x) = x^2 - 5$  Ⓑ $h(x) = (x - 4)^2$

**Think**

**How does g(x) differ from f(x)?**
For each value of $x$, the value of $g(x)$ is 5 less than the value of $f(x)$.

Translate the graph of $f$ down 5 units to get the graph of $g(x) = x^2 - 5$.

Translate the graph of $f$ to the right 4 units to get the graph of $h(x) = (x - 4)^2$.

**Got It? 2.** Graph each function. How is it a translation of $f(x) = x^2$?
  **a.** $g(x) = x^2 + 3$   **b.** $h(x) = (x + 1)^2$

The vertex form, $f(x) = a(x - h)^2 + k$, gives you information about the graph of $f$ without drawing the graph. If $a > 0$, $k$ is the minimum value of the function. If $a < 0$, $k$ is the maximum value.

 **Problem 3** Interpreting Vertex Form

For $y = 3(x - 4)^2 - 2$, what are the vertex, the axis of symmetry, the maximum or minimum value, the domain and the range?

**Plan**

**How do you use vertex form?**
Compare
$y = 3(x - 4)^2 - 2$
to vertex form
$y = a(x - h)^2 + k$
to find values for $a$, $h$, and $k$.

**Step 1** Compare: $y = 3(x - 4)^2 - 2$
  $y = a(x - h)^2 + k$

**Step 2** The vertex is $(h, k) = (4, -2)$.

**Step 3** The axis of symmetry is $x = h$, or $x = 4$.

**Step 4** Since $a > 0$, the parabola opens upward. $k = -2$ is the minimum value.

**Step 5** Domain: All real numbers. There is no restriction on the value of $x$.
  Range: All real numbers $\geq -2$, since the minimum value of the function is $-2$.

**Got It? 3.** What are the vertex, axis of symmetry, minimum or maximum, and domain and range of the function $y = -2(x + 1)^2 + 4$?

---

## Additional Problems

**1.** What is the graph of $f(x) = -\frac{1}{4}x^2$?

**ANSWER**

**2.** Graph each function. How is each graph a translation of $f(x) = x^2$?
  **a.** $g(x) = (x - 3)^2$
  **b.** $h(x) = x^2 + 1$

**ANSWER**
**a.**

**b.**

Translate $f(x) = x^2$ right 3 units to get $g(x) = (x - 3)^2$.

Translate $f(x) = x^2$ up 1 unit to get $h(x) = x^2 + 1$.

**3.** For $y = \frac{1}{2}(x - 3)^2 - 5$, what are the vertex, the axis of symmetry, the minimum or maximum value, the domain, and the range?

**ANSWER** The vertex is $(3, -5)$; the axis of symmetry is $x = 3$; $k = -5$ is the minimum value; the domain is all real numbers; and the range is all real numbers $\geq -5$.

**4.** What is the graph of $f(x) = -3(x + 5)^2 + 2$?

**ANSWER**

**5.** The arch of the Sidney Harbor Bridge is approximately 500 meters long and 85 meters high. What quadratic function models the curve of the arch? Assume the arch starts at $(0, 0)$.

**ANSWER**
$f(x) = -\frac{17}{12,500}(x - 250)^2 + 85$

You can use the vertex form of a quadratic function, $f(x) = a(x - h)^2 + k$, to transform the graph of the parent function $f(x) = x^2$.
• Stretch or compress the graph of $f(x) = x^2$ vertically by the factor $|a|$.
• If $a < 0$, reflect the graph across the $x$-axis.
• Shift the graph $|h|$ units horizontally and $|k|$ units vertically.

**take note**

### Key Concept  Translation of the Parabola

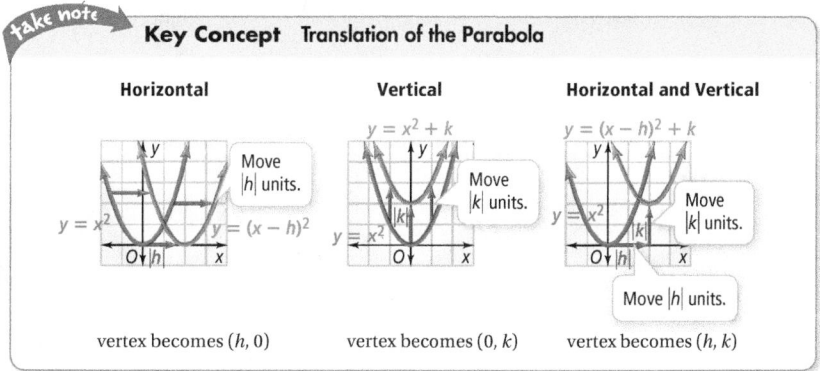

| Horizontal | Vertical | Horizontal and Vertical |
|---|---|---|
| vertex becomes $(h, 0)$ | vertex becomes $(0, k)$ | vertex becomes $(h, k)$ |

**Problem 4**  Using Vertex Form

**A** What is the graph of $f(x) = -2(x - 1)^2 + 3$?

**Step 1** Identify the constants $a = -2$, $h = 1$, and $k = 3$. Because $a < 0$, the parabola opens downward.

**Step 2** Plot the vertex $(h, k) = (1, 3)$ and draw the axis of symmetry $x = 1$.

$f(x) = -2(x - 1)^2 + 3$

**Step 3** Plot two points. $f(2) = -2(2 - 1)^2 + 3 = 1$. Plot $(2, 1)$ and the symmetric point $(0, 1)$.

**Step 4** Sketch the curve.

**B** Multiple Choice  What steps transform the graph of $y = x^2$ to $y = -2(x + 1)^2 + 3$?

Ⓐ Reflect across the $x$-axis, stretch by the factor 2, translate 1 unit to the right and 3 units up.

Ⓑ Stretch by the factor 2, translate 1 unit to the right and 3 units up.

Ⓒ Reflect across the $x$-axis, translate 1 unit to the left and 3 units up.

Ⓓ Stretch by the factor 2, reflect across the $x$-axis, translate 1 unit to the left and 3 units up.

The correct choice is D.

**Got It?  4.** What steps transform the graph of $y = x^2$ to $y = 2(x + 2)^2 - 5$?

---

---

## Answers

### Got It? (continued)

**2. a.** translated 3 units up

**b.** translated 1 unit to the left

**3.** vertex: $(-1, 4)$; axis of symmetry: $x = -1$; maximum: 4; domain: all real numbers, range: $y \leq 4$

**4.** stretch by the factor 2, translate 2 units to the left and 5 units down

**5.** $f(x) = -\frac{2}{9}(x - 2)^2 + 7$

### Lesson Check

**1.**

**2.** minimum

**3.** $y = -2(x - 0)^2 + 35$

**4.** when $a > 0$

**5.** No; $a$ must be $> 0$ or $< 0$.

**6.** $y = (x + 6)^2$ is the graph of $y = x^2$ translated 6 units to the left and has a minimum at $(-6, 0)$; $y = (x - 6)^2 + 7$ is the graph of $y = x^2$ translated 6 units to the right and 7 units up, with a minimum at $(6, 7)$.

### Practice and Problem-Solving Exercises

**7.**

**8.**

**9.**

**10.**

**11.**

**12.**

**13.**

**14.**

## Problem 5

Unlike Problems 1–4 that went from function to graph, this problem goes from graph to function.

> **Q** How can you tell from the picture that $a$ is negative? **[The path of the jump opens downward.]**
>
> **Q** What is the least information you need to write the equation? **[the vertex and one other point]**

### Got It?

**ERROR PREVENTION**

Suggest students sketch the path so they see the vertex is $(2, 7)$. Be aware of students simplifying $5 = a(5 - 2)^2 + 7$ as $5 = a(25 - 4) + 7$, which would give an answer of $a = -\frac{2}{21}$.

## 3 Lesson Check

### Do you know HOW?

- For Exercise 3, if students say the equation is already in vertex form, confirm understanding by asking for the values of $a$, $h$, and $k$.

### Do you UNDERSTAND?

- For Exercise 4, review the definition of vertex form on page 194. Explain that the constant linear function results when $a = 0$.

### Close

> **Q** How can you use a quadratic function written in vertex form to describe the graph of the parabola? **[The absolute value of $a$ in vertex form gives a stretch or compression of the parent function; the sign of $a$ gives the direction the parabola opens; $h$ gives the axis of symmetry; and $(h, k)$ is the vertex.]**

---

You can use the vertex form of a quadratic function to model a real-world situation.

 **Problem 5** Writing a Quadratic Function in Vertex Form

**Nature** The picture shows the jump of a dolphin. What quadratic function models the path of the dolphin's jump?

| Think | Write |
|---|---|
| What is the vertex? | The vertex is $(3, 7)$.<br>$h = 3, k = 7$ |
| Choose another point, $(9, 4)$, from the path. Substitute in the vertex form.<br><br>Solve for $a$. | $f(x) = a(x - h)^2 + k$<br>$4 = a(9 - 3)^2 + 7$<br>$4 = 36a + 7$<br>$-3 = 36a$<br>$a = -\frac{1}{12}$ |
| Substitute in the vertex form. | $f(x) = -\frac{1}{12}(x - 3)^2 + 7$<br>models the path of the dolphin's jump. |

**Got It?** **5.** Suppose the path of the jump changes so that the axis of symmetry becomes $x = 2$ and the height stays the same. If the path of the jump also passes through the point $(5, 5)$, what quadratic function would model this path?

### ✓ Lesson Check

**Do you know HOW?**

1. Graph the function $f(x) = -3x^2$.

2. Determine whether the function $f(x) = 0.25(2x - 15)^2 + 150$ has a maximum or a minimum value.

3. Rewrite $y = -2x^2 + 35$ in vertex form.

**Do you UNDERSTAND?**

4. **Vocabulary** When does the graph of a quadratic function have a minimum value?

5. **Reasoning** Is $y = 0(x - 4)^2 + 3$ a quadratic function? Explain.

6. **Compare and Contrast** Describe the differences between the graphs of $y = (x + 6)^2$ and $y = (x - 6)^2 + 7$.

---

## Answers

### Got It? (continued)
5. See page 197.

### Lesson Check
1–6. See page 197.

### Practice and Problem-Solving Exercises

15. translated 3 units up

16. translated 2 units to the right

17. translated 6 units down

18. translated 3 units to the left

## Practice and Problem-Solving Exercises

**Graph each function.**

 See Problem 1.

**7.** $y = -x^2$      **8.** $f(x) = 5x^2$      **9.** $y = \frac{2}{5}x^2$      **10.** $y = 2x^2$

**11.** $f(x) = 2\frac{1}{4}x^2$      **12.** $y = -\frac{4}{9}x^2$      **13.** $y = -7x^2$      **14.** $f(x) = 3\frac{2}{5}x^2$

**Graph each function. Describe how it was translated from $f(x) = x^2$.**    See Problem 2.

**15.** $f(x) = x^2 + 3$     **16.** $f(x) = (x - 2)^2$     **17.** $f(x) = x^2 - 6$     **18.** $f(x) = (x + 3)^2$

**19.** $f(x) = x^2 - 9$     **20.** $f(x) = (x + 5)^2$     **21.** $f(x) = x^2 + 1.5$     **22.** $f(x) = (x - 2.5)^2$

**Identify the vertex, the axis of symmetry, the maximum or minimum value, and the domain and the range of each function.**    See Problem 3.

**23.** $y = -1.5(x + 20)^2$     **24.** $f(x) = 0.1(x - 3.2)^2$     **25.** $f(x) = 24(x + 5.5)^2$

**26.** $y = 0.0035(x + 1)^2 - 1$     **27.** $f(x) = -(x - 4)^2 - 25$     **28.** $y = (x - 125)^2 + 125$

**Graph each function. Identify the axis of symmetry.**    See Problem 4.

**29.** $f(x) = (x - 1)^2 + 2$     **30.** $y = (x + 3)^2 - 4$     **31.** $f(x) = 2(x - 2)^2 + 5$

**32.** $y = -3(x + 7)^2 - 8$     **33.** $y = -(x - 1)^2 + 4$     **34.** $f(x) = -(x - 7)^2 + 10$

**Write a quadratic function to model each graph.**    See Problem 5.

**35.**      **36.**      **37.**

**38. Think About a Plan** A gardener is putting a wire fence along the edge of his garden to keep animals from eating his plants. If he has 20 meters of fence, what is the largest rectangular area he can enclose?
- To find the area of a rectangle, what two quantities do you need? Choose one to be your variable and write the other in terms of this variable.
- How can a graph help you solve this problem?
- What quadratic function represents the area of the garden?

**39. Manufacturing** The equation for the cost in dollars of producing computer chips is $C = 0.000015x^2 - 0.03x + 35$, where $x$ is the number of chips produced. Find the number of chips that minimizes the cost. What is the cost for that number of chips?

---

## 4 Practice

**ASSIGNMENT GUIDE**

Basic: 7–37 all, 38–41, 46–48, 51–57 odd

Average: 7–37 odd, 38–58

Advanced: 7–37 odd, 38–69

Standardized Test Prep: 70–73

Mixed Review: 74–85

**Reasoning** exercises have blue headings.

**Applications** exercises have red headings.

**EXERCISE 48:** Use the Think About a Plan worksheet in the **Practice and Problem Solving Workbook** (also available in the Teaching Resources in print and online) to further support students' development in becoming independent learners.

**HOMEWORK QUICK CHECK**

To check students' understanding of key skills and concepts, go over Exercises 15, 23, 38, 39, and 48.

---

**7–14.** See page 197.

**15–18.** See page 198.

**19.** translated 9 units down

**20.** translated 5 units to the left

**21.** translated 1.5 units up

**22.** translated 2.5 units to the right

**23.** vertex: $(-20, 0)$; axis of symmetry: $x = -20$; maximum: 0; domain: all real numbers, range: $y \le 0$

**24.** vertex: $(3.2, 0)$; axis of symmetry: $x = 3.2$; minimum: 0; domain: all real numbers, range: $y \ge 0$

**25.** vertex: $(-5.5, 0)$; axis of symmetry: $x = -5.5$; minimum: 0; domain: all real numbers, range: $y \ge 0$

**26.** vertex: $(-1, -1)$; axis of symmetry: $x = -1$; minimum: $-1$; domain: all real numbers, range: $y \ge -1$

**27.** vertex: $(4, -25)$; axis of symmetry: $x = 4$; maximum: $-25$; domain: all real numbers, range: $y \le -25$

**28.** vertex: $(125, 125)$; axis of symmetry: $x = 125$; minimum: 125; domain: all real numbers, range: $y \ge 125$

**29.** $x = 1$  

**30.** $x = -3$     **31.** $x = 2$

**32.** $x = -7$     **33.** $x = 1$

**34–39.** See page 200.

# Answers

## Practice and Problem-Solving
## Exercises (continued)

**34.** $x = 7$

**35.** $y = (x - 2)^2 + 5$

**36.** $y = 2(x + 1)^2 - 3$

**37.** $y = -\frac{1}{2}(x + 4)^2 + 2$

**38.** 25 m²      **39.** 1000 chips; $20

**40.** stretch vertically by a factor of 2, reflect across the x-axis, and translate 1 unit to the right

**41.** stretch vertically by a factor of 2, reflect across the x-axis, translate 1 unit to the left and 1 unit up

**42.** stretch vertically by a factor of 3, translate 2 units to the right and 3 units up

**43.** reflect across the x-axis, translate 4 units to the left and 5 units up

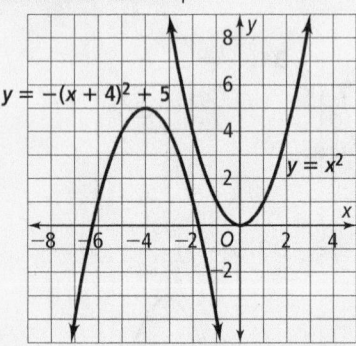

---

Describe how to transform the parent function $y = x^2$ to the graph of each function below. Graph both functions on the same axes.

**40.** $y = -2(x - 1)^2$    **41.** $y = -2(x + 1)^2 + 1$    **42.** $y = 3(x - 2)^2 + 3$

**43.** $y = -1(x + 4)^2 + 5$      **44.** $y = -0.25x^2 + 3$      **45.** $y = 0.2(x - 12)^2 - 3$

**46. Error Analysis** A classmate graphed $y = -2(x - 3)^2 + 4$ as shown. Explain your classmate's error. Graph the correct parabola.

**47. Writing** Describe the family of quadratic functions whose members each have (3, 4) as their vertex.

**48.** Write a quadratic function to represent the areas of all rectangles with a perimeter of 36 ft. Graph the function and describe the rectangle that has the largest area.

**Write the equation of each parabola in vertex form.**

**49.** vertex (1, 2), point (2, −5)      **50.** vertex (−3, 6), point (1, −2)

**51.** vertex (0, 5), point (1, −2)      **52.** vertex $\left(\frac{1}{4}, -\frac{3}{2}\right)$, point (1, 3)

In Chapter 2, you graphed absolute value functions as transformations of their parent function $y = |x|$. Similarly, you can graph a quadratic function as a transformation of the parent function $y = x^2$. Graph the following pairs of functions on the same set of axes. Determine how they are similar and how they are different.

**53.** $y = -|x - 2| + 1; y = -(x - 2)^2 + 1$    **54.** $y = 3|x + 1| - 2; y = 3(x + 1)^2 - 2$

**55.** $y = -2|x| + 4; y = -2x^2 + 4$      **56.** $y = |x + 3|; y = (x + 3)^2$

**57. Open-Ended** Write an equation of a parabola symmetric about $x = -10$.

**58. a. Technology** Determine the axis of symmetry for each parabola defined by the spreadsheet values at the right.
   **b.** How could you use the spreadsheet columns to verify that the axes of symmetry are correct?
   **c.** What functions in vertex form model the data? Check that the axes of symmetry are correct.

| | A | B |
|---|---|---|
| 1 | X1 | Y1 |
| 2 | 1 | −35 |
| 3 | 2 | −15 |
| 4 | 3 | −3 |
| 5 | 4 | 1 |
| 6 | 5 | −3 |

| | A | B |
|---|---|---|
| 1 | X2 | Y2 |
| 2 | 1 | 10 |
| 3 | 2 | 2 |
| 4 | 3 | 2 |
| 5 | 4 | 10 |
| 6 | 5 | 26 |

**Challenge**   Determine $a$ and $k$ so the given points are on the graph of the function.

**59.** (0, 1), (2, 1); $y = a(x - 1)^2 + k$    **60.** (−3, 2), (0, 11); $y = a(x + 2)^2 + k$

**61.** (1, 11), (2, −19); $y = a(x + 1)^2 + k$    **62.** (−2, 6), (3, 1); $y = a(x - 3)^2 + k$

**63. a.** In the function $y = ax^2 + bx + c$, $c$ represents the y-intercept. Find the value of the y-intercept in the function $y = a(x - h)^2 + k$.
   **b.** Under what conditions does $k$ represent the y-intercept?

---

**44.** compress vertically by a factor of $\frac{1}{4}$, reflect across the x-axis and translate 3 units up

**45.** compress vertically by a factor of 0.2, translate 12 units to the right and 3 units down

**46.** The classmate shifted the graph 4 units down and 3 units to the left instead of 4 units up and 3 units to the right.

**47.** parabola $y = a(x - 3)^2 + 4$ with vertex (3, 4) and $a > 0$ or $a < 0$

**48.** $y = 18x - x^2$ or $y = -(x - 9)^2 + 81$. The rectangle with the largest area will be 9 ft long and 9 feet wide.

**49.** $y = -7(x - 1)^2 + 2$

**50.** $y = -\frac{1}{2}(x + 3)^2 + 6$

**51.** $y = -7x^2 + 5$

**52.** $y = 8\left(x - \frac{1}{4}\right)^2 - \frac{3}{2}$

**53–63.** See page 201.

Find the quadratic function $y = a(x - h)^2$ whose graph passes through the given points.

**64.** $(-2, 1)$ and $(2, 1)$  **65.** $(-5, 2)$ and $(-1, 2)$  **66.** $(-1, -4)$ and $(7, -4)$

**67.** $(2, -1)$ and $(4, 0)$  **68.** $(-2, 18)$ and $(1, 0)$  **69.** $(1, -64)$ and $(-3, 0)$

## Standardized Test Prep

**70.** One parabola at the right has the equation $y = (x - 4)^2 + 2$. Which equation represents the second parabola?

Ⓐ $y = -(x - 4)^2 + 2$  Ⓒ $y = (x + 4)^2 - 2$

Ⓑ $y = (-x - 4)^2 + 2$  Ⓓ $y = -(x + 4)^2 - 2$

**71.** Which system has the unique solution $(1, 4)$?

Ⓕ $\begin{cases} y = x - 3 \\ x + y = 5 \end{cases}$  Ⓗ $\begin{cases} x + y = 5 \\ y = -x + 3 \end{cases}$

Ⓖ $\begin{cases} y = -x + 5 \\ x - y = -3 \end{cases}$  Ⓘ $\begin{cases} -x + y = 3 \\ 2x - 2y = -6 \end{cases}$

**72.** What is the formula for the surface area of a right circular cylinder, $S = 2\pi rh + 2\pi r^2$, solved for $h$?

Ⓐ $h = \frac{S}{4\pi r}$  Ⓑ $h = \frac{S}{2\pi r^2}$  Ⓒ $h = \frac{S}{2\pi r} - r$  Ⓓ $h = r - \frac{S}{2\pi r}$

**Short Response**

**73.** An athletic club has 225 feet of fencing to enclose a tennis court. What quadratic function can be used to find the maximum area of the tennis court? Find the maximum area, and the lengths of the sides of the resulting fence.

## Mixed Review

Solve each system of equations using a matrix.  ◀ See Lesson 3-6.

**74.** $\begin{cases} 3x - y = 7 \\ 2x + 2y = 10 \end{cases}$  **75.** $\begin{cases} 2x + 5y = 10 \\ -3x + y = 36 \end{cases}$  **76.** $\begin{cases} 3x + y - 2z = -3 \\ x - 3y - z = -2 \\ 2x + 2y + 3z = 11 \end{cases}$

Graph each inequality.  ◀ See Lesson 2-8.

**77.** $y > 3x + 1$  **78.** $y < -x + 4$  **79.** $y \geq \frac{1}{2}x - 2$

Determine whether each relation is a function.  ◀ See Lesson 2-1.

**80.** $\{(3, 0), (2, -1), (4, 2)\}$  **81.** $\{(1, 2), (1, 1), (-1, 1)\}$  **82.** $\{(1, 2), (-1, 2), (-1, 1)\}$

**Get Ready!**  To prepare for Lesson 4-2, do Exercises 83–85.

Find the vertex of the graph of each function.  ◀ See Lesson 2-7.

**83.** $y = -2|x|$  **84.** $y = |-x - 1|$  **85.** $y = 5|x - 5|$

---

**53.** similar: same vertex $(2, 1)$ and open downward, same domain (all real numbers), same range $(y \leq 1)$, same $x$-intercepts, $(1, 0)$, $(3, 0)$; different: $y = -|x - 2| + 1$ is an absolute value function with $y$-intercept $(0, -1)$ and $y = -(x - 2)^2 + 1$ is a quadratic function with $y$-intercept of $(0, -3)$.

$y = -(x - 2)^2 + 1$

**54.** similar: same vertex $(-1, -2)$ and open upward, same domain (all real numbers), same range $(y \geq -2)$, same $y$-intercept, $(0, 1)$; different: $y = 3|x + 1| - 2$ is an absolute value function with $x$-intercepts $\left(-\frac{1}{3}, 0\right)$ and $\left(-\frac{5}{3}, 0\right)$, and $y = 3(x + 1)^2 - 2$ is a quadratic function with $x$-intercepts $\left(-1 \pm \sqrt{\frac{2}{3}}, 0\right)$

$y = 3(x + 1)^2 - 2$
$y = 3|x + 1| - 2$

**55.** similar: same vertex $(0, 4)$ and open downward, same domain (all real numbers), same range $(y \leq 4)$, same $y$-intercept, $(0, 4)$; different: $y = -2|x| + 4$ is an absolute value function with $x$-intercepts $(\pm 2, 0)$ and $y = -2(x)^2 + 4$ is a quadratic function with $x$-intercepts $(\pm \sqrt{2}, 0)$

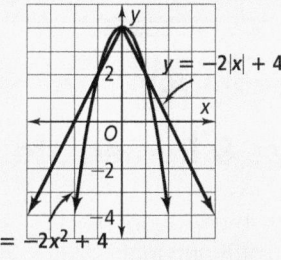

$y = -2|x| + 4$
$y = -2x^2 + 4$

**56.** similar: same vertex $(-3, 0)$ and open upward, same domain (all real numbers), same range $(y \geq 0)$, same $x$-intercept, $(-3, 0)$; different:

---

$y = |x + 3|$ is an absolute value function with $y$-intercept $(0, 3)$, and $y = (x + 3)^2$ is a quadratic function with $y$-intercept $(0, 9)$

$y = (x + 3)^2$
$y = |x + 3|$

**57.** Answers may vary. Sample: $y = (x + 10)^2 - 4$

**58. a.** $(x_1, y_1)$: $x = 4$; $(x_2, y_2)$: $x = 2.5$

  **b.** Expand the spreadsheet to have an equal number of values on each side of the axis of symmetry.

  **c.** $(x_1, y_1)$: $y = -4(x - 4)^2 + 1$; $(x_2, y_2)$: $y = 4(x - 2.5)^2 + 1$

**59.** Answers may vary. Sample: $k = -2, a = 3$; $y = 3(x - 1)^2 - 2$

**60.** Answers may vary. Sample: $a = 3, k = -1$; $y = 3(x + 2)^2 - 1$

**61.** Answers may vary. Sample: $a = -6, k = 35$; $y = -6(x + 1)^2 + 35$

**62.** Answers may vary. Sample: $a = \frac{1}{5}, k = 1$; $y = \frac{1}{5}(x - 3)^2 + 1$

**63. a.** $ah^2 + k$  **b.** when $h = 0$

**64.** $y = \frac{1}{4}x^2$  **65.** $y = \frac{1}{2}(x + 3)^2$

**66.** $y = -\frac{1}{4}(x - 3)^2$  **67.** $y = -\frac{1}{4}(x - 4)^2$

**68.** $y = 2(x - 1)^2$  **69.** $y = -4(x + 3)^2$

### Standardized Test Prep

**70.** A  **71.** G  **72.** C

**73. [2]** $2x + 2y = 225$
$2y = 225 - 2x$
$y = \frac{225}{2} - x$
$A = xy = x\left(\frac{225}{2} - x\right)$
$A = -x^2 + 112.5x$

Graph the function. There is a max. at about $(56.25, 3164.06)$, so the max. area is about $3164.06$ ft$^2$ and the length of each side is $56.25$ ft.

**[1]** correct area, incorrect length of each side OR a computational error

### Mixed Review

**74.** $(3, 2)$  **75.** $(-10, 6)$  **76.** $(1, 0, 3)$

**77.**   **78.**

**79.**   **80.** yes  **81.** no

**82.** no  **83.** $(0, 0)$  **84.** $(-1, 0)$  **85.** $(5, 0)$

## Additional Instructional Support

### Algebra 2 Companion

Students can use the **Algebra 2 Companion** worktext (4 pages) as you teach the lesson. Use the Companion to support

- New Vocabulary
- Key Concepts
- Got It for each Problem
- Lesson Check

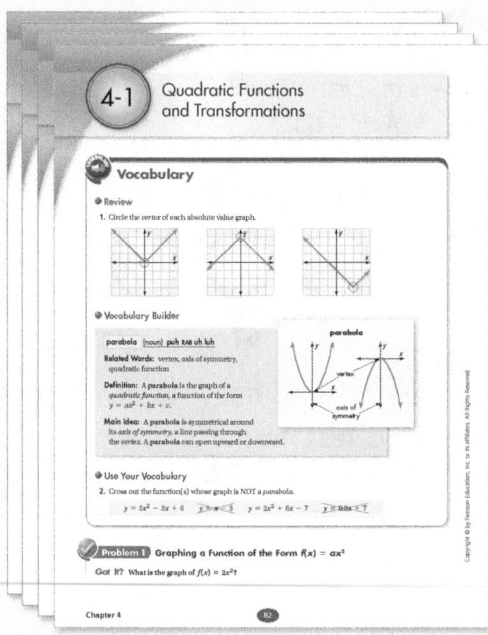

## 5 Assess & Remediate

### Lesson Quiz

1. What are the vertex, the axis of symmetry, the minimum or the maximum, the domain, and the range of $y = -5(x + 2)^2 - 8$?

2. What is the graph of $f(x) = \frac{1}{3}(x - 4)^2 - 1$?

3. **Do you UNDERSTAND?** A frog leaps 2 feet. The highest point in the jump is 6 inches. Assume the frog starts at (0, 0). What quadratic function models the path of the jump? Specify the units you use.

### ANSWERS TO LESSON QUIZ

1. The vertex is $(-2, -8)$; the axis of symmetry is $x = -2$; $k = -8$ is the maximum value; the domain is all real numbers; the range is all real numbers $\leq -8$.

2.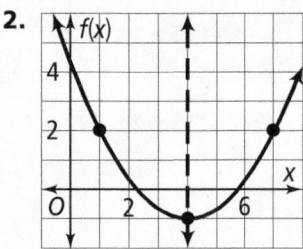

3. Samples: $f(x) = -\frac{1}{24}(x - 12)^2 + 6$ (inches)
   or $f(x) = -\frac{1}{2}(x - 1)^2 + \frac{1}{2}$ (feet)

### PRESCRIPTION FOR REMEDIATION

Use the student work on the Lesson Quiz to prescribe a differentiated review assignment:

| Points | Differentiated Remediation |
|--------|---------------------------|
| 0–1 | Intervention |
| 2 | On-level |
| 3 | Extension |

**PowerAlgebra.com**

## 5 Assess & Remediate

Assign the Lesson Quiz. Appropriate intervention, practice, or enrichment is automatically generated based on student performance.

## Intervention

- **Reteaching** (2 pages) Provides reteaching and practice exercises for the key lesson concepts. Use with struggling students or absent students.

- **English Language Learner Support** Helps students develop and reinforce mathematical vocabulary and key concepts.

### All-in-One Resources/Online
**Reteaching**

### All-in-One Resources/Online
**English Language Learner Support**

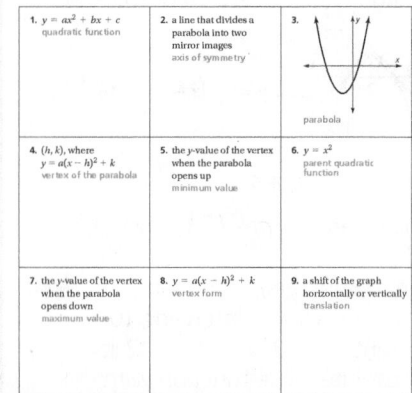

## ELL Support

**Use Manipulatives** Demonstrate translations with rubber stamps. Draw a parabola on a transparency, and move it around the coordinate plane. Model transformations with Silly Putty by making an impression or taking an image from a piece of newspaper and then stretching or compressing the image on the putty. Show students a picture of a fractal or some other artwork, and have them identify the transformations within it in words, using vocabulary terms.

# Differentiated Remediation *continued*

## On-Level

- **Practice** (2 pages) Provides extra practice for each lesson. For simpler practice exercises, use the Form K Practice pages found in the All-in-One Teaching Resources and online.

- **Think About a Plan** Helps students develop specific problem-solving skills and strategies by providing scaffolded guiding questions.

- **Standardized Test Prep** Focuses on all major exercises, all major question types, and helps students prepare for the high-stakes assessments.

## Extension

- **Enrichment** Provides students with interesting problems and activities that extend the concepts of the lesson.

- **Activities, Games, and Puzzles** Worksheets that can be used for concepts development, enrichment, and for fun!

---

### Practice and Problem Solving Wkbk/All-in-One Resources/Online
**Practice page 1**

### Practice and Problem Solving Wkbk/All-in-One Resources/Online
**Practice page 2**

### All-in-One Resources/Online
**Enrichment**

---

### Practice and Problem Solving Wkbk/All-in-One Resources/Online
**Think About a Plan**

### Practice and Problem Solving Wkbk/All-in-One Resources/Online
**Standardized Test Prep**

### Online Teacher Resource Center
**Activities, Games, and Puzzles**

# 1 Interactive Learning

## Solve It!

**PURPOSE** To use a quadratic model to determine the $y$-coordinate of the vertex of a parabola

**PROCESS** Students may

- graph the equation on a calculator and determine the maximum value of the function.
- estimate the $x$-coordinate of the vertex and use it to find the height.

### FACILITATE

**Q** What point on the curve represents the maximum height of the ball? Explain. **[The vertex; it is the turning point.]**

**Q** How do you find the vertex? **[Answers may vary. Sample: Graph the given equation on a calculator, and use the max function. The $x$- and $y$-values are the coordinates of the vertex.]**

**ANSWER** See Solve It in Answers on next page.

**CONNECT THE MATH** In the Solve It, students used the standard form of a quadratic function. In this lesson, they will use the properties of a quadratic function in standard form to model and graph parabolas.

# 2 Guided Instruction

## Problem 1      ERROR PREVENTION

**Q** What does $x = -2$ represent? **[−2 is the $x$-coordinate of the vertex, and $x = -2$ is the equation of the axis of symmetry.]**

**Q** What point can you use to find the range and the maximum or minimum of the parabola? **[the vertex]**

---

## Standard Form of a Quadratic Function

**Objective** To graph quadratic functions written in standard form

**Getting Ready!**

The function $h = -0.01x^2 + 0.9x$ models the height h of the soccer ball as it travels distance x. What is the maximum height of the ball? Explain.

The minimum height of the ball is $h = 0$. The ball is on the ground—twice.

**Lesson Vocabulary**
- standard form

In Lesson 4-1, you worked with quadratic functions written in vertex form. Now you will use quadratic functions in *standard form*. The **standard form** of a quadratic function is $f(x) = ax^2 + bx + c$, where $a \neq 0$.

**Essential Understanding** For any quadratic function $f(x) = ax^2 + bx + c$, the values of $a$, $b$, and $c$ provide key information about its graph.

You can find information about the graph of a quadratic function (such as the vertex) easily from the vertex form. Such information is "hidden" in standard form. However, standard form is easier to enter into a graphing calculator.

**Problem 1** Finding the Features of a Quadratic Function

**Graphing Calculator** What are the vertex, the axis of symmetry, the maximum or minimum value, and the range of $y = 2x^2 + 8x - 2$?

### Plan
**How can you use a calculator to find the features of a quadratic function in standard form?**
Graph the function. Then use the **CALC** and **TABLE** features.

Range: $y \geq -10$.

Minimum $x = -2$    $y = -10$

The vertex is $(-2, -10)$.

Notice the symmetry of $y$ values.

$-10$ is the minimum value.

Axis of symmetry is $x = -2$.

---

**Preparing to Teach**

**BIG ideas** Function     **UbD**
           Equivalence

### ESSENTIAL UNDERSTANDINGS

- Any quadratic function is a stretch, compression, reflection, and/or a translation of $y = x^2$.
- The standard form of a quadratic function is $f(x) = ax^2 + bx + c$, where $a \neq 0$.
- For any quadratic function $f(x) = ax^2 + bx + c$, the values of $a$, $b$, and $c$ provide key information about its graph.
- Standard form is "calculator ready" and a transformation of $y = x^2$.

### Math Background

$f(x) = ax^2 + bx + c$ is the standard form of a quadratic function. It is the form calculators use and the easiest model to find with systems of equations. Note that if $a = 0$, the function is linear rather than quadratic, so the graph is a line rather than a parabola. The values of $a$, $b$, and $c$ provide

the following information about the graph:

- whether the graph opens upward or downward
- the coordinates of the vertex
- the axis of symmetry
- the $y$-intercept.

This lesson examines the connection between standard form and vertex form.

### Support Student Learning

Use the **Algebra 2 Companion** to engage and support students during instruction. See Lesson Resources at the end of this lesson for details.

---

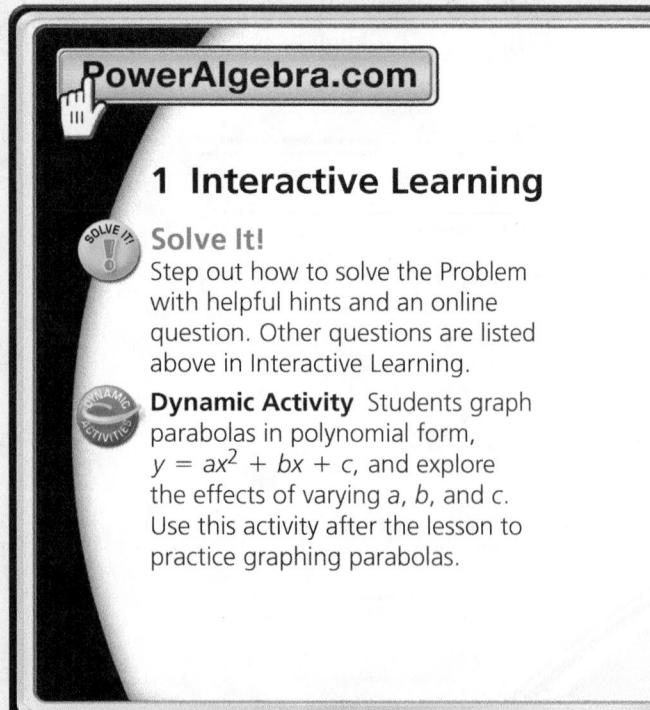

## PowerAlgebra.com

### 1 Interactive Learning

**Solve It!**
Step out how to solve the Problem with helpful hints and an online question. Other questions are listed above in Interactive Learning.

**Dynamic Activity** Students graph parabolas in polynomial form, $y = ax^2 + bx + c$, and explore the effects of varying $a$, $b$, and $c$. Use this activity after the lesson to practice graphing parabolas.

---

**Got It?** **1.** What are the vertex, axis of symmetry, maximum or minimum value, and range of $y = -3x^2 - 4x + 6$?

Got It?  SYNTHESIZING

**Q** Does this parabola contain a maximum or minimum value? Explain your reasoning.
**[maximum; because the parabola opens downward]**

You can find information about the quadratic function $f(x) = ax^2 + bx + c$ from the coefficients $a$ and $b$, and from the constant term $c$.

**take note**

**Dynamic Activity**
Quadratic Equations in Polynomial Form

### Properties   Quadratic Function in Standard Form

- The graph of $f(x) = ax^2 + bx + c$, $a \neq 0$, is a parabola.
- If $a > 0$, the parabola opens upward. If $a < 0$, the parabola opens downward.
- The axis of symmetry is the line $x = -\frac{b}{2a}$.
- The $x$-coordinate of the vertex is $-\frac{b}{2a}$. The $y$-coordinate of the vertex is the $y$-value of the function for $x = -\frac{b}{2a}$, or $y = f\left(-\frac{b}{2a}\right)$.
- The $y$-intercept is $(0, c)$.

$y = ax^2 + bx + c, a > 0$     $y = ax^2 + bx + c, a < 0$

**Here's Why It Works** You can expand the vertex form of a quadratic function to determine properties of the graph of a quadratic function written in standard form.

$$f(x) = a(x - h)^2 + k$$
$$= a(x^2 - 2hx + h^2) + k$$
$$= ax^2 - 2ahx + ah^2 + k$$
$$= ax^2 + (-2ah)x + (ah^2 + k)$$

Compare to the standard form, $f(x) = ax^2 + bx + c$.

$a = a$     $a$ in standard form is the same as $a$ in vertex form.

$b = -2ah$

$-\frac{b}{2a} = h$     Solve for $h$.

Since, $h = -\frac{b}{2a}$, the axis of symmetry is $x = -\frac{b}{2a}$ and the vertex is $(h, k) = \left(-\frac{b}{2a}, f\left(-\frac{b}{2a}\right)\right)$.

**Take Note**  ELL SUPPORT
Students may benefit from making a checklist for graphing quadratic functions using standard form. Have them design their own list to best meet their needs and to learn while making it.

For example, for the function $f(x) = ax^2 + bx + c$

[ ] $a \neq 0$

[ ] If $a > 0$, the parabola opens upward.

[ ] If $a < 0$, the parabola opens downward.

[ ] the axis of symmetry $x = \frac{-b}{2a}$

[ ] the vertex $\left(\frac{-b}{2a}, f\left(\frac{-b}{2a}\right)\right)$

[ ] the $y$-intercept $(0, c)$

**Here's Why It Works**
Although equivalent, different forms of equations present information differently. Have students list the steps for graphing using vertex form and using standard form.

## 2 Guided Instruction

 Each Problem is worked out and supported online.

**Problem 1**
Finding the Features of a Quadratic Function

**Problem 2**
Graphing a Function of the Form $y = ax^2 + bx + c$
*Animated*

**Problem 3**
Converting Standard Form to Vertex Form
*Animated*

**Problem 4**
Interpreting a Quadratic Graph

**Alternative Problem 4**
Interpreting a Quadratic Graph
*Animated*

**Support in Algebra 2 Companion**
- Vocabulary
- Key Concepts
- Got It?

## Answers

**Solve It!**
20.25 ft; graph and trace the function until the vertex is located. The $y$-coordinate of this point is the maximum height the ball will attain.

**Got It?**
**1.** vertex: $\left(-\frac{2}{3}, 7\frac{1}{3}\right)$; axis of symmetry: $x = -\frac{2}{3}$; maximum: $7\frac{1}{3}$; range: $y \leq 7\frac{1}{3}$

## Problem 2 — SYNTHESIZING

Q Why is it helpful to sketch the axis of symmetry? **[You can use reflection to find points on the curve on the opposite side of the axis.]**

Q Is (0, c) always the y-intercept? Explain. **[Yes; using standard form $y = ax^2 + bx + c$, substitute $x = 0$, which gives you $y = c$.]**

Q Can you always use the y-intercept and its reflection to find the second and third points? Explain. **[No, not when the vertex is on the y-axis.]**

### Got It?

Students may write the equation $x = -\frac{b}{2a}$ on their paper for each problem. By the end of the problem set, they will know the equation.

## Problem 3 — SYNTHESIZING

Students relate vertex form from a previous lesson to standard form.

Q What values do we know that will be used in this problem? **[Sample: a and b because they are used to find the vertex]**

Q What values must be found to write the equation in vertex form? **[h and k]**

Q How do you find k? **[k represents the y-coordinate of the vertex. Substitute the x-coordinate of the vertex in the standard form to solve for y.]**

### Got It? — ERROR PREVENTION

To eliminate arithmetic errors, use a calculator to simplify the equation after substitution.

---

 **Problem 2** Graphing a Function of the Form $y = ax^2 + bx + c$

**What is the graph of $y = x^2 + 2x + 3$?**

**Step 1** Identify $a$, $b$, and $c$.
$a = 1, b = 2, c = 3$

**Step 2** The axis of symmetry is $x = -\frac{b}{2a}$.
$$x = -\frac{2}{2(1)}$$
Lightly sketch the line $x = -1$.

**Step 3** The x-coordinate of the vertex is also $-\frac{b}{2a}$, or $-1$.
The y-coordinate is
$y = (-1)^2 + 2(-1) + 3 = 2$.
Plot the vertex $(-1, 2)$.

**Step 4** Since $c = 3$, the y-intercept is $(0, 3)$. The reflection of $(0, 3)$ across $x = -1$ is $(-2, 3)$. Plot both points.

**Step 5** $a > 0$ confirms that the graph opens upward. Draw a smooth curve through the points you found in Steps 3 and 4.

 Got It? **2.** What is the graph of $y = -2x^2 + 2x - 5$?

**Think**
**How can you use the axis of symmetry?**
The entire curve on one side of the axis is the mirror image of the curve on the other side.

---

 **Problem 3** Converting Standard Form to Vertex Form

**What is the vertex form of $y = 2x^2 + 10x + 7$?**

$y = 2x^2 + 10x + 7$ — Identify $a$ and $b$.

$x = -\frac{b}{2a}$ — Find the x-coordinate of the vertex.

$= -\frac{10}{2(2)}$

$= -2.5$

$y = 2(-2.5)^2 + 10(-2.5) + 7$ — Substitute $x = -2.5$ into the equation.

$= -5.5$

The vertex is $(-2.5, -5.5)$.

$y = a(x - h)^2 + k$ — Write the vertex form.

$y = 2[x - (-2.5)]^2 + (-5.5)$ — Substitute $a = 2, h = -2.5, k = -5.5$.

$y = 2(x + 2.5)^2 - 5.5$ — Simplify.

The vertex form is $y = 2(x + 2.5)^2 - 5.5$.

 Got It? **3.** What is the vertex form of $y = -x^2 + 4x - 5$?

**Plan**
**How do you find h, k, and a?**
Find the vertex. This gives you h and k. The value for a is the same in both forms.

---

# Additional Problems

**1.** What are the vertex, axis of symmetry, maximum or minimum value, and range of $y = -x^2 + 6x + 3$?

**ANSWER** $(3, 12)$; $x = 3$; max: 12; range: $y \le 12$

**2.** What is the graph of $y = 4x^2 - 16x + 10$?

**ANSWER**

**3.** What is the vertex form of $y = 2x^2 - 3x + 2$?

**ANSWER**
$y = 2(x - 0.75)^2 + 0.875$

**4.** A model for the performance of a stock is $P = -3d^2 + 50d$ where $d$ represents the days of trading and $P$ is the price per share. What is the maximum price per share of the stock?

**ANSWER** $208.33

# Answers

### Got It? (continued)

**2.**

**3.** $y = -(x - 2)^2 - 1$

**4. a.** 4 ft

**b.** because the y-intercept is (0, 0)

**Bridges** The New River Gorge Bridge in West Virginia is the world's largest steel single arch bridge. You can model the arch with the function $y = -0.000498x^2 + 0.847x$, where $x$ and $y$ are in feet. How high above the river is the arch? How long is the section of bridge above the arch?

Length of bridge above arch

Height of arch

516 ft

**Problem 4** SYNTHESIZING

**Q** What do you have to find first to determine the bridge height? Explain. **[The vertex; answers may vary. Sample: The vertex gives the height and half the length of the arch.]**

**Q** What quantities are added to find the height of the bridge above the river? Explain your reasoning. **[The $y$-coordinate of the vertex and 516; answers may vary. Sample: The $y$-coordinate of the vertex represents the height of the arch, and 516 is the vertical distance from the lowest part of river to the bottom of the arch.]**

**Q** What quantity is used to find the length of the bridge above the arch? Explain. **[The $x$-coordinate of the vertex. Since the vertex is in the middle of the bridge, $2x$ represents the entire horizontal distance between the $x$-intercepts of the arch.]**

**Know**

A function that models the arch and the vertical distance from the base of the supports to the water

**Need**

The height of the arch above the support base and the length of the bridge above the arch

**Plan**

Find the vertex. The $y$-coordinate is the height of the arch above the support base. The $x$-coordinate is half the distance between the supports.

**Think**

How can you tell that the quadratic function has a maximum value?

Since $a < 0$, the graph of the function opens down. The function has a maximum value.

**Step 1** Find the vertex of the arch.

$x = -\dfrac{b}{2a} = -\dfrac{0.847}{2(-0.000498)} \approx 850$

$y = -0.000498(850)^2 + 0.847(850) \approx 360$

The vertex is about (850, 360).

**Step 2** Find the height of the arch above its supports.

The $y$-coordinate of the vertex is the height of the arch above its supports. The arch is about 360 ft above its supports.

**Step 3** Find the height of the arch above the river.

The arch is about 360 ft + 516 ft = 876 ft above the river.

**Step 4** Find the length of the bridge above the arch.

The $x$-coordinate of the vertex is half the length of the bridge above the arch. The length of that part of the bridge is about 850 ft + 850 ft = 1700 ft long.

(850, 360)

The height is 360 ft.

$x = 850$

**Got It? 4. a.** The Zhaozhou Bridge in China is the oldest known arch bridge, dating to A.D. 605. You can model the support arch with the function $f(x) = -0.001075x^2 + 0.131148x$, where $x$ and $y$ are measured in feet. How high is the arch above its supports?

**b. Reasoning** Why does the model in part (a) not have a constant term?

**Got It?** SYNTHESIZING

**Q** Why might you want to solve this problem using a graphing calculator? **[Answers may vary. Sample: The numbers are decimals.]**

**Q** Where does the bridge start? **[on the ground at (0, 0)]**

## Lesson Check

**1.** vertex: (0, −4); axis of symmetry: $x = 0$; minimum: −4

**2.**

**3.**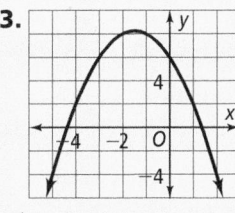

**4.** $y = (x - 1)^2 + 8$

**5.** $y = -\left(x - \dfrac{3}{2}\right)^2 + \dfrac{5}{4}$

**6.** Error in calculation of $x$. The correct calculation is:

$x = \dfrac{-(-4)}{2(2)} = 1$

$y = 2(1) - 4(1) - 3$

$= 2 - 4 - 3$

$= -5$

Vertex: (1, −5)

**7.** The vertex of a function written in vertex form can easily be determined. It is $(h, k)$ where $f(x) = a(x - h)^2 + k$. The vertex of a function in standard form is $\left(\dfrac{-b}{2a}, f\left(\dfrac{-b}{2a}\right)\right)$ where $f(x) = ax^2 + bx + c$.

## Practice and Problem-Solving Exercises

**8.** vertex: (−1, 0); axis of symmetry: $x = -1$; minimum: 0; range: $y \geq 0$

**9.** vertex: (1, 2); axis of symmetry: $x = 1$; maximum: 2; range: $y \leq 2$

**10.** vertex: (−2, −3); axis of symmetry: $x = -2$; minimum: 3; range: $y \geq -3$

**11.** vertex: (1, 6); axis of symmetry: $x = 1$; maximum: 6; range: $y \leq 6$

**12.** vertex: $\left(\dfrac{2}{3}, -3\dfrac{1}{3}\right)$; axis of symmetry: $x = \dfrac{2}{3}$; minimum: $-3\dfrac{1}{3}$; range: $y \geq -3\dfrac{1}{3}$

**13.** vertex: $\left(-\dfrac{3}{4}, 5\dfrac{1}{8}\right)$; axis of symmetry: $x = -\dfrac{3}{4}$; maximum: $5\dfrac{1}{8}$; range: $y \leq 5\dfrac{1}{8}$

**14.** vertex: $\left(\dfrac{3}{2}, -\dfrac{3}{2}\right)$; axis of symmetry: $x = \dfrac{3}{2}$; minimum: $-\dfrac{3}{2}$; range: $y \geq -\dfrac{3}{2}$

**15.** vertex: $\left(-\dfrac{1}{2}, \dfrac{1}{4}\right)$; axis of symmetry: $x = -\dfrac{1}{2}$; maximum: $\dfrac{1}{4}$; range: $y \leq \dfrac{1}{4}$

**16.** vertex: (0, 5); axis of symmetry: $x = 0$; minimum: 5; range: $y \geq 5$

# 3 Lesson Check

## Do you know HOW?

- For Exercise 1, if students have trouble identifying the parts of a parabola, have them review Problem 1 and make a list.
- For Exercises 2–3, if students have trouble graphing, suggest they start by graphing the axes of symmetry.

## Do you UNDERSTAND?

- For Exercise 7, if students have trouble comparing standard form with vertex form, suggest they use an actual function in both forms and compare the steps needed to find the vertex.

## Close

> **Q** How can you graph a quadratic function written in standard form? **[First find the axis of symmetry and vertex from $x = -\frac{b}{2a}$. See if $a > 0$ or $a < 0$. Find the $y$-intercept.]**
>
> **Q** What form provides easier access to the $y$-intercept and any $y$-values given an $x$-value? **[standard form]**

---

 **Lesson Check**

### Do you know HOW?

1. Identify the vertex, axis of symmetry, and the maximum or minimum value of the parabola at the right.

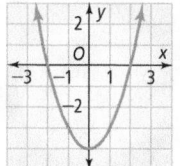

**Graph each function.**

2. $y = x^2 - 2x + 4$

3. $y = -x^2 - 3x + 6$

**Write each function in vertex form.**

4. $y = x^2 - 2x + 9$

5. $y = -x^2 + 3x - 1$

### Do you UNDERSTAND?

6. **Error Analysis** A student graphed the function $y = 2x^2 - 4x - 3$. Find and correct the error.

$$x = \frac{-4}{2(2)} = -1$$
$$y = 2(-1)^2 - 4(-1) - 3$$
$$= 2 + 4 - 3$$
$$= 3$$
$$\text{vertex } (-1, 3)$$

7. **Compare and Contrast** Explain the difference between finding the vertex of a function written in vertex form and finding the vertex of a function written in standard form.

---

## Practice and Problem-Solving Exercises

**A** Practice

Identify the vertex, the axis of symmetry, the maximum or minimum value, and the range of each parabola.  **See Problem 1.**

8. $y = x^2 + 2x + 1$
9. $y = -x^2 + 2x + 1$
10. $y = x^2 + 4x + 1$

11. $y = -x^2 + 2x + 5$
12. $y = 3x^2 - 4x - 2$
13. $y = -2x^2 - 3x + 4$

14. $y = 2x^2 - 6x + 3$
15. $y = -x^2 - x$
16. $y = 2x^2 + 5$

**Graph each function.**  **See Problem 2.**

17. $y = x^2 + 6x + 9$
18. $y = -x^2 - 3x + 6$
19. $y = 2x^2 + 4x$

20. $y = 4x^2 - 12x + 9$
21. $y = -6x^2 - 12x - 1$
22. $y = -\frac{3}{4}x^2 + 6x + 6$

23. $y = 3x^2 - 12x + 10$
24. $y = \frac{1}{2}x^2 + 2x - 8$
25. $y = -4x^2 - 24x - 36$

**Write each function in vertex form.**  **See Problem 3.**

26. $y = x^2 - 4x + 6$
27. $y = x^2 + 2x + 5$

28. $y = 4x^2 + 7x$
29. $y = 2x^2 - 5x + 12$

30. $y = -2x^2 + 8x + 3$
31. $y = \frac{9}{4}x^2 + 3x - 1$

32. **Economics** A model for a company's revenue from selling a software package is $R = -2.5p^2 + 500p$, where $p$ is the price in dollars of the software. What price will maximize revenue? Find the maximum revenue.  **See Problem 4.**

---

# Answers

**1–16.** See page 205.

17.
18.
19.
20.
21.
22.

23.
24.
25.

26. $y = (x - 2)^2 + 2$
27. $y = (x + 1)^2 + 4$
28. $y = 4\left(x + \frac{7}{8}\right)^2 - \frac{49}{16}$
29. $y = 2\left(x - \frac{5}{4}\right)^2 + \frac{71}{8}$
30. $y = -2(x - 2)^2 + 11$
31. $y = \frac{9}{4}\left(x + \frac{2}{3}\right)^2 - 2$
32. $100; $25,000

**Sketch each parabola using the given information.**

**33.** vertex $(3, 6)$, $y$-intercept 2

**34.** vertex $(-1, -4)$, $y$-intercept 3

**35.** vertex $(0, 5)$, point $(1, -2)$

**36.** vertex $(2, 3)$, point $(6, 9)$

**37. Think About a Plan** Suppose you work for a packaging company and are designing a box that has a rectangular bottom with a perimeter of 36 cm. The box must be 4 cm high. What dimensions give the maximum volume?
- How can you model the volume of the box with a quadratic function?
- What information can you get from the function to find the maximum volume?

**38. Landscaping** A town is planning a playground. It wants to fence in a rectangular space using an existing wall. What is the greatest area it can fence in using 100 ft of donated fencing?

$100 - 2\ell$

**For each function, the vertex of the function's graph is given. Find the unknown coefficients.**

**39.** $y = x^2 + bx + c$; $(3, -4)$

**40.** $y = -3x^2 + bx + c$; $(1, 0)$

**41.** $y = ax^2 + 10x + c$; $(-5, -27)$

**42.** $y = c - ax^2 - 2x$; $(-1, 3)$

**43. Physics** The equation for the motion of a projectile fired straight up at an initial velocity of 64 ft/s is $h = 64t - 16t^2$, where $h$ is height in feet and $t$ is time in seconds. Find the time the projectile needs to reach its highest point. How high will it go?

**44.** A student says that the graph of $y = ax^2 + bx + c$ gets wider as $a$ increases.
**a. Error Analysis** Use examples to show that the student is wrong.
**b. Writing** Summarize the relationship between $|a|$ and the width of the graph of $y = ax^2 + bx + c$.

**For each function, find the $y$-intercept.**

**45.** $y = (x - 1)^2 + 2$

**46.** $y = -3(x + 2)^2 - 4$

**47.** $y = -\frac{2}{3}(x - 9)^2$

**For each function, the vertex of the function's graph is given. Find $a$ and $b$.**

**48.** $y = ax^2 + bx - 27$; $(2, -3)$

**49.** $y = ax^2 + bx + 5$; $(-1, 4)$

**50.** $y = ax^2 + bx + 8$; $(2, -4)$

**51.** $y = ax^2 + bx$; $(-3, 2)$

**Sketch each parabola using the given information.**

**52.** axis of symmetry $x = 1$, $y$-intercept 3, point $(-1, 6)$

**53.** axis of symmetry $x = 2$, $y$-intercept 1, point $(3, 2.5)$

# 4 Practice

**33.**

**34.**

**35.**

**36.**

**37.** 4 cm × 9 cm × 9 cm
**38.** 1250 ft²
**39.** $b = -6$; $c = 5$
**40.** $b = 6$; $c = -3$
**41.** $a = 1$; $c = -2$
**42.** $a = 1$; $c = 2$
**43.** 2 s; 64 ft
**44. a.** Check students' work.
**b.** Answers may vary. Sample: The widths of the graphs of $y = ax^2 + bx + c$ and $y = -ax^2 + bx + c$ are the same. As $|a|$ increases, the widths of $y = ax^2 + bx + c$ and $y = -ax^2 + bx + c$ decrease.
**45.** $(0, 3)$
**46.** $(0, -16)$
**47.** $(0, -54)$
**48.** $a = -6$, $b = 24$
**49.** $a = 1$, $b = 2$
**50.** $a = 3$, $b = -12$

**51.** $a = -\frac{2}{9}$, $b = -\frac{4}{3}$

**52.**

**53.**

# Answers

## Standardized Test Prep

**54.** 15 min

**55.** 0

**56.** $19/h

## Mixed Review

**57.** $\frac{1}{4}$

**58.** $-2.5$

**59.** Explanations may vary. Sample: Elimination because the $x$'s have opposite signs; $(7, -1)$.

**60.** Explanations may vary. Sample: Substitution because the first equation is already solved for $y$; $(27, 15)$.

**61.** Explanations may vary. Sample: Elimination because you can multiply the second equation by $-3$ to eliminate $n$; $(3, 2)$.

**62.** vertex: $(-2, -1)$; axis of symmetry: $x = -2$; minimum at $(-2, -1)$; domain: all real numbers, range: $y \geq -1$

**63.** vertex: $(1, 3)$; axis of symmetry: $x = 1$; maximum at $(1, 3)$; domain: all real numbers, range: $y \leq 3$

**64.** vertex: $(3, -2)$; axis of symmetry: $x = 3$; minimum at $(3, -2)$; domain: all real numbers, range: $y \geq -2$

**65.** vertex: $(-3, 5)$; axis of symmetry: $x = -3$; maximum at $(-3, 5)$; domain: all real numbers, range: $y \leq 5$

**66.** vertex: $(-4, 0)$; axis of symmetry: $x = -4$; minimum at $(-4, 0)$; domain: all real numbers, range: $y \geq 0$

**67.** vertex: $(4, 6)$; axis of symmetry: $x = 4$; maximum at $(4, 6)$; domain: all real numbers, range: $y \leq 6$

**68.** $y = -(x - 1)^2 + 5$

**69.** $y = x^2 - 4$

**70.** $y = (x + 1)^2 - 2$

---

SAT/ACT

**54.** The time it takes to chalk a baseball diamond varies directly with the length of the side of the diamond. If it takes 10 minutes to chalk a little league diamond with 60 ft sides, how long will it take to chalk a major league baseball diamond with 90 ft sides?

**55.** What is the $x$-value of the vertex of the quadratic function $y = -5x^2 + \frac{4}{7}$?

**56.** Sarah works as a nanny and charges different rates for working during the week and the weekend. One week, she earned $902.50 working 45 hours, of which 5 hours were during the weekend. The following week she earned $1045 working 50 hours, of which 10 hours were during the weekend. What does Sarah charge per hour, in dollars, for working during the week?

## Mixed Review

Solve each equation.      ◀ **See Lesson 1-4.**

**57.** $0.6(y + 2) - 0.2(2 - y) = 1$

**58.** $3(a + 4) + 2(a - 1) = a$

For each system, choose the method of solving that seems easier to use.    ◀ **See Lessons 3-2 and 3-6.** Explain why you made each choice. Solve each system.

**59.** $\begin{cases} 3x - 5y = 26 \\ -2x - 3y = -11 \end{cases}$

**60.** $\begin{cases} y = \frac{2}{3}x - 3 \\ -x + 3y = 18 \end{cases}$

**61.** $\begin{cases} 2m + 3n = 12 \\ -5m + n = -13 \end{cases}$

**Get Ready!**    **To prepare for Lesson 4-3, do Exercises 62–70.**

Identify the vertex, the axis of symmetry, the maximum or minimum value, and    ◀ **See Lesson 4-2.** the domain and range of each function.

**62.** $y = 2(x + 2)^2 - 1$

**63.** $y = -(x - 1)^2 + 3$

**64.** $y = \frac{1}{2}(x - 3)^2 - 2$

**65.** $y = -\frac{2}{5}(x + 3)^2 + 5$

**66.** $y = 3(x + 4)^2$

**67.** $y = -7(x - 4)^2 + 6$

Write an equation in vertex form for each parabola.    ◀ **See Lesson 4-1.**

**68.**

**69.**

**70.**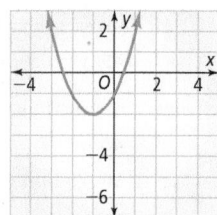

## Additional Instructional Support

### Algebra 2 Companion

Students can use the **Algebra 2 Companion** worktext (4 pages) as you teach the lesson. Use the Companion to support

- New Vocabulary
- Key Concepts
- Got It for each Problem
- Lesson Check

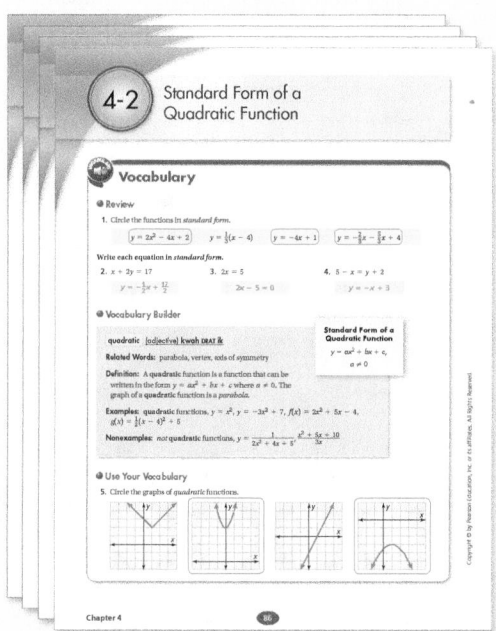

### ELL Support

**Focus on Language** Ask students what they know about the word *standard*. What are some common uses? [Standard deviation, standard English, standard time, standard methods, standard definitions, standard styles, educational standards, standard measurement, etc.] Thinking about these uses, what is the meaning of standard? [Usual, common, normal, familiar, basis of comparison, etc.] The standard form relates to a common form for all polynomial functions, including the linear function. The vertex form is a special form only for quadratics.

## 5 Assess & Remediate

### Lesson Quiz

1. What are the vertex, axis of symmetry, maximum or minimum value, and range of $y = 3x^2 + 6x - 1$?

2. What is the graph of $y = x^2 + 8x + 4$?

3. Write $y = -5x^2 + x + 1$ in vertex form.

4. **Do you UNDERSTAND?**
   A parabolic arch sculpture is on top of a city bank. A model of the arch is $y = -0.005x^2 + 0.3x$ where $x$ and $y$ are in feet.

   30′ Bank

   **a.** What is the distance from the highest point of the arch to the ground?

   **b.** What is the width of the bank building?

### ANSWERS TO LESSON QUIZ

1. $(-1, -4)$; $x = -1$; min: $-4$; range: $y \geq -4$

2.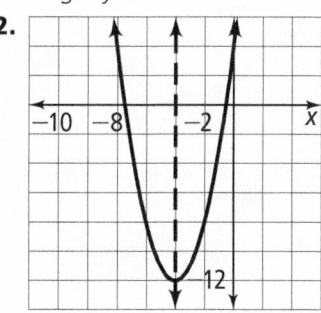

3. $y = -5(x - 0.1)^2 + 1.05$

4. **a.** 34.5 feet   **b.** 60 feet

### PRESCRIPTION FOR REMEDIATION

Use the student work on the Lesson Quiz to prescribe a differentiated review assignment:

| Points | Differentiated Remediation |
|--------|---------------------------|
| 0–2 | Intervention |
| 3 | On-level |
| 4 | Extension |

**PowerAlgebra.com**

### 5 Assess & Remediate

Assign the Lesson Quiz. Appropriate intervention, practice, or enrichment is automatically generated based on student performance.

## Intervention

- **Reteaching** (2 pages) Provides reteaching and practice exercises for the key lesson concepts. Use with struggling students or absent students.

- **English Language Learner Support** Helps students develop and reinforce mathematical vocabulary and key concepts.

### All-in-One Resources/Online
**Reteaching**

### All-in-One Resources/Online
**English Language Learner Support**

# Differentiated Remediation *continued*

## On-Level

- **Practice** (2 pages) Provides extra practice for each lesson. For simpler practice exercises, use the Form K Practice pages found in the All-in-One Teaching Resources and online.

- **Think About a Plan** Helps students develop specific problem-solving skills and strategies by providing scaffolded guiding questions.

- **Standardized Test Prep** Focuses on all major exercises, all major question types, and helps students prepare for the high-stakes assessments.

## Extension

- **Enrichment** Provides students with interesting problems and activities that extend the concepts of the lesson.

- **Activities, Games, and Puzzles** Worksheets that can be used for concepts development, enrichment, and for fun!

---

### Practice and Problem Solving Wkbk/ All-in-One Resources/Online
**Practice page 1**

### Practice and Problem Solving Wkbk/ All-in-One Resources/Online
**Practice page 2**

### All-in-One Resources/Online
**Enrichment**

---

### Practice and Problem Solving Wkbk/ All-in-One Resources/Online
**Think About a Plan**

### Practice and Problem Solving Wkbk/ All-in-One Resources/Online
**Standardized Test Prep**

### Online Teacher Resource Center
**Activities, Games, and Puzzles**

## 4-3 Modeling With Quadratic Functions

**Objective** To model data with quadratic functions

**SOLVE IT!**

**Getting Ready!**

You and a friend are tossing a ball back and forth. You each toss and catch the ball at waist level, 3 feet high. What equation, in standard form, models the path of the ball? Explain your reasoning.

You will have to decide where to locate the origin.

6 ft

10 ft

When you know the vertex and a point on a parabola, you can use vertex form to write an equation of the parabola. If you do not know the vertex, you can use standard form and any three points of the parabola to find an equation.

**Essential Understanding** Three noncollinear points, no two of which are in line vertically, are on the graph of exactly one quadratic function.

**Plan**

**How do you use the 3 given points?**
Use them to write a system of 3 equations. Solve the system to get a, b, and c.

**Problem 1** Writing an Equation of a Parabola

A parabola contains the points $(0, 0)$, $(-1, -2)$, and $(1, 6)$. What is the equation of this parabola in standard form?

Substitute the $(x, y)$ values into $y = ax^2 + bx + c$ to write a system of equations.

$y = ax^2 + bx + c$

$0 = a(0)^2 + b(0) + c \rightarrow c = 0$   Use $(0, 0)$.

$-2 = a(-1)^2 + b(-1) + c \rightarrow -2 = a - b + c$   Use $(-1, -2)$.

$6 = a(1)^2 + b(1) + c \rightarrow 6 = a + b + c$   Use $(1, 6)$.

Since $c = 0$, the resulting system has two variables. $\begin{cases} a - b = -2 \\ a + b = 6 \end{cases}$   Use elimination. $a = 2$ and $b = 4$.

Substitute $a = 2$, $b = 4$, and $c = 0$ into standard form: $y = 2x^2 + 4x + 0$.

$y = 2x^2 + 4x$ is the equation of the parabola that contains the given points.

**Got It?** 1. What is the equation of a parabola containing the points $(0, 0)$, $(1, -2)$, and $(-1, -4)$?

---

# 1 Interactive Learning

**Solve It!**

**PURPOSE** To introduce the idea that three points determine a quadratic function

**PROCESS** Students may place a coordinate system on the diagram and use vertex form of a quadratic function.

---

**FACILITATE**

**Q** How can you model the path with a parabola that has vertex $(0, 3)$? **[Sample: Assume the *y*-axis goes through the vertex and the *x*-axis is at waist level.]**

---

**ANSWER** See Solve It in Answers on next page.

**CONNECT THE MATH** In the Solve It, students use what they know about vertex form and standard form to write an equation of a parabola. In the lesson, they will use standard form and systems of equations to write equations of parabolas.

# 2 Guided Instruction

**Problem 1**

---

**Q** Use $y = ax^2 + bx + c$. Graph the three given points. What sign should you expect for *a*? Explain. **[Positive; because the parabola opens upward]**

**Q** How do you know you only need three points? **[You need one point to find each constant: *a*, *b*, and *c*.]**

---

## Got It?

---

**Q** Graph the points. What can you conclude about *a* and *c*? Explain. **[The parabola opens downward, so *a* < 0; the *y*-intercept is 0, so *c* = 0.]**

---

## 4-3 Preparing to Teach

**BIG** ideas **Function Equivalence**   **UbD**

**ESSENTIAL UNDERSTANDINGS**

- Any quadratic function is possibly a stretch, compression, reflection, and/or a translation of $y = x^2$.
- Three noncollinear points, no two of which are in line vertically, are on the graph of exactly one quadratic function.
- Standard form is "calculator ready".

### Math Background

Students should know that two points determine a line. The Essential Understanding extends this property. Since the points are on *exactly one* quadratic function, the three points *determine* this function. In the lesson, students will use the three points to write and solve a system of linear equations. This same method will be used to find a quadratic model for a real-world situation.

Be aware that a *quadratic model* can apply to a data set that contains more than three points. A quadratic model for three points is an exact fit, while a model for more than three points may be only an approximation. However, in some cases, a quadratic function *is* the exact fit for more than three data points. See the Lesson Check Exercises 2–3 for examples.

Once students have grasped this concept, you may wish to challenge them by asking how many points determine the graph of a cubic or higher-degree polynomial function.

### Support Student Learning

Use the **Algebra 2 Companion** to engage and support students during instruction. See Lesson resources at the end of this lesson for details.

**PowerAlgebra.com**

## 1 Interactive Learning

**Solve It!**

Step out how to solve the Problem with helpful hints and an online question. Other questions are listed above in Interactive Learning.

**Problem 2**      ERROR PREVENTION

**Q** How can you tell whether the equation is reasonable for this situation? **[Answers may vary. Sample: It is reasonable because $a < 0$, which means its graph opens downward, matching the path of the ball in the picture.]**

**Q** Could you use the equation to determine at what height the player released the ball? Explain. **[Yes; the player is standing at the origin, so substitute 0 for $x$ in the equation and solve for $y$.]**

## Got It?

**Q** For 2a, do you only need to determine whether the parabola passes through the point (5, 6)? Explain. **[No; you need to determine if the parabola passes *over* the point (5, 6).]**

For 2a, have students check their work: Substitute the given ordered pairs into the equation to check that they make the equation true. Graph the equation on a calculator and use the TRACE or TABLE feature to verify the graph goes under (5, 6).

---

 **Problem 2** Using a Quadratic Model

(4, 12)    (10, 12)

(2, 10)

**Basketball** A player throws a basketball toward the hoop. The basketball follows a parabolic path through the points shown. If the center of the hoop is at (12, 10), will the ball pass through the hoop? (You can think of the units as feet.)

**Step 1** Find a quadratic model.

Substitute the $x$ and $y$ values into the standard form of a quadratic function. The result is a system of three linear equations.

$$y = ax^2 + bx + c$$
$$10 = a(2)^2 + b(2) + c \qquad \text{Use (2, 10).}$$
$$12 = a(10)^2 + b(10) + c \qquad \text{Use (10, 12).}$$
$$12 = a(4)^2 + b(4) + c \qquad \text{Use (4, 12).}$$

Use one of the methods from Chapter 3. Solve. $\begin{cases} 4a + 2b + c = 10 \\ 100a + 10b + c = 12 \\ 16a + 4b + c = 12 \end{cases}$

The solution is $a = -0.125$, $b = 1.75$, and $c = 7$.

Substitute the values into the standard form of a quadratic function. An equation of the parabola is $y = -0.125x^2 + 1.75x + 7$.

**Think**

**In terms of the quadratic model, what does it mean for the ball to pass through the hoop?** The point (12, 10) is on the parabola. That is, the point (12, 10) satisfies the quadratic equation.

**Step 2** Use the quadratic model to see if the player makes the basket.

$$y = -0.125x^2 + 1.75x + 7$$
$$10 \stackrel{?}{=} -0.125(12)^2 + 1.75(12) + 7 \qquad \text{Substitute } (x, y) = (12, 10).$$
$$10 = 10 \checkmark$$

The point (12, 10) is on the parabola. The ball will pass through the hoop.

 **Got It?** **2. a.** The parabolic path of a thrown ball can be modeled by the table. The top of a wall is at (5, 6). Will the ball go over the wall? If not, will it hit the wall on the way up, or the way down?

**b. Reasoning** What is a reasonable domain and range for the function that models the path of the ball?

| x | y |
|---|---|
| 1 | 3 |
| 2 | 5 |
| 3 | 6 |

---

# Answers

### Solve It!

$y = -0.12x^2 + 1.2x + 3$, You catch the ball at (0, 3), and the vertex is the maximum, midway between you and your friend. Use the vertex (5, 6) and the point (0, 3) in the vertex form and solve for $a$. Then convert the vertex form to the standard form by squaring the binomial and simplifying.

### Got It?

**1.** $y = -3x^2 + x$

**2. a.** No; the ball will only reach a height of 5 when $x = 5$, which is lower than the top of the wall at (5, 6). The ball will hit the wall on its way down.

    **b.** domain: $0 \le x \le 7$, range: $0 \le y \le 6\frac{1}{8}$

**3.** $y = -0.329x^2 + 9.798x + 15.571$; 88.5°F at 2:53 P.M.

---

**PowerAlgebra.com**

## 2 Guided Instruction

Each Problem is worked out and supported online.

**Problem 1**
Writing an Equation of a Parabola
*Animated*

**Problem 2**
Using a Quadratic Model
*Animated*

**Problem 3**
Using a Quadratic Regression
*Animated*

**Support in Algebra 2 Companion**
• Vocabulary
• Key Concepts
• Got It?

When more than three data points suggest a quadratic function, you can use the quadratic regression feature of a graphing calculator to find a quadratic model.

## Problem 3 Using Quadratic Regression

The table shows a meteorologist's predicted temperatures for an October day in Sacramento, California.

**Sacramento, CA**

| Time | Predicted Temperature (°F) |
|---|---|
| 8 A.M. | 52 |
| 10 A.M. | 64 |
| 12 P.M. | 72 |
| 2 P.M. | 78 |
| 4 P.M. | 81 |
| 6 P.M. | 76 |

**A** What is a quadratic model for this data?

**Step 1** Enter the data. Use the 24-hour clock to represent times after noon.

**Think**

How do you write times using a 24-hour clock?
Add 12 to the number of hours past noon. So, 2 P.M. is 14:00 in the 24-hour clock.

**Step 2** Use **QuadReg**.

**Step 3** Graph the data and the function.

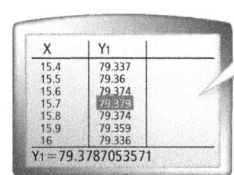

A quadratic model is reasonable.

A quadratic model for temperature is $y = -0.469x^2 + 14.716x - 36.121$.

**B** Use your model to predict the high temperature for the day. At what time does the high temperature occur?

Use the **Maximum** feature or tables.

16 represents 4 P.M. The maximum occurs at approximately 15.7, or about 3:42 P.M.

Predict the high temperature for the day to be 79.4°F at about 3:42 P.M.

**Denver, CO**

| Time | Predicted Temperature (°F) |
|---|---|
| 6 A.M. | 63 |
| 9 A.M. | 76 |
| 12 P.M. | 86 |
| 3 P.M. | 89 |
| 6 P.M. | 85 |
| 9 P.M. | 76 |

**Got It? 3.** The table shows a meteorologist's predicted temperatures for a summer day in Denver, Colorado. What is a quadratic model for this data? Predict the high temperature for the day. At what time does the high temperature occur?

### Problem 3

**Q** Are the calculated $y$-values equal to the Predicted Temperature values in the table? Explain why or why not. **[No; answers may vary. Sample: The $y$-values in the calculator table are values of the quadratic model for the data. The model is a function that approximates the data; it is not an exact fit.]**

**Q** What is the value of $R^2$ rounded to three decimal places? What does this answer indicate? Explain. **[0.992; answers may vary. Sample: It indicates that the model is a very close fit for the data because the value of $R^2$ is close to 1.]**

### Got It?

**Q** Using the model, what is your predicted high temperature? Justify your prediction. **[88.4°F; answers may vary. Sample: It is approximately the highest temperature value of the quadratic model. Although the predicted temperature for 3 P.M. is 89 degrees, it did not fit the model.]**

**Q** Which is an actual data point: (14.87, 88.4) or (15, 89)? Does that mean 89°F is the actual high temperature? Explain. **[(15, 89); no 89°F is a temperature predicted by a meteorologist.]**

# Additional Problems

**1.** A parabola contains the points (0, 0), (−1, 1), and (1, 5). What is the equation of this parabola in standard form?

**ANSWER** $y = 3x^2 + 2x$

**2.** You pitch a softball toward the catcher's mitt. The ball follows a parabolic path through the points shown. If the center of the catcher's mitt is at (0, 2), will the ball hit the center of the mitt? Explain.

(20, 8)  (30, 8)
(40, 6)

**ANSWER** Yes, because the point (0, 2) is on the graph of $y = -0.01x^2 + 0.5x + 2$, which is the parabola determined by the three points.

**3.** The table shows a meteorologist's predicted temperatures for a fall day in Baltimore, Maryland.

| Time | Predicted Temperature (°F) |
|---|---|
| 8 A.M. | 52 |
| 11 A.M. | 59 |
| 2 P.M. | 63 |
| 5 P.M. | 63 |
| 8 P.M. | 58 |
| 11 P.M. | 56 |

**a.** What is a quadratic model for this data? (Round numerical values to the nearest hundredth.)

**b.** Use your model to predict the high temperature for the day. At what time does the predicted high temperature occur?

**ANSWERS**

**a.** $y = -0.16x^2 + 5.14x + 21.60$

**b.** 62.9°F at about 4 P.M.

# 3 Lesson Check

## Do you know HOW?
- For Exercises 2–3, students will need to choose three of the given points to work with. Then, after finding the function, they will need to verify that *all* the given points satisfy that function.

## Do you UNDERSTAND?
- If students have trouble with Exercise 5, revisit Problem 2.

## Close

Q How can you write a quadratic function whose graph passes through three known points? **[Substitute the (x, y) values into $y = ax^2 + bx + c$ to write a system of equations, and then solve the system for a, b, and c.]**

Q How can you write a quadratic function that models data consisting of more than three points? **[Use quadratic regression.]**

---

 **Lesson Check**

**Do you know HOW?**

Find a quadratic function that includes each set of values.

**1.** $(1, 0), (2, -3), (3, -10)$

**2.**

| x | -2 | -1 | 0 | 1 | 2 |
|---|-----|-----|-----|------|------|
| y | 3.5 | 3.5 | 7.5 | 15.5 | 27.5 |

**3.**

| x | -2 | -1 | 0 | 1 |
|---|-------|-------|-------|------|
| y | -41.5 | -25.5 | -13.5 | -5.5 |

**Do you UNDERSTAND?**

**4. Compare and Contrast** How do you know whether to perform a linear regression or a quadratic regression for a given set of data?

**5. Reasoning** Explain how you can determine if the four points $(2, -8), (4, 3), (7, -1)$ and $(9, 5)$ lie on a single parabola.

**6. Error Analysis** Your classmate says he can write the equation of a quadratic function that passes through the points $(3, 4), (5, -2),$ and $(3, 0)$. Explain his error.

---

### Practice and Problem-Solving Exercises

**Ⓐ Practice**  Find an equation in standard form of the parabola passing through the points.  ◀ **See Problem 1.**

**7.** $(1, -2), (2, -2), (3, -4)$  **8.** $(1, -2), (2, -4), (3, -4)$  **9.** $(-1, 6), (1, 4), (2, 9)$

**10.** $(1, 1), (-1, -3), (-3, 1)$  **11.** $(3, -6), (1, -2), (6, 3)$  **12.** $(-2, 9), (-4, 5), (1, 0)$

**13.**

| x | f(x) |
|----|----|
| -1 | -1 |
| 1 | 3 |
| 2 | 8 |

**14.**

| x | f(x) |
|----|----|
| -1 | 17 |
| 1 | 17 |
| 2 | 8 |

**15.**

| x | f(x) |
|----|----|
| -1 | -4 |
| 1 | -2 |
| 2 | -4 |

**16. Communications** The table shows the percent of houses with cable TV in a city.  ◀ **See Problems 2 and 3.**

| Cable Television Access | | | | |
|---|---|---|---|---|
| Year | 1985 | 1990 | 1995 | 2000 | 2005 |
| % of Households | 46 | 59 | 66 | 68 | 69 |

    **a.** Find a quadratic model using 1985 as year 0, 1990 as year 5, and so on.
    **b.** Use the model to estimate the percent of households with cable TV in 1998.

**17. Physics** A man throws a ball off the top of a building and records the height of the ball at different times, as shown in the table.
    **a.** Find a quadratic model for the data.
    **b.** Use the model to estimate the height of the ball at 2.5 seconds.
    **c.** What is the ball's maximum height?

| Height of a Ball | |
|---|---|
| Time(s) | Height (ft) |
| 0 | 46 |
| 1 | 63 |
| 2 | 48 |
| 3 | 1 |

---

**PowerAlgebra.com**

## 3 Lesson Check

For a digital lesson check, use the Got It questions.

**Support in Algebra 2 Companion**
- Lesson Check

## 4 Practice

Assign homework to individual students or to an entire class.

---

# Answers

## Lesson Check

**1.** $y = -2x^2 + 3x - 1$

**2.** $y = 2x^2 + 6x + 7.5$

**3.** $y = -2x^2 + 10x - 13.5$

**4.** Answers may vary. Sample: A rough plot of the data will indicate whether the data are collinear (linear regression) or non-collinear where the data follows a curve (quadratic regression).

**5.** Answers may vary. Sample: A rough plot will show that the four points do *not* lie on a single parabola.

**6.** $y$ is not a function of $x$ since for one value of $x$, "3," there are 2 values of $y$, "4" and "0."

## Practice and Problem-Solving Exercises

**7.** $y = -x^2 + 3x - 4$

**8.** $y = x^2 - 5x + 2$

**9.** $y = 2x^2 - x + 3$

**10.** $y = x^2 + 2x - 2$

**11.** $y = x^2 - 6x + 3$

**12.** $y = -x^2 - 4x + 5$

**13.** $y = x^2 + 2x$

**14.** $y = -3x^2 + 20$

**15.** $y = -x^2 + x - 2$

**16. a.** $y = -0.083x^2 + 2.757x + 46.457$

    **b.** 68.3%

**17. a.** $y = -16x^2 + 33x + 46$, where $x$ is the number of seconds after release and $y$ is the height in ft

    **b.** 28.5 ft

    **c.** about 63 ft

B Apply

Determine whether a quadratic model exists for each set of values. If so, write the model.

**18.** $f(-2) = 16, f(0) = 0, f(1) = 4$

**19.** $f(0) = 5, f(2) = 3, f(-1) = 0$

**20.** $f(-1) = -4, f(1) = -2, f(2) = -1$

**21.** $f(-2) = 7, f(0) = 1, f(2) = 0$

**22. a.** **Geometry** Copy and complete the table. It shows the total number of segments whose endpoints are chosen from $x$ points, no three of which are collinear.

| Number of points, $x$ | 2 | 3 | ■ | ■ |
| --- | --- | --- | --- | --- |
| Number of segments, $y$ | 1 | 3 | ■ | ■ |

**b.** Write a quadratic model for the data.

**c.** Predict the number of segments that can be drawn using 10 points.

**23.** **Think About a Plan** The table shows the height of a column of water as it drains from its container. Use a quadratic model of this data to estimate the water level at 30 seconds.

- What system of equations can you use to solve this problem?
- How can you determine if your answer is reasonable?

**Water Levels**

| Elapsed Time (s) | Water Level (mm) |
| --- | --- |
| 0 | 120 |
| 20 | 83 |
| 40 | 50 |

**24.** A parabola contains the points $(-1, 8), (0, 4)$, and $(1, 2)$. Name another point also on the parabola.

**25. a.** **Postal Rates** Find a quadratic model for the data. Use 1981 as year 0.

**Price of First-Class Stamp**

| Year | 1981 | 1991 | 1995 | 1999 | 2001 | 2006 | 2007 | 2008 |
| --- | --- | --- | --- | --- | --- | --- | --- | --- |
| Price (cents) | 18 | 29 | 32 | 33 | 34 | 39 | 41 | 42 |

SOURCE: United States Postal Service

**b.** Describe a reasonable domain and range for your model. (*Hint:* This is a discrete, real situation.)

**c.** **Estimation** Estimate when first-class postage was 37 cents.

**d.** Use your model to predict when first-class postage will be 50 cents. Explain why your prediction may not be valid.

**26.** **Road Safety** The table below gives the stopping distance for an automobile under certain road conditions.

| Speed (mi/h) | 20 | 30 | 40 | 50 | 55 |
| --- | --- | --- | --- | --- | --- |
| Stopping Distance (ft) | 17 | 38 | 67 | 105 | 127 |

**a.** Find a linear model for the data.

**b.** Find a quadratic model for the data.

**c.** **Writing** Compare the models. Which is better? Explain.

**27.** **Open-Ended** Write three different quadratic functions, each with a graph that includes $(0, 0)$ and $(5, -1)$.

---

**18.** yes; $y = 4x^2$

**19.** yes; $y = -2x^2 + 3x + 5$

**20.** no

**21.** yes; $y = 0.625x^2 - 1.75x + 1$

**22. a.** $x$: 4, 5; $y$: 6, 10

**b.** $y = \frac{1}{2}x^2 - \frac{1}{2}x$

**c.** 45 segments

**23.** $y = 0.005x^2 - 1.95x + 120$; 66 mm

**24.** Answers may vary. Sample: (2, 2)

**25. a.** $y = -0.00357x^2 + 0.930x + 18.586$

**b.** Answers may vary. Sample: domain: integers from 0 to 27; range: whole numbers from 18 to 42

**c.** the year 2004

**d.** The year 2021; the year is outside the domain of the data pts.

**26. a.** $y = 3.157x - 52.335$

**b.** $y = 0.042x^2 - 0.041x + 0.889$

**c.** Answers may vary. Sample: Quadratic; the quadratic model comes closer to most data points than the linear model because the data follows a curve.

**27.** Answers may vary. Sample: $y = -\frac{1}{25}x^2$, $y = \frac{1}{25}x^2 - \frac{2}{5}x$, $y = \frac{1}{5}x^2 - \frac{6}{5}x$

**ASSIGNMENT GUIDE**

Basic: 7–17 all, 21–25

Average: 7–17 odd, 18–27

Advanced: 7–17 odd, 18–30

Standardized Test Prep: 31–34

Mixed Review: 35–45

**Reasoning** exercises have blue headings.

**Applications** exercises have red headings.

**EXERCISE 25:** Use the Think About a Plan worksheet in the **Practice and Problem Solving Workbook** (also available in the Teaching Resources in print and online) to further support students' development in becoming independent learners.

**HOMEWORK QUICK CHECK**

To check students' understanding of key skills and concepts, go over Exercises 7, 17, 22, 23, and 25.

# Answers

**28.** 3 pts.; answers may vary. Sample: you substitute $x$- and $y$-values into $y = ax^2 + bx + c$ to set up and solve a linear system to find the values of $a$, $b$, and $c$.

**29.** $(3, 5)$

**30. a.** You can find how high the arrow was when it was released.

**b.** The negative intercept tells you how much earlier you would have to shoot the arrow from height zero for its height to be described by the same function. The positive intercept tells you how many seconds after the release the arrow will take to hit the ground.

## Standardized Test Prep

**31.** A

**32.** I

**33.** D

**34.** [4] Let $d$ = number of dimes, let $q$ = number of quarters

$d + q = 42$

$q = 42 - d$

$0.10d + 0.25q = 6$

$0.1d + 0.25(42 - d) = 6$ (substitution)

$0.1d + 10.5 - 0.25d = 6$

$d = 30$

$(30) + q = 42$

$q = 12$

Mark has 12 quarters and 30 dimes. (OR solved by elimination)

[3] one computational error OR method used was not named

[2] only one value found

[1] correct answer, without work shown

## Mixed Review

**35.**

**36.**

**37.**

---

**28. Reasoning** What is the minimum number of data points you need to find a single quadratic model for a data set? Explain.

**29.** A parabola contains the points $(0, -4)$, $(2, 4)$, and $(4, 4)$. Find the vertex.

**30.** A model for the height of an arrow shot into the air is $h(t) = -16t^2 + 72t + 5$, where $t$ is time and $h$ is height. Without graphing, answer the following questions.
**a.** What can you learn by finding the graph's intercept with the $h$-axis?
**b.** What can you learn by finding the graph's intercept(s) with the $t$-axis?

## Standardized Test Prep

**SAT/ACT**

**31.** The graph of a quadratic function has vertex $(-3, -2)$. What is the axis of symmetry?

   Ⓐ $x = -3$     Ⓑ $x = 3$     Ⓒ $y = -2$     Ⓓ $y = 2$

**32.** Which function is NOT a quadratic function?

   Ⓕ $y = (x - 1)(x - 2)$     Ⓗ $y = 3x - x^2$

   Ⓖ $y = x^2 + 2x - 3$     Ⓘ $y = -x^2 + x(x - 3)$

**33.** Which is the composition $f(g(x))$, if $f(x) = -x - 3$ and $g(x) = 7 + 5x$?

   Ⓐ $f(g(x)) = 4x + 4$     Ⓒ $f(g(x)) = -5x - 8$

   Ⓑ $f(g(x)) = 4x - 10$     Ⓓ $f(g(x)) = -5x - 10$

**Extended Response**

**34.** Mark has 42 coins consisting of dimes and quarters. The total value of his coins is $6. How many of each type of coin does he have? Show all your work and explain what method you used to solve the problem.

## Mixed Review

Graph each function.    ◆ See Lesson 4-2.

**35.** $y = x^2 - 6x - 3$     **36.** $y = 2x^2 + 9x - 4$     **37.** $y = 3x^2 - 4x + 1$

Solve each system by elimination.    ◆ See Lesson 3-2.

**38.** $\begin{cases} x + y = 7 \\ 5x - y = 5 \end{cases}$     **39.** $\begin{cases} 2x - 3y = -14 \\ 3x - y = 7 \end{cases}$     **40.** $\begin{cases} x - 3y = 2 \\ x - 2y = 1 \end{cases}$

For Exercises 41–42, $y$ varies directly with $x$.    ◆ See Lesson 2-2.

**41.** If $y = 2$ when $x = 5$, find $y$ when $x = 2$.     **42.** If $y = -2$ when $x = 4$, find $y$ when $x = 7$.

**Get Ready!** To prepare for Lesson 4-4, do Exercises 43–45.

Simplify by combining like terms.    ◆ See Lesson 1-3.

**43.** $x^2 + x + 4x - 1$     **44.** $6x^2 - 4(3)x + 2x - 3$     **45.** $4x^2 - 2(5 - x) - 3x$

**38.** $(2, 5)$

**39.** $(5, 8)$

**40.** $(-1, -1)$

**41.** $\dfrac{4}{5}$

**42.** $-\dfrac{7}{2}$

**43.** $x^2 + 5x - 1$

**44.** $6x^2 - 10x - 3$

**45.** $4x^2 - x - 10$

## Additional Instructional Support

### Algebra 2 Companion

Students can use the **Algebra 2 Companion** worktext (4 pages) as you teach the lesson. Use the Companion to support

- New Vocabulary
- Key Concepts
- Got It for each Problem
- Lesson Check

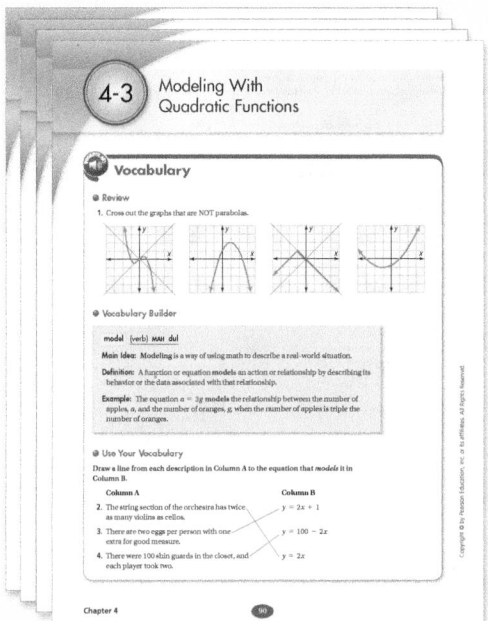

### ELL Support

**Focus on Language** Read the Essential Understanding aloud. You may also want to have students read it aloud. Use the following activity to have students explain the meaning in their own words. Draw three collinear points on the board and elicit why they do *not* satisfy all the stated conditions. Draw three noncollinear points, but with two of them in line vertically, and elicit why *they* do not satisfy all the stated conditions. Draw three noncollinear points with no two of them in line vertically, and elicit why *they do* satisfy all the stated conditions. Sketch a parabola-shaped curve through the points. Then draw several sets of points that satisfy the stated conditions and have student volunteers sketch parabola-shaped curves through them.

## 5 Assess & Remediate

### Lesson Quiz

1. Write in standard form the equation of the parabola that contains the points $(0, 0)$, $(-1, -5)$, and $(2, -2)$.

2. You throw a ball toward a trashcan. The ball follows a parabolic path through $(10, 10)$, $(14, 10)$, and $(20, 7)$. Will the ball pass through the center at $(0, 3)$?

3. **Do you UNDERSTAND?** The table shows predicted temperatures for a fall day in Orlando, Florida.

| Time | Predicted Temperature (°F) |
|---|---|
| 8 A.M. | 74 |
| 11 A.M. | 81 |
| 2 P.M. | 83 |
| 5 P.M. | 81 |
| 8 P.M. | 77 |
| 11 P.M. | 74 |

   a. Find a quadratic model for the data.

   b. Use your model to predict the high temperature for the day. At what time does the high temperature occur?

### ANSWERS TO LESSON QUIZ

1. $y = -2x^2 + 3x$

2. yes

3. a. $y = -0.15x^2 + 4.42x + 48.98$

   b. 81.5°F at about 3 P.M.

### PRESCRIPTION FOR REMEDIATION

Use the student work on the Lesson Quiz to prescribe a differentiated review assignment:

| Points | Differentiated Remediation |
|---|---|
| 0–1 | Intervention |
| 2 | On-level |
| 3 | Extension |

**PowerAlgebra.com**

### 5 Assess & Remediate

Assign the Lesson Quiz. Appropriate intervention, practice, or enrichment is automatically generated based on student performance.

## Intervention

- **Reteaching** (2 pages) Provides reteaching and practice exercises for the key lesson concepts. Use with struggling students or absent students.

- **English Language Learner Support** Helps students develop and reinforce mathematical vocabulary and key concepts.

### All-in-One Resources/Online
### Reteaching

**4-3 Reteaching**
Modeling With Quadratic Functions

Three non-collinear points, no two of which are in line vertically, are on the graph of exactly one quadratic function.

**Problem**

A parabola contains the points $(0, -2)$, $(-1, 5)$, and $(2, 2)$. What is the equation of this parabola in standard form?

If the parabola $y = ax^2 + bx + c$ passes through the point $(x, y)$, the coordinates of the point must satisfy the equation of the parabola. Substitute the $(x, y)$ values into $y = ax^2 + bx + c$ to write a system of equations.

First, use the point $(0, -2)$.   $y = ax^2 + bx + c$   Write the standard form.
$-2 = a(0)^2 + b(0) + c$   Substitute.
$-2 = c$   Simplify.

Use the point $(-1, 5)$ next.   $5 = a(-1)^2 + b(-1) + c$   Substitute.
$5 = a - b + c$   Simplify.

Finally, use the point $(2, 2)$.   $2 = a(2)^2 + b(2) + c$   Substitute.
$2 = 4a + 2b + c$   Simplify.

Because $c = -2$, the resulting system has two variables. Simplify the equations above.

$$a - b = 7$$
$$4a + 2b = 4$$

Use elimination to solve the system and obtain $a = 3$, $b = -4$, and $c = -2$. Substitute these values into the standard form $y = ax^2 + bx + c$.

The equation of the parabola that contains the given points is $y = 3x^2 - 4x - 2$.

**Exercises**

Find an equation in standard form of the parabola passing through the given points.

1. $(0, -1)$, $(1, 5)$, $(-1, -5)$   $y = x^2 + 5x - 1$    2. $(0, 4)$, $(-1, 9)$, $(2, 0)$   $y = x^2 - 4x + 4$
3. $(0, 1)$, $(1, 4)$, $(3, 22)$   $y = 2x^2 + x + 1$    4. $(1, -1)$, $(-2, 20)$, $(2, 0)$   $y = 2x^2 - 5x + 2$
5. $(-1, -5)$, $(0, -1)$, $(2, 1)$   $y = -x^2 + 3x - 1$    6. $(1, 3)$, $(-2, -3)$, $(-1, 3)$   $y = -2x^2 + 5$

### All-in-One Resources/Online
### English Language Learner Support

**4-3 ELL Support**
Modeling With Quadratic Functions

A football player kicks a football and records the height of the ball at different times. When kicked, at 0 seconds, the ball was 2 ft above the ground. One second later the ball was 28 ft above the ground, and 2 seconds after being kicked the ball was 20 ft above the ground. When will the ball hit the ground?

You wrote these steps to solve the problem on note cards, but they got mixed up.

| | |
|---|---|
| Substitute the $x$ and $y$ values into the standard form of a quadratic function. | Use the quadratic model to determine when the ball hits the ground. |
| Solve the system of three linear equations. | Substitute the values of $a$, $b$, and $c$ into the standard form of a quadratic function. |

Use the note cards to write the steps in order.

1. First, substitute the $x$- and $y$-values into the standard form of a quadratic function.

2. Second, solve the system of three linear equations.

3. Next, substitute the values of $a$, $b$, and $c$ into the standard form of a quadratic function.

4. Finally, use the quadratic model to determine when the ball hits the ground.

# Differentiated Remediation *continued*

## On-Level

- **Practice** (2 pages) Provides extra practice for each lesson. For simpler practice exercises, use the Form K Practice pages found in the All-in-One Teaching Resources and online.

- **Think About a Plan** Helps students develop specific problem-solving skills and strategies by providing scaffolded guiding questions.

- **Standardized Test Prep** Focuses on all major exercises, all major question types, and helps students prepare for the high-stakes assessments.

## Extension

- **Enrichment** Provides students with interesting problems and activities that extend the concepts of the lesson.

- **Activities, Games, and Puzzles** Worksheets that can be used for concepts development, enrichment, and for fun!

### Practice and Problem Solving Wkbk/ All-in-One Resources/Online
#### Practice page 1

### Practice and Problem Solving Wkbk/ All-in-One Resources/Online
#### Practice page 2

### All-in-One Resources/Online
#### Enrichment

### Practice and Problem Solving Wkbk/ All-in-One Resources/Online
#### Think About a Plan

### Practice and Problem Solving Wkbk/ All-in-One Resources/Online
#### Standardized Test Prep

### Online Teacher Resource Center
#### Activities, Games, and Puzzles

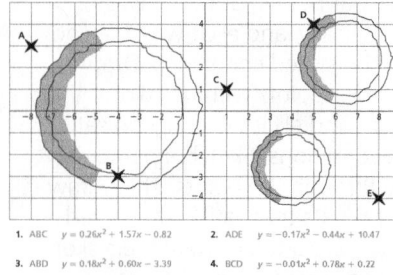

# Identifying Quadratic Data

You can identify perfect quadratic data when x-values are evenly spaced using the pattern in the differences between y-values.

## Example

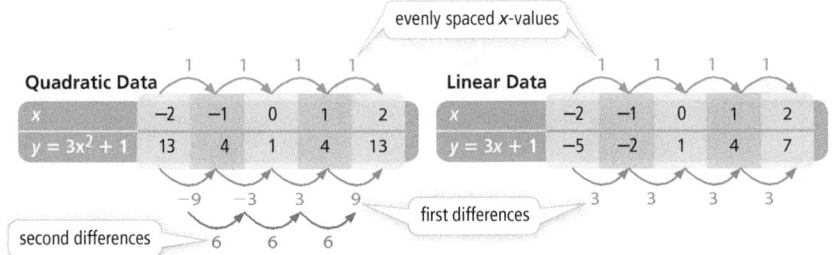

For linear data, the *first* differences of adjacent y-values are constant.
For quadratic data, the *second* differences are constant.

## Exercises

**Determine if each data set represents perfect quadratic data.**

**1.**

| x | y |
|----|----|
| −2 | −5 |
| −1 | 0 |
| 0 | 5 |
| 1 | 10 |
| 2 | 15 |

**2.**

| x | y |
|---|-----|
| 1 | 6 |
| 2 | 12 |
| 3 | 22 |
| 4 | 36 |
| 5 | 54 |
| 6 | 76 |
| 7 | 102 |

**3.**

| x | y |
|----|----|
| −2 | −8 |
| −1 | −1 |
| 0 | 0 |
| 1 | 1 |
| 2 | 8 |
| 3 | 27 |
| 4 | 64 |

**4.**

| x | y |
|------|-------|
| −3 | −1 |
| −2.5 | −3.75 |
| −2 | −6 |
| −1.5 | −7.75 |
| −1 | −9 |

**5.**

| x | y |
|----|-----|
| −3 | −13 |
| −1 | −8 |
| 1 | −5 |
| 3 | −4 |
| 5 | −5 |

**6. Reasoning** Can you use the method above to determine if a data set represents perfect linear or quadratic data if the x-values are *not* evenly spaced? Explain.

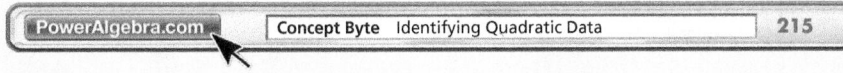

# Guided Instruction

**PURPOSE** To determine whether a data set represents perfect quadratic data

**PROCESS** Students find first and second differences of adjacent y-values to see whether a data set represents perfect quadratic data.

**DISCUSS**

**Q** What subtraction statement shows how to find the first first difference? the first second difference? **[4 − 13 = −9; −3 − (−9) = 6]**

**Q** What does *adjacent* mean? **[Answers may vary. Samples: consecutive, next to]**

**Q** The first differences are those of adjacent y-values. What are the second? **[differences of adjacent first differences]**

**Q** Could you use this method if each x in the table was not 1 unit from the previous x-values? Explain. **[Yes; as long as the x-values are evenly spaced.]**

Complete the table and find first and second differences to reinforce that x-values only need to be evenly spaced.

| x | −4 | −2 | 0 | 2 | 4 |
|----------------|----|----|---|---|---|
| $y = 3x^2 + 1$ | ■ | ■ | ■ | ■ | ■ |

## Exercises                     VISUAL LEARNERS

Have students copy the tables so they can draw the curves and write the differences.

**ERROR PREVENTION**

In Exercise 1, the second differences are all 0, which is constant. For data to be quadratic, the second differences must be a *nonzero* constant.

# Answers

**1.** no

**2.** yes

**3.** no

**4.** yes

**5.** yes

**6.** No; when x-values are not evenly spaced, linear or quadratic data will not necessarily have constant 1st or 2nd differences, and data that is neither linear nor quadratic may have constant 1st or 2nd differences.

# 1 Interactive Learning

## Solve It!

**PURPOSE** To identify factors of a number that have a given sum

**PROCESS** Students may
- write a linear equation to model each clue, and solve them as a system of equations.
- make tables with one row for factor pairs and one row for the sum of each pair.

**FACILITATE**

**Q** Can the two numbers on the cards be negative? Explain. **[Yes; the problem only says that the cards have numbers; it does not specify positive numbers.]**

**Q** What are all the pairs of numbers that have the product 5? **[1 and 5; −1 and −5]**

**Q** Which pair has a sum of 6? **[1 and 5]**

**Q** Does this mean that 1 and 5 are the only possible numbers that could be on your two cards? Explain. **[No; the two numbers can also have a product of 6 and a sum of 5, for example, 2 × 3 and 2 + 3.]**

**ANSWER** See Solve It in Answers on next page.

**CONNECT THE MATH** To solve the puzzle in the Solve It, students found sums and products of factors of given numbers. In this lesson, students use sums of factors to write equivalent quadratic expressions.

---

# 4-4 Factoring Quadratic Expressions

**Objectives** To find common and binomial factors of quadratic expressions
To factor special quadratic expressions

> **SOLVE IT!** **Getting Ready!**
>
> In a game, you see the two cards shown. You get two other cards with numbers. You win if
> 1. the product of your two numbers equals the number on one card shown, AND
> 2. the sum of your two numbers equals the number on the other card shown.
>
> What should your two cards be for you to win the game? Is there more than one answer? Explain.

*I know you can win this game!*

**Dynamic Activities**
Factoring
$x^2 + bx + c$
Factoring
$ax^2 + bx + c$

**Lesson Vocabulary**
- factoring
- greatest common factor (GCF) of an expression
- perfect square trinomial
- difference of two squares

Factors of a given number are numbers that have a product equal to the given number. Factors of a given expression are expressions that have a product equal to the given expression. **Factoring** is rewriting an expression as a product of its factors.

**Essential Understanding** You can factor many quadratic trinomials $(ax^2 + bx + c)$ into products of two binomials.

You can use the Distributive Property or the FOIL method to multiply two binomials. You can use FOIL in reverse to help you factor.

$$(x + 4)(x + 2) = (x + 4)(x) + (x + 4)(2) \qquad \text{Use the Distributive Property.}$$
$$= x(x) + 4(x) + x(2) + 4(2)$$
$$= x^2 + 6x + 8$$

$$(x + 4)(x + 2) = x(x) + x(2) + 4(x) + 4(2) \qquad \text{F: First; O: Outer; I: Inner; L: Last}$$
$$= x^2 + 6x + 8$$

To factor $x^2 + 6x + 8$, think of FOIL in reverse. Find two binomials for which the first terms have the product $x^2$, the products of the outer and inner terms have the sum $6x$, and the last terms have the product 8.

$$x^2 + 6x + 8 = (x + 4)(x + 2)$$

When you factor, a table of the different possible factors of the constant term may be helpful.

---

# 4-4 Preparing to Teach

**BIG idea** Solving Equations and Inequalities **UbD**

**ESSENTIAL UNDERSTANDINGS**
- Many quadratic trinomials ($ax^2 + bx + c$) can be factored into products of two binomials.
- The Distributive Property or FOIL method can be used to multiply two binomials. FOIL can be used in reverse to factor.

## Math Background

Students who are accustomed to factoring numbers are sometimes confused by the concept of factoring expressions. Point out the similarity between factoring numbers and factoring expressions. When you factor a number, you find pairs of numbers whose products are the original number. When you factor a quadratic expression, you find a pair of expressions whose product is the original expression.

Factoring is one way to solve quadratic equations. In this lesson, students will use the Distributive Property and the FOIL method. Factoring expressions is a skill that comes with practice. Allow students ample time to make sure they go through all the steps properly.

## Support Student Learning

Use the **Algebra 2 Companion** to engage and support students during instruction. See Lesson Resources at the end of this lesson for details.

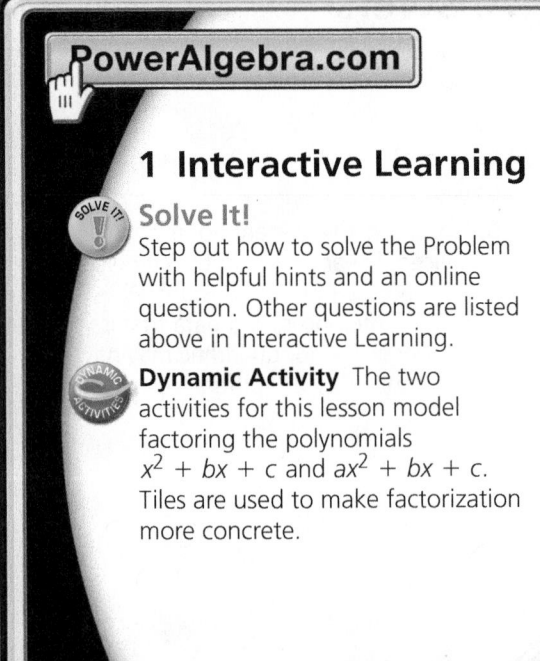

**PowerAlgebra.com**

## 1 Interactive Learning

**Solve It!**
Step out how to solve the Problem with helpful hints and an online question. Other questions are listed above in Interactive Learning.

**Dynamic Activity** The two activities for this lesson model factoring the polynomials $x^2 + bx + c$ and $ax^2 + bx + c$. Tiles are used to make factorization more concrete.

**Problem 1** Factoring $ax^2 + bx + c$ when $a = \pm 1$

**What is the expression in factored form?**

**Plan**

How can you *make a table* to find factors?
Use the first row to list sets of factors of the constant. Use the second row to find the sum of each set of factors.

**A** $x^2 + 9x + 20$

**Step 1** Find factors of 20 with sum 9.
Since both 20 and 9 are positive, both factors are positive.

| Factors of 20 | 1, 20 | 2, 10 | 4, 5 |
|---|---|---|---|
| Sum of factors | 21 | 12 | 9 |

**Step 2** Use the factors you found. Write the expression as the product of two binomials.

$x^2 + 9x + 20 = (x + 4)(x + 5)$   Use the factors 4 and 5.

**B** $x^2 + 14x - 72$

**Step 1** Find factors of $-72$ with sum 14.
Since $c < 0$, one factor is positive and the other is negative.
Since $b > 0$, the factor with greater absolute value is positive.

| Factors of -72 | -1, 72 | -2, 36 | -3, 24 | -4, 18 | -6, 12 | -8, 9 |
|---|---|---|---|---|---|---|
| Sum of factors | 71 | 34 | 21 | 14 | 6 | 1 |

**Step 2** Use the factors you found, $-4$ and 18. Write
$x^2 + 14x - 72 = (x - 4)(x + 18)$.

**C** $-x^2 + 13x - 12$

**Think**

Will factoring out $-1$ change the answer?
No; because the final factored expression will include $-1$ as a factor.

**Step 1** Rewrite the expression to show a trinomial with leading coefficient 1.

$-(x^2 - 13x + 12)$   Factor out $-1$.

**Step 2** Find factors of 12 with sum $-13$.

Since $c > 0$, both factors have the same sign.
Since $b < 0$, both factors must be negative.

| Factors of 12 | -1, -12 | -2, -6 | -3, -4 |
|---|---|---|---|
| Sum of factors | -13 | -8 | -7 |

**Step 3** Use the factors you found, $-1$ and $-12$. Write
$-x^2 + 13x - 12 = -(x^2 - 13x + 12) = -(x - 1)(x - 12)$.

 **Got It? 1.** What is the expression in factored form?
**a.** $x^2 + 14x + 40$      **b.** $x^2 - 11x + 30$      **c.** $-x^2 + 14x + 32$

---

# 2 Guided Instruction

**Problem 1**           **VISUAL LEARNERS**

In 1A, students factor quadratic expressions when $a = 1$ and $c > 0$. Use algebra tiles to model the factorization.

**Q** In 1B, how do you know that the first term in each binomial factor is $x$? **[The first terms have the product $x^2$.]**

**Q** In 1B, why are $-4$ and 18 used for the outer and inner terms? **[They are the only factors of $-72$ that have a sum of 14.]**

**Q** In 1C, if you did not factor out $-1$, what would be the first term in each binomial factor? Explain. **[$x$ and $-x$; they must have a product of $-x^2$.]**

**Got It?**           **ELL SUPPORT**

Students can make a list describing the signs of factors depending on the signs of $b$ and $c$. Use this to help find factors quickly or as a check.

**Signs of Factors**

| If a is not 1, factor it out first. | | |
|---|---|---|
| **$b$** | **$c$** | **Factors** |
| $+$ | $+$ | $+, +$ |
| $-$ | $-$ | $+, -$ [The factor with the greater absolute value is $-$] |
| $+$ | $-$ | $+, -$ [The factor with the greater absolute value is $+$] |
| $-$ | $+$ | $-, -$ |

          **EXTENSION**

Ask students to show examples for each combination of signs.

---

# 2 Guided Instruction

 Each Problem is worked out and supported online.

**Problem 1**
Factoring $ax^2 + bx + c$ when $a = \pm 1$

**Problem 2**
Finding Common Factors

**Problem 3**
Factoring $ax^2 + bx + c$ when $|a| \neq 1$
          *Animated*

**Problem 4**
Factoring a Perfect Square Trinomial
          *Animated*

**Problem 5**
Factoring a Difference of Two Squares
          *Animated*

**Support in Algebra 2 Companion**
• Vocabulary
• Key Concepts
• Got It?

---

# Answers

**Solve It!**
One card should be a 2, the other card should be a 3; yes; one card could be a 5 and the other card could be a 1.

**Got It?**
**1. a.** $(x + 10)(x + 4)$
    **b.** $(x - 5)(x - 6)$
    **c.** $-(x + 2)(x - 16)$

## Problem 2

Checking for a GCF to factor out is the first step when factoring any quadratic expression.

> **Q** If the expression were $6n^2 + 9$, what GCF would you factor out? If it were $6n^3 + 9n^2$? **[3; $3n^2$]**
>
> **Q** How do you know when you are finished factoring common terms out of an expression? **[The factoring is finished when the GCF is 1.]**

### Got It? ERROR PREVENTION

Students sometimes incorrectly factor the trinomial in 2b as $9(x - 2)(x + 1)$. Use the Distributive Property to show that this factorization in incorrect.

EXTENSION

> **Q** When the signs of the constants in the factor binomials are reversed, how does the trinomial change? **[The sign of the middle term in the trinomial is reversed.]**

## Problem 3

The only common factors of the terms in this trinomial are 1 and −1, so the GCF cannot be used to factor it.

> **Q** In 3A Step 3, why is $11x$ rewritten as $3x + 8x$? **[3 and 8 are factors of 24 with a sum of 11.]**
>
> **Q** Would this method work if you switched the order of $3x$ and $8x$? Explain. **[Yes; $2x^2 + 8x + 3x + 12 = 2x(x + 4) + 3(x + 4) = (2x + 3)(x + 4)$.]**

---

The **greatest common factor (GCF) of an expression** is a common factor of the terms in the expression. It is the common factor with the greatest coefficient and the greatest exponent. You can factor any expression that has a GCF not equal to 1.

 **Problem 2** Finding Common Factors

**What is the expression in factored form?**

**A** $6n^2 + 9n$

$$6n^2 + 9n = 3n(2n) + 3n(3) \qquad \text{Factor out the GCF, } 3n.$$
$$= 3n(2n + 3) \qquad \text{Use the Distributive Property.}$$

**B** $4x^2 + 20x - 56$

$$4x^2 + 20x - 56 = 4(x^2) + 4(5x) - 4(14) \qquad \text{Factor out the GCF, 4.}$$
$$= 4(x^2 + 5x - 14) \qquad \text{Use the Distributive Property.}$$
$$= 4(x - 2)(x + 7) \qquad \text{Factor the trinomial.}$$

**Got It?** **2.** What is the expression in factored form?

     **a.** $7n^2 - 21$      **b.** $9x^2 + 9x - 18$      **c.** $4x^2 + 8x + 12$

To factor a quadratic trinomial of the form $ax^2 + bx + c$ where $a \neq 1$, and there is no common factor, find factors of $ac$ that have sum $b$.

 **Problem 3** Factoring $ax^2 + bx + c$ when $|a| \neq 1$

**What is the expression in factored form?**

**A** $2x^2 + 11x + 12$

**Step 1** Since there is no common factor, find $ac$.

$$ac = 2(12) = 24$$

**Step 2** Since both $b$ and $ac$ are positive, find positive factors of 24 that have sum 11.

| Factors of 24 | 1, 24 | 2, 12 | 3, 8 | 4, 6 |
|---|---|---|---|---|
| Sum of factors | 25 | 14 | 11 | 10 |

**Step 3** Factor the trinomial as follows.

$$2x^2 + 11x + 12$$
$$2x^2 + 3x + 8x + 12 \qquad \text{Rewrite } bx \text{ using } b = 3 + 8.$$
$$x(2x + 3) + 4(2x + 3) \qquad \text{Find a common factor for the first two terms and another common factor for the last two terms.}$$
$$(x + 4)(2x + 3) \qquad \text{Rewrite using the Distributive Property.}$$

**Plan**

**Should you factor out a number, a variable, or both?**
Both; the two terms have numerical and variable common factors.

**Think**

**How should you make your table in this case?**
Use the first row to list sets of factors of ac. Use the second row as before, to find the sum of each set of factors.

**218** Chapter 4 Quadratic Functions and Equations

---

# Additional Problems

**1.** What is the expression in factored form? $x^2 + 7x + 6$

     **ANSWER** $(x + 1)(x + 6)$

**2.** What is the expression in factored form? $4x^2 - 28x$

     **ANSWER** $4x(x - 7)$

**3.** What is the expression in factored form?
$2x^2 + 5x - 12$

     **ANSWER** $(2x - 3)(x + 4)$

**4.** What is $x^2 - 12x + 36$ in factored form?

     **ANSWER** $(x - 6)^2$

**5.** What is $81x^2 - 100$ in factored form?

     **ANSWER** $(9x + 10)(9x - 10)$

**B** $4x^2 - 4x - 3$

**Think**

**Do you need positive or negative factors?**
You need one negative factor and one positive factor.

**Step 1** Since there is no common factor, find $ac$.

$$ac = 4(-3) = -12$$

**Step 2** Since $ac = -12 < 0$, find factors of $ac$ with opposite signs. Since $b < 0$, the factor with greater absolute value is negative.

| Factors of –12 | 1, –12 | 2, –6 | 3, –4 |
|---|---|---|---|
| Sum of factors | –11 | –4 | –1 |

**Step 3** Factor the trinomial as follows.

$4x^2 - 4x - 3$

$4x^2 + 2x - 6x - 3$     Rewrite $bx$ using $b = 2 - 6$.

$2x(2x + 1) - 3(2x + 1)$     Find a common factor for the first two terms and another common factor for the last two terms.

$(2x - 3)(2x + 1)$     Rewrite using the Distributive Property.

**Check** $(2x - 3)(2x + 1) = 4x^2 + 2x - 6x - 3$

$= 4x^2 - 4x - 3$ ✔

 **Got It? 3.** What is the expression in factored form? Check your answers.

   **a.** $4x^2 + 7x + 3$              **b.** $2x^2 - 7x + 6$

   **c. Reasoning** Can you factor the expression $2x^2 + 2x + 2$ into a product of two binomials? Explain.

A **perfect square trinomial** is a trinomial that is the square of a binomial. For example, $x^2 + 10x + 25 = (x + 5)^2$ is a perfect square trinomial.

If $ax^2 + bx + c$ is a perfect square trinomial, then $ax^2$ and $c$ are squares of the terms of the binomial and thus are both positive. $bx$ is twice the product of the terms of the binomial. $b$ is negative if the binomial terms have opposite signs.

Here is another way to represent the two forms of a perfect square trinomial.

---

**take note**    **Key Concept**   **Factoring Perfect Square Trinomials**

$$a^2 + 2ab + b^2 = (a + b)^2 \qquad\qquad a^2 - 2ab + b^2 = (a - b)^2$$

---

---

**VISUAL LEARNERS**

Students sometimes confuse terms when checking a factorization. Use a box to organize the process. Write each binomial in a row with one term in each column:

| | |
|---|---|
| 2x | −3 |
| 2x | +1 |

- Multiply down each column:
  $2x(2x) = 4x^2$
  $-3(+1) = -3$
- Multiply diagonally in both directions:
  $2x(+1) = 2x$
  $2x(-3) = -6x$
- Add all the products: $4x^2 - 4x - 3$

**Got It?**             **EXTENSION**

**Q** For 3c, what is the correct terminology to explain how the expression can be factored? [**Answers may vary. Sample: It can be factored as a product of one monomial and one trinomial: $2(x^2 + x + 1)$.**]

**Take Note**

The factoring methods used in previous sections can also be used to factor perfect square trinomials. For example:
$$x^2 + 10x + 25$$
$$= x^2 + 5x + 5x + 25$$
$$= x(x + 5) + 5(x + 5)$$
$$= (x + 5)(x + 5)$$
$$= (x + 5)^2.$$

---

## Answers

**Got It?** (continued)

**2. a.** $7(n^2 - 3)$

   **b.** $9(x + 2)(x - 1)$

   **c.** $4(x^2 + 2x + 3)$

**3. a.** $(x + 1)(4x + 3)$

   **b.** $(x - 2)(2x - 3)$

   **c.** No; $2x^2 + 2x + 2 = 2(x^2 + x + 1)$, there are no real factors of $a$ and $c$ whose product is 1 and whose sum is 1.

## Problem 4

**Q** How do the terms $4x^2$ and 36 help you identify it as a perfect square trinomial? **[Both terms are squares.]**

**Q** What must be true of the term $-24x$ for this expression to be a perfect square trinomial? **[Its absolute value must be twice the product of the square roots of $4x^2$ and 36 ($2x$ and 6).]**

### Got It?

A trinomial $ax^2 + bx + c$ is a perfect square only if
- both $ax^2$ and $c$ are squares,
- both $ax^2$ and $c$ are positive, AND
- $|b| = 2\sqrt{a} \cdot \sqrt{c}$.

### Take Note

A binomial is a difference of squares only if
- both $ax^2$ and $c$ are squares, AND
- $ax^2$ and $c$ have opposite signs.

## Problem 5

As long as the terms of a binomial have opposite signs, their order does not affect whether or not the expression is a difference of two squares.

**Q** Is $-25x^2 + 49$ a difference of two squares? Explain. **[yes; $49 - 25x^2 = (7 - 5x)(7 + 5x)$]**

### Got It?                                    EXTENSION

**Q** What are $a$ and $b$ in this problem? **[$4x$ and 9]**

---

 **Problem 4** Factoring a Perfect Square Trinomial

What is $4x^2 - 24x + 36$ in factored form?

| Think | Write |
|---|---|
| Write the expression. | $4x^2 - 24x + 36$ |
| You can do this in one step. | |
| Is the first term a perfect square? Yes, $4x^2$ is $(2x)^2$. | |
| Is the last term a perfect square? Yes, 36 is $6^2$. | $(2x - 6)^2$ |
| Is the middle term twice the product of 6 and $2x$? Yes, $2 \cdot 6 \cdot 2x = 24x$ | |
| There's a minus sign in the middle. You are done. | |
| You should check. | $(2x - 6)^2 = 4x^2 - 24x + 36$ ✔ |

**Got It?** **4.** What is $64x^2 - 16x + 1$ in factored form?

The expression $a^2 - b^2$ is the **difference of two squares**. There is a pattern to its factors.

**take note**

> **Key Concept** **Factoring a Difference of Two Squares**
>
> $$a^2 - b^2 = (a + b)(a - b)$$

**Think**

How can a binomial be the product of two binomials? If the outer and inner products of the binomials are opposites, their sum is zero.

**Problem 5** Factoring a Difference of Two Squares

What is $25x^2 - 49$ in factored form?

$25x^2 - 49 = (5x)^2 - 7^2$    Write as the difference of two squares.

$= (5x + 7)(5x - 7)$    Use the pattern for factoring a difference of two squares.

**Got It?** **5.** What is $16x^2 - 81$ in factored form?

---

# Answers

### Got It? (continued)
**4.** $(8x - 1)^2$
**5.** $(4x - 9)(4x + 9)$

### Lesson Check
**1.** $(x + 4)(x + 2)$
**2.** $(x - 12)(x - 1)$
**3.** $(x - 9)(x + 9)$
**4.** $(5y - 6)(5y + 6)$
**5.** $(y - 3)^2$      **6.** $(2x - 1)^2$
**7.** $5x$      **8.** $4a^2$
**9.** 6      **10.** $7h$

**11.** No; the middle term is not twice the product of the square root of the end terms.

**12.** For $a \neq 1$, look for two factors whose sum is $b$ and whose product is $ac$. For $a = 1$, look for two factors whose sum is $b$ and whose product is $c$.

**13.** $a^2 - 2ab + b^2 - 25$   Group the first 3 terms.
$= (a^2 - 2ab + b^2) - 25$
$= (a - b)^2 - 5^2$
$= (a - b - 5)(a - b + 5)$

## Lesson Check

**Do you know HOW?**

Factor each expression.

1. $x^2 + 6x + 8$     2. $x^2 - 13x + 12$

3. $x^2 - 81$     4. $25y^2 - 36$

5. $y^2 - 6y + 9$     6. $4x^2 - 4x + 1$

Find the GCF of each expression.

7. $15x^2 - 25x$     8. $4a^3 + 8a^2$

9. $18b^2 - 12b + 24$     10. $21h^3 + 35h^2 - 28h$

**Do you UNDERSTAND?**

11. **Vocabulary** Is $4b^2 - 26b + 169$ a perfect square trinomial? Explain.

12. **Compare and Contrast** How is factoring a trinomial $ax^2 + bx + c^2$ when $a \neq 1$ different from factoring a trinomial when $a = 1$? How is it similar?

13. **Reasoning** Explain how to rewrite the expression $a^2 - 2ab + b^2 - 25$ as the product of two trinomial factors. (*Hint:* Group the first three terms. What type of expression is this?)

## Practice and Problem-Solving Exercises

**Ⓐ Practice**    Factor each expression.       ◀ See Problem 1.

14. $x^2 + 3x + 2$     15. $x^2 + 5x + 6$     16. $x^2 + 7x + 10$

17. $x^2 + 10x + 16$     18. $y^2 + 15y + 36$     19. $x^2 + 22x + 40$

20. $x^2 - 3x + 2$     21. $-x^2 + 13x - 12$     22. $-r^2 + 11r - 18$

23. $x^2 - 10x + 24$     24. $d^2 - 12d + 27$     25. $x^2 - 13x + 36$

26. $x^2 - 5x - 14$     27. $-x^2 - x + 20$     28. $-x^2 + 3x + 40$

29. $c^2 + 2c - 63$     30. $x^2 + 10x - 75$     31. $-t^2 + 7t + 44$

Find the GCF of each expression. Then factor the expression.       ◀ See Problem 2.

32. $3a^2 + 9$     33. $25b^2 - 20b$     34. $x^2 - 2x$

35. $5t^2 - 5t - 10$     36. $14y^2 + 7y - 21$     37. $27p^2 - 9p + 18$

Factor each expression.       ◀ See Problems 3–5.

38. $3x^2 + 31x + 36$     39. $2x^2 - 19x + 24$     40. $5r^2 + 23r + 26$

41. $2m^2 - 11m + 15$     42. $5t^2 + 28t + 32$     43. $2x^2 - 27x + 36$

44. $3x^2 + 7x - 20$     45. $5y^2 + 12y - 32$     46. $7x^2 - 8x - 12$

47. $2z^2 + z - 28$     48. $3x^2 + 8x - 16$     49. $28k^2 + 13k - 6$

50. $x^2 + 2x + 1$     51. $t^2 - 14t + 49$     52. $k^2 - 18k + 81$

53. $4z^2 - 20z + 25$     54. $9x^2 + 48x + 64$     55. $81z^2 + 36z + 4$

56. $x^2 - 4$     57. $c^2 - 64$     58. $9x^2 - 1$

# 3 Lesson Check

## Do you know HOW?

- If students give the answers for Exercises 3 and 4 as $(x - 9)^2$ and $(5y - 6)^2$, refer them to Problem 5.
- For Exercise 6, suggest factoring out 4 from the expression: $4(x^2 - x + \frac{1}{4})$. If necessary, remind students that $-\frac{1}{2}(-\frac{1}{2}) = \frac{1}{4}$.
- For Exercises 7–10, have students factor out the GCF for each expression. Then challenge them to explain why each expression cannot be simplified further (other than by substituting a value for the variable).

## Do you UNDERSTAND?

- For Exercise 12, if students have trouble explaining their thinking, suggest that they use two example trinomials in their explanations.
- For Exercise 13, after students group the first three terms and recognize that they can be factored as $(a - b)^2$, suggest that they replace $(a - b)$ with a new variable. This should help students see that $(a - b)^2 - 25$ can be factored as a difference of squares.

## Close

> **Q** What is the purpose of factoring quadratic expressions? **[Answers may vary. Samples: to simplify an expression to identify values for its variable(s); to solve quadratic equations; to solve problems that can be modeled with parabolas]**

## Practice and Problem-Solving Exercises

**14.** $(x + 1)(x + 2)$   **15.** $(x + 2)(x + 3)$

**16.** $(x + 2)(x + 5)$   **17.** $(x + 2)(x + 8)$

**18.** $(y + 3)(y + 12)$

**19.** $(x + 2)(x + 20)$

**20.** $(x - 1)(x - 2)$

**21.** $-(x - 1)(x - 12)$

**22.** $-(r - 2)(r - 9)$

**23.** $(x - 4)(x - 6)$   **24.** $(d - 3)(d - 9)$

**25.** $(x - 4)(x - 9)$   **26.** $(x - 7)(x + 2)$

**27.** $-(x - 4)(x + 5)$

**28.** $-(x - 8)(x + 5)$

**29.** $(c - 7)(c + 9)$

**30.** $(x - 5)(x + 15)$

**31.** $-(t - 11)(t + 4)$

**32.** $3$; $3(a^2 + 3)$

**33.** $5b$; $5b(5b - 4)$

**34.** $x$; $x(x - 2)$

**35.** $5$; $5(t + 1)(t - 2)$

**36.** $7$; $7(2y + 3)(y - 1)$

**37.** $9$; $9(3p^2 - p + 2)$

**38.** $(3x + 4)(x + 9)$

**39.** $(x - 8)(2x - 3)$

**40.** $(r + 2)(5r + 13)$

**41.** $(m - 3)(2m - 5)$

**42.** $(t + 4)(5t + 8)$

**43.** $(x - 12)(2x - 3)$

**44.** $(x + 4)(3x - 5)$

**45.** $(y + 4)(5y - 8)$

**46.** $(x - 2)(7x + 6)$

**47.** $(z + 4)(2z - 7)$

**48.** $(x + 4)(3x - 4)$

**49.** $(4k + 3)(7k - 2)$

**50.** $(x + 1)^2$   **51.** $(t - 7)^2$

**52.** $(k - 9)^2$   **53.** $(2z - 5)^2$

**54.** $(3x + 8)^2$   **55.** $(9z + 2)^2$

**56.** $(x - 2)(x + 2)$

**57.** $(c - 8)(c + 8)$

**58.** $(3x - 1)(3x + 1)$

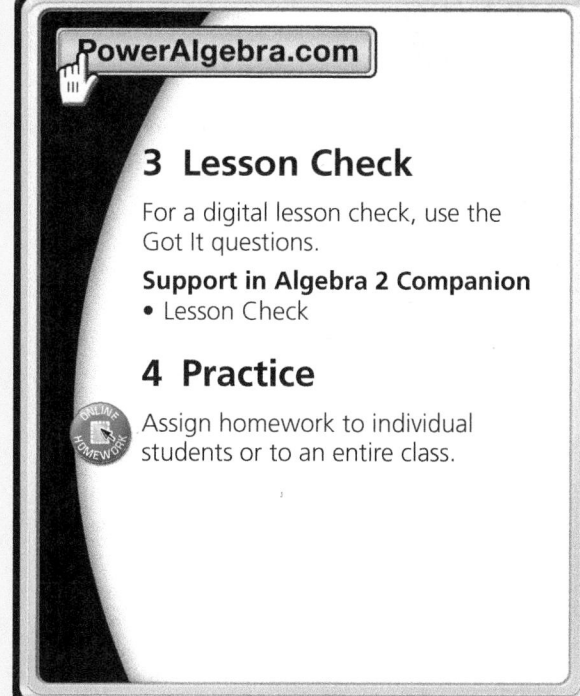

## PowerAlgebra.com

### 3 Lesson Check

For a digital lesson check, use the Got It questions.

**Support in Algebra 2 Companion**
- Lesson Check

### 4 Practice

Assign homework to individual students or to an entire class.

# 4 Practice

## ASSIGNMENT GUIDE

Basic: 14–58 all, 59–61, 79–82, 87, 90

Average: 15–57 odd, 59–90

Advanced: 15–57 odd, 59–102

Standardized Test Prep: 103–105

Mixed Review: 106–110

Reasoning exercises have blue headings.

Applications exercises have red headings.

EXERCISE 80: Use the Think About a Plan worksheet in the **Practice and Problem Solving Workbook** (also available in the Teaching Resources in print and online) to further support students' development in becoming independent learners.

## HOMEWORK QUICK CHECK

To check students' understanding of key skills and concepts, go over Exercises 33, 39, 59, 60, and 80.

---

 Apply

59. **Think About a Plan** Suppose you cut a small square from a square sheet of cardboard. Find the sides of one rectangle whose area is equal to the area of the remaining part.
    - How can you represent the remaining part as a combination of rectangles with known sides?
    - Can you factor the resulting expression?

60. The area in square centimeters of a square area rug is $25x^2 - 10x + 1$. What are the dimensions of the rug in terms of $x$?

**Factor each expression completely.**

61. $9x^2 - 36$
62. $18z^2 - 8$
63. $12y^2 - 75$
64. $64t^2 - 16$
65. $12x^2 + 36x + 27$
66. $16x^2 - 80x + 100$
67. $2a^2 - 16a + 32$
68. $3x^2 - 24x - 27$
69. $18b^2 + 24b - 10$
70. $4n^2 - 20n + 24$
71. $3y^2 + 24y + 45$
72. $-x^2 + 5x - 4$
73. $4x^2 - 22x + 10$
74. $\frac{1}{2}x^2 - \frac{1}{2}$
75. $-6z^2 - 600$
76. $2x^2 - 11x + 5$
77. $x^2 - y^2$
78. $-\frac{1}{16}s^2 + 1$

79. **Error Analysis** Your friend attempted to factor an expression as shown. Find the error in your friend's work. Then factor the expression correctly.

80. **Agriculture** The area in square feet of a rectangular field is $x^2 - 120x + 3500$. The width, in feet, is $x - 50$. What is the length, in feet?

**Find the GCF of each expression. Then factor the expression.**

81. $y^2 - y$
82. $ab^2 - b$
83. $10x^2 - 90$
84. $3t^2 - 24t$
85. $2x^2 - 74x + 12$
86. $x^2y^2 + xy$

87. What is the factored form of $4x^2 + 15x - 4$?
    - Ⓐ $(2x + 2)(2x - 2)$
    - Ⓒ $(4x + 1)(x - 4)$
    - Ⓑ $(2x - 4)(2x + 1)$
    - Ⓓ $(4x - 1)(x + 4)$

88. **Geometry** What is the volume of the shaded pipe with outer radius $R$, inner radius $r$, and height $h$ as shown? Express your answer in completely factored form.

89. **Open-Ended** Write a quadratic trinomial that you can factor, where $a \neq 1$, $ac > 0$, and $b < 0$. Factor the expression.

90. **Writing** Explain how to factor $3x^2 + 6x - 72$ completely.

Ⓒ Challenge **Factor each expression completely.**

91. $0.25t^2 - 0.16$
92. $8100x^2 - 10,000$
93. $(x + 3)^2 + 3(x + 3) - 54$
94. $(x - 2)^2 - 15(x - 2) + 56$
95. $6(x + 5)^2 - 5(x + 5) + 1$
96. $3(2a - 3)^2 + 17(2a - 3) + 10$

---

# Answers

## Practice and Problem-Solving Exercises (continued)

59. The rectangle would have one side equal to $x$ and one side equal to $x + 2y$.
60. $(5x - 1)$ cm by $(5x - 1)$ cm
61. $9(x + 2)(x - 2)$
62. $2(3z + 2)(3z - 2)$
63. $3(2y + 5)(2y - 5)$
64. $16(2t + 1)(2t - 1)$
65. $3(2x + 3)^2$
66. $4(2x - 5)^2$
67. $2(a - 4)^2$
68. $3(x + 1)(x - 9)$
69. $2(3b + 5)(3b - 1)$
70. $4(n - 2)(n - 3)$
71. $3(y + 3)(y + 5)$
72. $-(x - 1)(x - 4)$
73. $2(x - 5)(2x - 1)$

74. $\frac{1}{2}(x + 1)(x - 1)$
75. $-6(z^2 + 100)$
76. $(2x - 1)(x - 5)$
77. $(x - y)(x + y)$
78. $-\left(\frac{1}{4}s - 1\right)\left(\frac{1}{4}s + 1\right)$
79. The third line should be $x(2x - 5) - (2x - 5)$, and the final line should be $(x - 1)(2x - 5)$.
80. $(x - 70)$ ft
81. $y$; $y(y - 1)$
82. $b$; $b(ab - 1)$
83. 10; $10(x - 3)(x + 3)$
84. $3t$; $3t(t - 8)$
85. 2; $2(x^2 - 37x + 6)$
86. $xy$; $xy(xy + 1)$
87. D
88. $\pi h(R + r)(R - r)$
89. Check students' work.

90. Factor 3 from the terms to get $3(x^2 + 2x - 24)$. Look for numbers whose product is $-24$ and whose sum is 2. The numbers $-4$ and 6 work. The complete factorization is $3(x - 4)(x + 6)$.
91. $(0.5t + 0.4)(0.5t - 0.4)$
92. $100(9x - 10)(9x + 10)$
93. $(x + 12)(x - 3)$
94. $(x - 10)(x - 9)$
95. $(2x + 9)(3x + 14)$
96. $2(a + 1)(6a - 7)$

**97. Reasoning** Explain how to factor $4x^4 + 24x^3 + 32x^2$.

**Factor each expression completely.**

**98.** $x^4 - y^4$    **99.** $16x^4 - 625y^4$    **100.** $243a^5 - 3a$

**101.** When the expression $x^2 + bx - 24$ is factored completely, the difference of the factors is 11. Find both factors if it is known that $b$ is negative.

**102.** Prove that $n^3 - n$ is divisible by 3 for all positive integer values of $n$. (*Hint:* Factor the expression completely.)

## Standardized Test Prep

SAT/ACT

**103.** How can you write $(m - 5)(m + 4) + 8$ as a product of two binomials?
- **A** $(m - 1)(m + 8)$
- **C** $(m + 8)(m + 8)$
- **B** $(m - 4)(m + 3)$
- **D** $(m - 5)(8m + 32)$

**104.** The graph of a quadratic function has vertex $(7, 6)$. What is the axis of symmetry?
- **F** $x = 6$    **G** $y = 6$    **H** $x = 7$    **I** $y = 7$

**Extended Response**

**105.** Suppose you hit a baseball and its flight takes a parabolic path. The height of the ball at certain times appears in the table below.

| Time (s) | 0.5 | 0.75 | 1 | 1.25 |
|---|---|---|---|---|
| Height (ft) | 10 | 10.5 | 9 | 5.5 |

**a.** Find a quadratic model for the ball's height as a function of time.
**b.** Write the quadratic function in factored form.

## Mixed Review

**106.** Find a quadratic model for the values in the table.

| x | 0 | 5 | 10 | 15 | 20 |
|---|---|---|---|---|---|
| y | 17 | 39 | 54 | 61 | 61 |

◀ See Lesson 4-3.

**107. Coins** The combined mass of a penny, a nickel, and a dime is 9.8 g. Ten nickels and three pennies have the same mass as 25 dimes. Fifty dimes have the same mass as 18 nickels and 10 pennies. Write and solve a system of equations to find the mass of each type of coin.

◀ See Lesson 3-6.

**Get Ready!** **To prepare for Lesson 4-5, do Exercises 108–110.**

**Graph each function.**    ◀ See Lesson 4-2.

**108.** $y = x^2 - 2x - 5$    **109.** $y = x^2 - 4x + 4$    **110.** $y = -x^2 - 3x + 8$

## Mixed Review

**106.** $y = -0.149x^2 + 5.171x + 16.971$

**107.** penny: 2.5 g, nickel: 5 g, dime: 2.3 g

**108.**

**109.**

**110.**

**97.** Factor the GCF, $4x^2$, from the terms to get $4x^2(x^2 + 6x + 8)$. Look for numbers whose product is 8 and whose sum is 6. The numbers 4 and 2 work. The complete factorization is $4x^2(x + 4)(x + 2)$.

**98.** $(x - y)(x + y)(x^2 + y^2)$

**99.** $(2x - 5y)(2x + 5y)(4x^2 + 25y^2)$

**100.** $3a(3a - 1)(3a + 1)(9a^2 + 1)$

**101.** $(x - 8)(x + 3)$

**102.** Factor the expression completely to get $(n - 1)n(n + 1)$. The number 3 must go into exactly one of any three consecutive numbers.

## Standardized Test Prep

**103.** B

**104.** H

**105.** **[4] a.** By entering the given lists into a graphing calculator and then calculating the quadratic regression, you get $h = -16t^2 + 22t + 3$ as the quadratic model for the ball's height as a function of time.

**b.** $h = -16t^2 + 22t + 3$
$h = -[8t(2t - 3) + 1(2t - 3)]$
$h = -(2t - 3)(8t + 1)$

**[3]** computational error

**[2]** incorrect function, factored correctly OR correct function, factored incorrectly

**[1]** correct answers, without work shown

## Differentiated Remediation

## Additional Instructional Support

### Algebra 2 Companion

Students can use the **Algebra 2 Companion** worktext (4 pages) as you teach the lesson. Use the Companion to support

- New Vocabulary
- Key Concepts
- Got It for each Problem
- Lesson Check

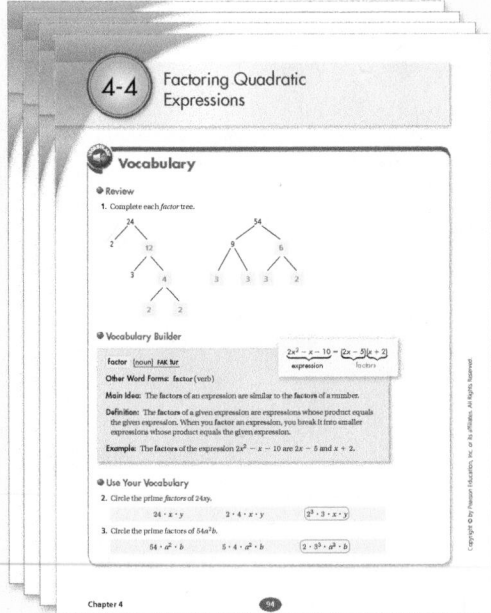

## 5 Assess & Remediate

### Lesson Quiz

1. **Do you UNDERSTAND?** What is the expression in factored form? $x^2 + 7x + 10$
2. What is the expression in factored form? $3x^2 + 21x + 18$
3. What is the expression in factored form? $3x^2 + 4x - 15$
4. What is $x^2 - 14x + 49$ in factored form?
5. What is $16x^2 - 25$ in factored form?

#### ANSWERS TO LESSON QUIZ

1. $(x + 5)(x + 2)$
2. $3(x + 6)(x + 1)$
3. $(3x - 5)(x + 3)$
4. $(x - 7)^2$
5. $(4x - 5)(4x + 5)$

## Intervention

- **Reteaching** (2 pages) Provides reteaching and practice exercises for the key lesson concepts. Use with struggling students or absent students.

- **English Language Learner Support** Helps students develop and reinforce mathematical vocabulary and key concepts.

### All-in-One Resources/Online
### Reteaching

## ELL Support

**Focus on Language** Write *binomial* and *trinomial* on the board. Underline the prefixes *bi-* and *tri-*. Explain that *bi-* means "two" and *tri-* means "three." A binomial has 2 terms, and a trinomial has 3 terms. Show pictures of a bicycle and a tricycle and use the number of wheels each has to help students understand the meaning and use of the two prefixes.

Ask students for examples of quadratic trinomials and binomials. Then have them make word cards for new terms. They should put familiar terms and illustrations on their cards.

### PRESCRIPTION FOR REMEDIATION

Use the student work on the Lesson Quiz to prescribe a differentiated review assignment:

| Points | Differentiated Remediation |
|--------|---------------------------|
| 0–2 | Intervention |
| 3–4 | On-level |
| 5 | Extension |

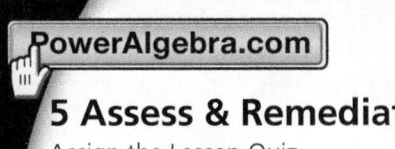

## 5 Assess & Remediate

Assign the Lesson Quiz. Appropriate intervention, practice, or enrichment is automatically generated based on student performance.

### All-in-One Resources/Online
### English Language Learner Support

# Differentiated Remediation *continued*

## On-Level

- **Practice** (2 pages) Provides extra practice for each lesson. For simpler practice exercises, use the Form K Practice pages found in the All-in-One Teaching Resources and online.

- **Think About a Plan** Helps students develop specific problem-solving skills and strategies by providing scaffolded guiding questions.

- **Standardized Test Prep** Focuses on all major exercises, all major question types, and helps students prepare for the high-stakes assessments.

## Extension

- **Enrichment** Provides students with interesting problems and activities that extend the concepts of the lesson.

- **Activities, Games, and Puzzles** Worksheets that can be used for concepts development, enrichment, and for fun!

---

### Practice and Problem Solving Wkbk/ All-in-One Resources/Online
**Practice page 1**

### Practice and Problem Solving Wkbk/ All-in-One Resources/Online
**Practice page 2**

### All-in-One Resources/Online
**Enrichment**

---

### Practice and Problem Solving Wkbk/ All-in-One Resources/Online
**Think About a Plan**

### Practice and Problem Solving Wkbk/ All-in-One Resources/Online
**Standardized Test Prep**

### Online Teacher Resource Center
**Activities, Games, and Puzzles**

# Answers

**Mid-Chapter Quiz**

**1.**

**2.**

**3.**

**4.**

**5.** axis of symmetry: $x = 3$; maximum: 14; domain: all real numbers, range: $y \leq 14$

**6.** axis of symmetry: $x = 6$; minimum: 7; domain: all real numbers, range: $y \geq 7$

**7.** axis of symmetry: $x = -2$; maximum: 1; domain: all real numbers, range: $y \leq 1$

**8.** axis of symmetry: $x = 1$; minimum: $-4$; domain: all real numbers, range: $y \geq -4$

**9.** $y = -3(x + 1)^2 - 5$; vertex: $(-1, -5)$; axis of symmetry: $x = -1$

**10.** $-2(m^2 - 8)$

**11.** $-x(x - 3)$

**12.** $(y - 12)(y - 1)$

**13.** $(k - 8)(k + 3)$

**14.** $(2y - 3)(2y + 3)$

**15.** $(n - 5)^2$

**16.** $(2x + 3)(x + 2)$

**17.** $y = x^2 + 6x + 3$

**18.** $y = 5x^2 - 10x$

**19.** $y = 2(x - 1)^2 - 2$

**20.** $y = -(x + 2)^2 + 4$

**21.** $3x^2(x - 6)(x + 2)$; $3x^2$, $x^2$, and $x + 2$ have no common factors except 1.

---

### Do you know HOW?

Graph each function.

**1.** $y = 4x^2 + 16x + 7$

**2.** $y = (x + 8)^2 - 3$

**3.** $y = -(x + 2)^2 - 7$

**4.** $y = -3x^2 - 2x + 1$

Identify the axis of symmetry, maximum or minimum value, and the domain and range of each function.

**5.** $y = -x^2 + 6x + 5$

**6.** $y = \frac{1}{2}(x - 6)^2 + 7$

**7.** $y = -3(x + 2)^2 + 1$

**8.** $y = 4x^2 - 8x$

**9.** Rewrite the equation $y = -3x^2 - 6x - 8$ in vertex form. Identify the vertex and the axis of symmetry of the graph.

Write each expression in factored form.

**10.** $16 - 2m^2$

**11.** $-x^2 + 3x$

**12.** $y^2 - 13y + 12$

**13.** $k^2 - 5k - 24$

**14.** $4y^2 - 9$

**15.** $-10n + 25 + n^2$

**16.** $2x^2 + 7x + 6$

Find a quadratic model in standard form for each set of values.

**17.** $(0, 3), (1, 10), (2, 19)$

**18.** $(0, 0), (1, -5), (2, 0)$

Write the equation of each parabola in vertex form.

**19.**

**20.**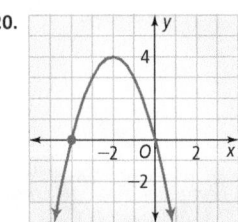

### Do you UNDERSTAND?

**21.** Write the expression $3x^4 - 12x^3 - 36x^2$ in factored form. Explain how you know the expression is completely factored.

**22.** **Open-Ended** Write the equation of a parabola with a vertex at $(3, 2)$. Name the axis of symmetry and the coordinates of two other points on the graph.

**23.** **Writing** Explain how to factor $25x^2 - 30x + 9$.

**24.** **Reasoning** Write the equation of two parabolas such that they have a common vertex and are reflections of each other across the $x$-axis.

**25.** Write the equation of a parabola in standard form and explain how to convert it to vertex form. How would you reverse the process?

**26.** What is the relationship between the $x$-intercepts of the graph of a quadratic function and the $x$-coordinate of the vertex of that graph? Explain how you determined your answer.

---

**22.** $y = a(x - 3)^2 + 2$; axis of symmetry: $x = 3$; answers may vary. Sample: if $a = -1$, then $(5, -2)$, $(1, -2)$

**23.** $25x^2 - 30x + 9$ is a perfect square trinomial. The first term is $(5x)^2$. The last term is $3^2$. The middle term is negative and twice the product of $5x$ and $3$: $(5x - 3)^2$

**24.** Answers may vary. Sample: $y = 2x^2$ and $y = -2x^2$

**25.** Standard form: $y = ax^2 + bx + c$; find the $x$-coordinate of the vertex: $x = -\frac{b}{2a}$; find the $y$-coordinate of the vertex by finding $y$ when $x = -\frac{b}{2a}$. Now that the vertex is known, write the eq. in vertex form. If the vertex is $(h, k)$ write: $y = a(x - h)^2 + k$. To reverse the process from vertex form to standard form, expand the squared binomial and simplify the eq.

**26.** If there are two $x$-intercepts, the $x$-coordinate of the vertex is the midpt. between the two $x$-intercepts. Explanations may vary. Sample: The vertex lies on the axis of symmetry, so the $x$-coordinate of the vertex must be halfway between the $x$-intercepts.

# Algebra Review
### For Use With Lesson 4-5
## Square Roots and Radicals

A radical symbol $\sqrt{\phantom{x}}$ indicates a square root. In general, $\sqrt{x^2} = |x|$ for all real numbers $x$.

### Square Roots

| **Multiplication Property of Square Roots** | **Division Property of Square Roots** |
|---|---|
| For any numbers $a \geq 0$ and $b \geq 0$, | For any numbers $a \geq 0$ and $b > 0$, |
| $\sqrt{ab} = \sqrt{a} \cdot \sqrt{b}.$ | $\sqrt{\dfrac{a}{b}} = \dfrac{\sqrt{a}}{\sqrt{b}}.$ |

### Example

Simplify each expression.

**Ⓐ** $\sqrt{50}$

$\sqrt{50} = \sqrt{25} \cdot \sqrt{2}$     Multiplication Property of Square Roots

$\quad\quad = 5\sqrt{2}$     Simplify.

**Ⓑ** $\sqrt{\dfrac{5}{11}}$

$\sqrt{\dfrac{5}{11}} = \dfrac{\sqrt{5}}{\sqrt{11}}$     Division Property of Square Roots

$\quad\quad = \dfrac{\sqrt{5}}{\sqrt{11}} \cdot \dfrac{\sqrt{11}}{\sqrt{11}}$     Multiply both the numerator and denominator by $\sqrt{11}$.

$\quad\quad = \dfrac{\sqrt{55}}{\sqrt{121}}$     Multiplication Property of Square Roots.

$\quad\quad = \dfrac{\sqrt{55}}{11}$     Simplify.

### Exercises

Simplify each radical expression.

1. $\sqrt{18}$      2. $\sqrt{75}$      3. $-\sqrt{32}$      4. $\sqrt{\dfrac{-5}{7}}$

5. $-\sqrt{\dfrac{7}{13}}$      6. $\sqrt{\dfrac{3}{15}}$      7. $-\sqrt{200}$      8. $5\sqrt{320}$

9. $(2\sqrt{27})^2$      10. $-\sqrt{10^4}$      11. $\sqrt{x^2 y^2}$      12. $\sqrt{\dfrac{8}{x^2}}$

13. $-\sqrt{\dfrac{7x^3}{5x}}$      14. $\sqrt{\dfrac{(-3)^4}{12}}$      15. $\sqrt{\dfrac{200}{28}}$      16. $\sqrt{120x}$

| PowerAlgebra.com | Review   Square Roots and Radicals | 225 |

---

# Guided Instruction

## Example
Students may wonder why $\dfrac{\sqrt{55}}{11}$ is considered simplified form for $\sqrt{\dfrac{5}{11}}$, noticing that it does not look simpler. Explain that it is both easier and more accurate to evaluate a radical expression if you do not have to divide by an endless decimal. To avoid such cumbersome divisions, it is customary to write radical expressions in a form that has no radicals in the denominator. (In Chapter 6, students will learn that this is called *rationalizing the denominator*.) Ask the students to compare the process of evaluating $\dfrac{\sqrt{3}}{\sqrt{10}}$ with the process of evaluating $\dfrac{\sqrt{3}}{10}$.

**Q** When can you use the Multiplication Property of Square Roots to simplify a radical? **[when the radicand can be factored]**

**Q** After applying the Division Property of Square Roots to a radical with a fractional radicand, how can you simplify it? **[Multiply both the numerator and denominator by a radical that makes the denominator a perfect square and simplify.]**

## Exercises     ERROR INTERVENTION
Students may think the simplified form of $\sqrt{x^2 y^2}$ is $xy$. Assign numeric values to $x$ and $y$ to show why $\sqrt{x^2 y^2} \neq xy$, such as $x = -3$ and $y = 4$. Elicit that $\sqrt{x^2 y^2} = \sqrt{x^2} \cdot \sqrt{y^2} = |x| \cdot |y| = |xy|$.

---

# Answers

## Algebra Review
1. $3\sqrt{2}$
2. $5\sqrt{3}$
3. $-4\sqrt{2}$
4. You cannot take the square root of a neg. no.
5. $\dfrac{-\sqrt{91}}{13}$
6. $\dfrac{\sqrt{5}}{5}$
7. $-10\sqrt{2}$
8. $40\sqrt{5}$
9. $108$
10. $-100$
11. $|xy|$
12. $\dfrac{2\sqrt{2}}{|x|}$
13. $\dfrac{-|x|\sqrt{35}}{5}$
14. $\dfrac{3\sqrt{3}}{2}$
15. $\dfrac{5\sqrt{14}}{7}$
16. $2\sqrt{30x}$

# 1 Interactive Learning

## Solve It!

**PURPOSE** To find an *x*-intercept of a parabola

**PROCESS** Students may

- use the ZERO function on a calculator.
- use symmetry, addition, and subtraction.

### FACILITATE

**Q** What is the vertex of the parabola? **[(6.4, 12.96)]**

**Q** What property of symmetry does a parabola have? **[A parabola is symmetric about the vertical line through its vertex.]**

**Q** What is the horizontal distance from *A* to the axis of symmetry? Explain. **[6.4 − (−8) = 14.4]**

**Q** How can you find the *x*-coordinate of *C*? **[Answers may vary. Sample: 6.4 + 14.4]**

**ANSWER** See Solve It in Answers on next page.

**CONNECT THE MATH** Students use either an equation or symmetry to find an *x*-intercept of a parabola. In the lesson, they learn that an *x*-intercept is a zero of a function and find zeros of quadratic functions by solving related equations.

# 2 Guided Instruction

## Take Note

**Q** Is it possible that both *a* and *b* are 0? Explain. **[Yes; $0 \cdot 0 = 0$.]**

## Problem 1

**Q** What are all the factor pairs of 6? **[(1)(6), (−1)(−6), (2)(3), (−2)(−3)]**

**Q** Which pair has the sum −5? **[−2 and −3]**

---

**Objectives** To solve quadratic equations by factoring
To solve quadratic equations by graphing

**Getting Ready!**

As part of an engineering project, your team is drawing a highway tunnel on a coordinate system. The tunnel opening is in the shape of a parabola. You need to finish the drawing. What are the coordinates of point *C*? Explain your reasoning.

*B* (6.4, 12.96)

*A* (−8, 0)    *C* (?, ?)

 **Dynamic Activity** Quadratics in Factored Form

**Lesson Vocabulary**
- zero of a function
- Zero-Product Property

Wherever the graph of a function $f(x)$ intersects the *x*-axis, $f(x) = 0$. A value of *x* for which $f(x) = 0$ is a **zero of the function**.

**Essential Understanding** To find the zeros of a quadratic function $y = ax^2 + bx + c$, solve the related quadratic equation $0 = ax^2 + bx + c$.

*Zeros of the Function*

You can solve some quadratic equations in standard form by factoring the quadratic expression and using the **Zero-Product Property**.

 **Property** Zero-Product Property

If $ab = 0$, then $a = 0$ or $b = 0$.

**Think**

What do you know about the factors of $x^2 - bx + c$?
The product of their constant terms is *c*. The sum is −*b*.

 **Problem 1** Solving a Quadratic Equation by Factoring

What are the solutions of the quadratic equation $x^2 - 5x + 6 = 0$?

$(x - 2)(x - 3) = 0$    Factor the quadratic expression.

$x - 2 = 0$ or $x - 3 = 0$    Use the Zero-Product Property.

$x = 2$ or $x = 3$    Solve for *x*.

The solutions are $x = 2$ and $x = 3$.

---

**BIG ideas** Solving Equations and Inequalities
Function

**UbD**

### ESSENTIAL UNDERSTANDINGS

- The zeros of a quadratic function $y = ax^2 + bx + c$ can be found by solving the related quadratic equation $0 = ax^2 + bx + c$.
- Some quadratic equations in standard form can be solved by factoring the quadratic expression and using the Zero-Product Property.
- The real solutions of a quadratic equation show the zeros of the related quadratic function and the *x*-intercepts of its graph.

## Math Background

The zeros of a quadratic function are equivalent to the *x*-intercepts of the graph of the function (where *y* is 0). Thus, finding the zeros of the quadratic function is a way of solving the related quadratic equation set equal to 0.

The following are equivalent:
- the zeros of a quadratic function

- the *x*-intercepts of the graph of the function
- the solutions of the related quadratic equation set equal to zero.

To solve a quadratic equation by factoring, you rely on the Zero-Product Property. Elicit that *a* and *b* represent any number or expression. The Zero-Product Property makes sense because for any product to be 0, one or both factors must be zero. Here is a quick proof by contradiction:

Assume $a, b \neq 0$.

$a \cdot b = 0$    Since $b \neq 0$, divide both sides by *b*

$a = 0$    Contradiction

## Support Student Learning

Use the **Algebra 2 Companion** to engage and support students during instruction. See Lesson Resources at the end of this lesson for details.

**PowerAlgebra.com**

# 1 Interactive Learning

**Solve It!**
Step out how to solve the Problem with helpful hints and an online question. Other questions are listed above in Interactive Learning.

**Dynamic Activity** This interactive graph lets students model polynomials in factored form, $a(x - r_1)(x - r_2) = 0$. Students will also see how polynomial form and factored forms relate.

**Got It? 1.** What are the solutions of the quadratic equation $x^2 - 7x = -12$?

**Problem 2**  Solving a Quadratic Equation With Tables

What are the solutions of the quadratic equation $5x^2 + 30x + 14 = 2 - 2x$?

$$5x^2 + 30x + 14 = 2 - 2x$$

$$5x^2 + 32x + 12 = 0 \qquad \text{Rewrite in standard form.}$$

Use your calculator's **TABLE** feature to find the zeros.

**Think**

What should you look for in the calculator table?
Look for $x$-values for which $y = 0$.

The solutions are $x = -6$ and $x = -0.4$.

 **Got It? 2.** What are the solutions of the quadratic equation $4x^2 - 14x + 7 = 4 - x$?

**Problem 3** Solving a Quadratic Equation by Graphing

What are the solutions of the quadratic equation $2x^2 + 7x = 15$?

$$2x^2 + 7x = 15$$

$$2x^2 + 7x - 15 = 0 \qquad \text{Rewrite in standard form.}$$

**Plan**

How can you use a graph to find the solutions?
Find the zeros of the related quadratic function.

The solutions are $x = -5$ and $x = 1.5$.

 **Got It? 3.** What are the solutions of the quadratic equation $x^2 + 2x - 24 = 0$?

---

**Got It?** ERROR PREVENTION

Students sometimes think $-4$ and $-3$ are solutions of $(x - 4)(x - 3) = 0$. Remind them to use the Zero-Product Property and then solve the two resulting equations.

### Problem 2

**Q** What is the related quadratic equation for the quadratic function $y_1$? **[$5x^2 + 32x + 12 = 0$]**

**Q** How is that equation related to the original equation in the problem? **[It is equivalent.]**

**Q** What are the zeros of the function $y_1$? Explain. **[$-6$ and $-0.4$; the zeros of a function are equivalent to the solutions of the related equation.]**

**Got It?** SYNTHESIZING

Students will not be able to find the noninteger zero by using 0.1 for the $x$-interval.

**Q** Between what $x$-values is the noninteger zero? Explain. **[0.2 and 0.3 because the $y$-values change sign]**

**Q** How can you find the noninteger zero? **[Change the $x$-interval to 0.01.]**

### Problem 3

An alternate method is to enter the left side of the equation in $y_1$ and the right side in $y_2$. Then find the intersection point.

**Got It?** EXTENSION

Students sometimes think they can find zeros by simply looking at a graph. To show why a better option is needed, have them find the solutions of $x^2 + 1.1x - 11.6 = 0$. **[2.9 and $-4$]**

---

## 2 Guided Instruction

 Each Problem is worked out and supported online.

**Problem 1**
Solving a Quadratic Equation by Factoring
*Animated*

**Problem 2**
Solving a Quadratic Equation With Tables
*Animated*

**Problem 3**
Solving a Quadratic Equation by Graphing

**Problem 4**
Using a Quadratic Equation
*Animated*

**Support in Algebra 2 Companion**
• Vocabulary
• Key Concepts
• Got It?

---

## Answers

**Solve It!**
$(20.8, 0)$; the vertex of the parabola is $(6.4, 12.96)$ so the parabola is symmetric over the line $x = 6.4$.

**Got It?**

**1.** $3, 4$

**2.** $3, \dfrac{1}{4}$

**3.** $-6, 4$

## Problem 4

Quadratic functions are models for many problems involving distance and movement. However, the function *graphs* do not necessarily show the path of the movement. The function graph in this problem models the actual path of a moving object.

---

**Q** In 4B, why does the maximum value of $f(x)$ occur midway between the zeros? **[Answers may vary. Sample: A quadratic function graph is symmetric about the vertical line through its vertex.]**

**Q** How does the shape of the calculator graph compare to the shape of the actual frog jump? **[Answers may vary. Sample: The scales on the axes are different, so the shape of the graph makes the jump appear higher than it really was.]**

---

Use the ZSquare option of the ZOOM feature to see the undistorted graph.

---

**Q** In 4C, the function $y = -0.029x^2 + 0.59x$ has a domain of all real numbers. What is its range? Explain. **[All real numbers less than or equal to 3.0, since 3.0 is approximately the maximum value of the function, and there is no minimum value.]**

**Q** What is the difference between the domain and range of the situational model? **[The domain is positive numbers less than 30, while the range is positive numbers less than 5.]**

---

### Got It?

An alternate method to find how high the soccer ball goes is to use the MAXIMUM option of the CALC feature.

---

 **Problem 4** Using a Quadratic Equation

**Competition** From the time Mark Twain wrote *The Celebrated Jumping Frog of Calaveras County* in 1865, frog-jumping competitions have been growing in popularity. The graph shows a function modeling the height of one frog's jump, where *x* is the distance, in feet, from the jump's start.

**Think**

How can you use a graphing calculator to determine the distance?
Graph the function and locate the point where the graph crosses the x-axis.

**A** How far did the frog jump?

The height of the jump is 0 at the start and end of the jump. Find the zeros of the function. Use a graphing calculator to find the zeros of the related function $y = -0.029x^2 + 0.59x$.

The frog jumped about 20.34 ft.

**B** How high did the frog jump?

The maximum height of the jump is the maximum value of the function. This occurs midway, at 10.17 ft from the start. Find *y* for $x = 10.17$.

$$y = -0.029(10.17)^2 + 0.59(10.17) \approx 3.0$$

The frog jumped to a height of about 3.0 ft.

**C** What is a reasonable domain and range for such a frog-jumping function?

While the function $y = -0.029x^2 + 0.59x$ has a domain of all real numbers, actual frog jumping does not allow negative values. So, a reasonable domain for frog-jumping distances is $0 \le x \le 30$. A reasonable range is $0 \le y \le 5$.

 **Got It? 4. a.** The function $y = -0.03x^2 + 1.60x$ models the path of a kicked soccer ball. The height is *y*, the distance is *x*, and the units are meters. How far does the soccer ball travel? How high does the soccer ball go? Describe a reasonable domain and range for the function.

**b. Reasoning** Are all domains and ranges reasonable for real-world situations? Explain.

---

# Additional Problems

**1.** What are the solutions of the quadratic equation $x^2 + 3x - 18 = 0$?

   **ANSWER** 3 and −6

**2.** What are the solutions of the quadratic equation $10x^2 + 2x - 46 = x - 4$?

   **ANSWER** 2 and −2.1

**3.** What are the solutions of the quadratic equation $5x^2 - 8 = 18x$?

   **ANSWER** −0.4 and 4

**4.** The function $f(x) = -0.002x^2 + 0.77x$ models the path of a baseball, where $f(x)$ gives the height of the ball and *x* gives the distance from where it is hit in feet.

   **a.** How far does the ball travel before hitting the ground?

   **b.** How high does the ball go?

   **c.** What is a reasonable domain and range for such a function?

   **ANSWERS**

   **a.** 385 ft

   **b.** about 74 ft

   **c.** Answers may vary. Sample: domain: $0 \le x \le 500$, range: $0 \le y \le 100$

## Lesson Check

### Do you know HOW?

Solve each equation by factoring.

1. $x^2 - 9 = 0$

2. $x^2 + 13x = -36$

3. $3x^2 - x - 2 = 0$

Solve by graphing.

4. $x^2 - 3x = 6$

5. $2x^2 - x = 11$

### Do you UNDERSTAND?

6. **Vocabulary** If 5 is a zero of the function $y = x^2 + bx - 20$, what is the value of $b$? Explain.

7. **Compare and Contrast** When is it easier to solve a quadratic equation by factoring than to solve it using a table?

8. **Reasoning** Using tables, how might you recognize that a quadratic equation likely has exactly one solution? no solutions?

## Practice and Problem-Solving Exercises

**A Practice** Solve each equation by factoring. Check your answers. ◆ See Problem 1.

9. $x^2 + 6x + 8 = 0$      10. $x^2 + 18 = 9x$      11. $2x^2 - x = 3$

12. $x^2 - 10x + 25 = 0$      13. $2x^2 + 6x = -4$      14. $3x^2 = 16x + 12$

15. $x^2 - 4x = 0$      16. $6x^2 + 4x = 0$      17. $2x^2 = 8x$

**Graphing Calculator** Solve each equation using tables. Give each answer to at most two decimal places. ◆ See Problem 2.

18. $x^2 + 5x + 3 = 0$      19. $x^2 - 11x + 24 = 0$      20. $x^2 - 7x = 11$

21. $2x^2 - x = 2$      22. $x^2 - 16x = 36$      23. $x^2 + 6x = 40$

24. $4x^2 = x + 3$      25. $5x^2 + x = 4$      26. $10x^2 + 3 = 11x$

**Graphing Calculator** Solve each equation by graphing. Give each answer to at most two decimal places. ◆ See Problem 3.

27. $6x^2 = -19x - 15$      28. $3x^2 - 5x - 4 = 0$      29. $5x^2 - 7x - 3 = 8$

30. $6x^2 + 31x = 12$      31. $1 = 4x^2 + 3x$      32. $\frac{1}{2}x^2 - x = 8$

33. $x^2 = 4x + 8$      34. $x^2 + 4x = 6$      35. $2x^2 - 2x - 5 = 0$

36. **Physics** An object is dropped from a height of 1700 ft above the ground. The function $h = -16t^2 + 1700$ gives the object's height $h$ in feet during free fall at $t$ seconds. ◆ See Problem 4.
   a. When will the object be 1000 ft above the ground?
   b. When will the object be 940 ft above the ground?
   c. What are a reasonable domain and range for the function $h$?

---

## 3 Lesson Check

### Do you know HOW?

- If students have trouble with Exercise 2, remind them to get 0 on one side of the equation.
- If students have trouble finding the actual factors for Exercises 1–3, they should revisit Lesson 4-4.

### Do you UNDERSTAND?

- If students have trouble with Exercise 6, remind them that (5, 0) makes the equation true.

### Close

**Q** What equation can you solve to find the zeros of $f(x) = 0.5x^2 + x - 1$? **[the related equation, $0.5x^2 + x - 1 = 0$]**

**Q** What is the first step in solving $3x^2 - 1 = 4x$? **[Put the equation in standard form by adding $-4x$ to both sides.]**

**Q** If $(3, -0.4)$ and $(3.6, 2)$ are on a parabola, where is a zero of the function? Explain. **[It is between 3 and 3.6. The two $y$-values have different signs, so there must be a point between them where the $y$-value passes through zero.]**

---

# Answers

### Got It? (continued)

4. **a.** $53\frac{1}{3}$ m; $21\frac{1}{3}$ m; answers may vary. Sample: domain: $0 \le x \le 60$, range: $0 \le y \le 30$

   **b.** No; domains and ranges are constrained by real-world limits.

### Lesson Check

1. $3, -3$      2. $-4, -9$

3. $-\frac{2}{3}, 1$      4. $4.372, -1.372$

5. $2.608, -2.108$

6. $-1$; since $y = 0$ when $x = 5$, substitute these values into the equation to find $b$.

7. when the coefficients are integers and a recognizable pattern of factoring is evident

8. One solution: when the table's range consists of zero and all positive numbers or zero and all negative numbers

   No solution: when the table does not include zero and the $y$-values are either all positive or all negative numbers

### Practice and Problem-Solving Exercises

9. $-4, -2$   10. $3, 6$    11. $-1, \frac{3}{2}$

12. $5$      13. $-2, -1$   14. $-\frac{2}{3}, 6$

15. $0, 4$     16. $-\frac{2}{3}, 0$   17. $0, 4$

18. $-4.30, -0.70$   19. $3, 8$

20. $-1.32, 8.32$   21. $-0.78, 1.28$

22. $18, -2$   23. $4, -10$   24. $1, -0.75$

25. $0.8, -1$     26. $0.5, 0.6$

27. $-1.67, -1.5$   28. $-0.59, 2.26$

29. $-0.94, 2.34$   30. $-5.53, 0.36$

31. $-1, 0.25$     32. $-3.12, 5.12$

33. $-1.46, 5.46$   34. $-5.16, 1.16$

35. $-1.16, 2.16$

36. **a.** about 6.61 s
   **b.** about 6.89 s
   **c.** domain: $0 \le t \le 10.4$, range: $0 \le h \le 1700$

**PowerAlgebra.com**

### 3 Lesson Check

For a digital lesson check, use the Got It questions.

**Support in Algebra 2 Companion**
- Lesson Check

### 4 Practice

Assign homework to individual students or to an entire class.

# 4 Practice

**ASSIGNMENT GUIDE**

Basic: 9–36 all, 37–43, 55

Average: 9–35 odd, 37–56

Advanced: 9–35 odd, 37–59

Standardized Test Prep: 60–63

Mixed Review: 64–75

**Reasoning** exercises have blue headings.

**Applications** exercises have red headings.

**EXERCISE 39:** Use the Think About a Plan worksheet in the **Practice and Problem Solving Workbook** (also available in the Teaching Resources in print and online) to further support students' development in becoming independent learners.

**HOMEWORK QUICK CHECK**

To check students' understanding of key skills and concepts, go over Exercises 11, 27, 37, 39, and 40.

---

 **Apply**

**37. Think About a Plan** Suppose you want to put a frame around the painting shown at the right. The frame will be the same width around the entire painting. You have 276 in.$^2$ of framing material. How wide should the frame be?
- What does 276 in.$^2$ represent in this situation?
- How can you write the dimensions of the frame using two binomials?

16 in.
24 in.

**38.** The period of a pendulum is the time the pendulum takes to swing back and forth. The function $L = 0.81t^2$ relates the length $L$ in feet of a pendulum to the time $t$ in seconds that it takes to swing back and forth. A convention center has a pendulum that is 90 feet long. Find the period.

**39. Landscaping** Suppose you have an outdoor pool measuring 25 ft by 10 ft. You want to add a cement walkway around the pool. If the walkway will be 1 ft thick and you have 304 ft$^3$ of cement, how wide should the walkway be?

**40. Error Analysis** A classmate solves the quadratic equation as shown. Find and correct the error. What are the correct solutions?

$$x^2 + 5x + 6 = 2$$
$$(x + 2)(x + 3) = 2$$
$$x = -2 \text{ or } x = -3$$

**41. Open-Ended** Write an equation with the given solutions.
a. 3 and 5  b. −3 and 2  c. −1 and −6

**Solve each equation by factoring, using tables, or by graphing. If necessary, round your answer to the nearest hundredth.**

**42.** $x^2 + 2x = 6 - 6x$     **43.** $6x^2 + 13x + 6 = 0$     **44.** $2x^2 + x - 28 = 0$

**45.** $2x^2 + 8x = 5x + 20$     **46.** $3x^2 + 7x = 9$     **47.** $2x^2 - 6x = 8$

**48.** $(x + 3)^2 = 9$     **49.** $x^2 + 4x = 0$     **50.** $x^2 = 8x - 7$

**51.** $x^2 - 3x = 6$     **52.** $4x^2 + 5x = 4$     **53.** $7x - 3x^2 = -10$

**Reasoning** The graphs of each pair of functions intersect. Find their points of intersection without using a calculator. (*Hint:* Solve as a system using substitution.)

**54.** $y = x^2$
$y = -\frac{1}{2}x^2 + \frac{3}{2}x + 3$

**55.** $y = x^2 - 2$
$y = 3x^2 - 4x - 2$

**56.** $y = -x^2 + x + 4$
$y = 2x^2 - 6$

**Challenge**

**57.** The equation $x^2 - 10x + 24 = 0$ can be written in factored form as $(x - 4)(x - 6) = 0$. How can you use this fact to find the vertex of the graph of $y = x^2 - 10x + 24$?

**58. a.** Let $a > 0$. Use algebraic or arithmetic ideas to explain why the lowest point on the graph of $y = a(x - h)^2 + k$ must occur when $x = h$.
**b.** Suppose that the function in part (*a*) is $y = a(x - h)^3 + k$. Is your reasoning still valid? Explain.

---

# Answers

## Practice and Problem-Solving Exercises (continued)

**37.** 3 in.

**38.** about 10.5 s

**39.** about 3.6 ft

**40.** The student needs to start by subtracting 2 from each side of the eq. The error is that the problem was done as if the eq. were equal to 0.
$$x^2 + 5x + 6 - 2 = 0$$
$$x^2 + 5x + 4 = 0$$
$$(x + 1)(x + 4) = 0$$
$$x = -1, -4$$

**41.** Answers may vary. Samples are given:
a. $x^2 - 8x + 15 = 0$
b. $x^2 + x - 6 = 0$
c. $x^2 + 7x + 6 = 0$

**42.** −8.69, 0.69

**43.** $-\frac{3}{2}, -\frac{2}{3}$

**44.** −4, 3.5     **45.** $-4, \frac{5}{2}$

**46.** −3.25, 0.92

**47.** −1, 4     **48.** −6, 0

**49.** −4, 0     **50.** 1, 7

**51.** 4.37, −1.37

**52.** −1.8, 0.55

**53.** $-1, \frac{10}{3}$

**54.** (−1, 1), (2, 4)

**55.** (0, −2), (2, 2)

**56.** $\left(-\frac{5}{3}, -\frac{4}{9}\right)$, (2, 2)

**57.** Solve $(x - 4)(x - 6) = 0$ to find that the zeros of $y = x^2 - 10x + 24$ are 4 and 6. Average 4 and 6 to get 5. This is the x-coordinate of the vertex. Substitute 5 for x in $x^2 - 10x + 24$ to find that −1 is the y-coordinate of the vertex. The vertex is (5, −1).

**58. a.** Answers may vary. Sample: If $x \neq h$, then $x - h$ will be nonzero, $(x - h)^2$ will be positive, and $a(x - h)^2$ will be positive. Adding a positive to k will always result in a number greater than k. So the pt. (h, k) is the lowest pt. when $x = h$ on the graph of $y = (x - h)^2 + k$.
**b.** No; $(x - h)^3$ can be negative.

**59. Physics** When serving in tennis, a player tosses the tennis ball vertically in the air. The height $h$ of the ball after $t$ seconds is given by the quadratic function $h(t) = -5t^2 + 7t$ (the height is measured in meters from the point of the toss).
  **a.** How high in the air does the ball go?
  **b.** Assume that the player hits the ball on its way down when it's 0.6 m above the point of the toss. For how many seconds is the ball in the air between the toss and the serve?

## Standardized Test Prep

SAT/ACT

**60.** What are the solutions of the equation $6x^2 + 9x - 15 = 0$?

Ⓐ $1, -15$  Ⓑ $1, -\frac{5}{2}$  Ⓒ $-1, -5$  Ⓓ $3, \frac{5}{2}$

**61.** The vertex of a parabola is $(3, 2)$. A second point on the parabola is $(1, 7)$. Which point is also on the parabola?

Ⓕ $(-1, 7)$  Ⓖ $(3, 7)$  Ⓗ $(5, 7)$  Ⓘ $(3, -2)$

**62.** For which quadratic function is $-3$ the constant term?

Ⓐ $y = (3x + 1)(-x - 3)$  Ⓒ $f(x) = (x - 3)(x - 3)$
Ⓑ $y = x^2 - 3x + 3$  Ⓓ $g(x) = -3x^2 + 3x + 9$

**Short Response**

**63.** What transformations are needed to go from the parent function $f(x) = x^2$ to the new function $g(x) = -3x^2 + 2$? Graph $g(x)$.

## Mixed Review

Factor each expression.  ◀ See Lesson 4-4.

**64.** $16x^2 - 1$  **65.** $5x^2 - 26x + 5$  **66.** $2x^2 + 13x - 7$

Solve each system by elimination. Check your answer.  ◀ See Lesson 3-5.

**67.** $\begin{cases} 7x - 2y - 5z = 24 \\ -x + 3y + 4z = -10 \\ x - y - z = 4 \end{cases}$  **68.** $\begin{cases} -2x + 9y - z = 8 \\ 3x - 4y + z = -5 \\ 5x + 5y - z = -10 \end{cases}$  **69.** $\begin{cases} x - 9y + 8z = -10 \\ x + y - z = 9 \\ -x - 9z = 2 \end{cases}$

Without graphing, identify the vertex, axis of symmetry, and transformations from the parent function $f(x) = |x|$.  ◀ See Lesson 2-7.

**70.** $y = |x + 9| + 4$  **71.** $y = |2x - 7|$  **72.** $y = \frac{3}{4}|x| - 1$

**Get Ready!**  To prepare for Lesson 4-6, do Exercises 73–75.

Simplify each expression.  ◀ See Lesson 4-4.

**73.** $(x + 4)(x + 4) - 3$  **74.** $(2x - 1)(2x - 1)$  **75.** $(x - 3)(x - 3)$

---

**59. a.** 2.45m
  **b.** $\approx 1.3$s

**Standardized Test Prep**
**60.** B
**61.** H
**62.** A
**63. [2]** reflection across the x-axis, followed by a vertical translation 2 units up, and stretched by a factor of 3

**[1]** correct transformations, with one error in graph

**Mixed Review**
**64.** $(4x - 1)(4x + 1)$
**65.** $(5x - 1)(x - 5)$
**66.** $(2x - 1)(x + 7)$
**67.** $(2, 0, -2)$
**68.** $(-2, 1, 5)$
**69.** $(7, 1, -1)$
**70.** vertex: $(-9, 4)$; axis of symmetry: $x = -9$; translation 9 units to the left and 4 units up
**71.** vertex: $\left(\frac{7}{2}, 0\right)$; axis of symmetry: $x = \frac{7}{2}$; stretch by a factor of 2, translation $3\frac{1}{2}$ units to the right
**72.** vertex: $(0, -1)$; axis of symmetry: $x = 0$; vert. compression by a factor of $\frac{3}{4}$, translation 1 unit down
**73.** $x^2 + 8x + 13$
**74.** $4x^2 - 4x + 1$
**75.** $x^2 - 6x + 9$

## Instructional Support

### Algebra 2 Companion
Students can use the **Algebra 2 Companion** worktext (4 pages) as you teach the lesson. Use the Companion to support

- New Vocabulary
- Key Concepts
- Got It for each Problem
- Lesson Check

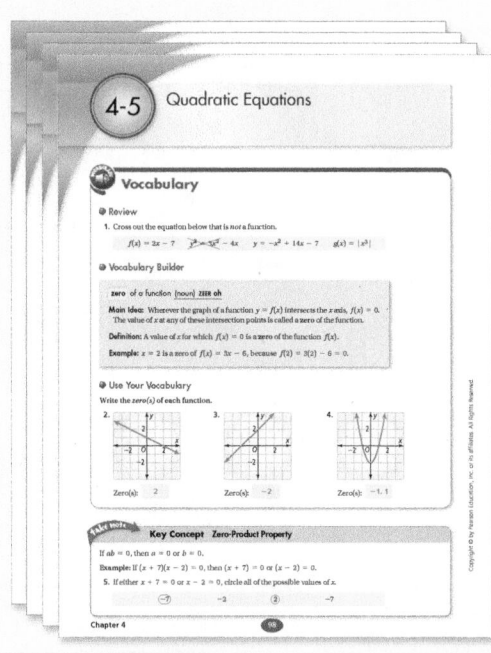

### ELL Support
**Use Graphic Organizers** Make the following reference display for the board or bulletin board.

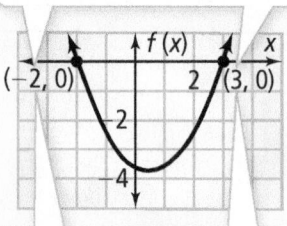

The zeros of the quadratic function $f(x) = x^2 - x - 6$ are $-2$ and $3$.

The solutions, or roots, of the related quadratic equation $x^2 - x - 6 = 0$ are $x = -2$ and $x = 3$.

## 5 Assess & Remediate

### Lesson Quiz
1. Solve $x^2 - 8x + 12 = 0$.
2. Solve $5x^2 - 4x - 7 = 1 - x$.
3. Solve $2x^2 + x = 10$.
4. **Do you UNDERSTAND?** The function $f(x) = -0.002x^2 + 0.66x$ models the path of a softball that is hit for a home run, where $f(x)$ gives the height of the ball and $x$ gives the distance from where it is hit in feet.
   a. How far does the ball travel before hitting the ground?
   b. How high does the ball go?
   c. What is a reasonable domain and range for a home run modeling function?

**ANSWERS TO LESSON QUIZ**
1. 6 and 2
2. $-1$ and 1.6
3. $-2.5$ and 2
4. a. 330 ft
   b. approximately 54.45 ft
   c. Answers may vary. Sample: domain: $0 \le x \le 330$, range: $0 \le y \le 54.45$

**PRESCRIPTION FOR REMEDIATION**
Use the student work on the Lesson Quiz to prescribe a differentiated review assignment:

| Points | Differentiated Remediation |
|---|---|
| 0–2 | Intervention |
| 3 | On-level |
| 4 | Extension |

**PowerAlgebra.com**
**5 Assess & Remediate**
Assign the Lesson Quiz. Appropriate intervention, practice, or enrichment is automatically generated based on student performance.

## Intervention

- **Reteaching** (2 pages) Provides reteaching and practice exercises for the key lesson concepts. Use with struggling students or absent students.
- **English Language Learner Support** Helps students develop and reinforce mathematical vocabulary and key concepts.

**All-in-One Resources/Online**
**Reteaching**

**All-in-One Resources/Online**
**English Language Learner Support**

# Differentiated Remediation *continued*

## On-Level

- **Practice** (2 pages) Provides extra practice for each lesson. For simpler practice exercises, use the Form K Practice pages found in the All-in-One Teaching Resources and online.

- **Think About a Plan** Helps students develop specific problem-solving skills and strategies by providing scaffolded guiding questions.
- **Standardized Test Prep** Focuses on all major exercises, all major question types, and helps students prepare for the high-stakes assessments.

## Extension

- **Enrichment** Provides students with interesting problems and activities that extend the concepts of the lesson.
- **Activities, Games, and Puzzles** Worksheets that can be used for concepts development, enrichment, and for fun!

### Practice and Problem Solving Wkbk/ All-in-One Resources/Online
**Practice page 1**

**4-5 Practice** Form G
Quadratic Equations

Solve each equation by factoring. Check your answers.

1. $x^2 - 2x - 24 = 0$  −4, 6
2. $3x^2 = x + 4$  −1, $\frac{4}{3}$
3. $x^2 - 6x + 9 = 0$  3
4. $3x^2 + 45 = 24x$  3, 5
5. $4x^2 + 6x = 0$  −$\frac{3}{2}$, 0
6. $7x^2 = 21x$  0, 3
7. $(x + 2)^2 = 49$  −9, 5
8. $x + 3 = 24x^2$  −$\frac{1}{3}$, $\frac{3}{8}$

Solve each equation using tables. Give each answer to at most two decimal places.

9. $5x^2 + 7x - 6 = 0$  −2, 0.6
10. $x^2 - 2x = 1$  −0.41, 2.41
11. $2x^2 - x = 5$  −1.35, 1.85
12. $x^2 - 4x + 2 = 0$  0.59, 3.41
13. $3x^2 + 7x = 1$  −2.47, 0.14
14. $2x^2 - 3x = 15$  −2.09, 3.59

Solve each equation by graphing. Give each answer to at most two decimal places.

15. $10x^2 = 4 - 3x$  −0.8, 0.5
16. $3x^2 + 2x = 2$  −1.22, 0.55
17. $4x^2 - x = 6$  −1.11, 1.36
18. $4x^2 + 3x = 6 - 2x$  −2, 0.75
19. $x^2 + 4 = 6x$  0.76, 5.24
20. $5 - x = \frac{1}{2}x^2$  −4.32, 2.32

21. A woman drops a front door key to her husband from their apartment window several stories above the ground. The function $h = -16t^2 + 64$ gives the height $h$ of the key in feet, $t$ seconds after she releases it.
   a. How long does it take the key to reach the ground? 2 s
   b. What are the reasonable domain and range for the function $h$?
   $0 \le t \le 2$; $0 \le h \le 64$

### Practice and Problem Solving Wkbk/ All-in-One Resources/Online
**Practice page 2**

**4-5 Practice** (continued) Form G
Quadratic Equations

22. The function $C = 75x + 2600$ gives the cost, in dollars, for a small company to manufacture $x$ items. The function $R = 225x - x^2$ gives the revenue, also in dollars, for selling $x$ items. How many items should the company produce so that the cost and revenue are equal? 20 or 130

23. The function $\bar{a} = 2.4t - 0.1t^2$ gives the amount $a$, in micromilligrams (mmg), of a drug in a patient's bloodstream $t$ hours after being ingested in tablet form. When is the amount of the drug equal to 8 mmg? (*Hint:* Multiply the equation you write by 10 before solving.) 4 h, 20 h

24. You use a rectangular piece of cardboard measuring 20 in. by 30 in. to construct a box. You cut squares with sides $x$ in. from each corner of the piece of cardboard and then fold up the sides to form the bottom.
   a. Write a function $A$ representing the area of the base of the box in terms of $x$. $A = (30 - 2x)(20 - 2x) = 4x^2 - 100x + 600$
   b. What is a reasonable domain for the function $A$? $0 < x < 10$
   c. Write an equation if the area of the base must be 416 in.$^2$. $4x^2 - 100x + 600 = 416$
   d. Solve the equation in part (c) for values of $x$ in the reasonable domain. 2
   e. What are the dimensions of the base of the box? 26 in. by 16 in.

Solve each equation by factoring, using tables, or by graphing. If necessary, round your answer to the nearest hundredth.

25. $9x^2 = 49$  −$\frac{7}{3}$, $\frac{7}{3}$
26. $x^2 + 10x + 17 = 0$  −7.83, −2.17
27. $4x^2 + 1 = 8x$  0.13, 1.87
28. $5x^2 - 2x - 7 = 0$  −1, $\frac{7}{5}$
29. $4(x^2 - x) = 19$  −1.74, 2.74
30. $25x^2 + 20x + 4 = 0$  −$\frac{2}{5}$
31. $3x^2 = 4x + 32$  −$\frac{8}{3}$, 4
32. $x^2 - 5x - 12 = 0$  −1.77, 6.77

### All-in-One Resources/Online
**Enrichment**

**4-5 Enrichment**
Quadratic Equations

**Fencing Costs**

Solve each of the following problems by using a quadratic equation.

1. The area of a rectangular field is 1200 m$^2$. Two parallel sides are fenced with aluminum at $20/m. The remaining two sides are fenced with steel at $10/m. The total cost of the fencing is $2200.
   a. What is the length of each side fenced with aluminum? 40 m, or 15 m
   b. What is the length of each side fenced with steel? 30 m, or 80 m, respectively

2. The perimeter of a rectangular field is 140 yards. The land sells for $10/yd$^2$ and the total cost of the land is $12,000. What are the dimensions of the field? 30 yd by 40 yd

3. The area of a rectangular field is 875 m$^2$. Two adjacent sides of the field are fenced with wood costing $5/m. The remaining two sides are fenced with steel costing $10/m. The total cost of the fencing is $900. What are the dimensions of the field? 25 m by 35 m

4. The area of a field shaped like a right triangle is 600 m$^2$. The legs of the field are fenced with steel at $10/m, while the hypotenuse is fenced with aluminum at $20/m. The perimeter of the field is 120 m. The total cost of the fencing is $1700.
   a. What is the length of each side fenced with steel? 30 m, and 40 m
   b. What is the length of the side fenced with aluminum? 50 m

5. The area of a field shaped like a right triangle is 750 m$^2$. One leg of the field is fenced with wood costing $5/yd. The remainder of the perimeter of the field is fenced with steel costing $10/yd. The perimeter of the field is 150 yd. The total cost of the fencing is $1200.
   a. What is the length of the leg fenced with wood? 60 yd
   b. What is the length of the leg fenced with steel? 25 yd

6. The area of a rectangular field is 1000 yd$^2$. Two parallel sides are fenced with aluminum at $15/yd. One of the remaining sides is fenced with steel at $10/yd, and all but 10 yd of the remaining side is fenced with wood costing $5/yd. The remaining 10 yd are left unfenced. The total cost of the fencing is $1525.
   a. What is the length of the side fenced with steel? 25 yd or 80 yd
   b. What is the length of each side fenced with aluminum? 40 yd, or 12½ yd, respectively

7. Two rectangular fields with identical shapes and areas are to be fenced side by side. The total area enclosed is 1200 yd$^2$. The shared side is fenced with wood costing $5/yd. The remaining perimeter of the two joined fields is fenced with aluminum at $15/yd. The total cost of the fencing is $2250.
   a. What is the length of the shared side? 30 yd, or 34⅔ yd
   b. What is the length of each side fenced with aluminum?
   30 yd and 20 yd, or 34⅔ yd and 17½ yd, respectively

### Practice and Problem Solving Wkbk/ All-in-One Resources/Online
**Think About a Plan**

**4-5 Think About a Plan**
Quadratic Equations

**Landscaping** Suppose you have an outdoor pool measuring 25 ft by 10 ft. You want to add a cement walkway around the pool. If the walkway will be 1 ft thick and you have 304 ft$^3$ of cement, how wide should the walkway be?

**Understanding the Problem**

1. Draw a diagram of the pool and the walkway. Let $x$ = the width of the walkway in feet.

2. If you lay the pieces of walkway end to end, what is the total length of the walkway? $4x + 70$

3. What is the thickness of the walkway? 1 ft

4. What is the problem asking you to determine?
   The width of a walkway that is $(4x + 70)$ ft long and 1 ft thick, that has volume 304 ft$^3$.

**Planning the Solution**

5. Write a quadratic equation to model the volume of the walkway. $V = 4x^2 + 70x$

6. What method can you use to find the solutions of your quadratic equation?
   Answers may vary. Sample: Substitute 304 for $V$ in the equation. Subtract 304 from each side to set it equal to zero. Graph $y = 4x^2 + 70x - 304$ on a graphing calculator and use the ZERO option in the CALC feature to solve for $x$.

**Getting an Answer**

7. How many solutions of your quadratic equation do you need to find? Explain.
   One; only one solution is positive, and a negative solution does not make sense.

8. How wide should the walkway be? about 3.6 ft

### Practice and Problem Solving Wkbk/ All-in-One Resources/Online
**Standardized Test Prep**

**4-5 Standardized Test Prep**
Quadratic Equations

**Gridded Response**

Solve each exercise and enter your answer in the grid provided.

1. What is the positive solution of the equation $x^2 + 2x = 35$? Solve by factoring.

2. What is the positive solution of the equation $5x^2 + 2x - 16 = 0$? Solve by factoring.

3. What is the positive solution of the equation $x^2 - 3x = 1$? Solve by using a table or by graphing. If necessary, round your answer to the nearest hundredth.

4. What is the positive solution of the equation $3x^2 - 5x - 7 = 0$? Solve by using a table or by graphing. If necessary, round your answer to the nearest hundredth.

5. What is the positive solution of the equation $\frac{1}{2}x^2 - 3x = 5$? Solve by using a table or by graphing. If necessary, round your answer to the nearest hundredth.

**Answers**

1.     2.     3.     4.     5.

### Online Teacher Resource Center
**Activities, Games, and Puzzles**

**4-5 Puzzle: Dominoes**
Quadratic Equations

Complete this puzzle with a partner.

**Materials**
- Twenty-four small index cards
- Transparent tape

**Goal**
- Find the solutions to the 24 quadratic equations given below.
- Make a card for each equation, writing the two solutions and the equation number, as shown in the example below.
- Tape the index cards together end to end to form the longest string possible. You can only tape together two cards when they share at least one solution (when the ends match).

**Example**
$x^2 + x - 6 = 0 \rightarrow (x + 3)(x - 2) = 0 \rightarrow x = -3$ or $x = 2$

Longest possible string uses all twenty-four cards. Answers may vary. Sample: 18, 1, 8, 15, 22, 5, 12, 19, 2, 9, 16, 23, 6, 13, 20, 3, 10, 17, 24, 7, 14, 21, 4, 11.

1. $x^2 + x - 6 = 0$
   $(x + 3)(x - 2) = 0$; $x = -3, 2$
2. $x^2 - 4x - 5 = 0$
   $(x + 1)(x - 5) = 0$; $x = -1, 5$
3. $x^2 - 25 = 0$
   $(x + 5)(x - 5) = 0$; $x = -5, 5$
4. $2x^2 + 3x - 5 = 0$
   $(2x - 5)(x - 1) = 0$; $x = -\frac{5}{2}, 1$
5. $2x^2 - 7x - 4 = 0$
   $(2x - 1)(x + 4) = 0$; $x = \frac{1}{2}, -4$
6. $5x^2 - 31x + 6 = 0$
   $(x - 6)(5x - 1) = 0$; $x = 6, \frac{1}{5}$
7. $x^2 + 2x - 24 = 0$
   $(x - 4)(x + 6) = 0$; $x = 4, -6$
8. $x^2 - 9x + 14 = 0$
   $(x - 2)(x - 7) = 0$; $x = 2, 7$
9. $3x^2 - 11x - 20 = 0$
   $(x - 5)(3x + 4) = 0$; $x = 5, -\frac{4}{3}$
10. $2x^2 - 11x + 5 = 0$
   $(x - 5)(2x - 1) = 0$; $x = 5, \frac{1}{2}$
11. $x^2 - 2x + 1 = 0$
   $(x - 1)^2 = 0$; $x = 1$
12. $x^2 - 4x - 32 = 0$
   $(x + 4)(x - 8) = 0$; $x = -4, 8$
13. $5x^2 - x = 0$
   $x(5x - 1) = 0$; $x = 0, \frac{1}{5}$
14. $3x^2 + 20x + 12 = 0$
   $(3x + 2)(x + 6) = 0$; $x = -\frac{2}{3}, -6$
15. $x^2 + 7x = 0$
   $x(x + 7) = 0$; $x = 7, 0$
16. $6x^2 - 12 = 0$
   $6(x - 3)(x + 2) = 0$; $x = -2, 3$
17. $6x^2 + 3x - 3 = 0$
   $3(2x - 1)(x + 1) = 0$; $x = -1, \frac{1}{2}$
18. $x^2 + 2x - 3 = 0$
   $(x - 1)(x + 3) = 0$; $x = 1, -3$
19. $x^2 - 7x - 8 = 0$
   $(x - 8)(x + 1) = 0$; $x = 8, -1$
20. $3x^2 + 15x = 0$
   $3x(x + 5) = 0$; $x = 0, -5$
21. $6x^2 + 19x + 10 = 0$
   $(2x + 5)(3x + 2) = 0$; $x = -\frac{5}{2}, -\frac{2}{3}$
22. $2x^2 - x = 0$
   $x(2x - 1) = 0$; $x = 0, \frac{1}{2}$
23. $2x^2 - 15x + 18 = 0$
   $(2x - 3)(x - 6) = 0$; $x = \frac{3}{2}, 6$
24. $x^2 - 3x - 4 = 0$
   $(x + 1)(x - 4) = 0$; $x = -1, 4$

# Guided Instruction

**PURPOSE** To write a quadratic function, given its zeros, or a quadratic equation, given its roots

**PROCESS** Students will
- write a quadratic function, given its zeros, or a quadratic equation, given its roots, in factored and standard form.
- find the sum and product of the roots of a quadratic equation in standard form.

**DISCUSS** Students expand what they know about zeros of linear functions to discover and apply properties of zeros of quadratic functions.

## Activity 1

**Q** What basic function satisfies 1a? **[Answers may vary. Sample: $f(x) = x - 3$]**

**Q** Are there any other nonzero linear functions that have a zero at $x = 3$? Explain. **[Yes; answers may vary. Sample: If you multiply $x - 3$ by any number, the new function will still have a zero at $x = 3$.]**

**Q** For Exercise 7, how could you write the equation in standard form so that $a$, $b$, and $c$ are integers? **[Multiply each term by 2.]**

## Activity 2                    ERROR PREVENTION

Since standard form of a quadratic equation is $ax^2 + bx + c = 0$, the use of $a$ and $b$ in the table may confuse students. To write $(x - a)(x - b)$ in standard form, just multiply the binomials.

## Exercises                    ERROR PREVENTION

For Exercise 10, watch for $x + 6 = 0$ or $x^2 - 6 = 0$. Suggest checking by substituting $-6$ into the equation. Refer to Questions 3–7 in Activity 1. Suggest the same process, using $-6$ and $-6$ as the pair.

---

The **root** of an equation is a value that makes the equation true. You can use the Zero-Product Property to write a quadratic function from its zeros or a quadratic equation from its roots.

### Activity 1

**1. a.** Write a nonzero linear function $f(x)$ that has a zero at $x = 3$.
   **b.** Write a nonzero linear function $g(x)$ that has a zero at $x = 4$.

**2. a.** For $f$ and $g$ from Exercise 1, write the product function $h(x) = f(x) \cdot g(x)$.
   **b.** What kind of function is $h(x)$?          **c.** Solve the equation $h(x) = 0$.

**Mental Math** Write a quadratic equation with each pair of values as roots.

**3.** 5 and 3          **4.** 2.5 and 4          **5.** $-4$ and 4          **6.** 5 and 10          **7.** $\frac{3}{2}$ and $-2$

You can also use zeros or roots to write quadratic expressions in standard form.

### Activity 2

**8. a.** Copy and complete the table. Write the product $(x - a)(x - b)$ in standard form for each pair $a$ and $b$.
   **b.** Is there a pattern in the table? Explain.

**9. a.** If you know the roots, you can write a quadratic function or equation in standard form. Explain how.
   **b.** Demonstrate your method for each pair of values in Exercises 3–7.

| $a$ | $b$ | $a+b$ | $ab$ | $(x-a)(x-b)$ |
|---|---|---|---|---|
| 4 | 5 | 9 | 20 | $x^2 - 9x + 20$ |
| $-4$ | 5 | 1 | $-20$ | ▨ |
| 4 | $-5$ | ▨ | ▨ | ▨ |
| $-4$ | $-5$ | ▨ | ▨ | ▨ |
| $-9$ | $-1$ | ▨ | ▨ | ▨ |
| $-2$ | 7 | ▨ | ▨ | ▨ |

### Exercises

**10.** Explain how to write a quadratic equation that has $-6$ as its only root.

**11.** Describe the family of quadratic functions that have zeros at $r$ and $s$. Sketch several members of the family in the coordinate plane.

**Find the sum and product of the roots for each quadratic equation.**

**12.** $2x^2 + 3x - 2 = 0$          **13.** $x^2 - 2x + 1 = 0$          **14.** $x^2 - 5x + 6 = 0$

**Given the sum and product of the roots, write a quadratic equation in standard form.**

**15.** sum $= -3$, product $= -18$          **16.** sum $= 4$, product $= 3$          **17.** sum $= 2$, product $= \frac{3}{4}$

---

# Answers

## Concept Byte

**1.** Answers may vary. Samples:
   **a.** $f(x) = x - 3$
   **b.** $g(x) = 2x - 8$

**2.** Answers may vary. Samples:
   **a.** $h(x) = (x - 3)(2x - 8)$
   **b.** quadratic
   **c.** 3, 4

**3.** $f(x) = (x - 5)(x - 3)$

**4.** $f(x) = (x - 2.5)(x - 4)$

**5.** $f(x) = (x - 4)(x - (-4))$ or $f(x) = (x - 4)(x + 4)$

**6.** $f(x) = (x - 5)(x - 10)$

**7.** $f(x) = \left(x - \frac{3}{2}\right)(x - (-2))$ or $f(x) = \left(x - \frac{3}{2}\right)(x + 2)$

**8. a.** $a + b$: $-1, -9, -10, 5$;
   $ab$: $-20, 20, 9, -14$;
   $(x - a)(x - b)$: $x^2 - x - 20$, $x^2 + x - 20, x^2 + 9x + 20$, $x^2 + 10x + 9, x^2 - 5x - 14$

**b.** Yes; the sum of the numbers is the opposite of the coefficients of the $x$-term; the product is the constant term.

**9. a.** For roots $a$ and $b$, the constant term is $ab$ and the $x$-coefficient is $-(a + b)$. The $x^2$-coefficient is 1.
   **b.** $x^2 - 8x + 15; x^2 - 6.5x + 10$;
   $x^2 - 16; x^2 - 15x + 50$;
   $x^2 + \frac{1}{2}x - 3$

**10.** If a quadratic function has only one root, then the corresponding quadratic expression is a perfect square. The eq. is $(x + 6)^2 = 0$.

**11.** $y = a(x - r)(x - s)$, $a \neq 0$; check students' sketches.

**12.** sum: $-\frac{3}{2}$; product: $-1$

**13.** sum: 2; product: 1

**14.** sum: 5; product: 6

**15.** $x^2 + 3x - 18 = 0$

**16.** $x^2 - 4x + 3 = 0$

**17.** $x^2 - 2x + \frac{3}{4} = 0$ or $4x^2 - 8x + 3 = 0$

# 4-6 Completing the Square

**Objectives** To solve equations by completing the square
To rewrite functions by completing the square

This suggests another way to write $(x + 3)^2$.

**Lesson Vocabulary**
• completing the square

Forming a square with model pieces provides a useful geometric image for completing a square algebraically.

**Essential Understanding** Completing a perfect square trinomial allows you to factor the completed trinomial as the square of a binomial.

You can solve an equation that contains a perfect square by finding square roots. The simplest of this type of equation has the form $ax^2 = c$.

**Problem 1** Solving by Finding Square Roots

**What is the solution of each equation?**

**Plan**

How is solving this equation like solving a linear equation?
You isolate the variable term.

**A** $4x^2 + 10 = 46$

$4x^2 = 36$ ← Rewrite in $ax^2 = c$ form. →

$\dfrac{4x^2}{4} = \dfrac{36}{4}$ ← Isolate $x^2$. →

$x^2 = 9$

$x = \pm 3$ ← Find square roots. →

**B** $3x^2 - 5 = 25$

$3x^2 = 30$

$\dfrac{3x^2}{3} = \dfrac{30}{3}$

$x^2 = 10$

$x = \pm\sqrt{10}$

**Got It?** **1.** What is the solution of each equation?

**a.** $7x^2 - 10 = 25$ **b.** $2x^2 + 9 = 13$

---

## 1 Interactive Learning

**Solve It!**
**PURPOSE** To build a model of a perfect square
**PROCESS** Students may
• arrange pieces by trial-and-error to get a square with the necessary side lengths.
• first draw a square with side length $x + 3$, and then fill the interior with pieces.

**FACILITATE**
**Q** Use two pieces to form a rectangle. What are its dimensions? **[Samples: a rectangle along a large square; $x$ by $x + 1$]**
**Q** If each side of the square is $x + 3$, what is the area of the square? Explain. **[$A = s^2 = (x + 3)^2 = x^2 + 6x + 9$]**

**ANSWER** See Solve It in Answers on next page.
**CONNECT THE MATH** In the Solve It, students model a perfect square expression. In the lesson, students will solve quadratic equations by algebraically forming perfect squares and finding square roots.

## 2 Guided Instruction

### Problem 1

**Q** Why is there a ±, and will it always be needed? **[When you take the square root there are two solutions: a positive and a negative. The ± gives both solutions, so you should always use it.]**

### Got It? EXTENSION

**Q** What happens if you try to solve $3x^2 + 16 = 1$? **[Answers may vary. Sample: You get $x = \pm\sqrt{-5}$, but no real number squared gives $-5$, so the equation does not have a real number solution.]**

---

# 4-6 Preparing to Teach

**BIG idea** **Solving Equations and Inequalities** UbD

**ESSENTIAL UNDERSTANDINGS**
• Completing a perfect square trinomial allows the completed trinomial to be factored as the square of a binomial.
• An equation that contains a perfect square can be solved by finding square roots. The simplest of this type of equation has the form $ax^2 = c$.
• The real solutions of a quadratic equation show the zeros of the related quadratic function and the $x$-intercepts of its graph.

## Math Background
Factoring, tables, and graphs give exact rational solutions or rational approximations. This lesson introduces two methods that may give exact irrational solutions:
• solving by finding square roots
• completing the square.

Both methods rely on isolating a perfect square variable expression on one side of the equation and finding square roots of both sides of the equation. When the isolated constant is positive but not a perfect square, the solutions are irrational. By adding a constant, you can turn *any* quadratic expression into a perfect square trinomial.

Note that completing the square yields the vertex form of a parabola.

## Support Student Learning
Use the **Algebra 2 Companion** to engage and support students during instructions. See Lesson Resources at the end of this lesson for details.

**PowerAlgebra.com**

## 1 Interactive Learning

**Solve It!**
Step out how to solve the Problem with helpful hints and an online question. Other questions are listed above in Interactive Learning.

**Dynamic Activity** The grid and algebra tiles in this activity can be manipulated to model factoring by completing the square. This is especially useful for visual learners.

## Problem 2

**Q** What is another way to find the area of the rectangular part? **[Answers may vary. Sample: Sum the area of two squares: $x^2 + x^2$.]**

**Q** How do you evaluate $\sqrt{\dfrac{2766}{2 + \frac{\pi}{8}}}$ on a calculator?

**[Answers may vary. Sample: Enter $\sqrt{(2766/(2+\pi/8))}$]**

### Got It?

**Q** If $x$ represents the shorter side of this window, what expression represents the length of the longer side? **[1.6x]**

**Q** Why are the final answers not $\pm$ a constant as in Problem 1? **[Length cannot be negative so only the positive solutions are needed.]**

## Problem 3

**Q** If the leading coefficient of a quadratic trinomial is 1, how do you recognize whether it is a perfect square trinomial? **[Answers may vary. Sample: For $x^2 + bx + c$ to be a perfect square, $c$ must be the square of half of $b$.]**

**Q** What happens if the constant on the right side is not a perfect square? **[Answers may vary. Sample: The solutions are irrational.]**

### Got It?                    ERROR PREVENTION

Watch that students take the square root of *both* sides of the equation rather than just the side with the perfect square trinomial. Also draw attention to the $\pm$.

---

 **Problem 2** Determining Dimensions

**Architecture** While designing a house, an architect used windows like the one shown here. What are the dimensions of the window if it has 2766 square inches of glass?

**Step 1** Find the area of the window.
The area of the rectangular part is $(2x)(x) = 2x^2$ in.$^2$.
The area of the semicircular part is
$$\frac{1}{2}\pi r^2 = \frac{1}{2}\pi\left(\frac{x}{2}\right)^2 = \frac{1}{2}\pi\frac{x^2}{4} = \frac{\pi}{8}x^2 \text{ in.}^2.$$
So, the total amount of glass used is
$2x^2 + \frac{\pi}{8}x^2 = 2766$ in.$^2$.

**Step 2** Solve for $x$.

**Think**

**Is the answer reasonable?**
Yes; the rectangular part is about $30 \times 70 = 2100$ in.$^2$. This leaves enough glass for the semicircle.

$\left(2 + \frac{\pi}{8}\right)x^2 = 2766$    Write the equation in $ax^2 = c$ form.

$x^2 = \dfrac{2766}{2 + \frac{\pi}{8}}$    Isolate $x^2$.

$x \approx \pm 34$    Find square roots. Use a calculator.

Length cannot be negative. So the rectangular portion of the window is 34 in. wide by 68 in. long. The semicircular top has a radius of 17 in.

 **Got It?** **2.** The lengths of the sides of a rectangular window have the ratio 1.6 to 1. The area of the window is 2822.4 in.$^2$. What are the window dimensions?

Sometimes an equation shows a perfect square trinomial equal to a constant. To solve, factor the perfect square trinomial into the square of a binomial. Then find square roots.

 **Problem 3** Solving a Perfect Square Trinomial Equation

What is the solution of $x^2 + 4x + 4 = 25$?

| Think | Write |
|---|---|
| Factor the perfect square trinomial. | $x^2 + 4x + 4 = 25$ <br> $(x + 2)^2 = 25$ |
| Find square roots. | $x + 2 = \pm 5$ |
| Rewrite as two equations. | $x + 2 = 5$ or $x + 2 = -5$ |
| Solve for $x$. | $x = 3$ or $x = -7$ |

**Got It?** **3.** What is the solution of $x^2 - 14x + 49 = 25$?

 **Dynamic Activity** Completing the Square

---

# Answers

## Solve It!
You need 1 "$x^2$", 6 "$x$"s, and 9 unit blocks. Line three "$x$"s to the right of the "$x^2$", and three "$x$"s below the "$x^2$". Complete the rest of the square using the nine unit blocks.

## Got It?
**1. a.** $\sqrt{5}, -\sqrt{5}$
  **b.** $\sqrt{2}, -\sqrt{2}$
**2.** 42 in. $\times$ 67.2 in.
**3.** 2, 12
**4. a.** 9
  **b.** No; $\left(\frac{b}{2}\right)^2 = \frac{b^2}{4}$, which is a function of $b$.

---

**PowerAlgebra.com**

## 2 Guided Instruction

Each Problem is worked out and supported online.

**Problem 1**
Solving by Finding Square Roots

**Problem 2**
Determining Dimensions
      *Animated*

**Problem 3**
Solving a Perfect Square Trinomial Equation

**Problem 4**
Completing the Square

**Problem 5**
Solving by Completing the Square
      *Animated*

**Problem 6**
Writing in Vertex Form
      *Animated*

**Support in Algebra 2 Companion**
• Vocabulary
• Key Concepts
• Got It?

If $x^2 + bx$ is not part of a perfect square trinomial, you can use the coefficient $b$ to find a constant $c$ so that $x^2 + bx + c$ is a perfect square. When you do this, you are **completing the square**. The diagram models this process.

$x^2 + bx$  $\quad x^2 + bx + \left(\frac{b}{2}\right)^2 \quad$  $\left(x + \frac{b}{2}\right)^2$

**Key Concept** Completing the Square

You can form a perfect square trinomial from $x^2 + bx$ by adding $\left(\frac{b}{2}\right)^2$.

$$x^2 + bx + \left(\frac{b}{2}\right)^2 = \left(x + \frac{b}{2}\right)^2$$

 **Problem 4** Completing the Square

What value completes the square for $x^2 - 10x$? Justify your answer.

 **Think**

Why do you want a perfect square trinomial?
You can factor a perfect square trinomial into the square of a binomial.

$x^2 - 10x$       Identify $b$; $b = -10$

$\left(\frac{b}{2}\right)^2 = \left(\frac{-10}{2}\right)^2 = (-5)^2 = 25$    Find $\left(\frac{b}{2}\right)^2$.

$x^2 - 10x + 25$       Add the value of $\left(\frac{b}{2}\right)^2$ to complete the square.

$x^2 - 10x + 25 = (x - 5)^2$    Rewrite as the square of a binomial.

 **Got It?** **4. a.** What value completes the square for $x^2 + 6x$?
      **b. Reasoning** Is it possible for more than one value to complete the square for an expression? Explain.

 **Key Concept** Solving an Equation by Completing the Square

1. Rewrite the equation in the form $x^2 + bx = c$. To do this, get all terms with the variable on one side of the equation and the constant on the other side. Divide all the terms of the equation by the coefficient of $x^2$ if it is not 1.
2. Complete the square by adding $\left(\frac{b}{2}\right)^2$ to each side of the equation.
3. Factor the trinomial.
4. Find square roots.
5. Solve for $x$.

PowerAlgebra.com    Lesson 4-6   Completing the Square      235

---

**Take Note**      VISUAL LEARNERS

**Q** How is the diagram of completing the square related to what you did in the Solve It? **[Answers may vary. Sample: In both cases, the pieces were squares and rectangles.]**

**Problem 4**
This problem illustrates the Essential Understanding that completing the square allows you to factor the completed trinomial as the square of a binomial.

**Q** Is the original expression $x^2 - 10x$ equivalent to the final expression $(x - 5)^2$? If not, how could you keep them equivalent? **[No; because 25 was added; subtract 25, or $(x - 5)^2 - 25$.]**

**Q** Is $(x - 5)^2$ the only square binomial equivalent to $x^2 - 10x + 25$? Explain. **[No; answers may vary. Sample: $(-x + 5)^2$ is too; the square of a number equals the square of its opposite.]**

**Got It?**
In the Exercises, students will see questions like this stated as fill-in-the-blank: "Complete the square: $x^2 + 6x + \square$"

**Q** What is the value of $b$? **[6]**
**Q** What is the value of $\frac{b}{2}$? **[3]**

**Take Note**      ELL SUPPORT
These steps can be paraphrased as 1) isolate, 2) divide, 3) complete, 4) factor, 5) square root, 6) solve. As you do examples in class, label each step with its number and paraphrased name. Encourage students to use a six-row graphic organizer with these steps to organize solutions to at least a few practice problems.

---

# Additional Problems

**1.** What is the solution of each equation?

   **a.** $3x^2 + 5 = 20$

   **b.** $8x^2 - 3 = 29$

   **ANSWERS**

   **a.** $\pm\sqrt{5}$

   **b.** $\pm 2$

**2.** The total area of three congruent circles is 500 cm². Find the approximate radius of each circle.

   **ANSWER** about 7.3 cm

**3.** What is the solution of $x^2 + 12x + 36 = 9$?

   **ANSWER** $-3$ or $-9$

**4.** What value completes the square for $x^2 + 14x$? Justify your answer.

   **ANSWER** 49;
   $x^2 + 14x + 49 = (x + 7)^2$

**5.** What is the solution of $3x^2 + 18x - 3 = 0$?

   **ANSWER** $-3 \pm \sqrt{10}$

**6.** What is $y = x^2 - 10x + 4$ in vertex form? Name the vertex and $y$-intercept.

   **ANSWER** $y = (x - 5)^2 - 21$;
   vertex $(5, -21)$;
   $y$-intercept $(0, 4)$

# Problem 5

> **Q** Why is 4 added to each side of the equation?
> **[Sample: On the left side, it completes the square; it is added on the right to keep the equation unchanged.]**
>
> **Q** If you solve a quadratic equation by completing the square and the solutions are integers, what does that indicate? **[Sample: You could also solve by factoring.]**
>
> **Q** What could you do if the "a" value does not divide evenly into each term of the quadratic equation? **[You divide by "a" anyway to get $x^2 + \frac{b}{a}x + \frac{c}{a}$, then take $\frac{b}{2a}$ and square it. Add and subtract $\frac{b^2}{4a^2}$.]**

## Got It?                    ERROR PREVENTION

> **Q** How do you get all $x$ terms alone on the left side? **[Subtract $x$ from each side, and subtract 3 from each side, in either order.]**

## Problem 6                    SYNTHESIZING
This problem connects concepts of Lessons 4-1 and 4-2 by converting standard to vertex form.

> **Q** What is $y = ax^2 + bx + c$ in vertex form?
> **[$y = a\left(x + \frac{b}{2a}\right)^2 + \frac{4ac - b^2}{4a}$]**

## Got It?
This is the first Problem or Got It that features an odd value of $b$. Be aware of students who may struggle with the fractions or decimals involved in completing the square.

---

 **Problem 5** Solving by Completing the Square

What is the solution of $3x^2 - 12x + 6 = 0$?

$$3x^2 - 12x + 6 = 0$$

$$3x^2 - 12x = -6 \qquad \text{Rewrite. Get all terms with } x \text{ on one side of the equation.}$$

$$\frac{3x^2}{3} - \frac{12x}{3} = \frac{-6}{3} \qquad \text{Divide each side by 3 so the coefficient of } x^2 \text{ will be 1.}$$

$$x^2 - 4x = -2 \qquad \text{Simplify.}$$

$$\left(\frac{b}{2}\right)^2 = \left(\frac{-4}{2}\right)^2 = (-2)^2 = 4 \qquad \text{Find } \left(\frac{b}{2}\right)^2 = 4.$$

$$x^2 - 4x + 4 = -2 + 4 \qquad \text{Add 4 to each side.}$$

$$(x - 2)^2 = 2 \qquad \text{Factor the trinomial.}$$

$$x - 2 = \pm\sqrt{2} \qquad \text{Find square roots.}$$

$$x = 2 \pm \sqrt{2} \qquad \text{Solve for } x.$$

**Think**
Is there a way to check without a calculator?
Yes; you can check that your solutions are reasonable by estimating.

Check your results on your calculator. Replace $x$ in the original equation with $2 + \sqrt{2}$ and $2 - \sqrt{2}$.

✓ **Got It? 5.** What is the solution of $2x^2 - x + 3 = x + 9$?

---

You can complete a square to change a quadratic function to vertex form.

**Plan**
What should be your first step?
Complete the square.

 **Problem 6** Writing in Vertex Form

What is $y = x^2 + 4x - 6$ in vertex form? Name the vertex and $y$-intercept.

$$y = x^2 + 4x - 6$$

$$y = x^2 + 4x + 2^2 - 6 - 2^2 \qquad \text{Add } \left(\frac{4}{2}\right)^2 = 2^2 \text{ to complete the square. Also, subtract } 2^2 \text{ to leave the function unchanged.}$$

$$y = (x + 2)^2 - 6 - 2^2 \qquad \text{Factor the perfect square trinomial.}$$

$$y = (x + 2)^2 - 10 \qquad \text{Simplify.}$$

The vertex is $(-2, -10)$. The $y$-intercept is $(0, -6)$.

Check with a graphing calculator.

✓ **Got It? 6.** What is $y = x^2 + 3x - 6$ in vertex form? Name the vertex and $y$-intercept.

---

# Answers

**Got It? (continued)**

**5.** $\frac{1}{2} \pm \frac{\sqrt{13}}{2}$

**6.** $y = \left(x + \frac{3}{2}\right)^2 - \frac{33}{4}$;

vertex: $\left(-\frac{3}{2}, -\frac{33}{4}\right)$;

$y$-intercept: $(0, -6)$

**Lesson Check**

**1.** 6, −6

**2.** 3, −3

**3.** 1

**4.** 25

**5.** 4

**6.** 36

**7.** 2500

**8.** 256

**9.** First, you rewrite the eq. to get all terms with $x$ on one side. Then, you find $\left(\frac{b}{2}\right)^2$ and add it

to both sides of the eq. Then, you factor the resulting trinomial.

**10.** $x^2 + 12x + 5 = 3$

$$x^2 + 12x = -2 \qquad \text{Rewrite to get all terms with } x \text{ on one side of the eq.}$$

$$\left(\frac{12}{2}\right)^2 = 6^2 = 36 \qquad \text{Find } \left(\frac{b}{2}\right)^2 = 36.$$

$$x^2 + 12x + 36 = -2 + 36 \qquad \text{Add 36 to each side.}$$

$$(x + 6)^2 = 34 \qquad \text{Factor the trinomial.}$$

**11.** Your friend should also have subtracted 49;

$$(x^2 - 14x + 49) + 36 - 49$$

$$= (x - 7)^2 - 13$$

## Lesson Check

### Do you know HOW?

**Solve each equation by finding square roots.**

**1.** $2x^2 = 72$       **2.** $6x^2 = 54$

**Complete the square.**

**3.** $x^2 + 2x + \blacksquare$      **4.** $x^2 + 10x + \blacksquare$

**5.** $x^2 - 4x + \blacksquare$      **6.** $x^2 + 12x + \blacksquare$

**7.** $x^2 + 100x + \blacksquare$     **8.** $x^2 - 32x + \blacksquare$

### Do you UNDERSTAND?

**9. Vocabulary** Explain the process of completing the square.

**10.** How can you rewrite the equation $x^2 + 12x + 5 = 3$ so the left side of the equation is in the form $(x + a)^2$?

**11. Error Analysis** Your friend completed the square and wrote the expression shown. Explain your friend's error and write the expression correctly.

$$x^2 - 14x + 36$$
$$x^2 - 14x + 49 + 36$$
$$(x - 7)^2 + 36$$

---

## Practice and Problem-Solving Exercises

**Ⓐ Practice**

**Solve each equation by finding square roots.**    🢠 **See Problem 1.**

**12.** $5x^2 = 80$     **13.** $x^2 - 4 = 0$     **14.** $2x^2 = 32$

**15.** $9x^2 = 25$     **16.** $3x^2 - 15 = 0$     **17.** $5x^2 - 40 = 0$

**18. Fitness** A rectangular swimming pool is 6 ft deep. One side of the pool is 2.5 times longer than the other. The amount of water needed to fill the swimming pool is 2160 cubic feet. Find the dimensions of the pool.    🢠 **See Problem 2.**

**Solve each equation.**    🢠 **See Problem 3.**

**19.** $x^2 + 6x + 9 = 1$     **20.** $x^2 - 4x + 4 = 100$     **21.** $x^2 - 2x + 1 = 4$

**22.** $x^2 + 8x + 16 = \frac{16}{9}$     **23.** $4x^2 + 4x + 1 = 49$     **24.** $x^2 - 12x + 36 = 25$

**25.** $25x^2 + 10x + 1 = 9$     **26.** $x^2 - 30x + 225 = 400$     **27.** $9x^2 + 24x + 16 = 36$

**Complete the square.**    🢠 **See Problem 4.**

**28.** $x^2 + 18x + \blacksquare$     **29.** $x^2 - x + \blacksquare$     **30.** $x^2 - 24x + \blacksquare$

**31.** $x^2 + 20x + \blacksquare$     **32.** $m^2 - 3m + \blacksquare$     **33.** $x^2 + 4x + \blacksquare$

**Solve each quadratic equation by completing the square.**    🢠 **See Problem 5.**

**34.** $x^2 + 6x - 3 = 0$     **35.** $x^2 - 12x + 7 = 0$     **36.** $x^2 + 4x + 2 = 0$

**37.** $x^2 - 2x = 5$     **38.** $x^2 + 8x = 11$     **39.** $x^2 + 12 = 10x$

**40.** $x^2 - 3x = x - 1$     **41.** $x^2 + 2 = 6x + 4$     **42.** $2x^2 + 2x - 5 = x^2$

**43.** $4x^2 + 10x - 3 = 0$     **44.** $9x^2 - 12x - 2 = 0$     **45.** $25x^2 + 30x = 12$

---

**1–11.** See page 236.

### Practice and Problem-Solving Exercises

**12.** 4, −4     **13.** 2, −2

**14.** 4, −4     **15.** $\frac{5}{3}, -\frac{5}{3}$

**16.** $\sqrt{5}, -\sqrt{5}$

**17.** $2\sqrt{2}, -2\sqrt{2}$

**18.** 12 ft × 30 ft × 6 ft

**19.** −4, −2

**20.** −8, 12     **21.** −1, 3

**22.** $-\frac{16}{3}, -\frac{8}{3}$

**23.** −4, 3

**24.** 1, 11

**25.** $-\frac{4}{5}, \frac{2}{5}$

**26.** 35, −5

**27.** $-\frac{10}{3}, \frac{2}{3}$

**28.** 81

**29.** $\frac{1}{4}$

**30.** 144

**31.** 100

**32.** $\frac{9}{4}$

**33.** 4

**34.** $-3 \pm 2\sqrt{3}$

**35.** $6 \pm \sqrt{29}$

**36.** $-2 \pm \sqrt{2}$

**37.** $1 \pm \sqrt{6}$

**38.** $-4 \pm 3\sqrt{3}$

**39.** $5 \pm \sqrt{13}$

**40.** $2 \pm \sqrt{3}$

**41.** $3 \pm \sqrt{11}$

**42.** $-1 \pm \sqrt{6}$

**43.** $-\frac{5}{4} \pm \frac{1}{4}\sqrt{37}$

**44.** $\frac{2}{3} \pm \frac{\sqrt{6}}{3}$

**45.** $-\frac{3}{5} \pm \frac{\sqrt{21}}{5}$

---

## 3 Lesson Check

### Do you know HOW?

- If students solve Exercises 1 and 2 by rewriting in standard form and factoring (as in Lesson 4-5), then suggest they also try finding square roots as in Problem 1.

### Do you UNDERSTAND?

- For Exercise 11, if students overlook the error, then have them look at the red numbers in Problem 6.

### Close

**Q** How does completing the square help solve any quadratic equation? **[Answers may vary. Sample: Completing the square creates a perfect square trinomial that factors as the square of a binomial; the quadratic equation is solved by finding square roots.]**

**PowerAlgebra.com**

## 3 Lesson Check

For a digital lesson check, use the Got It questions.

**Support in Algebra 2 Companion**
- Lesson Check

## 4 Practice

Assign homework to individual students or to an entire class.

Lesson 4-6   **237**

# 4 Practice

## ASSIGNMENT GUIDE

Basic: 12–51 all, 52–56 even, 62–66 even, 75

Average: 13–51 odd, 52–75

Advanced: 13–51 odd, 52–85

Standardized Test Prep: 86–89

Mixed Review: 90–100

Reasoning exercises have blue headings.

Applications exercises have red headings.

**EXERCISE 62:** Use the Think About a Plan worksheet in the **Practice and Problem Solving Workbook** (also available in the Teaching Resources in print and online) to further support students' development in becoming independent learners.

## HOMEWORK QUICK CHECK

To check students' understanding of key skills and concepts, go over Exercises 13, 35, 52, 62, and 75.

---

See Problem 6.

Rewrite each equation in vertex form.

**46.** $y = x^2 + 4x + 1$    **47.** $y = 2x^2 - 8x + 1$    **48.** $y = -x^2 - 2x + 3$

**49.** $y = x^2 + 4x - 7$    **50.** $y = 2x^2 - 6x - 1$    **51.** $y = -x^2 + 4x - 1$

**Ⓑ Apply**

**52. Think About a Plan** The area of the rectangle shown is 80 square inches. What is the value of $x$?
- How can you write an equation to represent 80 in terms of $x$?
- How can you find the value of $x$ by completing the square?

$x - 3$

$2x$

Find the value of $k$ that would make the left side of each equation a perfect square trinomial.

**53.** $x^2 + kx + 25 = 0$    **54.** $x^2 - kx + 100 = 0$    **55.** $x^2 - kx + 121 = 0$

**56.** $x^2 + kx + 64 = 0$    **57.** $x^2 - kx + 81 = 0$    **58.** $25x^2 - kx + 1 = 0$

**59.** $x^2 + kx + \frac{1}{4} = 0$    **60.** $9x^2 - kx + 4 = 0$    **61.** $36x^2 - kx + 49 = 0$

**62. Geometry** The table shows some possible dimensions of rectangles with a perimeter of 100 units. Copy and complete the table.
- **a.** Plot the points (width, area). Find a model for the data set.
- **b.** What is another point in the data set? Use it to verify your model.
- **c.** What is a reasonable domain for this function? Explain.
- **d.** Find the maximum possible area. What dimensions yield this area?
- **e.** Find a function for area in terms of width without using the table. Do you get the same model as in part (a)? Explain.

| Width | Length | Area |
|-------|--------|------|
| 1 | 49 | 49 |
| 2 | 48 | ■ |
| 3 | ■ | ■ |
| 4 | ■ | ■ |
| 5 | ■ | ■ |

Solve each quadratic equation by completing the square.

**63.** $x^2 + 5x - 3 = 0$      **64.** $x^2 + 3x = 2$

**65.** $x^2 - x = 5$      **66.** $x^2 + x - 1 = 0$

**67.** $3x^2 - 4x = 2$      **68.** $5x^2 - x = 4$

**69.** $x^2 + \frac{3}{4}x = \frac{1}{2}$      **70.** $2x^2 - \frac{1}{2}x = \frac{1}{8}$

**71.** $3x^2 + x = \frac{2}{3}$      **72.** $-x^2 + 2x + 4 = 0$

**73.** $-x^2 - 6x = 2$      **74.** $-0.25x^2 - 0.6x + 0.3 = 0$

**75. Football** The quadratic function $h = -0.01x^2 + 1.18x + 2$ models the height of a punted football. The horizontal distance in feet from the point of impact with the kicker's foot is $x$, and $h$ is the height of the ball in feet.
- **a.** Write the function in vertex form. What is the maximum height of the punt?
- **b.** The nearest defensive player is 5 ft horizontally from the point of impact. How high must the player reach to block the punt?
- **c.** Suppose the ball was not blocked but continued on its path. How far down the field would the ball go before it hit the ground?

---

# Answers

## Practice and Problem-Solving Exercises (continued)

**46.** $y = (x + 2)^2 - 3$

**47.** $y = 2(x - 2)^2 - 7$

**48.** $y = -(x + 1)^2 + 4$

**49.** $y = (x + 2)^2 - 11$

**50.** $y = 2\left(x - \frac{3}{2}\right)^2 - \frac{11}{2}$

**51.** $y = -(x - 2)^2 + 3$

**52.** 8 in.

**53.** 10, −10

**54.** 20, −20

**55.** 22, −22

**56.** 16, −16

**57.** 18, −18

**58.** 10, −10

**59.** 1, −1

**60.** 12, −12

**61.** 84, −84

**62.**

| Width | Length | Area |
|-------|--------|------|
| 1 | 49 | 49 |
| 2 | 48 | 96 |
| 3 | 47 | 141 |
| 4 | 46 | 184 |
| 5 | 45 | 225 |

**a.**

$A = -w^2 + 50w$

**b.** Check students' work.

**c.** $0 < w < 50$; since the perimeter is 100, the width would have to be less than 50. Also, width can't be negative so it would have to be greater than 0.

**d.** 625 units²; 25 units x 25 units

**e.** $A = w(50 - w)$; yes; the eqs. are equivalent.

**63.** $\frac{-5 \pm \sqrt{37}}{2}$

**64.** $\frac{-3 \pm \sqrt{17}}{2}$

**65.** $\frac{1 \pm \sqrt{21}}{2}$

**66.** $\frac{1 \pm \sqrt{5}}{2}$

**67.** $\frac{2 \pm \sqrt{10}}{3}$

**68.** $1, -\frac{4}{5}$

**69.** $\frac{-3 \pm \sqrt{41}}{8}$

**70.** $\frac{1 \pm \sqrt{5}}{8}$

**71.** $\frac{1}{3}, -\frac{2}{3}$

**72.** $1 \pm \sqrt{5}$

**73.** $-3 \pm \sqrt{7}$

**74.** $\frac{-6 \pm \sqrt{66}}{5}$

**75. a.** $-0.01(x - 59)^2 + 36.81$; 36.81 ft

**b.** 7.65 ft

**c.** about 120 ft

**Solve for $x$ in terms of $a$.**

**76.** $2x^2 - ax = 6a^2$     **77.** $3x^2 + ax = a^2$     **78.** $2a^2x^2 - 8ax = -6$

**79.** $4a^2x^2 + 8ax + 3 = 0$     **80.** $3x^2 + ax^2 = 9x + 9a$     **81.** $6a^2x^2 - 11ax = 10$

**82.** Solve $x^2 = (6\sqrt{2})x + 7$ by completing the square.

**Rewrite each equation in vertex form. Then find the vertex of the graph.**

**83.** $y = -4x^2 - 5x + 3$     **84.** $y = \frac{1}{2}x^2 - 5x + 12$     **85.** $y = -\frac{1}{5}x^2 + \frac{4}{5}x + \frac{11}{5}$

## Standardized Test Prep

SAT/ACT

**86.** The graph of which inequality has its vertex at $\left(2\frac{1}{2}, -5\right)$?

    Ⓐ $y < |2x - 5| + 5$        Ⓒ $y > |2x + 5| - 5$

    Ⓑ $y < |2x + 5| - 5$        Ⓓ $y > |2x - 5| - 5$

**87.** Which number is a solution of $|9 - x| = 9 + x$?

    Ⓕ $-3$        Ⓖ $0$        Ⓗ $3$        Ⓘ $6$

**88.** Joanne tosses an apple seed on the ground. It travels along a parabola with the equation $y = -x^2 + 4$. Assume the seed was thrown from a height of 4 ft. How many feet away from Joanne will the apple seed land?

    Ⓐ 1 ft        Ⓑ 2 ft        Ⓒ 4 ft        Ⓓ 8 ft

**Extended Response**

**89.** List the steps for solving the equation $x^2 - 9 = -8x$ by the completing the square method. Explain each step.

## Mixed Review

**Solve each equation by factoring. Check your answers.**    ◀ See Lesson 4-5.

**90.** $2x^2 - 3x + 1 = 0$     **91.** $x^2 - 4 = -3x$     **92.** $16 + 22x = 3x^2$

**Determine whether a quadratic model exists for each set of values. If so, write the model.**    ◀ See Lesson 4-3.

**93.** $(-4, 3), (-3, 3), (-2, 4)$     **94.** $\left(-1, \frac{1}{2}\right), (0, 2), (2, 2)$     **95.** $(0, 2), (1, 0), (2, 4)$

**Solve each system by elimination.**    ◀ See Lesson 3-2.

**96.** $\begin{cases} 2x + y = 4 \\ 3x - y = 6 \end{cases}$     **97.** $\begin{cases} 2x + y = 7 \\ -2x + 5y = -1 \end{cases}$     **98.** $\begin{cases} 2x + 4y = 10 \\ 3x + 5y = 14 \end{cases}$

**Get Ready!**   **To prepare for Lesson 4-7, do Exercises 99–100.**

**Evaluate each expression for the given values of the variables.**    ◀ See Lesson 1-3.

**99.** $b^2 - 4ac;\ a = 1,\ b = 6,\ c = 3$     **100.** $b^2 - 4ac;\ a = -5,\ b = 2,\ c = 4$

---

**76.** $-\dfrac{3a}{2}, 2a$

**77.** $\dfrac{-a \pm a\sqrt{13}}{6}$

**78.** $\dfrac{3}{a}, \dfrac{1}{a}, a \neq 0$

**79.** $-\dfrac{3}{2a}, -\dfrac{1}{2a}, a \neq 0$

**80.** $3, \dfrac{-3a}{a + 3}, a \neq -3$

**81.** $-\dfrac{2}{3a}, \dfrac{5}{2a}, a \neq 0$

**82.** $-5 + 3\sqrt{2}, 5 + 3\sqrt{2}$

**83.** $y = -4\left(x + \dfrac{5}{8}\right)^2 + \dfrac{73}{16}; \left(-\dfrac{5}{8}, \dfrac{73}{16}\right)$

**84.** $y = \dfrac{1}{2}(x - 5)^2 - \dfrac{1}{2}; \left(5, -\dfrac{1}{2}\right)$

**85.** $y = -\dfrac{1}{5}(x - 2)^2 + 3; (2, 3)$

**Standardized Test Prep**

**86.** D

**87.** G

**88.** B

**89.** [4] $x^2 - 9 = -8x$

$x^2 + 8x = 9$    Move the variables to the left side and the constant to the right by using the Add. Prop. of Eq.

$\left(\dfrac{8}{2}\right)^2 = 4^2 = 16$    Find $\left(\dfrac{b}{2}\right)^2 = 16$.

$x^2 + 8x + 16 = 9 + 16$    Add 16 to each side.

$(x + 4)^2 = 25$    Factor left side. Simplify right side.

$x + 4 = \pm 5$    Take the square root of each side.

$x = -4 \pm 5$    Add $-4$ to each side.

$x = -9, 1$    Simplify.

[3] computational error

[2] steps are listed, without explanations

[1] eq. is solved correctly, without work shown

**Mixed Review**

**90.** $\frac{1}{2}, 1$

**91.** $-4, 1$

**92.** $8, -\frac{2}{3}$

**93.** yes; $y = \frac{1}{2}x^2 + \frac{7}{2}x + 9$

**94.** yes; $y = -\frac{1}{2}x^2 + x + 2$

**95.** yes; $y = 3x^2 - 5x + 2$

**96.** $(2, 0)$

**97.** $(3, 1)$

**98.** $(3, 1)$

**99.** 24

**100.** 84

# Lesson Resources

## Differentiated Remediation

## Additional Instructional Support

### Algebra 2 Companion

Students can use the **Algebra 2 Companion** worktext (4 pages) as you teach the lesson. Use the Companion to support

- New Vocabulary
- Key Concepts
- Got It for each Problem
- Lesson Check

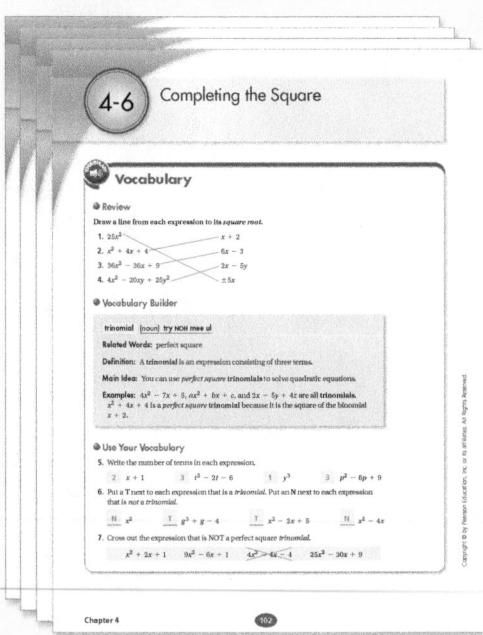

### ELL Support

**Use Manipulatives** Let students use algebra tiles (or photocopied cut-outs of the pieces shown in the Solve It) to model completing the square when $a = 1$ and $b$ is even. In Problem 4, for example, students can arrange one large square ($x^2$) and 10 rectangles ($10x$) into the best possible square. (To model the fact that $10x$ is negative, students can flip the rectangles over to the *opposite* sides.) Then students can see that 25 unit squares are needed to literally complete the square.

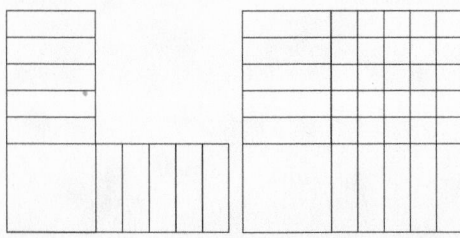

Give students different equations to model. Have them sketch it and describe how their model can be used to solve the problem.

## 5 Assess & Remediate

### Lesson Quiz

**1.** What is the solution of $6x^2 = 42$?

**2.** A rectangle is constructed on a semicircle so that the length equals the diameter. The rectangle is 3 times as long as it is wide. The total area of this figure is 750 in.$^2$. Find the approximate dimensions of the rectangle.

**3.** What is the solution of $x^2 - 14x + 49 = 4$?

**4.** Complete the square: $x^2 - 8x + \square$.

**5.** Solve $x^2 - 10x + 22 = 0$.

**6. Do you UNDERSTAND?** Explain the process of rewriting $y = x^2 + 2x + 26$ in vertex form.

### ANSWERS TO LESSON QUIZ

**1.** $\pm\sqrt{7}$

**2.** about 10.7 in. by 32.1 in.

**3.** 5 or 9

**4.** 16

**5.** $5 \pm \sqrt{3}$

**6.** Answers may vary. Sample: Complete the square by adding 1, which is the square of half of 2; keep the equation unchanged by also subtracting 1, $y = x^2 + 2x + 1 + 26 - 1$; rewrite the perfect square trinomial as the square of a binomial and add the constants, $y = (x + 1)^2 + 25$.

### PRESCRIPTION FOR REMEDIATION

Use the student work on the Lesson Quiz to prescribe a differentiated review assignment:

| Points | Differentiated Remediation |
|--------|---------------------------|
| 0–2 | Intervention |
| 3–5 | On-level |
| 6 | Extension |

**PowerAlgebra.com**

### 5 Assess & Remediate

Assign the Lesson Quiz. Appropriate intervention, practice, or enrichment is automatically generated based on student performance.

## Intervention

- **Reteaching** (2 pages) Provides reteaching and practice exercises for the key lesson concepts. Use with struggling students or absent students.

- **English Language Learner Support** Helps students develop and reinforce mathematical vocabulary and key concepts.

### All-in-One Resources/Online
**Reteaching**

### All-in-One Resources/Online
**English Language Learner Support**

# Differentiated Remediation *continued*

## On-Level

- **Practice** (2 pages) Provides extra practice for each lesson. For simpler practice exercises, use the Form K Practice pages found in the All-in-One Teaching Resources and online.

- **Think About a Plan** Helps students develop specific problem-solving skills and strategies by providing scaffolded guiding questions.

- **Standardized Test Prep** Focuses on all major exercises, all major question types, and helps students prepare for the high-stakes assessments.

## Extension

- **Enrichment** Provides students with interesting problems and activities that extend the concepts of the lesson.

- **Activities, Games, and Puzzles** Worksheets that can be used for concepts development, enrichment, and for fun!

---

### Practice and Problem Solving Wkbk/ All-in-One Resources/Online
**Practice page 1**

**4-6 Practice** — Form G
Completing the Square

Solve each equation by finding square roots.

1. $3x^2 = 75$  ±5
2. $5x^2 - 45 = 0$  ±3
3. $4x^2 - 49 = 0$  $±\frac{7}{2}$
4. $6x^2 = 216$  ±6
5. $2x^2 = 14$  ±√7
6. $3x^2 - 96 = 0$  ±4√2

7. A box is 4 in. high. Its length is 1.5 times its width. The volume of the box is 1350 in.². What are the width and length of the box?  15 in.; 22.5 in.

Solve each equation.

8. $x^2 + 12x + 36 = 25$  −11, −1
9. $x^2 - 10x + 25 = 144$  −7, 17
10. $x^2 + 6x + 9 = \frac{49}{4}$  $-\frac{13}{2}, \frac{1}{2}$
11. $x^2 - 22x + 121 = 225$  −4, 26
12. $16x^2 + 8x + 1 = 16$  $-\frac{5}{4}, \frac{3}{4}$
13. $25x^2 - 30x + 9 = 81$  $-\frac{6}{5}, \frac{12}{5}$

Complete the square.

14. $x^2 + 22x + 121$
15. $x^2 - 30x + 225$
16. $x^2 + 5x + \frac{25}{4}$
17. $x^2 - \frac{1}{2}x + \frac{1}{16}$
18. $25x^2 + 10x + 1$
19. $4x^2 - 12x + 9$

Solve each quadratic equation by completing the square.

20. $x^2 + 10x - 1 = 0$  $-5 ± √26$
21. $x^2 + 2x - 7 = 0$  $-1 ± 2√2$
22. $-x^2 + 6x + 10 = 0$  $3 ± √19$
23. $x^2 + 5x = 3x + 11$  $-1 ± 2√3$
24. $3x^2 + 4x = 2x^2 + 3$  $-2 ± √7$
25. $x^2 - 2x - \frac{3}{4} = 0$  $\frac{2 ± √7}{2}$
26. $-0.2x^2 + 0.4x + 0.8 = 0$  $1 ± √5$
27. $4x^2 + 20x + 1 = 0$  $\frac{-5 ± 2√6}{2}$

---

### Practice and Problem Solving Wkbk/ All-in-One Resources/Online
**Think About a Plan**

**4-6 Think About a Plan**
Completing the Square

**Geometry** The table shows some possible dimensions of rectangles with a perimeter of 100 units. Copy and complete the table.
a. Plot the points (width, area). Find a model for the data set.
b. What is another point in the data set? Use it to verify your model.
c. What is a reasonable domain for this function? Explain.
d. What is the maximum possible area. What are its dimensions?
e. Find an equation for area in terms of width without using the table. Do you get the same equation as in part (a)? Explain.

| Width | Length | Area |
|---|---|---|
| 1 | 49 | 49 |
| 2 | 48 | 96 |
| 3 | 47 | 141 |
| 4 | 46 | 184 |
| 5 | 45 | 225 |

1. What points should you plot? Plot the points on the graph.
   (1, 49), (2, 96), (3, 141), (4, 184), (5, 225)

2. Use your graphing calculator to find a model for the data set. $A = -x^2 + 50x$

3. What is another point in the data set? Use it to verify your model.
   Answers may vary. Sample: (6, 264); 264 $\stackrel{?}{=} -(6)^2 + 50(6)$; 264 = 264

4. What does the domain of your function represent?
   the width of the rectangle

5. The domain must be greater than __0__ and less than __50__.

6. A reasonable domain is:
   all real numbers greater than 0 and less than 50

7. Write the vertex form of your function.  $A = -(x - 25)^2 + 625$

8. The maximum possible area is __625 units²__.
   The dimensions of this rectangle are __25 units__ by __25 units__.

9. If the width of the rectangle is x, then the length is __50 − x__.
   Area = [ length ] times [ width ] = [ (50 − x) ] · [ x ] = $-x^2 + 50x$

10. Is the equation in Exercise 9 the same as your model in Exercise 2? Explain.
    Yes; the functions are the same.

---

### Practice and Problem Solving Wkbk/ All-in-One Resources/Online
**Practice page 2**

**4-6 Practice** (continued) — Form G
Completing the Square

Rewrite each equation in vertex form.

28. $y = x^2 - 6x + 4$  $y = (x - 3)^2 - 5$
29. $y = x^2 + 14x + 50$  $y = (x + 7)^2 + 1$
30. $y = 3x^2 + 8x + 2$  $y = 3(x + \frac{4}{3})^2 - \frac{10}{3}$
31. $y = -2x^2 + 6x - 2$  $y = -2(x - \frac{3}{2})^2 + \frac{5}{2}$

Find the value of k that would make the left side of each equation a perfect square trinomial.

32. $x^2 + kx + 196 = 0$  28
33. $64x^2 - kx + 1 = 0$  16
34. $x^2 - kx + 16 = 0$  8
35. $4x^2 - kx + 9 = 0$  12
36. $16x^2 + kx + 9 = 0$  24
37. $\frac{1}{4}x^2 - kx + \frac{1}{25} = 0$  $\frac{1}{5}$

38. The quadratic function $d = -t^2 + 4t + 33$ models the depth of water in a flood channel after a rainstorm. The time in hours after it stops raining is $t$ and $d$ is the depth of the water in feet.
    a. Solve the equation $-t^2 + 4t + 33 = 0$.  $2 ± √37$
    b. Approximate the positive solution found in part (a) to two decimal places.  8.08
    c. Interpret the answer to part (b) in terms of the problem.
       The water level will be 0 ft after about 8 h.

39. While in orbit, a space scientist measures the pressure inside a container as it is being heated and then cooled. She records the information and discovers the pressure $p$, in pounds per square inch, is related to the time $t$ in minutes after the experiment begins according to the equation $p = -0.2t^2 + 1.6t$.
    a. Complete the square in the expression $-0.2t^2 + 1.6t$.  $-0.2(t - 4)^2 + 1.6t - 3.2$
    b. Rewrite the equation for $p$ in vertex form.  $p = -0.2(t - 4)^2 + 3.2$
    c. What is a reasonable domain for this function? Explain.  $0 ≤ t ≤ 8$; other values of $t$ result in negative values for $p$.
    d. When does the maximum pressure occur? What is the maximum pressure?  4 min; 3.2 lbs/in.²

---

### Practice and Problem Solving Wkbk/ All-in-One Resources/Online
**Standardized Test Prep**

**4-6 Standardized Test Prep**
Completing the Square

**Multiple Choice**

For Exercises 1–6, choose the correct letter.

1. What are the solutions of the equation $36x^2 - 12x + 1 = 1$?  D
   Ⓐ 4, 8   Ⓑ $-\frac{1}{6}, \frac{1}{6}$   Ⓒ $-\frac{1}{2}, \frac{1}{6}$   Ⓓ $0, \frac{1}{3}$

2. What are the solutions of the equation $2x^2 + 16x + 28 = 0$?  G
   Ⓕ $-4 ± √30$   Ⓖ $-4 ± √2$   Ⓗ $4 ± √2$   Ⓘ $4 ± √30$

3. Which value completes the square for $x^2 - 3x$?  A
   Ⓐ $\frac{9}{4}$   Ⓑ $\frac{3}{2}$   Ⓒ $-\frac{3}{2}$   Ⓓ $-\frac{9}{4}$

4. Which value for k would make the left side of $x^2 + kx + \frac{49}{64} = 0$ a perfect square trinomial?  H
   Ⓕ 7   Ⓖ $\frac{7}{2}$   Ⓗ $\frac{7}{4}$   Ⓘ $\frac{7}{8}$

5. What are the solutions of the equation $x^2 = 8x - 1$?  C
   Ⓐ $-4 ± √17$   Ⓑ $-4 ± √15$   Ⓒ $4 ± √15$   Ⓓ $4 ± √17$

6. Which equation is the vertex form of $y = -3x^2 + 12x - 7$?  G
   Ⓕ $y = -3(x - 2)^2 - 5$   Ⓖ $y = -3(x - 2)^2 + 5$
   Ⓗ $y = -3(x + 2)^2 - 5$   Ⓘ $y = -3(x + 2)^2 + 5$

**Short Response**

7. The equation $p = -x^2 + 8x + 5$ gives the price $p$, in dollars, for a product when $x$ million units are produced.
   a. What are the solutions of the equation $-x^2 + 8x + 5 = 0$?
   b. What is the positive solution to part (a) rounded to two decimal places? What does this solution mean in terms of this problem?
   [2] a. $4 ± √21$ b. 8.58; the price will be $0 when 8.58 million units are produced.
   [1] incorrect solution OR incorrect interpretation
   [0] no answers given

---

### All-in-One Resources/Online
**Enrichment**

**4-6 Enrichment**
Completing the Square

You can approximate square roots with an interesting quadratic relationship.

1. Multiply $(a + \frac{b}{2a})^2$. $a^2 + b + \frac{b^2}{4a^2}$

2. What happens to the value of a fraction as the denominator gets larger?
   As the denominator gets larger, the fraction becomes smaller.

If $a$ is much larger than $b$, the value of the fraction $\frac{b^2}{4a^2}$ is very small and has little effect in the expression $a^2 + b + \frac{b^2}{4a^2}$. So when $a$ is much larger than $b$, you can write

$$\left(a + \frac{b}{2a}\right)^2 ≈ a^2 + b$$

$$a + \frac{b}{2a} ≈ \sqrt{a^2 + b}$$

If you can write a number as $a^2 + b$ where $a > b$, then an approximate value of its square root is $a + \frac{b}{2a}$.

For example, to approximate $\sqrt{17}$, let $a = 4$ and $b = 1$.

$$\sqrt{17} = \sqrt{4^2 + 1} \text{ so } \sqrt{17} ≈ a + \frac{b}{2a} = 4 + \frac{1}{2(4)} ≈ 4.125$$

Evaluate this square root on a calculator.

$$\sqrt{17} ≈ 4.123$$

Use the formula to approximate each square root. Then find each square root using your calculator. Round to the nearest thousandth.

3. $\sqrt{26}$  5.100; 5.099
4. $\sqrt{404}$  20.100; 20.100
5. $\sqrt{174}$  13.192; 13.191
6. $\sqrt{1773}$  42.107; 42.107
7. $\sqrt{963}$  31.032; 31.032
8. $\sqrt{83}$  9.111; 9.110

---

### Online Teacher Resource Center
**Activities, Games, and Puzzles**

**4-6 Puzzle: Dot Mania**
Completing the Square

This puzzle can be done individually or with a partner. You will need three different-colored pencils or pens.

There are fifteen quadratic expressions labeled a. through o. below. Find the value that needs to be added to make an expression that is a perfect square. Then replace each letter with its perfect-square value in the dot-to-dot puzzle.

Next connect the following sets of numbers with a segment. Stop your segment after completing each set and then move to the next set and start a new segment. Use different-colored pencils or pens as indicated.

| Color 1 | Color 2 | Color 3 |
|---|---|---|
| 1–4 | 37–41 | 51–55 |
| 5–8 | 42–46 | 56–61 |
| 9–12 | 47–48 | 62–63 |
| 13–16 | 49–50 | 64–65 |
| 17–22 | | 66–70 |
| 23–24 | | 71–72 |
| 25–26 | | 73–74 |
| 27–28 | | 75–80 |
| 29–30 | | |
| 31–36 | | |

a. $x^2 + 12x$  36
b. $x^2 - 2x$  1
c. $x^2 + 16x$  64
d. $2x^2 - 12x$  18
e. $3x^2 - 12x$  12
f. $\frac{1}{4}x^2 - 2x$  4
g. $\frac{1}{3}x^2 + 6x$  27
h. $x^2 - 14x$  49
i. $x^2 - 10x$  25
j. $\frac{2}{5}x^2 + 6x$  15
k. $2x^2 - 24x$  72
l. $x^2 + 6x$  9
m. $\frac{2}{3}x^2 + 12x$  54
n. $\frac{1}{2}x^2 + 12x$  24
o. $\frac{1}{2}x^2 - 4x$  16

When the segments are connected, you will have a diagram and can answer the following questions.

1. What is the area of the region that "completes the square"? $b^2$

2. What is the connection between the figure you made and the algebraic process of completing the square?
   Check students' work.

# 1 Interactive Learning

## Solve It!

**PURPOSE** To write quadratic functions whose graphs have 2, 1, or 0 $x$-intercepts

**PROCESS** Students may

- pick the vertex point and use one of the endpoints to find an equation in vertex form.
- pick any third point and use a system of three equations or quadratic regression to find an equation in standard form.

---

**FACILITATE**

**Q** If the smile crosses the $x$-axis twice, what coordinates do you estimate for intercepts? **[Answers may vary. Sample: (3, 0), (5, 0)]**

**Q** What is the axis of symmetry of the smile? Explain. **[$x = 4$; fold the face in half on that line.]**

---

**ANSWER** See Solve It in Answers on next page.

**CONNECT THE MATH** In the Solve It, students use points to write quadratic functions whose graphs have 2, 1, or 0 $x$-intercepts. In the lesson, they will evaluate the discriminant to identify whether 2, 1, or 0 real solutions exist for a quadratic equation.

SYNTHESIZING

Refer to page 235 and the steps in the Take Note section while presenting this derivation. Steps 1 and 2 are reversed in this derivation.

---

**Q** Why can you divide by $a$ before rewriting so all terms with a variable are on one side? **[Subtracting $c$ then dividing by $a$ or dividing by $a$ then subtracting $\frac{c}{a}$ both result in $-\frac{c}{a}$ on the right.]**

---

**Objectives** To solve quadratic equations using the Quadratic Formula
To determine the number of solutions by using the discriminant

You have to restrict the domain of each function to $2 \leq x \leq 6$.

**Getting Ready!**

On this happy face, what quadratic function graphs a smile that
- crosses the $x$-axis twice?
- touches the $x$-axis once?
- misses the $x$-axis completely?

Copy and show each completed face on graph paper. Explain why each mouth meets the given condition.

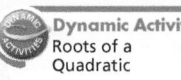 **Dynamic Activity** Roots of a Quadratic

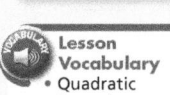 **Lesson Vocabulary**
- Quadratic Formula
- discriminant

Another way to solve a quadratic equation $ax^2 + bx + c = 0$ is by completing a square and then factoring.

**Essential Understanding** You can solve a quadratic equation $ax^2 + bx + c = 0$ in more than one way. In general, you can find a formula that gives values of $x$ in terms of $a$, $b$, and $c$.

Here's how to solve $ax^2 + bx + c = 0$ to get the *Quadratic Formula*.

$$ax^2 + bx + c = 0$$

$$x^2 + \frac{b}{a}x + \frac{c}{a} = 0 \qquad \text{Divide each side by } a.$$

$$x^2 + \frac{b}{a}x = -\frac{c}{a} \qquad \text{Rewrite so all terms containing } x \text{ are on one side.}$$

$$x^2 + \frac{b}{a}x + \left(\frac{b}{2a}\right)^2 = \left(\frac{b}{2a}\right)^2 - \frac{c}{a} \qquad \text{Complete the square.}$$

$$\left(x + \frac{b}{2a}\right)^2 = \frac{b^2 - 4ac}{4a^2} \qquad \text{Factor the perfect square trinomial. Also, simplify.}$$

$$x + \frac{b}{2a} = \pm\sqrt{\frac{b^2 - 4ac}{4a^2}} \qquad \text{Find square roots.}$$

$$x = -\frac{b}{2a} \pm \frac{\sqrt{b^2 - 4ac}}{2a} \qquad \text{Solve for } x. \text{ Also, simplify the radical.}$$

$$x = \frac{-b \pm \sqrt{b^2 - 4ac}}{2a} \qquad \text{Simplify.}$$

---

##  4-7 Preparing to Teach

**BIG idea** Solving Equations and Inequalities          UbD

**ESSENTIAL UNDERSTANDINGS**

- A quadratic equation $ax^2 + bx + c = 0$ can be solved by a formula that gives values of $x$ in terms of $a$, $b$, and $c$.
- The real solutions of a quadratic equation show the zeros of the related quadratic function and the $x$-intercepts of its graph.

### Math Background

One way of solving a quadratic equation is to use the Quadratic Formula. It is derived by completing the square to solve for $x$ in terms of $a$, $b$, and $c$ in the literal equation $ax^2 + bx + c = 0$. Unlike factoring, the Quadratic Formula can be used to solve any quadratic equation. It is simpler than completing the square in many cases.

Students sometimes get caught up in the computation and lose sight that they are solving quadratic equations. Emphasize the algebraic and graphical connections between solutions, zeroes, and $x$-intercepts. Students should be able to visualize a parabola when solving a quadratic equation and use the discriminant to determine how the parabola intersects the $x$-axis.

### Support Student Learning

Use the **Algebra 2 Companion** to engage and support students during instruction. See Lesson Resources at the end of this lesson for details.

### PowerAlgebra.com

## 1 Interactive Learning

**Solve It!**
Step out how to solve the Problem with helpful hints and an online question. Other questions are listed above in Interactive Learning.

**Dynamic Activity** Students find the roots of quadratic equations by graphing the parabola. They can compare the graphs of quadratic functions and associated solutions.

**Key Concept** The Quadratic Formula

To solve the quadratic equation $ax^2 + bx + c = 0$, use the **Quadratic Formula**.

$$x = \frac{-b \pm \sqrt{b^2 - 4ac}}{2a}$$

 **Problem 1** Using the Quadratic Formula

**What are the solutions? Use the Quadratic Formula.**

**A** $2x^2 - x = 4$

**Plan**
**Should you write the equation in standard form?**
Yes; write the equation in standard form to identify $a$, $b$, and $c$.

$$2x^2 - x = 4$$

$$2x^2 - x - 4 = 0 \qquad \text{Write in standard form.}$$

$$a = 2, b = -1, c = -4 \qquad \text{Find the values of } a, b, \text{ and } c.$$

$$x = \frac{-b \pm \sqrt{b^2 - 4ac}}{2a} \qquad \text{Write the Quadratic Formula.}$$

$$= \frac{-(-1) \pm \sqrt{(-1)^2 - 4(2)(-4)}}{2(2)} \qquad \text{Substitute for } a, b, \text{ and } c.$$

$$= \frac{1 \pm \sqrt{33}}{4} \qquad \text{Simplify.}$$

$$= \frac{1 + \sqrt{33}}{4} \text{ or } \frac{1 - \sqrt{33}}{4}$$

**Check** Use a graphing calculator to graph $y = 2x^2 - x - 4$. The $x$-intercepts are about $-1.186 \approx \frac{1 - \sqrt{33}}{4}$ and $1.686 \approx \frac{1 + \sqrt{33}}{4}$, as expected.

Zero
X=-1.186141  Y=0

**B** $x^2 + 6x + 9 = 0$

$$x^2 + 6x + 9 = 0$$

$$a = 1, b = 6, c = 9 \qquad \text{Find the values of } a, b, \text{ and } c.$$

$$x = \frac{-6 \pm \sqrt{6^2 - 4(1)(9)}}{2(1)} \qquad \text{Substitute into } \frac{-b \pm \sqrt{b^2 - 4ac}}{2a}.$$

$$= \frac{-6 \pm \sqrt{36 - 36}}{2} \qquad \text{Simplify.}$$

$$= \frac{-6 \pm \sqrt{0}}{2}$$

$$= -3$$

**Think**
**Why is there only one solution?**
Because if you add or subtract zero you get the same number.

 **Got It?** **1.** What are the solutions? Use the Quadratic Formula.
**a.** $x^2 + 4x = -4$  **b.** $x^2 + 4x - 3 = 0$

# 2 Guided Instruction

## Take Note  SYNTHESIZING
The Quadratic Formula solves any quadratic equation, including those that cannot be solved by factoring.

## Problem 1  ERROR PREVENTION
Students must write the quadratic equation in standard form before using the Quadratic Formula. Be sure students use the correct order of operations when simplifying the expressions.

**Q** Why are there two solutions to 1A? **[Answers may vary. Sample: The graph of the related function intersects the *x*-axis twice.]**

**Q** For 1B, what would a graph of the related function look like? **[Answers may vary. Sample: The parabola touches but does not cross the *x*-axis.]**

**Q** If the solution(s) are integers, what does that indicate about the quadratic equation? **[Answers may vary. Sample: The equation could also be solved by factoring.]**

## Got It?  ERROR PREVENTION
Some students may solve 1a by factoring. For 1b, watch that students reduce the square root and common factors in all terms.

**Q** For 1a, what must you do before applying the Quadratic Formula? **[Rewrite the equation in standard form.]**

---

# 2 Guided Instruction

 Each Problem is worked out and supported online.

**Problem 1**
Using the Quadratic Formula
*Animated*

**Problem 2**
Applying the Quadratic Formula
*Animated*

**Problem 3**
Using the Discriminant

**Problem 4**
Using the Discriminant to Solve a Problem
*Animated*

**Support in Algebra 2 Companion**
• Vocabulary
• Key Concepts
• Got It?

---

# Answers

## Solve It!
Answers may vary. Sample:
$y = 0.375x^2 - 3x + 5.5$ crosses the $x$-axis twice because it has two real roots;

$y = 0.25(x - 4)^2$ touches the $x$-axis once because the vertex is the only root;

$y = 0.125(x - 4)^2 + 0.5$ misses the $x$-axis completely because it has no real roots.

## Problem 2

Students solve a real-world problem by applying the Quadratic Formula to a quadratic model. This is the first example students see where the value of $a$ is negative.

**Q** Why was 200 substituted into the equation? **[The variable $p$ represents profit, and the desired profit is $200.]**

**Q** If the band sells the CDs for the smallest price of $15.28, will the profit be exactly $200? [Answers may vary. Samples: No, because 15.28 was a rounded value; if you substitute 15.28 into the original equation for profit, $p \approx 199.96$.]**

## Got It?

**Q** How does this problem differ from Problem 2? **[You need to substitute 100 for $p$.]**

## Take Note                    ERROR PREVENTION

Emphasize that the discriminant is the expression *under* the radical symbol. The symbol itself is not part of the discriminant.

**Q** In terms of $a$, $b$, and $c$, when is the discriminant zero? **[The discriminant is zero when $b^2$ is equal to $4ac$.]**

---

**Fundraising** Your school's jazz band is selling CDs as a fundraiser. The total profit $p$ depends on the amount $x$ that your band charges for each CD. The equation $p = -x^2 + 48x - 300$ models the profit of the fundraiser. What is the least amount, in dollars, you can charge for a CD to make a profit of $200?

$$p = -x^2 + 48x - 300$$

$$200 = -x^2 + 48x - 300 \qquad \text{Substitute 200 for } p.$$

$$0 = -x^2 + 48x - 500 \qquad \text{Write the equation in standard form.}$$

$$a = -1, b = 48, c = -500 \qquad \text{Find the values of } a, b, \text{ and } c.$$

$$x = \frac{-48 \pm \sqrt{48^2 - 4(-1)(-500)}}{2(-1)} \qquad \text{Substitute into } \frac{-b \pm \sqrt{b^2 - 4ac}}{2a}.$$

$$x = \frac{-48 \pm \sqrt{304}}{-2} \qquad \text{Simplify.}$$

$$x \approx 15.282 \text{ or } x \approx 32.717 \qquad \text{Use a calculator.}$$

The least amount you can charge is $15.29 for each CD to make a profit of $200.

The answer is 15.29.

### Think

**Does it make sense that two different prices can yield the same profit?**
Yes. You can generate a given profit either by selling many CDs at a low price, or fewer CDs at a high price.

✓ **Got It?** **2. a.** In Problem 2, what is the least amount you can charge for each CD to make a $100 profit?

**b. Reasoning** Would a negative profit make sense in this problem? Explain.

---

A quadratic equation can have two real solutions ($x^2 = 4$), one real solution ($x^2 = 0$), or no real solutions ($x^2 = -4$). In the Quadratic Formula, the value under the radical symbol, $b^2 - 4ac$, tells you how many real-number solutions exist.

In Problem 1(a), $b^2 - 4ac > 0$ and there are two real solutions. In Problem 1(b), $b^2 - 4ac = 0$ and there is only one real solution.

### take note    Key Concept   Discriminant

The **discriminant** of a quadratic equation in the form $ax^2 + bx + c = 0$ is the value of the expression $b^2 - 4ac$.

$$x = \frac{-b \pm \sqrt{b^2 - 4ac}}{2a} \leftarrow \text{discriminant}$$

---

# Additional Problems

**1.** What are the solutions? Use the Quadratic Formula.
$5x^2 - 2x = 2$
**ANSWER** $\frac{1}{5} \pm \frac{\sqrt{11}}{5}$

**2.** You sell wrapping paper as a charity fundraiser. The equation $p = -6x^2 + 280x - 1200$ models the total profit $p$ as a function of the price $x$ per roll of paper. What is the smallest amount in dollars you can charge per roll of wrapping paper to make a profit of $1500?
**ANSWER** $13.62

**3.** What is the number of real solutions of $-x^2 + 14x = 49$?
**ANSWER** one real solution

**4.** A rocket is launched from the ground with an initial vertical velocity of 150 ft/s. The function $h = -16t^2 + 150t$ models the height in feet of the rocket at time $t$ in seconds. Will the rocket reach a height of 300 ft? Explain your answer.
**ANSWER** Yes; the discriminant is positive, so there are two real solutions for time $t$ when the rocket's height is 300 ft.

# Answers

**Got It?**
**1. a.** $-2$
**b.** $-2 \pm \sqrt{7}$

**Discriminants and Solutions of Quadratic Equations**

| Value of the Discriminant | Number of Solutions for $ax^2 + bx + c = 0$ | x-intercepts of Graph of Related Function $y = ax^2 + bx + c$ |
|---|---|---|
| $b^2 - 4ac > 0$ | two real solutions | two x-intercepts |
| $b^2 - 4ac = 0$ | one real solution | one x-intercept |
| $b^2 - 4ac < 0$ | no real solutions | no x-intercepts |

This table connects the discriminant, solutions, and x-intercepts.

**ELL SUPPORT**

**Q** How could you paraphrase the entries in the first column? **[Answers may vary. Samples: discriminant is positive, discriminant is zero, and discriminant is negative]**

**Q** What is the root word for *discriminant*? **[*discriminate* (which means to distinguish)]**

**VISUAL LEARNERS**

Some students think that "no real solutions" means an equation is entirely nonsensical. Highlight the last row of this table and point out that the graph of the corresponding quadratic function *does* exist; it simply has no x-intercepts.

### Problem 3

**Problem 3 Using the Discriminant**

What is the number of real solutions of $-2x^2 - 3x + 5 = 0$?

**Think**

Find the values of a, b, and c.

Evaluate $b^2 - 4ac$.

Interpret the discriminant.

**Write**

$a = -2, b = -3, c = 5$

$b^2 - 4ac = (-3)^2 - 4(-2)(5)$
$= 49$

The discriminant is positive. The equation has two real solutions.

**Q** In terms of the Quadratic Formula, why are there two real solutions? **[Answers may vary. Sample: In the Quadratic Formula, the square root follows ±; that means the Quadratic Formula will contain ±√49 or ±7, and two real values can be calculated.]**

**Q** What would the graph of $y = -2x^2 - 3x + 5$ look like? **[The parabola opens downward and intersects the x-axis twice.]**

**Got It? 3.** What is the number of real solutions of each equation?
   **a.** $2x^2 - 3x + 7 = 0$          **b.** $x^2 = 6x + 5$

### Got It?

**ERROR PREVENTION**

**Q** How can you check your work? **[Answers may vary. Sample: Graph the related function using a calculator, and check the number of x-intercepts.]**

PowerAlgebra.com          Lesson 4-7   The Quadratic Formula          243

**2. a.** $10.74
   **b.** Yes; a neg. profit means more money was spent than earned.
**3. a.** no real solutions
   **b.** two real solutions

## Problem 4

**Q** Why use the discriminant here instead of the Quadratic Formula? **[Answers may vary. Sample: You only need to know whether a real solution exists, not its actual value.]**

**Q** What would a positive discriminant mean here? **[The ball reaches 115 ft twice on its path.]**

**Q** If the ball's maximum height were 115 ft, what would happen to the discriminant? **[It would be zero since the maximum occurs once.]**

### Got It?

**Q** How does this height compare to 115 ft? **[higher]**

**Q** Why does it help to compare the heights? **[Answers may vary. Sample: The ball never reaches 115 ft, so it never reaches higher.]**

# 3 Lesson Check

### Do you know HOW?   ERROR INTERVENTION

• For Exercises 1–4, to avoid sign errors, suggest students circle each coefficient, including the leading + or −.

### Do you UNDERSTAND?

• For Exercises 8 and 10, if students unsuccessfully use trial-and-error, refer them to page 243 to help them find an equation.

### Close

**Q** Is the Quadratic Formula the best way to solve a quadratic equation? **[Answers may vary. Sample: The Quadratic Formula solves any quadratic equation, but other methods might be easier for certain equations.]**

---

**Problem 4** Using the Discriminant to Solve a Problem

**Projectile Motion** You hit a golf ball into the air from a height of 1 in. above the ground with an initial vertical velocity of 85 ft/s. The function $h = -16t^2 + 85t + \frac{1}{12}$ models the height, in feet, of the ball at time $t$, in seconds. Will the ball reach a height of 115 ft?

**Plan**

**What value should you substitute for $h$?**
You are trying to determine whether the ball will reach 115 ft. Replace $h$ with 115.

$$h = -16t^2 + 85t + \frac{1}{12}$$

$$115 = -16t^2 + 85t + \frac{1}{12} \qquad \text{Substitute 115 for } h.$$

$$0 = -16t^2 + 85t - 114\tfrac{11}{12} \qquad \text{Write the equation in standard form.}$$

$$a = -16, b = 85, c = -114\tfrac{11}{12} \qquad \text{Find the values of } a, b, \text{ and } c.$$

$$b^2 - 4ac = 85^2 - 4(-16)\left(-114\tfrac{11}{12}\right) \qquad \text{Evaluate the discriminant.}$$

$$= 7225 - 7354\tfrac{2}{3} \qquad \text{Simplify.}$$

$$= -129\tfrac{2}{3}$$

The discriminant is negative. The equation $115 = -16t^2 + 85t + \frac{1}{12}$ has no real solutions. The golf ball will not reach a height of 115 feet.

**Got It?** **4. Reasoning** Without solving an equation, will the golf ball in Problem 4 reach a height of 110 ft? Explain.

---

 **Lesson Check**

### Do you know HOW?

Solve each equation using the Quadratic Formula.

**1.** $x^2 - 5x - 7 = 0$

**2.** $x^2 + 3x - 13 = 0$

**3.** $2x^2 - 5x - 3 = 0$

**4.** $3x^2 - 4x + 3 = 0$

Find the discriminant of each quadratic equation. Determine the number of real solutions.

**5.** $-x^2 + 2x - 9 = 0$

**6.** $x^2 + 17x + 4 = 0$

**7.** $x^2 - 6x + 9 = 0$

### Do you UNDERSTAND?

**8. Reasoning** For what values of $k$ does the equation $x^2 + kx + 9 = 0$ have one real solution? two real solutions?

**9. Error Analysis** Your friend concluded that because two discriminants are equal, the solutions to the two equations are the same. Explain your friend's error. Give an example of two quadratic equations that disprove this conclusion.

**10. Reasoning** If one quadratic equation has a positive discriminant, and another quadratic equation has a discriminant equal to 0, can the two quadratic equations share a solution? Explain why or why not. If so, give two quadratic equations that meet this criterion.

---

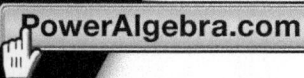

## 3 Lesson Check

For a digital lesson check, use the Got It questions.
**Support in Algebra 2 Companion**
• Lesson Check

## 4 Practice

Assign homework to individual students or to an entire class.

---

# Answers

### Got It? (continued)

**4.** Yes;
$$b^2 - 4ac = (85)^2 - 4(-16)\left(-109\tfrac{11}{12}\right)$$
$$= 190\tfrac{1}{3}.$$
The discriminant is positive. So the eq. has two real solutions.

### Lesson Check

**1.** $\dfrac{5 \pm \sqrt{53}}{2}$

**2.** $\dfrac{-3 \pm \sqrt{61}}{2}$

**3.** $3, -\dfrac{1}{2}$

**4.** no real solutions

**5.** −32; no real solutions

**6.** 273; two real solutions

**7.** 0; one real solution

**8.** $k = \pm 6$ for one real solution; $k > 6$ or $k < -6$ for two real solutions

**9.** Answers may vary. Sample: The discriminants of eqs. with one real solution are all zero and thus equal, but the solutions may or may not be equal. An example is $x^2 - 8x + 16$ and $x^2 - 4x + 4$. Each has a discriminant of zero, but the solutions are 4 and 2.

**10.** Yes; the eqs. can share common factors such as for $x^2 + 2x - 8$ where the discriminant is 36 and the solutions are 2 and −4, and $x^2 - 4x + 4$ where the discriminant is zero and the solution is 2.

## Practice and Problem-Solving Exercises

**A** Practice

**Solve each equation using the Quadratic Formula.**

 See Problem 1.

**11.** $x^2 - 4x + 3 = 0$    **12.** $x^2 + 8x + 12 = 0$    **13.** $2x^2 + 5x = 7$

**14.** $3x^2 + 2x - 1 = 0$    **15.** $x^2 + 10x = -25$    **16.** $2x^2 - 5 = -3x$

**17.** $x^2 = 3x - 1$    **18.** $6x - 5 = -x^2$    **19.** $3x^2 = 2(2x + 1)$

**20.** $2x(x - 1) = 3$    **21.** $x(x - 5) = -4$    **22.** $12x + 9x^2 = 5$

**23. Fundraising** Your class is selling boxes of flower seeds as a fundraiser. The total ◀ **See Problem 2.** profit $p$ depends on the amount $x$ that your class charges for each box of seeds. The equation $p = -0.5x^2 + 25x - 150$ models the profit of the fundraiser. What's the smallest amount, in dollars, that you can charge and make a profit of at least $125?

**24. Baking** Your local bakery sells more bagels when it reduces prices, but then its profit changes. The function $y = -1000x^2 + 1100x - 2.5$ models the bakery's daily profit in dollars, from selling bagels, where $x$ is the price of a bagel in dollars. What's the highest price the bakery can charge, in dollars, and make a profit of at least $200?

**Evaluate the discriminant for each equation. Determine the number of real** ◀ **See Problem 3.** **solutions.**

**25.** $x^2 + 4x + 5 = 0$    **26.** $x^2 - 4x - 5 = 0$    **27.** $-4x^2 + 20x - 25 = 0$

**28.** $-2x^2 + x - 28 = 0$    **29.** $2x^2 + 7x - 15 = 0$    **30.** $6x^2 - 2x + 5 = 0$

**31.** $-2x^2 + 7x = 6$    **32.** $x^2 - 12x + 36 = 0$    **33.** $x^2 + 8x = -16$

**34.** $3x^2 + x = -3$    **35.** $x + 2 = -3x^2$    **36.** $12x(x + 1) = -3$

**37. Business** The weekly revenue for a company is $r = -3p^2 + 60p + 1060$, ◀ **See Problem 4.** where $p$ is the price of the company's product. Use the discriminant to find whether there is a price for which the weekly revenue would be $1500.

**38. Physics** The equation $h = 80t - 16t^2$ models the height $h$ in feet reached in $t$ seconds by an object propelled straight up from the ground at a speed of 80 ft/s. Use the discriminant to find whether the object will ever reach a height of 90 ft.

**B** Apply

**39. Think About a Plan** The area of a rectangle is 36 in.$^2$. The perimeter of the rectangle is 36 in. What are the dimensions of the rectangle to the nearest hundredth of an inch?
• How can you write an equation using one variable to find the dimensions of the rectangle?
• How can the discriminant of the equation help you solve the problem?

**40. Writing** Summarize how to use the discriminant to analyze the types of solutions of a quadratic equation.

---

## Practice and Problem-Solving Exercises

**11.** 1, 3

**12.** −6, −2

**13.** $-\frac{7}{2}$, 1

**14.** $-1, \frac{1}{3}$

**15.** −5

**16.** $-\frac{5}{2}$, 1

**17.** $\frac{3 \pm \sqrt{5}}{2}$

**18.** $-3 \pm \sqrt{14}$

**19.** $\frac{2 \pm \sqrt{10}}{3}$

**20.** $\frac{1 \pm \sqrt{7}}{2}$

**21.** 1, 4

**22.** $-\frac{5}{3}, \frac{1}{3}$

**23.** $16.34

**24.** $.86

**25.** −4; no real solutions

**26.** 36; two

**27.** 0; one

**28.** −223; no real solutions

**29.** 169; two

**30.** −116; no real solutions

**31.** 1; two

**32.** 0; one

**33.** 0; one

**34.** −35; no real solutions

**35.** −23; no real solutions

**36.** 0; one

**37.** no

**38.** yes

**39.** 2.29 in. × 15.71 in.

**40.** Answers may vary. Sample: Assume the coefficients are real numbers. If the discriminant is negative, then there is no real solution. If the discriminant is zero, then there is one real solution. If the discriminant is positive, then there are two real solutions.

# 4 Practice

**ASSIGNMENT GUIDE**

Basic: 11–38 all, 39–42, 57–59, 67

Average: 11–37 odd, 39–69

Advanced: 11–37 odd, 39–77

Standardized Test Prep: 78–81

Mixed Review: 82–90

**Reasoning** exercises have blue headings.

**Applications** exercises have red headings.

**EXERCISE 57:** Use the Think About a Plan worksheet in the **Practice and Problem Solving Workbook** (also available in the Teaching Resources in print and online) to further support students' development in becoming independent learners.

**HOMEWORK QUICK CHECK**

To check students' understanding of key skills and concepts, go over Exercises 13, 23, 39, 57, and 67.

# Answers

## Practice and Problem-Solving
## Exercises (continued)

**41.** $-\frac{1}{6}$, 1

**42.** $-1.24$, 1.38

**43.** $-2.49$, 0.89

**44.** $-2.90$, 1.90

**45.** $-0.19$, 2.69

**46.** $-0.81$, 0.31

**47.** 1, 10

**48.** 0, 42

**49.** $-\frac{3}{2}$, $\frac{1}{2}$

**50.** $-3.45$, 1.45

**51.** $-1.70$, 4.70

**52.** $-7$, 7

**53.** $-8.47$, 0.47

**54.** $-\frac{1}{2}$, $\frac{3}{2}$

**55.** 1.47, $-7.47$

**56. a.** Answers may vary. Sample: Graph $y = 0.4409x^2 - 5.1724x + 99.0321$ and $y = 100$. The $x$-coordinate of the point where they intersect is the year when 100 million tons were released in the air. The graph of $y = 0.4409x^2 - 5.1724x + 99.0321$ is above the graph of $y = 100$ when more than 100 million tons were released.

  **b.** Write $y = 0.4409x^2 - 5.1724x + 99.0321 > 100$. Subtract 100 from both sides to get $y = 0.4409x^2 - 5.1724x - 0.9679 < 0$. Use the Quadratic Formula to solve.

  **c.** Check students' work.

**57.** about 1.89 s

**58.** two

**59.** one

**60.** none

**61.** two

**62.** two

**63.** two

**64.** two

**65.** two

**66.** none

**67. a.** $k$ such that $|k| < 12$

  **b.** 12 or $-12$

  **c.** $k$ such that $|k| > 12$

**68. a.** II

  **b.** III

  **c.** I

**69. a.** $x^2 = 100\pi$

  **b.** 17.72 cm

---

Solve each equation using any method. When necessary, round real solutions to the nearest hundredth.

**41.** $6x^2 - 5x - 1 = 0$

**42.** $7x^2 - x - 12 = 0$

**43.** $5x^2 + 8x - 11 = 0$

**44.** $4x^2 + 4x = 22$

**45.** $2x^2 - 1 = 5x$

**46.** $2x^2 + x = \frac{1}{2}$

**47.** $x^2 = 11x - 10$

**48.** $5x^2 = 210x$

**49.** $4x^2 + 4x = 3$

**50.** $2x^2 + 4x = 10$

**51.** $x^2 - 3x - 8 = 0$

**52.** $-3x^2 + 147 = 0$

**53.** $x^2 + 8x = 4$

**54.** $4x^2 - 4x - 3 = 0$

**55.** $x^2 = 11 - 6x$

**56. Air Pollution** The function $y = 0.4409x^2 - 5.1724x + 99.0321$ models the emissions of carbon monoxide in the United States since 1987, where $y$ represents the amount of carbon monoxide released in a year in millions of tons, and $x = 0$ represents the year 1987.

  **a.** How can you use a graph to estimate the year in which more than 100 million tons of carbon monoxide were released into the air?

  **b.** How can you use the Quadratic Formula to estimate the year in which more than 100 million tons of carbon monoxide were released into the air?

  **c.** Which method do you prefer? Explain why.

**57. Sports** A diver dives from a 10 m springboard. The equation $f(t) = -4.9t^2 + 4t + 10$ models her height above the pool at time $t$ in seconds. At what time does she enter the water?

**Without graphing, determine how many $x$-intercepts each function has.**

**58.** $y = -2x^2 + 3x - 1$

**59.** $y = 0.25x^2 + 2x + 4$

**60.** $y = x^2 + 3x + 5$

**61.** $y = -x^2 + 3x + 10$

**62.** $y = 3x^2 - 10x + 6$

**63.** $y = 10x^2 + 13x - 3$

**64.** $y = x^2 + 17x - 2$

**65.** $y = -5x^2 - 4x + 3$

**66.** $y = 7x^2 - 2x + 9$

**67. Reasoning** Determine the value(s) of $k$ for which $3x^2 + kx + 12 = 0$ has each type of solution.

  **a.** no real solutions

  **b.** exactly one real solution

  **c.** two real solutions

**68.** Use the discriminant to match each function with its graph.

  **a.** $f(x) = x^2 - 4x + 2$

  **b.** $f(x) = x^2 - 4x + 4$

  **c.** $f(x) = x^2 - 4x + 6$

  **I.**

  **II.**

  **III.**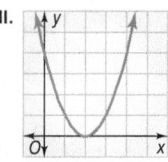

**69. a. Geometry** Write an equation to find the dimensions of a square that has the same area as a circle with a radius of 10 cm.

  **b.** Find the length of a side of the square, to the nearest hundredth centimeter.

**Challenge** Write a quadratic equation with the given solutions.

**70.** $\dfrac{3 + \sqrt{5}}{2}, \dfrac{3 - \sqrt{5}}{2}$     **71.** $\dfrac{-5 + \sqrt{13}}{2}, \dfrac{-5 - \sqrt{13}}{2}$     **72.** $\dfrac{-5 + \sqrt{17}}{4}, \dfrac{-5 - \sqrt{17}}{4}$

Solve each equation.

**73.** $|5 - 2x^2| = 5$     **74.** $|x^2 - 4x| = 3$     **75.** $|x^2 + 4x + 3| = 8$

**76.** Use the Quadratic Formula to prove each statement.
   **a.** The sum of the solutions of the quadratic equation $ax^2 + bx + c = 0$ is $-\dfrac{b}{a}$.
   **b.** The product of the solutions of the quadratic equation $ax^2 + bx + c = 0$ is $\dfrac{c}{a}$.

**77.** Explain the meaning of the value $\dfrac{\sqrt{b^2 - 4ac}}{2a}$ in terms of the graph of the standard quadratic function $y = ax^2 + bx + c$.

---

## Standardized Test Prep

**SAT/ACT**

GRIDDED RESPONSE

**78.** How many different real solutions are there for $2x^2 - 3x + 5 = 0$?

**79.** What is the $y$-value of the $y$-intercept of the quadratic function $y = 2(x + 2)^2 - 5$?

**80.** What is the $x$-value in the solution to the system $\begin{cases} 3x + y = -7 \\ 2x - 2y = -10 \end{cases}$?

**81.** The graph of the system of inequalities $\begin{cases} y \le \frac{1}{2}x + 3 \\ y \ge 6x - 30 \\ x \ge 0 \\ y \ge 0 \end{cases}$ is shown at the right.

What is the maximum value of the function $P = 3x - 4y$ for the $(x, y)$ pairs in the bounded region shown?

---

## Mixed Review

Solve each equation by completing the square.     ◀ See Lesson 4-6.

**82.** $x^2 - 8x - 20 = 0$     **83.** $2y^2 = 4y - 1$     **84.** $x^2 - 3x - 8 = 0$

Simplify by combining like terms.     ◀ See Lesson 1-3.

**85.** $z^2 + 8z^2 - 2z + 5z$     **86.** $4k - x - 3k + 5x$     **87.** $4y - (2y + 3x) - 5x$

**Get Ready!** To prepare for Lesson 4-8, do Exercises 88–90.     ◀ See p. 973.

Simplify each expression.

**88.** $\sqrt{(-2)^2 + 8^2}$     **89.** $\sqrt{3^2 + 4^2}$     **90.** $\sqrt{5^2 + (-12)^2}$

 PowerAlgebra.com    Lesson 4-7   The Quadratic Formula    **247**

---

### Standardized Test Prep

**78.** 0
**79.** 3
**80.** −3
**81.** 15

### Mixed Review

**82.** −2, 10
**83.** $\dfrac{2 \pm \sqrt{2}}{2}$
**84.** $\dfrac{3 \pm \sqrt{41}}{2}$
**85.** $9z^2 + 3z$
**86.** $4x + k$
**87.** $2y - 8x$
**88.** $2\sqrt{17}$
**89.** 5
**90.** 13

---

**70.** Answers may vary. Sample:
$x^2 - 3x + 1 = 0$

**71.** Answers may vary. Sample:
$x^2 + 5x + 3 = 0$

**72.** Answers may vary. Sample:
$2x^2 + 5x + 1 = 0$

**73.** $0, \pm\sqrt{5}$

**74.** $1, 3, 2 \pm 7$

**75.** $-5, 1$

**76. a.** $-\dfrac{b}{2a} + \dfrac{\sqrt{b^2 - 4ac}}{2a} + \left(-\dfrac{b}{2a}\right) - \dfrac{\sqrt{b^2 - 4ac}}{2a}$

$= \dfrac{(-2b)}{2a} = -\dfrac{b}{a}$

**b.** $\left(-\dfrac{b}{2a} + \dfrac{\sqrt{b^2 - 4ac}}{2a}\right) \times \left(-\dfrac{b}{2a} - \dfrac{\sqrt{b^2 - 4ac}}{2a}\right)$

$= \left(-\dfrac{b}{2a}\right)^2 - \left(\dfrac{\sqrt{b^2 - 4ac}}{2a}\right)^2$

$= \dfrac{(4ac)}{4a^2} = \dfrac{c}{a}$

**77.** The absolute value of $\dfrac{\sqrt{b^2 - 4ac}}{2a}$ is the distance from the axis of symmetry to the $x$-intercepts, if the discriminant is nonnegative.

# Lesson Resources

## Additional Instructional Support

### Algebra 2 Companion

Students can use the **Algebra 2 Companion** worktext (4 pages) as you teach the lesson. Use the Companion to support

- New Vocabulary
- Key Concepts
- Got It for each Problem
- Lesson Check

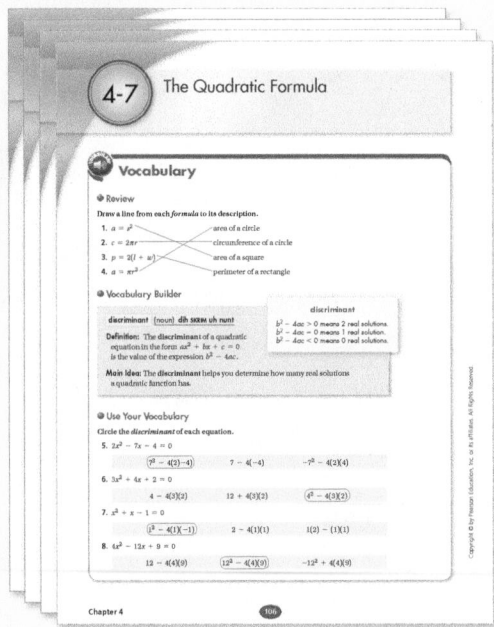

### ELL Support

**Use Manipulatives** Colored pencils and corresponding colored sticky notes are useful when students first practice the Quadratic Formula in Problem 1. Let students use colored pencils to write a "shell" of the formula with colored blanks.

$$x = \frac{-\boxed{b} \pm \sqrt{\boxed{b}^2 - 4 \cdot \boxed{a} \cdot \boxed{c}}}{2 \cdot \boxed{a}}.$$

After writing each equation in standard form and identifying the values of a, b, and c, have students copy the values onto color-coded sticky notes (e.g., blue for a, red for b, and green for c). Students fill each blank in the formula with an appropriate note. Then, as the expression is simplified, students can use larger yellow sticky notes to cover and replace parts of the formula.

## 5 Assess & Remediate

### Lesson Quiz

1. Solve $2x^2 + 3x = 6$ using the Quadratic Formula.

2. The equation $p = -5x^2 + 100x - 250$ models the profit p in dollars from selling pizzas, where x is the price per pizza in dollars. What is the highest price you can charge per pizza to profit $100?

3. Use the discriminant to determine the number of real solutions of $3x^2 - x = -1$.

4. **Do you UNDERSTAND?** You hit a ball from 4 ft above the ground with an initial vertical velocity of v ft/s. The function $h = -16t^2 + vt + 4$ models the height h in feet of the ball at time t in seconds. Explain how to find the initial velocity for which the ball reaches a maximum height of 40 ft.

### ANSWERS TO LESSON QUIZ

1. $\dfrac{-3}{4} \pm \dfrac{\sqrt{57}}{4}$

2. $15.48

3. discriminant $= -11$; no real solutions

4. Answers may vary. Sample: The maximum or minimum of a quadratic function occurs only once; if the ball reaches a maximum height of 40 ft, then $40 = -16t^2 + vt + 4$, or $0 = -16t^2 + vt - 36$, has one real solution and the discriminant is zero; solve $v^2 - 4(-16)(-36) = 0$ or $v = \pm 48$. The positive initial velocity is 48 ft/s.

### PRESCRIPTION FOR REMEDIATION

Use the student work on the Lesson Quiz to prescribe a differentiated review assignment:

| Points | Differentiated Remediation |
|--------|---------------------------|
| 0–2 | Intervention |
| 3 | On-level |
| 4 | Extension |

### 5 Assess & Remediate

Assign the Lesson Quiz. Appropriate intervention, practice, or enrichment is automatically generated based on student performance.

## Intervention

- **Reteaching** (2 pages) Provides reteaching and practice exercises for the key lesson concepts. Use with struggling students or absent students.

- **English Language Learner Support** Helps students develop and reinforce mathematical vocabulary and key concepts.

**All-in-One Resources/Online**

**Reteaching**

**All-in-One Resources/Online**

**English Language Learner Support**

# Differentiated Remediation *continued*

## On-Level

- **Practice** (2 pages) Provides extra practice for each lesson. For simpler practice exercises, use the Form K Practice pages found in the All-in-One Teaching Resources and online.

- **Think About a Plan** Helps students develop specific problem-solving skills and strategies by providing scaffolded guiding questions.

- **Standardized Test Prep** Focuses on all major exercises, all major question types, and helps students prepare for the high-stakes assessments.

## Extension

- **Enrichment** Provides students with interesting problems and activities that extend the concepts of the lesson.

- **Activities, Games, and Puzzles** Worksheets that can be used for concepts development, enrichment, and for fun!

---

### Practice and Problem Solving Wkbk/All-in-One Resources/Online
**Practice page 1**

4-7 Practice — Form G
The Quadratic Formula

Solve each equation using the Quadratic Formula.

1. $x^2 - 8x + 15 = 0$   3, 5
2. $x^2 + 12x + 35 = 0$   −7, −5
3. $3x^2 + 5x = 2$   −2, $\frac{1}{3}$
4. $2x^2 + 3 = 7x$   $\frac{1}{2}$, 3
5. $x^2 + 16 = 8x$   4
6. $x^2 = x - 1$   $\frac{1}{2} \pm \sqrt{3}$
7. $x(2x - 5) = 12$   $-\frac{3}{2}$, 4
8. $-3x^2 - 8x + 16 = 0$   −4, $\frac{4}{3}$
9. $x^2 + 4x = 3$   $-2 \pm \sqrt{7}$
10. $x^2 + 10x + 22 = 0$   $-5 \pm \sqrt{3}$
11. $4x(x + 1) = 7$   $\frac{-1 \pm 2\sqrt{2}}{2}$
12. $x(2x - 3) = 9$   $-\frac{3}{2}$, 3

13. The principal at a high school is planning a concert to raise money for the music programs. He determines the profit $p$ from ticket sales depends on the price $t$ of a ticket according to the equation $p = -200t^2 + 3600t - 6400$. All amounts are in dollars. If the goal is to raise $8500, what is the smallest amount the school should charge for a ticket to the concert?   $6.45

14. The equation $y = x^2 - 12x + 45$ models the number of books $y$ sold in a bookstore $x$ days after an award-winning author appeared at an autograph-signing reception. What was the first day that at least 100 copies of the book were sold?   day 16

15. The height of the tide measured at a seaside community varies according to the number of hours $t$ after midnight. If the height $h$, in feet, is currently given by the equation $h = -\frac{1}{2}t^2 + 6t - 9$, when will the tide first be at 6 ft?   about 3.55 h past midnight or about 3:33 A.M.

16. The height $h$, in feet, of a model rocket $t$ seconds after launch is given by $h = 256t - 16t^2$. As the rocket descends, it deploys a recovery parachute when it reaches 200 ft above the ground. At what time does the parachute deploy?   about 15.2 s

### Practice and Problem Solving Wkbk/All-in-One Resources/Online
**Practice page 2**

4-7 Practice (continued) — Form G
The Quadratic Formula

Evaluate the discriminant for each equation. Determine the number of real solutions.

17. $x^2 + 5x + 8 = 0$   −7; none
18. $x^2 - 5x + 4 = 0$   9; two
19. $-9x^2 + 12x - 4 = 0$   0; one
20. $-3x^2 + 5x - 4 = 0$   −23; none
21. $4x^2 + 4x = -1$   0; one
22. $6x^2 = x + 2$   49; two
23. $5x + 1 = 3x^2$   37; two
24. $4x^2 - x + 3 = 0$   −47; none
25. $4x^2 + 36x + 81 = 0$   0; one
26. $5x^2 = 3x - 2$   −31; none
27. $16x^2 - 56x + 49 = 0$   0; one
28. $4x^2 - 16x + 11 = 0$   80; two

29. In Exercise 16, the height of the rocket was given by $h = 256t - 16t^2$. Use the discriminant to answer the following questions.
   a. Will the rocket reach an altitude of 1000 ft?   yes
   b. Will the rocket reach an altitude of 1024 ft?   yes
   c. Will the rocket reach an altitude of 1048 ft?   no

30. The number $n$ of people using the elevator in an office building every hour is given by $n = t^2 - 10t + 40$. In this equation, $t$ is the number of hours after the building opens in the morning, $0 \le t \le 12$. Will the number of people using the elevator ever be less than 15 in any one hour? Use the discriminant to answer.   no

Solve each equation using any method. When necessary, round real solutions to the nearest hundredth.

31. $4x^2 + x - 3 = 0$   −1, $\frac{3}{4}$
32. $5x^2 - 6x - 2 = 0$   −0.27, 1.47
33. $x^2 - 5x - 9 = 0$   −1.41, 6.41
34. $15x^2 - 2x - 1 = 0$   $-\frac{1}{5}$, $\frac{1}{3}$
35. $2x^2 = 5x - 3$   1, $\frac{3}{2}$
36. $4x^2 + 3x = 5$   −1.55, 0.80

### All-in-One Resources/Online
**Enrichment**

4-7 Enrichment
The Quadratic Formula

The value of the discriminant of a quadratic equation tells you how many solutions the quadratic equation will have and the type of solutions they will be. The discriminant can also tell you if the quadratic equation is factorable.

Factor each of the following quadratic equations, if possible. Then determine the value of the discriminant for each equation.

1. $6x^2 - 11x + 3 = 0$   $(3x - 1)(2x - 3)$; 49
2. $4x^2 - x - 7 = 0$   not factorable; 113
3. $x^2 + 7x + 10 = 0$   $(x + 5)(x + 2)$; 9
4. $16x^2 - 7x = 0$   $x(16x + 1)$; 64
5. $x^2 + x - 5 = 0$   not factorable; 21
6. $2x^2 + 5x - 1 = 0$   not factorable; 33
7. $x^2 - 11x + 30 = 0$   $(x - 5)(x - 6)$; 1
8. $x^2 + 9x + 2 = 0$   not factorable; 73
9. $x^2 + 5x - 8 = 0$   not factorable; 57
10. $3x^2 + 8x + 4 = 0$   $(3x + 2)(x + 2)$; 16
11. $x^2 - 7x - 5 = 0$   not factorable; 69
12. $x^2 + 4x + 3 = 0$   $(x + 3)(x + 1)$; 4

Copy and complete the table using your previous answers.

| Discriminants of quadratics that are factorable | 49 | 9 | 64 | 1 | 16 | 4 |
| Discriminants of quadratics that are not factorable | 113 | 21 | 33 | 73 | 57 | 69 |

13. What types of numbers did you get for the values of the discriminants for the quadratics that were factorable?   The numbers are all perfect squares.

14. Writing How can the value of the discriminant tell you if a quadratic equation is factorable?   Answers may vary. Sample: If the discriminant is a perfect square, the equation will be factorable.

### Practice and Problem Solving Wkbk/All-in-One Resources/Online
**Think About a Plan**

4-7 Think About a Plan
The Quadratic Formula

Sports A diver dives from a 10 m springboard. The equation $f(t) = -4.9t^2 + 4t + 10$ models her height above the pool at time $t$. At what time does she enter the water?

**Understanding the Problem**

1. What does the function represent?
   the diver's height above the water at time $t$ in seconds

2. What is the problem asking you to determine?
   at what time the diver's height above the water equals 0

3. Do you need to use the height of the springboard to solve the problem? Explain.
   No; you don't use the height of the springboard. You only need to find the zeros of the function.

**Planning the Solution**

4. What are three possible methods for solving this problem?
   Graph the equation, factor the equation, use the Quadratic Formula.

5. If a solution exists, which method will give an exact solution? Explain.
   The Quadratic Formula; you can only estimate from a graph, and not all equations have expressions that are factorable.

**Getting an Answer**

6. Is there more than one reasonable solution to the problem? Explain.
   No; the equation has two zeros, but one of them is negative. Time moves forward and cannot be negative.

7. At what time does the diver enter the water?
   The diver enters the water about 1.89 s after starting her dive.

### Practice and Problem Solving Wkbk/All-in-One Resources/Online
**Standardized Test Prep**

4-7 Standardized Test Prep
The Quadratic Formula

**Multiple Choice**

For Exercises 1–6, choose the correct letter.

1. What is the solution of $3x^2 + 2x - 5 = 0$? Use the Quadratic Formula.   A
   A) $-\frac{5}{3}$, 1   B) $-1$, $\frac{5}{3}$   C) $1$, $\frac{5}{3}$   D) $-5$, $1\frac{1}{3}$

2. What is the solution of $2x^2 - 8x + 3 = 0$? Use the Quadratic Formula.   H
   F) $\frac{-4 \pm \sqrt{22}}{2}$   G) $\frac{-4 \pm \sqrt{10}}{2}$   H) $\frac{4 \pm \sqrt{10}}{2}$   I) $\frac{4 \pm \sqrt{22}}{2}$

3. What is the solution of $x^2 - 5x = 5$? Use the Quadratic Formula.   D
   A) $-5$, 1   B) $-1$, 5   C) $\frac{5 \pm \sqrt{5}}{2}$   D) $\frac{5 \pm 3\sqrt{5}}{2}$

4. What is the solution of $x^2 = 6x - 3$? Use the Quadratic Formula.   I
   F) $-3 \pm \sqrt{6}$   G) $-3$   H) 3   I) $3 \pm \sqrt{6}$

5. What is the discriminant of the equation $3x^2 - 7x + 1 = 0$?   B
   A) 61   B) 37   C) $\sqrt{37}$   D) $-19$

6. What is the discriminant of the equation $4x^2 + 28x + 49 = 0$?   H
   F) 5472   G) $-756$   H) 0   I) 1568

**Extended Response**

7. The equation $d = n^2 - 12n + 43$ models the number of defective items $d$ produced in a manufacturing process when there are $n$ workers in a restricted area. Use the discriminant to answer the following questions. Show your work.
   a. Will the number of defective items ever be 10?
   b. Will the number of defective items ever be 7?
   c. Will the number of defective items ever be 5?
   [4] a. yes; b. yes; c. no; the answers are based on the value of the discriminant for each case: (a) 12, (b) 0, and (c) −8.
   [3] appropriate method with one computational error
   [2] appropriate method with several computational errors
   [1] correct answers but no work shown
   [0] incorrect answers and no work shown OR no answers given

### Online Teacher Resource Center
**Activities, Games, and Puzzles**

4-7 Game: Risk and Reward
The Quadratic Formula

Provide the host with the following questions and answers for the given categories and point values.

**Vocabulary**

| Points | Question | Answer |
|---|---|---|
| 10 | quadratic equation | an equation that can be written in the form $ax^2 + bx + c = 0$ |
| 20 | vertex | the lowest (or highest) point on the graph of a quadratic function, or the intersection of a parabola with its axis of symmetry |
| 30 | parabola | the graph of a quadratic function |
| 40 | discriminant | for a quadratic function $f(x) = ax^2 + bx + c$, the value $b^2 - 4ac$ |
| 50 | quadratic formula | $x = \frac{-b \pm \sqrt{b^2 - 4ac}}{2a}$, the solutions of the quadratic function $f(x) = ax^2 + bx + c$ |

**With**

| Points | Question | Answer |
|---|---|---|
| 10 | $x^2 + 2x - 8 = 0$ | −4, 2 |
| 20 | $9x^2 + 16 = -24x$ | $-\frac{4}{3}$ |
| 30 | $2x^2 + 4x - 6 = 0$ | −3, 1 |
| 40 | $x^2 - 10x + 18 = 0$ | $5 \pm \sqrt{7}$ |
| 50 | $4x^2 + 4x - 1 = 0$ | $\frac{-1 \pm \sqrt{2}}{2}$ |

**Without**

| Points | Question | Answer |
|---|---|---|
| 10 | $x^2 - 4x - 21 = 0$ | −3, 7 |
| 20 | $4x^2 - 36x + 81 = 0$ | $\frac{9}{2}$ |
| 30 | $6x^2 + 11x - 10 = 0$ | $-\frac{5}{2}$, $\frac{2}{3}$ |
| 40 | $x^2 + 6x - 11 = 0$ | $-3 \pm 2\sqrt{5}$ |
| 50 | $6x^2 + 2x = 1$ | $\frac{-1 \pm \sqrt{7}}{6}$ |

**Number/Type**

| Points | Question | Answer |
|---|---|---|
| 10 | $4x^2 + 4x - 3 = 0$ | 2 real |
| 20 | $25x^2 - 30x = -9$ | 1 real |
| 30 | $4x^2 - 7x + 5 = 0$ | 2 complex |
| 40 | $3x^2 - 5x - 2$ | 2 real |
| 50 | $\frac{1}{2}x^2 + \frac{4}{3}x + 1 = 0$ | 2 complex |

# 1 Interactive Learning

## Solve It!

**PURPOSE** To explore a function that simulates a cycle of powers for $-1$ or $i = \sqrt{-1}$

**PROCESS** Students may make and complete a table that only uses powers of $a$, replace the powers of $a$ with appropriate powers of $b$, $c$, and $d$, and identify the pattern of reducing the powers.

### FACILITATE

**Q** Which letter can you multiply $a$ by and get $a$? What kind of number is this? **[$d$; an identity]**

**Q** How can you simplify $a^6$? **[Answers may vary. Sample: Rewrite as $a^4 a^2 = b$.]**

**Q** How can you simplify $a^{4n}$? **[$(a^4)^n = d$]**

**ANSWER** See Solve It in Answers on next page.
**CONNECT THE MATH** In the Solve It, students identify a pattern of powers using the base $a$. In this lesson, students will apply the properties of powers of $i$.

# 2 Guided Instruction

## Take Note

SYNTHEZISING

**Q** Why must $a$ be a positive number? **[Sample: show by counterexample. Let $a = -1$. Then, $\sqrt{-(-1)} = \sqrt{-1 \cdot -1} = \sqrt{-1} \cdot \sqrt{-1} = i \cdot i = -1$. However, $\sqrt{-(-1)} = \sqrt{1} = 1$, which is a contradiction.]**

---

**Objectives** To identify, graph, and perform operations with complex numbers
To find complex number solutions of quadratic equations

One of $a$, $b$, $c$, and $d$ acts like an identity element.

**Getting Ready!**

Here is a partially-completed multiplication table.
If you know that
$a \cdot a = a^2 = b$, $a \cdot b = a \cdot a^2 = a^3 = c$,
$a^4 = d$, and $a^5 = a$,
how would you complete the table? What is $a^{99}$?
Explain your reasoning.

| $\cdot$ | $a$ | $b$ | $c$ | $d$ |
|---|---|---|---|---|
| $a$ | $b$ | $c$ | ▪ | ▪ |
| $b$ | ▪ | ▪ | ▪ | ▪ |
| $c$ | ▪ | ▪ | ▪ | ▪ |

### Lesson Vocabulary

- imaginary unit
- imaginary number
- complex number
- pure imaginary number
- complex number plane
- absolute value of a complex number
- complex conjugates

In Chapter 1, you learned about different subsets of real numbers. The set of real numbers is itself a subset of a larger set of numbers, the *complex numbers*. Curiously, the complex numbers include a number like $a$ in the Solve It. Its fifth power is itself.

**Essential Understanding** The complex numbers are based on a number whose square is $-1$.

The **imaginary unit** $i$ is the complex number whose square is $-1$. So, $i^2 = -1$, and $i = \sqrt{-1}$.

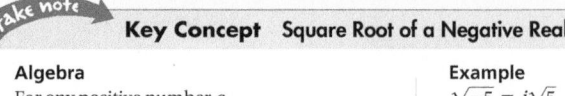

**Key Concept** Square Root of a Negative Real Number

**Algebra**
For any positive number $a$,
$\sqrt{-a} = \sqrt{-1 \cdot a} = \sqrt{-1} \cdot \sqrt{a} = i\sqrt{a}$.

**Example**
$\sqrt{-5} = i\sqrt{5}$

Note that $(\sqrt{-5})^2 = (i\sqrt{5})^2 = i^2(\sqrt{5})^2 = -1 \cdot 5 = -5$ (not 5).

---

## 4-8 Preparing to Teach

### BIG idea Solving Equations and Inequalities    UbD

#### ESSENTIAL UNDERSTANDINGS

- Every quadratic equation has complex number solutions (that sometimes are real numbers).
- The imaginary unit is the complex number whose square is $-1$. So $i^2 = -1$ and $i = \sqrt{-1}$.
- The real solutions of a quadratic equation show the zeros of the related quadratic function and the $x$-intercepts of its graph.

### Math Background

The set of complex numbers includes imaginary and real numbers, as shown in Lesson 1-2. Thus, every quadratic equation has solutions, and some may be imaginary.

Be aware of the common misconception that imaginary numbers do not really exist. Imaginary

numbers were introduced to solve quadratic equations of the form $x^2 + k = 0$, where $k > 0$. The imaginary unit $i$ is a number, not a variable, and is defined as $\sqrt{-1}$. In general, you cannot order complex numbers, since they cannot be graphed on the real number line.

Complex numbers have numerous applications in many fields including engineering, science, physics, and computer graphics.

### Support Student Learning

Use the **Algebra 2 Companion** to engage and support students during instruction. See Lesson Resources at the end of this lesson for details.

**PowerAlgebra.com**

## 1 Interactive Learning

### Solve It!
Step out how to solve the Problem with helpful hints and an online question. Other questions are listed above in Interactive Learning.

**Problem 1** Simplifying a Number Using $i$

How do you write $\sqrt{-18}$ by using the imaginary unit $i$?

$$\sqrt{-18} = \sqrt{-1 \cdot 18}$$
$$= \sqrt{-1} \cdot \sqrt{18} \quad \text{Multiplication Property of Square Roots}$$
$$= i \cdot \sqrt{18} \quad \text{Definition of } i$$
$$= i \cdot 3\sqrt{2} \quad \text{Simplify.}$$
$$= 3i\sqrt{2}$$

**Got It?** **1.** How do you write each number in parts (a)–(c) by using the imaginary unit $i$?

 **a.** $\sqrt{-12}$ **b.** $\sqrt{-25}$ **c.** $\sqrt{-7}$
 **d.** Reasoning Explain why $\sqrt{-64} \neq -\sqrt{64}$.

An **imaginary number** is any number of the form $a + bi$, where $a$ and $b$ are real numbers and $b \neq 0$. Imaginary numbers and real numbers together make up the set of *complex numbers*.

### Key Concept Complex Numbers

You can write a **complex number** in the form $a + bi$, where $a$ and $b$ are real numbers.

If $b = 0$, the number $a + bi$ is a real number.

If $a = 0$ and $b \neq 0$, the number $a + bi$ is a **pure imaginary number**.

$$a + bi$$
Real part, Imaginary part

**Complex Numbers ($a + bi$)**

| Real Numbers ($a + 0i$) | Imaginary Numbers ($a + bi$, $b \neq 0$) |
| | Pure Imaginary Numbers ($0 + bi$, $b \neq 0$) |

In the **complex number plane**, the point $(a, b)$ represents the complex number $a + bi$. To graph a complex number, locate the real part on the horizontal axis and the imaginary part on the vertical axis.

The **absolute value of a complex number** is its distance from the origin in the complex plane.

$$|a + bi| = \sqrt{a^2 + b^2}$$

$$|3 - 2i| = \sqrt{13}$$

---

## Problem 1

By convention, $i$ is written before the radical.

**Q** Why is it better to write $i\sqrt{18}$ rather than $\sqrt{18}i$? **[so that you do not mistakenly think that the $i$ is under the radical]**

**Q** How do you know that both ways are equivalent? **[because of the Commutative Property of Multiplication]**

### Got It?

**Q** For 1d, consider $\sqrt{-64} = \sqrt{-1 \cdot 64}$. Can you move $-1$ outside of the radical? Explain. **[No; since $\sqrt{-1}$ does not equal $-1$, you cannot move it outside of the radical.]**

### Take Note

Complex numbers and imaginary numbers are not synonymous; the set of complex numbers consists of both real and imaginary numbers.

**Q** How is the absolute value of a complex number like the absolute value of a real number? **[Answers may vary. Sample: They both represent the distance from the point to the origin.]**

**Q** Where does the formula $\sqrt{a^2 + b^2}$ come from? **[The distance formula is the distance from the origin to ($a, b$) derived using the Pythagorean Theorem.]**

---

## 2 Guided Instruction

Each Problem is worked out and supported online.

**Problem 1**
Simplifying a Number Using $i$

**Problem 2**
Graphing in the Complex Number Plane

**Problem 3**
Adding and Subtracting Complex Numbers

**Alternative Problem 3**
Adding and Subtracting Complex Numbers
*Animated*

**Problem 4**
Multiplying Complex Numbers

**Problem 5**
Dividing Complex Numbers
*Animated*

**Problem 6**
Finding Pure Imaginary Solutions

**Problem 7**
Finding Imaginary Solutions
*Animated*

## Answers

### Solve It!

| · | a | b | c | d |
|---|---|---|---|---|
| a | b | c | d | a |
| b | c | d | a | b |
| c | d | a | b | c |

$a^{99} = c$; $99 \div 4 = 24$ with a remainder of 3, and $a^3 = c$.

### Got It?

 **1. a.** $2i\sqrt{3}$
   **b.** $5i$
   **c.** $i\sqrt{7}$
   **d.** $8i \neq -8$

## Problem 2

VISUAL LEARNERS

**Q** What determines the horizontal position of a complex number? **[the real part]**

**Q** What determines the vertical position of a complex number? **[the imaginary part]**

### Got It?

**Q** What type of numbers lie on the imaginary axis? **[pure imaginary numbers]**

**Q** What type of numbers lie on the real axis? **[real numbers]**

**Q** If $a + bi$ lies in Quadrant II, then is $a$ positive or negative? $b$? **[negative; positive]**

## Problem 3

**Q** Is it possible to add two complex numbers and get a real number? Explain. **[Yes; real numbers are a subset of complex numbers. If the imaginary parts of the complex numbers are additive inverses, the sum is real. For example, $4 - 2i + 3 + 2i = 7$.]**

**Q** Is it possible to add two real numbers and get an imaginary number? Explain. **[No; the set of real numbers is closed under addition.]**

### Got It?                    ERROR PREVENTION

When subtracting imaginary numbers, the subtraction sign must be distributed over both the real and imaginary parts.

**Q** Are the numbers in 3d additive inverses? Explain. **[No; the sum is $18i$, not 0.]**

---

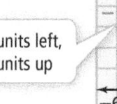 **Problem 2** Graphing in the Complex Number Plane

**What are the graph and absolute value of each number?**

**A** $-5 + 3i$

$$|-5 + 3i| = \sqrt{(-5)^2 + 3^2}$$
$$= \sqrt{34}$$

6 units up

5 units left, 3 units up

**Think**

Where is a pure imaginary number in the complex plane?
The real part of a pure imaginary number is 0. The number must be on the imaginary axis.

**B** $6i$

$$|6i| = |0 + 6i|$$
$$= \sqrt{0^2 + 6^2}$$
$$= \sqrt{36}$$
$$= 6$$

✓ **Got It?** **2.** What are the graph and absolute value of each number?

**a.** $5 - i$ **b.** $-3 - 2i$ **c.** $1 + 4i$

---

**Essential Understanding** You can define operations on the set of complex numbers so that when you restrict the operations to the subset of real numbers, you get the familiar operations on the real numbers.

To add or subtract complex numbers, combine the real parts and the imaginary parts separately. If the sum of two complex numbers is 0, or $0 + 0i$, then each number is the opposite, or additive inverse, of the other. The associative and commutative properties apply to complex numbers as well.

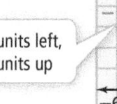 **Problem 3** Adding and Subtracting Complex Numbers

**What is each sum or difference?**

**A** $(4 - 3i) + (-4 + 3i)$

$4 + (-4) + (-3i) + 3i$    Use the commutative and associative properties.

$0 + 0 = 0$           $4 - 3i$ and $-4 + 3i$ are additive inverses.

**B** $(5 - 3i) - (-2 + 4i)$

$5 - 3i + 2 - 4i$    To subtract, add the opposite.

$5 + 2 - 3i - 4i$    Use the commutative and associative properties

$7 - 7i$          Simplify.

**Plan**

How is adding complex numbers similar to adding algebraic expressions?
Adding the real parts and imaginary parts separately is like adding like terms.

✓ **Got It?** **3.** What is each sum or difference?

**a.** $(7 - 2i) + (-3 + i)$    **b.** $(1 + 5i) - (3 - 2i)$

**c.** $(8 + 6i) - (8 - 6i)$    **d.** $(-3 + 9i) + (3 + 9i)$

---

# Additional Problems

**1.** How do you write $\sqrt{-24}$ using the imaginary unit $i$?

**ANSWER** $2i\sqrt{6}$

**2.** What are the graph and absolute value of each complex number?

**a.** $1 - 3i$

**b.** $-4 + i$

**ANSWERS**

**a.** $\sqrt{10}$

**b.** $\sqrt{17}$

**3.** What is each sum or difference?

**a.** $(2 + i) + (-3 + 3i)$

**b.** $(5 + i) + (5 - i)$

**c.** $(-6 - 2i) - (4 + 2i)$

**ANSWERS**

**a.** $-1 + 4i$

**b.** $10$

**c.** $-10 - 4i$

**4.** What is each product?

**a.** $-i(4 - 8i)$

**b.** $(5 - 7i)(-4 - 3i)$

**ANSWERS**

**a.** $-8 - 4i$

**b.** $-41 + 13i$

**5.** What is each quotient?

**a.** $\dfrac{7i}{8 + i}$

**b.** $\dfrac{5 + 2i}{3 - 2i}$

**ANSWERS**

**a.** $\dfrac{7}{65} + \dfrac{56}{65}i$

**b.** $\dfrac{11}{13} + \dfrac{16}{13}i$

**6.** What are the solutions of $3x^2 + 12 = 0$?

**ANSWER** $\pm 2i$

**7.** What are the solutions of $-x^2 + 4x - 5 = 0$?

**ANSWER** $2 + i, 2 - i$

You multiply complex numbers $a + bi$ and $c + di$ as you would multiply binomials. For imaginary parts $bi$ and $di$, $(bi)(di) = bd(i)^2 = bd(-1) = -bd$.

### Problem 4  Multiplying Complex Numbers

**What is each product?**

Ⓐ $(3i)(-5 + 2i)$

| | |
|---|---|
| $-15i + 6i^2$ | Distributive Property |
| $-15i + 6(-1)$ | Substitute $-1$ for $i^2$. |
| $-6 - 15i$ | Simplify. |

**Think**

How do you multiply two binomials?
Multiply each term of one binomial by each term of the other binomial.

Ⓑ $(4 + 3i)(-1 - 2i)$

$-4 - 8i - 3i - 6i^2$

$-4 - 8i - 3i - 6(-1)$ ⟵ Substitute $-1$ for $i^2$.

$2 - 11i$

Ⓒ $(-6 + i)(-6 - i)$

$36 + 6i - 6i - i^2$

$36 + 6i - 6i - (-1)$

$37$

✔ **Got It?** **4.** What is each product?

**a.** $(7i)(3i)$ **b.** $(2 - 3i)(4 + 5i)$ **c.** $(-4 + 5i)(-4 - 5i)$

In Problem 4(c), the product is a real number. Number pairs of the form $a + bi$ and $a - bi$ are **complex conjugates**. The product of complex conjugates is a real number.

$$(a + bi)(a - bi) = a^2 - (bi)^2 = a^2 - b^2i^2 = a^2 - b^2(-1) = a^2 + b^2$$

You can use complex conjugates to simplify quotients of complex numbers.

### Problem 5  Dividing Complex Numbers

**Plan**

What is the goal?
Write the quotient in the form $a + bi$.

**What is each quotient?**

Ⓐ $\dfrac{9 + 12i}{3i}$

$\dfrac{9 + 12i}{3i} \cdot \dfrac{-3i}{-3i}$ ⟶ Multiply numerator and denominator by the complex conjugate of the denominator.

$\dfrac{-27i - 36i^2}{-9i^2}$

$\dfrac{-27i - 36(-1)}{-9(-1)}$ ⟶ Substitute $-1$ for $i^2$.

$\dfrac{36 - 27i}{9}$

$4 - 3i$

Ⓑ $\dfrac{2 + 3i}{1 - 4i}$

$\dfrac{2 + 3i}{1 - 4i} \cdot \dfrac{1 + 4i}{1 + 4i}$

$\dfrac{2 + 8i + 3i + 12i^2}{1 + 4i - 4i - 16i^2}$

$\dfrac{2 + 8i + 3i + 12(-1)}{1 + 4i - 4i - 16(-1)}$

$\dfrac{-10 + 11i}{17}$

$-\dfrac{10}{17} + \dfrac{11}{17}i$

✔ **Got It?** **5.** What is each quotient?

**a.** $\dfrac{5 - 2i}{3 + 4i}$ **b.** $\dfrac{4 - i}{6i}$ **c.** $\dfrac{8 - 7i}{8 + 7i}$

---

**Problem 4**

**Q** Is it possible to multiply two imaginary numbers and get a real number? Explain. **[Yes; the set of imaginary numbers is not closed under multiplication. For example, $i \cdot i = -1$, a real number.]**

**Q** What is the absolute value of each complex number in 4C? How does it compare to the product? **[Each absolute value is $\sqrt{37}$, and the product is 37, which is the absolute value squared.]**

**Q** How are the numbers in 4C related? **[Answers may vary. Sample: They are factors of a difference of two squares.]**

**Got It?**

**Q** What method of multiplying binomials can you use to multiply complex numbers? **[Answers may vary. Sample: FOIL]**

**Problem 5**

**Q** Why is $\dfrac{-10 + 11i}{17}$ rewritten as $-\dfrac{10}{17} + \dfrac{11i}{17}$? **[because $-\dfrac{10}{17} + \dfrac{11i}{17}$ is in $a + bi$ form]**

**Q** Could you solve 5A by multiplying the fraction by $\dfrac{i}{i}$? Explain. **[Yes; $i$ would be eliminated from the denominator.]**

**Q** Could you do the same for 5B? Explain. **[No; the denominator would still be a complex number.]**

**Got It?**

**Q** What is the complex conjugate of $6i$? Explain. **[$-6i$; $6i = 0 + 6i$, so the conjugate is $0 - 6i = -6i$.]**

---

# Answers

## Got It? (continued)

**2. a.**  $; \sqrt{26}$

**b.**  $; \sqrt{13}$

**c.**  $; \sqrt{17}$

**3. a.** $4 - i$

**b.** $-2 + 7i$

**c.** $12i$

**d.** $18i$

**4. a.** $-21$

**b.** $23 - 2i$

**c.** $41$

**5. a.** $\dfrac{7}{25} - \dfrac{26}{25}i$

**b.** $-\dfrac{1}{6} - \dfrac{2}{3}i$

**c.** $\dfrac{15}{113} - \dfrac{112}{113}i$

## Problem 6

**Q** When a quadratic equation has no linear term, what are the possible solutions? **[two real or two pure imaginary solutions]**

**Q** How many solutions are there? Identify them. **[2; 4i and −4i]**

**Q** How are the solutions related? Explain. **[Samples: They are additive inverses; their sum is 0, and they are complex conjugates.]**

### Got It?

**Q** How can you check your answer? **[Substitute the solutions into the original equation.]**

## Problem 7

**Q** What is a quick way to identify whether a quadratic equation has complex solutions? **[Determine whether the discriminant of the quadratic formula is positive or negative.]**

**Q** Why does the number of real solutions not affect the *y*-intercept? **[The *y*-intercept of a quadratic function is always the function's value at *x* = 0.]**

**Q** What would be a good way to check whether the answer is reasonable? **[Answers may vary. Sample: Graph the associated function and see whether it has any real solutions.]**

### Got It?

**Q** If you know the solutions are imaginary, why does it make sense that the graph does not cross the *x*-axis? **[because *x*-intercepts occur at real number solutions]**

---

**Essential Understanding** Every quadratic equation has complex number solutions (that sometimes are real numbers).

Some quadratic equations have pure imaginary solutions.

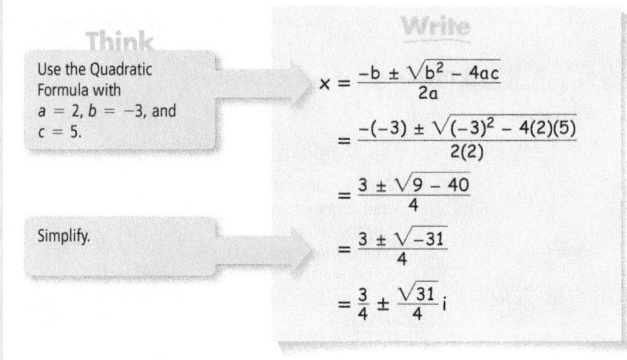

**Problem 6** Finding Pure Imaginary Solutions

What are the solutions of $2x^2 + 32 = 0$?

$$2x^2 + 32 = 0$$

$$2x^2 = -32 \quad \text{Isolate } x^2.$$

$$x^2 = -16 \quad \text{Divide both sides by 2.}$$

$$x = \pm\sqrt{-16} \quad \text{Find square roots.}$$

$$x = \pm 4i \quad \text{Simplify.}$$

**Plan**

**How do you solve a quadratic equation of the form $ax^2 + c = 0$?**
Use properties of equality to isolate the variable.

**Got It? 6.** What are the solutions of each equation?

    **a.** $5x^2 + 20 = 0$         **b.** $x^2 + 15 = 0$

Some quadratic equations have solutions that are imaginary numbers.

**Problem 7** Finding Imaginary Solutions

What are the solutions of $2x^2 - 3x + 5 = 0$?

**Think**

Use the Quadratic Formula with $a = 2$, $b = -3$, and $c = 5$.

Simplify.

**Write**

$$x = \frac{-b \pm \sqrt{b^2 - 4ac}}{2a}$$

$$= \frac{-(-3) \pm \sqrt{(-3)^2 - 4(2)(5)}}{2(2)}$$

$$= \frac{3 \pm \sqrt{9 - 40}}{4}$$

$$= \frac{3 \pm \sqrt{-31}}{4}$$

$$= \frac{3}{4} \pm \frac{\sqrt{31}}{4} i$$

**Got It? 7.** What are the solutions of each equation?

    **a.** $3x^2 - x + 2 = 0$         **b.** $x^2 - 4x + 5 = 0$

---

# Answers

**7.** error in the sign of the last term of the first line, which carries through to the end of the calculation; the line should be: "... $= 16 + 28i - 28i - 49i^2$

$$= 16 + 49$$

$$= 65.$$"

## Got It? (continued)

**6. a.** $\pm 2i$

   **b.** $\pm i\sqrt{15}$

**7. a.** $\frac{1}{6} \pm \frac{i\sqrt{23}}{6}$

   **b.** $2 \pm i$

## Lesson Check

**1.** $5i\sqrt{3}$         **2.** 5

**3.** $\pm 4i$         **4.** $7 - 3i$

**5.** $13 - 6i$

**6.** The add. inv. of a complex number, $a + bi$, is the opposite of the complex number, or $-a - bi$. The complex conjugate of a complex number, $a + bi$, is the real part plus the opposite of the imaginary part of the complex number, or $a - bi$.

**Lesson Check**

**Do you know HOW?**

1. Simplify $\sqrt{-75}$ by using the imaginary number $i$.

2. Find the absolute value of $4 - 3i$.

3. Solve the equation $x^2 + 16 = 0$. Check your answers.

Simplify each expression.

4. $(4 - 2i) - (-3 + i)$

5. $(2 + i)(4 - 5i)$

**Do you UNDERSTAND?**

6. **Vocabulary** Explain the difference between the additive inverse of a complex number and a complex conjugate.

7. **Error Analysis** Describe and correct the error made in simplifying the expression $(4 - 7i)(4 + 7i)$.

$$(4 - 7i)(4 + 7i) = 16 + 28i - 28i + 49i^2$$
$$= 16 - 49$$
$$= -33$$

  **Practice and Problem-Solving Exercises**

**A** Practice

Simplify each number by using the imaginary number $i$.     ◀ **See Problem 1.**

8. $\sqrt{-4}$    9. $\sqrt{-7}$    10. $\sqrt{-15}$    11. $\sqrt{-81}$    12. $\sqrt{-50}$

Plot each complex number and find its absolute value.     ◀ **See Problem 2.**

13. $2i$    14. $5 + 12i$    15. $2 - 2i$    16. $1 - 4i$    17. $3 - 6i$

Simplify each expression.     ◀ **See Problems 3 and 4.**

18. $(2 + 4i) + (4 - i)$    19. $(-3 - 5i) + (4 - 2i)$    20. $(7 + 9i) + (-5i)$

21. $(12 + 5i) - (2 - i)$    22. $(-6 - 7i) - (1 + 3i)$    23. $(8 + i)(2 + 7i)$

24. $(-6 - 5i)(1 + 3i)$    25. $(-6i)^2$    26. $(9 + 4i)^2$

Write each quotient as a complex number.     ◀ **See Problem 5.**

27. $\dfrac{3 - 2i}{5i}$    28. $\dfrac{-2i}{1 + i}$    29. $\dfrac{4 - 3i}{-1 - 4i}$

30. $\dfrac{i + 2}{i - 2}$    31. $\dfrac{4}{2 - 3i}$    32. $\dfrac{3 + 2i}{(1 + i)^2}$

Solve each equation. Check your answer.     ◀ **See Problem 6.**

33. $x^2 + 25 = 0$    34. $2x^2 + 1 = 0$    35. $3s^2 + 2 = -62$

36. $x^2 = -7$    37. $x^2 + 36 = 0$    38. $-5x^2 - 3 = 0$

Find all solutions to each quadratic equation.     ◀ **See Problem 7.**

39. $x^2 + 2x + 3 = 0$    40. $-3x^2 + x - 3 = 0$    41. $2x^2 - 4x + 7 = 0$

42. $x^2 - 2x + 2 = 0$    43. $x^2 + 5 = 4x$    44. $2x(x - 3) = -5$

---

# 3 Lesson Check

### Do you know HOW?    ERROR INTERVENTION

• For Exercise 2, if students have difficulty with the definition of absolute value of complex numbers, compare it to the absolute value of a real number by drawing a graph and showing that absolute value is the distance from the origin. If needed, revisit Problem 2, or use Additional Problem 2.

### Do you UNDERSTAND?

• In Exercise 7, students should see that the negative sign is not correctly distributed. If they have trouble understanding multiplication of complex numbers, compare it to multiplying binomials, and show more examples. If needed, revisit Problem 4, or use Additional Problem 4.

### Close

**Q** Is the square of a complex number always a real number? Explain. **[No; only the square of a pure imaginary number is always a real number.]**

**Q** How could you simplify $i^5$? **[Use the rules of exponents; $i^5 = (i^4)i = (1)i = i$.]**

---

**1–7.** See page 252.

## Practice and Problem-Solving Exercises

8. $2i$       9. $i\sqrt{7}$

10. $i\sqrt{15}$   11. $9i$    12. $5i\sqrt{2}$

13.  ; 2

14.  ; 13

15.  ; $2\sqrt{2}$

16. ; $\sqrt{17}$

17. ; $3\sqrt{5}$

18. $6 + 3i$     19. $1 - 7i$

20. $7 + 4i$     21. $10 + 6i$

22. $-7 - 10i$   23. $9 + 58i$

24. $9 - 23i$    25. $-36$

26. $65 + 72i$   27. $-\dfrac{2}{5} - \dfrac{3}{5}i$

28. $-1 - i$     29. $\dfrac{8}{17} + \dfrac{19}{17}i$

30. $-\dfrac{3}{5} - \dfrac{4}{5}i$   31. $\dfrac{8}{13} + \dfrac{12}{13}i$

32. $1 - \dfrac{3}{2}i$     33. $\pm 5i$

34. $\pm i\dfrac{\sqrt{2}}{2}$     35. $\pm 8i\dfrac{\sqrt{3}}{3}$

36. $\pm i\sqrt{7}$     37. $\pm 6i$

38. $\pm i\dfrac{\sqrt{15}}{5}$    39. $-1 \pm i\sqrt{2}$

40. $\dfrac{1}{6} \pm \dfrac{i\sqrt{35}}{6}$   41. $1 \pm i\dfrac{\sqrt{10}}{2}$

42. $1 \pm i$      43. $2 \pm i$

44. $\dfrac{3}{2} \pm \dfrac{i}{2}$

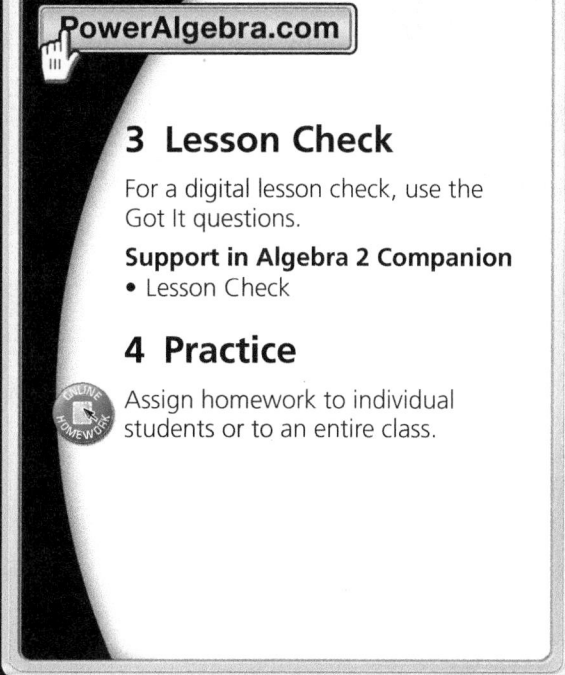

**PowerAlgebra.com**

## 3 Lesson Check

For a digital lesson check, use the Got It questions.

**Support in Algebra 2 Companion**
• Lesson Check

## 4 Practice

Assign homework to individual students or to an entire class.

# 4 Practice

## ASSIGNMENT GUIDE

Basic: 8–44 all, 45, 46–50 even, 56, 57

Average: 9–43 odd, 45–69

Advanced: 9–43 odd, 45–72

Standardized Test Prep: 73–76

Mixed Review: 77–89

**Reasoning** exercises have blue headings.

**Applications** exercises have red headings.

**EXERCISE 57:** Use the Think About a Plan worksheet in the **Practice and Problem Solving Workbook** (also available in the Teaching Resources in print and online) to further support students' development in becoming independent learners.

## HOMEWORK QUICK CHECK

To check students' understanding of key skills and concepts, go over Exercises 27, 39, 46, 56, and 57.

---

 **Apply**

**45. a.** Name the complex number represented by each point on the graph at the right.
   **b.** Find the additive inverse of each number.
   **c.** Find the complex conjugate of each number.
   **d.** Find the absolute value of each number.

**46. Think About a Plan** In the complex number plane, what geometric figure describes the complex numbers with absolute value 10?
   - What does the absolute value of a complex number represent?
   - How can you use the complex number plane to solve this problem?

**47.** Solve $(x + 3i)(x - 3i) = 34$.

**Simplify each expression.**

**48.** $(8i)(4i)(-9i)$

**49.** $(2 + \sqrt{-1}) + (-3 + \sqrt{-16})$

**50.** $(4 + \sqrt{-9}) + (6 - \sqrt{-49})$

**51.** $(10 + \sqrt{-9}) - (2 + \sqrt{-25})$

**52.** $(8 - \sqrt{-1}) - (-3 + \sqrt{-16})$

**53.** $2i(5 - 3i)$

**54.** $-5(1 + 2i) + 3i(3 - 4i)$

**55.** $(3 + \sqrt{-4})(4 + \sqrt{-1})$

**56. Open-Ended** In the equation $x^2 - 6x + c = 0$, find values of $c$ that will give:
   **a.** two real solutions     **b.** two imaginary solutions     **c.** one real solution

**57.** A student wrote the numbers 1, 5, $1 + 3i$, and $4 + 3i$ to represent the vertices of a quadrilateral in the complex number plane. What type of quadrilateral has these vertices?

The multiplicative inverse of a complex number $z$ is $\frac{1}{z}$ where $z \neq 0$. Find the multiplicative inverse, or reciprocal, of each complex number. Then use complex conjugates to simplify. Check each answer by multiplying it by the original number.

**58.** $2 + 5i$

**59.** $8 - 12i$

**60.** $a + bi$

**Find the sum and product of the roots of each equation.**

**61.** $x^2 - 2x + 3 = 0$

**62.** $5x^2 + 2x + 1 = 0$

**63.** $-2x^2 + 3x - 3 = 0$

For $ax^2 + bx + c = 0$, the sum of the roots is $-\frac{b}{a}$ and the product of the roots is $\frac{c}{a}$. Find a quadratic equation for each pair of roots. Assume $a = 1$.

**64.** $-6i$ and $6i$

**65.** $2 + 5i$ and $2 - 5i$

**66.** $4 - 3i$ and $4 + 3i$

Two complex numbers $a + bi$ and $c + di$ are equal when $a = c$ and $b = d$. Solve each equation for $x$ and $y$.

**67.** $2x + 3yi = -14 + 9i$

**68.** $3x + 19i = 16 - 8yi$

**69.** $-14 - 3i = 2x + yi$

---

# Answers

## Practice and Problem-Solving Exercises (continued)

**45. a.** A: $-5$; B: $3 + 2i$; C: $2 - i$; D: $3i$; E: $-6 - 4i$; F: $-1 + 5i$

**b.** A: 5; B: $-3 - 2i$; C: $-2 + i$; D: $-3i$; E: $6 + 4i$; F: $1 - 5i$

**c.** A: $-5$; B: $3 - 2i$; C: $2 + i$; D: $-3i$; E: $-6 + 4i$; F: $-1 - 5i$

**d.** A: 5; B: $\sqrt{13}$; C: $\sqrt{5}$; D: 3; E: $2\sqrt{13}$; F: $\sqrt{26}$

**46.** a circle

**47.** $-5, 5$

**48.** $288i$

**49.** $-1 + 5i$

**50.** $10 - 4i$

**51.** $8 - 2i$

**52.** $11 - 5i$

**53.** $6 + 10i$

**54.** $7 - i$

**55.** $10 + 11i$

**56. a.** $c < 9$

**b.** $c > 9$

**c.** $c = 9$

**57.** trapezoid

**58.** $\frac{2}{29} - \frac{5}{29}i$

**59.** $\frac{1}{26} + \frac{3}{52}i$

**60.** $\frac{a}{a^2 + b^2} - \frac{bi}{a^2 + b^2}$

**61.** sum: 2, product: 3

**62.** sum: $-\frac{2}{5}$, product: $\frac{1}{5}$

**63.** sum: $\frac{3}{2}$, product: $\frac{3}{2}$

**64.** Answers may vary. Sample: $x^2 + 36 = 0$

**65.** Answers may vary. Sample: $x^2 - 4x + 29 = 0$

**66.** Answers may vary. Sample: $x^2 - 8x + 25 = 0$

**67.** $x = -7, y = 3$

**68.** $x = \frac{16}{3}, y = -\frac{19}{8}$

**69.** $x = -7, y = -3$

**Challenge**

**70.** Show that the product of any complex number $a + bi$ and its complex conjugate is a real number.

**71.** For what real values of $x$ and $y$ is $(x + yi)^2$ an imaginary number?

**72.** **Reasoning** True or false: The conjugate of the additive inverse of a complex number is equal to the additive inverse of the conjugate of that complex number. Explain your answer.

## Standardized Test Prep

**SAT/ACT**

**73.** How can you rewrite the expression $(8 - 5i)^2$ in the form $a + bi$?

   Ⓐ $39 + 80i$     Ⓑ $39 - 80i$     Ⓒ $69 + 80i$     Ⓓ $69 - 80i$

**74.** How many solutions does the quadratic equation $4x^2 - 12x + 9 = 0$ have?

   Ⓕ two real solutions        Ⓗ two imaginary solutions

   Ⓖ one real solution         Ⓘ one imaginary solution

**75.** What are the solutions of $3x^2 - 2x - 4 = 0$?

   Ⓐ $\dfrac{1 \pm \sqrt{13}}{3}$    Ⓑ $\dfrac{1 \pm i\sqrt{11}}{3}$    Ⓒ $\dfrac{-1 \pm \sqrt{13}}{3}$    Ⓓ $\dfrac{-1 \pm i\sqrt{11}}{3}$

**Short Response**

**76.** Using factoring, what are all four solutions to $x^4 - 16 = 0$? Show your work.

## Mixed Review

Solve each equation using the Quadratic Formula.    ◆ **See Lesson 4-7.**

**77.** $2x^2 + 3x - 4 = 0$       **78.** $4x^2 + x = 1$       **79.** $x^2 = -7x - 8$

Graph each function. Identify the axis of symmetry.    ◆ **See Lesson 4-1.**

**80.** $y = -2(x + 1)^2 - 3$     **81.** $y = \frac{1}{2}(x - 4)^2 + 1$     **82.** $y = 3(x - 1)^2 - 5$

Write an equation for each line.    ◆ **See Lesson 2-3.**

**83.** $m = 3$ and the $y$-intercept is $-4$     **84.** $m = -0.5$ and the $y$-intercept is $-2$

**85.** $m = -7$ and the $y$-intercept is $10$     **86.** $m = 2$ and the $y$-intercept is $8$

**Get Ready!**    **To prepare for Lesson 4-9, do Exercises 87–89.**    ◆ **See Lesson 3-3.**

Solve each system of inequalities by graphing.

**87.** $\begin{cases} y < 2x + 4 \\ y \geq |x - 3| + 2 \end{cases}$     **88.** $\begin{cases} y > -x \\ y < -|x + 1| \end{cases}$     **89.** $\begin{cases} y \leq |x| + 2 \\ y \geq -\frac{1}{2}x + 4 \end{cases}$

**83.** $y = 3x - 4$
**84.** $y = -0.5x - 2$
**85.** $y = -7x + 10$
**86.** $y = 2x + 8$

**87.**

**88.**

no solution

**89.**

 **PowerAlgebra.com**     Lesson 4-8   Complex Numbers       **255**

---

**70.** $(a + bi)(a - bi) = a^2 + b^2$; since $a$ and $b$ are real, so is $a^2 + b^2$.

**71.** all nonzero numbers $x$ and $y$ such that $|x| = |y|$

**72.** True; the add. inv. of $a + bi$ is $-a - bi$ and the conjugate of $-a - bi$ is $-a + bi$. The conjugate of $a + bi$ is $a - bi$ and the add. inv. of $a - bi$ is $-a + bi$.

## Standardized Test Prep

**73.** B      **74.** G      **75.** A

**76.** **[2]** $\pm 2, \pm 2i$;
$$x^4 - 16 = (x^2 - 4)(x^2 + 4)$$
$$= (x - 2)(x + 2)$$
$$(x^2 + 4)$$
$$x - 2 = 0, x + 2 = 0,$$
$$x^2 + 4 = 0$$
$$x = 2 \quad x = -2 \quad x = \pm 2i$$

  **[1]** appropriate method, with one computational error

## Mixed Review

**77.** $\dfrac{-3 \pm \sqrt{41}}{4}$

**78.** $\dfrac{-1 \pm \sqrt{17}}{8}$

**79.** $\dfrac{-7 \pm \sqrt{17}}{2}$

**80.**  ; axis of symmetry: $x = -1$

**81.**  ; axis of symmetry: $x = 4$

**82.**  ; axis of symmetry: $x = 1$

## Additional Instructional Support

### Algebra 2 Companion

Students can use the **Algebra 2 Companion** worktext (4 pages) as you teach the lesson. Use the Companion to support

- New Vocabulary
- Key Concepts
- Got It for each Problem
- Lesson Check

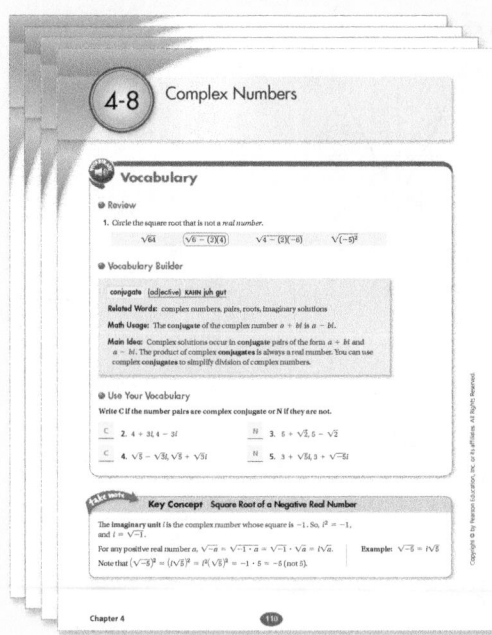

### ELL Support

**Connect to Prior Knowledge** Go back to the table in Lesson 4-7 on page 243. Point out the last example, where the discriminant is less than zero. The table tells you that there are no real solutions. Ask students what that means in terms of complex solutions. [There will be 2 complex solutions.]

Point out the graphs in the table. Real solutions only occur where the graph crosses the *x*-axis. Unlike real solutions, complex solutions cannot be identified on the parabola. However, you can still use the graph to determine that there are no real solutions and then know that there are complex solutions.

## 5 Assess & Remediate

### Lesson Quiz

1. **Do you UNDERSTAND?** How do you write $\sqrt{-20}$ using the imaginary unit $i$?
2. What are the graph and absolute value of $2 + 2i$?
3. What is the sum $(7 + 2i) + (5 - 3i)$?
4. What is the product $(-2 + 5i)(-1 + 4i)$?
5. What is the quotient $\frac{7 + 4i}{2 - 3i}$?
6. What are the solutions of $2x^2 + 18 = 0$?
7. Find the solutions of $6x^2 + 4x = -11$.

### ANSWERS TO LESSON QUIZ

1. $2i\sqrt{5}$
2. $2\sqrt{2}$

3. $12 - i$
4. $-18 - 13i$
5. $\frac{2}{13} + \frac{29}{13}i$
6. $\pm 3i$
7. $-\frac{1}{3} \pm \frac{i\sqrt{62}}{6}$

**PRESCRIPTION FOR REMEDIATION**
Use the student work on the Lesson Quiz to prescribe a differentiated review assignment:

| Points | Differentiated Remediation |
|--------|---------------------------|
| 0–2 | Intervention |
| 3–6 | On-level |
| 7 | Extension |

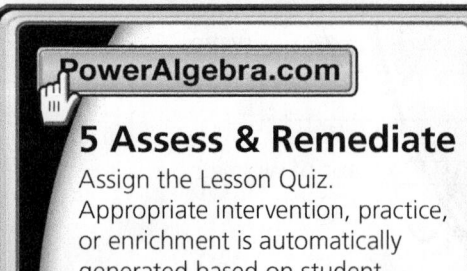

**PowerAlgebra.com**

### 5 Assess & Remediate

Assign the Lesson Quiz. Appropriate intervention, practice, or enrichment is automatically generated based on student performance.

## Intervention

- **Reteaching** (2 pages) Provides reteaching and practice exercises for the key lesson concepts. Use with struggling students or absent students.
- **English Language Learner Support** Helps students develop and reinforce mathematical vocabulary and key concepts.

### All-in-One Resources/Online
**Reteaching**

**4-8** Reteaching
Complex Numbers

- A *complex number* consists of a real part and an imaginary part. It is written in the form $a + bi$, where $a$ and $b$ are real numbers.
- $i = \sqrt{-1}$ and $i^2 = (\sqrt{-1})(\sqrt{-1}) = -1$
- When adding or subtracting complex numbers, combine the real parts and then combine the imaginary parts.
- When multiplying complex numbers, use the Distributive Property or FOIL.

**Problem**
What is $(3 - i) + (2 + 3i)$?

$(3 - i) + (2 + 3i)$
$= \boxed{3} - \boxed{i} + \boxed{2} + \boxed{3i}$  Circle real parts. Put a square around imaginary parts.
$= (3 + 2) + (-1 + 3)i$  Combine.
$= 5 + 2i$  Simplify.

**Problem**
What is the product $(7 - 3i)(-4 + 9i)$?
Use FOIL to multiply:

$(7 - 3i)(-4 + 9i) = 7(-4) + 7(9i) + (-3i)(-4) + (-3i)(9i)$
$(7 - 3i)(-4 + 9i)$     $= -28 + 63i + 12i - 27i^2$
First $= 7(-4)$         $= -28 + 75i - 27i^2$
Outer $= 7(9i)$         You can simplify the expression by substituting $-1$ for $i^2$.
Inner $= (-3i)(-4)$     $(7 - 3i)(-4 + 9i) = -28 + 75i - 27(-1)$
Last $= (-3i)(9i)$      $= -1 + 75i$

**Exercises**
Simplify each expression.

1. $2i + (-4 - 2i)$    2. $(3 - i)(2 + i)$     3. $(4 + 3i)(1 + 2i)$
   $-4$                   $5 + 5i$                $-2 + 11i$

4. $3(1 - 2i)$         5. $3(4 - i)$          6. $3 - (-2 + 3i) + (-5 + i)$
   $6 + 3i$              $3 + 12i$               $-2i$

7. $4i(6 - 2i)$        8. $(5 + 6i) + (-2 + 4i)$   9. $9(11 + 5i)$
   $8 + 24i$             $3 + 10i$                  $99 + 45i$

### All-in-One Resources/Online
**English Language Learner Support**

**4-8** ELL Support
Complex Numbers

Complete the vocabulary chart by filling in the missing information.

| Word or Word Phrase | Definition | Picture or Example |
|---------------------|------------|--------------------|
| imaginary unit | The *imaginary unit i* is a complex number whose square is $-1$. | $i = \sqrt{-1}$ |
| pure imaginary number | A *pure imaginary number* is of the form $a + bi$, where $a = 0$ and $b \neq 0$. | 1. Answers may vary. Sample: $5i$ |
| complex number | 2. any number of the form $a + bi$ where $a$ and $b$ are real numbers | $7 - 4i$ |
| complex number plane | In the *complex number plane*, the point $(a, b)$ represents the complex number $a + bi$. To graph, locate the real part on the horizontal axis and the imaginary part on the vertical axis. | 3. |
| absolute value of a complex number | 4. Answers may vary. Sample: The absolute value of a complex number is its distance from the origin in the complex number plane. | $|8 + 6i| = \sqrt{8^2 + 6^2} = 10$ |
| complex conjugates | number pairs of the form $a + bi$ and $a - bi$ | 5. Answers may vary. Sample: $-3 + 4i$ and $-3 - 4i$ |

# Differentiated Remediation *continued*

## On-Level

- **Practice** (2 pages) Provides extra practice for each lesson. For simpler practice exercises, use the Form K Practice pages found in the All-in-One Teaching Resources and online.

- **Think About a Plan** Helps students develop specific problem-solving skills and strategies by providing scaffolded guiding questions.

- **Standardized Test Prep** Focuses on all major exercises, all major question types, and helps students prepare for the high-stakes assessments.

## Extension

- **Enrichment** Provides students with interesting problems and activities that extend the concepts of the lesson.

- **Activities, Games, and Puzzles** Worksheets that can be used for concepts development, enrichment, and for fun!

---

### Practice and Problem Solving Wkbk/ All-in-One Resources/Online
**Practice page 1**

### Practice and Problem Solving Wkbk/ All-in-One Resources/Online
**Practice page 2**

### All-in-One Resources/Online
**Enrichment**

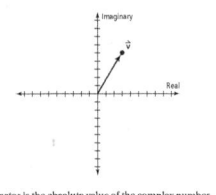

---

### Practice and Problem Solving Wkbk/ All-in-One Resources/Online
**Think About a Plan**

### Practice and Problem Solving Wkbk/ All-in-One Resources/Online
**Standardized Test Prep**

### Online Teacher Resource Center
**Activities, Games, and Puzzles**

# Guided Instruction

**PURPOSE** To investigate and use different methods to solve quadratic inequalities

**PURPOSE** To investigate and use different methods to solve quadratic inequalities
**PROCESS** Students will solve quadratic inequalities by
- factoring.
- using a table for the related function.
- graphing the related quadratic function.
- solving the related quadratic equation.

---

**DISCUSS**

**Q** What do the *x*-intercepts of a parabola represent? **[The *x*-values for which the related function equals zero.]**

**Q** What do all points above the *x*-axis have in common? **[The *y*-value is positive.]**

---

## Example 1

---

**Q** If one factor is positive and the other is negative, what is the sign of the product? **[negative]**

**Q** If the product of two numbers is positive, what do you know about the signs of the numbers? **[both are positive or both are negative]**

**Q** What is true about all negative numbers? **[They are less than zero.]**

---

## Activity

To solve a quadratic inequality by using a table, you must have a table of solutions for the related quadratic function.

---

**Q** What are the *x*-intercepts of the related quadratic function? **[(1, 0) and (5, 0)]**

**Q** Is it possible that any negative *y*-values exist for *x*-values less than 0 or greater than 6? Explain. **[Answers may vary. Sample: No; the parabola opens upward, so the function increases for $x \leq 0$ and $x \geq 6$.]**

---

To solve some quadratic inequalities, relate the quadratic expression to 0 and factor. To determine the sign of each factor, use what you know about multiplying positive and negative numbers.

### Example 1

**Solve each inequality algebraically.**

a. $2x^2 - 14x < 0$

| | |
|---|---|
| $2x(x - 7) < 0$ | Factor. |
| $2x > 0$ and $(x - 7) < 0$, or $2x < 0$ and $(x - 7) > 0$ | The product is negative, so the two factors must have *different* signs. |
| $x > 0$ and $x < 7$, or $x < 0$ and $x > 7$ | Simplify. |
| $0 < x < 7$ | No value can be both greater than 7 and less than 0. |

b. $2x^2 - 14x > 0$

| | |
|---|---|
| $2x(x - 7) > 0$ | Factor. |
| $2x > 0$ and $(x - 7) > 0$, or $2x < 0$ and $(x - 7) < 0$ | The product is positive, so the two factors must have the *same* signs. |
| $x > 0$ and $x > 7$, or $x < 0$ and $x < 7$ | Simplify. |
| $x > 7$ or $x < 0$ | A value that is greater than both 0 and 7 is always greater than 7. A value that is less than both 0 and 7 is always less than 0. |

You can use a table to solve inequalities by analyzing the values of *y* around 0.

### Activity

Use a table to find the solutions of $x^2 - 6x + 5 < 0$.

| x | y |
|---|---|
| 0 | 5 |
| 1 | 0 |
| 2 | -3 |
| 3 | -4 |
| 4 | -3 |
| 5 | 0 |
| 6 | 5 |

1. What happens to the value of *y* when $0 \leq x \leq 6$?
2. Does this make sense when you think of the shape of the graph of $y = x^2 - 6x + 5$? Explain.
3. What *x*-values in the table make the inequality $x^2 - 6x + 5 < 0$ true?
4. What are the solutions of $x^2 - 6x + 5 < 0$?

You can determine the solution of a quadratic inequality based on how many times and where the graph of the related function crosses the *x*-axis. The graph could open upward or downward, and could intersect the *x*-axis at 0, 1, or 2 points.

---

# Answers

**Activity**

1. Values range from positive to zero to negative and then back to zero and positive.
2. Yes; the shape is a parabola that dips below the *x*-axis and then comes back up.
3. 2, 3, 4
4. $1 < x < 5$

You can solve inequalities of the form $ax^2 + bx + c > 0$ or $ax^2 + bx + c < 0$ by graphing the corresponding function and seeing where the graph is above or below the $x$-axis.

## Example 2

Find the solution sets for $\frac{1}{4}(x-2)^2 - 1 > 0$ and $\frac{1}{4}(x-2)^2 - 1 < 0$.

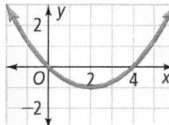

The solution set for $\frac{1}{4}(x-2)^2 - 1 > 0$ is all $x$-values of points on the parabola that lie above the $x$-axis.

$$x < 0 \text{ or } x > 4$$

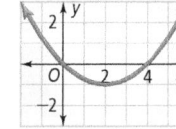

The solution set for $\frac{1}{4}(x-2)^2 - 1 < 0$ is all $x$-values of points on the parabola that lie below the $x$-axis.

$$0 < x < 4$$

## Example 3

Solve $-2x^2 - 8x - 6 < 0$.

**Think:** Since the coefficient of $x^2$ is less than zero, the graph of $y = -2x^2 - 8x - 6$ opens downward.

**Solve:** Find where $-2x^2 - 8x - 6$ equals 0.

$$-2x^2 - 8x - 6 = 0$$
$$-2(x^2 + 4x + 3) = 0$$
$$-2(x + 3)(x + 1) = 0$$
$$x = -3 \text{ or } x = -1$$

The graph of $y = -2x^2 - 8x - 6$ opens down and crosses the $x$-axis at $x = -3$ and $x = -1$. The solution of $-2x^2 - 8x - 6 < 0$ is $x < -3$ or $x > -1$.

## Exercises

**5.** Solve each inequality. Graph your solution on a number line.

   **a.** $x^2 < 36$       **b.** $x^2 - 9 > 0$       **c.** $x^2 < -4$       **d.** $x^2 - 3x - 18 > 0$

**6.** How can you use the graph of $y = 3x - 4$ to solve the linear inequality $3x - 4 < 0$? Graph the solution.

**7.** How can you solve the absolute value inequality $|-3x + 4| > 0$?

**8.** Example 2 shows two possible graphs for a quadratic inequality. What other possibilities are there?

**9.** Describe the graphs of possible solutions of $ax^3 + bx^2 + cx + d > 0$.

---

## Example 2

The previous activity alluded to the graphical connection between solutions of a quadratic function and solutions of a quadratic inequality. This example solidifies that connection by finding when the $y$-values of a parabola are positive or negative.

**Q** Are the $x$-intercepts part of either solution? Why or why not? [**No; the $x$-intercepts represent $\frac{1}{4}(x-2)^2 - 1 = 0$, so they are not part of the solution sets of the strict inequalities.**]

**Q** Will $ax^2 + bx + c < 0$ always have a solution? Explain. [**No; a parabola entirely above the $x$-axis never has negative $y$-values.**]

## Example 3

This method is related to the tabular method in the Activity. Both require finding the zeros of the quadratic function. However, while the Activity uses the table to determine the sign of the function around the zeros, Example 3 uses prior knowledge about the direction of a parabola based on the leading coefficient.

**Q** Without actually making one, what would a table of values for $y = -2x^2 - 8x - 6$ look like? [**Answers may vary. Sample: The $y$-values would be zero for $x = -3$ and $x = -1$, negative for $x < -3$ or $x > -1$ and positive for $-3 < x < -1$.**]

**Q** Why does it matter whether the graph opens upward or downward? [**Answers may vary. Sample: Assuming the graph intersects the $x$-axis, the direction in which the graph opens determines where $y$ is positive or negative.**]

---

**5. a.** $-6 < x < 6$

**b.** $x > 3$ or $x < -3$

**c.** no solution

**d.** $x < -3$ or $x > 6$

**6.** Graph $y = 3x - 4$ and shade the $x$-values for which the line is below the $x$-axis.

**7.** Absolute value is always nonnegative, thus $|-3x + 4| > 0$ for all values of $x$, $x \neq \frac{4}{3}$.

**8.** intersects the $x$-axis at one point:

does not intersect the $x$-axis:

**9.** Graphs of solutions of $ax^3 + bx^2 + cx + d > 0$ could be: for $a > 0$, $x > n$ or $n < x < m$ and $x > k$; for $a < 0$, $x < n$, or $x < n$ and $n < x < m$, or $x < n$ and $m < x < k$, where $n$, $m$, and $k$ are real solutions of the equation $ax^3 + bx^2 + cx + d = 0$ with $n < m < k$.

# 1 Interactive Learning

## Solve It!
**PURPOSE** To use inequalities to define a region bounded by quadratic functions
**PROCESS** Students may
- write a system of inequalities of two of the three functions from Lesson 4-7 Solve It.
- solve a simpler problem by finding a linear function for the top "lip" of the mouth.

### FACILITATE
**Q** What points must the functions share? Why? **[The functions must share (2, 1) and (6, 1) because they are the corners of the mouth.]**

**Q** Are the "lips" part of the inside of the mouth? Explain. **[Answers may vary. Sample: Yes; the lips form the boundary of the inside.]**

**Q** Do you need to restrict the domain? Explain. **[Answers may vary. Sample: No; the intersection of the inequalities already restricts $2 \leq x \leq 6$.]**

**ANSWER** See Solve It in Answers on next page.
**CONNECT THE MATH** In the Solve it, students combine their knowledge of inequalities and graphs of quadratic functions to describe a region bounded by parabolas. In this lesson, students solve quadratic systems by graphing or substitution.

# 2 Guided Instruction

## Take Note
**VISUAL LEARNERS**
The number of solutions of a Linear-Quadratic system indicates the number of points of intersection in the graphs of the functions.

---

**Objectives** To solve and graph systems of linear and quadratic equations
To solve and graph systems of quadratic inequalities

**Dynamic Activity** Systems of Quadratic Inequalities

**Getting Ready!**

In the Lesson 4-7 Solve It, you put a mouth on this face. What second quadratic function would you graph to open the mouth? Show the completed face. What quadratic statements could you write to shade the inside of the mouth? Explain your reasoning.

By drawing a second parabola in the Solve It, you created a quadratic system.

**Essential Understanding** You can solve systems involving quadratic equations using methods similar to the ones used to solve systems of linear equations.

The points where the graphs of the equations intersect represent the solutions of a system.

### take note

**Key Concept** Solutions of a Linear-Quadratic System

A system of one quadratic equation and one linear equation can have two solutions, one solution, or no solution.

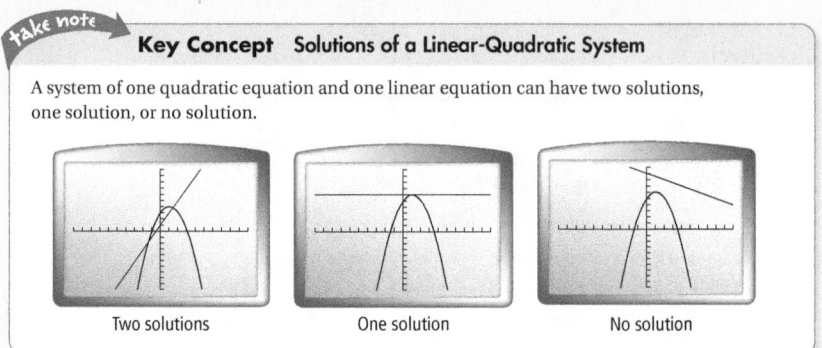

| Two solutions | One solution | No solution |

---

**BIG** ideas **Equivalence Functions** **UbD**
**Function**
**Solving Equations**
**and Inequalities**

**ESSENTIAL UNDERSTANDINGS**
- Systems involving quadratic equations can be solved using methods similar to the ones used to solve systems of linear equations.
- Any quadratic function is a stretch, compression, reflection, and/or a translation of $y = x^2$.
- The points where the graphs of the equations intersect represent the solutions of a system.

## Math Background
Students are familiar with solving systems of linear equations and inequalities. In this lesson, they will solve nonlinear systems of equations and inequalities. The methods used to solve nonlinear systems are the same methods used to solve linear systems: substitution, elimination, and graphing.

Students often shade inequalities incorrectly when solving by graphing. Like linear inequalities,

students should use a test point to determine whether to shade inside or outside of the parabola.

For students who still struggle with the graphing aspect, teach these basic steps:
1. Use the inequality symbol to determine whether the graph should have a dotted or solid line.
2. Graph the parabola.
3. Choose a point inside the parabola, and determine whether it is a solution of the inequality.
4. If the point is a solution, shade inside the parabola; otherwise shade outside the parabola.

## Support Student Learning
Use the **Algebra 2 Companion** to engage and support students during instruction. See Lesson Resources at the end of this lesson for details.

---

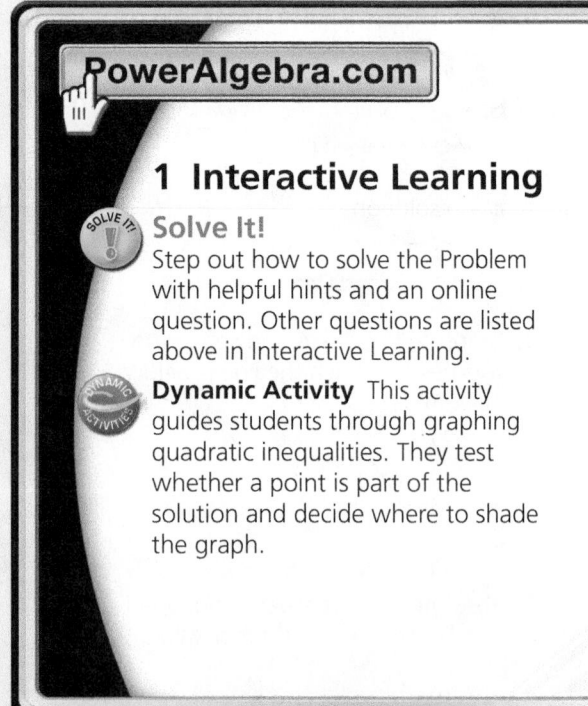

## PowerAlgebra.com

### 1 Interactive Learning

**Solve It!**
Step out how to solve the Problem with helpful hints and an online question. Other questions are listed above in Interactive Learning.

**Dynamic Activity** This activity guides students through graphing quadratic inequalities. They test whether a point is part of the solution and decide where to shade the graph.

**Problem 1** Solving a Linear-Quadratic System by Graphing

**Multiple Choice** Which numbers are *y*-values of the solutions of the system of equations? $\begin{cases} y = -x^2 + 5x + 6 \\ y = x + 6 \end{cases}$

**Plan**
How can you graph these two equations?
Use slope-intercept form to graph the linear equation. Make a table of values to graph the quadratic equation.

Ⓐ 4 only     Ⓑ 6 only     Ⓒ 4 and 6     Ⓓ 6 and 10

Graph the equations. Find their intersections.

The solutions appear to be (0, 6) and (4, 10).

**Check**

| $y = -x^2 + 5x + 6$ | $y = x + 6$ |
|---|---|
| $6 \stackrel{?}{=} -(0)^2 + 5(0) + 6$ | $6 \stackrel{?}{=} 0 + 6$ |
| $6 = 6$ ✔ | $6 = 6$ ✔ |
| $y = -x^2 + 5x + 6$ | $y = x + 6$ |
| $10 \stackrel{?}{=} -(4)^2 + 5(4) + 6$ | $10 \stackrel{?}{=} 4 + 6$ |
| $10 = 10$ ✔ | $10 = 10$ ✔ |

The *y*-values of the solutions are 6 and 10, choice D.

 **Got It? 1.** What is the solution of the system? $\begin{cases} y = x^2 + 6x + 9 \\ y = x + 3 \end{cases}$

**Q** What are the *x*-values of the solutions? **[0 and 4]**

**Q** What does it mean algebraically for a point to be the intersection of the graphs of two functions? **[The coordinates are a solution to both equations.]**

**Q** Can you solve any linear-quadratic systems by graphing? Explain. **[Answers may vary. Sample: No; if the intersection points do not fall on the grid, you could only estimate.]**

**Got It?**
A graphing calculator could also be used to find the intersections.

**Q** How many times do the graphs intersect? **[twice]**

---

 **Problem 2** Solving a Linear-Quadratic System Using Substitution

What is the solution of the system of equations? $\begin{cases} y = -x^2 - x + 6 \\ y = x + 3 \end{cases}$

**Think**        **Write**

| Think | Write |
|---|---|
| Substitute *x* + 3 for *y* in the quadratic equation. | $x + 3 = -x^2 - x + 6$ |
| Write in standard form. | $x^2 + 2x - 3 = 0$ |
| Factor. Solve for *x*. | $(x - 1)(x + 3) = 0$ <br> $x = 1 \text{ or } x = -3$ |
| Substitute for *x* in $y = x + 3$. | $x = 1 \rightarrow y = 1 + 3 = 4$ <br> $x = -3 \rightarrow y = -3 + 3 = 0$ <br> The solutions are (1, 4) and (−3, 0). |

 **Got It? 2.** What is the solution of the system? $\begin{cases} y = -x^2 - 3x + 10 \\ y = x + 5 \end{cases}$

**Q** If the linear equation had been in $ax + by + c = 0$ form, what would have been a good first step and why? **[Solve the equation for *y* so you could easily set the two equations equal to each other by substitution.]**

**Q** Does it matter which equation you substitute the *x*-values into? Explain. **[No; the solutions need to satisfy both equations.]**

**Got It?**

**Q** Without graphing how can you tell how many times the functions intersect? **[Sample: The *y*-intercept of the parabola is above the *y*-intercept of the line and the parabola opens downward, so they intersect at two points.]**

---

## 2 Guided Instruction

Each Problem is worked out and supported online.

**Problem 1**
Solving a Linear-Quadratic System by Graphing
*Animated*

**Problem 2**
Solving a Linear-Quadratic System Using Substitution
*Animated*

**Problem 3**
Solving a Quadratic System of Equations
*Animated*

**Problem 4**
Solving a Quadratic System of Inequalities

**Support in Algebra 2 Companion**
• Vocabulary
• Key Concepts
• Got It?

## Answers

**Solve It!**
$y = -0.25(x - 4)^2 + 2$ will open the mouth.
To shade the inside of the mouth, write:
$y \geq 0.25(x - 4)^2$ and $y \leq -0.25(x - 4)^2 + 2$.

**Got It?**
1. (−3, 0), (−2, 1)
2. (−5, 0), (1, 6)

## Problem 3

A system of two quadratic equations could also be solved by graphing or using substitution.

---

**Q** Why would adding the two equations together to eliminate $x^2$ not be useful? **[There are still two variables; neither $x$ nor $y$ is eliminated.]**

**Q** If you use the elimination method, which variable would you eliminate? **[Eliminate $y$, so you are left with an equation in only one variable.]**

**Q** Does each method produce the same solutions? Explain why. **[Yes; the points of intersection are conceptually equivalent to the algebraic solutions.]**

---

### EXTENSION

**Q** A linear-quadratic system can have 2, 1, or no solutions. What are the possibilities for a quadratic-quadratic system? **[There can be infinitely many, 2, 1, or 0 solutions.]**

### Got It?

**Q** Why do the numbers of solutions in 3a and 3b differ? **[Answers may vary. Sample: Between 3a and 3b, the function $y = -x^2 + 5$ is translated down 10 units to become $y = -x^2 - 5$, so the parabolas no longer intersect.]**

### SYNTHESIZING

If time allows, have students solve Problem 3 or Got It 3a by the elimination method to verify that it produces the same solutions.

---

**Plan**

**Which variable should you substitute for?**
You can substitute for either variable, but substituting for $y$ results in a simple equation.

---

You can solve quadratic-quadratic systems using the same methods you used for linear-quadratic systems.

 **Problem 3** Solving a Quadratic System of Equations

What is the solution of the system? $\begin{cases} y = -x^2 - x + 12 \\ y = x^2 + 7x + 12 \end{cases}$

**Method 1** Use substitution.

Substitute $y = -x^2 - x + 12$ for $y$ in the second equation. Solve for $x$.

| | |
|---|---|
| $-x^2 - x + 12 = x^2 + 7x + 12$ | Substitute for $y$. |
| $-2x^2 - 8x = 0$ | Write in standard form. |
| $-2x(x + 4) = 0$ | Factor. |
| $x = 0 \text{ or } x = -4$ | Solve for $x$. |

Substitute each value of $x$ into either equation. Solve for $y$.

| | |
|---|---|
| $y = x^2 + 7x + 12$ | $y = x^2 + 7x + 12$ |
| $y = (0)^2 + 7(0) + 12$ | $y = (-4)^2 + 7(-4) + 12$ |
| $y = 0 + 0 + 12 = 12$ | $y = 16 - 28 + 12 = 0$ |

The solutions are $(0, 12)$ and $(-4, 0)$.

**Method 2** Graph the equations.

Use a graphing calculator.
Define functions $Y_1$ and $Y_2$.

Use the **INTERSECT** feature to find the points of intersection.

The solutions are $(-4, 0)$ and $(0, 12)$.

 **Got It?** **3.** What is the solution of each system of equations?

**a.** $\begin{cases} y = x^2 - 4x + 5 \\ y = -x^2 + 5 \end{cases}$     **b.** $\begin{cases} y = x^2 - 4x + 5 \\ y = -x^2 - 5 \end{cases}$

---

# Additional Problems

**1.** What is the solution of the system?
$\begin{cases} y = x^2 - 2x + 1 \\ y = x - 3 \end{cases}$

**ANSWER** no solution

**2.** What is the solution of the system?
$\begin{cases} y = x^2 + 3x + 9 \\ y = -3x + 4 \end{cases}$

**ANSWER** $(-5, 19)$ and $(-1, 7)$

**3.** What is the solution of the system?
$\begin{cases} y = x^2 + 9x + 7 \\ y = -x^2 + 3x + 7 \end{cases}$

**ANSWER** $(-3, -11)$ and $(0, 7)$

**4.** What is the solution to this system of inequalities?
$\begin{cases} y \geq x^2 + 5x - 8 \\ y < -x^2 + 3x + 4 \end{cases}$

**ANSWER**

# Answers

**Got It? (continued)**

**3. a.** $(0, 5)$, $(2, 1)$

**b.** no solution

**4. a.**

**b.** infinite, one, or none

## Lesson Check

**1.** $(1, 2)$, $(2, 3)$

**2.** $(1, -1)$, $(2, 0)$

**3.** $(2, -5)$, $\left(-\frac{4}{3}, \frac{25}{9}\right)$

**4.**

**5.**

**6.** For each system of eqs., linear or quadratic, to solve the system you need to find the pt. (or pts.) of intersection or, in the case of inequalities, the regions of intersection. A linear system of eqs. can have one, infinite, or no solutions, whereas a quadratic system of eqs. can have one, two, infinite, or no solutions.

You can use the techniques for solving a linear system of inequalities to solve a quadratic system of inequalities.

Problem 4 **Solving a Quadratic System of Inequalities**

Plan

**How can you find the solution?**
Graph each inequality and find the region where the graphs overlap.

What is the solution of the system of inequalities? $\begin{cases} y < -x^2 - 9x - 2 \\ y > x^2 - 2 \end{cases}$

Graph the first inequality.

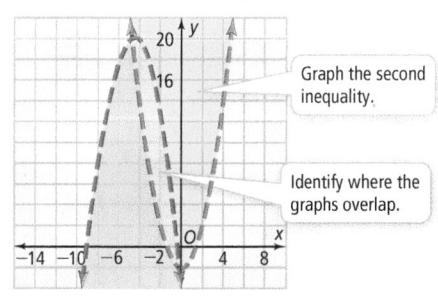

Graph the second inequality.

Identify where the graphs overlap.

The solution of this system is the region where the graphs overlap. The region contains no boundary points.

 **Got It?** **4. a.** What is the solution of this system of inequalities? $\begin{cases} y \le -x^2 - 4x + 3 \\ y > x^2 + 3 \end{cases}$

   **b. Reasoning** How many solutions can a system of inequalities have?

 **Lesson Check**

**Do you know HOW?**

Solve each system by substitution.

**1.** $\begin{cases} y = x^2 - 2x + 3 \\ y = x + 1 \end{cases}$

**2.** $\begin{cases} y = 2x^2 - 5x + 2 \\ y = x - 2 \end{cases}$

**3.** $\begin{cases} y = x^2 - 3x - 3 \\ y = -2x^2 - x + 5 \end{cases}$

Solve each system by graphing.

**4.** $\begin{cases} y > 2x^2 + x + 3 \\ y < -x^2 - 4x + 1 \end{cases}$

**5.** $\begin{cases} y > -3x^2 - 6x + 1 \\ y < -2x^2 - 3x + 5 \end{cases}$

**Do you UNDERSTAND?**

**6. Compare and Contrast** How are solving systems of two linear equations or inequalities and solving systems of two quadratic equations or inequalities alike? How are they different?

**7. Reasoning** How many points of intersection can graphs of the following types of functions have? Draw graphs to justify your answers.
   **a.** a linear function and a quadratic function
   **b.** two quadratic functions
   **c.** a quadratic function and an absolute value function (*Hint:* Graph $y = x^2$ and $y = |x|$ together. Can you transform one of the graphs slightly to increase the number of intersections?)

---

Problem 4

**Q** What is the domain of the solution? **[−4.5 < x < 0]**
**Q** What is the range of the solution? **[−2 < y < 18.25]**
**Q** Will two quadratic inequalities always intersect? Why? **[No. A quadratic inequality opening upward with a positive minimum, shaded inside, will not intersect with a quadratic inequality opening downward with a negative maximum, shaded inside.]**

**Got It?** ERROR PREVENTION

**Q** Does the region contain any boundary points? Explain. **[Yes; the first inequality is not strict, so that parabola is included for −2 < x < 0.]**

# 3 Lesson Check

**Do you know HOW?** ERROR INTERVENTION
• Exercise 4 has a very narrow region of overlap. If students assume that there is no solution, then suggest they graph the parabolas on a calculator and zoom in on the intersection.

**Do you UNDERSTAND?** TACTILE LEARNERS
• For Exercise 7, if students have difficulty visualizing intersections, have them sketch the curves on patty paper and explore different ways to position one curve on top of another.

**Close**

**Q** How are linear systems similar to, yet different from, quadratic systems? **[Answers may vary. Sample: Both kinds of systems are similar because they can be solved by graphing or substitution; they are different because only a quadratic system can have exactly two solutions.]**

---

# Answers

**1–6.** See page 260.
**7. a.** two, one, or zero

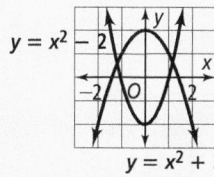

**b.** two, one, or zero

$y = x^2 - 2$
$y = x^2 + 2$
$y = x^2$
$y = x^2 + 1$
$y = -x^2$
$y = -x^2$

**c.** four, three, two, one, or zero

$y = x^2 - 1$
$y = -|x|$

**PowerAlgebra.com**

## 3 Lesson Check

For a digital lesson check, use the Got It questions.

**Support in Algebra 2 Companion**
• Lesson Check

## 4 Practice

Assign homework to individual students or to an entire class.

# 4 Practice

## ASSIGNMENT GUIDE

Basic: 8–28 all, 29–31, 39–41, 47

Average: 9–27 odd, 29–55

Advanced: 9–27 odd, 29–61

Standardized Test Prep: 62–65

Mixed Review: 66–77

Reasoning exercises have blue headings.

Applications exercises have red headings.

**EXERCISE 47:** Use the Think About a Plan worksheet in the **Practice and Problem Solving Workbook** (also available in the Teaching Resources in print and online) to further support students' development in becoming independent learners.

## HOMEWORK QUICK CHECK

To check students' understanding of key skills and concepts, go over Exercises 9, 15, 29, 40, and 47.

---

## Practice and Problem-Solving Exercises

 **Practice**

Solve each system by graphing. Check your answers.  ◀ See Problem 1.

8. $\begin{cases} y = -x^2 + 2x + 1 \\ y = 2x + 1 \end{cases}$

9. $\begin{cases} y = x^2 - 2x + 1 \\ y = 2x + 1 \end{cases}$

10. $\begin{cases} y = x^2 - x + 3 \\ y = -2x + 5 \end{cases}$

11. $\begin{cases} y = 2x^2 + 3x + 1 \\ y = -2x + 1 \end{cases}$

12. $\begin{cases} y = -x^2 - 3x + 2 \\ y = x + 6 \end{cases}$

13. $\begin{cases} y = -x^2 - 2x - 2 \\ y = x - 4 \end{cases}$

Solve each system by substitution. Check your answers.  ◀ See Problem 2.

14. $\begin{cases} y = x^2 + 4x + 1 \\ y = x + 1 \end{cases}$

15. $\begin{cases} y = -x^2 + 2x + 10 \\ y = x + 4 \end{cases}$

16. $\begin{cases} y = -x^2 + x - 1 \\ y = -x - 1 \end{cases}$

17. $\begin{cases} y = 2x^2 - 3x - 1 \\ y = x - 3 \end{cases}$

18. $\begin{cases} y = x^2 - 3x - 20 \\ y = -x - 5 \end{cases}$

19. $\begin{cases} y = -x^2 - 5x - 1 \\ y = x + 2 \end{cases}$

Solve each system.  ◀ See Problem 3.

20. $\begin{cases} y = x^2 + 5x + 1 \\ y = x^2 + 2x + 1 \end{cases}$

21. $\begin{cases} y = x^2 - 2x - 1 \\ y = -x^2 - 2x - 1 \end{cases}$

22. $\begin{cases} y = -x^2 - 3x - 2 \\ y = x^2 + 3x + 2 \end{cases}$

23. $\begin{cases} y = -x^2 - x - 3 \\ y = 2x^2 - 2x - 3 \end{cases}$

24. $\begin{cases} y = -3x^2 - x + 2 \\ y = x^2 + 2x + 1 \end{cases}$

25. $\begin{cases} y = x^2 + 2x + 1 \\ y = x^2 + 2x - 1 \end{cases}$

Solve each system by graphing.  ◀ See Problem 4.

26. $\begin{cases} y > x^2 + 2x \\ y > x^2 - 1 \end{cases}$

27. $\begin{cases} y > x^2 - 3x \\ y < 2x^2 - 3x \end{cases}$

28. $\begin{cases} y < -x^2 - 3x \\ y > x^2 - 1 \end{cases}$

**Apply**

29. **Think About a Plan** A manufacturer is making cardboard boxes by cutting out four equal squares from the corners of the rectangular piece of cardboard and then folding the remaining part into a box. The length of the cardboard piece is 1 in. longer than its width. The manufacturer can cut out either 3 × 3 in. squares, or 4 × 4 in. squares. Find the dimensions of the cardboard for which the volume of the boxes produced by both methods will be the same.
   • How can you represent the volume of the box using one variable?
   • What system of equations can you write?
   • Which method can you use to solve the system?

30. **Open-Ended** Can you solve the system of equations shown by graphing? Justify your answer. Can you solve this system using another method? If so, solve the system and explain why you chose that method.  $\begin{cases} x = y^2 + 2y + 1 \\ y = x - 4 \end{cases}$

Solve each system by substitution.

31. $\begin{cases} x + y = 3 \\ y = x^2 - 8x - 9 \end{cases}$

32. $\begin{cases} y - 2x = x + 5 \\ y + 1 = x^2 + 5x + 3 \end{cases}$

33. $\begin{cases} y - \frac{1}{2}x^2 = 1 + 3x \\ y + \frac{1}{2}x^2 = x \end{cases}$

34. $\begin{cases} x + y - 2 = 0 \\ x^2 + y - 8 = 0 \end{cases}$

35. $\begin{cases} x^2 - y = x + 4 \\ x - 1 = y + 3 \end{cases}$

36. $\begin{cases} 2y = y - x^2 + 1 \\ y = x^2 - 5x - 2 \end{cases}$

---

# Answers

## Practice and Problem-Solving Exercises (continued)

8. (0, 1);

9. (0, 1), (4, 9);

10. (−2, 9), (1, 3);

11. $(0, 1), \left(-\frac{5}{2}, 6\right)$;

12. (−2, 4);

13. $\left(\dfrac{-3 + \sqrt{17}}{2}, \dfrac{-11 + \sqrt{17}}{2}\right),$ $\left(\dfrac{-3 - \sqrt{17}}{2}, \dfrac{-11 - \sqrt{17}}{2}\right)$ $\approx (0.56, -3.44), (-3.56, -7.56)$

14. (0, 1), (−3, −2)  15. (3, 7), (−2, 2)

16. (0, −1), (2, −3)  17. (1, −2)

18. (5, −10), (−3, −2)

19. $(-3 + \sqrt{6}, -1 + \sqrt{6}),$ $(-3 - \sqrt{6}, -1 - \sqrt{6})$

20. (0, 1)  21. (0, −1)

22. (−1, 0), (−2, 0)

23. $(0, -3), \left(\frac{1}{3}, -\frac{31}{9}\right)$

24. $(-1, 0), \left(\frac{1}{4}, \frac{25}{16}\right)$

**25–36.** See page 263.

**Graph the solution to each set of inequalities.**

**37.** $\begin{cases} y < -3x^2 + 1 \\ y > x^2 - x - 5 \end{cases}$
**38.** $\begin{cases} y < 3x^2 + 2x + 1 \\ y > 2x^2 - x + 1 \end{cases}$
**39.** $\begin{cases} y > x^2 - 5x + 4 \\ y > x^2 + 3x + 2 \end{cases}$

**40. Error Analysis** A classmate graphed the system of inequalities and concluded that because the shaded regions do not intersect, there are no solutions to the system. Describe and correct the error.

$\begin{cases} y \le x^2 - 4x + 6 \\ y \ge x^2 - 4x + 2 \end{cases}$

**Solve each system.**

**41.** $\begin{cases} y = 3x^2 - 2x - 1 \\ y = x - 1 \end{cases}$
**42.** $\begin{cases} y = -x^2 + x - 5 \\ y = x - 5 \end{cases}$
**43.** $\begin{cases} y = x^2 - 3x - 2 \\ y = 4x + 28 \end{cases}$

**44.** $\begin{cases} y = \frac{1}{2}x^2 + 4x + 4 \\ y = -4x + 12\frac{1}{2} \end{cases}$
**45.** $\begin{cases} y = -\frac{3}{4}x^2 - 4x \\ y = 3x + 8 \end{cases}$
**46.** $\begin{cases} y = -\frac{1}{4}x^2 + x + 1 \\ y = x - 4 \end{cases}$

**47. Business** A company's weekly revenue $R$ is given by the formula $R = -p^2 + 30p$, where $p$ is the price of the company's product. The company is considering hiring a distributor, which will cost the company $4p + 25$ per week.
 **a.** Use a system of equations to find the values of the price $p$ for which the product will still remain profitable if they hire this distributor.
 **b.** Which value of $p$ will maximize the profit after including the distributor cost?

**Solve each system.**

**48.** $\begin{cases} y = 5x^2 + 9x + 4 \\ y = -5x + 3 \end{cases}$
**49.** $\begin{cases} y = -7x^2 - 9x + 6 \\ y = \frac{1}{2}x + 11 \end{cases}$

**50.** $\begin{cases} y = x^2 + 3x + 6 \\ y = -x + 2 \end{cases}$
**51.** $\begin{cases} y = -4x^2 + 7x + 1 \\ y = 3x + 2 \end{cases}$

**52. Reasoning** Sketch the graphs of $y = 2x^2 + 4x - 5$ and $y = x^2 + 2x - 3$. Change these equations into inequalities so the system has solutions that comprise:
 **a.** two non-overlapping regions
 **b.** one bounded region

**Solve the systems by graphing. For each system indicate one point in the solution set.**

**53.** $\begin{cases} y < x^2 - 1 \\ y > 3x^2 - 3 \end{cases}$
**54.** $\begin{cases} y > x^2 \\ y < -x^2 + 1 \end{cases}$
**55.** $\begin{cases} y > (x - 3)^2 + 4 \\ y < -(x - 3)^2 + 5 \end{cases}$

**Challenge**

**56.** Find a value of $a$ for which the line $y = x + a$ separates the parabolas $y = x^2 - 3x + 2$ and $y = -x^2 + 8x - 15$.

---

**40.** The solution of the system is the common area (shaded) on the graph. So, yes, there are solutions, even though the graphs of the parabolas do not intersect.

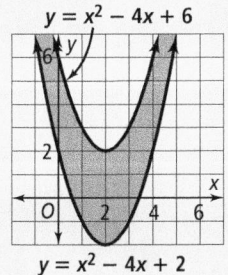

$y = x^2 - 4x + 6$

$y = x^2 - 4x + 2$

**41.** $(0, -1), (1, 0)$

**42.** $(0, -5)$

**43.** $(10, 68), (-3, 16)$

**44.** $(-17, 80.5), (1, 8.5)$

**45.** $(-8, -16), \left(-\frac{4}{3}, 4\right)$

**46.** $(4.47, 0.47), (-4.47, -8.47)$

**47. a.** $0 < p < 25$    **b.** $13$

**48.** $\left(\frac{-7 + 2\sqrt{11}}{5}, 10 - 2\sqrt{11}\right),$

$\left(\frac{-7 - 2\sqrt{11}}{5}, 10 + 2\sqrt{11}\right)$

$\approx (-0.0734, 3.3668), (-2.7266, 16.6332)$

**49.** no solution

**50.** $(-2, 4)$     **51.** $\left(\frac{1}{2}, \frac{7}{2}\right)$

**52.**

$y = x^2 + 2x - 3$

$y = 2x^2 + 4x - 5$

 **a.**

$y > x^2 + 2x - 3$

$y < 2x^2 + 4x - 5$

 **b.**

$y \le x^2 + 2x - 3$

$y \ge 2x^2 + 4x - 5$

**53.**

; $(0, -2)$

$y = x^2 - 1$

$y = 3x^2 - 3$

**54.**

$y = x^2$; $\left(0, \frac{1}{2}\right)$

$y = -x^2 + 1$

**55.**

; $\left(3, \frac{9}{2}\right)$

$y = (x - 3)^2 + 4$

$y = -(x - 3)^2 + 5$

**56.** Answers may vary. Sample: $-2.5$

---

**25.** no solution

**26.**

**27.**

**28.**

**29.** width $= 20.45$ in. and length $= 21.45$ in.; or width $= 6.55$ in. and length $= 7.55$ in.

**30.** The system can be solved by graphing or substitution: $(5.30, 1.30), (1.70, -2.30)$. To solve graphically, solve the first equation for $y$: $y = -1 \pm \sqrt{x}$.

Then graph $y = -1 + \sqrt{x}$ and $y = -1 - \sqrt{x}$ along with the second equation.

**31.** $(8.42, -5.42), (-1.42, 4.42)$

**32.** $(-3, -4), (1, 8)$

**33.** $\left(-1, -\frac{3}{2}\right)$

**34.** $(3, -1), (-2, 4)$

**35.** $(0, -4), (2, -2)$

**36.** $(3, -8), (-0.5, 0.75)$

**37.**

**38.**

**39.**

# Answers

## Practice and Problem-Solving Exercises (continued)

**57.** never; $x^2 + c \neq x^2 + d$

**58.** always; $(0, c)$

**59.** always; $\left( \dfrac{-a-b}{2}, \dfrac{a^2 - 2ab + b^2}{2} \right)$

**60.** sometimes; for example, no solution if $a > 0, c > 0, b < 0, d < 0$

**61.** $\sqrt{5} - 1$ units

## Standardized Test Prep

**62.** C

**63.** F

**64.** C

**65.** [2] $x = \dfrac{-b \pm \sqrt{b^2 - 4ac}}{2a}$

$x = \dfrac{-(5) \pm \sqrt{(5)^2 - 4(-3)(4)}}{2(-3)}$

$x = \dfrac{5 \pm \sqrt{73}}{6}$

[1] appropriate method, with one computational error

## Mixed Review

**66.** $-4 + 3i$

**67.** $7 + 7i$

**68.** $3 + 3i$

**69.** $-1, -\dfrac{3}{2}$

**70.** $1, 3$

**71.** $\dfrac{3}{5}$

**72.** $y = -(k - 2)^2 + 10$

**73.** $y = (x + 3)^2 - 8$

**74.** $y = 2(n - 2)^2 - 11$

**75.** $11q$

**76.** $2a^2 b + ab^2$

**77.** $-y^2 + 2y$

---

Determine whether the following systems *always, sometimes,* or *never* have solutions. (Assume that different letters refer to unequal constants.) Explain.

**57.** $\begin{cases} y = x^2 + c \\ y = x^2 + d \end{cases}$

**58.** $\begin{cases} y = ax^2 + c \\ y = bx^2 + c \end{cases}$

**59.** $\begin{cases} y = (x + a)^2 \\ y = (x + b)^2 \end{cases}$

**60.** $\begin{cases} y = a(x + m)^2 + c \\ y = b(x + n)^2 + d \end{cases}$

**61.** Find the side of the square with vertical and horizontal sides inscribed in the region representing the solution of the system $\begin{cases} y \leq -x^2 + 1 \\ y \geq x^2 - 1 \end{cases}$.

## Standardized Test Prep

**SAT/ACT**

**62.** How many solutions does the system have? $\begin{cases} y = -\frac{1}{4}x^2 - 2x \\ y = x^2 + \frac{3}{4} \end{cases}$

  Ⓐ 0      Ⓑ 1      Ⓒ 2      Ⓓ 3

**63.** Which expression is equivalent to $(-3 + 2i)(2 - 3i)$?

  Ⓕ $13i$      Ⓖ $12$      Ⓗ $12 + 13i$      Ⓘ $-12$

**64.** Which expression is equivalent to $(2 - 7i) \div (2i)^3$?

  Ⓐ $\frac{7}{8} - \frac{1}{4}i$      Ⓑ $\frac{1}{4} - \frac{7}{8}i$      Ⓒ $\frac{7}{8} + \frac{1}{4}i$      Ⓓ $\frac{1}{4} + \frac{7}{8}i$

**Short Response**

**65.** Solve the equation $-3x^2 + 5x + 4 = 0$. Show your work.

## Mixed Review

Find the sum or difference.      ◆ See Lesson 4-8.

**66.** $(1 - i) + (-5 + 4i)$      **67.** $(3 + 4i) - (-4 - 3i)$      **68.** $(1 + i) + (2 + 2i)$

Solve each equation using the Quadratic Formula.      ◆ See Lesson 4-7.

**69.** $2m^2 + 5m + 3 = 0$      **70.** $p^2 - 4p + 3 = 0$      **71.** $25x^2 - 30x + 9 = 0$

Rewrite each equation in vertex form.      ◆ See Lesson 4-6.

**72.** $y = -k^2 + 4k + 6$      **73.** $y = x^2 + 6x + 1$      **74.** $y = 2n^2 - 8n - 3$

**Get Ready!**   **To prepare for Lesson 5-1, do Exercises 75–77.**

Simplify by combining like terms.      ◆ See Lesson 1-3.

**75.** $3q + 9q - q$      **76.** $-2ab^2 + 2a^2b + 3ab^2$      **77.** $-4y^2 + 2y + 3y^2$

## Additional Instructional Support

### Algebra 2 Companion

Students can use the **Algebra 2 Companion** worktext (4 pages) as you teach the lesson. Use the Companion to support

- New Vocabulary
- Key Concepts
- Got It for each Problem
- Lesson Check

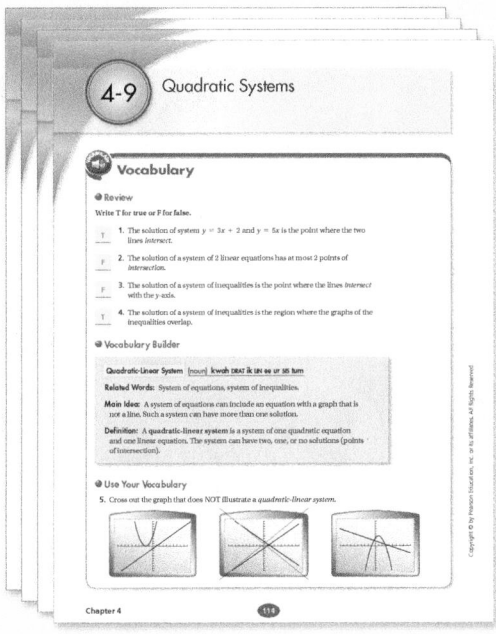

### ELL Support

**Use Manipulatives** Sketch a line on 2 transparencies and a parabola on 2 more transparencies.

First, review the number of real solutions of a system of 2 linear equations. Demonstrate the number of intersections (solutions) for each: none (parallel lines), 1, or infinitely many (the lines coincide).

Then, show a line and a parabola. It is possible that they do not intersect at all, at 1 point, or at 2 points. They will not, however, intersect at infinitely many points.

Finally, show the 2 parabolas. Demonstrate where they intersect at no points, 1 point, 2 points, and infinitely many points.

## 5 Assess & Remediate

### Lesson Quiz

1. **Do you UNDERSTAND?** How many solutions can a linear-quadratic system have? Explain what the number of solutions means about a graph of the system.

2. Solve and check: $\begin{cases} y = x^2 - 6x + 12 \\ y = x + 2 \end{cases}$

3. Solve and check: $\begin{cases} y = x^2 - 3x + 6 \\ y = -x^2 + 7x + 6 \end{cases}$

4. Solve: $\begin{cases} y > x^2 - x + 1 \\ y < -x^2 + x + 5 \end{cases}$

### ANSWERS TO LESSON QUIZ

1. Answers may vary. Samples: There can be 2, 1, or no solutions. 2 solutions means the line intersects the parabola twice; 1 solution means a line intersects the parabola once; no solution means the line never intersects the parabola.

2. (2, 4) and (5, 7)

3. (0, 6) and (5, 16)

4.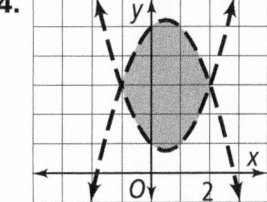

### PRESCRIPTION FOR REMEDIATION

Use the student work on the Lesson Quiz to prescribe a differentiated review assignment:

| Points | Differentiated Remediation |
|--------|---------------------------|
| 0–2 | Intervention |
| 3 | On-level |
| 4 | Extension |

**PowerAlgebra.com**

### 5 Assess & Remediate

Assign the Lesson Quiz. Appropriate intervention, practice, or enrichment is automatically generated based on student performance.

## Intervention

- **Reteaching** (2 pages) Provides reteaching and practice exercises for the key lesson concepts. Use with struggling students or absent students.

- **English Language Learner Support** Helps students develop and reinforce mathematical vocabulary and key concepts.

### All-in-One Resources/Online
**Reteaching**

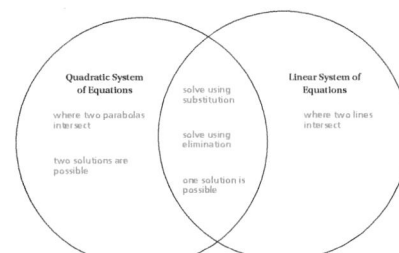

### All-in-One Resources/Online
**English Language Learner Support**

# Differentiated Remediation *continued*

## On-Level

- **Practice** (2 pages) Provides extra practice for each lesson. For simpler practice exercises, use the Form K Practice pages found in the All-in-One Teaching Resources and online.

- **Think About a Plan** Helps students develop specific problem-solving skills and strategies by providing scaffolded guiding questions.

- **Standardized Test Prep** Focuses on all major exercises, all major question types, and helps students prepare for the high-stakes assessments.

## Extension

- **Enrichment** Provides students with interesting problems and activities that extend the concepts of the lesson.

- **Activities, Games, and Puzzles** Worksheets that can be used for concepts development, enrichment, and for fun!

---

**Practice and Problem Solving Wkbk/ All-in-One Resources/Online**
### Practice page 1

**Practice and Problem Solving Wkbk/ All-in-One Resources/Online**
### Practice page 2

**Practice and Problem Solving Wkbk/ All-in-One Resources/Online**
### Think About a Plan

**Practice and Problem Solving Wkbk/ All-in-One Resources/Online**
### Standardized Test Prep

**All-in-One Resources/Online**
### Enrichment

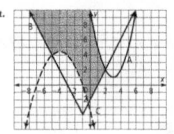

**Online Teacher Resource Center**
### Activities, Games, and Puzzles

## Concept Byte
EXTENSION

# Powers of Complex Numbers

You can use the rules for multiplying complex numbers to find powers of complex numbers.

## Example 1

Compute and graph $(2i)^n$, for $n = 0, 1, 2$, and $3$.

| n | $(2i)^n$ |
|---|---|
| 0 | $(2i)^0 = 1$ |
| 1 | $(2i)^1 = 2i$ |
| 2 | $(2i)^2 = 4i^2 = 4(-1) = -4$ |
| 3 | $(2i)^3 = 8i^3 = 8(i^2 \cdot i) = 8(-1 \cdot i) = -8i$ |

imaginary axis
$0 + 2i$
$-4 + 0i$    real axis
$1 + 0i$    8
$-4i$
$-8i$
$0 - 8i$

## Example 2

Compute and graph $(2 - 3i)^n$, for $n = 0, 1, 2$, and $3$.

| n | $(2 - 3i)^n$ |
|---|---|
| 0 | $(2 - 3i)^0 = 1$ |
| 1 | $(2 - 3i)^1 = 2 - 3i$ |
| 2 | $(2 - 3i)^2 = 4 - 6i - 6i + 9i^2 = 4 - 12i + 9(-1) = -5 - 12i$ |
| 3 | $(2 - 3i)^3 = -10 - 24i + 15i + 36i^2 = -10 - 9i + 36(-1) = -46 - 9i$ |

imaginary axis
$10i$    real axis
$1 + 0i$
$-50$ $-40$ $-30$ $-20$ $-10$
$2 - 3i$
$-10i$
$-46 - 9i$    $-5 - 12i$

## Exercises

1. Based on the graph in Example 1, predict the location of $(2i)^5$.

2. Compute and graph $(-3i)^n$ for $n = 0, 1, 2$, and $3$.

3. **a.** Connect the points from the graph in Example 1 with a smooth curve. Estimate $(2i)^{\frac{1}{2}}$.
   **b.** Use a graphing calculator to compute $(2i)^{\frac{1}{2}}$. Does it fall on the curve? Was it close to your estimate?

4. Use a graphing calculator to find values of $(2 - 3i)^n$ for $n = 0.5, 1.5$, and $2.5$. Copy the graph and add these points.

5. Compute and graph $(3 - 4i)^n$ for $n = 0, 1, 2$, and $3$.

## Guided Instruction

**PURPOSE** To investigate powers of complex numbers

**PROCESS** Students will
- use repeated multiplication to algebraically evaluate powers of complex numbers.
- use a calculator to evaluate fractional powers of complex numbers.
- graph powers of a complex number.

**DISCUSS**                              **VISUAL LEARNERS**

The graph of a complex number raised to successively higher powers circles around the origin in a rapidly expanding pattern.

> **Q** How can you evaluate the square of a complex number? **[Answers may vary. Sample: Write as a product of binomials and use FOIL.]**

### Example 1

> **Q** In what direction does the curve move around the origin? **[counterclockwise]**
> **Q** Which powers are on the imaginary axis? real axis? **[odd powers; even powers]**

**VISUAL**
Compare the graphs to reinforce the difference between pure imaginary and complex numbers.

### Example 2

> **Q** Do any of the positive integer powers lie on the axes? Explain. **[No; the positive integer values are neither real numbers nor pure imaginary numbers.]**

### Exercises

> **Q** For Exercise 4, do the powers lie on the graph where you would expect them to be—between the integer powers? Explain. **[Answers may vary. Sample: Yes; they lie on the spiral curve.]**

# Answers

## Exercises

**1.** $0 + 32i$

**2.**

imaginary axis
$20i$
$10i$
real axis
$-30$ $-20$ $-10$
$-10i$

$(1 + 0i, 0 - 3i, -9 + 0i, 0 + 27i)$

**3. a.** $1 + i$
   **b.** $1 + i$; yes

**4.** $n = 0.5, 1.674 - 0.896i$
   $n = 1.5, 0.6604 - 6.8144i$
   $n = 2.5, -19.1225 - 15.6099i$

imaginary axis
$20i$
$10i$
real axis
$-40$ $-30$ $-20$ $-10$

**5.** $n = 0, 1$
   $n = 1, 3 - 4i$
   $n = 2, -7 - 24i$
   $n = 3, -117 - 44i$

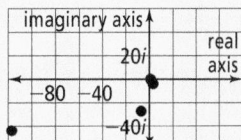

imaginary axis
real axis
$20i$
$-80$ $-40$
$-40i$

# Performance Task

## Pull It All Together

The concepts and skills required to solve these problems are from several lessons within this chapter and from earlier chapters. As students solve these problems, they will demonstrate their reasoning strategies and their growth as independent problem solvers.

The following questions are designed to
- help support students as they do the Tasks.
- gauge the amount of support students need as they become independent problem solvers.

### Task 1

Compare the coefficients of standard and vertex form of a quadratic function by converting from standard to vertex form.
- What does the coefficient of the $x^2$ term have to be before you can complete the square?
- Knowing the quadratic formula might help you if you get stuck while converting the standard form to vertex form. What is the quadratic formula?

### Task 2

Find the equation of a quadratic function that models three given data points and then use the model to extend the data.
- What values of the equation $y = ax^2 + bx + c$ do you know? How many equations will be in the system you will solve?
- Can you use a graphing calculator to find the quadratic equation that models the path of the arrow?
- What value of $y$ represents the ground?
- Could 2d have more than one solution? Do both solutions make sense?

---

> To solve these problems, you will pull together many concepts and skills related to solving quadratic equations. Be sure to show your work and justify your reasoning.

**BIG idea** Equivalence and Function

The parameters $a$, $b$, $c$, $h$, and $k$ in the standard and vertex forms of a quadratic function give information on how the graph of the function relates to the graph of the parent function $y = x^2$.

Standard form: $y = ax^2 + bx + c$    Vertex form: $y = a(x - h)^2 + k$

### Task 1

**Refer to the two forms shown above.**

**a.** What information do the parameters, or combinations of parameters, provide about the graph of the quadratic function?

**b.** Begin with standard form. Transform it to vertex form. What are the values of $h$ and $k$ in terms of $a$, $b$, and $c$?

**c.** Show how the Quadratic Formula follows from your result in part (b). *Hint:* Set the expression in your vertex form equal to 0. Then solve by factoring.

**BIG idea** Solving Equations and Inequalities

A problem may require different types of equation solving. You should know when and how to use a graphing calculator to help you with your work.

### Task 2

**You shoot an arrow at a target. The parabolic path of your arrow passes through the points shown in the table.**

| x | y |
|---|---|
| 30 | 6 |
| 60 | 7 |
| 100 | 4 |

**a.** Find a quadratic function in standard form that models the path of your arrow. *Hint:* The three points are $(x, y)$-values that satisfy $y = ax^2 + bx + c$.

**b.** If the $y$-value represents height above the ground, for what value of $x$ would your arrow hit the ground if you miss the target?

**c.** If the target bull's-eye is at $x = 100$, at what height should the bull's-eye be for your arrow to hit it?

**d.** If the target bull's-eye is at height $y = 2.98$, at what value of $x$ should the bull's-eye be for the arrow to hit it?

---

# Assess
# Performance

## Pull It All Together

See p. 49 for a holistic scoring rubric to gauge a student's progress on Understanding the Problem, Planning a Solution, Getting an Answer, and Assessing Autonomy.

### SOLUTION OUTLINES

**1. a.** First step: Using the standard form:

a indicates a stretch or compression factor and is the same in both the standard and vertex form.

c is the $y$-intercept

$-\frac{b}{2a}$ is the $x$-coordinate of the vertex.

The line $x = -\frac{b}{2a}$ is the axis of symmetry.

Second step: Using the vertex form:

h is the $x$-coordinate of the vertex. It also indicates how many units the graph shifts to the right or left.

k is the $y$-coordinate of the vertex. It also indicates how many units the graph shifts up or down.

**b.** First step: Using the standard form, find the $x$-coordinate of the vertex. $\left(-\frac{b}{2a}\right)$

Second step: Find the $y$-coordinate of the vertex by substituting the $x$-value you found in Step 1 into the equation and solving for $y$. $\left(\frac{-b^2 + 4ac}{4a}\right)$

So, $h = -\frac{b}{2a}$ and $k = \frac{-b^2 + 4ac}{4a}$.

Third step: Substitute the values of $h$ and $k$ into the vertex form, $y = a(x - h)^2 + k$.

$\left(y = a\left(x + \frac{b}{2a}\right)^2 + \frac{-b^2 + 4ac}{4a}\right)$

**c.** First step: Use the equation you found in part (b),

$y = a\left(x + \frac{b}{2a}\right)^2 + \frac{-b^2 + 4ac}{4a}$.

Second step: Set the equation equal to 0;

$0 = a\left(x + \frac{b}{2a}\right)^2 + \frac{-b^2 + 4ac}{4a}$.

Third step: Add the opposite of $a\left(x + \frac{b}{2a}\right)^2$ to each side of the equation.

Fourth step: Divide each side of the equation by $-a$.

Fifth step: Take the square root of each side.

Sixth step: Add the opposite of $\frac{b}{2a}$ to each side.

Seventh step: Rewrite the right-hand side of the equation as a single fraction. (The result should be the Quadratic Formula.)

**2. a.** First step: Use the **STAT** feature to enter the given points in your graphing calculator. Enter the $x$-values in L1 and the $y$-values in L2.

Second step: Use **QuadReg** to find the equation of the parabola. ($y = -0.0015x^2 + 0.1726x + 2.214$)

**b.–d.** See next page.

Connecting **BIG** ideas and Answering the Essential Questions

**1 Equivalence**
Vertex form of a quadratic function shows the vertex of the parabola. Standard form is "calculator ready." Both forms give additional information.

**2 Function**
Any quadratic function is possibly a stretch or compression, a reflection, and a translation of $y = x^2$.

**3 Solving Equations and Inequalities**
The real solutions of a quadratic equation show the zeros of the related quadratic function and the $x$-intercepts of its graph.

**The Different Forms of a Quadratic Function (Lessons 4-1 and 4-2)**

$y = 2(x - 1)^2 + 3$ has vertex $(1, 3)$ and opens upward $(2 > 0)$.

$y = -2x^2 + 4x + 1$ has vertex with $x$-coordinate $-\frac{4}{2(-2)} = 1$ and opens downward $(-2 < 0)$.

Each has axis of symmetry $x = 1$.
Each is a stretch of $y = x^2$ by the factor 2.

**Helpful Aids for Solving Quadratic Equations (Lessons 4-4, 4-6, 4-8)**

Factor a quadratic: $-16x^2 + 12x + 4$
$\qquad = -4(4x + 1)(x - 1)$

Complete the square: $x^2 + 4x + 1$
$= x^2 + 4x + \left(\frac{4}{2}\right)^2 + 1 - \left(\frac{4}{2}\right)^2$
$= (x + 2)^2 - 3$
Complex numbers: $x^2 + 1 = (x + i)(x - i)$
$\qquad\qquad$ where $i = \sqrt{-1}$.

**Modeling With Quadratics (Lessons 4-3 and 4-9)**

$y = -16x^2 + 12x + 4$ can model the height $y$ in feet reached by the coin tossed by the referee before the game. $x$ represents time in seconds.

**Solving Quadratic Equations (Lessons 4-5, 4-7)**

$-16x^2 + 12x + 4 = 0 \quad \rightarrow$
$-4(4x + 1)(x - 1) = 0 \quad \rightarrow$
$x = -\frac{1}{4}$ or $x = 1$.

$-2x^2 + 4x + 1 = 0 \quad \rightarrow$
$x = \frac{-4 \pm \sqrt{4^2 - 4(-2)(1)}}{2(-2)} \quad \rightarrow$
$x = 1 + \frac{\sqrt{6}}{2}$ or $x = 1 - \frac{\sqrt{6}}{2}$.

 **Chapter Vocabulary**

- absolute value of a complex number (p. 249)
- axis of symmetry (p. 194)
- completing the square (p. 235)
- complex conjugate (p. 251)
- complex number (p. 249)
- complex number plane (p. 249)
- difference of two squares (p. 220)
- discriminant (p. 242)
- factoring (p. 216)
- greatest common factor (p. 218)
- imaginary number (p. 249)
- imaginary unit (p. 248)
- maximum value (p. 195)
- minimum value (p. 195)
- parabola (p. 194)
- perfect square trinomial (p. 219)
- pure imaginary number (p. 249)
- quadratic formula (p. 240)
- quadratic function (p. 194)
- standard form (p. 202)
- vertex form (p. 194)
- vertex of the parabola (p. 194)
- zero of a function (p. 226)
- zero product property (p. 226)

**Choose the correct term to complete each sentence.**

1. To solve an equation by factoring, the equation should first be written in (standard form/vertex form).

2. The value of $b^2 - 4ac$ for the equation $ax^2 + bx + c = 0$ is called the (discriminant/difference of two squares).

3. The number $a + bi$, where $b = 0$, is an example of a(n) (imaginary/complex) number.

---

**BIG** idea **Equivalence**
**ESSENTIAL QUESTION** What are the advantages of a quadratic function in vertex form? in standard form?
**ANSWER** Vertex form of a quadratic function shows the vertex of the parabola. Standard form is "calculator ready." Both forms give additional information.

**BIG** idea **Function**
**ESSENTIAL QUESTION** How is any quadratic function related to the parent quadratic function $y = x^2$?
**ANSWER** Any quadratic function is possibly a stretch or compression, a reflection, and/or a translation of $y = x^2$.

**BIG** idea **Solving Equations**
**ESSENTIAL QUESTION** How are the real solutions of a quadratic equation related to the graph of the related quadratic function?
**ANSWER** The real solutions of a quadratic equation show the zeros of the related quadratic function and the $x$-intercepts of its graph.

---

**SOLUTION OUTLINES** (continued)

**b.** Possible Plan: Using your graphing calculator, graph the equation you found in part (a). Find the value of $x$ when the parabola intersects the $x$-axis. ($\approx 126.7$)

**c.** Find the $y$-value when $x = 100$. ($\approx 4.5$ ft)

**d.** Find the $x$-value when $y = 2.98$. ($\approx 110$)

**Chapter Review**

1. standard
2. discriminant
3. complex

---

Use the following prompts as you review this chapter with your students. The prompts are designed to help you assess your students' understanding of the Big Ideas they have studied.

- Compare and contrast vertex and standard form of a quadratic function. What information does each form give you? Which would you use to graph the function?
- Why might you factor a quadratic equation? What does the Zero-Product Property tell you about the factors?
- What information does the discriminant give you about the number and type of solutions to a quadratic equation?
- When is a complex number the solution to a quadratic equation?
- Compare and contrast factoring, completing the square, and using the Quadratic Formula to solve a quadratic equation. Under what circumstances would you use each one?

# Answers

## Chapter Review (continued)

**4.** vertex: $(-2, -6)$; axis of symmetry: $x = -2$; minimum: $-6$; domain: all real numbers; range: $y \geq -6$

**5.** vertex: $(3, 2)$; axis of symmetry: $x = 3$; maximum: $2$; domain: all real numbers; range: $y \leq 2$

**6.** vertex: $(1, 5)$; axis of symmetry: $x = 1$; minimum: $5$; domain: all real numbers; range: $y \geq 5$

**7.** vertex: $(-9, -4)$; axis of symmetry: $x = -9$; minimum: $-4$; domain: all real numbers; range: $y \geq -4$

**8.**  translation 4 units up

**9.**  translation 9 units to the right and 2 units up

**10.**  vert. compression by a factor of $\frac{1}{2}$, translation 1 unit to the left and 5 units down

**11.** $y = 2(x - 2)^2 + 1$

**12.** $y = \left(-\frac{1}{3}\right)(x + 5)^2 + 4$

---

### Quick Review

You can write every **quadratic function** in the form $f(x) = ax^2 + bx + c$, where $a \neq 0$. A **parabola** is the graph of a quadratic function. Every parabola has a vertex and an axis of symmetry. Shown below is the graph of the quadratic parent function $f(x) = x^2$.

The **vertex form** of a quadratic function is $f(x) = a(x - h)^2 + k$, where $a \neq 0$. The vertex of the parabola formed by a quadratic function is $(h, k)$.

If $a > 0$, $k$ is the **minimum value** of the function.

If $a < 0$, $k$ is the **maximum value** of the function. The axis of symmetry is given by $x = h$.

### Example

What is the vertex, axis of symmetry, maximum or minimum, and domain and range of the function $f(x) = 5(x - 7)^2 + 2$?

| | |
|---|---|
| $a = 5, h = 7, k = 2$ | Identify $a$, $h$, and $k$. |
| vertex: $(7, 2)$ | Find the vertex: $(h, k)$. |
| axis of symmetry: $x = 7$ | The axis of symmetry is at $x = h$. |
| $k = 2$ is a minimum | Since $a > 0$, $k$ is a minimum. |
| domain: all real numbers | There are no restrictions on $x$. |
| range: $y \geq 2$. | Since the minimum is 2, $y \geq 2$. |

### Exercises

Identify the vertex, axis of symmetry, maximum or minimum, and domain and range of each function.

**4.** $f(x) = 4(x + 2)^2 - 6$

**5.** $f(x) = -(x - 3)^2 + 2$

**6.** $f(x) = 10(x - 1)^2 + 5$

**7.** $f(x) = 2(x + 9)^2 - 4$

Graph each function. Describe each transformation of the parent function $f(x) = x^2$.

**8.** $f(x) = x^2 + 4$

**9.** $f(x) = (x - 9)^2 + 2$

**10.** $f(x) = \frac{1}{2}(x + 1)^2 - 5$

Write the equation of each parabola in vertex form.

**11.**

**12.**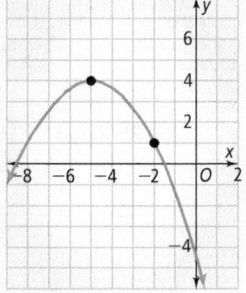

## 4-2 Standard Form of a Quadratic Function

### Quick Review

The **standard form** of a quadratic function is $f(x) = ax^2 + bx + c$, where $a \neq 0$. When $a > 0$, the parabola opens up. When $a < 0$, the parabola opens down.

The axis of symmetry is the line $x = -\frac{b}{2a}$. The vertex is $\left(-\frac{b}{2a}, f\left(-\frac{b}{2a}\right)\right)$, and the $y$-intercept is $(0, c)$.

### Example

What are the vertex, the axis of symmetry and $y$-intercept of the graph of the function $f(x) = x^2 - 6x + 8$?

axis of symmetry: $x = -\left(\frac{-6}{2(1)}\right) = 3$

vertex: $(3, -1)$

$y$-intercept: $(0, 8)$

### Exercises

**Graph each function.**

**13.** $f(x) = x^2 + 6x + 5$   **14.** $f(x) = x^2 - 7x - 18$

**15.** $f(x) = x^2 - 7x + 12$   **16.** $f(x) = x^2 - 9$

**Write each function in vertex form.**

**17.** $f(x) = 4x^2 - 8x + 2$   **18.** $f(x) = x^2 - 8x + 12$

**19.** $f(x) = 8x^2 + 8x - 12$   **20.** $f(x) = -2x^2 - 6x + 10$

**21. Physics** The equation $h = -16t^2 + 32t + 9$ gives the height of a ball, $h$, in feet above the ground, at $t$ seconds after the ball is thrown upward. How many seconds after the ball is thrown will it reach its maximum height? What is its maximum height?

## 4-3 Modeling With Quadratic Functions

### Quick Review

You can use quadratic functions to model real world data. You can find a quadratic function to model data that passes through any three non-collinear points given that no two of the points lie on a vertical line.

### Example

Find the equation of the parabola that passes through the points $(-2, 8)$, $(0, -2)$, and $(1, 2)$.

$y = ax^2 + bx + c$ — Use the standard form of a quadratic function.

$\begin{cases} 8 = a(-2)^2 + b(-2) + c \\ -2 = a(0)^2 + b(0) + c \\ 2 = a(1)^2 + b(1) + c \end{cases}$ — Substitute the $(x, y)$ values to write a system of equations.

$\begin{cases} 4a - 2b + c = 8 \\ c = -2 \\ a + b + c = 2 \end{cases}$

$a = 3, b = 1, c = -2$ — Solve the system of equations.

$y = 3x^2 + x - 2$ — Substitute $a$, $b$, and $c$ to find the quadratic function.

### Exercises

**Find the equation of the parabola that passes through each set of points.**

**22.** $(0, 5), (2, -3), (-1, 12)$

**23.** $(2, 0), (3, -2), (1, -2)$

**24.** $(4, 10), (0, -18), (-2, -20)$

**25.** $(0, -7), (7, -14), (-3, -19)$

**26. Track and Field** The table shows the height of a javelin as it is thrown and travels across a horizontal distance. Use your calculator to find a quadratic model to represent the path of the javelin.

| Distance (m) | Height (m) |
|---|---|
| 5 | 2 |
| 18 | 5 |
| 33 | 8 |
| 55 | 6 |
| 68 | 4 |
| 74 | 3 |

**13.**

**14.**

**15.**

**16.**

**17.** $f(x) = 4(x - 1)^2 - 2$

**18.** $f(x) = (x - 4)^2 - 4$

**19.** $f(x) = 8\left(x + \frac{1}{2}\right)^2 - 14$

**20.** $f(x) = -2\left(x + \frac{3}{2}\right)^2 + \frac{29}{2}$

**21.** 1s; 25 ft

**22.** $y = x^2 - 6x + 5$

**23.** $y = -2x^2 + 8x - 8$

**24.** $y = x^2 + 3x - 18$

**25.** $y = -0.5x^2 + 2.5x - 7$

**26.** $y = -0.0043x^2 + 0.3521x + 0.3691$

# Answers

## Chapter Review (continued)

**27.** $(x - 6)(x - 2)$

**28.** $(3x - 4)(x + 5)$

**29.** $-2(2x - 1)(x - 3)$

**30.** $(x + 10)(x + 4)$

**31.** $(x - 7)^2$

**32.** $(3x + 5)^2$

**33.** $4(3x - 2)(3x + 2)$

**34.** $(5x - 2)(5x + 2)$

**35.** $6x; 6x(x - 4)$

**36.** $7; -7(2x^2 + 7)$

**37.** $-2, 6$

**38.** $-2, \dfrac{7}{2}$

**39.** $-4, 2$

**40.** $-9, 2$

**41.** $1, -2.6;$

**42.** $1.345, -3.345;$

**43.** $1.618, -0.618;$

**44.** $3.236, -1.236;$

**45.** $2, 4$

**46.** no real solutions

**47.** $4.56, 0.44$

**48.** $2, 4$

---

## 4-4 Factoring Quadratic Expressions

### Quick Review

To factor an expression of the form $ax^2 + bx + c$, when $a \neq 1$, you find numbers that have the product $ac$ and sum $b$. You can also factor an expression using the FOIL method in reverse or by finding the greatest common factor (GCF).

### Example

Factor the expression $5x^2 + 13x + 6$.

| | |
|---|---|
| $ac = (5)(6) = 30$ | Find $ac$. |
| $30 = 1 \cdot 30 = 2 \cdot 15 = 3 \cdot 10 = 5 \cdot 6$ | Find the factors of $ac$. |
| $b = 13 = 3 + 10$ | Find two factors that sum to $b$. |
| $5x^2 + 10x + 3x + 6$ | Rewrite $bx$. |
| $5x(x + 2) + 3(x + 2)$ | Find the common factors. |
| $(5x + 3)(x + 2)$ | Rewrite using the Distributive Property. |

### Exercises

Factor each expression.

**27.** $x^2 - 8x + 12$     **28.** $3x^2 + 11x - 20$

**29.** $-4x^2 + 14x - 6$     **30.** $x^2 + 14x + 40$

Factor each perfect square trinomial.

**31.** $x^2 - 14x + 49$     **32.** $9x^2 + 30x + 25$

Factor each difference of two squares.

**33.** $36x^2 - 16$     **34.** $25x^2 - 4$

Find the GCF of each expression. Then factor each expression.

**35.** $6x^2 - 24x$     **36.** $-14x^2 - 49$

---

## 4-5 Solving Quadratic Equations

### Quick Review

The **zeros** of a quadratic function are the solutions of the related quadratic equation. You can find the zeros from a table or from the $x$-intercepts of the parabola that is the graph of the function. You can also find them by **factoring the standard form of a quadratic equation**, $ax^2 + bx + c = 0$, and using the **Zero-Product Property**.

### Example

Solve $2x^2 + 6x = 8$ by factoring.

| | |
|---|---|
| $2x^2 + 6x - 8 = 0$ | Rewrite the equation in standard form. |
| $2(x^2 + 3x - 4) = 0$ | Factor out the GCF, 2. |
| $2(x + 4)(x - 1) = 0$ | Factor the quadratic expression. |
| $2(x + 4) = 0 \text{ or } x - 1 = 0$ | Use the Zero-Product Property. |
| $x = -4 \text{ or } x = 1$ | Solve. |

### Exercises

Solve each equation by factoring.

**37.** $x^2 = 4x + 12$     **38.** $2x^2 - 3x - 14 = 0$

**39.** $x^2 + 2x = 8$     **40.** $x^2 + 7x = 18$

Solve each equation by graphing.

**41.** $5x^2 + 8x - 13 = 0$     **42.** $9 - 4x = 2x^2$

**43.** $x^2 - x = 1$     **44.** $x^2 - 2x - 4 = 0$

Solve each equation by using a table.

**45.** $x^2 - 6x + 8 = 0$     **46.** $9x - 14 = 3x^2$

**47.** $x^2 - 5x + 2 = 0$     **48.** $2x^2 - 12x = -16$

## 4-6 Completing the Square

### Quick Review

If you cannot solve a quadratic equation by factoring, you can use **completing the square**. You write one side as a perfect square trinomial and then take square roots. You can also convert a quadratic function from standard form to vertex form by completing the square.

### Example

Solve $x^2 + 6x - 7 = 0$ by completing the square.

| | |
|---|---|
| $x^2 + 6x = 7$ | Rewrite the equation so the constant is by itself. |
| $\left(\frac{b}{2}\right)^2 = \left(\frac{6}{2}\right)^2 = 3^2 = 9$ | Find $\left(\frac{b}{2}\right)^2$. |
| $x^2 + 6x + 9 = 7 + 9$ | Add $\left(\frac{b}{2}\right)^2$ to each side. |
| $(x + 3)^2 = 16$ | Factor and simplify. |
| $x + 3 = \pm 4$ | Take the square root of each side. |
| $x = 1$ or $x = -7$ | Solve for $x$. |

### Exercises

Solve each equation by finding square roots.

**49.** $4x^2 = 16$      **50.** $4x^2 - 20 = 0$

**51.** $5x^2 - 45 = 0$      **52.** $3x^2 = 36$

What values complete each square?

**53.** $x^2 - 6x$      **54.** $x^2 + 3x$

Solve each equation by completing the square.

**55.** $x^2 + 8x + 6 = 0$      **56.** $x^2 - 10x = 13$

**57.** $9x^2 + 6x + 1 = 4$      **58.** $x^2 - 2x + 4 = 0$

**59.** $x^2 + 3x = -25$      **60.** $4x^2 - x - 3 = 0$

## 4-7 The Quadratic Formula

### Quick Review

You can solve a quadratic equation in the form $ax^2 + bx + c = 0$ by using the **Quadratic Formula**, $x = \frac{-b \pm \sqrt{b^2 - 4ac}}{2a}$. The **discriminant** of a quadratic equation in standard form is the value of the expression $b^2 - 4ac$. You can use it to find the quantity and type of solutions of a quadratic equation.

### Example

Use the Quadratic Formula to solve $2x^2 - 6x = -3$.

| | |
|---|---|
| $2x^2 - 6x + 3 = 0$ | Write the equation in standard form. |
| $a = 2, b = -6, c = 3$ | Identify $a$, $b$, and $c$. |
| $x = \frac{-(-6) \pm \sqrt{(-6)^2 - 4(2)(3)}}{2(2)}$ | Substitute $a$, $b$, and $c$ into the quadratic formula. |
| $x = \frac{6 \pm \sqrt{12}}{4} = \frac{3 \pm \sqrt{3}}{2}$ | Simplify. |

### Exercises

Solve each equation using the quadratic formula.

**61.** $3x^2 + 5x = 8$      **62.** $x^2 = 6x - 9$

**63.** $x(x - 3) = 4$      **64.** $5x^2 - 7x - 3 = 0$

Determine the discriminant of each equation. How many real solutions does each equation have?

**65.** $4x^2 - 2x = 10$      **66.** $x^2 - 5x + 7 = 0$

**67.** $3x^2 + 3 = 6x$      **68.** $7 - 3x = 8x^2$

**69. Gardening** Margaret is planning a rectangular garden. Its length is 4 ft less than twice its width. Its area is 170 ft². What are the dimensions of the garden?

**49.** $\pm 2$

**50.** $\pm \sqrt{5}$

**51.** $\pm 3$

**52.** $\pm 2\sqrt{3}$

**53.** 9

**54.** $\frac{9}{4}$

**55.** $-4 \pm \sqrt{10}$

**56.** $5 \pm \sqrt{38}$

**57.** $-1, \frac{1}{3}$

**58.** $1 \pm i\sqrt{3}$

**59.** $\frac{-3}{2} \pm \frac{i\sqrt{91}}{2}$

**60.** $1, -\frac{3}{4}$

**61.** $1, -\frac{8}{3}$

**62.** 3

**63.** $4, -1$

**64.** $1.744, -0.344$

**65.** 164; two

**66.** $-3$; none

**67.** 0; one

**68.** 233; two

**69.** $10.2736$ ft $\times$ $16.5472$ ft

# Answers

## Chapter Review (continued)

**70.** $2i\sqrt{6}$

**71.** $-3 + i\sqrt{2}$

**72.** $-50 + 40i$

**73.** $6 + 4i\sqrt{6}$

**74.** $3 + 9i$

**75.** $13 + 20i$

**76.** $21 - 25i$

**77.** $-12 - 15i$

**78.** $-3 - 2i$

**79.** $-\frac{1}{2} - \frac{1}{2}i$

**80.** $\pm 3i$

**81.** $\frac{1}{5} \pm \frac{2}{5}i$

**82.** $2 \pm i\sqrt{6}$

**83.** $\frac{-4}{7} \pm \frac{i\sqrt{26}}{7}$

**84.** $(7, -6), (-2, 12)$

**85.** $(5, -27), (-2, 8)$

**86.** $(-5, 37), (3, -27);$

**87.** $(6.32, 15.64), (-3.32, -3.64);$

**88.**

**89.**

---

### Quick Review

A **complex number** is written in the form $a + bi$, where $a$ and $b$ are real numbers, and $i$ is equal to $\sqrt{-1}$. If $b = 0$, $a + bi$ is a real number. If $b \neq 0$, $a + bi$ is an **imaginary number**. You can use the Quadratic Formula or completing the square to find the imaginary solutions of quadratic equations.

### Example

Use the Quadratic Formula to solve $3x^2 - 4x + 2 = 0$.

$x = \dfrac{-(-4) \pm \sqrt{(-4)^2 - 4(3)(2)}}{2(3)}$    Enter $a$, $b$, and $c$ into the quadratic formula.

$x = \dfrac{4 \pm \sqrt{16 - 24}}{6} = \dfrac{4 \pm \sqrt{-8}}{6}$    Simplify.

$x = \dfrac{2}{3} \pm \dfrac{\sqrt{2}}{3}i$    Write the solutions.

### Exercises

Simplify each expression using the imaginary unit $i$.

**70.** $\sqrt{-24}$     **71.** $\sqrt{-2} - 3$

**72.** $(4 + \sqrt{-25})(\sqrt{-100})$    **73.** $2\sqrt{-24} + 6$

Simplify each expression.

**74.** $(9 + 7i) - (6 - 2i)$    **75.** $(3 + 11i) + (10 + 9i)$

**76.** $(1 - 9i)(3 + 2i)$    **77.** $(3i)^2 - 3(1 + 5i)$

**78.** $\dfrac{4 - 6i}{2i}$     **79.** $\dfrac{2 - 3i}{1 + 5i}$

Solve each equation.

**80.** $x^2 + 9 = 0$    **81.** $5x^2 - 2x + 1 = 0$

**82.** $-x^2 + 4x = 10$    **83.** $7x^2 + 8x = -6$

---

## 4-9 Quadratic Systems

### Quick Review

A system of quadratic equations can be solved by substitution or by graphing. You can use these methods to solve a linear-quadratic system or a quadratic-quadratic system. Use graphing to solve a quadratic system of inequalities.

### Example

Use substitution to solve $\begin{cases} y = 2x^2 + 2x - 10 \\ y = x^2 + 5x - 6 \end{cases}$.

$2x^2 + 2x - 10 = x^2 + 5x - 6$    Substitute for $y$.

$x^2 - 3x - 4 = 0$    Rewrite in standard form.

$(x + 1)(x - 4) = 0$    Factor.

$x = -1$ or $x = 4$    Solve for $x$.

$y = (-1)^2 + 5(-1) - 6 = -10$    Substitute for $x$ then solve for $y$.

$y = (4)^2 + 5(4) - 6 = 30$

$(-1, -10)$ and $(4, 30)$    Write solutions as ordered pairs.

### Exercises

Solve each system by substitution.

**84.** $\begin{cases} y = x^2 - 7x - 6 \\ y = 8 - 2x \end{cases}$

**85.** $\begin{cases} y = -x^2 - 2x + 8 \\ y = x^2 - 8x - 12 \end{cases}$

Solve each system by graphing.

**86.** $\begin{cases} y = -x^2 - 10x + 12 \\ y = x^2 - 6x - 18 \end{cases}$

**87.** $\begin{cases} y = x^2 - x - 18 \\ y = 2x + 3 \end{cases}$

Solve each system of inequalities.

**88.** $\begin{cases} y < x + 4 \\ y \geq x^2 + 2x + 2 \end{cases}$

**89.** $\begin{cases} y > 3x^2 - 10x - 8 \\ y < x^2 - 5x + 4 \end{cases}$

**MathXL® for School**
Go to PowerAlgebra.com

## Do you know HOW?

**Sketch a graph of the quadratic function with the given vertex and through the given point. Then write the equation of the parabola in vertex form and describe how the function was transformed from the parent function $y = x^2$.**

1. vertex $(0, 0)$, point $(-3, 3)$

2. vertex $(1, 5)$, point $(2, 1)$

**Graph each quadratic function. Identify the axis of symmetry, the vertex, and the domain and the range of each function.**

3. $y = x^2 - 7$

4. $y = x^2 + 2x + 6$

5. $y = -x^2 + 5x - 3$

**Simplify each expression.**

6. $\sqrt{-16}$

7. $4\sqrt{-9} - 2$

8. $(2 + 3i)(8 - 5i)$

9. $(-3 + 2i) - (6 + i)$

10. $\frac{4 + 2i}{2 - i}$

**Factor each expression completely.**

11. $2y^2 - 8y$

12. $3x^2 + 8x - 3$

13. $9w^2 - 30w + 25$

**Solve each quadratic equation.**

14. $x^2 - 25 = 0$

15. $x^2 - 2x + 3 = 0$

16. $x^2 - 8x = -6$

**Solve the following systems of equations.**

17. $\begin{cases} y = 3x^2 - x + 1 \\ y = 3x^2 + x - 1 \end{cases}$

18. $\begin{cases} y = -x^2 + 2x - 3 \\ y = 4x - 3 \end{cases}$

**Solve the following systems of inequalities.**

19. $\begin{cases} y > 2x^2 + 5x + 1 \\ y < -2x^2 - 5x - 1 \end{cases}$

20. $\begin{cases} y < x^2 - x + 2 \\ y > x^2 - 1 \end{cases}$

**Evaluate the discriminant of each equation. How many real and imaginary solutions does each have?**

21. $x^2 + 6x - 7 = 0$

22. $3x^2 - x + 3 = 0$

23. $-4x^2 - 4x + 1 = 0$

## Do you UNDERSTAND?

24. **Writing** Compare graphing a number on the complex plane to graphing a point on the coordinate plane. How are they similar? How are they different?

25. **Open-Ended** Sketch the graph of a quadratic function $f(x) = ax^2 + bx + c$ that has no real zeros. How does this relate to the solutions of the related equation $ax^2 + bx + c = 0$?

26. **Physics** A model for the path of a toy rocket is given by $h = 68t - 4.9t^2$, where $h$ is the altitude in meters and $t$ is the time in seconds. Explain how to find both the maximum altitude of the rocket and how long it takes to reach that altitude.

27. How many solutions are possible for:
    **a.** a system of two quadratic equations?
    **b.** a system of two quadratic inequalities?
    Explain your answers.

## Answers

### Chapter Test

1.

   $y = \frac{1}{3}x^2$, vertically compressed by a factor of $\frac{1}{3}$

2.

   $y = -4(x - 1)^2 + 5$, reflected across the $x$-axis, vertically stretched by a factor of 4, translated 1 unit to the right and 5 units up

3.

   axis of symmetry: $x = 0$; vertex $(0, -7)$; domain: all real numbers, range: $y \geq -7$

4.

   axis of symmetry: $x = -1$; vertex $(-1, 5)$; domain: all real numbers, range: $y \geq 5$

5.

   axis of symmetry: $x = \frac{5}{2}$; vertex $\left(\frac{5}{2}, \frac{13}{4}\right)$; domain: all real numbers, range: $y \leq \frac{13}{4}$

6. $4i$

7. $-2 + 12i$

8. $31 + 14i$

9. $-9 + i$

10. $\frac{6}{5} + \frac{8}{5}i$

11. $2y(y - 4)$

12. $(3x - 1)(x + 3)$

13. $(3w - 5)^2$

14. $\pm 5$

15. $1 \pm i\sqrt{2}$

16. $4 \pm \sqrt{10}$

17. $(1, 3)$

18. $(0, -3)$, $(-2, -11)$

19.

20.

21. 64; two real

22. $-35$; two imaginary

23. 32; two real

24. Answers may vary. Sample: In the coordinate plane you graph ordered pairs $(a, b)$; in the complex plane you graph complex numbers $a + bi$. For both you find $a$ on the horizontal axis and you find $b$ on the vertical axis.

25. Answers may vary. Sample: Below is the graph $y = -x^2 - 4x - 6$. There will only be imaginary solutions to the equation: $-x^2 - 4x - 6 = 0$.

26. To find the maximum altitude of the rocket (235.92 m), either look at a table or graph the function and trace to locate the vertex. The $h$-value of the vertex is the maximum altitude of the rocket. The $t$-value of the vertex (6.939 s) is the amount of time the rocket takes to reach that altitude.

27. **a.** zero, one, or two solutions
    **b.** zero, one, or an infinite number of solutions

**PowerAlgebra.com**

**MathXL for School**
Prepare students for the Mid-Chapter Quiz and Chapter Test with online practice and review.

| Item Number | Lesson |
|---|---|
| 1 | 4-6 |
| 2 | 3-5 |
| 3 | 4-5 |
| 4 | 4-8 |
| 5 | 4-8 |
| 6 | 4-2 |
| 7 | 4-1 |
| 8 | 4-2 |
| 9 | 4-2 |
| 10 | 2-2 |
| 11 | 3-3 |
| 12 | 3-2 |
| 13 | 2-7 |
| 14 | 3-4 |
| 15 | 1-6 |
| 16 | 1-4 |
| 17 | 4-7 |
| 18 | 4-6 |
| 19 | 4-2 |
| 20 | 3-2 |
| 21 | 2-4 |
| 22 | 2-4 |
| 23 | 4-4, 4-5 |
| 24 | 3-2 |
| 25 | 2-4 |
| 26 | 4-4 |
| 27 | 3-2 |
| 28 | 3-2 |
| 29 | 2-8 |
| 30 | 1-6 |
| 31 | 3-4 |

# 4 Cumulative Test Prep

## TIPS FOR SUCCESS

Some questions on tests require that you model a word problem with a quadratic function.

### TIP 1

To identify the function, use what you already know. You know that the perimeter of a rectangle is $2(\ell + w)$ and the area is $\ell \cdot w$.

Roy has a 400 foot roll of wire. He wants to use it to fence in a rectangular area. What is the maximum area of the enclosed space?

- (A) 20,000 square feet
- (B) 10,000 square feet
- (C) 200 square feet
- (D) 100 square feet

### TIP 2

Use the information from the problem. The perimeter is 400, so $2(\ell + w) = 400$. Solve for $w$: $w = 200 - \ell$.

### Think It Through

Substitute for $w$ in the area formula:
$$A = f(\ell) = \ell \cdot (200 - \ell)$$
$$= -\ell^2 + 200\ell.$$

The maximum value is the $y$-coordinate of the vertex, $f\left(-\frac{b}{2a}\right) = f(100) = 10{,}000$. So, the maximum area Roy can enclose is 10,000 square feet.

The correct answer is B.

## Vocabulary Builder

As you solve test items, you must understand the meanings of mathematical terms. Match each term with its mathematical meaning.

**A.** axis of symmetry

**B.** discriminant

**C.** imaginary number

**D.** Zero-Product Property

**E.** parabola

**F.** perfect square trinomial

**G.** completing the square

**I.** value of $b^2 - 4ac$ for the equation $ax^2 + bx + c = 0$

**II.** If $ab = 0$, then $a = 0$ or $b = 0$.

**III.** line that divides a parabola into two parts that are mirror images

**IV.** $a + bi$, $a$ and $b$ are real numbers and $b \neq 0$

**V.** square of a binomial

**VI.** process of finding the last term to make a perfect square trinomial

**VII.** graph of a quadratic function

## Multiple Choice

Read each question. Then write the letter of the correct answer on your paper.

**1.** Which equation is equivalent to $x^2 + 24x + 100 = -46$?
- (A) $(x + 12)^2 = -2$
- (B) $(x - 12)^2 = -2$
- (C) $(x - 12)^2 = 2$
- (D) $(x + 12)^2 = 2$

**2.** What is the solution of the following system of equations?
$$\begin{cases} x + y + z = 13 \\ 2x - y = 4 \\ x + z = -3 \end{cases}$$
- (F) $x = 10, y = 16, z = 13$
- (G) $x = 16, y = 28, z = -19$
- (H) $x = 10, y = 16, z = -13$
- (I) $x = -16, y = -28, z = 19$

# Answers

## Vocabulary Builder
**A.** III
**B.** I
**C.** IV
**D.** II
**E.** VII
**F.** V
**G.** VI

## Multiple Choice
**1.** A
**2.** H

**3.** What are the factors of the quadratic function graphed below?

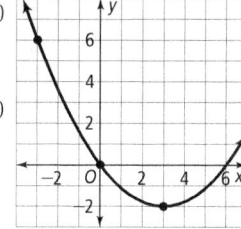

- Ⓐ $(x + 3)$ and $(x + 2)$
- Ⓑ $x$ and $(x - 6)$
- Ⓒ $x$ and $(x + 6)$
- Ⓓ $(x - 3)$ and $(x + 2)$

**4.** Which equation has $-1 \pm i$ as its solution?

- Ⓕ $x^2 - 2x - 2 = 0$
- Ⓖ $2x^2 - 2x - 1 = 0$
- Ⓗ $2x^2 + 2x + 1 = 0$
- Ⓘ $x^2 + 2x + 2 = 0$

**5.** Which number is equivalent to $\sqrt{-169} - 64$?

- Ⓐ $8 - 13i$
- Ⓒ $-64 - 13i$
- Ⓑ $-64 + 13i$
- Ⓓ $64 - 13i$

**6.** The graph of which quadratic function includes the points $(-5, 0)$ and $(-1, 0)$?

- Ⓕ $y = (x + 5)^2 - 1$
- Ⓖ $y = x^2 + 6x + 5$
- Ⓗ $y = x^2 - 6x + 5$
- Ⓘ $y = (x - 5)^2 - 1$

**7.** What is the transformation of the graph of $y = (x + 3)^2 - 2$ from its parent function $y = x^2$?

- Ⓐ 3 units left and 2 units down
- Ⓑ 3 units right and 2 units up
- Ⓒ 6 units right and 2 units up
- Ⓓ 2 units left and 3 units down

**8.** What is the axis of symmetry for the graph of the quadratic equation $y = -3x^2 - 12 + 12x$?

- Ⓕ $x = -2$
- Ⓗ $x = 12$
- Ⓖ $x = 2$
- Ⓘ $x = -12$

**9.** What are the domain and range of the function graphed below?

- Ⓐ Domain: All real numbers
  Range: All real numbers $\leq 3$
- Ⓑ Domain: All real numbers
  Range: All real numbers $\geq 3$
- Ⓒ Domain: All real numbers between $-5$ and $-1$
  Range: All real numbers $\leq 3$
- Ⓓ Domain: All real numbers between $-5$ and $-1$
  Range: All real numbers $\geq 3$

**10.** Which equation DOES NOT represent a direct variation?

- Ⓕ $x - 5y = 0$
- Ⓗ $y + 5 = 3x - 5$
- Ⓖ $\frac{y}{x} = \frac{4}{3}$
- Ⓘ $x = \frac{y}{-5}$

**11.** What is the solution of $\begin{cases} -y = 3x - 1 \\ 2y = -x - 2 \end{cases}$?

- Ⓐ $x = 20, y = -11$
- Ⓒ $x = -20, y = 11$
- Ⓑ $x = \frac{4}{5}, y = -\frac{7}{5}$
- Ⓓ $x = -\frac{4}{5}, y = \frac{7}{5}$

**12.** Which system of equations is graphed below?

- Ⓕ $\begin{cases} y - 3 = 5x \\ y - x = 3 \end{cases}$
- Ⓖ $\begin{cases} y + 3 = 5x \\ y + x = 3 \end{cases}$
- Ⓗ $\begin{cases} -y + 3 = -5x \\ y + x = -3 \end{cases}$
- Ⓘ $\begin{cases} y + 3 = -5x \\ -y + x = 3 \end{cases}$

**13.** What is the vertex of $y = -2|x + 4| - 5$?

- Ⓐ $(-2, -5)$
- Ⓒ $(4, -5)$
- Ⓑ $(-4, -5)$
- Ⓓ $(2, -5)$

**3.** B
**4.** I
**5.** B
**6.** G
**7.** A
**8.** G
**9.** A
**10.** H
**11.** B
**12.** G
**13.** B

# Answers

## Cumulative Test Prep (continued)

**14.** G **15.** B **16.** G **17.** 15.25 **18.** 8

**19.** 4 **20.** 4 **21.** 4 **22.** $\frac{3}{8}$ **23.** 2

**24.** 18 **25.** $\frac{7}{3}$ **26.** 5

**27.** **[2]** Let $s$ = rate of the swimmer and let $c$ = rate of the current:

$$s + c = \frac{1000}{15}$$

$$s - c = \frac{1000}{30}$$

$$2s = \frac{3000}{30} \quad \text{Add the eqs.}$$

$$s = \frac{3000}{60}$$

$$s - c = \frac{1000}{30}$$

$$\left(\frac{3000}{60}\right) - c = \frac{1000}{30}$$

$$c = \frac{3000}{60} = 1000 \text{ m/h (or 1 km/h)}$$

(OR another appropriate method)

**[1]** computational error OR correct solution, without work shown

**28.** **[2]** Let $\ell$ = length of garden and let $w$ = width of garden:

$$\ell + 2w = 81$$

$$\ell = 81 - 2w$$

$$\ell w = A$$

$$(81 - 2w)w = A \quad \text{Substitute for } \ell.$$

$$81w - 2w^2 = A$$

Graph the function on a graphing calculator and calculate the maximum: (20.25, 820.125). The maximum area, 820.125 ft², occurs when the width is 20.25 ft.

$$\ell w = A$$

$$\ell(20.25) = 40.5$$

$$\ell = 40.5$$

The dimensions should be 20.25 ft × 40.5 ft.

**[1]** appropriate methods with one computational error OR correct answer, without work shown

**29.** **[2]** Rewrite the inequality as $y < 2|x - 3| - 4$.
This is a transformation of the parent function $y = |x|$. Vertically stretch by a factor of 2, translate 3 units to the right and 4 units down. Shade the region below the graph.

**[1]** parent funcion not named

**30.** **[4]** $\frac{64 + 51}{2} = 57.5$ cm

$\frac{64 - 51}{2} = 6.5$ cm

$|x - 57.5| \leq 6.5$

51  64

**[3]** inequality is written correctly, but graph is drawn with open circles

**14.** Which system of inequalities is graphed below?

 F $\begin{cases} y \leq -1 \\ y + x \geq 2 \end{cases}$

 G $\begin{cases} y \geq -1 \\ y + x \leq 2 \end{cases}$

 H $\begin{cases} y < 1 \\ y + x > -2 \end{cases}$

 I $\begin{cases} y > 1 \\ y + x < -2 \end{cases}$

**15.** What are the solutions of $|3x - 5| = 2$?

Ⓐ $x = -1$ and $x = \frac{7}{3}$

Ⓑ $x = 1$ and $x = \frac{7}{3}$

Ⓒ $x = 1$ and $x = \frac{1}{5}$

Ⓓ $x = -1$ and $x = \frac{1}{5}$

**16.** The formula for the total surface area of a regular right pentagonal prism is $A = ap + pH$. Solve this equation for $p$.

Ⓕ $p = \frac{a + H}{A}$

Ⓗ $p = A - \frac{a}{H}$

Ⓖ $p = \frac{A}{a + H}$

Ⓘ $p = \frac{H - a}{A}$

### GRIDDED RESPONSE

**17.** What is the discriminant of the equation $1.5x^2 - 2.5x - 1.5 = 0$?

**18.** Find the positive value of $k$ that would make the expression $4x^2 + kx + 4$ a perfect square trinomial.

**19.** When $y = -3x^2 - 18x - 23$ is written in vertex form $y = a(x - h)^2 + k$, what is the value of $k$?

**20.** What is the value of $x$ in the system of equations $\begin{cases} 2y = x - 2 \\ y - x = -3 \end{cases}$?

**21.** Line A is perpendicular to $x + 3y = 5$ and passes through the point $(-1, 1)$. What is the $y$-intercept of Line A?

**22.** What is the slope of the line that passes through $(5, 1)$ and $(-3, -2)$?

**23.** What is the sum of the zeros of $f(x) = x^2 - 2x - 8$?

**24.** A piggy bank contains $2.40 in nickels and dimes. If there are 33 coins in all, how many nickels are there?

**25.** What is the slope of the line parallel to $3y - 7x = 15$?

**26.** Claudia has a rectangular flowerbed. She decided that the original width $w$, in feet, was too small, so she increased the width by 3 feet. She also changed the length to be 1 foot less than twice the original width. The new area of her flowerbed is 72 square feet. How many feet wide was the original flowerbed?

### Short Response

**27.** A swimmer swam 1000 meters downstream in 15 minutes and swam back in 30 minutes against the current. What was the rate of the swimmer in still water? How fast was the current?

**28.** A horticulturalist is building a fence around a rectangular garden using the side of a building for one side of the enclosure. She has 81 feet of fencing. What should the dimensions of the enclosure be so that she can maximize the garden's area?

**29.** Explain how you would graph $y + 4 < 2|x - 3|$ on a coordinate grid.

### Extended Response

**30.** A hat company is designing a one-size-fits-all hat with a strap in the back that makes the hat smaller or larger. Head sizes normally range from 51 to 64 centimeters. What absolute value inequality models the different sizes of the hat? Graph the solution.

**31.** Robby decided to earn extra money by making and selling brownies and cookies. He had space in his oven to make at most 80 brownies and cookies. Each brownie cost $.10 to make and each cookie cost $.05 to make. He had $6 to spend on ingredients.
 **a.** Write a system of inequalities to represent the situation.
 **b.** Graph the system, choose one point in the feasible region, and explain what the point means in terms of the problem.
 **c.** If Robby makes a profit of $.25 on each brownie and $.20 on each cookie, how many of each dessert should he make to maximize his profit?

**[2]** correct inequality, without graph drawn

**[1]** correct inequality, without graph drawn, without work shown

**31.** **[4]** Let $b$ = number of brownies and let $c$ = number of cookies.
 **a.** $b + c \leq 80$
 $0.1b + 0.05c \leq 6$
 **b.** The feasible region is any point that is below *both* lines. The point $(c, b)$ represents the situation in which Robby makes $c$ cookies and $b$ brownies.

 **c.** Let $P$ = profit, then $P = .25b + .2c$. Test the vertices to find the maximum profit:
 (0, 60): 0.25 (60) + 0.2(0) = 15
 (40, 40): 0.25 (40) + 0.2(40) = 18
 (80, 0): 0.25 (0) + 0.2(80) = 16
 Robby should make 40 cookies and 40 brownies.

**[3]** appropriate methods with one computational error OR feasible region is not shaded in graph

**[2]** correct answer for parts (a) − (b) only

**[1]** correct answer, without explanations or work shown

# Get Ready!

Lesson 4-2 ◆ **Graphing Quadratic Functions**

Graph each function.

**1.** $f(x) = x^2 - 8x + 7$    **2.** $f(x) = -\frac{1}{2}x^2 - 4x - 4$    **3.** $f(x) = x^2 + 4x + 4$

Lesson 4-3 ◆ **Writing Equations of Parabolas**

Write in standard form the equation of the parabola passing through the given points.

**4.** $(-1, -6), (-3, -4), (2, 6)$    **5.** $(3, 4), (-2, 9), (2, 1)$    **6.** $(-5, -8), (4, -8), (-3, 6)$

Lesson 4-5 ◆ **Solving Quadratic Equations by Graphing**

Solve each equation by graphing. Round to the nearest hundredth.

**7.** $1 = 4x^2 + 3x$    **8.** $\frac{1}{2}x^2 + x - 14 = 0$    **9.** $5x^2 + 30x = 12$

Lesson 4-5 ◆ **Solving Quadratic Equations by Factoring**

Solve each equation by factoring.

**10.** $x^2 - x - 20 = 0$    **11.** $x^2 + 6x - 27 = 0$    **12.** $3x^2 - 9x + 6 = 0$

Lesson 4-7 ◆ **Finding the Number and Type of Solutions**

Evaluate the discriminant of each equation. Tell how many solutions each equation has and whether the solutions are real or imaginary.

**13.** $x^2 - 12x + 30 = 0$    **14.** $-4x^2 + 20x - 25 = 0$    **15.** $2x^2 = 8x - 8$

 **Looking Ahead Vocabulary**

**16.** A *turning point* is a place where a graph changes direction. Suppose you start hiking north on a winding trail, and the trail makes a turn and heads south, and then north again. If you make a total of 3 of these 180 degree turns, in which direction will you be hiking after the last turn?

**17.** A *relative maximum* is the greatest value in a region. The highest point in Maine is Mt. Katahdin at 5267 ft. How might that compare to the highest point in the United States? What might the relative maximum of a graph be?

**18.** A contraction is a shortened form of a word or phrase. The expanded form of the contraction "don't" is "do not." You can *expand* a math phrase by multiplying it out. For example, $(x - 2)^2 = (x - 2)(x - 2) = x^2 - 4x + 4$. Expand $(2x + 1)^2$.

## Answers

### Get Ready!

**1.**

**2.**

**3.**

**4.** $y = x^2 + 3x - 4$

**5.** $y = x^2 - 2x + 1$

**6.** $y = -x^2 - x + 12$    **7.** $0.25, -1$

**8.** $-6.39, 4.39$    **9.** $-6.38, 0.38$

**10.** $-4, 5$    **11.** $-9, 3$    **12.** $1, 2$

**13.** 24; two real solutions

**14.** 0; one real solution

**15.** 0; one real solution    **16.** south

**17.** The highest pt. in Maine may be lower than the highest pt. in the United States. The relative maximum of a graph for a given region is the maximum for that region only, whereas the maximum of the graph may be greater than or equal to the relative maximum for the region.

**18.** $4x^2 + 4x + 1$

# Chapter 5 Overview

## UbD Understanding by Design

Chapter 5 expands on students' understandings and skills related to functions, equations, and graphs. In this chapter, students will develop the answers to the Essential Questions posed on the opposite page as they learn the concepts and skills bulleted below.

### BIG idea Functions

**ESSENTIAL QUESTION** What does the degree of a polynomial tell you about its related polynomial function?

- Students will write a polynomial function given a polynomial equation.
- Students will identify the degree of a polynomial equation.
- Students will identify the highest power of a polynomial function.

### BIG idea Equivalence

**ESSENTIAL QUESTION** For a polynomial function, how are factors, zeros, and *x*-intercepts related?

- Students will write a polynomial given its factors or zeros.
- Students will identify the zeros of a polynomial function by finding the *x*-intercepts of its graph.

### BIG idea Solving Equations and Inequalities

**ESSENTIAL QUESTION** For a polynomial equation, how are factors and roots related?

- Students will factor a polynomial equation.
- Students will apply the Zero-Product Property.

**CHAPTER 5**

# Polynomials and Polynomial Functions

## PowerAlgebra.com

Your place to get all things digital

**Download videos** connecting math to your world.

VIDEO

**Math definitions** in English and Spanish

VOCABULARY

**The online** Solve It will get you in gear for each lesson.

SOLVE IT!

**Interactive!** Vary numbers, graphs, and figures to explore math concepts.

DYNAMIC ACTIVITIES

**Download** Step-by-Step Problems with Instant Replay.

ONLINE PROBLEMS

**Get and view your** assignments online.

ONLINE HOMEWORK

**Extra practice and** review online

MathXL® FOR SCHOOL

*Polynomial functions are used to model all kinds of real-world situations, like the energy produced by a turbine.*

*In this chapter, you will also learn theorems that will help you when working with polynomial functions and equations.*

## Vocabulary

**English/Spanish Vocabulary Audio Online:**

| English | Spanish |
|---|---|
| end behavior, *p. 282* | comportamiento extremo |
| monomial, *p. 280* | monomio |
| multiplicity, *p. 291* | multiplicidad |
| Pascal's Triangle, *p. 327* | Triángulo de Pascal |
| polynomial function, *p. 280* | función polinomial |
| relative maximum, *p. 291* | máximo relativo |
| relative minimum, *p. 291* | mínimo relativo |
| standard form of a polynomial function, *p. 281* | forma normal de una función polinomial |
| synthetic division, *p. 306* | división sintética |
| turning point, *p. 282* | punto de giro |

## Chapter 5 Overview

Use these online assets to engage your students. These include support for the Solve It and step-by-step solutions for Problems.

 Show the student-produced video demonstrating relevant and engaging applications of the new concepts in the chapter.

 Find online definitions for new terms in English and Spanish.

 Start each lesson with an attention-getting Problem. View the Problem online with helpful hints.

**My Math Video**

## BIG ideas

1 **Function**
   **Essential Question** What does the degree of a polynomial tell you about its related polynomial function?

2 **Equivalence**
   **Essential Question** For a polynomial function, how are factors, zeros, and x-intercepts related?

3 **Solving Equations and Inequalities**
   **Essential Question** For a polynomial equation, how are factors and roots related?

## Chapter Preview

5-1 **Polynomial Functions**
5-2 **Polynomials, Linear Factors, and Zeros**
5-3 **Solving Polynomial Equations**
5-4 **Dividing Polynomials**
5-5 **Theorems About Roots of Polynomial Equations**
5-6 **The Fundamental Theorem of Algebra**
5-7 **The Binomial Theorem**
5-8 **Polynomial Models in the Real World**
5-9 **Transforming Polynomial Functions**

PowerAlgebra.com | Chapter 5 Polynomials and Polynomial Functions | 279

**My Math Video**
Use this picture to introduce the concept of a polynomial function as a model.

**Q** One kind of turbine is a wind turbine. As the wind speed increases, the power output increases, levels off, and then decreases. What would a graph of the power output as a function of wind speed look like? **[a curve that increases, levels off, and then curves back downward]**

**Q** The graph is modeled by a function called a *polynomial function*. How might a polynomial model for the power output of a wind turbine be used? **[to determine the wind speed that maximizes power output]**

 Increase students' depth of knowledge with interactive online activities.

 Show Problems from each lesson solved step by step. Instant replay allows students to go at their own pace when studying online.

 Assign homework to individual students or to an entire class.

 Prepare students for the Mid-Chapter Quiz and Chapter Test with online practice and review.

# POLYNOMIALS AND POLYNOMIAL FUNCTIONS
# Math Background

**UbD**

## Function

**BIG idea** A function is a relationship between variables in which each value of the input variable is associated with a unique value of the output variable. Functions can be represented in a variety of ways, such as graphs, tables, equations, or words. Each representation is particularly useful in certain situations. Some important families of functions are developed through transformations of the simplest form of the function.

**ESSENTIAL UNDERSTANDINGS**

**5-1** A polynomial function has distinguishing "behaviors." You can look at its algebraic form and know something about its graph. You can look at its graph and know something about its algebraic form.

**5-2** Knowing the zeros of a polynomial function can help you understand the behavior of its graph.

**5-3** If $(x - a)$ is a factor of a polynomial, then the polynomial has value 0 when $x = a$. If $a$ is a real number, then the graph of the polynomial has $(a, 0)$ as an $x$–intercept.

**5-9** The graph of the function $y = af(x - h) + k$ is a vertical stretch or compression by a factor $|a|$, a horizontal shift of $h$ units, and a vertical shift of $k$ units of the graph of $y = f(x)$.

## Equivalence

**BIG idea** A single quantity may be represented by many different expressions. The facts about a quantity may be expressed by many different equations (or inequalities).

**ESSENTIAL UNDERSTANDINGS**

**5-1 to 5-3** See above.

**5-4** You can divide polynomials using steps that are similar to the long-division steps that you use to divide whole numbers.

**5-5** The factors of the numbers $a_n$ and $a_0$ in $P(x) = a_n x^n + a_{n-1} x^{n-1} + \ldots a_1 x + a_0$ can help you factor $P(x)$ and solve the equation $P(x) = 0$.

**5-6** The degree of a polynomial equation tells you how many roots the equation has.

**5-7** You can use a pattern of coefficients and the pattern $a^n, a^{n-1}b, a^{n-2}b^2, \ldots, a^1b^{n-1}, b^n$, to write the expansion of $(a + b)^n$.

## Solving Equations & Inequalities

**BIG idea** Solving an equation is the process of rewriting the equation to make what it says about its variable(s) as simple as possible. Properties of numbers and equality can be used to transform an equation (or inequality) into equivalent, simpler equations (or inequalities) in order to find solutions. Useful information about equations and inequalities (including solutions) can be found by analyzing graphs or tables. The numbers and types of solutions vary predictably, based on the type of equation.

**ESSENTIAL UNDERSTANDINGS**

**5-5 to 5-6** See above.

## Polynomial Functions

The degree of a polynomial equation is the greatest degree among its monomial terms. The degree provides information about the end behavior, turning points, and number of solutions for the polynomial function.

## End Behavior and Turning Points

The end behavior describes the graph at the far left and at the far right. A turning point is where the graph changes direction. You can determine end behavior and turning points from the degree of the polynomial.

**Degree is Odd**
- even number of turning points
- $a > 0$, ends down then up
- $a < 0$, ends up then down

**Degree is Even**
- odd number of turning points
- $a > 0$, both ends up
- $a < 0$, both ends down

**Examples:**

$y = -x^3 + 4x^2 - 7$

$y = x^4 - 4x^2$

$y = -x^4 + 4x^2 + 2x - 3$

$y = x^5 - 4x^3 + 4x + 2$

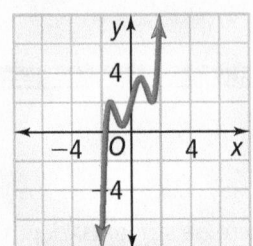

### Common Errors When Graphing and Describing Quadratic Functions

Students often reach for their graphing calculators when asked to graph. By accepting the graph on the screen without visualizing the function first, students do not develop their ability to recognize graphing errors. Sharpen students' visualization skills by having them sketch graphs (not on the coordinate plane) using only paper and pencil. Include graphs of fourth and fifth degree functions. Features of the graph must include:
- the correct shape and orientation
- the correct number of turning points
- correct end behavior

Then have students use their graphing calculators to check their sketches.

## Zeros of Polynomial Equations

The **Fundamental Theorem of Algebra** and its corollary state that every polynomial has complex solutions and the degree of the polynomial equation gives the number of roots.

Students can use a combination of graphing, theorems, and factoring techniques to find all solutions of many polynomials. For example,

**Find all solutions for $y = x^3 - x^2 - 3x - 9$.**

The number of complex roots is 3.

**Step 1)** Use a graphing calculator to find the single real root (3).

**Step 2)** Use synthetic division to find the polynomial factor.

$$\begin{array}{r|rrrr} 3 & 1 & -1 & -3 & -9 \\ & & 3 & 6 & 9 \\ \hline & 1 & 2 & 3 & 0 \end{array}$$

So $(x - 3)(x^2 + 2x + 3)$

**Step 3)** Use the quadratic formula to determine the roots for the quadratic polynomial.

$$x = \frac{-b \pm \sqrt{b^2 - 4ac}}{2a} = \frac{-2 \pm \sqrt{2^2 - 4(1)(3)}}{2(1)}$$
$$= -1 \pm i\sqrt{2}$$

**The roots are 3, $-1 + i\sqrt{2}$, $-1 - i\sqrt{2}$.**

The following theorems can help identify all complex roots of polynomials with rational coefficients.

### Conjugate Root Theorem

- If $a + \sqrt{b}$ is an irrational root with $a$ and $b$ rational, then $a - \sqrt{b}$ is also a root.
- If $a + bi$ is a complex root with $a$ and $b$ real, then $a - bi$ is also a root.

### Rational Roots Theorem

*Possible* roots for a polynomial function with integer coefficients are determined by the reduced form of $\frac{p}{q}$ where $p$ is a factor of the constant and $q$ is a factor of the leading coefficient.

### Common Errors When Finding Zeros of Polynomial Equations

**Rational Root Theorem** Students often believe that the numbers $\frac{p}{q}$ *must* be solutions. Remind students they represent only *possible* roots and must be checked to determine if they are solutions.

**Synthetic Division** Errors include forgetting to include terms with the coefficient of 0. If the highest degree is 4, for example, there must be a coefficient for $x^3$, $x^2$, and $x$.

## Writing Polynomial Functions

Real-world applications of polynomial functions include fitting a function to a given set of points. Note that most real-world data do not fit a function exactly. Statistical measures such as $R^2$ can help determine whether the function is a good fit. However, it is also possible that data are modeled by a certain function only over a certain domain. Both the behavior of the function and $R^2$ must be analyzed.

Care must always be taken when making predictions based on models. For example, estimating within the domain (**interpolation**) often yields reliable results. Estimating outside the domain (**extrapolation**) yields less reliable results.

### Writing a Function from Zeros

If the zeros of a function are known, a polynomial can be written to satisfy the zeros. Because $b$ is a root of $P(x)$ if $(x - b)$ is a factor, you can write factors of a polynomial function when given the zeros.

**Example:** Write a polynomial function in standard form with roots $-2$ and $2$.

Write the roots as factors, and then multiply.
$(x + 2)(x - 2) = x^2 - 4$

Note that different functions can have the same zeros. Both functions below have roots $-2$ and $2$.

$y = x^2 - 4$

$y = -x^2 + 4$

### Writing a Function from Other Points

The $n + 1$ principle states that for any $n + 1$ points in the coordinate plane that pass a vertical line test, there is a unique polynomial with degree at most $n$ that fits the points.

### Common Errors When Writing Polynomial Function

**Using Zeros** Students may forget some zeros come in pairs. For example, if $3 + i$ is a root, then $3 - i$ is also a root.

**Using Other Points** Students may choose regression equations based only on the $R^2$ value. Non-numerical information must also be weighed. Data should be viewed as plotted points first to determine the most appropriate function.

CHAPTER 5

# POLYNOMIALS AND POLYNOMIAL FUNCTIONS
# Pacing and Assignment Guide

| | | TRADITIONAL | | | BLOCK |
|---|---|---|---|---|---|
| Lesson | Teaching Day(s) | Basic | Average | Advanced | Block |
| 5-1 | 1 | Problems 1–2<br>Exs. 8–31, 57–70 | Problems 1–2<br>Exs. 9–31 odd, 57–70 | Problems 1–4<br>Exs. 9–39 odd, 40–70 | **Day 1**<br>Problems 1–4<br>Exs. 9–39 odd,<br>40–53, 57–70 |
| | 2 | Problems 3–4<br>Exs. 32–39, 40–50 even, 51 | Problems 3–4<br>Exs. 33–39 odd, 40–53 | | |
| 5-2 | 1 | Problems 1–4<br>Exs.7–34, 57–69 | Problems 1–4<br>Exs. 7–33 odd, 57–69 | Problems 1–4<br>Exs. 7–33 odd, 57–69 | **Day 2**<br>Problems 1–6<br>Exs. 7–39 odd,<br>40–54, 57–69 |
| | 2 | Problems 5–6<br>Exs. 35–39, 41–43, 45–47,<br>50–52 | Problems 5–6<br>Exs. 35–39 odd, 40–54 | Problems 5–6<br>Exs. 35–39 odd, 40–56 | |
| 5-3 | 1 | Problems 1–2<br>Exs. 10–24, 61–72 | Problems 1–2<br>Exs. 11–23 odd, 61–72 | Problems 1–2<br>Exs. 11–37 odd, 39–72 | **Day 3**<br>Problems 1–4<br>Exs. 11–37 odd,<br>39–57, 61–72 |
| | 2 | Problems 3–4<br>Exs. 25–38, 40–50 even,<br>51–54 | Problems 3–4<br>Exs. 25–37 odd, 39–57 | | |
| 5-4 | 1 | Problems 1–2<br>Exs. 9–20, 67–85 | Problems 1–2<br>Exs. 9–19 odd, 67–85 | Problems 1–2<br>Exs. 9–19 odd, 67–85 | **Day 4**<br>Problems 1–5<br>Exs. 9–39 odd,<br>40–62, 67–85 |
| | 2 | Problems 3–5<br>Exs. 21–41, 43, 48, 50 | Problems 3–5<br>Exs. 21–39 odd, 40–62 | Problems 3–5<br>Exs. 21–39 odd, 40–66 | |
| 5-5 | 1 | Problems 1–2<br>Exs. 9–17, 50–62 | Problems 1–2<br>Exs. 9–17 odd, 50–62 | Problems 1–2<br>Exs. 9–17 odd, 50–62 | **Day 5**<br>Problems 1–5<br>Exs. 9–31 odd,<br>33–46, 50–62 |
| | 2 | Problems 3–5<br>Exs. 18–32, 34–40 even,<br>42–45 | Problems 3–5<br>Exs. 19–31 odd, 33–46 | Problem 3–5<br>Exs. 19–31 odd, 33–49 | |
| 5-6 | 1 | Problem 1<br>Exs. 8–15, 50–65 | Problems 1–2<br>Exs. 9–25 odd, 26–46, 50–65 | Problems 1–2<br>Exs. 9–25 odd, 26–65 | **Day 6**<br>Problems 1–2<br>Exs. 9–25 odd,<br>26–46, 50–65 |
| | 2 | Problem 2<br>Exs. 16–25, 26–30 even,<br>38–40, 44, 46 | | | |
| 5-7 | 1 | Problems 1–2<br>Exs. 8–24, 30, 31, 44, 45,<br>54–68 | Problems 1–2<br>Exs. 9–23 odd, 24–46, 54–68 | Problems 1–2<br>Exs. 9–23 odd, 24–68 | Problems 1–2<br>Exs. 9–23 odd,<br>24–46, 54–68 |
| 5-8 | 1 | Problems 1–4<br>Exs. 8–25, 28, 31, 34, 38–58 | Problems 1–4<br>Exs. 9–23 odd, 24–35, 38–58 | Problems 1–4<br>Exs. 9–25 odd, 26–58 | **Day 7**<br>Problems 1–4<br>Exs. 9–23 odd,<br>24–35, 38–58 |
| 5-9 | 1 | Problems 1–2<br>Exs. 7–18, 47–58 | Problems 1–2<br>Exs. 7–25 odd, 27–43, 47–58 | Problems 1–4<br>Exs. 7–25 odd, 27–58 | Problems 1–4<br>Exs. 7–25 odd,<br>27–43, 47–58 |
| | 2 | Problems 3–4<br>Exs. 19–28, 30–36 even,<br>40, 41 | | | |
| Review | 1 | Chapter 5 Review | Chapter 5 Review | Chapter 5 Review | **Day 8**<br>Chapter 5 Review<br>Chapter 5 Test |
| Assess | 1 | Chapter 5 Test | Chapter 5 Test | Chapter 5 Test | |
| **Total** | | **18 Days** | **16 Days** | **14 Days** | **8 Days** |

# Resources

| | For the Chapter | 5-1 | 5-2 | 5-3 | 5-4 | 5-5 | 5-6 | 5-7 | 5-8 | 5-9 |
|---|---|---|---|---|---|---|---|---|---|---|
| **Planning** | | | | | | | | | | |
| Teacher Center Online Planner & Grade Book | I | I | I | I | I | I | I | I | I | I |
| **Interactive Learning & Guided Instruction** | | | | | | | | | | |
| My Math Video | I | | | | | | | | | |
| Solve It! | | I TM | I TM | I TM | I TM | I TM | I TM | I TM | I TM | I TM |
| Student Companion (SP)* | | P M | P M | P M | P M | P M | P M | P M | P M | P M |
| Vocabulary Support | | I P M | I P M | I P M | I P M | I P M | I P M | I P M | I P M | I P M |
| Got It? Support | | I P | I P | I P | I P | I P | I P | I P | I P | I P |
| Dynamic Activity | | | I | | I | | | | | |
| Online Problems | | I | I | I | I | I | I | I | I | I |
| Additional Problems | | M | M | M | M | M | M | M | M | M |
| English Language Learner Support (TR) | | E P M | E P M | E P M | E P M | E P M | E P M | E P M | E P M | E P M |
| Activities, Games, and Puzzles | | E M | E M | E M | E M | E M | E M | E M | E M | E M |
| Teaching With TI Technology With CD-ROM | | | ✓ P | | | | | | | |
| TI-Nspire™ Support CD-ROM | | ✓ | ✓ | ✓ | ✓ | ✓ | ✓ | ✓ | ✓ | ✓ |
| **Lesson Check & Practice** | | | | | | | | | | |
| Student Companion (SP)* | | P M | P M | P M | P M | P M | P M | P M | P M | P M |
| Lesson Check Support | | I P | I P | I P | I P | I P | I P | I P | I P | I P |
| Practice and Problem Solving Workbook (SP) | | P | P | P | P | P | P | P | P | P |
| Think About a Plan (TR)* | | E P M | E P M | E P M | E P M | E P M | E P M | E P M | E P M | E P M |
| Practice Form G (TR)* | | E P M | E P M | E P M | E P M | E P M | E P M | E P M | E P M | E P M |
| Standardized Test Prep (TR)* | | P M | P M | P M | P M | P M | P M | P M | P M | P M |
| Practice Form K (TR)* | | E P M | E P M | E P M | E P M | E P M | E P M | E P M | E P M | E P M |
| Extra Practice | E M | | | | | | | | | |
| Find the Errors! | M | | | | | | | | | |
| Enrichment (TR) | | E P M | E P M | E P M | E P M | E P M | E P M | E P M | E P M | E P M |
| Answers and Solutions CD-ROM | ✓ | ✓ | ✓ | ✓ | ✓ | ✓ | ✓ | ✓ | ✓ | ✓ |
| **Assess & Remediate** | | | | | | | | | | |
| ExamView CD-ROM | ✓ | ✓ | ✓ | ✓ | ✓ | ✓ | ✓ | ✓ | ✓ | ✓ |
| Lesson Quiz | | I TM | I TM | I TM | I TM | I TM | I TM | I TM | I TM | I TM |
| Quizzes and Tests Form G (TR)* | E P M | | | | E P M | | | | | E P M |
| Quizzes and Tests Form K (TR)* | E P M | | | | E P M | | | | | E P M |
| Reteaching (TR)* | | E P M | E P M | E P M | E P M | E P M | E P M | E P M | E P M | E P M |
| Performance Tasks (TR)* | P M | | | | | | | | | |
| Cumulative Review (TR)* | P M | | | | | | | | | |
| Progress Monitoring Assessments | I P M | | | | | | | | | |

(TR) Available in All-In-One Teaching Resources     * Spanish available

# 1 Interactive Learning

## Solve It!

**PURPOSE** To look for patterns in a sequence using common differences and then use those patterns to find unknown terms of the sequence

**PROCESS** Students may

- make a table and fill it in using addition and subtraction and then work backward beginning with the last column.
- look for a pattern rule and use the rule to find the eighth number.

---

**FACILITATE**

**Q** Copy the information in a table with four columns and eight rows. What number goes under the 46? How do you know? **[106; 156 − 50 = 106]**

**Q** Find the values represented by the question marks in the diagram. What do you notice about the third differences? **[They are all 24.]**

**Q** How can you use the third differences column to find the original sequence of numbers? **[Work backward, using addition.]**

---

**ANSWER** See Solve It in Answers on next page.

**CONNECT THE MATH** The Solve It uses the patterns of differences. In the lesson, students will examine difference patterns to determine the degree of a polynomial.

---

## 5-1 Polynomial Functions

**Objectives** To classify polynomials
To graph polynomial functions and describe end behavior

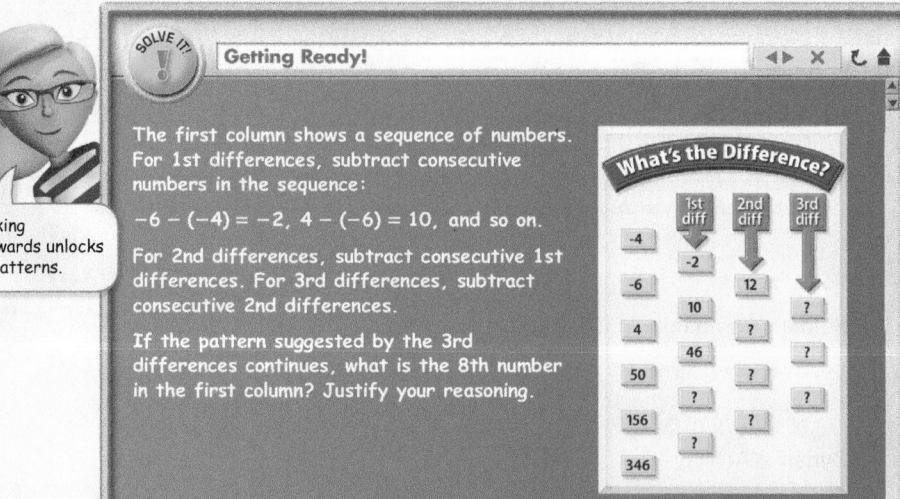

> **Getting Ready!**
>
> The first column shows a sequence of numbers. For 1st differences, subtract consecutive numbers in the sequence:
>
> $-6 - (-4) = -2$, $4 - (-6) = 10$, and so on.
>
> For 2nd differences, subtract consecutive 1st differences. For 3rd differences, subtract consecutive 2nd differences.
>
> If the pattern suggested by the 3rd differences continues, what is the 8th number in the first column? Justify your reasoning.

Working backwards unlocks the patterns.

**Lesson Vocabulary**
- monomial
- degree of a monomial
- polynomial
- degree of a polynomial
- polynomial function
- standard form of a polynomial function
- turning point
- end behavior

The sequence of numbers in the first column above are values of a particular *polynomial function*. For such a sequence, you can use patterns of 1st differences, 2nd differences, 3rd differences, and so on, to learn more about the polynomial function.

**Essential Understanding** A polynomial function has distinguishing "behaviors." You can look at its algebraic form and know something about its graph. You can look at its graph and know something about its algebraic form.

A **monomial** is a real number, a variable, or a product of a real number and one or more variables with whole-number exponents. The **degree of a monomial** in one variable is the exponent of the variable. A **polynomial** is a monomial or a sum of monomials. The **degree of a polynomial** in one variable is the greatest degree among its monomial terms.

A polynomial with the variable $x$ defines a **polynomial function** of $x$. The degree of the polynomial function is the same as the degree of the polynomial.

---

## 5-1 Preparing to Teach

**BIG** ideas Equivalence
Function
**UbD**

**ESSENTIAL UNDERSTANDINGS**
- The algebraic form of a polynomial function gives information about its graph. Its graph gives information about its algebraic form.
- The shape and the end behavior of the graph of a polynomial is determined by the degree of the polynomial and by the sign of the leading coefficient.
- It's possible to determine the degree of a polynomial by analyzing the first, second, etc., differences of its $y$-values.

## Math Background

The algebraic form of a polynomial function reveals certain information about the graph.

The degree of a polynomial function affects the shape of its graph.

- For a polynomial function of degree $n$, its graph has at most $n − 1$ turning points.

- The graph of a polynomial function of odd degree has an even number of turning points.
- The graph of a polynomial function of even degree has an odd number of turning points.

The degree of a polynomial function affects the end behavior, which can then be sketched using the leading coefficient of the polynomial function.

Similarly, the graph of a polynomial function reveals information about the algebraic form. The graph indicates whether the degree of the polynomial function is even or odd and whether the leading coefficient is positive or negative.

## Support Student Learning

Use the **Algebra 2 Companion** to engage and support students during instruction. See Lesson Resources at the end of this lesson for details.

**PowerAlgebra.com**

## 1 Interactive Learning

### Solve It!
Step out how to solve the Problem with helpful hints and an online question. Other questions are listed above in Interactive Learning.

## Key Concept  Standard Form of a Polynomial Function

The **standard form of a polynomial function** arranges the terms by degree in descending numerical order.

A polynomial function $P(x)$ in standard form is

$$P(x) = a_n x^n + a_{n-1} x^{n-1} + \cdots + a_1 x + a_0,$$

where $n$ is a nonnegative integer and $a_n, \ldots, a_0$ are real numbers.

$$P(x) = 4x^3 + 3x^2 + 5x - 2$$

Cubic term | Quadratic term | Linear term | Constant term

You can classify a polynomial by its degree or by its number of terms. Polynomials of degrees zero through five have specific names, as shown in this table.

| Degree | Name Using Degree | Polynomial Example | Number of Terms | Name Using Number of Terms |
|--------|-------------------|--------------------|-----------------|----------------------------|
| 0 | constant | $5$ | 1 | monomial |
| 1 | linear | $x + 4$ | 2 | binomial |
| 2 | quadratic | $4x^2$ | 1 | monomial |
| 3 | cubic | $4x^3 - 2x^2 + x$ | 3 | trinomial |
| 4 | quartic | $2x^4 + 5x^2$ | 2 | binomial |
| 5 | quintic | $-x^5 + 4x^2 + 2x + 1$ | 4 | polynomial of 4 terms |

###  Problem 1  Classifying Polynomials

Write each polynomial in standard form. What is the classification of each polynomial by degree? by number of terms?

**Think**

*How do you write a polynomial in standard form?*
Combine like terms if possible. Then, write the terms with their degrees in descending order.

**A** $3x + 9x^2 + 5$

$9x^2 + 3x + 5$

The polynomial has degree 2 and 3 terms. It is a quadratic trinomial.

**B** $4x - 6x^2 + x^4 + 10x^2 - 12$

$x^4 + 4x^2 + 4x - 12$

The polynomial has degree 4 and 4 terms. It is a quartic polynomial of 4 terms.

 **Got It?**  **1.** Write each polynomial in standard form. What is the classification of each by degree? by number of terms?

**a.** $3x^3 - x + 5x^4$      **b.** $3 - 4x^5 + 2x^2 + 10$

---

# 2 Guided Instruction

## Take Note

**Q** In how many different orders could you write the terms of $3x^2 + 2x + 1$? **[6]**

**Q** In how many different orders could you write the terms of $4x^3 - 3x^2 + 3x + 2$? **[24]**

**Q** Why have a standard form for writing polynomial functions? **[Answers may vary. Samples: so everyone writes polynomial functions the same way; similar to having spelling rules for language]**

**Q** Why does a constant term have a degree of zero? **[Because $x^0 = 1$. For example, 5 could be written as $5x^0$.]**

Emphasize that the term with the greatest power in a polynomial function has the most influence over the behavior of the graph of the function.

## Problem 1
Remind students to be careful of the signs as they reorder the terms of a polynomial to put it in standard form.

**Q** In 1B, where did the $4x^2$ come from? **[combining like terms]**

## Got It?      ERROR PREVENTION

**Q** What do you have to do before classifying each polynomial? **[Answers may vary. Sample: Put them in standard form and combine like terms.]**

---

# 2 Guided Instruction

 Each Problem is worked out and supported online.

**Problem 1**
Classifying Polynomials

**Problem 2**
Describing End Behavior of Polynomial Functions

**Problem 3**
Graphing Cubic Functions
*Animated*

**Alternative Problem 3**
Graphing Cubic Functions
*Animated*

**Problem 4**
Using Differences to Determine Degree
*Animated*

**Support in Algebra 2 Companion**
• Vocabulary
• Key Concepts
• Got It?

# Answers

## Solve It!
1074; work backwards using the constant third difference, 24, to find the first and second differences and the seventh and eighth numbers in the first column.

## Got It?
**1. a.** $5x^4 + 3x^3 - x$; quartic trinomial
    **b.** $-4x^5 + 2x^2 + 13$; quintic trinomial

To help students synthesize the information in the table of end behaviors on p. 282, sketch examples and discuss the simplest polynomial functions of even and odd degree: quadratic and linear.

The graph of a quadratic function in standard form $y = ax^2 + bx + c$ opens upward or downward based upon the leading term. If $a$ is positive, the parabola opens upward and the end behavior is up and up. If $a$ is negative, the parabola opens downward and the end behavior is down and down.

The graph of a linear function in slope-intercept form $y = mx + b$ is a line with slope $m$. Here, $m$ is analogous to the coefficient $a$. If $m$ is positive, the line rises from left to right and the end behavior is down and up. If $m$ is negative, the line falls from left to right and has end behavior up and down.

## Problem 2

**Q** Why does the end behavior of a polynomial function not rely on any term other than the leading term? **[The leading term has the greatest degree, so as the value of $x$ approaches positive infinity or negative infinity, the magnitude of the leading term is far greater than any other term.]**

**Q** If you forget the rules in the table regarding end behavior, how could you determine end behavior on your own? **[Answers may vary. Sample: Substitute extreme negative and positive integer values for $x$ and determine only the sign of the leading term; if the leading term is positive, that end's behavior is up; if the leading term is negative, that end's behavior is down.]**

---

The degree of a polynomial function affects the shape of its graph and determines the maximum number of **turning points**, or places where the graph changes direction. It also affects the **end behavior**, or the directions of the graph to the far left and to the far right.

For polynomial functions of degree one or greater, there are four types of end behavior as you move to the left and move to the right, away from the origin: *up and up, down and down, down and up,* and *up and down.*

| Up and Up | Down and Down | Down and Up | Up and Down |
|---|---|---|---|
|  |  |  | 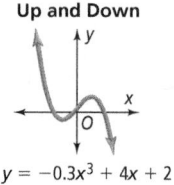 |
| $y = x^4 - 3x^3 + 5x$ | $y = -x^2 + 6x$ | $y = x^3$ | $y = -0.3x^3 + 4x + 2$ |

You can determine the end behavior of a polynomial function of degree $n$ from the leading term $ax^n$ of the standard form.

**End Behavior of a Polynomial Function of Degree $n$ With Leading Term $ax^n$ (Moving Away From the Origin)**

| | $n$ Even | $n$ Odd |
|---|---|---|
| $a$ Positive | Up and Up | Down and Up |
| $a$ Negative | Down and Down | Up and Down |

**Problem 2** Describing End Behavior of Polynomial Functions

Consider the leading term of each polynomial function. What is the end behavior of the graph? Check your answer with a graphing calculator.

**A** $y = 4x^3 - 3x$

The leading term is $4x^3$. Since $n$ is odd and $a$ is positive, the end behavior is down and up.

**B** $y = -2x^4 + 8x^3 - 8x^2 + 2$

The leading term is $-2x^4$. Since $n$ is even and $a$ is negative, the end behavior is down and down.

**Think**

**What do $a$ and $n$ represent?**
$a$ is the coefficient of the leading term. $n$ is the exponent of the leading term.

**Check**

The solution checks.

**Check**

The solution checks.

---

# Additional Problems

**1.** Write $-3x + 4x^3 + 7x - 3$ in standard form. What is the classification of this polynomial by its degree? by its number of terms?

**ANSWER** $4x^3 + 4x - 3$; cubic trinomial

**2.** Consider the leading term of $y = 3x^4 - 2x^3 + x - 1$. What is the end behavior of the graph?

**ANSWER** up and up

**3.** What is the graph of $y = 3 - 2x^3 + x$? Describe the graph.

**ANSWER** up and down; two turning points

**4.** What is the degree of the polynomial function that generates the data shown in the table?

| x | y |
|---|---|
| −2 | −13 |
| −1 | −4 |
| 0 | −1 |
| 1 | 2 |
| 2 | 11 |
| 3 | 32 |
| 4 | 71 |

**ANSWER** 3

**Got It?** **2.** Consider the leading term of $y = -4x^3 + 2x^2 + 7$. What is the end behavior of the graph?

In general, the graph of a polynomial function of degree $n$ ($n \geq 1$) has at most $n - 1$ turning points. The graph of a polynomial function of odd degree has an even number of turning points. The graph of a polynomial function of even degree has an odd number of turning points.

This information, combined with end behavior, determines possible shapes that the graph of a polynomial function can have.

Degree: 1
Zero turning point

Degree: 2
One turning point

Degree: 3
Zero or two turning points

 **Problem 3** Graphing Cubic Functions

What is the graph of each cubic function? Describe the graph.

**A** $y = \frac{1}{2}x^3$

**B** $y = 3x - x^3$

**Step 1** **Step 2**

| x | y |
|---|---|
| −2 | −4 |
| −1 | −0.5 |
| 0 | 0 |
| 1 | 0.5 |
| 2 | 4 |

**Step 1** **Step 2**

| x | y |
|---|---|
| −2 | 2 |
| −1 | −2 |
| 0 | 0 |
| 1 | 2 |
| 2 | −2 |

**Step 3**
The end behavior is down and up. There are no turning points.

**Step 3**
The end behavior is up and down. There are two turning points.

**Got It?** **3.** What is the graph of each cubic function? Describe the graph.
   **a.** $y = -x^3 + 2x^2 - x - 2$    **b.** $y = x^3 - 1$

**Plan**

**How can you graph a polynomial function?**
Make a table of values to help you sketch the middle part of the graph. Use what you know about end behavior to sketch the ends of the graph.

---

# Answers

## Got It? (continued)

**2.** up and down

**3. a.** end behavior: up and down; two turning points

**b.** end behavior: down and up; no turning points

**Q** At least how many ordered pairs do you need to calculate second differences? Explain. **[Three; you need two first differences to calculate a second difference, and you need three *y*-values for two first differences.]**

**Q** Are four ordered pairs enough to determine whether a cubic function could have generated the data? Explain. **[No; with four ordered pairs you will be able to calculate only one third difference, which isn't enough to conclude that all of the third differences are constant.]**

## Problem 4

**Q** What kind of polynomial function has constant second differences? **[quadratic]**

**Q** What kind of polynomial function has constant first differences? **[linear]**

**Q** The polynomial function that generates the data has two turning points, at $x = -2$ and $x \approx 1.33$. What happens to the first differences around these values? **[The signs of the first-difference values change from negative to positive or from positive to negative.]**

## Got It?

**Q** How do you calculate the first value in the first differences? What is the difference? **[Subtract 23 from $-16$; $-16 - 23 = -39$.]**

---

Suppose you are given a set of polynomial function outputs. You know that their inputs are an ordered set of *x*-values in which consecutive *x*-values differ by a constant. By analyzing the differences of consecutive *y*-values, it is possible to determine the least-degree polynomial function that could generate the data.

If the first differences are constant, the function is linear. If the second differences (but not the first) are constant, the function is quadratic. If the third differences (but not the second) are constant, the function is cubic, and so on.

**Problem 4** Using Differences to Determine Degree

**What is the degree of the polynomial function that generates the data shown at the right?**

| x | y |
|---|---|
| −3 | −1 |
| −2 | −7 |
| −1 | −3 |
| 0 | 5 |
| 1 | 11 |
| 2 | 9 |
| 3 | −7 |

**Know** — A set of polynomial function values

**Need** — Degree of the polynomial function

**Plan** — Check first differences of *y*-values. Then check second differences, third differences, and so on until they are constant.

**Think**
**How do you find the second differences?**
Subtract the consecutive first differences.

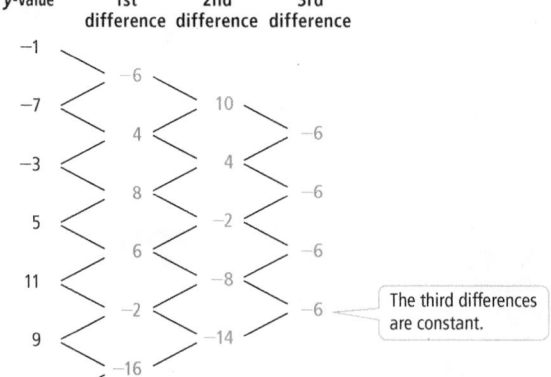

The third differences are constant.

The degree of the polynomial function is 3.

**Got It?** **4. a.** What is the degree of the polynomial function that generates the data shown at the right?
**b. Reasoning** What is an example of a polynomial function whose fifth differences are constant but whose fourth differences are not constant?

| x | y |
|---|---|
| −3 | 23 |
| −2 | −16 |
| −1 | −15 |
| 0 | −10 |
| 1 | −13 |
| 2 | −12 |
| 3 | 29 |

---

# Answers

## Got It? (continued)

**4. a.** degree: 4
    **b.** Answers may vary. Sample: $y = x^5$

## Lesson Check

**Do you know HOW?**

Classify each polynomial by degree and by number of terms.

**1.** $5x^3$

**2.** $6x^2 + 4x - 2$

Write each polynomial in standard form.

**3.** $7x + 3 + 5x^2$

**4.** $-3 + 9x$

**Do you UNDERSTAND?**

**5. Vocabulary** Describe the end behavior of the graph of $y = -2x^7 - 8x$.

**6. Reasoning** Can the graph of a polynomial function be a straight line? If so, give an example.

**7. Error Analysis** Your friend claims the graph of the function $y = 4x^3 + 4$ has only one turning point. Describe the error your friend made and give the correct number of turning points.

### Practice and Problem-Solving Exercises

 **Practice**

Write each polynomial in standard form. Then classify it by degree and by number of terms.

*See Problem 1.*

**8.** $7x + 3x + 5$

**9.** $5 - 3x$

**10.** $2m^2 - 3 + 7m$

**11.** $-x^3 + x^4 + x$

**12.** $-4p + 3p + 2p^2$

**13.** $5a^2 + 3a^3 + 1$

**14.** $-x^5$

**15.** $3 + 12x^4$

**16.** $6x^3 - x^3$

**17.** $7x^3 - 10x^3 + x^3$

**18.** $4x + 5x^2 + 8$

**19.** $x^2 - x^4 + 2x^2$

Determine the end behavior of the graph of each polynomial function.

*See Problem 2.*

**20.** $y = -7x^3 + 8x^2 + x$

**21.** $y = -3x + 6x^2 - 1$

**22.** $y = 1 - 4x - 6x^3 - 15x^6$

**23.** $y = 8x^{11} - 2x^9 + 3x^6 + 4$

**24.** $y = -x^5 - 15x^7 - 4x^9$

**25.** $y = -3 - 6x^5 - 9x^8$

**26.** $y = x^4 - 7x^2 + 3$

**27.** $y = -8x^7 + 16x^6 + 9$

**28.** $y = -14x^6 + 11x^5 - 11$

**29.** $y = -x^3 - x^2 + 3$

**30.** $y = x^3 - 14x - 4$

**31.** $y = 5 - 17x^7 + 9x^{10}$

Describe the shape of the graph of each cubic function by determining the end behavior and number of turning points.

*See Problem 3.*

**32.** $y = 3x^3 - x - 3$

**33.** $y = -9x^3 - 2x^2 + 5x + 3$

**34.** $y = 10x^3 + 9$

**35.** $y = 3x^3$

**36.** $y = -4x^3 - 5x^2$

**37.** $y = 8x^3$

Determine the degree of the polynomial function with the given data.

*See Problem 4.*

**38.**

| x | −2 | −1 | 0 | 1 | 2 |
|---|----|----|---|---|---|
| y | 16 | 7 | 2 | 1 | 4 |

**39.**

| x | −2 | −1 | 0 | 1 | 2 |
|---|----|----|---|---|---|
| y | −15 | −9 | −9 | −9 | −3 |

---

**Do you know HOW?**

- For Exercises 1–2, students may confuse the terminology for degree and number of terms. One way to remember is that the name using the degree refers to the shape of the graph, and the name using number of terms always ends in "nomial," which comes from the Greek word for "law."

**Do you UNDERSTAND?**

- If students have difficulty with Exercises 5 or 7, suggest that they try graphing the given polynomial functions.

**Close**

**Q** What does the degree of a polynomial function tell you about its graph? **[information about the end behavior and possible shape]**

**Q** Why should you write polynomial functions in standard form? **[Answers may vary. Samples: so the same polynomial is written the same way by everyone; so the leading term is the term of greatest degree; to make it easier to determine graph behavior]**

---

## Lesson Check

**1.** cubic monomial

**2.** quadratic trinomial

**3.** $5x^2 + 7x + 3$  **4.** $9x - 3$

**5.** up and down

**6.** Yes, the graph of a linear binomial or linear monomial is a straight line; $f(x) = 2x$

**7.** The graph of $y = 4x^3 + 4$ has no turning points, *not* one turning point.

## Practice and Problem-Solving Exercises

**8.** $10x + 5$; linear binomial

**9.** $-3x + 5$; linear binomial

**10.** $2m^2 + 7m - 3$; quadratic trinomial

**11.** $x^4 - x^3 + x$; quartic trinomial

**12.** $2p^2 - p$; quadratic binomial

**13.** $3a^3 + 5a^2 + 1$; cubic trinomial

**14.** $-x^5$; quintic monomial

**15.** $12x^4 + 3$; quartic binomial

**16.** $5x^3$; cubic monomial

**17.** $-2x^3$; cubic monomial

**18.** $5x^2 + 4x + 8$; quadratic trinomial

**19.** $-x^4 + 3x^2$; quartic binomial

**20.** up and down    **21.** up and up

**22.** down and down   **23.** down and up

**24.** up and down    **25.** down and down

**26.** up and up      **27.** up and down

**28.** down and down  **29.** up and down

**30.** down and up    **31.** up and up

**32.** end behavior: down and up; two turning pts.

**33.** end behavior: up and down; two turning pts.

**34.** end behavior: down and up; no turning pts.

**35.** end behavior: down and up; no turning pts.

**36.** end behavior: up and down; two turning pts.

**37.** end behavior: down and up; no turning pts.

**38.** 2        **39.** 3

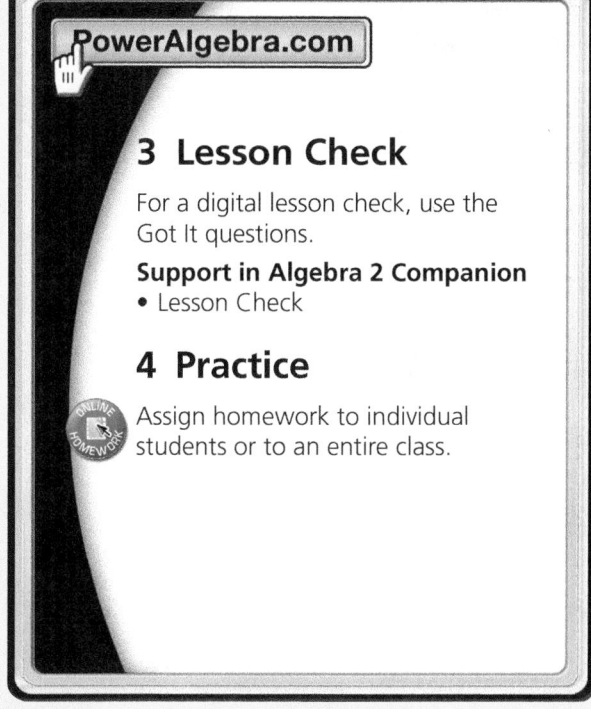

**PowerAlgebra.com**

## 3 Lesson Check

For a digital lesson check, use the Got It questions.

**Support in Algebra 2 Companion**
- Lesson Check

## 4 Practice

Assign homework to individual students or to an entire class.

# 4 Practice

## ASSIGNMENT GUIDE

Basic: 8–39 all, 40–50 even, 51

Average: 9–39 odd, 40–53

Advanced: 9–39 odd, 40–56

Standardized Test Prep: 57–60

Mixed Review: 61–70

**Reasoning** exercises have blue headings.

**Applications** exercises have red headings.

**EXERCISE 51:** Use the Think About a Plan worksheet in the **Practice and Problem Solving Workbook** (also available in the Teaching Resources in print and online) to further support students' development in becoming independent learners.

## HOMEWORK QUICK CHECK

To check students' understanding of key skills and concepts, go over Exercises 13, 33, 40, 48, and 51.

---

 **Apply**

**40. Think About a Plan** The data shows the power generated by a wind turbine. The $x$ column gives the wind speed in meters per second. The $y$ column gives the power generated in kilowatts. What is the degree of the polynomial function that models the data?

- What are the first differences of the $y$-values?
- What are the second differences of the $y$-values?
- When are the differences constant?

| x | y |
|---|---|
| 5 | 10 |
| 6 | 17.28 |
| 7 | 27.44 |
| 8 | 40.96 |
| 9 | 58.32 |

**Classify each polynomial by degree and by number of terms. Simplify first if necessary.**

**41.** $a^2 + a^3 - 4a^4$

**42.** $7$

**43.** $2x(3x)$

**44.** $(2a - 5)(a^2 - 1)$

**45.** $(-8d^3 - 7) + (-d^3 - 6)$

**46.** $b(b - 3)^2$

**Determine the sign of the leading coefficient and the least possible degree of the polynomial function for each graph.**

**47.** **48.** **49.**

**50. Open-Ended** Write an equation for a polynomial function that has three turning points and end behavior up and up.

**51.** Show that the third differences of a polynomial function of degree 3 are nonzero and constant. First, use $f(x) = x^3 - 3x^2 - 2x - 6$. Then show third differences are nonzero and constant for $f(x) = ax^3 + bx^2 + cx + d, a \neq 0$.

**52. Reasoning** Suppose that a function pairs elements from set $A$ with elements from set $B$. A function is called *onto* if it pairs every element in $B$ with at least one element in $A$. For each type of polynomial function, and for each set $B$, determine whether the function is *always*, *sometimes*, or *never* onto.
- **a.** linear; $B$ = all real numbers
- **b.** quadratic; $B$ = all real numbers
- **c.** quadratic; $B$ = all real numbers greater than or equal to 4
- **d.** cubic; $B$ = all real numbers

**53.** Make a table of second differences for each polynomial function. Using your tables, make a conjecture about the second differences of quadratic functions.
- **a.** $y = 2x^2$
- **b.** $y = 5x^2$
- **c.** $y = 5x^2 - 2$
- **d.** $y = 7x^2$
- **e.** $y = 7x^2 + 1$
- **f.** $y = 7x^2 + 3x + 1$

---

# Answers

## Practice and Problem-Solving Exercises (continued)

**40.** 3

**41.** $-4a^4 + a^3 + a^2$; quartic trinomial

**42.** 7; constant monomial

**43.** $6x^2$; quadratic monomial

**44.** $2a^3 - 5a^2 - 2a + 5$; cubic polynomial of 4 terms

**45.** $-9d^3 - 13$; cubic binomial

**46.** $b^3 - 6b^2 + 9b$; cubic trinomial

**47.** negative; 3

**48.** positive; 3

**49.** positive; 4

**50.** Answers may vary. Sample: $x^4 - 10x^2 + 9$

**51.** For $f(x) = x^3 - 3x^2 - 2x - 6$,

| x | f(x) | 1st diff | 2nd diff | 3rd diff |
|---|------|----------|----------|----------|
| 0 | −6 | | | |
| | | −4 | | |
| 1 | −10 | | 0 | |
| | | −4 | | 6 |
| 2 | −14 | | 6 | |
| | | 2 | | 6 |
| 3 | −12 | | 12 | |
| | | 14 | | 6 |
| 4 | 2 | | 18 | |
| | | 32 | | |
| 5 | 34 | | | |

For $f(x) = ax^3 + bx^2 + cx + d$,

| x | f(x) | 1st diff | 2nd diff | 3rd diff |
|---|------|----------|----------|----------|
| 0 | d | | | |
| | | a + b + c | | |
| 1 | a + b + c + d | | 6a + 2b | |
| | | 7a + 3b + c | | 6a |
| 2 | 8a + 4b + 2c + d | | 12a + 2b | |
| | | 19a + 5b + c | | 6a |
| 3 | 27a + 9b + 3c + d | | 18a + 2b | |
| | | 37a + 7b + c | | 6a |
| 4 | 64a + 16b + 4c + d | | 24a + 2b | |
| | | 61a + 9b + c | | |
| 5 | 125a + 25b + 5c + d | | | |

**Challenge**

**54.** Copy and complete the table, which shows the first and second differences in $y$-values for consecutive $x$-values for a polynomial function of degree 2.

| x | y | 1ˢᵗ diff. | 2ⁿᵈ diff. |
|---|---|---|---|
| −3 | 14 | −8 | 2 |
| −2 | 6 |  | 2 |
| −1 |  | −4 | 2 |
| 0 | −4 | −2 | 2 |
| 1 |  | 0 | 2 |
| 2 | −6 |  |  |
| 3 |  |  |  |

**55.** The outputs for a certain function are 1, 2, 4, 8, 16, 32, and so on.
  **a.** Find the first differences of this function.
  **b.** Find the second differences of this function.
  **c.** Find the tenth difference of this function.
  **d.** Can you find a polynomial function that matches the original outputs? Explain your reasoning.

**56. Reasoning** A cubic polynomial function $f$ has leading coefficient 2 and constant term 7. If $f(1) = 7$ and $f(2) = 9$, what is $f(-2)$? Explain how you found your answer.

## Standardized Test Prep

SAT/ACT

**57.** Which expression is a cubic polynomial?
   Ⓐ $x^3$   Ⓑ $3x + 3$   Ⓒ $2x^2 + 3x - 1$   Ⓓ $3x$

**58.** Which equation has $-3 \pm 5i$ as its solutions?
   Ⓕ $x^2 + 6x = -34$   Ⓖ $x^2 + 6x = -14$   Ⓗ $x^2 + 3x = 4$   Ⓘ $x^2 + 3x = 2$

**59.** What is the discriminant of $qx^2 + rx + s = 0$?
   Ⓐ $qrs$   Ⓑ $q^2 - 4rs$   Ⓒ $r^2 - 4qs$   Ⓓ $s^2 - 4qr$

**Short Response**

**60.** What is a simpler form of $x^2(3x^2 - 2x) - 3x^4$? Classify the polynomial by degree and by number of terms.

## Mixed Review

Solve each system of equations.                    ◀ See Lesson 4-9.

**61.** $\begin{cases} y = x^2 - 3x - 7 \\ y = -2x + 3 \end{cases}$   **62.** $\begin{cases} y = x^2 + x - 20 \\ y = x^2 + 2x \end{cases}$   **63.** $\begin{cases} y = 3x^2 + 8x - 3 \\ y = x^2 - 9 \end{cases}$

Write an equation of each line in standard form with integer coefficients.   ◀ See Lesson 2-4.

**64.** $y = 7x + 0.4$   **65.** $y = -3x - 2.5$   **66.** $y = -\frac{2}{7}x + 4$   **67.** $y = 1.2x - 0.5$

**Get Ready!**  To prepare for Lesson 5-2, do Exercises 68–70.

Factor each quadratic expression.                    ◀ See Lesson 4-4.

**68.** $x^2 + 7x + 12$   **69.** $x^2 + 8x - 20$   **70.** $x^2 - 14x + 24$

---

**52. a.** sometimes
  **b.** never
  **c.** sometimes
  **d.** always

**53. a.**

| x | y | 1ˢᵗ diff | 2ⁿᵈ diff |
|---|---|---|---|
| −2 | 8 | −6 | 4 |
| −1 | 2 | −2 | 4 |
| 0 | 0 | 2 | 4 |
| 1 | 2 | 6 |  |
| 2 | 8 |  |  |

**b.**

| x | y | 1ˢᵗ diff | 2ⁿᵈ diff |
|---|---|---|---|
| −2 | 20 | −15 | 10 |
| −1 | 5 | −5 | 10 |
| 0 | 0 | 5 | 10 |
| 1 | 5 | 15 |  |
| 2 | 20 |  |  |

**c.**

| x | y | 1ˢᵗ diff | 2ⁿᵈ diff |
|---|---|---|---|
| −2 | 18 | −15 | 10 |
| −1 | 3 | −5 | 10 |
| 0 | −2 | 5 | 10 |
| 1 | 3 | 15 |  |
| 2 | 18 |  |  |

**d.**

| x | y | 1ˢᵗ diff | 2ⁿᵈ diff |
|---|---|---|---|
| −2 | 28 | −21 | 14 |
| −1 | 7 | −7 | 14 |
| 0 | 0 | 7 | 14 |
| 1 | 7 | 21 |  |
| 2 | 28 |  |  |

**e.**

| x | y | 1ˢᵗ diff | 2ⁿᵈ diff |
|---|---|---|---|
| −2 | 29 | −21 | 14 |
| −1 | 8 | −7 | 14 |
| 0 | 1 | 7 | 14 |
| 1 | 8 | 21 |  |
| 2 | 29 |  |  |

**f.**

| x | y | 1ˢᵗ diff | 2ⁿᵈ diff |
|---|---|---|---|
| −2 | 23 | −18 | 14 |
| −1 | 5 | −4 | 14 |
| 0 | 1 | 10 | 14 |
| 1 | 11 | 24 |  |
| 2 | 35 |  |  |

Second differences of quadratic functions are constant.

**54.** missing values: $y$: 0, −6, −4; first differences: −6, 2

**55. a.** 1, 2, 4, 8, 16, 32 ...
   **b.** 1, 2, 4, 8, 16, 32 ...
   **c.** 1, 2, 4, 8, 16, 32 ...
   **d.** No; the differences will never be constant, therefore there is no polynomial function that matches the outputs.

**56.** −35; Let $y = 2x^3 + bx^2 + cx + 7$. Evaluate $f(1) = 7$ and $f(2) = 9$ to find a system of equations for $b$ and $c$. $b = -5$ and $c = 3$, so $f(-2) = -35$.

## Standardized Test Prep

**57.** A

**58.** F

**59.** C

**60.** **[2]** $x^2(3x^2 - 2x) - 3x^4 = 3x^4 - 2x^3 - 3x^4 = -2x^3$; The degree is 3 and there is 1 term, so this is a cubic monomial.

  **[1]** no explanation given

## Mixed Review

**61.** (3.7, −4.4), (−2.7, 8.4)

**62.** (−20, 360)

**63.** (−3, 0), (−1, −8)

**64.** $35x - 5y = -2$

**65.** $6x + 2y = -5$

**66.** $2x + 7y = 28$

**67.** $12x - 10y = 5$

**68.** $(x + 4)(x + 3)$

**69.** $(x + 10)(x - 2)$

**70.** $(x - 12)(x - 2)$

## Differentiated Remediation

Available in editable format online.

## Additional Instructional Support

### Algebra 2 Companion

Students can use the **Algebra 2 Companion** worktext (4 pages) as you teach the lesson. Use the Companion to support

- New Vocabulary
- Key Concepts
- Got It for each Problem
- Lesson Check

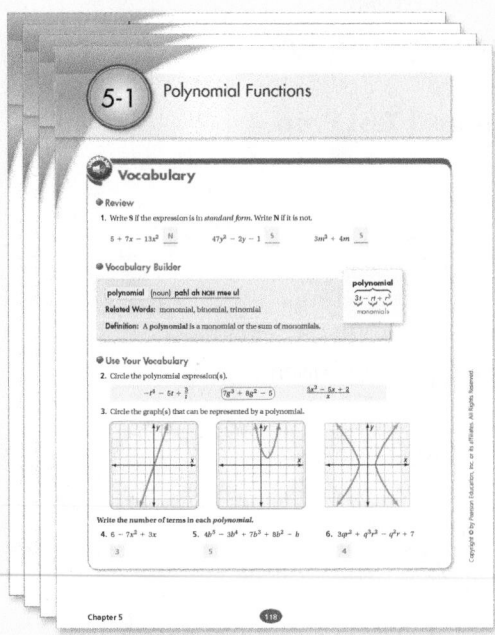

### ELL Support

**Use Role Playing** To help students learn the vocabulary for classifying polynomials, play the following game:

Divide students into groups of three. One student says what the degree of a polynomial is and how many terms it has. For example, "I am a polynomial of degree 2 with 1 term. What am I?" One of the other two students responds, naming the polynomial. For example, "You are a quadratic monomial." The other student checks the answer.

You might want to start by allowing the students to look at the table in the book and then closing the book and continuing.

## 5 Assess & Remediate

### Lesson Quiz

1. Write $2x^3 - 3x^2 + x^5$ in standard form. What is the classification of this polynomial by its degree? by its number of terms?

2. Consider the leading term of $y = -2x^2 - 3x + 3$. What is the end behavior of the graph?

3. Describe the end behavior and number of turning points in the graph of $y = x^3 + x + 3$.

4. **Do you UNDERSTAND?** What is the degree of the polynomial function that generates the data shown in the table?

| x | y |
|---|---|
| 1 | −2 |
| 2 | 0 |
| 3 | 6 |
| 4 | 16 |
| 5 | 30 |
| 6 | 48 |
| 7 | 70 |
| 8 | 96 |

### ANSWERS TO LESSON QUIZ

1. $x^5 + 2x^3 - 3x^2$; quintic trinomial
2. down and down
3. The end behavior is down and up. There are no turning points.
4. 2

### PRESCRIPTION FOR REMEDIATION

Use the student work on the Lesson Quiz to prescribe a differentiated review assignment:

| Points | Differentiated Remediation |
|--------|---------------------------|
| 0–2 | Intervention |
| 3 | On-level |
| 4 | Extension |

### PowerAlgebra.com

#### 5 Assess & Remediate

Assign the Lesson Quiz. Appropriate intervention, practice, or enrichment is automatically generated based on student performance.

## Intervention

- **Reteaching** (2 pages) Provides reteaching and practice exercises for the key lesson concepts. Use with struggling students or absent students.

- **English Language Learner Support** Helps students develop and reinforce mathematical vocabulary and key concepts.

# Differentiated Remediation _continued_

Available in editable format online.

## On-Level

- **Practice** (2 pages) Provides extra practice for each lesson. For simpler practice exercises, use the Form K Practice pages found in the All-in-One Teaching Resources and online.

- **Think About a Plan** Helps students develop specific problem-solving skills and strategies by providing scaffolded guiding questions.

- **Standardized Test Prep** Focuses on all major exercises, all major question types, and helps students prepare for the high-stakes assessments.

## Extension

- **Enrichment** Provides students with interesting problems and activities that extend the concepts of the lesson.

- **Activities, Games, and Puzzles** Worksheets that can be used for concepts development, enrichment, and for fun!

---

### Practice and Problem Solving Wkbk/ All-in-One Resources/Online
**Practice page 1**

### Practice and Problem Solving Wkbk/ All-in-One Resources/Online
**Practice page 2**

### All-in-One Resources/Online
**Enrichment**

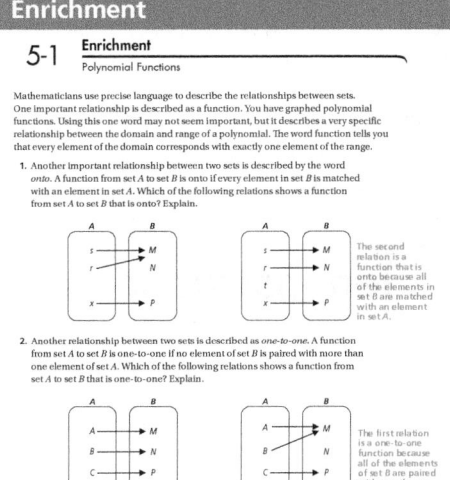

---

### Practice and Problem Solving Wkbk/ All-in-One Resources/Online
**Think About a Plan**

### Practice and Problem Solving Wkbk/ All-in-One Resources/Online
**Standardized Test Prep**

### Online Teacher Resource Center
**Activities, Games, and Puzzles**

# 1 Interactive Learning

## Solve It!

**PURPOSE** To explore the product of linear factors numerically, algebraically, and graphically

**PROCESS** Students may select several $x$-values, find corresponding $y$-values for each line, calculate the products, and plot product points. Alternatively, they may find the algebraic product $(x + 1)(x - 1)$ and use the quadratic polynomial to find product points and/or graph the parabola.

### FACILITATE

**Q** How can $1.5 \cdot 3.5$ be expressed as the product of a sum and a difference? **[Samples: $(2.5 - 1)(2.5 + 1)$; $(x - 1)(x + 1)$ for $x = 2.5$]**

**Q** Which $x$-values result in a product of 0? What is special about those? **[−1 and 1; each of the lines has an $x$-intercept for those $x$-values.]**

**ANSWER** See Solve It in Answers on next page.
**CONNECT THE MATH** In the Solve It, students see numerical and graphical equivalence between the product of two linear factors and a quadratic function. The lesson solidifies connections between factors, roots, zeros, and $x$-intercepts of polynomials, related functions, and graphs.

## 2 Guided Instruction

### Problem 1

**Q** Why do the constants of the factors of the quadratic trinomial have different signs? **[Sample: The constant of the trinomial is negative.]**

### Got It?

**Q** What is the first step to factor this polynomial? **[Factor out the GCF, $x$.]**

---

**Objectives** To analyze the factored form of a polynomial
To write a polynomial function from its zeros

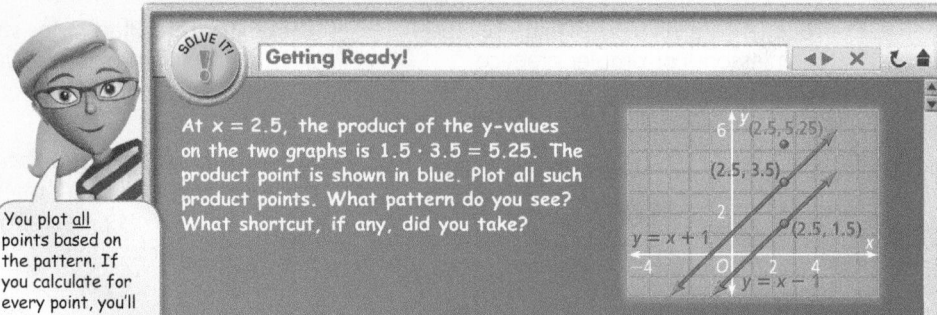

**Getting Ready!**

At $x = 2.5$, the product of the $y$-values on the two graphs is $1.5 \cdot 3.5 = 5.25$. The product point is shown in blue. Plot all such product points. What pattern do you see? What shortcut, if any, did you take?

You plot <u>all</u> points based on the pattern. If you calculate for every point, you'll never get done.

### Lesson Vocabulary

- factor theorem
- multiple zero
- multiplicity
- relative maximum
- relative minimum

If $P(x)$ is a polynomial function, the solutions of the related polynomial equation $P(x) = 0$ are the zeros of the function.

**Essential Understanding** Finding the zeros of a polynomial function will help you factor the polynomial, graph the function, and solve the related polynomial equation.

In Chapter 4, you solved a quadratic equation of the form $x^2 + bx + c = 0$ by factoring. You wrote it using *linear factors* in the form $(x - r_1)(x - r_2) = 0$. Then you applied the Zero-Product Property to find the solutions $x = r_1$ and $x = r_2$. You can solve some polynomial equations $a_n x^n + a_{n-1} x^{n-1} + \cdots + a_0 = 0$ in much the same way.

### Plan

**How do you write the factored form of a polynomial?**
Write the polynomial as a product of factors. Make sure each factor cannot be factored any further.

**Problem 1** Writing a Polynomial in Factored Form

**What is the factored form of $x^3 - 2x^2 - 15x$?**

$$x^3 - 2x^2 - 15x = x(x^2 - 2x - 15) \qquad \text{Factor out the GCF, } x.$$
$$= x(x - 5)(x + 3) \qquad \text{Factor } x^2 - 2x - 15.$$

**Check** $\quad x(x - 5)(x + 3) = x(x^2 - 2x - 15) \qquad$ Multiply $(x - 5)(x + 3)$.
$$= x^3 - 2x^2 - 15x \ ✔ \qquad \text{Distributive Property}$$

**Got It?** **1.** What is the factored form of $x^3 - x^2 - 12x$?

---

### BIG ideas Equivalence
Function

**UbD**

#### ESSENTIAL UNDERSTANDINGS
- Knowing the zeros of a polynomial function gives information about its graph.
- A polynomial of degree $n$ has $n$ linear factors. The graph of the related function crosses the $x$-axis an even or odd number of times depending on whether $n$ is even or odd.
- $(x - a)$ is linear factor if and only if $a$ is a zero.

### Math Background
The linear factors of a polynomial are closely connected to the zeros of the related polynomial function. By applying the Zero Product Property, each linear factor is set equal to zero and solved

to obtain the zeros. The Factor Theorem makes the connection explicit, stating that $x - a$ is a linear factor when the value of $a$ is a zero of the related polynomial function.

Thus the zeros of a polynomial function identify
- the linear factors of the polynomial.
- the $x$-intercepts of the function's graph.
- the solutions to $P(x) = 0$.

### Support Student Learning
Use the **Algebra 2 Companion** to engage and support students during instruction. See Lesson Resources at the end of this lesson for details.

### PowerAlgebra.com

## 1 Interactive Learning

### Solve It!
Step out how to solve the Problem with helpful hints and an online question. Other questions are listed above in Interactive Learning.

**Dynamic Activity** The activity gives students practice graphing linear factors and their corresponding polynomials and using graphs to find roots of polynomials.

## Key Concepts Roots, Zeros, and *x*-intercepts

The following are equivalent statements about a real number $b$ and a polynomial $P(x) = a_n x^n + a_{n-1} x^{n-1} + \cdots + a_1 x + a_0$.

- $x - b$ is a linear factor of the polynomial $P(x)$.
- $b$ is a zero of the polynomial function $y = P(x)$.
- $b$ is a root (or solution) of the polynomial equation $P(x) = 0$.
- $b$ is an $x$-intercept of the graph of $y = P(x)$.

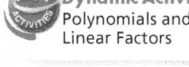
**Dynamic Activity**
Polynomials and
Linear Factors

### Problem 2 Finding Zeros of a Polynomial Function

**What are the zeros of $y = (x + 2)(x - 1)(x - 3)$? Graph the function.**

| Know | Need | Plan |
|------|------|------|
| Polynomial function | • Zeros <br> • Additional points <br> • End behavior | • Use the Zero-Product Property to find zeros. <br> • Find points between the zeros. <br> • Sketch the graph. |

**Think**

Does knowing the zeros of a function give you enough information to sketch it?

No; several different cubic functions could pass through $(-2, 0)$, $(1, 0)$, and $(3, 0)$.

**Step 1** Use the Zero-Product Property to find the zeros.

$(x + 2)(x - 1)(x - 3) = 0$

so $x + 2 = 0$ or $x - 1 = 0$ or $x - 3 = 0$.
The zeros of the function are $-2$, $1$, and $3$.

**Step 2** Find points for $x$-values between the zeros.
Evaluate $y = (x + 2)(x - 1)(x - 3)$ for $x = -1, 0,$ and $2$.

$(-1 + 2)(-1 - 1)(-1 - 3) = 8 \quad (-1, 8)$

$(0 + 2)(0 - 1)(0 - 3) = 6 \quad (0, 6)$

$(2 + 2)(2 - 1)(2 - 3) = -4 \quad (2, -4)$

**Step 3** Determine the end behavior.
The function $y = (x + 2)(x - 1)(x - 3)$ is cubic. The coefficient of $x^3$ is $+1$, so the end behavior is *down and up*.

**Step 4** Use the zeros: $(-2, 0)$, $(1, 0)$, $(3, 0)$; the additional points: $(-1, 8)$, $(0, 6)$, $(2, -4)$; and end behavior to sketch the graph.

 **Got It? 2.** What are the zeros of $y = x(x - 3)(x + 5)$? Graph the function.

The Factor Theorem describes the relationship between the linear factors of a polynomial and the zeros of a polynomial.

---

**Take Note**

An example might help students better understand the equivalent statements:

Let $P(x) = -x^3 + 2x + 4$, and let $x = 2$.

Then $P(2) = -(2)^3 + 2(2) + 4 = 0$.

Therefore,

- $x - 2$ is a factor of $-x^3 + 2x + 4$.
- 2 is a zero for the polynomial function $P(x)$.
- 2 is a solution to the equation $-x^3 + 2x + 4 = 0$.
- The point $(2, 0)$ is an $x$-intercept of the graph of $P(x) = -x^3 + 2x + 4$.

**Problem 2**

**Q** What is the value of $y$ for any zero of a polynomial function? **[0]**

**Q** How does the graph of this function show that $-2$, $1$, and $3$ are the zeros of the function? **[The graph of the function intersects the $x$-axis at $-2$, $1$, and $3$.]**

**Got It?**

Use this polynomial to emphasize that 0 can be a zero of a polynomial function if one of the factors of the polynomial is $x$.

---

## 2 Guided Instruction

Each Problem is worked out and supported online.

**Problem 1**
Writing a Polynomial in Factored Form

**Problem 2**
Finding Zeros of a Polynomial Function

**Problem 3**
Writing a Polynomial Function From Its Zeros
*Animated*

**Problem 4**
Finding the Multiplicity of a Zero
*Animated*

**Problem 5**
Identifying Relative Maximums and Minimums

**Problem 6**
Using a Polynomial to Maximize Volume

**Alternative Problem 6**
Using a Polynomial to Maximize Volume
*Animated*

**Support in Algebra 2 Companion**
- Vocabulary
- Key Concepts
- Got It?

---

## Answers

**Solve It!**
The product pts. form a parabola. The pts. can be found by plotting $y = (x + 1)(x - 1) = x^2 - 1$.

**Got It?**

**1.** $x(x - 4)(x + 3)$

**2.** $0, 3, -5$;

**Take Note**      EXTENSION

"If and only if" means that the reverse of the statement is also true: If $x - a$ is a factor, then $x = a$ is a zero; and if $x = a$ is a zero, then $x - a$ is a factor.

## Problem 3

> **Q** In 3A, could the factors $(x + 2)(x - 2)(x - 3)$ be rewritten as $(x^2 - 4)(x - 3)$? Explain. **[Yes; $(x + 2)(x - 2)$ are the factors of a difference of two squares: $(x^2 - 2^2)$.]**

EXTENSION

If a polynomial function is of degree $n$, then there are at most $n - 1$ turning points in the graph of that function. This means that in Problem 3, $f(x)$ has at most 2 turning points and $g(x)$ has at most 3 turning points. The graphs of both functions on this page show all the turning points of those functions.

## Got It?

ERROR PREVENTION

> **Q** What is the difference between a quartic polynomial and a quadratic polynomial? **[A quartic polynomial is of degree 4 and has the form $ax^4 + bx^3 + cx^2 + dx + e$, while a quadratic polynomial is of degree 2 and has the form $ax^2 + bx + c$.]**

**Theorem**   **Factor Theorem**

The expression $x - a$ is a factor of a polynomial if and only if the value $a$ is a zero of the related polynomial function.

### Problem 3   Writing a Polynomial Function From Its Zeros

**A** What is a cubic polynomial function in standard form with zeros $-2$, 2, and 3?

**Plan**

**How can you use the zeros to find the function?**
By the Factor Theorem, $a$ is a zero means that $x - a$ is a factor of the related polynomial.

$$-2 \quad\quad 2 \quad\quad 3 \quad\quad\quad\quad -2, 2, \text{ and } 3 \text{ are zeros.}$$
$$\downarrow \quad\quad \downarrow \quad\quad \downarrow$$

| | |
|---|---|
| $f(x) = (x + 2)(x - 2)(x - 3)$ | Write a linear factor for each zero. |
| $= (x + 2)(x^2 - 5x + 6)$ | Multiply $(x-2)$ and $(x-3)$. |
| $= x(x^2 - 5x + 6) + 2(x^2 - 5x + 6)$ | Distributive Property |
| $= x^3 - 5x^2 + 6x + 2x^2 - 10x + 12$ | Distributive Property |
| $= x^3 - 3x^2 - 4x + 12$ | Simplify. |

The cubic polynomial $f(x) = x^3 - 3x^2 - 4x + 12$ has zeros $-2$, 2, and 3.

**B** What is a quartic polynomial function in standard form with zeros $-2$, $-2$, 2, and 3?

$$-2 \quad\quad -2 \quad\quad 2 \quad\quad 3 \quad\quad\quad -2, -2, 2, \text{ and } 3 \text{ are zeros.}$$
$$\downarrow \quad\quad \downarrow \quad\quad \downarrow \quad\quad \downarrow$$

| | |
|---|---|
| $g(x) = (x + 2)(x + 2)(x - 2)(x - 3)$ | Write a linear factor for each zero. |
| $= x^4 - x^3 - 10x^2 + 4x + 24$ | Simplify. |

The quartic polynomial $g(x) = x^4 - x^3 - 10x^2 + 4x + 24$ has zeros $-2$, $-2$, 2, and 3.

**C** Graph both functions. How do the graphs differ? How are they similar?

Both screens:
x-scale: 1
y-scale: 5

Both graphs have $x$-intercepts at $-2$, 2, and 3. The cubic has down-and-up end behavior. The quartic has up-and-up end behavior.

The cubic function has two turning points, and it crosses the $x$-axis at $-2$. The quartic function touches the $x$-axis at $-2$ but does not cross it. The quartic function has three turning points.

> **Got It?**   **3. a.** What is a quadratic polynomial function with zeros 3 and $-3$?
> **b.** What is a cubic polynomial function with zeros 3, 3, and $-3$?
> **c.** **Reasoning** Graph both functions. How do the graphs differ? How are they similar?

# Additional Problems

**1.** What is the factored form of $x^3 + x^2 - 12x$?

**ANSWER** $x(x + 4)(x - 3)$

**2.** What are the zeros of $y = (x - 3)(x + 4)(x - 1)$? Graph the function.

**ANSWER** 3, $-4$, 1

**3.** What is a cubic polynomial function in standard form with zeros 1, $-1$, and 4?

**ANSWER** $x^3 - 4x^2 - x + 4$

**4.** What are the zeros of $f(x) = x^3 - 5x^2 + 3x + 9$? What are the multiplicities? How does the graph behave at these zeros?

**ANSWER** 3 with a multiplicity of 2: the graph only touches the $x$-axis and turns around; $-1$ with a multiplicity of 1: the graph crosses the $x$-axis.

**5.** What are the relative maximum and minimum of $f(x) = x^3 - 9x$? Round to the nearest tenth.

**ANSWER** relative maximum: $(-1.7, 10.4)$; relative minimum: $(1.7, -10.4)$

**6.** A designer wants to make a rectangular prism box with maximum volume, while keeping the sum of its length, width, and height 12 in. The length must be 3 times the height. What should each dimension be?

**ANSWER** length: 6 in., width = 4 in., height = 2 in.

You can write the polynomial functions in Problem 3 in factored form as $f(x) = (x + 2)(x - 2)(x - 3)$ and $g(x) = (x + 2)^2(x - 2)(x - 3)$. In $g(x)$ the repeated linear factor $x + 2$ makes $-2$ a **multiple zero**.

In particular, since the linear factor $x + 2$ appears twice, you can say that $-2$ is a zero of **multiplicity** 2. In general, $a$ is a zero of multiplicity $n$ means that $x - a$ appears $n$ times as a factor.

 take note

### Key Concept   How Multiple Zeros Affect a Graph

If $a$ is a zero of multiplicity $n$ in the polynomial function $y = P(x)$, then the behavior of the graph at the $x$-intercept $a$ will be close to linear if $n = 1$, close to quadratic if $n = 2$, close to cubic if $n = 3$, and so on.

 **Problem 4**   Finding the Multiplicity of a Zero

**What are the zeros of $f(x) = x^4 - 2x^3 - 8x^2$? What are their multiplicities? How does the graph behave at these zeros?**

$$f(x) = x^4 - 2x^3 - 8x^2$$
$$= x^2(x^2 - 2x - 8) \quad \text{Factor out the GCF, } x^2.$$
$$= x^2(x + 2)(x - 4) \quad \text{Factor } (x^2 - 2x - 8).$$

Since $x^2 = (x - 0)^2$, the number 0 is a zero of multiplicity 2. The numbers $-2$ and 4 are zeros of multiplicity 1.

The graph looks close to linear at the $x$-intercepts $-2$ and 4. It resembles a parabola at the $x$-intercept 0.

**Think**

**How can you find the multiplicities?**
Factor the polynomial. Find the number of times each linear factor appears.

✓ **Got It?** **4.** What are the zeros of $f(x) = x^3 - 4x^2 + 4x$? What are their multiplicities? How does the graph behave at these zeros?

If the graph of a polynomial function has several turning points, the function can have a **relative maximum** and a **relative minimum**. A relative maximum is the value of the function at an up-to-down turning point. A relative minimum is the value of the function at a down-to-up turning point.

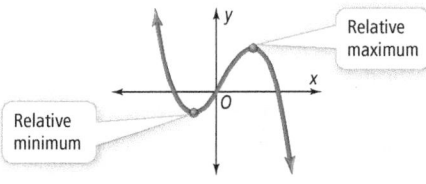

Relative maximum

Relative minimum

**Take Note**   EXTENSION

This discussion of how multiple zeros affect a graph can be extended with the following facts:

- If $a$ is a zero of **even** multiplicity, then the graph of its function touches the $x$-axis at $a$ and turns around.
- If $a$ is a zero of **odd** multiplicity, then the graph of its function crosses the $x$-axis at $a$.

### Problem 4

**Q** How does this graph show that 0 is a multiple zero of the function? **[The graph has a turning point at (0, 0).]**

**Q** What is the end behavior of this function's graph? **[up and up]**

### Got It?   VISUAL LEARNERS

Since $x$ is a common factor of this function, students can conclude that 0 is a zero with a multiplicity of 1. Note that this fact is displayed in the function's graph where it crosses the $x$-axis at (0, 0).

EXTENSION

Only polynomials of degree greater than 2 can have more than one maximum or minimum value. If $n$ is the degree of a polynomial function, then $n - 1$ is the greatest possible total number of minimum and maximum values for that function.

## Answers

### Got It? (continued)

**3. a.** $f(x) = x^2 - 9$

**b.** $P(x) = x^3 - 3x^2 - 9x + 27$

**c.**

Both graphs have $x$-intercepts of 3 and $-3$.
The quadratic has up and up end behavior and one turning pt., and the cubic has down and up end behavior and two turning pts.

**4.** 0 is a zero of multiplicity 1, the graph looks close to linear at $x = 0$; 2 is a zero of multiplicity 2, the graph looks close to quadratic at $x = 2$.

## Problem 5

To see the graph of the function as shown on this page, students should change the RANGE settings on their calculators to Ymax = 100 and Ymin = −100.

**Q** Why is (−4, 80) called a relative maximum of this function? **[It is a turning point of the function's graph, but it is not the greatest (absolute maximum) value of the function.]**

### Got It?

**Q** How many x-intercepts does this graph have? **[3]**
**Q** What is the greatest number of relative maximums and relative minimums this graph can have? How do you know? **[2; it is a polynomial of degree 3.]**

## Problem 6

**Q** What do the values of x represent? **[the height of the camera]**
**Q** What do the values of y represent? **[the volume of the camera]**
**Q** What does the point (1.6, 7.68) represent? **[A camera that is 1.6 in. tall will have the maximum volume of 7.68 in.$^3$.]**

### Got It?                    ERROR PREVENTION

**Q** What expression from the Problem do you have to change? **[Change the expression for the camera's width based on the new sum of its dimensions.]**

---

  **Problem 5** Identifying a Relative Maximum and Minimum

**What are the relative maximum and minimum of $f(x) = x^3 + 3x^2 − 24x$?**

Use a graphing calculator to find a relative maximum and a relative minimum.

**Think**

**How is a relative maximum different from a maximum at the vertex of a parabola?**
A relative maximum is the greatest y-value in the "neighborhood" of its x-value. The maximum at the vertex of a parabola is the greatest y-value for *all* x-values.

Relative maximum

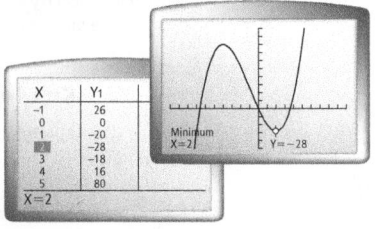

Relative minimum

The relative maximum is 80 at $x = −4$ and the relative minimum is $−28$ at $x = 2$.

 **Got It?** **5.** What are the relative maximum and minimum of $f(x) = 3x^3 + x^2 − 5x$?

 **Problem 6** Using a Polynomial Function to Maximize Volume

**Technology** The design of a digital box camera maximizes the volume while keeping the sum of the dimensions at 6 inches. If the length must be 1.5 times the height, what should each dimension be?

**Step 1** Define a variable x.

Let $x$ = the height of the camera.

**Step 2** Determine length and width.

length = 1.5x; width = $6 − (x + 1.5x) = 6 − 2.5x$

**Think**

What is the formula for the volume of a "box"?
$V = \ell wh$

**Step 3** Model the volume.

$V = (\text{length})(\text{width})(\text{height}) = (1.5x)(6 − 2.5x)(x)$
$= −3.75x^3 + 9x^2$

**Step 4** Graph the polynomial function. Use the **MAXIMUM** feature to find that the maximum volume is 7.68 in.$^3$ for a height of 1.6 in.

height $= x = 1.6$
length $= 1.5x = 1.5(1.6) = 2.4$
width $= 6 − 2.5x = 6 − 2.5(1.6) = 2$

The dimensions of the camera should be 2.4 in. long by 2 in. wide by 1.6 in. high.

 **Got It?** **6.** What is the maximum volume of the camera in Problem 6, if the sum of the dimensions is at most 4 inches?

---

# Answers

## Got It?

**5.** relative maximum: (−0.86, 3.13); relative minimum: (0.64, −2)

**6.** 2.28 in.$^3$

## Lesson Check

**1.** 0, 6
**2.** −4, 5
**3.** −12, 7, 9
**4.** $f(x) = x^3 − x$
**5.** $h(x) = x^4 + 4x^3 − 26x^2 − 60x + 225$
**6.** Error in writing the factors: a function that has zeros at 3 and −1 has factors of $x − 3$ and $x + 1$ *not* $x + 3$ and $x − 1$, so $f(x) = x^2 − 2x − 3$ *not* $x^2 + 2x − 3$.

## Practice and Problem-Solving Exercises

**7.** $x(x + 5)(x + 2)$
**8.** $x(x − 9)(x + 2)$
**9.** $x(x − 7)(x + 3)$

**10.** $x(x − 6)(x + 6)$
**11.** $x(x + 4)^2$
**12.** $3x(3x − 1)(x + 1)$
**13.** 1, −2;

**14.** 2, −9;

**15.** 0, −5, 8;

**16.** −1, 2, 3;

**17.** −1, 1, 2;

**18.** 0, −2, −3;

**19.** $y = x^3 − 18x^2 + 107x − 210$
**20.** $y = x^3 + x^2 − 2x$
**21.** $y = x^3 + 9x^2 + 15x − 25$

**Lesson Check**

**Do you know HOW?**

Find the zeros of each function.

1. $y = x(x - 6)$

2. $y = (x + 4)(x - 5)$

3. $y = (x + 12)(x - 9)(x - 7)$

4. Write a polynomial function in standard form with zeros $-1$, $1$, and $0$.

**Do you UNDERSTAND?**

5. **Vocabulary** Write a polynomial function $h$ in standard form that has 3 and $-5$ as zeros of multiplicity 2.

6. **Error Analysis** Your friend says that to write a function that has zeros 3 and $-1$, you should multiply the two factors $(x + 3)$ and $(x - 1)$ to get $f(x) = x^2 + 2x - 3$. Describe and correct your friend's error.

  **Practice and Problem-Solving Exercises**

 **Practice**

Write each polynomial in factored form. Check by multiplication. ◀ See Problem 1.

7. $x^3 + 7x^2 + 10x$     8. $x^3 - 7x^2 - 18x$     9. $x^3 - 4x^2 - 21x$

10. $x^3 - 36x$     11. $x^3 + 8x^2 + 16x$     12. $9x^3 + 6x^2 - 3x$

Find the zeros of each function. Then graph the function. ◀ See Problem 2.

13. $y = (x - 1)(x + 2)$     14. $y = (x - 2)(x + 9)$     15. $y = x(x + 5)(x - 8)$

16. $y = (x + 1)(x - 2)(x - 3)$     17. $y = (x + 1)(x - 1)(x - 2)$     18. $y = x(x + 2)(x + 3)$

Write a polynomial function in standard form with the given zeros. ◀ See Problem 3.

19. $x = 5, 6, 7$     20. $x = -2, 0, 1$     21. $x = -5, -5, 1$     22. $x = 3, 3, 3$

23. $x = 1, -1, -2$     24. $x = 0, 4, -\frac{1}{2}$     25. $x = 0, 0, 2, 3$     26. $x = -1, -2, -3, -4$

Find the zeros of each function. State the multiplicity of multiple zeros. ◀ See Problem 4.

27. $y = (x + 3)^3$     28. $y = x(x - 1)^3$

29. $y = 2x^3 + x^2 - x$     30. $y = 3x^3 - 3x$

31. $y = (x - 4)^2$     32. $y = (x - 2)^2(x - 1)$

33. $y = (2x + 3)(x - 1)^2$     34. $y = (x + 1)^2(x - 1)(x - 2)$

Find the relative maximum and relative minimum of the graph of each function. ◀ See Problem 5.

35. $f(x) = x^3 + 4x^2 - 5x$     36. $f(x) = -x^3 + 16x^2 - 76x + 96$

37. $f(x) = -4x^3 + 12x^2 + 4x - 12$     38. $f(x) = x^3 - 7x^2 + 7x + 15$

22. $y = x^3 - 9x^2 + 27x - 27$

23. $y = x^3 + 2x^2 - x - 2$

24. $y = x^3 - \frac{7}{2}x^2 - 2x$

25. $y = x^4 - 5x^3 + 6x^2$

26. $y = x^4 + 10x^3 + 35x^2 + 50x + 24$

27. $-3$ (multiplicity 3)

28. $0$, $1$ (multiplicity 3)

29. $-1, 0, \frac{1}{2}$

30. $-1, 0, 1$

31. $4$ (multiplicity 2)

32. $1, 2$ (multiplicity 2)

33. $-\frac{3}{2}$, $1$ (multiplicity 2)

34. $-1$ (multiplicity 2), $1, 2$

35. relative maximum: $(-3.19, 24.2)$; relative minimum: $(0.52, -1.38)$

36. relative maximum: $(7.10, 5.05)$; relative minimum: $(3.57, -16.9)$

37. relative maximum: $(2.15, 12.32)$; relative minimum: $(-0.15, -12.32)$

38. relative maximum: $(0.57, 16.9)$; relative minimum: $(4.10, -5.05)$

---

## 3 Lesson Check

### Do you know HOW?     ERROR INTERVENTION

- If students confuse the signs of their zeros, then have them write each factor in a separate equation equal to 0 and solve each for $x$.
- For Exercise 4, remind students that here standard form means that all the factors are multiplied out and the polynomial's terms are written in order, starting with the greatest degree.

### Do you UNDERSTAND?

- For Exercise 5, point out that the problem does not state that 3 and $-5$ are the *only* zeros of the polynomial. Challenge students to write three different polynomial functions that match the description.
- If students have difficulty identifying or explaining the error for Exercise 6, suggest that they start by solving the problem correctly and then use their own process to identify and describe the error.

### Close

Q What do the zeros of a polynomial function tell you about the function's graph? **[The zeros tell the $x$-intercepts.]**

**PowerAlgebra.com**

## 3 Lesson Check

For a digital lesson check, use the Got It questions.

**Support in Algebra 2 Companion**
- Lesson Check

## 4 Practice

Assign homework to individual students or to an entire class.

# 4 Practice

**ASSIGNMENT GUIDE**

Basic: 7–39 all, 41–43, 45–47, 50–52

Average: 7–39 odd, 40–54

Advanced: 7–39 odd, 40–56

Standardized Test Prep: 57–60

Mixed Review: 61–69

**Reasoning** exercises have blue headings.

**Applications** exercises have red headings.

**EXERCISE 46:** Use the Think About a Plan worksheet in the **Practice and Problem Solving Workbook** (also available in the Teaching Resources in print and online) to further support students' development in becoming independent learners.

**HOMEWORK QUICK CHECK**

To check students' understanding of key skills and concepts, go over Exercises 19, 27, 43, 45, and 46.

---

**39. Metalwork** A metalworker wants to make an open box from a sheet of metal, by cutting equal squares from each corner as shown.
   a. Write expressions for the length, width, and height of the open box.
   b. Use your expressions from part (a) to write a function for the volume of the box. (*Hint:* Write the function in factored form.)
   c. Graph the function. Then find the maximum volume of the box and the side length of the cut-out squares that generates this volume.

◆ See Problem 6.

12 in.

16 in.

**B** **Apply**    **Write each function in factored form. Check by multiplication.**

**40.** $y = 3x^3 - 27x^2 + 24x$    **41.** $y = -2x^3 - 2x^2 + 40x$    **42.** $y = x^4 + 3x^3 - 4x^2$

**43. Think About a Plan** A storage company needs to design a new storage box that has twice the volume of its largest box. Its largest box is 5 ft long, 4 ft wide, and 3 ft high. The new box must be formed by increasing each dimension by the same amount. Find the increase in each dimension.
   • How can you write the dimensions of the new storage box as polynomial expressions?
   • How can you use the volume of the current largest box to find the volume of the new box?

**44. Carpentry** A carpenter hollowed out the interior of a block of wood as shown at the right.
   a. Express the volume of the original block and the volume of the wood removed as polynomials in factored form.
   b. What polynomial represents the volume of the wood remaining?

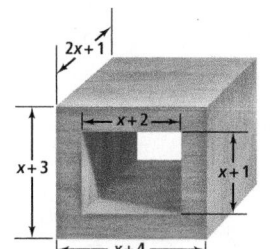

2x+1

x+2

x+3

x+1

x+4

**45. Geometry** A rectangular box is $2x + 3$ units long, $2x - 3$ units wide, and $3x$ units high. What is its volume, expressed as a polynomial?

**46. Measurement** The volume in cubic feet of a CD holder can be expressed as $V(x) = -x^3 - x^2 + 6x$, or, when factored, as the product of its three dimensions. The depth is expressed as $2 - x$. Assume that the height is greater than the width.
   a. Factor the polynomial to find linear expressions for the height and the width.
   b. Graph the function. Find the $x$-intercepts. What do they represent?
   c. What is a realistic domain for the function?
   d. What is the maximum volume of the CD holder?

**Find the relative maximum, relative minimum, and zeros of each function.**

**47.** $y = 2x^3 - 23x^2 + 78x - 72$   **48.** $y = 8x^3 - 10x^2 - x - 3$   **49.** $y = (x + 1)^4 - 1$

**50. Open-Ended** Write a polynomial function with the following features: it has three distinct zeros; one of the zeros is 1; another zero has a multiplicity of 2.

**51. Writing** Explain how the graph of a polynomial function can help you factor the polynomial.

**For each function, determine the zeros. State the multiplicity of any multiple zeros.**

**52.** $f(x) = x^3 - 36x$    **53.** $y = (x + 1)(x - 4)(3 - 2x)$    **54.** $y = (x + 7)(5x + 2)(x - 6)^2$

---

# Answers

**Practice and Problem-Solving Exercises (continued)**

**39. a.** $\ell = 16 - 2x$; $w = 12 - 2x$; $h = x$
   **b.** $V = x(16 - 2x)(12 - 2x)$
   **c.**

Maximum
X=2.2629672   Y=194.06736

194 in.³, 2.26 in.

**40.** $y = 3x(x - 8)(x - 1)$

**41.** $y = -2x(x + 5)(x - 4)$

**42.** $y = x^2(x + 4)(x - 1)$

**43.** 1 ft increase in each dimension

**44. a.** $V_B = (2x + 1)(x + 3)(x + 4)$
   $V_W = (2x + 1)(x + 1)(x + 2)$
   **b.** $V = 8x^2 + 24x + 10$

**45.** $V = 12x^3 - 27x$

**46. a.** $x(x + 3)(2 - x)$; $h = x + 3$; $w = x$
   **b.**

0, −3, 2; where the volume is zero
   **c.** $0 < x < 2$
   **d.** about 4.06 ft³

**47.** relative maximum: (2.53, 10.51); relative minimum: (5.14, −7.14); $\frac{3}{2}$, 4, 6

**48.** relative maximum: (−0.05, −2.98); relative minimum: (0.88, −6.17); 1.5

**49.** no relative maximum; relative minimum: (−1, −1); −2, 0

**50.** Answers may vary. Sample: $y = x^4 - x^2$

**51.** Answers may vary. Sample: The linear factors can be determined by examining the $x$-intercepts of the graph.

**52.** 0, 6, −6

**53.** −1, 4, $\frac{3}{2}$

**54.** −7, −$\frac{2}{5}$, 6 (multiplicity 2)

**55.** Find a fourth-degree polynomial function with zeros 1, −1, $i$, and −$i$. Write the function in factored form.

**56. a.** Compare the graphs of $y = (x + 1)(x + 2)(x + 3)$ and $y = (x − 1)(x − 2)(x − 3)$. What transformation could you use to describe the change from one graph to the other?

　　**b.** Compare the graphs of $y = (x + 1)(x + 3)(x + 7)$ and $y = (x − 1)(x − 3)(x − 7)$. Does the transformation that you chose in part (a) still hold true? Explain.

　　**c.** Make a Conjecture What transformation could you use to describe the effect of changing the signs of the zeros of a polynomial function?

## Standardized Test Prep

 SAT/ACT

**57.** The three most frequent letters in the English language are E, T, and A. They represent, on average, 30% of all letters. The most frequent letter, E, is 4% more frequent than the second most frequent letter, T. The combined frequency of T and A is 4% greater than the frequency of E. Approximately how many E's can you expect to encounter in a 500-letter paragraph?

　　Ⓐ 49　　　　　Ⓑ 65　　　　　Ⓒ 72　　　　　Ⓓ 88

**58.** Which expression is the factored form of $x^3 + 2x^2 − 5x − 6$?

　　Ⓕ $(x + 1)(x + 1)(x − 6)$　　　　Ⓗ $(x + 2)(2x − 5)(x − 6)$

　　Ⓖ $(x + 3)(x + 1)(x − 2)$　　　　Ⓘ $(x − 3)(x − 1)(x + 2)$

**59.** A ball with a 3 in. radius has volume $V_1$. A second ball has a 9 in. radius and volume $V_2$. Which equation represents the volume of the second ball in terms of the first?

　　Ⓐ $V_2 = 3V_1$　　Ⓑ $V_2 = 27V_1$　　Ⓒ $V_2 = V_1^2$　　Ⓓ $V_2 = 9V_1^2$

Extended Response

**60.** What is the polynomial function, in factored form, whose zeros are −2, 5, and 6, and whose leading coefficient is −2? Graph this function and find any relative minimums or maximums.

## Mixed Review

Write each polynomial in standard form. Then classify it by degree and by number of terms.　　 See Lesson 5-1.

**61.** $x^2 − 1 − 3x^5 + 2x^2$　　**62.** $−2x^3 − 7x^4 + x^3$　　**63.** $6x + x^3 − 6x − 2$

Factor each expression.　　 See Lesson 4-4.

**64.** $x^2 + 5x + 4$　　**65.** $x^2 − 2x − 15$　　**66.** $x^2 − 12x + 36$

Get Ready! To prepare for Lesson 5-3, do Exercises 67–69.

Solve each quadratic equation using any method.　　See Lesson 4-7.

**67.** $x^2 + x − 6 = 0$　　**68.** $2x^2 − 7x + 3 = 0$　　**69.** $4x^2 − 25 = 0$

---

**65.** $(x − 5)(x + 3)$

**66.** $(x − 6)^2$

**67.** $−3, 2$

**68.** $\frac{1}{2}, 3$

**69.** $\pm\frac{5}{2}$

---

**55.** $y = x^4 − 1$

**56. a.** Answers may vary. Sample: translation 4 units to the right

　　**b.** No; the second graph is not the result of a horizontal translation.

　　**c.** Answers may vary. Sample: rotation of 180° about the origin

## Standardized Test Prep

**57.** B

**58.** G

**59.** B

**60.** [4] $y = −2(x + 2)(x − 5)(x − 6)$
$y = −2(x + 2)(x^2 − 11x + 30)$
$y = −2(x^3 − 11x^2 + 30x + 2x^2 − 22x + 60)$
$y = −2(x^3 − 9x^2 + 8x + 60)$
$y = −2x^3 + 18x^2 − 16x − 120$

Use a graphing calculator to find the relative maximum at (5.52, 3.75) and relative minimum at (0.48, −123.75).

[3] appropriate methods, but with one computational error

[2] function found and graphed correctly, but the relative maximum and relative minimum not found

[1] correct function, without work shown

## Mixed Review

**61.** $−3x^5 + 3x^2 − 1$; quintic trinomial

**62.** $−7x^4 − x^3$; quartic binomial

**63.** $x^3 − 2$; cubic binomial

**64.** $(x + 4)(x + 1)$

## Additional Instructional Support

### Algebra 2 Companion

Students can use the **Algebra 2 Companion** worktext (4 pages) as you teach the lesson: Use the Companion to support

- New Vocabulary
- Key Concepts
- Got It for each Problem
- Lesson Check

### ELL Support

**Focus on Language** Ask the students, "What does *relative* mean?" [Samples: dependent upon other conditions for its specific nature, size, etc.; treated in relation to something else; comparative] Ask, "What are some synonyms?" [Samples: conditional; subject; dependent] Ask, "What are the relative maximums and minimum relative to? Why?" [Sample: The points directly around them: among these points, the relative maximum is the greatest *y*-value, and the relative minimum is the least *y*-value.]

## 5 Assess & Remediate

### Lesson Quiz

1. Factor $x^3 + 4x^2 - 5x$.
2. What are the zeros of $y = (x + 1)(x - 3)(x + 2)$?
3. What is a cubic polynomial function in standard form with zeros 4, −1, and 2?
4. What are the zeros of $f(x) = x^3 - 3x^2 + 2x$? What are the multiplicities? How does the graph behave at these zeros?
5. What are the relative maximum and minimum of $f(x) = x^3 - 4x$? Round to the nearest tenth.
6. **Do you UNDERSTAND?** A designer is making a rectangular prism box with maximum volume, with the sum of its length, width, and height 8 in. The length must be 2 times the width. What should each dimension be? Round to the nearest tenth of an inch.

### ANSWERS TO LESSON QUIZ

1. $x(x - 1)(x + 5)$
2. −1, 3, −2
3. $x^3 - 5x^2 + 2x + 8$
4. 0, 1, and 2; each has a multiplicity of 1; the graph crosses the *x*-axis and appears linear at each zero.
5. relative min: (1.2, −3.1); relative max: (−1.2, 3.1)
6. width: 1.8 in.
   length: 3.6 in.
   height: 2.6 in.

### PRESCRIPTION FOR REMEDIATION

Use the student work on the Lesson Quiz to prescribe a differentiated review assignment:

| Points | Differentiated Remediation |
|--------|----------------------------|
| 0–3 | Intervention |
| 4–5 | On-level |
| 6 | Extension |

**PowerAlgebra.com**

### 5 Assess & Remediate

Assign the Lesson Quiz. Appropriate intervention, practice, or enrichment is automatically generated based on student performance.

## Differentiated Remediation

Available in editable format online.

### Intervention

- **Reteaching** (2 pages) Provides reteaching and practice exercises for the key lesson concepts. Use with struggling students or absent students.
- **English Language Learner Support** Helps students develop and reinforce mathematical vocabulary and key concepts.

#### All-in-One Resources/Online
**Reteaching**

**5-2** **Reteaching**
Polynomials, Linear Factors, and Zeros

The Factor Theorem tells you that if you know the zeros of a polynomial function, you can write the polynomial.

**Factor Theorem**
The expression $x - a$ is a factor of a polynomial if and only if the value $a$ is a zero of the related polynomial function.

**Problem**
What is a cubic polynomial function in standard form with zeros 0, 4, and −2?

Each zero ($a$) is part of a linear factor of the polynomial, so you can write each factor as ($x - a$).

$$(x - a_1)(x - a_2)(x - a_3)$$ Set up the cubic polynomial factors.
$$a_1 = 0, a_2 = 4, a_3 = -2$$ Assign the zeros.
$$(x - 0)(x - 4)[x - (-2)]$$ Substitute the zeros into the factors.
$$f(x) = x(x - 4)(x + 2)$$ Write the polynomial function in factored form.
$$f(x) = x(x^2 - 2x - 8)$$ Multiply $(x - 4)(x + 2)$.
$$f(x) = x^3 - 2x^2 - 8x$$ Multiply by $x$ using the Distributive Property.

The polynomial function written in standard form is $f(x) = x^3 - 2x^2 - 8x$.

**Exercises**
Write a polynomial function in standard form with the given zeros.

1. $5, -1, 3$   $f(x) = x^3 - 7x^2 + 7x + 15$
2. $1, 7, -5$   $f(x) = x^3 - 3x^2 - 33x + 35$
3. $-1, 1, -6$   $f(x) = x^3 + 6x^2 - x - 6$
4. $2, -2, -3$   $f(x) = x^3 + 3x^2 - 4x - 12$
5. $2, 1, 3$   $f(x) = x^3 - 6x^2 + 11x - 6$
6. $3, -3, -1$   $f(x) = x^3 + x^2 - 9x + 18$
7. $0, -8, 2$   $f(x) = x^3 + 6x^2 - 16x$
8. $-10, 0, 2$   $f(x) = x^3 + 8x^2 - 20x$
9. $-2, 2, -\frac{3}{2}$   $f(x) = x^3 + \frac{3}{2}x^2 - 4x - 6$
10. $-1, \frac{2}{3}$   $f(x) = x^2 + \frac{1}{3}x - \frac{2}{3}$

#### All-in-One Resources/Online
**English Language Learner Support**

**5-2** **ELL Support**
Polynomials, Linear Factors, and Zeros

There are two sets of note cards below that show how to write a cubic polynomial function with zeros −3, 1, and 4 in standard form. The set on the left explains the thinking. The set on the right shows the steps. Write the thinking and the steps in the correct order.

| Think Cards | Write Cards |
|---|---|
| Multiply (x − 1) and (x − 4). | $x(x^2 - 5x + 4) + 3(x^2 - 5x + 4)$ $= x^3 - 5x^2 + 4x + 3x^2 - 15x + 12$ |
| Use the Distributive Property to multiply (x + 3) and (x² − 5x + 4). | $(x + 3)(x^2 - 5x + 4)$ |
| Simplify. | $x^3 - 2x^2 - 11x + 12$ |
| Write a linear factor for each zero. | $f(x) = (x + 3)(x - 1)(x - 4)$ |

| Think | Write |
|---|---|
| **First,** you should write a linear factor for each zero. | **Step 1** $f(x) = (x + 3)(x - 1)(x - 4)$ |
| **Second,** you should multiply (x − 1) and (x − 4). | **Step 2** $(x + 3)(x^2 - 5x + 4)$ |
| **Then,** you should use the Distributive Property to multiply (x + 3) and (x² − 5x + 4). | **Step 3** $x(x^2 - 5x + 4) + 3(x^2 - 5x + 4) = x^3 - 5x^2 + 4x + 3x^2 - 15x + 12$ |
| **Finally,** you should simplify. | **Step 4** $x^3 - 2x^2 - 11x + 12$ |

# Differentiated Remediation *continued*

Available in editable format online.

## On-Level

- **Practice** (2 pages) Provides extra practice for each lesson. For simpler practice exercises, use the Form K Practice pages found in the All-in-One Teaching Resources and online.

- **Think About a Plan** Helps students develop specific problem-solving skills and strategies by providing scaffolded guiding questions.

- **Standardized Test Prep** Focuses on all major exercises, all major question types, and helps students prepare for the high-stakes assessments.

## Extension

- **Enrichment** Provides students with interesting problems and activities that extend the concepts of the lesson.

- **Activities, Games, and Puzzles** Worksheets that can be used for concepts development, enrichment, and for fun!

---

### Practice and Problem Solving Wkbk/ All-in-One Resources/Online
#### Practice page 1

**5-2 Practice** — *Form G*
Polynomials, Linear Factors, and Zeros

Write each polynomial in factored form. Check by multiplication.

1. $2x^3 + 10x^2 + 12x$  $\;2x(x + 2)(x + 3)$
2. $x^4 - x^3 - 6x^2$  $\;x^2(x + 2)(x - 3)$
3. $-3x^3 + 18x^2 - 27x$  $\;-3x(x - 3)^2$
4. $x^3 - 2x^2 + x$  $\;x(x - 1)^2$
5. $x^3 + 7x^2 + 15x + 9$  $\;(x + 3)^2(x + 1)$
6. $2x^4 + 23x^3 + 60x^2 - 125x - 500$  $\;(x + 4)(2x - 5)(x + 5)^2$

Find the zeros of each function. Then graph the function.

7. $y = (x + 1)(x - 1)(x - 3)$  $\;-1, 1, 3$
8. $y = (x + 2)(x - 3)$  $\;-2, 3$
9. $y = x(x - 2)(x + 5)$  $\;-5, 0, 2$

10. $y = (x - 6)(x + 3)$  $\;6, -3$
11. $y = (x + 4)^2(x + 1)$  $\;-4, -4, -1$
12. $y = (x - 1)(x + 7)$  $\;1, -7$

Write a polynomial function in standard form with the given zeros.

13. $x = -1, 3, 4$  $\;y = x^3 - 6x^2 + 5x + 12$
14. $x = 4, 2, -3, 0$  $\;y = x^4 - 3x^3 - 10x^2 + 24x$
15. $x = -3, 0, 0, 5$  $\;y = x^4 - 2x^3 - 15x^2$
16. $x = 1, 1, 2$  $\;y = x^3 - 4x^2 + 5x - 2$
17. $x = -1, 5, -2$  $\;y = x^3 - 2x^2 - 13x - 10$
18. $x = -6, 0$  $\;y = x^2 + 6x$

Find the zeros of each function. State the multiplicity of multiple zeros.

19. $y = (x - 5)^3$  $\;5,$ multiplicity 3
20. $y = x(x - 8)^2$  $\;0; 8,$ multiplicity 2
21. $y = (x - 2)(x + 7)^3$  $\;2; -7,$ multiplicity 3
22. $y = x^4 - 8x^3 + 16x^2$  $\;0,$ multiplicity 2; 4, multiplicity 2
23. $y = 9x^3 - 81x$  $\;-3, 0, 3$
24. $y = (2x + 5)(x - 3)^2$  $\;-\frac{5}{2}; 3,$ multiplicity 2

---

### Practice and Problem Solving Wkbk/ All-in-One Resources/Online
#### Practice page 2

**5-2 Practice** *(continued)* — *Form G*
Polynomials, Linear Factors, and Zeros

Find the relative maximum and relative minimum of the graph of each function.

25. $f(x) = x^3 - 7x^2 + 10x$
rel. max.: 4.06; rel. min.: −8.21
26. $f(x) = x^3 - x^2 - 9x + 9$
rel. max.: 16.9; rel. min.: −5.05
27. $f(x) = x^4 + x^3 - 3x^2 - 5x - 2$
rel. min.: about −8.54
28. $f(x) = x^2 - 6x + 9$
rel. min.: 0

29. A rectangular box has a square base. The combined length of a side of the square base, and the height is 20 in. Let $x$ be the length of a side of the base of the box.
a. Write a polynomial in factored form modeling the volume $V$ of the box.  $\;V = x^2(20 - x)$
b. What is the maximum possible volume of the box?  about 1185 in.$^3$

30. **Reasoning** A polynomial function has a zero at $x = -2a$. Find one of its factors.  $\;(x + 2a)$

31. The side of a cube measures $3x + 2$ units long. Express the volume of the cube as a polynomial.  $\;27x^3 + 54x^2 + 36x + 8$

32. **Writing** The volume of a box is $x^3 - 3x^2 + 3x - 1$ cubic units. Explain how to find the length of a side if the box is a cube.  The factors of this polynomial are $(x - 1)(x - 1)(x - 1)$. Because all three factors are equal, and the sides of the box are equal, the side length would be $x - 1$.

33. You have a block of wood that you want to use to make a sculpture. The block is currently $3x$ units wide, $4x$ units high, and $5x$ units deep. You need to remove 1 unit from each dimension before you can begin your sculpture.
a. What is the original volume of the block?  $60x^3$ cubic units
b. What is the new volume of the block?  $60x^3 - 47x^2 + 12x - 1$ cubic units
c. What is the volume of the wood that you remove?  $47x^2 - 12x + 1$ cubic units

34. What are the zeros and the multiplicity of each zero for the polynomial function $x^4 - 2x^2 + 1$? 1 of multiplicity 2, −1 of multiplicity 2

35. **Error Analysis** On your homework, you wrote that the polynomial function from the given zeros $x = 3, 0, -9, 1$ is $y = x^4 + 5x^3 - 33x^2 + 27x$. Your friend wrote that the polynomial function is $y = x^3 + 5x^2 - 33x + 27$. Who is correct? What mistake was made?  You are correct. Your friend did not include the factor with the zero $x = 0$ from the polynomial. It should include the factor $(x - 0)$.

---

### All-in-One Resources/Online
#### Enrichment

**5-2 Enrichment**
Polynomials, Linear Factors, and Zeros

**Fast Factorization of Monic Trinomials**

Thus far, you have factored trinomials primarily by trial and error. This method can be quite slow, especially if the constant term of a quadratic trinomial is, for example, 72, since there are many different ways to factor this number: 1 and 72, 2 and 36, 3 and 24, 4 and 18, 6 and 12, 8 and 9. With larger numbers, the trial-and-error method becomes time-consuming.

A polynomial is called monic if the coefficient of the term of highest degree is 1. Monic quadratic trinomials can be factored quite rapidly using a combination of difference of squares and equation solving.

Suppose that we wish to factor the monic quadratic trinomial $x^2 + bx + c$. Assume there are numbers $r$ and $s$ such that

$$x^2 + bx + c = [(x + r) + s][(x + r) - s]$$
$$= (x + r)^2 - s^2$$
$$= x^2 + 2rx + r^2 - s^2$$

Subtracting $x^2$ from both sides results in

$$bx + c = 2rx + r^2 - s^2$$

Therefore, $b = 2r$ and $c = r^2 - s^2$.

Solve for $r$ and $s$ in terms of $b$ and $c$.

$$r = \frac{b}{2} \qquad s = \sqrt{\left(\frac{b}{2}\right)^2 - c}$$

The following example shows how this technique works.

Factor: $x^2 - 6x - 72$ $\quad b = -6, c = -72$
$$r = \frac{b}{2} = -3 \qquad s = \sqrt{9 - (-72)}$$
$$= \sqrt{81} = 9$$
So $x^2 - 6x - 72 = [(x - 3) + 9][(x - 3) - 9]$
$$= (x + 6)(x - 12)$$

Verify that this is the correct factorization.
$(x + 6)(x - 12) = x^2 - 12x + 6x - 72 = x^2 - 6x - 72$

Use this technique for each of the following.

1. $x^2 - 60x + 864$  $\;(x - 24)(x - 36)$
2. $x^2 - 25x + 144$  $\;(x - 9)(x - 16)$
3. $x^2 - 28x - 128$  $\;(x - 32)(x + 4)$
4. $x^2 - 44x - 540$  $\;(x - 54)(x + 10)$
5. $x^2 + 81x + 990$  $\;(x + 15)(x + 66)$
6. $x^2 - 50x - 576$  $\;(x - 32)(x - 18)$
7. $x^2 + 17x - 168$  $\;(x - 7)(x + 24)$
8. $x^2 - 17x - 630$  $\;(x - 35)(x + 18)$

---

### Practice and Problem Solving Wkbk/ All-in-One Resources/Online
#### Think About a Plan

**5-2 Think About a Plan**
Polynomials, Linear Factors, and Zeros

**Measurement** The volume in cubic feet of a CD holder can be expressed as $V(x) = -x^3 - x^2 + 6x$, or, when factored, as the product of its three dimensions. The depth is expressed as $2 - x$. Assume that the height is greater than the width.
a. Factor the polynomial to find linear expressions for the height and the width.
b. Graph the function. Find the $x$-intercepts. What do they represent?
c. What is a realistic domain for the function?
d. What is the maximum volume of the CD holder?

1. What do you know about the factors of the polynomial?
One of the factors is $(2 - x)$.

2. Factor the polynomial.
$V(x) = -x^3 - x^2 + 6x = \boxed{2 - x}\left(\boxed{x}\right)\left(\boxed{x + 3}\right)$

3. What are the height and width of the CD holder? How do you know which factor is the height and which factor is the width?
height $x + 3$; width: $x$; the height is greater than the width, and $x + 3$ is greater than $x$.

4. Graph the function on a graphing calculator. How can you find the $x$-intercepts?
Set the factors equal to zero and solve or use the zero feature.

5. What are the $x$-intercepts? What do they represent?
−3, 0, 2; values of $x$ that result in a volume of 0

6. What are the limits of each of the factors? What is a realistic domain for the function? Explain.
Each dimension of the CD holder must be greater than 0, so each factor should be greater than 0. So $2 - x > 0$, $x > 0$, and $x + 3 > 0$. The solution of all three inequalities is $0 < x < 2$.

7. How can you find the maximum volume of the CD holder?
Find the maximum value of the function in the domain $0 < x < 2$. Use the maximum feature of the CALC menu with LeftBound = 0 and RightBound = 2.

8. What is the maximum volume of the CD holder?  about 4.06 ft$^3$

---

### Practice and Problem Solving Wkbk/ All-in-One Resources/Online
#### Standardized Test Prep

**5-2 Standardized Test Prep**
Polynomials, Linear Factors, and Zeros

**Multiple Choice**

For Exercises 1–6, choose the correct letter.

1. What are the zeros of the polynomial function $y = (x - 3)(2x + 1)(x - 1)$? C
A. $\frac{1}{2}, 1, 3$
B. $-1, 1, 3$
C. $-\frac{1}{2}, 1, 3$
D. $-3, \frac{1}{2}, -1$

2. What is the factored form of $2x^3 + 5x^2 - 12x$? H
F. $(x + 4)(2x - 3)$
G. $x(x + 4)(2x - 3)$
H. $(x - 4)(2x + 3)$
I. $x(x - 4)(2x + 3)$

3. Which is the cubic polynomial in standard form with roots 3, −6, and 0? D
A. $x^2 - 3x - 18$
B. $x^2 + 3x - 18$
C. $x^3 - 3x^2 - 18x$
D. $x^3 + 3x^2 - 18x$

4. What is the relative minimum and relative maximum of $f(x) = 6x^3 - 5x + 12$? I
F. min 0, max 0
G. min −5, max 6
H. min −1.5, max 12
I. min 10.2, max 13.8

5. What is the multiplicity of the zero of the polynomial function $f(x) = (x + 5)^4$? A
A. 4
B. 5
C. 20
D. 625

6. For the polynomial function $y = (x - 2)^3$, which behavior will the graph exhibit at the $x$-intercept? H
F. linear
G. quadratic
H. cubic
I. quartic

**Short Response**

7. A rectangular box is 24 in. long, 12 in. wide, and 18 in. high. If each dimension is increased by $x$ in., what is the polynomial function in standard form that models the volume $V$ of the box? Show your work.
[2] $V = x^3 + 54x^2 + 936x + 5184$ in.$^3$
[1] correct process with one computational error OR correct polynomial without work shown
[0] incorrect answer and no work shown OR no answer given

---

### Online Teacher Resource Center
#### Activities, Games, and Puzzles

**5-2 Puzzle: Made in the Shade**
Polynomials, Linear Factors, and Zeros

Find the zeros of each polynomial below. For each corresponding row, shade in each number that is a zero. The illustration made from shading the squares suggests the answer to the riddle below.

A. $P(x) = x(x^2 - 1)$
$\;-1, 0, 1$
B. $P(x) = x(x + 2)(x + 1)(x^2 + 2x - 3)$
$\;-3, -2, -1, 0, 1$
C. $P(x) = x(x + 4)(x + 3)(x + 1)(x - 1)$
$\;-4, -3, -1, 0, 1$
D. $P(x) = x(x^2 - 25)(x^2 + 4x + 3)$
$\;-5, -3, -1, 0, 5$
E. $P(x) = (x^2 + x - 20)(x + 2)(x^2 + 4x + 3)$
$\;-5, -3, -2, -1, 4$
F. $P(x) = (x^2 - 9)(x^2 - 25)$
$\;-5, -3, 3, 5$
G. $P(x) = (x^2 + 9x + 20)(x^2 - 5x + 6)(x - 5)$
$\;-5, -4, 2, 3, 5$
H. $P(x) = (x^2 - 9)(x - 4)(x^2 - 9x + 20)$
$\;2, 3, 4, 5$
I. $P(x) = x^2 - 6x + 9$
$\;3$
J. $P(x) = (x^2 - 4x + 4)(x^2 + 4x + 4)$
$\;2$
K. $P(x) = x(x^2 - 2x + 1)(x - 2)$
$\;0, 1, 2$

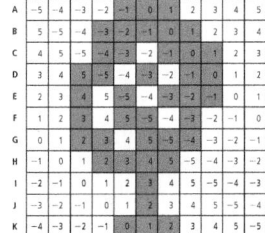

**Riddle:** This grows above the ground, but the solutions to the polynomials above lie beneath. And as it grows, it provides shade to those underneath. What is it?  a tree

---

# 1 Interactive Learning

## Solve It!

**PURPOSE** To model a polynomial with tiles
**PROCESS** Students may arrange the pieces so that the *x*-by-*x* squares are arranged vertically or horizontally.

### FACILITATE

**Q** Where do the *x*-by-1 pieces have to be arranged in relationship to the *x*-by-*x* pieces? **[The sides with length *x* have to touch.]**

**Q** Where do the 1-by-1 pieces have to be arranged? **[They must be arranged so that they complete the rectangle.]**

**Q** Why can the 1-by-1 squares not be arranged in a 12-by-1 row? **[You do not have a 12 unit piece to line up with the side of the 12-by-1 row to form a rectangle.]**

**Q** What polynomial do the pieces represent? Factor it. **[$2x^2 + 11x + 12$; $(2x + 3)(x + 4)$]**

**ANSWER** See Solve It in Answers on next page.
**CONNECT THE MATH** The Solve It is a visual model of factoring, where students use tiles representing each part of the polynomial to create a rectangle. Students will use factoring in the lesson to solve polynomial equations.

# 2 Guided Instruction

## Problem 1

**Q** When should you use the quadratic formula to solve a quadratic polynomial equation? **[when the discriminant is less than zero or when the polynomial does not factor]**

---

## 5-3 Solving Polynomial Equations

**Objectives** To solve polynomial equations by factoring
To solve polynomial equations by graphing

**Getting Ready!**

Can you arrange all of these pieces to make a rectangle with no pieces overlapping and no gaps? If you can, make a sketch. If you cannot, explain why.

I count 2 pieces with area $x^2$, 11 with area $x$, and 12 with area 1. The rectangle would have the same total area.

**Lesson Vocabulary**
- sum of cubes
- difference of cubes

Factoring a polynomial like $ax^2 + bx + c$ can help you solve a polynomial equation like $ax^2 + bx + c = 0$.

**Essential Understanding** If $(x - a)$ is a factor of a polynomial, then the polynomial has value 0 when $x = a$. If $a$ is a real number, then the graph of the polynomial has $(a, 0)$ as an *x*-intercept.

To solve a polynomial equation by factoring:

**1.** Write the equation in the form $P(x) = 0$ for some polynomial function *P*.
**2.** Factor $P(x)$. Use the Zero Product Property to find the roots.

### Problem 1 Solving Polynomial Equations Using Factors

**What are the real or imaginary solutions of each polynomial equation?**

**A** $2x^3 - 5x^2 = 3x$

**Plan**
What does it mean if *x* is a common factor of every term in $P(x)$? You can write $P(x)$ as $xQ(x)$, so 0 will be a solution of $P(x) = 0$.

| | |
|---|---|
| $2x^3 - 5x^2 - 3x = 0$ | Rewrite in the form $P(x) = 0$. |
| $x(2x^2 - 5x - 3) = 0$ | Factor out the GCF, *x*. |
| $x(2x + 1)(x - 3) = 0$ | Factor $2x^2 - 5x - 3$. |
| $x = 0$  or  $2x + 1 = 0$  or  $x - 3 = 0$ | Zero Product Property |
| $x = 0$      $x = -\frac{1}{2}$      $x = 3$ | Solve each equation for *x*. |

The solutions are $0$, $-\frac{1}{2}$, and $3$.

---

## 5-3 Preparing to Teach

**BIG ideas** Equivalence
Function
Solving Equations and Inequalities

**UbD**

### ESSENTIAL UNDERSTANDINGS

- If $(x - a)$ is a factor of a polynomial, then the polynomial has value 0 when $x = a$. If $a$ is a real number, then the graph of the polynomial has $(a, 0)$ as an *x*-intercept.
- Knowing the zeros of a polynomial function gives information about its graph.
- A polynomial of degree *n* has *n* linear factors. The graph of the related function crosses the *x*-axis an even or odd number of times depending on whether *n* is even or odd.

### Math Background

The real solutions to a polynomial equation give the *x*-intercepts of the graph of the polynomial function. Students previously found *x*-intercepts when they solved even the simplest one-step equation. You can demonstrate this with the following steps:

- start with a simple equation, such as $y = x + 4$;
- set the equation equal to 0: $x + 4 = 0$;
- solve for *x*: $x = -4$;
- find the *x*-intercept of the graph of the related function, $f(x) = x + 4$: $(-4, 0)$.
- Note that this is the same as $(a, 0)$. If you substitute *a* into $f(x)$ and evaluate the expression, the result would be 0.

This activity connects the advanced solving of polynomial equations of a greater degree to solving equations of degree one. It also connects the techniques that students use to solve various kinds of equations.

### Support Student Learning

Use the **Algebra 2 Companion** to engage and support students during instruction. See Lesson Resources at the end of this lesson for details.

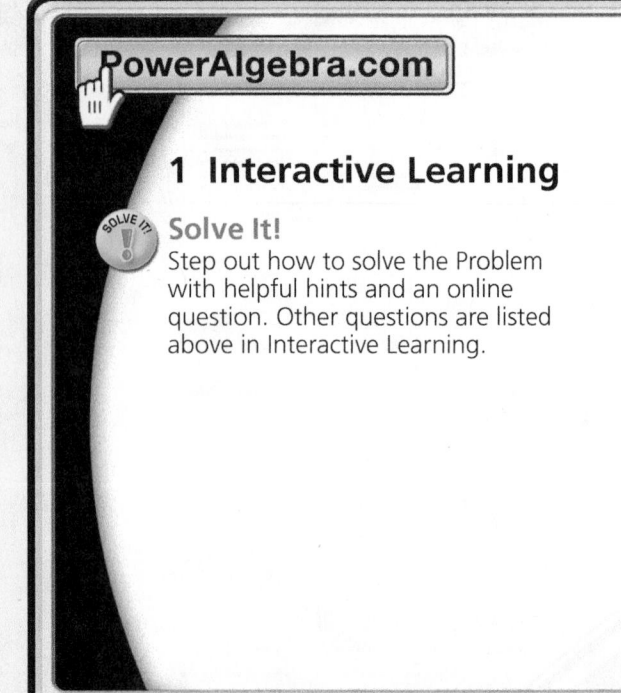

**PowerAlgebra.com**

## 1 Interactive Learning

### Solve It!

Step out how to solve the Problem with helpful hints and an online question. Other questions are listed above in Interactive Learning.

**B** $3x^4 + 12x^2 = 6x^3$

**Think**
How will the solution be similar to the solution of the equation in part (a)?
Both equations have 0 as a solution, but here it will have a multiplicity of 2.

| | |
|---|---|
| $3x^4 - 6x^3 + 12x^2 = 0$ | Rewrite in the form $P(x) = 0$. |
| $x^4 - 2x^3 + 4x^2 = 0$ | Multiply by $\frac{1}{3}$ to simplify. |
| $x^2(x^2 - 2x + 4) = 0$ | Factor out the GCF, $x^2$. |
| $x^2 = 0$ or $x^2 - 2x + 4 = 0$ | Zero Product Property |

$$x = 0 \quad \begin{vmatrix} x = \dfrac{-(-2) \pm \sqrt{(-2)^2 - 4(1)(4)}}{2(1)} \\[2mm] x = \dfrac{2 \pm \sqrt{-12}}{2} = \dfrac{2 \pm 2i\sqrt{3}}{2} = 1 \pm i\sqrt{3} \end{vmatrix}$$

> Use the Quadratic Formula to solve $x^2 - 2x + 4 = 0$. Substitute $a = 1$, $b = -2$, and $c = 4$.

The solutions are 0, $1 + i\sqrt{3}$, and $1 - i\sqrt{3}$.

**Got It?** **1.** What are the real or imaginary solutions of each equation?
**a.** $(x^2 - 1)(x^2 + 4) = 0$  **b.** $x^5 + 4x^3 = 5x^4 - 2x^3$

**Got It?**      **ERROR PREVENTION**
In 1a, watch for students who attempt to factor $x^2 + 4$ as if it were $x^2 - 4$.

**Q** In 1b, in what order do you need to arrange the terms of the polynomial equation? **[Put the polynomial equation in terms of descending powers of $x$.]**

**Take Note**
It may be helpful to review each type of factoring listed in the Take Note.

Have students make their own examples of each technique, such as the following examples:

Factoring out the GCF
$6x^3 + 15x^2 + 9x = 3x(2x^2 + 5x + 3)$

Quadratic Trinomials
$8x^2 + 10x - 3 = (4x - 1)(2x + 3)$

Perfect Square Trinomials
$4x^2 + 12x + 9 = (2x + 3)^2$

Difference of Squares
$x^2 - 36 = (x + 6)(x - 6)$

Factoring by Grouping
$2x^3 - 2x^2 + 3x - 3 = 2x^2(x - 1) + 3(x - 1)$
$\qquad\qquad\qquad\quad = (2x^2 + 3)(x - 1)$

Sum or Difference of Cubes
$x^3 - 27 = (x - 3)(x^2 + 3x + 9)$

---

**Concept Summary**    **Polynomial Factoring Techniques**

| Techniques | Examples |
|---|---|
| **Factoring out the GCF** <br> Factor out the greatest common factor of all the terms. | $15x^4 - 20x^3 + 35x^2$ <br> $= 5x^2(3x^2 - 4x + 7)$ |
| **Quadratic Trinomials** <br> For $ax^2 + bx + c$, find factors with product $ac$ and sum $b$. | $6x^2 + 11x - 10$ <br> $= (3x - 2)(2x + 5)$ |
| **Perfect Square Trinomials** <br> $a^2 + 2ab + b^2 = (a + b)^2$ <br> $a^2 - 2ab + b^2 = (a - b)^2$ | $x^2 + 10x + 25 = (x + 5)^2$ <br> $x^2 - 10x + 25 = (x - 5)^2$ |
| **Difference of Squares** <br> $a^2 - b^2 = (a + b)(a - b)$ | $4x^2 - 15 = (2x + \sqrt{15})(2x - \sqrt{15})$ |
| **Factoring by Grouping** <br> $ax + ay + bx + by$ <br> $= a(x + y) + b(x + y)$ <br> $= (a + b)(x + y)$ | $x^3 + 2x^2 - 3x - 6$ <br> $= x^2(x + 2) + (-3)(x + 2)$ <br> $= (x^2 - 3)(x + 2)$ |
| **Sum or Difference of Cubes** <br> $a^3 + b^3 = (a + b)(a^2 - ab + b^2)$ <br> $a^3 - b^3 = (a - b)(a^2 + ab + b^2)$ | $8x^3 + 1 = (2x + 1)(4x^2 - 2x + 1)$ <br> $8x^3 - 1 = (2x - 1)(4x^2 + 2x + 1)$ |

---

## 2 Guided Instruction

Each Problem is worked out and supported online.

**Problem 1**
Solving Polynomial Equations Using Factors
*Animated*

**Problem 2**
Solving Polynomial Equations by Factoring
*Animated*

**Problem 3**
Finding Real Roots by Graphing

**Problem 4**
Modeling a Problem Situation
*Animated*

**Support in Algebra 2 Companion**
• Vocabulary
• Key Concepts
• Got It?

## Answers

**Solve It!**
yes;

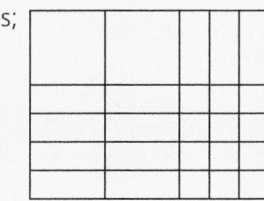

**Got It?**
**1. a.** $\pm 1$, $\pm 2i$
     **b.** 0, 2, 3

## Here's Why It Works

Review the most common perfect cubes with students:

$2^3 = 8$
$3^3 = 27$
$4^3 = 64$
$5^3 = 125$
$6^3 = 216$

For $a^3 - b^3$, the steps are as follows.

$a^3 - b^3 = a^3 - a^2b + a^2b - ab^2 + ab^2 - b^3$
$\quad\quad\quad = a^2(a - b) + ab(a - b) + b^2(a - b)$
$\quad\quad\quad = (a - b)(a^2 + ab + b^2)$

> **Q** How is the first step equivalent to adding zero?
> **[The expressions $-a^2b$ and $a^2b$ cancel each other out, as do the expressions $-ab^2$ and $ab^2$.]**

## Problem 2

> **Q** Will a graph help you check all the solutions of a polynomial equation? Explain. **[Answers may vary. Sample: Only if all the solutions are real, since the imaginary solutions will not show on a graph.]**
>
> **Q** How can you check the imaginary solutions? **[Substitute each solution for $x$ in the expression and see if it simplifies to zero.]**

## Got It?                    ERROR PREVENTION

> **Q** In 2a, if you simply take the fourth root of 16, will you get all of the solutions? Explain. **[No; answers may vary. Sample: You will miss the solution $-2$ and the imaginary solutions $2i$ and $-2i$.]**

---

The sum and difference of cubes is a new factoring technique.

**Here's Why It Works** Factoring $a^3 + b^3 = (a + b)(a^2 - ab + b^2)$:

$a^3 + b^3 = a^3 + a^2b - a^2b - ab^2 + ab^2 + b^3$    Add 0.
$\quad\quad\quad = a^2(a + b) - ab(a + b) + b^2(a + b)$    Factor out $a^2$, $-ab$, and $b^2$.
$\quad\quad\quad = (a + b)(a^2 - ab + b^2)$    Factor out $(a + b)$.

For $a^3 - b^3 = (a - b)(a^2 + ab + b^2)$, you can follow steps similar to those above, or you can factor $a^3 - b^3$ as the sum of cubes $a^3 + (-b)^3$.

**Problem 2** Solving Polynomial Equations by Factoring

**What are the real or imaginary solutions of each polynomial equation?**

**A** $x^4 - 3x^2 = 4$

$\quad\quad x^4 - 3x^2 - 4 = 0$    Rewrite in the form $P(x) = 0$.
$\quad\quad\quad a^2 - 3a - 4 = 0$    Let $a = x^2$.
$\quad\quad\quad (a - 4)(a + 1) = 0$    Factor.
$\quad\quad (x^2 - 4)(x^2 + 1) = 0$    Replace $a$ with $x^2$.
$(x + 2)(x - 2)(x^2 + 1) = 0$    Factor $x^2 - 4$ as a difference of squares.

It follows from the Zero Product Property that $x = 2$, $x = -2$, or $x^2 = -1$. Solving $x^2 = -1$ yields two imaginary roots: $x = i$ or $x = -i$.

**Check** Graph the related function $y = x^4 - 3x^2 - 4$.

The graph shows zeros at $x = 2$ and $x = -2$. It also shows three turning points. This means that there are imaginary roots, which do not appear on the graph.

**B** $x^3 = 1$

$\quad\quad x^3 - 1 = 0$    Rewrite in the form $P(x) = 0$.
$(x - 1)(x^2 + x + 1) = 0$    Factor the difference of cubes.

It follows from the Zero Product Property that $x = 1$ or $x^2 + x + 1 = 0$. Use the Quadratic Formula to solve $x^2 + x + 1 = 0$.

$$x = \frac{-(1) \pm \sqrt{(1)^2 - 4(1)(1)}}{2(1)} = \frac{-1 \pm \sqrt{-3}}{2} = \frac{-1 \pm i\sqrt{3}}{2}$$

The three solutions of $x^3 = 1$ are $1$, $-\frac{1}{2} + i\frac{\sqrt{3}}{2}$, and $-\frac{1}{2} - i\frac{\sqrt{3}}{2}$.

**Got It?** **2.** What are the real or imaginary solutions of each polynomial equation?

   **a.** $x^4 = 16$      **b.** $x^3 = 8x - 2x^2$      **c.** $x(x^2 + 8) = 8(x + 1)$

**Think**

How can you write the polynomial in quadratic form?
Write in terms of $x^2$:
$(x^2)^2 - 3(x^2) - 4 = 0$,
which shows the factorable quadratic form $a^2 - 3a - 4 = 0$.

---

# Additional Problems

**1.** What are the real or imaginary solutions of $4x^3 - 6x^2 = 4x$?

   **ANSWERS** $-\frac{1}{2}$, 0, 2

**2.** What are the real or imaginary solutions of the equation $2x^3 = -54$?

   **ANSWER** $-3$; $\frac{3 \pm i\sqrt{3}}{2}$

**3.** What are the real solutions of $2x^3 + 5 = 3x^2 - 2x$?

   **ANSWER** $-0.84$

**4.** What are three consecutive even integers whose product is 4 times their sum?

   **ANSWERS** 2, 4, 6 or $-6, -4, -2$

While factoring is an effective way to solve a polynomial equation, you can also find the real roots quickly by using a graphing calculator.

Plan

**Why is it helpful to graph $Y_1$ and $Y_2$?**
The values of $x$ for which $Y_1 = Y_2$ are the solutions of the original equation.

**Problem 3** Finding Real Roots by Graphing

**What are the real solutions of the equation $x^3 + 5 = 4x^2 + x$?**

**Method 1** Graph $Y_1 = x^3 + 5$ and $Y_2 = 4x^2 + x$. Use the **INTERSECT** feature to find the $x$ values of the points of intersection.

These two intersection points are visible in the standard viewing window.

You must adjust the window to obtain this point of intersection.

Intersection X=-1.093763 Y=3.6915105

Intersection X=1.1629619 Y=6.572883

Intersection X=3.9308016 Y=65.735606

Approximate solutions are $x = -1.09$, $x = 1.16$, and $x = 3.93$.

**Method 2** Rewrite the equation as $x^3 - 4x^2 - x + 5 = 0$. Graph the related function $y = x^3 - 4x^2 - x + 5$. Use the **ZERO** feature.

Zero X=-1.093763 Y=0

Zero X=1.1629619 Y=0

Zero X=3.9308016 Y=0

The solutions are the same as identified using Method 1.

Approximate solutions are $x = -1.09$, $x = 1.16$, and $x = 3.93$.

**Check** Verify the solutions by showing that they satisfy the original equation. Show values of $y_1 = x^3 + 5$ and $y_2 = 4x^2 + x$ in a table.

The solution checks.

| X | Y₁ | Y₂ |
|---|-----|-----|
| 1.09 | 3.69 | 3.69 |
| 1.16 | 6.57 | 6.57 |
| 3.93 | 65.7 | 65.7 |

X=

 **Got It?** **3. a.** What are the real solutions of the equation $x^3 + x^2 = x - 1$?
**b. Reasoning** In Problem 3, which method seems to be an easier and more reliable way to find the solutions of an equation? Explain.

---

**Problem 3**

**Q** Why might you miss some real solutions when you use a calculator? [**Some solutions may not be visible in the standard viewing window.**]

**Q** Which value is the solution, the $x$ or the $y$? [**The $x$-value is always the solution.**]

**Q** How does Method 1 work? [**It works like solving a system of equations.**]

**Got It?**

**Q** Compare and contrast the two methods. Which do you prefer? [**Answers may vary. Sample: For the first method, you do not need to write the equation in standard form, just graph each side of the equation as a separate function and find the intersections. For the second method, you do have to rewrite the equation, but then you can find the zeros as you normally would, and the solutions all lie along the $x$-axis, which simplifies the choice of Ymin and Ymax. Both methods use calculator features.**]

---

# Answers

**2. a.** $\pm 2, \pm 2i$

  **b.** $0, -4, 2$

  **c.** $2, -1 \pm i\sqrt{3}$

**3. a.** $-1.84$

  **b.** The second method seems to be a more reliable way to find the solutions because you do not risk missing a pt. of intersection.

## Problem 4

**Q** Could you let another child's age be $x$? Explain. **[Yes, if you changed the expressions that represented the other ages.]**

**Q** When you know the value of $x$, how do you find the other ages? **[Go back to the expressions for the other children's ages and substitute for $x$ in the expressions.]**

### Got It?    ERROR PREVENTION

**Q** What are consecutive integers? **[integers whose difference is one]**

# 3 Lesson Check

## Do you know HOW?

• For Exercises 1–6, if students forget how to factor the polynomials, have them look up and list the different methods they have used and identify which method works best for each polynomial.

## Do you UNDERSTAND?

• Before trying Exercise 7, have students write the definition of sum of cubes, difference of cubes, and difference of squares in their own words.

## Close

**Q** What is the advantage of solving polynomial equations algebraically rather than by using a graph? **[Solving algebraically finds all the solutions, while solving with a graph finds only the real solutions. Solving algebraically provides exact answers, while solving with a graph may only give a decimal approximation.]**

---

**Problem 4** Modeling a Problem Situation

Close friends Stacy, Una, and Amir were all born on July 4. Stacy is one year younger than Una. Una is two years younger than Amir. On July 4, 2010, the product of their ages was 2300 more than the sum of their ages. How old was each friend on that day?

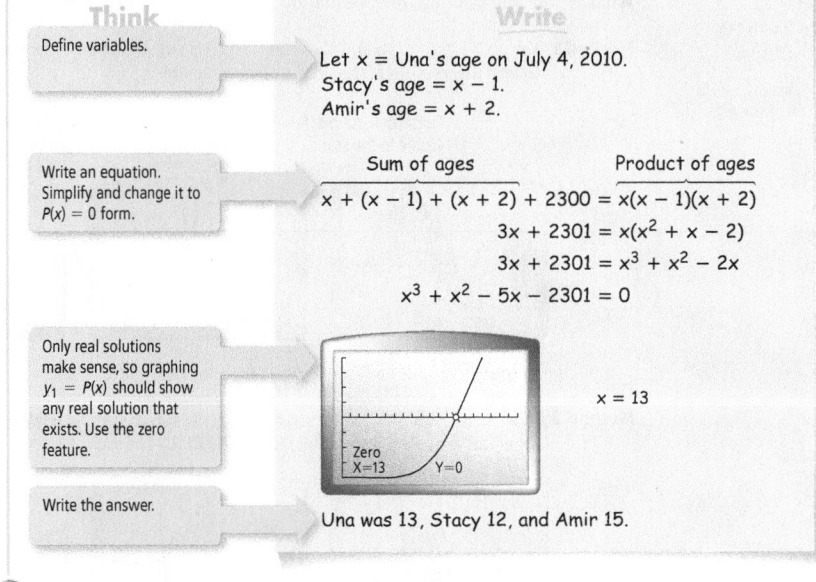

**Think**

Define variables.

Write an equation. Simplify and change it to $P(x) = 0$ form.

Only real solutions make sense, so graphing $y_1 = P(x)$ should show any real solution that exists. Use the zero feature.

Write the answer.

**Write**

Let $x =$ Una's age on July 4, 2010.
Stacy's age $= x - 1$.
Amir's age $= x + 2$.

$$\overbrace{x + (x - 1) + (x + 2)}^{\text{Sum of ages}} + 2300 = \overbrace{x(x - 1)(x + 2)}^{\text{Product of ages}}$$
$$3x + 2301 = x(x^2 + x - 2)$$
$$3x + 2301 = x^3 + x^2 - 2x$$
$$x^3 + x^2 - 5x - 2301 = 0$$

$x = 13$

Zero
X=13    Y=0

Una was 13, Stacy 12, and Amir 15.

**Got It?** **4.** What are three consecutive integers whose product is 480 more than their sum?

### Lesson Check

#### Do you know HOW?

Factor each polynomial.

**1.** $x^2 - 3x - 18$      **2.** $x^3 - 27$

**3.** $x^3 + 3x^2 + 4x + 12$      **4.** $x^4 - 2x^2 - 8$

Solve each equation by factoring.

**5.** $2x^2 + 7x - 4 = 0$

**6.** $2x^3 + 2x^2 - 4x = 0$

#### Do you UNDERSTAND?

**7. Vocabulary** Identify each expression as a sum of cubes, difference of cubes, or difference of squares.
  **a.** $x^2 - 64$      **b.** $x^3 + 8$
  **c.** $x^3 - 125$      **d.** $x^2 - 81$

**8. Reasoning** Which method of solving polynomial equations will not identify the imaginary roots? Explain.

**9. Reasoning** Show two different ways to find the real roots of the polynomial equation $0 = x^6 - x^2$. Show your steps.

---

### PowerAlgebra.com

## 3 Lesson Check

For a digital lesson check, use the Got It questions.

**Support in Algebra 2 Companion**
• Lesson Check

## 4 Practice

Assign homework to individual students or to an entire class.

# Answers

## Got It? (continued)

**4.** 7, 8, 9

## Lesson Check

**1.** $(x - 6)(x + 3)$

**2.** $(x - 3)(x^2 + 3x + 9)$

**3.** $(x^2 + 4)(x + 3)$

**4.** $(x - 2)(x + 2)(x^2 + 2)$

**5.** $-4, \frac{1}{2}$      **6.** $-2, 0, 1$

**7. a.** difference of squares
   **b.** sum of cubes
   **c.** difference of cubes
   **d.** difference of squares

**8.** Graphing; imaginary numbers don't exist on the $x$-axis.

**9.** Method 1: Graph $y = x^6 - x^2$. Find the zeros for the real solutions.

Method 2: Factor and solve $x$ for $x^6 - x^2 = 0$.
$$x^2(x^4 - 1) = x^2(x^2 - 1)(x^2 + 1)$$
$$= x^2(x - 1)(x + 1)(x^2 + 1)$$
$$x = 0, \pm 1$$

## Practice and Problem-Solving Exercises

**A  Practice**  Find the real or imaginary solutions of each equation by factoring.  ◆ **See Problems 1 and 2.**

**10.** $x^3 + 64 = 0$

**11.** $x^3 - 1000 = 0$

**12.** $125x^3 - 27 = 0$

**13.** $64x^3 - 1 = 0$

**14.** $x^3 + 2x^2 + 5x + 10 = 0$

**15.** $6x^2 + 13x - 5 = 0$

**16.** $0 = x^3 - 27$

**17.** $0 = x^3 - 64$

**18.** $8x^3 = 1$

**19.** $64x^3 = -8$

**20.** $x^4 - 10x^2 = -9$

**21.** $x^4 - 8x^2 = -16$

**22.** $x^4 - 12x^2 = 64$

**23.** $x^4 + 7x^2 = 18$

**24.** $x^4 + 4x^2 = 12$

Find the real solutions of each equation by graphing.  ◆ **See Problem 3.**

**25.** $x^3 - 4x^2 - 7x = -10$

**26.** $3x^3 - 6x^2 - 9x = 0$

**27.** $4x^3 - 8x^2 + 4x = 0$

**28.** $6x^2 = 48x$

**29.** $x^3 + 3x^2 + 2x = 0$

**30.** $2x^3 + 5x^2 = 7x$

**31.** $4x^3 = 4x^2 + 3x$

**32.** $2x^4 - 5x^3 - 3x^2 = 0$

**33.** $x^2 - 8x + 7 = 0$

**34.** $x^4 - 4x^3 - x^2 + 16x = 12$

**35.** $x^3 - x^2 - 16x = 20$

**36.** $3x^3 + 12x^2 - 3x = 12$

 **Graphing Calculator**  Write an equation to model each situation. Then solve each equation by graphing.  ◆ **See Problem 4.**

**37.** The Johnson twins were born two years after their older sister. This year, the product of the three siblings ages is exactly 4558 more than the sum of their ages. How old are the twins?

**38.** The product of three consecutive integers is 210. What are the numbers?

**B  Apply**  Solve each equation.

**39.** $x^3 + 13x = 10x^2$

**40.** $x^3 - 6x^2 + 6x = 0$

**41.** $12x^3 = 60x^2 + 75x$

**42.** $125x^3 + 216 = 0$

**43.** $81x^3 - 192 = 0$

**44.** $x^4 - 64 = 0$

**45.** $-2x^4 - 100 = 0$

**46.** $27 = -x^4 - 12x^2$

**47.** $x^5 - 5x^3 + 4x = 0$

**48.** $5x^3 = 5x^2 + 12x$

**49.** $x^3 + x^2 + x + 1 = 0$

**50.** $x^3 + 1 = x^2 + x$

**51. Think About a Plan**  The width of a plastic storage box is 1 ft longer than the height. The length is 4 ft longer than the height. The volume is 36 ft³. What are the dimensions of the box?
- What is the formula for the volume of a rectangular prism?
- What variable expressions represent the length, height, and width?
- What equation represents the volume of the plastic storage box?

**52. Error Analysis**  A student claims that 1, 2, 3, and 4 are the zeros of a cubic polynomial function. Explain why the student is mistaken.

**53. Geometry**  The width of a box is 2 m less than the length. The height is 1 m less than the length. The volume is 60 m³. What is the length of the box?

## 4 Practice

**ASSIGNMENT GUIDE**
Basic: 10–38 all, 50–54
Average: 11–37 odd, 39–57
Advanced: 1–37 odd, 39–60
Standardized Test Prep: 61–64
Mixed Review: 65–72

**Reasoning** exercises have blue headings.

**Applications** exercises have red headings.

**EXERCISE 53:** Use the Think About a Plan worksheet in the **Practice and Problem Solving Workbook** (also available in the Teaching Resources in print and online) to further support students' development in becoming independent learners.

**HOMEWORK QUICK CHECK**
To check students' understanding of key skills and concepts, go over Exercises 21, 25, 51, 52, and 53.

## Practice and Problem-Solving Exercises

**10.** $-4, 2 \pm 2i\sqrt{3}$

**11.** $10, -5 \pm 5i\sqrt{3}$

**12.** $\frac{3}{5}, \frac{-3 \pm 3i\sqrt{3}}{10}$

**13.** $\frac{1}{4}, \frac{-1 \pm i\sqrt{3}}{8}$

**14.** $-2, \pm i\sqrt{5}$

**15.** $\frac{1}{3}, -\frac{5}{2}$

**16.** $3, \frac{-3 \pm 3i\sqrt{3}}{2}$

**17.** $4, -2 \pm 2i\sqrt{3}$

**18.** $\frac{1}{2}, \frac{-1 \pm i\sqrt{3}}{4}$

**19.** $-\frac{1}{2}, \frac{1 \pm i\sqrt{3}}{4}$

**20.** $\pm 1, \pm 3$

**21.** $\pm 2$

**22.** $\pm 4, \pm 2i$

**23.** $\pm\sqrt{2}, \pm 3i$

**24.** $\pm\sqrt{2}, \pm i\sqrt{6}$

**25.** $-2, 1, 5$

**26.** $-1, 0, 3$

**27.** $0, 1$

**28.** $0, 8$

**29.** $0, -1, -2$

**30.** $0, -3.5, 1$

**31.** $0, -0.5, 1.5$

**32.** $-0.5, 0, 3$

**33.** $1, 7$

**34.** $-2, 1, 2, 3$

**35.** $-2, 5$

**36.** $-4, -1, 1$

**37.** 16 yrs old; $x^2(x + 2) = 3x + 4560$;

**38.** 5, 6, 7; $x(x + 1)(x + 2) = 210$;

**39.** $0, 5 \pm 2\sqrt{3}$

**40.** $0, 3 \pm \sqrt{3}$

**41.** $0, \frac{5 \pm 5\sqrt{2}}{2}$

**42.** $-\frac{6}{5}, \frac{3 \pm 3i\sqrt{3}}{5}$

**43.** $\frac{4}{3}, \frac{-2 \pm 2i\sqrt{3}}{3}$

**44.** $\pm 2\sqrt{2}, \pm 2i\sqrt{2}$

**45.** $1.9(1 \pm i), -1.9(1 \pm i)$

**46.** $\pm 3i, \pm i\sqrt{3}$

**47.** $0, \pm 1, \pm 2$

**48.** $0, \frac{1}{2} \pm \frac{\sqrt{265}}{10}$

**49.** $-1, \pm i$

**50.** $-1, 1$

**51.** 2 ft × 3 ft × 6 ft

**52.** A cubic function can have at most 3 zeros.

**53.** 5 m

# Answers

## Practice and Problem-Solving Exercises
(continued)

**54.** $-\frac{5}{2}$, 1; $y = (2x + 5)(x - 1)$;

**55.** $\pm 3$, $\pm 1$; $y = (x - 1)(x + 1)(x - 3)(x + 3)$;

**56.** $-1$, 2; $y = (x + 1)(x - 2)^2$;

**57.** Check students' work.

**58.** The geometric figure consists of either 2 cubes or 3 rectangular blocks, each with total volume equal.

$V_{\text{large cube}} = a(a)[(a - b) + b] = a^3$

$V_{\text{small cube}} = b(b)[(a + b) - a] = b^3$

$V_{\text{total 2 cubes}} = V_{\text{large cube}} + V_{\text{small cube}} = a^3 + b^3$

$V_{\text{top rectangular block}} = a(a)(a - b) = a^2(a - b)$

$V_{\text{small bottom rectangular block}} = a(b)(a - b)$
$\qquad\qquad = ab(a - b)$

$V_{\text{long bottom rectangular block}} = b(b)(a + b)$
$\qquad\qquad = b^2(a + b)$

$V_{\text{total 3 rectangular blocks}} = a^2(a - b) + ab(a - b)$
$\qquad\qquad + b^2(a + b)$
$\qquad\qquad = a(a - b)(a + b) + b^2(a + b)$
$\qquad\qquad = (a + b)[a(a - b) + b^2]$
$\qquad\qquad = (a + b)(a^2 - ab + b^2)$

So, $V_{\text{total 2 cubes}} = V_{\text{total 3 rectangular blocks}}$
$\qquad a^3 + b^3 = (a + b)(a^2 - ab + b^2)$.

**59.** Answers may vary. Sample:
$f(x) = 4x(x + 12)\left(x - \frac{1}{4}\right)\left(x - \frac{1}{6}\right)$
$p(x) = x(x + 12)(4x - 1)(6x - 1)$

**60.** $\dfrac{-1 \pm i\sqrt{3}}{2}$

## Standardized Test Prep

**61.** C  **62.** I  **63.** B

**64.** [2] Let $q$ = number of quarters and let $d$ = number of dimes:
$q + d = 12$
$\qquad q = 12 - d$

---

Graph each function to find the zeros. Rewrite the function with the polynomial in factored form.

**54.** $y = 2x^2 + 3x - 5$  **55.** $y = x^4 - 10x^2 + 9$  **56.** $y = x^3 - 3x^2 + 4$

**57.** Open-Ended To solve a polynomial equation, you can use any combination of graphing, factoring, and the Quadratic Formula. Write and solve an equation to illustrate each method.

Ⓒ Challenge **58.** The geometric figure at the right has volume $a^3 + b^3$. You can split it into three rectangular blocks (including the long one with side $a + b$). Explain how to use this figure to prove the factoring formula for the sum of cubes, $a^3 + b^3 = (a + b)(a^2 - ab + b^2)$.

**59.** Open-Ended Find equations for two different polynomial functions whose zeros include $-12$, 0, $\frac{1}{4}$, and $\frac{1}{6}$.

**60.** What are the complex solutions of $x^5 + x^3 + 2x = 2x^4 + x^2 + 1$?

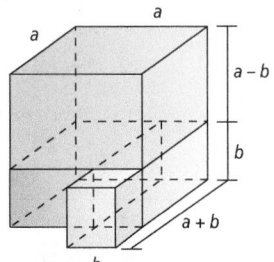

### Standardized Test Prep

SAT/ACT **61.** Which value is NOT a solution to the equation $x^4 - 3x^2 - 54 = 0$?
Ⓐ $-3$  Ⓑ $3$  Ⓒ $-3i$  Ⓓ $-i\sqrt{6}$

**62.** Ava drove 3 hours at 45 miles per hour. How many miles did she drive?
Ⓕ 45 miles  Ⓖ 48 miles  Ⓗ 90 miles  Ⓘ 135 miles

**63.** Which polynomial has the complex roots $1 + i\sqrt{2}$ and $1 - i\sqrt{2}$?
Ⓐ $x^2 + 2x + 3$  Ⓑ $x^2 - 2x + 3$  Ⓒ $x^2 + 2x - 3$  Ⓓ $x^2 - 2x - 3$

Short Response **64.** Sam has only quarters and dimes in his pocket. He has a total of 12 coins, totaling $1.95. How many of each coin does Sam have?

### Mixed Review

Write each polynomial in factored form. Check by multiplication. ◆ See Lesson 5-2.

**65.** $3x^2 - 18x + 24$  **66.** $2x^4 + 6x^3 - 18x^2 - 54x$  **67.** $x^4 - 4x^3 - 5x^2$

Solve each equation by factoring. Check your answers. ◆ See Lesson 4-5.

**68.** $x^2 - 4x = 12$  **69.** $x^2 + 1 = 37$  **70.** $2x^2 - 5x - 3 = 0$

**Get Ready!** To prepare for Lesson 5-4, do Exercises 71 and 72.

Evaluate each expression for the given values of the variables. ◆ See Lesson 1-3.

**71.** $\dfrac{16(x - 4)(y - 2)}{4(x - 3)y}$; $x = 1$ and $y = -2$  **72.** $\dfrac{2(x + 5)y}{10(x - 4)(y - 2)}$; $x = 1$ and $y = -2$

---

$.25q + 0.1d = 1.95$
$.25(12 - d) + 0.1d = 1.95$ Substitue for $q$.
$3 - 0.15d = 1.95$
$-0.15d = -1.05$
$d = 7$

$q = 12 - (7)$ Substitute for $d$.
$q = 5$
Sam has five quarters and seven dimes. (OR another appropriate method)

[1] correct answers, without work shown

### Mixed Review
**65.** $3(x - 4)(x - 2)$
**66.** $2x(x + 3)^2(x - 3)$
**67.** $x^2(x - 5)(x + 1)$
**68.** $-2$, 6
**69.** $\pm 6$
**70.** $-\frac{1}{2}$, 3
**71.** 12
**72.** $-\frac{1}{5}$

## Differentiated Remediation
Available in editable format online.

## Additional Instructional Support

### Algebra 2 Companion
Students can use the **Algebra 2 Companion** worktext (4 pages) as you teach the lesson. Use the Companion to support

- New Vocabulary
- Key Concepts
- Got It for each Problem
- Lesson Check

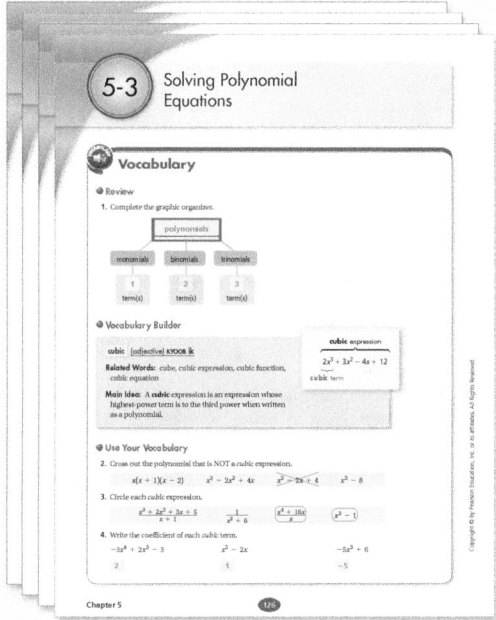

### ELL Support
**Use Graphic Organizers** Help students make a flow chart for finding the roots of a polynomial function. It should include both algebraic and graphing methods.

For example, write the polynomial function $P$ in the form $P(x) = 0$.

Then factor $P(x)$ (list and describe the methods) and use the Factor Theorem to list the roots.

Or graph the polynomial function with a graphing calculator. Then identify the real zeros.

## 5 Assess & Remediate

### Lesson Quiz

1. What are the real or imaginary solutions of $2x^3 + 7x^2 = 15x$?
2. What are the real or imaginary solutions of $2x^4 - 7x^2 = 4$?
3. What are the real solutions of $x^3 - 2x = 3x^2 - 1$?
4. **Do you UNDERSTAND?** Yun Sil added twice as many new songs on her MP3 player as Matt, who added 5 more new songs on his MP3 player than Sierra. The sum of the songs added on all three players is 15 more than the cube of the number of songs added on Sierra's player. How many songs did each person add?

### ANSWERS TO LESSON QUIZ

1. $0, \frac{3}{2}, -5$
2. $-2, 2, \frac{i\sqrt{2}}{2}, \frac{-i\sqrt{2}}{2}$
3. $-0.834, 0.343, 3.491$
4. Yun Sil added 14; Matt added 7; Sierra added 2.

**PRESCRIPTION FOR REMEDIATION**
Use the student work on the Lesson Quiz to prescribe a differentiated review assignment:

| Points | Differentiated Remediation |
|--------|----------------------------|
| 0–2 | Intervention |
| 3 | On-level |
| 4 | Extension |

**PowerAlgebra.com**

## 5 Assess & Remediate
Assign the Lesson Quiz. Appropriate intervention, practice, or enrichment is automatically generated based on student performance.

## Intervention

- **Reteaching** (2 pages) Provides reteaching and practice exercises for the key lesson concepts. Use with struggling students or absent students.
- **English Language Learner Support** Helps students develop and reinforce mathematical vocabulary and key concepts.

### All-in-One Resources/Online
**Reteaching**

**5-3 Reteaching**
Solving Polynomial Equations

**Problem**

What are the real or imaginary solutions of the polynomial equation $2x^3 + 16 = 0$?

$$2x^3 + 16 = 0$$
$$2(x^3 + 8) = 0 \quad \text{Factor out the GCF. In this case, it is 2.}$$
$$2(x + 2)(x^2 - 2x + 4) = 0 \quad \text{Factor the remaining cubic expression.}$$
$$x + 2 = 0 \text{ or } x^2 - 2x + 4 = 0 \quad \text{Use the Zero-Product Property.}$$
$$x = -2 \text{ or } x = \frac{2 \pm \sqrt{4 - 4(1)(4)}}{2(1)} \quad \text{Solve each equation for } x. \text{ Use the Quadratic Formula when necessary.}$$
$$x = -2 \text{ or } x = \frac{2 \pm 2i\sqrt{3}}{2}$$
$$x = -2 \text{ or } x = 1 \pm i\sqrt{3} \quad \text{Simplify.}$$

The solutions are $-2$ and $1 \pm i\sqrt{3}$.

**Exercises**

Find the real or imaginary solutions of each polynomial equation.

1. $x^3 - 8 = 0$
2. $4x^3 + 4 = 0$
3. $x^4 - x^2 - 72 = 0$
4. $x^4 + 9x^2 = -20$
5. $x^4 - 27 = 0$
6. $8x^3 = -1$
7. $7x^4 - 28x^2 = 21$
8. $x^3 = 64$
9. $8x^3 + 27 = 0$
10. $x^4 - 7x^2 = -12$
11. $2x^4 + 16x^2 = 40$
12. $x^4 - 16x = 0$
13. $9x^4 - 25 = 0$
14. $2x^4 - x^2 = 3$
15. $x^4 + 5x^2 = -4$
16. $x^6 - 7x^2 - 8 = 0$
17. $2x^3 + 16 = 0$
18. $x^4 - 5x^2 - 24 = 0$

### All-in-One Resources/Online
**English Language Learner Support**

**5-3 ELL Support**
Solving Polynomial Equations

**Problem**

What are the real or imaginary solutions of the equation $4x^3 + 2x^2 = 2x$? Explain your work.

$$4x^3 + 2x^2 = 2x \quad \text{Write the original equation.}$$
$$4x^3 + 2x^2 - 2x = 0 \quad \text{Rewrite in the form } P(x) = 0.$$
$$2x^3 + x^2 - x = 0 \quad \text{Multiply by } \tfrac{1}{2} \text{ to simplify.}$$
$$x(2x^2 + x - 1) = 0 \quad \text{Factor out the GCF, } x.$$
$$x(2x - 1)(x + 1) = 0 \quad \text{Factor } 2x^2 + x - 1.$$
$$x = 0 \text{ or } 2x - 1 = 0 \text{ or } x + 1 = 0 \quad \text{Zero Product Property.}$$
$$x = 0 \quad x = \tfrac{1}{2} \quad x = -1 \quad \text{Solve each equation for } x.$$

**Exercises**

What are the real or imaginary solutions of the equation $2x^3 + x^2 = 6x$? Explain your work.

$$2x^3 + x^2 = 6x \quad \text{Write the original equation.}$$
$$2x^3 + x^2 - 6x = 0 \quad \text{Rewrite in the form } P(x) = 0.$$
$$x(2x^2 + x - 6) = 0 \quad \text{Factor out the GCF, } x.$$
$$x(2x - 3)(x + 2) = 0 \quad \text{Factor } 2x^2 + x - 6.$$
$$x = 0 \text{ or } 2x - 3 = 0 \text{ or } x + 2 = 0 \quad \text{Zero Product Property.}$$
$$x = 0 \quad x = \tfrac{3}{2} \quad x = -2 \quad \text{Solve each equation for } x.$$

What are the real or imaginary solutions of the equation $3x^3 + 7x^2 = 6x$? Explain your work.

$$3x^3 + 7x^2 = 6x \quad \text{Write the original equation.}$$
$$3x^3 + 7x^2 - 6x = 0 \quad \text{Rewrite in the form } P(x) = 0.$$
$$x(3x^2 + 7x - 6) = 0 \quad \text{Factor out the GCF, } x.$$
$$x(3x - 2)(x + 3) = 0 \quad \text{Factor } 3x^2 + 7x - 6.$$
$$x = 0, 3x - 2 = 0, x + 3 = 0 \quad \text{Zero Product Property.}$$
$$x = 0, x = \tfrac{2}{3}, x = -3 \quad \text{Solve each equation for } x.$$

# Differentiated Remediation *continued*

Available in editable format online.

## On-Level

- **Practice** (2 pages) Provides extra practice for each lesson. For simpler practice exercises, use the Form K Practice pages found in the All-in-One Teaching Resources and online.

- **Think About a Plan** Helps students develop specific problem-solving skills and strategies by providing scaffolded guiding questions.
- **Standardized Test Prep** Focuses on all major exercises, all major question types, and helps students prepare for the high-stakes assessments.

## Extension

- **Enrichment** Provides students with interesting problems and activities that extend the concepts of the lesson.
- **Activities, Games, and Puzzles** Worksheets that can be used for concepts development, enrichment, and for fun!

---

### Practice and Problem Solving Wkbk/ All-in-One Workbook/Resources/Online
**Practice page 1**

### Practice and Problem Solving Wkbk/ All-in-One Workbook/Resources/Online
**Practice page 2**

### All-in-One Resources/Online
**Enrichment**

---

### Practice and Problem Solving Wkbk/ All-in-One Workbook Resources/Online
**Think About a Plan**

### Practice and Problem Solving Wkbk/ All-in-One Workbook/Resources/Online
**Standardized Test Prep**

### Online Teacher Resource Center
**Activities, Games, and Puzzles**

## 5-4 Dividing Polynomials

**Objectives** To divide polynomials using long division
To divide polynomials using synthetic division

Getting Ready!

In how many ways is it possible to replace the squares with single digit numbers to complete a correct division problem? Justify your answer.

**Dynamic Activity** Synthetic Division

**Lesson Vocabulary**
• synthetic division
• Remainder Theorem

Long division is one of many methods you can use to divide whole numbers.

**Essential Understanding** You can divide polynomials using steps that are similar to the long-division steps that you use to divide whole numbers.

When you try to factor a polynomial, you are trying to find a divisor of the polynomial that gives a quotient (the other factor) and remainder 0. This suggests that being able to divide one polynomial by another could help you factor polynomials.

Numerical long division and polynomial long division are similar.

**Numerical Long Division**  **Polynomial Long Division**

$$
\begin{array}{r}
32 \\
21\overline{)672} \\
\underline{63} \\
42 \\
\underline{42} \\
0
\end{array}
$$

21 divides into
67 3 times
21 divides into
42 2 times

$$
\begin{array}{r}
3x + 2 \\
2x + 1\overline{)6x^2 + 7x + 2} \\
\underline{6x^2 + 3x} \\
4x + 2 \\
\underline{4x + 2} \\
0
\end{array}
$$

$(2x + 1)$ divides into
$(6x^2 + 7x)$ $3x$ times
$(2x + 1)$ divides into
$(4x + 2)$ 2 times

The remainder from each division above is 0, so 21 is a factor of 672 and $2x + 1$ is a factor of $6x^2 + 7x + 2$.

---

# 1 Interactive Learning

## Solve It!

**PURPOSE** To review long division
**PROCESS** Students may
• estimate the dividend to determine the value of the missing digits.
• guess and check to determine the value of the missing digits.

### FACILITATE

**Q** Using rules for divisibility, are there any digits that you can eliminate for the divisor? **[0, 5]**

**Q** Can you use 24 as your divisor? Explain. **[No; in this case, the first number below the divisor would be 96, which does not end in 2.]**

**Q** Is it possible for 7 to be the digit before the 2 in the first row under the dividend? Explain. **[No; when you subtract 110 − 72 = 38 and 38 is greater than the divisor.]**

**ANSWER** See Solve It in Answers on next page.
**CONNECT THE MATH** The Solve It uses a puzzle to review long division. The students will use these skills when they divide polynomials.

---

## 5-4 Preparing to Teach

**BIG idea** Solving Equations and Inequalities

**UbD**

### ESSENTIAL UNDERSTANDING

• Polynomials can be divided using steps that are similar to the long-division steps that are used to divide whole numbers.

### Math Background

An algorithm is a specific set of instructions used to solve a problem. The Division Algorithm for Polynomials is a generalized version of the technique of long division in arithmetic. For polynomials $P(x)$ and $D(x)$, with $D(x)$ not equal to zero, there exist polynomials $Q(x)$ and $R(x)$ such that $P(x) = D(x) Q(x) + R(x)$. If $R(x) = 0$, then $D(x)$ is a factor of $P(x)$. Students divide polynomials using the process of long division and then move to dividing polynomials using synthetic division, which can be completed only if the factor is linear. Both methods are shown in order to illustrate the relationship between long division and synthetic division.

The Euclidean Algorithm works in a method similar to the Division Algorithm for polynomials and is used to find the greatest common divisor for two polynomials. For polynomials $P(x)$ and $D(x)$, with $D(x)$ not equal to zero and the degree of $D(x) <$ the degree of $P(x)$, use the following iteration:
• Use long division to find $P(x) = D(x) Q(x) + R(x)$. If $R(x) = 0$, then $D(x)$ is the greatest common divisor.
• If $R(x)$ is not equal to zero, divide $D(x)$ by $R(x)$. Use long division to find $D(x) = R(x) Q_2(x) + R_2(x)$. If $R_2(x) = 0$, then $R(x)$ is the greatest common factor.
• If $R_2(x)$ is not equal to zero, repeat the process dividing $R(x)$ by $R_2(x)$.

### Support Student Learning

Use the **Algebra 2 Companion** to engage and support students during instruction. See Lesson Resources at the end of this lesson for details.

**PowerAlgebra.com**

## 1 Interactive Learning

**Solve It!**
Step out how to solve the Problem with helpful hints and an online question. Other questions are listed above in Interactive Learning.

**Dynamic Activity** Students who have difficulty understanding synthetic division are lead through the process step by step as they model situations with numbered tiles.

# 2 Guided Instruction

## Problem 1

**Q** In what order should you arrange the terms when you divide polynomials? **[descending]**

**Q** How do you determine where to place the first term in the quotient? **[The term of the quotient is placed over the term in the dividend of the same degree.]**

**Q** How do you know when you are finished dividing the polynomial? **[The degree of the remainder is less than the divisor.]**

### Got It?
When performing long division, have students use a colored pencil to change the sign of each term being subtracted.

$$x - 7 \overline{)\,3x^2 - 29x + 56} \qquad x - 7 \overline{)\,3x^2 - 29x + 56}$$
$$\underline{3x^2 - 21x} \qquad\qquad \underline{-3x^2 + 21x}$$

with $3x$ above each.

### Take Note

**Q** When you divide a polynomial by a binomial and there is no remainder, what does that tell you about the quotient? **[The quotient is a factor of the dividend.]**

---

 **Problem 1** Using Polynomial Long Division

Use polynomial long division to divide $4x^2 + 23x - 16$ by $x + 5$. What is the quotient and remainder?

$$
\begin{array}{r}
4x \\
x + 5 \overline{)\,4x^2 + 23x - 16} \\
\underline{4x^2 + 20x} \\
3x - 16
\end{array}
$$

Divide: $\frac{4x^2}{x} = 4x$.

Multiply: $4x(x + 5) = 4x^2 + 20x$.

Subtract to get $3x$. Bring down $-16$.

Repeat the process of dividing, multiplying, and subtracting.

$$
\begin{array}{r}
4x \ + \ 3 \\
x + 5 \overline{)\,4x^2 + 23x - 16} \\
\underline{4x^2 + 20x} \\
3x - 16 \\
\underline{3x + 15} \\
-31
\end{array}
$$

Divide: $\frac{3x}{x} = 3$

Multiply: $3(x + 5) = 3x + 15$.

Subtract to get $-31$.

The quotient is $4x + 3$ with remainder $-31$. ⟨ You can say, $4x + 3$, R $-31$. ⟩

**Think**
How can you check your result?
Show that (divisor)(quotient) + remainder = dividend.

**Check**

$(x + 5)(4x + 3) - 31 = (4x^2 + 3x + 20x + 15) - 31$ — Multiply $(x + 5)(4x + 3)$.
$= 4x^2 + 23x - 16$ ✔ — Simplify.

**Got It? 1.** Use polynomial long division to divide $3x^2 - 29x + 56$ by $x - 7$. What is the quotient and remainder?

---

**take note** ➤ **Key Concept** The Division Algorithm for Polynomials

You can divide polynomial $P(x)$ by polynomial $D(x)$ to get polynomial quotient $Q(x)$ and polynomial remainder $R(x)$. The result is $P(x) = D(x)Q(x) + R(x)$.

$$
\begin{array}{r}
Q(x) \\
D(x) \overline{)\,P(x)} \\
\cdot \\
\cdot \\
\cdot \\
\overline{R(x)}
\end{array}
$$

If $R(x) = 0$, then $P(x) = D(x)Q(x)$ and $D(x)$ and $Q(x)$ are factors of $P(x)$.

To use long division, $P(x)$ and $D(x)$ should be in standard form with zero coefficients where appropriate. The process stops when the degree of the remainder, $R(x)$, is less than the degree of the divisor, $D(x)$.

---

## 2 Guided Instruction

 Each Problem is worked out and supported online.

**Problem 1**
Using Polynomial Long Division
*Animated*

**Problem 2**
Checking Factors

**Problem 3**
Using Synthetic Division
*Animated*

**Problem 4**
Using Synthetic Division to Solve a Problem

**Problem 5**
Evaluating a Polynomial

**Alternative Problem 5**
Evaluating a Polynomial
*Animated*

**Support in Algebra 2 Companion**
• Vocabulary
• Key Concepts
• Got It?

## Answers

**Solve It!**
One way: $1105 \div 23 = 48$, R 1; begin with $11 \div 2 \approx 5$, but 5 times any number results in a multiple of 5, not 2. So, the first number in the dividend must be 4. Next, think $4 \times 2\blacksquare = \blacksquare2.4 \times 3 = 12$, so the divisor must be 23. Once you know the divisor, you can fill in the rest of the blanks by doing long division. ($4 \times 23 = 92$; $110 - 92 = 18$; bring down the 5; $185 \div 23 \approx 8$; $8 \times 23 = 184$; the remainder is 1)

**Got It?**
**1.** $3x - 8$, R 0
**2. a.** yes; $P(x) = (x + 5)(x^4 - 1)$
   **b.** $(x + 2)(3x + 1)$

**Problem 2** Checking Factors

**A** Is $x^2 + 1$ a factor of $3x^4 - 4x^3 + 12x^2 + 5$?

$$
\begin{array}{r}
3x^2 - 4x + 9 \\
x^2 + 0x + 1 \overline{\smash{)}3x^4 - 4x^3 + 12x^2 + 0x + 5} \\
\underline{3x^4 + 0x^3 + 3x^2} \\
-4x^3 + 9x^2 + 0x \\
\underline{-4x^3 + 0x^2 - 4x} \\
9x^2 + 4x + 5 \\
\underline{9x^2 + 0x + 9} \\
4x - 4
\end{array}
$$

Include $0x$ terms.

The degree of the remainder is less than the degree of the divisor. Stop!

The remainder is not zero. $x^2 + 1$ is not a factor of $3x^4 - 4x^3 + 12x^2 + 5$.

**B** Is $x - 2$ a factor of $P(x) = x^5 - 32$? If it is, write $P(x)$ as a product of two factors.

**Step 1** Use the Factor Theorem to determine if $x - 2$ is a factor of $x^5 - 32$.

$$
\begin{aligned}
P(2) &= 2^5 - 32 \\
&= 32 - 32 \\
&= 0
\end{aligned}
$$

Since $P(2) = 0$, $x - 2$ is a factor of $P(x)$.

**Step 2** Use polynomial long division to find the other factor.

$$
\begin{array}{r}
x^4 + 2x^3 + 4x^2 + 8x + 16 \\
x - 2 \overline{\smash{)}x^5 + 0x^4 + 0x^3 + 0x^2 + 0x - 32} \\
\underline{x^5 - 2x^4} \\
2x^4 + 0x^3 \\
\underline{2x^4 - 4x^3} \\
4x^3 + 0x^2 \\
\underline{4x^3 - 8x^2} \\
8x^2 + 0x \\
\underline{8x^2 - 16x} \\
16x - 32 \\
\underline{16x - 32} \\
0
\end{array}
$$

$$P(x) = (x - 2)(x^4 + 2x^3 + 4x^2 + 8x + 16)$$

 **Got It?** **2. a.** Is $x^4 - 1$ a factor of $P(x) = x^5 + 5x^4 - x - 5$? If it is, write $P(x)$ as a product of two factors.

 **b.** *Reasoning* Use the fact that $12 \cdot 31 = 372$ to write $3x^2 + 7x + 2$ as the product of two factors.

**Plan**

**Can you use the Factor Theorem to help answer this question?**
Yes; recall that if $P(a) = 0$, then $x - a$ is a factor of $P(x)$.

PowerAlgebra.com
Lesson 5-4  Dividing Polynomials  305

**Problem 2**
When solving a long division problem, students may not recognize that a term is missing from either the dividend or the divisor. Remind students to write the terms in descending order and write a zero for any missing terms.

**Q** What terms are missing in 2A? **[The *x* term is missing in the dividend and divisor.]**

**Q** What is the purpose of the $0x$ term? **[It serves as a placeholder for the missing term.]**

**Q** Why must you stop dividing when the degree of the remainder is less than the degree of the divisor? **[There is no polynomial term that you can multiply the divisor by to get rid of the first term of the remainder.]**

**EXTENSION**

**Q** $x^2 - 1$ is a factor of $x^3 - 2x^2 - x + 2$. How do the factors of $x^2 - 1$ ($x + 1$ and $x - 1$) relate to $x^3 - 2x^2 - x + 2$? **[$x + 1$ and $x - 1$ are also factors of $x^3 - 2x^2 - x + 2$]**

**Got It?**  **ERROR PREVENTION**

**Q** Can you use the Factor Theorem to answer 2a? Explain why or why not. **[No; samples: $x^4 - 1$ is not a linear factor; $x^4 - 1$ is not in the form $x - a$; $x^4 - 1$ cannot be factored into real linear factors.]**

# Additional Problems

**1.** Use polynomial long division to divide $5x^2 + 2x + 3$ by $x + 1$. What are the quotient and remainder?

**ANSWER** $5x - 3$, R6

**2.** Is $x^2 - 2$ a factor of $P(x) = x^4 - x^2 - 2$? If it is, write $P(x)$ as a product of two factors.

**ANSWER** Yes; $(x^2 - 2)(x^2 + 1)$

**3.** Use synthetic division to divide $4x^3 - 3x^2 + 2x - 3$ by $x - 1$. What are the quotient and the remainder?

**ANSWER** $4x^2 + x + 3$; remainder 0

**4.** The polynomial $x^3 + 9x^2 + 23x + 15$ expresses the volume, in cubic inches, of a box, and the length is $(x + 5)$ inches. What are the other two dimensions of the box?

**ANSWER** $(x + 1)$ and $(x + 3)$

**5.** Given that $P(x) = x^4 + 6x^3 + 9x^2 + 3x - 3$, what is $P(4)$?

**ANSWER** 793

## Problem 3

Make sure students include the sign when writing the coefficients of the terms for synthetic division.

> **Q** Why is the sign of the $x + 2$ term reversed when completing the synthetic division? **[The term has to be in the form $x - a$, so you must rewrite $x + 2$ as $x - (-2)$.]**
>
> **Q** How would you describe the arithmetic process of synthetic division? **[A number above the line is added and a number below the line is multiplied by the divisor, moving over one space to the right.]**
>
> **Q** What does the final number in the bottom row represent? **[The number 0 means the divisor is a factor of the dividend. If the final number is other than 0, then it is a remainder.]**

## Got It?

> **Q** What do you need to do first? **[Answers may vary. Sample: Identify the divisor, 7.]**

## Problem 4

> **Q** After you complete the synthetic division, what is the next step? **[Factor the trinomial.]**
>
> **Q** How could you check your work? **[Use a graphing calculator to graph the given function and then calculate the zeros, or multiply the factors together and see if the result matches the original dividend.]**

---

**Synthetic division** simplifies the long-division process for dividing by a linear expression $x - a$. To use synthetic division, write the coefficients (including zeros) of the polynomial in standard form. Omit all variables and exponents. For the divisor, reverse the sign (use $a$). This allows you to add instead of subtract throughout the process.

 **Problem 3** Using Synthetic Division

Use synthetic division to divide $x^3 - 14x^2 + 51x - 54$ by $x + 2$. What is the quotient and remainder?

**Think**
To divide by $x + 2$ what number do you use for the synthetic divisor?
$x + 2 = x - (-2)$ so use $-2$.

**Step 1** Reverse the sign of $+2$. Write the coefficients of the polynomial.

$$-2 \underline{\,|\, 1 \;\; -14 \;\; 51 \;\; -54}$$

**Step 2** Bring down the first coefficient.

$$\begin{array}{r|rrrr} -2 & 1 & -14 & 51 & -54 \\ \hline & 1 \end{array}$$

**Step 3** Multiply the coefficient by the divisor. Add to the next coefficient.

$$\begin{array}{r|rrrr} -2 & 1 & -14 & 51 & -54 \\ & & -2 \\ \hline & 1 & -16 \end{array}$$

**Step 4** Continue multiplying and adding through the last coefficient.

$$\begin{array}{r|rrrr} -2 & 1 & -14 & 51 & -54 \\ & & -2 & 32 & -166 \\ \hline & 1 & -16 & 83 & -220 \end{array}$$

The quotient is $x^2 - 16x + 83$, R $-220$.

 **Got It?** **3.** Use synthetic division to divide $x^3 - 57x + 56$ by $x - 7$. What is the quotient and remainder?

---

**Problem 4** Using Synthetic Division to Solve a Problem

**Crafts** The polynomial $x^3 + 7x^2 - 38x - 240$ expresses the volume, in cubic inches, of the shadow box shown.

Ⓐ What are the dimensions of the box? (*Hint:* The length is greater than the height (or depth).)

**Plan**
How can you use the picture to help solve the problem?
The picture gives the width of box. Remember for a rectangular prism, $V = \ell \times w \times h$.

$$\begin{array}{r|rrrr} -5 & 1 & 7 & -38 & -240 \\ & & -5 & -10 & 240 \\ \hline & 1 & 2 & -48 & 0 \end{array}$$

$$x^2 + 2x - 48 = (x - 6)(x + 8)$$

So, $x^3 + 7x^2 - 38x - 240 = (x + 5)(x^2 + 2x - 48)$
$$= (x + 5)(x - 6)(x + 8)$$

The length, width, and height (or depth) of the box are $(x + 8)$ in., $(x + 5)$ in., and $(x - 6)$ in., respectively.

---

# Answers

**Got It?** (continued)

**3.** $x^2 + 7x - 8$, R 0

**B** If the width of the box is 15 in., what are the other two dimensions?

The width of the box is $x + 5$. So if $x + 5 = 15$, then $x = 10$.

Substitute for $x$ to find the length and height (or depth).

Length: $x + 8 = 10 + 8 = 18$ in.
Height: $x - 6 = 10 - 6 = 4$ in.

 **Got It?** **4.** If the polynomial $x^3 + 6x^2 + 11x + 6$ expresses the volume, in cubic inches, of the box, and the width is $(x + 1)$ in., what are the dimensions of the box?

The **Remainder Theorem** provides a quick way to find the remainder of a polynomial long-division problem.

 **Theorem    The Remainder Theorem**

If you divide a polynomial $P(x)$ of degree $n \geq 1$ by $x - a$, then the remainder is $P(a)$.

**Here's Why It Works** When you divide polynomial $P(x)$ by $D(x)$, you find $P(x) = D(x)Q(x) + R(x)$.

$P(x) = (x - a)Q(x) + R(x)$    Substitute $(x - a)$ for $D(x)$.

$P(a) = (a - a)Q(a) + R(a)$    Evaluate $P(a)$. Substitute $a$ for $x$.

$\quad\quad = R(a)$    Simplify.

 **Problem 5** **Evaluating a Polynomial**    **GRIDDED RESPONSE**

**Think**

Is there a way to find $P(3)$ without substituting?
Use synthetic division. $P(3)$ is the remainder.

Given that $P(x) = x^5 - 2x^3 - x^2 + 2$, what is $P(3)$?

By the Remainder Theorem, $P(3)$ is the remainder when you divide $P(x)$ by $x - 3$.

$$\begin{array}{r|rrrrrr} 3 & 1 & 0 & -2 & -1 & 0 & 2 \\ & & 3 & 9 & 21 & 60 & 180 \\ \hline & 1 & 3 & 7 & 20 & 60 & 182 \end{array}$$

$P(3) = 182$.

 **Got It?** **5.** Given that $P(x) = x^5 - 3x^4 - 28x^3 + 5x + 20$, what is $P(-4)$?

---

**Got It?**     EXTENSION

**Q** What are the length, width, height, and volume of the box when $x = 5$? **[$(x + 1)(x + 2)(x + 3)$; the width is 6 in., the other two dimensions are 7 in. and 8 in., and the volume is 336 in.$^3$.]**

**Take Note**

**Q** Divide $4x^2 - 5x - 20$ by $x - 4$ using synthetic division. What is the remainder? **[24]**

**Here's Why It Works**

**Q** What is $P(4)$ for $P(x) = 4x^2 - 5x - 20$? **[24]**

**Q** What is the connection between dividing the polynomial by $x - 4$ and evaluating the polynomial when $x = 4$? **[When the polynomial was evaluated at $x = 4$, the result, $P(4)$, is the same as the remainder when the polynomial was divided by $x - 4$.]**

**Problem 5**

**Q** When you use synthetic division, how do you determine the degree of the first term in the quotient? **[The degree of the quotient is one less than the degree of the dividend polynomial.]**

**Q** What is an advantage of using synthetic division and the Remainder Theorem to evaluate a polynomial? **[You minimize the calculations required of substituting the value for $x$ and evaluating.]**

**Got It?**

**Q** When determining $P(-4)$, what factor are you dividing by? **[$x + 4$]**

---

**4.** width: $(x + 1)$ in.; height: $(x + 2)$ in.;
length: $(x + 3)$ in.

**5.** 0

# 3 Lesson Check

## Do you know HOW?

- For Exercises 1–5, remind students that the binomial needs to be in the form $x - a$. If the form is $x + a$, students will need to rewrite the term as $x - (-a)$.

## Do you UNDERSTAND?

- For Exercise 7, suggest students discuss what could happen if the terms of both polynomials are not written in descending order. **[You may not be able to subtract the terms as you divide.]**

## Close

> **Q** How are long division and synthetic division similar? **[They can both be used to divide a polynomial by a binomial.]**
>
> **Q** How are long division and synthetic division different? **[Synthetic division can only be performed on a linear binomial factor, whereas long division can be used to divide any two polynomials.]**
>
> **Q** What is an example of polynomial division that can be performed using synthetic division? that cannot be performed using synthetic division? **[Answers may vary. Samples: $3x^2 + 2x + 1$ divided by $x + 2$; $6x^2 + 2x - 1$ divided by $x^2 - 1$]**

---

 **Lesson Check**

### Do you know HOW?

Divide using any method.

1. $(2x^2 + 7x + 11) \div (x + 2)$

2. $(x^3 + 5x^2 + 11x + 15) \div (x + 3)$

3. $(x^3 - x^2 - 4x + 4) \div (x - 2)$

4. $(4x^3 + 21x^2 - x - 24) \div (x + 5)$

5. $(9x^3 - 15x^2 + 4x) \div (x - 3)$

### Do you UNDERSTAND?

6. **Reasoning** A polynomial $P(x)$ is divided by a binomial $x - a$. The remainder is 0. What conclusion can you draw? Explain.

7. **Writing** Explain why it is important to have the terms of both polynomials written in descending order of degree before dividing.

8. **Open-Ended** Write a polynomial division that has a quotient of $x + 3$ and a remainder of 2.

---

 **Practice and Problem-Solving Exercises**

**A** Practice ⟳

**Divide using long division. Check your answers.**  ◀ See Problem 1.

9. $(x^2 - 3x - 40) \div (x + 5)$

10. $(3x^2 + 7x - 20) \div (x + 4)$

11. $(x^3 + 3x^2 - x + 2) \div (x - 1)$

12. $(2x^3 - 3x^2 - 18x - 8) \div (x - 4)$

13. $(3x^3 + 9x^2 + 8x + 4) \div (x + 2)$

14. $(9x^2 - 21x - 20) \div (x - 1)$

15. $(x^2 - 7x + 10) \div (x + 3)$

16. $(x^3 - 13x - 12) \div (x - 4)$

**Determine whether each binomial is a factor of $x^3 + 4x^2 + x - 6$.**  ◀ See Problem 2.

17. $x + 1$    18. $x + 2$    19. $x + 3$    20. $x - 3$

**Divide using synthetic division.**  ◀ See Problem 3.

21. $(x^3 + 3x^2 - x - 3) \div (x - 1)$

22. $(x^3 - 4x^2 + 6x - 4) \div (x - 2)$

23. $(x^3 - 7x^2 - 7x + 20) \div (x + 4)$

24. $(x^3 - 3x^2 - 5x - 25) \div (x - 5)$

25. $(x^2 + 3) \div (x - 1)$

26. $(3x^3 + 17x^2 + 21x - 9) \div (x + 3)$

27. $(x^3 + 27) \div (x + 3)$

28. $(6x^2 - 8x - 2) \div (x - 1)$

**Use synthetic division and the given factor to completely factor each polynomial function.**  ◀ See Problem 4.

29. $y = x^3 + 2x^2 - 5x - 6; (x + 1)$

30. $y = x^3 - 4x^2 - 9x + 36; (x + 3)$

31. **Geometry** The volume, in cubic inches, of the decorative box shown can be expressed as the product of the lengths of its sides as $V(x) = x^3 + x^2 - 6x$. What linear expressions with integer coefficients represent the length and height of the box?

$x$

---

**PowerAlgebra.com**

## 3 Lesson Check

For a digital lesson check, use the Got It questions.

**Support in Algebra 2 Companion**
- Lesson Check

## 4 Practice

Assign homework to individual students or to an entire class.

---

# Answers

## Lesson Check

1. $2x + 3$, R 5
2. $x^2 + 2x + 5$
3. $x^2 + x - 2$
4. $4x^2 + x - 6$, R 26
5. $9x^2 + 12x + 40$, R 120
6. $x - a$ is a factor of $P(x)$.
7. The polynomials need to be written in standard form since the leading coefficient of both polynomials determines the leading term of the quotient.
8. Check students' work.

## Practice and Problem-Solving Exercises

9. $x - 8$
10. $3x - 5$
11. $x^2 + 4x + 3$, R 5
12. $2x^2 + 5x + 2$
13. $3x^2 + 3x + 2$
14. $9x - 12$, R $-32$
15. $x - 10$, R 40
16. $x^2 + 4x + 3$
17. no
18. yes
19. yes
20. no
21. $x^2 + 4x + 3$
22. $x^2 - 2x + 2$
23. $x^2 - 11x + 37$, R $-128$
24. $x^2 + 2x + 5$
25. $x + 1$, R 4
26. $3x^2 + 8x - 3$
27. $x^2 - 3x + 9$
28. $6x - 2$, R $-4$
29. $y = (x + 1)(x + 3)(x - 2)$
30. $y = (x + 3)(x - 4)(x - 3)$
31. width $= x$; length $= x + 3$; height $= x - 2$

Use synthetic division and the Remainder Theorem to find $P(a)$.

See Problem 5.

**32.** $P(x) = x^3 + 4x^2 - 8x - 6; a = -2$

**33.** $P(x) = x^3 + 4x^2 + 4x; a = -2$

**34.** $P(x) = x^3 - 7x^2 + 15x - 9; a = 3$

**35.** $P(x) = x^3 + 7x^2 + 4x; a = -2$

**36.** $P(x) = 6x^3 - x^2 + 4x + 3; a = 3$

**37.** $P(x) = 2x^3 - x^2 + 10x + 5; a = \frac{1}{2}$

**38.** $P(x) = 2x^3 + 4x^2 - 10x - 9; a = 3$

**39.** $P(x) = 2x^4 + 6x^3 + 5x^2 - 45; a = -3$

 **Apply**

**40. Think About a Plan** Your friend multiplies $x + 4$ by a quadratic polynomial and gets the result $x^3 - 3x^2 - 24x + 30$. The teacher says that everything is correct except for the constant term. Find the quadratic polynomial that your friend used. What is the correct result of multiplication?
- What does the fact that all the terms except for the constant are correct tell you?
- How can polynomial division help you solve this problem?
- What is the connection between the remainder of the division and your friend's error?

**41. Error Analysis** A student used synthetic division to divide $x^3 - x^2 - 2x$ by $x + 1$. Describe and correct the error shown.

**42. Reasoning** When a polynomial is divided by $(x - 5)$, the quotient is $5x^2 + 3x + 12$ with remainder 7. Find the polynomial.

**43. Geometry** The expression $\frac{1}{3}(x^3 + 5x^2 + 8x + 4)$ represents the volume of a square pyramid. The expression $x + 1$ represents the height of the pyramid. What expression represents the side length of the base? (*Hint:* The formula for the volume of a pyramid is $V = \frac{1}{3}Bh$.)

Divide.

**44.** $(2x^3 + 9x^2 + 14x + 5) \div (2x + 1)$

**45.** $(x^4 + 3x^2 + x + 4) \div (x + 3)$

**46.** $(x^5 + 1) \div (x + 1)$

**47.** $(x^4 + 4x^3 - x - 4) \div (x^3 - 1)$

**48.** $(3x^4 - 5x^3 + 2x^2 + 3x - 2) \div (3x - 2)$

Determine whether each binomial is a factor of $x^3 + x^2 - 16x - 16$.

**49.** $x + 2$ **50.** $x - 4$ **51.** $x + 1$ **52.** $x - 1$

Use synthetic division to determine whether each binomial is a factor of $3x^3 + 10x^2 - x - 12$.

**53.** $x + 3$ **54.** $x - 1$ **55.** $x + 2$ **56.** $x - 4$

Divide using synthetic division.

**57.** $(x^4 - 2x^3 + x^2 + x - 1) \div (x - 1)$

**58.** $(x^4 + 3x^3 + 3x^2 + 4x + 3) \div (x + 1)$

**59.** $(x^4 + 3x^3 + 7x^2 + 26x + 15) \div (x + 3)$

**60.** $(x^4 - 6x^2 - 27) \div (x + 2)$

**61.** $(x^4 - 5x^2 + 4x + 12) \div (x + 2)$

**62.** $\left(x^4 - \frac{9}{2}x^3 + 3x^2 - \frac{1}{2}x\right) \div \left(x - \frac{1}{2}\right)$

**ASSIGNMENT GUIDE**

Basic: 9–39 all, 40, 41, 43, 48, 50

Average: 9–39 odd, 40–62

Advanced: 9–39 odd, 40–66

Standardized Test Prep: 67–70

Mixed Review: 71–85

**Reasoning** exercises have blue headings.

**Applications** exercises have red headings.

**EXERCISE 43:** Use the Think About a Plan worksheet in the **Practice Problem Solving Workbook** (also available in the Teaching Resources in print and online) to further support students' development in becoming independent learners.

**HOMEWORK QUICK CHECK**

To check students' understanding of key skills and concepts, go over Exercises 13, 29, 40, 41, and 43.

---

**32.** 18

**33.** 0

**34.** 0

**35.** 12

**36.** 168

**37.** 10

**38.** 51

**39.** 0

**40.** $x^2 - 7x + 4$; $x^3 - 3x^2 - 24x + 16$

**41.** There are 2 errors. The constant term of the dividend is missing and the divisor is $-1$ *not* 1:
$x^3 - x^2 - 2x = (x + 1)(x^2 - 2x)$
$= x(x + 1)(x - 2)$

**42.** $5x^3 - 22x^2 - 3x - 53$

**43.** $x + 2$

**44.** $x^2 + 4x + 5$

**45.** $x^3 - 3x^2 + 12x - 35$, R 109

**46.** $x^4 - x^3 + x^2 - x + 1$

**47.** $x + 4$

**48.** $x^3 - x^2 + 1$

**49.** no

**50.** yes

**51.** yes

**52.** no

**53.** yes

**54.** yes

**55.** no

**56.** no

**57.** $x^3 - x^2 + 1$

**58.** $x^3 + 2x^2 + x + 3$

**59.** $x^3 + 7x + 5$

**60.** $x^3 - 2x^2 - 2x + 4$, R $-35$

**61.** $x^3 - 2x^2 - x + 6$

**62.** $x^3 - 4x^2 + x$

# Answers

## Practice and Problem-Solving Exercises
(continued)

**63. a.** $x + 1$
**b.** $x^2 + x + 1$
**c.** $x^3 + x^2 + x + 1$
**d.** $(x - 1)(x^4 + x^3 + x^2 + x + 1)$

**64.** 1
**65.** $x + 2i$
**66.** negative

## Standardized Test Prep

**67.** D
**68.** I
**69.** A
**70. [4]** $\pi r^2 = A$

$$r^2 = \frac{A}{\pi}$$

$$r = \sqrt{\frac{A}{\pi}}$$

$$r = \sqrt{\frac{(78.5)}{3.14}} = \sqrt{25}$$

$$r = 5 \text{ cm}$$

**[3]** appropriate methods, but with one computational error

**[2]** solved for $r$ incorrectly, radius found appropriately, given previous results

**[1]** correct equation and radius, without work shown

## Mixed Review

**71.** $0, -1$
**72.** $0, 1$
**73.** $-5, 0, 5$
**74.** $\dfrac{-3 \pm \sqrt{17}}{2}$
**75.** $-1 \pm \sqrt{3}$
**76.** $1, -\dfrac{5}{7}$
**77.** $\dfrac{5 \pm \sqrt{5}}{2}$
**78.** $3 \pm \sqrt{2}$
**79.** $\dfrac{-7 \pm \sqrt{5}}{2}$
**80.**
**81.**

**82.**

**83.** 24
**84.** 5
**85.** $23 - 11i$

---

**63. Reasoning** Divide. Look for patterns in your answers.
**a.** $(x^2 - 1) \div (x - 1)$     **b.** $(x^3 - 1) \div (x - 1)$     **c.** $(x^4 - 1) \div (x - 1)$
**d.** Using the patterns, factor $x^5 - 1$.

**64. Reasoning** The remainder from the division of the polynomial $x^3 + ax^2 + 2ax + 5$ by $x + 1$ is 3. Find $a$.

**65.** Use synthetic division to find $(x^2 + 4) \div (x - 2i)$.

**66. Writing** Suppose 3, $-1$, and 5 are zeros of a cubic polynomial function $f(x)$. What is the sign of $f(1) \cdot f(4)$? (*Hint:* Sketch the graph; consider all possibilities.)

## Standardized Test Prep

**SAT/ACT**

**67.** What is the remainder when $x^2 - 5x + 7$ is divided by $x + 1$?
Ⓐ 1     Ⓑ 3     Ⓒ 11     Ⓓ 13

**68.** What is the least degree of a polynomial that has a zero of multiplicity 3 at 1, a zero of multiplicity 1 at 0, and a zero of multiplicity 2 at 2?
Ⓕ 3     Ⓖ 4     Ⓗ 5     Ⓘ 6

**69.** The equation $y = 0.17x$ represents your weight, in pounds, on the Moon $y$ in relation to your weight on Earth $x$. If Al weighs 130 lb on Earth, what would he weigh on the Moon?
Ⓐ 22.1 lb     Ⓑ 92.3 lb     Ⓒ 130 lb     Ⓓ 764.7 lb

**Extended Response**

**70.** The formula for the area of a circle is $A = \pi r^2$. Solve the equation for $r$. If the area of a circle is 78.5 cm², what is the radius? Use 3.14 for $\pi$.

## Mixed Review

**Find the real solutions of each equation by factoring.**     *See Lesson 5-3.*

**71.** $x^3 + 2x^2 + x = 0$     **72.** $2x^4 - 2x^3 + 2x^2 = 2x$     **73.** $5x^5 = 125x^3$

**Solve each equation using the Quadratic Formula.**     *See Lesson 4-7.*

**74.** $x^2 + 3x - 2 = 0$     **75.** $2x^2 + 4x - 4 = 0$     **76.** $7x^2 - 2x - 5 = 0$

**77.** $x^2 - 5x = -5$     **78.** $x^2 - 6x = -7$     **79.** $x^2 + 7x + 11 = 0$

**Find the solution of each system by graphing.**     *See Lesson 3-3.*

**80.** $\begin{cases} y < 2x + 3 \\ y > -x \end{cases}$     **81.** $\begin{cases} y > x - 4 \\ y > 4 - \frac{1}{3}x \end{cases}$     **82.** $\begin{cases} y < -|x| + 3 \\ y > x + 1 \end{cases}$

**Get Ready!** To prepare for Lesson 5-5, do Exercises 83–85.

**Simplify each expression.**     *See Lesson 4-8.*

**83.** $(-4i)(6i)$     **84.** $(2 + i)(2 - i)$     **85.** $(4 - 3i)(5 + i)$

# Differentiated Remediation

Available in editable format online.

## Additional Instructional Support

### Algebra 2 Companion

Students can use the **Algebra 2 Companion** worktext (4 pages) as you teach the lesson. Use the Companion to support

- New Vocabulary
- Key Concepts
- Got It for each Problem
- Lesson Check

### ELL Support

**Focus on Communication** Divide the class into pairs. Give each pair of students a synthetic division problem. Have the students work them out together in the following manner: One student explicitly states the steps to be taken and why, and the other student does the writing. When they finish, they reverse roles with another problem.

## 5 Assess & Remediate

### Lesson Quiz

1. Use polynomial long division to divide $2x^2 + 3x - 1$ by $x + 4$. What are the quotient and remainder?

2. Is $x^2 - 1$ a factor of $P(x) = 2x^4 + 7$? If it is, write $P(x)$ as a product of two factors.

3. Use synthetic division to divide $x^3 - 3x^2 + x - 8$ by $x - 1$. What are the quotient and the remainder?

4. **Do you UNDERSTAND?** The polynomial $x^3 + 12x^2 + 39x + 28$ expresses the volume, in cubic inches, of a box, and the length is $(x + 7)$ inches. What are the other dimensions of the box?

5. Given that $P(x) = x^5 - 3x^3 - x^2 + 1$, what is $P(2)$?

### ANSWERS TO LESSON QUIZ

1. $2x - 5$, R19
2. $x^2 - 1$ is not a factor.
3. The quotient is $x^2 - 2x - 1$, R $-9$.
4. $(x + 1)$ and $(x + 4)$
5. 5

### PRESCRIPTION FOR REMEDIATION

Use the student work on the Lesson Quiz to prescribe a differentiated review assignment:

| Points | Differentiated Remediation |
|--------|---------------------------|
| 0–2 | Intervention |
| 3–4 | On-level |
| 5 | Extension |

**PowerAlgebra.com**

### 5 Assess & Remediate

Assign the Lesson Quiz. Appropriate intervention, practice, or enrichment is automatically generated based on student performance.

## Intervention

- **Reteaching** (2 pages) Provides reteaching and practice exercises for the key lesson concepts. Use with struggling students or absent students.

- **English Language Learner Support** Helps students develop and reinforce mathematical vocabulary and key concepts.

### All-in-One Resources/Online
#### Reteaching

**5-4 Reteaching**
Dividing Polynomials

### All-in-One Resources/Online
#### English Language Learner Support

**5-4 ELL Support**
Dividing Polynomials

# Differentiated Remediation *continued*

Available in editable format online.

## On-Level

- **Practice** (2 pages) Provides extra practice for each lesson. For simpler practice exercises, use the Form K Practice pages found in the All-in-One Teaching Resources and online.

- **Think About a Plan** Helps students develop specific problem-solving skills and strategies by providing scaffolded guiding questions.

- **Standardized Test Prep** Focuses on all major exercises, all major question types, and helps students prepare for the high-stakes assessments.

## Extension

- **Enrichment** Provides students with interesting problems and activities that extend the concepts of the lesson.

- **Activities, Games, and Puzzles** Worksheets that can be used for concepts development, enrichment, and for fun!

---

### Practice and Problem Solving Wkbk/ All-in-One Resources/Online
#### Practice page 1

### Practice and Problem Solving Wkbk/ All-in-One Resources/Online
#### Practice page 2

### All-in-One Resources/Online
#### Enrichment

### Practice and Problem Solving Wkbk/ All-in-One Resources/Online
#### Think About a Plan

### Practice and Problem Solving Wkbk/ All-in-One Resources/Online
#### Standardized Test Prep

### Online Teacher Resource Center
#### Activities, Games, and Puzzles

## Do you know HOW?

For each polynomial function, describe the end behavior of its graph.

**1.** $f(x) = x^8 - 8x^4 + 6x^2$

**2.** $f(x) = -x^4 - x^3 + 1$

**3.** $f(x) = x^7 - 3x^5 - 5x^3$

**4.** What is the degree of the function that generates the data shown?

| x | y |
|----|-----|
| -3 | 159 |
| -2 | 29 |
| -1 | -1 |
| 0 | -3 |
| 1 | -1 |
| 2 | 29 |
| 3 | 159 |

Find all the solutions of each equation by factoring.

**5.** $x^3 - 5x^2 = 36x$

**6.** $27x^3 = 8$

**7.** $x^4 - 20x^2 + 64 = 0$

**8.** $x^3 + 125 = 0$

**9.** Use the Remainder Theorem and synthetic division to find $P(4)$ for $P(x) = 2x^4 - 3x^2 + 4x - 1$.

You have several boxes with the same dimensions. They have a combined volume of $2x^4 + 4x^3 - 18x^2 - 4x + 16$. Determine whether each binomial below could represent the number of boxes you have.

**10.** $x - 1$

**11.** $x + 2$

**12.** $2x + 8$

Write each polynomial in standard form. Then classify it by degree and number of terms.

**13.** $-2x^3 + 6 - x^3 + 5x$

**14.** $3(x - 1)(x + 4)$

Describe the shape of the graph of each cubic function by determining the end behavior and number of turning points.

**15.** $y = -5x^3$

**16.** $y = 3x^3 + 4x^2 + 2x - 1$

## Do you UNDERSTAND?

**17.** You buy equal numbers of containers of strawberries, blueberries, and cherries. Cherries are $1 more per container than blueberries, which are $1 more per container than strawberries. The product of the 3 individual prices is 5 times the total cost of one container of each fruit.
   **a.** Write a polynomial function to model the cost of your purchase.
   **b.** Graph to find the price of each container.
   **c.** Writing Explain how you used the graph to find the prices.

**18.** A cylinder has a radius of $3x - 2$ and a height of $3 - 2x$.
   **a.** Use 3.14 as $\pi$ and graph the equation for the volume.
   **b.** Find the relative maximum.
   **c.** Reasoning What kind of limitation on the radius would make your answer in part (b) the maximum possible volume?

**19.** Open-Ended Write a polynomial function in factored form with at least three zeros that are negative, one of which has multiplicity 2.

**18. a.** $V = 3.14(3x - 2)^2(3 - 2x)$

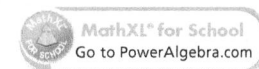

   **b.** $(1.22, 4.85)$

   **c.** $x \geq \dfrac{2}{3}$

**19.** Answers may vary. Sample:
   $f(x) = (x + 1)(x + 2)(x + 3)^2$

# Answers

**1.** up and up

**2.** down and down

**3.** down and up

**4.** 4

**5.** $-4, 0, 9$

**6.** $\dfrac{2}{3}, \dfrac{-1 \pm i\sqrt{3}}{3}$

**7.** $\pm 4, \pm 2$

**8.** $-5, \dfrac{5 \pm 5i\sqrt{3}}{2}$

**9.** 479

**10.** yes

**11.** no

**12.** yes

**13.** $-3x^3 + 5x + 6$; cubic trinomial

**14.** $3x^2 + 9x - 12$; quadratic trinomial

**15.** up and down; no turning pts.

**16.** down and up; no turning pts.

**17. a.** $P(x) = x^3 + 3x^2 - 13x - 15$

   **b.** strawberries: $3; blueberries: $4; cherries: $5

   **c.** The positive zero ($x = 3$) of the function in part (a) is the solution.

# 1 Interactive Learning

## Solve It!

**PURPOSE** To use factors to solve a puzzle
**PROCESS** Students may
- list the factors of 6 and 4.
- find fractions whose sum of the numerator and denominator is 5.
- test each fraction to see if it is greater than its square.

---

**FACILITATE**

**Q** What are the factors of 6? [$\pm 1, \pm 2, \pm 3, \pm 6$]

**Q** What are the factors of 4? [$\pm 1, \pm 2, \pm 4$]

**Q** Following the clues, what fractions can you write whose numerator and denominator add to 5? [$\frac{1}{4}, \frac{3}{2}, \frac{6}{-1}$]

**Q** Which fraction is greater than its square? [$\frac{1}{4}$]

---

**ANSWER** See Solve It in Answers on next page.
**CONNECT THE MATH** Students use factors to solve the Solve It. In this lesson students will apply the Rational Root Theorem using factors to generate possible rational roots of a polynomial equation.

## 2 Guided Instruction

### Take Note
**ERROR PREVENTION**
The Rational Root Theorem does not necessarily give the zeros of the equation. It provides a list of first guesses to test as roots.

---

## 5-5 Theorems About Roots of Polynomial Equations

**Objectives** To solve equations using the Rational Root Theorem
To use the Conjugate Root Theorem

**Lesson Vocabulary**
- Rational Root Theorem
- Conjugate Root Theorem
- Descartes' Rule of Signs

Factoring the polynomial $P(x) = a_n x^n + a_{n-1} x^{n-1} + \cdots + a_1 x + a_0$ can be challenging, especially when both $a_n$ and $a_0$ have many factors.

**Essential Understanding** The factors of the numbers $a_n$ and $a_0$ in $P(x) = a_n x^n + a_{n-1} x^{n-1} + \cdots + a_1 x + a_0$ can help you factor $P(x)$ and solve the equation $P(x) = 0$.

One way to find a root of the polynomial equation $P(x) = 0$ is to guess and check. This is inefficient unless there is a way to minimize the number of guesses, or possible roots. The **Rational Root Theorem** does just that.

**Theorem   Rational Root Theorem**

Let $P(x) = a_n x^n + a_{n-1} x^{n-1} + \cdots + a_1 x + a_0$ be a polynomial with integer coefficients. There are a limited number of possible roots of $P(x) = 0$:
- Integer roots must be factors of $a_0$.
- Rational roots must have reduced form $\frac{p}{q}$ where $p$ is an integer factor of $a_0$ and $q$ is an integer factor of $a_n$.

| Factors of the leading coefficient: $\pm 1, \pm 3, \pm 7,$ and $\pm 21.$ | $21x^2 + 29x + 10 = 0$ | Factors of the constant term: $\pm 1, \pm 2, \pm 5,$ and $\pm 10.$ |

$$x^2 + \frac{29}{21}x + \frac{10}{21} = 0$$

$$\left(x + \frac{2}{3}\right)\left(x + \frac{5}{7}\right) = 0 \quad \text{The roots are } -\frac{2}{3} \text{ and } -\frac{5}{7}.$$

---

## 5-5 Preparing to Teach

**BIG ideas** Solving Equations and Inequalities
Equivalence

**UbD**

### ESSENTIAL UNDERSTANDINGS
- The factors of the numbers $a_n$ and $a_0$ in $P(x) = a_n x^n + a_{n-1} x^{n-1} + \ldots a_1 x + a_0$ can be used to factor $P(x)$ and solve the equation $P(x) = 0$.
- $(x - a)$ is linear factor if and only if $a$ is a root of the related polynomial equation.

### Math Background
When used together, the Rational Root Theorem, the Conjugate Root Theorem, and Descartes' Rule of Signs are powerful tools to solve polynomial equations.
- The Rational Root Theorem creates a finite list of possible rational roots of a polynomial equation with rational coefficients.
- The Conjugate Root Theorem is helpful when the polynomial equation has irrational or imaginary roots. Once an irrational or imaginary root is

found, remaining members of the conjugate pairs can be stated. This theorem gives a way to generate remaining roots for many polynomials with rational or real coefficents.
- Descartes' Rule of Signs indicates the number of positive and negative real roots. Multiple real roots are counted multiple times to get the number of roots.

Therefore, the use of these theorems is important when solving polynomial equations. When combined with factoring, the Quadratic Formula, and synthetic division, the theorems will be invaluable when working with higher-order polynomial equations.

### Support Student Learning
Use the **Algebra 2 Companion** to engage and support students during instruction. See Lesson Resources at the end of this lesson for details.

---

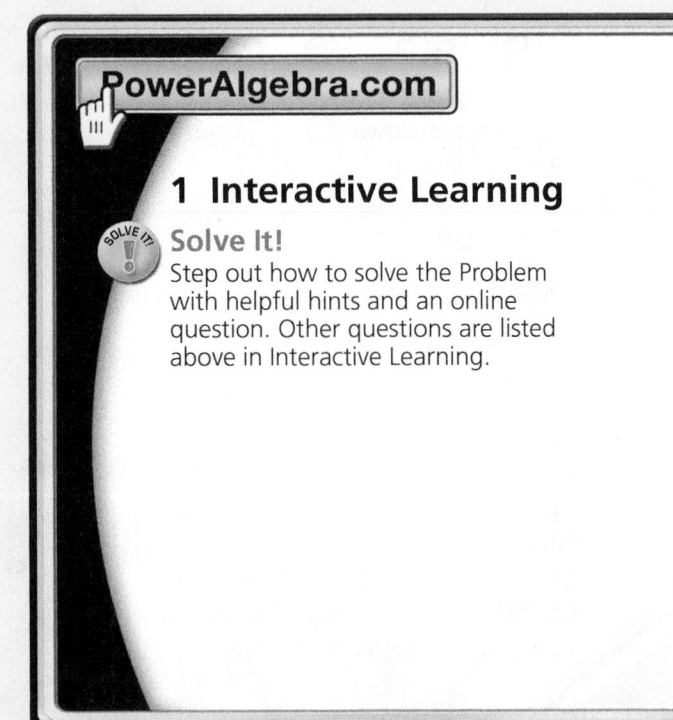

**PowerAlgebra.com**

## 1 Interactive Learning

### Solve It!
Step out how to solve the Problem with helpful hints and an online question. Other questions are listed above in Interactive Learning.

**Problem 1** Finding a Rational Root

What are the rational roots of $2x^3 - x^2 + 2x + 5 = 0$?

The only possible rational roots have the form $\frac{\text{factor of constant term}}{\text{factor of leading coefficient}}$.

The constant factors are $\pm 1, \pm 5$. The leading coefficient factors are $\pm 1, \pm 2$. The only possible rational roots are $\pm 1, \pm 5, \pm \frac{1}{2}, \pm \frac{5}{2}$.

The table shows the values of the function $y = P(x)$ for the possible roots.

| x | 1 | −1 | 5 | −5 | $\frac{1}{2}$ | $-\frac{1}{2}$ | $\frac{5}{2}$ | $-\frac{5}{2}$ |
|---|---|---|---|---|---|---|---|---|
| P(x) | 8 | 0 | 240 | −280 | 6 | $\frac{7}{2}$ | 35 | $-\frac{75}{2}$ |

The only rational root of $2x^3 - x^2 + 2x + 5 = 0$ is $-1$.

 **Got It? 1.** What are the rational roots of $3x^3 + 7x^2 + 6x - 8 = 0$?

Once you find one root, use synthetic division to factor the polynomial. Continue finding roots and dividing until you have a second-degree polynomial. Use the Quadratic Formula to find the remaining roots.

 **Problem 2** Using the Rational Root Theorem

What are the rational roots of $15x^3 - 32x^2 + 3x + 2 = 0$?

| Know | Need | Plan |
|---|---|---|
| Coefficients and the constant term of the polynomial | The roots of the polynomial equation | • Find one root.<br>• Factor until you get a quadratic.<br>• Use the Quadratic Formula to find the other roots. |

**Step 1** The constant term factors are $\pm 1$ and $\pm 2$. The leading coefficient factors are $\pm 1, \pm 3, \pm 5$, and $\pm 15$.

**Step 2** The possible rational roots are: $\pm 1, \pm 2, \pm \frac{1}{3}, \pm \frac{2}{3}, \pm \frac{1}{5}, \pm \frac{2}{5}, \pm \frac{1}{15}$, and $\pm \frac{2}{15}$.

**Step 3** Test each possible rational root in $15x^3 - 32x^2 + 3x + 2$ until you find a root.
Test 1: $15(1)^3 - 32(1)^2 + 3(1) + 2 = -12 \neq 0$
Test 2: $15(2)^3 - 32(2)^2 + 3(2) + 2 = 0$     So 2 is a root.

**Step 4** Factor the polynomial by using synthetic division:
$P(x) = (x - 2)(15x^2 - 2x - 1)$.

$$\begin{array}{r|rrrr} 2 & 15 & -32 & 3 & 2 \\ & & 30 & -4 & -2 \\ \hline & 15 & -2 & -1 & 0 \end{array}$$

**Step 5** Since $15x^2 - 2x - 1 = (5x + 1)(3x - 1)$, the other roots are $-\frac{1}{5}$ and $\frac{1}{3}$.

The rational roots of $15x^3 - 32x^2 + 3x + 2 = 0$ are $2, -\frac{1}{5}$, and $\frac{1}{3}$.

 **Got It? 2.** What are the rational roots of $2x^3 + x^2 - 7x - 6 = 0$?

---

## Problem 1    SYNTHESIZING

**Q** What can you conclude about the roots of the polynomial function if $P(x) \neq 0$ for all possible rational roots? **[The polynomial function has no rational roots, but it may have imaginary, complex, or irrational roots.]**

### Got It?    SYNTHESIZING

**Q** How many possible rational roots are there? **[16]**

## Problem 2    SYNTHESIZING

**Q** What is an advantage of combining the theorem with synthetic division? **[Answers may vary. Sample: It may save time, especially if the remaining quadratic polynomial is factorable.]**

**Q** If the remaining polynomial is not factorable, what techniques could be used to find the remaining roots? **[The Quadratic Formula could be used on a quadratic, or you could use a calculator.]**

### Got It?    ERROR PREVENTION

**Q** What possible roots would you substitute in first? Explain. **[Answers may vary. Sample: 1 and −1, since they are the easiest to calculate.]**

**Q** How could you use your calculator to make the substitution accurate? **[On the TI-84 or TI-85, store the polynomial in $Y_1$ using the Y = menu. Store the root to be tested in x. Use VARS→Y−VARS→ 1: Function $Y_1$ to evaluate.]**

---

## 2 Guided Instruction

 Each Problem is worked out and supported online.

**Problem 1**
Finding a Rational Root
*Animated*

**Problem 2**
Using the Rational Root Theorem

**Problem 3**
Using the Conjugate Root Theorem to Identify Roots

**Problem 4**
Using Conjugates to Construct a Polynomial

**Alternative Problem 4**
Using Conjugates to Construct a Polynomial
*Animated*

**Problem 5**
Using Descartes' Rule of Signs
*Animated*

**Support in Algebra 2 Companion**
• Vocabulary
• Key Concepts
• Got It?

---

# Answers

### Solve It!

$\frac{1}{4}$  There are two pairs of numbers that have a sum of 5: 1 and 4; 2 and 3. Try each pair to see if the numbers satisfy the constraints. Only $\frac{1}{4}$ satisfies all the constraints.

### Got It?

**1.** $\frac{2}{3}$

**2.** $2, -1, -\frac{3}{2}$

## Take Note

**SYNTHESIZING**

In the book, $a + bi$ is referred to as complex and $bi$ as pure imaginary. The Conjugate Root Theorem as it applies to complex numbers is sometimes called the Imaginary Root Theorem.

### Problem 3

**SYNTHESIZING**

**Q** How do you know that this polynomial function has at most 4 roots? **[It is a quartic polynomial function.]**

**Q** Could a third-degree polynomial function with rational coefficients have the roots $2 - i$ and $\sqrt{3}$? Why or why not? **[No; by the Conjugate Root Theorem $2 + i$ and $-\sqrt{3}$ would also have to be roots of the function. A third-degree polynomial function cannot have 4 roots.]**

### Got It?

**ERROR PREVENTION**

**Q** Is $\frac{5}{2}$ part of a conjugate pair? Why or why not? **[No; $\frac{5}{2}$ is a rational root. The Conjugate Root Theorem applies to irrational and imaginary roots.]**

### Problem 4

**ERROR PREVENTION**

**Q** After applying the Conjugate Root Theorem, how do you know that you have all of the roots? **[Check the degree of the polynomial function. Since the problem refers to a third-degree polynomial function and 2 roots are given, one more root is needed.]**

### Got It?

**ERROR PREVENTION**

**Q** How would you write the factors of the polynomial? **[$(x - (2 - 3i))(x - (2 + 3i))(x - 8)(x - 2)$]**

---

Recall from Lesson 4-8 that the complex numbers $a + bi$ and $a - bi$ are conjugates. Similarly, the irrational numbers $a + \sqrt{b}$ and $a - \sqrt{b}$ are conjugates. If a complex number or an irrational number is a root of a polynomial equation with rational coefficients, so is its conjugate.

**take note**

**Theorem   Conjugate Root Theorem**

If $P(x)$ is a polynomial with *rational* coefficients, then irrational roots of $P(x) = 0$ that have the form $a + \sqrt{b}$ occur in conjugate pairs. That is, if $a + \sqrt{b}$ is an irrational root with $a$ and $b$ rational, then $a - \sqrt{b}$ is also a root.

If $P(x)$ is a polynomial with *real* coefficients, then the complex roots of $P(x) = 0$ occur in conjugate pairs. That is, if $a + bi$ is a complex root with $a$ and $b$ real, then $a - bi$ is also a root.

 **Problem 3** Using the Conjugate Root Theorem to Identify Roots

A quartic polynomial $P(x)$ has rational coefficients. If $\sqrt{2}$ and $1 + i$ are roots of $P(x) = 0$, what are the two other roots?

Since $P(x)$ has rational coefficients and $0 + \sqrt{2}$ is a root of $P(x) = 0$, it follows from the Conjugate Root Theorem that $0 - \sqrt{2}$ is also a root.

Since $P(x)$ has real coefficients and $1 + i$ is a root of $P(x) = 0$, it follows that $1 - i$ is also a root.

The two other roots are $-\sqrt{2}$ and $1 - i$.

**Think**

Do you have real coefficients?
All rational numbers are real numbers. Therefore the rational coefficients are real coefficients.

 **Got It? 3.** A cubic polynomial $P(x)$ has real coefficients. If $3 - 2i$ and $\frac{5}{2}$ are two roots of $P(x) = 0$, what is one additional root?

 **Problem 4** Using Conjugates to Construct a Polynomial

**Multiple Choice** What is a third-degree polynomial function $y = P(x)$ with rational coefficients so that $P(x) = 0$ has roots $-4$ and $2i$?

&#9398; $P(x) = x^3 - 2x^2 - 16x + 32$

&#9399; $P(x) = x^3 - 4x^2 + 4x - 16$

&#9400; $P(x) = x^3 + 4x^2 + 4x + 16$

&#9401; $P(x) = x^3 + 4x^2 - 4x - 16$

Since $2i$ is a root, then $-2i$ is also a root.

$P(x) = (x + 2i)(x - 2i)(x + 4)$   Write the polynomial function.

$= (x^2 + 4)(x + 4)$   Multiply the complex conjugates.

$= x^3 + 4x^2 + 4x + 16$   Write the polynomial function in standard form.

The equation $x^3 + 4x^2 + 4x + 16 = 0$ has rational coefficients and has roots $-4$ and $2i$. The correct answer is C.

**Think**

Does the Conjugate Root Theorem apply to $-4$?
No; the theorem does not apply because $-4$ is neither irrational nor imaginary.

**Got It? 4.** What quartic polynomial equation has roots $2 - 3i$, 8, 2?

---

# Additional Problems

**1.** What are the rational roots of $x^3 - 5x^2 - 2x + 10 = 0$?

**ANSWER** 5

**2.** What are the rational roots of $x^3 - 2x^2 - 5x + 6 = 0$?

**ANSWER** 1, $-2$, 3

**3.** A cubic polynomial $P(x)$ has rational coefficients. If $2 + 3i$ and $\frac{2}{3}$ are two roots of $P(x) = 0$, what is one additional root?

**ANSWER** $2 - 3i$

**4.** What is a quartic polynomial function $P(x)$ with rational coefficients so that $P(x) = 0$ has roots 1, 3, and $1 + 2i$?

**ANSWER**
$x^4 - 6x^3 + 16x^2 - 26x + 15$

**5.** What does Descartes' Rule of Signs tell you about the real roots of $P(x) = -x^4 + x^3 - 2x^2 + x + 1 = 0$?

**ANSWER** 1 or 3 positive, 1 negative

The French mathematician René Descartes (1596–1650) recognized a connection between the roots of a polynomial equation and the $+$ and $-$ signs of the standard form.

> **Theorem** Descartes' Rule of Signs
>
> Let $P(x)$ be a polynomial with real coefficients written in standard form.
> - The number of positive real roots of $P(x) = 0$ is either equal to the number of sign changes between consecutive coefficients of $P(x)$ or is less than that by an even number.
> - The number of negative real roots of $P(x) = 0$ is either equal to the number of sign changes between consecutive coefficients of $P(-x)$ or is less than that by an even number.
>
> In both cases, count multiple roots according to their multiplicity.

### Problem 5  Using Descartes' Rule of Signs

**What does Descartes' Rule of Signs tell you about the real roots of $x^3 - x^2 + 1 = 0$?**

There are two sign changes, $+$ to $-$ and $-$ to $+$.
Therefore, there are either 0 or 2 positive real roots.

$P(-x) = (-x)^3 - (-x)^2 + 1 = -x^3 - x^2 + 1 = 0$ has only one sign change $-$ to $+$. There is one negative real root.

Recall that graphs of cubic functions have zero or two turning points. Because the graph already shows two turning points, it will not change direction again. So there are no positive real roots.

**Think**
Why can't there be zero negative real roots?
The number of negative roots is equal to 1 or is less than 1 by an even number. Zero is less than 1 by an odd number.

 **Got It? 5. a.** What does Descartes' Rule of Signs tell you about the real roots of $2x^4 - x^3 + 3x^2 - 1 = 0$?
**b. Reasoning** Can you confirm real and complex roots graphically? Explain.

### ✓ Lesson Check

**Do you know HOW?**

Use the Rational Root Theorem to list all possible rational roots for each equation.

1. $x^2 + x - 2 = 0$

2. $2x^3 - x^2 - 6 = 0$

3. $3x^4 + 2x^2 - 12 = 0$

Write a polynomial function with rational coefficients so that $P(x) = 0$ has the given roots.

4. 5 and 9          5. $-4$ and $2i$

**Do you UNDERSTAND?**

6. **Vocabulary** Give an example of a conjugate pair.

7. **Reasoning** In the statements below, $r$ and $s$ represent integers. Is each statement *always*, *sometimes*, or *never* true? Explain.
   **a.** A root of the equation $3x^3 + rx^2 + sx + 8 = 0$ could be 5.
   **b.** A root of the equation $3x^3 + rx^2 + sx + 8 = 0$ could be $-2$.

8. **Error Analysis** A student claims that $-4i$ is the only imaginary root of a polynomial equation that has real coefficients. What is the student's mistake?

---

## Take Note                    SYNTHESIZING

This theorem implies that two tests must be done on a polynomial function to determine both positive and negative real roots.

### Problem 5                   SYNTHESIZING

> **Q** Suppose $P(x) = x^4 - x^2 = 0$. Why does Descartes' Rule of Signs say $P(x)$ has one positive and one negative root? **[0 is neither positive nor negative.]**

### Got It?                     EXTENSION

> **Q** What part of the polynomial indicates that $P(x) \neq P(-x)$? **[The odd exponent of the second term guarantees that the sign of this term will change in $P(-x)$.]**

## 3 Lesson Check

### Do you know HOW?      ERROR INTERVENTION
- For Exercises 1–3, if students mistakenly list multiples of the same root, encourage them to simplify all roots and check that each is different.

### Do you UNDERSTAND? ERROR INTERVENTION
- For Exercise 7, students must focus on the constant term and the leading coefficient. Refer to the Rational Root Theorem and Problem 1.

### Close

> **Q** What is the difference between the Rational Root Theorem and the Conjugate Root Theorem? **[The Rational Root Theorem generates a list of possible rational roots of a given polynomial function. The Conjugate Root Theorem generates additional irrational, imaginary, or complex roots when some roots are given.]**

---

# Answers

## Got It? (continued)

3. $3 + 2i$

4. $P(x) = x^4 - 14x^3 + 69x^2 - 194x + 208$

5. **a.** There are three or one positive real roots and one negative real root. The graph confirms one negative and one positive real root.

   **b.** Real roots can be confirmed graphically because they are $x$-intercepts. Complex roots cannot be confirmed graphically because they have an imaginary component.

## Lesson Check

1. $\pm 1, \pm 2$

2. $\pm 1, \pm 2, \pm 3, \pm 6, \pm \frac{1}{2}, \pm \frac{3}{2}$

3. $\pm 1, \pm 2, \pm 3, \pm 4, \pm 6, \pm 12, \pm \frac{1}{3}, \pm \frac{2}{3}, \pm \frac{4}{3}$

4. $P(x) = x^2 - 14x + 45$

5. $P(x) = x^3 + 4x^2 + 4x + 16$

6. Answers may vary. Samples: $1 + 2i$ and $1 - 2i$; $1 + \sqrt{2}$ and $1 - \sqrt{2}$

7. **a.** never; 5 does not divide 8 evenly.
   **b.** always; $-2$ divides 8 evenly.

8. Complex number roots come in pairs; if $-4i$ is a root, so is $4i$.

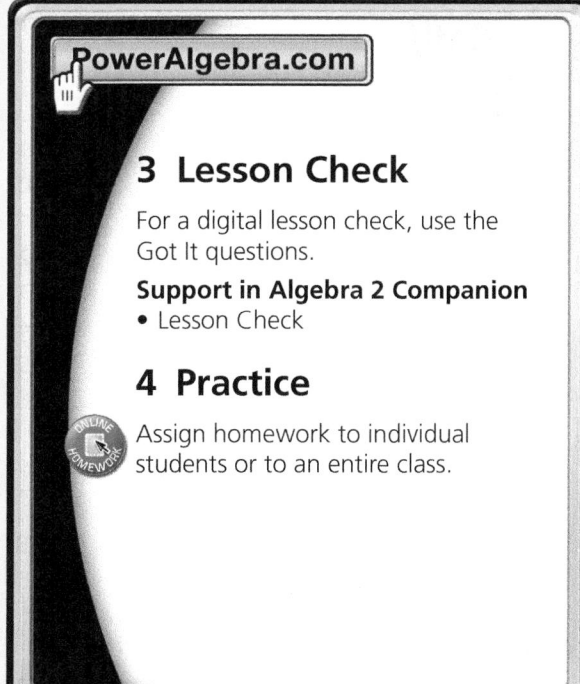

**PowerAlgebra.com**

### 3 Lesson Check

For a digital lesson check, use the Got It questions.

**Support in Algebra 2 Companion**
- Lesson Check

### 4 Practice

Assign homework to individual students or to an entire class.

# 4 Practice

## ASSIGNMENT GUIDE

Basic: 9–32 all, 34–40 even, 42–45

Average: 9–31 odd, 33–46

Advanced: 9–31 odd, 33–49

Standardized Test Prep: 50–54

Mixed Review: 55–62

**Reasoning** exercises have blue headings.

**Applications** exercises have red headings.

**EXERCISE 45:** Use the Think About a Plan worksheet in the **Practice and Problem Solving Workbook** (also available in the Teaching Resources in print and online) to further support students' development in becoming independent learners.

## HOMEWORK QUICK CHECK

To check students' understanding of key skills and concepts, go over Exercises 9, 19, 42, 44, and 45.

---

## Practice and Problem-Solving Exercises

**A Practice**

Use the Rational Root Theorem to list all possible rational roots for each equation. Then find any actual rational roots.　◀ See Problems 1 and 2.

**9.** $x^3 - 4x + 1 = 0$　　**10.** $x^3 + 2x - 9 = 0$　　**11.** $2x^3 - 5x + 4 = 0$

**12.** $3x^3 + 9x - 6 = 0$　　**13.** $4x^3 + 2x - 12 = 0$　　**14.** $6x^3 + 2x - 18 = 0$

**15.** $7x^3 - x^2 + 4x + 10 = 0$　**16.** $8x^3 + 2x^2 - 5x + 1 = 0$　**17.** $10x^3 - 7x^2 + x - 10 = 0$

A polynomial function $P(x)$ with rational coefficients has the given roots. Find two additional roots of $P(x) = 0$.　◀ See Problem 3.

**18.** $-2i$ and $\sqrt{10}$　**19.** $14 - \sqrt{2}$ and $-6i$　**20.** $i$ and $7 + 8i$　　**21.** $-\sqrt{3}$ and $5 - \sqrt{11}$

Write a polynomial function with rational coefficients so that $P(x) = 0$ has the given roots.　◀ See Problem 4.

**22.** 7 and 12　　**23.** $-9$ and $-15$　　**24.** $-10i$　　　**25.** $3i + 9$

**26.** 4, 16, and $1 + 19i$　**27.** $13i$ and $5 + 10i$　**28.** $11 - 2i$ and $8 + 13i$　**29.** $17 - 4i$ and $12 + 5i$

What does Descartes' Rule of Signs say about the number of positive real roots and negative real roots for each polynomial function?　◀ See Problem 5.

**30.** $P(x) = x^2 + 5x + 6$　　**31.** $P(x) = 9x^3 - 4x^2 + 10$　　**32.** $P(x) = 8x^3 + 2x^2 - 14x + 5$

**B Apply**

Find all rational roots for $P(x) = 0$.

**33.** $P(x) = 2x^3 - 5x^2 + x - 1$　　　**34.** $P(x) = 6x^4 - 13x^3 + 13x^2 - 39x - 15$

**35.** $P(x) = 7x^3 - x^2 - 5x + 14$　　　**36.** $P(x) = 3x^4 - 7x^3 + 10x^2 - x + 12$

**37.** $P(x) = 6x^4 - 7x^2 - 3$　　　　**38.** $P(x) = 2x^3 - 3x^2 - 8x + 12$

Write a polynomial function $P(x)$ with rational coefficients so that $P(x) = 0$ has the given roots.

**39.** $-6$, 3, and $-15i$　　**40.** $4 + \sqrt{5}$ and $8i$　　**41.** $-5 - 7i$ and $2 - \sqrt{11}$

**42. Think About a Plan** You are building a square pyramid out of clay and want the height to be 0.5 cm shorter than twice the length of each side of the base. If you have 18 cm³ of clay, what is the greatest height you could use for your pyramid?
- How can drawing a diagram help you solve this problem?
- What is the formula for the volume of a pyramid?
- What equation can you solve to find the height of the pyramid?

**43. Error Analysis** Your friend is using Descartes' Rule of Signs to find the number of negative real roots of $x^3 + x^2 + x + 1 = 0$. Describe and correct the error.

> $P(-x) = (-x)^3 + (-x)^2 + (-x) + 1$
> $= -x^3 - x^2 - x + 1$
> Because there is only one sign change in $P(-x)$, there must be one negative real root.

**44. Reasoning** A quartic equation with integer coefficients has two real roots and one imaginary root. Explain why the fourth root must be imaginary.

---

# Answers

## Practice and Problem-Solving Exercises

**9.** $\pm 1$; no rational roots

**10.** $\pm 1, \pm 3, \pm 9$; no rational roots

**11.** $\pm 1, \pm 2, \pm 4, \pm\frac{1}{2}$; no rational roots

**12.** $\pm 1, \pm 2, \pm 3, \pm 6, \pm\frac{1}{3}, \pm\frac{2}{3}$; no rational roots

**13.** $\pm 1, \pm 2, \pm 3, \pm 4, \pm 6, \pm 12, \pm\frac{1}{4}, \pm\frac{1}{2}, \pm\frac{3}{4}, \pm\frac{3}{2}$; no rational roots

**14.** $\pm 1, \pm 2, \pm 3, \pm 6, \pm 9, \pm 18, \pm\frac{1}{6}, \pm\frac{1}{3}, \pm\frac{1}{2}, \pm\frac{3}{2}, \pm\frac{2}{3}, \pm\frac{9}{2}$; no rational roots

**15.** $\pm 1, \pm 2, \pm 5, \pm 10, \pm\frac{1}{7}, \pm\frac{2}{7}, \pm\frac{5}{7}, \pm\frac{10}{7}$; no rational roots

**16.** $\pm 1, \pm\frac{1}{8}, \pm\frac{1}{4}, \pm\frac{1}{2}; -1, \frac{1}{4}, \frac{1}{2}$

**17.** $\pm 1, \pm 2, \pm 5, \pm 10, \pm\frac{1}{2}, \pm\frac{5}{2}, \pm\frac{1}{5}, \pm\frac{2}{5}, \pm\frac{1}{10}$; no rational roots

**18.** $2i, -\sqrt{10}$

**19.** $14 + \sqrt{2}, 6i$

**20.** $-i, 7 - 8i$

**21.** $\sqrt{3}, 5 + \sqrt{11}$

**22.** $P(x) = x^2 - 19x + 84$

**23.** $P(x) = x^2 + 24x + 135$

**24.** $P(x) = x^2 + 100$

**25.** $P(x) = x^2 - 18x + 90$

**26.** $P(x) = x^4 - 22x^3 + 466x^2 - 7368x + 23,168$

**27.** $P(x) = x^4 - 10x^3 + 294x^2 - 1690x + 21,125$

**28.** $P(x) = x^4 - 38x^3 + 710x^2 - 7126x + 29,125$

**29.** $P(x) = x^4 - 588x^3 + 1290x^2 - 13,066x + 51,545$

**30.** no positive real roots; two or no negative real roots

**31.** two or no positive real roots; one negative real root

**32.** two or no positive real roots; one negative real root

**33.** no rational roots

**34.** $\frac{5}{2}, -\frac{1}{3}$

**35.** no rational roots

**36.** no rational roots

**37.** no rational roots

**38.** $\frac{3}{2}, -2; 2$

**39.** $P(x) = x^4 + 3x^3 + 207x^2 + 675x - 4050$

**40.** $P(x) = x^4 - 8x^3 + 75x^2 - 512x + 704$

**41.** $P(x) = x^4 + 6x^3 + 27x^2 - 366x - 518$

**42.** $\approx 5.67$ cm

**43.** Error in second line, sign of second term; the line should be: $P(-1) = -x^3 + x^2 - x + 1$. Since there are three sign changes in $P(-x)$, there are three or one negative real roots.

**44.** Imaginary roots come in pairs; the imaginary root's conjugate is also a root.

**45. Gardening** A gardener is designing a new garden in the shape of a trapezoid. She wants the shorter base to be twice the height and the longer base to be 4 feet longer than the shorter base. If she has enough topsoil to create a 60 ft² garden, what dimensions should she use for the garden?

**46. Open-Ended** Write a fourth-degree polynomial equation with integer coefficients that has two irrational roots and two imaginary roots.

Ⓒ **Challenge**

**47. a.** Find a polynomial equation in which $1 + \sqrt{2}$ is the only root.
    **b.** Find a polynomial equation with root $1 + \sqrt{2}$ of multiplicity 2.
    **c.** Find $c$ such that $1 + \sqrt{2}$ is a root of $x^2 - 2x + c = 0$.

**48. a.** Using *real* and *imaginary* as types of roots, list all possible combinations of root type for a fourth-degree polynomial equation.
    **b.** Repeat the process for a fifth-degree polynomial equation.
    **c. Make a Conjecture** Make a conjecture about the number of real roots of an odd-degree polynomial equation.

**49. Writing** A student states that $2 + \sqrt{3}$ is a root of $x^2 - 2x - (3 + 2\sqrt{3}) = 0$. The student claims that $2 - \sqrt{3}$ is another root of the equation by the Conjugate Root Theorem. Explain how you would respond to the student.

---

## Standardized Test Prep

SAT/ACT

**50.** What is a positive root of $-5x^3 - 2x^2 + 9x + 30 = 0$?

**51.** What is the remainder when you divide $x^3 + 2x^2 - x - 6$ by $x - 1$?

**52.** A polynomial with rational coefficients has roots $-3i$ and $8 + \sqrt{7}$. What is the minimum degree of the polynomial?

**53.** What is the value of $y$ in the solution of the system of equations? $\begin{cases} 10x + 24y = 9 \\ 8x + 60y = 14 \end{cases}$

**54.** What is the value of the greater solution of the equation $6x^2 - 17x + 5 = 0$?

---

## Mixed Review

**Divide.** ◀ See Lesson 5-4.

**55.** $(x^3 + 5x^2 - 3) \div (x - 1)$    **56.** $(8x^3 + 12x^2 + 7) \div (x + 6)$    **57.** $(7x^2 + 11x - 4) \div (x + 2)$

**Solve.** ◀ See Lesson 4-8.

**58.** $7x^2 + 63 = 0$         **59.** $x^2 + 81 = 0$         **60.** $2x^2 + 288 = 0$

**Get Ready!** To prepare for Lesson 5-6, do Exercises 61 and 62.

Write each polynomial in standard form. Then classify it by degree and by number of terms. ◀ See Lesson 5-1.

**61.** $6x^2 + 11 - 5x^4 + 9x$         **62.** $13x - 4x^5 + 7x^3 + 2$

---

---

**45.** height: 5 ft; bases: 10 ft, 14 ft

**46.** Answers may vary. Sample: $x^4 - x^2 - 2 = 0$; roots: $\pm\sqrt{2}, \pm i$

**47.** Answers may vary. Samples:
    **a.** $x - 1 - \sqrt{2} = 0$
    **b.** $x^2 - 2(1 + \sqrt{2})x + (1 + \sqrt{2})^2 = 0$
    **c.** $-1$

**48. a.** two real, two imaginary; four imaginary; four real
    **b.** five real; three real, two imaginary; four imaginary, one real
    **c.** Answers may vary. Sample: It must have at least one real solution.

**49.** Answers may vary. Sample: You cannot use the Conjugate Root Theorem for irrational roots unless the equation has rational coefficients.

## Standardized Test Prep

**50.** 2

**51.** $-4$

**52.** 4

**53.** $\frac{1}{6}$

**54.** 2.5

## Mixed Review

**55.** $x^2 + 6x + 6$, R 3

**56.** $8x^2 - 36x + 216$, R $-1289$

**57.** $7x - 3$, R 2

**58.** $\pm 3i$

**59.** $\pm 9i$

**60.** $\pm 12i$

**61.** $-5x^4 + 6x^2 + 9x + 11$; quartic polynomial of four terms

**62.** $-4x^5 + 7x^3 + 13x + 2$; quintic polynomial of four terms

# Lesson Resources

## Differentiated Remediation
Available in editable format online.

## Additional Instructional Support

### Algebra 2 Companion
Students can use the **Algebra 2 Companion** worktext (4 pages) as you teach the lesson. Use the Companion to support

- New Vocabulary
- Key Concepts
- Got It for each Problem
- Lesson Check

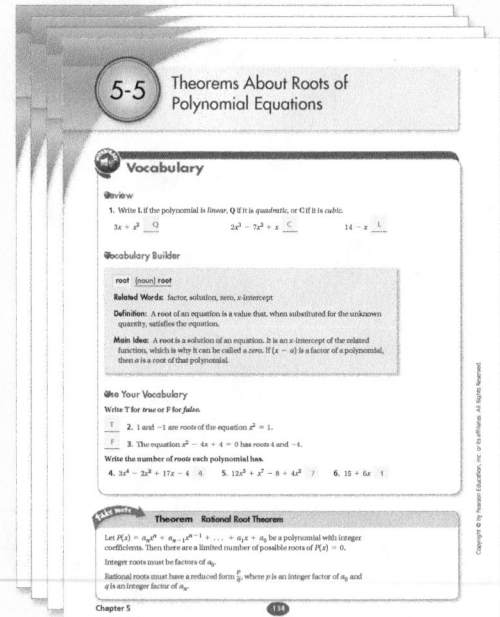

## 5 Assess & Remediate

### Lesson Quiz

**1.** What are the rational roots of $3x^3 - 6x^2 - x + 2 = 0$?

**2.** What are the rational roots of $3x^3 - 2x^2 - 19x - 6 = 0$?

**3. Do you UNDERSTAND?** A quartic polynomial $P(x)$ has rational coefficients. If $2 - i$ and $-\sqrt{5}$ are roots of $P(x) = 0$, what are the other two roots?

**4.** What is a third-degree polynomial function $P(x)$ with rational coefficients so that $P(x) = 0$ has roots $-3$ and $i$?
- **A.** $P(x) = x^3 - 3x^2 + x - 3$
- **B.** $P(x) = x^3 + 3x^2 + x + 3$
- **C.** $P(x) = x^3 - 5x^2 - x + 3$
- **D.** $P(x) = x^3 + 5x^2 + x + 3$

**5.** What does Descartes' Rule of Signs tell you about the real roots of $x^3 - x^2 + x + 1 = 0$?

### ANSWERS TO LESSON QUIZ

**1.** 2

**2.** $-2, 3, -\dfrac{1}{3}$

**3.** $2 + i, \sqrt{5}$

**4.** B

**5.** 0 or 2 positive, 1 negative

## Intervention

- **Reteaching** (2 pages) Provides reteaching and practice exercises for the key lesson concepts. Use with struggling students or absent students.

- **English Language Learner Support** Helps students develop and reinforce mathematical vocabulary and key concepts.

### All-in-One Resources/Online
#### Reteaching

**5-5 Reteaching**
Theorems About Roots of Polynomials Equations

**Problem**
What are the rational roots of $6x^4 + 29x^3 + 40x^2 + 7x - 12 = 0$?

**Step 1** Determine the factors of the constant term and the factors of the leading coefficient.
constant term: 12    factors: $\pm 1, \pm 2, \pm 3, \pm 4, \pm 6, \pm 12$
leading coefficient: 6    factors: $\pm 1, \pm 2, \pm 3, \pm 6$

**Step 2** Find all the possible roots by dividing the factors of the constant term by the factors of the leading coefficient. $\pm 1, \pm 2, \pm 3, \pm 4, \pm 6, \pm 12, \pm\frac{1}{2}, \pm\frac{3}{2}, \pm\frac{1}{3}, \pm\frac{2}{3}, \pm\frac{4}{3}$

**Step 3** Substitute each possible root into the polynomial until you find one that causes the polynomial to equal zero. This is one rational root.
Test $-\frac{3}{2}: 6\left(-\frac{3}{2}\right)^4 + 29\left(-\frac{3}{2}\right)^3 + 40\left(-\frac{3}{2}\right)^2 + 7\left(-\frac{3}{2}\right) - 12 = 0$ $-\frac{3}{2}$ is a rational root.

**Step 4** Factor the polynomial by synthetic division using the first rational root as the divisor.

**Step 5** If the dividend is a second-degree polynomial, factor to find any additional rational roots. If the dividend does not factor, there are no additional rational roots. If the dividend is greater than a second-degree polynomial, repeat Steps 1–4 until the dividend is a second-degree polynomial.
$6x^2 + 12x - 6 = 0$ does not factor. The rational roots of $6x^4 + 29x^3 + 40x^2 + 7x - 12$ are $-\frac{3}{2}$ and $-\frac{4}{3}$.

**Exercises**
Find all rational roots for $P(x) = 0$.
1. $P(x) = x^3 - x^2 - 8x + 12$ $-3, 2$
2. $P(x) = x^4 - 49x^2$ $0, 7, -7$
3. $P(x) = 2x^3 - 7x^2 - 21x + 54$ $-3, 2, \frac{9}{2}$
4. $P(x) = x^4 - 2x^3 - 3$ $-1$

## ELL Support
**Use Role Playing** Assign #11,18, 26, 30, 33, and 39 from the Practice Exercises. Divide the class into groups of four. In each group, two students assume the role of the teacher. Using their notes, they ask the other two students to solve the problems and to state their steps as they work through each problem. "For Ex. 11, first we list the factors of 1 and 9. Then we use the Rational Root Theorem by . . . " After completing problems #11,18, and 26, the roles are switched and the second set of problems is completed.

### PRESCRIPTION FOR REMEDIATION
Use the student work on the Lesson Quiz to prescribe a differentiated review assignment:

| Points | Differentiated Remediation |
|---|---|
| 0–2 | Intervention |
| 3–4 | On-level |
| 5 | Extension |

## 5 Assess & Remediate
Assign the Lesson Quiz. Appropriate intervention, practice, or enrichment is automatically generated based on student performance.

### All-in-One Resources/Online
#### English Language Learner Support

**5-5 ELL Support**
Theorems About Roots of Polynomial Equations

**Problem**
What are the rational roots of $6x^3 - 17x^2 - 4x + 3 = 0$? Explain your work.

$6x^3 - 17x^2 - 4x + 3 = 0$    Write the original equation.
Constant term: $\pm 1, \pm 3$    Identify the factors of the constant term.
Leading coefficient: $\pm 1, \pm 2, \pm 3, \pm 6$    Identify the leading coefficient.
$\pm 1, \pm\frac{1}{2}, \pm\frac{1}{3}, \pm\frac{1}{6}, \pm 3, \pm\frac{3}{2}$    Use the Rational Root Theorem to identify the possible rational roots.
$6(3)^3 - 17(3)^2 - 4(3) + 3 = 0$    Test the possible rational roots.
$3\,|\,6\ -17\ -4\ \ 3$    Factor the polynomial using synthetic division.
$\underline{\ \ \ \ 18\ \ \ 3\ -3}$
$6\ \ \ 1\ -1\ \ 0$
$P(x) = (x - 3)(6x^2 + x - 1)$
$6x^2 + x - 1 = (3x - 1)(2x + 1)$    Find the other rational roots.
$3\left(\frac{1}{3}\right) - 1 = 0$
$2\left(-\frac{1}{2}\right) + 1 = 0$
The rational roots are $3, \frac{1}{3}$, and $-\frac{1}{2}$.

**Exercise**
What are the rational roots of $4x^3 - 8x^2 + x + 3 = 0$? Explain your work.

$4x^3 - 8x^2 + x + 3 = 0$    Write the original equation.
Constant term: $\pm 1, \pm 3$    Identify the factors of the constant term.
Leading coefficient: $\pm 1, \pm 2, \pm 4$    Identify the leading coefficient.
$\pm 1, \pm\frac{1}{2}, \pm\frac{1}{4}, \pm 3, \pm\frac{3}{2}, \pm\frac{3}{4}$    Use the Rational Root Theorem to identify the possible rational roots.
$4(1)^3 - 8(1)^2 + 1 + 3 = 0$    Test the possible rational roots.
$1\,|\,4\ -8\ \ \ 1\ \ \ 3$    Factor the polynomial using synthetic division.
$\underline{\ \ \ \ \ 4\ -4\ -3}$
$4\ -4\ -3\ \ 0$
$P(x) = (x - 1)(4x^2 - 4x - 3)$
$4x^2 - 4x - 3 = (2x + 1)(2x - 3)$    Find the other rational roots.
$2\left(-\frac{1}{2}\right) + 1 = 0$
$2\left(\frac{3}{2}\right) - 3 = 0$
The rational roots are $1, -\frac{1}{2}$, and $\frac{3}{2}$.

# Differentiated Remediation *continued*

Available in editable format online.

## On-Level

- **Practice** (2 pages) Provides extra practice for each lesson. For simpler practice exercises, use the Form K Practice pages found in the All-in-One Teaching Resources and online.

- **Think About a Plan** Helps students develop specific problem-solving skills and strategies by providing scaffolded guiding questions.

- **Standardized Test Prep** Focuses on all major exercises, all major question types, and helps students prepare for the high-stakes assessments.

## Extension

- **Enrichment** Provides students with interesting problems and activities that extend the concepts of the lesson.

- **Activities, Games, and Puzzles** Worksheets that can be used for concepts development, enrichment, and for fun!

---

### Practice and Problem Solving Wkbk/All-in-One Resources/Online
**Practice page 1**

### Practice and Problem Solving Wkbk/All-in-One Resources/Online
**Practice page 2**

### All-in-One Resources/Online
**Enrichment**

---

### Practice and Problem Solving Wkbk/All-in-One Resources/Online
**Think About a Plan**

### Practice and Problem Solving Wkbk/All-in-One Resources/Online
**Standardized Test Prep**

### Online Teacher Resource Center
**Activities, Games, and Puzzles**

# Guided Instruction

**PURPOSE** To solve polynomial inequalities

**PROCESS** Students will
- find the zeros of a polynomial.
- sketch the graph of a polynomial function.
- use the shape of the graph and the zeros to write the solution of the inequality.

**DISCUSS**

## Example 1                    SYNTHESIZING

> **Q** Using the zeros as markers, how many pieces of the curve are in the solution set? **[2]**
>
> **Q** What inequality represents the leftmost piece? Why? **[$x < -1$, because the cubic graph will remain below the x-axis for all values less than $-1$ (to the left of $-1$).]**
>
> **Q** What is the inequality that represents the other piece? Why? **[$-\frac{2}{3} < x < \frac{3}{4}$; the graph is below the x-axis between these values.]**
>
> **Q** Will the graph remain above the x-axis for all values greater than $\frac{3}{4}$? Why? **[Yes; the shape of the graph indicates this.]**

## Example 2                    SYNTHESIZING

> **Q** Why is there only one zero? **[The graph intersects the x-axis in only 1 point.]**
>
> **Q** What part of the graph will be the solution? Why? **[The polynomial is greater than 0 where the graph is above the x-axis, to the left of 6.53.]**

---

You can use what you know about factoring and graphing polynomials to help you solve polynomial inequalities.

## Example 1

Solve $12x^3 + 11x^2 - 7x - 6 < 0$.

By the Rational Root Theorem and the Factor Theorem, $(x + 1)$ is one factor.

So, $12x^3 + 11x^2 - 7x - 6 = (x + 1)(12x^2 - x - 6)$
$$= (x + 1)(3x + 2)(4x - 3)$$

The zeros of the polynomial are $-1$, $-\frac{2}{3}$, and $\frac{3}{4}$.

You know the graph of a cubic polynomial with a positive leading coefficient has the shape shown at the right. The polynomial is less than 0 where the graph is below the x-axis.

Thus, $x < -1$ and $-\frac{2}{3} < x < \frac{3}{4}$ is the solution of the inequality.

## Example 2

Solve $-x^3 + 12x^2 - 44x + 54 > 0$.

You know the shape of the graph. Use a graphing calculator to find the only zero at $x = 6.53$.

The graph is above the x-axis when $x < 6.53$. Therefore, the solution of the inequality is $x < 6.53$.

## Exercises

**Solve each inequality.**

**1.** $8x^2 - 2x - 21 > 0$

**2.** $-16x^2 + 104x - 169 < 0$

**3.** $x^3 - 20x^2 - 100x + 2000 > 0$

**4.** $-10x^3 + x^2 - 10x + 1 > 0$

**5.** $x(x^2 + 1) > 2(2x^2 - 3)$

**6.** $7x^3 \leq x^2 + 66x$

**7.** $x^3 - 11x^2 + 32x - 28 \geq 0$

**8.** $11x^3 - 76x^2 + 80x + 192 > 0$

**9. Reasoning** If $Q(x)$ is a quartic polynomial, one possible solution of $Q(x) < 0$ is an interval of numbers, not including endpoints. Describe other possible solutions.

---

# Answers

## Exercises

**1.** $x < -1.5$ or $x > 1.75$

**2.** all real values of $x$, $x \neq 3.25$

**3.** $-10 < x < 10$ or $x > 20$

**4.** $x < \frac{1}{10}$

**5.** $-1 < x < 2$ or $x > 3$

**6.** $x \leq -3$ or $0 \leq x \leq \frac{22}{7}$

**7.** $x \geq 7$ or $x = 2$

**8.** $x > -\frac{12}{11}$, $x \neq 4$

**9.** Check students' work.

# 5-6 The Fundamental Theorem of Algebra

**Objective** To use the Fundamental Theorem of Algebra to solve polynomial equations with complex solutions

These graphs are on complex planes.

**Getting Ready!**

The first graph shows the three complex-number solutions of $x^3 - 1 = 0$. The second graph shows the six solutions of $x^6 - 1 = 0$. How many complex number solutions does $x^{12} - 1 = 0$ have? What are they?

**Lesson Vocabulary**
• Fundamental Theorem of Algebra

You can factor any polynomial of degree $n$ into $n$ linear factors, but sometimes the factors will involve imaginary numbers.

**Essential Understanding** The degree of a polynomial equation tells you how many roots the equation has.

It is easy to see graphically that every polynomial function of degree 1 has a single zero, the $x$-intercept. However, there appear to be three possibilities for polynomials of degree 2. They correspond to these three graphs:

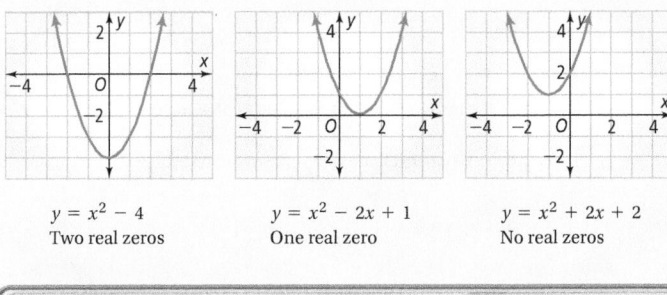

$y = x^2 - 4$
Two real zeros

$y = x^2 - 2x + 1$
One real zero

$y = x^2 + 2x + 2$
No real zeros

---

# 1 Interactive Learning

**Solve It!**

**PURPOSE** To realize that the number of roots of a polynomial equation is the same as the degree

**PROCESS** Students may

• notice the relationship between the exponent and the number of complex solutions.

• notice the pattern of the complex solutions on the unit circle.

**FACILITATE**

**Q** How are the three equations different? **[The powers of the $x$-term are different.]**

**Q** How does the exponent seem to affect the number of solutions? **[As the exponent doubles, the number of solutions doubles.]**

**Q** The solutions are all located on the unit circle. How are they spaced? **[evenly]**

**Q** Where are the solutions of $x^{12} - 1 = 0$ located? **[Answers may vary. Sample: in the same place as the solutions for $x^6 - 1$ plus midway between each of these solutions]**

**ANSWER** See Solve It in Answers on next page.

**CONNECT THE MATH** In the Solve It, students use patterns to identify the number and type of complex solutions of a polynomial equation. In this lesson, they will use the fact that the number of complex solutions of a polynomial equation is equal to its degree.

---

# 5-6 Preparing to Teach

**BIG ideas** Solving Equations and Inequalities
Equivalence

**UbD**

**ESSENTIAL UNDERSTANDING**

• The degree of a polynomial equation tells how many roots the equation has.

## Math Background

This lesson is students' first introduction to the Fundamental Theorem of Algebra. It is important to note that this theorem does not *find* the roots of a function but instead identifies how many roots a function has.

This lesson applies and combines the theorems and techniques in the chapter to find roots of a polynomial function of degree $n \geq 1$.

A polynomial function with no constant term has 0 as one of its rational roots. Also, a polynomial function with odd degree and real coefficients must

have a root in the set of real numbers. Show this by graphing. Based on the rules for end behavior, it is possible that the graph of a polynomial function of an even degree will never cross the $x$-axis, but a polynomial function of an odd degree must.

## Support Student Learning

Use the **Algebra 2 Companion** to engage and support students during instruction. See Lesson Resources at the end of this lesson for details.

**PowerAlgebra.com**

# 1 Interactive Learning

**Solve It!**

Step out how to solve the Problem with helpful hints and an online question. Other questions are listed above in Interactive Learning.

# 2 Guided Instruction

## Take Note
SYNTHESIZING

The polynomial equation must be set equal to 0. Review that complex roots include real roots and imaginary roots.

## Problem 1
SYNTHESIZING

Students apply the Fundamental Theorem of Algebra to find all complex roots of the polynomial equation. They must have previous knowledge of the Rational Root Theorem, the Factor Theorem, and synthetic division.

> **Q** How are the rational roots found? **[According to the Rational Root Theorem, the possible rational roots are $x = \pm\frac{p}{q}$, where $p$ represents the integer factors of the constant term and $q$ represents the integer factors of the leading coefficient.]**
>
> **Q** What could you do instead of factoring $x^4 - 3x^2 - 4$? **[Answers may vary. Sample: Substitute the possible rational roots. If the value of the polynomial equals 0, use synthetic division.]**
>
> **Q** How would you check your result? **[Multiply the binomials to make sure that you get the original polynomial.]**

## Got It?
ERROR PREVENTION

> **Q** Since there is no constant term, what will be your first step after the equation is in standard form? **[Factor $x$ from the polynomial.]**

---

However, by factoring, you can see that each related equation has two roots.

$$x^2 - 4 = (x - 2)(x + 2) = 0 \qquad \text{two real roots, 2 and } -2$$
$$x^2 - 2x + 1 = (x - 1)(x - 1) = 0 \qquad \text{a root of multiplicity } two \text{ at 1}$$
$$x^2 + 2x + 2 = (x - (-1 + i))(x - (-1 - i)) = 0 \qquad \text{two complex roots, } -1 + i \text{ and } -1 - i$$

Every quadratic polynomial equation has two roots, every cubic polynomial equation has three roots, and so on.

This result is related to the *Fundamental Theorem of Algebra*. The German mathematician Carl Friedrich Gauss (1777–1855) is credited with proving this theorem.

> **take note**
>
> **Theorem  The Fundamental Theorem of Algebra**
>
> If $P(x)$ is a polynomial of degree $n \geq 1$, then $P(x) = 0$ has exactly $n$ roots, including multiple and complex roots.

 **Problem 1**  Using the Fundamental Theorem of Algebra

What are all the roots of $x^5 - x^4 - 3x^3 + 3x^2 - 4x + 4 = 0$?

| Know | Need | Plan |
|------|------|------|
| The polynomial equation has degree 5. There are 5 roots. | The zeros of the function | Use the Rational Root and Factor Theorems, synthetic division, and factoring. |

**Step 1**  The polynomial is in standard form. The possible rational roots are $\pm 1$, $\pm 2$, $\pm 4$.

**Step 2**  Evaluate the related polynomial function for $x = 1$. Since $P(1) = 0$, 1 is a root and $x - 1$ is a factor. Use synthetic division to factor out $x - 1$:

```
 1 | 1  -1  -3   3  -4   4
   |     1   0  -3   0  -4
   ---------------------------
     1   0  -3   0  -4   0
```

**Think**

How many linear factors will there be?
If there are five roots, there must be five linear factors.

**Step 3**  Continue factoring until you have five linear factors.

$$x^5 - x^4 - 3x^3 + 3x^2 - 4x + 4 = (x - 1)(x^4 - 3x^2 - 4)$$
$$= (x - 1)(x^2 - 4)(x^2 + 1)$$
$$= (x - 1)(x - 2)(x + 2)(x - i)(x + i)$$

**Step 4**  The roots are 1, 2, $-2$, $i$, and $-i$.

By the Fundamental Theorem of Algebra, these are the only roots.

 **Got It?  1.** What are all the roots of the equation $x^4 + 2x^3 = 13x^2 - 10x$?

---

# Answers

## Solve It!

$12; \pm 1, \pm \dfrac{\sqrt{3} \pm i}{2}, \pm \dfrac{1}{2}i, \dfrac{1 \pm i\sqrt{3}}{2}, \pm i, \dfrac{-1 \pm i\sqrt{3}}{2}$

## Got It?

**1.** 0, 1, $-5$, 2       **2. a.** $-1$, 2, $\dfrac{1 \pm i\sqrt{23}}{4}$

**b.** i. A 5th degree polynomial function has four, two, or no turning pts. Three turning pts. are visible, so there must be a fourth one. This will turn the graph back across the $x$-axis.

ii. The Fundamental Thm. of Algebra states there will be five roots, and the Conjugate Root Thm. requires pairs of irrational or complex roots. Only two zeros appear in the graph, so there are three zeros remaining. Of the remaining roots, either there are three real roots, or one real and two complex roots. Either way, there is at least one real root that does not appear as a real zero in the graph.

---

**PowerAlgebra.com**

# 2 Guided Instruction

Each Problem is worked out and supported online.

> **Problem 1**
> Using the Fundamental Theorem of Algebra
> *Animated*

> **Problem 2**
> Finding All the Zeros of a Polynomial Function
> *Animated*

## Support in Algebra 2 Companion
- Vocabulary
- Key Concepts
- Got It?

**Problem 2** Finding All the Zeros of a Polynomial Function

**What are the zeros of** $f(x) = x^4 + x^3 - 7x^2 - 9x - 18$?

**Step 1** Use a graphing calculator to find any real roots. The graph of $y = x^4 + x^3 - 7x^2 - 9x - 18$ shows real zeros at $x = -3$ and $x = 3$.

Zero X=-3 Y=0    Zero X=3 Y=0

> **Think**
>
> **Does the graph show all of the real roots?**
> Yes; the graphs of quartic functions have one or three turning points. Since the graph shows three turning points, it will not turn again to cross the x-axis a third time.

**Step 2** Factor out the linear factors $x + 3$ and $x - 3$. Use synthetic division twice.

$$\begin{array}{r|rrrrr} -3 & 1 & 1 & -7 & -9 & -18 \\ & & -3 & 6 & 3 & 18 \\ \hline & 1 & -2 & -1 & -6 & 0 \end{array}$$

$$\begin{array}{r|rrrr} 3 & 1 & -2 & -1 & -6 \\ & & 3 & 3 & 6 \\ \hline & 1 & 1 & 2 & 0 \end{array}$$

$$x^4 + x^3 - 7x^2 - 9x - 18 = (x + 3)(x^3 - 2x^2 - x - 6)$$
$$= (x + 3)(x - 3)(x^2 + x + 2)$$

**Step 3** Use the Quadratic Formula. Find the complex roots of $x^2 + x + 2 = 0$.

$a = 1, b = 1, c = 2$    Identify the values of a, b, and c.

$\dfrac{-1 \pm \sqrt{1^2 - 4(1)(2)}}{2(1)}$    Substitute.

$\dfrac{-1 \pm \sqrt{-7}}{2}$    Simplify.

The complex roots are $\dfrac{-1 + i\sqrt{7}}{2}$ and $\dfrac{-1 - i\sqrt{7}}{2}$.

**Step 4** The four zeros of the function are $-3, 3, \dfrac{-1 + i\sqrt{7}}{2}$, and $\dfrac{-1 - i\sqrt{7}}{2}$.

By the Fundamental Theorem of Algebra, there can be no other zeros.

**Got It?** **2. a.** What are all the zeros of the function $g(x) = 2x^4 - 3x^3 - x - 6$?
**b. Reasoning** The graph of
$f(x) = x^5 + 4x^4 - 3x^3 - 12x^2 - 4x - 4$ is shown at the right.
  **i.** Use the turning points to explain why the graph does NOT show all of the real zeros of the function.
  **ii.** The graph of $g(x) = f(x) + 4$ is a translation of the graph of $f$ up 4 units. How many real zeros of $g$ will the graph of $g$ show? Explain.

---

## Problem 2  SYNTHESIZING

Students use a graphing calculator to determine the real roots of the polynomial function and determine the remaining complex roots using the Quadratic Formula.

**Q** What are some advantages and disadvantages of using a calculator to find the real roots? **[Answers may vary. Sample: Adjusting the window to generate a complete graph may be difficult, but once the complete graph is visible, the real roots are easy to find.]**

**Q** Why is synthetic division used twice? **[The graph shows 2 real roots.]**

**Q** Why is the Quadratic Formula used? **[The trinomial of degree 2 cannot be factored, and there are no more possible real roots.]**

## Got It?  ERROR PREVENTION

**Q** How many times will you use synthetic division in 2a? Why? **[The graph indicates that there are 2 real roots, so synthetic division will be used twice.]**

**Q** How many turning points does a fifth-degree polynomial function have? **[A fifth-degree polynomial function can have 0, 2, or 4 turning points.]**

---

# Additional Problems

**1.** What are all the complex roots of $x^5 - x^4 - 7x^3 + 7x^2 - 18x + 18 = 0$?
**ANSWER** $1, \pm 3, \pm i\sqrt{2}$

**2.** What are the zeros of $f(x) = x^4 + 2x^3 - 4x^2 - 7x - 2$?
**ANSWER** $-1, 2, \dfrac{-3 \pm \sqrt{5}}{2}$

## Take Note

If students have trouble seeing how the third statement implies the first two, present the following. Choose any polynomial function of degree $n \geq 1$. By the third statement, the function has at least one complex zero. Factor it out. The remaining polynomial is of degree $n - 1$. If $n - 1 \geq 1$, the new polynomial must also have at least one complex zero. Factor it out. Continue until the degree of the remaining polynomial is $n - n$, or zero.

> **Q** The original polynomial can be represented as the product of how many linear factors? **[n]**

# 3 Lesson Check

## Do you know HOW?

- Exercises 1 and 2 only require students to find the *number* of roots. This is a direct application of the Fundamental Theorem of Algebra.

## Do you UNDERSTAND?

- For Exercise 6, review that a root of multiplicity 2 means that there are 2 identical roots. If students have difficulty, then they should use the roots to work backward to find the polynomial function.
- For Exercise 7, suggest that students examine Problems 1 and 2. Hint: Look at the degrees of the polynomial functions.

## Close

> **Q** How can the Fundamental Theorem of Algebra help you to solve polynomial equations? **[Answers may vary. Sample: The Fundamental Theorem of Algebra indicates the *number* of complex roots. When you identify the actual roots, you can use this number as a check.]**

**Concept Summary** The Fundamental Theorem of Algebra

Here are equivalent ways to state the Fundamental Theorem of Algebra. You can use any one of these statements to prove the others.

- Every polynomial equation of degree $n \geq 1$ has exactly $n$ roots, including multiple and complex roots.
- Every polynomial of degree $n \geq 1$ has $n$ linear factors.
- Every polynomial function of degree $n \geq 1$ has at least one complex zero.

### Lesson Check

**Do you know HOW?**

Find the number of roots for each equation.

**1.** $5x^4 + 12x^3 - x^2 + 3x + 5 = 0$

**2.** $-x^{14} - x^8 - x + 7 = 0$

Find all the zeros for each function.

**3.** $y = x^3 - 5x^2 + 16x - 80$

**4.** $y = x^4 - 2x^3 + x^2 - 2x$

**Do you UNDERSTAND?**

**5. Vocabulary** Given a polynomial equation of degree $n$, explain how you determine the number of roots of the equation.

**6. Open-Ended** Write a polynomial function of degree 4 with rational coefficients and two complex zeros of multiplicity 2.

**7. Writing** Describe when to use synthetic division and when to use the Quadratic Formula to determine the linear factors of a polynomial.

### Practice and Problem-Solving Exercises

**A** Practice

Without using a calculator, find all the roots of each equation. **See Problem 1.**

**8.** $x^3 - 3x^2 + x - 3 = 0$

**9.** $x^3 + x^2 + 4x + 4 = 0$

**10.** $x^3 + 4x^2 + x - 6 = 0$

**11.** $x^3 - 5x^2 + 2x + 8 = 0$

**12.** $x^4 + 4x^3 + 7x^2 + 16x + 12 = 0$

**13.** $x^4 - 4x^3 + x^2 + 12x - 12 = 0$

**14.** $x^5 + 3x^3 - 4x = 0$

**15.** $x^5 - 8x^3 - 9x = 0$

Find all the zeros of each function. **See Problem 2.**

**16.** $y = 2x^3 + x^2 + 1$

**17.** $f(x) = x^3 - 3x^2 + x - 3$

**18.** $g(x) = x^3 - 5x^2 + 5x - 4$

**19.** $y = x^3 - 2x^2 - 3x + 6$

**20.** $y = x^4 - 6x^2 + 8$

**21.** $f(x) = x^4 - 3x^2 - 4$

**22.** $y = x^3 - 3x^2 - 9x$

**23.** $y = x^3 + 6x^2 + x + 6$

**24.** $y = x^4 + 3x^3 + x^2 - 12x - 20$

**25.** $y = x^4 + x^3 - 15x^2 - 16x - 16$

## Answers

### Lesson Check

**1.** four roots

**2.** fourteen roots

**3.** $5, \pm 4i$

**4.** $0, 2, \pm i$

**5.** By the Fundamental Thm. of Algebra, a polynomial equation of degree $n$ has exactly $n$ roots.

**6.** Answers may vary. Sample: $y = x^4 + 8x^2 + 16$

**7.** Use synthetic division to test for and factor out linear factors until a quadratic factor is obtained. Then use the Quadratic Formula if the quadratic factor cannot be factored further.

### Practice and Problem-Solving Exercises

**8.** $3, \pm i$

**9.** $-1, \pm 2i$

**10.** $-3, -2, 1$

**11.** $-1, 2, 4$

**12.** $-3, -1, \pm 2i$

**13.** $2, \pm \sqrt{3}$

**14.** $0, \pm 1, \pm 2i$

**15.** $0, \pm 3, \pm i$

**16.** $-1; \dfrac{1 \pm i\sqrt{7}}{4}$

**17.** $3, \pm i$

**18.** $4; \dfrac{1 \pm i\sqrt{3}}{2}$

**19.** $2, \pm \sqrt{3}$

**20.** $\pm 2, \pm \sqrt{2}$

**21.** $\pm 2, \pm i$

**22.** $0; \dfrac{3 \pm 3\sqrt{5}}{2}$

**23.** $-6, \pm i$

**24.** $\pm 2, \dfrac{-3 \pm i\sqrt{11}}{2}$

**25.** $\pm 4, \dfrac{-1 \pm i\sqrt{3}}{2}$

---

# 3 Lesson Check

For a digital lesson check, use the Got It questions.

**Support in Algebra 2 Companion**
- Lesson Check

# 4 Practice

Assign homework to individual students or to an entire class.

**Apply**

For each equation, state the number of complex roots, the possible number of real roots, and the possible rational roots.

**26.** $2x^4 - x^3 + 2x^2 + 5x - 26 = 0$

**27.** $x^5 - x^3 - 11x^2 + 9x + 18 = 0$

**28.** $-12 + x + 10x^2 + 3x^3 = 0$

**29.** $4x^6 - x^5 - 24 = 0$

Find all the zeros of each function.

**30.** $y = x^3 - 4x^2 + 9x - 36$

**31.** $f(x) = x^3 + 2x^2 - 5x - 10$

**32.** $y = 2x^3 - 3x^2 - 18x - 8$

**33.** $y = 3x^3 - 7x^2 - 14x + 24$

**34.** $g(x) = x^3 - 4x^2 - x + 22$

**35.** $y = x^3 - x^2 - 3x - 9$

**36.** $y = x^4 - x^3 - 5x^2 - x - 6$

**37.** $y = 2x^4 + 3x^3 - 17x^2 - 27x - 9$

**38. Think About a Plan** A polynomial function, $f(x) = x^4 - 5x^3 - 28x^2 + 188x - 240$, is used to model a new roller coaster section. The loading zone will be placed at one of the zeros. The function has a zero at 5. What are the possible locations for the loading zone?
- Can you determine how many zeros you need to find?
- How can you use polynomial division?
- What other methods can be helpful?

**39. Bridges** A twist in a river can be modeled by the function $f(x) = \frac{1}{3}x^3 + \frac{1}{2}x^2 - x$, $-3 \le x \le 2$. A city wants to build a road that goes directly along the $x$-axis. How many bridges would it have to build?

**40. Error Analysis** Maurice says: "Every linear function has exactly one zero. It follows from the Fundamental Theorem of Algebra." Cheryl disagrees. "What about the linear function $y = 2$?" she asks. "Its graph is a line, but it has no $x$-intercept." Whose reasoning is incorrect? Where is the flaw?

Determine whether each of the following statement is *always*, *sometimes*, or *never* true.

**41.** A polynomial function with real coefficients has real zeros.

**42.** Polynomial functions with complex coefficients have one complex zero.

**43.** A polynomial function that does not intercept the $x$-axis has complex roots only.

**44. Reasoning** A 4th degree polynomial function has zeros at 3 and $5 - i$. Can $4 + i$ also be a zero of the function? Explain your reasoning.

**45. Open-Ended** Write a polynomial function that has four possible rational zeros but no actual rational zeros.

**46.** Three roots of a polynomial equation with real coefficients are 3, $5 - 3i$, and $-3i$. Which number MUST also be a root of the equation?

    I. $-3$          II. $5 + 3i$          III. $3i$

  Ⓐ II only      Ⓑ I and II only      Ⓒ II and III only      Ⓓ I, II, and III

# 4 Practice

**ASSIGNMENT GUIDE**

Basic: 8–25 all, 26–30 even, 38–40, 44, 46

Average: 9–25 odd, 26–46

Advanced: 9–25 odd, 26–49

Standardized Test Prep: 50–53

Mixed Review: 54–65

**Reasoning** exercises have blue headings.

**Applications** exercises have red headings.

**EXERCISE 39:** Use the Think About a Plan worksheet in the **Practice and Problem Solving Workbook** (also available in the Teaching Resources in print and online) to further support students' development in becoming independent learners.

**HOMEWORK QUICK CHECK**

To check students' understanding of key skills and concepts, go over Exercises 9, 17, 38, 39, and 44.

---

**26.** four complex roots; four, two, or no real roots; possible rational roots: $\pm\frac{1}{2}, \pm1, \pm2, \pm\frac{13}{2}, \pm13, \pm26$

**27.** five complex roots; one, three, or five real roots; possible rational roots: $\pm1, \pm2, \pm3, \pm6, \pm9, \pm18$

**28.** three complex roots; one or three real roots; possible rational roots: $\pm\frac{1}{3}, \pm\frac{2}{3}, \pm1, \pm\frac{4}{3}, \pm2, \pm3, \pm4, \pm6, \pm12$

**29.** six complex roots; zero, two, four, or six real roots; possible rational roots: $\pm\frac{1}{4}, \pm\frac{1}{2}, \pm\frac{3}{4}, \pm1, \pm\frac{3}{2}, \pm2, \pm3, \pm4, \pm6, \pm8, \pm12, \pm24$

**30.** $4, \pm3i$

**31.** $-2, \pm\sqrt{5}$

**32.** $-2, -\frac{1}{2}, 4$

**33.** $-2, \frac{4}{3}, 3$

**34.** $-2, 3 \pm i\sqrt{2}$

**35.** $3, -1 \pm i\sqrt{2}$

**36.** $-2, 3, \pm i$

**37.** $-\frac{1}{2}, -1, \pm3$

**38.** $-6, 2, 4,$ or 5

**39.** 3 bridges

**40.** Maurice is incorrect. Although every function of degree 1 has exactly one zero, $y = 2$ is a function of degree 0 but it is still a linear function. So linear functions with degree zero may have no zero or $x$-intercept.

**41.** sometimes

**42.** never

**43.** always

**44.** No; a 4th degree polynomial has four roots. If $5 - i$ is a root, then by the Conjugate Root Theorem $5 + i$ must also be a root. Likewise, if $4 + i$ is a root, then $4 - i$ must also be a root. This would result in five roots, which is impossible.

**45.** Answers may vary. Sample: $y = x^4 + 3x^2 + 2$

**46.** C

# Answers

## Practice and Problem-Solving Exercises (continued)

**47.** Given any polynomial eq. of odd degree $n \geq 1$, the eq. has exactly $n$ roots. Since imaginary roots occur in pairs, a polynomial of odd degree $n$ will have an even number of imaginary roots and thus an odd number of real roots. So, any odd degree polynomial eq. with real coefficients has at least one real root.

**48.** 5

**49.** 5th degree; rational zero:
$$-\frac{5}{6}(x - \sqrt{2})(x + \sqrt{2})(x - \sqrt{3})(x + \sqrt{3})(x + \frac{5}{6})$$
$$= x^5 + \frac{5}{6}x^4 - 5x^3 - \frac{25}{6}x^2 + 6x + 5.$$

## Standardized Test Prep

**50.** B

**51.** G

**52.** D

**53.** **[2]** Substitute $(2, -2)$ into both inequalities to see if the pt. satisfies both inequalities. If it does, then $(2, -2)$ is a solution of the system. If one or both inequalities are not satisfied by the pt. $(2, -2)$, then $(2, -2)$ is not a solution of the system.

**[1]** incomplete explanation

## Mixed Review

**54.** $x^4 + 6x^3 + 14x^2 + 24x + 40 = 0$

**55.** $3 \pm 2\sqrt{2}$

**56.** $\dfrac{-5 \pm i\sqrt{47}}{4}$

**57.** $\dfrac{3 \pm i\sqrt{23}}{4}$

**58.** $f(x) = -x^2 + 2x + 3$

**59.** $f(x) = 2x^2 + 24x + 75$

**60.** $x^3 + 3x^2 + 3x + 1$

**61.** $x^3 - 9x^2 + 27x - 27$

**62.** $x^4 - 8x^3 + 24x^2 - 32x + 16$

**63.** $x^2 - 2x + 1$

**64.** $x^3 + 15x^2 + 75x + 125$

**65.** $-x^3 + 12x^2 + 48x + 64$

---

 **Challenge**

**47.** Use the Fundamental Theorem of Algebra and the Conjugate Root Theorem to show that any odd degree polynomial equation with real coefficients has at least one real root.

**48. Reasoning** What is the maximum number of points of intersection between the graphs of a quartic and a quintic polynomial function?

**49. Reasoning** What is the least possible degree of a polynomial with rational coefficients, leading coefficient 1, constant term 5, and zeros at $\sqrt{2}$ and $\sqrt{3}$? Show that such a polynomial has a rational zero and indicate this zero.

## Standardized Test Prep

**SAT/ACT**

**50.** How many roots does $f(x) = x^4 + 5x^3 + 3x^2 + 2x + 6$ have?

  Ⓐ 5    Ⓑ 4    Ⓒ 3    Ⓓ 2

**51.** Which translation takes $y = |x + 2| - 1$ to $y = |x| + 2$?

  Ⓕ 2 units right, 3 units down    Ⓗ 2 units left, 3 units up

  Ⓖ 2 units right, 3 units up    Ⓘ 2 units left, 3 units down

**52.** What is the factored form of the expression $x^4 - 3x^3 + 2x^2$?

  Ⓐ $x^2(x - 1)(x + 2)$    Ⓒ $x^2(x + 1)(x - 2)$

  Ⓑ $x^2(x + 1)(x + 2)$    Ⓓ $x^2(x - 1)(x - 2)$

**Short Response**

**53.** How would you test whether $(2, -2)$ is a solution of the system? $\begin{cases} y < -2x + 3 \\ y \geq x - 4 \end{cases}$

## Mixed Review

**54.** Find a fourth-degree polynomial equation with real coefficients that has $2i$ and $-3 + i$ as roots.   ◀ See Lesson 5-5.

Solve each equation using the Quadratic Formula.   ◀ See Lesson 4-7.

**55.** $x^2 - 6x + 1 = 0$    **56.** $2x^2 + 5x = -9$    **57.** $2(x^2 + 2) = 3x$

Determine whether a quadratic model exists for each set of values. If so, write the model.   ◀ See Lesson 4-3.

**58.** $f(-1) = 0, f(2) = 3, f(1) = 4$    **59.** $f(-4) = 11, f(-5) = 5, f(-6) = 3$

**Get Ready!** To prepare for Lesson 5-7, do Exercises 60–65.   ◀ See Lesson 4-2.

Write each polynomial in standard form.

**60.** $(x + 1)^3$    **61.** $(x - 3)^3$    **62.** $(x - 2)^4$

**63.** $(x - 1)^2$    **64.** $(x + 5)^3$    **65.** $(4 - x)^3$

# Lesson Resources

## Additional Instructional Support

### Algebra 2 Companion

Students can use the **Algebra 2 Companion** worktext (4 pages) as you teach the lesson. Use the Companion to support

- New Vocabulary
- Key Concepts
- Got It for each Problem
- Lesson Check

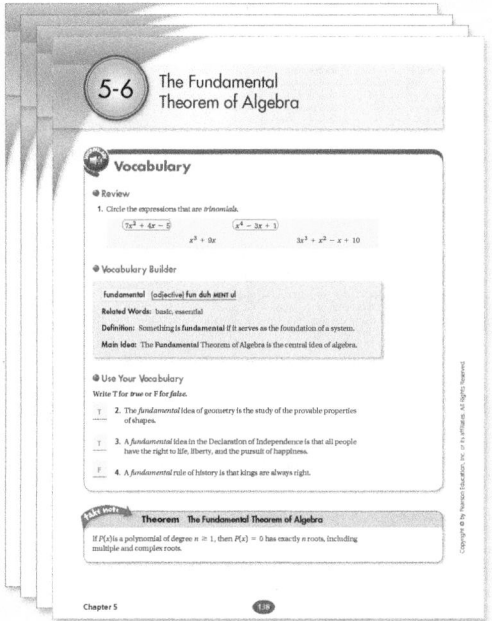

### ELL Support

**Use Graphic Organizers** Have students label six index cards as shown. Add notes to the bottom three cards such as, "Use synthetic division when a real root is known," and "Use factoring when the polynomial is factorable." When solving a problem, students line up the first three cards as indicated. The last three cards depend on the problem.

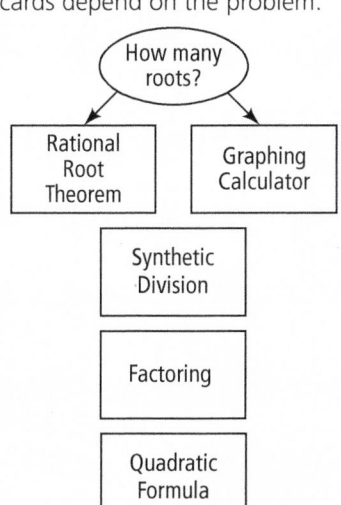

## 5 Assess & Remediate

### Lesson Quiz

1. What are all the complex roots of $x^4 - 8x^2 = x^3 - 8x$?

2. **Do you UNDERSTAND?** What are the zeros of $f(x) = x^4 + x^3 - 3x^2 - 4x - 4$?

**ANSWERS TO LESSON QUIZ**

1. $0, 1, \pm 2\sqrt{2}$
2. $\pm 2, \dfrac{-1 \pm i\sqrt{3}}{2}$

### PRESCRIPTION FOR REMEDIATION

Use the student work on the Lesson Quiz to prescribe a differentiated review assignment:

| Points | Differentiated Remediation |
|--------|----------------------------|
| 0 | Intervention |
| 1 | On-level |
| 2 | Extension |

**PowerAlgebra.com**

### 5 Assess & Remediate

Assign the Lesson Quiz. Appropriate intervention, practice, or enrichment is automatically generated based on student performance.

## Differentiated Remediation

Available in editable format online.

### Intervention

- **Reteaching** (2 pages) Provides reteaching and practice exercises for the key lesson concepts. Use with struggling students or absent students.

- **English Language Learner Support** Helps students develop and reinforce mathematical vocabulary and key concepts.

**All-in-One Resources/Online**
**Reteaching**

**All-in-One Resources/Online**
**English Language Learner Support**

# Differentiated Remediation *continued*

Available in editable format online.

## On-Level

- **Practice** (2 pages) Provides extra practice for each lesson. For simpler practice exercises, use the Form K Practice pages found in the All-in-One Teaching Resources and online.

- **Think About a Plan** Helps students develop specific problem-solving skills and strategies by providing scaffolded guiding questions.

- **Standardized Test Prep** Focuses on all major exercises, all major question types, and helps students prepare for the high-stakes assessments.

## Extension

- **Enrichment** Provides students with interesting problems and activities that extend the concepts of the lesson.

- **Activities, Games, and Puzzles** Worksheets that can be used for concepts development, enrichment, and for fun!

---

### Practice and Problem Solving Wkbk/All-in-One Resources/Online
**Practice page 1**

*5-6 Practice — Form G — The Fundamental Theorem of Algebra*

### Practice and Problem Solving Wkbk/All-in-One Resources/Online
**Practice page 2**

*5-6 Practice (continued) — Form G — The Fundamental Theorem of Algebra*

### All-in-One Resources/Online
**Enrichment**

*5-6 Enrichment — The Fundamental Theorem of Algebra*

---

### Practice and Problem Solving Wkbk/All-in-One Resources/Online
**Think About a Plan**

*5-6 Think About a Plan — The Fundamental Theorem of Algebra*

### Practice and Problem Solving Wkbk/All-in-One Resources/Online
**Standardized Test Prep**

*5-6 Standardized Test Prep — The Fundamental Theorem of Algebra*

### Online Teacher Resource Center
**Activities, Games, and Puzzles**

*5-6 Puzzle: An Unlikely Find — The Fundamental Theorem of Algebra*

## Concept Byte

For Use With Lesson 5-7

# Pascal's Triangle

You are standing at the corner of the grid shown at the right (point A1). You are only permitted to travel down or to the right. The only way to get to point A2 is by traveling down one unit. To get to point B1, travel to the right one unit. There is one way to get to point B1. There is also one way to get to point A2, however there are 2 ways to get to point B2.

You are here →

## Exercises

1. What are the two different ways you can get from point A1 to point B2?

2. Copy the grid. Travel only down or to the right. In how many ways can you get from point A1 to point A3?

3. Use your copy of the grid from Exercise 2. In how many ways can you get from point A1 to point C2?

4. In how many ways can you get to point B5 from your starting point, A1?

5. Mark the number of ways you can get to each point on the grid from point A1.

6. **Reasoning** Describe any patterns you see in the numbers on the grid.

7. Describe how the numbers increase in each row. How can you tell the next number in each row without counting the number of paths from A1?

8. **a.** Make a copy of your completed grid. Color a shaded square around every number that is a multiple of 2. (You may need to extend the grid to see a pattern.)
   **b.** The pattern you see in part (a) resembles the Sierpinski triangle. Look at page 10, exercise 42 to see a Sierpinski triangle. Find another way to describe how to obtain this pattern.

9. **Writing** The completed grid is called Pascal's Triangle. Rotate your copy of the grid 45° clockwise so that point A1 is at the top. Explain why the grid is called a triangle.

10. Find the sum of the rows of the rotated grid. (These would be diagonals in the original grid.) What pattern do you find?

# Guided Instruction

**PURPOSE** To explore and discover the pattern of Pascal's Triangle

**PROCESS** Students will

- follow the rules on how to travel in the grid.
- trace and count the number of paths from the starting point to different points on the grid.
- describe patterns that they see.
- generalize the pattern.

**DISCUSS** The rows and columns of the grid are symmetric. As you progress along each row or the column of the same number, the number of paths is the same.

**Q** Could you count the number of paths from B2 to A1? Explain. **[No, you can only move to the right and down.]**

**Q** Which points do you think will have the greatest number of paths? **[Answers may vary. Sample: The ones along the diagonal because you can combine moving right and down in the greatest number of ways.]**

## Exercises

To help ensure that students find every possible path, suggest that they count all of the paths that begin by moving to the right first, and then all of the paths that begin by moving down first.

**Q** What is the number of paths for points in Row 1? For Column A? **[They are all 1.]**

**Q** What is the pattern of the number of paths for each consecutive point in Row 2? **[The numbers are increasing by 1.]**

**Q** How does Row 2 compare to Column 2? **[They are the same.]**

# Answers

## Exercises

1. A1 → B1 → B2; A1 → A2 → B2

2. 1     3. 3     4. 5

5.

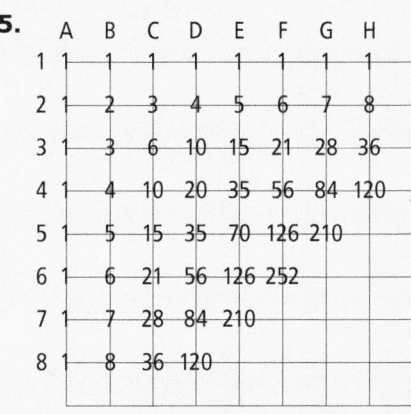

6. Answers may vary. Sample: The outer edges are all ones. Row 2 and Column B are consecutive positive integers.

7. Each number in a row is the sum of the number that precedes it and the number in the same column in the row above it.

8. a.

**8.b.–10.** See back of book.

# 1 Interactive Learning

## Solve It!

**PURPOSE** To find patterns within the numbers of ways to choose items from a group

**PROCESS** Students may

- make systematic lists of all arrangements and count the number of unique subgroups.
- solve simpler problems with fewer letters and recognize geometric or numeric patterns.
- use prior knowledge of counting techniques to calculate the number of combinations.

### FACILITATE

**Q** In the diagram shown, why is BA not listed? **[Order is not important; BA is equivalent to AB.]**

**Q** How does the diagram represent a "systematic" method? **[The first row shows A paired with all other letters; the second row shows B paired with all other letters except A; the third row shows C paired with all other letters except A or B; the last row shows D paired with all other letters except A, B, or C.]**

**ANSWER** See Solve It in Answers on next page.

**CONNECT THE MATH** In the Solve It, students use patterns to calculate numbers of combinations. Numbers of combinations may also be calculated from the coefficients of a binomial expansion or Pascal's Triangle.

---

**Objectives** To expand a binomial using Pascal's Triangle
To use the Binomial Theorem

**Getting Ready!**

When counting seems complicated, it helps to be systematic.

How many unique letter combinations are possible using each of the following?
a. 2 of 5 letters   b. 3 of 5 letters
c. 2 of 6 letters   d. 4 of 6 letters
e. 3 of 6 letters
Justify your reasoning.

<u>Hint:</u> Use the diagram, a previous response, or both. The same letters in different orders are one combination.

AB  AC  AD  AE
BC  BD  BE
CD  CE

A  B  C  D  E

**Lesson Vocabulary**
- expand
- Pascal's Triangle
- Binomial Theorem

There is a connection between the triangular pattern of numbers in the Solve It and the expansion of $(a + b)^n$.

**Essential Understanding** You can use a pattern of coefficients and the pattern $a^n, a^{n-1}b, a^{n-2}b^2, \ldots, a^2b^{n-2}, ab^{n-1}, b^n$ to write the expansion of $(a + b)^n$.

You can *expand* $(a + b)^3$ using the Distributive Property.

$$(a + b)^3 = (a + b)(a + b)(a + b) = a^3 + 3a^2b + 3ab^2 + b^3$$

To **expand** the power of a binomial in general, first multiply as needed. Then write the polynomial in standard form.

Consider the expansions of $(a + b)^n$ for the first few values of $n$:

| Row | Power | Expanded Form | Coefficients Only |
|---|---|---|---|
| 0 | $(a + b)^0$ | 1 | 1 |
| 1 | $(a + b)^1$ | $1a^1 + 1b^1$ | 1  1 |
| 2 | $(a + b)^2$ | $1a^2 + 2a^1b^1 + 1b^2$ | 1  2  1 |
| 3 | $(a + b)^3$ | $1a^3 + 3a^2b^1 + 3a^1b^2 + 1b^3$ | 1  3  3  1 |
| 4 | $(a + b)^4$ | $1a^4 + 4a^3b^1 + 6a^2b^2 + 4a^1b^3 + 1b^4$ | 1  4  6  4  1 |

---

## 5-7 Preparing to Teach

**BIG idea** Equivalence   **UbD**

### ESSENTIAL UNDERSTANDINGS

- A pattern of coefficients and the pattern $a^n, a^{n-1}b, a^{n-2}b^2, \ldots, a^1b^{n-1}, b^n$, can be used to write the expansion of $(a + b)^n$.
- To expand the power of a binomial in general, first multiply as needed. Then write the polynomial in standard form.

### Math Background

This lesson shows three methods to expand binomials. For binomial $(a + b)^n$:

#### DISTRIBUTIVE PROPERTY

- Remove the power by rewriting the binomial as a product of $n$ binomials.
- Multiply out, one binomial at a time.
- Simplify by combining like terms.

The Distributive Property works well if $n$ is small. If $n$ is large, calculations are time-consuming and lead to errors.

#### PASCAL'S TRIANGLE

- Generate $n + 1$ rows of Pascal's Triangle.
- Use the numbers of the $n + 1$ row of the triangle in order as coefficients of $a^n + a^{n-1}b + \ldots + ab^{n-1} + b^n$.

Pascal's Triangle is useful when $a$ and $b$ are both variables. Students may consider it a trick or shortcut.

#### BINOMIAL THEOREM

- Generate $n + 1$ rows of Pascal's Triangle.
- Let $P_0, P_1, \ldots, P_n$ be the numbers of the $n + 1$ row in order.
- Use the general formula $(a + b)^n = P_0a^n + P_1a^{n-1}b + \ldots + P_{n-1}ab^{n-1} + P_nb^n$.
- If $a$ or $b$ is not a variable, simplify.

### Support Student Learning

Use the **Algebra 2 Companion** to engage and support students during instruction. See Lesson Resources at the end of this lesson for details.

---

**PowerAlgebra.com**

## 1 Interactive Learning

### Solve It!

Step out how to solve the Problem with helpful hints and an online question. Other questions are listed above in Interactive Learning.

The "coefficients only" column matches the numbers in *Pascal's Triangle*. **Pascal's Triangle**, named for the French mathematician Blaise Pascal (1623-1662), is a triangular array of numbers in which the first and last number of each row is 1. Each of the other numbers in the row is the sum of the two numbers above it.

For example, to generate row 5, use the sums of the adjacent elements in the row above it.

**Pascal's Triangle**

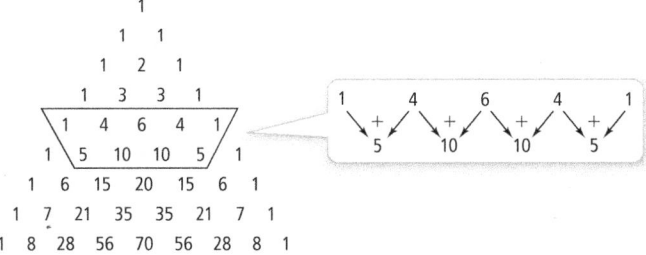

**Plan**

What row of Pascal's Triangle should you use for this expansion?
The expression is raised to the 6th power so use the 6th row.

**Problem 1** Using Pascal's Triangle

**What is the expansion of $(a + b)^6$? Use Pascal's Triangle.**

The exponents for $a$ begin with 6 and decrease to 0. ⌐

$$1a^6b^0 + 6a^5b^1 + 15a^4b^2 + 20a^3b^3 + 15a^2b^4 + 6a^1b^5 + 1a^0b^6$$

The exponents for $b$ begin with 0 and increase to 6. ⌐

$$(a + b)^6 = a^6 + 6a^5b + 15a^4b^2 + 20a^3b^3 + 15a^2b^4 + 6ab^5 + b^6.$$

 **Got It?** **1.** What is the expansion of $(a + b)^8$? Use Pascal's Triangle.

The **Binomial Theorem** gives a general formula for expanding a binomial.

**take note**

**Theorem** Binomial Theorem

For every positive integer $n$,
$$(a + b)^n = P_0a^n + P_1a^{n-1}b + P_2a^{n-2}b^2 + \cdots + P_{n-1}ab^{n-1} + P_nb^n$$
where $P_0, P_1, \ldots, P_n$ are the numbers in the $n$th row of Pascal's Triangle.

# 2 Guided Instruction

To help students better understand Pascal's Triangle, use the following activity:
- Close the book.
- Place the 1 on the top of your page.
- Write two more 1's below it.
- Generate each row. For each new term, add the adjacent terms above it.
- Make your triangle as large as you can, and compare it with a partner's triangle.

## Problem 1

It is possible to expand the power by repeatedly applying the Distributive Property, but the method of using Pascal's Triangle is much simpler.

**Q** How many terms are in the expansion? **[7]**
**Q** Do you see any pattern in the coefficients? **[They increase from the left to the middle, and decrease from the middle to the right in symmetrical fashion.]**

## Got It?

It can be helpful to include the powers $a^0$ and $b^0$ in the expansion to see how the power of each variable is incremented in each term.

**Q** What would be the coefficient of $a^{20}$ in $(a + b)^{20}$? **[1]**

## Take Note

The rules for expanding the square or cube of a binomial are the same as in the Binomial Theorem for $n = 2$ and $n = 3$.

**Q** Which coefficients are the same as the power of the binomial? **[The second and the second to last.]**

# 2 Guided Instruction

 Each Problem is worked out and supported online.

**Problem 1**
Using Pascal's Triangle
*Animated*

**Problem 2**
Expanding a Binomial
*Animated*

**Support in Algebra 2 Companion**
- Vocabulary
- Key Concepts
- Got It?

# Answers

## Solve It!

**a.** 10; AB, AC, AD, AE, BC, BD, BE, CD, CE, DE
**b.** 10; ABC, ABD, ABE, ACD, ACE, ADE, BCD, BCE, BDE, CDE
**c.** 15; the combinations from part (a) and AF, BF, CF, DF, EF
**d.** 15; add an F to all combinations in part (b), and ABCD, ABCE, BCDE, ABDE, ACDE
**e.** 20; the combinations from part (b) and ABF, ACF, ADF, AEF, BCF, BDF, BEF, CDF, CEF, DEF

## Got It?

**1.** $a^8 + 8a^7b + 28a^6b^2 + 56a^5b^3 + 70a^4b^4 + 56a^3b^5 + 28a^2b^6 + 8ab^7 + b^8$

## Problem 2

When a binomial has a term with a coefficient other than 1, the coefficients of the expansion are not the same as the numbers in Pascal's Triangle.

> **Q** Which terms in the expansion have a negative coefficient? **[the terms with even powers of $x$]**

### Got It?

> **Q** In 2a, how can you write the binomial in the form $(a + b)^n$? **[$(2x - 3)^4 = (2x + (-3))^4$]**
>
> **Q** Which terms in the expansion have a negative coefficient? **[the terms with odd powers of $x$]**

## 3 Lesson Check

### Do you know HOW?

- In Exercises 3–4, the students may be confused by the coefficients of $x$ or $a$. Suggest that they expand the binomial, replacing "$x$" with "$2x$" or "$a$" with "$3a$" in parentheses, and then simplify.

### Do you UNDERSTAND?

- For Exercise 6, if students have difficulty understanding the relationship, suggest that they solve a problem with each method. Then have them compare the processes.

### Close

> **Q** For what powers do the rows of Pascal's Triangle repeat the same number in the middle? **[odd powers]**
>
> **Q** Why is it easier to use the Binomial Theorem than expanding the power using the Distributive Property? **[Answers may vary. Sample: For greater powers, there are too many terms to write out to use the Distributive Property easily.]**

---

When you use the Binomial Theorem to expand $(x - 2)^4$, $a = x$ and $b = -2$. To expand a binomial such as $(3x - 2)^5$, $a = 3x$ so remember that $a^4 = (3x)^4$ not $3x^4$.

 **Problem 2** Expanding a Binomial

**What is the expansion of $(3x - 2)^5$? Use the Binomial Theorem.**

| Think | | Write |
|---|---|---|
| For $(3x - 2)^5$, use the 5th row of Pascal's Triangle. | → | **Pascal's Triangle** <br> 1 <br> 1   1 <br> 1   2   1 <br> 1   3   3   1 <br> 1   4   6   4   1 <br> $\boxed{1\ \ 5\ \ 10\ \ 10\ \ 5\ \ 1}$ |
| The Binomial Theorem uses a binomial sum. | → | $(3x - 2)^5 = (3x + (-2))^5$ |
| Apply the Binomial Theorem. | → | $= (3x)^5 + 5(3x)^4(-2)^1 + 10(3x)^3(-2)^2$ <br> $+ 10(3x)^2(-2)^3 + 5(3x)^1(-2)^4 + 1(-2)^5$ |
| Simplify. | → | $= 243x^5 - 810x^4 + 1080x^3 - 720x^2 + 240x - 32$ |

 **Got It?** **2. a.** What is the expansion of $(2x - 3)^4$? Use the Binomial Theorem.

**b. Reasoning** Consider the following:

$$11^0 = 1 \quad 11^1 = 11 \quad 11^2 = 121 \quad 11^3 = 1331 \quad 11^4 = 14641$$

Why do these powers of 11 have digits that mirror Pascal's Triangle?

---

### ✓ Lesson Check

**Do you know HOW?**

Use Pascal's Triangle to expand each binomial.

1. $(x + a)^3$

2. $(x - 2)^5$

3. $(2x + 4)^2$

4. $(3a - 2)^3$

**Do you UNDERSTAND?**

5. **Vocabulary** Tell whether each expression can be expanded using the Binomial Theorem.
   **a.** $(2a - 6)^4$   **b.** $(5x^2 + 1)^5$   **c.** $(x^2 - 3x - 4)^3$

6. **Writing** Describe the relationship between Pascal's Triangle and the Binomial Theorem.

7. **Reasoning** Using Pascal's Triangle, determine the number of terms in the expansion of $(x + a)^{12}$. How many terms are there in the expansion of $(x + a)^n$?

---

## Additional Problems

1. What is the expansion of $(x + 3)^4$?

   **ANSWER**
   $x^4 + 12x^3 + 54x^2 + 108x + 81$

2. What is the expansion of $(3 - z)^3$?

   **ANSWER** $27 - 27z + 9z^2 - z^3$

## Answers

### Got It? (continued)

**2. a.** $16x^4 - 96x^3 + 216x^2 - 216x + 81$

**b.** If you express 11 as $(10 + 1)$ and calculate the powers using Pascal's triangle, it will be the coefficients.

### Lesson Check

1. $x^3 + 3x^2a + 3xa^2 + a^3$

2. $x^5 - 10x^4 + 40x^3 - 80x^2 + 80x - 32$

3. $4x^2 + 16x + 16$

4. $27a^3 - 54a^2 + 36a - 8$

5. **a.** yes   **b.** yes   **c.** no

6. The coefficients for the expansion of $(a + b)^n$ are equal to the numbers in the $n$th row of Pascal's Triangle, respectively.

7. 13; $n + 1$

---

**PowerAlgebra.com**

## 3 Lesson Check

For a digital lesson check, use the Got It questions.

**Support in Algebra 2 Companion**
- Lesson Check

## 4 Practice

Assign homework to individual students or to an entire class.

## Practice and Problem-Solving Exercises

See Problems 1 and 2.

**A** Practice

Expand each binomial.

**8.** $(x - y)^3$     **9.** $(a + 2)^4$     **10.** $(6 + a)^6$     **11.** $(x - 5)^3$

**12.** $(y + 1)^8$     **13.** $(x + 2)^{10}$     **14.** $(b - 4)^7$     **15.** $(b + 3)^9$

**16.** $(2x - y)^7$     **17.** $(a + 3b)^4$     **18.** $(4x + 2)^6$     **19.** $(4 - x)^8$

**20.** $(4x + 5)^2$     **21.** $(3a - 7)^3$     **22.** $(2a + 16)^6$     **23.** $(3y - 11)^4$

**B** Apply

**24. Think About a Plan** The side length of a cube is $\left(x^2 - \frac{1}{2}\right)$. Determine the volume of the cube.
- Rewrite the binomial as a sum.
- Consider $(a + b)^n$. Identify $a$ and $b$ in the given binomial.
- Which row of Pascal's Triangle can be used to expand the binomial?

**25.** In the expansion of $(2m - 3n)^9$, one of the terms contains $m^3$.
   **a.** What is the exponent of $n$ in this term?
   **b.** What is the coefficient of this term?

**Find the specified term of each binomial expansion.**

**26.** Fourth term of $(x + 2)^5$        **27.** Third term of $(x - 3)^6$

**28.** Third term of $(3x - 1)^5$       **29.** Fifth term of $(a + 5b^2)^4$

**30. Reasoning** Explain why the coefficients in the expansion of $(x + 2y)^3$ do not match the numbers in the 3rd row of Pascal's Triangle.

**31. Compare and Contrast** What are the benefits and challenges of using the Binomial Theorem when expanding $(2x + 3)^2$? Using FOIL? Which method would you choose when expanding $(2x + 3)^6$? Why?

**Expand each binomial.**

**32.** $(2x - 2y)^6$     **33.** $(x^2 + 4)^{10}$     **34.** $(x^2 - y^2)^3$     **35.** $(a - b^2)^5$

**36.** $(3x + 8y)^3$     **37.** $(4x - 7y)^4$     **38.** $(7a + 2y)^{10}$     **39.** $(4x^3 + 2y^2)^6$

**40.** $(3b - 36)^7$     **41.** $(5a + 2b)^3$     **42.** $(b^2 - 2)^8$     **43.** $(-2y^2 + x)^5$

**44. Geometry** The side length of a cube is given by the expression $(2x + 8)$. Write a binomial power for the area of a face of the cube and for the volume of the cube. Then use the Binomial Theorem to expand and rewrite the powers in standard form.

**45. Writing** Explain why the terms of $(x - y)^n$ have alternating positive and negative signs.

**46. Error Analysis** A student expands $(3x - 8)^4$ as shown below. Describe and correct the student's error.

$$(3x - 8)^4 = (3x)^4 + 4(3x)^3(-8) + 6(3x)^2(-8)^2 + 4(3x)(-8)^3 + (-8)^4$$
$$= 3x^4 - 96x^3 + 1152x^2 - 6144x + 4096$$

---

**ASSIGNMENT GUIDE**
Basic: 8–23, 24, 30, 31, 44, 45
Average: 9–23 odd, 24–46
Advanced: 9–23 odd, 24–53
Standardized Test Prep: 54–57
Mixed Review: 58–68

**Reasoning** exercises have blue headings.

**Applications** exercises have red headings.

**EXERCISE 44:** Use the Think About a Plan worksheet in the **Practice and Problem Solving Workbook** (also available in the Teaching Resources in print and online) to further support students' development in becoming independent learners.

**HOMEWORK QUICK CHECK**
To check students' understanding of key skills and concepts, go over Exercises 9, 11, 24, 44, and 45.

---

## Practice and Problem-Solving Exercises

**8.** $x^3 - 3x^2y + 3xy^2 - y^3$

**9.** $a^4 + 8a^3 + 24a^2 + 32a + 16$

**10.** $46{,}656 + 46{,}656a + 19{,}440a^2 + 4320a^3 + 540a^4 + 36a^5 + a^6$

**11.** $x^3 - 15x^2 + 75x - 125$

**12.** $y^8 + 8y^7 + 28y^6 + 56y^5 + 70y^4 + 56y^3 + 28y^2 + 8y + 1$

**13.** $x^{10} + 20x^9 + 180x^8 + 960x^7 + 3360x^6 + 8064x^5 + 13{,}440x^4 + 15{,}360x^3 + 11{,}520x^2 + 5120x + 1024$

**14.** $b^7 - 28b^6 + 336b^5 - 2240b^4 + 8960b^3 - 21{,}504b^2 + 28{,}672b - 16{,}384$

**15.** $b^9 + 27b^8 + 324b^7 + 2268b^6 + 10{,}206b^5 + 30{,}618b^4 + 61{,}236b^3 + 78{,}732b^2 + 59{,}049b + 19{,}683$

**16.** $128x^7 - 448x^6y + 672x^5y^2 - 560x^4y^3 + 280x^3y^4 - 84x^2y^5 + 14xy^6 - y^7$

**17.** $a^4 + 12a^3b + 54a^2b^2 + 108ab^3 + 81b^4$

**18.** $4096x^6 + 12{,}288x^5 + 15{,}360x^4 + 10{,}240x^3 + 3840x^2 + 768x + 64$

**19.** $65{,}536 - 131{,}072x + 114{,}688x^2 - 57{,}344x^3 + 17{,}920x^4 - 3584x^5 + 448x^6 - 32x^7 + x^8$

**20.** $16x^2 + 40x + 25$

**21.** $27a^3 - 189a^2 + 441a - 343$

**22.** $64a^6 + 3072a^5 + 61{,}440a^4 + 655{,}360a^3 + 3{,}932{,}160a^2 + 12{,}582{,}912a + 16{,}777{,}216$

**23.** $81y^4 - 1188y^3 + 6534y^2 - 15{,}972y + 14{,}641$

**24.** $V = x^6 - \frac{3}{2}x^4 + \frac{3}{4}x^2 - \frac{1}{8}$

**25. a.** 6       **b.** 489,888

**26.** $80x^2$       **27.** $135x^4$

**28.** $270x^3$       **29.** $625b^8$

**30.** Because the coefficient of 2 in $2y^2$ will affect the terms.

**31.** The challenge of the Binomial Theorem occurs when there is a coefficient with the $x$. However, it is much more efficient to use the Binomial Theorem than FOIL when expanding a binomial that is raised to a high power.

**32.** $64x^6 - 384x^5y + 960x^4y^2 - 1280x^3y^3 + 960x^2y^4 - 384xy^5 + 64y^6$

**33.** $x^{20} + 40x^{18} + 720x^{16} + 7680x^{14} + 53{,}760x^{12} + 258{,}048x^{10} + 860{,}160x^8 + 1{,}966{,}080x^6 + 2{,}949{,}120x^4 + 2{,}621{,}440x^2 + 1{,}048{,}576$

**34.** $x^6 - 3x^4y^2 + 3x^2y^4 - y^6$

**35.** $a^5 - 5a^4b^2 + 10a^3b^4 - 10a^2b^6 + 5ab^8 - b^{10}$

**36.** $27x^3 + 216x^2y + 576xy^2 + 512y^3$

**37–46.** See next page.

# Answers

## Practice and Problem-Solving Exercises
(continued)

**37.** $256x^4 - 1792x^3y$
$+ 4704x^2y^2 - 5488xy^3 + 2401y^4$

**38.** $282{,}475{,}249a^{10} + 807{,}072{,}140a^9y +$
$1{,}037{,}664{,}180a^8y^2 + 790{,}601{,}280a^7y^3 +$
$395{,}300{,}640a^6y^4 + 135{,}531{,}648a^5y^5 +$
$32{,}269{,}440a^4y^6 + 5{,}268{,}480a^3y^7 +$
$564{,}480a^2y^8 + 35{,}840ay^9 + 1024y^{10}$

**39.** $4096x^{18} + 12{,}288x^{15}y^2 + 15{,}360x^{12}y^4 +$
$10{,}240x^9y^6 + 3840x^6y^8 + 768x^3y^{10} + 64y^{12}$

**40.** $2187b^7 - 183{,}708b^6 + 6{,}613{,}488b^5 -$
$132{,}269{,}760b^4 + 1{,}587{,}237{,}120b^3 -$
$11{,}428{,}107{,}264b^2 + 45{,}712{,}429{,}056b -$
$78{,}364{,}164{,}096$

**41.** $125a^3 + 150a^2b + 60ab^2 + 8b^3$

**42.** $b^{16} - 16b^{14} + 112b^{12} - 448b^{10} + 1120b^8 -$
$1792b^6 + 1792b^4 - 1024b^2 + 256$

**43.** $-32y^{10} + 80y^8x - 80y^6x^2 + 40y^4x^3 -$
$10y^2x^4 + x^5$

**44.** Area $= (2x + 8)^2 = 4x^2 + 32x + 64$;
Volume $= (2x + 8)^3 = 8x^3 + 96x^2 + 384x + 512$

**45.** Answers may vary. Sample: Since one of the
terms is negative $(-y)$ and it is alternately
raised to odd and even powers; the term is
negative when raised to an odd power and
positive when raised to an even power.

**46.** In the expression on the right, the student
did not simplify each power of $3x$ before
multiplying.
$81x^4 - 864x^3 + 3456x^2 - 6144x + 4096$.

**47.** $-29{,}113 + 17{,}684i$

**48.** $702 - 486i$

**49.** $(x^{14} - 21x^{10} + 35x^6 - 7x^2) + i(-7x^{12} +$
$35x^8 - 21x^4 + 1)$

**50.** $n = 10$; $a = 2$

**51.** $\frac{1}{64}$

**52. a.** $-4$
**b.** $(1 - i)^4 = 1 - 4i - 6 + 4i + 1 = -4$

**53.** $(-1 + i\sqrt{3})^3 = -1 + 3i\sqrt{3}$
$+ 9 - 3i\sqrt{3} = 8$

## Standardized Test Prep

**54.** C **55.** G **56.** B

**57. [4]** Let $c_a$ = the first company's cost per
month and let $c_b$ = the second company's
cost per month: $c_a = 2.25t + 7.95$ and
$c_b = 2.75t$

$$c_a = c_b$$
$$2.25t + 7.95 = 2.75t$$
$$7.95 = 0.5t$$
$$15.9 = t$$

The cost will be equal after 15.9 hours of use.
**[3]** appropriate method, but with one
computational error

---

**47.** $(7 + \sqrt{-16})^5$ **48.** $(\sqrt{-81} - 3)^3$ **49.** $(x^2 - i)^7$

**50.** The first term in the expansion of a binomial $(ax + by)^n$ is $1024x^{10}$. Find $a$ and $n$.

**51.** Determine the coefficient of $x^7y$ in the expansion of $\left(\frac{1}{2}x + \frac{1}{4}y\right)^8$.

**52. a.** Expand $(1 + i)^4$.
**b.** Verify that $1 - i$ is a fourth root of $-4$ by repeating the process in part (a) for
$(1 - i)^4$.

**53.** Verify that $-1 + \sqrt{3}i$ is a cube root of 8 by expanding $(-1 + \sqrt{3}i)^3$.

### Standardized Test Prep

**SAT/ACT**

**54.** What is the fourth term in the expansion of $(2a + 4b)^5$?
- Ⓐ $256a^4b$
- Ⓑ $768a^3b^2$
- Ⓒ $2560a^2b^3$
- Ⓓ $2048ab^4$

**55.** Suppose $y$ varies directly with $x$. If $x$ is 30 when $y$ is 10, what is $x$ when $y$ is 9?
- Ⓕ $3$
- Ⓖ $27$
- Ⓗ $29$
- Ⓘ $\frac{300}{9}$

**56.** Which of following is a root of $9x^2 - 30x + 25 = 0$?
- Ⓐ $x = \frac{3}{5}$
- Ⓑ $x = \frac{5}{3}$
- Ⓒ $x = -\frac{5}{3}$
- Ⓓ $x = -\frac{3}{5}$

**Extended Response**

**57.** One company charges a monthly fee of $7.95 and $2.25 per hour for Internet
access. Another company does not charge a monthly fee, but charges $2.75 per
hour for Internet access. Write a system of equations to represent the cost $c$ for $t$
hours of access in one month for each company. Then find how many hours of use
it will take for the costs to be equal.

### Mixed Review

**Find all the roots of each equation.** ◆ See Lesson 5-6.

**58.** $x^4 + 7x^3 + 20x^2 + 29x + 15 = 0$ **59.** $x^5 - x^4 + 10x^3 - 10x^2 + 9x - 9 = 0$

**60.** $2x^3 + 11x^2 + 14x + 8 = 0$ **61.** $x^4 - x^3 + 6x^2 - 13x + 7 = 0$

**Simplify each expression.** ◆ See Lesson 4-8.

**62.** $(5i - 4)(-2i + 7)$ **63.** $(-3i)(20i)(10i)$

**64.** $\frac{-6 - 2i}{3 + i}$ **65.** $\frac{11i + 9}{2 - i}$

**Get Ready!** **To prepare for Lesson 5-8, do Exercises 66–68.**

**Write each polynomial in standard form. Then classify it by degree and by
number of terms.** ◆ See Lesson 5-1.

**66.** $5x^2 - x + 2x^3 + 9$ **67.** $1 + 4x - 7x^2$ **68.** $-9x^2 + x - 3x^3 - 8 + 12x^4$

---

**[2]** incorrect system solved correctly
OR correct system solved
incorrectly

**[1]** correct answers, without work
shown

## Mixed Review

**58.** $-3, -1, \frac{-3 \pm i\sqrt{11}}{2}$

**59.** $1, \pm i, \pm 3i$

**60.** $-4, \frac{-3 \pm i\sqrt{7}}{4}$

**61.** $1, \frac{-1 \pm 3i\sqrt{3}}{2}$

**62.** $-18 + 43i$ **63.** $600i$

**64.** $-2$

**65.** $\frac{7}{5} + \frac{31}{5}i$

**66.** $2x^3 + 5x^2 - x + 9$; cubic polynomial
of 4 terms

**67.** $-7x^2 + 4x + 1$; quadratic trinomial

**68.** $12x^4 - 3x^3 - 9x^2 + x - 8$; quartic
polynomial of 5 terms

# Lesson Resources

## Additional Instructional Support

### Algebra 2 Companion

Students can use the **Algebra 2 Companion** worktext (4 pages) as you teach the lesson. Use the Companion to support

- New Vocabulary
- Key Concepts
- Got It for each Problem
- Lesson Check

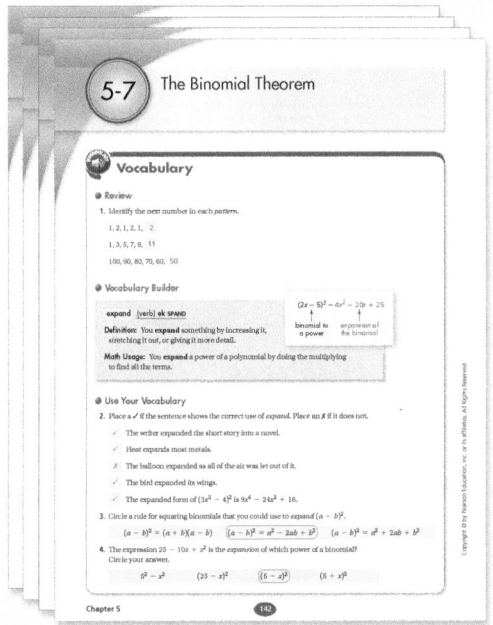

### ELL Support

**Assess Understanding** Write the binomial power $(3x - 7)^3$ on the board. Ask a volunteer what the first step in expanding the power must be before they can use Pascal's Triangle or the Binomial Theorem. [It must be rewritten in the form $(a + b)^n$.] Have another volunteer explain how to handle the negative term and how the exponent helps them identify the row of Pascal's Triangle they must use.

## 5 Assess & Remediate

### Lesson Quiz

**1.** What is the expansion of $(a + b)^4$?

**2. Do you UNDERSTAND?** What is the expansion of $(y - 4)^3$?

**ANSWERS TO LESSON QUIZ**

**1.** $a^4 + 4a^3b + 6a^2b^2 + 4ab^3 + b^4$

**2.** $y^3 - 12y^2 + 48y - 64$

**PRESCRIPTION FOR REMEDIATION**

Use the student work on the Lesson Quiz to prescribe a differentiated review assignment:

| Points | Differentiated Remediation |
|--------|----------------------------|
| 0 | Intervention |
| 1 | On-level |
| 2 | Extension |

**PowerAlgebra.com**

### 5 Assess & Remediate

Assign the Lesson Quiz. Appropriate intervention, practice, or enrichment is automatically generated based on student performance.

## Differentiated Remediation

Available in editable format online.

### Intervention

- **Reteaching** (2 pages) Provides reteaching and practice exercises for the key lesson concepts. Use with struggling students or absent students.

- **English Language Learner Support** Helps students develop and reinforce mathematical vocabulary and key concepts.

**All-in-One Resources/Online**
**Reteaching**

**All-in-One Resources/Online**
**English Language Learner Support**

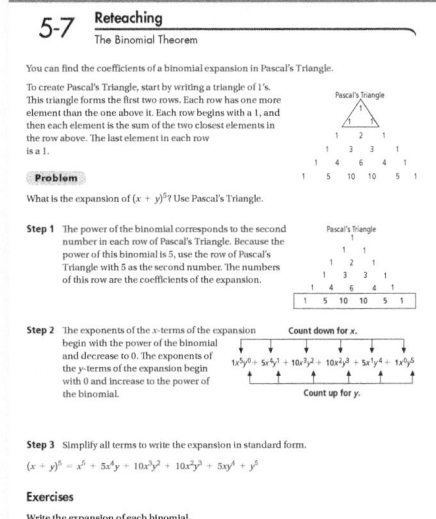

# Differentiated Remediation *continued*

Available in editable format online.

## On-Level

- **Practice** (2 pages) Provides extra practice for each lesson. For simpler practice exercises, use the Form K Practice pages found in the All-in-One Teaching Resources and online.

- **Think About a Plan** Helps students develop specific problem-solving skills and strategies by providing scaffolded guiding questions.

- **Standardized Test Prep** Focuses on all major exercises, all major question types, and helps students prepare for the high-stakes assessments.

## Extension

- **Enrichment** Provides students with interesting problems and activities that extend the concepts of the lesson.

- **Activities, Games, and Puzzles** Worksheets that can be used for concepts development, enrichment, and for fun!

---

### Practice and Problem Solving Wkbk/All-in-One Resources/Online
**Practice page 1**

**5-7 Practice** — Form G
The Binomial Theorem

**Expand each binomial.** *See answers below.*

1. $(x + 2)^4$  2. $(a + 2)^7$  3. $(x + y)^5$  4. $(d - 2)^8$
5. $(2x - 3)^8$  6. $(x - 1)^9$  7. $(2x^2 - 2y^2)^8$  8. $(a^2 + 2y)^7$
9. $(n - 3)^7$  10. $(2n + 2)^4$  11. $(n - 6)^5$  12. $(n - 1)^8$
13. $(2a + 2)^3$  14. $(x^2 - y)^4$  15. $(2x + 3y)^5$  16. $(2x^2 + y^2)^8$
17. $(x^2 - y^2)^3$  18. $(2b + y)^4$  19. $(3m - 2n)^5$  20. $(x^3 - y^4)^6$

**Find the specified term of each binomial expansion.**

21. third term of $(x + 3)^{12}$  594x^{10}  22. second term of $(x + 3)^9$  27x^8
23. twelfth term of $(2 + x)^{11}$  x^{11}  24. third term of $(2 - x)^{12}$  264x^{10}
25. eighth term of $(x - 2y)^{10}$  -823,680x^3y^7  26. seventh term of $(x - 2y)^8$  64y^6
27. fifth term of $(x^2 + y^2)^{13}$  715x^{18}y^8  28. fourth term of $(x^2 - 2y)^{11}$  -1320x^{16}y^3

29. The term $126x^a d^4$ appears in the expansion of $(c + d)^n$. What is $n$?  9

30. The coefficient of the second term in the expansion of $(r + s)^n$ is 7. Find the value of $n$, and write the complete term.  n = 7; 7r^6s

**State the number of terms in each expansion and give the first two terms.**

31. $(d + e)^{12}$  13; d^{12} + 12d^{11}e  32. $(x - y)^{15}$  16; x^{15} - 15x^{14}y  33. $(2a + b)^6$  7; 32a^5 + 80a^4b
34. $(x - 3y)^7$  8; x^7 - 21x^6y  35. $(4 - 2x)^8$  9; 65,536 - 262,144x  36. $(x^2 + y^2)^6$  7; x^{12} + 6x^{10}y

37. The side of a number cube is $x + 4$ units long. Write a binomial for the volume of the number cube. Use the Binomial Theorem to expand and rewrite the expression in standard form.  $(x + 4)^3 = x^3 + 12x^2 + 48x + 64$

---

### Practice and Problem Solving Wkbk/All-in-One Resources/Online
**Practice page 2**

**5-7 Practice** *(continued)* — Form G
The Binomial Theorem

**Expand each binomial.**

38. $(x + 1)^7$
x^7 + 7x^6 + 21x^5 + 35x^4 + 35x^3 + 21x^2 + 7x + 1

39. $(x + 4)^8$
x^8 + 32x^7 + 448x^6 + 3584x^5 + 17,920x^4 + 57,344x^3 + 114,688x^2 + 131,072x + 65,536

40. $(x - 3y)^6$
x^6 - 18x^5y + 135x^4y^2 - 540x^3y^3 + 1215x^2y^4 - 1458xy^5 + 729y^6

41. $(x + 2)^5$
x^5 + 10x^4 + 40x^3 + 80x^2 + 80x + 32

42. $(x - 2)^5$
x^{10} - 5x^8y^2 + 10x^6y^4 - 10x^4y^6 + 5x^2y^8 - y^{10}

43. $(3 + y)^5$
y^5 + 15y^4 + 90y^3 + 270y^2 + 405y + 243

44. $(x^2 + 3)^6$
x^{12} + 18x^{10} + 135x^8 + 540x^6 + 1215x^4 + 1458x^2 + 729

45. $(x - 5)^7$
x^7 - 35x^6 + 525x^5 - 4375x^4 + 21,875x^3 - 65,625x^2 + 109,375x - 78,125

46. $(x - y)^8$
x^8 - 16x^7y + 96x^6y^2 - 256x^5y^3 + 256y^8

47. **Open-Ended** Write a binomial in the form $(a + b)^n$ that has 3 as the coefficient of the first term.  Answers may vary. Any binomial that has an a-term coefficient of $\sqrt[3]{3}$.

48. Use Pascal's Triangle to determine the binomial of the expanded expression $x^6 + 6x^5 + 15x^4 + 20x^3 + 15x^2 + 6x + 1$.  $(x + 1)^6$

49. **Error Analysis** Your friend expands the binomial $(x - 2)^5$ as $x^6 + 12x^5 - 30x^4 + 160x^3 - 240x^2 + 192x + 64$. What mistake did your friend make? What is the correct expansion?  Your friend used $b = 2$ instead of $b = -2$; $x^6 - 12x^5 + 30x^4 - 160x^3 + 240x^2 - 192x + 64$

50. **Reasoning** Without writing any of the previous terms, how do you know that 2187 is the eighth term of the expansion of $(x + 3)^7$?  According to Pascal's Triangle, the eighth term of a binomial with $n = 7$ is equal to $1a^0b^7$. In this binomial $a = x$ and $b = 3$. $1x^03^7 = 2187$.

51. In the expansion of $(3x - y)^8$, one of the terms contains the factor $y^4$.
a. What is the exponent of 3x in this term?  4
b. What is the coefficient of this term?  135

52. You are shipping a cubic glass sculpture. Each side of the sculpture is $x$ in. long. To adequately protect the sculpture, the shipping box must leave room for 5 in. of padding on either side in every dimension. Write and expand a binomial for the volume of the shipping box.  $V = (x + 5)^3 = x^3 + 15x^2 + 75x + 125$ in.^3

---

### All-in-One Resources/Online
**Enrichment**

**5-7 Enrichment**
The Binomial Theorem

Pascal's Triangle is helpful for expanding powers of a binomial sum, but what if you wanted to expand $(a + b)^{20}$? You may not want to write out all of the rows of Pascal's Triangle. In cases like this, you can use another form of the Binomial Theorem.

1. This form of the Binomial Theorem uses the operation called factorial. The expression 4! is read "four factorial" and is computed by multiplying all of the counting numbers from 4 down to 1. So, $4! = 4 \times 3 \times 2 \times 1 = 24$. What is 5!?  $5! = 5 \times 4 \times 3 \times 2 \times 1 = 120$

2. An unexpected fact arises for 0!. 0! is defined as 1. Fractions involving factorials can be simplified first. Rewrite each factorial in the fraction $\frac{6!}{3!}$ as multiplication and then reduce. What is the simplified form?  $\frac{6 \times 5 \times 4 \times 3 \times 2 \times 1}{3 \times 2 \times 1}$; $6 \times 5 \times 4$

Expressions involving factorials can be used to write a different form of the Binomial Theorem. This form states that the $k$th term in the expansion of $(a + b)^n$ is $\frac{n!}{(k - 1)![n - (k - 1)]!}a^{n - k + 1}b^{k - 1}$.

3. Find the third term in the expansion of $(a + b)^8$ using the Binomial Theorem. What value will you substitute in for $n$? What value will you substitute in for $k$?  $n = 8; k = 3; 28a^6b^2$

4. Use Pascal's Triangle to verify that you have found the correct third term.  Answers may vary. Sample: The correct row is 1, 8, 28, 56, 70, 56, 28, 8, 1, and the third number, 28, is the correct coefficient.

**Use the Binomial Theorem to find the indicated term of each expansion.**

5. fifth term of $(x + y)^{10}$  1365x^{11}y^8

6. ninth term of $(x + 3)^{10}$  295,245x^2

7. twelfth term of $(2x + y)^{22}$  1,444,724,736x^{11}y^{11}

---

### Practice and Problem Solving Wkbk/All-in-One Resources/Online
**Think About a Plan**

**5-7 Think About a Plan**
The Binomial Theorem

**Geometry** The side length of a cube is given by the expression $(2x + 8)$. Write a binomial expression for the area of a face of the cube and the volume of the cube. Then use the Binomial Theorem to expand and rewrite the expressions in standard form.

**Understanding the Problem**

1. What is the formula for the area of a face of a cube?  $A = s^2$

2. What is the formula for the volume of a cube?  $V = s^3$

3. What is the problem asking you to determine?  expressions in standard form for the face area and volume of a cube with side length $(2x + 8)$

**Planning the Solution**

4. What is a binomial expression for the area of a face of this cube?  $(2x + 8)^2$

5. What is a binomial expression for the volume of this cube?  $(2x + 8)^3$

6. How can you use the Binomial Theorem to expand these expressions?  Answers may vary. Sample: Use $n = 2$ for the expression for area and use $n = 3$ for the expression for volume. For both expressions, $a = 2x$ and $b = 8$.

**Getting an Answer**

7. What is an expression for the area of a face of the cube written in standard form?  $4x^2 + 32x + 64$

8. What is an expression for the volume of the cube written in standard form?  $8x^3 + 96x^2 + 384x + 512$

---

### Practice and Problem Solving Wkbk/All-in-One Resources/Online
**Standardized Test Prep**

**5-7 Standardized Test Prep**
The Binomial Theorem

**Multiple Choice**

For Exercises 1–7, choose the correct letter.

1. What is the expanded form of $(a - b)^3$?  D
A. $a^3 + a^2b + ab^2 + b^3$
B. $a^3 - a^2b + ab^2 - b^3$
C. $a^3 + 3a^2b + 3ab^2 + b^3$
D. $a^3 - 3a^2b + 3ab^2 - b^3$

2. What is the third term in the expansion of $(x - y)^7$?  F
F. $21x^5y^2$  G. $-7x^6y$  H. $7x^6y$  I. $-21x^5y^2$

3. What is the coefficient of the third term in the expansion of $(2x - y)^5$?  D
A. $-80$  B. 32  C. 40  D. 80

4. Which term in the expansion of $(2a - 3b)^6$ has coefficient 2160?  G
F. second term  G. third term  H. fourth term  I. fifth term

5. What is $n$ if $-448x^5y^2$ appears in the expansion of $(x - 2y)^n$?  C
A. 6  B. 7  C. 8  D. 9

6. What is the 6th term in the 12th line of Pascal's Triangle?  G
F. 252  G. 462  H. 792  I. 1287

7. What is the expanded form of $(2x - y)^5$?  B
A. $32x^5 + 80x^4y + 80x^3y^2 + 40x^2y^3 + 10xy^4 + y^5$
B. $32x^5 - 80x^4y + 80x^3y^2 - 40x^2y^3 + 10xy^4 - y^5$
C. $2x^5 + 5x^4y + 20x^3y^2 + 20x^2y^3 + 10xy^4 + y^5$
D. $2x^5 - 5x^4y + 20x^3y^2 - 20x^2y^3 + 10xy^4 - y^5$

**Short Response**

8. The coefficient of the fourth term in the expansion of $(x + y)^n$ is 84.
a. What is the value of $n$?
b. What is the complete term?
[2] $n = 9$; the complete term is $84(x)^6(y)^3 = 84x^6y^3$.
[1] incorrect number for $n$ OR incorrect complete term
[0] no answers given

---

### Online Teacher Resource Center
**Activities, Games, and Puzzles**

**5-7 Puzzle: Pyramid Power**
The Binomial Theorem

Find each of the specified coefficients of $(a + b)^n$ and circle them in the diagram.

1. the coefficient in $(a + b)^2$ not equal to the others  2
2. the coefficient of $ab^2$ in $(a + b)^3$  3
3. the coefficient of $a^4$ in $(a + b)^4$  1
4. the coefficient of $ab^4$ in $(a + b)^5$  5
5. the coefficients of $a^4b^2$ and $a^2b^4$ in $(a + b)^6$  15, 20
6. the coefficient of $a^3b^4$ in $(a + b)^7$  35
7. the coefficients of $a^6b^2$ and of $a^2b^6$ in $(a + b)^8$  28, 28
8. the coefficient of $a^8$ in $(a + b)^9$  1
9. the coefficient of $a^2b^8$ in $(a + b)^{10}$  252
10. the coefficients of $a^7b^4$ and of $a^4b^7$ in $(a + b)^{11}$  330, 330
11. the coefficient of $a^5b^7$ in $(a + b)^{12}$  792
12. the coefficient of $a^3b^9$ in $(a + b)^{13}$  1716
13. the coefficients of $a^7b^7$ and $a^4b^{10}$ in $(a + b)^{14}$  3432, 1001

What is the sum of the circled numbers?  7562

---

## 5-8 Polynomial Models in the Real World

**Objective** To fit data to linear, quadratic, cubic, or quartic models

There is more than one way to solve this problem.

**Getting Ready!**

You are designing a patio. Square A is where you will place your grill. You are experimenting with your design by varying the size of square B. The table shows the total patio area for each of five different lengths x.

| Length x (m) | 1 | 2 | 3 | 4 | 5 |
|---|---|---|---|---|---|
| Total Area (m²) | 13 | 20 | 29 | 40 | ? |

Based on the pattern in the table, find the total area when x is 5. What type of polynomial function does the data fit? Explain.

Polynomial functions can be degree 0 (constant), degree 1 (linear), degree 2 (quadratic), degree 3 (cubic), and so on.

**Essential Understanding** You can use polynomial functions to model many real-world situations. The behavior of the graphs of polynomial functions of different degrees can suggest what type of polynomial will best fit a particular data set.

You can use a graphing calculator to help you find functions that model the data in the table shown here.

Enter the data into calculator lists **L1** and **L2**. Use three different regressions: **LINREG**, **QUADREG**, and **CUBICREG**.

Graph each regression function and the scatter plot of the data in the same window. For this data, the cubic function appears to be a perfect fit.

| x | y |
|---|---|
| 0 | 10.1 |
| 5 | 2.8 |
| 10 | 8.1 |
| 15 | 16.0 |
| 20 | 17.8 |

# 1 Interactive Learning

## Solve It!

**PURPOSE** To use first and second differences to identify a pattern and to determine the degree of a polynomial function

**PROCESS** Students may determine the degree of the polynomial function by
• finding differences.
• plotting the data and evaluating the shape of the graph.

---

**FACILITATE**

**Q** What are the first differences of the areas? **[7, 9, 11]**

**Q** What is the pattern? **[Differences increase by 2.]**

**Q** What is the missing value? **[53]**

**Q** What are the second differences? **[all 2]**

**Q** What degree polynomial function is indicated? **[degree 2]**

---

**ANSWER** See Solve It in Answers on next page.

**CONNECT THE MATH** In the Solve It, differences may be used to determine the degree of a polynomial function that fits a set of data. In the lesson, students use polynomial models to solve real-world problems.

# 2 Guided Instruction

Note that if you use QuarticReg to model the data, the coefficient of the $x^4$ term will be very close to zero and the QuarticReg curve will be very similar to the CubicReg curve.

---

## 5-8 Preparing to Teach

**BIG idea** Function

**ESSENTIAL UNDERSTANDING**

• The behavior of the graphs of polynomial functions of different degrees can suggest which will best fit a particular real-world data set.

### Math Background

Just as two points can be used to determine a unique line and three points not on the same line determine a unique quadratic function, polynomial functions of various degrees can be found that perfectly match a given data set that passes the vertical-line test. Regression analysis (LinReg, QuadReg, etc.) can also be used to determine best-fitting polynomial models for a given data set. The polynomial model can then be used to make predictions. Such models may not

always be the best even though they match the data perfectly. The best model often depends on the nature of the situation. If the situation being modeled is essentially a quadratic relationship based on principles of physics, then a quadratic model will most likely best fit the data and result in the most reliable predictions. One must be cautious when using any model not to be too confident of predictions outside of the domain of the data.

### Support Student Learning

Use the **Algebra 2 Companion** to engage and support students during instruction. See Lesson Resources at the end of this lesson for details.

**PowerAlgebra.com**

## 1 Interactive Learning

**Solve It!**

Step out how to solve the Problem with helpful hints and an online question. Other questions are listed above in Interactive Learning.

## Take Note

This result follows from the fact that an *n*th-degree polynomial function

$P(x) = a_n x^n + a_{n-1} x^{n-1} + \ldots a_1 x^1 + a_0 x^0$ is uniquely determined by the values of its $n + 1$ numerical coefficients $a_0, \ldots, a_n$. Given a set of $n + 1$ points, a system of $n + 1$ linear equations can be written and solved to determine the values of $a_0$ to $a_n$.

## Problem 1

**Q** How can you verify that the points *do not* lie on a line or a parabola? **[Find the differences, starting with the fourth point. Since neither the first nor the second differences are constant, the four points do not lie on either a line or a parabola.]**

## Got It?

**Q** How do you know that the four points do not lie on a line? **[You cannot use differences since the changes in *x* are not constant. But if you calculate slopes between each pair of points you see that the slopes are not all the same, so the points cannot all lie on one line.]**

**Q** The degree of the polynomial function whose graph passes through these four points is at most what? **[$n + 1 = 4$, so $n = 3$, and the polynomial function is at most a cubic.]**

---

 **Key Concept** The (*n* + 1) Point Principle

For any set of $n + 1$ points in the coordinate plane that pass the vertical line test, there is a unique polynomial of degree at most $n$ that fits the points perfectly.

This principle confirms that any two points determine a unique line. Three points that are not on a line determine a unique parabola. Four points that are not on a line or a parabola determine a unique cubic, and so forth.

### Problem 1 Using A Polynomial Function to Model Data

**What polynomial function has a graph that passes through the four points (0, −3), (1, −1), (2, 5), and (−1, −7)?**

**Step 1** By the $(n + 1)$ Point Principle, there is a cubic polynomial $y = ax^3 + bx^2 + cx + d$ that fits the points perfectly.

Substitute the *x*- and *y*-values of the four points to get four linear equations in four unknowns.

$-3 = a(0)^3 + b(0)^2 + c(0) + d$        $0a + 0b + 0c + 1d = -3$

$-1 = a(1)^3 + b(1)^2 + c(1) + d$        $1a + 1b + 1c + 1d = -1$

$5 = a(2)^3 + b(2)^2 + c(2) + d$        $8a + 4b + 2c + 1d = 5$

$-7 = a(-1)^3 + b(-1)^2 + c(-1) + d$        $-1a + 1b - 1c + 1d = -7$

**Step 2** Write the system in augmented matrix form. Use the **RREF()** function to find the coefficient values *a*, *b*, *c*, and *d*.

**Step 3** $a = 1, b = -1, c = 2,$ and $d = -3$. The polynomial function is $y = x^3 - x^2 + 2x - 3$.

**Check** Use **CUBICREG** with the four given points.

The solution checks.

 **Got It?** **1.** What polynomial function has a graph that passes through the four points (−2, 1), (0, 5), (2, 9), and (3, 36)?

---

**Plan**

How can you use the four points to find a system of equations? Substitute each point into a polynomial function.

---

## Answers

### Solve It!

53 m²; quadratic; second differences are constant

### Got It?

**1.** $y = 1.667x^3 + 1.3 \times 10^{-12} x^2 - 4.667x + 5$

**2.** 22.56 billion lb

**3.** Answers may vary. Sample: The cubic model would fit the data better than the linear model because of the $(n + 1)$ Pt. Principle. Both models have down and up end behavior and increasing growth. The cubic shows slowing growth followed by rapidly increasing growth.

---

**PowerAlgebra.com**

## 2 Guided Instruction

 Each Problem is worked out and supported online.

**Problem 1**
Using A Polynomial Function to Model Data
*Animated*

**Problem 2**
Modeling Data

**Problem 3**
Comparing Models
*Animated*

**Problem 4**
Using Interpolation and Extrapolation
*Animated*

**Support in Algebra 2 Companion**
• Vocabulary
• Key Concepts
• Got It?

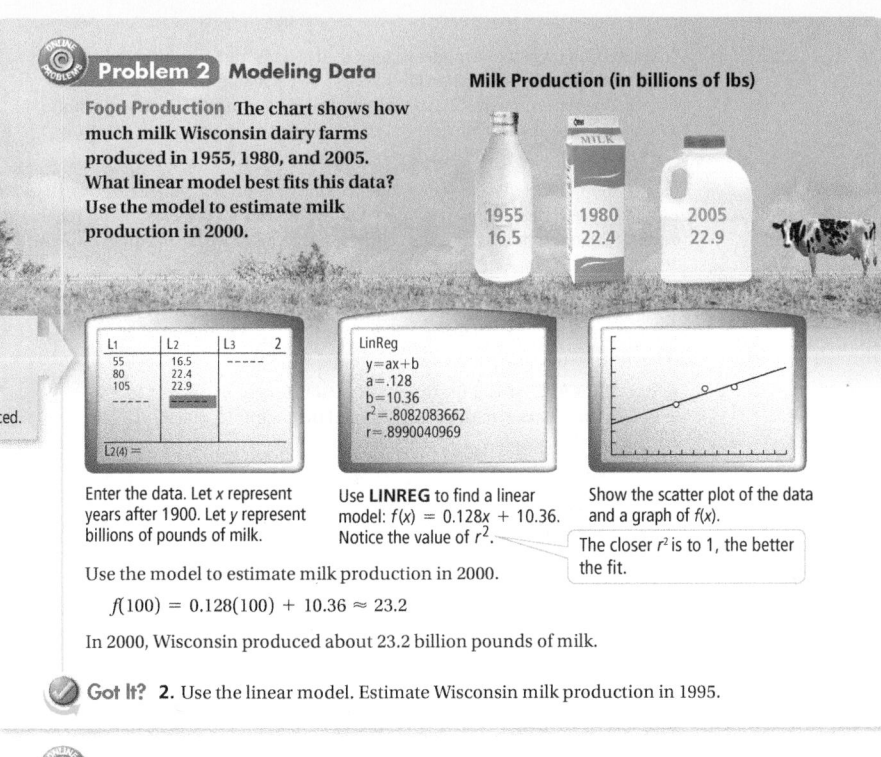

### Problem 2 Modeling Data

**Food Production** The chart shows how much milk Wisconsin dairy farms produced in 1955, 1980, and 2005. What linear model best fits this data? Use the model to estimate milk production in 2000.

**Milk Production (in billions of lbs)**

| 1955 | 1980 | 2005 |
|------|------|------|
| 16.5 | 22.4 | 22.9 |

**Think**

**What data should you enter?**
Enter the years, after 1900, and billions of pounds of milk produced.

| L1 | L2 | L3 | 2 |
|----|----|----|---|
| 55 | 16.5 | ----- | |
| 80 | 22.4 | | |
| 105 | 22.9 | | |

L2(4) =

Enter the data. Let $x$ represent years after 1900. Let $y$ represent billions of pounds of milk.

**LinReg**
$y = ax + b$
$a = .128$
$b = 10.36$
$r^2 = .8082083662$
$r = .8990040969$

Use **LINREG** to find a linear model: $f(x) = 0.128x + 10.36$. Notice the value of $r^2$.

Show the scatter plot of the data and a graph of $f(x)$.

The closer $r^2$ is to 1, the better the fit.

Use the model to estimate milk production in 2000.

$$f(100) = 0.128(100) + 10.36 \approx 23.2$$

In 2000, Wisconsin produced about 23.2 billion pounds of milk.

 **Got It? 2.** Use the linear model. Estimate Wisconsin milk production in 1995.

### Problem 3 Comparing Models

**Food Production** The graph shows the quadratic model for the milk production data in Problem 2. The quadratic model fits the data points exactly because of the $(n + 1)$ Point Principle. Given that both models are good fits, which seems more likely to represent milk production over time?

**Linear Model:** This model continually rises.

**Quadratic Model:** This model has down-and-down end behavior. It shows slowing growth, a turning point, and then a decline, eventually to 0 and negative values.

Despite the $R^2$ value of 1 for the quadratic model, the linear model is more likely to represent milk production over time since it shows a continuing increase.

**Think**

**Is the quadratic model reasonable?**
No; the quadratic model will show milk production eventually decreasing to below zero.

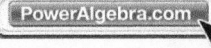 **Got It? 3.** If four data points were given, would a cubic function be the best model for the data? Explain your answer.

---

### Problem 2

**Q** There are three points. Why choose a linear function model and not a quadratic function model? **[You *could* use a quadratic model, but the scatter plot shows that a line is a good fit.]**

### Got It?

**Q** What value of $x$ should you use to predict milk production in 1995? **[Let $x = 95$, since $x$ represents years after 1900.]**

### Problem 3

Either model can be used for estimating production within the domain of the data. The quadratic model only appears to result in questionable results when you make a prediction well outside of the domain of the data.

### Got It?

A cubic function would match four data points exactly but will not necessarily result in a better model. The result would depend on what the fourth data point is.

**Q** What is the end behavior of a cubic polynomial function? **[down and up, or up and down]**

**Q** Are either of these end behaviors reasonable? **[Down and up end behavior might be reasonable, but up and down behavior is not.]**

---

## Additional Problems

**1.** What polynomial function has a graph that passes through the points $(-2, 13)$, $(0, 9)$, $(1, 4)$, and $(2, 5)$?

**ANSWER** $y = x^3 - 6x + 9$

**2.** What is the linear model that best fits the data? Use the model to estimate egg consumption in 1995.

| Year | US Per Capita Egg Consumption |
|------|-------------------------------|
| 1970 | 302 |
| 1980 | 266 |
| 1990 | 231 |
| 2000 | 247 |

**ANSWER** $y = -2x + 431.5$ ($x$ = years after 1900); 241.5 eggs in 1995

**3.** What is the quadratic model that best fits the above data? Use the model to estimate egg consumption in 1995.

**ANSWER**
$0.13x^2 - 24.1x + 1354.5$; 238.25 eggs in 1995

**4.** Which is the better model for estimating egg consumption between 1970 and 2000? Which is better for extrapolating egg consumption beyond 2000?

**ANSWER** The quadratic model is better for interpolation. The quadratic model is also better for extrapolation beyond year 2000, but neither model is reliable.

Remember: **in**terpolate refers to **in**side the domain of the data while **ex**trapolate refers to **out**side the domain of the data.

## Problem 4

**Q** When the $x$ value is low, what is the magnitude of the $x^3$ term? Explain. **[The $x^3$ coefficient is low, so the $x^3$ term is low when the $x$ value is low.]**

**Q** For larger values of $x$, $(x > 100)$, what happens to the $x^3$ term? **[It gets very large very quickly and dominates the behavior of the model.]**

### Got It?

**Q** What does the scatter plot indicate about the rate of increase of the data? **[The scatter plot shows a behavior of increasing at an increasing rate.]**

**Q** How will a linear model that fits this data when $x$ is small fit the data for large values of $x$? **[It will tend to underestimate the data for large values of $x$.]**

---

When deciding whether a model is reliable, it is important to consider the source of the data. Data generated by a law of physics or a geometric formula will have a mathematical model that fits the data and yields accurate predictions. With other data, such as sales records, you can approximate the data only within, or close to, the domain over which it was generated.

Using a model to predict a $y$-value "outside" the domain of a data set is *extrapolation*. Estimating within the domain is *interpolation*. Interpolation usually yields reliable estimates. Extrapolation becomes less reliable as you move farther away from the data.

### Problem 4  Using Interpolation and Extrapolation

**Cheese Consumption**  The table shows average annual consumption of cheese per person in the U. S. for selected years from 1910 to 2001.

**A** Use **CUBICREG**. Model the data with a cubic function. Graph the function with a scatter plot of the data.

**Cheese Consumption**

| Year | Pounds Consumed |
|------|-----------------|
| 1910 | 4 |
| 1940 | 5 |
| 1970 | 8 |
| 1975 | 10 |
| 1995 | 25 |
| 2001 | 30 |

SOURCE: U.S. Department of Agriculture

Since $R^2$ is close to 1, the fit is good. The cubic model is approximately $y = 0.0000924x^3 - 0.00958x^2 + 0.311x + 1.802$.

**B** Use the model to estimate cheese consumption for 1980, 2000, and 2012. In which estimate do you have the most confidence? The least confidence? Explain.

Use the cubic model from part A to estimate the cheese consumption for each year:

1980: 12.6 lb of cheese per person
2000: 29.4 lb of cheese per person
2012: 46.2 lb of cheese per person

**Think**

**What affects your confidence in drawing conclusions from the model?**
Your confidence can waver where model behavior is extreme or where there are large gaps in the data.

You can be confident in interpolating the estimates for 1980 (**Y1(80)**) and 2000 (**Y1(100)**) because the cheese consumption fits the pattern of increase shown in the table. You should have the least confidence in the extrapolated 2012 (**Y1(112)**) estimate because the cubic model increases so quickly beyond 2001.

```
Y1 (80)
        12.63416396
Y1 (100)
        29.44524491
Y1 (112)
        46.21454748
■
```

**Got It?  4. a.** Use **LINREG** to find a linear model for cheese consumption. Graph it with a scatter plot.

**b. Reasoning**  Use the model to estimate consumption for 1980, 2000, and 2012. In which of these estimates do you have the most confidence? The least confidence? Explain.

---

# Answers

## Got It? (continued)

**4. a.** $y = 0.269867411x - 3.919692952$

**b.** 1980: 17.7 lb; 2000: 23.07 lb; 2012: 26.31 lb; most confident for the yrs 1980 and 2000, since they are within the domain of the data set; least confident for the yr 2012, since it is outside of the domain of the data set

## Lesson Check

### Do you know HOW?

Determine which type of model best fits each set of points.

**1.** $(-2, -1)$, $(0, 3)$, and $(2, 7)$

**2.** $(0, 3)$, $(3, 4)$, and $(5, 6)$

**3.** $(2, 3)$, $(4, 2)$, $(6, 4)$, and $(8, 5)$

**4.** $(-5, 6)$, $(-4, 3)$, $(0, 2)$, $(2, 4)$, and $(5, 10)$

### Do you UNDERSTAND?

**5. Vocabulary** Explain which form of estimation, interpolation or extrapolation, is more reliable.

**6. Reasoning** Is it possible to create a cubic function that passes through $(0, 0)$, $(-1, 1)$, $(-2, 2)$, and $(-3, 9)$? Explain.

**7. Writing** The $R^2$ value for a quartic model is 0.94561. The $R^2$ value for a cubic model of the same data is 0.99817. Which model seems to show a better fit? Explain.

## Practice and Problem-Solving Exercises

 **Practice** Find a polynomial function whose graph passes through each set of points.  **See Problem 1.**

**8.** $(0, 5)$ and $(2, -13)$

**9.** $(-2, -4)$ and $(8, 1)$

**10.** $(-5, 14)$ and $(1, -16)$

**11.** $(7, 13)$, $(10, -11)$, and $(0, 4)$

**12.** $(-2, -16)$, $(3, 11)$, and $(0, 2)$

**13.** $(-1, 8)$, $(5, -4)$, and $(7, 8)$

**14.** $(-1, -15)$, $(1, -7)$, and $(6, -22)$

**15.** $(-1, 9)$, $(0, 6)$, $(1, 5)$, and $(2, 18)$

For each set of data, compare two models and determine which one best fits the data. Which model seems more likely to represent each set of data over time? **See Problems 2 and 3.**

**16.** U.S. Federal Spending

| Year | Total (billions $) |
|---|---|
| 1965 | 630 |
| 1980 | 1,300 |
| 1995 | 1,950 |
| 2005 | 2,650 |

**17.** World Population

| Year | Average Growth Rate (%) |
|---|---|
| 1972 | 1.96 |
| 1982 | 1.73 |
| 1992 | 1.5 |
| 2002 | 1.22 |

**18.** U.S. Homes

| Year | Average Sale Price (thousands $) |
|---|---|
| 1990 | 149 |
| 1995 | 158 |
| 2000 | 207 |

**19.** U.S. Crude Oil and Petroleum

| Month (2008) | Products Supplied (millions of barrels/day) |
|---|---|
| 2 | 19.782 |
| 4 | 19.768 |
| 6 | 19.553 |

---

## 3 Lesson Check

### Do you know HOW?

- Not every set of $n + 1$ points determines an $n$th-degree polynomial function. For example, 3 or more points might all lie on a line. Students may be able to use differences to determine the degree of the polynomial function that fits a given set of points.

- For Exercises 1–4, if students have trouble identifying the type of model that best fits the given data, have them review the $(n + 1)$ Point Principle and look at Problem 1.

### Do you UNDERSTAND?

- For Exercise 5, remind students that interpolation refers to inside the domain of the data and that extrapolation refers to outside of the domain of the data.

- For Exercise 6, if students do not remember the meanings of "cubic" or "quartic," review Lesson 5–1 on classification of polynomial functions by degree.

### Close

**Q** Why is it useful to represent data with a mathematical model? **[Answers may vary. Sample: A model allows one to make estimations and predictions.]**

**Q** What determines whether a model is a good model? **[Answers may vary. Sample: A good model closely matches the data in the region of interest.]**

---

## Lesson Check

**1.** linear

**2.** quadratic

**3.** cubic

**4.** quartic

**5.** interpolation since the data point is within the domain of the data set

**6.** yes, since the four pts. pass the vertical line test a cubic function will fit the pts; $y = -x^3 - 3x^2 - 3x$

**7.** cubic model; the closer $R^2$ is to 1, the better the fit

## Practice and Problem-Solving Exercises

**8.** $y = -9x + 5$

**9.** $y = \frac{1}{2}x - 3$

**10.** $y = -5x - 11$

**11.** $y = -0.929x^2 + 7.786x + 4$

**12.** $y = -1.2x^2 + 6.6x + 2$

**13.** $y = x^2 - 6x + 1$

**14.** $y = -x^2 + 4x - 10$

**15.** $y = 2x^3 + x^2 - 4x + 6$

**16.** (where $x =$ yrs after 1900) linear: $y = 49.238x - 2614.286$, cubic: $y = 0.028x^3 - 6.711x^2 + 578.194x - 16226.667$; cubic; linear

**17.** (where $x =$ yrs after 1900) quadratic: $y = -1.25 \times 10^{-4}x^2 - 0.003x + 2.804$, cubic: $y = -8.33 \times 10^{-6}x^3 + 0.002x^2 - 0.190x + 8.142$; cubic; cubic

**18.** (where $x =$ yrs after 1900) linear: $y = 5.8x - 379.667$, quadratic: $y = 0.8x^2 - 146.2x + 6827$; linear; linear

**19.** linear: $y = -0.057x + 19.93$, quadratic: $y = -0.025x^2 + 0.14x + 19.595$; quadratic; quadratic

PowerAlgebra.com

## 3 Lesson Check

For a digital lesson check, use the Got It questions.

**Support in Algebra 2 Companion**
- Lesson Check

## 4 Practice

Assign homework to individual students or to an entire class.

# 4 Practice

## ASSIGNMENT GUIDE

Basic: 8–25, 28, 31, 34

Average: 9–23 odd, 24–35

Advanced: 9–23 odd, 24–37

Standardized Test Prep: 38–42

Mixed Review: 43–58

Reasoning exercises have blue headings.

Applications exercises have red headings.

**EXERCISE 31:** Use the Think About a Plan worksheet in the **Practice and Problem Solving Workbook** (also available in the Teaching Resources in print and online) to further support students' development in becoming independent learners.

## HOMEWORK QUICK CHECK

To check students' understanding of key skills and concepts, go over Exercises 17, 21, 28, 31, and 34.

---

**Use your models from Exercises 16-19 to make predictions.**

◀ See Problem 4.

**20.** Estimate total U.S. federal spending for 1990 and 2010.

**21.** Estimate the average annual growth rate of the world population for 1950, 1988, and 2010.

**22.** Estimate the average sale price of homes sold in the United States for 1985, 1999, and 2020.

**23.** Estimate the number of barrels of crude oil and petroleum supplied per day for January, March, and October of 2008.

**Ⓑ Apply**

**Find a cubic and a quartic model for each set of values. Explain why one models the data better.**

**24.**

| x | −2 | −1 | 0 | 2 | 3 |
|---|---|---|---|---|---|
| y | −25 | −4 | 3 | 23 | 40 |

**25.**

| x | −2 | −1 | 0 | 1 | 2 |
|---|---|---|---|---|---|
| y | −65 | −14 | −4 | 2 | 90 |

**Find a polynomial function whose graph passes through the points.**

**26.** $(−14, 14)$, $(−10, 0)$, $(0, −1)$, $(8, 0)$, and $(12, 4)$

**27.** $(−3, −50)$, $(−2, −4)$, $(−1, 10)$, $(0, 7)$, and $(2, −23)$

**28. Think About a Plan** The table at the right shows the amount of carbon dioxide in the Earth's atmosphere for selected years. Predict the amount of carbon dioxide in the Earth's atmosphere in 2022. How confident are you in your prediction?
- How can you plot the data? (*Hint:* Let $x$ equal the years after 1900.)
- What polynomial model should you use?

| Year | $CO_2$ in atmosphere (ppm) |
|---|---|
| 1968 | 324.14 |
| 1983 | 343.91 |
| 1998 | 367.68 |
| 2003 | 376.68 |
| 2008 | 385.60 |

Source: The Weather Channel

**Find a cubic model for each set of values. Then use the regression coefficient of each model to determine whether the model is a good fit.**

**29.** $(−5, −60)$, $(−1, −5)$, $(0, 0.5)$, $(1, 8)$, $(5, 17)$, $(10, 32)$

**30.** $(8, −101)$, $(−1, 10)$, $(−8, 47)$, $(−10, 59)$

**31. Air Travel** The table shows the percent of on-time flights for selected years. Find a polynomial function to model the data. Use 1998 as Year 0.

| Year | 1998 | 2000 | 2002 | 2004 | 2006 |
|---|---|---|---|---|---|
| On-time Flights (%) | 77.20 | 72.59 | 82.14 | 78.08 | 75.45 |

Source: U.S. Bureau of Transportation Statistics

**32. Writing** Explain two ways to find a polynomial function to model a given set of data.

---

# Answers

## Practice and Problem-Solving Exercises (continued)

**20.** 1990: $1863.69 billion; 2010: $3439.57 billion

**21.** 1950: 2.60%; 1988: 1.23%; 2010: 0.35%

**22.** 1985: $113,300; 1999: $194,500; 2020: $316,300

**23.** January: 19.714 million barrels/day; March: 19.8 million barrels/day; October: 18.535 million barrels/day

**24.** cubic: $y = 0.922x^3 − 1.462x^2 + 7.978x + 4.681$;
quartic: $y = −\frac{1}{3}x^4 + \frac{5}{3}x^3 + \frac{1}{3}x^2 + \frac{16}{3}x + 3$; quartic, $(R^2 = 1)$

**25.** cubic: $y = 10.25x^3 + 5x^2 − 2.25x − 8.2$;
quartic: $y = 2.042x^4 + 10.25x^3 − 4.042x^2 − 2.25x − 4$; quartic, $(R^2 = 1)$

**26.** $y = 0.001x^4 − 0.002x^3 − 0.035x^2 + 0.293x − 1$

**27.** $y = −0.275x^4 + 0.85x^3 − 4.025x^2 − 8.15x + 7$

**28.** 407.37 ppm; quite confident because both the linear and the quartic functions yield close to the same prediction. Also, for the linear function, $r^2 = .9965291461$ and for the quartic function, $R^2 = 1$. Although 2022 is outside the domain, the data goes far enough back to make this a reasonable prediction.

**29.** $y = 0.0611511911x^3 − 0.9276466231x^2 + 6.184642324x + 1.750778723$; $R^2 = 0.9994739765$; good fit

**30.** $y = −0.0288800705x^3 − 0.469356261x^2 − 7.401675485x + 3.038800705$; $R^2 = 1$; good fit

**31.** Answers may vary. Sample: $f(x) = 0.111x^4 − 1.916x^3 + 10.147x^2 − 15.825x + 77.2$

**32.** Method 1: Graph the scatter plot and determine which regression model best fits the data. Method 2: Enter the data into your calculator, and use the regression function with the correlation function closest to 1 as the model.

**33. Error Analysis** The table at the right shows the number of students enrolled in a high school personal finance course. A student says that a cubic model would best fit the data based on the $(n + 1)$ Point Principle. Explain why a quadratic model might be more appropriate.

| Year | Number of Students Enrolled |
| --- | --- |
| 2000 | 50 |
| 2004 | 65 |
| 2008 | 94 |
| 2010 | 110 |

**34. Compare and Contrast** The table shows the United States gross domestic product for selected years. Construct curves using cubic regression and quartic regression to model the data. Which curve seems most likely to model gross domestic product over the years?

| Year | 1960 | 1970 | 1980 | 1990 | 2000 |
| --- | --- | --- | --- | --- | --- |
| GDP (billions $) | 526.4 | 1038.5 | 2789.5 | 5803.1 | 9817.0 |

**35.** The table below shows the percentage of the U.S. labor force in unions for selected years between 1955 and 2005.

| Year | 1955 | 1960 | 1965 | 1970 | 1975 | 1980 | 1985 | 1990 | 1995 | 2000 | 2005 |
| --- | --- | --- | --- | --- | --- | --- | --- | --- | --- | --- | --- |
| % | 33.2 | 31.4 | 28.4 | 27.3 | 25.5 | 21.9 | 18.0 | 16.1 | 14.9 | 13.5 | 12.5 |

   **a.** Make a scatter plot of the data. Which kind of polynomial model seems to be most appropriate?
   **b.** Use a graphing calculator to find the type of model from part (a).
   **c.** Use the model you found in part (b) to predict the percent of the labor force in unions in the year 2020.
   **d. Reasoning** Do you have much confidence in this prediction? Explain.

 **Challenge**

**36.** Your friend's teacher showed the class a graph of a cubic polynomial in the ZDecimal window, which is $[-4.7, 4.7]$ by $[-3.1, 3.1]$. She then challenged the class to find the polynomial *without using cubic regression on their calculators*, and your friend succeeded. Follow your friend's steps and see if you can find the polynomial.
   **a.** The graph resembles a parabola with vertex $(2, 0)$ near $x = 2$. Find the equation in standard form for that parabola.
   **b.** Find the equation of a line in slope-intercept form through $(-2, 0)$ with slope 1. Multiply the linear expression by the quadratic expression from part (a) to get a cubic. (Leave it in factored form.) Graph the cubic function. What do you notice about the zeros and the $y$-intercept of the cubic function?
   **c.** Multiply the cubic by a constant to change the $y$-intercept to 2. Graph the function to see if you've found the right polynomial. What is the function?

**37.** The graph at the right is that of a certain quartic polynomial in the ZDecimal window, which is $[-4.7, 4.7]$ by $[-3.1, 3.1]$. Find the equation of the quartic *without using quartic regression on your calculator*. You may leave it in factored form.

---

**b.** The model is $y = 0.00022688423x^3 - 0.0525547786x^2 + 3.505260295x - 38.64568765$.
**c.** 17.3%
**d.** no; $R^2 \neq 1$

**36. a.** $y = x^2 - 4x + 4$
   **b.** $y = (x - 2)^2(x + 2)$; the zeros are perfect, but the $y$-intercept (8) is too large.
   **c.** $y = \frac{1}{4}(x - 2)^2(x + 2)$

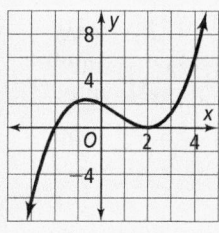

**37.** $y = \frac{1}{8}(x^2 - 4)^2$

---

**33.** A quadratic model would be more appropriate, given the real world context. According to the cubic model, there would be a negative number of students enrolled in the course in the year 2024.

**34.** cubic:
$y = -0.01988x^3 + 10.676431x^2 - 1086.25x + 31,565.157$,
$R^2 = 0.9999803248$;

quartic:
$y = -0.00192x^4 + 0.36145x^3 - 34.558x^2 + 1269.845 - 13,892.5$,
$R^2 = 1$;

The quartic is the best model since $R^2 = 1$.

**35. a.**

A cubic model seems to be most appropriate.

# Answers

## Standardized Test Prep

**38.** 71.409 s

**39.** 1

**40.** 2

**41.** $-\dfrac{7}{8}$

**42.** 5

## Mixed Review

**43.** $32x^5 + 240x^4 + 720x^3 + 1080x^2 + 810x + 243$

**44.** $1331x^3 - 363x^2 + 33x - 1$

**45.** $4096 - 6144x + 3456x^2 - 864x^3 + 81x^4$

**46.** $64 + 432x + 972x^2 + 729x^3$

**47.** $|x - 8| < 1$

**48.** $\left|x - \dfrac{3}{8}\right| \le \dfrac{1}{8}$

**49.** $|y - 2.8| < 1.1$

**50.** $|t - 750| < 250$

**51.** $s = \sqrt{A}$

**52.** $\ell = \dfrac{P}{2} - w$

**53.** $r = \dfrac{C}{2\pi}$

**54.** $b = \dfrac{A}{h}$

**55.**

**56.**

**57.**

**58.**

---

**SAT/ACT**

**38.** The table shows the time it takes a computer program to run, given the number of files used as input. Using a cubic model, what do you predict the run time will be if the input consists of 1000 files?

| Files | Time(s) |
|-------|---------|
| 100 | 0.5 |
| 200 | 0.9 |
| 300 | 3.5 |
| 400 | 8.2 |
| 500 | 14.8 |

**39.** Suppose you hit a ball and its flight follows the graph of $f(x) = -16x^2 + 20x + 3$. How many seconds will it take for the ball to hit the ground? Round your answer to the nearest second.

**40.** What is the multiplicity of the zeros of $y = 16x^2 - 8x + 1$?

**41.** What is the slope of the line shown?

**42.** What is the degree of the polynomial function $y = -9x^3 - 5x^2 - 2x^5 + 4x + x^4 + 1$?

## Mixed Review

**Expand each binomial.**     ◆ **See Lesson 5-7.**

**43.** $(2x + 3)^5$

**44.** $(11x - 1)^3$

**45.** $(8 - 3x)^4$

**46.** $(4 + 9x)^3$

**Write each compound inequality as an absolute value inequality.**     ◆ **See Lesson 1-6.**

**47.** $7 < x < 9$

**48.** $\dfrac{1}{4} \le x \le \dfrac{1}{2}$

**49.** $1.7 < y < 3.9$

**50.** $500 < t < 1000$

**Solve each formula for the indicated variable.**     ◆ **See Lesson 1-4.**

**51.** $A = s^2$, for $s$

**52.** $P = 2(l + w)$, for $l$

**53.** $C = 2\pi r$, for $r$

**54.** $A = bh$, for $b$

**Get Ready!**    To prepare for Lesson 5-9, do Exercises 55–58.

**Graph each function.**     ◆ **See Lesson 4-1.**

**55.** $y = x^2$

**56.** $y = -4x^2$

**57.** $y = x^2 + 3$

**58.** $y = -7x^2 - 1$

# Additional Instructional Support

## Algebra 2 Companion

Students can use the **Algebra 2 Companion** worktext (4 pages) as you teach the lesson. Use the Companion to support

- New Vocabulary
- Key Concepts
- Got It for each Problem
- Lesson Check

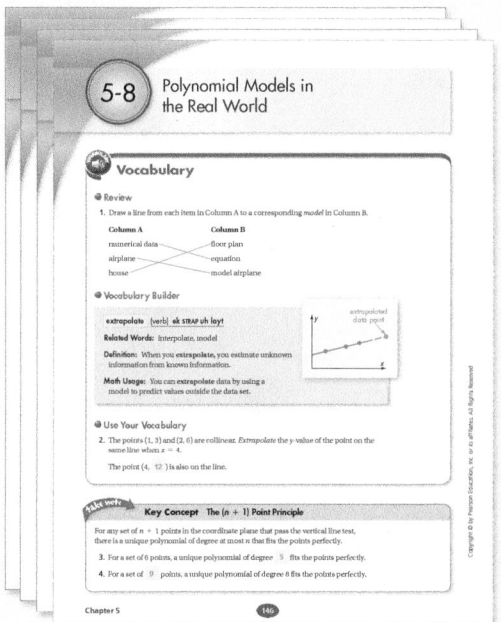

## ELL Support

**Focus on Communication** Discuss the idea of confidence in general and with regard to estimations. Ask the following questions to help increase students' understanding of the concept of confidence:

- What would you feel more confident walking over: a bridge made of steel or one made of balsa wood?
- What song would you feel more confident singing: one you have heard only once or one you have heard 150 times?
- [Bring in a jar of pennies or other objects] What number of pennies would you feel confident estimating that the jar contains? If I say it holds 3, should I be confident about my answer? What if I say 10,000? 500? Why or why not?
- Suppose we hold a competition to guess how many siblings total this class has. Should I be confident about guessing that there are 4 siblings total? 1000? Explain.

# 5 Assess & Remediate

## Lesson Quiz

1. What polynomial function has a graph that passes through the three points $(-1, -4)$, $(0, -5)$, and $(1, -2)$?

2. **Do you UNDERSTAND?** Determine and compare quadratic and cubic models that fit the data in the table. Which model is best?

| Speed (mi/h) | Total Stopping Distance (feet) |
|---|---|
| 20 | 43 |
| 30 | 80 |
| 40 | 126 |
| 50 | 183 |
| 60 | 251 |

3. Using the models developed above, what is the predicted total stopping distance from 80 mi/h? Round to the nearest foot.

### ANSWERS TO LESSON QUIZ

1. $y = 2x^2 + x - 5$

2. $y = 0.05214x^2 + 1.018571x + 2.0$ or $y = 0.00017x^3 + 0.03214x^2 + 1.76190x - 6.400$

   Both models match the data well. It is not obvious which is better.

3. 417 ft (Quadratic model) or 426 ft (Cubic model)

### PRESCRIPTION FOR REMEDIATION

Use the student work on the Lesson Quiz to prescribe a differentiated review assignment:

| Points | Differentiated Remediation |
|---|---|
| 0–1 | Intervention |
| 2 | On-level |
| 3 | Extension |

**PowerAlgebra.com**

## 5 Assess & Remediate

Assign the Lesson Quiz. Appropriate intervention, practice, or enrichment is automatically generated based on student performance.

## Intervention

- **Reteaching** (2 pages) Provides reteaching and practice exercises for the key lesson concepts. Use with struggling students or absent students.
- **English Language Learner Support** Helps students develop and reinforce mathematical vocabulary and key concepts.

### All-in-One Resources/Online
**Reteaching**

5-8 **Reteaching**
Polynomial Models in the Real World

**Problem**

What polynomial function has a graph that passes through the four points $(0, -1)$, $(-1, -7)$, $(2, 17)$, and $(-2, -27)$?

**Step 1** Use the $(n + 1)$ Point Principle to determine the degree $(n)$ of the polynomial that fits these points perfectly. In this case $n + 1 = 4$, so the degree of the polynomial is 3 and the polynomial that fits these points will be $y = ax^3 + bx^2 + cx + d$.

**Step 2** Substitute the $x$- and $y$-values from the four points given in the problem. Now you have four linear equations in four unknowns $(a, b, c, d)$.

$a(0)^3 + b(0)^2 + c(0) + d = -1$    or    $0a + 0b + 0c + d = -1$
$a(-1)^3 + b(-1)^2 + c(-1) + d = -7$    or    $-a + b - c + d = -7$
$a(2)^3 + b(2)^2 + c(2) + d = 17$    or    $8a + 4b + 2c + d = 17$
$a(-2)^3 + b(-2)^2 + c(-2) + d = -27$    or    $-8a + 4b - 2c + d = -27$

**Step 3** Enter the coefficients from the four linear equations as a matrix in your graphing calculator.

**Step 4** Recall that the **rref** function on your calculator returns the reduced row echelon form of a matrix. The last column of the reduced row echelon form is the solution to the system of equations represented by the matrix.

Use the **rref** function to determine the coefficient values $a, b, c, d$.
$a = 2, b = -1, c = 3, d = -1$
So, the polynomial function is $y = 2x^3 - x^2 + 3x - 1$.

**Step 5** Use the CubicReg calculator function with the four original points to check your answer.

**Exercises**

Find the polynomial function that passes through each set of points.

1. $(1, -4)$, $(-2, 38)$, $(0, 2)$, $(-1, 10)$   $y = -3x^3 + x^2 - 4x + 2$

2. $(1, -5)$, $(-3, 39)$, and $(0, -6)$   $y = 4x^2 - 3x - 6$

### All-in-One Resources/Online
**English Language Learner Support**

5-8 **ELL Support**
Polynomial Models in the Real World

Match each word phrase in Column A with the matching item in Column B.

Column A
1. interpolation
2. $(n + 1)$ Point Principle
3. extrapolation
4. $R^2$ value

Column B
A. estimating outside the domain
B. measures the fit between a model and a set of data
C. estimating within the domain
D. used to find a model that fits a set of data

Match each graph in Column A with the matching term in Column B.

Column A
5. C
6. A
7. B

Column B
A. linear
B. quadratic
C. cubic

8. Which form of estimation is more reliable: interpolation or extrapolation?
interpolation

# Differentiated Remediation *continued*

Available in editable format online.

## On-Level

- **Practice** (2 pages) Provides extra practice for each lesson. For simpler practice exercises, use the Form K Practice pages found in the All-in-One Teaching Resources and online.

- **Think About a Plan** Helps students develop specific problem-solving skills and strategies by providing scaffolded guiding questions.

- **Standardized Test Prep** Focuses on all major exercises, all major question types, and helps students prepare for the high-stakes assessments.

## Extension

- **Enrichment** Provides students with interesting problems and activities that extend the concepts of the lesson.

- **Activities, Games, and Puzzles** Worksheets that can be used for concepts development, enrichment, and for fun!

---

### Practice and Problem Solving Wkbk/ All-in-One Resources/Online
**Practice page 1**

### Practice and Problem Solving Wkbk/ All-in-One Resources/Online
**Practice page 2**

### All-in-One Resources/Online
**Enrichment**

### Practice and Problem Solving Wkbk/ All-in-One Resources/Online
**Think About a Plan**

### Practice and Problem Solving Wkbk/ All-in-One Resources/Online
**Standardized Test Prep**

### Online Teacher Resource Center
**Activities, Games, and Puzzles**

## 5-9 Transforming Polynomial Functions

**Objective** To apply transformations to graphs of polynomials

Remember you transformed the graphs of quadratic and absolute value functions.

**Getting Ready!**

The graph of the parent cubic function $f(x) = x^3$ is one of the graphs at the right. The other graph is a transformation $g$ of the parent function. What is an equation for $g$? How do you know?

**Lesson Vocabulary**
• power function
• constant of proportionality

Recall that you can obtain the graph of any quadratic function from the graph of the parent quadratic function, $y = x^2$, using one or more basic transformations. You will find that this is not true of cubic functions.

**Essential Understanding** The graph of the function $y = af(x - h) + k$ is a vertical stretch or compression by the factor $|a|$, a horizontal shift of $h$ units, and a vertical shift of $k$ units of the graph of $y = f(x)$.

**Problem 1** Transforming $y = x^3$

What is an equation of the graph of $y = x^3$ under a vertical compression by the factor $\frac{1}{2}$ followed by a reflection across the $x$-axis, a horizontal translation 3 units to the right, and then a vertical translation 2 units up?

**Think**

How is translating this cubic function like translating a quadratic function?
In each case you replace $x$ with $x - h$ to translate $h$ units to the right.

**Step 1** Multiply by $\frac{1}{2}$ to compress.

$$y = x^3 \longrightarrow y = \frac{1}{2}x^3$$

**Step 2** Multiply by $-1$ to reflect.

$$y = \frac{1}{2}x^3 \longrightarrow y = -\frac{1}{2}x^3$$

**Step 3** Replace $x$ with $x - 3$ to translate horizontally.

$$y = -\frac{1}{2}x^3 \longrightarrow y = -\frac{1}{2}(x - 3)^3$$

**Step 4** Add 2 to translate vertically.

$$y = -\frac{1}{2}(x - 3)^3 \longrightarrow y = -\frac{1}{2}(x - 3)^3 + 2$$

PowerAlgebra.com    Lesson 5-9   Transforming Polynomial Functions    339

# 1 Interactive Learning

**Solve It!**

**PURPOSE** To identify the translations used to transform one cubic function into another
**PROCESS** Students may
• use the coordinates of the inflection point of the transformed function to identify the horizontal and vertical translations.
• compare the shapes of the graphs to see that the offspring function is simply a translation.

**FACILITATE**

**Q** What is the equation for the parent cubic function? **[$y = x^3$]**

**Q** Which equation on the grid shows the parent function $y = x^3$? Explain. **[The blue one; it goes through (0, 0); the red one does not.]**

**Q** How do you know the offspring function is simply a translation of $y = x^3$? **[The graphs have the same shape.]**

**ANSWER** See Solve It in Answers on next page.
**CONNECT THE MATH** In the Solve It, students apply what they know about transforming functions to solve the problem. In the lesson, students will transform polynomial functions of degrees 3 and 4.

# 2 Guided Instruction

**Problem 1**

**Q** How do you translate a cubic function two units to the right? **[Use 2 for $h$; subtract 2 from the $x$ inside the parentheses.]**

**Q** How do you translate a cubic function three units down? **[Use $-3$ for $k$; subtract 3 from the constant term.]**

## 5-9 Preparing to Teach

**BIG idea Functions**        **UbD**
**ESSENTIAL UNDERSTANDING**

• The graph of the function $y = af(x - h) + k$ is a vertical stretch or compression by the factor $|a|$, a horizontal shift of $h$ units, and a vertical shift of $k$ units of the graph of $y = f(x)$.

**Math Background**
Recall that this text defines a *parent function* as "the simplest form of a set of functions that form a family." The functions (or offspring) in the family are created by applying transformations to the parent function.

The most common of these transformations are translation, reflection across the $x$-axis, and stretch or compression. Students have explored transforming parent functions for linear, quadratic, and absolute value functions. This lesson focuses on polynomial functions of degrees 3 and 4.

The transformations used in this lesson change the values and sometimes the number of the real zeros.

At this level, working with parent functions and their offspring helps reinforce the idea that classes of functions can be recognized by the shapes of their graphs.

In subsequent courses, students will learn that transformations can be used to simplify polynomial functions; for example, the general quintic equation can be reduced to the form $x^5 + px + q = 0$ by applying the appropriate series of transformations.

**Support Student Learning**
Use the **Algebra 2 Companion** to engage and support students during instruction. See Lesson Resources at the end of this lesson for details.

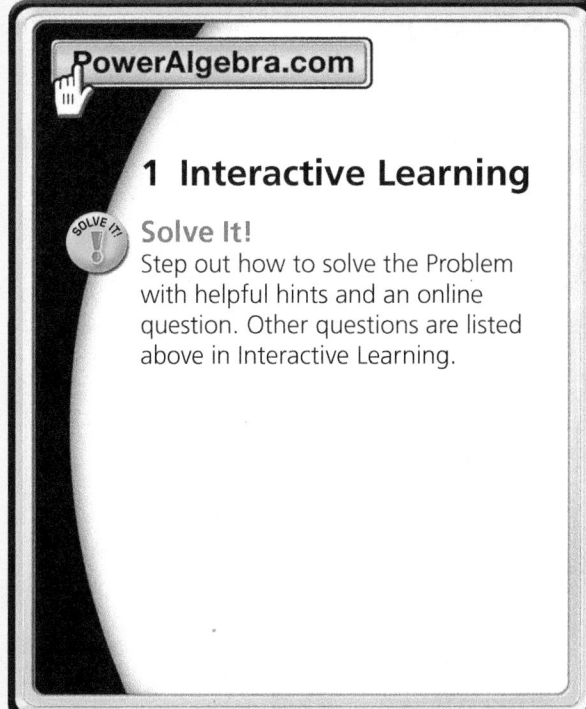

**PowerAlgebra.com**

## 1 Interactive Learning

**Solve It!**
Step out how to solve the Problem with helpful hints and an online question. Other questions are listed above in Interactive Learning.

**Lesson 5-9   339**

## Got It?

**Q** How can you check your answer by graphing? **[Compare the graph of the cubic function to the description of the transformations to make sure they match.]**

## Problem 2

**Q** How can you find the real zeros of $y = -3(x - 1)^3 + 8$? **[Set $y$ equal to 0 and solve for $x$.]**

**Q** How can you find the real zeros of the general form $y = -a(x - h)^3 + k$? What form will your answer have? **[Use the same procedure. Set $y$ equal to 0 and solve for $x$. It will be a literal expression in the three variables $a$, $h$, and $k$.]**

## Got It?

**Q** How do you know before you start that the function will have only one real zero? **[It is a transformation of the parent cubic function, and that function has only one real zero.]**

Students who have difficulty using the formula may want to solve the problem algebraically or by graphing.

---

 **Got It?** **1.** What is an equation of the graph of $y = x^3$ under a vertical stretch by the factor 2 followed by a horizontal translation 3 units to the left and then a vertical translation 4 units down?

The graph shows $y = x^3$ and the graphs that result from the transformations in Problem 1.

In general, $y = a(x - h)^3 + k$ represents all of the cubic functions you can obtain by stretching, compressing, reflecting, or translating the cubic parent function $y = x^3$.

 **Problem 2** Finding Zeros of a Transformed Cubic Function

**Multiple Choice** If $a$, $h$, and $k$ are real numbers and $a \neq 0$, how many distinct real zeros does $y = -a(x - h)^3 + k$ have?

  Ⓐ 0        Ⓑ 1        Ⓒ 2        Ⓓ 3

$$-a(x - h)^3 + k = 0 \qquad x \text{ is a zero means it is an } x\text{-intercept, so } y = 0.$$
$$-a(x - h)^3 = -k \qquad \text{Subtract } k \text{ from each side.}$$
$$(x - h)^3 = \frac{k}{a} \qquad \text{Divide each side by } -a.$$
$$x - h = \sqrt[3]{\frac{k}{a}} \qquad \text{Take the cube root of each side.}$$
$$x = \sqrt[3]{\frac{k}{a}} + h \qquad \text{Solve for } x.$$

Disregarding multiplicities, the function has a single real zero. The correct answer is B.

 **Got It?** **2.** What are all the real zeros of the function $y = 3(x - 1)^3 + 6$?

Problems 1 and 2 together illustrate that the graph of an "offspring" function of the parent cubic function $y = x^3$ has only one $x$-intercept.

The graph of the cubic function $y = x^3 - 2x^2 - 5x + 6$ has three $x$-intercepts. You cannot obtain this function or others like it by transforming the parent cubic function $y = x^3$ using stretches, reflections, and translations.

Similarly, some quartic functions are simple transformations of $y = x^4$ and some are not.

**Plan**

**How can you find the zeros of a function?**
Set the function equal to 0 and solve for $x$.

---

## Answers

### Solve It!

$g(x) = (x - 3)^3 + 2$; it is translated 3 units to the right and 2 units up.

### Got It?

**1.** $y = 2(x + 3)^3 - 4$

**2.** $1 - \sqrt[3]{2}$

**3. a.** Answers may vary. Sample:
   $y = x^4 - 6x^3 + x^2 - 6x$

   **b.** Yes; $-f(x)$ is the function reflected across the $x$-axis, so the zeros will stay the same.

---

 **PowerAlgebra.com**

## 2 Guided Instruction

Each Problem is worked out and supported online.

**Problem 1**
Transforming $y = x^3$
*Animated*

**Alternative Problem 1**
Transforming $y = x^3$

**Problem 2**
Finding Zeros of a Transformed Cubic Function
*Animated*

**Problem 3**
Constructing a Quartic Function with Two Real Zeros
*Animated*

**Problem 4**
Modeling with a Power Function

**Support in Algebra 2 Companion**
• Vocabulary
• Key Concepts
• Got It?

---

## Problem 3   Constructing a Quartic Function with Two Real Zeros

**What is a quartic function with only two real zeros, $x = 5$ and $x = 9$?**

**Method 1** Use transformations.

First, find a quartic with zeros at $\pm 2$.
Translate the basic quartic 16 units down:
$y = x^4 \rightarrow y = x^4 - 16$

9 is 7 units to the right of 2.
Translate 7 units to the right.
$y = x^4 - 16 \rightarrow y = (x - 7)^4 - 16$

A quartic function with its only real zeros at 5 and 9 is
$y = (x - 7)^4 - 16$.

$\boxed{y = x^4}$

$\boxed{y = x^4 - 16} \quad \boxed{y = (x - 7)^4 - 16}$

**Method 2** Use algebraic methods.

$$y = (x - 5)(x - 9) \cdot Q(x)$$
$$= (x - 5)(x - 9)(x^2 + 1)$$
$$= (x^2 - 14x + 45)(x^2 + 1)$$
$$= x^4 - 14x^3 + 46x^2 - 14x + 45$$

Make $Q(x)$ a quadratic with no real zeros.

Another quartic function with its only real zeros at
5 and 9 is $y = x^4 - 14x^3 + 46x^2 - 14x + 45$.

**Think**

**What should you use for $Q(x)$?**
Choose $Q(x)$ to be a quadratic with no real zeros. Keep it simple, such as $x^2 + 1$.

✓ **Got It?**   **3. a.** What is a quartic function $f(x)$ with only two real zeros, $x = 0$ and $x = 6$?
     **b. Reasoning** Does the quartic function $-f(x)$ have the same zeros? Explain.

The "offspring" of the parent function $y = x^4$ is a subfamily of all quartic polynomials. This subfamily consists of quartics of the form $y = a(x - h)^4 + k$. These functions also belong to another category of polynomials, and in this category you can generate families as usual.

### Key Concept   Power Functions

**Definition**

A **power function** is a function of the form
$y = a \cdot x^b$, where $a$ and $b$ are nonzero real numbers.

**Examples**

$y = 0.5x^6 \qquad y = \frac{1}{2}x^2$

$y = -4x^{\frac{2}{3}} \qquad y = x^{0.25}$

If the exponent $b$ in $y = ax^b$ is a positive integer, the function is also a *monomial function*.

If $y = ax^b$ describes $y$ as a power function of $x$, then $y$ *varies directly with*, or is *proportional to*, the $b$th power of $x$. The constant $a$ is the **constant of proportionality**. Power functions arise in many real-world contexts related to the concept of direct variation, which you studied in Chapter 2.

---

**Problem 3**
In Method 1, it may be difficult for students to understand why they start by translating the function 16 units down. Have them graph the parent function $y = x^4$.

**Q** What points on the graph of $y = x^4$ have $+2$ and $-2$ as the $x$-coordinates? **(2, 16) and (−2, 16)]**
**Q** How far apart are these points? **[4 units]**
**Q** If you translate $y = x^4$ 16 units down, how far apart will the zeros be? **[4 units]**

### Got It?

**Q** Why are there many different answers to this problem? Hint: Look at the solution steps in Method 2. **[The function $Q(x)$ could be any quadratic function, so there is an infinite number of solutions.]**

### Take Note

**Q** How does setting $h$ and $k$ equal to 0 in $y = a(x - h)^4 + k$ change the transformed quartic function to the fourth-degree power function? **[Substituting 0 for $h$ and $k$ in $y = a(x - h)^4 - k$ gives $y = a(x - 0)^4 + 0$, which simplifies to $y = ax^4$, which is the fourth-degree power function.]**

---

# Additional Problems

**1.** What cubic function do you obtain by applying the following transformations to $y = x^3$: vertical stretch by the factor 3; reflection in the $x$-axis; vertical translation 5 units up?

**ANSWER** $y = -3x^3 + 5$

**2.** What are all the real zeros of $y = \frac{1}{2}(x - 2)^3 - 3$?

**ANSWER** 3.82

**3.** What is a quartic function with only two real zeros: $x = -4$ and $x = -6$?

**ANSWER** Answers may vary. Samples: $y = (x + 5)^4 - 1$; $y = x^4 + 10x^3 + 25x^2 + 10x + 24$

**4.** A wind turbine generates 1200 kW of power in a 20 mi/h wind. How much power does this turbine generate in a 12 mi/h wind? Use the formula for $P$ as a power function of velocity, $P = av^3$.

**ANSWER** 259.2 kW, or about 259 kW

## Problem 4

Q What is a method for using the direct variation equation $y = kx$ to solve a problem when you are given one set of values for $x$ and $y$? **[Write the equation $y = kx$. Use the given values to find $k$. Substitute any value for $x$ to find $y$.]**

Q The point $(2, 2)$ is on the graph of the power function $y = ax^2$. What is $a$? What is the point with 5 as its $x$-coordinate? **[$a = 0.5$; $(5, 12.5)$]**

### Got It?

Q Why is the constant of proportionality different from the variation equation in the Problem? **[The values of $P$ and $v$ do not vary directly with the values of $P$ and $v$ in the Problem because the units have been changed.]**

## 3 Lesson Check

### Do you know HOW?   ERROR INTERVENTION

• If students have trouble with Exercises 1–3, remind them that they can find the zeros either algebraically or by graphing, and then use the other method to check.

### Do you UNDERSTAND?

• If students are confused by Exercise 5 because they know some cubic functions have 3 real roots, remind them that these functions cannot be obtained by transformations. Have them experiment with a graphing calculator to see for themselves.

### Close

Q What are the relationships among these sets?
Set $A$ = {all cubic polynomial functions}
Set $B$ = {transformed cubic polynomial functions}
Set $C$ = {third-degree power functions}
**[$B$ is a subset of $A$, and $C$ is a subset of $B$.]**

---

 **Problem 4** Modeling With a Power Function

**Wind-Generated Power** Wind farms are a source of renewable energy found around the world. The power $P$ (in kilowatts) generated by a wind turbine varies directly as the cube of the wind speed $v$ (in meters per second). The picture shows the power output of one turbine at one wind speed. To the nearest kilowatt, how much power does this turbine generate in a 10 m/s wind?

Wind 8 m/s
Electric Power 600 kW

**Think**

How is this problem like the direct variation you studied in Chapter 2?
With the direct variation, $y = kx$, you use a first power. Here you use a third power.

The formula for $P$ as a power function of $v$ is $P = a \cdot v^3$. From the picture, $P = 600$ when $v = 8$, or $600 = a \cdot 8^3$. Solve for $a$.

$600 = a \cdot 8^3$    Use values of $P$ and $v$ to find $a$.

$600 = 512a$

$a \approx 1.1719$

$P \approx 1.1719v^3$.    Use the value of $a$ in the original formula.

$P \approx 1.1719 \cdot 10^3 = 1171.9$.    Substitute 10 for $v$ and simplify.

This turbine generates about 1172 kW of power in a 10 m/s wind.

 **Got It? 4.** Another turbine generates 210 kW of power in a 12 mi/h wind. How much power does this turbine generate in a 20 mi/h wind?

---

**Lesson Check**

**Do you know HOW?**

Find all the real zeros of each function.

1. $y = -(x + 3)^3 + 1$

2. $y = -8(x - 5)^3 - 64$

3. $y = \frac{9}{2}(x - 1)^3 + \frac{4}{3}$

**Do you UNDERSTAND?**

4. **Vocabulary** Is the function $y = 4x^3 + 5$ an example of a power function? Explain.

5. **Error Analysis** Your friend says that he has found a way to transform the graph of $y = x^3$ to obtain three real roots. Using the graph of the function, explain why this is impossible.

6. **Compare and Contrast** How are the graphs of $y = x^3$ and $y = 4x^3$ alike? How are they different? What transformation was used to get the second equation?

---

## Answers

### Got It? (continued)

**4.** 972 kW

### Lesson Check

**1.** −2

**2.** 3

**3.** $\frac{1}{3}$

**4.** No; a power function is of the form $y = ax^b$, where $y$ varies directly with the $b$th power of $x$.

**5.** $y = x^3$ has end behavior of down and up with no turning pt. Thus, at most, there is one real root.

**6.** Both $y = x^3$ and $y = 4x^3$ pass through the origin, have the same end behavior of down and up, and no turning pts. $y = 4x^3$ is $y = x^3$ stretched vertically by a factor of 4.

---

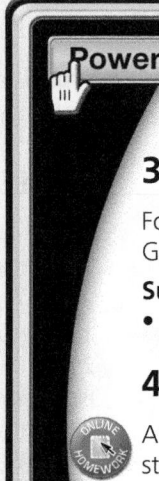

**PowerAlgebra.com**

## 3 Lesson Check

For a digital lesson check, use the Got It questions.

**Support in Algebra 2 Companion**
• Lesson Check

## 4 Practice

 Assign homework to individual students or to an entire class.

## Practice and Problem-Solving Exercises

◀ See Problem 1.

**Ⓐ Practice**    Determine the cubic function that is obtained from the parent function $y = x^3$ after each sequence of transformations.

**7.** a vertical stretch by a factor of 3;
a reflection across the $x$-axis;
a vertical translation 2 units up;
and a horizontal translation 1 unit right

**8.** a vertical stretch by a factor of 2;
a vertical translation 4 units up;
and a horizontal translation 3 units left

**9.** a reflection across the $y$-axis;
a vertical translation 1 unit down;
and a horizontal translation 5 units left

**10.** a vertical translation 3 units down;
and a horizontal translation 2 units right

**11.** a vertical stretch by a factor of 3;
a reflection across the $y$-axis;
a vertical translation $\frac{3}{4}$ unit up;
and a horizontal translation $\frac{1}{2}$ unit left

**12.** a vertical stretch by a factor of $\frac{5}{3}$;
a reflection across the $x$-axis;
a vertical translation 4 units down;
and a horizontal translation 3 units right

Find all the real zeros of each function.    ◀ See Problem 2.

**13.** $y = -27(x - 2)^3 + 8$

**14.** $y = -\frac{1}{8}(x - 7)^3 - 8$

**15.** $y = -3\left(x + \frac{4}{5}\right)^3 + \frac{8}{9}$

**16.** $y = -16(x + 3)^3 + 9$

**17.** $y = 4(x - 1)^3 + 10$

**18.** $y = 2(x + 5)^3 + 10$

Find a quartic function with the given $x$-values as its only real zeros.    ◀ See Problem 3.

**19.** $x = 2$ and $x = -1$

**20.** $x = -3$ and $x = -4$

**21.** $x = -1$ and $x = 3$

**22.** $x = 4$ and $x = 2$

**23.** $x = -4$ and $x = -1$

**24.** $x = -3$ and $x = 2$

**25. Cooking** The number of pepperoni slices that Kim puts on a pizza varies directly as the square of the diameter of the pizza. If she puts 15 slices on a 10" diameter pizza, how many slices should she put on a 16" diameter pizza?    ◀ See Problem 4.

**26. Volume** The amount of water that a spherical tank can hold varies directly as the cube of its radius. If a tank with radius 7.5 ft holds 1767 ft$^3$ of water, how much water can a tank with radius 16 ft hold?

**Ⓑ Apply**    **27. Think About a Plan** The kinetic energy generated by a 5 lb ball is represented by the formula $K = \frac{1}{2}(5)v^2$. If the ball is thrown with a velocity of 6 ft/sec, how much kinetic energy is generated?
- What does 5 represent in the function?
- What number should you substitute for $v$?

---

## 4 Practice

### ASSIGNMENT GUIDE

Basic: 7–26 all, 27, 28, 30–36 even, 40, 41

Average: 7–25 odd, 27–43

Advanced: 7–25 odd, 27–46

Standardized Test Prep: 47–49

Mixed Review: 50–58

**Reasoning** exercises have blue headings.

**Applications** exercises have red headings.

**EXERCISE 40:** Use the Think About a Plan worksheet in the **Practice and Problem Solving Workbook** (also available in the Teaching Resources in print and online) to further support students' development in becoming independent learners.

### HOMEWORK QUICK CHECK

To check students' understanding of key skills and concepts, go over Exercises 7, 13, 27, 34, and 40.

---

### Practice and Problem-Solving Exercises

**7.** $y = -3(x - 1)^3 + 2$

**8.** $y = 2(x + 3)^3 + 4$

**9.** $y = -(x + 5)^3 - 1$

**10.** $y = (x - 2)^3 - 3$

**11.** $y = -3\left(x + \frac{1}{2}\right)^3 + \frac{3}{4}$

**12.** $y = -\frac{5}{3}(x - 3)^3 - 4$

**13.** $\frac{8}{3}$

**14.** 3

**15.** $-\frac{2}{15}$

**16.** $-3 + \frac{1}{4}\sqrt[3]{36}$

**17.** $1 - \frac{1}{2}\sqrt[3]{20}$

**18.** $-5 - \sqrt[3]{5}$

For Exercises 19–24, answers may vary.
Samples:

**19.** $x^4 - x^3 - x^2 - x - 2$

**20.** $x^4 + 7x^3 + 13x^2 + 7x + 12$

**21.** $x^4 - 2x^3 - 2x^2 - 2x - 3$

**22.** $x^4 - 6x^3 + 9x^2 - 6x + 8$

**23.** $x^4 + 5x^3 + 5x^2 + 5x + 4$

**24.** $x^4 + x^3 - 5x^2 + x - 6$

**25.** $38.4 \approx 38$ slices

**26.** 17,155.9 ft$^3$

**27.** 90 lb·ft$^2$/s$^2$

# Answers

## Practice and Problem-Solving Exercises
(continued)

**28.** Yes; using parent function $y = x^3$, stretch vertically by a factor of 3.

**29.** Yes; using parent function $y = x^2$, stretch vertically by a factor of 2, then translate 5 units up and 3 units to the right.

**30.** no

**31.** Yes; using parent function $y = x^2$, translate 9 units down and 4 units to the right.

**32.** Yes; using parent function $y = x^4$, translate 2 units to the left.

**33.** Yes; using parent function $y = x^3$, stretch vertically by a factor of 4 and reflect across the *x*-axis.

**34.** translation 4 units up and 1 unit to the left

**35.** reflection across the *x*-axis, vert. stretch by a factor of 2, translation 1 unit up and 1 unit to the right

**36.** reflection across the *x*-axis, translation 2 units down and 3 units to the right

**37.** vert. stretch by a factor of 3, translation 2 units down and 1 unit to the right

**38.** vert. stretch by a factor of 5, translation 1 unit up and 1 unit to the right

**39.** reflection across the *x*-axis, translation 2 units up and 4 units to the right

**40.** 40 lb · ft$^2$/s$^2$

**41.** The parent function, $y = x^5$, has only one *x*-intercept.

**42.** Some quartic polynomials have four *x*-intercepts and cannot be written in that form; $y = x^4 - 20x^2 + 64$; $y = x^4 - 5x^2 + 4$.

**43.** Error in (2) "a transformation of $y = x^2$." Some polynomials do not contain an $x^2$ term.

---

Determine whether each function can be obtained from the parent function, $y = x^n$, using basic transformations. If so, describe the sequence of transformations.

**28.** $y = 3x^3$

**29.** $y = 2(x - 3)^2 + 5$

**30.** $y = x^3 - x$

**31.** $y = x^2 - 8x + 7$

**32.** $y = (x + 2)^4$

**33.** $y = -4x^3$

Determine the transformations that were used to change the graph of the parent function $y = x^3$ to each of the following graphs.

**34.**

**35.**

**36.**

**37.**

**38.**

**39.**

**40. Physics** The formula $K = \frac{1}{2}mv^2$ represents the kinetic energy of an object. If the kinetic energy of a ball is 10 lb-ft$^2$/s$^2$ when it is thrown with a velocity of 4 ft/s, how much kinetic energy is generated if the ball is thrown with a velocity of 8 ft/s?

**41. Reasoning** Explain why the basic transformations of the parent function $y = x^5$ will only generate functions that can be written in the form $y = a(x - h)^5 + k$.

**42. Reasoning** Explain why some quartic polynomials cannot be written in the form $y = a(x - h)^4 + k$. Give two examples.

**43. Error Analysis** Your friend claims he can write any cubic polynomial as the sum of two functions: (1) a cubic monomial and (2) a transformation of $y = x^2$. Explain why your friend's claim is incorrect.

$$P(x) = ax^3 + bx^2 + cx + d$$
cubic   transformation
monomial   of $y = x^2$

**Challenge**
**44. Reasoning** Find a sequence of basic transformations by which the polynomial function $y = 2x^3 - 6x^2 + 6x + 5$ can be derived from the cubic function $y = x^3$.

**45. Physics** For a constant resistance $R$ (in ohms), the power $P$ (in watts) dissipated across two terminals of a battery varies directly as the square of the current $I$ (in amps). If a battery connected in a circuit dissipates 24 watts of power for 2 amps of current flow, how much power would be dissipated when the current flow is 5 amps?

**46. Writing** Give an argument that shows that *every* polynomial family of degree $n > 2$ contains polynomials that cannot be generated from the basic function $y = x^n$ by using stretches, compressions, reflections, and translations.

## Standardized Test Prep

Use the graph to answer questions 47–49.

 **SAT/ACT**

**47.** Which equation does the graph represent?

Ⓐ $y = (x + 2)^2 - 1$   Ⓒ $y = (x - 2)^2 + 1$
Ⓑ $y = (x - 2)^2 - 1$   Ⓓ $y = (x - 2)^4 - 1$

**48.** If $y = f(x)$ is an equation for the graph, what are factors of $f(x)$?
Ⓕ $(x - 1)$ and $(x + 3)$   Ⓗ $(x + 1)$ and $(x - 3)$
Ⓖ $(x - 1)$ and $(x - 3)$   Ⓘ $(x + 1)$ and $(x + 3)$

**Short Response**
**49.** If $y = ax^2 + bx + c$ is an equation for the graph, what type of number is its discriminant?

## Mixed Review

Find a polynomial function whose graph passes through the given points.      See Lesson 5-8.

**50.** $(-1, 4), (0, -2), (1, -2), (2, -8)$     **51.** $(-2, -17), (0, -3), (1, -5), (3, 63)$

Write an equation of each line.     See Lesson 2-4.

**52.** slope $= -\frac{4}{5}$; through $(-1, 4)$     **53.** slope $= -3$; through $(2, -1)$

Determine whether each relation is a function.     See Lesson 2-1.

**54.** $\{(0, -1), (-1, 3), (2, 3), (-3, 3)\}$     **55.** $\{(-4, 0), (-7, 0), (-4, 1), (-7, 1)\}$

**Get Ready!** To prepare for Lesson 6-1, do Exercises 56–58.

Factor each expression.     See Lesson 5-2.

**56.** $x^{10} + x^2$     **57.** $x^4 - y^4$     **58.** $169x^6y^{12} - 13x^3y^6$

**44.** vert. stretch by a factor of 2, translation 7 units up and 1 unit to the right

**45.** 150 watts

**46.** Even-degree parent functions and their offspring have two $x$-intercepts, odd-degree parent functions and their offspring have one $x$-intercept. Polynomial functions of degree $n$ have as many as $n$ $x$-intercepts; for example: $y = x^3 - 2x^2 - 5x + 6$ (with three $x$-intercepts) cannot be generated from the parent function $y = x^3$ (with one $x$-intercept).

## Standardized Test Prep
**47.** B
**48.** G
**49. [2]** $y = (x - 2)^2 - 1$
$= x^2 - 4x + 4 - 1$
$= x^2 - 4x + 3$

The discriminant is:
$b^2 - 4ac = (-4)^2 - 4(1)(3) = 4$
which is positive.

**[1]** appropriate methods, with one computational error

## Mixed Review
**50.** $y = -2x^3 + 3x^2 - x - 2$
**51.** $y = 3x^3 - 5x - 3$
**52.** $y = -\frac{4}{5}x + \frac{16}{5}$
**53.** $y = -3x + 5$
**54.** yes
**55.** no
**56.** $x^2(x^8 + 1)$
**57.** $(x - y)(x + y)(x^2 + y^2)$
**58.** $13x^3y^6(13x^3y^6 - 1)$

# Additional Instructional Support

## Algebra 2 Companion

Students can use the **Algebra 2 Companion** worktext (4 pages) as you teach the lesson. Use the Companion to support

- New Vocabulary
- Key Concepts
- Got It for each Problem
- Lesson Check

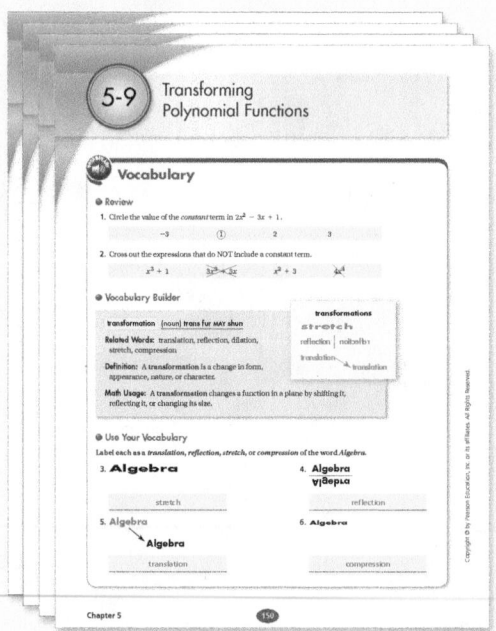

## ELL Support

**Focus on Language** Ask students to consider each of the following and determine whether they are *always*, *sometimes*, or *never* true and explain why:

- A parent function has the same number of zeros as its offspring. [Sometimes true; a horizontal translation does not change the number of zeros but a vertical translation sometimes does]
- A parent function has the same degree as its offspring. [Always true, by definition. No transformation can change the degree of a function.]
- A parent function has the same leading coefficient as its offspring. [Sometimes true; vertical and horizontal translations do not change the leading coefficient; however, a vertical stretch or compression or reflection does.]

# 5 Assess & Remediate

## Lesson Quiz

1. What function do you obtain by applying the following transformations to $y = x^3$: reflection in the x-axis; horizontal translation 2 units right; vertical translation 1 unit down?

2. What are the real zeros of $y = -2(x + 3)^3 + 8$?

3. What is a quartic function with only two real zeros, $x = 7$ and $x = 13$?

4. **Do you UNDERSTAND?** A wind turbine generates 100 kW of power in a 10 mi/h wind. How much power does this turbine generate in a 25 mi/h wind? Use the formula for $P$ as a power function of velocity, $P = av^3$.

### ANSWERS TO LESSON QUIZ

1. $y = -(x - 2)^3 - 1$

2. one; $-1.41$

3. Answers may vary. Samples:
$y = (x - 10)^4 - 81$;
$y = x^4 - 20x^3 + 92x^2 - 20x + 91$

4. 1562.5 kW

### PRESCRIPTION FOR REMEDIATION

Use the student work on the Lesson Quiz to prescribe a differentiated review assignment:

| Points | Differentiated Remediation |
|--------|---------------------------|
| 0–2 | Intervention |
| 3 | On-level |
| 4 | Extension |

## 5 Assess & Remediate

Assign the Lesson Quiz. Appropriate intervention, practice, or enrichment is automatically generated based on student performance.

# Differentiated Remediation

Available in editable format online.

## Intervention

- **Reteaching** (2 pages) Provides reteaching and practice exercises for the key lesson concepts. Use with struggling students or absent students.

- **English Language Learner Support** Helps students develop and reinforce mathematical vocabulary and key concepts.

### All-in-One Resources/Online
### Reteaching

### All-in-One Resources/Online
### English Language Learner Support

# Differentiated Remediation *continued*

Available in editable format online.

## On-Level

- **Practice** (2 pages) Provides extra practice for each lesson. For simpler practice exercises, use the Form K Practice pages found in the All-in-One Teaching Resources and online.

- **Think About a Plan** Helps students develop specific problem-solving skills and strategies by providing scaffolded guiding questions.

- **Standardized Test Prep** Focuses on all major exercises, all major question types, and helps students prepare for the high-stakes assessments.

## Extension

- **Enrichment** Provides students with interesting problems and activities that extend the concepts of the lesson.

- **Activities, Games, and Puzzles** Worksheets that can be used for concepts development, enrichment, and for fun!

---

### Practice and Problem Solving Wkbk/All-in-One Resources/Online
**Practice page 1**

### Practice and Problem Solving Wkbk/All-in-One Resources/Online
**Practice page 2**

### All-in-One Resources/Online
**Enrichment**

---

### Practice and Problem Solving Wkbk/All-in-One Resources/Online
**Think About a Plan**

### Practice and Problem Solving Wkbk/All-in-One Resources/Online
**Standardized Test Prep**

### Online Teacher Resource Center
**Activities, Games, and Puzzles**

# Performance Task

## Pull It All Together

The concepts and skills required to solve these problems are from several lessons within this chapter and from earlier chapters. As students solve these problems, they will demonstrate their reasoning strategies and their growth as independent problem solvers.

The following questions are designed to
- Help support students as they do the Tasks.
- Gauge the amount of support students need as they become independent problem solvers.

### Task 1

Factor a polynomial and use the linear factors to solve a problem.
- What linear factor is given in the Task description?
- How can you tell which linear factor will yield a higher value in the context of the problem?
- Could the value of $x$ be less than or equal to one?

### Task 2

Use algebraic properties and the Binomial Theorem to rewrite and expand a binomial raised to a power.
- How can you rewrite $[(a - b) + 1]^5$ so that $b$ is grouped with 1 instead of $a$?

### Task 3

Use factoring techniques to find zeros and write polynomials as products of linear factors.
- How will finding the complete factorization of one of the polynomials help you complete the task?
- What are all the factors of 6?
- How can a polynomial of degree four and a polynomial of degree three have the same linear factors?

---

## Pull It All Together

**BIG idea** Function

You can represent quantities using variables and algebraic expressions. You can represent some relationships between quantities using equations.

### Task 1

The polynomial $2x^3 + 9x^2 + 4x - 15$ represents the volume in cubic feet of a rectangular holding tank at a fish hatchery. The depth of the tank is $(x - 1)$ feet. The length is 13 feet.

**a.** Use synthetic division to help you factor the volume polynomial. How many linear factors should you look for? What are they?

**b.** Assume the length is the greatest dimension. Which linear factor represents the 13-ft length? What are the dimensions of the tank? What is its volume? What is the value of $x$? Do you get the same volume if you substitute the value of $x$ into $2x^3 + 9x^2 + 4x - 15$?

**BIG idea** Equivalence

You can use the Binomial Theorem and properties of algebra to rewrite some powers.

### Task 2

Show that the following equation is true for all values of $a$ and $b$.

$$[(a - b) + 1]^5 = a^5 - 5a^4(b - 1) + 10a^3(b - 1)^2 - 10a^2(b - 1)^3 + 5a(b - 1)^4 - (b - 1)^5$$

**BIG idea** Solving Equations and Inequalities

A polynomial $P(x)$ of degree $n$, $n \geq 1$, and its related polynomial function $y = P(x)$ have $n$ complex zeros. The zeros are identical to the $n$ complex roots of the related polynomial equation $P(x) = 0$.

### Task 3

Four of these five polynomial functions have identical zeros. The fifth has exactly two zeros in common with each of the other functions. Write this fifth function as a product of its linear factors.

$$P_1(x) = x^3 - 6x^2 + 11x - 6$$
$$P_2(x) = x^4 - 5x^3 + 7x^2 - 5x + 6$$
$$P_3(x) = x^4 - 7x^3 + 17x^2 - 17x + 6$$
$$P_4(x) = x^4 - 8x^3 + 23x^2 - 28x + 12$$
$$P_5(x) = x^4 - 9x^3 + 29x^2 - 39x + 18$$

To solve these problems, you will pull together concepts and skills related to working with polynomials and their related functions and equations.

---

# Assess
# Performance

## Pull It All Together

See p. 49 for a holistic scoring rubric to gauge a student's progress on Understanding the Problem, Planning a Solution, Getting an Answer, and Assessing Autonomy.

### SOLUTION OUTLINES

**1. a.** First step: Since the given expression is cubic, you should look for 3 linear factors.

Second step: Divide $2x^3 + 9x^2 + 4x - 15$ by $(x - 1)$ using synthetic division. (The result is $2x^2 - 11x + 15$.)

Third step: Factor your result from Step 2. $[(2x + 5)(x + 3)]$

So, the 3 linear factors are $(x - 1)$, $(2x + 5)$, and $(x + 3)$.

**b.** Possible Plan: Use the linear factor $(2x + 5)$ to represent the length. Since the $x$-value is double the $x$-value in the other 2 factors, it will be the largest value. Set the factor equal to 13 and solve for $x$. Use the value of $x$ to find the other two dimensions. ($x = 4$; The other 2 dimensions are 3 ft and 7 ft.)

**2.** First step: Use the Binomial Theorem to expand $[(a - b) + 1]^5$.

Second step: Expand each term of the binomial expansion.

Third step: Regroup factors and use factor by grouping to show that the left-hand side of the equation is equal to the right-hand side.

**3.** Possible Plan: Find the zeros of each of the polynomials using the Rational Root and Factor Theorems, synthetic division, and factoring. Then compare the zeros. (The polynomial with only 2 common factors is $P_2$. Its linear factors are $(x - 2)$, $(x - 3)$, and $(x^2 + 1)$. So, its zeros are $i$, $-i$, 2, and 3. The other four polynomials have zeros 1, 2, and 3.)

# 5 Chapter Review

Connecting **BIG** ideas and Answering the Essential Questions

**1 Function**
A polynomial of degree $n$ has $n$ linear factors. The graph of the related function crosses the $x$-axis an even or odd number of times depending on whether $n$ is even or odd.

**Polynomial Functions, Zeros, and Linear Factors (Lessons 5-1 and 5-2)**
$y = 2x^3 + 7x^2 - 9$ has 3 linear factors $(x + 3)$, $(2x + 3)$, $(x - 1)$, it crosses the $x$-axis 3 times—at $(-3, 0)$, $\left(-\frac{3}{2}, 0\right)$, and $(1, 0)$. Its end behavior is down and up.

**2 Equivalence**
$(x - a)$ is a linear factor if and only if $a$ is a zero, and if and only if $(a, 0)$ is an $x$-intercept when $a$ is a real number.

**Theorems About Roots of Polynomial Equations (Lesson 5-5)**
$P(x) = 2x^3 + 7x^2 - 9$ and $Q(x) = 2x^3 + 5x^2 + 9$ each have degree 3 so $P(x) = 0$ and $Q(x) = 0$ each have 3 complex roots.
Each has $\pm 1, \pm 3, \pm 9, \pm\frac{1}{2}, \pm\frac{3}{2}, \pm\frac{9}{2}$ as its possible rational roots.
$P(-3) = 0$, so $x + 3$ is a factor of $2x^3 + 7x^2 - 9$.
$Q(-3) = 0$, so $x + 3$ is a factor of $2x^3 + 5x^2 + 9$.

**Solving Polynomial Equations (Lesson 5-3)**
$2x^3 + 7x^2 - 9 = 0$ has factored form $(x + 3)(2x + 3)(x - 1) = 0$. It has 3 roots or solutions, $x = -3$, $x = -\frac{3}{2}$, and $x = 1$.

**The Fundamental Theorem of Algebra (Lesson 5-6)**
$2x^3 + 5x^2 + 9 = 0$ has factored form $(x + 3)(2x^2 - x + 3) = 0$. It has 3 roots or solutions, $x = -3$, $x = \frac{1}{4} - \frac{\sqrt{23}}{4}i$, and $x = \frac{1}{4} + \frac{\sqrt{23}}{4}i$.

**3 Solving Equations and Inequalities**
$(x - a)$ is a linear factor if and only if $a$ is a root of the related polynomial equation.

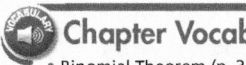 **Chapter Vocabulary**

- Binomial Theorem (p. 327)
- Conjugate Root Theorem (p. 314)
- constant of proportionality (p. 341)
- degree of a monomial (p. 280)
- degree of a polynomial (p. 280)
- Descartes' Rule of Signs (p. 315)
- difference of cubes (p. 297)
- end behavior (p. 282)
- expand a binomial (p. 326)
- Factor Theorem (p. 290)

- Fundamental Theorem of Algebra (p. 320)
- monomial (p. 280)
- multiple zero (p. 291)
- multiplicity (p. 291)
- Pascal's Triangle (p. 327)
- polynomial (p. 280)
- polynomial function (p. 280)
- power function (p. 341)
- Rational Root Theorem (p. 312)

- relative maximum (p. 291)
- relative minimum (p. 291)
- Remainder Theorem (p. 307)
- standard form of a polynomial function (p. 281)
- sum of cubes (p. 297)
- synthetic division (p. 306)
- turning point (p. 282)

**Match each vocabulary term with the description that best fits it.**

**1.** Conjugate Root Theorem
**2.** Fundamental Theorem of Algebra
**3.** Rational Root Theorem
**4.** Remainder Theorem

**A.** determines $P(a)$ by dividing the polynomial by $x - a$
**B.** the degree equals the number of roots
**C.** minimizes guessing fraction and integer solutions
**D.** complex numbers as roots come in pairs

## Answers

**1.** D
**2.** B
**3.** C
**4.** A

**BIG** idea **Function**
**ESSENTIAL QUESTION** What does the degree of a polynomial tell you about its related polynomial function?
**ANSWER** A polynomial of degree $n$ has $n$ linear factors. The graph of the related function crosses the $x$-axis an even or odd number of times depending on whether $n$ is even or odd.

**BIG** idea **Equivalence**
**ESSENTIAL QUESTION** For a polynomial function, how are factors, zeros, and $x$-intercepts related?
**ANSWER** $(x - a)$ is a linear factor if and only if $a$ is a zero and if and only if $(a, 0)$ is an $x$-intercept when $a$ is a real number.

**BIG** idea **Solving Equations and Inequalities**
**ESSENTIAL QUESTION** For a polynomial equation, how are factors and roots related?
**ANSWER** $(x - a)$ is a linear factor if and only if $a$ is a root of the related polynomial equation.

## Summative Questions UbD

Use the following prompts as you review this chapter with your students. The prompts are designed to help you assess your students' understanding of the Big Ideas they have studied.

- What must be true about the divisor when you use synthetic division?
- If you know the degree of a polynomial, what can you tell about its zeros?
- The vertex of a parabola is either the maximum or minimum value of the function. How are these different from the relative maximums and minimums of polynomial functions? How are they similar?
- When is Pascal's Triangle a better tool than the Distributive Property to expand the power of a binomial?
- What is a multiple zero? Graphically, when do they occur?

# Answers

## Chapter Review (continued)

**5.** $y = -x^4 + 12$; quartic binomial; down and down

**6.** $y = x^2 - x + 7$; quadratic trinomial; up and up

**7.** $y = -x^4 + 2x^3 + 3x^2 - 6x + 12$; quartic polynomial of five terms; down and down

**8.** $y = x^3 + 2x^2 - 4x + 8$; cubic polynomial of four terms; down and up

**9.** $y = x^4 - 3x^3 + 3x^2 + 10$; quartic polynomial of four terms; up and up

**10.** 3

**11.** If $n$ is even there are an odd number of turning points; if $n$ is odd there are an even number of turning points.

**12.** $f(x) = x^3 - 4x^2 - 11x - 6$

**13.** $f(x) = x^3 - x^2 - 2x$

**14.** $f(x) = x^3 - 6x^2 + 11x - 6$

**15.** $f(x) = x^3 - 3x^2 - 6x + 8$

**16.** $0$, $-2$ (multiplicity 3)

**17.** 2 (multiplicity 2), $-2$ (multiplicity 2)

**18.** $0$, $-\dfrac{1}{2}$, 1

**19.** 5, $-2$ (multiplicity 2)

**20.** relative maximum: $(0.8672, -1.9351)$; relative minimums: $(0, -3)$, $(2.8828, -12.1704)$; zeros: $x = -0.5992$, $x = 3.7115$

**21.** relative maximum: $(-0.8441, 9.3023)$; relative minimum: $(0.7108, -0.0964)$; zeros: $x = -1.6180$, $x = 0.6180$, $x = 0.8$

**22.** relative minimum: $(1, -4)$; zeros: $x = -0.2490$, $x = 1.6633$

**23.** relative maximum: $(-0.4142, -3.3432)$; relative minimum: $(2.4142, -14.6569)$; zero: $x = 4$

---

## 5-1 Polynomial Functions

### Quick Review

The **standard form of a polynomial function** is $P(x) = a_n x^n + a_{n-1}x^{n-1} + \cdots + a_1 x + a_0$, where $n$ is a nonnegative integer and the coefficients are real numbers. A **polynomial function** is classified by degree. Its degree is the highest degree among its monomial term(s). The degree determines the possible number of **turning points** in the graph and the **end behavior** of the graph.

### Example

Write the polynomial function in standard form and classify it by degree. How many terms does it have? What are the possible numbers of turning points of the graph of $P(x)$ given the degree of the polynomial?

$$P(x) = -4x^2 + x^4$$

Standard form arranges the terms by decreasing exponents, or $P(x) = x^4 - 4x^2$. Its degree is 4, so $x^4 - 4x^2$ is a quartic binomial. It has two terms. The graph of a quartic polynomial function can have either one or three turning points.

### Exercises

Write each polynomial function in standard form, classify it by degree, and determine the end behavior of its graph.

**5.** $y = 12 - x^4$

**6.** $y = x^2 + 7 - x$

**7.** $y = 2x^3 - 6x + 3x^2 - x^4 + 12$

**8.** $y = 2x^2 + 8 - 4x + x^3$

**9.** $y = 10 - 3x^3 + 3x^2 + x^4$

**10.** If the volume of a cube can be represented by a polynomial of degree 9, what is the degree of the polynomial that represents each side length?

**11.** A polynomial function $P(x)$ has degree $n$. If $n$ is even, is the number of turning points of the graph of $P(x)$ even or odd? What can you say about the number of turning points if $n$ is odd?

---

## 5-2 Polynomials, Linear Factors, and Zeros

### Quick Review

For any real number $a$ and polynomial $P(x)$, if $x - a$ is a **factor** of $P(x)$, then $a$ is:

- a **zero** of $y = P(x)$
- a **root** (or **solution**) of $P(x) = 0$, and
- an **x-intercept** of the graph of $y = P(x)$.

If $a$ is a **multiple zero**, its **multiplicity** is the same as the number of times $x - a$ appears as a factor.

A turning point is a **relative maximum** or **relative minimum** of a polynomial function.

### Example

Find the zeros for $y = 3x^3 - 6x^2 + 3x$ and state the multiplicity of any multiple zeros.

$y = 3x(x^2 - 2x + 1)$    Factor out the GCF, $3x$.

$y = 3x(x - 1)(x - 1)$    Factor the quadratic.

The zeros are 0, and 1 with multiplicity 2.

### Exercises

Write a polynomial function with the given zeros.

**12.** $x = -1, -1, 6$      **13.** $x = -1, 0, 2$

**14.** $x = 1, 2, 3$      **15.** $x = -2, 1, 4$

Find the zeros of each function. State the multiplicity of any multiple zeros.

**16.** $y = 3x(x + 2)^3$      **17.** $y = x^4 - 8x^2 + 16$

**18.** $y = 4x^3 - 2x^2 - 2x$      **19.** $y = (x - 5)(x + 2)^2$

Use a graphing calculator to find the relative maximum, relative minimum, and zeros of each function.

**20.** $y = x^4 - 5x^3 + 5x^2 - 3$

**21.** $y = 5x^3 + x^2 - 9x + 4$

**22.** $y = x^4 - 4x - 1$

**23.** $y = x^3 - 3x^2 - 3x - 4$

## 5-3 Solving Polynomial Equations

### Quick Review

One way to solve a polynomial equation is by factoring. First write the equation in the form $P(x) = 0$, where $P(x)$ is the polynomial. Then factor the polynomial. Last, use the Zero-Product Property to find the solutions, or roots. The solutions may be real or imaginary. Real solutions and approximations of irrational solutions can also be found by using a graphing calculator.

### Example

Solve $x^3 + 4x^2 = 12x$ by factoring.

$$x^3 + 4x^2 - 12x = 0 \qquad \text{Set equal to 0.}$$
$$x(x - 2)(x + 6) = 0 \qquad \text{Factor the left side.}$$
$$x = 0, x - 2 = 0, x + 6 = 0 \qquad \text{Zero Product Property.}$$
$$x = 0, x = 2, x = -6 \qquad \text{Solve each equation.}$$

The solutions are 0, 2, and $-6$.

### Exercises

Find the real or imaginary solutions of each equation by factoring.

**24.** $x^2 - 11x = -24$     **25.** $4x^2 = -4x - 1$

**26.** $3x^3 + 3x^2 = 27x$     **27.** $2x^2 + 3 = 4x$

Find the real roots of each equation by graphing.

**28.** $x^4 + 3x^2 - 2x + 5 = 0$

**29.** $x^2 + 3 = x^3 - 5$

**30.** The height and width of a rectangular prism are each 2 inches shorter than the length of the prism. The volume of the prism is 40 cubic inches. Approximate the dimensions of the prism to the nearest hundredth.

## 5-4 Dividing Polynomials

### Quick Review

You can divide a polynomial by one of its factors to find another factor. When you divide by a linear factor, you can simplify this division by writing only the coefficients of each term. This is called **synthetic division**. The **Remainder Theorem** says that $P(a)$ is the remainder when you divide $P(x)$ by $x - a$.

### Example

Let $P(x) = 3x^2 - 13x + 15$. What is $P(3)$?

According to the Remainder Theorem, $P(3)$ is the remainder when you divide $P(x)$ by $x - 3$.

$$\begin{array}{r|rrr} 3 & 3 & -13 & 15 \\ & & 9 & -12 \\ \hline & 3 & -4 & 3 \end{array}$$

Put the opposite of the constant in the divisor at the top left.

The quotient is $3x - 4$ with remainder 3, so $P(3) = 3$.

### Exercises

Divide using long division. Check your answers.

**31.** $(x^3 + 7x^2 + 15x + 9) \div (x + 1)$

**32.** $(2x^3 - 7x^2 - 7x + 13) \div (x - 4)$

Determine whether each binomial is a factor of $x^3 + x^2 - 10x + 8$.

**33.** $x - 2$        **34.** $x - 4$

Divide using synthetic division.

**35.** $(x^3 + 5x^2 - x - 5) \div (x + 5)$

**36.** $(2x^3 + 14x^2 - 58x) \div (x + 10)$

**37.** $(5x^3 + 8x^2 - 60) \div (x - 2)$

Use the Remainder Theorem to determine the value of $P(a)$.

**38.** $P(x) = 2x^3 + 5x^2 + 7x - 4, a = -2$

**39.** $P(x) = x^3 - 4x^2 + 2x + 3, a = 1$

**24.** 3, 8

**25.** $-\dfrac{1}{2}$

**26.** 0, $\dfrac{-1 \pm \sqrt{37}}{2}$

**27.** $\dfrac{2 \pm i\sqrt{2}}{2}$

**28.** no real roots;

**29.** 2.3949;

**30.** 4.87 in. $\times$ 2.87 in. $\times$ 2.87 in.

**31.** $x^2 + 6x + 9$

**32.** $2x^2 + x - 3$, R 1

**33.** yes

**34.** no

**35.** $x^2 - 1$

**36.** $2x^2 - 6x + 2$, R $-20$

**37.** $5x^2 + 18x + 36$, R 12

**38.** $-14$

**39.** 2

# Answers

## Chapter Review (continued)

**40.** $\pm1, \pm2, \pm3, \pm6$

**41.** $\pm1, \pm2, \pm\frac{1}{3}, \pm\frac{2}{3}$

**42.** $\pm1, \pm2, \pm3, \pm4, \pm6, \pm12, \pm\frac{1}{4}, \pm\frac{1}{2},$ $\pm\frac{3}{4}, \pm\frac{3}{2}$

**43.** $\pm1, \pm7, \pm\frac{1}{3}, \pm\frac{7}{3}$

**44.** $-3$

**45.** $-5$

**46.** $1, -4, -\frac{1}{2}$

**47.** $1, -2, -\frac{2}{3}$

**48.** $1 + i$

**49.** $5 - \sqrt{3}, \sqrt{2}$

**50.** $3i, -7i$

**51.** $-2 - \sqrt{11}, -4 + 6i$

**52.** $y = x^2 - 17x + 70$

**53.** $y = x^3 + 3x^2 + 25x + 75$

**54.** $y = x^2 - 12x + 37$

**55.** $y = x^4 - 4x^3 - 10x^2 + 68x - 80$

**56.** one positive real zero; two or no negative real zeros

**57.** two or no positive real zeros; one negative real zero

**58.** four, two, or no positive real zeros; no negative real zeros

**59.** two or no positive real zeros; two or no negative real zeros

---

## 5-5 Theorems About Roots of Polynomial Equations

### Quick Review

The **Rational Root Theorem** gives a way to determine the possible roots of a polynomial equation $P(x) = 0$. If the coefficients of $P(x)$ are all integers, then every root of the equation can be written in the form $\frac{p}{q}$, where $p$ is a factor of the constant term and $q$ is a factor of the leading coefficient.

The **Conjugate Root Theorem** states that if $P(x)$ is a polynomial with rational coefficients, then irrational roots that have the form $a + \sqrt{b}$ and imaginary roots of $P(x) = 0$ come in conjugate pairs. Therefore, if $a + \sqrt{b}$ is an irrational root, where $a$ and $b$ are rational, then $a - \sqrt{b}$ is also a root. Likewise, if $a + bi$ is a root, where $a$ and $b$ are real and $i$ is the imaginary unit, then $a - bi$ is also a root.

**Descartes' Rule of Signs** gives a way to determine the possible number of positive and negative real roots by analyzing the signs of the coefficients. The number of positive real roots is equal to the number of sign changes in consecutive coefficients of $P(x)$, or is less than that by an even number. The number of negative real roots is equal to the number of sign changes in consecutive coefficients of $P(-x)$, or is less than that by an even number.

### Example

Find the rational roots of $P(x) = 0$ if $P(x) = 2x^3 - 4x^2 - 10x + 12$.

List the possible roots: $\pm\frac{1}{2}, \pm1, \pm\frac{3}{2}, \pm2, \pm3, \pm4, \pm6, \pm12$.
Use synthetic division to test roots.

$$
\begin{array}{r|rrrr}
3 & 2 & -4 & -10 & 12 \\
  &   & 6  & 6   & -12 \\
\hline
  & 2 & 2  & -4  & 0 \\
\end{array}
$$

So $x - 3$ and $(2x^2 + 2x - 4)$ are factors of $P(x)$.

$P(x) = (x - 3)(2x^2 + 2x - 4)$

Factor the quadratic.

$P(x) = 2(x - 3)(x + 2)(x - 1)$

Solve $2(x - 3)(x + 2)(x - 1) = 0$.

$x = 3, x = -2,$ or $x = 1$

The rational roots are $3, -2,$ and $1$.

### Exercises

List the possible rational roots of $P(x)$ given by the Rational Root Theorem.

**40.** $P(x) = x^3 + 4x^2 - 10x + 6$

**41.** $P(x) = 3x^3 - x^2 - 7x + 2$

**42.** $P(x) = 4x^4 - 2x^3 + x^2 - 12$

**43.** $P(x) = 3x^4 - 4x^3 - x^2 - 7$

Find any rational roots of $P(x)$.

**44.** $P(x) = x^3 + 2x^2 + 4x + 21$

**45.** $P(x) = x^3 + 5x^2 + x + 5$

**46.** $P(x) = 2x^3 + 7x^2 - 5x - 4$

**47.** $P(x) = 3x^4 + 2x^3 - 9x^2 + 4$

A polynomial $P(x)$ has rational coefficients. Name additional roots of $P(x)$ given the following roots.

**48.** $1 - i$ and $5$

**49.** $5 + \sqrt{3}$ and $-\sqrt{2}$

**50.** $-3i$ and $7i$

**51.** $-2 + \sqrt{11}$ and $-4 - 6i$

Write a polynomial function with the given roots.

**52.** $7$ and $10$

**53.** $-3$ and $5i$

**54.** $6 - i$

**55.** $3 + i, 2,$ and $-4$

Determine the possible number of positive real zeros and negative real zeros for each polynomial function given by Descartes' Rule of Signs.

**56.** $P(x) = 5x^3 + 7x^2 - 2x - 1$

**57.** $P(x) = -3x^3 + 11x^2 + 12x - 8$

**58.** $P(x) = 6x^4 - x^3 + 5x^2 - x + 9$

**59.** $P(x) = -x^4 - 3x^3 + 8x^2 + 2x - 14$

## 5-6 The Fundamental Theorem of Algebra

### Quick Review

The **Fundamental Theorem of Algebra** states that if $P(x)$ is a polynomial of degree $n$, where $n \geq 1$, then $P(x) = 0$ has exactly $n$ roots. This includes multiple and complex roots.

### Example

Use the Fundamental Theorem of Algebra to determine the number of roots for $x^4 + 2x^2 - 3 = 0$.

Because the polynomial is of degree 4, it has 4 roots.

### Exercises

**Find the number of roots for each equation.**

**60.** $x^3 - 2x + 5 = 0$

**61.** $2 - x^4 + x^2 = 0$

**62.** $-x^5 - 6 = 0$

**63.** $5x^4 - 7x^6 + 2x^3 + 8x^2 + 4x - 11 = 0$

**Find all the zeros for each function.**

**64.** $P(x) = x^3 + 5x^2 - 4x - 2$

**65.** $P(x) = x^4 - 4x^3 - x^2 + 20x - 20$

**66.** $P(x) = 2x^3 - 3x^2 + 3x - 2$

**67.** $P(x) = x^4 - 4x^3 - 16x^2 + 21x + 18$

## 5-7 The Binomial Theorem

### Quick Review

Rows 0–5 of Pascal's Triangle are shown below.

```
            1
          1   1
        1   2   1
      1   3   3   1
    1   4   6   4   1
  1   5  10  10   5   1
```

The **Binomial Theorem** uses Pascal's Triangle to expand binomials. For a positive integer $n$,
$(a + b)^n = P_0 a^n + P_1 a^{n-1}b + P_2 a^{n-2}b^2 + \cdots + P_{n-1}ab^{n-1} + P_n b^n$, where $P_0, P_1, \ldots P_n$ are the coefficients of the $n$th row of Pascal's Triangle.

### Example

Use the binomial theorem to expand $(2x + 3)^3$.

$(2x + 3)^3$

$= 1(2x)^3 + 3(2x)^2(3) + 3(2x)(3)^2 + 1(3)^3$

$= 8x^3 + 36x^2 + 54x + 27$

### Exercises

**68.** How many numbers are in the eighth row of Pascal's Triangle?

**69.** List the numbers in the eighth row of Pascal's Triangle.

**70.** How many numbers are in the fifteenth row of Pascal's Triangle?

**71.** What is the third number in the fifteenth row of Pascal's Triangle?

**Use the Binomial Theorem to expand each binomial.**

**72.** $(x + 9)^3$      **73.** $(b + 2)^4$

**74.** $(3a + 1)^3$      **75.** $(x - 5)^3$

**76.** $(x - 2y)^3$      **77.** $(3a + 4b)^5$

**78.** $(x + 1)^6$      **79.** $(2x - 1)^6$

**Find the coefficient of the $x^2$ term in each binomial expansion.**

**80.** $(3x + 4)^3$      **81.** $(ax - c)^4$

**60.** 3

**61.** 4

**62.** 5

**63.** 6

**64.** $1, -3 \pm \sqrt{7}$

**65.** $2, \pm\sqrt{5}$

**66.** $1, \dfrac{1 \pm i\sqrt{15}}{4}$

**67.** $-3, 6, \dfrac{1 \pm \sqrt{5}}{2}$

**68.** 9

**69.** 1, 8, 28, 56, 70, 56, 28, 8, 1

**70.** 16

**71.** 105

**72.** $x^3 + 27x^2 + 243x + 729$

**73.** $b^4 + 8b^3 + 24b^2 + 32b + 16$

**74.** $27a^3 + 27a^2 + 9a + 1$

**75.** $x^3 - 15x^2 + 75x - 125$

**76.** $x^3 - 6x^2y + 12xy^2 - 8y^3$

**77.** $243a^5 + 1620a^4b + 4320a^3b^2 + 5760a^2b^3 + 3840ab^4 + 1024b^5$

**78.** $x^6 + 6x^5 + 15x^4 + 20x^3 + 15x^2 + 6x + 1$

**79.** $64x^6 - 192x^5 + 240x^4 - 160x^3 + 60x^2 - 12x + 1$

**80.** 108

**81.** $6a^2c^2$

# Answers

## Chapter Review (continued)

**82.** $y = 3.5x^2 - 4.5x + 5$

**83.** $y = 2.082999x - 2.475234$;
$y = 0.086232x^2 + 0.008929x + 5.963724$;
$y = -0.002554x^3 + 0.178307x^2 - 0.913645x + 8.205128$; cubic is best fit since $R^2 = 1$.

**84.** $y = -5.8667x^3 + 120.5333x^2 - 629.2667x + 1421$; $1097.2 \approx 1097$

**85.** $y = -(x - 2)^3 + 1$

**86.** $y = 6(x + 3)^3$

**87.** Answers may vary. Sample:
$y = x^4 - 10x^3 + 25x^2 - 10x + 24$

**88.** $y = 0.3x^5 + 3$

## 5-8 Polynomial Models in the Real World

### Quick Review

A data set can be modeled by a polynomial function. Methods of finding a model that fits the data include the $(n + 1)$ Point Principle and **regression**. Linear, quadratic, cubic, and quartic regressions can be performed on a graphing calculator. A higher $R^2$ value means a better fit. Once the equation that models the data is known, it can be used to make predictions.

### Example

For the data set (8, 30), (10, 45), and (11, 65), predict $y$ when $x = 15$.

Enter 8, 10, and 11 in **L1** and 30, 45, and 65 in **L2**. Choose **LINREG** to find the regression model $y \approx 11.071x - 60.357$. The $r^2$ value is about 0.928.

Now try **QUADREG**. The model is $y \approx 4.17x^2 - 67.5x + 303.3$ with an $R^2$ value of 1. Assuming the model makes sense in context, it fits the data better.

Using the quadratic model, when $x = 15$, $y \approx 228.3$.

### Exercises

**82.** Write a polynomial function whose graph passes through (0, 5), (2, 10), and (1, 4). Use a regression to check your answer.

**83.** Find a linear, a quadratic, and a cubic model for the data. Which model best fits the data?

| x | 3 | 8 | 15 | 21 |
|---|---|---|----|----|
| y | 7 | 11 | 26 | 44 |

**84.** Use **CUBICREG** to model the data below. Then use the model to estimate the population in 2008. Let $x$ be the number of years after 2000.

| Year | 2004 | 2007 | 2009 | 2010 |
|------|------|------|------|------|
| Population | 457 | 910 | 1244 | 1315 |

## 5-9 Transforming Polynomial Functions

### Quick Review

A polynomial function can be transformed into other polynomial functions using stretches, reflections, and translations. The monomial function $y = ax^b$ is called a **power function**.

### Example

This is the graph of a cubic function. Determine which sequence of transformations you can apply to the graph of the parent function $y = x^3$ to get this graph. Write an equation for the graph.

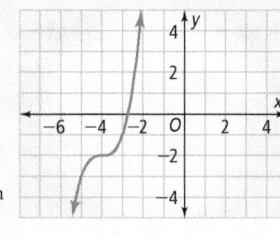

Translate the parent function 4 units left and 2 units down:
$y = (x + 4)^3 - 2$

### Exercises

**Determine the cubic function obtained from the parent function $y = x^3$ after each sequence of transformations.**

**85.** a reflection across the $x$-axis;
a translation 1 unit up;
and a translation 2 units right

**86.** a vertical stretch by a factor of 6;
and a translation 3 units left

**87.** Find a quartic function whose only real zeros are 4 and 6.

**88.** The parent power function $y = x^5$ is translated 3 units up and is compressed by the factor 0.3. Write the function.

# 5 Chapter Test

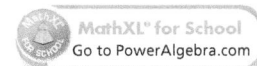

MathXL® for School
Go to PowerAlgebra.com

## Do you know HOW?

**Write each polynomial function in standard form. Then classify it by degree and by number of terms and describe its end behavior.**

1. $y = 3x^2 - 7x^4 + 9 - x^4$

2. $y = 2x(x^2 - 3)(x^2 + 2)$

3. $y = (t - 2)(t + 1)(t + 1)$

**Write a polynomial function for each set of zeros.**

4. $x = 1, 2, \frac{3}{5}$

5. $x = \sqrt{2}, -i$

6. $x = 3 + i, -1 - \sqrt{5}$

**Find the quotient and remainder.**

7. $(x^2 + 3x - 4) \div (x - 1)$

8. $(x^3 + 7x^2 - 5x - 6) \div (x + 2)$

9. $(2x^3 + 9x^2 + 11x + 3) \div (2x + 3)$

**For each equation, state the number of complex roots, the possible number of real roots, and the possible rational roots.**

10. $3x^4 + 5x^3 - 2x^2 + x - 9 = 0$

11. $x^7 - 2x^5 - 4x^3 - 2x - 1 = 0$

**For each equation, find all the roots.**

12. $3x^4 - 11x^3 + 15x^2 - 9x + 2 = 0$

13. $x^3 - x^2 - x - 2 = 0$

14. One $x$-intercept of the graph of the cubic function $f(x) = x^3 - 2x^2 - 111x - 108$ is $-9$. What are the other zeros?

**Use synthetic division and the Remainder Theorem to find $P(a)$.**

15. $P(x) = 6x^4 + 19x^3 - 2x^2 - 44x - 24; a = -\frac{2}{3}$

16. $P(x) = x^4 + 3x^3 - 7x^2 - 9x + 12; a = 3$

17. $P(x) = x^3 + 3x^2 - 5x - 4; a = -1$

**Expand each binomial.**

18. $(x + z)^5$

19. $(1 - 2t)^2$

20. Graph and write the equation of the cubic function that is obtained from the parent function $y = x^3$ after this sequence of transformations: vertical stretch by a factor of 2, reflection across the $x$-axis, translation 3 units down and 4 units right.

## Do you UNDERSTAND?

21. **Physics** You take measurements of the distance traveled by an object that is increasing its speed at a constant rate. The distance traveled as a function of time can be modeled by a quadratic function.
    a. Write a quadratic function that models distances of 10 ft at 1 sec, 30 ft at 2 sec, and 100 ft at 4 sec.
    b. Find the zeros of the function.
    c. **Reasoning** Describe what each zero represents for this real-world situation.

22. **Writing** For the polynomial $x^6 - 64$, could you apply the Difference of Cubes? Difference of Squares? Explain your answers.

23. The number of pairs of shoes Emily buys varies directly as the square of the area of the floor of her closet. If she can fit 12 pairs of shoes when her closet was 10 square feet, how many pairs of shoes will she fit when the area of her closet floor is 18 square feet?

22. both; difference of squares:
$x^6 - 64 = (x^2 - 4)(x^4 + 4x^2 + 16) = (x - 2)(x + 2)(x^2 + 2x + 4)(x^2 - 2x + 4)$;
difference of cubes:
$x^6 - 64 = (x^3 - 8)(x^3 + 8) = (x - 2)(x + 2)(x^2 + 2x + 4)(x^2 - 2x + 4)$

23. 38 pairs of shoes

## Answers

1. $y = -8x^4 + 3x^2 + 9$; quartic trinomial; down and down

2. $y = 2x^5 - 2x^3 - 12x$; quintic trinomial; down and up

3. $y = t^3 - 3t - 2$; cubic trinomial; down and up

4. $p(x) = 5x^3 - 18x^2 + 19x - 6$

5. $p(x) = x^4 - x^2 - 2$

6. $p(x) = x^4 - 4x^3 - 6x^2 + 44x - 40$

7. $x + 4$, R 0

8. $x^2 + 5x - 15$, R 24

9. $x^2 + 3x + 1$, R 0

10. four complex roots; three or one positive real root, 1 negative real root; possible rational roots: $\pm 1, \pm 3, \pm 9, \pm\frac{1}{3}$

11. seven complex roots; one positive real root, two or no negative real roots; possible rational roots: $\pm 1$

12. $\frac{2}{3}, 1$

13. $2, \frac{-1 \pm i\sqrt{3}}{2}$

14. $-1, 12$

15. 0

16. 84

17. 3

18. $x^5 + 5x^4z + 10x^3z^2 + 10x^2z^3 + 5xz^4 + z^5$

19. $1 - 4t + 4t^2$

20. $y = -2(x - 4)^3 - 3$

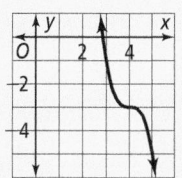

21. a. $d = 5t^2 + 5t$
    b. $0, -1$
    c. $-1$ is outside the real-world problem's domain, and 0 is "time zero," or takeoff.

PowerAlgebra.com

MathXL for School
Prepare students for the Mid-Chapter Quiz and Chapter Test with online practice and review.

| Item Number | Lesson |
|:-----------:|:------:|
| 1 | 3-2 |
| 2 | 5-1 |
| 3 | 3-2 |
| 4 | 5-4 |
| 5 | 5-2 |
| 6 | 1-4 |
| 7 | 5-2 |
| 8 | 3-3 |
| 9 | 1-6 |
| 10 | 2-7 |
| 11 | 2-2 |
| 12 | 5-5 |
| 13 | 4-8 |
| 14 | 5-2 |
| 15 | 2-2 |
| 16 | 5-3 |
| 17 | 5-3 |
| 18 | 4-7 |
| 19 | 2-4 |
| 20 | 4-2 |
| 21 | 4-6 |
| 22 | 4-1 |

# 5 Cumulative Test Prep

## TIPS FOR SUCCESS

Some problems require you to simplify expressions that contain imaginary numbers.

### TIP 1
When multiplying binomials, you should use the Distributive Property.

Which expression is equivalent to $(3 - 4i)(2 + i)$?

- (A) $2 - 5i$
- (B) $2 + 5i$
- (C) $10 - 5i$
- (D) $10 + 5i$

### TIP 2
Recall that $i^2 = -1$.

**Think It Through**

$$(3 - 4i)(2 + i)$$
$$= 6 + 3i - 8i - 4i^2$$
$$= 6 - 5i - 4(-1)$$
$$= 10 - 5i$$

The correct answer is C.

### Vocabulary Review

As you solve test items, you must understand the meanings of mathematical terms. Match each term with its mathematical meaning.

**A.** multiplicity

**B.** synthetic division

**C.** Conjugate Root Theorem

**D.** relative maximum

**E.** polynomial

**I.** the process of dividing a polynomial by a linear factor, omitting all variables and exponents

**II.** if $a + bi$ is an irrational root where $a$ and $b$ are real numbers, then $a - bi$ is also a root

**III.** a monomial or the sum of monomials

**IV.** the greatest $y$-value in a region of a graph

**V.** the number of times a zero is repeated in a polynomial function

### Multiple Choice

Read each question. Then write the letter of the correct answer on your paper.

**1.** Which statement is true about this system of linear equations?

$$\begin{cases} 3x - 4y = 12 \\ 6x - 8y = 12 \end{cases}$$

- (A) The solution is $(0, -1)$.
- (B) The solution is $(8, 4)$.
- (C) There is no solution because the lines are parallel.
- (D) There are infinitely many solutions because the lines are coinciding.

**2.** Which of the following statements is *never* true about a quartic function?

- (F) The end behavior of the function is up and up.
- (G) The function has 4 zeros.
- (H) The function has 4 turning points.
- (I) The function has complex roots.

# Answers

## Cumulative Test Prep
**A.** V
**B.** I
**C.** II
**D.** IV
**E.** III

## Multiple Choice
**1.** C
**2.** H

**3.** Tia deposited $x$ dollars in a bank account that paid 4% interest. She also deposited $y$ dollars in a bank account that paid 8% interest. The system below represents one year's interest on Tia's deposits.

$$\begin{cases} 0.04x + 0.08y = 240 \\ \phantom{00} 0.04x = 0.08y \end{cases}$$

Based on the solution of the system of equations, which of the following can you conclude?

- Ⓐ Tia deposited \$3000 in each account, and the amounts of interest earned were \$240 and \$120.
- Ⓑ Tia deposited \$3000 in each account, and the amount of interest earned in each account was \$120.
- Ⓒ The deposit amounts were \$3000 and \$1500, and the amounts of interest earned in each account were \$240 and \$120.
- Ⓓ The deposit amounts were \$3000 and \$1500, and the amount of interest earned in each account was \$120.

**4.** The total area of the parallelogram below is $4x^4 + 3x^3 - 14x^2 + 33x - 35$. Which of the following expressions best represents the length of the base of the parallelogram? (*Hint:* $A = bh$)

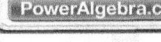

- Ⓕ $x^3 + 2x^2 - x + 7$
- Ⓖ $x^3 - 2x^2 + x - 7$
- Ⓗ $4x^4 + 3x^3 - 14x^2 + 33x - 7$
- Ⓘ $x^3 + 5x^2 - x + 5$

**5.** Which point corresponds to a zero of the function $f(x) = x^2 + 2x - 15$?

- Ⓐ $(0, -15)$       Ⓒ $(-5, 0)$
- Ⓑ $(5, 0)$        Ⓓ $(-3, 0)$

**6.** Solve the equation $x^2 + 3w = P$ for $x$.

- Ⓕ $x = P - 3w$       Ⓗ $x = \pm\sqrt{P - 3w}$
- Ⓖ $x = \pm\sqrt{\frac{P}{3w}}$       Ⓘ $x = \pm\sqrt{P + 3w}$

**7.** A bridge supported by a parabolic arch spans a stream of water 180 feet wide. There must be a clearance of at least 40 feet over a 100-foot channel in the middle of the stream. The origin is placed at water level directly below the center of the arch. Which equation best represents the situation?

- Ⓐ $y = 140(x + 180)(x - 180)$
- Ⓑ $y = -\frac{1}{140}(x + 90)(x - 90)$
- Ⓒ $y = -\frac{1}{140}(x + 40)(x - 40)$
- Ⓓ $y = 140(x + 40)(x - 40)$

**8.** Sofia has \$25 in her savings account. She plans to deposit between \$5 and \$10 each week into her account. On the graph, line $m$ represents a deposit of exactly \$5 per week and line $n$ represents a deposit of exactly \$10 per week.

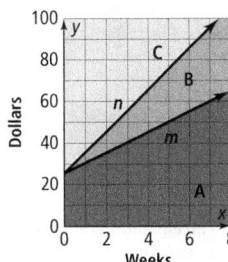

If Sofia deposits between \$5 and \$10 per week, which region on the graph represents all possible balances in her account?

- Ⓕ A        Ⓗ C
- Ⓖ B        Ⓘ A and C combined

**3.** D
**4.** F
**5.** C
**6.** H
**7.** B
**8.** G

# Answers

**9.** B
**10.** F
**11.** 1250
**12.** 1
**13.** 1
**14.** 6
**15.** 6
**16.** 2
**17.** 1
**18.** 2
**19.** [2] The slope of line $m$ is $\frac{3}{4}$, so the slope of

line $n = \dfrac{-1}{\left(\frac{3}{4}\right)} = \dfrac{-4}{3}$. Point P is (1, 3).

$$y - (3) = \left(-\frac{4}{3}\right)(x - 1)$$
$$y - 3 = -\frac{4}{3}x + \frac{4}{3}$$
$$y = -\frac{4}{3}x + \frac{13}{3}$$

[1] appropriate methods, with one computational error

**20.** [2]
when the cat is at (2,3)

[1] graph is correct, but furthest location from pole is incorrect

**21.** [2]   $x^2 - 4x = 8$
$x^2 - 4x + 4 = 8 + 4$
$(x - 2)^2 = 12$
$x - 2 = \pm\sqrt{12}$
$x = 2 \pm 2\sqrt{3}$

This eq. could be solved using the Quadratic Formula, but not by factoring.

[1] appropriate methods, with one computational error OR correct method and solution, without other methods mentioned

**22.** [4] **a.** Reflect across the $x$-axis; translate 4 units to the right and 4 units up.

**b.** Zeros at $x = 2, 6$; the function crosses the axis and $y = 0$ at $x = 2$ and $x = 6$.

**c.** $y = -(x - 4)^2 + 4$

**d.** Check points such as (2, 0), (4, 4), and (6, 0) to test the accuracy of the function.

[3] three parts answered correctly

[2] two parts answered correctly OR three parts answered correctly, without explanations given

[1] one part answered correctly

---

**9.** Solve the absolute value inequality $-2\,|x - 3| \le -16$.

Ⓐ $x \le -3$ or $x \ge 4$   Ⓒ $-5 \le x \le 11$
Ⓑ $x \le -5$ or $x \ge 11$   Ⓓ $-11 \le x \le 5$

**10.** Which equation does the graph represent?

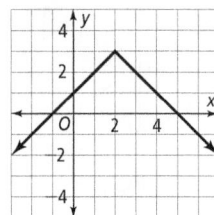

Ⓕ $y = -|x - 2| + 3$   Ⓗ $y = |x - 2| + 3$
Ⓖ $y = -|x - 3| + 2$   Ⓘ $y = |x + 2| + 3$

**GRIDDED RESPONSE**

**11.** The power created by a wind turbine varies directly as the cube of the wind speed in miles per hour. A turbine with 30% efficiency spinning in a 50 mile per hour wind can be expected to produce approximately 10,000 watts of electricity. How many watts would the same turbine produce in a 25 mile per hour wind? If necessary, round your answer to the nearest whole number.

**12.** One root of a cubic equation is $2i$. How many real roots does the equation have?

**13.** What is the value of the real part of the quotient of $(6 + 4i)$ and $(5 - i)$?

**14.** If the solutions of an equation are $-1$, 2, and 5, what is the sum of the zeros of the related function?

**15.** Assume $y$ varies directly with $x$. If $y = -3$ when $x = -\frac{2}{5}$, what is $x$ when $y$ is 45?

**16.** What is the $x$-coordinate of the point where a relative maximum of $g(x) = -2x^3 + 6x^2 - 10$ occurs?

**17.** Using a graph, find the real zero of the function $y = 2x^3 - 2x^2 + x - 1$.

**18.** How many imaginary roots does $x^2 - 5x + 10 = 0$ have?

**Short Response**

**19.** The graph shows line $m$ and point $P$. Write the equation of a line $n$ that goes through point $P$ and is perpendicular to line $m$. Show your work.

**20.** A cat ran around part of a telephone pole on a path modeled by the equation $y = -x^2 + 4x - 1$. Graph the cat's path in the first quadrant. If the pole is at (2, 0), at what point is the cat furthest from the pole?

**21.** Solve the equation $x^2 - 4x = 8$ by completing the square. Explain whether you could have solved this equation by factoring or using the Quadratic Formula.

**Extended Response**

**22.** Use the graph to answer the questions below.

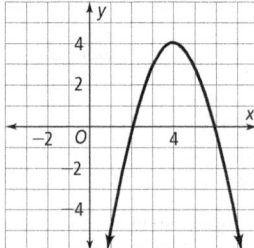

**a.** Describe the sequence of transformations that would take the graph of the parent function $y = x^2$ to the graph shown.

**b.** Identify the zeros of the function represented in the graph and explain your reasoning.

**c.** Write the equation of the function in the graph.

**d.** Explain how you could check to see that the equation is correct.

# Get Ready!

**CHAPTER 6**

 **Finding the Domain and Range of Functions**

*Lessons 2-1 and 4-1*

Find the domain and range of each function.

**1.** $\{(1, 2), (2, 3), (3, 4), (4, 5)\}$     **2.** $\{(1, 2), (2, 2), (3, 2), (4, 2)\}$

**3.** $f(x) = (x - 4)^2 - 8$     **4.** $f(x) = 2x^2 + 3$

*Lesson 4-1*

 **Graphing Quadratic Functions**

Graph each function.

**5.** $y = 2x^2 - 4$     **6.** $y = -3(x^2 + 1)$     **7.** $y = \frac{1}{2}(x - 3)^2 + 1$

*Lesson 4-4*

 **Multiplying Binomials**

Multiply.

**8.** $(3y - 2)(y - 4)$     **9.** $(7a + 10)(7a - 10)$     **10.** $(x - 3)(x + 6)(x + 1)$

*Lessons 4-5 and 5-3*

 **Solving by Factoring**

Solve each equation by factoring.

**11.** $x^2 - 5x - 14 = 0$     **12.** $2x^2 - 11x + 15 = 0$     **13.** $3x^2 + 10x - 8 = 0$

**14.** $12x^2 - 12x + 3 = 0$     **15.** $8x^2 - 98 = 0$     **16.** $x^4 - 14x^2 + 49 = 0$

## Looking Ahead Vocabulary

**17.** Combining two or more elements forms composite chemical mixtures. In some cases, if you change the order in which you mix two chemicals, it can produce very different results. A *composite function* is made by combining two functions. If you are buying a $60 shirt and there is a 50% off sale and you have a $10 coupon, does it make a difference which discount is applied first?

**18.** One-to-one relationships describe situations where people are matched with unique identifiers, such as their social security numbers. A function is a relation that matches $x$ values to $y$ values. What do you suppose a *one-to-one function* is?

**19.** In an orchestra, the principal player is chosen among all the other musicians that play a certain instrument to sit in the first chair and lead his section. In math, what do you suppose a *principal root* is?

 **PowerAlgebra.com** | Chapter 6   Radical Functions and Rational Exponents | 357

---

 **Get Ready!**

Assign this diagnostic assessment to determine if students have the prerequisite skills for Chapter 6.

| Lesson | Skill |
|--------|-------|
| 2-1 and 4-1 | Find the Domain and Range of Functions |
| 4-1 | Graph Quadratic Functions |
| 4-4 | Multiply Binomials |
| 4-5 and 5-3 | Solve by Factoring |

To remediate students, select from these resources (available for every lesson).
• Online Problems (PowerAlgebra.com)
• Reteaching (All-in-One Teaching Resources)
• Practice (All-in-One Teaching Resources)

## Why Students Need These Skills

**FINDING THE DOMAIN AND RANGE OF FUNCTIONS**
Finding the domain and range of functions is essential to understanding and describing inverse functions.

**GRAPHING QUADRATIC FUNCTIONS**
Graphing quadratic functions is essential to graphing square root functions, which are the inverse of quadratic functions with a restricted domain.

**MULTIPLYING BINOMIALS**
Multiplying binomials is an essential skill when multiplying binomial radical expressions.

**SOLVING BY FACTORING**
Solving by factoring is an important component of solving square root and other radical equations.

## Looking Ahead Vocabulary

**COMPOSITE FUNCTION** Two different discounts are being applied. Have students determine both prices depending on the order in which they are applied.

**ONE-TO-ONE FUNCTION** Ask students what must be true about the domain and range of a one-to-one function.

**PRINCIPAL ROOT** Ask students to consider what a root is, for example, the square root of 4. Ask them if there is more than one possible root and why.

---

# Answers

## Get Ready!

**1.** domain: $\{1, 2, 3, 4\}$, range: $\{2, 3, 4, 5\}$

**2.** domain: $\{1, 2, 3, 4\}$, range: $\{2\}$

**3.** domain: all real numbers, range: $y \geq -8$

**4.** domain: all real numbers, range: $y \geq 3$

**5.**

**6.**

**7.**

**8.** $3y^2 - 14y + 8$

**9.** $49a^2 - 100$

**10.** $x^3 + 4x^2 - 15x - 18$

**11.** $-2, 7$     **12.** $\frac{5}{2}, 3$

**13.** $-4, \frac{2}{3}$     **14.** $\frac{1}{2}$

**15.** $\pm\frac{7}{2}$     **16.** $\pm\sqrt{7}$

**17.** Yes; it is a better deal to first take 50% off the shirt and then use the $10 coupon.

**18.** A "one-to-one function" is a function where there is exact correspondence of every element of the domain with exactly one element of the range.

**19.** the nonnegative root

# Chapter 6 Overview

Chapter 6 expands on student understandings and skills related to radical functions and rational exponents. In this chapter, students will develop the answers to the Essential Questions posed on the opposite page as they learn the concepts and skills bulleted below.

## BIG idea Equivalence

**ESSENTIAL QUESTION** To simplify the *n*th root of an expression, what must be true about the expression?
• Students will simplify radical expressions.

## BIG idea Solving Equations

**ESSENTIAL QUESTION** When you square each side of an equation, is the resulting equation equivalent to the original?
• Students will solve radical equations.
• Students will determine the domain of radical functions.
• Students will check for extraneous solutions.

## BIG idea Functions

**ESSENTIAL QUESTION** How are a function and its inverse function related?
• Students will find inverse functions.
• Students will graph functions and their inverses.

**CHAPTER**
**6**

# Radical Functions and Rational Exponents

**PowerAlgebra.com**

Your place to get all things digital

**VIDEO**
Download videos connecting math to your world.

**VOCABULARY**
Math definitions in English and Spanish

**SOLVE IT!**
The online Solve It will get you in gear for each lesson.

**DYNAMIC ACTIVITIES**
Interactive! Vary numbers, graphs, and figures to explore math concepts.

**ONLINE PROBLEMS**
Download Step-by-Step Problems with Instant Replay.

**ONLINE HOMEWORK**
Get and view your assignments online.

**MathXL® FOR SCHOOL**
Extra practice and review online

In this chapter, you will learn how to work with radicals, whether they occur by themselves or as parts of functions or equations; whether they appear with the symbol $\sqrt{\phantom{x}}$ or as fractional exponents. In a sense, radicals are the inverses of powers. Mountain climbers need to be aware of air pressure, which can be calculated using fractional exponents.

## Vocabulary

**English/Spanish Vocabulary Audio Online:**

| English | Spanish |
| --- | --- |
| composite function, *p. 399* | función compuesta |
| inverse function, *p. 405* | función inversa |
| *n*th root, *p. 361* | raíz *n*-ésima |
| principal root, *p. 361* | raíz principal |
| radical equation, *p. 390* | ecuación radical |
| radicand, *p. 362* | radicando |
| rational exponent, *p. 382* | exponente racional |
| rationalize the denominator, *p. 369* | racionalizar el denominador |
| square root equation, *p. 390* | ecuación de raíz cuadrada |
| square root function, *p. 415* | función de raíz cuadrada |

**PowerAlgebra.com**

## Chapter 6 Overview

Use these online assets to engage your students. These include support for the Solve It and step-by-step solutions for Problems.

Show the student-produced video demonstrating relevant and engaging applications of the new concepts in the chapter.

Find online definitions for new terms in English and Spanish.

Start each lesson with an attention-getting Problem. View the Problem online with helpful hints.

## My Math Video

Use this picture to introduce the concept of a fractional exponent. Air pressure decreases exponentially with respect to altitude. An approximate formula for air pressure at an altitude of $h$ (meters) is $P = P_0 \cdot 2^{-\frac{h}{5600}}$, where $P_0$ is the air pressure at sea level, measured in standard atmospheres.

**Q** How does low air pressure affect breathing? **[You have to breathe more quickly in order to get enough oxygen.]**

**Q** How is the mountain climber in the picture dealing with the low air pressure? **[The climber is using an oxygen supply.]**

**Q** Why is it important for mountain climbers to know the air pressure at certain altitudes? **[Knowing the air pressure allows them to be prepared to protect themselves.]**

**EXTENSION**

Have students research the behavior of graphs of functions with fractional exponents. Have them use graphing calculators and begin with a simple function, such as $f(x) = x^{\frac{1}{2}}$. Have them describe what happens to the graph when they increase or decrease the numerator or denominator of the fractional exponent.

## BIG ideas

**1 Equivalence**
**Essential Question** To simplify the $n$th root of an expression, what must be true about the expression?

**2 Solving Equations and Inequalities**
**Essential Question** When you square each side of an equation, is the resulting equation equivalent to the original?

**3 Function**
**Essential Question** How are a function and its inverse function related?

## Chapter Preview

6-1 Roots and Radical Expressions
6-2 Multiplying and Dividing Radical Expressions
6-3 Binomial Radical Expressions
6-4 Rational Exponents
6-5 Solving Square Root and Other Radical Equations
6-6 Function Operations
6-7 Inverse Relations and Functions
6-8 Graphing Radical Functions

PowerAlgebra.com | Chapter 6 Radical Functions and Rational Exponents | 359

 Increase students' depth of knowledge with interactive online activities.

 Show Problems from each lesson solved step by step. Instant replay allows students to go at their own pace when studying online.

 Assign homework to individual students or to an entire class.

 Prepare students for the Mid-Chapter Quiz and Chapter Test with online practice and review.

## Equivalence

**BIG** idea A single quantity may be represented by many different expressions. The facts about a quantity may be expressed by many different equations (or inequalities).

### ESSENTIAL UNDERSTANDINGS

**6-1** Corresponding to every power, there is a root. For example, just as there are squares (second powers), there are square roots. Just as there are cubes (third powers), there are cube roots, and so on.

**6-2** If $\sqrt[n]{a}$ and $\sqrt[n]{b}$ are real numbers, then $\sqrt[n]{a} \cdot \sqrt[n]{b} = \sqrt[n]{ab}$.

**6-3** You can combine like radicals using properties of real numbers.

**6-4** You can write a radical expression in an equivalent form using a fractional (rational) exponent instead of a radical sign.

**6-5** Solving a square root equation may require that you square each side of the equation. This can introduce extraneous solutions.

**6-6** You can add, subtract, multiply, and divide functions based on how you perform these operations for real numbers. One difference, however, is that you must consider the domain of each function.

## Solving Equations & Inequalities

**BIG** idea Solving an equation is the process of rewriting the equation to make what it says about its variable(s) as simple as possible. Properties of numbers and equality can be used to transform an equation (or inequality) into equivalent, simpler equations (or inequalities) in order to find solutions. Useful information about equations and inequalities (including solutions) can be found by analyzing graphs or tables. The numbers and types of solutions vary predictably, based on the type of equation.

### ESSENTIAL UNDERSTANDINGS

**6-7** The inverse of a function may or may not be a function.

**6-8** A square root function is the inverse of a quadratic function that has a restricted domain.

## Function

**BIG** idea A function is a relationship between variables in which each value of the input variable is associated with a unique value of the output variable. Functions can be represented in a variety of ways, such as graphs, tables, equations, or words. Each representation is particularly useful in certain situations. Some important families of functions are developed through transformations of the simplest form of the function.

### ESSENTIAL UNDERSTANDINGS

**6-6 to 6-8** See above.

## Radical Expressions

### Simplifying Radical Expressions

The practical value of simplifying numerical radicals has diminished with the widespread use of calculators. There is even reason to question whether, for example, $\frac{\sqrt{21}}{42}$ is still a "simpler form" of $\frac{1}{\sqrt{84}}$. Nonetheless, the simplification techniques used in this chapter provide practice making transformations between equivalent expressions.

Like radical terms can be *combined*. Simplify radical terms to determine whether they can be combined.

**Example:** $\sqrt{75} + 2\sqrt{3}$
$$5\sqrt{3} + 2\sqrt{3} = 7\sqrt{3}$$

### Property For Products And Quotients

If $\sqrt[n]{a}$ and $\sqrt[n]{b}$ are real numbers, then

- $\sqrt[n]{a}\ \sqrt[n]{b} = \sqrt[n]{ab}$

- $\frac{\sqrt[n]{a}}{\sqrt[n]{b}} = \sqrt[n]{\frac{a}{b}}$ when $b \neq 0$.

**Example:** $\sqrt{5}(\sqrt{10} + 4)$
$$\sqrt{50} + 4\sqrt{5} = 5\sqrt{2} + 4\sqrt{5}$$

The product of **conjugates** results in no radical terms. Therefore, conjugates are used for rationalizing denominators.

**Example:** $\frac{4}{x + \sqrt{3}}$

$$= \frac{4}{x + \sqrt{3}} \cdot \frac{x - \sqrt{3}}{x - \sqrt{3}}$$

$$= \frac{4x - 4\sqrt{3}}{(x)^2 - \left(\sqrt{3}\right)^2}$$

$$= \frac{4x - 4\sqrt{3}}{x^2 - 3}$$

### Function Operations

When adding, subtracting, multiplying or dividing functions, the domain will consist of the x-values of both functions.

### Common Errors When Using Radical Expressions

**Finding Roots** Errors occur when students do not note the value of the index. For example, $\sqrt{64} = 8$ but $\sqrt[3]{64} = 4$.

**Simplifying Variables** Students might attempt to take the root of a variable exponent. For example, they may believe that $\sqrt{x^{16}}$ is equal to $x^4$. Remind them that $\sqrt{x^2} = x$ so $\sqrt{x^{16}} = x^8$.

**Finding Domain** The domains of even roots may be different than the domains for odd roots. For example, the domain of $y = \sqrt{x - 3}$ is $x \geq 3$. However, the domain of $y = \sqrt[3]{x - 3}$ is all real numbers because a negative radicand is possible in a cube root.

# Rational Exponents and Radical Equations

## Rational Exponents

Radical terms can be written using rational exponents. The denominator of the exponent is the index of the root. The numerator is the power. The term can be simplified by finding the root and then raising it to the power or vice versa.

$$16^{\frac{3}{2}} = \sqrt[2]{16^3} \qquad \text{or} \qquad 16^{\frac{3}{2}} = \left(\sqrt{16}\right)^3$$
$$= \sqrt{4096} \qquad\qquad\qquad = 4^3$$
$$= 64 \qquad\qquad\qquad\quad = 64$$

## Radical Equations

A radical equation has a variable in the radicand or a variable with a rational exponent. Solve radical equations by raising each side to the power suggested by the index. Emphasize that raising each side to a power can create **extraneous solutions.**

**Example:** $\sqrt{30 - 2x} = x - 3$
$$30 - 2x = (x - 3)^2$$
$$30 - 2x = x^2 - 6x + 9$$
$$x^2 - 4x - 21 = 0$$
$$(x - 7)(x + 3) = 0$$
$$x = 7; \ x = -3$$

**Check:** $\sqrt{30 - 14} = 7 - 3$
$$\sqrt{16} = 4 \ ✔$$
$$\sqrt{30 - (-6)} = -3 - 3$$
$$\sqrt{36} \ne -6, \text{ thus } -3 \text{ is extraneous}$$

Solve equations with rational exponents by using the reciprocal of the power.

**Example:** $n^{\frac{3}{4}} = 27 \ .$
$$\left(n^{\frac{3}{4}}\right)^{\frac{4}{3}} = 27^{\frac{4}{3}}$$
$$n = \left(\sqrt[3]{27}\right)^4$$
$$= 81$$

## Common Errors When Solving Radical Equations

**Squaring Both Sides:** When squaring both sides, students might raise each term to the power rather than the entire polynomial. For example, students might solve $\sqrt{x} = x + 2$ by writing the right side as $x^2 + 2^2$ and not $(x + 2)^2 = x^2 + 4x + 4$.

**Extraneous Solutions:** Remind students that raising both sides of the equation to a power can introduce extraneous solutions. Students must check every apparent solution to be sure it is not extraneous. Suggest to students that they graph each side of the equation to find whether the graphs intersect in order to determine approximate solutions.

# Graphing Radical Functions

## Inverses

The inverse of a function is found by switching the $x$- and $y$-values in a function. The inverse may or may not be a function.

**Example:** Find the graphs of $y = x^2 + 4$ and its inverse.

Inverse:  $x = y^2 + 4$
$$x - 4 = y^2$$
$$\pm\sqrt{x - 4} = y$$

The **composition of functions** is used to determine whether functions are inverses of each other.

Functions $f^{-1}$ and $f$ are inverses if $(f^{-1} \circ f)(x) = x$ and $(f \circ f^{-1})(x) = x$.

**Example:** Are $f(x) = 3x - 6$ and $g(x) = \frac{1}{3}x + 2$ inverses?

$(f \circ g)(x) = 3\left(\frac{1}{3}x + 2\right) - 6 \quad (g \circ f)(x) = \frac{1}{3}(3x - 6) + 2$
$$= x \qquad\qquad\qquad\qquad\qquad = x$$

The functions are inverses.

## Transformations

Transformations of radical functions can be found by graphing the parent function, then reflecting, stretching, or translating.

- $y = -\sqrt{x}$ indicates reflection in the x-axis.
- For $y = a\sqrt{x}$, the graph stretches for $a > 1$ and shrinks for $0 < a < 1$ by the factor $a$.
- The transformed function $y = \sqrt{x - h} + k$ is shifted horizontally by $h$ and vertically by $k$.

**Example:** Graph $y = \sqrt{x - 2} + 4$

Shift the parent function 2 units to the right then 4 units up.

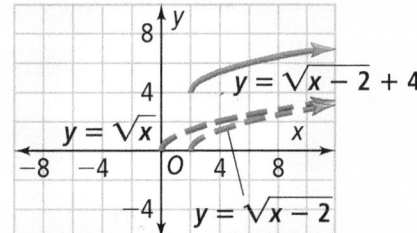

## Common Errors When Graphing Radical Functions

**Finding the Inverse:** Algebraic errors often occur when finding the inverse of a function. Suggest students graph the function and its inverse to determine visually if the inverse is correct.

**Transformations:** Students might shift a function horizontally by $-h$ rather than $h$. Remind students the function $y = \sqrt{x - 5}$ is shifted five units to the *right*.

# RADICAL FUNCTIONS AND RATIONAL EXPONENTS
# Pacing and Assignment Guide

| Lesson | Teaching Day(s) | TRADITIONAL Basic | Average | Advanced | BLOCK Block |
|--------|-----------------|-------|---------|----------|-------|
| 6-1 | 1 | Problems 1–4 Exs. 10–30, 33–37, 56–67 | Problems 1–4 Exs. 11–29 odd, 31–48, 56–67 | Problems 1–4 Exs. 10–30 odd, 31–67 | **Day 1** Problems 1–4 Exs. 11–29 odd, 31–48, 56–67 |
| 6-2 | 1 | Problems 1–3 Exs. 10–36, 80–98 | Problems 1–5 Exs. 11–51 odd, 52–75, 80–98 | Problems 1–5 Exs. 11–51 odd, 52–98 | Problems 1–5 Exs. 11–51 odd, 52–75, 80–98 |
| | 2 | Problems 4–5 Exs. 37–55, 58–64 even | | | |
| 6-3 | 1 | Problems 1–3 Exs. 10–22, 69–91 | Problems 1–3 Exs. 11–21 odd, 69–91 | Problems 1–3 Exs. 11–21 odd, 69–91 | **Day 2** Problems 1–6 Exs. 11–35 odd, 37–64, 69–91 |
| | 2 | Problems 4–6 Exs. 23–40, 53, 54–58 even | Problems 4–6 Exs. 23–35 odd, 37–64 | Problems 4–6 Exs. 23–35 odd, 37–68 | |
| 6-4 | 1 | Problems 1–3 Exs. 10–38, 98–119 | Problems 1–3 Exs. 11–37 odd, 98–119 | Problems 1–6 Exs. 10–66 odd, 67–119 | **Day 3** Problems 1–6 Exs. 11–65 odd, 67–90, 98–119 |
| | 2 | Problems 4–6 Exs. 39–67, 72–82 even | Problems 4–6 Exs. 39–65 odd, 67–90 | | |
| 6-5 | 1 | Problems 1–3 Exs. 9–25, 73–96 | Problems 1–3 Exs. 9–25 odd, 73–96 | Problems 1–3 Exs. 9–25 odd, 73–96 | **Day 4** Problems 1–5 Exs. 9–43 odd, 45–67, 73–96 |
| | 2 | Problems 4–5 Exs. 26–47, 57–60, 63–65 | Problems 4–5 Exs. 27–43 odd, 45–67 | Problems 4–5 Exs. 27–43 odd, 45–72 | |
| 6-6 | 1 | Problems 1–2 Exs. 9–26, 86–106 | Problems 1–2 Exs. 9–25 odd, 86–106 | Problems 1–4 Exs. 9–57 odd, 59–106 | **Day 5** Problems 1–4 Exs. 9–57 odd, 59–78, 86–106 |
| | 2 | Problems 3–4 Exs. 27–59, 61, 69–73 | Problems 3–4 Exs. 27–57 odd, 59–78 | | |
| 6-7 | 1 | Problems 1–3 Exs. 8–29, 75–95 | Problems 1–3 Exs. 9–29 odd, 75–95 | Problems 1–3 Exs. 9–29 odd, 75–95 | **Day 6** Problems 1–6 Exs. 9–41 odd, 42–67, 75–95 |
| | 2 | Problems 4–6 Exs. 30–43, 48–54 even, 65 | Problems 4–6 Exs. 31–41 odd, 42–67 | Problems 4–6 Exs. 31–41 odd, 42–74 | |
| 6-8 | 1 | Problems 1–3 Exs. 7–20, 60–76 | Problems 1–3 Exs. 7–19 odd, 60–76 | Problems 1–3 Exs. 7–19 odd, 60–76 | **Day 7** Problems 1–6 Exs. 7–35 odd, 37–54, 60–76 |
| | 2 | Problems 4–6 Exs. 21–36, 37–39, 43, 53 | Problems 4–6 Exs. 21–35 odd, 37–54 | Problems 4–6 Exs. 21–35 odd, 37–59 | |
| Review | 1 | Chapter 6 Review | Chapter 6 Review | Chapter 6 Review | **Day 8** Chapter 6 Review Chapter 6 Test |
| Assess | 1 | Chapter 6 Test | Chapter 6 Test | Chapter 6 Test | |
| **Total** | | **17 Days** | **16 Days** | **14 Days** | **8 Days** |

Note: Pacing does not include Concept Bytes and other feature pages.

# Resources

| | For the Chapter | 6-1 | 6-2 | 6-3 | 6-4 | 6-5 | 6-6 | 6-7 | 6-8 |
|---|---|---|---|---|---|---|---|---|---|
| **Planning** | | | | | | | | | |
| Teacher Center Online Planner & Grade Book | I | I | I | I | I | I | I | I | I |
| **Interactive Learning & Guided Instruction** | | | | | | | | | |
| My Math Video | I | | | | | | | | |
| Solve It! | | I TM | I TM | I TM | I TM | I TM | I TM | I TM | I TM |
| Student Companion (SP)* | | P M | P M | P M | P M | P M | P M | P M | P M |
| *Vocabulary Support* | | I P M | I P M | I P M | I P M | I P M | I P M | I P M | I P M |
| *Got It? Support* | | I P | I P | I P | I P | I P | I P | I P | I P |
| Dynamic Activity | I | | | | | | | | I |
| Online Problems | | I | I | I | I | I | I | I | I |
| Additional Problems | | M | M | M | M | M | M | M | M |
| English Language Learner Support (TR) | | E P M | E P M | E P M | E P M | E P M | E P M | E P M | E P M |
| Activities, Games, and Puzzles | | E M | E M | E M | E M | E M | E M | E M | E M |
| Teaching With TI Technology With CD-ROM | | | | | | | | | ✓ P |
| TI-Nspire™ Support CD-ROM | | ✓ | ✓ | ✓ | ✓ | ✓ | ✓ | ✓ | ✓ |
| **Lesson Check & Practice** | | | | | | | | | |
| Student Companion (SP)* | | P M | P M | P M | P M | P M | P M | P M | P M |
| *Lesson Check Support* | | I P | I P | I P | I P | I P | I P | I P | I P |
| Practice and Problem Solving Workbook (SP) | | P | P | P | P | P | P | P | P |
| *Think About a Plan* (TR)* | | E P M | E P M | E P M | E P M | E P M | E P M | E P M | E P M |
| *Practice Form G* (TR)* | | E P M | E P M | E P M | E P M | E P M | E P M | E P M | E P M |
| *Standardized Test Prep* (TR)* | | P M | P M | P M | P M | P M | P M | P M | P M |
| Practice *Form K* (TR)* | | E P M | E P M | E P M | E P M | E P M | E P M | E P M | E P M |
| Extra Practice | E M | | | | | | | | |
| Find the Errors! | M | | | | | | | | |
| Enrichment (TR) | | E P M | E P M | E P M | E P M | E P M | E P M | E P M | E P M |
| Answers and Solutions CD-ROM | ✓ | ✓ | ✓ | ✓ | ✓ | ✓ | ✓ | ✓ | ✓ |
| **Assess & Remediate** | | | | | | | | | |
| ExamView CD-ROM | ✓ | ✓ | ✓ | ✓ | ✓ | ✓ | ✓ | ✓ | ✓ |
| Lesson Quiz | | I TM | I TM | I TM | I TM | I TM | I TM | I TM | I TM |
| Quizzes and Tests *Form G* (TR)* | E P M | | | | E P M | | | | E P M |
| Quizzes and Tests *Form K* (TR)* | E P M | | | | E P M | | | | E P M |
| Reteaching (TR)* | | E P M | E P M | E P M | E P M | E P M | E P M | E P M | E P M |
| Performance Tasks (TR)* | P M | | | | | | | | |
| Cumulative Review (TR)* | P M | | | | | | | | |
| Progress Monitoring Assessments | I P M | | | | | | | | |

(TR) Available in All-In-One Teaching Resources  * Spanish available

# Guided Instruction

**PURPOSE** To review and practice using the properties of exponents in preparation to simplify expressions containing exponents

**PROCESS** Students will
- review properties of exponents.
- apply exponent properties to simplify expressions containing exponents so that only positive exponents are used.

**DISCUSS**

**Q** Does a negative exponent change the sign of an answer? Explain. **[No, a negative exponent changes the base to its reciprocal, which does not affect the sign of either the base or the answer. For example, $4^{-3} = \left(\frac{1}{4}\right)^3$.]**

To explain the multiplication and division properties, you may use concrete examples:

$x^5 \cdot x^3 = (x \cdot x \cdot x \cdot x \cdot x)(x \cdot x \cdot x) = x^8$

$\dfrac{x^7}{x^3} = \dfrac{x \cdot x \cdot x \cdot x \cdot x \cdot x \cdot x}{x \cdot x \cdot x} = x^4$

Students may question in what order to use the properties when more than one applies. Have them rework parts (a) and (b) applying the properties in a different order. If the expressions are rewritten with positive exponents, everyone will get the same simplified expression.

**EXTENSION**

**Q** What are the restrictions on a variable when it is in the denominator of an expression? **[The denominator cannot be 0, so the variable cannot be a number that would make it 0.]**

**Q** Can an expression such as $x^0$ be in the denominator of an expression? Explain. **[Yes, since the value of $x^0$ is always 1.]**

---

Chapter 6

## Concept Byte
For Use With Lesson 6-1
REVIEW

## Properties of Exponents

Exponents indicate powers. The table below lists the properties of exponents. Assume that no denominator is equal to zero and that $m$ and $n$ are integers.

**take note**

**Properties** **Properties of Exponents**

- $a^0 = 1, a \neq 0$
- $\dfrac{a^m}{a^n} = a^{m-n}$

- $a^{-n} = \dfrac{1}{a^n}$
- $(ab)^n = a^n b^n$
- $(a^m)^n = a^{mn}$

- $a^m \cdot a^n = a^{m+n}$
- $\left(\dfrac{a}{b}\right)^n = \dfrac{a^n}{b^n}$

### Example

Simplify and rewrite each expression using only positive exponents.

a. $(5a^3)(-3a^{-4})$

$(5a^3)(-3a^{-4}) = 5(-3)a^{(3+(-4))}$

$= -15a^{-1}$

$= \dfrac{-15}{a}$, or $-\dfrac{15}{a}$

b. $(-4x^{-3}y^5)^2$

$(-4x^{-3}y^5)^2 = (-4)^2(x^{-3})^2(y^5)^2$

$= 16x^{-6}y^{10}$

$= \dfrac{16y^{10}}{x^6}$

c. $\dfrac{4ab^6c^3}{a^5bc^3}$

$\dfrac{4ab^6c^3}{a^5bc^3} = 4a^{(1-5)}b^{(6-1)}c^{(3-3)}$

$= 4a^{-4}b^5c^0$

$= \dfrac{4b^5}{a^4}$

### Exercises

Simplify each expression. Use only positive exponents.

1. $(2a^3)(5a^4)$

2. $(-3x^2)(-4x^{-2})$

3. $(3x^2y^3)^2$

4. $(3x^{-4}y^3)^2$

5. $\dfrac{4a^8}{2a^4}$

6. $\dfrac{12x^5y^3}{4x^{-1}}$

7. $\dfrac{(6x^3)^0}{3xy^2}$

8. $\left(\dfrac{2x^4}{3}\right)^3$

9. $(-4m^2n^3)(2mn)$

10. $(2x^3y^7)^{-2}$

11. $\dfrac{(3r^{-2}s^3t^0)^{-3}}{3rs}$

12. $(h^7k^3)^0$

13. $\dfrac{r^2s^4t^6}{r^3s^4t^{-6}}$

14. $\dfrac{x^2y}{4} \cdot \dfrac{16x}{y}$

15. $(s^4t)^2(st)$

16. $\left(\dfrac{1}{h^{-2}}\right)^{-1} \cdot h^3$

17. $\dfrac{1}{a^2b^{-3}}(a^2b^{-3})^{-1}$

18. $\left(\dfrac{r^{-1}s^2t^{-3}}{r^{-2}s^0t^1}\right)^{-1}$

19. **Reasoning** Your friend tells you that $(k^2)^{-5} = -k^{10}$. Did she apply the properties of exponents correctly? Explain why or why not.

## Answers

### Concept Byte

1. $10a^7$

2. $12$

3. $9x^4y^6$

4. $\dfrac{9y^6}{x^8}$

5. $2a^4$

6. $3x^6y^3$

7. $\dfrac{1}{3xy^2}$

8. $\dfrac{8x^{12}}{27}$

9. $-8m^3n^4$

10. $\dfrac{1}{4x^6y^{14}}$

11. $\dfrac{r^5}{81s^{10}}$

12. $1$

13. $\dfrac{t^{12}}{r}$

14. $4x^3$

15. $s^9t^3$

16. $h$

17. $\dfrac{b^6}{a^4}$

18. $\dfrac{t^4}{s^2r}$

19. No; $(k^2)^{-5} \neq -k^{10}$; by the prop. of exponents, $(k^2)^{-5} = k^{2(-5)} = k^{-10} = \dfrac{1}{k^{10}}$.

# 6-1 Roots and Radical Expressions

**Objective** To find $n$th roots

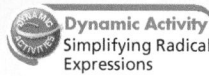
Dynamic Activity
Simplifying Radical Expressions

Lesson Vocabulary
• $n$th root
• principal root
• radicand
• index

**Getting Ready!**

This equation contains an infinite radical. Square each side. You get a quadratic equation. Are the two solutions of the quadratic equation also solutions of this equation? Explain your reasoning.

$$x = \sqrt{1 + \sqrt{1 + \sqrt{1 + \ldots}}}$$

In Chapter 5, you used *root* to represent a solution of an equation. For example, 2 is a root of the equation $x^3 = 8$. For such a simple power equation, you can simply refer to 2 as a cube root of 8.

**Essential Understanding** Corresponding to every power, there is a root. For example, just as there are squares (second powers), there are square roots. Just as there are cubes (third powers), there are cube roots, and so on.

$5^2 = 25$    5 is a square root of 25.
$5^3 = 125$    5 is a cube root of 125.
$5^4 = 625$    5 is a fourth root of 625.
$5^5 = 3125$    5 is a fifth root of 3125.

This pattern suggests a definition of an $n$th root.

**take note**

### Key Concept    The $n$th Root

If $a^n = b$, with $a$ and $b$ real numbers and $n$ a positive integer, then $a$ is an **$n$th root** of $b$.

**If $n$ is odd...**
there is one real $n$th root of $b$, denoted in radical form as $\sqrt[n]{b}$.

**If $n$ is even...**
• and $b$ is positive, there are two real $n$th roots of $b$. The positive root is the **principal root** (or principal $n$th root) and its symbol is $\sqrt[n]{b}$. The negative root is its opposite, or $-\sqrt[n]{b}$.
• and $b$ is negative, there are no real $n$th roots of $b$.

The only $n$th root of 0 is 0.

## 1 Interactive Learning

### Solve It!
**PURPOSE** To take roots and apply substitution to solve a quadratic equation
**PROCESS** Students may
• square both sides of the equation, substitute $x$ for the infinite radical, and solve.
• use a calculator to evaluate the infinite radical until an approximate value is reached.

**FACILITATE**
**Q** What is $\left(\sqrt{1 + \sqrt{1 + \sqrt{1 + }}}\right)^2$?
$[1 + \sqrt{1 + \sqrt{1 + \ldots}}]$
**Q** How can you rewrite $x^2 = 1 + \sqrt{1 + \sqrt{1 + \ldots}}$ without radicals? **[Substitute $x$ for the equivalent radical: $x^2 = 1 + x$.]**
**Q** Can you get an exact solution for $\sqrt{1 + \sqrt{1 + \sqrt{1 \ldots}}}$ on a calculator? Explain. **[No; you can only get an approximation.]**
**Q** Why is the original equation called an infinite radical? **[because the right side of the equation is never-ending]**

**ANSWER** See Solve It in Answers on next page.
**CONNECT THE MATH** The Solve It uses roots, radical expressions, substitution, and the Quadratic Formula to find solutions to the equation algebraically. In the lesson, students find real and principal roots and discover their properties.

## 2 Guided Instruction

### Take Note

**Q** Why do negative radicands have no real roots when the index is even? **[There is no real number whose square or other even power is negative.]**

---

# 6-1 Preparing to Teach

**BIG idea Equivalence**    **UbD**
**ESSENTIAL UNDERSTANDINGS**
• Corresponding to every power, there is a root. For example, just as there are squares (second powers), there are square roots. Just as there are cubes (third powers), there are cube roots, and so on.
• The $n$th root of an expression that contains an $n$th power as a factor can be simplified.
$$\sqrt[n]{x^n} = x^{\frac{n}{n}} = \begin{cases} x, & \text{if } n \text{ is odd} \\ |x|, & \text{if } n \text{ is even} \end{cases}$$

## Math Background
Depending on the sign of the radicand, the root corresponding to every real power is not necessarily a real number.

Specifically, if the index is even, the root of a negative number is not a real number. For example, the square root of $-9$ cannot be 3 or $-3$ since $3^2 = 9$ and $(-3)^2 = 9$. The

two complex square roots of $-9$ are $3i$ and $-3i$.

When finding the roots of variables, students may be confused by the placement of the absolute value signs. They are needed if and only if all of the following are true:
• the index is even,
• the power of the variable in the radicand is even, and
• the power of the variable in the root is odd.
The absolute value will ensure that an even root is always nonnegative.

Note that although there are two real $n$th roots of $b$ when $n$ is even and $b$ is positive, only the positive root is the principal root, $\sqrt[n]{b}$. The negative root is represented as $-\sqrt[n]{b}$. So, in Problems 2–4 where students are asked to find various roots $\sqrt[n]{b}$, they should give only the one positive root.

**PowerAlgebra.com**

## 1 Interactive Learning

### Solve It!
Step out how to solve the Problem with helpful hints and an online question. Other questions are listed above in Interactive Learning.

**Dynamic Activity** This activity guides students through simplifying radical expressions by ordering the appropriate solution steps. Use this activity for practice after the lesson.

## Problem 1

**Q** How do you find the fourth root of a fraction, like $\frac{16}{81}$? **[Consider the numerator and denominator separately, and find the root of each. The fourth root of 16 is 2 and the fourth root of 81 is 3, hence the fourth root of $\frac{16}{81}$ is $\frac{2}{3}$.]**

**Q** You can find the cube root of $-1000$ by solving $x^3 + 1000 = 0$. According to the Fundamental Theorem of Algebra, how many roots does $x^3 + 1000 = 0$ have? How many are real? **[Since the degree of this polynomial equation is 3, it has 3 complex solutions. Only one of them, $-10$, is real.]**

## Got It?

**Q** Can the square root of a negative number ever be real? Explain. **[No, because the square of a real number can never be negative.]**

## Problem 2

**Q** Instead of guess-and-check, what is another efficient way to find a root? **[Answers may vary. Sample: Use prime factorization. For example, $-8 = (-1)(2)(2)(2) = (-2)(-2)(-2) = (-2)^3$]**

**Q** For 2D, $(-2)^2$ also equals 4. Why is $-2$ not listed as a root? **[$-2$ is not listed as a root because $\sqrt{4}$ represents the positive square root.]**

---

You use a radical sign to indicate a root. The number under the radical sign is the **radicand**. The **index** gives the degree of the root.

### Problem 1 Finding All Real Roots

**A** What are the real cube roots of 0.008, $-1000$, and $\frac{1}{27}$?

$0.008 = (0.2)^3$    0.2 is the only real cube root of 0.008.

$-1000 = (-10)^3$    $-10$ is the only real cube root of $-1000$.

$\frac{1}{27} = \left(\frac{1}{3}\right)^3$    $\frac{1}{3}$ is the only real cube root of $\frac{1}{27}$.

**B** What are the real fourth roots of 1, $-0.0001$, and $\frac{16}{81}$?

Since 1 is positive, there are two real fourth roots.

$1 = 1^4$    1 is a real fourth root of 1.

$1 = (-1)^4$    $-1$ is the other real fourth root of 1.

Since $-0.0001$ is negative, there are no real fourth roots of $-0.0001$.

Since $\frac{16}{81}$ is positive, there are two real fourth roots.

$\frac{16}{81} = \left(\frac{2}{3}\right)^4$    $\frac{2}{3}$ is a real fourth root of $\frac{16}{81}$.

$\frac{16}{81} = \left(-\frac{2}{3}\right)^4$    $-\frac{2}{3}$ is the other real fourth root of $\frac{16}{81}$.

**Got It?** **1. a.** What are the real fifth roots of 0, $-1$, and 32?

     **b.** What are the real square roots of 0.01, $-1$, and $\frac{36}{121}$?

     **c.** Reasoning Explain why a negative real number $b$ has no real $n$th roots if $n$ is even.

According to the Fundamental Theorem of Algebra, $x^4 - 1 = 0$ has four roots, only two of which are real. In this chapter, the focus is on real roots only.

### Problem 2 Finding Roots

What is each real-number root?

**A** $\sqrt[3]{-8}$                 **B** $\sqrt{0.04}$

$(-2)^3 = -8$             $(0.2)^2 = 0.04$    $(-0.2)^2 = 0.04$ also, but

So, $\sqrt[3]{-8} = -2$.          So, $\sqrt{0.04} = 0.2$.    $\sqrt{0.04}$ represents the positive square root.

**C** $\sqrt[4]{-1}$                 **D** $\sqrt{(-2)^2}$

There is no real root because     $\sqrt{(-2)^2} = \sqrt{4} = 2$.

there is no real number whose

fourth power is $-1$.

### Plan

**How many real cube roots are there?**
A cube root is the same as a third root, and 3 is odd. So there is only one real cube root of a number.

### Plan

**How can you find a cube root?**
Work backwards. Find a number whose cube is the radicand.

---

# Answers

## Solve It!

No; the solutions of the quadratic eq. are $\frac{1 \pm \sqrt{5}}{2}$.

The solution to the original equation is $\frac{1 + \sqrt{5}}{2}$, since the solution must be positive.

## Got It?

**1. a.** 0; $-1$; 2

     **b.** $\pm 0.1$; no real square root; $\pm \frac{6}{11}$

     **c.** Any negative number multiplied by itself an even number of times will always be positive. Therefore, there can be no real $n$th roots (where $n$ is even) for a negative number $b$.

**2. a.** $-3$        **c.** 7

     **b.** no real root    **d.** no real root

**3. a.** $9x^2$    **b.** $a^4b^5$    **c.** $|x^3|y^4$

---

**PowerAlgebra.com**

# 2 Guided Instruction

Each Problem is worked out and supported online.

### Problem 1
Finding All Real Roots
*Animated*

### Problem 2
Finding Roots

### Problem 3
Simplifying Radical Expressions
*Animated*

### Problem 4
Using a Radical Expression
*Animated*

### Support in Algebra 2 Companion
• Vocabulary
• Key Concepts
• Got It?

**Got It?** 2. What is each real-number root?

a. $\sqrt[3]{-27}$    b. $\sqrt[4]{-81}$    c. $\sqrt{(-7)^2}$    d. $\sqrt{-49}$

It is tempting to conclude that $\sqrt[n]{a^n} = a$ for all real numbers $a$, but part (d) of Problem 2 shows that this is not the case. If $n$ is even, then $\sqrt[n]{a^n}$ is positive even if $a$ itself is negative.

**Property** *n*th Roots of *n*th Powers

For any real number $a$, $\sqrt[n]{a^n} = \begin{cases} a & \text{if } n \text{ is odd} \\ |a| & \text{if } n \text{ is even} \end{cases}$

It is easy to overlook this rule for simplifying radicals. It is particularly important that you remember it when the radicand contains a variable expression. You must *include* the absolute value when $n$ is even, and you must *omit* it when $n$ is odd.

**Problem 3** Simplifying Radical Expressions

What is a simpler form of each radical expression?

**Plan**
How can you get started?
You're simplifying a square root, so use properties of exponents to write the *entire* radicand as a perfect square.

**A** $\sqrt{16x^8}$

$\sqrt{16x^8} = \sqrt{4^2(x^4)^2} = \sqrt{(4x^4)^2} = |4x^4| = 4x^4$

You need to include absolute value symbols because the index of a square root is 2, which is even. However, $|4x^4| = 4x^4$ because $x^4$ is always nonnegative.

**B** $\sqrt[3]{a^6b^9}$

$\sqrt[3]{a^6b^9} = \sqrt[3]{(a^2)^3(b^3)^3} = \sqrt[3]{(a^2b^3)^3} = a^2b^3$

The index is odd, so you cannot include absolute value symbols here.

**C** $\sqrt[4]{x^8y^{12}}$

$\sqrt[4]{x^8y^{12}} = \sqrt[4]{(x^2)^4(y^3)^4} = \sqrt[4]{(x^2y^3)^4} = x^2|y^3|$

The index is even. The absolute value symbols ensure that the root is positive when $y^3$ is negative. Absolute value symbols are not needed for $x^2$ since $x^2$ is always nonnegative.

**Got It?** 3. What is the simplified form of each radical expression?

a. $\sqrt{81x^4}$    b. $\sqrt[3]{a^{12}b^{15}}$    c. $\sqrt[4]{x^{12}y^{16}}$

---

## Got It?   ERROR PREVENTION

**Q** In 2c, is $-7$ a root? Why or why not? **[$-7$ is a real square root of 49 but not a principal root. The form $\sqrt{a}$ calls for the principal square root of $a$, and the principal square root cannot be negative.]**

Note that this statement is true since $\sqrt[n]{a^n}$ is a principal root when $n$ is even, so it must be nonnegative.

## Take Note

**Q** Why is it necessary to include absolute value bars when $n$ is even? **[Answers may vary. Sample: The absolute value bars ensure that the root is nonnegative. For example, $\sqrt{x^2} = x$ is false when $x$ is negative, while $\sqrt{x^2} = |x|$ is true.]**

## Problem 3

**Q** Why is $\sqrt{x^2} = |x|$, but $\sqrt{x^4} = x^2$? **[The absolute value bars are unnecessary for $x^2$ because $x^2$ is always nonnegative.]**

**Q** Why does 3B not have absolute value bars around the answer? **[Absolute value is not needed because the index is odd.]**

## Got It?   ERROR PREVENTION

You may want to quickly review operations with exponents to help with factoring:
$a^{12} = a^{4(3)} = (a^4)^3$.

**Q** What should you do first? **[Answers may vary. Sample: Factor the radicand, and identify the multiples of the given power.]**

---

# Additional Problems

**1.** What are all the real square roots of $-0.81$, $\frac{25}{49}$, and 121?

**ANSWER** none; $\frac{5}{7}$ and $-\frac{5}{7}$; 11 and $-11$

**2.** What is each real-number root of $\sqrt{0.36}$, $\sqrt[3]{-1}$ and $\sqrt{(-17)^2}$?

**ANSWER** 0.6, $-1$; 17

**3.** What is the simplified form of each radical?

a. $\sqrt{25a^4}$

b. $\sqrt[4]{p^{12}q^4}$

**ANSWERS a.** $5a^2$   **b.** $|p^3q|$

**4.** The speed $s$ in meters per second of a car leaving a skid mark $d$ meters long after the brakes are applied is given by the formula $s = \sqrt{15d}$. If you measure a skid mark and it is 180 m long, how fast was the car going before it braked?

**ANSWER** about 52 m/s

**Problem 4**

> **Q** Why does the formula contain the number 10? **[Ten is the square root of the highest possible score achievable on the test.]**

A good point for discussion here is the fairness of adjusting test scores. Students may have an initial negative reaction to a student gaining 24 points versus a student gaining only 5 points. Point out that the person at the bottom of the scoring is still at the bottom.

### Got It?

> **Q** The raw scores of 0 and 100 are not altered by the formula. Do you think this is a good idea? Explain. **[Sample: Yes; no one can score more than 100 with this formula, and it does not make sense to give points to someone who scored zero.]**

## 3 Lesson Check

### Do you know HOW?

- For Exercises 1–3, remind students to use the Take Note table (p. 361) to determine how many real roots they should find.

### Do you UNDERSTAND? ERROR INTERVENTION

- If students have trouble finding the error in Exercise 7, remind them that the four is an index, not a divisor.

### Close

> **Q** Why does a positive integer have two real square roots but only one real cube root? **[Either a negative number squared or a positive number squared will produce a positive number, but only a positive number cubed will produce a positive number.]**

**Problem 4** Using a Radical Expression

**Academics** Some teachers adjust test scores when a test is difficult. One teacher's formula for adjusting scores is $A = 10\sqrt{R}$, where $A$ is the adjusted score and $R$ is the raw score. If the raw scores on one test range from 36 to 90, what is the range of the adjusted scores?

| Think | Write |
|---|---|
| You have to adjust the lowest raw score and the highest raw score. | $10\sqrt{36} = 10(6) = 60$ <br> $10\sqrt{90} \approx 10(9.487) = 94.87 \approx 95$ |
| The other adjusted scores must be between the lowest and highest adjusted scores. | The adjusted scores range from 60 to 95. |

**Got It?** 4. In Problem 4, what are the adjusted scores for raw scores of 0 and 100?

### Lesson Check

**Do you know HOW?**

Find all the real square roots of each number.

**1.** 25 **2.** 0.16 **3.** −64

Simplify each radical expression.

**4.** $\sqrt{9b^2}$ **5.** $\sqrt{a^8 b^{18}}$ **6.** $\sqrt[3]{-125a^3}$

**Do you UNDERSTAND?**

**7. Error Analysis** A student said the only fourth root of 16 is 2. Describe and correct his error.

**8. Vocabulary** Explain the difference between a real root and the principal root.

**9. Reasoning** A number has only one real $n$th root. What can you conclude about the index $n$?

### Practice and Problem-Solving Exercises

**A Practice** Find all the real square roots of each number. *See Problem 1.*

**10.** 225 **11.** 0.0049 **12.** $-\frac{1}{121}$ **13.** $\frac{64}{169}$

Find all the real cube roots of each number.

**14.** −64 **15.** 0.125 **16.** $-\frac{27}{216}$ **17.** 0.000343

Find all the real fourth roots of each number.

**18.** 16 **19.** −16 **20.** 0.0081 **21.** $\frac{10,000}{81}$

## 3 Lesson Check

For a digital lesson check, use the Got It questions.

**Support in Algebra 2 Companion**
- Lesson Check

## 4 Practice

Assign homework to individual students or to an entire class.

## Answers

### Got It? (continued)

**4.** 0; 100

### Lesson Check

**1.** ±5
**2.** ±0.4
**3.** no real roots
**4.** $3|b|$
**5.** $a^4|b^9|$
**6.** $-5a$
**7.** 16 has two real fourth roots, 2 and −2.
**8.** The real roots of a number are the positive and negative (but not imaginary) roots of the number; the principal root of a number is the nonnegative root of the number.
**9.** $n$ is odd.

### Practice and Problem-Solving Exercises

**10.** ±15
**11.** ±0.07
**12.** none
**13.** $\pm\frac{8}{13}$
**14.** −4
**15.** 0.5
**16.** $-\frac{1}{2}$
**17.** 0.07
**18.** ±2
**19.** none
**20.** ±0.3
**21.** $\pm\frac{10}{3}$

Find each real root.

 **See Problem 2.**

**22.** $\sqrt{36}$  **23.** $\sqrt{0.25}$  **24.** $-\sqrt[3]{64}$  **25.** $\sqrt[3]{-27}$

Simplify each radical expression. Use absolute value symbols when
needed.

 **See Problem 3.**

**26.** $\sqrt{16x^2}$  **27.** $\sqrt[3]{27y^6}$  **28.** $\sqrt[4]{x^{20}y^{28}}$  **29.** $\sqrt[5]{32y^{10}}$

**30. Grades** In many classes, a passing test grade is 70. Using the
formula $A = 10\sqrt{R}$, what raw score would a student need to
get a passing grade after her score is adjusted?

 **See Problem 4.**

 **Apply**

Find the two real solutions of each equation.

**31.** $x^2 = 100$  **32.** $x^4 = 1$  **33.** $x^2 = 0.25$  **34.** $x^4 = \frac{16}{81}$

**35. Think About a Plan** The radius of a spherical balloon can be expressed as $r = \sqrt[3]{\frac{3V}{4\pi}}$
inches, where $r$ is the radius and $V$ is the volume of the balloon in cubic inches. If
air is pumped to inflate the balloon from 500 cubic inches to 800 cubic inches, by
how many inches has the radius of the balloon increased?
- What was the radius of the balloon originally?
- What was the radius after inflating the balloon to 800 cubic inches?
- How can you use the two radii to find the amount of increase?

**36. Electricity** The voltage $V$ of an audio system's speaker can be represented by
$V = 4\sqrt{P}$, where $P$ is the power of the speaker. An engineer wants to design a
speaker with 400 watts of power. What will the voltage be?

**37. Boat Building** Boat builders share an old rule of thumb for sailboats. The
maximum speed $K$ in knots is 1.35 times the square root of the length $L$ in feet of
the boat's waterline.
**a.** A customer is planning to order a sailboat with a maximum speed of 12 knots.
How long should the waterline be?
**b.** How much longer would the waterline have to be to achieve a maximum speed
of 15 knots?

Simplify each radical expression. Use absolute value symbols when needed.

**38.** $\sqrt[3]{0.125}$  **39.** $\sqrt[3]{\frac{8}{216}}$  **40.** $\sqrt[4]{0.0016}$  **41.** $\sqrt[4]{\frac{1}{256}}$  **42.** $\sqrt[4]{16c^4}$

**43. Open-Ended** Write three radical expressions that simplify to $-2x^2$.

**44. Reasoning** For what positive integers $n$ is each of the statements true?
**a.** If $x^n = b$, then $x$ is an $n$th root of $b$.
**b.** If $x^n = b$, then $x = \sqrt[n]{b}$.

Is each equation *always*, *sometimes*, or *never* true? Explain your answer.

**45.** $\sqrt{x^4} = x^2$  **46.** $\sqrt{x^6} = x^3$  **47.** $\sqrt[3]{x^8} = x^2$  **48.** $\sqrt[3]{x^3} = |x|$

 PowerAlgebra.com — Lesson 6-1 Roots and Radical Expressions — 365

---

# 4 Practice

**ASSIGNMENT GUIDE**

Basic: 10–30 all, 33–37

Average: 11–29 odd, 31–48

Advanced: 11–29 odd, 31–55

Standardized Test Prep: 56–59

Mixed Review: 60–67

**Reasoning** exercises have blue headings.

**Applications** exercises have red headings.

**EXERCISE 37:** Use the Think About a Plan
worksheet in the **Practice and Problem Solving
Workbook** (also available in the Teaching Resources
in print and online) to further support students'
development in becoming independent learners.

**HOMEWORK QUICK CHECK**

To check students' understanding of key skills and
concepts, go over Exercises 21, 29, 34, 35, and 37.

---

**22.** 6

**23.** 0.5

**24.** −4

**25.** −3

**26.** $4|x|$

**27.** $3y^2$

**28.** $|x^5 y^7|$

**29.** $2y^2$

**30.** 49

**31.** $\pm 10$

**32.** $\pm 1$

**33.** $\pm 0.5$

**34.** $\pm \frac{2}{3}$

**35.** about 0.8 in.

**36.** 80 volts

**37. a.** about 79.01 ft
**b.** about 44.44 ft

**38.** 0.5

**39.** $\frac{1}{3}$

**40.** 0.2

**41.** $\frac{1}{4}$

**42.** $2|c|$

**43.** Answers may vary. Sample:
$\sqrt[3]{-8x^6}$, $-\sqrt[4]{16x^8}$, $\sqrt[5]{-32x^{10}}$

**44. a.** for all positive integers
**b.** for all odd positive integers

**45.** all; $x^2$ is always nonnegative

**46.** sometimes; they are equal for $x \geq 0$

**47.** sometimes; they are equal for
$x = -1, 0, 1$

**48.** sometimes; they are equal for $x \geq 0$

# Answers

## Practice and Problem-Solving Exercises
(continued)

**49.** even: $|m|$; odd: $m$

**50.** even: $m^2$; odd: $m^2$

**51.** even: $|m^3|$; odd: $m^3$

**52.** even: $m^4$; odd: $m^4$

**53.** 48

**54.** No; the square root of 4 is $\pm 2$.

**55.** a diagonal of a square with side 5

## Standardized Test Prep

**56.** B

**57.** G

**58.** C

**59.** [4] System:
$-35 = (-3)^3 a + (-3)^2 b + (-3)c + d$,
$1 = (0)^3 a + (0)^2 b + (0)c + d$, $3 = (2)^3 a +$
$(2)^2 b + (2)c + d$, $7 = (4)^3 a + (4)^2 b +$
$(4)c + d$ (OR equivalent system); solution:
$a = 0.35, b = -1.85, c = 3.3, d = 1$,
cubic polynomial: $y = 0.35x^3 -$
$1.85x^2 + 3.3x + 1$.

[3] appropriate methods, but with one
computational error

[2] incorrect system solved correctly OR
correct system solved incorrectly; function
written appropriately, given previous
results

[1] correct function, without work shown

## Mixed Review

**60.** $y = (x + 2)^3 + 3$

**61.** $y = \frac{1}{2}x^3 - 2$

**62.** $1, \frac{3}{4}$

**63.** $\frac{5 \pm i\sqrt{11}}{6}$

**64.** $\frac{11}{6}$

**65.** $2x^3 y^3$

**66.** $\frac{ac}{3}$

**67.** $\frac{4}{x^2}$

---

**Simplify each radical expression if $n$ is even, and then if $n$ is odd.**

**49.** $\sqrt[n]{m^n}$     **50.** $\sqrt[n]{m^{2n}}$     **51.** $\sqrt[n]{m^{3n}}$     **52.** $\sqrt[n]{m^{4n}}$

**53. Reasoning** How many square roots of integers are in the interval between 24 and 25?

**54. Reasoning** The square root of a positive integer is either a positive integer or an irrational number. Is this a true statement or not? Explain your reasoning.

**55. Geometry** Without using a calculator, determine which is greater: the altitude of an equilateral triangle with side 8 or the diagonal of a square with side 5. Show your work.

## Standardized Test Prep

**SAT/ACT**

**56.** Which equation has more than one real-number solution?
- (A) $x^2 = 0$
- (B) $x^2 = 1$
- (C) $x^2 = -1$
- (D) $x^3 = -1$

**57.** According to the Rational Root Theorem, which of the following is NOT a possible root of the polynomial equation $7x^5 + 3x^2 - 4x + 21 = 0$?
- (F) $\frac{1}{7}$
- (G) $\frac{1}{3}$
- (H) 3
- (I) 7

**58.** The fuse of a three-break firework rocket is programmed to ignite three times with 2-second intervals between the ignitions. When the rocket is shot vertically in the air, its height $h$ in feet after $t$ seconds is given by the formula $h(t) = -5t^2 + 70t$. At how many seconds after the shot should the firework technician set the timer of the first ignition to make the second ignition occur when the rocket is at its highest point?
- (A) 3
- (B) 9
- (C) 5
- (D) 7

**Extended Response**

**59.** Write a system of equations to find a cubic polynomial that goes through $(-3, -35)$, $(0, 1)$, $(2, 3)$, and $(4, 7)$.

## Mixed Review

**Determine the cubic function that is obtained from the parent function $y = x^3$ after each sequence of transformations.**    ◆ See Lesson 5-9.

**60.** translation up 3 units and to the left 2 units

**61.** vertical compression by a factor of $\frac{1}{2}$, translation down 2 units

**Solve each equation by using the Quadratic Formula.**    ◆ See Lesson 4-7.

**62.** $-4x^2 + 7x - 3 = 0$     **63.** $3x^2 - 5x + 3 = 0$     **64.** $36x^2 - 132x + 121 = 0$

**Get Ready!**   To prepare for Lesson 6-2, do Exercises 65–67.

**Simplify each algebraic expression.**    ◆ See Lesson 1-3.

**65.** $\frac{14x^7 y^9}{7x^4 y^6}$     **66.** $\frac{3abc}{9b}$     **67.** $\frac{20x}{5x^3}$

## Additional Instructional Support

### Algebra 2 Companion

Students can use the **Algebra 2 Companion** worktext (4 pages) as you teach the lesson. Use the Companion to support

- New Vocabulary
- Key Concepts
- Got It for each Problem
- Lesson Check

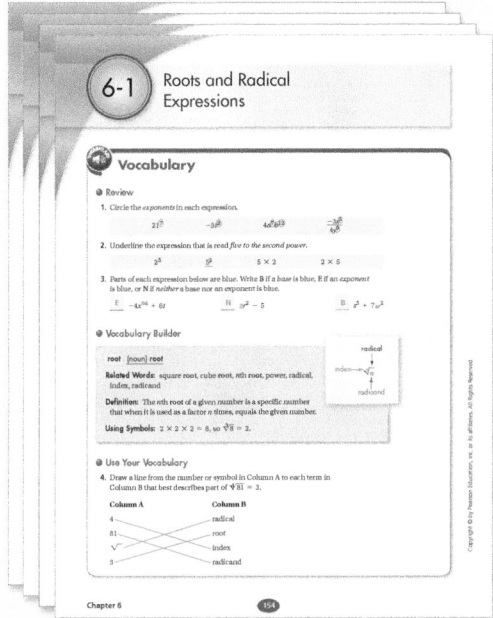

### ELL Support

**Use Manipulatives** Divide students into small groups. Give each group 25 tiles and 125 small cubes (or less, 16 tiles and 64 cubes, or 9 tiles and 27 cubes, or 4 tiles and 8 cubes, as materials allow). Have them model $5^2$ and $\sqrt{25}$ with tiles, and $5^3$ and $\sqrt[3]{125}$ with cubes. Repeat using 4, 3, and 2 instead of 5. Have students identify and name the index and radicand of each.

Discuss the shape of each figure. What does $5^2$ look like? [a 5 × 5 square] What represents $\sqrt{25}$? [5 tiles, or one side of the square] What does $5^3$ look like? [a 5 × 5 × 5 cube] What represents $\sqrt[3]{125}$? [5 tiles, or one edge of the cube]

You may also want to make the following poster for the classroom or vocabulary board:

$$\sqrt[\text{Index}]{\text{Radicand}}$$

## 5 Assess & Remediate

### Lesson Quiz

1. What are the real cube roots of $-64$, $0.001$, and $\frac{27}{125}$?
2. What is each real-number root of $\sqrt{0.16}$, $\sqrt[3]{-343}$ and $\sqrt{(-5)^2}$?
3. What is the simplified form of $\sqrt{9x^2}$ and of $\sqrt[3]{x^6y^{15}}$?
4. **Do you UNDERSTAND?** The formula $d = 1.35\sqrt{h}$ models the distance $d$ in miles from the horizon where $h$ is the distance in feet from a person's eyes to the water. If you are standing in a boat and the distance from the water to your eyes is 8 ft, what is your distance from the horizon to the nearest hundredth of a mile?

### ANSWERS TO LESSON QUIZ

1. $-4$; $0.1$; $\frac{3}{5}$
2. $0.4$; $-7$; $5$
3. $3|x|$; $x^2y^5$
4. $3.82$ mi

### PRESCRIPTION FOR REMEDIATION

Use the student work on the Lesson Quiz to prescribe a differentiated review assignment:

| Points | Differentiated Remediation |
|--------|----------------------------|
| 0–2 | Intervention |
| 3 | On-level |
| 4 | Extension |

### PowerAlgebra.com

## 5 Assess & Remediate

Assign the Lesson Quiz. Appropriate intervention, practice, or enrichment is automatically generated based on student performance.

## Intervention

- **Reteaching** (2 pages) Provides reteaching and practice exercises for the key lesson concepts. Use with struggling students or absent students.
- **English Language Learner Support** Helps students develop and reinforce mathematical vocabulary and key concepts.

### All-in-One Resources/Online
### Reteaching

### All-in-One Resources/Online
### English Language Learner Support

# Differentiated Remediation *continued*

## On-Level

- **Practice** (2 pages) Provides extra practice for each lesson. For simpler practice exercises, use the Form K Practice pages found in the All-in-One Teaching Resources and online.

- **Think About a Plan** Helps students develop specific problem-solving skills and strategies by providing scaffolded guiding questions.
- **Standardized Test Prep** Focuses on all major exercises, all major question types, and helps students prepare for the high-stakes assessments.

## Extension

- **Enrichment** Provides students with interesting problems and activities that extend the concepts of the lesson.
- **Activities, Games, and Puzzles** Worksheets that can be used for concepts development, enrichment, and for fun!

---

### Practice and Problem Solving Wkbk/ All-in-One Resources/Online
**Practice page 1**

**6-1 Practice** — Form G
Roots and Radical Expressions

Find all the real square roots of each number.

1. 400  −20, 20
2. −196  no real square roots
3. 10,000  −100, 100
4. 0.0625  −0.25, 0.25

Find all the real cube roots of each number.

5. 216  6
6. −343  −7
7. −0.064  −0.4
8. $\frac{1000}{27}$  $\frac{10}{3}$

Find all the real fourth roots of each number.

9. −81  no real fourth roots
10. 256  −4, 4
11. 0.0001  −0.1, 0.1
12. 625  −5, 5

Find each real root.

13. $\sqrt{144}$  12
14. $-\sqrt{25}$  −5
15. $\sqrt{-0.01}$  not a real number
16. $\sqrt[3]{0.001}$  0.1

17. $\sqrt[4]{0.0081}$  0.3
18. $\sqrt[3]{27}$  3
19. $\sqrt[3]{-27}$  −3
20. $\sqrt{0.09}$  0.3

Simplify each radical expression. Use absolute value symbols when needed.

21. $\sqrt{81x^4}$  9x²
22. $\sqrt{121y^{10}}$  11|y⁵|
23. $\sqrt[3]{8g^6}$  2g²

24. $\sqrt[3]{125x^9}$  5x³
25. $\sqrt[5]{243x^5y^{15}}$  3xy³
26. $\sqrt{(x-9)^2}$  x − 9

27. $\sqrt{25(x+2)^4}$  5(x + 2)²
28. $\sqrt[3]{\frac{64x^6}{343}}$  $\frac{4x^2}{7}$
29. $\sqrt[3]{-0.008}$  −0.2

30. $\sqrt[4]{\frac{x^4}{81}}$  $\frac{|x|}{3}$
31. $\sqrt{36x^2y^6}$  6|x|y³
32. $\sqrt[3]{(m-n)^3}$  (m − n)

33. A cube has volume $V = s^3$, where s is the length of a side. Find the side length for a cube with volume 8000 cm³.  20 cm

34. The temperature T in degrees Celsius (°C) of a liquid t minutes after heating is given by the formula $T = 8\sqrt{t}$. When is the temperature 48°C?  36 min

---

### Practice and Problem Solving Wkbk/ All-in-One Resources/Online
**Practice page 2**

**6-1 Practice** (continued) — Form G
Roots and Radical Expressions

Find the two real solutions of each equation.

35. $x^2 = 4$  −2, 2
36. $x^4 = 81$  −3, 3
37. $x^2 = 0.16$  −0.4, 0.4
38. $x^2 = \frac{16}{49}$  $-\frac{4}{7}, \frac{4}{7}$
39. $x^4 = \frac{16}{625}$  $-\frac{2}{5}, \frac{2}{5}$
40. $x^2 = \frac{121}{25}$  $-\frac{11}{5}, \frac{11}{5}$
41. $x^2 = 0.000009$  −0.003, 0.003
42. $x^4 = 0.0001$  −0.1, 0.1

43. The number of new customers n that visit a dry cleaning shop in one year is directly related to the amount a (in dollars) spent on advertising. This relationship is represented by $n^3 = 13,824a$. To attract 480 new customers, how much should the owners spend on advertising during the year?  $8000

44. **Geometry** The volume V of a sphere with radius r is given by the formula $V = \frac{4}{3}\pi r^3$.
   a. What is the radius of a sphere with volume 36π cubic inches?  3 in.
   b. If the volume increases by a factor of 8, what is the new radius?  6 in.

45. A clothing manufacturer finds the number of defective blouses d is a function of the total number of blouses n produced at her factory. This function is $d = 0.000005n^2$.
   a. What is the total number of blouses produced if 45 are defective?  3000
   b. If the number of defective blouses increases by a factor of 9, how does the total number of blouses change?  It has tripled.

46. The velocity of a falling object can be found using the formula $v^2 = 64h$, where v is the velocity (in feet per second) and h is the distance the object has already fallen.
   a. What is the velocity of the object after a 10-foot fall?  about 25.30 ft/sec
   b. How much does the velocity increase if the object falls 20 feet rather than 10 feet?  about 10.48 ft/sec

---

### All-in-One Resources/Online
**Enrichment**

**6-1 Enrichment**
Roots and Radical Expressions

**Rounding Roots and Radicals**

Computers treat radicals such as $\sqrt{2}$ as if they were rounded to a preassigned number of decimal places. Most computers round numbers according to an algorithm that uses the largest integer less than or equal to a given number. This function is called the greatest integer function and is written as $y = [x]$.

As you can see, the graph of the greatest integer function is not continuous. The open circles indicate that the endpoint is not included as part of the graph.

The command INT in most popular spreadsheet programs serves the same purpose as the greatest integer function. For instance, INT(3.84) = 3; INT(−1.99) = −2; INT(7) = 7.

To round a number x to r decimal places, a computer performs the following procedure:

**Step 1** Multiply x by 10ʳ.
**Step 2** Add 0.5 to the result.
**Step 3** Find INT of the result.
**Step 4** Multiply the result by $10^{-r}$.

Fill in the table below to see how this procedure works.

| x | r | Step 1 | Step 2 | Step 3 | Step 4 |
|---|---|--------|--------|--------|--------|
| 11.4825 | 3 | 11482.5 | 11483 | 11483 | 11.483 |
| 132.718 | 2 | 13271.8 | 13272.3 | 13272 | 132.72 |
| 34.999 | 1 | 349.99 | 350.49 | 350 | 35.0 |

A computer that rounds numbers after each operation may introduce rounding errors into calculations. To see the effects of rounding errors, perform each of the following computations for x = 2 and different r values. First find the given root and write the answer to r + 1 digits after the decimal. Carry out the four steps to get the answer and then raise the result to the given power. Write the answer again to r + 1 digits after the decimal and carry out the four steps to get the final answer.

| x | r | $\left(\sqrt{x}\right)^2$ | $\left(\sqrt[3]{x}\right)^3$ |
|---|---|------|------|
| 2 | 6 | 2.000001 | 2.000000 |
| 2 | 3 | 1.999 | 2.000 |
| 2 | 1 | 2.0 | 2.2 |

---

### Practice and Problem Solving Wkbk/ All-in-One Resources/Online
**Think About a Plan**

**6-1 Think About a Plan**
Roots and Radical Expressions

**Boat Building** Boat builders share an old rule of thumb for sailboats. The maximum speed K in knots is 1.35 times the square root of the length L in feet of the boat's waterline.
   a. A customer is planning to order a sailboat with a maximum speed of 12 knots. How long should the waterline be?
   b. How much longer would the waterline have to be to achieve a maximum speed of 15 knots?

1. Write an equation to relate the maximum speed K in knots to the length L in feet of a boat's waterline.  $K = 1.35\sqrt{L}$

2. How can you find the length of a sailboat's waterline if you know its maximum speed?
   Substitute the maximum speed for K and solve the resulting equation for L

3. A customer is planning to order a sailboat with a maximum speed of 12 knots. How long should the waterline be?  about 79 ft

4. How can you find how much longer the waterline would have to be to achieve a maximum speed of 15 knots, compared to a maximum speed of 12 knots?
   Subtract the waterline length needed for a 12-knot maximum speed from the waterline length needed for a 15-knot maximum speed

5. If a customer wants a sailboat with a maximum speed of 15 knots, how long should the waterline be?  about 123 ft

6. How much longer would the waterline have to be to achieve a maximum speed of 15 knots?  about 44 ft

---

### Practice and Problem Solving Wkbk/ All-in-One Resources/Online
**Standardized Test Prep**

**6-1 Standardized Test Prep**
Roots and Radical Expressions

**Multiple Choice**

For Exercises 1–6, choose the correct letter.

1. What is the real square root of 0.00647  B
   Ⓐ 0.4   Ⓒ 0.04
   Ⓑ 0.08   Ⓓ no real square root

2. What is the real cube root of −64?  G
   Ⓕ 4   Ⓗ −8
   Ⓖ −4   Ⓘ no real cube root

3. What is the real fourth root of $-\frac{16}{81}$?  D
   Ⓐ $\frac{2}{3}$   Ⓒ $-\frac{4}{9}$
   Ⓑ $-\frac{2}{3}$   Ⓓ no real fourth root

4. What is the value of $\sqrt[3]{-0.027}$?  F
   Ⓕ −0.3   Ⓗ −0.03
   Ⓖ 0.3   Ⓘ 0.03

5. What is the simplified form of the expression $\sqrt{4x^2y^4}$?  B
   Ⓐ 2xy²   Ⓒ 4xy²
   Ⓑ 2|x|y²   Ⓓ 2|xy|

6. What are the real solutions of the equation $x^4 = 81$?  H
   Ⓕ −9, 9   Ⓗ −3, 3
   Ⓖ 3   Ⓘ −3

**Short Response**

7. The volume V of a cube with side length s is $V = s^3$. A cubical storage bin has volume 5832 cubic inches. What is the length of the side of the cube? Show your work.
   [2] $V = s^3$, 5832 = s³, $s = \sqrt[3]{5832} = 18$; 18 in.
   [1] incorrect side length OR no work shown
   [0] incorrect answer and no work shown OR no answer given

---

### Online Teacher Resource Center
**Activities, Games, and Puzzles**

**6-1 Game: The Spiral Boardwalk**
Roots and Radical Expressions

This is a game for two or more players. Each player will use a pencil to trace his or her path on the spiral of the game board provided.
- Make cards by cutting out each root expression below. Mix up the cards and place them face down on the table.
- Each player starts at the dot closest to the center of the spiral and moves along the Xs.
- In turn, a player selects an expression from the table.
- The player simplifies the expression.
- If the simplified expression is an integer, the player advances (clockwise) or retreats (counterclockwise) by the number of steps indicated by the integer. A positive integer is an advance. A negative integer is a retreat. Players do not retreat farther than the starting dot. If the simplified expression is not an integer, the player does not move.
- When you have finished with a card, place it back in the pile (face down) and shuffle the deck before your opponent goes.
- Players check each other's answers. If an answer is incorrect, the player loses his or her turn. If players cannot agree on an answer, they should ask the teacher.
- The player to advance the farthest or cross the finish line first wins.

| $\sqrt[3]{64}$ 2 | $\sqrt[3]{125}$ 5 | $\sqrt[4]{81}$ 3 | $\sqrt[3]{-27}$ −3 | $-\sqrt[3]{64}$ 4 |
|---|---|---|---|---|
| $\sqrt[3]{8}$ 2 | $\sqrt[5]{-32}$ −2 | $\sqrt[4]{625}$ 5 | $-\sqrt{16}$ −4 | $-\sqrt[3]{-27}$ 3 |
| $\sqrt[6]{64}$ 4 | $\sqrt[4]{2^{16}}$ 2 | $\sqrt[5]{3^7}$ 3 | $-\sqrt[3]{-125}$ 5 | $-\sqrt[4]{16}$ −2 |
| $-\sqrt[3]{8}$ −2 | $\sqrt[3]{3^9}$ 3 | $\sqrt[4]{4^{10}}$ | $\frac{\sqrt[3]{216}}{2}$ | $\frac{-\sqrt[3]{125}}{5}$ |
| $\sqrt[3]{\frac{16}{2}}$ 2 | $2\sqrt[3]{27}$ 6 | $-2\sqrt[4]{81}$ −6 | $\sqrt[3]{27} \times \sqrt[3]{-16}$ −6 | $0.5\sqrt[3]{64}$ 2 |

---

## 6-2 Multiplying and Dividing Radical Expressions

**Objective** To multiply and divide radical expressions

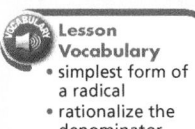

**Getting Ready!**

You can cut the 36-square into four 9-squares or nine 4-squares. What other n-square can you cut into sets of smaller squares in two ways? Is there a square you can cut into smaller squares in three ways? Explain your reasoning.

Cutting *n*-squares into 1-squares doesn't count.

Knowing the perfect squares greater than 1 (namely, 4, 9, 16, and so on) will help you simplify some radical expressions.

**Lesson Vocabulary**
• simplest form of a radical
• rationalize the denominator

**Essential Understanding** You can simplify a radical expression when the exponent of one factor of the radicand is a multiple of the radical's index.

You can simplify the product of powers that have the same exponent. Similarly, you can simplify the product of radicals that have the same index.

| Same Exponent | Same Index |
|---|---|
| $2^2 \cdot 3^2 = (2 \cdot 3)^2$ | $\sqrt{2} \cdot \sqrt{3} = \sqrt{2 \cdot 3}$ |
| $4^3 \cdot 5^3 = (4 \cdot 5)^3$ | $\sqrt[3]{4} \cdot \sqrt[3]{5} = \sqrt[3]{4 \cdot 5}$ |

**Property** Combining Radical Expressions: Products

If $\sqrt[n]{a}$ and $\sqrt[n]{b}$ are real numbers, then $\sqrt[n]{a} \cdot \sqrt[n]{b} = \sqrt[n]{ab}$.

**Problem 1** Multiplying Radical Expressions

**Can you simplify the product of the radical expressions? Explain.**

Ⓐ $\sqrt[3]{6} \cdot \sqrt{2}$

No. The indexes are different. The property above does not apply.

Ⓑ $\sqrt[3]{-4} \cdot \sqrt[3]{2}$

Yes. $\sqrt[3]{-4} \cdot \sqrt[3]{2} = \sqrt[3]{-4(2)} = \sqrt[3]{-8} = -2$.

**Plan**

What allows you to use the property for multiplying radicals? The radicals must be real numbers. The indexes must be the same.

PowerAlgebra.com | Lesson 6-2 Multiplying and Dividing Radical Expressions | 367

## 1 Interactive Learning

### Solve It!
**PURPOSE** To use sums of perfect squares to solve a problem
**PROCESS** Students may
• find the perfect squares that sum to 48.
• use trial and error by drawing and counting.

**Q** What is the factored form of 36? How does this relate to the two ways that you can divide a 36-square into smaller squares as shown? **[36 = 2 · 2 · 3 · 3 = 4 · $3^2$ = $2^2$ · 9; the factored form illustrates why a 36-square can be divided into four 3-by-3 squares or nine 2-by-2 squares. A 36-square can be divided in the two ways shown because 36 is the product of 2 squares.]**

**ANSWER** See Solve It in Answers on next page.
**CONNECT THE MATH** The Solve It is solved by finding factors and recognizing perfect squares. In the lesson, students find factors and use perfect squares to simplify radical expressions.

## 2 Guided Instruction

### Take Note

**Q** How can this property be used to simplify $\sqrt[n]{a} \cdot \sqrt[n]{b}$ when the radicals alone cannot be simplified? **[Answers may vary. Sample: You may be able to factor ab into factors of powers of a multiple of n. For example, $\sqrt[3]{4} \cdot \sqrt[3]{2} = \sqrt[3]{8} = \sqrt[3]{2^3} = 2$.]**

### Problem 1

**Q** Do the radicands also need to be the same to use the property for multiplying radicals? Explain. **[No; only the indexes need to be the same.]**

## 6-2 Preparing to Teach

**BIG idea Equivalence** UbD

**ESSENTIAL UNDERSTANDINGS**
• If $\sqrt[n]{a}$ and $\sqrt[n]{b}$ are real numbers, then $\sqrt[n]{a} \cdot \sqrt[n]{b} = \sqrt[n]{ab}$.
• A radical expression can be simplified when the exponent of one factor of the radicand is a multiple of the radical's index.
• The product of powers that have the same exponent can be simplified.
• The product of radicals that have the same index can be simplified.

### Math Background
The fact that you can simplify a radical expression when the exponent of one factor of the radicand is a multiple of the radical's index is general and may be difficult to understand. Restate it in terms of the square root: You can simplify a square root expression if the exponent of a factor in the radicand is a multiple of 2.

For example, the expression $\sqrt{5^4 \cdot 7}$ has the factor $5^4$ in the radicand. Four is a multiple of 2, so the radicand can be simplified:

$\sqrt{5^4 \cdot 7} = 5^2\sqrt{7} = 25\sqrt{7}$.

In general, a radical expression is considered simplified if the radicand cannot be reduced.

This lesson focuses on the properties for multiplying and dividing radicals. These properties apply only to real numbers, as shown in the following proof by contradiction:

• Assume the product property holds true for complex numbers.
• Thus $i \cdot i = \sqrt{-1} \cdot \sqrt{-1} = \sqrt{-1 \cdot -1} = \sqrt{1} = 1$.
• However, $i \cdot i = -1$, which is a contradiction.
• The property does not hold true for complex numbers.

Note that absolute value symbols are generally needed when simplifying roots with even-numbered indexes, as shown in Lesson 6-1.

### PowerAlgebra.com

## 1 Interactive Learning

**Solve It!**
Step out how to solve the Problem with helpful hints and an online question. Other questions are listed above in Interactive Learning.

## Got It?

Q If the radicands are the same, is that enough to simplify a product using the Combining Radicals: Products property? Explain. **[You can only simplify a product when the indexes are also the same and both radicands are real. Otherwise you cannot use the property for multiplying radicals.]**

## Problem 2

Q When can you simplify a cubic radical? **[when the radicand contains perfect cube factors]**

## Got It?

Q What will you do first? **[Answers may vary. Sample: Factor the radicand and write it in terms of all the perfect cubes.]**

## Problem 3

Q Solve $\sqrt{2x^{12}} \cdot \sqrt{9x^3}$ in the following two ways:
**a.** Simplify, then multiply.
**b.** Multiply, then simplify.
What is the solution in each case?
**[$3x^7\sqrt{2x}$; both methods give the same answer.]**

## Got It?                           EXTENSION

Q What is the simplest form of $\sqrt[3]{45x^5y^3} \cdot \sqrt[3]{35xy^4}$?
**[$x^2y^2\sqrt[3]{1575y}$]**

---

 **Got It?** **1.** Can you simplify the product of the radical expressions? Explain.
**a.** $\sqrt[4]{7} \cdot \sqrt[5]{7}$          **b.** $\sqrt[5]{-5} \cdot \sqrt[5]{-2}$

If the radicand of $\sqrt[n]{a}$ has a perfect $n$th power among its factors, you can *reduce* the radical. If you reduce a radical as much as possible, the radical is in **simplest form**. For example, consider $\sqrt{24}$ and $\sqrt[3]{24}$.

$$\sqrt{24} = \sqrt{4 \cdot 6} = \sqrt{2^2 \cdot 6} = \sqrt{2^2} \cdot \sqrt{6} = 2\sqrt{6} \qquad 2\sqrt{6} \text{ is in simplest form.}$$

$$\sqrt[3]{24} = \sqrt[3]{8 \cdot 3} = \sqrt[3]{2^3 \cdot 3} = \sqrt[3]{2^3} \cdot \sqrt[3]{3} = 2\sqrt[3]{3} \qquad 2\sqrt[3]{3} \text{ is in simplest form.}$$

 **Problem 2** Simplifying a Radical Expression

**What is the simplest form of $\sqrt[3]{54x^5}$ ?**

**Think**
How do you know when you are done simplifying?
You are done when the radicand contains no perfect cube factors.

$$\sqrt[3]{54x^5} = \sqrt[3]{3^3 \cdot 2 \cdot x^2 \cdot x^3} \qquad \text{Find all perfect cube factors.}$$
$$= \sqrt[3]{3^3x^3} \cdot \sqrt[3]{2x^2} \qquad \sqrt[n]{ab} = \sqrt[n]{a} \cdot \sqrt[n]{b}$$
$$= 3x\sqrt[3]{2x^2} \qquad \text{Simplify.}$$

 **Got It?** **2.** What is the simplest form of $\sqrt[3]{128x^7}$?

Problem 2 involves simplifying a cube root, so absolute value symbols are not needed. Remember that to combine $\sqrt[n]{a}$ and $\sqrt[n]{b}$ by multiplication, both radical expressions must be real numbers.

 **Problem 3** Simplifying a Product

**What is the simplest form of $\sqrt{72x^3y^2} \cdot \sqrt{10xy^3}$?**

**Think**                  **Write**

You need to multiply the radicands and find the perfect square factors.

$$\sqrt{72x^3y^2} \cdot \sqrt{10xy^3} = \sqrt{(72x^3y^2)(10xy^3)}$$
$$= \sqrt{720x^4y^5}$$
$$= \sqrt{12^2(5)(x^2)^2(y^2)^2y}$$
$$= \sqrt{12^2(x^2)^2(y^2)^2} \cdot \sqrt{5y}$$

Now find square roots. Since $\sqrt{72x^3y^2}$ and $\sqrt{10xy^3}$ must be real numbers, $x$ and $y$ are nonnegative, so no absolute value symbols are needed.

$$= 12|x^2y^2| \cdot \sqrt{5y}$$
$$= 12x^2y^2\sqrt{5y}$$

The simplest form is $12x^2y^2\sqrt{5y}$.

 **Got It?** **3.** What is the simplest form of $\sqrt{45x^5y^3} \cdot \sqrt{35xy^4}$?

---

# Answers

## Solve It!
Answers may vary. Sample: The number of different ways an $n$-square can be cut is the number of different divisors of $\sqrt{n}$, excluding 1 and $\sqrt{n}$.

## Got It?
**1. a.** No; the indexes are different.
   **b.** Yes; $\sqrt[5]{10}$
**2.** $4x^2\sqrt[3]{2x}$
**3.** $15x^3y^3\sqrt{7y}$
**4. a.** $5|x|$
   **b.** yes; $\dfrac{3x^2\sqrt{2x}}{x\sqrt{2x}} = 3x$

---

**PowerAlgebra.com**

## 2 Guided Instruction

Each Problem is worked out and supported online.

**Problem 1**
Multiplying Radical Expressions

**Alternative Problem 1**
Multiplying Radical Expressions
*Animated*

**Problem 2**
Simplifying a Radical Expression

**Problem 3**
Simplifying a Product
*Animated*

**Problem 4**
Dividing Radical Expressions

**Problem 5**
Rationalizing the Denominator
*Animated*

**Support in Algebra 2 Companion**
• Vocabulary
• Key Concepts
• Got It?

Since you define division in terms of multiplication, you can extend the property for multiplying radical expressions. If the indexes are the same, you can write a quotient of roots as a root of a quotient.

| Multiplying | Dividing |
|---|---|
| $\sqrt{2} \cdot \sqrt{3} = \sqrt{2 \cdot 3}$ | $\dfrac{\sqrt{2}}{\sqrt{3}} = \sqrt{\dfrac{2}{3}}$ |
| $\sqrt[3]{4} \cdot \sqrt[3]{5} = \sqrt[3]{4 \cdot 5}$ | $\dfrac{\sqrt[3]{4}}{\sqrt[3]{5}} = \sqrt[3]{\dfrac{4}{5}}$ |

 take note

**Property  Combining Radical Expressions: Quotients**

If $\sqrt[n]{a}$ and $\sqrt[n]{b}$ are real numbers and $b \neq 0$, then $\dfrac{\sqrt[n]{a}}{\sqrt[n]{b}} = \sqrt[n]{\dfrac{a}{b}}$.

 **Problem 4  Dividing Radical Expressions**

What is the simplest form of the quotient?

**Think**

Do you need to include absolute value symbols?
No. Both the divisor and dividend already require that $x$ be nonnegative.

Ⓐ $\dfrac{\sqrt{18x^5}}{\sqrt{2x^3}}$

$\dfrac{\sqrt{18x^5}}{\sqrt{2x^3}} = \sqrt{\dfrac{18x^5}{2x^3}}$

$= \sqrt{9x^2}$

$= 3x$

Ⓑ $\dfrac{\sqrt[3]{162y^5}}{\sqrt[3]{3y^2}}$

$\dfrac{\sqrt[3]{162y^5}}{\sqrt[3]{3y^2}} = \sqrt[3]{\dfrac{162y^5}{3y^2}}$

$= \sqrt[3]{54y^3}$

$= \sqrt[3]{27y^3} \cdot \sqrt[3]{2}$

$= \sqrt[3]{3^3 y^3} \cdot \sqrt[3]{2}$

$= 3y\sqrt[3]{2}$

 **Got It?  4. a.** What is the simplest form of $\dfrac{\sqrt{50x^6}}{2x^4}$?

**b. Reasoning** Can you simplify the expression in Problem 4(a) by first simplifying $\sqrt{18x^5}$ and $\sqrt{2x^3}$? Explain.

Another way to simplify a radical expression is to **rationalize the denominator**. You rewrite the expression so that there are no radicals in any denominator and no denominator in any radical.

Multiply by 1.

$\dfrac{1}{\sqrt{2}} = \dfrac{1}{\sqrt{2}}\left(\dfrac{\sqrt{2}}{\sqrt{2}}\right) = \dfrac{\sqrt{2}}{2}$  The product of $\sqrt{2}$ and itself is a rational number, 2.

**Take Note**

**Q** How is the property for dividing radicals like the property for multiplying radicals? How are they different?  **[Answers may vary. Sample: Both properties combine the two radicands under one radical. For division, one radicand is divided by the other; for multiplication, the radicands are multiplied together.]**

**Problem 4**

**Q** What are the possible values for $x$ in 4A? Why?  **[The value of $x$ must be greater than zero; a value of 0 would result in an undefined number, and a negative value would result in an imaginary numerator and denominator.]**

**Got It?**

**Q** How do a radical and its simplest form compare?  **[They are equivalent.]**

**Q** Do you need to show absolute value in your answer for 4a? Explain.  **[Yes. The index is even, the exponents under the radical are even and the simplified exponent is odd.]**

## Additional Problems

**1.** Can you simplify the product $\sqrt[4]{125} \cdot \sqrt[4]{405}$? Explain.
**ANSWER** Yes; the indexes are the same. 15

**2.** What is the simplest form of $\sqrt[3]{135x^5}$?
**ANSWER** $3x\sqrt[3]{5x^2}$

**3.** What is the simplest form of $\sqrt{48x^5y^2} \cdot \sqrt{50x^2y^4}$?
**ANSWER** $20x^3|y^3|\sqrt{6x}$

**4.** What is the simplest form of $\dfrac{\sqrt[3]{189x^7}}{\sqrt[3]{7x^2}}$?
**ANSWER** $3x\sqrt[3]{x^2}$

**5.** What is the simplest form of $\sqrt[3]{\dfrac{4x^4}{32yz^3}}$?
**ANSWER** $\dfrac{x\sqrt[3]{xy^2}}{2yz}$

## Problem 5

**Q** What is an advantage to writing the numerator and denominator using prime factors? **[You can determine what is needed to get a perfect cube.]**

**Q** In the problem, why can you multiply the numerator and denominator by $\sqrt[3]{2 \cdot 3^2 yz^2}$ without changing the value of the fraction? **[You are multiplying by a factor of 1.]**

### Got It?

**Q** What factor do you multiply the numerator and denominator by to rationalize the denominator? Explain. **[$\sqrt[3]{5^2 y}$; this will make the denominator a perfect cube.]**

# 3 Lesson Check

### Do you know HOW?
• For Exercise 3, have students circle the index on each term as a reminder that indexes must be the same.

### Do you UNDERSTAND?
• For Exercise 7, have students factor the radicand using factors that are perfect cubes.
• For Exercise 8, review with students what constitutes a real number.

### Close

**Q** How do you know if your radical expression is simplified? **[The radical expression contains no radicand with a perfect *n*th power other than 1, there is no radical in the denominator, and there is no denominator in any radical.]**

---

 **Problem 5** Rationalizing the Denominator

**Multiple Choice** What is the simplest form of $\sqrt[3]{\dfrac{5x^2}{12y^2z}}$?

A $\dfrac{\sqrt[3]{90x^2yz^2}}{6yz}$  B $\dfrac{\sqrt[3]{5x^2}}{\sqrt[3]{12y^2z}}$  C $\dfrac{5\sqrt[3]{x^2yz^2}}{yz}$  D $5\sqrt[3]{x^2z}$

**How do you choose what to multiply by?** Choose a cube root with a radicand that will make each factor of the radicand in the denominator a perfect cube.

$$\sqrt[3]{\dfrac{5x^2}{12y^2z}} = \dfrac{\sqrt[3]{5x^2}}{\sqrt[3]{2^2 \cdot 3y^2z}}$$
The radicand in the denominator needs 2, $3^2$, $y$, and $z^2$ to make the factors perfect cubes.

$$= \dfrac{\sqrt[3]{5x^2}}{\sqrt[3]{2^2 \cdot 3y^2z}} \cdot \dfrac{\sqrt[3]{2 \cdot 3^2 yz^2}}{\sqrt[3]{2 \cdot 3^2 yz^2}}$$
Multiply the numerator and denominator by $\sqrt[3]{2 \cdot 3^2 yz^2}$.

$$= \dfrac{\sqrt[3]{90x^2yz^2}}{\sqrt[3]{2^3 \cdot 3^3 y^3 z^3}}$$

$$= \dfrac{\sqrt[3]{90x^2yz^2}}{2 \cdot 3yz}$$
Simplify.

$$= \dfrac{\sqrt[3]{90x^2yz^2}}{6yz}$$

The correct answer is A.

**Got It?** **5. a.** What is the simplest form of $\dfrac{\sqrt[3]{7x}}{\sqrt[3]{5y^2}}$?

**b. Reasoning** Which choice in Problem 5 could be eliminated immediately? Explain your reasoning.

---

### ✓ Lesson Check

**Do you know HOW?**

Multiply, if possible. Then simplify.

1. $\sqrt{2} \cdot \sqrt{5}$

2. $\sqrt[3]{-27} \cdot \sqrt[3]{4}$

3. $\sqrt[3]{2} \cdot \sqrt[2]{7}$

4. $\sqrt{3} \cdot \sqrt{-4}$

Divide and simplify.

5. $\dfrac{\sqrt[3]{15x^2}}{\sqrt[3]{5x}}$

6. $\dfrac{\sqrt{21x^{10}}}{\sqrt{7x^5}}$

**Do you UNDERSTAND?**

7. **Vocabulary** Write the simplest form of $\sqrt[3]{32x^4}$.

8. **Reasoning** For what values of $x$ is $\sqrt{-4x^3}$ real? Justify your reasoning.

9. **Error Analysis** Explain the error in this simplification of radical expressions.

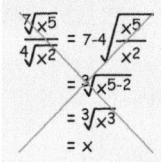

$$\dfrac{\sqrt[7]{x^5}}{\sqrt[4]{x^2}} = 7 - 4\sqrt{\dfrac{x^5}{x^2}}$$
$$= \sqrt[3]{x^{5-2}}$$
$$= \sqrt[3]{x^3}$$
$$= x$$

---

## Answers

### Got It? (continued)

**5. a.** $\dfrac{\sqrt[3]{175xy}}{5y}$

**b.** D; there is no $y$ in the expression.

### Lesson Check

1. $\sqrt{10}$

2. $-3\sqrt[3]{4}$

3. Cannot be simplified; the indexes are different.

4. No real solutions; $\sqrt{-4}$ is not a real number.

5. $\sqrt[3]{3x}$

6. $x^2\sqrt{3x}$

7. $2x\sqrt[3]{4x}$

8. $x \le 0$; for $x \le 0$, $-4x^3 \ge 0$ and $\sqrt{-4x^3}$ is real.

9. error in line 1: $\dfrac{\sqrt[7]{x^5}}{\sqrt[4]{x^2}} \ne 7 - 4\sqrt{\dfrac{x^5}{x^2}}$

## Practice and Problem-Solving Exercises

 **Practice**

**Multiply, if possible. Then simplify.**

See Problem 1.

**10.** $\sqrt{8} \cdot \sqrt{32}$     **11.** $\sqrt[3]{4} \cdot \sqrt[3]{16}$     **12.** $\sqrt[3]{9} \cdot \sqrt[3]{-81}$

**13.** $\sqrt[4]{8} \cdot \sqrt[3]{32}$     **14.** $\sqrt{-5} \cdot \sqrt{5}$     **15.** $\sqrt[3]{-5} \cdot \sqrt[3]{-25}$

**16.** $\sqrt[3]{9} \cdot \sqrt[3]{-24}$     **17.** $\sqrt[3]{-12} \cdot \sqrt[3]{-18}$     **18.** $\sqrt{50} \cdot \sqrt{75}$

**Simplify.**

See Problem 2.

**19.** $\sqrt{20x^3}$     **20.** $\sqrt[3]{81x^3}$     **21.** $\sqrt{50x^5}$

**22.** $\sqrt[3]{32a^5}$     **23.** $\sqrt[3]{54y^{10}}$     **24.** $\sqrt{200a^6b^7}$

**25.** $\sqrt[3]{-250x^6y^5}$     **26.** $\sqrt[4]{64x^3y^6}$     **27.** $\sqrt[5]{-32x^6y^7}$

**Multiply and simplify.**

See Problem 3.

**28.** $\sqrt[3]{6} \cdot \sqrt[3]{16}$     **29.** $\sqrt{8y^5} \cdot \sqrt{40y^2}$     **30.** $\sqrt{8x^5} \cdot \sqrt{3x}$

**31.** $4\sqrt{2x} \cdot 5\sqrt{6xy^2}$     **32.** $3\sqrt[3]{5y^3} \cdot 2\sqrt[3]{50y^4}$     **33.** $-\sqrt[3]{2x^2y^2} \cdot 2\sqrt[3]{15x^5y}$

**34.** $\sqrt[4]{81x^5y^4} \cdot \sqrt[4]{32x^3y}$     **35.** $2\sqrt[3]{2xy^2} \cdot \sqrt[3]{4x^2y^5}$     **36.** $3\sqrt[4]{18a^9} \cdot \sqrt[4]{6ab^2}$

**Divide and simplify.**

See Problem 4.

**37.** $\dfrac{\sqrt{500}}{\sqrt{5}}$     **38.** $\dfrac{\sqrt{48x^3}}{\sqrt{3xy^2}}$     **39.** $\dfrac{\sqrt{56x^5y^5}}{\sqrt{7xy}}$

**40.** $\dfrac{\sqrt[3]{250x^7y^3}}{\sqrt[3]{2x^2y}}$     **41.** $\dfrac{\sqrt[3]{48x^3y^2}}{\sqrt[3]{6x^4y}}$     **42.** $\dfrac{\sqrt{20ab}}{\sqrt{45a^2b^3}}$

**Rationalize the denominator of each expression.**

See Problem 5.

**43.** $\dfrac{\sqrt{x}}{\sqrt{2}}$     **44.** $\dfrac{\sqrt{5}}{\sqrt{8x}}$     **45.** $\dfrac{\sqrt[3]{x}}{\sqrt[3]{2}}$

**46.** $\sqrt[3]{\dfrac{5}{3x}}$     **47.** $\dfrac{\sqrt[4]{2}}{\sqrt[4]{5}}$     **48.** $\dfrac{15\sqrt{60x^5}}{3\sqrt{12x}}$

**49.** $\dfrac{\sqrt{3xy^2}}{\sqrt{5xy^3}}$     **50.** $\dfrac{\sqrt{5x^4y}}{\sqrt{2x^2y^3}}$     **51.** $\dfrac{\sqrt[3]{12ab^3c^2}}{\sqrt[3]{10a^3bc}}$

**B Apply**

**52. Think About a Plan** The formula $t = \sqrt{\dfrac{2s}{a}}$ shows the time $t$ that any vehicle takes to travel a distance $s$ at a constant acceleration $a$, starting from rest. What is the difference in time between a car accelerating at $16 \text{ m/s}^2$ and one accelerating at $25 \text{ m/s}^2$ for a distance of 200 m?

- What is the time that a car accelerating at $16 \text{ m/s}^2$ takes to travel 200 m?
- What is the time that a car accelerating at $25 \text{ m/s}^2$ takes to travel 200 m?

**53. Geometry** The base of a triangle is $\sqrt{18}$ cm and its height is $\sqrt{8}$ cm. Find its area.

---

## 4 Practice

**ASSIGNMENT GUIDE**

Basic: 10–51 all, 52–55, 58–64 even, 71

Average: 11–51 odd, 52–75

Advanced: 11–51 odd, 52–79

Standardized Test Prep: 80–84

Mixed Review: 85–98

**Reasoning** exercises have blue headings.

**Applications** exercises have red headings.

**EXERCISE 55:** Use the Think About a Plan worksheet in the **Practice and Problem Solving Workbook** (also available in the Teaching Resources in print and online) to further support students' development in becoming independent learners.

**HOMEWORK QUICK CHECK**

To check students' understanding of key skills and concepts, go over Exercises 31, 49, 52, 55, and 71.

---

## Practice and Problem-Solving Exercises

**10.** 16

**11.** 4

**12.** −9

**13.** not possible

**14.** $5i$

**15.** 5

**16.** −6

**17.** 6

**18.** $25\sqrt{6}$

**19.** $2x\sqrt{5x}$

**20.** $3x\sqrt[3]{3}$

**21.** $5x^2\sqrt{2x}$

**22.** $2a\sqrt[3]{4a^2}$

**23.** $3y^3\sqrt[3]{2y}$

**24.** $10|a^3|b^3\sqrt{2b}$

**25.** $-5x^2y\sqrt[3]{2y^2}$

**26.** $2|y|\sqrt[4]{4x^3y^2}$

**27.** $-2xy\sqrt[5]{xy^2}$

**28.** $2\sqrt[3]{12}$

**29.** $8y^3\sqrt{5y}$

**30.** $2x^3\sqrt{6}$

**31.** $40x|y|\sqrt{3}$

**32.** $30y^2\sqrt[3]{2y}$

**33.** $-2x^2y\sqrt[3]{30x}$

**34.** $6x^2y\sqrt[4]{2y}$

**35.** $4\,xy^2\sqrt[3]{y}$

**36.** $3a^2\sqrt[4]{108a^2b^2}$

**37.** 10

**38.** $\dfrac{4x}{|y|}$

**39.** $2x^2y^2\sqrt{2}$

**40.** $5x\sqrt[3]{x^2y^2}$

**41.** $\dfrac{2\sqrt[3]{x^2y}}{x}$

**42.** $\dfrac{2\sqrt{a}}{3ab}$

**43.** $\dfrac{\sqrt{2x}}{2}$

**44.** $\dfrac{\sqrt{10x}}{4x}$

**45.** $\dfrac{\sqrt[3]{4x}}{2}$

**46.** $\dfrac{\sqrt[3]{45x^2}}{3x}$

**47.** $\dfrac{\sqrt[4]{250}}{5}$

**48.** $5x^2\sqrt{5}$

**49.** $\dfrac{\sqrt{15y}}{5y}$

**50.** $\dfrac{|x|\sqrt{10}}{y}$

**51.** $\dfrac{\sqrt[3]{150ab^2c}}{5a}$

**52.** 1 s

**53.** 6 cm²

# Answers

## Practice and Problem-Solving Exercises
(continued)

**54.** $v = \dfrac{\sqrt{Fmr}}{m}$

**55.** about 212 mi/h

**56. a.** $\dfrac{\sqrt{6} + 3}{15}$

  **b.** $\dfrac{\sqrt{6} + 3}{15}$

  **c.** Answers may vary. Sample: first simplify the denominator. Since $\sqrt{98} = \sqrt{2(49)} = 7\sqrt{2}$, to rationalize the denominator, multiply the fraction by $\dfrac{\sqrt{2}}{\sqrt{2}}$. This yields $\dfrac{\sqrt{2(2)} + \sqrt{3(2)}}{7\sqrt{2(2)}} = \dfrac{2 + \sqrt{6}}{14}$.

**57.** $5\sqrt{10}$

**58.** $4\sqrt[3]{5}$

**59.** $3x^6y^5\sqrt{2y}$

**60.** $20x^2y^3\sqrt{y}$

**61.** $10 + 7\sqrt{2}$

**62.** $5 + 5\sqrt{3}$

**63.** $\dfrac{|x|\sqrt{10y}}{2y^2}$

**64.** $\dfrac{5\sqrt{14x}}{21x}$

**65.** $\dfrac{\sqrt[3]{3x^2}}{3x}$

**66.** $\dfrac{2\sqrt[3]{25x}}{x}$

**67.** $\dfrac{\sqrt[3]{2xy^2}}{xy}$

**68.** $\dfrac{\sqrt{33x}}{-4x}$

**69.** $4$ g/cm$^3$

**70.** For some values; it is easy to see that the equation is true if $x = 0$ or $x = 1$, but when $x < 0$, $\sqrt{x^3}$ is not a real number and $\sqrt[3]{x^2}$ is.

**71.** Check students' work.

**72.** A product of two square roots can be simplified in this way only if the square roots are real numbers. $\sqrt{-2}$ and $\sqrt{-8}$ are not real numbers.

**73.** always

**74.** sometimes

**75.** sometimes

**76.** $2xy$

**77.** $2\sqrt{5}$

**78.** $\dfrac{\sqrt[6]{x^4y^3}}{y}$

**79.** $a = -2c,\ b = -6d$

---

**54. Physics** The formula $F = \dfrac{mv^2}{r}$ gives the centripetal force $F$ of an object of mass $m$ moving along a circle of radius $r$, where $v$ is the tangential velocity of the object. Solve the formula for $v$. Rationalize the denominator.

**55. Satellites** The circular velocity $v$ in miles per hour of a satellite orbiting Earth is given by the formula $v = \sqrt{\dfrac{1.24 \times 10^{12}}{r}}$, where $r$ is the distance in miles from the satellite to the center of the Earth. How much greater is the velocity of a satellite orbiting at an altitude of 100 mi than the velocity of a satellite orbiting at an altitude of 200 mi? (The radius of the Earth is 3950 mi.)

**56. a.** Simplify $\dfrac{\sqrt{2} + \sqrt{3}}{\sqrt{75}}$ by multiplying the numerator and denominator by $\sqrt{75}$.

  **b.** Simplify the expression in (a) by multiplying by $\sqrt{3}$ instead of $\sqrt{75}$.

  **c.** Explain how you would simplify $\dfrac{\sqrt{2} + \sqrt{3}}{\sqrt{98}}$.

**Simplify each expression. Rationalize all denominators.**

**57.** $\sqrt{5} \cdot \sqrt{50}$

**58.** $\sqrt[3]{4} \cdot \sqrt[3]{80}$

**59.** $\sqrt{x^5y^5} \cdot 3\sqrt{2x^7y^6}$

**60.** $5\sqrt{2xy^6} \cdot 2\sqrt{2x^3y}$

**61.** $\sqrt{2}(\sqrt{50} + 7)$

**62.** $\sqrt{5}(\sqrt{5} + \sqrt{15})$

**63.** $\dfrac{\sqrt{5x^4}}{\sqrt{2x^2y^3}}$

**64.** $\dfrac{5\sqrt{2}}{3\sqrt{7x}}$

**65.** $\dfrac{1}{\sqrt[3]{9x}}$

**66.** $\dfrac{10}{\sqrt[3]{5x^2}}$

**67.** $\dfrac{\sqrt[3]{14}}{\sqrt[3]{7x^2y}}$

**68.** $\dfrac{3\sqrt{11x^3y}}{-2\sqrt{12x^4y}}$

**69. Physics** The mass $m$ of an object is $\sqrt{80}$ g and its volume $V$ is $\sqrt{5}$ cm$^3$. Use the formula $D = \dfrac{m}{V}$ to find the density $D$ of the object.

**70. Writing** Does $\sqrt{x^3} = \sqrt[3]{x^2}$ for *all, some,* or *no* values of $x$? Explain.

**71. Open-Ended** Of the equivalent expressions $\sqrt{\dfrac{2}{3}}, \dfrac{\sqrt{2}}{\sqrt{3}}$ and $\dfrac{\sqrt{6}}{3}$, which do you prefer to use for finding a decimal approximation with a calculator? Justify your reasoning.

**72. Error Analysis** Explain the error in this simplification of radical expressions.

$\sqrt{-2} \cdot \sqrt{-8} = \sqrt{-2(-8)} = \sqrt{16} = 4$

**Determine whether each expression is *always, sometimes,* or *never* a real number. Assume that $x$ can be any real number.**

**73.** $\sqrt[3]{-x^2}$

**74.** $\sqrt{-x^2}$

**75.** $\sqrt{-x}$

**Challenge**

**Simplify each expression. Rationalize all denominators.**

**76.** $\sqrt{\sqrt{16x^4y^4}}$

**77.** $\sqrt{\sqrt[3]{8000}}$

**78.** $\sqrt[6]{\dfrac{y^{-3}}{x^{-4}}}$

**79. Reasoning** When $\sqrt{x^ay^b}$ is simplified, the result is $\dfrac{1}{x^cy^{3d}}$, where $c$ and $d$ are positive integers. Express $a$ in terms of $c$, and $b$ in terms of $d$.

## Standardized Test Prep

**SAT/ACT**

**80.** What is the simplified form of the expression $\dfrac{3}{\sqrt{18xy^2}}$ if $x$ and $y$ are positive?

Ⓐ $\dfrac{\sqrt{2x}}{2xy}$     Ⓑ $\dfrac{\sqrt{2y}}{2xy}$     Ⓒ $\dfrac{\sqrt{54xy^2}}{2xy}$     Ⓓ $\dfrac{\sqrt{27xy^2}}{2xy}$

**81.** What are the solutions, in simplest form, of the quadratic equation $3x^2 + 6x - 5 = 0$?

Ⓕ $\dfrac{-6 \pm \sqrt{96}}{6}$     Ⓖ $\dfrac{-6 \pm i\sqrt{24}}{6}$     Ⓗ $\dfrac{-3 \pm 2\sqrt{6}}{3}$     Ⓘ $\dfrac{-3 \pm i\sqrt{6}}{3}$

**82.** Which inequality is shown by the graph at the right?

Ⓐ $y \geq \frac{2}{3}|x - 1| - 2$       Ⓒ $y \geq \frac{3}{2}|x - 1| - 2$

Ⓑ $y \geq \frac{2}{3}|x - 2| - 1$       Ⓓ $y \geq \left|\frac{2}{3}x - 1\right| - 2$

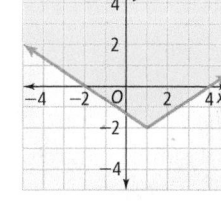

**83.** A triangle has the dimensions shown below.

What is the height of a triangle with equal area but a base of 36?

Ⓕ $\frac{h}{3}$      Ⓖ $\frac{2h}{3}$      Ⓗ $2h$      Ⓘ $3h$

**Short Response**

**84.** Find the axis of symmetry of the graph of the function $y = -2x^2 - 5x + 4$. Show your work.

## Mixed Review

Simplify each radical expression. Use absolute value symbols when needed.    ◀ See Lesson 6-1.

**85.** $\sqrt{121a^{90}}$      **86.** $\sqrt{81c^{48}d^{64}}$      **87.** $\sqrt[3]{64a^{81}}$      **88.** $\sqrt[5]{32y^{25}}$

Divide using synthetic division.    ◀ See Lesson 5-4.

**89.** $(y^3 - 64) \div (y + 4)$          **90.** $(6a^3 + a^2 - a + 4) \div (a + 1)$

Complete each square.    ◀ See Lesson 4-6.

**91.** $x^2 + 10x + \blacksquare$      **92.** $x^2 - 10x + \blacksquare$      **93.** $x^2 + 11x + \blacksquare$      **94.** $x^2 - 11x + \blacksquare$

**Get Ready!**    To prepare for Lesson 6-3, do Exercises 95–98.

Write each quotient as a complex number in the form $a \pm bi$.    ◀ See Lesson 4-8.

**95.** $\dfrac{2}{3 - i}$      **96.** $\dfrac{5}{2 + 3i}$      **97.** $\dfrac{4}{4 + i}$      **98.** $\dfrac{-1}{7 - 5i}$

---

## Standardized Test Prep

**80.** A

**81.** H

**82.** A

**83.** F

**84.** [2] $x = \dfrac{-b}{2a} = \dfrac{-5}{4}$

[1] correct answer, but without work shown

## Mixed Review

**85.** $11|a^{45}|$

**86.** $9c^{24}d^{32}$

**87.** $4a^{27}$

**88.** $2y^5$

**89.** $y^2 - 4y + 16, R -128$

**90.** $6a^2 - 5a + 4$

**91.** 25

**92.** 25

**93.** $\dfrac{121}{4}$

**94.** $\dfrac{121}{4}$

**95.** $\dfrac{3}{5} + \dfrac{1}{5}i$

**96.** $\dfrac{10}{13} - \dfrac{15}{13}i$

**97.** $\dfrac{16}{17} - \dfrac{4}{17}i$

**98.** $\dfrac{-7}{74} - \dfrac{5}{74}i$

# Differentiated Remediation

## Additional Instructional Support

### Algebra 2 Companion

Students can use the **Algebra 2 Companion** worktext (4 pages) as you teach the lesson. Use the Companion to support

- New Vocabulary
- Key Concepts
- Got It for each Problem
- Lesson Check

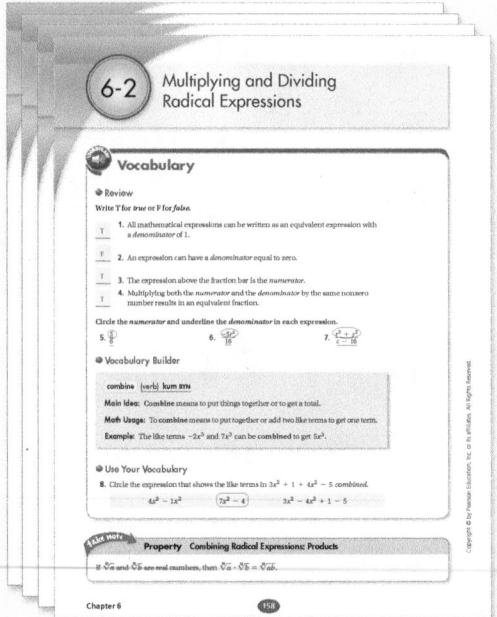

### ELL Support

**Focus on Language** Write the following radical expression on the board: $\frac{\sqrt[3]{12x}}{\sqrt[3]{4y}}$.

Have volunteers come up and label each of the following as you call them out:
- radicals
- radicands
- indexes
- numerator
- denominator
- variables

Practice using the vocabulary. Ask, "When can you use the properties for multiplying and dividing *radicals*?" [When the *indexes* are the same and the *radicals* are real.]

## 5 Assess & Remediate

### Lesson Quiz

**1.** Can you simplify the product $\sqrt[4]{64} \cdot \sqrt[4]{32}$? Explain.

**2.** What is the simplest form of $\sqrt[4]{162x^6}$?

**3.** What is the simplest form of $\sqrt{54x^4y^3} \cdot \sqrt{72xy^6}$?

**4.** What is the simplest form of $\frac{\sqrt{64x^7}}{\sqrt{4x^3}}$?

**5.** **Do you UNDERSTAND?** What is the simplest form of $\sqrt[3]{\frac{7x^2}{15yz^2}}$?

### ANSWERS TO LESSON QUIZ

**1.** Yes, the indexes are the same. $4\sqrt[4]{8}$

**2.** $3|x| \sqrt[4]{2x^2}$

**3.** $36x^2y^4\sqrt{3xy}$

**4.** $4x^2$

**5.** $\frac{\sqrt[3]{1575x^2y^2z}}{15yz}$

### PRESCRIPTION FOR REMEDIATION

Use the student work on the Lesson Quiz to prescribe a differentiated review assignment:

| Points | Differentiated Remediation |
|--------|---------------------------|
| 0–2 | Intervention |
| 3–4 | On-level |
| 5 | Extension |

**PowerAlgebra.com**

### 5 Assess & Remediate

Assign the Lesson Quiz. Appropriate intervention, practice, or enrichment is automatically generated based on student performance.

## Intervention

- **Reteaching** (2 pages) Provides reteaching and practice exercises for the key lesson concepts. Use with struggling students or absent students.

- **English Language Learner Support** Helps students develop and reinforce mathematical vocabulary and key concepts.

### All-in-One Resources/Online
**Reteaching**

**6-2 Reteaching**
Multiplying and Dividing Radical Expressions

### All-in-One Resources/Online
**English Language Learner Support**

**6-2 ELL Support**
Multiplying and Dividing Radical Expressions

# Differentiated Remediation *continued*

## On-Level

- **Practice** (2 pages) Provides extra practice for each lesson. For simpler practice exercises, use the Form K Practice pages found in the All-in-One Teaching Resources and online.

- **Think About a Plan** Helps students develop specific problem-solving skills and strategies by providing scaffolded guiding questions.

- **Standardized Test Prep** Focuses on all major exercises, all major question types, and helps students prepare for the high-stakes assessments.

## Extension

- **Enrichment** Provides students with interesting problems and activities that extend the concepts of the lesson.

- **Activities, Games, and Puzzles** Worksheets that can be used for concepts development, enrichment, and for fun!

### Practice and Problem Solving Wkbk/All-in-One Resources/Online
**Practice page 1**

### Practice and Problem Solving Wkbk/All-in-One Resources/Online
**Practice page 2**

### All-in-One Resources/Online
**Enrichment**

### Practice and Problem Solving Wkbk/All-in-One Resources/Online
**Think About a Plan**

### Practice and Problem Solving Wkbk/All-in-One Resources/Online
**Standardized Test Prep**

### Online Teacher Resource Center
**Activities, Games, and Puzzles**

# 1 Interactive Learning

## Solve It!

**PURPOSE** To find areas and perimeters of triangles to introduce a common use of radical expressions

**PROCESS** Students may

- sketch the triangles to scale and continue the pattern, calculating area and perimeter.
- know that an isosceles right triangle has a base angle of 45 degrees, so 8 triangles encircle $O$.
- find a pattern of hypotenuse lengths and areas of each triangle and use it to find the area of the entire figure.

---

**FACILITATE**

**Q** Is there a pattern for the hypotenuse of an isosceles right triangle with side $s$? **[Yes; the length of the hypotenuse is $s\sqrt{2}$.]**

**Q** How can you calculate the perimeter of the figure? **[Sketch the figure and add the lengths of the segments on the figure's exterior.]**

---

**ANSWER** See Solve It in Answers on next page.
**CONNECT THE MATH** The Solve It is solved using formulas for area and perimeter. In the lesson students add and subtract radical expressions, simplifying before adding or subtracting.

# 2 Guided Instruction

## Take Note

Combining like terms is similar to combining like radicals. For example, $2x^3 + 3x^3 = 5x^3$ is analogous to $2\sqrt[3]{x} + 3\sqrt[3]{x} = 5\sqrt[3]{x}$.

---

## 6-3 Binomial Radical Expressions

**Objective** To add and subtract radical expressions

**Lesson Vocabulary**
- like radicals

**Like radicals** are radical expressions that have the same index and radicand.

**Essential Understanding** You can combine like radicals using properties of real numbers.

Here is how you can combine like radicals using the Distributive Property.

| Like Radicals With Numbers | Like Radicals With Variables |
|---|---|
| $\sqrt{2} + 3\sqrt{2} = 4\sqrt{2}$ | $\sqrt{5xy} + 8\sqrt{5xy} = 9\sqrt{5xy}$ |
| $\sqrt[3]{7} - 5\sqrt[3]{7} = -4\sqrt[3]{7}$ | $\sqrt[3]{9x^2y} - 8\sqrt[3]{9x^2y} = -7\sqrt[3]{9x^2y}$ |

**Property** Combining Radical Expressions: Sums and Differences

Use the Distributive Property to add or subtract like radicals.
$$a\sqrt[n]{x} + b\sqrt[n]{x} = (a + b)\sqrt[n]{x} \qquad a\sqrt[n]{x} - b\sqrt[n]{x} = (a - b)\sqrt[n]{x}$$

Combining radical expressions is different from *adding* them. The sum of any two real numbers is a real number, so you can add $\sqrt{2}$ and $\sqrt{3}$ to get the real number $\sqrt{2} + \sqrt{3}$. However, you cannot *combine* the result into a single radical, so $\sqrt{2} + \sqrt{3} \neq \sqrt{5}$.

$$\begin{array}{ll} \sqrt{2} \approx 1.414 & \sqrt{5} \approx 2.236 \\ + \sqrt{3} \approx 1.732 & \\ \hline \sqrt{2} + \sqrt{3} \approx 3.146 & \neq 2.236 \end{array}$$

---

## 6-3 Preparing to Teach

**BIG idea** Equivalence **UbD**

**ESSENTIAL UNDERSTANDING**

- Like radicals can be combined using properties of real numbers.

### Math Background

Identifying and combining like radicals is similar to the Algebra 1 skill of identifying and combining like terms in polynomials. The lesson then uses combining like radicals as a springboard for several advanced skills with multiple-term radical expressions. All have connections to prior math content:

- Simplifying before combining like radicals connects to reducing radicals from Lesson 6-2.
- Multiplying binomial radical expressions relates to multiplying polynomials with the FOIL method from Algebra 1, multiplying radical expressions from Lesson 6-2, and multiplying complex numbers from Lesson 4-8.
- Writing and multiplying conjugates connects to differences of two squares from Algebra 1 and complex numbers from Lesson 4-8.

- Rationalizing two-term denominators is an extension of rationalizing single-term denominators from Lesson 6-2 and connects to rationalizing complex denominators in Lesson 4-8.

You can improve student success with Lesson 6-3 by pointing out any or all of these connections. Doing so helps students view the lesson as new applications of previously mastered skills, rather than a new set of disconnected rules.

### Support Student Learning

Use the **Algebra 2 Companion** to engage and support students during instruction. See Lesson Resources at the end of this lesson for details.

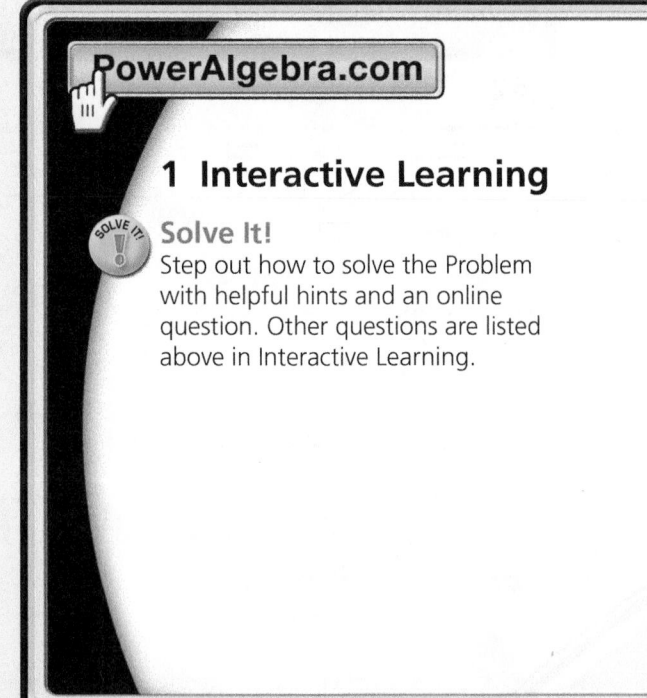

**PowerAlgebra.com**

## 1 Interactive Learning

**Solve It!**
Step out how to solve the Problem with helpful hints and an online question. Other questions are listed above in Interactive Learning.

**What is the simplified form of each expression?**

**Ⓐ** $3\sqrt{5x} - 2\sqrt{5x}$

$$3\sqrt{5x} - 2\sqrt{5x} = (3-2)\sqrt{5x} \qquad \text{Distributive Property}$$
$$= \sqrt{5x} \qquad\qquad \text{Simplify.}$$

**Ⓑ** $6x^2\sqrt{7} + 4x\sqrt{5}$

The radicands are different. You cannot combine the expressions.

**Ⓒ** $12\sqrt[3]{7xy} - 8\sqrt[5]{7xy}$

The indexes are different. You cannot combine the expressions.

 **Got It?** **1.** What is the simplified form of each expression?
  **a.** $7\sqrt[3]{5} - 4\sqrt{5}$  **b.** $3x\sqrt{xy} + 4x\sqrt{xy}$  **c.** $17\sqrt[5]{3x^2} - 15\sqrt[5]{3x^2}$

**Think**

**Can you always simplify a radical sum?**
No. The radicands and the indexes must be the same.

 **Problem 2** Using Radical Expressions

**Architecture** In the stained-glass window design, the side of each small square is 5 in. Find the perimeter of the window to the nearest tenth of an inch.

Length of the diagonal of a square with side $s$: $s\sqrt{2}$.
Length of the diagonal of each 5-inch square: $5\sqrt{2}$.

Length of the window:  $l = 3(5\sqrt{2}) = 15\sqrt{2}$
Width of the window:  $w = 2(5\sqrt{2}) = 10\sqrt{2}$

$$
\begin{aligned}
\text{Perimeter} &= 2l + 2w \\
&= 2(15\sqrt{2}) + 2(10\sqrt{2}) &&\text{Substitute for length and width.} \\
&= 30\sqrt{2} + 20\sqrt{2} &&\text{Simplify.} \\
&= 50\sqrt{2} &&\text{Distributive Property} \\
&\approx 70.7 &&\text{Use a calculator to approximate.}
\end{aligned}
$$

The perimeter of the window is about 70.7 inches.

**Think**

**Does it make sense that you have a radical expression as the answer?**
Yes, because perimeter is a linear measure, and there is no squaring in the calculations.

 **Got It?** **2. a.** Find the perimeter of the window if the side of each small square is 6 in.
  **b.** **Reasoning** Describe a different sequence of steps which you could use to compute the perimeter of the window.

---

## Problem 1 — VISUAL LEARNERS

For 1A, you can model the problem with congruent physical or sketched tiles each labeled $\sqrt{5x}$. Model $3\sqrt{5x}$ as three tiles, $\boxed{\sqrt{5x}}\ \boxed{\sqrt{5x}}\ \boxed{\sqrt{5x}}$. Then model the subtraction by removing two tiles.

**Q** What property allows you to write $\sqrt{5x}$ instead of $1\sqrt{5x}$? **[Identity Property of Multiplication]**

## Got It? — ERROR PREVENTION

Be aware of students who attempt to operate with the radicands. For example, in 1b watch for $7x\sqrt{2xy}$ (incorrect because the like radical $\sqrt{xy}$ should remain unchanged by the Distributive Property).

## Problem 2

**Q** By the Pythagorean Theorem, why does a square of side $s$ have diagonal $s\sqrt{2}$? **[The diagonal creates two isosceles right triangles with legs $s$ and hypotenuse $d$:** $d^2 = s^2 + s^2$ **and** $d = \sqrt{2s^2} = s\sqrt{2}$**.]**

## Got It?

Challenge students to find a pattern for the perimeter when the side of each square is 5 in. and 6 in., and then extend the pattern for any size square.

**Q** If each small square is $x$ in. on a side, what radical expression represents the perimeter? **[$10x\sqrt{2}$]**

---

## 2 Guided Instruction

Each Problem is worked out and supported online.

**Problem 1**
Adding and Subtracting Radical Expressions

**Problem 2**
Using Radical Expressions
*Animated*

**Problem 3**
Simplifying Before Adding or Subtracting
*Animated*

**Problem 4**
Multiplying Binomial Radical Expressions

**Problem 5**
Multiplying Conjugates

**Problem 6**
Rationalizing the Denominator
*Animated*

**Support in Algebra 2 Companion**
• Vocabulary
• Key Concepts
• Got It?

## Answers

### Solve It!
8; an isosceles triangle has base angle of 45° and $\frac{360}{45} = 8$. area: 127.5, perimeter: $30 + 15\sqrt{2}$

### Got It?
**1. a.** The indexes are different. You cannot combine the expressions.

  **b.** $7x\sqrt{xy}$

  **c.** $2\sqrt[5]{3x^2}$

**2. a.** about 84.9 in.

  **b.** The length of the diagonal of a square of side 6 can be found using the Pythagorean Thm. to be $\sqrt{6^2 + 6^2} = \sqrt{72}$. Using this information you can calculate the perimeter of the window and simplify the expression at the end.

## Problem 3

Although you cannot combine radicals with different radicands, it may be possible to simplify the radicals so that the radicands are the same.

> **Q** Why did the solution not factor $\sqrt{12}$ as $\sqrt{6 \cdot 2}$? **[To reduce a square root, you need perfect squares among the factors of the radicand; neither 6 nor 2 are perfect squares.]**
>
> **Q** How can you check that $\sqrt{12} + \sqrt{75} - \sqrt{3}$ is equivalent to $6\sqrt{3}$? **[Sample: Use a calculator to find that the decimal approximations are equivalent.]**

### Got It?

If students have trouble remembering or recognizing perfect cubes, suggest using any recognizable factors, leading toward prime factors; then look for cubed factors. For example, $\sqrt[3]{250} = \sqrt[3]{25 \cdot 10} = \sqrt[3]{5 \cdot 5 \cdot 2 \cdot 5} = \sqrt[3]{5^3 \cdot 2}$.

## Problem 4

> **Q** How does $2\sqrt{2} \cdot 4\sqrt{2}$ simplify to 16? Support your answer with the properties of real numbers. **[Sample: $2\sqrt{2} \cdot 4\sqrt{2} = 2 \cdot 4 \cdot \sqrt{2} \cdot \sqrt{2}$ by the Commutative Property of Multiplication, then $2 \cdot 4 \cdot \sqrt{2} \cdot \sqrt{2} = 8 \cdot \sqrt{4}$ by the Associative Property of Multiplication, and $8 \cdot \sqrt{4} = 8 \cdot 2 = 16$.]**

### Got It?                     ERROR PREVENTION

Be aware of students who correctly use the FOIL method but then incorrectly simplify each product. For example, the "outer" product $3 \cdot 4\sqrt{5}$ could become $12\sqrt{15}$ (incorrectly multiplied 3 by both 4 and 5), or the "inner" product $2\sqrt{5} \cdot 2$ could become $2\sqrt{10}$ (incorrectly multiplied 5 by 2 because they are adjacent).

---

When you have a sum or difference of radical expressions, you should simplify each expression so that you can find all the like radicals.

 **Problem 3** Simplifying Before Adding or Subtracting

**What is the simplest form of the expression?** $\sqrt{12} + \sqrt{75} - \sqrt{3}$

| Think | Write |
|---|---|
| To simplify each radical expression, factor each radicand. | $\sqrt{12} + \sqrt{75} - \sqrt{3}$ <br> $= \sqrt{4 \cdot 3} + \sqrt{25 \cdot 3} - \sqrt{3}$ <br> $= \sqrt{2^2 \cdot 3} + \sqrt{5^2 \cdot 3} - \sqrt{3}$ <br> $= \sqrt{2^2}\sqrt{3} + \sqrt{5^2}\sqrt{3} - \sqrt{3}$ |
| These are like radicals. Combine them. Remember $\sqrt{3} = 1\sqrt{3}$. | $= 2\sqrt{3} + 5\sqrt{3} - \sqrt{3}$ <br> $= 6\sqrt{3}$ |

 **Got It? 3.** What is the simplest form of the expression? $\sqrt[3]{250} + \sqrt[3]{54} - \sqrt[3]{16}$

---

You can use the FOIL method to multiply binomials that have radical expressions. Remember that the FOIL method ensures that you multiply each term of one binomial by each term of the other.

 **Problem 4** Multiplying Binomial Radical Expressions

**What is the product of each radical expression?**

**Plan**
How do you multiply two binomials?
Use the FOIL method: **F**irst, **O**uter, **I**nner, **L**ast. Then simplify.

**A** $(4 + 2\sqrt{2})(5 + 4\sqrt{2})$

$(4 + 2\sqrt{2})(5 + 4\sqrt{2})$

$= 4 \cdot 5 + 4 \cdot 4\sqrt{2} + 2\sqrt{2} \cdot 5 + 2\sqrt{2} \cdot 4\sqrt{2}$  Distribute.

$= 20 + 16\sqrt{2} + 10\sqrt{2} + 16$  Multiply.

$= 36 + 26\sqrt{2}$  Combine like radicals.

**B** $(3 - \sqrt{7})(5 + \sqrt{7})$

$(3 - \sqrt{7})(5 + \sqrt{7})$

$= 3 \cdot 5 + 3\sqrt{7} - \sqrt{7} \cdot 5 - \sqrt{7} \cdot \sqrt{7}$  Distribute.

$= 15 - 2\sqrt{7} - 7$  Multiply and combine like radicals.

$= 8 - 2\sqrt{7}$  Simplify.

**Got It? 4.** What is the product $(3 + 2\sqrt{5})(2 + 4\sqrt{5})$?

---

# Additional Problems

**1.** What is the simplified form of each expression?

   **a.** $14a\sqrt{7bc} + 5a\sqrt{7bc}$

   **b.** $3\sqrt[5]{x} - \sqrt[5]{3x}$

   **ANSWERS**

   **a.** $19a\sqrt{7bc}$

   **b.** cannot be simplified

**2.** This tile design is made of congruent right triangles with base 1 ft and height 2 ft. Find the perimeter of the tile to the nearest tenth of a foot.

2 ft
90°
1 ft

   **ANSWER** $4\sqrt{5}$ ft $\approx 8.9$ ft

**3.** What is the simplest form of the expression? $\sqrt{28} - \sqrt{175} + \sqrt{63}$

   **ANSWER** 0

**4.** What is the product? $(1 + 2\sqrt{7})(4 - 3\sqrt{7})$

   **ANSWER** $-38 + 5\sqrt{7}$

**5.** What is the product? $(5 + 3\sqrt{2})(5 - 3\sqrt{2})$

   **ANSWER** 7

**6.** How can you write the expression $\frac{11}{6 + \sqrt{3}}$ with a rationalized denominator?

   **ANSWER** $\frac{6 - \sqrt{3}}{3}$

Conjugates are expressions, like $\sqrt{a} + \sqrt{b}$ and $\sqrt{a} - \sqrt{b}$, that differ only in the signs of the second terms. When $a$ and $b$ are rational numbers, the product of two radical conjugates is a rational number.

Problem 5 **Multiplying Conjugates**

**What is the product $(5 - \sqrt{7})(5 + \sqrt{7})$?**

$(5 - \sqrt{7})(5 + \sqrt{7}) = 5 \cdot 5 + 5\sqrt{7} - 5\sqrt{7} - (\sqrt{7})^2$    Distribute.

$\qquad\qquad\qquad\qquad = 25 - 7$    Simplify.

$\qquad\qquad\qquad\qquad = 18$

**Got It? 5.** What is each product?

**a.** $(6 - \sqrt{12})(6 + \sqrt{12})$        **b.** $(3 + \sqrt{8})(3 - \sqrt{8})$

Sometimes a denominator is a sum or difference involving radicals. If the radical expressions are square roots, you can rationalize the denominator by multiplying the numerator and the denominator by the conjugate of the denominator.

Problem 6 **Rationalizing the Denominator**

**How can you write the expression with a rationalized denominator?**

$\dfrac{3\sqrt{2}}{\sqrt{5} - \sqrt{2}}$

$\dfrac{3\sqrt{2}}{\sqrt{5} - \sqrt{2}} = \dfrac{3\sqrt{2}}{\sqrt{5} - \sqrt{2}} \cdot \dfrac{\sqrt{5} + \sqrt{2}}{\sqrt{5} + \sqrt{2}}$    Multiply. Use the conjugate of the denominator.

$\qquad\qquad = \dfrac{3\sqrt{2}(\sqrt{5} + \sqrt{2})}{(\sqrt{5})^2 - (\sqrt{2})^2}$    The radicals in the denominator cancel out.

$\qquad\qquad = \dfrac{3(\sqrt{2} \cdot \sqrt{5} + \sqrt{2} \cdot \sqrt{2})}{5 - 2}$    Distribute $\sqrt{2}$ in the numerator.

$\qquad\qquad = \dfrac{3(\sqrt{10} + 2)}{3}$    Simplify.

$\qquad\qquad = \sqrt{10} + 2$

**Got It? 6.** How can you write the expression with a rationalized denominator?

**a.** $\dfrac{2\sqrt{7}}{\sqrt{3} - \sqrt{5}}$        **b.** $\dfrac{4x}{3 - \sqrt{6}}$

**c.** *Reasoning* Suppose you were going to rationalize the denominator of $\dfrac{1 - \sqrt{8}}{2 - \sqrt{8}}$. Would you simplify $\sqrt{8}$ before or after rationalizing? Explain your answer.

---

**Problem 5**          SYNTHESIZING

**Q** How could you use the difference of two squares instead of the FOIL method to find this product?
$[(5 - \sqrt{7})(5 + \sqrt{7}) = 5^2 - (\sqrt{7})^2 = 25 - 7 = 18]$

### Got It?

**Q** Note that $\sqrt{12} = 2\sqrt{3}$. Is it advantageous to simplify the radicals before multiplying conjugates? Explain. **[Sample: No; $(\sqrt{12})^2 = 12$ is easier than $(2\sqrt{3})^2 = 2^2 \cdot (\sqrt{3})^2 = 4 \cdot 3 = 12$.]**

**Problem 6**

**Q** Why can you not cancel $\sqrt{2}$ in the original $\dfrac{3\sqrt{2}}{\sqrt{5} + \sqrt{2}}$, but you can cancel 3 in $\dfrac{3(\sqrt{10} + 2)}{3}$? **[Sample: Fractions are reduced by canceling common factors in the numerator and denominator; in $\dfrac{3\sqrt{2}}{\sqrt{5} + \sqrt{2}}$, $\sqrt{2}$ is an *addend* of the denominator, not a *factor*.]**

### Got It?      ERROR PREVENTION

Be aware of students who try to rationalize two-term denominators using only a single term as they did in Lesson 6-2. For example, in 6b, some students may try to multiply by $\dfrac{\sqrt{6}}{\sqrt{6}}$ instead of $\dfrac{3 + \sqrt{6}}{3 + \sqrt{6}}$.

---

# Answers

### Got It? (continued)

**3.** $6\sqrt[3]{2}$

**4.** $46 + 16\sqrt{5}$

**5. a.** 24
    **b.** 1

**6. a.** $-\sqrt{21} - \sqrt{35}$
    **b.** $\frac{1}{3}(12x + 4x\sqrt{6})$
    **c.** after rationalizing; When the numerator is multiplied by the conjugate of the denominator it is more convenient if $\sqrt{8}$ is not yet simplified.

# 3 Lesson Check

## Do you know HOW?  ERROR INTERVENTION

- If students operate with the radicands when combining like radicals in Exercises 1 and 3, have them underline the like radicals. By the Distributive Property, the like radical remains unchanged during the process.
- If students multiply only the first non-radical terms and the last radical terms in Exercises 6 and 7, then have them look at the proper use of the FOIL method in Problem 4.

## Do you UNDERSTAND?

- Extend Exercise 8 by asking students to justify why the expressions in (a) and (c) are not pairs of like radicals. **[The pairs in (a) and (c) do not have the same radicands.]**

## Close

> **Q** What process do you use to identify like radicals? **[Answers may vary. Sample: First check that the indexes are the same; then simplify each radical to simplest form and check that the remaining radicands are the same.]**

---

## Lesson Check

### Do you know HOW?

Simplify if possible.

**1.** $10\sqrt{6} + 2\sqrt{6}$  **2.** $3\sqrt{2} + 4\sqrt[3]{2}$

**3.** $8\sqrt{3x} - 5\sqrt{3x}$  **4.** $5\sqrt{3} + \sqrt{12}$

Multiply.

**5.** $(4 + \sqrt{3})(4 - \sqrt{3})$

**6.** $(5 + 2\sqrt{5})(7 + 4\sqrt{5})$

**7.** $(2 + 3\sqrt{2})(1 - 3\sqrt{2})$

### Do you UNDERSTAND?

**8. Vocabulary** Determine whether each of the following is a pair of like radicals. If so, add them.
  **a.** $3x\sqrt{11}$ and $3x\sqrt{10}$
  **b.** $2\sqrt{3xy}$ and $7\sqrt{3xy}$
  **c.** $12\sqrt{13y}$ and $12\sqrt{6y}$

**9. Compare and Contrast** How are the processes of multiplying radical expressions and multiplying polynomial expressions alike? How are the processes different?

---

## Practice and Problem-Solving Exercises

**Practice**  Simplify if possible.  ◆ See Problem 1.

**10.** $5\sqrt{6} + \sqrt{6}$  **11.** $6\sqrt[3]{3} - 2\sqrt[3]{3}$  **12.** $4\sqrt{3} + 4\sqrt[3]{3}$

**13.** $3\sqrt{x} - 5\sqrt{x}$  **14.** $14\sqrt{x} + 3\sqrt{y}$  **15.** $7\sqrt[3]{x^2} - 2\sqrt[3]{x^2}$

**16.** The design of a garden path uses stone pieces shaped as squares with a side length of 15 in. Find the length of the path.  ◆ See Problem 2.

Simplify.  ◆ See Problem 3.

**17.** $6\sqrt{18} + 3\sqrt{50}$  **18.** $14\sqrt{20} - 3\sqrt{125}$  **19.** $\sqrt{18} + \sqrt{32}$

**20.** $\sqrt[3]{54} + \sqrt[3]{16}$  **21.** $3\sqrt[3]{81} - 2\sqrt[3]{54}$  **22.** $\sqrt[4]{32} + \sqrt[4]{48}$

Multiply.  ◆ See Problem 4.

**23.** $(3 + \sqrt{5})(1 + \sqrt{5})$  **24.** $(2 + \sqrt{7})(1 + 3\sqrt{7})$  **25.** $(3 - 4\sqrt{2})(5 - 6\sqrt{2})$.

**26.** $(\sqrt{3} + \sqrt{5})^2$  **27.** $(\sqrt{13} + 6)^2$  **28.** $(2\sqrt{5} + 3\sqrt{2})^2$

Multiply each pair of conjugates.  ◆ See Problem 5.

**29.** $(5 - \sqrt{11})(5 + \sqrt{11})$  **30.** $(4 - 2\sqrt{3})(4 + 2\sqrt{3})$

**31.** $(2\sqrt{6} + 8)(2\sqrt{6} - 8)$  **32.** $(\sqrt{3} + \sqrt{5})(\sqrt{3} - \sqrt{5})$

Rationalize each denominator. Simplify your answer.  ◆ See Problem 6.

**33.** $\dfrac{4}{1 + \sqrt{3}}$  **34.** $\dfrac{4}{3\sqrt{3} - 2}$  **35.** $\dfrac{5 + \sqrt{3}}{2 - \sqrt{3}}$  **36.** $\dfrac{3 + \sqrt{8}}{2 - 2\sqrt{8}}$

---

## 3 Lesson Check

For a digital lesson check, use the Got It questions.

**Support in Algebra 2 Companion**
- Lesson Check

## 4 Practice

Assign homework to individual students or to an entire class.

# Answers

## Lesson Check

**1.** $12\sqrt{6}$
**2.** cannot combine
**3.** $3\sqrt{3x}$
**4.** $7\sqrt{3}$
**5.** 13
**6.** $75 + 34\sqrt{5}$
**7.** $-16 - 3\sqrt{2}$
**8. a.** not like radicals
   **b.** $9\sqrt{3xy}$
   **c.** not like radicals
**9.** They are alike in that you can also use the FOIL method and Distr. Prop. to multiply binomial radical expressions; they are different in that you cannot multiply like radicands together if they do not have the same index.

## Practice and Problem-Solving Exercises

**10.** $6\sqrt{6}$  **11.** $4\sqrt[3]{3}$
**12.** cannot combine
**13.** $-2\sqrt{x}$
**14.** cannot combine
**15.** $5\sqrt[3]{x^2}$
**16.** about 127.3 in.
**17.** $33\sqrt{2}$  **18.** $13\sqrt{5}$
**19.** $7\sqrt{2}$  **20.** $5\sqrt[3]{2}$
**21.** $9\sqrt[3]{3} - 6\sqrt[3]{2}$
**22.** $2\sqrt[4]{2} + 2\sqrt[4]{3}$
**23.** $8 + 4\sqrt{5}$
**24.** $23 + 7\sqrt{7}$
**25.** $63 - 38\sqrt{2}$
**26.** $8 + 2\sqrt{15}$
**27.** $49 + 12\sqrt{13}$
**28.** $38 + 12\sqrt{10}$
**29.** 14  **30.** 4  **31.** $-40$

**37. Think About a Plan** The design on a parquet floor, shown at the right, is made of equilateral triangles. The side of a large triangle is 6 in., and the side of a small triangle is 3 in. Find the total area of the design to the nearest tenth of a square inch.
- How many large and how many small triangles form the design?
- Can you express the area of an equilateral triangle through its side?

**Simplify.**

**38.** $\sqrt{72} + \sqrt{32} + \sqrt{18}$

**39.** $\sqrt{75} + 2\sqrt{48} - 5\sqrt{3}$

**40.** $5\sqrt{32x} + 4\sqrt{98x}$

**41.** $\sqrt{75} - 4\sqrt{18} + 2\sqrt{32}$

**42.** $4\sqrt{216y^2} + 3\sqrt{54y^2}$

**43.** $3\sqrt[3]{16} - 4\sqrt[3]{54} + \sqrt[3]{128}$

**44.** $(1 + \sqrt{72})(5 + \sqrt{2})$

**45.** $(\sqrt{3} - \sqrt{7})(\sqrt{3} + 2\sqrt{7})$

**46.** $(\sqrt{y} + \sqrt{2})(\sqrt{y} - 7\sqrt{2})$

**47.** $(\sqrt{12} + \sqrt{72})^2$

**48.** $(\sqrt{1.25} - \sqrt{1.8})(\sqrt{5} + \sqrt{0.2})$

**49.** $(\sqrt{a+1} + \sqrt{a-1})(\sqrt{a+1} - \sqrt{a-1})$

**50. Error Analysis** Describe and correct the error made while simplifying the expression $\frac{3 + \sqrt{2}}{3 - \sqrt{2}}$.

$$\frac{3 + \sqrt{2}}{3 - \sqrt{2}} = \frac{3 + \sqrt{2}}{3 - \sqrt{2}} \cdot \frac{3 + \sqrt{2}}{3 + \sqrt{2}}$$
$$= \frac{3^2 + (\sqrt{2})^2}{3^2 - (\sqrt{2})^2} = \frac{9 + 2}{9 - 2} = \frac{11}{7}$$

**51. Chemistry** A scientist found that $x$ grams of Metal $A$ is completely oxidized in $2x\sqrt{3}$ seconds and $x$ grams of Metal $B$ is completely oxidized in $6x\sqrt{3}$ seconds. How much faster is Metal $A$ oxidized than Metal $B$?

**52. Reasoning** Describe the possible values of $a$ such that $\sqrt{72} + \sqrt{a}$ simplifies to a single term.

**53. Writing** Discuss the advantages and disadvantages of first simplifying $\sqrt{72} + \sqrt{32} + \sqrt{18}$ in order to estimate its decimal value.

**54. Geometry** Show that a right triangle with legs of lengths $\sqrt{2} - 1$ and $\sqrt{2} + 1$ is similar to a right triangle with legs of lengths $6 - \sqrt{32}$ and 2.

**55. Open-Ended** Find two pairs of conjugates with a product of 3.

**Rationalize the denominators and simplify.**

**56.** $\frac{4 + \sqrt{27}}{2 - 3\sqrt{27}}$

**57.** $\frac{4 + \sqrt{6}}{\sqrt{2} + \sqrt{3}}$

**58.** $\frac{5 - \sqrt{21}}{\sqrt{3} - \sqrt{7}}$

**59.** $\frac{\sqrt{44x^2}}{\sqrt{11} + 3}$

**60.** $\frac{\sqrt{2} + \sqrt{6}}{\sqrt{1.5} + \sqrt{0.5}}$

**61.** $\frac{\sqrt{27} - \sqrt{5}}{\sqrt{15} - 3}$

**62.** $\frac{4 + \sqrt[3]{2}}{\sqrt[3]{2}}$

**63.** $\frac{5 + \sqrt[4]{x}}{\sqrt[4]{x}}$

**64.** $\frac{4 - 2\sqrt[3]{6}}{\sqrt[3]{4}}$

## 4 Practice

**ASSIGNMENT GUIDE**
Basic: 10–36 all, 37–40, 53, 54–58 even
Average: 11–35 odd, 37–64
Advanced: 11–35 odd, 37–68
Standardized Test Prep: 69–73
Mixed Review: 74–91

**Reasoning** exercises have blue headings.

**Applications** exercises have red headings.

**EXERCISE 54:** Use the Think About a Plan worksheet in the **Practice and Problem Solving Workbook** (also available in the Teaching Resources in print and online) to further support students' development in becoming independent learners.

**HOMEWORK QUICK CHECK**
To check students' understanding of key skills and concepts, go over Exercises 29, 33, 37, 40, and 54.

## Answers

**32.** $-2$

**33.** $-2 + 2\sqrt{3}$

**34.** $\frac{12\sqrt{3} + 8}{23}$

**35.** $13 + 7\sqrt{3}$

**36.** $\frac{11 + 8\sqrt{2}}{-14}$

**37.** $140.3$ in.$^2$

**38.** $13\sqrt{2}$

**39.** $8\sqrt{3}$

**40.** $48\sqrt{2x}$

**41.** $5\sqrt{3} - 4\sqrt{2}$

**42.** $33|y|\sqrt{6}$

**43.** $-2\sqrt[3]{2}$

**44.** $17 + 31\sqrt{2}$

**45.** $-11 + \sqrt{21}$

**46.** $y - 6\sqrt{2y} - 14$

**47.** $84 + 24\sqrt{6}$

**48.** $-0.6$

**49.** $2$

**50.** In the second step, the student did not use the FOIL method correctly. The steps should be:

$$\cdots = \frac{3^2 + 6\sqrt{2} + (\sqrt{2})^2}{3^2 - (\sqrt{2})^2}$$
$$= \frac{9 + 6\sqrt{2} + 2}{9 - 2}$$
$$= \frac{11 + 6\sqrt{2}}{7}$$

**51.** $4x\sqrt{3}$ s

**52.** $a$ must be twice a perfect square.

**53.** Answers may vary. Sample: Without simplifying first, you must estimate three square roots and then add the estimates. If they are first simplified, then they can be combined as $13\sqrt{2}$. Then only one square root need be estimated.

**54.** $\frac{\sqrt{2} - 1}{\sqrt{2} + 1} = \frac{6 - \sqrt{32}}{2} = 3 - 2\sqrt{2}$

**55.** Answers may vary. Sample: $(\sqrt{7} + 2)(\sqrt{7} - 2), (2\sqrt{2} + \sqrt{5})(2\sqrt{2} - \sqrt{5})$

**56.** $\frac{89 + 42\sqrt{3}}{-239}$

**57.** $2\sqrt{3} - \sqrt{2}$

**58.** $\frac{1}{2}(\sqrt{3} - \sqrt{7})$

**59.** $11|x| - 3|x|\sqrt{11}$

**60.** $2$

**61.** $\frac{3\sqrt{5} + 2\sqrt{3}}{3}$

**62.** $1 + 2\sqrt[3]{4}$

**63.** $\frac{x + 5\sqrt[4]{x^3}}{x}$

**64.** $2\sqrt[3]{2} - \sqrt[3]{12}$

# Answers

## Practice and Problem-Solving Exercises
(continued)

**65.** $-\frac{1}{2}$

**66.** $4\sqrt{3}$

**67.** $a = 0$ and $b \geq 0$, or $b = 0$ and $a \geq 0$

**68. a.** $m > n$

    **b.** $m$ must be even or $n$ must be odd, where $m > n$

    **c.** $m$ must be even, where $m > n$

## Standardized Test Prep

**69.** 13

**70.** 2

**71.** $\frac{15}{7}$

**72.** $\frac{5}{2}$

**73.** 9

## Mixed Review

**74.** $3\sqrt[3]{2}$

**75.** $\frac{2\sqrt[3]{x^2}}{x}$

**76.** 4

**77.** 6

**78.** $2x$

**79.** $7x^2\sqrt{2}$

**80.** $x\sqrt{15}$

**81.** $15x^2$

**82.** $2, -1 \pm i\sqrt{3}$

**83.** $-10, 5 \pm 5i\sqrt{3}$

**84.** $\frac{1}{5}, \frac{-1 \pm i\sqrt{3}}{10}$

**85.** $\sqrt{7}$ (multiplicity 2), $-\sqrt{7}$ (multiplicity 2)

**86.** $\frac{2\sqrt{5}}{5}$ (multiplicity 2), $-\frac{2\sqrt{5}}{5}$ (multiplicity 2)

**87.** $\pm\frac{1}{3}, \pm\frac{1}{3}i$

**88.** $x^6$

**89.** $p^5q^5$

**90.** $2^9$, or 512

**91.** $3^3$, or 27

---

 **Challenge**    Add or subtract.

**65.** $\dfrac{1}{1 - \sqrt{5}} + \dfrac{1}{1 + \sqrt{5}}$

**66.** $\dfrac{4}{\sqrt{5} - \sqrt{3}} - \dfrac{4}{\sqrt{5} + \sqrt{3}}$

**67.** For what values of $a$ and $b$ does $\sqrt{a} + \sqrt{b} = \sqrt{a + b}$?

**68.** In the expression $\sqrt[n]{x^m}$, $m$ and $n$ are positive integers and $x$ is a real number. The expression can be simplified.

    **a.** If $x > 0$, what are the possible values for $m$ and $n$?

    **b.** If $x < 0$, what are the possible values for $m$ and $n$?

    **c.** If $x < 0$, and an absolute value symbol is needed in the simplified expression, what are the possible values of $m$ and $n$?

## Standardized Test Prep

**GRIDDED RESPONSE**

**SAT/ACT**

**69.** What is the value of the expression $(5 - 2\sqrt{3})(5 + 2\sqrt{3})$?

**70.** What is the value of $z$ in the solution of the system of equations below?

$$\begin{cases} 2x - 3y + z = 6 \\ -x + y - 2z = -5 \\ 3x - y - 3z = -7 \end{cases}$$

**71.** What is the $y$-value of the $y$-intercept of the line $5x - 7y = -15$?

**72.** What is the slope of a line perpendicular to the line $2x + 5y = 10$?

**73.** What is the value of $p$ for which the equation $x^2 - 12x + 4p = 0$ has exactly one real root?

## Mixed Review

Simplify each expression. Rationalize all denominators.    ◀ **See Lesson 6-2.**

**74.** $\sqrt[3]{3} \cdot \sqrt[3]{18}$     **75.** $\sqrt[3]{\dfrac{4}{0.5x}}$     **76.** $\dfrac{\sqrt{32}}{\sqrt{2}}$     **77.** $\dfrac{\sqrt{216}}{\sqrt{6}}$

**78.** $\sqrt[3]{2x^2} \cdot \sqrt[3]{4x}$     **79.** $\sqrt{7x} \cdot \sqrt{14x^3}$     **80.** $\sqrt{3x} \cdot \sqrt{5x}$     **81.** $\sqrt{9x^2} \cdot \sqrt{25x^2}$

Find the real and imaginary solutions of each equation.    ◀ **See Lesson 5-3.**

**82.** $2x^3 - 16 = 0$     **83.** $x^3 + 1000 = 0$     **84.** $125x^3 - 1 = 0$

**85.** $x^4 - 14x^2 + 49 = 0$     **86.** $25x^4 - 40x^2 + 16 = 0$     **87.** $81x^4 - 1 = 0$

**Get Ready!**    To prepare for Lesson 6-4, do Exercises 88–91.

Simplify.    ◀ **See p. 970.**

**88.** $(x^2)^3$     **89.** $(pq)^5$     **90.** $(2^4)(2^5)$     **91.** $(3^{-2})(3^5)$

## Additional Instructional Support

### Algebra 2 Companion

Students can use the **Algebra 2 Companion** worktext (4 pages) as you teach the lesson. Use the Companion to support

- New Vocabulary
- Key Concepts
- Got It for each Problem
- Lesson Check

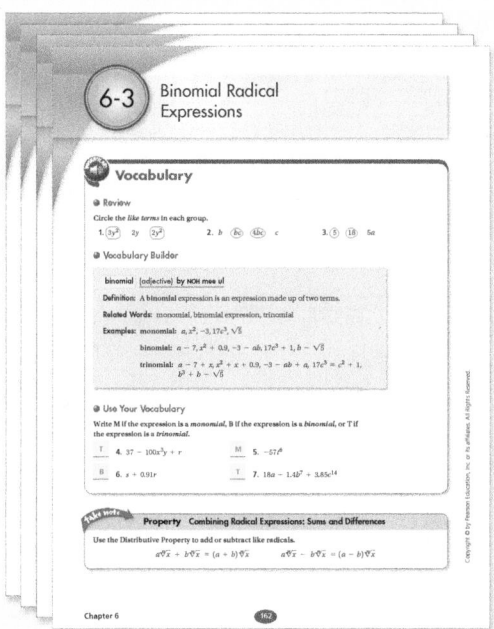

### ELL Support

**Use Graphic Organizers** Have students fold a sheet of paper in half to make two columns. Label one column Like Radicals and the other Unlike Radicals. Have students work in groups of two or three to write at least five pairs of radical expressions that fit in each column.

Circulate and challenge students to write pairs that either appear to be like terms but are not (e.g., $\sqrt{2}$ and $\sqrt[3]{2}$) or do not appear to be like terms but are (e.g., $\sqrt{2}$ and $\sqrt{50}$). Come back together as a class and have each group share at least one pair from each column.

Encourage students to use the correct vocabulary. For example, "$\sqrt{2}$ and $\sqrt[3]{2}$ have the same *radicand* but are not *like radicals* because their *indexes* are different." Students may add illustrative examples to their own graphic organizers.

## 5 Assess & Remediate

### Lesson Quiz

1. What is the simplified form of $15\sqrt[4]{8y^3} - 6\sqrt[4]{8y^3} + \sqrt[4]{y^3}$?

2. **Do you UNDERSTAND?** This wall-hanging is made of congruent 30°-60°-90° triangles with height 6 cm and hypotenuse 12 cm. What is the perimeter of the wall hanging to the nearest tenth of a centimeter?

3. What is the simplest form of the expression? $\sqrt{180} - \sqrt{80} + \sqrt{45}$

4. What is the product? $(4 - \sqrt{3})(5 - 6\sqrt{3})$

5. What is the product? $(8 + \sqrt{20})(8 - \sqrt{20})$

6. How can you write the expression with a rationalized denominator? $\dfrac{3\sqrt{7}}{\sqrt{7} + \sqrt{3}}$

### ANSWERS TO LESSON QUIZ

1. $9\sqrt[4]{8y^3} + \sqrt[4]{y^3}$

2. $(24 + 24\sqrt{3})$ cm $\approx 65.6$ cm

3. $5\sqrt{5}$

4. $38 - 29\sqrt{3}$

5. $44$

6. $\dfrac{21 - 3\sqrt{21}}{4}$

### PRESCRIPTION FOR REMEDIATION

Use the student work on the Lesson Quiz to prescribe a differentiated review assignment:

| Points | Differentiated Remediation |
|--------|---------------------------|
| 0–3 | Intervention |
| 4–5 | On-level |
| 6 | Extension |

**PowerAlgebra.com**

## 5 Assess & Remediate

Assign the Lesson Quiz. Appropriate intervention, practice, or enrichment is automatically generated based on student performance.

## Intervention

- **Reteaching** (2 pages) Provides reteaching and practice exercises for the key lesson concepts. Use with struggling students or absent students.

- **English Language Learner Support** Helps students develop and reinforce mathematical vocabulary and key concepts.

### All-in-One Resources/Online
### Reteaching

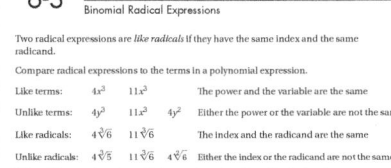

### All-in-One Resources/Online
### English Language Learner Support

# Differentiated Remediation *continued*

## On-Level

- **Practice** (2 pages) Provides extra practice for each lesson. For simpler practice exercises, use the Form K Practice pages found in the All-in-One Teaching Resources and online.

- **Think About a Plan** Helps students develop specific problem-solving skills and strategies by providing scaffolded guiding questions.

- **Standardized Test Prep** Focuses on all major exercises, all major question types, and helps students prepare for the high-stakes assessments.

## Extension

- **Enrichment** Provides students with interesting problems and activities that extend the concepts of the lesson.

- **Activities, Games, and Puzzles** Worksheets that can be used for concepts development, enrichment, and for fun!

---

### Practice and Problem Solving Wkbk/ All-in-One Resources/Online
#### Practice page 1

**6-3 Practice** — Form G
Binomial Radical Expressions

*(reduced worksheet image)*

### Practice and Problem Solving Wkbk/ All-in-One Resources/Online
#### Practice page 2

**6-3 Practice (continued)** — Form G
Binomial Radical Expressions

*(reduced worksheet image)*

### All-in-One Resources/Online
#### Enrichment

**6-3 Enrichment**
Binomial Radical Expressions

*(reduced worksheet image)*

---

### Practice and Problem Solving Wkbk/ All-in-One Resources/Online
#### Think About a Plan

**6-3 Think About a Plan**
Binomial Radical Expressions

*(reduced worksheet image)*

### Practice and Problem Solving Wkbk/ All-in-One Resources/Online
#### Standardized Test Prep

**6-3 Standardized Test Prep**
Binomial Radical Expressions

*(reduced worksheet image)*

### Online Teacher Resource Center
#### Activities, Games, and Puzzles

**6-3 Activity: Bringing Closure**
Binomial Radical Expressions

*(reduced worksheet image)*

## 6-4 Rational Exponents

**Objective** To simplify expressions with rational exponents

**SOLVE IT!**

**Getting Ready!** ◄► ✕ ↺ ⌂

This is a 1-square.

[1 Square]

The first diagram shows how to cut two linked 1-squares into congruent pieces, each with size $\frac{2}{3}$. Show how to cut the three linked 1-squares into congruent pieces, each with size $\frac{3}{4}$. Explain why you cannot cut them into congruent pieces, each with size $\frac{4}{5}$.

*It is easy to cut one 1-square into congruent pieces, each with size $\frac{1}{2}$.*

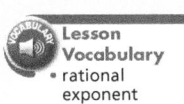

**Lesson Vocabulary**
• rational exponent

If $a^x = \sqrt[4]{a^3}$, then by definition, $a^x \cdot a^x \cdot a^x \cdot a^x = a^3$. By adding exponents, $a^{4x} = a^3$, so $x$ is $\frac{3}{4}$. This suggests an alternative notation for radical expressions in which, for example, $\sqrt[4]{a^3} = a^{\frac{3}{4}}$.

**Essential Understanding** You can write a radical expression in an equivalent form using a fractional (rational) exponent instead of a radical sign.

In general, $\sqrt[n]{x} = x^{\frac{1}{n}}$ for any positive integer $n$. Like the radical form, the exponent form indicates the principal root.

$$\sqrt{36} = 36^{\frac{1}{2}} \qquad \sqrt[3]{64} = 64^{\frac{1}{3}} \qquad \sqrt[4]{16} = 16^{\frac{1}{4}}$$

**Think**
What does the denominator of the fractional exponent represent?
The denominator of the fraction is the index of the radical.

 **Problem 1** Simplifying Expressions with Rational Exponents

What is the simplified form of each expression?

**A** $216^{\frac{1}{3}}$

$216^{\frac{1}{3}} = \sqrt[3]{216}$ ◄ Rewrite as radicals.

$= \sqrt[3]{6^3}$

$= 6$

**B** $7^{\frac{1}{2}} \cdot 7^{\frac{1}{2}}$

$7^{\frac{1}{2}} \cdot 7^{\frac{1}{2}} = \sqrt{7} \cdot \sqrt{7}$

$= \sqrt{7 \cdot 7}$

$= \sqrt{7^2}$

$= 7$

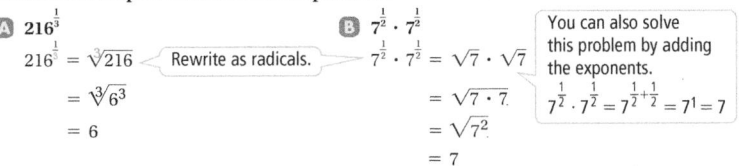

You can also solve this problem by adding the exponents.

$7^{\frac{1}{2}} \cdot 7^{\frac{1}{2}} = 7^{\frac{1}{2}+\frac{1}{2}} = 7^1 = 7$

---

## 1 Interactive Learning

**Solve It!**

**PURPOSE** To use multiplication and division of fractions to prove a task is impossible

**PROCESS** Students may
• sketch the squares and use trial and error to cut the 1-squares into 4 congruent pieces.
• determine the number of congruent pieces of size $\frac{3}{4}$ that can be cut by dividing 3 by $\frac{3}{4}$.

**FACILITATE**

**Q** How can you find the number of congruent pieces of size $\frac{3}{4}$ that can be cut from the three 1-squares? **[by dividing: $3 \div \frac{3}{4} = 4$]**

**Q** Suppose you attempt to cut the 1-squares into congruent pieces of size $\frac{4}{5}$. How many pieces would you cut? **[$3 \div \frac{4}{5} = \frac{15}{4} = 3.75$]**

**Q** Is 3 evenly divisible by $\frac{3}{4}$? $\frac{4}{5}$? **[yes; no]**

**ANSWER** See Solve It in Answers on next page.

**CONNECT THE MATH** The students use multiplication and division of fractions to find the solutions for the Solve It. These skills are reinforced in the lesson as they use properties of rational exponents to simplify expressions with rational exponents as well as convert between exponential and radical form.

## 2 Guided Instruction

**Problem 1**

**Q** The exponent $\frac{1}{2}$ indicates a square root. What does the exponent $\frac{1}{3}$ indicate? **[a cube root]**

---

## 6-4 Preparing to Teach

**BIG idea Equivalence** UbD

**ESSENTIAL UNDERSTANDINGS**

• A radical expression can be written in an equivalent form using a fractional (rational) exponent instead of a radical sign.

• $\sqrt[n]{x} = x^{\frac{1}{n}}$ for any positive integer $n$. Like the radical form, the exponent form indicates the principal root.

• The $n$th root of an expression that contains an $n$th power as a factor can be simplified.

$$\sqrt[n]{x^n} = x^{\frac{n}{n}} = \begin{cases} x, & \text{if } n \text{ is odd} \\ |x|, & \text{if } n \text{ is even} \end{cases}$$

### Math Background

Extending exponents to include those that are not integers not only gives an alternative way to write radical expressions, but also allows students to apply all the previously learned properties of exponents to expressions containing radicals. When powers are extended to include all rational exponents, it is customary to restrict bases to the set of positive real numbers, so that all the familiar laws of exponents *do* hold.

At first glance, changing the expression $ab^2\sqrt{3a}$ to the exponential form $3^{\frac{1}{2}}a^{\frac{3}{2}}b^{\frac{4}{2}}$ does not appear to achieve any simplification. The advantages of this type of change may only be clear to students when they are computing products and quotients.

Students may question why radicals can be expressed as fractional exponents. Explain that $(x^{\frac{1}{n}})^n = x^{\frac{n}{n}} = x$ by the laws of exponents, and $(\sqrt[n]{x})^n = x$ or $|x|$, so it makes sense to define $x^{\frac{1}{n}}$ as $\sqrt[n]{x}$.

### Support Student Learning

Use the **Algebra 2 Companion** to engage and support students during instruction. See Lesson Resources at the end of this lesson for details.

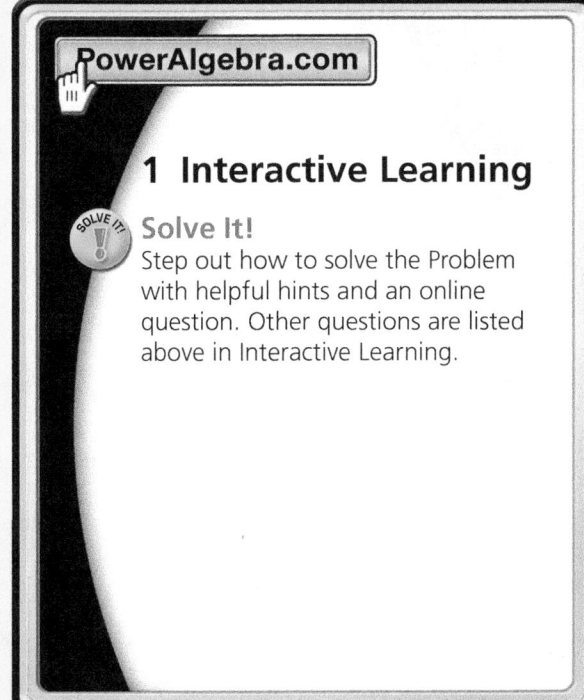

**PowerAlgebra.com**

## 1 Interactive Learning

**Solve It!**
Step out how to solve the Problem with helpful hints and an online question. Other questions are listed above in Interactive Learning.

## Got It?

Students may use calculators with an $x^y$ key to check these answers.

### Take Note

- Use the example $\sqrt[3]{x} \cdot \sqrt[6]{x}$ to show students the advantages of changing radicals to exponential expressions.
- Once the expression has been converted to $x^{\frac{1}{3}} \cdot x^{\frac{1}{6}}$, students can use the laws of exponents to show $x^{\frac{1}{3}} \cdot x^{\frac{1}{6}} = x^{\frac{1}{2}} = \sqrt{x}$.
- Have a volunteer use 64 for $x$ to confirm this result.

## Problem 2

**Q** What is 2 to the 7th power? What is the value of $x^{\frac{3}{7}}$ for $x = 128$? Which form allows you to evaluate the expression for $x = 128$ without using a calculator? **[128; 8; radical form]**

## Got It?

**ERROR PREVENTION**

Model this sequence of steps for converting a fractional exponent to a radical expression:
$x^{\frac{2}{3}} = (x^2)^{\frac{1}{3}} = \sqrt[3]{x^2}$.

**Q** What part of a fractional exponent is the index of the radical? **[the denominator]**

---

**C** $5^{\frac{1}{4}} \cdot 125^{\frac{1}{4}}$

| | |
|---|---|
| $5^{\frac{1}{4}} \cdot 125^{\frac{1}{4}} = \sqrt[4]{5} \cdot \sqrt[4]{125}$ | Rewrite as radicals. |
| $= \sqrt[4]{5 \cdot 125}$ | Property for multiplying radical expressions |
| $= \sqrt[4]{625}$ | Multiply. |
| $= \sqrt[4]{5^4}$ | Rewrite the radicand. |
| $= 5$ | Simplify. |

 **Got It?** **1.** What is the simplified form of each expression?

    **a.** $64^{\frac{1}{2}}$     **b.** $11^{\frac{1}{2}} \cdot 11^{\frac{1}{2}}$     **c.** $3^{\frac{1}{2}} \cdot 12^{\frac{1}{2}}$

If $\sqrt[n]{x} = x^{\frac{1}{n}}$, it follows from the Laws of Exponents that for all real numbers $\sqrt[n]{x^m} = (x^m)^{\frac{1}{n}} = (x^{\frac{1}{n}})^m = \left(\sqrt[n]{x}\right)^m$. This leads to the definition of a rational exponent.

### Key Concept   Rational Exponent

If the $n$th root of $a$ is a real number, $m$ is an integer, and $\frac{m}{n}$ is in lowest terms, then
$$a^{\frac{1}{n}} = \sqrt[n]{a} \text{ and } a^{\frac{m}{n}} = \sqrt[n]{a^m} = \left(\sqrt[n]{a}\right)^m. \qquad \text{If } m \text{ is negative, } a \neq 0.$$

**Problem 2** **Converting Between Exponential and Radical Form**

**A** What are $x^{\frac{3}{7}}$ and $y^{-3.5}$ in radical form?
$$x^{\frac{3}{7}} = \sqrt[7]{x^3} \text{ or } (\sqrt[7]{x})^3$$
$$y^{-3.5} = y^{-\frac{7}{2}}$$
$$= \frac{1}{y^{\frac{7}{2}}}$$
$$= \frac{1}{\sqrt{y^7}} = \frac{1}{\sqrt{y^6 y}} = \frac{1}{y^3 \sqrt{y}} \text{ or } \frac{\sqrt{y}}{y^4}$$

**B** What are $\sqrt{a^5}$ and $(\sqrt[5]{b})^3$ in exponential form?
$$\sqrt{a^5} = (a^5)^{\frac{1}{2}} = a^{\frac{5}{2}}$$
$$(\sqrt[5]{b})^3 = (b^{\frac{1}{5}})^3 = b^{\frac{3}{5}}$$

 **Got It?** **2. a.** What are the expressions $w^{-\frac{5}{8}}$ and $w^{0.2}$ in radical form?

    **b.** What are the expressions $\sqrt[4]{x^3}$ and $(\sqrt[5]{y})^4$ in exponential form?

    **c.** Reasoning Refer to the definition of rational exponent. Explain the need for the restriction that $a \neq 0$ if $m$ is negative.

**Think**

Does the fraction $\frac{3}{7}$ first need to be simplified?
No. The fraction is already in lowest terms.

**Chapter 6** Radical Functions and Rational Exponents

---

## 2 Guided Instruction

Each Problem is worked out and supported online.

**Problem 1**
Simplifying Expressions with Rational Exponents

**Problem 2**
Converting Between Exponential and Radical Form
    *Animated*

**Problem 3**
Using Rational Exponents

**Problem 4**
Combining Radical Expressions
    *Animated*

**Problem 5**
Simplifying Numbers With Rational Exponents

**Problem 6**
Writing Expressions in Simplest Form

**Support in Algebra 2 Companion**
- Vocabulary
- Key Concepts
- Got It?

## Answers

### Solve It!

You can determine how many congruent pieces to make by finding $3 \div \frac{3}{4} = 4$. Since $\frac{4}{5}$ does not divide 3 evenly, you cannot cut three 1-squares into congruent pieces of size $\frac{4}{5}$.

### Got It?

**1. a.** 8     **b.** 11     **c.** 6

**2. a.** $\frac{\sqrt[8]{w^3}}{w}$, $\sqrt[5]{w}$   **b.** $x^{\frac{3}{4}}$, $y^{\frac{4}{5}}$

    **c.** If $m$ is negative, $a$ is in the denominator and $\frac{1}{a}$ is undefined when $a = 0$.

**3. a.** The length of a Venusian year is about 0.61 Earth years.

    **b.** The length of a Jovian year is about 12.76 Earth years.

**Chapter 6**

**Problem 3** Using Rational Exponents

**Planetary Motion** Kepler's Third Law of Orbital Motion shows how you can approximate the period $P$ (in Earth years) it takes a planet to complete one orbit of the sun. Use the function $P = d^{\frac{3}{2}}$, where $d$ is the distance from the planet to the sun in astronomical units (AU—about 93,000,000 miles or the distance from Earth to the sun). How many Earth years does it take Mars to orbit the sun?

$$P = d^{\frac{3}{2}} \qquad \text{Write the formula.}$$
$$= (1.52)^{\frac{3}{2}} \qquad \text{Substitute for } d.$$
$$\approx 1.87 \qquad \text{Use a calculator.}$$

It takes Mars approximately 1.87 Earth years to orbit the sun.

✓ **Got It?** **3.** Find the approximate length (in Earth years) of each planet's year.
  **a.** A Venusian year if Venus is 0.72 AU from the sun
  **b.** A Jovian year if Jupiter is 5.46 AU from the sun

**Plan**

**How can you find a $\frac{3}{2}$ power on a calculator?**
You can use ⌃.
◁ 3 ÷ 2 ▷.
You can also cube the number and then take the square root, or take the square root then cube.

All the properties of integer exponents apply to rational exponents.

**take note**

**Properties** Properties of Rational Exponents

Let $m$ and $n$ represent rational numbers. Assume that no denominator equals 0.

| Property | Example | Property | Example |
|---|---|---|---|
| $a^m \cdot a^n = a^{m+n}$ | $8^{\frac{1}{3}} \cdot 8^{\frac{2}{3}} = 8^{\frac{1}{3}+\frac{2}{3}} = 8^1 = 8$ | $a^{-m} = \frac{1}{a^m}$ | $9^{-\frac{1}{2}} = \frac{1}{9^{\frac{1}{2}}} = \frac{1}{3}$ |
| $(a^m)^n = a^{mn}$ | $(5^{\frac{1}{2}})^4 = 5^{\frac{1}{2} \cdot 4} = 5^2 = 25$ | $\frac{a^m}{a^n} = a^{m-n}$ | $\frac{7^{\frac{3}{2}}}{7^{\frac{1}{2}}} = 7^{\frac{3}{2}-\frac{1}{2}} = 7^1 = 7$ |
| $(ab)^m = a^m b^m$ | $(4 \cdot 5)^{\frac{1}{2}} = 4^{\frac{1}{2}} \cdot 5^{\frac{1}{2}} = 2 \cdot 5^{\frac{1}{2}}$ | $\left(\frac{a}{b}\right)^m = \frac{a^m}{b^m}$ | $\left(\frac{5}{27}\right)^{\frac{1}{3}} = \frac{5^{\frac{1}{3}}}{27^{\frac{1}{3}}} = \frac{5^{\frac{1}{3}}}{3}$ |

**Problem 3**
An astronomical unit is approximately the mean distance between the Earth and the sun. It is a derived constant and used to indicate distances within the solar system.

**Q** Which planet will take longer to orbit the sun: Mars or Neptune? Why? **[Neptune; it is farther from the sun. As $d$ increases, so does $P$.]**

**Q** How is $P^2 = d^3$ another way of writing the relationship in the problem? **[$P^2 = d^3$, so $\sqrt{P^2} = \sqrt{d^3}$: $P = d^{\frac{3}{2}}$.]**

**Got It?**      ERROR PREVENTION
Students may get a more accurate solution with this type of problem if they first convert the fraction $\frac{3}{2}$ to a decimal. Entering 1.5 may be easier than entering $\frac{3}{2}$.

**Take Note**      AUDITORY LEARNERS
List on the board these names of the properties shown in the chart. Have students match each name to its algebraic statement.

     Power of a Product
     Negative Exponent
     Product of Powers
     Power of a Quotient
     Quotient of Powers
     Power of a Power

If students seem at all uncertain of these properties, have them work in pairs or small groups to write several more numerical examples of each property.

---

# Additional Problems

**1.** What is the simplified form of each expression?

**a.** $625^{\frac{1}{4}}$

**b.** $12^{\frac{1}{2}} \cdot 12^{\frac{1}{2}}$

**c.** $12^{\frac{1}{3}} \cdot 18^{\frac{1}{3}}$

**ANSWERS**
**a.** 5
**b.** 12
**c.** 6

**2. a.** What are $-2y^{\frac{4}{5}}$ and $d^{-\frac{3}{2}}$ in radical form?

**b.** What are $\sqrt{ab^3}$ and $\sqrt[3]{w^2}$ in exponential form?

**ANSWERS**

**a.** $-2\sqrt[5]{y^4},\ \frac{\sqrt{d}}{d^2}$

**b.** $a^{\frac{1}{2}}b^{\frac{3}{2}},\ w^{\frac{2}{3}}$

**3.** For a $\frac{1}{4}$-in.-thick cookie, the diameter $d$ of the cookie is related to the diameter $c$ of the ball of dough by

$d = 1.6c^{\frac{3}{2}}$. What is the diameter to the nearest tenth of an inch of a cookie made from a 2 in. ball of dough?

**ANSWER** 4.5 in.

**4.** What is $\sqrt[6]{10}(\sqrt[3]{10})$ in simplest form?

**ANSWER** $\sqrt{10}$

**5.** What is each number in simplest form?

**a.** $(-64)^{\frac{5}{3}}$

**b.** $32^{-1.2}$

**ANSWERS**

**a.** $-1024$

**b.** $\frac{1}{64}$

**6.** What is each expression in simplest form?

**a.** $(9y\sqrt{x})^{\frac{3}{2}}$

**b.** $(27x^6y^9)^{-\frac{1}{3}}$

**ANSWERS**

**a.** $27y^{\frac{3}{2}}x^{\frac{3}{4}}$

**b.** $\frac{1}{3x^2y^3}$

## Problem 4

**Q** Is the statement $x^2y^2 = (xy)^4$ true? Why or why not? Give a specific example. **[No; you cannot add the exponents unless the bases are the same. For $x = 8$ and $y = 3$, $8^2 \cdot 3^2 = 576$ and $(8 \cdot 3)^4 = 331{,}776$.]**

**Q** How is radical multiplication like multiplying exponential expressions? **[Answers may vary. Sample: You may not be able to simplify the product unless the same expression is under both radical signs.]**

## Got It?

**Q** How can you check your result for 4b? **[Substitute a numerical value, such as $x = 64$.]**

## Problem 5

**Q** How are the two methods for 5A different? **[Method 1 changes the base to a power of 2; method 2 converts the expression to a fraction with a positive exponent and then to radical form.]**

**Q** How are the two methods for 5B different? **[Method 1 changes the base to a power of $-2$; method 2 converts the expression to radical form.]**

---

Recall from Lesson 6-2 that you simplified products or quotients involving radical expressions only when they had the same index. However, you can combine radical expressions with different indexes if you convert them to expressions with rational exponents.

### Problem 4  Combining Radical Expressions

What is $\dfrac{\sqrt[4]{x^3}}{\sqrt[8]{x^2}}$ in simplest form?

**Think**

The radicands are different, but both are powers of the same variable. Write the expressions using exponents.

$$\dfrac{\sqrt[4]{x^3}}{\sqrt[8]{x^2}} = \dfrac{x^{\frac{3}{4}}}{x^{\frac{2}{8}}}$$

Use the division property for exponents. Subtract the exponents.

$$= x^{\frac{3}{4} - \frac{2}{8}}$$
$$= x^{\frac{3}{4} - \frac{1}{4}}$$

Simplify, and write in either exponential or radical form.

$$= x^{\frac{1}{2}} = \sqrt{x}$$

**Got It?** **4.** What is each product or quotient in simplest form?

**a.** $\sqrt{3}\left(\sqrt[4]{3}\right)$     **b.** $\dfrac{\sqrt{x^3}}{\sqrt[3]{x^2}}$     **c.** $\sqrt{7}\left(\sqrt[3]{7}\right)$

---

You can simplify a number with a rational exponent by using the properties of exponents or by converting the expression to a radical expression.

### Problem 5  Simplifying Numbers With Rational Exponents

What is each number in simplest form?

**A** $16^{-2.5}$

**Plan**

**What is the first step?** Rewrite the decimal exponent as a fraction in lowest terms.

**Method 1**

$$16^{-2.5} = 16^{-\frac{5}{2}}$$
$$= (2^4)^{-\frac{5}{2}}$$
$$= 2^{4 \cdot -\frac{5}{2}}$$
$$= 2^{-10}$$
$$= \dfrac{1}{2^{10}} = \dfrac{1}{1024}$$

**Method 2**

$$16^{-2.5} = 16^{-\frac{5}{2}}$$
$$= \dfrac{1}{16^{\frac{5}{2}}}$$
$$= \dfrac{1}{(\sqrt{16})^5}$$
$$= \dfrac{1}{4^5}$$
$$= \dfrac{1}{1024}$$

---

# Answers

## Got It? (continued)

**4. a.** $\sqrt[4]{27}$

   **b.** $\sqrt[6]{x^5}$

   **c.** $\sqrt[6]{16{,}807}$

**B** $(-32)^{\frac{4}{5}}$

**Method 1**

$$(-32)^{\frac{4}{5}} = ((-2)^5)^{\frac{4}{5}}$$
$$= (-2)^{5 \cdot \frac{4}{5}}$$
$$= (-2)^4$$
$$= 16$$

**Method 2**

$$(-32)^{\frac{4}{5}} = (\sqrt[5]{-32})^4$$
$$= (\sqrt[5]{(-2)^5})^4$$
$$= (-2)^4$$
$$= 16$$

 **Got It? 5.** What is each number in simplest form?

**a.** $32^{-\frac{3}{5}}$      **b.** $16^{\frac{3}{4}}$      **c.** $9^{-3.5}$

To write an expression with rational exponents in simplest form, write every exponent as a positive number.

**Problem 6** Writing Expressions in Simplest Form

**What is each expression in simplest form?**

Plan

What is the first step in simplifying a radical expression using the properties of exponents?
Rewrite the radicals using rational exponents.

**A** $\left(-8x\sqrt{xy}\right)^{\frac{2}{3}}$

$$\left(-8x\sqrt{xy}\right)^{\frac{2}{3}} = (-8)^{\frac{2}{3}} \cdot x^{\frac{2}{3}} \cdot ((xy)^{\frac{1}{2}})^{\frac{2}{3}}$$
$$= ((-2)^3)^{\frac{2}{3}} \cdot x^{\frac{2}{3}} \cdot (xy)^{\frac{1}{3}}$$
$$= (-2)^2 \cdot x^{\frac{2}{3}} \cdot x^{\frac{1}{3}} \cdot y^{\frac{1}{3}}$$
$$= 4xy^{\frac{1}{3}}, \text{ or } 4x\sqrt[3]{y}$$

**B** $\left(16y^{-8}\right)^{-\frac{3}{4}}$

$$(16y^{-8})^{-\frac{3}{4}} = 16^{-\frac{3}{4}} \cdot y^{-8 \cdot -\frac{3}{4}}$$
$$= (2^4)^{-\frac{3}{4}} \cdot y^6$$
$$= 2^{-3}y^6$$
$$= \frac{y^6}{8}$$

 **Got It? 6.** What is each expression in simplest form?

**a.** $(8x^{15})^{-\frac{1}{3}}$      **b.** $\left(9x\sqrt[4]{y}\right)^{\frac{3}{2}}$

**Lesson Check**

**Do you know HOW?**

Simplify each expression.

**1.** $125^{\frac{1}{3}}$      **2.** $5^{\frac{1}{2}} \cdot 5^{\frac{1}{2}}$

**3.** $25^{-\frac{3}{2}}$      **4.** $4^{-3.5}$

**5.** $\sqrt{11}(\sqrt[4]{11})$      **6.** $\frac{\sqrt[3]{x}}{\sqrt[6]{x^5}}$

**Do you UNDERSTAND?**

**7. Open-Ended** Find a nonzero number $q$ such that $q(1 - 2^{\frac{1}{2}})$ is a rational number. Explain.

**8. Error Analysis** Explain why this simplification is incorrect.

**9. Reasoning** Explain why $(-64)^{\frac{1}{3}} = -64^{\frac{1}{3}}$ but $(-64)^{\frac{1}{2}} \neq -64^{\frac{1}{2}}$.

---

**Got It?**

**Q** Since you have two methods to solve these problems, what might be an effective check? [**Samples: Solve using one method and check by solving using the other; check with a calculator.**]

Problem 6

**Q** What do you think is the easiest way to remove all of the radical signs? [**Answers may vary. Sample: Rewrite the expressions in exponential form.**]

**Got It?**      ERROR PREVENTION

**Q** Could an expression be in simplest form if it had a radical sign in the denominator? Explain. [**No; by definition, a simplified expression cannot have a radical sign in the denominator.**]

# 3 Lesson Check

## Do you know HOW?

- If students are unsure how to start Exercise 4, suggest that they first change the exponent to a fraction.

## Do you UNDERSTAND?

- In Exercise 8, emphasize the distinction between $(5 \cdot 5)^{\frac{1}{2}}$ and $5 \cdot (5)^{\frac{1}{2}}$: the parentheses change the order of operations.

## Close

**Q** How are rational exponents related to radicals? [**The numerator of the exponent is the power of the number under the radical sign. The denominator is the index of the radical, so $x^{\frac{m}{n}} = \sqrt[n]{x^m}$.**]

---

**5. a.** $\frac{1}{8}$

   **b.** $8$

   **c.** $\frac{1}{2187}$

**6. a.** $\frac{1}{2x^5}$

   **b.** $27x\sqrt[8]{x^4y^3}$

**Lesson Check**

**1.** $5$

**2.** $5$

**3.** $\frac{1}{125}$

**4.** $\frac{1}{128}$

**5.** $\sqrt[4]{11^3}$

**6.** $\frac{\sqrt{x}}{x}$

**7.** $(1 + \sqrt{2})$ or any nonzero rational number times $(1 + \sqrt{2})$

**8.** error in third line, second term; $5(5^{\frac{1}{2}}) = 5^{\frac{3}{2}}$. The third and fourth lines should be:
$$20 - 5^{\frac{3}{2}}$$
$$20 - 5\sqrt{5}$$

**9.** $(-64)^{\frac{1}{3}} = \sqrt[3]{-64} = -4$ and $-64^{\frac{1}{3}} = -\sqrt[3]{64} = -4$; $(-64)^{\frac{1}{2}} = \sqrt{-64}$, which is not a real number, but $-64^{\frac{1}{2}} = -\sqrt{64} = -8$, which is a real number.

# 4 Practice

## ASSIGNMENT GUIDE
Basic: 10–66 all, 67, 72–82 even

Average: 11–65 odd, 67–90

Advanced: 11–65 odd, 67–97

Standardized Test Prep: 98–101

Mixed Review: 102–119

**Reasoning** exercises have blue headings.

**Applications** exercises have red headings.

**EXERCISE 78:** Use the Think About a Plan worksheet in the **Practice and Problem Solving Workbook** (also available in the Teaching Resources in print and online) to further support students' development in becoming independent learners.

## HOMEWORK QUICK CHECK
To check students' understanding of key skills and concepts, go over Exercises 37, 51, 67, 78, and 82.

---

## Practice and Problem-Solving Exercises

**A Practice**

Simplify each expression.   *See Problem 1.*

**10.** $36^{\frac{1}{2}}$  **11.** $27^{\frac{1}{3}}$  **12.** $49^{\frac{1}{2}}$

**13.** $10^{\frac{1}{2}} \cdot 10^{\frac{1}{2}}$  **14.** $(-3)^{\frac{1}{3}} \cdot (-3)^{\frac{1}{3}} \cdot (-3)^{\frac{1}{3}}$  **15.** $7^{\frac{1}{2}} \cdot 21^{\frac{1}{2}}$

**16.** $2^{\frac{1}{2}} \cdot 32^{\frac{1}{2}}$  **17.** $3^{\frac{1}{3}} \cdot 9^{\frac{1}{3}}$  **18.** $3^{\frac{1}{4}} \cdot 27^{\frac{1}{4}}$

Write each expression in radical form.   *See Problem 2.*

**19.** $x^{\frac{1}{6}}$  **20.** $x^{\frac{1}{5}}$  **21.** $x^{\frac{2}{7}}$  **22.** $y^{\frac{2}{5}}$

**23.** $y^{-\frac{9}{8}}$  **24.** $t^{-\frac{3}{4}}$  **25.** $x^{1.5}$  **26.** $y^{1.2}$

Write each expression in exponential form.

**27.** $\sqrt{-10}$  **28.** $\sqrt{7x^3}$  **29.** $\sqrt{(7x)^3}$  **30.** $(\sqrt{7x})^3$

**31.** $\sqrt[3]{a^2}$  **32.** $(\sqrt[3]{a})^2$  **33.** $\sqrt[4]{c^2}$  **34.** $\sqrt[3]{(5xy)^6}$

**Optimal Height** The optimal height $h$ of the letters of a message printed on pavement is given by the formula $h = \frac{0.00252 d^{2.27}}{e}$. Here $d$ is the distance of the driver from the letters and $e$ is the height of the driver's eye above the pavement. All of the distances are in meters. Find $h$ for the given values of $d$ and $e$.   *See Problem 3.*

**35.** $d = 100$ m, $e = 1.2$ m  **36.** $d = 50$ m, $e = 1.2$ m

**37.** $d = 50$ m, $e = 2.3$ m  **38.** $d = 25$ m, $e = 2.3$ m

Find each product or quotient.   *See Problem 4.*

**39.** $(\sqrt[4]{6})(\sqrt[3]{6})$  **40.** $\frac{\sqrt[9]{y^3}}{\sqrt[3]{y^9}}$  **41.** $\sqrt{5} \cdot \sqrt[5]{5}$  **42.** $\sqrt[7]{7} \cdot \sqrt[3]{7}$

**43.** $\frac{\sqrt[6]{4}}{\sqrt[3]{4}}$  **44.** $\sqrt[4]{18} \cdot \sqrt{12}$  **45.** $\frac{\sqrt{6}}{\sqrt[3]{36}}$  **46.** $\frac{\sqrt{x^4 y}}{\sqrt[4]{x^2 y^8}}$

Simplify each number.   *See Problem 5.*

**47.** $8^{\frac{2}{3}}$  **48.** $64^{\frac{2}{3}} 64^{\frac{2}{3}}$  **49.** $(-8)^{\frac{2}{3}}$  **50.** $(-32)^{\frac{6}{5}}$

**51.** $(32)^{-\frac{4}{5}}$  **52.** $4^{1.5}$  **53.** $16^{1.5}$  **54.** $10,000^{0.75}$

Write each expression in simplest form.   *See Problem 6.*

**55.** $\left(x^{\frac{2}{3}}\right)^{-3}$  **56.** $\left(x^{-\frac{4}{7}}\right)^7$  **57.** $\left(3x^{\frac{2}{3}}\right)^{-1}$  **58.** $5\left(x^{\frac{2}{3}}\right)^{-1}$

**59.** $\left(-27x^{-9}\right)^{\frac{1}{3}}$  **60.** $\left(-32y^{15}\right)^{\frac{1}{5}}$  **61.** $\left(x^{\frac{1}{2}} y^{-\frac{2}{3}}\right)^{-6}$  **62.** $\left(x^{\frac{2}{3}} y^{-\frac{1}{6}}\right)^{-12}$

**63.** $\left(\frac{x^3}{x^{-1}}\right)^{-\frac{1}{4}}$  **64.** $\left(\frac{x^2}{x^{-11}}\right)^{\frac{1}{3}}$  **65.** $\left(\frac{x^{\frac{1}{4}}}{y^{-\frac{3}{4}}}\right)^{12}$  **66.** $\left(\frac{x^{-\frac{2}{3}}}{y^{-\frac{1}{3}}}\right)^{15}$

---

## 3 Lesson Check

For a digital lesson check, use the Got It questions.

**Support in Algebra 2 Companion**
• Lesson Check

## 4 Practice

Assign homework to individual students or to an entire class.

---

# Answers

## Practice and Problem-Solving Exercises

**10.** 6  **11.** 3

**12.** 7  **13.** 10

**14.** −3  **15.** $7\sqrt{3}$

**16.** 8  **17.** 3

**18.** 3  **19.** $\sqrt[6]{x}$

**20.** $\sqrt[5]{x}$  **21.** $\sqrt[7]{x^2}$ or $(\sqrt[7]{x})^2$

**22.** $\sqrt[5]{y^2}$ or $(\sqrt[5]{y})^2$  **23.** $\frac{1}{\sqrt[8]{y^9}}$ or $\frac{1}{(\sqrt[8]{y})^9}$

**24.** $\frac{1}{\sqrt[4]{t^3}}$ or $\frac{1}{(\sqrt[4]{t})^3}$  **25.** $\sqrt{x^3}$ or $(\sqrt{x})^3$

**26.** $\sqrt[5]{y^6}$ or $(\sqrt[5]{y})^6$  **27.** $(-10)^{\frac{1}{2}}$

**28.** $7^{\frac{1}{2}}x^{\frac{3}{2}}$  **29.** $(7x)^{\frac{3}{2}}$

**30.** $(7x)^{\frac{3}{2}}$  **31.** $a^{\frac{2}{3}}$

**32.** $a^{\frac{2}{3}}$  **33.** $c^{\frac{1}{2}}$

**34.** $25x^2y^2$  **35.** $\approx 72.8$ m

**36.** $\approx 15.1$ m  **37.** $\approx 7.9$ m

**38.** $\approx 1.6$ m  **39.** $\sqrt[12]{6^7}$

**40.** $\frac{\sqrt[3]{y}}{y^3}$  **41.** $\sqrt[10]{5^7}$

**42.** $\sqrt[21]{7^{10}}$  **43.** $\frac{\sqrt[3]{4}}{2}$

**44.** $6\sqrt[4]{2}$  **45.** $\frac{\sqrt[6]{7776}}{6}$

**46.** $\frac{x\sqrt{xy}}{y^2}$  **47.** 4

**48.** 256  **49.** 4

**50.** 64  **51.** $\frac{1}{16}$

**52.** 8  **53.** 64

**54.** 1000  **55.** $\frac{1}{x^2}$

**56.** $\frac{1}{x^4}$  **57.** $\frac{\sqrt[3]{x}}{3x}$

**58.** $\frac{5\sqrt[3]{x}}{x}$  **59.** $-\frac{3}{x^3}$

**60.** $-2y^3$  **61.** $\frac{y^4}{x^3}$

**62.** $\frac{y^2}{x^8}$  **63.** $\frac{1}{x}$

**64.** $x^{\frac{13}{3}}$  **65.** $x^3y^9$

**66.** $\frac{y^5}{x^{10}}$

**Apply**

**67. Think About a Plan** The ratio $R$ of radioactive carbon to nonradioactive carbon left in a sample of an organism that died $T$ years ago can be approximated by the formula $R = A(2.7)^{-\frac{T}{8033}}$. Here $A$ is the ratio of radioactive carbon to nonradioactive carbon in the living organism. What percent of $A$ is left after 2000 years? After 4000 years? After 8000 years?
- What are the known and unknown values?
- How can you use the properties of exponents to solve this problem?

**68.** The expression $0.036m^{\frac{3}{4}}$ is used in the study of fluids. Which best represents the value of the expression for $m = 46 \times 10^4$?

   (A) 636          (B) 1460          (C) 1660          (D) 16,600

**Simplify each number.**

**69.** $(-343)^{\frac{1}{3}}$         **70.** $(-243)^{\frac{1}{5}}$         **71.** $32^{1.2}$

**72.** $243^{1.2}$         **73.** $64^{3.5}$         **74.** $100^{4.5}$

**75.** $-(-27)^{-\frac{4}{3}}$         **76.** $\dfrac{1000^{\frac{4}{3}}}{100^{\frac{3}{2}}}$         **77.** $25^{\frac{3}{2}}$

**78. Science** A desktop world globe has a volume of about 1386 cubic inches. The radius of Earth is approximately equal to the radius of the globe raised to the 10th power. Find the radius of Earth. (*Hint:* Use the formula $V = \frac{4}{3}\pi r^3$ for the volume of a sphere.)

**Simplify each expression.**

**79.** $x^{\frac{2}{7}} \cdot x^{\frac{3}{14}}$         **80.** $y^{\frac{1}{2}} \cdot y^{\frac{3}{10}}$         **81.** $x^{\frac{3}{5}} \div x^{\frac{3}{10}}$

**82.** $y^{\frac{5}{7}} \div y^{\frac{3}{14}}$         **83.** $\dfrac{x^{\frac{2}{3}} y^{-\frac{1}{4}}}{x^{\frac{1}{2}} y^{-\frac{1}{2}}}$         **84.** $\dfrac{x^{\frac{1}{2}} y^{-\frac{1}{3}}}{x^{\frac{3}{4}} y^{\frac{1}{2}}}$

**85.** $\left(\dfrac{16x^{14}}{81y^{18}}\right)^{\frac{1}{2}}$         **86.** $\left(\dfrac{81y^{16}}{16x^{12}}\right)^{\frac{1}{2}}$         **87.** $\left(\dfrac{8x^6}{27y^9}\right)^{\frac{1}{3}}$

**88. Open-Ended** Find three nonzero numbers $a$ such that $a\left(4 + 5^{\frac{1}{2}}\right)$ is a rational number. Can $a$ itself be a rational number? Explain.

**89. a. Reasoning** Show that $\sqrt[4]{x^2} = \sqrt{x}$ by using the definition of fourth root.
    **b. Reasoning** Show that $\sqrt[4]{x^2} = \sqrt{x}$ by rewriting $\sqrt[4]{x^2}$ in exponential form.

**90. Simplify $4^{\frac{1}{2}} \cdot 4^{\frac{1}{2}}$ using the following methods. Show all your work.**
    **a.** Use the properties of exponents.
    **b.** Simplify each term in the product, then multiply.
    **c.** Convert to radical form, then simplify.

**67.** about 78%; 61%; 37%

**68.** A

**69.** $-7$

**70.** $-3$

**71.** 64

**72.** 729

**73.** 2,097,152

**74.** 1,000,000,000 or $10^9$

**75.** $-\dfrac{1}{81}$

**76.** 10

**77.** 125

**78.** about 251,000,000 in., or 3961 mi

**79.** $x^{\frac{1}{2}}$

**80.** $y^{\frac{4}{5}}$

**81.** $x^{\frac{3}{10}}$

**82.** $y^{\frac{1}{2}}$

**83.** $x^{\frac{1}{6}}y^{\frac{1}{4}}$

**84.** $\dfrac{x^{\frac{3}{4}}y^{\frac{1}{6}}}{xy}$

**85.** $\dfrac{4x^7}{9y^9}$

**86.** $\dfrac{9y^8}{4x^6}$

**87.** $\dfrac{2x^2}{3y^3}$

**88.** Answers may vary. Sample: $4 - 5^{\frac{1}{2}}$, $2\left(4 - 5^{\frac{1}{2}}\right), \dfrac{4 - 5^{\frac{1}{2}}}{2}$;

No, if $a$ is rational and the product is rational, then $4 + 5^{\frac{1}{2}}$ would have to be rational.

**89. a.** $\sqrt{x} \cdot \sqrt{x} \cdot \sqrt{x} \cdot \sqrt{x} = x \cdot x = x^2$ so $\sqrt[4]{x^2} = \sqrt{x}$

    **b.** $\sqrt[4]{x^2} = (x^2)^{\frac{1}{4}} = x^{\frac{2}{4}} = x^{\frac{1}{2}} = \sqrt{x}$

**90. a.** $4^{\frac{1}{2}} \times 4^{\frac{1}{2}} = 4^1 = 4$

    **b.** $4^{\frac{1}{2}} \times 4^{\frac{1}{2}} = 2 \times 2 = 4$

    **c.** $\sqrt{4} \times \sqrt{4} = \sqrt{16} = 4$

# Answers

## Practice and Problem-Solving Exercises (continued)

**91.** 49

**92.** 9

**93.** $x^{2\pi}$

**94.** 1

**95.** $3^{\sqrt{2}}$

**96.** 9

**97.** 33.13 mi/h

## Standardized Test Prep

**98.** 2

**99.** 12

**100.** 3

**101.** 3

## Mixed Review

**102.** $4\sqrt[3]{3}$

**103.** $21\sqrt{2}$

**104.** $1 + 3\sqrt{5}$

**105.** $-7$

**106.** $-8\sqrt{3}$

**107.** $9\sqrt[4]{2}$

**108.** $4x(x^2 - 2x + 4)$

**109.** $(x + 2)^2$

**110.** $(x - 9)^2$

**111.** $(4a - 3b)(4a + 3b)$

**112.** $(5x - 4y)^2$

**113.** $(3x + 8)^2$

**114.** $-3, 2$

**115.** $7, -2$

**116.** $-\dfrac{3}{2}, 1$

**117.** $-\dfrac{1}{3}, 2$

**118.** $-\dfrac{5}{2}, \dfrac{1}{2}$

**119.** $-\dfrac{2}{3}, \dfrac{3}{2}$

---

**C** Challenge You can define the rules for irrational exponents so that they have the same properties as rational exponents . Use those properties to simplify each expression.

**91.** $\left(7^{\sqrt{2}}\right)^{\sqrt{2}}$

**92.** $\dfrac{3^{3+\sqrt{5}}}{3^{1+\sqrt{5}}}$

**93.** $\dfrac{x^{4\pi}}{x^{2\pi}}$

**94.** $5^{2\sqrt{3}} \cdot 25^{-\sqrt{3}}$

**95.** $9^{\frac{1}{\sqrt{2}}}$

**96.** $\left(3^{2+\sqrt{2}}\right)^{2-\sqrt{2}}$

**97. Weather** Using data for the effect of temperature and wind on an exposed face, the National Weather Service uses the following formula to determine wind chill.

Wind Chill Index $= 35.74 + 0.6215T - 35.75V^{0.16} + 0.4275TV^{0.16}$

$T$ is the temperature in degrees Fahrenheit and $V$ is the velocity of the wind in miles per hour. Frostbite occurs in about 15 minutes when the wind chill index is $-20$. Find the wind velocity that produces a wind chill index of $-20$ when the temperature is 5°F.

## Standardized Test Prep

GRIDDED RESPONSE

SAT/ACT

**98.** What is the simplified value of $\left(\frac{1}{64}\right)^{-\frac{1}{6}}$?

**99.** What positive value of $b$ makes $9x^2 - bx + 4$ a perfect square trinomial?

**100.** How many real roots does the cubic polynomial equation $x^3 - 7x^2 + 13x - 4 = 0$ have?

**101.** What is the $y$-value of the $y$-intercept of the graph of $f(x) = 4|x - 2| - 5$?

## Mixed Review

Simplify.

See Lesson 6-3.

**102.** $6\sqrt[3]{3} - 2\sqrt[3]{3}$

**103.** $3\sqrt{18} + 2\sqrt{72}$

**104.** $(\sqrt{5} - 1)(\sqrt{5} + 4)$

**105.** $(1 - 2\sqrt{2})(1 + 2\sqrt{2})$

**106.** $2\sqrt{12} - 4\sqrt{27}$

**107.** $\sqrt[4]{162} + 3\sqrt[4]{32}$

Factor each expression completely.

See Lesson 4-4.

**108.** $4x^3 - 8x^2 + 16x$

**109.** $x^2 + 4x + 4$

**110.** $x^2 - 18x + 81$

**111.** $16a^2 - 9b^2$

**112.** $25x^2 - 40xy + 16y^2$

**113.** $9x^2 + 48x + 64$

**Get Ready!** To prepare for Lesson 6-5, do Exercises 114–119.

Solve by factoring. Check your answers.

See Lesson 4-5.

**114.** $x^2 = -x + 6$

**115.** $x^2 = 5x + 14$

**116.** $2x^2 + x = 3$

**117.** $3x^2 - 2 = 5x$

**118.** $4x^2 = -8x + 5$

**119.** $6x^2 = 5x + 6$

# Lesson Resources

## Additional Instructional Support

### Algebra 2 Companion

Students can use the **Algebra 2 Companion** worktext (4 pages) as you teach the lesson. Use the Companion to support

- New Vocabulary
- Key Concepts
- Got It for each Problem
- Lesson Check

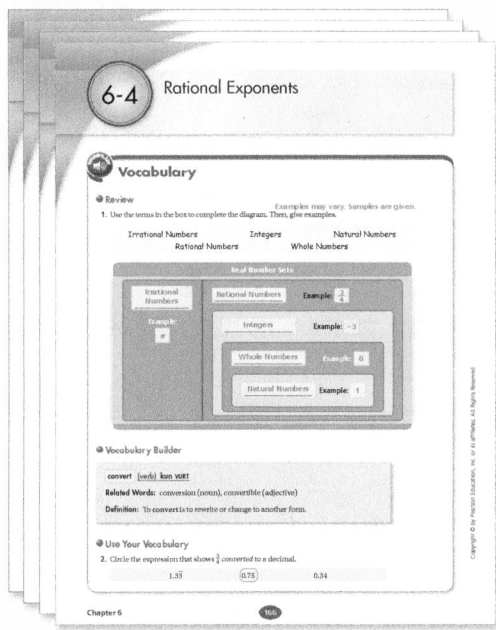

### ELL Support

**Connect to Prior Knowledge** Write the terms *integer* and *rational number* on the board. Ask, "What is an integer? Give some examples." [a positive or negative whole number or zero; 4, −28, 0] "What is a rational number? Give some examples." [A number that can be expressed as a fraction; $\frac{1}{2}$, 3.8, 22] Change the terms to *integer exponent* and *rational exponent*. Ask, "What is an integer exponent? What are some examples?" [an exponent that is an integer, $81^{-3}$, $4^2$] "What is a rational exponent? What are some examples?" [an exponent that is a rational number, $81^{\frac{2}{3}}$, $16^{1.5}$]

## 5 Assess & Remediate

### Lesson Quiz

1. What is the simplified form of $2^{\frac{1}{2}} \cdot 32^{\frac{1}{2}}$?
2. What is $x^{\frac{1}{2}}y^{\frac{2}{3}}$ in radical form?
3. **Do you UNDERSTAND?** The surface area $A$ of a cube is related to its volume $V$ by $A = 6 \cdot V^{\frac{2}{3}}$. If the volume of a cube is 35 cubic centimeters, what is its surface area to the nearest square centimeter?
4. What is $\dfrac{\sqrt[6]{w^5}}{\sqrt[3]{w^2}}$ in simplest form?
5. What is the simplest form of $64^{\frac{5}{6}}$?
6. What is the simplest form of $\sqrt[3]{8x^2y^7}$?

### ANSWERS TO LESSON QUIZ

1. 8
2. $\sqrt{x} \cdot \sqrt[3]{y^2}$
3. 64 square centimeters
4. $\sqrt[6]{w}$
5. 32
6. $2x^{\frac{2}{3}}y^{\frac{7}{3}}$

**PRESCRIPTION FOR REMEDIATION**
Use the student work on the Lesson Quiz to prescribe a differentiated review assignment:

| Points | Differentiated Remediation |
|--------|---------------------------|
| 0–3 | Intervention |
| 4–5 | On-level |
| 6 | Extension |

**PowerAlgebra.com**

### 5 Assess & Remediate
Assign the Lesson Quiz. Appropriate intervention, practice, or enrichment is automatically generated based on student performance.

## Intervention

- **Reteaching** (2 pages) Provides reteaching and practice exercises for the key lesson concepts. Use with struggling students or absent students.
- **English Language Learner Support** Helps students develop and reinforce mathematical vocabulary and key concepts.

**All-in-One Resources/Online**
**Reteaching**

6-4 Reteaching
Rational Exponents

**All-in-One Resources/Online**
**English Language Learner Support**

6-4 ELL Support
Rational Exponents

# Differentiated Remediation continued

## On-Level

- **Practice** (2 pages) Provides extra practice for each lesson. For simpler practice exercises, use the Form K Practice pages found in the All-in-One Teaching Resources and online.

- **Think About a Plan** Helps students develop specific problem-solving skills and strategies by providing scaffolded guiding questions.
- **Standardized Test Prep** Focuses on all major exercises, all major question types, and helps students prepare for the high-stakes assessments.

## Extension

- **Enrichment** Provides students with interesting problems and activities that extend the concepts of the lesson.
- **Activities, Games, and Puzzles** Worksheets that can be used for concepts development, enrichment, and for fun!

### Practice and Problem Solving Wkbk/All-in-One Workbook/Resources/Online
**Practice page 1**

### Practice and Problem Solving Wkbk/All-in-One Workbook/Resources/Online
**Practice page 2**

### All-in-One Resources/Online
**Enrichment**

### Practice and Problem Solving Wkbk/All-in-One Workbook Resources/Online
**Think About a Plan**

### Practice and Problem Solving Wkbk/All-in-One Workbook/Resources/Online
**Standardized Test Prep**

### Online Teacher Resource Center
**Activities, Games, and Puzzles**

## Do you know HOW?

**Find all the real square roots of each number.**

**1.** 100

**2.** 0.49

**Simplify each radical expression. Use absolute value symbols when needed.**

**3.** $\sqrt{36x^2}$

**4.** $\sqrt[3]{0.008y^3x^6}$

**Simplify.**

**5.** $\sqrt{50x^4y^8}$

**6.** $\sqrt[4]{32m^7n^9}$

**Multiply and simplify.**

**7.** $6\sqrt{4x^2} \cdot 2\sqrt{9x^2y^2}$

**8.** $\sqrt[3]{9} \cdot \sqrt[3]{9}$

**9.** $\sqrt[4]{16x^8} \cdot \sqrt[4]{x^{14}}$

**Divide and simplify.**

**10.** $\dfrac{\sqrt{36x^4}}{\sqrt{9x^6}}$

**11.** $\dfrac{\sqrt[3]{64x^9y^3}}{\sqrt[3]{8x^3}}$

**Simplify. Rationalize all denominators.**

**12.** $10\sqrt[3]{81} - 8\sqrt[3]{24}$

**13.** $\dfrac{4 + \sqrt{12}}{4 - \sqrt{12}}$

**14.** $\sqrt{48} - 3\sqrt{27} + 2\sqrt{75}$

**15.** $(3 + \sqrt{63})(1 + \sqrt{7})$

**16.** $\dfrac{\sqrt{x}}{\sqrt{6y^3}}$

**Write each expression in exponential form.**

**17.** $-\sqrt{17}$

**18.** $\sqrt[3]{y^8}$

**Write each expression in radical form.**

**19.** $m^{\frac{3}{7}}$

**20.** $y^{-\frac{4}{3}}$

**Simplify each expression.**

**21.** $(-27)^{\frac{2}{3}}$

**22.** $(16)^{\frac{3}{4}}$

**Write each expression in simplest form.**

**23.** $7\sqrt[3]{2x} - 3\sqrt[3]{2x}$

**24.** $2\sqrt{32x^2} + 3\sqrt{72x^2}$

**25.** $\sqrt[3]{125x^6} - \sqrt[3]{27x^6}$

**26.** $\sqrt[4]{7} - \sqrt[3]{7}$

**27.** $(\sqrt{y} - \sqrt{3})(\sqrt{y} + 2\sqrt{3})$

**28.** $\left(16x^{\frac{1}{4}}y^{\frac{3}{4}}\right)^{-4}$

**29.** $\left(\dfrac{x^{\frac{1}{3}}}{y^{\frac{2}{3}}}\right)^9$

**30.** $\left(\dfrac{x^{-10}}{x^5}\right)^{\frac{2}{5}}$

**31.** The radius of a circle can be expressed as $r = \sqrt{\dfrac{A}{\pi}}$ inches where $r$ is the radius and $A$ is the area of the circle. If the area of a circle is $169\pi$ in.$^2$, what is its radius?

### Do you UNDERSTAND?

**32.** What are the real roots of $\sqrt{-16}$? Explain.

**33.** **Error Analysis** Identify the error in this statement.
$$\frac{\sqrt[3]{x}}{\sqrt[3]{y}} \cdot \frac{\sqrt[3]{y}}{\sqrt[3]{y}} = \frac{\sqrt[3]{xy}}{y}$$

**34.** **Reasoning** If $0^{\frac{2}{3}} = 0$, why is $0^{-\frac{2}{3}}$ undefined?

**35.** Given that $x$ and $y$ are integers, explain why the product of $x + \sqrt{y}$ and its conjugate will always be an integer.

**36.** **Reasoning** Explain why $(-8)^{\frac{1}{2}} \neq -(8)^{\frac{1}{2}}$, but $(-27)^{\frac{1}{3}} = -(27)^{\frac{1}{3}}$.

**32.** There are no real roots of $\sqrt{-16}$; there is no real number $a$ such that $a^2 = -16$.

**33.** error in multiplication of the denominators:
$$\frac{\sqrt[3]{x}}{\sqrt[3]{y}} \cdot \frac{\sqrt[3]{y}}{\sqrt[3]{y}} = \frac{\sqrt[3]{xy}}{\sqrt[3]{y^2}} = \sqrt[3]{\frac{x}{y}}$$

**34.** $0^{-\frac{2}{3}} = \frac{1}{0}$, which is undefined.

**35.** The product of two integers will always be an integer, and the product $\sqrt{y} \cdot \sqrt{y} = y$, an integer. The other terms will cancel out and the difference of two integers is an integer.

**36.** $(-8)^{\frac{1}{2}} = \sqrt{-8}$, which is not a real number, but $-(8)^{\frac{1}{2}} = -\sqrt{8}$, which is a real number; $(-27)^{\frac{1}{3}} = \sqrt[3]{-27} = -3$, and $-\sqrt[3]{27} = -(3) = -3$

# Answers

**1.** $\pm 10$

**2.** $\pm 0.7$

**3.** $6|x|$

**4.** $0.2x^2y$

**5.** $5x^2y^4\sqrt{2}$

**6.** $2mn^2\sqrt[4]{2m^3n}$

**7.** $72x^2|y|$

**8.** $3\sqrt[3]{3}$

**9.** $2x^5\sqrt{x}$

**10.** $\dfrac{2}{|x|}$

**11.** $2x^2y$

**12.** $14\sqrt[3]{3}$

**13.** $7 + 4\sqrt{3}$

**14.** $5\sqrt{3}$

**15.** $24 + 6\sqrt{7}$

**16.** $\dfrac{\sqrt{6xy}}{6y^2}$

**17.** $-17^{\frac{1}{2}}$

**18.** $y^{\frac{8}{3}}$

**19.** $\sqrt[7]{m^3}$

**20.** $\dfrac{\sqrt[3]{y^2}}{y^2}$

**21.** 9

**22.** 8

**23.** $4\sqrt[3]{2x}$

**24.** $26|x|\sqrt{2}$

**25.** $2x^2$

**26.** cannot be simplified

**27.** $y + \sqrt{3y} - 6$

**28.** $\dfrac{1}{65{,}536\,xy^3}$

**29.** $\dfrac{x^3}{y^6}$

**30.** $\dfrac{1}{x^6}$

**31.** 13 in.

# 1 Interactive Learning

## Solve It!

**PURPOSE** To use the Pythagorean Theorem to solve a real-world problem with a solution that can be written in either decimal or radical form

**PROCESS** Students may use the Pythagorean Theorem to solve for the distance due east that the car will travel to reach the range of 6 mi.

### FACILITATE

**Q** How can you draw a diagram that represents the location of the car when it is 6 mi away from the cell phone tower? **[Sketch a segment from the tower to the road, east of the car, and label the segment 6 mi. Mark the intersection of the segment and road.]**

**Q** What formula can you use to find the distance the car must travel to reach the 6-mi range? Explain. **[The Pythagorean Theorem; the diagram is a right triangle.]**

**ANSWER** See Solve It in Answers on next page.
**CONNECT THE MATH** The Pythagorean Theorem determines the distance the car can travel before the end of the effective range. The Solve It is a real-world application of square root equations, which students solve in the lesson.

# 2 Guided Instruction

## Problem 1

**Q** What does it mean to "isolate the radical expression"? **[manipulate the equation so that the radical is alone on one side of the equals sign]**

# Solving Square Root and Other Radical Equations

**Objective** To solve square root and other radical equations

**Lesson Vocabulary**
• radical equation
• square root equation

A **radical equation** is an equation that has a variable in a radicand or a variable with a rational exponent. If the radical has index 2, the equation is a **square root equation**. In this lesson, assume that all radicals and expressions with rational exponents represent real numbers.

**Essential Understanding** Solving a square root equation may require that you square each side of the equation. This can introduce extraneous solutions.

To solve a radical equation, isolate the radical on one side of the equation. Then raise each side to the power suggested by the index.

**Problem 1** Solving a Square Root Equation

**What is the solution of** $3 + \sqrt{2x - 3} = 8$?

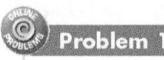
**Think**
**Do you need to introduce a ± sign here?**
No, when you take the square root of each side of an equation you do, but here you are squaring both sides of the equation.

$$3 + \sqrt{2x - 3} = 8$$
$$\sqrt{2x - 3} = 5 \quad \text{Isolate the radical expression.}$$
$$(\sqrt{2x - 3})^2 = 5^2 \quad \text{Square each side.}$$
$$2x - 3 = 25$$
$$2x = 28 \quad \text{Add 3 to each side.}$$
$$x = 14 \quad \text{Divide each side by 2.}$$

---

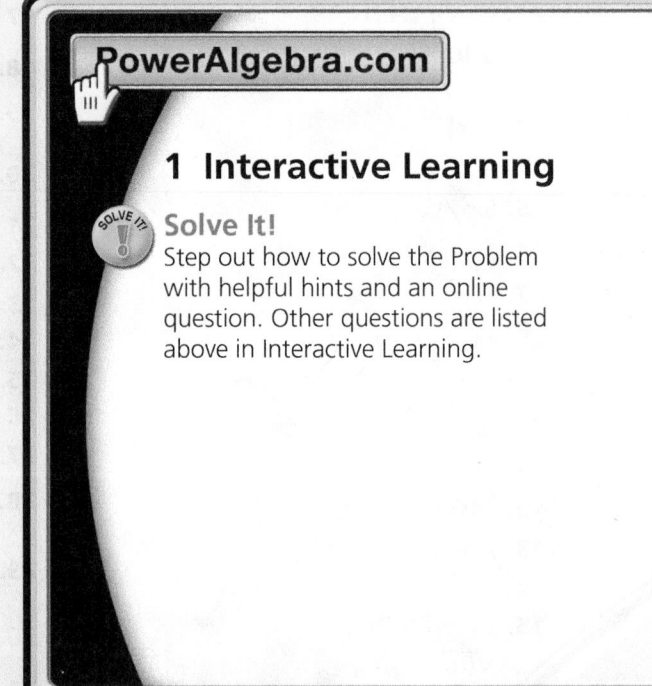 

**BIG** ideas **Equivalence**    **UbD**
              **Solving Equations and Inequalities**

### ESSENTIAL UNDERSTANDINGS

• Solving a square root equation may require squaring each side of the equation. This can introduce extraneous solutions.

• A radical equation can be solved by isolating the radical on one side of the equation, then raising each side to the power suggested by the index.

• The $n$th root of an expression that contains an $n$th power as a factor can be simplified.
$$\sqrt[n]{x^n} = x^{\frac{n}{n}} = \begin{cases} x, & \text{if } n \text{ is odd} \\ |x|, & \text{if } n \text{ is even} \end{cases}$$

### Math Background

Squaring both sides of an equation does not always produce an equivalent equation. The extraneous solutions that may be introduced are solutions to the transformed equation but are not solutions to the original equation. Because of this, it is critical that students always check their answers in the

**390**   **Chapter 6**

original equation. Alternatively, students can graph both sides of the original equation as separate functions and find all intersection points. If a solution is not an intersection, it is extraneous.

Solving a radical equation can be compared to solving any other equation for the variable. Isolate the radical first as you would the variable in another equation.

Solving a square root equation is both similar to and different from solving other kinds of equations in the following ways:

• Similar: The goal is to isolate the variable on one side of the equation by using inverse operations.

• Different: Extraneous (incorrect) solutions can occur.

### Support Student Learning

Use the **Algebra 2 Companion** to engage and support students during instruction. See Lesson Resources at the end of this lesson for details.

**PowerAlgebra.com**

## 1 Interactive Learning

### Solve It!

Step out how to solve the Problem with helpful hints and an online question. Other questions are listed above in Interactive Learning.

**Check**

$$3 + \sqrt{2x - 3} = 8 \quad \text{Write the original equation.}$$

$$3 + \sqrt{2(14) - 3} \stackrel{?}{=} 8 \quad \text{Substitute 14 for } x.$$

$$3 + \sqrt{25} \stackrel{?}{=} 8 \quad \text{Simplify.}$$

$$3 + 5 \stackrel{?}{=} 8$$

$$8 = 8 \checkmark$$

 **Got It? 1.** What is the solution of $\sqrt{4x + 1} - 5 = 0$?

To solve equations of the form $x^{\frac{m}{n}} = k$, raise each side of the equation to the power $\frac{n}{m}$, the reciprocal of $\frac{m}{n}$. If either $m$ or $n$ is even, then $\left(x^{\frac{m}{n}}\right)^{\frac{n}{m}} = |x|$.

**Problem 2** Solving Other Radical Equations

**A** What is the solution of $3(x + 1)^{\frac{2}{3}} = 12$?

| Know | Need | Plan |
|---|---|---|
| • The equation<br>• The power of the exponential expression | Solution of the equation | • Isolate the exponential expression.<br>• Use the inverse of the power to simplify and solve the equation. |

**Think**

How can you get rid of the rational exponent?
Raise each side to the reciprocal power.

$$3(x + 1)^{\frac{2}{3}} = 12$$

$$(x + 1)^{\frac{2}{3}} = 4 \quad \text{Divide each side by 3.}$$

$$\left((x + 1)^{\frac{2}{3}}\right)^{\frac{3}{2}} = 4^{\frac{3}{2}} \quad \text{Raise each side to the } \frac{3}{2} \text{ power.}$$

$$(x + 1)^{\frac{6}{6}} = 4^{\frac{3}{2}}$$

$$|x + 1| = 8 \quad \longleftarrow \boxed{\text{Since the numerator of } \frac{2}{3} \text{ is even, } (x^{\frac{2}{3}})^{\frac{3}{2}} = |x|}$$

$$x + 1 = \pm 8$$

$$x = 7 \text{ or } x = -9$$

The solutions are 7 and $-9$.

**Check**

$$3(x + 1)^{\frac{2}{3}} = 12 \qquad\qquad 3(x + 1)^{\frac{2}{3}} = 12$$

$$3(7 + 1)^{\frac{2}{3}} \stackrel{?}{=} 12 \qquad\qquad 3(-9 + 1)^{\frac{2}{3}} \stackrel{?}{=} 12$$

$$3(2^3)^{\frac{2}{3}} \stackrel{?}{=} 12 \qquad\qquad 3((-2)^3)^{\frac{2}{3}} \stackrel{?}{=} 12$$

$$3(2)^2 \stackrel{?}{=} 12 \qquad\qquad 3(-2)^2 \stackrel{?}{=} 12$$

$$12 = 12 \checkmark \qquad\qquad 12 = 12 \checkmark$$

**Got It?**

**Q** What is the first step you would take to solve this equation? Why? [**Add 5 to both sides of the equation. This will isolate the radical.**]

**Problem 2**
Raising each side of an equation to the reciprocal of the radical's power removes the radical from the equation.

**Q** Why should you raise each side of the equation to the $\frac{3}{2}$ power? [**Answers may vary: Samples: $\frac{3}{2}$ is the reciprocal of $\frac{2}{3}$; to remove the radical from the equation.**]

**Q** Why is it necessary to check each solution? [**Raising both sides of an equation to a power may introduce extraneous solutions.**]

## 2 Guided Instruction

 Each Problem is worked out and supported online.

**Problem 1**
Solving a Square Root Equation

**Problem 1 Alternative**
Solving a Square Root Equation
*Animated*

**Problem 2**
Solving Other Radical Equations

**Problem 3**
Using Radical Equations

**Problem 4**
Checking for Extraneous Solutions
*Animated*

**Problem 5**
Solving an Equation with Two Radicals
*Animated*

**Support in Algebra 2 Companion**
• Vocabulary
• Key Concepts
• Got It?

# Answers

**Solve It!**

about 5.2 mi; $6^2 - 3^2 \approx 5.2^2$

**Got It?**

**1.** 6

## Got It?

If students have difficulty understanding why it is a good idea to use reciprocals to solve radical equations, show them how to solve an equation without using a rational exponent for the radical:

$2(x + 3)^{\frac{2}{3}} = 8$
$2\sqrt[3]{(x + 3)^2} = 8$
$\sqrt[3]{(x + 3)^2} = 4$
$\left(\sqrt[3]{(x + 3)^2}\right)^3 = 4^3$
$(x + 3)^2 = 64$
$\sqrt{(x + 3)^2} = \sqrt{64}$
$x + 3 = \pm 8$
$x = 5$ or $x = -11$

## Problem 3

Q Why should you use 1,200 m for the diameter in this equation instead of 1.2 km? **[Answers may vary. Sample: The formula uses meters and cubic meters.]**

Q Why should you use the word *about* in the answer? **[The problem states that all values are approximate.]**

## Got It?

Q What should you do first before substituting values into the equation? **[Convert 1 km to meters.]**

---

**B** What is the solution of $3\sqrt[5]{(x + 1)^3} + 1 = 25$?

$3\sqrt[5]{(x + 1)^3} + 1 = 25$

$3(x + 1)^{\frac{3}{5}} + 1 = 25$    Rewrite the radical using a rational exponent.

$3(x + 1)^{\frac{3}{5}} = 24$    Subtract 1 from each side.

$(x + 1)^{\frac{3}{5}} = 8$    Divide each side by 3.

$\left((x + 1)^{\frac{3}{5}}\right)^{\frac{5}{3}} = 8^{\frac{5}{3}}$    Raise each side to the $\frac{5}{3}$ power.

$x + 1 = 32$    Simplify.

$x = 31$    Subtract 1 from each side.

The solution is 31.

**Think**

**Why is isolating the variable important?** If you raise each side of $3\sqrt[5]{(x + 1)^3} + 1 = 25$ to the $\frac{5}{3}$ power you will end up with a more complicated equation, not a simpler one.

✓ **Got It? 2.** What are the solution(s) of $2(x + 3)^{\frac{3}{5}} = 8$?

---

**Problem 3** Using Radical Equations

**Earth Science** For Meteor Crater in Arizona, the formula $d = 2\sqrt[3]{\dfrac{V}{0.3}}$ relates the diameter $d$ of the rim (in meters) to the volume $V$ (in cubic meters). What is the volume of Meteor Crater? (All values are approximate.)

1.2 km

**Think**

**What is the diameter in meters?**
$1.2 \text{ km} = 1.2 \times 1000 \text{ m}$.

$d = 2\sqrt[3]{\dfrac{V}{0.3}}$

$1200 = 2\sqrt[3]{\dfrac{V}{0.3}}$    Substitute 1200 for $d$.

$600 = \sqrt[3]{\dfrac{V}{0.3}}$    Divide each side by 2.

$600^3 = \dfrac{V}{0.3}$    Cube each side.

$0.3 \cdot 600^3 = V$    Multiply each side by 0.3.

$V = 64{,}800{,}000$    Simplify.

The volume of Meteor Crater is about 64,800,000 m$^3$.

✓ **Got It? 3.** Suppose the diameter of a similarly shaped crater is 1 km. What is the volume of the crater? Use the formula given in Problem 3.

---

# Additional Problems

**1.** What is the solution of $\sqrt{x + 4} + 6 = 7$?

**ANSWER** $-3$

**2.** What is the solution of $(6x + 9)^{\frac{1}{3}} - 5 = -2$?

**ANSWER** 3

**3.** A parabolic goblet with a cup that is as wide as it is tall holds $1.74r^3$ oz of water when it is full, where $r$ is the radius in inches of the circular rim. What is the radius, to the nearest hundredth of an inch, of a goblet that holds 9 oz?

**ANSWER** about 1.73 in.

**4.** What is the solution of $\sqrt{5x + 14} = x$? Check your results.

**ANSWER** 7

**5.** What is the solution of $2 + \sqrt{x - 6} = \sqrt{x + 10}$?

**ANSWER** 15

When you raise each side of an equation to a power, it is possible to introduce extraneous solutions. Therefore, it becomes very important that you check all solutions in the original equation. A correct solution will give a true statement. An extraneous solution will give a false statement.

 **Problem 4** Checking for Extraneous Solutions

**Think**

**How do you square a binomial?**
Use the formula,
$(a + b)^2 = a^2 + 2ab + b^2$.

**What is the solution of $\sqrt{x + 7} - 5 = x$? Check your results.**

$$\sqrt{x + 7} - 5 = x$$

$\sqrt{x + 7} = x + 5$     Isolate the radical.

$(\sqrt{x + 7})^2 = (x + 5)^2$     Square each side.

$x + 7 = x^2 + 10x + 25$     Simplify.

$0 = x^2 + 9x + 18$     Combine like terms.

$0 = (x + 3)(x + 6)$     Factor.

$x = -3 \text{ or } x = -6$     Zero-Product Property

**Check**

$\sqrt{x + 7} - 5 = x$                  $\sqrt{x + 7} - 5 = x$

$\sqrt{-3 + 7} - 5 \overset{?}{=} -3$          $\sqrt{-6 + 7} - 5 \overset{?}{=} -6$

$\sqrt{4} - 5 \overset{?}{=} -3$                $\sqrt{1} - 5 \overset{?}{=} -6$

$2 - 5 \overset{?}{=} -3$                  $1 - 5 \overset{?}{=} -6$

$-3 = -3$ ✔                    $-4 \neq -6$

The only solution is $-3$.                           false

 **Got It?** **4. a.** What is the solution of $\sqrt{5x - 1} + 3 = x$? Check your results.
         **b. Reasoning** When should you check for extraneous solutions? Explain.

In this lesson you studied algebraic methods of solving square root and radical equations. In Lesson 6-8 you will study the graphs of square root functions. These graphs can help you find solutions and identify extraneous solutions.

The calculator screen shows the graphs **Y1 = $\sqrt{(x + 7)}$ − 5** and **Y2 = x**. From the graph, it is clear that $-3$ is a solution of $\sqrt{x + 7} - 5 = x$, and $-6$ is not a solution.

**Problem 4**           SYNTHESIZING
Sometimes students assume that all negative numbers are extraneous solutions for square root equations. Use this problem to emphasize that some negative numbers do satisfy the original radical equation.

**Q** How do you check an equation for extraneous solutions? **[Substitute each possible solution for x in the original equation and check to see if the equation is true.]**

**Q** Why is $-6$ called an extraneous solution for this equation? **[When it is substituted for x in the original equation, it gives a false statement.]**

**Got It?**

**Q** Will you have to check for extraneous solutions for this problem? Explain your answer. **[Yes; to solve the problem, you will have to square both sides of the equation, which may introduce extraneous solutions.]**

**Q** If you solve a square root equation by graphing, will you have to check for extraneous solutions? Explain. **[No; if a solution is extraneous, it will not be on the graph.]**

# Answers

## Got It? (continued)

**2.** 5, $-11$

**3.** 37,500,000 m$^3$

**4. a.** 10

     **b.** when you raise each side of an equation to a power

## Problem 5

Q Why do you square both sides of this equation *twice* to solve it? **[because squaring the first time did not eliminate both radicals]**

**ERROR PREVENTION**

In this problem, students may do the following:
$(\sqrt{2x+1})^2 - (\sqrt{x})^2 = 1^2$
or $(\sqrt{2x+1})^2 = 1^2 + (\sqrt{x})^2$. Emphasize that they must raise each *side* to the *n*th power, not each *term*.

### Got It?

Q Which radical should you isolate first? Explain.
**[$\sqrt{5x+4}$; it is more complicated.]**

## 3 Lesson Check

### Do you know HOW?
• For Exercises 1–6, emphasize that the first step for solving any radical equation is to isolate the radical on one side of the equation.

### Do you UNDERSTAND?
• In Exercise 7, make sure students realize that the number they are looking for is *not* a solution to the equation.

### Close

Q What are the steps to solving a radical equation?
**[Sample: Isolate the radical on one side of the equation. Raise both sides to the power that is the reciprocal of the radical. Simplify. Repeat if there are more radicals. Solve the resulting polynomial equation; check for extraneous solutions.]**

PowerAlgebra.com

### 3 Lesson Check

For a digital lesson check, use the Got It questions.

**Support in Algebra 2 Companion**
• Lesson Check

### 4 Practice

Assign homework to individual students or to an entire class.

---

If an equation contains two radical expressions (or two terms with rational exponents), isolate one of the radicals (or one of the terms), then eliminate it (or its rational exponent). Isolate the more complicated radical expression first. In the resulting equation, simplify the expressions before you eliminate the second radical.

 **Problem 5** Solving an Equation With Two Radicals

What is the solution of $\sqrt{2x+1} - \sqrt{x} = 1$?

**Plan**

 Which radical expression should you isolate first? Isolate the more complicated radical first, $\sqrt{2x+1}$.

$$\sqrt{2x+1} - \sqrt{x} = 1$$

| | |
|---|---|
| $\sqrt{2x+1} = \sqrt{x} + 1$ | Isolate the more complicated radical. |
| $(\sqrt{2x+1})^2 = (\sqrt{x}+1)^2$ | Square each side. |
| $2x + 1 = x + 2\sqrt{x} + 1$ | |
| $x = 2\sqrt{x}$ | Isolate $2\sqrt{x}$. |
| $x^2 = (2\sqrt{x})^2$ | Square each side. |
| $x^2 = 4x$ | |
| $x^2 - 4x = 0$ | Subtract $4x$ from each side. |
| $x(x-4) = 0$ | Factor. |
| $x = 0 \text{ or } x = 4$ | Zero-Product Property |

**Check**

$$\sqrt{2x+1} - \sqrt{x} = 1$$
$$\sqrt{2(0)+1} - \sqrt{0} \stackrel{?}{=} 1$$
$$\sqrt{1} - 0 \stackrel{?}{=} 1$$
$$1 - 0 \stackrel{?}{=} 1$$
$$1 = 1 ✔$$

$$\sqrt{2x+1} - \sqrt{x} = 1$$
$$\sqrt{2(4)+1} - \sqrt{4} \stackrel{?}{=} 1$$
$$\sqrt{9} - \sqrt{4} \stackrel{?}{=} 1$$
$$3 - 2 \stackrel{?}{=} 1$$
$$1 = 1 ✔$$

The solutions are 0 and 4.

 **Got It? 5.** What is the solution of $\sqrt{5x+4} - \sqrt{x} = 4$?

### Lesson Check

**Do you know HOW?**

Solve. Check for extraneous solutions.

1. $\sqrt{4x-23} - 3 = 2$
2. $-\sqrt[3]{x} + 3 = 0$
3. $5\sqrt{x} + 7 = 8$
4. $3\sqrt{x} = 6$
5. $5 - 2\sqrt{x} = 3$
6. $\sqrt[3]{x} = 8$

**Do you UNDERSTAND?**

7. **Vocabulary** Which value, 12 or 3, is an extraneous solution of $x - 6 = \sqrt{3x}$? Explain your reasoning.

8. **Compare and Contrast** How is solving a square root equation similar to solving an absolute value equation? How is it different?

---

# Answers

### Got It? (continued)
**5.** 9

### Lesson Check
**1.** 12
**2.** 27
**3.** $\frac{1}{25}$
**4.** 4
**5.** 1
**6.** 512
**7.** 3; The solution of 3 yields a negative value for $x - 6$, but the right side of the equation ($\sqrt{3(3)}$) cannot be negative.
**8.** Solving square root equations is different from solving absolute value equations in that you use a different technique to isolate the variable. In square root equations, you square each side. In absolute value equations, you write two new equations and solve both. Solving square root equations is similar to solving absolute value equations in that both can introduce extraneous solutions.

## Practice and Problem-Solving Exercises

Solve.

See Problem 1.

**9.** $3\sqrt{x} + 3 = 15$     **10.** $4\sqrt{x} - 1 = 3$     **11.** $\sqrt{x+3} = 5$

**12.** $\sqrt{x+1} = 4$     **13.** $\sqrt{2x-1} = 3$     **14.** $\sqrt{x+2} - 2 = 0$

**15.** $\sqrt{3x+4} = 4$     **16.** $\sqrt{2x+3} - 7 = 0$     **17.** $\sqrt{6-3x} - 2 = 0$

Solve.

See Problem 2.

**18.** $(x+5)^{\frac{2}{3}} = 4$     **19.** $(x+2)^{\frac{2}{3}} = 9$     **20.** $3(x-2)^{\frac{3}{4}} = 24$

**21.** $3(x+3)^{\frac{3}{4}} = 81$     **22.** $(x+1)^{\frac{3}{2}} - 2 = 25$     **23.** $3 + (4-x)^{\frac{3}{2}} = 11$

**24. Volume** A spherical water tank holds 9000 ft³ of water. What is the diameter of the tank? $\left(Hint: d = \sqrt[3]{\frac{6V}{\pi}}\right)$

See Problem 3.

**25. Hydraulics** The formula $d = \sqrt{\frac{4Q}{\pi v}}$ models the diameter of a pipe where $Q$ is the maximum flow of water in a pipe, and $v$ is the velocity of the water. What is the diameter of a pipe that allows a maximum flow of 30 ft³/min of water flowing at a velocity of 400 ft/min? Round your answer to the nearest inch.

Solve. Check for extraneous solutions.

See Problem 4.

**26.** $\sqrt{3x+7} = x - 1$     **27.** $(5-x)^{\frac{1}{2}} = x + 1$     **28.** $\sqrt{-3x-5} = x + 3$

**29.** $\sqrt{11x+3} - 2x = 0$     **30.** $(5x-4)^{\frac{1}{2}} - x = 0$     **31.** $\sqrt{3x+13} - 5 = x$

**32.** $\sqrt{x+7} + 5 = x$     **33.** $(x+3)^{\frac{1}{2}} - 1 = x$     **34.** $\sqrt{x+7} - x = 1$

Solve. Check for extraneous solutions.

See Problem 5.

**35.** $\sqrt{3x} = \sqrt{x+6}$     **36.** $(2x)^{\frac{1}{2}} = (x+5)^{\frac{1}{2}}$

**37.** $(7x+6)^{\frac{1}{2}} - (9+4x)^{\frac{1}{2}} = 0$     **38.** $\sqrt{3x+2} - \sqrt{2x+7} = 0$

**39.** $(x+5)^{\frac{1}{2}} - (5-2x)^{\frac{1}{4}} = 0$     **40.** $(x-2)^{\frac{1}{2}} - (28-2x)^{\frac{1}{4}} = 0$

**41.** $\sqrt{5-x} - \sqrt{x} = 1$     **42.** $\sqrt{3x+1} - \sqrt{x+1} = 2$

**43.** $\sqrt{2x+6} - \sqrt{x-1} = 2$     **44.** $\sqrt{3-x} + \sqrt{x+2} = 3$

**45. Think About a Plan** A hexagonal tray of vegetables has an area of 450 cm². What is the length of each side of the hexagon?
- What is the area of the triangle at the bottom in terms of the side length?
- How can you use the diagram at the right to find the formula for the area of the hexagon? (*Hint:* Six triangles make one hexagon.)

**46. Traffic Signs** A stop sign is a regular octagon, formed by cutting triangles off the corners of a square. If a stop sign measures 36 in. from top to bottom, what is the length of each side?

$\frac{s\sqrt{3}}{2}$

## Answers

### Practice and Problem-Solving Exercises

**9.** 16
**10.** 1
**11.** 22
**12.** 15
**13.** 5
**14.** 2
**15.** 4
**16.** 23
**17.** $\frac{2}{3}$
**18.** 3, −13
**19.** −29, 25
**20.** 18
**21.** 78
**22.** 8
**23.** 0
**24.** about 25.8 ft
**25.** about 4 in.
**26.** 6
**27.** 1
**28.** −2
**29.** 3
**30.** 1, 4
**31.** −3, −4
**32.** 9
**33.** 1
**34.** 2
**35.** 3
**36.** 5
**37.** 1
**38.** 5
**39.** −2
**40.** 6
**41.** 1
**42.** 8
**43.** 5
**44.** −1, 2
**45.** $10\sqrt[4]{3}$ cm, or about 13.16 cm
**46.** $36\sqrt{2} - 36$

## 4 Practice

**ASSIGNMENT GUIDE**

Basic: 9–44, 45–47, 57–60, 63–65

Average: 9–43 odd, 45–67

Advanced: 9–43 odd, 45–72

Standardized Test Prep: 73–76

Mixed Review: 77–96

**Reasoning** exercises have blue headings.

**Applications** exercises have red headings.

**EXERCISE 46:** Use the Think About a Plan worksheet in the **Practice and Problem Solving Workbook** (also available in the Teaching Resources in print and online) to further support students' development in becoming independent learners.

**HOMEWORK QUICK CHECK**

To check students' understanding of key skills and concepts, go over Exercises 25, 37, 45, 46, and 60.

# Answers

## Practice and Problem-Solving Exercises
(continued)

**47.** 5

**48.** B

**49.** 8

**50.** 4

**51.** 5

**52.** 23

**53.** 1

**54.** 6.5

**55.** 9, −7

**56.** $\frac{81}{16}$

**57.** 9

**58.** 11

**59.** $x = 4$ is a solution, but $x = 1$ is an extraneous solution.

**60.** $d = \frac{v^2}{64}$

**61.** Answers may vary. Sample:
$\sqrt{x - 3} = \sqrt{3x + 5}$

**62. a.** A counterexample is $a = 3, b = -3$.
   **b.** A counterexample is $a = -5, b = 3$.

**63.** C

**64.** 1

**65.** 0, 2

**66.** 2

**67.** 0

---

**47. Mental Math** What is the solution? $\sqrt{x + 11} = 4$

**48.** You can find the area $A$ of a square whose side is $s$ units with the formula $A = s^2$. What is the best estimate for the side of a square with an area of $32\ m^2$?

    Ⓐ 4.2 m            Ⓒ 8.0 m

    Ⓑ 5.7 m            Ⓓ 16 m

**Solve. Check for extraneous solutions.**

**49.** $3\sqrt{2x} - 3 = 9$

**50.** $2(2x)^{\frac{1}{3}} + 1 = 5$

**51.** $\sqrt{2x - 1} - 3 = 0$

**52.** $(2x + 3)^{\frac{1}{2}} - 7 = 0$

**53.** $\sqrt{x^2 + 3} = x + 1$

**54.** $(2x + 3)^{\frac{3}{4}} - 3 = 5$

**55.** $2(x - 1)^{\frac{4}{3}} + 4 = 36$

**56.** $x^{\frac{1}{2}} - (x - 5)^{\frac{1}{2}} = 2$

**57.** $\sqrt{x} = \sqrt{x - 8} + 2$

**58.** $(x - 3)^{\frac{2}{3}} = x - 7$

**59. Error Analysis** A student said that 4 and 1 are the solutions of the problem shown. Describe and correct the student's error.

$$\sqrt{x} + 2 = x$$
$$\sqrt{x} = x - 2$$
$$(\sqrt{x})^2 = (x - 2)^2$$
$$x = x^2 - 4x + 4$$
$$0 = x^2 - 5x + 4$$
$$0 = (x - 4)(x - 1)$$

**60. Physics** The velocity $v$ of an object dropped from a tall building is given by the formula $v = \sqrt{64d}$, where $d$ is the distance the object has dropped. Solve the formula for $d$.

**61. Open-Ended** Write an equation that has two radical expressions and no real roots.

**62. Reasoning** You have solved equations containing square roots by squaring each side. You were using the property that if $a = b$ then $a^2 = b^2$. Show that the following statements are *not* true for all real numbers.
   **a.** If $a^2 = b^2$ then $a = b$.
   **b.** If $a \leq b$ then $a^2 \leq b^2$.

**63.** A teacher asked students why it is necessary to check for extraneous roots when squaring both sides of the equation. Which of the following answers is the best? Is this answer complete? Explain.
   Ⓐ Because the squared equation can have negative roots.
   Ⓑ Because squaring is multiplication, and any multiplication is a potential source of extraneous roots.
   Ⓒ Because when you square both sides of the equation $a = b$, you add to the solution set the roots of the equation $a = -b$.
   Ⓓ Because any operation with an equation may result in extraneous roots.

**Solve. Check for extraneous solutions.**

**64.** $\sqrt{x + 1} + \sqrt{2x} = \sqrt{5x + 3}$

**65.** $\sqrt{x + \sqrt{2x}} = \sqrt{2x}$

**66.** $\sqrt{x + \sqrt{2x}} = 2$

**67.** $\sqrt{\sqrt{x + 25}} = \sqrt{x + 5}$

**68. Reasoning** Devise a plan to find the value of $x$.

$$x = \sqrt{2 + \sqrt{2 + \sqrt{2 + \cdots}}}$$

**For each set of values, determine which is greater without using a calculator.**

**69.** $\sqrt{6}$ or $\sqrt{2} + 1$

**70.** $\sqrt{3} + \sqrt{11}$ or 5

**71.** $\sqrt{10}$ or $\sqrt{2} + \sqrt{3}$

**72.** $\sqrt{19} + \sqrt{3}$ or $\sqrt{5} + \sqrt{13}$

## Standardized Test Prep

**SAT/ACT**

**73.** What is the solution of $(x + 2)^{\frac{3}{4}} = 27$?

Ⓐ $x = 27$     Ⓑ $x = 79$     Ⓒ $x = 81$     Ⓓ $x = 83$

**74.** A problem on a test asked students to solve a fifth-degree polynomial equation with rational coefficients. Adam found the following roots: $-11.5$, $\sqrt{2}$, $\frac{2i + 6}{2}$, $-\sqrt{2}$ and $3 - i$. His teacher wrote that four of these roots are correct, and one is incorrect. Which root is incorrect?

Ⓕ $-11.5$     Ⓖ $\sqrt{2}$     Ⓗ $\frac{2i + 6}{2}$     Ⓘ $3 - i$

**75.** Which expression represents the solution of the equation $\frac{x}{y} = \frac{c}{a + b}$ solved for $a$?

Ⓐ $\frac{c}{b} - \frac{x}{y}$     Ⓑ $\frac{yc}{a + b}$     Ⓒ $\frac{yc}{x} + b$     Ⓓ $\frac{yc - xb}{x}$

**Short Response**

**76.** To rationalize the denominator of $\sqrt[4]{\frac{4}{25}}$, by what number would you multiply the numerator and denominator of the fraction?

## Mixed Review

**Simplify each number.**    ◆ See Lesson 6-4.

**77.** $81^{\frac{1}{4}}$

**78.** $4^{\frac{1}{2}}$

**79.** $125 \cdot 125^{\frac{1}{3}}$

**80.** $32 \cdot 256^{\frac{1}{2}}$

**81.** $100^{-\frac{3}{2}}$

**82.** $64^{\frac{2}{3}}$

**83.** $25^{1.5}$

**84.** $6^{\frac{1}{2}} \cdot 12^{\frac{1}{2}}$

**Solve each equation by factoring. Check your answers.**    ◆ See Lesson 4-5.

**85.** $x^2 - 7x + 12 = 0$

**86.** $x^2 - 8x + 15 = 0$

**87.** $x^2 + 9x + 20 = 0$

**88.** $3x^2 + 8x + 4 = 0$

**89.** $9x^2 + 15x + 4 = 0$

**90.** $4x^2 + 11x + 6 = 0$

**Get Ready!**   **To prepare for Lesson 6-6, do Exercises 91–96.**

**Find the domain and range of each relation, and determine whether it is a function.**    ◆ See Lesson 2-1.

**91.** $\{(0, -5), (2, -3), (4, -1)\}$

**92.** $\{(-1, 2), (0, 0), (1, 1)\}$

**93.** $\{(-2, -2), (0, 0), (1, 1)\}$

**94.** $\{(3, -1), (4, -1), (5, -1)\}$

**95.** $\{(0, 0), (1, 0), (2, 1), (2, 2)\}$

**96.** $\{(0, -2), (0, 0), (0, 2)\}$

---

**88.** $-2, -\frac{2}{3}$

**89.** $-\frac{1}{3}, -\frac{4}{3}$

**90.** $-2, -\frac{3}{4}$

**91.** domain: $\{0, 2, 4\}$, range: $\{-5, -3, -1\}$; yes

**92.** domain: $\{-1, 0, 1\}$, range: $\{2, 0, 1\}$; yes

**93.** domain: $\{-2, 0, 1\}$, range: $\{-2, 0, 1\}$; yes

**94.** domain: $\{3, 4, 5\}$, range: $\{-1\}$; yes

**95.** domain: $\{0, 1, 2\}$, range: $\{0, 1, 2\}$; no

**96.** domain: $\{0\}$, range: $\{-2, 0, 2\}$; no

---

**68.** Plan 1: Use a calculator to evaluate $\sqrt{2}$ and record it. Add 2, take the square root, and record it. Repeat this procedure about seven times until it becomes clear that the values are approaching 2.
Plan 2: The given eq. is equivalent to $x = \sqrt{2 + x}$. Solve this eq. to find that $x = 2$.

**69.** $\sqrt{6}$

**70.** $\sqrt{3} + \sqrt{11}$

**71.** $\sqrt{10}$

**72.** $\sqrt{19} + \sqrt{3}$

**Standardized Test Prep**

**73.** B

**74.** F

**75.** D

**76.** [2]

$$\sqrt[4]{25^3}; \frac{\sqrt[4]{4}}{\sqrt[4]{25}} \cdot \frac{\sqrt[4]{25^3}}{\sqrt[4]{25^3}} = \frac{\sqrt[4]{62,500}}{25}$$

$$= \frac{\sqrt[4]{625} \cdot \sqrt[4]{100}}{25} = \frac{5\sqrt[4]{100}}{25} = \frac{\sqrt[4]{100}}{5}$$

**[1]** correct answer, but without any work shown

**Mixed Review**

**77.** 3

**78.** 2

**79.** 625

**80.** 512

**81.** $\frac{1}{1000}$

**82.** 16

**83.** 125

**84.** $6\sqrt{2}$

**85.** 3, 4

**86.** 3, 5

**87.** $-5, -4$

## Additional Instructional Support

### Algebra 2 Companion

Students can use the **Algebra 2 Companion** worktext (4 pages) as you teach the lesson. Use the Companion to support

- New Vocabulary
- Key Concepts
- Got It for each Problem
- Lesson Check

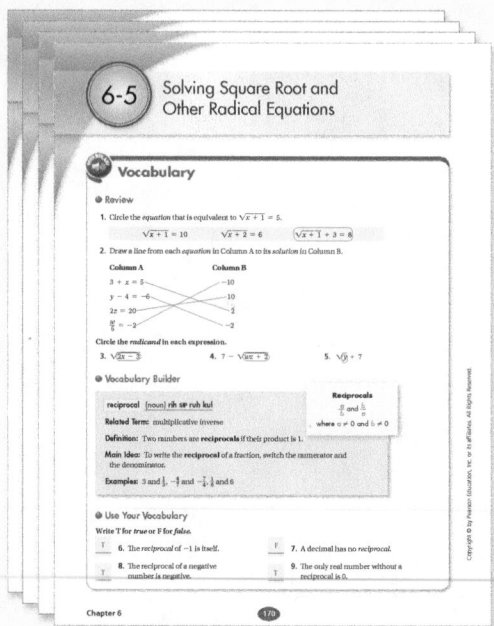

## 5 Assess & Remediate

### Lesson Quiz

1. What is the solution of $\sqrt{x - 2} + 1 = 5$?

2. What is the solution of $(4x + 1)^{\frac{1}{4}} - 4 = -1$?

3. **Do you UNDERSTAND?** The radius $r$ of a sphere is related to its volume $V$ by $r = \sqrt[3]{\dfrac{3V}{4\pi}}$. If the radius of a sphere is 3 centimeters, what is its volume?

4. What is the solution of $\sqrt{x - 1} = x - 7$? Check your results.

5. What is the solution of $\sqrt{2x - 2} + \sqrt{x} = 7$?

### ANSWERS TO LESSON QUIZ

1. 18
2. 20
3. about 113 cubic centimeters
4. 10
5. 9

## ELL Support

**Focus on Language** Use examples and nonexamples to help students understand the definition of *radical equation* given in this lesson.

Write these equations on the board:

$4 = 2x$  $\qquad$  $4 = \sqrt{2x}$

$4 = \sqrt{2} + x$  $\qquad$  $4 = \sqrt{2 + x}$

Point to each equation and ask, "What are these?" [equations]

Point to $x$ in each equation and ask, "What are these?" [variables]

Point to the radicand in the last three equations and ask, "What are these?" [radicands]

Point to $x$ in the last two equations and ask, "Where is the variable?" [in a radicand]

Say, "A radical equation has a variable in a radicand." Then, point to each equation and ask, "Does this equation have a variable in a radicand?"

### PRESCRIPTION FOR REMEDIATION

Use the student work on the Lesson Quiz to prescribe a differentiated review assignment:

| Points | Differentiated Remediation |
|--------|---------------------------|
| 0–2 | Intervention |
| 3–4 | On-level |
| 5 | Extension |

## 5 Assess & Remediate

Assign the Lesson Quiz. Appropriate intervention, practice, or enrichment is automatically generated based on student performance.

## Intervention

- **Reteaching** (2 pages) Provides reteaching and practice exercises for the key lesson concepts. Use with struggling students or absent students.

- **English Language Learner Support** Helps students develop and reinforce mathematical vocabulary and key concepts.

### All-in-One Resources/Online
### Reteaching

**6-5 Reteaching**
Solving Square Root and Other Radical Equations

Equations containing radicals can be solved by isolating the radical on one side of the equation, and then raising both sides to the same power that would undo the radical.

**Problem**

What is the solution of the radical equation? $2\sqrt{2x + 2} - 2 = 10$

| | |
|---|---|
| $2\sqrt{2x + 2} - 2 = 10$ | |
| $2\sqrt{2x + 2} = 12$ | Add 2 to each side. |
| $\sqrt{2x + 2} = 6$ | Divide each side by 2. |
| $(\sqrt{2x + 2})^2 = 6^2$ | Square each side to undo the radical. |
| $2x + 2 = 36$ | Simplify. |
| $2x = 34$ | Subtract 2 from each side. |
| $x = 17$ | Divide each side by 2. |

Check the solution in the original equation.

**Check**

| | |
|---|---|
| $2\sqrt{2x + 2} - 2 = 10$ | Write the original equation. |
| $2\sqrt{2(17) + 2} - 2 \stackrel{?}{=} 10$ | Replace $x$ by 17. |
| $2\sqrt{36} - 2 \stackrel{?}{=} 10$ | Simplify. |
| $12 - 2 \stackrel{?}{=} 10$ | |
| $10 = 10 ✓$ | |

The solution is 17.

**Exercises**

Solve. Check your solutions.

1. $x^{\frac{1}{2}} = 13$  169

2. $3\sqrt{2x} = 12$  8

3. $\sqrt{3x} + 5 = 11$  12

4. $(2x + 4)^{\frac{1}{2}} - 1 = 4$  7

5. $(6 - x)^{\frac{1}{2}} + 2 = 5$  -3

6. $\sqrt{3x + 13} = 4$  1

7. $(x + 2)^{\frac{1}{2}} - 5 = 0$  23

8. $\sqrt{3 - 2x} - 2 = 3$  -11

9. $\sqrt[3]{3x + 2} - 3 = 0$  5

### All-in-One Resources/Online
### English Language Learner Support

**6-5 ELL Support**
Solving Square Root and Other Radical Equations

**Problem**

Solve the equation $4\sqrt[3]{(y + 2)^2} + 3 = 19$. Justify your steps. Then check your solution.

| | |
|---|---|
| $4(y + 2)^{\frac{2}{3}} + 3 = 19$ | Rewrite the radical using a rational exponent. |
| $4(y + 2)^{\frac{2}{3}} = 16$ | Subtract 3 from each side. |
| $(y + 2)^{\frac{2}{3}} = 4$ | Divide each side by 4. |
| $\left[(y + 2)^{\frac{2}{3}}\right]^{\frac{3}{2}} = 4^{\frac{3}{2}}$ | Raise each side to the $\frac{3}{2}$ power. |
| $(y + 2) = 8$ | Simplify the exponents. |
| $y = 6$ | Solve for $y$. |

| Check | | |
|---|---|---|
| | $4\sqrt[3]{(6 + 2)^2} + 3 = 19$ | Substitute 6 for $y$. |
| | $4\sqrt[3]{8^2} + 3 = 19$ | Add. |
| | $4 \cdot 4 + 3 = 19$ | Simplify the radical. |
| | $19 = 19$ | Simplify. |

**Exercise**

Solve the equation $9\sqrt{(2x - 4)^4} + 2 = 38$. Justify your steps. Then check your solution.

| | |
|---|---|
| $9(2x - 4)^{\frac{4}{2}} + 2 = 38$ | Rewrite the radical using a rational exponent. |
| $9(2x - 4)^2 = 36$ | Subtract 2 from each side and simplify the exponent. |
| $(2x - 4)^2 = 4$ | Divide each side by 9. |
| $\left[(2x - 4)^2\right]^{\frac{1}{2}} = 4^{\frac{1}{2}}$ | Raise each side to the $\frac{1}{2}$ power. |
| $(2x - 4) = 2$ | Simplify the exponents. |
| $x = 3$ | Solve for $x$. |

| Check | | |
|---|---|---|
| | $9\sqrt{(2 \cdot 3 - 4)^4} + 2 = 38$ | Substitute 3 for $x$. |
| | $9\sqrt{16} + 2 = 38$ | Simplify the expression under the radical. |
| | $38 = 38$ | Simplify. |

# Differentiated Remediation *continued*

## On-Level

- **Practice** (2 pages) Provides extra practice for each lesson. For simpler practice exercises, use the Form K Practice pages found in the All-in-One Teaching Resources and online.

- **Think About a Plan** Helps students develop specific problem-solving skills and strategies by providing scaffolded guiding questions.
- **Standardized Test Prep** Focuses on all major exercises, all major question types, and helps students prepare for the high-stakes assessments.

## Extension

- **Enrichment** Provides students with interesting problems and activities that extend the concepts of the lesson.
- **Activities, Games, and Puzzles** Worksheets that can be used for concepts development, enrichment, and for fun!

---

### Practice and Problem Solving Wkbk/ All-in-One Resources/Online
**Practice page 1**

### Practice and Problem Solving Wkbk/ All-in-One Resources/Online
**Practice page 2**

### All-in-One Resources/Online
**Enrichment**

### Practice and Problem Solving Wkbk/ All-in-One Resources/Online
**Think About a Plan**

### Practice and Problem Solving Wkbk/ All-in-One Resources/Online
**Standardized Test Prep**

### Online Teacher Resource Center
**Activities, Games, and Puzzles**

# 1 Interactive Learning

## Solve It!

**PURPOSE** To write and subtract equations to solve a percentage problem

**PROCESS** Students may

- find the final cost using each option, and find the difference.
- write general equations to represent both options, identify which equation gives a lower price, and find the difference between the equations to find how much money is saved.

### FACILITATE

**Q** How can you represent a payment including a 5% sales tax before the discount? **[(1.05)$x$, where $x$ is the cost before the sales tax]**

**Q** Can you write mathematical expressions to represent both options? Explain. **[yes; (1.05)$x$ − 50 and ($x$ − 50)1.05, where $x$ is the original cost]**

**ANSWER** See Solve It in Answers on next page.

**CONNECT THE MATH** The students write and subtract equations in the Solve It. In the lesson, students add and subtract functions and prove that function composition is not commutative.

# 2 Guided Instruction

## Take Note
**AUDITORY LEARNERS**

The symbols may confuse some students, and they may think that the parentheses imply multiplication. Read each operation out loud, using the correct terminology. For example, "The sum of $f$ and $g$ of $x$ equals the sum of $f$ of $x$ and $g$ of $x$."

---

## 6-6 Function Operations

**Getting Ready!**

You want to buy a sofa that has already been marked down by $100. The furniture store may add the 5% sales tax before applying the additional discount, or it may add the sales tax after applying the additional discount. Which way is better for you, the customer? How much better?

Make sure you get the best bargain!

Clearance sale
Take $50 off

**Lesson Vocabulary**
- composite function

The final cost of the sofa in the Solve It involves two functions: one that gives an additional discount and one that multiplies to find the sales tax.

**Essential Understanding** You can add, subtract, multiply, and divide functions based on how you perform these operations for real numbers. One difference, however, is that you must consider the domain of each function.

### Key Concepts  Function Operations

| | |
|---|---|
| Addition | $(f + g)(x) = f(x) + g(x)$ |
| Subtraction | $(f - g)(x) = f(x) - g(x)$ |
| Multiplication | $(f \cdot g)(x) = f(x) \cdot g(x)$ |
| Division | $\left(\dfrac{f}{g}\right)(x) = \dfrac{f(x)}{g(x)}, g(x) \neq 0$ |

The domains of the sum, difference, product, and quotient functions consist of the $x$-values that are in the domains of *both* $f$ and $g$. Also, the domain of the quotient function does not contain any $x$-value for which $g(x) = 0$.

---

# 6-6 Preparing to Teach

## BIG idea Function  **UbD**

### ESSENTIAL UNDERSTANDINGS

- Functions can be added, subtracted, multiplied, and divided based on how these operations are performed for real numbers. One difference, however, is that the domain of each function must be considered.
- The $n$th root of an expression that contains an $n$th power as a factor can be simplified.

$$\sqrt[n]{x^n} = x^{\frac{n}{n}} = \begin{cases} x, & \text{if } n \text{ is odd} \\ |x|, & \text{if } n \text{ is even} \end{cases}$$

## Math Background

The notation for the composition of two functions is easily confused with the notation for the product of two functions.

Highlight the differences:

- While multiplication of functions is commutative, composition of functions generally is not. Problem 4 in the text highlights this; the price is different when the coupon is applied first than when the discount is applied first.

---

- The product of two functions involves multiplying each term of one function by each term of the other. The composition of two functions involves replacing the variable of one function with the expression equal to the other function.
- By definition, the composition of the function $f$ with the function $g$ can also be written as $f(g(x))$. This is in contrast to the product of $f$ and $g$ which can be written as $f(x) \cdot g(x)$.

## Support Student Learning

Use the **Algebra 2 Companion** to engage and support students during instruction. See Lesson Resources at the end of this lesson for details.

---

**PowerAlgebra.com**

# 1 Interactive Learning

## Solve It!

Step out how to solve the Problem with helpful hints and an online question. Other questions are listed above in Interactive Learning.

### Problem 1  Adding and Subtracting Functions

Let $f(x) = 4x + 7$ and $g(x) = \sqrt{x} + x$. What are $f + g$ and $f - g$? What are their domains?

$$(f + g)(x) = f(x) + g(x) = (4x + 7) + (\sqrt{x} + x) = 5x + \sqrt{x} + 7$$
$$(f - g)(x) = f(x) - g(x) = (4x + 7) - (\sqrt{x} + x) = 3x - \sqrt{x} + 7$$

**Think**

**What determines the domain of $g$?**
Because there is a square root of $x$, $x$ must be $\geq 0$.

The domain of $f$ is the set of all real numbers. The domain of $g$ is all $x \geq 0$. The domain of both $f + g$ and $f - g$ is the set of numbers common to the domains of both $f$ and $g$, which is all $x \geq 0$.

**Got It?  1.** Let $f(x) = 2x^2 + 8$ and $g(x) = x - 3$. What are $f + g$ and $f - g$? What are their domains?

### Problem 2  Multiplying and Dividing Functions

Let $f(x) = x^2 - 9$ and $g(x) = x + 3$. What are $f \cdot g$ and $\frac{f}{g}$ and their domains?

$$(f \cdot g)(x) = f(x) \cdot g(x) = (x^2 - 9)(x + 3)$$
$$= x^3 + 3x^2 - 9x - 27$$
$$\left(\frac{f}{g}\right)(x) = \frac{f(x)}{g(x)} = \frac{x^2 - 9}{x + 3} = \frac{(x - 3)(x + 3)}{x + 3} = x - 3, x \neq -3$$

**Think**

**Is the domain of $\frac{f}{g}$ the domain of $x - 3$?**
No; The fraction can only be simplified and the function is only defined when $g(x) \neq -3$.

The domain of both $f$ and $g$ is the set of real numbers, so the domain of $f \cdot g$ is also the set of real numbers.
The domain of $\frac{f}{g}$ is the set of all real numbers except $x \neq -3$, because $g(-3) = 0$. The definition of $\frac{f}{g}$ requires that you consider the zero denominator in the *original* expression for $\frac{f(x)}{g(x)}$ despite the fact that the simplified form has the domain all real numbers.

**Got It?  2.** Let $f(x) = 3x^2 - 11x - 4$ and $g(x) = 3x + 1$. What are $f \cdot g$ and $\frac{f}{g}$ and their domains?

The diagram shows what happens when you apply one function $g(x)$ after another function $f(x)$.

The output from the first function becomes the input for the second function. When you combine two functions as in the diagram, you form a **composite function**.

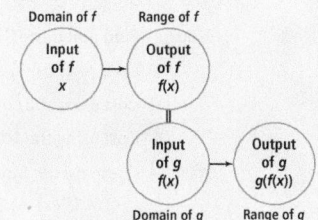

---

## Problem 1

**Q** How do you add or subtract functions? [**By definition, you add or subtract the functions' expressions resulting in one expression that is equal to the new function.**]

### Got It?

**Q** When simplified, why does $(f - g)(x) = 2x^2 - x + 11$ instead of $2x^2 - x + 5$? [**Since $g(x)$ is in parentheses when the subtraction is done, the subtraction sign gets distributed, yielding $2x^2 + 8 - x + 3$ before the answer is simplified.**]

## Problem 2

**Q** How does the domain of $\left(\frac{f}{g}\right)(x)$ compare to the domain of $\left(\frac{g}{f}\right)(x)$? [**The domain of $\left(\frac{f}{g}\right)(x)$ excludes only $-3$ while the domain of $\left(\frac{g}{f}\right)(x)$ excludes both $-3$ and 3.**]

### Got It?

**Q** Why do you factor $3x^2 - 11x - 4$ when dividing but not when multiplying? [**Answers may vary. Sample: When you divide, you end up with a fraction, and factoring the numerator makes it possible to simplify the denominator. When you multiply, you will have no denominator so you do not need to simplify it.**]

---

## 2 Guided Instruction

Each Problem is worked out and supported online.

**Problem 1**
Adding and Subtracting Functions
*Animated*

**Problem 2**
Multiplying and Dividing Functions
*Animated*

**Problem 3**
Composing Functions
*Animated*

**Problem 4**
Using Composite Functions

**Support in Algebra 2 Companion**
• Vocabulary
• Key Concepts
• Got It?

## Answers

**Solve It!**
It is better for the customer to take the additional discount before adding the sales tax; $2.50

**Got It?**
**1.** $(f + g)(x) = 2x^2 + x + 5$, domain: all real numbers; $(f - g)(x) = 2x^2 - x + 11$, domain: all real numbers

**2.** $(f \cdot g)(x) = 9x^3 - 30x^2 - 23x - 4$, domain: all real numbers; $\left(\frac{f}{g}\right)(x) = x - 4$, domain: all real numbers except $x = -\frac{1}{3}$

## Take Note

**ERROR PREVENTION**

Stress that the symbol ∘ is not related to multiplication, though it looks like the symbol · for multiplication. You can read "g ∘ f" as "g composed with f."

## Problem 3

**Q** What is the range of $g(f(x))$? **[all real numbers greater than or equal to 0]**

## Got It?

**Q** What is the difference between the two methods? Which do you prefer? **[Answers may vary. Sample: In Method 1, you first find the function rule for $(g \circ f)(x)$, and in Method 2 you directly find the value of $(g \circ f)(-3)$. I prefer Method 1 because you can look at the function rule.]**

## Problem 4

**Q** Which discount would you want to be applied first? **[the 10% student discount]**

**Q** Is the composition of functions commutative? Explain. **[No; if it were, it would not matter which discount you applied first, and you would get the same answer both ways. Since you pay less when you apply the 10% discount first, the composition of these functions is not commutative.]**

---

**take note** **Key Concept** **Composition of Functions**

The composition of function $g$ with function $f$ is written as $g \circ f$ and is defined as $(g \circ f)(x) = g(f(x))$. The domain of $g \circ f$ consists of the $x$-values in the domain of $f$ for which $f(x)$ is in the domain of $g$.

$$(g \circ f)(x) = g(\underbrace{f(x)}_{\textstyle \frac{1}{2}})$$ 
1. Evaluate $f(x)$ first.
2. Then use $f(x)$ as the input for $g$.

Function composition is not commutative since $f(g(x))$ does not always equal $g(f(x))$.

### Problem 3 Composing Functions

GRIDDED RESPONSE

Let $f(x) = x - 5$ and $g(x) = x^2$. What is $(g \circ f)(-3)$?

**Method 1**

$(g \circ f)(x) = g(f(x))$

$\qquad = g(x - 5) = (x - 5)^2$

$(g \circ f)(-3) = (-3 - 5)^2$

$\qquad = (-8)^2$

$\qquad = 64$

**Method 2**

$(g \circ f)(-3) = g(f(-3))$

$\qquad = g(-3 - 5)$

$\qquad = g(-8)$

$\qquad = (-8)^2$

$\qquad = 64$

**Think**

Which function is substituted into the other?
Use $f(x)$ as the input for $g$.

**Got It?** **3.** What is $(f \circ g)(-3)$ for the functions $f$ and $g$ defined in Problem 3?

### Problem 4 Using Composite Functions

You have a coupon good for $5 off the price of any large pizza. You also get a 10% discount on any pizza if you show your student ID. How much more would you pay for a large pizza if the cashier applies the coupon first?

| Know | Need | Plan |
|---|---|---|
| The coupon value and the discount rate | The difference between the results of applying the discount or coupon first | • Compose two functions in two ways.<br>• Then find the difference in their results. |

**Step 1** Find functions $C$ and $D$ that model the cost of a large pizza.

Let $x =$ the price of a large pizza.

Cost using the coupon: $C(x) = x - 5$

Cost using the 10% discount: $D(x) = x - 0.1x = 0.9x$

**Step 2** Compose the functions to apply the discount and then the coupon.

$(C \circ D)(x) = C(D(x))$ \qquad Apply the discount, $D(x)$, first.

$\qquad = C(0.9x) = 0.9x - 5$

---

# Additional Problems

**1.** Let $f(x) = 5x^3 + 1$ and $g(x) = x^2 - 4$. What are $f + g$ and $f - g$? What are their domains?

**ANSWER**
$(f + g)(x) = 5x^3 + x^2 - 3$;
$(f - g)(x) = 5x^3 - x^2 + 5$;
the domain of each is all real numbers.

**2.** Let $f(x) = x^2 + x - 6$ and $g(x) = x - 2$. What are $f \cdot g$ and $\frac{f}{g}$ and their domains?

**ANSWER**
$(f \cdot g)(x) = x^3 - x^2 - 8x + 12$
$\left(\frac{f}{g}\right)(x) = x + 3$; the domain of $(f \cdot g)(x)$ is all real numbers; the domain of $\left(\frac{f}{g}\right)(x)$ is all real numbers except $x = 2$.

**3.** Let $f(x) = x^2 + 1$ and $g(x) = x - 2$. What is $(g \circ f)(-2)$?

**ANSWER** 3

**4.** A car manufacturer offers a $2000 rebate, but the buyer must pay the 7% sales tax on the full price of the car. Write a composite function to represent the cost to purchase a car listed for $x$ dollars.

**ANSWER**
$f(x) = 1.07x$;
$g(x) = x - 2000$;
$(g \circ f)(x) = 1.07x - 2000$

# Answers

## Got It? (continued)

**3.** 4

**4.** Let $D(x) =$ cost after applying the 15% store discount, $E(x) =$ cost after applying the 20% employee discount, and $x =$ cost of items, then $D(x) = 0.85x$ and $E(x) = 0.80x$.

**a.** $(E \circ D)(x) = 0.68x$

**b.** $(D \circ E)(x) = 0.68x$

**c.** The total discounts are the same.

**Step 3** Compose the functions to apply the coupon and then the discount.

$(D \circ C)(x) = D(C(x))$    Apply the coupon, $C(x)$, first.

$\qquad\qquad = D(x - 5) = 0.9(x - 5) = 0.9x - 4.5$

**Step 4** Subtract the functions to find how much more you would pay if the cashier applies the coupon first.

$(D \circ C)(x) - (C \circ D)(x) = (0.9x - 4.5) - (0.9x - 5)$

$\qquad\qquad\qquad\qquad\qquad = -4.5 + 5$

$\qquad\qquad\qquad\qquad\qquad = 0.5$

You pay $.50 more if the cashier applies the coupon first.

 **Got It?** **4.** A store is offering a 15% discount on all items. Also, employees get a 20% employee discount. Write composite functions
  **a.** to model taking the 15% discount and then the 20% discount.
  **b.** to model taking the 20% discount and then the 15% discount.
  **c.** Reasoning If you were an employee, which discount would you take first? Why?

---

 **Lesson Check**

**Do you know HOW?**

Let $f(x) = 3x - 2$ and $g(x) = x^2 + 1$. Perform each function operation.

**1.** $(f \cdot g)(x)$        **2.** $(f - g)(x)$

**3.** $(f \circ g)(x)$       **4.** $f(x) + g(x)$

**5.** $g(x) - f(x)$     **6.** $f(x) - g(x)$

**Do you UNDERSTAND?**

**7.** Error Analysis Your friend used some simple functions and found that $(f \circ g)(x) = (g \circ f)(x)$, and concluded that function composition is commutative. Give an example to show that your friend is mistaken.

**8.** Open-Ended Find two functions $f$ and $g$ such that $f(g(x)) = x$ for all real numbers $x$.

---

 **Practice and Problem-Solving Exercises**

 **Practice** Let $f(x) = 7x + 5$ and $g(x) = x^2$. Perform each function operation and then find the domain of the result.     ◆ See Problems 1 and 2.

**9.** $(f + g)(x)$      **10.** $(f - g)(x)$      **11.** $(g - f)(x)$

**12.** $(f \cdot g)(x)$      **13.** $\frac{f}{g}(x)$      **14.** $\frac{g}{f}(x)$

Let $f(x) = 2 - x$ and $g(x) = \frac{1}{x}$. Perform each function operation and then find the domain of the result.

**15.** $(f + g)(x)$      **16.** $(f - g)(x)$      **17.** $(g - f)(x)$

**18.** $(f \cdot g)(x)$      **19.** $\frac{f}{g}(x)$      **20.** $\frac{g}{f}(x)$

---

**Got It?**

In contrast to Problem 4, the composition of $D$ and $E$ does happen to be commutative.

**Q** How is it that $(D \circ E)(x) = (E \circ D)(x)$ when functions in previous problems did not commute? **[Answers may vary. Sample: These two functions only involve multiplication, and multiplication is associative and commutative.]**

## 3 Lesson Check

**Do you know HOW?**

• If students have difficulty combining functions algebraically, have them use the Take Notes "Function Operations" and "Composition of Functions" to write out the five definitions on an index card to refer to until they are comfortable with them.

**Do you UNDERSTAND?**

• For Exercise 7, if students have trouble understanding that composition of functions is not commutative, review how the operation is different from multiplication. Explain that finding one counterexample is enough to prove that composition of functions is not commutative.

**Close**

**Q** How are multiplying two functions and composing two functions the same? How are they different? **[Answers may vary. Sample: In both cases, you form a new function. The product of two functions is found by multiplying the expressions for the functions. When composing functions, the output of one function becomes the input of the other function.]**

---

**Lesson Check**

**1.** $3x^3 - 2x^2 + 3x - 2$

**2.** $-x^2 + 3x - 3$

**3.** $3x^2 + 1$

**4.** $x^2 + 3x - 1$

**5.** $x^2 - 3x + 3$

**6.** $-x^2 + 3x - 3$

**7.** Answers may vary. Sample: $f(x) = 3x^2 + 1$, $g(x) = 2x + 1$; $(f \circ g)(x) = 12x^2 + 12x + 4$; $(g \circ f)(x) = 6x^2 + 3$

**8.** Answers may vary. Sample: $f(x) = 2x$, $g(x) = 0.5x$; $f(g(x)) = x$

**Practice and Problem-Solving Exercises**

**9.** $x^2 + 7x + 5$; domain: all real numbers

**10.** $-x^2 + 7x + 5$; domain: all real numbers

**11.** $x^2 - 7x - 5$; domain: all real numbers

**12.** $7x^3 + 5x^2$; domain: all real numbers

**13.** $\frac{7x + 5}{x^2}$; domain: all real numbers except $x = 0$

**14.** $\frac{x^2}{7x + 5}$; domain: all real numbers except $x = -\frac{5}{7}$

**15.** $2 - x + \frac{1}{x}$; domain: all real numbers except $x = 0$

**16.** $2 - x - \frac{1}{x}$; domain: all real numbers except $x = 0$

**17.** $\frac{1}{x} + x - 2$; domain: all real numbers except $x = 0$

**18.** $\frac{2 - x}{x}$; domain: all real numbers except $x = 0$

**19.** $2x - x^2$; domain: all real numbers except $x = 0$

**20.** $\frac{1}{2x - x^2}$; domain: all real numbers except $x = 0, 2$

---

**PowerAlgebra.com**

## 3 Lesson Check

For a digital lesson check, use the Got It questions.

**Support in Algebra 2 Companion**
• Lesson Check

## 4 Practice

Assign homework to individual students or to an entire class.

# 4 Practice

## ASSIGNMENT GUIDE

Basic: 9–58 all, 59, 61, 69–73 odd

Average: 9–57 odd, 59–78

Advanced: 9–57 odd, 59–85

Standardized Test Prep: 86–89

Mixed Review: 90–106

Reasoning exercises have blue headings.

Applications exercises have red headings.

**EXERCISE 61:** Use the Think About a Plan worksheet in the **Practice and Problem Solving Workbook** (also available in the Teaching Resources in print and online) to further support students' development in becoming independent learners.

## HOMEWORK QUICK CHECK

To check students' understanding of key skills and concepts, go over Exercises 17, 51, 59, 61, and 71.

---

Let $f(x) = 2x^2 + x - 3$ and $g(x) = x - 1$. Perform each function operation and then find the domain.

**21.** $(f + g)(x)$ **22.** $(f - g)(x)$ **23.** $(g - f)(x)$

**24.** $(f \cdot g)(x)$ **25.** $\frac{f}{g}(x)$ **26.** $\frac{g}{f}(x)$

Let $g(x) = 2x$ and $h(x) = x^2 + 4$. Find each value or expression. ◆ See Problem 3.

**27.** $(h \circ g)(1)$ **28.** $(h \circ g)(-5)$ **29.** $(h \circ g)(-2)$

**30.** $(g \circ h)(-2)$ **31.** $(g \circ h)(0)$ **32.** $(g \circ h)(a)$

**33.** $(g \circ g)(a)$ **34.** $(h \circ h)(a)$ **35.** $(h \circ g)(a)$

Let $f(x) = x^2$ and $g(x) = x - 3$. Find each value or expression.

**36.** $(g \circ f)(-2)$ **37.** $(f \circ g)(-2)$ **38.** $(g \circ f)(0)$

**39.** $(f \circ g)(0)$ **40.** $(g \circ f)(3.5)$ **41.** $(f \circ g)(3.5)$

**42.** $(f \circ g)(a)$ **43.** $(g \circ f)(-a)$ **44.** $(f \circ g)(-a)$

**45. Sales** A computer store offers a 5% discount off the list price $x$ for any computer ◆ See Problem 4. bought with cash, rather than put on credit. At the same time, the manufacturer offers a $200 rebate for each purchase of a computer.
  **a.** Write a function $f(x)$ to represent the price after the cash discount.
  **b.** Write a function $g(x)$ to represent the price after the $200 rebate.
  **c.** Suppose the list price of a computer is $1500. Use a composite function to find the price of the computer if the discount is applied before the rebate.
  **d.** Suppose the list price of a computer is $1500. Use a composite function to find the price of the computer if the rebate is applied before the discount.

**46. Economics** Suppose the function $f(x) = 0.15x$ represents the number of U.S. dollars equivalent to $x$ Chinese yuan and the function $g(y) = 14.07y$ represents the number of Mexican pesos equivalent to $y$ U.S. dollars.
  **a.** Write a composite function that represents the number of Mexican pesos equivalent to $x$ Chinese yuan.
  **b.** Find the value in Mexican pesos of an item that costs 15 Chinese yuan.

Let $f(x) = 2x + 5$ and $g(x) = x^2 - 3x + 2$. Perform each function operation and then find the domain.

**47.** $f(x) + g(x)$ **48.** $3f(x) - 2$ **49.** $g(x) - f(x)$

**50.** $-2g(x) + f(x)$ **51.** $f(x) - g(x) + 10$ **52.** $4f(x) + 2g(x)$

**53.** $-f(x) + 4g(x)$ **54.** $f(x) - 2g(x)$ **55.** $f(x) \cdot g(x)$

**56.** $-3f(x) \cdot g(x)$ **57.** $\frac{f(x)}{g(x)}$ **58.** $\frac{5f(x)}{g(x)}$

# Answers

## Practice and Problem-Solving Exercises (continued)

**21.** $2x^2 + 2x - 4$; domain: all real numbers

**22.** $2x^2 - 2$; domain: all real numbers

**23.** $-2x^2 + 2$; domain: all real numbers

**24.** $2x^3 - x^2 - 4x + 3$; domain: all real numbers

**25.** $2x + 3$; domain: all real numbers except $x = 1$

**26.** $\frac{1}{2x + 3}$; domain: all real numbers except $x = -\frac{3}{2}, 1$

**27.** 8

**28.** 104

**29.** 20

**30.** 16

**31.** 8

**32.** $2a^2 + 8$

**33.** $4a$

**34.** $a^4 + 8a^2 + 20$

**35.** $4a^2 + 4$

**36.** 1

**37.** 25

**38.** −3

**39.** 9

**40.** 9.25

**41.** 0.25

**42.** $a^2 - 6a + 9$

**43.** $a^2 - 3$

**44.** $a^2 + 6a + 9$

**45. a.** $f(x) = 0.95x$
  **b.** $g(x) = x - 200$
  **c.** $1225
  **d.** $1235

**46. a.** $(g \circ f)(x) = 2.1105x$
  **b.** 31.6575 pesos

**47.** $x^2 - x + 7$; domain: all real numbers

**48.** $6x + 13$; domain: all real numbers

**49.** $x^2 - 5x - 3$; domain: all real numbers

**50.** $-2x^2 + 8x + 1$; domain: all real numbers

**51.** $-x^2 + 5x + 13$; domain: all real numbers

**52.** $2x^2 + 2x + 24$; domain: all real numbers

**53.** $4x^2 - 14x + 3$; domain: all real numbers

**54.** $-2x^2 + 8x + 1$; domain: all real numbers

**55.** $2x^3 - x^2 - 11x + 10$; domain: all real numbers

**56.** $-6x^3 + 3x^2 + 33x - 30$; domain: all real numbers

**57.** $\frac{2x + 5}{x^2 - 3x + 2}$; domain: all real numbers except $x = 1$ and 2

**58.** $\frac{10x + 25}{x^2 - 3x + 2}$; domain: all real numbers except $x = 1$ and 2

**59. Think About a Plan** A craftsman makes and sells violins. The function
$I(x) = 5995x$ represents the income in dollars from selling $x$ violins. The function
$P(y) = y - 100,000$ represents his profit in dollars if he makes an income of
$y$ dollars. What is the profit from selling 30 violins?
• How can you write a composite function to represent the craftsman's profit?
• How can you use the composite function to find the profit earned when he sells
30 violins?

**60.** Suppose your teacher offers to give the whole class a bonus if everyone passes
the next math test. The teacher says she will give everyone a 10-point bonus and
increase everyone's grade by 9% of their score.
**a.** You earned a 75 on the test. Would you rather have the 10-point bonus first and
then the 9% increase, or the 9% increase first and then the 10-point bonus?
**b. Reasoning** Is this the best plan for all students? Explain.

**61. Sales** A salesperson earns a 3% bonus on weekly sales over $5000. Consider the
following functions.

$$g(x) = 0.03x \qquad\qquad h(x) = x - 5000$$

**a.** Explain what each function above represents.
**b.** Which composition, $(h \circ g)(x)$ or $(g \circ h)(x)$, represents the weekly bonus?
Explain.

**62.** If $(f \circ g)(x) = x^2 - 6x + 8$ and $g(x) = x - 3$, what is $f(x)$?

**Let $g(x) = 3x + 2$ and $f(x) = \dfrac{x - 2}{3}$. Find each value.**

**63.** $f(g(1))$      **64.** $g(f(-4))$      **65.** $f(g(0))$      **66.** $g(f(2))$

**67.** $g(g(0))$      **68.** $(g \circ g)(1)$      **69.** $(f \circ g)(-2)$      **70.** $(f \circ f)(0)$

**71. Geometry** You toss a pebble into a pool of water and watch the circular ripples
radiate outward. You find that the function $r(x) = 12.5x$ describes the radius $r$, in
inches, of a circle $x$ seconds after it was formed. The function $A(x) = \pi x^2$ describes
the area $A$ of a circle with radius $x$.
**a.** Find $(A \circ r)(x)$ when $x = 2$. Interpret your answer.
**b.** Find the area of a circle 4 seconds after it was formed.

**For each pair of functions, find $f(g(x))$ and $g(f(x))$.**

**72.** $f(x) = 3x, g(x) = x^2$            **73.** $f(x) = x + 3, g(x) = x - 5$

**74.** $f(x) = 3x^2 + 2, g(x) = 2x$       **75.** $f(x) = \dfrac{x - 3}{2}, g(x) = 2x - 3$

**76.** $f(x) = -x - 7, g(x) = 4x$        **77.** $f(x) = \dfrac{x + 5}{2}, g(x) = x^2$

**78. Open-Ended** Write a function rule that approximates each value.
**a.** The amount you save is a percent of what you earn. (You choose the percent.)
**b.** The amount you earn depends on how many hours you work. (You choose the
hourly wage.)
**c.** Write and simplify a composite function that expresses your savings as a
function of the number of hours you work. Interpret your results.

---

**59.** $79,850

**60. a.** 10-point bonus first then the 9%
increase

**b.** Yes; the "10-point bonus first then
the 9% increase" is $1.09x + 10.9$
and the "9% increase first then the
10-point bonus" is $1.09x + 10$.
The first option is 0.9 points
greater than the second option.

**61. a.** $g(x)$ is the bonus earned when $x$ is
the amount of sales over $5000.
$h(x)$ is the excess sales over $5000.

**b.** $(g \circ h)(x)$; you first need to find
the excess sales over $5000 to
calculate the bonus.

**62.** $f(x) = x^2 - 1$

**63.** 1

**64.** −4

**65.** 0

**66.** 2

**67.** 8

**68.** 17

**69.** −2

**70.** $-\dfrac{8}{9}$

**71. a.** $\approx 1963$; The area after 2 seconds is
about 1963 in.$^2$
**b.** $\approx 7854$ in.$^2$

**72.** $3x^2$; $9x^2$

**73.** $x - 2$; $x - 2$

**74.** $12x^2 + 2$; $6x^2 + 4$

**75.** $x - 3$; $x - 6$

**76.** $-4x - 7$; $-4x - 28$

**77.** $\dfrac{x^2 + 5}{2}$; $\dfrac{x^2 + 10x + 25}{4}$

**78.** Answers may vary. Samples:
**a.** $g(x) = 0.12x$
**b.** $f(x) = 9.50x$
**c.** $(g \circ f)(x) = 1.14x$; Your savings will
be $1.14 for each hour you work.

# Answers

## Practice and Problem-Solving Exercises
(continued)

**79.** $x^7 - x^6 - 16x^5 + 10x^4 + 85x^3 - 25x^2 - 150x$; domain: all real numbers

**80.** $\dfrac{x^2 + 2x}{x - 3}$, domain: all real numbers except $x = 3$, $\sqrt{5}$ and $-\sqrt{5}$

**81.** $\dfrac{x - 3}{x^2 + 2x}$; domain: all real numbers except $x = 0$, $-2$, $\sqrt{5}$ and $-\sqrt{5}$

**82.** $\dfrac{1}{x}$

**83.** 2

**84.** 4

**85.** $8a + 4h$

## Standardized Test Prep

**86.** D

**87.** H

**88.** C

**89.** **[2]** Look at the 5th number in Row 7 of Pascal's triangle to find the coefficient of the $x^3y^4$ term in the expansion of $(x + y)^7$. $35(3x)^3 (-y)^4 = 945x^3y^4$, so 945 is the coefficient.

**[1]** correct coefficient, but without work shown

## Mixed Review

**90.** 1

**91.** $-3$

**92.** 4

**93.** 3

**94.** 2

**95.** 3

**96.** $x^8 + 32x^7 + 448x^6 + 3584x^5 + 17{,}920x^4 + 57{,}344x^3 + 114{,}688x^2 + 131{,}072x + 65{,}536$

**97.** $x^6 + 6x^5y + 15x^4y^2 + 20x^3y^3 + 15x^2y^4 + 6xy^5 + y^6$

**98.** $16x^4 - 32x^3y + 24x^2y^2 - 8xy^3 + y^4$

**99.** $128x^7 - 1344x^6y + 6048x^5y^2 - 15{,}120x^4y^3 + 22{,}680x^3y^4 - 20{,}412x^2y^5 + 10{,}206xy^6 - 2187y^7$

**100.** $59{,}049 - 65{,}610x + 29{,}160x^2 - 6480x^3 + 720x^4 - 32x^5$

**101.** $1024x^5 - 1280x^4y + 640x^3y^2 - 160x^2y^3 + 20xy^4 - y^5$

**102.** $x^8 + 4x^7 + 6x^6 + 4x^5 + x^4$

**103.** $x^{12} + 12x^{10}y^3 + 60x^8y^6 + 160x^6y^9 + 240x^4y^{12} + 192x^2y^{15} + 64y^{18}$

**104.** no solution

**105.** $(2, 2)$

**106.** $(1, 1)$

---

**Challenge** Let $f(x) = x^4 + 2x^3 - 5x^2 - 10x$ and $g(x) = x^3 - 3x^2 - 5x + 15$. Perform each function operation and simplify, and then find the domain.

**79.** $f(x) \cdot g(x)$

**80.** $\dfrac{f(x)}{g(x)}$

**81.** $\dfrac{g(x)}{f(x)}$

Find each composition of functions. Simplify your answer.

**82.** Let $f(x) = \frac{1}{x}$. Find $f(f(f(x)))$.

**83.** Let $f(x) = 2x - 3$. Find $\dfrac{f(1 + h) - f(1)}{h}$, $h \neq 0$.

**84.** Let $f(x) = 4x - 1$. Find $\dfrac{f(a + h) - f(a)}{h}$, $h \neq 0$.

**85.** Let $f(x) = 4x^2 - 1$. Find $\dfrac{f(a + h) - f(a)}{h}$, $h \neq 0$.

## Standardized Test Prep

**SAT/ACT**

**86.** Let $f(x) = x + 5$ and $g(x) = x^2 - 25$. What is the domain of $\frac{f}{g}(x)$?

Ⓐ All real numbers    Ⓒ All real numbers except $-5$

Ⓑ All real numbers except 5    Ⓓ All real numbers except $-5$ and 5

**87.** Let $g(x) = x - 3$ and $h(x) = x^2 + 6$. What is $(h \circ g)(1)$?

Ⓕ $-14$    Ⓖ 4    Ⓗ 10    Ⓘ 15

**88.** Which number is a solution of $|3 - 2x| < 5$?

Ⓐ $-6$    Ⓑ $-1$    Ⓒ 2    Ⓓ 4

**Short Response**

**89.** What is the coefficient of the $x^3y^4$ term in the expansion of $(3x - y)^7$? Show your work.

## Mixed Review

**Solve. Check for extraneous solutions.**    See Lesson 6-5.

**90.** $\sqrt{x^2 + 3} = x + 1$    **91.** $x + 8 = (x^2 + 16)^{\frac{1}{2}}$    **92.** $\sqrt{x^2 + 9} = x + 1$

**93.** $(x^2 - 9)^{\frac{1}{2}} - x = -3$    **94.** $\sqrt{x^2 + 12} - 2 = x$    **95.** $(3x)^{\frac{1}{2}} = (x + 6)^{\frac{1}{2}}$

**Expand each binomial.**    See Lesson 5-7.

**96.** $(x + 4)^8$    **97.** $(x + y)^6$    **98.** $(2x - y)^4$    **99.** $(2x - 3y)^7$

**100.** $(9 - 2x)^5$    **101.** $(4x - y)^5$    **102.** $(x^2 + x)^4$    **103.** $(x^2 + 2y^3)^6$

**Get Ready!** To prepare for Lesson 6-7, do Exercises 104–106.

**Graph and solve each system.**    See Lesson 3-1.

**104.** $\begin{cases} y = x - 6 \\ y = x + 6 \end{cases}$    **105.** $\begin{cases} y = 0.5x + 1 \\ y = 2x - 2 \end{cases}$    **106.** $\begin{cases} y = \frac{x + 4}{5} \\ y = 5x - 4 \end{cases}$

## Differentiated Remediation

## Additional Instructional Support

### Algebra 2 Companion

Students can use the **Algebra 2 Companion** worktext (4 pages) as you teach the lesson. Use the Companion to support

- New Vocabulary
- Key Concepts
- Got It for each Problem
- Lesson Check

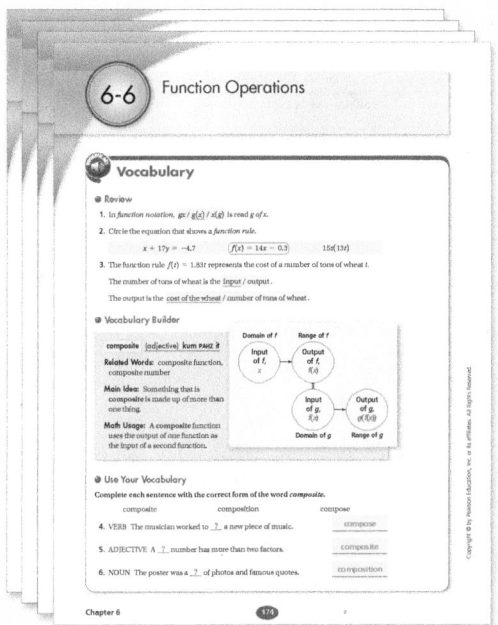

### ELL Support

**Connect to Prior Knowledge** You may want to discuss the background behind Problem 4 before teaching it.

Ask students the following questions: "What is a discount?" [a reduction in price] "What is a coupon? How does it work?" [a discount from the original price. It may be a certain dollar amount, or a percentage of the total price.]

"Suppose you have a coupon for $5 off of a purchase. Does the amount you spend affect your savings? Explain." [No; the coupon will save you just $5 regardless of how much you spend.]

"Suppose you have a coupon for 20% off. Does the amount you spend affect your savings? Explain." [Yes; the more you spend, the more total money you will save.]

## 5 Assess & Remediate

### Lesson Quiz

1. Let $f(x) = \sqrt{x} - 4$ and $g(x) = x + 6$. What are $f + g$ and $f - g$? What are their domains?

2. Let $f(x) = x^2 - 16$ and $g(x) = x - 4$. What are $f \cdot g$ and $\frac{f}{g}$? What are their domains?

3. Let $f(x) = x - 2$ and $g(x) = x^3$. What is $(f \circ g)(2)$?

4. **Do you UNDERSTAND?** The function $f(x) = 12x$ gives the number of inches in $x$ feet and $g(x) = 3.28x$ gives the approximate number of feet in $x$ meters. Write a composite function that could be used to convert meters to inches.

### ANSWERS TO LESSON QUIZ

1. $(f + g)(x) = \sqrt{x} + x + 2$;
$(f - g)(x) = \sqrt{x} - x - 10$; the domain of each is $x \geq 0$.

2. $(f \cdot g)(x) = x^3 - 4x^2 - 16x + 64$; $\left(\frac{f}{g}\right)(x) = x + 4$; the domain of $(f \cdot g)(x)$ is all real numbers; the domain of $\left(\frac{f}{g}\right)(x)$ is all real numbers except $x = 4$.

3. 6

4. $(f \circ g)(x) = 39.36x$

### PRESCRIPTION FOR REMEDIATION

Use the student work on the Lesson Quiz to prescribe a differentiated review assignment:

| Points | Differentiated Remediation |
|--------|----------------------------|
| 0–2 | Intervention |
| 3 | On-level |
| 4 | Extension |

**PowerAlgebra.com**

## 5 Assess & Remediate

Assign the Lesson Quiz. Appropriate intervention, practice, or enrichment is automatically generated based on student performance.

## Intervention

- **Reteaching** (2 pages) Provides reteaching and practice exercises for the key lesson concepts. Use with struggling students or absent students.
- **English Language Learner Support** Helps students develop and reinforce mathematical vocabulary and key concepts.

### All-in-One Resources/Online
#### Reteaching

#### 6-6 Reteaching
Function Operations

When you combine functions using addition, subtraction, multiplication, or division, the domain of the resulting function has to include the domains of both of the original functions.

**Problem**

Let $f(x) = x^2 - 4$ and $g(x) = \sqrt{x}$. What is the solution of each function operation? What is the domain of the result?

a. $(f + g)(x) = f(x) + g(x) = (x^2 - 4) + (\sqrt{x}) = x^2 + \sqrt{x} - 4$
b. $(f - g)(x) = f(x) - g(x) = (x^2 - 4) - (\sqrt{x}) = x^2 - \sqrt{x} - 4$
c. $(g - f)(x) = g(x) - f(x) = (\sqrt{x}) - (x^2 - 4) = -x^2 + \sqrt{x} + 4$
d. $(f \cdot g)(x) = f(x) \cdot g(x) = (x^2 - 4)(\sqrt{x}) = x^2\sqrt{x} - 4\sqrt{x}$

The domain of $f$ is all real numbers. The domain of $g$ is all $x \geq 0$. For parts a–d, there are no additional restrictions on the values for $x$, so the domain for each of these is $x \geq 0$.

e. $\frac{f}{g}(x) = \frac{f(x)}{g(x)} = \frac{x^2 - 4}{\sqrt{x}} = \frac{(x^2 - 4)\sqrt{x}}{x}$

As before, the domain is $x \geq 0$. But, because the denominator cannot be zero, eliminate any values of $x$ for which $g(x) = 0$. The only value for which $\sqrt{x}$ is 0 is $x = 0$. Therefore, the domain of $\frac{f}{g}$ is $x > 0$.

f. $\frac{g}{f}(x) = \frac{g(x)}{f(x)} = \frac{\sqrt{x}}{x^2 - 4}$

Similarly, begin with $x \geq 0$ and eliminate any values of $x$ that make the denominator $f(x)$ zero: $x^2 - 4 = 0$ when $x = -2$ and $x = 2$. Therefore, the domain of $\frac{g}{f}$ is $x \geq 0$ combined with $x \neq -2$ and $x \neq 2$. In other words, the domain is $x \geq 0$ and $x \neq 2$, or all nonnegative numbers except 2.

**Exercises**

Let $f(x) = 4x - 3$ and $g(x) = x^2 + 2$. Perform each function operation and then find the domain of the result.

1. $(f + g)(x)$
$x^2 + 4x - 1$; all real numbers

2. $(f - g)(x)$
$-x^2 + 4x - 5$; all real numbers

3. $(g - f)(x)$
$x^2 - 4x + 5$; all real numbers

4. $(f \cdot g)(x)$
$4x^3 - 3x^2 + 8x - 6$; all real numbers

5. $\frac{f}{g}(x)$
$\frac{4x - 3}{x^2 + 2}$; all real numbers

6. $\frac{g}{f}(x)$
$\frac{x^2 + 2}{4x - 3}$; $x \neq \frac{3}{4}$

### All-in-One Resources/Online
#### English Language Learner Support

#### 6-6 ELL Support
Function Operations

Darnell wrote the steps to compose the following functions on index cards, but the cards got mixed up.

Let $f(x) = x + 7$ and $g(x) = x^3$. What is $(g \circ f)(-4)$?

| Subtract 4 from 7. | Substitute −4 for x in f(x). |
|---|---|
| Raise 3 to the 3rd power. | Substitute 3 into g(x). |

Use the note cards to write the steps in order.

1. First, substitute −4 for x in f(x).

2. Second, subtract 4 from 7.

3. Then, substitute 3 into g(x).

4. Finally, raise 3 to the 3rd power.

# Differentiated Remediation *continued*

## On-Level

- **Practice** (2 pages) Provides extra practice for each lesson. For simpler practice exercises, use the Form K Practice pages found in the All-in-One Teaching Resources and online.

- **Think About a Plan** Helps students develop specific problem-solving skills and strategies by providing scaffolded guiding questions.

- **Standardized Test Prep** Focuses on all major exercises, all major question types, and helps students prepare for the high-stakes assessments.

## Extension

- **Enrichment** Provides students with interesting problems and activities that extend the concepts of the lesson.

- **Activities, Games, and Puzzles** Worksheets that can be used for concepts development, enrichment, and for fun!

---

### Practice and Problem Solving Wkbk/ All-in-One Resources/Online
#### Practice page 1

### Practice and Problem Solving Wkbk/ All-in-One Resources/Online
#### Practice page 2

### All-in-One Resources/Online
#### Enrichment

---

### Practice and Problem Solving Wkbk/ All-in-One Resources/Online
#### Think About a Plan

### Practice and Problem Solving Wkbk/ All-in-One Resources/Online
#### Standardized Test Prep

### Online Teacher Resource Center
#### Activities, Games, and Puzzles

## 6-7 Inverse Relations and Functions

**Objective** To find the inverse of a relation or function

**Getting Ready!**

What is wrong with the headline? Why? What headline would you have written?

*The Community Times*                    Thursday Morning Edition

**Mayor's Salary Restored**
At last night's meeting, the town council approved a 20% increase in the mayor's salary. This follows last year's 20% decrease. The Mayor's comment was

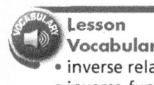

**Lesson Vocabulary**
• inverse relation
• inverse function
• one-to-one function

If a relation pairs element *a* of its domain to element *b* of its range, the **inverse relation** pairs *b* with *a*. So, if (*a*, *b*) is an ordered pair of a relation, then (*b*, *a*) is an ordered pair of its inverse. If both a relation and its inverse happen to be functions, they are **inverse functions**.

**Essential Understanding** The inverse of a function may or may not be a function.

This diagram shows a relation *r* (a function) and its inverse (not a function). The range of the relation is the domain of the inverse. The domain of the relation is the range of the inverse.

| Relation *r* | |
|---|---|
| Domain | Range |
| 1.2 | 1 |
| 1.4 | |
| 1.6 | 2 |
| 1.9 | |

| Inverse of *r* | |
|---|---|
| Domain | Range |
| 1 | 1.2 |
| | 1.4 |
| 2 | 1.6 |
| | 1.9 |

**Think**
(0, −1) is in *s*. How do you find the corresponding pair in the inverse of *s*?
Switch the coordinates. (−1, 0) is in the inverse of *s*.

**Problem 1** Finding the Inverse of a Relation

**A** What is the inverse of relation *s*?

**Relation *s***

| x | y |
|---|---|
| 0 | −1 |
| 2 | 0 |
| 3 | 2 |
| 4 | 3 |

Switch the *x* and *y* values to get the inverse.

**Inverse of Relation *s***

| x | y |
|---|---|
| −1 | 0 |
| 0 | 2 |
| 2 | 3 |
| 3 | 4 |

---

### Solve It!

**PURPOSE** To explore the outcome of increasing and decreasing a value by the same percentage
**PROCESS** Students may
• choose a starting salary for the mayor and find the salary for each year based on it.
• generalize the salaries for each year based on a starting salary *x*.

**FACILITATE**

**Q** How can you represent a 20% cut in pay of a salary *x*? **[(.80)*x*]**

**Q** How can you represent a 20% increase in a salary *x*? **[(1.2)*x*]**

**Q** How can you represent the mayor's salary this year? **[(1.2)(.8)*x*]**

**Q** If the council restored the mayor's salary to its first-year level, what should that value equal? Does it? **[*x*; no]**

**Q** Which is greater: *x*% of a greater number or lesser number? **[*x*% of a greater number, unless *x* is negative]**

**ANSWER** See Solve It in Answers on next page.
**CONNECT THE MATH** In the Solve It students use percentages to determine why the headline is incorrect, that is, increasing a salary by 20% does not "undo" the 20% decrease from the previous year. In the lesson, students find inverse functions, which "undo" what another function does.

# 2 Guided Instruction

## Problem 1

**Q** How are the columns of the table of *s* and its inverse related? **[They are reversed.]**

---

## 6-7 Preparing to Teach

**BIG** ideas **Functions**
    **Solving Equations and Inequalities**     **UbD**

**ESSENTIAL UNDERSTANDINGS**
• The inverse of a function may or may not be a function.
• When you square each side of an equation, the resulting equation may have more solutions than the original equation.
• If *f* and $f^{-1}$ are functions and if either maps *a* to *b*, then the other maps *b* to *a*, i.e., $(f \circ f^{-1})(a) = (f^{-1} \circ f)(a) = a$.
• The range of the relation is the domain of the inverse. The domain of the relation is the range of the inverse.

### Math Background

The following is a simple way to illustrate inverse functions and their composition:

There is a formula used to convert US dollars to euros, and there is a formula to convert euros back to US dollars. If you compose these two functions on the same day, you will be right back with the currency you started with. These are called inverse functions.

Be careful to differentiate between inverse functions and the inverse of a function. The inverse of a function may not be a function.

The inverse of a function will only be a function if the function is one-to-one.

A common mistake students make is confusing *f* inverse with *f* to the negative one. Make sure to clarify that the notation for *f* inverse is $f^{-1}(x)$ and for *f* to the negative one is $f(x)^{-1}$.

### Support Student Learning

Use the **Algebra 2 Companion** to engage and support students during instruction. See Lesson Resources at the end of this lesson for details.

**PowerAlgebra.com**

## 1 Interactive Learning

**Solve It!**
Step out how to solve the Problem with helpful hints and an online question. Other questions are listed above in Interactive Learning.

## Got It?

Q What points are on the graph of the inverse of $t$?
[(−5, 0), (−4, 1), (−3, 2), (−3, 3)]

## Problem 2

Q What is the output of the inverse of the function?
[the input of the original function]

Q Is the inverse of $y$ a function? Explain. [No,
because for every $x$-value except −1 there are
two $y$-values.]

## Got It?

Q How does the slope of the function relate to the
slope of its inverse? [It is the reciprocal.]

## Problem 3

To reflect a graph over the line $y = x$, plot the
points $(y, x)$ for points $(x, y)$ that are on the original
graph.

Q What is the shape of the graph of the inverse
relation? [It is a parabola that opens rightward.]

Q Is the inverse of $y$ a function? Explain. [No, it does
not pass the vertical-line test.]

## Got It?

Q How are the intercepts of the graph of the
function and the graph of the inverse relation
related? [They are switched. For example, (0, 8)
is the $y$-intercept of the function and (8, 0) is the
$x$-intercept of the graph of the inverse relation.]

---

**B** What are the graphs of $s$ and its inverse?

  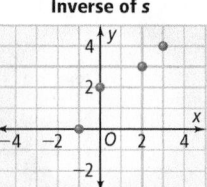

Got It? 1. a. What are the graphs of $t$ and its inverse?
   b. Reasoning Is $t$ a function? Is the inverse
      of $t$ a function? Explain.

**Relation $t$**

| $x$ | 0 | 1 | 2 | 3 |
|---|---|---|---|---|
| $y$ | −5 | −4 | −3 | −3 |

As shown in Problem 1, the graphs of a relation and its inverse are the reflections of
each other in the line $y = x$. If you describe a relation or function by an equation in
$x$ and $y$, you can switch $x$ and $y$ to get an equation for the inverse.

**Problem 2  Finding an Equation for the Inverse**

**Think**
Why do you solve
for $y$?
If you solve the equation
for $y$, you can use it to
easily generate ordered
pairs that are part of the
inverse relation.

What is the inverse of the relation described by $y = x^2 - 1$?

$$y = x^2 - 1$$
$$x = y^2 - 1 \quad \text{Switch } x \text{ and } y.$$
$$x + 1 = y^2 \quad \text{Add 1 to each side.}$$
$$\pm\sqrt{x + 1} = y \quad \text{Find the square root of each side to solve for } y.$$

Got It? 2. What is the inverse of $y = 2x + 8$?

**Problem 3  Graphing a Relation and Its Inverse**

**Think**
What does the
graph of $y = x^2 - 1$
look like?
The graph of $y = x^2 - 1$
is a translation of $y = x^2$
down one unit.

What are the graphs of $y = x^2 - 1$ and its inverse, $y = \pm\sqrt{x + 1}$?

The graph of $y = x^2 - 1$ is a parabola that opens
upward with vertex $(0, -1)$. The graph of the inverse
is the reflection of the parabola in the line $y = x$.

Got It? 3. What are the graphs of $y = 2x + 8$ and
   its inverse?

---

## Answers

### Solve It!
A 20% increase in pay after a 20% decrease in pay
will not restore the mayor's salary to the same
amount. If he made $x$ dollars a year originally, he
would make $0.8x$ dollars a year after the cut in pay.
Then he would make only $1.2(0.8x) = 0.96x$ after
the increase. He is still making 4% less than his
original salary.

### Got It?
**1. a.**

**1b–4.** See page 408.

---

**PowerAlgebra.com**

## 2 Guided Instruction

Each Problem is worked out and
supported online.

**Problem 1**
Finding the Inverse of a Relation

**Problem 2**
Finding an Equation for the Inverse

**Problem 2 Alternative**
Finding an Equation for the Inverse
*Animated*

**Problem 3**
Graphing a Relation and Its Inverse

**Problem 4**
Finding an Inverse Function
*Animated*

**Problem 5**
Finding the Inverse of a Formula

**Problem 6**
Composing Inverse Functions
*Animated*

**Problem 6 Alternative**
Composing Inverse Functions

The inverse of a function $f$ is denoted by $f^{-1}$. You read $f^{-1}$ as "the inverse of $f$" or as "$f$ inverse." The notation $f(x)$ is used for functions, but the relation $f^{-1}$ may not even be a function.

**Problem 4** Finding an Inverse Function

Consider the function $f(x) = \sqrt{x - 2}$.

**A** What are the domain and range of $f$?

The radicand cannot be negative, so the numbers $x \geq 2$ make up the domain. The principal square root is nonnegative, so the numbers $y \geq 0$ make up the range.

**B** What is $f^{-1}$, the inverse of $f$?

$$f(x) = \sqrt{x - 2}$$
$$y = \sqrt{x - 2} \quad \text{Rewrite the equation using } y.$$
$$x = \sqrt{y - 2} \quad \text{Switch } x \text{ and } y. \text{ Since } x \text{ equals a principal square root, } x \geq 0.$$
$$x^2 = y - 2 \quad \text{Square both sides.}$$
$$y = x^2 + 2 \quad \text{Solve for } y.$$

So, $f^{-1}(x) = x^2 + 2$, for $x \geq 0$.

**C** What are the domain and range of $f^{-1}$?

Part (b) shows that the domain of $f^{-1}$ is the range of $f$—the numbers $x \geq 0$. Since $x^2 \geq 0$, $x^2 + 2 \geq 2$. Therefore, the numbers $y \geq 2$ make up the range of $f^{-1}$. Note that the range of $f^{-1}$ is the same as the domain of $f$.

**D** Is $f^{-1}$ a function? Explain.

For each $x$ in the domain ($x \geq 0$) of $f^{-1}$, there is only one value of $y$ in the range. So $f^{-1}(x) = x^2 + 2$, $x \geq 0$, is a function.

**Think**

**How could a graph help you check your answer?**
You could graph $f^{-1}$ and see whether the graph passes the vertical line test. If it does, $f^{-1}$ is a function.

 **Got It?** 4. Let $g(x) = 6 - 4x$.
 a. What are the domain and range of $g$?
 b. What is the inverse of $g$?
 c. What are the domain and range of $g^{-1}$?
 d. Is $g^{-1}$ a function? Explain.

Functions that model real-world behavior are often expressed as formulas with meaningful variables, like $A = \pi r^2$ for the area of a circle. Strictly speaking, the inverse formula would be $r^2 = \pi A$, but this expresses a false relationship between $A$ and $r$. It is better to leave the variables in place and solve for $r$ as a function of $A$.

$$A = \pi r^2 \quad \text{Original formula.}$$
$$r = \sqrt{\tfrac{A}{\pi}} \quad \text{Same formula, but inversely expressed.}$$

**Problem 4**
In this problem, the domain of the inverse function is restricted, as not all valid inputs of the function are in the range of the original function.

**Q** How does knowing the domain and range of $y = \sqrt{x}$ help you find the domain and range of $f(x)$? **[Answers may vary. Sample: By knowing the translation of two units to the right, you can see that the range is the same and the domain is translated two units to the right.]**

**Q** How can you determine whether an inverse of a function is itself a function? **[You can use the same methods you use to determine whether any other relation is a function: use the vertical-line test, or determine whether for each $x$ in the domain there is only one value of $y$ in the range.]**

**Got It?**

**Q** What is the graph of $g(x)$? **[It is a line.]**

**Q** How could you determine where this line and the graph of the inverse of its function intersect? **[Answers may vary. Sample: This is the point where $y = x$.]**

# Additional Problems

**1.** Relation $v$

| x | -2 | -1 | 0 | 1 |
|---|----|----|---|---|
| y | 2 | 0 | 3 | 0 |

 a. What is the inverse of relation $v$?
 b. What are the graphs of $v$ and its inverse?

**ANSWERS**

a. Inverse

| x | 2 | 0 | 3 | 0 |
|---|---|---|---|---|
| y | -2 | -1 | 0 | 1 |

b.

**2.** What is the inverse of the relation described by $y = 5x^2 + 2$?

**ANSWER** $y = \pm\sqrt{\dfrac{x - 2}{5}}$

**3.** What is the graph of $y = 5x^2 + 2$ and its inverse?

**ANSWER**

**4.** Consider the function $g(x) = -\tfrac{2}{3}x + 7$.
 a. What are the domain and range of $g$?
 b. What is $g^{-1}$, the inverse of $g$?
 c. What are the domain and range of $g^{-1}$?
 d. Is $g^{-1}$ a function? Explain.

**ANSWERS**
a. domain is all real numbers; range is all real numbers
b. $g^{-1}(x) = -\tfrac{3}{2}x + 10.5$
c. domain is all real numbers; range is all real numbers
d. Yes; for each $x$ in the domain, there is only one value of $y$ in the range.

**5.** The formula for finding the area of a circle is $A = \pi r^2$. What is the inverse of this function? What is the radius of a circle with area 30 ft²?

**ANSWER** $r = \sqrt{\tfrac{A}{\pi}} \approx 3.09$ ft

**6.** For $h(x) = \dfrac{3}{2 - x}$, what is each of the following?
 a. $h^{-1}(x)$
 b. $(h \circ h^{-1})(2)$
 c. $(h^{-1} \circ h)(2)$

**ANSWERS**
a. $h^{-1}(x) = -\tfrac{3}{x} + 2$
b. 2
c. undefined

Lesson 6-7 **407**

## Problem 5     ERROR PREVENTION

Previously, students switched the variables when finding an inverse. This is to find the resulting inverse relation with *y* as the traditional dependent variable. However, in real-world applications, the dependence of variables is fixed and their order should not be switched.

---

**Q** What is the input and output of *d*? Its inverse? **[The input of *d* is time and the output is distance. The input of its inverse is distance and its output is time.]**

---

### Got It?

The formula in this question assumes that the initial velocity of the object is 0 when it begins to fall due to gravity.

---

**Q** What value of *d* do you use to find the velocity? **[24 m]**

**Q** What would be the velocity if the height of the cliff were 12 m? 36 m? **[approximately 15.3 m/s; 26.6 m/s]**

---

### Take Note

---

**Q** Why does it make sense that the composition of inverse functions leaves *x* unchanged when *x* is in both respective domains? **[Answers may vary. Sample: The inverse functions "undo" each other, leaving *x* unchanged.]**

---

 **Problem 5** Finding the Inverse of a Formula

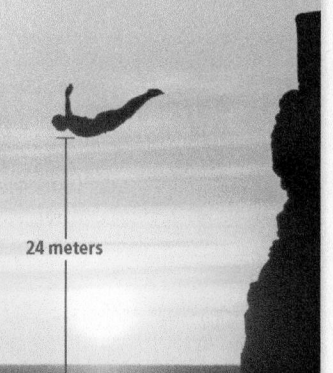

The function $d = 4.9t^2$ represents the distance *d*, in meters, that an object falls in *t* seconds due to Earth's gravity. Find the inverse of this function. How long, in seconds, does it take for the cliff diver shown to reach the water below?

$d = 4.9t^2$

$t^2 = \dfrac{d}{4.9}$    Solve for *t*. Do not switch the variables.

$t = \sqrt{\dfrac{d}{4.9}}$    Time must be nonnegative.

$= \sqrt{\dfrac{24}{4.9}}$    Substitute 24 for *d*.

$\approx 2.2$    Use a calculator.

It will take about 2.2 seconds for the diver to reach the water.

**Think**

**Why shouldn't you interchange the variables?**
Interchanging the variables leads to a false relationship between distance and time.

24 meters

**Got It?**   **5.** The function $d = \frac{v^2}{19.6}$ relates the distance *d*, in meters, that an object has fallen to its velocity *v*, in meters per second. Find the inverse of this function. What is the velocity of the cliff diver in meters per second as he enters the water?

You know that for any function *f*, each *x*-value in the domain corresponds to exactly one *y*-value in the range. For a **one-to-one function**, it is also true that each *y*-value in the range corresponds to exactly one *x*-value in the domain. A one-to-one function *f* has an inverse $f^{-1}$ that is also a function. If *f* maps *a* to *b*, then $f^{-1}$ must map *b* to *a*.

Domain of *f*    Range of *f*
Range of $f^{-1}$    Domain of $f^{-1}$

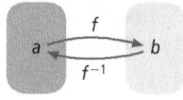

*take note*   **Key Concept**   **Composition of Inverse Functions**

If *f* and $f^{-1}$ are inverse functions, then

$(f^{-1} \circ f)(x) = x$ and $(f \circ f^{-1})(x) = x$ for *x* in the domains of *f* and $f^{-1}$, respectively.

This says that the composition of a function and its inverse is essentially the identity function, $id(x) = x$, or $y = x$.

---

## Answers

### Got It? (continued)

**1b.** *t* is a function; the inverse of *t* is not a function; there are 2 *y*-values for one *x*-value.

**2.** $y = \dfrac{x}{2} - 4$

**3.**
$y = 2x + 8$
$y = 0.5x - 4$

**4. a.** domain: all real numbers; range: all real numbers

   **b.** $g^{-1}(x) = -\frac{1}{4}x + \frac{3}{2}$

   **c.** domain: all real numbers; range: all real numbers

**d.** Yes; for each *x* in the domain of $g^{-1}$, there is only one value of *y* in the range.

**5.** $v = \sqrt{19.6d}$; about 21.7 m/s

**6. a.** $g^{-1}(x) = \dfrac{4 - 2x}{x}$

   **b.** 0 is not in the domain of $g^{-1}$ so $(g \circ g^{-1})(0)$ does not exist.

   **c.** 0

### Lesson Check

**1.** $f^{-1}(x) = \dfrac{x - 3}{4}$; yes

**2.** $f^{-1}(x) = \pm\sqrt{x + 1}$; no

**3.** $f^{-1}(x) = -1 \pm \sqrt{x}$; no

**4. a.** $h^{-1}(x) = -\frac{1}{x} - 2$

   **b.** −2.25    **c.** 0

**5.** no; yes

**6.** 2, 5

**7.** Answers may vary. Samples: $f(x) = 2x + 1$ and $g(x) = x - 2$; $f(x) = x^2$ and $g(x) = x + 1$

### Practice and Problem-Solving Exercises

**8.**

| x | 0 | 1 | 0 | 2 |
|---|---|---|---|---|
| y | 1 | 2 | 3 | 4 |

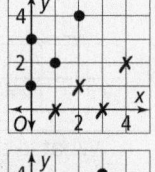

**9.**

| x | 0 | 1 | 2 | 3 |
|---|---|---|---|---|
| y | 1 | 2 | 3 | 4 |

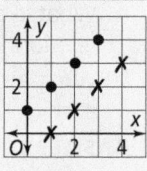

**10.**

| x | 0 | 1 | 4 | 9 |
|---|---|---|---|---|
| y | 0 | 1 | 2 | 3 |

**11.**

| x | 2 | 2 | 2 | 2 |
|---|---|---|---|---|
| y | −3 | −2 | −1 | 0 |

**Problem 6** Composing Inverse Functions

For $f(x) = \frac{1}{x-1}$, what is each of the following?

**A** $f^{-1}(x)$

$$f(x) = \frac{1}{x-1}$$

$$y = \frac{1}{x-1} \qquad \text{Rewrite the equation using } y.$$

$$x = \frac{1}{y-1} \qquad \text{Switch } x \text{ and } y.$$

$$x(y-1) = 1 \qquad \text{Solve for } y.$$

$$y - 1 = \frac{1}{x}$$

$$y = \frac{1}{x} + 1$$

So $f^{-1}(x) = \frac{1}{x} + 1$.

**Think**

**Is this a function?**
Yes. For each value of $x$, there is only one value for $y$.

**B** $(f \circ f^{-1})(1)$

$$(f \circ f^{-1})(1) = f(f^{-1}(1))$$

$$= f\left(\frac{1}{1} + 1\right)$$

$$= f(2)$$

$$= \frac{1}{2-1} = 1$$

**C** $(f^{-1} \circ f)(1)$

$$(f^{-1} \circ f)(1) = f^{-1}(f(1))$$

$$= f^{-1}\left(\frac{1}{1-1}\right)$$

$$= f^{-1}\left(\frac{1}{0}\right) \quad \text{undefined}$$

1 is not in the domain of $f$. Therefore $(f^{-1} \circ f)(1)$ does not exist.

**Got It? 6.** Let $g(x) = \frac{4}{x+2}$. What is each of the following?
**a.** $g^{-1}(x)$ **b.** $(g \circ g^{-1})(0)$ **c.** $(g^{-1} \circ g)(0)$

 **Lesson Check**

**Do you know HOW?**

Find the inverse of each function. Is the inverse a function?

**1.** $f(x) = 4x + 3$

**2.** $f(x) = x^2 - 1$

**3.** $f(x) = (x+1)^2$

**4.** For $h(x) = \frac{1}{x+2}$, find:
**a.** $h^{-1}(x)$
**b.** $h^{-1}(4)$
**c.** Value of $x$ for which the equality $(h \circ h^{-1})(x) = x$ does not hold.

**Do you UNDERSTAND?**

**5. Vocabulary** Does every function have an inverse which is a function? Does every relation have an inverse which is a relation?

**6. Reasoning** A function consists of the pairs $(2, 3)$, $(x, 4)$, and $(5, 6)$. What values, if any, may $x$ not assume?

**7. Error Analysis** A classmate says that $(f \circ g)^{-1}(x) = (f^{-1} \circ g^{-1})(x)$. Show that this is incorrect by finding examples of $f(x)$ and $g(x)$ for which the equation does not hold.

---

**Problem 6**

**Q** Why is the function defined at $x = 1$ in 6B but not in 6C? **[The composition $f^{-1} \circ f$ creates a zero denominator at $x = 1$, while $f \circ f^{-1}$ does not.]**

**Got It?**

**Q** At what value of $x$ would $(g^{-1} \circ g)(x)$ be undefined? **[$x = -2$]**

# 3 Lesson Check

**Do you know HOW?**
• For Exercises 1–3, if students have difficulty finding an inverse function algebraically, have them list the steps: 1) switch the variables and 2) solve for $y$.

**Do you UNDERSTAND?**
• For Exercise 7, remind students that an example cannot show that something is true, but one counterexample is enough to prove that something is not true.

**Close**

**Q** How can you tell from the graph of a function whether its inverse is a function? **[Answers may vary. Sample: If no horizontal line intersects the graph of $f$ in more than one point, then $f^{-1}$ will be a function.]**

---

# Answers

**12.** $y = \frac{1}{3}x - \frac{1}{3}$; yes

**13.** $y = \frac{1}{2}x + \frac{1}{2}$; yes

**14.** $y = -\frac{1}{3}x + \frac{4}{3}$; yes

**15.** $y = \pm\sqrt{\frac{5-x}{2}}$; no

**16.** $y = \pm\sqrt{x-4}$; no

**17.** $y = \pm\sqrt{\frac{x+5}{3}}$; no

**18.** $y = \pm\sqrt{x} + 8$; no

**19.** $y = \frac{4 \pm \sqrt{x}}{3}$; no

**20.** $y = \frac{1 \pm \sqrt{x-5}}{2}$; no

**21.**

**22.**

**23.**

 **PowerAlgebra.com**

# 3 Lesson Check

For a digital lesson check, use the Got It questions.

**Support in Algebra 2 Companion**
• Lesson Check

# 4 Practice

Assign homework to individual students or to an entire class.

# 4 Practice

**ASSIGNMENT GUIDE**

Basic: 8–41 all, 42, 43, 48–54 even, 65

Average: 9–41 odd, 42–67

Advanced: 9–41 odd, 42–74

Standardized Test Prep: 75–78

Mixed Review: 79–95

**Reasoning** exercises have blue headings.

**Applications** exercises have red headings.

**EXERCISE 65:** Use the Think About a Plan worksheet in the **Practice and Problem Solving Workbook** (also available in the Teaching Resources in print and online) to further support students' development in becoming independent learners.

**HOMEWORK QUICK CHECK**

To check students' understanding of key skills and concepts, go over Exercises 33, 37, 48, 54, and 65.

---

## Practice and Problem-Solving Exercises

**A Practice**   Find the inverse of each relation. Graph the given relation and its inverse.   ◆ See Problem 1.

**8.**

| x | y |
|---|---|
| 1 | 0 |
| 2 | 1 |
| 3 | 0 |
| 4 | 2 |

**9.**

| x | y |
|---|---|
| 1 | 0 |
| 2 | 1 |
| 3 | 2 |
| 4 | 3 |

**10.**

| x | y |
|---|---|
| 0 | 0 |
| 1 | 1 |
| 2 | 4 |
| 3 | 9 |

**11.**

| x | y |
|---|---|
| −3 | 2 |
| −2 | 2 |
| −1 | 2 |
| 0 | 2 |

Find the inverse of each function. Is the inverse a function?   ◆ See Problem 2.

**12.** $y = 3x + 1$
**13.** $y = 2x - 1$
**14.** $y = 4 - 3x$

**15.** $y = 5 - 2x^2$
**16.** $y = x^2 + 4$
**17.** $y = 3x^2 - 5$

**18.** $y = (x - 8)^2$
**19.** $y = (3x - 4)^2$
**20.** $y = (1 - 2x)^2 + 5$

Graph each relation and its inverse   ◆ See Problem 3.

**21.** $y = 2x - 3$
**22.** $y = 3 - 7x$
**23.** $y = -x$

**24.** $y = 3x^2$
**25.** $y = -x^2$
**26.** $y = 4x^2 - 2$

**27.** $y = (x - 1)^2$
**28.** $y = (2 - x)^2$
**29.** $y = (3 - 2x)^2 - 1$

For each function, find the inverse and the domain and range of the function and its inverse. Determine whether the inverse is a function.   ◆ See Problem 4.

**30.** $f(x) = 3x + 4$
**31.** $f(x) = \sqrt{x - 5}$

**32.** $f(x) = \sqrt{x + 7}$
**33.** $f(x) = \sqrt{-2x + 3}$

**34.** $f(x) = 2x^2 + 2$
**35.** $f(x) = -x^2 + 1$

**36. Temperature** The formula for converting from Celsius to Fahrenheit temperatures is $F = \frac{9}{5}C + 32$.   ◆ See Problem 5.

   **a.** Find the inverse of the formula. Is the inverse a function?
   **b.** Use the inverse to find the Celsius temperature that corresponds to 25°F.

**37. Geometry** The formula for the volume of a sphere is $V = \frac{4}{3}\pi r^3$.
   **a.** Find the inverse of the formula. Is the inverse a function?
   **b.** Use the inverse to find the radius of a sphere that has a volume of 35,000 ft³.

For Exercises 38–41, $f(x) = 10x - 10$. Find each value.   ◆ See Problem 6.

**38.** $(f^{-1} \circ f)(10)$
**39.** $(f \circ f^{-1})(-10)$

**40.** $(f^{-1} \circ f)(0.2)$
**41.** $(f \circ f^{-1})(d)$

---

# Answers

## Practice and Problem-Solving Exercises (continued)

**24.**

**25.**

**26.**

**27.**

**28.**

**29.**

**30.** $f^{-1}(x) = \frac{x - 4}{3}$, domain of f: all real numbers, range of f: all real numbers, domain of $f^{-1}$: all real numbers, range of $f^{-1}$: all real numbers; $f^{-1}$ is a function.

**31.** $f^{-1}(x) = x^2 + 5$, $x \geq 0$; domain of f: $x \geq 5$, range of f: $y \geq 0$, domain of $f^{-1}$: $x \geq 0$, range of $f^{-1}$: $y \geq 5$; $f^{-1}$ is a function.

**32.** $f^{-1}(x) = x^2 - 7$, $x \geq 0$; domain of f: $x \geq -7$, range of f: $y \geq 0$, domain of $f^{-1}$: $x \geq 0$, range of $f^{-1}$: $y \geq -7$; $f^{-1}$ is a function.

**33.** $f^{-1}(x) = \frac{3 - x^2}{2}$, $x \geq 0$; domain of f: $x \leq \frac{3}{2}$, range of f: $y \geq 0$, domain of $f^{-1}$: $x \geq 0$, range of $f^{-1}$: $y \leq \frac{3}{2}$; $f^{-1}$ is a function.

**34.** $f^{-1}(x) = \pm\sqrt{\frac{x - 2}{2}}$, domain of f: all real numbers, range of f: $y \geq 2$, domain of $f^{-1}$: $x \geq 2$, range of $f^{-1}$: all real numbers; $f^{-1}$ is not a function.

**35.** $f^{-1}(x) = \pm\sqrt{1 - x}$, domain of f: all real numbers, range of f: $y \leq 1$, domain of $f^{-1}$: $x \leq 1$, range of $f^{-1}$: all real numbers; $f^{-1}$ is not a function.

**36–41.** See next page.

**Find the inverse of each function. Is the inverse a function?**

**42.** $f(x) = x^3$    **43.** $f(x) = x^4$    **44.** $f(x) = \frac{2x^2}{5} + 1$

**45.** $f(x) = 1.5x^2 - 4$    **46.** $f(x) = \frac{3x^2}{4}$    **47.** $f(x) = \sqrt{2x - 1} + 3$

**48. Think About a Plan** The velocity of the water that flows from an opening at the base of a tank depends on the height of water above the opening. The function $v(x) = \sqrt{2gx}$ models the velocity $v$ in feet per second where $g$, the acceleration due to gravity, is about 32 ft/s² and $x$ is the height in feet of the water. What is the depth of water when the flow is 40 ft/s, and when the flow is 20 ft/s?
- How can you use inverse functions to help you find the answer?
- What restrictions are on the domain of $v(x)$? of $v^{-1}(x)$?

**49.** Let $f(x) = 3x^2 - 4$ and $g(x) = x - 2$. Calculate $(f \circ g^{-1})(x)$ for $x = -3$.

**50. Writing** Explain how you can find the range of the inverse of $f(x) = \sqrt{x - 1}$ without finding the inverse itself.

**For each function, find the inverse and the domain and range of the function and its inverse. Determine whether the inverse is a function.**

**51.** $f(x) = -\sqrt{x}$    **52.** $f(x) = \sqrt{x} + 3$    **53.** $f(x) = \sqrt{-x + 3}$

**54.** $f(x) = \sqrt{x + 2}$    **55.** $f(x) = \frac{x^2}{2}$    **56.** $f(x) = \frac{1}{x^2}$

**57.** $f(x) = (x - 4)^2$    **58.** $f(x) = (7 - x)^2$    **59.** $f(x) = \frac{1}{(x + 1)^2}$

**60.** $f(x) = 4 - 2\sqrt{x}$    **61.** $f(x) = \frac{3}{\sqrt{x}}$    **62.** $f(x) = \frac{1}{\sqrt{-2x}}$

**63. a. Open-Ended** Copy the mapping diagram at the right. Complete it by writing members of the domain and range and connecting them with arrows so that $r$ is a function and $r^{-1}$ is not a function.

Relation $r$

**b.** Repeat part (a) so that $r$ is not a function and $r^{-1}$ is a function.

**64. Reasoning** Relation $r$ has one element in its domain and two elements in its range. Is $r$ a function? Is the inverse of $r$ a function? Explain.

**65. Geometry** Write a function that gives the length of the hypotenuse of an isosceles right triangle with side length $s$. Evaluate the inverse of the function to find the side length of an isosceles right triangle with a hypotenuse of 6 in.

**66. Open-Ended** Write a function $f$ such that the graph of $f^{-1}$ lies only in Quadrants III and IV.

**67. Reasoning** To determine if the inverse of function $f$ is also a function, you can use a *horizontal line test*. It says that if no horizontal line intersects the graph of the function $f$ in more than one point, then the inverse of $f$ is a function.
**a.** Explain why the horizontal line test works.
**b.** The graph of a polynomial function passes through the points $(-1, 1)$, $(0, 4)$ and $(2, 3)$. Can its inverse be a function?

## Answers

**36. a.** $C = \frac{5}{9}(F - 32)$; yes    **b.** $-3.9°C$

**37. a.** $r = \sqrt[3]{\frac{3V}{4\pi}}$; yes    **b.** 20.29 ft

**38.** 10

**39.** $-10$

**40.** 0.2

**41.** d

**42.** $f^{-1}(x) = \sqrt[3]{x}$; yes

**43.** $f^{-1}(x) = \pm\sqrt[4]{x}$; no

**44.** $f^{-1}(x) = \pm\sqrt{\frac{5x - 5}{2}}$; no

**45.** $f^{-1}(x) = \pm\sqrt{\frac{2x + 8}{3}}$; no

**46.** $f^{-1}(x) = \pm 2\sqrt{\frac{x}{3}}$; no

**47.** $f^{-1}(x) = \frac{x^2 - 6x + 10}{2}$, $x \geq 3$; yes

**48.** 25 ft; 6.25 ft

**49.** $-1$

**50.** The range of the inverse of $f$ is the domain of $f$, which is $x \geq 1$.

**51.** $f^{-1}(x) = x^2$, $x \leq 0$; domain of $f$: $x \geq 0$, range of $f$: $y \leq 0$, domain of $f^{-1}$: $x \leq 0$, range of $f^{-1}$: $y \geq 0$; $f^{-1}$ is a function.

**52.** $f^{-1}(x) = (x - 3)^2$, $x \geq 3$; domain of $f$: $x \geq 0$, range of $f$: $y \geq 3$, domain of $f^{-1}$: $x \geq 3$, range of $f^{-1}$: $y \geq 0$; $f^{-1}$ is a function.

**53.** $f^{-1}(x) = 3 - x^2$, domain of $f$: $x \leq 3$, range of $f$: $y \geq 0$, domain of $f^{-1}$: $x \geq 0$, range of $f^{-1}$: $y \leq 3$; $f^{-1}$ is a function.

**54.** $f^{-1}(x) = x^2 - 2$, domain of $f$: $x \geq -2$, range of $f$: $y \geq 0$, domain of $f^{-1}$: $x \geq 0$, range of $f^{-1}$: $y \geq -2$; $f^{-1}$ is a function.

**55.** $f^{-1}(x) = \pm\sqrt{2x}$, domain of $f$: all real numbers, range of $f$: $y \geq 0$, domain of $f^{-1}$: $x \geq 0$, range of $f^{-1}$: all real numbers; $f^{-1}$ is not a function.

**56.** $f^{-1}(x) = \pm\frac{1}{\sqrt{x}}$, domain of $f$: $x \neq 0$, range of $f$: $y > 0$, domain of $f^{-1}$: $x > 0$, range of $f^{-1}$: $y \neq 0$; $f^{-1}$ is not a function.

**57.** $f^{-1}(x) = \pm\sqrt{x} + 4$, domain of $f$: all real numbers, range of $f$: $y \geq 0$, domain of $f^{-1}$: $x \geq 0$, range of $f^{-1}$: all real numbers; $f^{-1}$ is not a function.

**58.** $f^{-1}(x) = 7 \pm \sqrt{x}$, domain of $f$: all real numbers, range of $f$: $y \geq 0$, domain of $f^{-1}$: $x \geq 0$, range of $f^{-1}$: all real numbers; $f^{-1}$ is not a function.

**59.** $f^{-1}(x) = \pm\frac{1}{\sqrt{x}} - 1$, domain of $f$: $x \neq -1$, range of $f$: $y > 0$, domain of $f^{-1}$: $x > 0$, range of $f^{-1}$: $y \neq -1$; $f^{-1}$ is not a function.

**60.** $f^{-1}(x) = \left(\frac{4 - x}{2}\right)^2$, $x \leq 4$; domain of $f$: $x \geq 0$, range of $f$: $y \leq 4$, domain of $f^{-1}$: $x \leq 4$, range of $f^{-1}$: $y \geq 0$; $f^{-1}$ is a function.

**61.** $f^{-1}(x) = \left(\frac{3}{x}\right)^2$, $x > 0$; domain of $f$: $x > 0$, range of $f$: $y > 0$, domain of $f^{-1}$: $x > 0$, range of $f^{-1}$: $y > 0$; $f^{-1}$ is a function.

**62.** $f^{-1}(x) = -\frac{1}{2}\left(\frac{1}{x}\right)^2$, $x \geq 0$; domain of $f$: $x < 0$, range of $f$: $y > 0$, domain of $f^{-1}$: $x > 0$, range of $f^{-1}$: $y < 0$; $f^{-1}$ is a function.

**63. a.**

**b.**

**64.** $r$ is not a function because there are two $y$-values for one $x$-value. $r^{-1}$ is a function because each of its $x$-values has one $y$-value.

**65.** $h = s\sqrt{2}$; $s = \frac{h\sqrt{2}}{2} = 3\sqrt{2} \approx 4.2$ in.

**66.** Answers may vary. Sample: $f(x) = \sqrt{-(x + 1)} - 2$

**67. a.** The horizontal line test tells you if there is more than one $x$-value for every $y$-value. Since the graph of $f^{-1}$ interchanges the $x$ and $y$ values of $f$, if $f$ passes the horizontal line test, $f^{-1}$ will pass the vertical line test and it will be a function.

**b.** no

# Answers

## Practice and Problem-Solving Exercises
(continued)

**68.** $f^{-1}(x) = \sqrt[3]{5x}$; yes

**69.** $f^{-1}(x) = x^3 + 5$; yes

**70.** $f^{-1}(x) = 27x^3$; yes

**71.** $f^{-1}(x) = 2 + \sqrt[3]{x}$; yes

**72.** $f^{-1}(x) = x^4$, $x \geq 0$; yes

**73.** $f^{-1}(x) = \pm\sqrt[4]{\frac{5x}{6}}$; no

**74.** Yes; $f(x)$ is a one-to-one function, and its graph will pass the horizontal line test.

## Standardized Test Prep

**75.** D

**76.** F

**77.** B

**78.** **[4]** To find the $x$-intercepts of $f(x)$:
$$0 = (x + 1)^2 - 2$$
$$2 = (x + 1)^2$$
$$\pm\sqrt{2} = x + 1$$
$-1 \pm \sqrt{2} = x$, so $x$-intercepts are $(-1 \pm \sqrt{2}, 0)$. To find the $y$-intercept of $f(x)$: $f(x) = (0 + 1)^2 - 2 = -1$, so the $y$-intercept is $(0, -1)$. To find the inverse of $f(x)$:
$$x = (y + 1)^2 - 2$$
$$\pm\sqrt{x + 2} = y + 1$$
$-1 \pm \sqrt{x + 2} = y$,
so $f^{-1}(x) = -1 \pm \sqrt{x + 2}$; $f^{-1}(x)$ is not a function.

**[3]** appropriate methods, but with one computational error

**[2]** intercepts found correctly, but inverse function is incorrect

**[1]** correct answers, but without work shown

## Mixed Review

**79.** $2x + 7$

**80.** $-x - 10$

**81.** $-\frac{3}{2}x + 11$

**82.** $2x^2 + 28x$

**83.** $32$

**84.** $2x + 28$

**85.** $-2$

**86.** no real root

**87.** $3$

**88.** $-3$

**89.** $-3$

**90.** $0.4$

**91.** $30$

**92.** $0.05$

**93.**

**Challenge**  Find the inverse of each function. Is the inverse a function?

**68.** $f(x) = \frac{1}{5}x^3$

**69.** $f(x) = \sqrt[3]{x - 5}$

**70.** $f(x) = \frac{\sqrt[3]{x}}{3}$

**71.** $f(x) = (x - 2)^3$

**72.** $f(x) = \sqrt[4]{x}$

**73.** $f(x) = 1.2x^4$

**74.** Function $f(x)$ is defined the following way:
- if $x$ is an integer, then $f(x) = x + 1$;
- for all other $x$, $f(x) = x + 2$.

Is the inverse of $f(x)$ a function? Explain.

## Standardized Test Prep

**SAT/ACT**

**75.** Which pair of words make this sentence FALSE?
The product of two ____(I)____ numbers is always a (n) ____(II)____ number.

 Ⓐ (I) complex; (II) complex

 Ⓒ (I) rational; (II) real

 Ⓑ (I) real; (II) complex

 Ⓓ (I) imaginary; (II) imaginary

**76.** If $f(x) = x + 1$ and $g(x) = x^2 - 3x - 4$, what is $(f \circ g)(x)$?

 Ⓕ $x^2 - 3x - 3$   Ⓖ $x^2 - x - 6$   Ⓗ $x^2 - x$   Ⓘ $x^2 - x - 3$

**77.** What is the simplified form of $\left(a^{\frac{2}{3}}b^{\frac{3}{4}}\right)^2$?

 Ⓐ $a^{\frac{4}{9}}b^{\frac{9}{16}}$   Ⓑ $a^{\frac{4}{3}}b^{\frac{3}{2}}$   Ⓒ $ab$   Ⓓ $(ab)^{\frac{17}{6}}$

**Extended Response**

**78.** Let $f(x) = (x + 1)^2 - 2$. Find the $x$- and $y$-intercepts of $f(x)$ and the inverse of $f(x)$. Is the inverse a function?

## Mixed Review

Let $f(x) = 4x$, $g(x) = \frac{1}{2}x + 7$, and $h(x) = -2x + 4$. Perform each function operation.   ◀ See Lesson 6-6.

**79.** $(g \circ f)(x)$

**80.** $(h \circ g)(x)$

**81.** $h(x) + g(x)$

**82.** $f(x) \cdot g(x)$

**83.** $(f \circ g)(x) + h(x)$

**84.** $(f \circ g)(x)$

Find each real root.   ◀ See Lesson 6-1.

**85.** $-\sqrt[4]{16}$

**86.** $\sqrt[4]{-16}$

**87.** $\sqrt[5]{243}$

**88.** $-\sqrt[5]{243}$

**89.** $\sqrt[5]{-243}$

**90.** $\sqrt[3]{0.064}$

**91.** $\sqrt[4]{810,000}$

**92.** $\sqrt[4]{\frac{1}{160,000}}$

**Get Ready!**   **To prepare for Lesson 6-8, do Exercises 93–95.**

Graph each function.   ◀ See Lesson 4-1.

**93.** $y = -x^2 - 1$

**94.** $y = -(x + 1)^2 + 1$

**95.** $y = 3x^2 + 3$

**94.**

**95.**

## Additional Instructional Support

### Algebra 2 Companion

Students can use the **Algebra 2 Companion** worktext (4 pages) as you teach the lesson. Use the Companion to support

- New Vocabulary
- Key Concepts
- Got It for each Problem
- Lesson Check

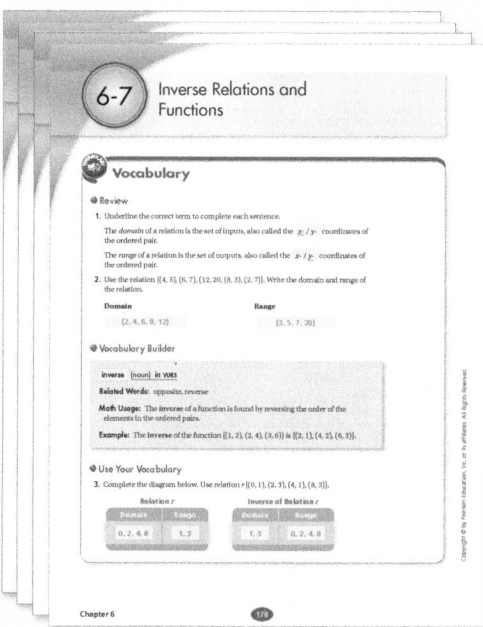

### ELL Support

**Assess Understanding** Ask students the following questions:

- What are some other real-world examples of inverses? [converting currencies, converting from the metric system to the customary, system, unit conversion]
- Are these inverses functions? How do you know? [The ones listed above are, because you can convert both ways and always get the same answer.]
- Can you think of an example of a real-world relation that is not a function and its inverse? [Perhaps a dictionary that translates one language to another. Both languages will have several words with the same meaning.]

Explain to students that the word *inverse* applies in many mathematical contexts as well. Have students ask each other questions that use the word *inverse*:

- What number is the additive inverse of 3? Multiplicative inverse of 3? $[-3; \frac{1}{3}]$
- What is the inverse operation of subtraction? Multiplication? [addition; division]

## 5 Assess & Remediate

### Lesson Quiz

1. What is the inverse of the relation described by $y = 2x^2 + 7$?

2. Consider the function $h(x) = 4\sqrt{x+3}$.
   a. Find the domain and range of $h$.
   b. What is the inverse of $h$?
   c. Find the domain and range of $h^{-1}$.
   d. Is $h^{-1}$ a function? Explain.

3. **Do you UNDERSTAND?** The formula for converting temperatures from degrees Fahrenheit $F$ to degrees Celsius $C$ is $C = \frac{5}{9}(F - 32)$. What is the inverse function? What is the temperature in Fahrenheit when it is 12 degrees Celsius?

4. Let $k(x) = \frac{2}{x-1}$. What is each of the following?
   a. $k^{-1}(x)$
   b. $(k \circ k^{-1})(1)$
   c. $(k^{-1} \circ k)(1)$

### ANSWERS TO LESSON QUIZ

1. $y = \pm\sqrt{\dfrac{x-7}{2}}$

2. a. domain is $x \geq -3$; range is $y \geq 0$
   b. $h^{-1}(x) = \dfrac{x^2}{16} - 3$ for $x \geq 0$
   c. domain is $x \geq 0$; range is $y \geq -3$
   d. Yes; for each $x$ in the domain, there is only one value of $y$ in the range.

3. $F = \dfrac{9}{5}C + 32$; 53.6°F

4. a. $k^{-1}(x) = \dfrac{2}{x} + 1$
   b. 1
   c. undefined

### PRESCRIPTION FOR REMEDIATION

Use the student work on the Lesson Quiz to prescribe a differentiated review assignment:

| Points | Differentiated Remediation |
|--------|----------------------------|
| 0–2 | Intervention |
| 3 | On-level |
| 4 | Extension |

**PowerAlgebra.com**

### 5 Assess & Remediate

Assign the Lesson Quiz. Appropriate intervention, practice, or enrichment is automatically generated based on student performance.

## Intervention

- **Reteaching** (2 pages) Provides reteaching and practice exercises for the key lesson concepts. Use with struggling students or absent students.

- **English Language Learner Support** Helps students develop and reinforce mathematical vocabulary and key concepts.

### All-in-One Resources/Online
**Reteaching**

6-7 Reteaching
Inverse Relations and Functions

### All-in-One Resources/Online
**English Language Learner Support**

6-7 ELL Support
Inverse Relations and Functions

# Differentiated Remediation *continued*

## On-Level

- **Practice** (2 pages) Provides extra practice for each lesson. For simpler practice exercises, use the Form K Practice pages found in the All-in-One Teaching Resources and online.

- **Think About a Plan** Helps students develop specific problem-solving skills and strategies by providing scaffolded guiding questions.

- **Standardized Test Prep** Focuses on all major exercises, all major question types, and helps students prepare for the high-stakes assessments.

## Extension

- **Enrichment** Provides students with interesting problems and activities that extend the concepts of the lesson.

- **Activities, Games, and Puzzles** Worksheets that can be used for concepts development, enrichment, and for fun!

### Practice and Problem Solving Wkbk/ All-in-One Resources/Online
**Practice page 1**

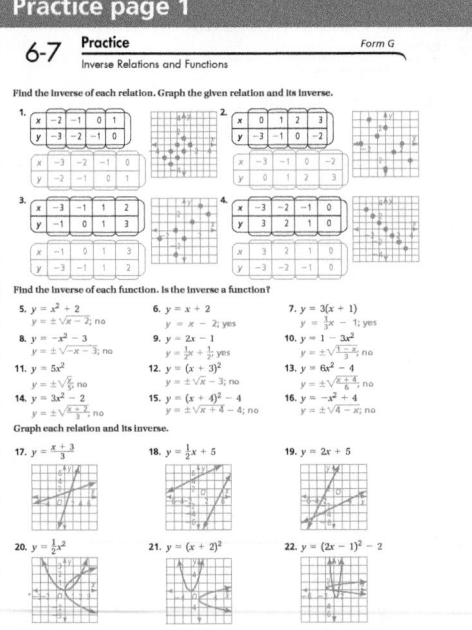

### Practice and Problem Solving Wkbk/ All-in-One Resources/Online
**Practice page 2**

### All-in-One Resources/Online
**Enrichment**

### Practice and Problem Solving Wkbk/ All-in-One Resources/Online
**Think About a Plan**

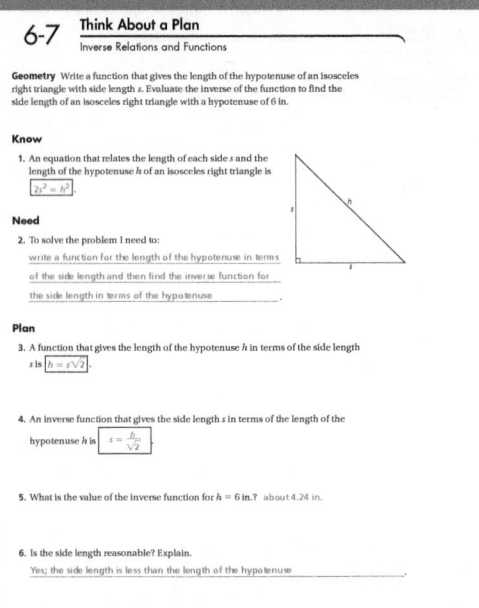

### Practice and Problem Solving Wkbk/ All-in-One Resources/Online
**Standardized Test Prep**

### Online Teacher Resource Center
**Activities, Games, and Puzzles**

# Graphing Inverses

You can graph inverses of functions on a graphing calculator by using the **DrawInv** feature or by using parametric equations. It takes more keystrokes to set up parametric equations, but once you do you can easily change from one function to another and quickly see the graphs of the new function and its inverse.

## Activity

Graph $y = 0.3x^2 + 1$ and its inverse.

**Method 1** Use the **DrawInv** feature.

**Step 1** Press (y=) and enter the equation. Press (zoom) **5** to see a graph of the function with equal *x*- and *y*-intervals.

**Step 2** Press (2nd) (draw) **8**. You will see **DrawInv** followed by a flashing cursor. Select equation $Y_1$ by pressing (vars) ▷ **1 1**. Press (enter) to see the graph of the function and its inverse.

**Method 2** Use parametric equations.

**Step 1** Set to parametric mode. Press (mode), select **Par**, and press (2nd) (quit).

**Step 2** Enter the given equation in parametric form. Press (y=) and enter the equations $X_{1T} = T$ and $Y_{1T} = .3T^2 + 1$.

**Step 3** Now use $X_{2T} = Y_{1T}$ and $Y_{2T} = X_{1T}$ to interchange the *x*- and *y*-values of the first parametric equation. Press (y=) and move the cursor to follow $X_{2T} =$. Select $Y_{1T}$ by pressing (vars) ▷ **2 2**. Enter the equation $Y_{2T} = X_{1T}$ in a similar fashion.

**Step 4** Press (zoom) **5**. Adjust the **Window** so that **Tmin** and **Tmax** approximately agree with **Xmin** and **Xmax**. Press (graph) to see the graph of the function and its inverse.

## Exercises

Graph each function and its inverse with a graphing calculator. Then sketch the graphs.

1. $y = x^2 - 5$
2. $y = (x - 3)^2$
3. $y = 0.01x^4$
4. $y = 0.5x^3 - 3$

5. **Writing** Change the parametric equation $X_{2T} = Y_{1T}$ in Method 2, Step 3 to $X_{2T} = -Y_{1T}$. Describe the graph that results.

6. Explain how once you set up parametric equations, you can change from one function to another and quickly see the graphs of the new function and its inverse.

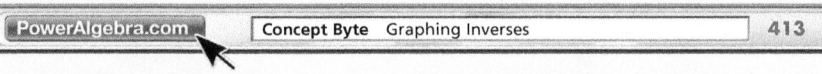

# Guided Instruction

**PURPOSE** To use a graphing calculator to graph inverse functions

**PROCESS** Students will
- use a graphing calculator to graph a function and its inverse.
- use parametric functions to graph a family of functions and their inverses.
- analyze the parametric family of functions and inverses.

**DISCUSS**
The **DrawInv** feature is used to find the graph of the inverse relation. This can be used to view the shape of the graph and find particular points on the graph. It will not, however, provide the equation that defines the inverse.

**Q** What is the advantage of using parametric equations to graph the function? **[Answers may vary. Sample: You can easily change the function and its inverse slightly to observe the differences.]**

## Activity
Parametric equations can be confusing, since they introduce an additional variable. Explain that *T* acts as the variable *x* throughout and that Step 3 acts like switching the variables when solving for an inverse relation by hand.

**Q** Do you get the same graphs using Method 1 and Method 2? **[yes]**

**Q** In Method 2, why does it make sense to define $X_{2T}$ and $Y_{2T}$ this way? **[You find the inverse function by switching *x* and *y*.]**

# Answers

## Exercises

**1.**

**2.**

**3.**

**4.**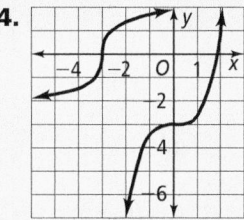

**5.** The graph is the reflection of the first graph across the *x*-axis.

**6.** Answers may vary. Sample: Using parametric equations, you only have to change $Y_{1T}$ to see a new function and its inverse.

# 1 Interactive Learning

## Solve It!

**PURPOSE** Combine area formulas to write an equation and solve for the radius of a circle

**PROCESS** Students may draw an equilateral triangle by connecting the centers of each cylinder, draw three rectangles by drawing two radii out of each cylinder that will make a right angle with the strip, and use area formulas to write an expression that represents the cross-sectional area of the strip.

---

**FACILITATE**

**Q** Why would it help to divide the cross-sectional area of the strip into geometric shapes that you recognize? **[You can write equations for the areas of the shapes that you recognize and set their sum equal to 115.]**

**Q** Into which shapes can you divide the cross-sectional area? **[1 equilateral triangle, 3 rectangles, and 3 thirds of a circle]**

**Q** What are the area formulas that you need to use?

**[area of an equilateral triangle $= \frac{s^2\sqrt{3}}{4}$; area of a rectangle $= \ell w$; area of a circle $= 2\pi r$]**

---

**ANSWER** See Solve It in Answers on next page.

**CONNECT THE MATH** In the Solve It, students use the formulas for the area of a circle, a rectangle, and an equilateral triangle to write a square root equation for the radius of each cylinder. In this lesson, students graph square root and radical functions.

---

# 6-8 Graphing Radical Functions

**Objective** To graph square root and other radical functions

**Getting Ready!**

A red plastic strip binds the three identical cylinders. The cross-sectional area enclosed by the strip is 115 cm². What is the radius of each cylinder? What is the length of the plastic strip?

*This is what I would call an irrational radius.*

**Lesson Vocabulary**
• radical function
• square root function

The formula $A = \pi r^2$ shows that area is a quadratic function of the radius of a circle. The formula $r = \frac{1}{\sqrt{\pi}}\sqrt{A}$ shows that the radius of a circle is a square root function of the area.

**Essential Understanding** A square root function is the inverse of a quadratic function that has a restricted domain.

A horizontal line can intersect the graph of $f(x) = x^2$ in two points—where $f(-2) = f(2)$, for example. Thus, a vertical line can intersect the graph of $f^{-1}$ in two points. $f^{-1}$ is *not* a function because it fails the vertical line test.

However, you can restrict the domain of $f$ so that the inverse of the restricted function is a function.

---

# 6-8 Preparing to Teach

**BIG** ideas **Function**
**Solving Equations and Inequalities**

**ESSENTIAL UNDERSTANDINGS**

• A square root function is the inverse of a quadratic function that has a restricted domain.
• When you square each side of an equation, the resulting equation may have more solutions than the original equation.
• If $f$ and $f^{-1}$ are functions and if either maps $a$ to $b$, then the other maps $b$ to $a$, i.e., $(f \circ f^{-1})(a) = (f^{-1} \circ f)(a) = a$.

## Math Background

Square root functions are important because they are inverses of quadratic functions, so they model the same real-world behavior as quadratic polynomials, but in reverse.

The graphs of square root functions are halves of parabolic curves opening sideways.

The methods for graphing radical functions are similar to those presented for other functions in previous chapters.

Graphs whose equations have the form $y = a(x - h)^2 + k$ are translated $h$ units horizontally and $k$ units vertically from the graph of $y = ax^2$. This holds true for functions of the form $y = a\sqrt[n]{x - h} + k$; the graphs are transformations of the graph of the parent function $y = \sqrt[n]{x}$.

In this lesson, students will use graphing calculators to graph radical functions and determine the solutions to problems.

**Support Student Learning**

Use the **Algebra 2 Companion** to engage and support students during instruction. See Lesson Resources at the end of this lesson for details.

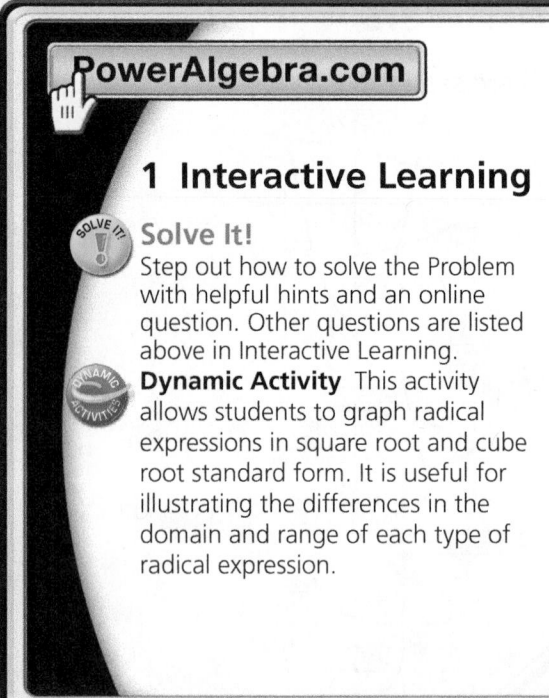

**PowerAlgebra.com**

## 1 Interactive Learning

**Solve It!**
Step out how to solve the Problem with helpful hints and an online question. Other questions are listed above in Interactive Learning.

**Dynamic Activity** This activity allows students to graph radical expressions in square root and cube root standard form. It is useful for illustrating the differences in the domain and range of each type of radical expression.

Inverses of the power functions $y = x^n$ (with domains restricted as needed) form parent functions $y = \sqrt[n]{x}$ for families of **radical functions**. In particular, $f(x) = \sqrt{x}$ is the parent for the family of **square root functions**. Members of this family have the general form $f(x) = a\sqrt{x - h} + k$.

**take note**

### Key Concepts    Families of Radical Functions

| | Square Root | Radical |
|---|---|---|
| Parent function: | $y = \sqrt{x}$ | $y = \sqrt[n]{x}$ |
| Reflection in $x$-axis: | $y = -\sqrt{x}$ | $y = -\sqrt[n]{x}$ |
| Stretch $(a > 1)$, shrink $(0 < a < 1)$ by the factor $a$: | $y = a\sqrt{x}$ | $y = a\sqrt[n]{x}$ |
| Translation: Horizontal by $h$ Vertical by $k$ | $y = \sqrt{x - h} + k$ | $y = \sqrt[n]{x - h} + k$ |

**Think**

**How is $y = \sqrt{x} + k$ related to the parent function $y = \sqrt{x}$?**
It is related to the parent function in the same way that $y = f(x) + k$ is related to $y = f(x)$. It is a vertical translation of $k$ units.

**Problem 1** Translating a Square Root Function Vertically

**What are the graphs of $y = \sqrt{x} - 2$ and $y = \sqrt{x} + 1$?**

The graph of $y = \sqrt{x} - 2$ is the graph of $y = \sqrt{x}$ shifted down 2 units.

The graph of $y = \sqrt{x} + 1$ is the graph of $y = \sqrt{x}$ shifted up 1 unit.

The domains of both functions are the set of nonnegative numbers, but their ranges differ.

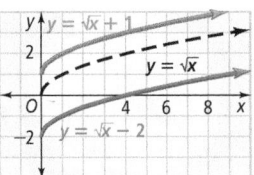

✓ **Got It?** **1.** What are the graphs of $y = \sqrt{x} + 2$ and $y = \sqrt{x} - 3$?

**Think**

**How is $y = \sqrt{x - h}$ related to the parent function $y = \sqrt{x}$?**
It is a horizontal translation of $h$ units.

**Problem 2** Translating a Square Root Function Horizontally

**What are the graphs of $y = \sqrt{x + 4}$ and $y = \sqrt{x - 1}$?**

The graph of $y = \sqrt{x + 4}$ is the graph of $y = \sqrt{x}$ shifted left 4 units.

The graph of $y = \sqrt{x - 1}$ is the graph of $y = \sqrt{x}$ shifted right 1 unit.

The ranges of both functions are the set of nonnegative numbers, but their domains differ.

✓ **Got It?** **2.** What are the graphs of $y = \sqrt{x - 3}$ and $y = \sqrt{x + 2}$?

---

## 2 Guided Instruction

### Take Note

**Q** What is the difference between a square root function and a radical function? **[A square root function has an index of 2. A radical function can have an index of any number.]**

### Problem 1

**Q** What do you notice about the placement of the $k$-value for each given function? **[The $k$-value is outside the radical sign.]**

**Q** How does the sign of the $k$ affect the graph? **[A positive $k$ shifts the graph up and a negative $k$ shifts the graph down.]**

**Q** Why do the graphs look similar? **[They have the same parent function.]**

### Got It?

**Q** When graphing square root functions, why choose $x$-values that are perfect squares? **[They yield whole number range values, which are easier to graph.]**

### Problem 2

**Q** What do you notice about the $h$-value for each function? **[It is under the radical sign.]**

**Q** How can you obtain the graph of $y = \sqrt{x + 2}$ from the graph of $y = \sqrt{x}$? **[Shift the graph two units to the left.]**

### Got It?                    ERROR PREVENTION

Students may translate the graph in the wrong direction. Have them circle the sign of the $h$-value and write an arrow in the direction of the translation.

---

## 2 Guided Instruction

 Each Problem is worked out and supported online.

**Problem 1**
Translating a Square Root Function Vertically

**Problem 2**
Translating a Square Root Function Horizontally
*Animated*

**Problem 3**
Graphing a Square Root Function
*Animated*

**Problem 4**
Solving a Radical Equation by Graphing

**Problem 5**
Graphing a Cube Root Function
*Animated*

**Problem 6**
Rewriting a Radical Function

**Support in Algebra 2 Companion**
• Vocabulary
• Key Concepts
• Got It?

---

## Answers

**Solve It!**
$r \approx 3.3$ cm; length $\approx 39.9$ cm

**Got It?**
**1.**

**2.**

## Problem 3

**Q** What is the effect of $a$ on the graph with a value between 0 and 1? **[The graph is shrunk.]**

**Q** How would the graph of $y = \frac{1}{2}\sqrt{x-3} - 1$ compare to the graph of $y = -\frac{1}{2}\sqrt{x-3} + 1$? **[The graph would be reflected across the x-axis and shifted down two units.]**

### Got It?
**VISUAL LEARNERS**

**Q** In the equation $y = a\sqrt{x-h} + k$ what does each variable do to the parent function $y = \sqrt{x}$? **[a is a vertical stretch or shrink, h is a horizontal translation, k is a vertical translation]**

## Problem 4

**Q** Why is the equation $y = \sqrt[3]{x - 1950}$ entered as $y = (x - 1950)^{(1/3)}$ on a graphing calculator? **[Rewriting a radical in exponential form is a general way to enter radicals with an index greater than 2.]**

### Got It?

**Q** What effect does the change in population have on the two equations? **[The first equation remains the same. The second equation changes to $y_2 = 275{,}000$.]**

---

Recall from Lesson 2-7 that for any transformation, $y = af(x - h) + k$ of the parent function $f(x)$, $a$ indicates a vertical stretch or shrink.

Similarly, for the combined transformation $y = a\sqrt{x - h} + k$, $a$ indicates a vertical stretch ($|a| > 1$) or shrink ($|a| < 1$). A negative value of $a$ indicates a reflection in the $x$-axis.

### Problem 3 Graphing a Square Root Function

**What is the graph of $y = -\frac{1}{2}\sqrt{x - 3} + 1$?**

**Think**
What would be good points to choose?
Points that have integer $x$- and $y$-coordinates.

**Step 1** Choose several points from the parent function $y = \sqrt{x}$.

**Step 2** Multiply the $y$-coordinates by $a = -\frac{1}{2}$. This shrinks the parent graph vertically by the factor $\frac{1}{2}$ and reflects the result in the $x$-axis.

**Step 3** The values of $h$ and $k$ give the horizontal and vertical translations. Translate the graph from Step 2 to the right 3 units and up 1 unit.

**Got It? 3.** What is the graph of $y = 3\sqrt{x + 2} - 4$?

### Problem 4 Solving a Radical Equation by Graphing

**Multiple Choice** You can model the population $P$ of Corpus Christi, Texas, between the years 1970 and 2005 by the radical function $P(x) = 75{,}000\sqrt[3]{x - 1950}$, where $x$ is the year. Using this model, in what year was the population of Corpus Christi 250,000?

Ⓐ 1980　　Ⓑ 1983　　Ⓒ 1987　　Ⓓ 1990

For $P = 250{,}000$, solve the equation $250{,}000 = 75{,}000\sqrt[3]{x - 1950}$.

**Think**
How can you rewrite a radical function using an exponent?
You can write a radical function $y = \sqrt[n]{x}$ as $y = x^{\frac{1}{n}}$.

Graph **Y1 = 75000(X − 1950)^(1/3)** and **Y2 = 250000**. Adjust the window to find where the graphs intersect.

Use the **INTERSECT** feature to find the $x$-coordinate of the intersection.

In the year 1987, the population of Corpus Christi was 250,000. The correct answer is C.

Intersection X=1987.04　Y=250000

**Got It? 4.** In what year was the population of Corpus Christi 275,000?

Problem 4 uses a transformation of $y = \sqrt[3]{x}$. The function $f(x) = \sqrt[3]{x}$ is the inverse of $g(x) = x^3$. Unlike $y = \sqrt{x}$, the domain and range of $f(x) = \sqrt[3]{x}$ are all real numbers.

---

# Additional Problems

**1.** What are the graphs of $y = \sqrt{x} + 4$ and $y = \sqrt{x} - 4$?

**ANSWER**

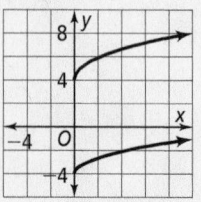

**2.** What are the graphs of $y = \sqrt{x - 2}$ and $y = \sqrt{x + 7}$?

**ANSWER**

**3.** What is the graph of $y = 2\sqrt{x + 1} - 2$?

**ANSWER**

**4.** You can model the radius of a sphere by $r = \sqrt[3]{\frac{3V}{4\pi}}$. If the radius of a child's spherical balloon is 4.5 inches, what is the volume of the balloon to the nearest cubic inch? (Use 3.14 for $\pi$.)

**ANSWER** approximately 382 in³

**5.** What is the graph of $y = 2\sqrt[3]{x + 2} - 3$?

**ANSWER**

**6.** How can you rewrite $y = \sqrt{4x - 12}$ so you can graph it using transformations? Describe the graph.

**ANSWER** $y = 2\sqrt{x - 3}$; graph of $y = \sqrt{x}$ translated 3 units right, stretched by a factor of 2

# Answers

### Got It? (continued)

**3.**

**4.** 1999

**5.**

**6. a.** $y = \sqrt[3]{8x + 32} - 2$ is the graph of $y = 2\sqrt[3]{x}$ translated 4 units to the left and 2 units down.

**b.** $y = 9|x + 2|$; the graph of $y = 9|x + 2|$ is the graph of $y = 9|x|$ translated 2 units to the left; You are rewriting the function so that $x$ has a coefficient of 1.

The patterns for graphing square root functions apply to other radical functions.

**Problem 5** Graphing a Cube Root Function

What is the graph of $y = 2\sqrt[3]{x + 1} - 4$?

**Step 1** Graph the parent function, $y = \sqrt[3]{x}$.

**Step 2** Multiply the $y$-coordinates by 2. This stretches the graph vertically.

**Step 3** Translate the graph from step 2, 1 unit to the left and 4 units down.

Step 2

Step 1

Step 3

**Got It? 5.** What is the graph of $y = 3 - \frac{1}{2}\sqrt[3]{x - 2}$?

You can graph functions of the form $y = \sqrt[n]{bx + c}$ using transformations, if you can simplify the radicand so that $x$ has a coefficient of 1. This is also true for functions in the form $y = a\sqrt[n]{bx + c} + k$.

**Problem 6** Rewriting a Radical Function

How can you rewrite $y = \sqrt{9x + 18}$ so you can graph it using transformations? Describe the graph.

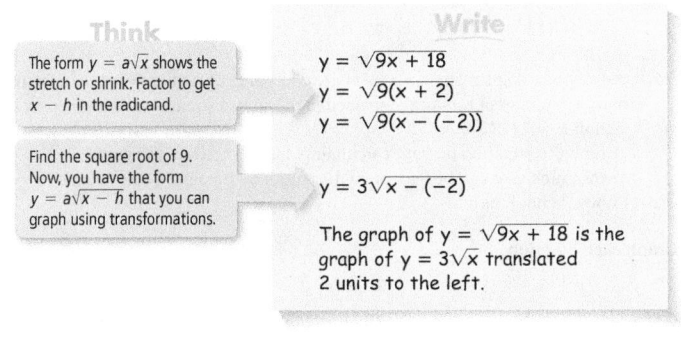

**Think**

The form $y = a\sqrt{x}$ shows the stretch or shrink. Factor to get $x - h$ in the radicand.

Find the square root of 9. Now, you have the form $y = a\sqrt{x - h}$ that you can graph using transformations.

**Write**

$y = \sqrt{9x + 18}$
$y = \sqrt{9(x + 2)}$
$y = \sqrt{9(x - (-2))}$

$y = 3\sqrt{x - (-2)}$

The graph of $y = \sqrt{9x + 18}$ is the graph of $y = 3\sqrt{x}$ translated 2 units to the left.

**Got It? 6. a.** How can you rewrite $y = \sqrt[3]{8x + 32} - 2$ so you can graph it using transformations? Describe the graph.

    **b. Reasoning** Describe the graph of $y = |9x + 18|$ by rewriting it in the form $y = a|x - h|$. How is this similar to rewriting $y = \sqrt{9x + 18}$ in Problem 6?

**Problem 5**     ERROR PREVENTION
When graphing a square root or cube root function, students sometimes try to simplify the numbers under the radical with the numbers outside the radical. Try circling each change from the parent function with a colored pencil.

**Q** When graphing cube root functions, why do you want to select $x$-values that are perfect cubes? **[You will get whole number values, which are easier to graph.]**

**Got It?**

**Q** What is the difference between the graph of $y = 3 - \frac{1}{2}\sqrt[3]{x - 2}$ and the graph of $y = -\frac{1}{2}\sqrt[3]{x - 2} + 3$? **[The two graphs are the same. The value of $k$ was moved before the radical in the first function; this can be done since $k$ is not contained under the radical sign.]**

**Problem 6**
Some radical equations are more easily graphed after they have been written in the form $y = a\sqrt[n]{x - h} + k$.

**Q** Why do you need to factor the 9 and take the square root? **[to find the stretch or shrink factor]**
**Q** How does the 3 change the graph? **[It stretches the graph.]**

**Got It?**
Have students graph the equation two ways:
**a.** by graphing the given equation
**b.** by using transformations

**Q** Which method do you prefer? **[Answers will vary. Results will be the same using both methods.]**

---

# Answers

## Lesson Check

**1.**

**2.**

**3.** $y = 2\sqrt{x - 1}$; the graph of $y = 2\sqrt{x}$ translated 1 unit to the right

**4.** $y = 2\sqrt[3]{x + 2}$; the graph of $y = 2\sqrt[3]{x}$ translated 2 units to the left

**5.** When $|a| < 1$, $a$ will vertically compress $y = a\sqrt{x}$ and when $|a| > 1$, $a$ will vertically stretch $y = a\sqrt{x}$; this is similar to its effect on other functions.

**6.** $g(x)$ is the reflection of $f(x)$ across the $x$-axis and again across $x = -1$.

## Practice and Problem-Solving Exercises

**7.**

**8.**

**9.**

**10.**

**11.**

**12.**

**13.**

**14.**

# 3 Lesson Check

## Do you know HOW?

• For Exercises 1 and 2, if students are having difficulty graphing the function, have them first graph the parent function.

## Do you UNDERSTAND?

• For Exercise 5, have students graph several functions with positive and negative values for *a*.

• For Exercise 6, have students graph each function using different colored pencils. Make sure students understand the meaning of a reflection.

## Close

> **Q** How is the graph of $y = 3\sqrt[3]{x + 3} - 2$ transformed from the graph of $y = 3\sqrt[3]{x}$? **[The graph is shifted 3 units left and 2 units down.]**

---

 **Lesson Check**

### Do you know HOW?

Graph each function.

**1.** $y = -\sqrt{x + 3}$     **2.** $y = -\sqrt[3]{x} + 5$

Rewrite each function so you can graph it using transformations of its parent function. Describe the graph.

**3.** $y = \sqrt{4x - 4}$     **4.** $y = \sqrt[3]{8x + 16}$

### Do you UNDERSTAND?

**5. Writing** Explain the effect that *a* has on the graph of $y = a\sqrt{x}$. How does this compare to its effect on other functions you have studied?

**6. Error Analysis** Your friend states that the graph of the function $g(x) = \sqrt{-x - 1}$ is a reflection of the graph of the function $f(x) = -\sqrt{x + 1}$ across the *x*-axis. Describe your friend's error.

---

  ## Practice and Problem-Solving Exercises

**A Practice**

Graph each function.        **◀ See Problems 1 and 2.**

**7.** $y = \sqrt{x} + 1$    **8.** $y = \sqrt{x} - 2$    **9.** $y = \sqrt{x} - 4$    **10.** $y = \sqrt{x} + 5$

**11.** $y = \sqrt{x - 3}$    **12.** $y = \sqrt{x + 1}$    **13.** $y = \sqrt{x + 6}$    **14.** $y = \sqrt{x - 4}$

Graph each function.        **◀ See Problem 3.**

**15.** $y = 3\sqrt{x}$     **16.** $y = -\sqrt{x - 1}$     **17.** $y = -5\sqrt{x + 2}$

**18.** $y = -0.5\sqrt{x} + 3$     **19.** $y = \frac{1}{2}\sqrt{x + 2} - 1$     **20.** $y = 3\sqrt{x + 1} + 4$

Solve each square root equation by graphing. Round the answer to the nearest hundredth, if necessary. If there is no solution, explain why.    **◀ See Problem 4.**

**21.** $\sqrt{x - 3} = 12$     **22.** $\sqrt{2x - 3} = 4$     **23.** $\sqrt{2x + 5} = \sqrt{2 - x}$

**24. Landscaping** A sprinkler can water between 1 and 130 square yards of a lawn. The length *L* in inches of rotating pipe needed to water *A* square yards is given by the function $L = 117.75\sqrt{A}$.

   **a.** Graph the equation on your calculator. Make a sketch of the graph.

   **b.** How much area can be watered if the length of the pipe is 500, 800, or 1,300 inches long?

Graph each function.        **◀ See Problem 5.**

**25.** $y = \sqrt[3]{x + 5}$     **26.** $y = \sqrt[3]{x} - 4$     **27.** $y = \sqrt[3]{x + 2} - 7$

**28.** $y = -\sqrt[3]{x + 3} - 1$     **29.** $y = 2\sqrt[3]{x - 6} - 9$     **30.** $y = \frac{1}{2}\sqrt[3]{x - 1} + 3$

Rewrite each function to make it easy to graph using transformations of its parent function. Describe the graph.    **◀ See Problem 6.**

**31.** $y = \sqrt{9x - 9}$     **32.** $y = -\sqrt{16x + 32}$     **33.** $y = -2\sqrt{4x + 16}$

**34.** $y = \sqrt[3]{64x + 128}$     **35.** $y = \sqrt{25x + 125} - 3$     **36.** $y = \sqrt[3]{8x - 24} + 1$

---

# Answers

## Practice and Problem-Solving Exercises (continued)

**15.**

**16.**

**17.**

**18.**

**19.**

**20.**

**21.** 147    **22.** 9.5    **23.** −1

**24. a.**

**b.** ≈18 sq yds, ≈46 sq yds, ≈122 sq yds

**25.**

**26.**

## 3 Lesson Check

For a digital lesson check, use the Got It questions.

**Support in Algebra 2 Companion**
• Lesson Check

## 4 Practice

Assign homework to individual students or to an entire class.

**Apply**

**37. Think About a Plan** The time $t$ in seconds for a pendulum to complete one full cycle is given by the function $t = 1.11\sqrt{l}$, where $l$ is the length of the pendulum in feet. How long is a pendulum that takes 4.5 seconds to complete one full cycle? 6 seconds to complete one full cycle? Round your answers to the nearest hundredth.
- How can you use a graph to approximate the length of a pendulum?
- How can you check your answers algebraically?

**Graph each function. Find the domain and range.**

**38.** $y = 4\sqrt[3]{x - 2} + 1$     **39.** $y = \frac{1}{2}\sqrt{x - 1} + 3$     **40.** $y = 3\sqrt[3]{x - 6} + 2$

**41.** Suppose that a function pairs elements from set $A$ with elements from set $B$. Recall that a function is called *onto* if every element in $B$ is paired with at least one element in $A$.

  **a.** The graph shows a transformation of $y = \sqrt{x}$. Write the function.
  **b.** What are the domain and range of the function?
  **c.** For the domain, is the function onto the set of nonnegative real numbers? Explain.

**42. Open-Ended** Write a radical function such that for its domain, the function is onto the set of real numbers such that $y \le 3$.

**Rewrite each function to make it easy to graph using transformations of its parent function. Describe the graph.**

**43.** $y = \sqrt{25x - 100} - 1$     **44.** $y = \sqrt{36x + 108} + 4$     **45.** $y = -\sqrt[3]{8x - 2}$

**46.** $y = \sqrt{\frac{x-1}{4}} - 2$     **47.** $y = 10 - \sqrt[3]{\frac{x+3}{27}}$     **48.** $y = \sqrt{\frac{x}{9} + 1} + 5$

**Graphing Calculator** Solve the following radical equations.

**49.** $2\sqrt{x} = \sqrt{(x + 1)}$     **50.** $\sqrt{(x + 3)} = 4\sqrt{(x)} - 2$     **51.** $\sqrt[3]{x - 1} = \sqrt{x} - 1$

**52. a.** Solve $3 - \sqrt{(x - 3)} = x$ algebraically.
  **b.** Solve the equation from part (a) graphically.
  **c.** What do you notice about your answer to part (a) compared to your answer to part (b)?

**53. Electronics** The size of a computer monitor is given as the length of the screen's diagonal $d$ in inches. The equation $d = \frac{5}{6}\sqrt{3A}$ models the length of a diagonal of a monitor screen with area $A$ in square inches.
  **a.** Graph the equation on your calculator.
  **b.** Suppose you want to buy a new monitor with a screen that is twice the area of your old screen. Your old screen has a diagonal of 15 inches. What will be the diagonal of your new screen?

**54. Physics** You can model time $t$, in seconds, an object takes to reach the ground falling from height $H$, in meters, by $t(H) = \sqrt{\frac{2H}{g}}$. The value of $g$ is 9.81 m/s$^2$. If an object takes 7 seconds to fall to the ground, what was its initial height?

PowerAlgebra.com     Lesson 6-8   Graphing Radical Functions     419

---

# 4 Practice

**ASSIGNMENT GUIDE**

Basic: 7–36 all, 37–39, 43, 53

Average: 7–35 odd, 37–54

Advanced: 7–35 odd, 37–59

Standardized Test Prep: 60–63

Mixed Review: 64–76

**Reasoning** exercises have blue headings.

**Applications** exercises have red headings.

**EXERCISE 53:** Use the Think About a Plan worksheet in the **Practice and Problem Solving Workbook** (also available in the Teaching Resources in print and online) to further support students' development in becoming independent learners.

**HOMEWORK QUICK CHECK**

To check students' understanding of key skills and concepts, go over Exercises 17, 33, 37, 43, and 53.

---

**27.**

**28.**

**29.**

**30.**

**31.** $y = 3\sqrt{x - 1}$; the graph of $y = 3\sqrt{x}$ translated 1 unit to the right

**32.** $y = -4\sqrt{x + 2}$; the graph of $y = -4\sqrt{x}$ translated 2 units to the left

**33.** $y = -4\sqrt{x + 4}$; the graph of $y = -4\sqrt{x}$ translated 4 units to the left

**34.** $y = 4\sqrt[3]{x + 2}$; the graph of $y = 4\sqrt[3]{x}$ translated 2 units to the left

**35.** $y = 5\sqrt{x + 5} - 3$; the graph of $y = 5\sqrt{x}$ translated 5 units to the left and 3 units down

**36.** $y = 2\sqrt[3]{x - 3} + 1$; the graph of $y = 2\sqrt[3]{x}$ translated 3 units to the right and 1 unit up

**37.** graph $l$ vs. $t$ and find the value of $l$ for $t = 4.5$ and $t = 6$; use the equation $t = 1.11\sqrt{l}$ and substitute $t = 4.5$ and $t = 6$; $\approx 16.44$ ft; $\approx 29.22$ ft

**38.**  domain: all real numbers, range: all real numbers

**39.**  domain: $x \ge 1$, range: $y \ge 3$

**40.**  domain: all real numbers, range: all real numbers

**41. a.** $y = \sqrt{x - 2} - 2$
  **b.** domain: $x \ge 2$, range: $y \ge -2$
  **c.** No; the function pairs the number 3 with the number $-1$, which is not a non-negative real number.

**42.–54.** See next page.

**Lesson 6-8    419**

# Answer

## Practice and Problem-Solving Exercises (continued)

**42.** Sample: $y = -\sqrt{x-2} + 3$

**43. a.** $y = 5\sqrt{x-4} - 1$; the graph of $y = 5\sqrt{x}$, translated 4 units to the right and 1 unit down

**44.** $y = 6\sqrt{x+3} + 4$; the graph of $y = 6\sqrt{x}$, translated 3 units to the left and 4 units up

**45.** $y = -2\sqrt[3]{x - \frac{1}{4}}$; the graph of $y = -2\sqrt[3]{x}$, translated $\frac{1}{4}$ unit to the right

**46.** $y = \frac{1}{2}\sqrt{x-1} - 2$; the graph of $y = \frac{1}{2}\sqrt{x}$, translated 1 unit to the right and 2 units down

**47.** $y = 10 - \frac{1}{3}\sqrt[3]{x+3}$; the graph of $y = -\frac{1}{3}\sqrt[3]{x}$, translated 3 units to the left and 10 units up

**48.** $y = \frac{1}{3}\sqrt{x+9} + 5$; the graph of $y = \frac{1}{3}\sqrt{x}$, translated 9 units to the left and 5 units up

**49.** $\frac{1}{3}$     **50.** 1     **51.** 0, 1, 9

**52. a.** $x = 3$     **b.**
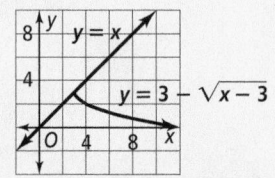

**c.** There is an extraneous solution that must be eliminated when solving algebraically.

**53. a.**

**b.** 21.2 in.

**54.** 240.345 m

**55.** $y = -\sqrt{8}\sqrt{x - \frac{3}{4}}$; the graph of $y = -\sqrt{8x}$, translated $\frac{3}{4}$ unit to the right; domain: $x \geq \frac{3}{4}$, range: $y \leq 0$

**56.** $y = \sqrt{3}\sqrt{x - \frac{5}{3}} + 6$; the graph of $y = \sqrt{3x}$, translated $\frac{5}{3}$ units to the right and 6 units up; domain: $x \geq \frac{5}{3}$, range: $y \geq 6$

**57.** $y = -\sqrt{12}\sqrt{x + \frac{3}{2}} - 3$; the graph of $y = -\sqrt{12x}$, translated $\frac{3}{2}$ units to the left and 3 units down; domain: $x \geq -\frac{3}{2}$, range: $y \leq -3$

**58. a.**

**b.** The graph of $y = \sqrt{h - x}$ is a reflection of the graph of $y = \sqrt{x - h}$ across the line $x = h$.

**59.** for all odd positive integers

---

Rewrite each function to make it easy to graph using transformations of its parent function. Describe the graph. Find the domain and range of each function.

**55.** $y = -\sqrt{2(4x - 3)}$     **56.** $y = \sqrt{3x - 5} + 6$     **57.** $y = -3 - \sqrt{12x + 18}$

**58. a.** Graph $y = \sqrt{-x}$, $y = \sqrt{1 - x}$, and $y = \sqrt{2 - x}$.
  **b. Make a Conjecture** How does the graph of $y = \sqrt{h - x}$ differ from the graph of $y = \sqrt{x - h}$?

**59.** For what positive integers $n$ are the domain and range of $y = \sqrt[n]{x}$ the set of real numbers? Assume that $x$ is a real number.

## Standardized Test Prep

**SAT/ACT**

**60.** How is the graph of $y = \sqrt{x} - 5$ translated from the graph of $y = \sqrt{x}$?
  Ⓐ shifted 5 units left          Ⓒ shifted 5 units up
  Ⓑ shifted 5 units right         Ⓓ shifted 5 units down

**61.** Which absolute value inequality has the graph shown here?
  Ⓕ $|x - 1| \leq 3$      Ⓗ $|x + 1| \leq 3$
  Ⓖ $|x - 1| \geq 3$      Ⓘ $|x + 1| \geq 3$

**62.** Which polynomial cannot be factored in the real number system?
  Ⓐ $x^2 - 3x + 2$     Ⓑ $x^2 + 4$     Ⓒ $4x^2 - 1$     Ⓓ $2x^2y - 2xy^2$

**Short Response**

**63.** How do the domains and ranges of the functions $f(x) = \sqrt{x - 1}$ and $g(x) = \sqrt{x} - 1$ compare?

## Mixed Review

Find the inverse of each function. Is the inverse a function?          **◀ See Lesson 6-7.**

**64.** $f(x) = \frac{2}{3}x - 3$     **65.** $f(x) = \sqrt{x + 3} - 4$     **66.** $f(x) = (2x + 1)^2$

Rationalize the denominator of each expression. Assume that all variables are positive.          **◀ See Lesson 6-2.**

**67.** $\dfrac{\sqrt{36x^3}}{\sqrt{12y}}$     **68.** $\sqrt{\dfrac{3x}{2y}}$     **69.** $\dfrac{\sqrt[3]{x}}{\sqrt[3]{3y}}$     **70.** $\sqrt[5]{\dfrac{3x^3}{2y}}$

Solve using the Quadratic Formula.          **◀ See Lesson 4-7.**

**71.** $x^2 - 9x + 15 = 0$     **72.** $3x^2 + 9x = 27$     **73.** $5x^2 + x = 3$

**Get Ready!   To prepare for Lesson 7-1, do Exercises 74–76.**

Evaluate each expression for the given value of $x$.          **◀ See Lesson 1-3.**

**74.** $2^x$ for $x = 3$     **75.** $4^{x+1}$ for $x = 1$     **76.** $2^{3x+4}$ for $x = -1$

---

## Standardized Test Prep

**60.** D      **61.** F      **62.** B

**63.** **[2]** For $f(x) = \sqrt{x - 1}$ the domain is $x \geq 1$ and range is $y \geq 0$. For $g(x) = \sqrt{x} - 1$ the domain is $x \geq 0$ and range is $y \geq -1$.

**[1]** incorrect statement of either one domain or one range

## Mixed Review

**64.** $f^{-1}(x) = \dfrac{3(x + 3)}{2}$; yes

**65.** $f^{-1}(x) = (x + 4)^2 - 3$, $x \geq -4$; yes

**66.** $f^{-1}(x) = \dfrac{-1 \pm \sqrt{x}}{2}$; no

**67.** $\dfrac{x\sqrt{3xy}}{y}$     **68.** $\dfrac{\sqrt{6xy}}{2y}$     **69.** $\dfrac{\sqrt[3]{9xy^2}}{3y}$

**70.** $\dfrac{\sqrt[5]{48x^3y^4}}{2y}$     **71.** $\dfrac{9 \pm \sqrt{21}}{2}$

**72.** $\dfrac{-3 \pm 3\sqrt{5}}{2}$     **73.** $\dfrac{-1 \pm \sqrt{61}}{10}$

**74.** 8     **75.** 16     **76.** 2

# Additional Instructional Support

## Algebra 2 Companion

Students can use the **Algebra 2 Companion** worktext (4 pages) as you teach the lesson. Use the Companion to support

- New Vocabulary
- Key Concepts
- Got It for each Problem
- Lesson Check

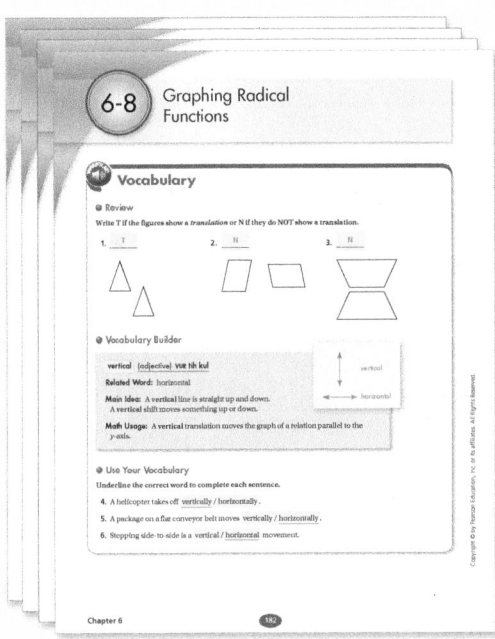

## ELL Support

**Focus on Language** To help students remember that the domain is the set of $x$-values and the range is the set of $y$-values, state that $d$ comes before $r$ as $x$ comes before $y$ alphabetically.

**Role Playing** On a number of index cards equal to half the class, write either $f(x)$ or $g(x)$ and list 2–3 transformations to be performed on the function. Divide the class in pairs. Tell them that $f(x) = x^2$ and $g(x) = x^3$. Pass out an index card to one student in each pair. Without showing it to his or her partner, the student with the card graphs the given transformed function. Then, the partner tells the first student whether the function is a transformation of $f(x)$ or of $g(x)$ and identifies the transformations. Together, they write the equation of the function.

Then they shuffle the cards and switch roles to play again.

# 5 Assess & Remediate

## Lesson Quiz

1. What is the graph of $y = 2\sqrt{x - 2} - 1$?
2. **Do you UNDERSTAND?** The speed of a tsunami $s$ (in meters/second) is approximated by $s = \sqrt{gd}$, where $g$ is the acceleration due to gravity (9.8 m/s²) and $d$ is the depth of the water (in meters). If the speed of a tsunami is 200 m/s, about how deep is the water?
3. How can you rewrite $y = \sqrt{4x + 16}$ so you can graph it using transformations? Describe the graph.

### ANSWERS TO LESSON QUIZ

1.

2. about 4082 meters
3. $y = 2\sqrt{x + 4}$; the graph is shifted 4 units left and stretched by a factor of 2.

### PRESCRIPTION FOR REMEDIATION

Use the student work on the Lesson Quiz to prescribe a differentiated review assignment:

| Points | Differentiated Remediation |
|--------|---------------------------|
| 0–1 | Intervention |
| 2 | On-level |
| 3 | Extension |

**PowerAlgebra.com**

## 5 Assess & Remediate

Assign the Lesson Quiz. Appropriate intervention, practice, or enrichment is automatically generated based on student performance.

# Intervention

- **Reteaching** (2 pages) Provides reteaching and practice exercises for the key lesson concepts. Use with struggling students or absent students.
- **English Language Learner Support** Helps students develop and reinforce mathematical vocabulary and key concepts.

## All-in-One Resources/Online
### Reteaching

**6-8 Reteaching**
Graphing Radical Functions

## All-in-One Resources/Online
### English Language Learner Support

**6-8 ELL Support**
Graphing Radical Functions

# Differentiated Remediation *continued*

## On-Level

- **Practice** (2 pages) Provides extra practice for each lesson. For simpler practice exercises, use the Form K Practice pages found in the All-in-One Teaching Resources and online.

- **Think About a Plan** Helps students develop specific problem-solving skills and strategies by providing scaffolded guiding questions.
- **Standardized Test Prep** Focuses on all major exercises, all major question types, and helps students prepare for the high-stakes assessments.

## Extension

- **Enrichment** Provides students with interesting problems and activities that extend the concepts of the lesson.
- **Activities, Games, and Puzzles** Worksheets that can be used for concepts development, enrichment, and for fun!

---

### Practice and Problem Solving Wkbk/All-in-One Resources/Online
#### Practice page 1

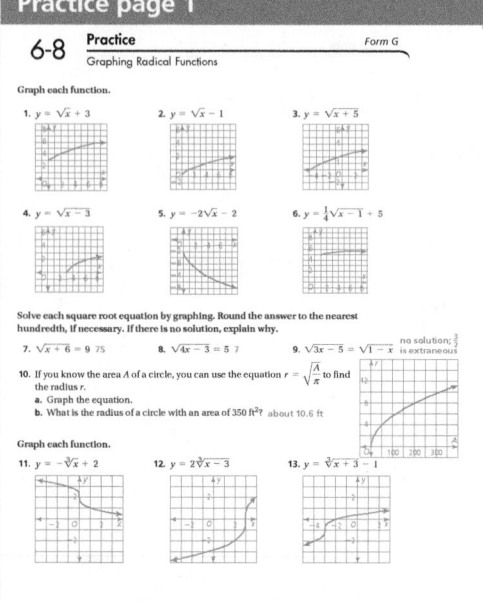

### Practice and Problem Solving Wkbk/All-in-One Resources/Online
#### Practice page 2

### All-in-One Resources/Online
#### Enrichment

### Practice and Problem Solving Wkbk/All-in-One Resources/Online
#### Think About a Plan

### Practice and Problem Solving Wkbk/All-in-One Resources/Online
#### Standardized Test Prep

### Online Teacher Resource Center
#### Activities, Games, and Puzzles

# 6 Pull It **All Together**

To solve these problems, you will pull together concepts and skills related to roots and radical functions.

**BIG idea** Solving Equations and Inequalities

Solving an equation is the process of rewriting the equation to make what it says about its variables as simple as possible.

## Task 1

An environmental equipment supplier sells hemispherical holding ponds for treatment of chemical waste. The volume of a pond is $V_1 = \frac{1}{2}\left(\frac{4}{3}\pi r_1^3\right)$, where $r_1$ is the radius in feet. The supplier also sells cylindrical collecting tanks. A collecting tank fills completely and then drains completely to fill the empty pond. The volume of the tank is $V_2 = 12\pi r_2^2$, where $r_2$ is the radius of the tank.

a. Since $V_1 = V_2$, write an equation that shows $r_1$ as a function of $r_2$. Write an equation that shows $r_2$ as a function of $r_1$.

b. You want to double the radius of the pond. How will the radius of the tank change?

**BIG idea** Solving Equations and Inequalities
The numbers and types of solutions vary based on the type of equation.

**BIG idea** Function
You can represent functions in a variety of ways (such as graphs, tables, equations, or words). Each representation is particularly useful in certain situations.

## Task 2

Suppose $f(x) = \sqrt{x + 1}$.

a. What are the domain and range of $f$?

b. Find $f^{-1}(x)$. What are its domain and range? Be careful!

c. Show that $(f \circ f^{-1})(a) = a = (f^{-1} \circ f)(a)$ for any $a$ in the respective domains.

d. Solve the equation $f(x) = f^{-1}(x)$. Remember to check for extraneous roots.

e. Graph the functions $f$ and $f^{-1}$. Be sure that you accurately represent the domains of each function. Interpret graphically the solution(s) you found to the equation in part (d).

# Performance Task **UbD**

## Pull It All Together

The concepts and skills required to solve these problems are from several lessons within this chapter and from earlier chapters. As students solve these problems, they will demonstrate their reasoning strategies and their growth as independent problem solvers.

### Task 1

Solve a problem using algebra and the mathematical operations that are the inverses of squaring and cubing.

• Once you solve for $r_1$ as a function of $r_2$, do you have to go back to the original equation to find $r_2$ as a function of $r_1$?

• What numbers can you use for $r_1$ to compare how $r_2$ changes when $r_1$ doubles?

### Task 2

Find inverses and solve equations using algebraic methods, analyze functions for domain and range, and graphically interpret solutions of equations.

• Why does the graph of a quadratic equation not have an inverse? How can restricting the domain change this?

• What formula can you use to solve a quadratic equation if the quadratic expression does not factor? What algebraic method can you use?

• A graph and its inverse are symmetric about what line?

# Assess
# Performance **UbD**

## Pull It All Together

See p. 49 for a holistic scoring rubric to gauge a student's progress on Understanding the Problem, Planning a Solution, Getting an Answer, and Assessing Autonomy.

### SOLUTION OUTLINES

**1. a.** Possible Plan: Set $\frac{1}{2}\left(\frac{4}{3}\pi r_1^3\right)$ equal to $12\pi r_2^2$ and solve for $r_1$. Then solve it a second time only solving for $r_2$. $\left(r_1 = \sqrt[3]{18 r_2^2}\ \text{and}\ r_2 = \sqrt{32 r_1^3}\right)$

**b.** Possible Plan: Use the equation from part (a) that shows $r_2$ as a function of $r_1$. Then double the radius of $r_1$. (The radius of the tank will be $\frac{1}{16}$ the size of the pond after doubling the size of the pond.)

**2. a.** Domain: $x \geq -1$, range: $f(x) \geq 0$

**b.** First step: Switch $x$ and $y$.
Second step: Square each side of the equation.
Third step: Add $-1$ to each side.
($f^{-1}(x) = x^2 - 1$; domain: all real numbers, range: $f^{-1}(x) \geq -1$)

**c.** Possible Plan: Substitute $f^{-1}$ into $f$ and use the rule for $f(x)$.
Then substitute $f$ into $f^{-1}$ and use the rule for $f^{-1}(x)$.
$\left[\left(f \cdot f^{-1}\right)(a) = \sqrt{a^2 - 1 + 1} = \sqrt{a^2} = a;\right.$
$\left.\left(f^{-1} \cdot f\right)(a) = \left(\sqrt{a+1}\right)^2 - 1 = a + 1 - 1 = a\right]$

**d.** First step: Write $f(x) = f^{-1}(x)$ as $\sqrt{x+1} = x^2 - 1$.
Second step: Square each side of the equation.
Third step: Add $-x$ and $-1$ to each side of the equation.
Solve using a graphing calculator.
($0 = x^4 - 2x^2 - x$; $x = 0, -1, 1.6,$ and $0.6$.) The roots $0$ and $0.6$ are extraneous.

**e.**

The graphs of $f$ and $f^{-1}$ intersect at $(-1, 0)$ and about $(1.62, 1.62)$.

**Pull It All Together** 421

# Essential Questions

## BIG idea Equivalence

**ESSENTIAL QUESTION** To simplify the *n*th root of an expression, what must be true about the expression?

**ANSWER** You can simplify the *n*th root of an expression that contains an *n*th power as a factor.

$$\sqrt[n]{x^n} = x^{\frac{n}{n}} = \begin{cases} x, & n \text{ odd} \\ |x|, & n \text{ even} \end{cases}$$

## BIG idea Solving Equations

**ESSENTIAL QUESTION** When you square each side of an equation, is the resulting equation equivalent to the original?

**ANSWER** When you square each side of an equation, the resulting equation may have more solutions than the original equation.

## BIG idea Functions

**ESSENTIAL QUESTION** How are a function and its inverse function related?

**ANSWER** If $f$ and $f^{-1}$ are inverse functions and if one maps $a$ to $b$, then the other maps $b$ to $a$, i.e.,

$$\left(f \circ f^{-1}\right)(a) = \left(f^{-1} \circ f\right)(a) = a$$

---

# 6 Chapter Review

## Connecting BIG ideas and Answering the Essential Questions

**1 Equivalence**
You can simplify the *n*th root of an expression that contains an *n*th power as a factor.

$$\sqrt[n]{x^n} = x^{\frac{n}{n}} = \begin{cases} x, & n \text{ odd} \\ |x|, & n \text{ even} \end{cases}$$

**Radical Expressions and Rational Exponents (Lessons 6-1, 6-2 and 6-4)**

$$\sqrt[3]{-8x^5} \cdot \sqrt[3]{x^2} = \sqrt[3]{-8x^7}$$
$$= \sqrt[3]{(-2)^3 x^6 \cdot x}$$
$$= -2x^2 \sqrt[3]{x}$$

$$(-8x^5)^{\frac{1}{3}} (x^2)^{\frac{1}{3}} = (-8x^7)^{\frac{1}{3}}$$
$$= ((-2)^3 \cdot x^6 \cdot x)^{\frac{1}{3}}$$
$$= -2x^2 x^{\frac{1}{3}}$$

**Solving Square Root Equations (Lesson 6-5)**

$$x - 2 = \sqrt{x}$$
$$x^2 - 4x + 4 = x$$
$$x^2 - 5x + 4 = 0$$
$$(x - 4)(x - 1) = 0$$
$$x = 4 \text{ or } x = 1$$
$$4 - 2 = \sqrt{4} \checkmark$$
$$1 - 2 \neq \sqrt{1} \ ✗$$

**2 Solving Equations and Inequalities**
When you square each side of an equation, the resulting equation may have more solutions than the original equation.

**Inverse Relations and Functions (Lesson 6-7)**

The inverse of $y = \sqrt{x} + 2, x \geq 0, y \geq 2$ is $x = \sqrt{y} + 2$, or $\sqrt{y} = x - 2$, or $y = (x - 2)^2, y \geq 0, x \geq 2$.

**Graphing Radical Functions (Lesson 6-8)**

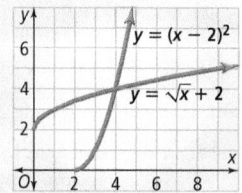

**3 Function**
If $f$ and $f^{-1}$ are inverse functions and if one maps $a$ to $b$, then the other maps $b$ to $a$, i.e.,
$$(f \circ f^{-1})(a) = (f^{-1} \circ f)(a)$$
$$= a.$$

## Chapter Vocabulary

- composite function (p. 399)
- index (p. 362)
- inverse function (p. 405)
- inverse relation (p. 405)
- like radicals (p. 374)
- *n*th root (p. 361)
- one-to-one function (p. 408)
- principal root (p. 361)
- radical equation (p. 390)
- radical function (p. 415)
- radicand (p. 362)
- rational exponent (p. 382)
- rationalize the denominator (p. 369)
- simplest form of a radical (p. 368)
- square root equation (p. 390)
- square root function (p. 415)

**Choose the correct term to complete each sentence.**

1. The number under a radical sign is called the (index/radicand).

2. (Radical functions/Inverse functions) are of the form $f(x) = \sqrt[n]{x}$.

3. A radical expression can always be rewritten using a(n) (rational exponent/inverse relation).

4. When two functions are combined so the range of one becomes the domain of the other, the resulting function is called a (square root function/composite function).

---

# Summative Questions UbD

Use the following prompts as you review this chapter with your students. The prompts are designed to help you assess your students' understanding of the Big Ideas they have studied.

- Under what conditions can you simplify a radical expression? How do the conditions change depending on the operation involved?
- What properties would you use to write $\left(9x^{-4}\right)^{-\frac{1}{2}}$ in simplest form?
- What would be your first step in the solution of $2(x + 1)^{\frac{2}{3}} = 8$?
- What operations can you perform on functions? For each, how do you determine the domain of the new function?

# Answers

## Chapter Review

1. radicand
2. radical functions
3. rational exponent
4. composite function
5. $\pm 5$
6. $\pm 0.7$
7. $-2$
8. $-2$

# 6-1 Roots and Radical Expressions

## Quick Review

You can simplify a radical expression by finding the roots. The **principal root** of a number with two real roots is the positive root. The principal **nth root** of $b$ is written as $\sqrt[n]{b}$, where $b$ is the **radicand** and $n$ is the **index** of the radical expression.

For any real number $a$, $\sqrt[n]{a^n} = \begin{cases} a \text{ if } n \text{ is odd} \\ |a| \text{ if } n \text{ is even} \end{cases}$.

## Example

What is the simplified form of $\sqrt{36x^6}$?

$\sqrt{6^2 x^6}$     Find the root of the integer.

$= \sqrt{6^2 (x^3)^2}$     Find the root of the variable.

$= 6|x^3|$     Take the square root of each term. Since the index is even, include the absolute value symbol to ensure that the root is positive even when $x^3$ is negative.

## Exercises

**Find each real root.**

5. $\sqrt{25}$          6. $\sqrt{0.49}$

7. $\sqrt[3]{-8}$         8. $-\sqrt[3]{8}$

**Simplify each radical expression. Use absolute value symbols when needed.**

9. $\sqrt{81x^2}$        10. $\sqrt[3]{64x^6}$

11. $\sqrt[4]{16x^{12}}$      12. $\sqrt[5]{0.00032x^5}$

13. $\sqrt{\dfrac{9x^4}{36}}$       14. $\sqrt[3]{125x^6y^9}$

# 6-2 Multiplying and Dividing Radical Expressions

## Quick Review

If $\sqrt[n]{a}$ and $\sqrt[n]{b}$ are real numbers, then $(\sqrt[n]{a})(\sqrt[n]{b}) = \sqrt[n]{ab}$, and, if $b \neq 0$, then $\dfrac{\sqrt[n]{a}}{\sqrt[n]{b}} = \sqrt[n]{\dfrac{a}{b}}$.

To **rationalize the denominator** of an expression, rewrite it so that the denominator contains no radical expressions.

## Example

What is the simplest form of $\sqrt{32x^2y} \cdot \sqrt{18xy^3}$?

$\sqrt{(32x^2y)(18xy^3)}$     Combine terms.

$= \sqrt{(4^2 \cdot 2x^2y)(3^2 \cdot 2xy^3)}$     Factor.

$= \sqrt{4^2 \cdot 3^2 \cdot 2^2 x^3 y^4}$     Consolidate like terms.

$= \sqrt{4^2 \cdot 3^2 \cdot 2^2 (x^2 x)(y^2)^2}$     Identify perfect squares.

$= 4 \cdot 3 \cdot 2xy^2 \sqrt{x} = 24xy^2 \sqrt{x}$     Extract perfect squares.

## Exercises

**Multiply if possible. Then simplify.**

15. $\sqrt[3]{9} \cdot \sqrt[3]{3}$     16. $\sqrt[3]{-7} \cdot \sqrt[3]{49}$     17. $\sqrt{2} \cdot \sqrt{8}$

**Multiply and simplify.**

18. $\sqrt{8x^2} \cdot \sqrt{2x^2}$       19. $5\sqrt[3]{9y^2} \cdot \sqrt[3]{24y}$

**Divide and simplify.**

20. $\sqrt{\dfrac{128}{8}}$    21. $\dfrac{\sqrt[3]{81x^5y^3}}{\sqrt[3]{3x^2}}$    22. $\dfrac{\sqrt[4]{162x^4}}{\sqrt[4]{2y^8}}$

**Divide. Rationalize all denominators.**

23. $\dfrac{\sqrt{8}}{\sqrt{6}}$    24. $\dfrac{\sqrt{3x^5}}{8x^2}$    25. $\dfrac{\sqrt[3]{6x^2y^4}}{2\sqrt[3]{5x^7y}}$

9. $9|x|$

10. $4x^2$

11. $2|x^3|$

12. $0.2x$

13. $\dfrac{x^2}{2}$

14. $5x^2y^3$

15. $3$

16. $-7$

17. $4$

18. $4x^2$

19. $30y$

20. $4$

21. $3xy$

22. $\dfrac{3|x|}{y^2}$

23. $\dfrac{2\sqrt{3}}{3}$

24. $\dfrac{\sqrt{3x}}{8}$

25. $\dfrac{y\sqrt[3]{150x}}{10x^2}$

# Answers

## Chapter Review (continued)

**26.** $22\sqrt{3}$

**27.** $26\sqrt{5x}$

**28.** $x\sqrt[3]{2}$

**29.** $14 + 7\sqrt{2}$

**30.** $-6$

**31.** $100 + 10\sqrt{6} - 10\sqrt{3} - 3\sqrt{2}$

**32.** $\dfrac{5 + 2\sqrt{5}}{5}$

**33.** $\dfrac{9 + 3\sqrt{2}}{7}$

**34.** $5$

**35.** $3$

**36.** $4$

**37.** $25$

**38.** $x$

**39.** $-2y^3$

**40.** $81x^2y^4$

**41.** $\dfrac{1}{x^3y^6}$

**42.** $\dfrac{1}{x}$

**43.** $x^3y^6$

## 6-3 Binomial Radical Expressions

### Quick Review

**Like radicals** have the same index and the same radicand. Use the distributive property to add and subtract them. Use the FOIL method to multiply binomial radical expressions. To rationalize a denominator that is a square root binomial, multiply the numerator and denominator by the conjugate of the denominator.

### Example

What is the simplified form of $\sqrt{18} + \sqrt{50} - \sqrt{8}$?

$$\sqrt{18} + \sqrt{50} - \sqrt{8}$$
$$= \sqrt{3^2 \cdot 2} + \sqrt{5^2 \cdot 2} - \sqrt{2^2 \cdot 2} \quad \text{Factor.}$$
$$= 3\sqrt{2} + 5\sqrt{2} - 2\sqrt{2} \quad \text{Simplify each radical.}$$
$$= (3 + 5 - 2)\sqrt{2} \quad \text{Combine like terms.}$$
$$= 6\sqrt{2} \quad \text{Simplify.}$$

### Exercises

**Add or subtract if possible.**

**26.** $10\sqrt{27} - 4\sqrt{12}$

**27.** $3\sqrt{20x} + 8\sqrt{45x} - 4\sqrt{5x}$

**28.** $\sqrt[3]{54x^3} - \sqrt[3]{16x^3}$

**Multiply.**

**29.** $(3 + \sqrt{2})(4 + \sqrt{2})$

**30.** $(\sqrt{5} + \sqrt{11})(\sqrt{5} - \sqrt{11})$

**31.** $(10 + \sqrt{6})(10 - \sqrt{3})$

**Divide. Rationalize all denominators.**

**32.** $\dfrac{2 + \sqrt{5}}{\sqrt{5}}$  **33.** $\dfrac{3 + \sqrt{18}}{1 + \sqrt{8}}$

## 6-4 Rational Exponents

### Quick Review

You can rewrite a radical expression with a rational exponent. By definition, if the $n$th root of $a$ is a real number and $m$ is an integer, then $a^{\frac{m}{n}} = \sqrt[n]{a^m} = (\sqrt[n]{a})^m$; if $m$ is negative then $a \neq 0$. Rational exponents can be used to simplify radical expressions.

### Example

Multiply and simplify $\sqrt{x}\left(\sqrt[4]{x^3}\right)$.

$$\sqrt{x}\left(\sqrt[4]{x^3}\right) = x^{\frac{1}{2}} \cdot x^{\frac{3}{4}} \quad \text{Rewrite with rational exponents.}$$
$$= x^{\frac{5}{4}} \quad \text{Combine exponents.}$$
$$= \sqrt[4]{x^5} \quad \text{Rewrite as a radical expression.}$$

### Exercises

**Simplify each expression.**

**34.** $25^{\frac{1}{2}}$  **35.** $81^{\frac{1}{4}}$

**36.** $16^{\frac{1}{3}} \cdot 4^{\frac{1}{3}}$  **37.** $5^{\frac{3}{2}} \cdot 5^{\frac{1}{2}}$

**Write each expression in simplest form.**

**38.** $\left(x^{\frac{1}{4}}\right)^4$  **39.** $\left(-8y^9\right)^{\frac{1}{3}}$

**40.** $\left(\sqrt{9xy^2}\right)^4$  **41.** $\left(x^{\frac{1}{6}} y^{\frac{1}{3}}\right)^{-18}$

**42.** $\left(\dfrac{x^4}{x^{-1}}\right)^{-\frac{1}{5}}$  **43.** $\left(\dfrac{x^{\frac{1}{3}}}{y^{-\frac{2}{3}}}\right)^9$

# 6-5 Solving Square Root and Other Radical Equations

## Quick Review

To solve a **radical equation**, you must isolate a radical expression on one side of the equation. You can then rewrite the radical expression using a rational exponent and use the reciprocal of the exponent to solve the equation.

For example, to solve a square root equation, you square each side of the equation. Check all possible solutions in the original equation to eliminate extraneous solutions.

## Example

What is the solution of $4(x - 2)^{\frac{2}{3}} = 16$?

$(x - 2)^{\frac{2}{3}} = 4$     Isolate the radical.

$((x - 2)^{\frac{2}{3}})^{\frac{3}{2}} = 4^{\frac{3}{2}}$     Raise both sides to the $\frac{3}{2}$ power.

$(x - 2)^{\frac{6}{6}} = 4^{\frac{3}{2}}$     Law of exponents.

$|x - 2| = 8$     Simplify.

$x = 10$ or $x = -6$     Solve for x.

## Exercises

**Solve each equation. Check for extraneous solutions.**

**44.** $2 + \sqrt{x + 5} = 4$     **45.** $3\sqrt{2x + 6} = 18$

**46.** $5(3x + 1)^{\frac{1}{4}} = 10$     **47.** $4(3x - 3)^{\frac{2}{3}} = 36$

**48.** $\sqrt{3x + 3} - 1 = x$     **49.** $\sqrt{x + 6} + 2 = x + 6$

**50.** $\sqrt{5x + 1} - 2\sqrt{x} = 1$     **51.** $\sqrt{2x + 9} - \sqrt{x} = 3$

**52. Electricity** The power $P$, in watts, that a circular solar cell produces and the radius of the cell $r$ in centimeters are related by the square root equation $r = \sqrt{\frac{P}{0.02\pi}}$. About how much power is produced by a cell with a radius of 12 cm?

# 6-6 Function Operations

## Quick Review

When performing function operations, you can use the same rules you used for real numbers, but you must take into consideration the domain and range of each function. The composition of function $g$ with function $f$ is defined as $(g \circ f)(x) = g(f(x))$.

## Example

Let $f(x) = x + 3$ and $g(x) = x^2 - 2$. What is $(g \circ f)(-2)$?

$g(f(-2)) = g((-2) + 3)$     Evaluate $f(-2)$.

$= g(1)$     Simplify.

$= (1)^2 - 2$     Evaluate $g(f(-2))$.

$= -1$     Simplify.

Therefore, $(g \circ f)(-2) = -1$

## Exercises

**Let $f(x) = x - 4$ and $g(x) = x^2 - 16$. Perform each function operation and then find the domain.**

**53.** $f(x) + g(x)$     **54.** $g(x) - f(x)$

**55.** $f(x) \cdot g(x)$      **56.** $\frac{g(x)}{f(x)}$

**Let $g(x) = 5x - 2$ and $h(x) = x^2 + 1$. Find the value of each expression.**

**57.** $(h \circ g)(-1)$     **58.** $(h \circ g)(0)$

**59.** $(g \circ h)(2)$     **60.** $(g \circ h)(a)$

**61. Discounts** A grocery store is offering a 50% discount off a $4.00 box of cereal. You also have a $1.00 off coupon for the same cereal. Use a composite function to show whether it is better to use the coupon before or after the store discount.

**44.** $-1$

**45.** 15

**46.** 5

**47.** 10, $-8$

**48.** 2, $-1$

**49.** $-2$

**50.** 0, 16

**51.** 0, 36

**52.** 9.05 W

**53.** $x^2 + x - 20$; domain: all real numbers

**54.** $x^2 - x - 12$; domain: all real numbers

**55.** $x^3 - 4x^2 - 16x + 64$; domain: all real numbers

**56.** $x + 4$; domain: all real numbers except $x = 4$

**57.** 50

**58.** 5

**59.** 23

**60.** $5a^2 + 3$

**61.** $D(C(x)) = 0.5x - 0.5$, $C(D(x)) = 0.5x - 1$; use the coupon after the store discount.

# Answers

## Chapter Review (continued)

**62.** $f^{-1}(x) = \pm\sqrt{\dfrac{x+8}{2}}$; no

**63.** $f^{-1}(x) = 5 - \dfrac{1}{3}x$; yes

**64.** $f^{-1}(x) = x^2 - 6$; yes

**65.** $f^{-1}(x) = \dfrac{3 \pm \sqrt{x}}{2}$; no

**66.**  domain of $f$: all real numbers, range of $f$: all real numbers, domain of $f^{-1}$: all real numbers, range of $f^{-1}$: all real numbers

**67.** domain of $f$: all real numbers, range of $f$: $y \geq 0$; domain of $f^{-1}$: $x \geq 0$, range of $f^{-1}$: all real numbers

**68.** domain of $f$: $x \geq 3$, range of $f$: $y \geq 0$, domain of $f^{-1}$: $x \geq 0$, range of $f^{-1}$: $y \geq 3$

**69.** domain of $f$: all real numbers, range of $f$: $y \leq 6$, domain of $f^{-1}$: $x \leq 6$, range of $f^{-1}$: all real numbers

**70.** $s = \sqrt[3]{V}$; 4 ft

**71.** domain: $x \geq 0$, range: $y \geq -5$

**72.** domain: $x \geq -8$, range: $y \geq 0$

---

## 6-7 Inverse Relations and Functions

### Quick Review

If a relation or a function is described by an equation in $x$ and $y$, you can interchange $x$ and $y$ to get the inverse. The domain of a function becomes the range of its inverse, and the range of a function becomes the domain of its inverse.

### Example

What is the inverse of $f(x) = \sqrt{x - 10}$?

| | |
|---|---|
| $y = \sqrt{x - 10}$ | Rewrite using $y$. |
| $x = \sqrt{y - 10}$ | Interchange the $x$ and $y$ values. |
| $x^2 = y - 10$ | Square each side. |
| $y = x^2 + 10$ | Solve for $y$. |
| $f^{-1}(x) = x^2 + 10$ | Write the inverse function. |

The domain of $f(x)$ is $x \geq 10$, which means the range of $f^{-1}(x)$ is $y \geq 10$. Also, since the range of $f(x)$ is $y \geq 0$, the domain of $f^{-1}(x)$ is $x \geq 0$.

### Exercises

**Find the inverse of each function. Determine whether each inverse is a function.**

**62.** $f(x) = 2x^2 - 8$    **63.** $f(x) = 15 - 3x$

**64.** $f(x) = \sqrt{x + 6}$    **65.** $f(x) = (2x - 3)^2$

**Graph each function and its inverse. Describe the domain and range of each.**

**66.** $f(x) = 4x - 1$    **67.** $f(x) = (x + 3)^2$

**68.** $f(x) = \sqrt{x - 3}$    **69.** $f(x) = 6 - 5x^2$

**70. Geometry** The volume of cube is determined by the formula $V = s^3$, where $s$ is the length of one side. Find the inverse formula. Use it to find the side length of a cube with a volume of 64 ft$^3$.

---

## 6-8 Graphing Radical Functions

### Quick Review

The function $f(x) = \sqrt{x}$ is the parent function of the **square root function** $f(x) = a\sqrt{x - h} + k$. The graph of $f(x) = a\sqrt{x}$ is a stretch ($a > 1$) or a shrink ($0 < a < 1$) of the parent function. The graph of $f(x) = a\sqrt{x - h} + k$ is a translation $h$ units horizontally and $k$ units vertically of $y = a\sqrt{x}$. The graph of $f(x) = \sqrt[3]{x}$ is transformed by $a$, $h$, and $k$ in the same way as the graph of $f(x) = \sqrt{x}$.

### Example

Describe the graph of $y = \sqrt{4x + 12}$.

| | |
|---|---|
| $y = \sqrt{4x + 12}$ | |
| $y = \sqrt{4(x + 3)}$ | Factor the polynomial. |
| $y = 2\sqrt{x + 3}$ | Simplify the radical. |

The graph of $y = \sqrt{4x + 12}$ is the graph of $y = 2\sqrt{x}$ translated 3 units to the left.

### Exercises

**Graph each function. Find the domain and range.**

**71.** $y = \sqrt{x} - 5$    **72.** $y = \sqrt{x + 8}$

**73.** $y = 5\sqrt{x} + 9$    **74.** $y = -\sqrt{x - 4}$

**75.** $y = \sqrt[3]{x + 10}$    **76.** $y = -\sqrt[3]{x - 2} + 5$

**Rewrite each function to make it easy to graph using transformations. Describe each graph.**

**77.** $y = \sqrt{9x - 27} + 4$    **78.** $y = -3\sqrt{4x - 16}$

**79.** $y = \sqrt[3]{8x + 24}$    **80.** $y = \sqrt{\dfrac{x - 4}{4}} + 6$

**Solve each equation by graphing.**

**81.** $5 = -\sqrt{x - 3}$

**82.** $\sqrt{8x - 16} = 2\sqrt{x + 2}$

**73.** domain: $x \geq 0$, range: $y \geq 9$

**74.** domain: $x \geq 4$, range: $y \leq 0$

**75.** domain: all real numbers, range: all real numbers

**76.** domain: all real numbers, range: all real numbers

**77.** $y = 3\sqrt{x - 3} + 4$ the graph of $y = 3\sqrt{x}$ translated 3 units to the right and 4 units up

**78.** $y = -6\sqrt{x - 4}$; the graph of $y = -6\sqrt{x}$ translated 4 units to the right

**79.** $y = 2\sqrt[3]{x + 3}$; the graph of $y = 2\sqrt[3]{x}$ translated 3 units to the left

**80.** $y = \dfrac{1}{2}\sqrt{x - 4} + 6$; the graph of $y = \dfrac{1}{2}\sqrt{x}$ translated 4 units to the right and 6 units up

**81.** no solution

**82.** 6

## Do you know HOW?

Simplify each radical expression. Use absolute value symbols when needed.

**1.** $\sqrt{54x^3y^5}$

**2.** $\sqrt[3]{-0.027}$

**3.** $\sqrt[5]{-64x^{14}y^{20}}$

Simplify each expression. Rationalize all denominators.

**4.** $\sqrt{7x^3} \cdot \sqrt{14x}$

**5.** $\dfrac{1 - \sqrt{3x}}{\sqrt{6x}}$

**6.** $\sqrt{48} + 2\sqrt{27} + 5\sqrt{12}$

**7.** $(3 + 2\sqrt{5})(1 - \sqrt{20})$

**8.** $4\sqrt{7xz} + 2\sqrt{7xz}$

**9.** $\dfrac{5\sqrt{2}}{\sqrt{7} - \sqrt{2}}$

Simplify each expression.

**10.** $(125)^{-\frac{2}{3}}$

**11.** $x^{\frac{1}{6}} \cdot x^{\frac{1}{3}}$

**12.** $\left(\dfrac{8x^9y^3}{27x^2y^{12}}\right)^{\frac{2}{3}}$

**13.** $\sqrt{8x^5} - \sqrt{18x^5}$

Solve each equation. Check for extraneous solutions.

**14.** $\sqrt{x - 3} = x - 5$

**15.** $\sqrt{x + 4} = \sqrt{3x}$

**16.** $2(x - 1)^{\frac{3}{4}} = 16$

**17.** $\sqrt{x + 3} - 1 = x$

Let $f(x) = x - 2$ and $g(x) = x^2 - 3x + 2$. Perform each function operation and then find the domain.

**18.** $-2g(x) + f(x)$

**19.** $-f(x) \cdot g(x)$

**20.** $\dfrac{g(x)}{f(x)}$

Find each product or quotient.

**21.** $\sqrt{5}\,(\sqrt[4]{5})$

**22.** $\dfrac{\sqrt{x^3}}{\sqrt[5]{x^2}}$

For each pair of functions, find $(g \circ f)(x)$ and $(f \circ g)(x)$.

**23.** $f(x) = x^2 - 2$, $g(x) = 4x + 1$

**24.** $f(x) = 2x^2 + x - 7$, $g(x) = -3x - 1$

Find the inverse of each function. Is the inverse a function?

**25.** $f(x) = (x + 3)^2 + 1$

**26.** $f(x) = \sqrt{2x + 1}$

**27.** $g(x) = 3x^3 - 4$

**28.** $f(x) = \frac{1}{4}x$

Rewrite each function to make it easy to graph using transformations. Describe the graph.

**29.** $y = \sqrt{16x + 80} - 1$    **30.** $y = \sqrt{9x + 3}$

Graph. Find the domain and range of each function.

**31.** $y = 2\sqrt{x} + 3$

**32.** $y = -\sqrt{2x + 3}$

**33.** $y = \sqrt{x + 3} - 4$

## Do you UNDERSTAND?

**34. Writing** Explain why $-108$ has no real 6th roots.

**35. Open-Ended** Write a relation that is not a function, but whose inverse is a function.

**36. Measurement** The time $t$ in seconds for a swinging pendulum to complete one full cycle is given by the function $t = 0.2\sqrt{l}$, where $l$ is the length of the pendulum in centimeters. To the nearest tenth, how long is a full cycle if the pendulum is 10 cm long? 20 cm long? How long, in centimeters, is a pendulum that takes 2 seconds for one full cycle?

**30.** $y = 3\sqrt{x + \frac{1}{3}}$; the graph of $y = 3\sqrt{x}$ translated $\frac{1}{3}$ units to the left

**31.**  domain: $x \geq 0$, range: $y \geq 3$

**32.** domain: $x \geq -\frac{3}{2}$, range: $y \leq 0$

**33.** domain: $x \geq -3$, range: $y \geq -4$

**34.** $\sqrt[6]{-108}$ has no real roots, since there is no real number $x$ such that $x^6 = -108$.

**35.** Answers may vary. Sample: $f(x) = \pm\sqrt{x}$ is not a function, but $f^{-1}(x) = x^2$ is a function.

**36.** 0.6 s; 0.9 s; 100 cm

## Answers

**1.** $3|x|y^2\sqrt{6xy}$

**2.** $-0.3$

**3.** $-2x^2y^4\sqrt[5]{2x^4}$

**4.** $7x^2\sqrt{2}$

**5.** $\dfrac{\sqrt{6x} - 3x\sqrt{2}}{6x}$

**6.** $20\sqrt{3}$

**7.** $-17 - 4\sqrt{5}$

**8.** $6\sqrt{7xz}$

**9.** $2 + \sqrt{14}$

**10.** $\dfrac{1}{25}$

**11.** $x^{\frac{1}{2}}$

**12.** $\dfrac{4x^4\sqrt[3]{x^2}}{9y^6}$

**13.** $-x^2\sqrt{2x}$

**14.** 7

**15.** 2

**16.** 17

**17.** 1

**18.** $-2x^2 + 7x - 6$; domain: all real numbers

**19.** $-x^3 + 5x^2 - 8x + 4$; domain: all real numbers

**20.** $x - 1$; domain: all real numbers except $x = 2$

**21.** $\sqrt[4]{125}$

**22.** $x\sqrt[10]{x}$

**23.** $(g \circ f)(x) = 4x^2 - 7$; $(f \circ g)(x) = 16x^2 + 8x - 1$

**24.** $(g \circ f)(x) = -6x^2 - 3x + 20$; $(f \circ g)(x) = 18x^2 + 9x - 6$

**25.** $f^{-1}(x) = -3 \pm \sqrt{x - 1}$; no

**26.** $f^{-1}(x) = \dfrac{x^2 - 1}{2}$, $x \geq 0$; yes

**27.** $g^{-1}(x) = \sqrt[3]{\dfrac{x + 4}{3}}$; yes

**28.** $f^{-1}(x) = 4x$; yes

**29.** $y = 4\sqrt{x + 5} - 1$; the graph of $y = 4\sqrt{x}$ translated 5 units to the left and 1 unit down

**PowerAlgebra.com**

**MathXL for School**

Prepare students for the Mid-Chapter Quiz and Chapter Test with online practice and review.

| Item Number | Lesson |
|---|---|
| 1 | 5-5 |
| 2 | 1-4 |
| 3 | 5-3 |
| 4 | 2-2 |
| 5 | 2-7 |
| 6 | 4-1 |
| 7 | 6-2 |
| 8 | 4-6 |
| 9 | 4-8 |
| 10 | 1-6 |
| 11 | 2-4 |
| 12 | 6-4 |
| 13 | 3-5 |
| 14 | 4-8 |
| 15 | 4-1 |
| 16 | 5-4 |
| 17 | 6-6 |
| 18 | 3-1 |
| 19 | 3-2 |
| 20 | 5-5 |
| 21 | 4-7 |
| 22 | 6-2 |
| 23 | 6-5 |
| 24 | 6-4 |
| 25 | 3-2 |
| 26 | 4-6 |
| 27 | 4-2 |
| 28 | 3-2 |
| 29 | 5-5 |
| 30 | 5-1 |
| 31 | 6-1 |
| 32 | 6-3 |
| 33 | 6-6 |

# 6 Cumulative Test Prep

## TIPS FOR SUCCESS

Some problems require you to find the inverse of a function.

What is the inverse of the function $y = x^2 + 3$?

- Ⓐ $y = x - 3$
- Ⓑ $y = \pm \sqrt{x - 3}$
- Ⓒ $y = \pm \sqrt{x^2 + 3}$
- Ⓓ $y = (x - 3)^2$

### TIP 1
To find the inverse of a function, interchange x and y.

### TIP 2
After you interchange x and y, solve for y.

**Think It Through**
$y = x^2 + 3$
$x = y^2 + 3$
$x - 3 = y^2$
$\pm \sqrt{x - 3} = y$
$y = \pm \sqrt{x - 3}$

The correct answer is B.

 ## Vocabulary Review

As you solve test items, you must understand the meanings of mathematical terms. Match each term with its mathematical meaning.

A. radicand

B. index

C. composite function

D. inverse functions

E. radical function

I. the combination of two functions such that the output from the first becomes the input for the second

II. the degree of a root in a radical expression

III. the number under the radical sign in a radical expression

IV. a function that can be written in the form $f(x) = a\sqrt[n]{x - h} + k$

V. the range of one function is the domain of the other and vice versa

## Multiple Choice

Read each question. Then write the letter of the correct answer on your paper.

1. Find all the roots of $2x^4 + x^3 - 8x^2 - 4x = 0$.
   - Ⓐ $x = -2, x = -0.5, x = 0, x = 2$
   - Ⓑ $x = -2, x = -0.5, x = 2$
   - Ⓒ $x = -2, x = 0.5, x = 0, x = 2$
   - Ⓓ $x = -2, x = 0.5, x = 2$

2. Solve the equation $ax^2 + bx + c = 0$ for $b$.
   - Ⓕ $b = -cx - ax^2$
   - Ⓖ $b = \frac{-c - ax^2}{x}$
   - Ⓗ $b = -(cx - ax^2)$
   - Ⓘ $b = \frac{-(c - ax^2)}{x}$

3. Use the sum of cubes formula to factor $x^3 + 64$.
   - Ⓐ $(x + 4)(x^2 - 4x + 4)$
   - Ⓑ $(x + 4)(x^2 + 4x + 4)$
   - Ⓒ $(x + 4)(x^2 - 4x + 16)$
   - Ⓓ $(x + 4)(x^2 + 4x + 16)$

# Answers

## Vocabulary Review
A III
B II
C I
D V
E IV

## Multiple Choice
1. A
2. G
3. C

**4.** The time it takes to copy pages varies directly with the number of pages being copied. The copier at your office can copy 21 color pages per minute and 40 black and white pages per minute. Approximately how long will it take to copy 60 color pages and 35 black and white pages?

   (F) 0.9 minute     (H) 2.9 minutes

   (G) 2.5 minutes     (I) 3.7 minutes

**5.** Which equation is modeled by the graph?

   (A) $y = |2x - 3|$     (C) $y = |2x + 3|$

   (B) $y = 2|x - 3|$     (D) $y = 2|x + 3|$

**6.** What are the vertex and axis of symmetry for the given parabola?

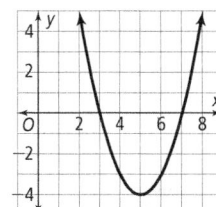

   (F) $(-4, 5), y = 5$     (H) $(5, -4), y = -4$

   (G) $(-4, 5), x = 5$     (I) $(5, -4), x = 5$

**7.** What is the product of $\sqrt[3]{3}$ and $\sqrt[5]{3}$?

   (A) $\sqrt[8]{3}$     (C) $\sqrt[15]{3^8}$

   (B) $\sqrt[8]{9}$     (D) $\sqrt[8]{3^{15}}$

**8.** Solve the equation $x^2 - 6x = 3$ by completing the square.

   (F) $-3 \pm 2\sqrt{3}$     (H) $-3 \pm 3\sqrt{2}$

   (G) $3 \pm 2\sqrt{3}$     (I) $3 \pm 3\sqrt{2}$

**9.** Solve $7x^2 + 196 = 0$ for $x$.

   (A) $\pm 4i\sqrt{7}$     (C) $\pm 2i\sqrt{7}$

   (B) $\pm 4\sqrt{7}$     (D) $\pm 2\sqrt{7}$

**10.** Which inequality is modeled by the graph?

   (F) $k + 1 \le 7$     (H) $k - 4 \le 3$

   (G) $|k + 1| \le 7$     (I) $|k - 4| \le 3$

**11.** Which equation represents a line that contains the point $(3, 2)$ and is parallel to $y = 3x - 12$?

   (A) $y = \frac{1}{3}x - 7$     (C) $y = 3x - 3$

   (B) $y = 3x - 7$     (D) $y = \frac{1}{3}x - 3$

**12.** Which is the first *incorrect* step in simplifying $\sqrt[3]{x^9 y^6 z}$?

Step 1: $\sqrt[3]{x^9 y^6 z} = \sqrt[3]{x^9} \cdot \sqrt[3]{y^6} \cdot \sqrt[3]{z}$

Step 2: $= x^3 \cdot \sqrt[3]{y^6} \cdot \sqrt[3]{z}$

Step 3: $= x^3 \cdot y^3 \cdot \sqrt[3]{z}$

   (F) Step 1

   (G) Step 2

   (H) Step 3

   (I) Each step is correct.

**13.** A photographer is promoting three photo specials. How much does it cost for each type of print?

   (A) $5 \times 7$ costs $7, $3 \times 5$ costs $5, Wallet costs $3

   (B) $5 \times 7$ costs $11, $3 \times 5$ costs $7, Wallet costs $3

   (C) $5 \times 7$ costs $12, $3 \times 5$ costs $11, Wallet costs $7

   (D) $5 \times 7$ costs $7, $3 \times 5$ costs $5, Wallet costs $5

**14.** What is an equivalent form of $\frac{5}{2 + 2i}$?

   (F) $\frac{5}{4i}$     (H) $\frac{5 + 5i}{4}$

   (G) $\frac{10 - 10i}{4 - 4i}$     (I) $\frac{5 - 5i}{4}$

**4.** I
**5.** C
**6.** I
**7.** C
**8.** G
**9.** C
**10.** I
**11.** B
**12.** H
**13.** A
**14.** I

# Answers

**15.** C
**16.** F
**17.** 10
**18.** 9
**19.** 32
**20.** 2
**21.** 2
**22.** 1
**23.** $\frac{4}{3}$
**24.** $\frac{1}{64}$
**25.** 210
**26.** $-2$
**27.** [2] **a.** domain of $f$: all real numbers, range of $f$: $y \geq 4$; domain of $g$: all real numbers, range of $g$: all real numbers
   **b.** $f(x) + g(x) = (x^2 + 4) + (3x - 1) = x^2 + 3x + 3$
   **c.** all real numbers
   [1] one incorrect statement of a domain or a range
**28.** [2] hat: $25, shirt: $20

   [1] graph is not labeled appropriately
**29.** [2] $y = 3(x - 16)(x - (1 - 2i))(x - (1 + 2i))$, multiply the constant terms only:
   $3(-16)(-1 + 2i)(-1 - 2i) = -240$
   [1] constant term is correct, but no work is shown OR one computational error
**30.** [2] degree: 6, polynomial of 4 terms; down and down end behavior with one turning point
   [1] end behavior is described correctly, but no other description is given
**31.** sometimes
**32.** always
**33.** [4] **a.** rebate: $R(x) = 5x$, where $x$ is the number of CDs bought; discount: $M(y) = 0.15y$, where $y$ is the amount of money paid
   **b.** If the rebate is taken off first, the customer will pay $(13x - 5x)(1 - 0.15) = 6.8x$. If the discount is given first, the customer will pay $(1 - 0.15)(13x) - 5x = 6.05x$. The customer receives the greatest discount if the 15% off is taken before the $5 rebate is applied.

---

**15.** The graph shows a transformation of $f(x) = x^2$. What is an equation of the graph?

(A) $g(x) = (x - 2)^2 - 3$  (C) $g(x) = (x + 2)^2 - 3$
(B) $g(x) = (x - 2)^2 + 3$  (D) $g(x) = (x + 2)^2 + 3$

**16.** The total cost of $x + 2$ markers is $x^3 + 5x^2 + 2x - 8$. What is the cost of each marker?

(F) $x^2 + 3x - 4$    (H) $x^2 - 3x - 4$
(G) $x^2 - 3x + 4$    (I) $x^2 + 5x + 2$

### GRIDDED RESPONSE

**17.** Let $g(x) = x - 3$ and $h(x) = x^2 + 6$. What is $(h \circ g)(1)$?

**18.** A laptop comes without any programs installed on it. Each program costs $20 and the laptop you want costs $319. What is the greatest number of programs you can buy if you want to spend at most $500 for the laptop?

**19.** You are building an entertainment center with shelves that are $x$ in. deep by $x$ in. long. The height of the unit will be twice the depth. If the volume of the unit will be 8,192 in³, what is the height, in inches, of the entertainment center?

**20.** Use Descartes' Rule of Signs to find the maximum number of positive real roots of $P(x) = 5x^4 + x^3 - 4x^2 + 3x + 1 = 0$.

**21.** Using the discriminant, determine the number of real roots of the equation $2x^2 + 3x = 4$.

**22.** What is the quotient $\dfrac{\sqrt[3]{8x^6 y^{12}}}{\sqrt{4x^4 y^8}}$?

**23.** What is the solution of $4 + \sqrt{3x + 5} = 7$?

---

**24.** Simplify the expression $256^{-\frac{3}{4}}$.

**25.** All 385 tickets for a high-school play sold in 10 days. The ticket receipts totaled $1960. If the cost of a child's ticket was $4 and the cost of an adult's ticket was $6, how many adult tickets were sold?

**26.** What is the $x$-value of the $x$-intercept of the graph of $f(x) = x^2 + 4x + 4$?

### Short Response

**27.** You are given that $f(x) = x^2 + 4$ and $g(x) = 3x - 1$.
   **a.** What are the domain and range of $f(x)$ and $g(x)$?
   **b.** Find $f(x) + g(x)$.
   **c.** What is the domain of your answer to part (b)?

**28.** Two friends went shopping together. One friend bought 2 hats and 1 shirt and spent $70, while the other friend bought 1 hat and 3 shirts and spent $85. Use a graph to determine the costs of each shirt and hat.

**29.** A student found that a cubic function has zeros 16 and $1 - 2i$ with a leading coefficient of 3. What is the constant term of this polynomial function with real coefficients?

**30.** Describe the graph of the polynomial function $f(x) = -x^6 + 3x^5 + 4x - 10$. What is its end behavior?

Decide whether the following statements are *always*, *sometimes*, or *never* true.

**31.** If $n$ is a real number, then $0^n = 0$.

**32.** If $a$ and $b$ are rational numbers, then the product of $(a + \sqrt{b})$ and its conjugate is a rational number.

### Extended Response

**33.** An online music store is having a promotion. Customers receive a $5 rebate if they buy any regular priced CD at $13 each. They can also receive 15% off if they register as a store member.
   **a.** What functions model the two discounts?
   **b.** In which order should the discounts be applied for the customer to receive the greatest discount?
   **c.** Use your answer from part (b) to determine the amount a customer will save if she buys 5 CDs.

---

   **c.** 5 CDs at regular price costs
   $13(5) = $60
   5 CDs at a discount costs
   $6.05(5) = $30.25
   The customer saves $29.75.
   [3] appropriate methods, but with one computational error
   [2] incorrect function(s), but work done appropriately given previous results
   [1] correct answers, but without work shown

---

# Get Ready!

Lesson 1-3  **Evaluating Expressions**

Evaluate each expression for $x = -2, 0,$ and $2.$

**1.** $10^{x+1}$  **2.** $\left(\frac{3}{2}\right)^x$  **3.** $-5^{x-2}$  **4.** $-(3)^{0.5x}$

Lesson 2-5 **Using Linear Models**

Draw a scatter plot and find the line of best fit for each set of data.

**5.** $(0, 2), (1, 4), (2, 6.5), (3, 8.5), (4, 10), (5, 12), (6, 14)$

**6.** $(3, 100), (5, 150), (7, 195), (9, 244), (11, 296), (13, 346), (15, 396)$

Lessons 4-1 and 5-9 **Graphing Transformations**

Identify the parent function of each equation. Graph each equation as a transformation of its parent function.

**7.** $y = (x + 5)^2 - 3$  **8.** $y = -2(x - 6)^3$

Lesson 6-4 **Simplifying Rational Exponents**

Simplify each expression.

**9.** $\left(x^{\frac{1}{5}}\right)^{10}$  **10.** $\left(-8x^3\right)^{\frac{4}{3}}$

Lesson 6-7 **Finding Inverses**

Find the inverse of each function. Is the inverse a function?

**11.** $y = 10 - 2x^2$  **12.** $y = (x + 4)^3 - 1$

## Looking Ahead Vocabulary

**13.** In advertising, the *decay factor* describes how an advertisement loses its effectiveness over time. In math, would you expect a decay factor to increase or decrease the value of $y$ as $x$ increases?

**14.** There are many different kinds of growth patterns. Patterns that increase by a constant rate are linear. Patterns that grow *exponentially* increase by an ever-increasing rate. If your allowance doubles each week, does that represent linear growth or exponential growth?

**15.** The word *asymptote* comes from a Greek word meaning "not falling together." When looking at the end behavior of a function, do you expect the graph to intersect its asymptote?

**PowerAlgebra.com**  Chapter 7  Exponential and Logarithmic Functions  431

---

---

# Answers

## Get Ready!

**1.** 0.1; 10; 1000

**2.** $\frac{4}{9}$; 1; $\frac{9}{4}$

**3.** $-\frac{1}{625}$; $-\frac{1}{25}$; $-1$

**4.** $-\frac{1}{3}$; $-1$; $-3$

**5.**  ; $y \approx 1.98x + 2.20$

**6.**  ; $y \approx 24.66x + 24.77$

**7.** $y = x^2$

**8.** $y = x^3$

**9.** $x^2$

**10.** $16x^4$

**11.** $y = \pm\sqrt{\frac{10 - x}{2}}$; no

**12.** $y = -4 + \sqrt[3]{x + 1}$; yes

**13.** decrease

**14.** exponential

**15.** no

# Chapter 7 Overview

## UbD Understanding by Design

Chapter 7 expands on student understandings and skills related to exponential and logarithmic functions. In this chapter, students will develop the answers to the Essential Questions posed on the opposite page as they learn the concepts and skills bulleted below.

### BIG idea Modeling

**ESSENTIAL QUESTION** How do you model a quantity that changes regularly over time by the same percentage?
- Students will model situations with exponential functions.

### BIG idea Equivalence

**ESSENTIAL QUESTION** How are exponents and logarithms related?
- Students will use exponents to solve logarithmic equations and logarithms to solve exponential equations.

### BIG idea Function

**ESSENTIAL QUESTION** How are exponential functions and logarithmic functions related?
- Students will show that exponents and logarithms are inverse functions.
- Students will graph exponential and logarithmic functions.

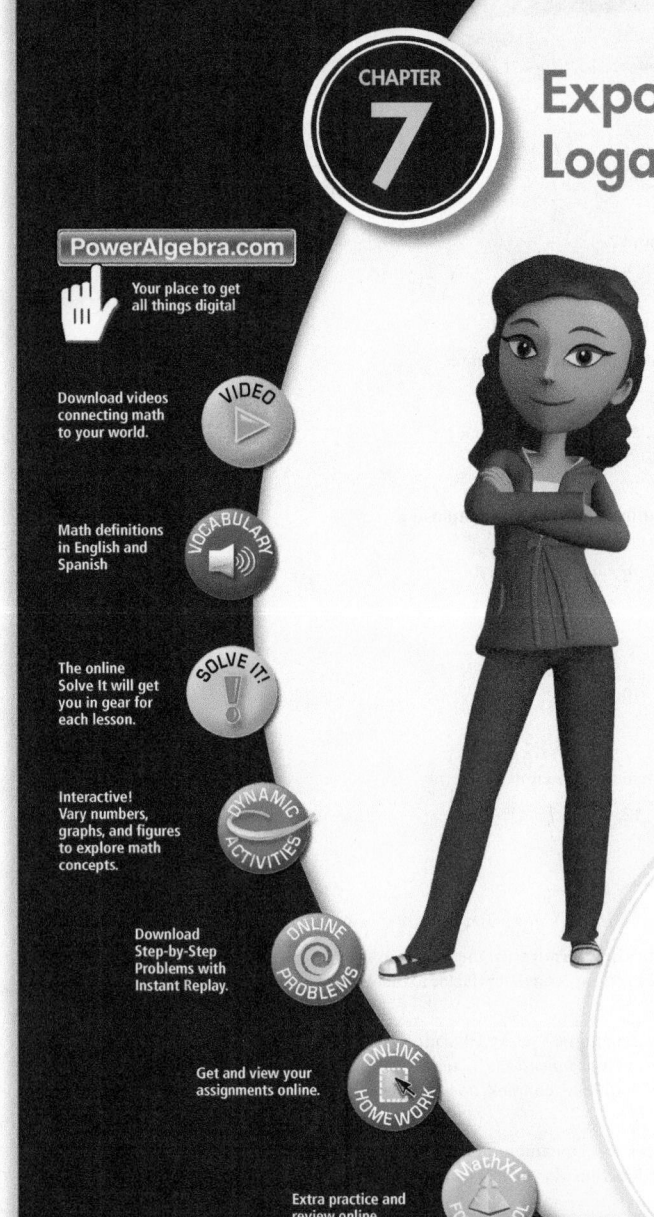

**PowerAlgebra.com**

Your place to get all things digital

**Download videos** connecting math to your world.

VIDEO

**Math definitions** in English and Spanish

VOCABULARY

**The online Solve It** will get you in gear for each lesson.

SOLVE IT!

**Interactive!** Vary numbers, graphs, and figures to explore math concepts.

DYNAMIC ACTIVITIES

**Download Step-by-Step Problems** with Instant Replay.

ONLINE PROBLEMS

**Get and view your assignments online.**

ONLINE HOMEWORK

**Extra practice and review online**

MathXL FOR SCHOOL

# CHAPTER 7
# Exponential and Logarithmic Functions

Logarithms provide a way to work with the inverses of exponential functions. Exponential functions model what some might call "explosive" growth, but logarithmic values grow very slowly. Decibels are logarithms that measure sound, and when sound energy increases dramatically, the decibel values creep upward. A few extra decibels can bust your eardrums!

## Vocabulary

**English/Spanish Vocabulary Audio Online:**

| English | Spanish |
|---|---|
| asymptote, *p. 435* | asíntota |
| Change of Base Formula, *p. 464* | fórmula de cambio de base |
| common logarithm, *p. 453* | logaritmo común |
| exponential equation, *p. 469* | ecuación exponencial |
| exponential function, *p. 434* | función exponencial |
| exponential growth, *p. 435* | incremento exponencial |
| logarithm, *p. 451* | logaritmo |
| logarithmic equation, *p. 471* | ecuación logarítmica |
| logarithmic function, *p. 454* | función logarítmica |
| natural logarithmic function, *p. 478* | función logarítmica natural |

**PowerAlgebra.com**

## Chapter 7 Overview

Use these online assets to engage your students. These include support for the Solve It and step-by-step solutions for Problems.

 Show the student-produced video demonstrating relevant and engaging applications of the new concepts in the chapter.

 Find online definitions for new terms in English and Spanish.

 Start each lesson with an attention-getting Problem. View the Problem online with helpful hints.

## My Math Video

## BIG ideas

1 **Modeling**
**Essential Question** How do you model a quantity that changes regularly over time by the same percentage?

2 **Equivalence**
**Essential Question** How are exponents and logarithms related?

3 **Function**
**Essential Question** How are exponential functions and logarithmic functions related?

## Chapter Preview

7-1 **Exploring Exponential Models**
7-2 **Properties of Exponential Functions**
7-3 **Logarithmic Functions as Inverses**
7-4 **Properties of Logarithms**
7-5 **Exponential and Logarithmic Equations**
7-6 **Natural Logarithms**

PowerAlgebra.com | **Chapter 7** Exponential and Logarithmic Functions | 433

---

## My Math Video
Use this photo to introduce the concept of logarithmic functions.

**Q** What is being shown in the photo? **[A DJ spinning a record]**

**Q** What do decibels measure? **[sound]**

**Q** If someone told you that the music is just a few decibels louder than what is safe, should you be concerned? Why or why not? **[Yes; an increase of just a few decibels is dramatically louder.]**

**Q** Why might you want to use a logarithmic function to model sound rather than a linear one? **[Sample: The numbers for decibels are smaller for extremely loud sounds and easier to work with than they would be for a linear model.]**

EXTENSION
Have students research other types of logarithmic models, such as the Richter scale or the pH scale.

---

 Increase students' depth of knowledge with interactive online activities.

 Show Problems from each lesson solved step by step. Instant replay allows students to go at their own pace when studying online.

 Assign homework to individual students or to an entire class.

 Prepare students for the Mid-Chapter Quiz and Chapter Test with online practice and review.

# EXPONENTIAL AND LOGARITHMIC FUNCTIONS
# Math Background

**UbD**

## Modeling

**BIG** idea  Many real-world mathematical problems can be represented algebraically. These representations can lead to algebraic solutions. A function that models a real-world situation can then be used to make estimates or predictions about future occurrences.

**ESSENTIAL UNDERSTANDINGS**

**7-1**   You can represent repeated multiplication with a function in the form of $y = ab^x$ where $b$ is a positive number other than 1.

**7-4**   Logarithms and exponents have corresponding properties.

## Equivalence

**BIG** idea  A single quantity may be represented by many different expressions. The facts about a quantity may be expressed by many different equations (or inequalities).

**ESSENTIAL UNDERSTANDINGS**

**7-1**   See above.

**7-3**   The exponential function $y = b^x$ is one-to-one, so its inverse $x = b^y$ is a function. To express "$y$ as a function of $x$" for the inverse, write $y = \log_b x$.

**7-4**   Logarithms and exponents have corresponding properties.

**7-5**   You can use logarithms to solve exponential equations. You can use exponents to solve logarithmic equations.

**7-6**   The functions $y = e^x$ and $y = \ln x$ are inverse functions. Just as before, this means that if $a = e^b$, then $b = \ln a$, and vice versa.

## Function

**BIG** idea  A function is a relationship between variables in which each value of the input variable is associated with a unique value of the output variable. Functions can be represented in a variety of ways, such as graphs, tables, equations, or words. Each representation is particularly useful in certain situations. Some important families of functions are developed through transformations of the simplest form of the function.

**ESSENTIAL UNDERSTANDINGS**

**7-1**   See above.

**7-2**   The factor $a$ in $y = ab^x$ can stretch or compress, and possibly reflect the graph of the parent function $y = b^x$.

**7-3**   The exponential function $y = b^x$ is one-to-one, so its inverse $x = b^y$ is a function. To express "$y$ as a function of $x$" for the inverse, write $y = \log_b x$.

**7-5 to 7-6**  See above.

## Exponential and Logarithmic Models

### Exponential Models

The function $y = ab^x$, represents
- exponential growth if $a > 0$ and $b > 1$
- exponential decay if $a > 0$ and $0 < b < 1$

| Growth | Decay |
|--------|-------|

The factor $a$ can stretch, compress, or reflect the graph of the parent function $y = b^x$.

Translations occur for nonzero values of $h$ (horizontal) and $k$ (vertical) in the function $y = ab^{(x-h)} + k$.

### Logarithmic Models

The equation $y = \log_b x$ is the inverse of the exponential function $y = b^x$. The common log is a logarithm with base 10. It is commonly written without the base. So $\log_{10} x = \log x$.

The fact that exponential and logarithmic functions are inverses can be used to find values of logarithms.

### Common Errors When Using Exponential and Logarithmic Models

**Exponential Models**  Students may make errors when converting the factors for growth and decay from percent to decimal. For example, a growth rate of 3% indicates that the value $b$ should be 1.03. Remind students to check the first few terms to be sure their models are correct.

**Logarithmic Models**  Students sometimes confuse the domain and range of logarithmic models. Point out that because the functions are inverses of each other, the domain and range of the exponential model are the range and domain of the logarithmic model.

## Solving Logarithmic Equations

The properties of logarithms can be used to solve logarithmic equations.

For any positive numbers $m$, $n$, and $b$ where $b \neq 1$:

**Product Property** $\quad \log_b mn = \log_b m + \log_b n$

**Quotient Property** $\quad \log_b \frac{m}{n} = \log_b m - \log_b n$

**Power Property** $\quad \log_b m^n = n \log_b m$

**Example:** What is the solution of $\log 3 + \log 2x = 2$?

$$\log 3 + \log 2x = 2$$
$$\log(6x) = 2 \qquad \text{Product Property}$$
$$10^{\log 6x} = 10^2 \qquad \text{Exponential Form}$$
$$6x = 100$$
$$x = \frac{50}{3}$$

### Natural Logarithms

Natural logarithms (ln) are logarithms to the base $e$. They follow the same rules and properties as logarithms to other bases. The functions $y = e^x$ and $y = \ln x$ are inverse functions.

**Example:** What are the solutions of $\ln 3x^2 - 2 \ln 3 = 2$?

$$\ln 3x^2 - 2 \ln 3 = 2$$
$$\ln 3x^2 - \ln 3^2 = 2 \qquad \text{Power Property}$$
$$\ln \frac{x^2}{3} = 2 \qquad \text{Quotient Property}$$
$$\frac{x^2}{3} = e^2 \qquad \text{Exponential Form}$$
$$x^2 \approx 22.1672$$
$$x \approx \pm 4.708$$

### Common Errors When Solving Logarithmic Equations

**Quotient Property** Students sometimes mistakenly apply the Quotient Property in the reverse order. Point out that the log of the numerator is the first term in the subtraction expression.

**Exponential Form** Errors occur when students write logarithmic equations in exponential form. Encourage them to write steps as needed. For example, in the natural logarithm example above, write $e^{\ln \frac{x^2}{3}} = e^2$ to get the equation in exponential form. Because natural log and $e$ are inverses, the left side of the equation becomes $\frac{x^2}{3}$.

## Solving Exponential Equations

### Solve Algebraically

Exponential equations can be solved by taking logarithms of each side. Although logarithms to any base can be used, common logs and natural logs are generally used.

**Example:** Solve $13^{n+10} = 80$.

$$13^{n+10} = 80$$
$$\log 13^{n+10} = \log 80$$
$$(n + 10)(\log 13) = \log 80 \qquad \text{Power Property}$$
$$n + 10 = \frac{\log 80}{\log 13}$$
$$n \approx -8.9216$$

An equation need not contain $e$ to use the natural log.

**Example:** What is the solution of $5^x = 30$?

$$5^x = 30 \qquad\qquad 5^x = 30$$
$$x \ln 5 = \ln 30 \qquad x \log 5 = \log 30$$
$$x = \frac{\ln 30}{\ln 5} \qquad\qquad x = \frac{\log 30}{\log 5}$$
$$x \approx 2.113 \qquad\qquad x \approx 2.113$$

### Solve Graphically

Both exponential and logarithmic equations can be solved using a graph or table.

**Example:** Solve $3^{4x} = 500$.

Enter $3^{(4x)}$ in $Y_1$ and 500 in $Y_2$. Find the intersection.

Solve using the table.

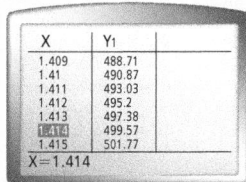

### Common Errors When Solving Exponential Equations

**Same Bases:** A method for solving exponential equations involves equating the exponents if the bases are the same. Students may try to equate the exponents when the bases are not the same. Different bases require the use of logarithms. Have students check their answers to be sure their solution is correct.

**Logs of negative numbers:** Students can often be confused as to the restrictions for the variables and logarithmic equations. Point out that a positive number to any power can never been negative. Therefore, it is not possible to find a logarithm of a negative number. For example, there is no solution to the equation $10^x = -100$.

# CHAPTER 7

## EXPONENTIAL AND LOGARITHMIC FUNCTIONS
# Pacing and Assignment Guide

| | | TRADITIONAL | | | BLOCK |
|---|---|---|---|---|---|
| **Lesson** | **Teaching Day(s)** | **Basic** | **Average** | **Advanced** | **Block** |
| **7-1** | **1** | Problems 1–2<br>Exs. 10–32, 34–40 even, 46–63 | Problems 1–5<br>Exs. 11–29 odd, 30–41, 46–63 | Problems 1–5<br>Exs. 11–29 odd, 30–63 | **Day 1**<br>Problems 1–5<br>Exs. 11–29 odd, 30–41, 46–63 |
| **7-2** | **1** | Problems 1–5<br>Exs. 7–33, 35, 38–42 even, 45–63 | Problems 1–5<br>Exs. 7–29 odd, 31–42, 45–63 | Problems 1–5<br>Exs. 7–29 odd, 31–63 | Problems 1–5<br>Exs. 7–29 odd, 31–42, 45–63 |
| **7-3** | **1** | Problems 1–3<br>Exs. 12–35, 85–98 | Problems 1–3<br>Exs. 13–35 odd, 85–98 | Problems 1–3<br>Exs. 13–35 odd, 85–98 | **Day 2**<br>Problems 1–5<br>Exs. 13–43 odd, 44–79, 85–98 |
| | **2** | Problems 4–5<br>Exs. 36–47, 58–61, 72–76 even | Problems 4–5<br>Exs. 37–43 odd, 44–79 | Problems 4–5<br>Exs. 37–43 odd, 44–84 | |
| **7-4** | **1** | Problems 1–2<br>Exs. 9–29, 80–95 | Problems 1–2<br>Exs. 9–29 odd, 80–95 | Problems 1–2<br>Exs. 9–29 odd, 80–95 | **Day 3**<br>Problems 1–4<br>Exs. 9–37 odd, 39–74, 80–95 |
| | **2** | Problems 3–4<br>Exs. 30–38, 43–47, 50–60 even | Problems 3–4<br>Exs. 31–37 odd, 39–74 | Problems 3–4<br>Exs. 31–37 odd, 39–79 | |
| **7-5** | **1** | Problems 1–3<br>Exs. 7–30, 84–100 | Problems 1–3<br>Exs. 7–29 odd, 84–100 | Problems 1–3<br>Exs. 7–29 odd, 84–100 | **Day 4**<br>Problems 1–6<br>Exs. 7–45 odd, 46–78, 84–100 |
| | **2** | Problems 4–6<br>Exs. 31–46, 48–54 even, 60, 61 | Problems 4–6<br>Exs. 31–45 odd, 46–78 | Problems 4–6<br>Exs. 31–45 odd, 46–83 | |
| **7-6** | **1** | Problems 1–2<br>Exs. 11–28, 66–84 | Problems 1–2<br>Exs. 11–27 odd, 66–84 | Problems 1–2<br>Exs. 11–27 odd, 66–84 | **Day 5**<br>Problems 1–4<br>Exs. 11–39 odd, 40–59, 66–84 |
| | **2** | Problems 3–4<br>Exs. 29–44, 52, 53 | Problems 3–4<br>Exs. 29–39 odd, 40–59 | Problems 3–4<br>Exs. 29–39 odd, 40–65 | |
| **Review** | **1** | Chapter 7 Review | Chapter 7 Review | Chapter 7 Review | **Day 6**<br>Chapter 7 Review<br>Chapter 7 Test |
| **Assess** | **1** | Chapter 7 Test | Chapter 7 Test | Chapter 7 Test | |
| **Total** | | **12 Days** | **12 Days** | **12 Days** | **6 Days** |

Note: Pacing does not include Concept Bytes and other feature pages.

# Resources

| | For the Chapter | 7-1 | 7-2 | 7-3 | 7-4 | 7-5 | 7-6 |
|---|---|---|---|---|---|---|---|
| **Planning** | | | | | | | |
| Teacher Center Online Planner & Grade Book | I | I | I | I | I | I | I |
| **Interactive Learning & Guided Instruction** | | | | | | | |
| My Math Video | I | | | | | | |
| Solve It! | | I TM | I TM | I TM | I TM | I TM | I TM |
| Student Companion (SP)* | | P M | P M | P M | P M | P M | |
|   *Vocabulary Support* | | I P M | I P M | I P M | I P M | I P M | I P M |
|   *Got It? Support* | | I P | I P | I P | I P | I P | I P |
| Dynamic Activity | | I | I | I | | | |
| Online Problems | | I | I | I | I | I | I |
| Additional Problems | | M | M | M | M | M | M |
| English Language Learner Support (TR) | | E P M | E P M | E P M | E P M | E P M | E P M |
| Activities, Games, and Puzzles | | E M | E M | E M | E M | E M | E M |
| Teaching With TI Technology With CD-ROM | | ✓ P | ✓ P | | | | |
| TI-Nspire™ Support CD-ROM | | ✓ | ✓ | ✓ | ✓ | ✓ | ✓ |
| **Lesson Check & Practice** | | | | | | | |
| Student Companion (SP)* | | P M | P M | P M | P M | P M | P M |
|   *Lesson Check Support* | | I P | I P | I P | I P | I P | I P |
| Practice and Problem Solving Workbook (SP) | | P | P | P | P | P | P |
|   *Think About a Plan* (TR)* | | E P M | E P M | E P M | E P M | E P M | E P M |
|   *Practice Form G* (TR)* | | E P M | E P M | E P M | E P M | E P M | E P M |
|   *Standardized Test Prep* (TR)* | | P M | P M | P M | P M | P M | P M |
| Practice *Form K* (TR)* | | E P M | E P M | E P M | E P M | E P M | E P M |
| Extra Practice | E M | | | | | | |
| Find the Errors! | M | | | | | | |
| Enrichment (TR) | | E P M | E P M | E P M | E P M | E P M | E P M |
| Answers and Solutions CD-ROM | ✓ | ✓ | ✓ | ✓ | ✓ | ✓ | ✓ |
| **Assess & Remediate** | | | | | | | |
| ExamView CD-ROM | ✓ | ✓ | ✓ | ✓ | ✓ | ✓ | |
| Lesson Quiz | | I TM | I TM | I TM | I TM | I TM | I TM |
| Quizzes and Tests *Form G* (TR)* | E P M | | | E P M | | | E P M |
| Quizzes and Tests *Form K* (TR)* | E P M | | | E P M | | | E P M |
| Reteaching (TR)* | | E P M | E P M | E P M | E P M | E P M | E P M |
| Performance Tasks (TR)* | P M | | | | | | |
| Cumulative Review (TR)* | P M | | | | | | |
| Progress Monitoring Assessments | I P M | | | | | | |

(TR) Available in All-In-One Teaching Resources   * Spanish available

# 1 Interactive Learning

## Solve It!

**PURPOSE** To express an exponential pattern in algebraic terms

**PROCESS** Students may
- sketch simpler models and extrapolate results to apply to more complex models.
- write an equation for the model.

### FACILITATE

**Q** How many times does the original bottom ring move? **[once]**

**Q** How many times does the smallest ring move from its original position to its final position if there are $n$ rings? Explain. **[$2^{n-1}$ times; the smallest ring gets every second move. In between moving it, there is only one legal move that is not moving it again.]**

**Q** Is there a post you have to move the smallest ring to as the first move if you want the final stack on a specific post? Explain. **[Yes; for $n$ odd, move it to the post where you want the stack, and for $n$ even, move it to the post where you do not want the stack.]**

**ANSWER** See Solve It in Answers on next page.

**CONNECT THE MATH** The Solve It introduces an exponential expression as part of a solution to a problem. In the lesson students will write and use exponential equations to solve problems.

# 2 Guided Instruction

## Problem 1

**Q** What would happen to the graph of $2^x$ if the 2 was replaced by a 5? **[The graph would be steeper.]**

**Objective** To model exponential growth and decay

**Getting Ready!**

You are to move the stack of 5 rings to another post. Here are the rules.
- A move consists of taking the top ring from one post and placing it onto another post.
- You can move only one ring at a time.
- Do not place a ring on top of a smaller ring.

What is the fewest number of moves needed? How many moves are needed for 10 rings? 20 rings? Explain.

*This is a famous puzzle. Variations of it show up in many video games.*

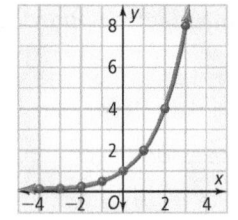

### Lesson Vocabulary
- exponential function
- exponential growth
- exponential decay
- asymptote
- growth factor
- decay factor

The number of moves needed for additional rings in the Solve It suggests a pattern that approximates repeated multiplication.

**Essential Understanding** You can represent repeated multiplication with a function of the form $y = ab^x$ where $b$ is a positive number other than 1.

An **exponential function** is a function with the general form $y = ab^x$, $a \neq 0$, with $b > 0$, and $b \neq 1$. In an exponential function, the base $b$ is a constant. The exponent $x$ is the independent variable with domain the set of real numbers.

### Plan

**How does making a table help you sketch the graph?** The table shows coordinates of several points on the graph.

## Problem 1 Graphing an Exponential Function

**What is the graph of $y = 2^x$?**

**Step 1** Make a table of values.

| x | $2^x$ | y |
|---|---|---|
| −4 | $2^{-4}$ | $\frac{1}{16} = 0.0625$ |
| −3 | $2^{-3}$ | $\frac{1}{8} = 0.125$ |
| −2 | $2^{-2}$ | $\frac{1}{4} = 0.25$ |
| −1 | $2^{-1}$ | $\frac{1}{2} = 0.5$ |

| x | $2^x$ | y |
|---|---|---|
| 0 | $2^0$ | 1 |
| 1 | $2^1$ | 2 |
| 2 | $2^2$ | 4 |
| 3 | $2^3$ | 8 |

**Step 2** Plot and connect the points.

**BIG** ideas Equivalence
Function
Modeling

**UbD**

### ESSENTIAL UNDERSTANDINGS
- Repeated multiplication can be represented with a function in the form of $y = ab^x$ where $b$ is a positive number other than 1.
- An exponential function is a function with the general form $y = ab^x$, $a \neq 0$, with $b > 0$, and $b \neq 1$. In an exponential function, the base $b$ is a constant. The exponent $x$ is the independent variable with domain the set of real numbers.

## Math Background

Exponential notation is a simplified way to represent repeated multiplication. For example, $2 \cdot 2 \cdot 2 \cdot 2 \cdot 2 \cdot 2 \cdot 2 = 2^7$. Repeated multiplication by the same factor can be represented by an exponential function.

Such functions have the form $y = ab^x$ where $b$ is greater than 0 and not equal to 1, and $x$ is any real number.

For $a > 0$, the value of $b$ determines whether the function grows or decays exponentially:
- When $b > 1$, the function *grows* exponentially.
- When $0 < b < 1$, the function *decays* exponentially.

Note that if $b = 1$, the function would simplify to $y = a$, which is a constant function.

Exponential functions can be used to model many real-world situations, including half-life, radiometric dating, interest-bearing savings accounts, population growth, and a bouncing ball.

## Support Student Learning

Use the **Algebra 2 Companion** to engage and support students during instruction. See Lesson Resources at the end of this lesson for details.

**PowerAlgebra.com**

## 1 Interactive Learning

**Solve It!**

Step out how to solve the Problem with helpful hints and an online question. Other questions are listed above in Interactive Learning.

**Dynamic Activity** Students can use this interactive graph to explore exponential growth and decay. They can manipulate the sliders to vary the values of $a$ and $b$ in the equation $y = a \cdot b^x$.

**Got It?** **1.** What is the graph of each function?

**a.** $y = 4^x$  **b.** $y = \left(\frac{1}{3}\right)^x$  **c.** $y = 2(3)^x$

**d. Reasoning** What generalizations can you make about the domain, range, and *y*-intercepts of these functions?

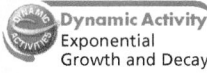
**Dynamic Activity**
Exponential
Growth and Decay

Two types of exponential behavior are *exponential growth* and *exponential decay*.

For **exponential growth**, as the value of *x* increases, the value of *y* increases. For **exponential decay**, as the value of *x* increases, the value of *y* decreases, approaching zero.

The exponential functions shown here are *asymptotic* to the *x*-axis. An **asymptote** is a line that a graph approaches as *x* or *y* increases in absolute value.

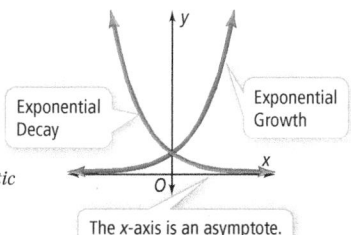

Exponential Decay

Exponential Growth

The *x*-axis is an asymptote.

**take note**

### Concept Summary  Exponential Functions

For the function $y = ab^x$,

- if $a > 0$ and $b > 1$, the function represents exponential growth.
- if $a > 0$ and $0 < b < 1$, the function represents exponential decay.

In either case, the *y*-intercept is $(0, a)$, the domain is all real numbers, the asymptote is $y = 0$, and the range is $y > 0$.

**Problem 2** **Identifying Exponential Growth and Decay**

Identify each function or situation as an example of exponential growth or decay. What is the *y*-intercept?

**A** $y = 12(0.95)^x$

Since $0 < b < 1$, the function represents exponential decay. The *y*-intercept is $(0, a) = (0, 12)$.

**B** $y = 0.25(2)^x$

Since $b > 1$, the function represents exponential growth. The *y*-intercept is $(0, a) = (0, 0.25)$.

**Think**

What quantity does the *y*-intercept represent?
The *y*-intercept is the amount of money at $t = 0$, which is the initial investment.

**C** You put $1000 into a college savings account for four years. The account pays 5% interest annually.

The amount of money in the bank grows by 5% annually. It represents exponential growth. The *y*-intercept is 1000, which is the dollar value of the initial investment.

 **Got It?** **2.** Identify each function or situation as an example of exponential growth or decay. What is the *y*-intercept?

**a.** $y = 3(4^x)$  **b.** $y = 11(0.75^x)$

**c.** You put $2000 into a college savings account for four years. The account pays 6% interest annually.

**PowerAlgebra.com**  Lesson 7-1  Exploring Exponential Models  **435**

---

**Q** How do you know what numbers to select for the *x* values? **[You should select values that are positive, negative, and zero.]**

### Take Note

The graph of an exponential growth function, $y = ab^x$ when $a > 0$ and $b > 1$, is a curve that rises from left to right. It gets steeper as *x* increases.

The graph of an exponential decay function, $y = ab^x$ when $a > 0$ and $0 < b < 1$, is a curve that falls from left to right. It gets less steep as *x* increases. In both types of exponential functions the *x*-axis is a horizontal asymptote of the graph.

### Problem 2

**Q** In the exponential growth function represented by $y = ab^x$, what represents the *y*-intercept? **[a]**

### Got It?

**Q** What is the *y*-intercept of an exponential function with no stated *a* value? Explain. **[(0,1); answers may vary. Sample: The function $f(x) = b^x$, is the parent function for the family of exponential growth functions with base *b*. To determine the *y*-intercept, evaluate $b^x$ when *x* is set equal to zero: $b^0 = 1$. Therefore, the *y*-intercept is the ordered pair (0, 1).]**

---

## 2 Guided Instruction

 Each Problem is worked out and supported online.

### Problem 1
Graphing an Exponential Function

### Problem 2
Identifying Exponential Growth and Decay
*Animated*

### Problem 3
Modeling Exponential Growth
*Animated*

### Problem 4
Using Exponential Growth

### Problem 5
Writing an Exponential Function

### Support in Algebra 2 Companion
- Vocabulary
- Key Concepts
- Got It?

---

## Answers

### Solve It!
31; 1023; 1048575; The number of moves follows the pattern $2^x - 1$.

### Got It?

**1. a.**   **b.**

**c.**

**d.** domain: all real numbers, range: $y > 0$; *y*-intercept: $(0, a)$ where $y = ab^x$

**2. a.** exponential growth; 3

**b.** exponential decay; 11

**c.** exponential growth; 2000

## Take Note

**Q** Does $t$ always represent time in years? Explain.
[No; time may need to be calculated in units other than years, for example, some bacteria grow exponentially in hours or minutes.]

## Problem 3

**Q** When is an exponential function an appropriate model? [If finding the solution would require iterative multiplication, an exponential model is appropriate.]

**Q** Why would you advise a friend who wants to make his savings account grow as much as possible not to withdraw the interest at the end of each year? [If you leave the interest in the account, the savings account will pay interest on the interest, but if you withdraw the interest, the account will only pay interest on the original principal.]

### ERROR PREVENTION

Even advanced students may occasionally write a 5% growth rate as 1.5 or a growth rate of 4.5% as 1.45. Making students aware of the error may help prevent it.

### EXTENSION

**Q** How much money would you have if you invested the money at the end of first grade? [$1710.34]

## Got It?                    EXTENSION

**Q** What model will you use? [$A(t) = a(1 + r)^t$, where $t$ is the number of years since the money was invested and $A(t)$ is the amount in the account after each year]

---

For exponential growth $y = ab^x$, with $b > 1$, the value $b$ is the **growth factor**. A quantity that exhibits exponential growth increases by a constant percentage each time period. The percentage increase $r$, written as a decimal, is the *rate of increase* or *growth rate*. For exponential growth, $b = 1 + r$.

For exponential decay, $0 < b < 1$ and $b$ is the **decay factor**. The quantity decreases by a constant percentage each time period. The percentage decrease, $r$, is the *rate of decay*. Usually a rate of decay is expressed as a negative quantity, so $b = 1 + r$.

### Key Concept    Exponential Growth and Decay

You can model exponential growth or decay with this function.

| Amount after $t$ time periods |  | Rate of growth ($r > 0$) or decay ($r < 0$) |

$$A(t) = a(1 + r)^t$$

| Initial amount |  | Number of time periods |

For growth or decay to be exponential, a quantity changes by a fixed percentage each time period.

### Problem 3   Modeling Exponential Growth

You invested $1000 in a savings account at the end of 6th grade. The account pays 5% annual interest. How much money will be in the account after six years?

**Step 1** Determine if an exponential function is a reasonable model.

The money grows at a fixed rate of 5% per year. An exponential model is appropriate.

**Step 2** Define the variables and determine the model.

Let $t =$ the number of years since the money was invested.
Let $A(t) =$ the amount in the account after each year.

A reasonable model is $A(t) = a(1 + r)^t$.

**Think**

What is the growth rate $r$?
It is the annual interest rate, written as a decimal: 5% = 0.05.

**Step 3** Use the model to solve the problem.

$$A(6) = 1000(1 + 0.05)^6 \quad \text{Substitute } a = 1000, r = 0.05, \text{ and } t = 6.$$
$$= 1000(1.05)^6 \quad \text{Simplify.}$$
$$\approx \$1340.10$$

The account contains $1340.10 after six years.

 **Got It?  3.** Suppose you invest $500 in a savings account that pays 3.5% annual interest. How much will be in the account after five years?

---

# Additional Problems

**1.** What is the graph of $y = 3.1^x$?

**ANSWER**

**2.** Identify $y = 0.7^x$ as an example of exponential growth or decay. What is the $y$-intercept?

**ANSWER** decay; (0, 1)

**3.** You buy a savings bond for $25 that pays a yearly interest rate of 4.2%. What will the savings bond be worth after fifteen years?

**ANSWER** $46.34

**4.** You open a savings account that pays 4.5% annual interest. If your initial investment is $300 and you make no additional deposits or withdrawals, how many years will it take for the account to grow to at least $500?

**ANSWER** 12 years

**5.** The initial value of a car is $30,000. After one year, the value of the car is $20,000. Estimate the value of the car after five years.

**ANSWER** $3950.62

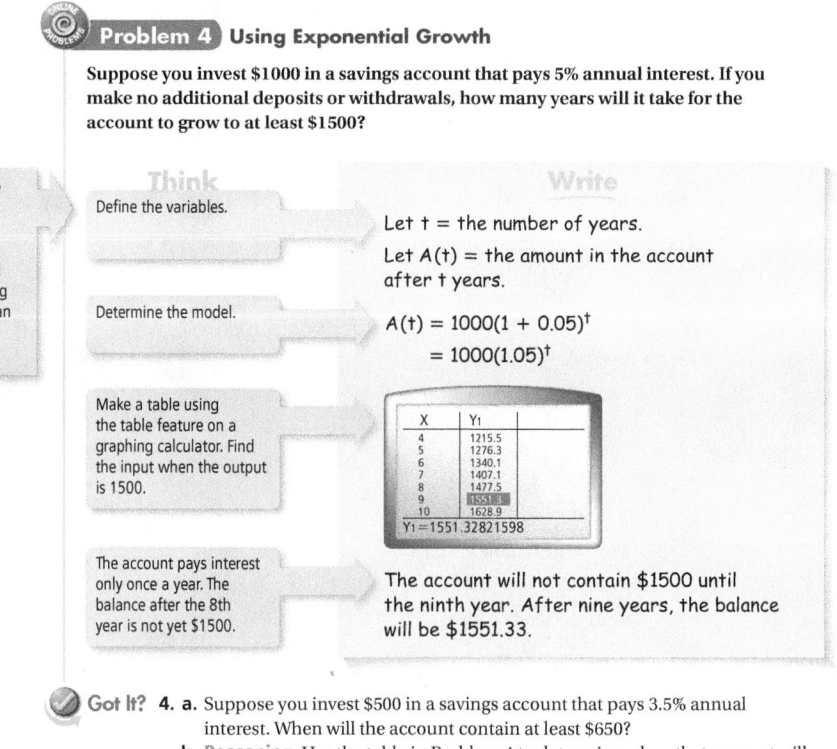

## Problem 4 · Using Exponential Growth

Suppose you invest $1000 in a savings account that pays 5% annual interest. If you make no additional deposits or withdrawals, how many years will it take for the account to grow to at least $1500?

**Plan**

**How can you make a table to solve this problem?**
Define the variables, write an equation and enter it into a graphing calculator. Then you can inspect a table to find the solution.

**Think**

Define the variables.

Determine the model.

Make a table using the table feature on a graphing calculator. Find the input when the output is 1500.

The account pays interest only once a year. The balance after the 8th year is not yet $1500.

**Write**

Let $t$ = the number of years.

Let $A(t)$ = the amount in the account after $t$ years.

$A(t) = 1000(1 + 0.05)^t$
$\quad = 1000(1.05)^t$

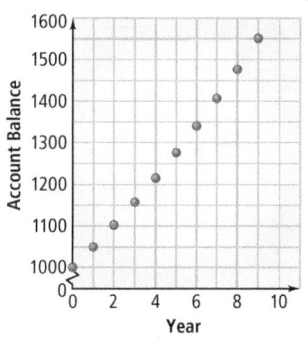

| X | Y₁ |
|---|-----|
| 4 | 1215.5 |
| 5 | 1276.3 |
| 6 | 1340.1 |
| 7 | 1407.1 |
| 8 | 1477.5 |
| 9 | 1551.3 |
| 10 | 1628.9 |

Y₁=1551.32821598

The account will not contain $1500 until the ninth year. After nine years, the balance will be $1551.33.

**Got It?** **4. a.** Suppose you invest $500 in a savings account that pays 3.5% annual interest. When will the account contain at least $650?

**b.** *Reasoning* Use the table in Problem 4 to determine when that account will contain at least $1650. Explain.

Exponential functions are often discrete. In Problem 4, interest is paid only once a year. So the graph consists of individual points corresponding to $t = 1, 2, 3$, and so on. It is not continuous. Both the table and the graph show that there is never *exactly* $1500 in the account and that the account will not contain more than $1500 until the ninth year.

To model a discrete situation using an exponential function of the form $y = ab^x$, you need to find the growth or decay factor $b$. If you know $y$-values for two consecutive $x$-values, you can find the rate of change $r$, and then find $b$ using $r = \frac{(y_2 - y_1)}{y_1}$ and $b = 1 + r$.

**Problem 4** EXTENSION

**Q** If you withdrew the interest at the end of each year, how long would it take the savings account to pay you $500? Explain. **[The account would pay you $50 each year, so it would take ten years, which is a year longer than if you leave the interest in the account.]**

**Q** If you double the original investment, would the amount in the account at the end of the term also double? Explain. **[Yes; you are changing the constant of multiplication, so your end value will change by that same constant.]**

**Q** Use tables to answer the following questions. Would doubling the interest rate from the original rate or doubling the time double the final amount from the original final amount? Why? **[No; answers may vary. Samples: $(1 + 2r)^t$ does not equal $2(1 + r)^t$; $(1 + r)^{2t}$ does not equal $2(1 + r)^t$.]**

### Got It?

**Q** Is an exponential function a reasonable model for this situation? Explain. **[Yes; answers may vary. Sample: Your savings account grows at a fixed, constant rate per year, so an exponential model is appropriate.]**

## Answers

### Got It? (continued)
**3.** $593.84
**4. a.** after 8 yrs
   **b.** after 11 yrs; then the account contains $1710.34.

## Problem 5

**Q** What is the meaning of 0.8? **[Each year, the population is 80% of what it was the year before.]**

**Q** If the trend has been occurring since the Iberian Lynx was placed on the Endangered Species List in 1970, how many Iberian Lynx were there when it was placed on the list? Do you think this is reasonable? Explain. **[About 236,658; sample: yes; $236{,}658(.8)^{33} \approx 150$.]**

**EXTENSION**

**Q** Can you sketch a graph of what a population recovery would look like? **[Answers may vary. Sample: A population recovery graph would begin to turn upward.]**

### Got It?

**Q** If the trend continues, in what year will there be no hope of a wild Iberian Lynx population recovery (excluding captive animals)? **[In 2023, there will be fewer than two wild Iberian lynx, so there will be no possibility of a wild Iberian lynx mating pair.]**

---

 **Problem 5** Writing an Exponential Function

**Endangered Species** The table shows the world population of the Iberian lynx in 2003 and 2004. If this trend continues and the population is decreasing exponentially, how many Iberian lynx will there be in 2014?

Use the general form of the exponential equation, $y = ab^x = a(1 + r)^x$.

**Step 1** Define the variables.

Let $x$ = the number of years since 2003.
Let $y$ = the population of the Iberian lynx.

**Step 2** Determine $r$.

Use the populations for 2003 and 2004.

$$r = \frac{y_2 - y_1}{y_1}$$
$$= \frac{120 - 150}{150}$$
$$= -0.2$$

**Step 3** Use $r$ to determine $b$.

$$b = 1 + r = 1 + (-0.2) = 0.8$$

**Step 4** Write the model.

$$y = ab^x$$
$$150 = a(0.8)^0$$
$$150 = a$$

> Solve for $a$ using the initial values $x = 0$ and $y = 150$.

The model is $y = 150(0.8)^x$.

**Step 5** Use the model to find the population in 2014. For the year 2014, $x = 2014 - 2003 = 11$.

$$y = 150(0.8)^x$$
$$= 150(0.8)^{11}$$
$$\approx 13$$

If the 2003–2004 trend continues, there will be approximately 13 Iberian lynx in the wild in 2014.

**Think**
How can you find the value of $r$?
You can use the populations for two consecutive years to find $r$.

**Think**
How do you find the $x$-value corresponding to 2014?
The initial $x$-value corresponds to 2003, so find the difference.

**World Population of Iberian Lynx**

| Year | 2003 | 2004 |
|------|------|------|
| Population | 150 | 120 |

 **Got It?** **5. a.** For the model in Problem 5, what will be the world population of Iberian lynx in 2020?
  **b. Reasoning** If you graphed the model in Problem 5, would it ever cross the $x$-axis? Explain.

---

# Answers

### Got It? (continued)

**5. a.** $\approx 3$

  **b.** No; the function is asymptotic to the $x$-axis.

### Lesson Check

**1.** decay; 10  **2.** growth; 0.75
**3.** growth; 1  **4.** decay; 1
**5.**

**6.**

**7.** If $a > 0$ and $b > 1$, then the function represents exponential growth; if $a > 0$ and $0 < b < 1$, then the function represents exponential decay.

**8. a.** quadratic; degree 2 with $3x^2$ as the leading term

  **b.** exponential; the equation is of the form $y = ab^x$

  **c.** linear; degree 1 with $x$ as the leading term

  **d.** exponential; the equation is of the form $y = ab^x$

**9.** $0.3 < 1$, so 0.3 is the decay factor

### Practice and Problem-Solving Exercises

**10.**

**11.**

**12.**

**13.**

## Lesson Check

### Do you know HOW?

Without graphing, determine whether the function represents exponential growth or exponential decay. Then find the $y$-intercept.

**1.** $y = 10(0.45)^x$      **2.** $y = 0.75(4)^x$

**3.** $y = 3^x$      **4.** $y = 0.95^x$

Graph each function.

**5.** $A(t) = 3(1.04)^t$      **6.** $A(t) = 7(0.6)^t$

### Do you UNDERSTAND?

**7. Vocabulary** Explain how you can tell if $y = ab^x$ represents exponential growth or exponential decay.

**8. Reasoning** Identify each function as *linear*, *quadratic*, or *exponential*. Explain your reasoning.
 **a.** $y = 3(x + 1)^2$    **b.** $y = 4(3)^x$
 **c.** $y = 2x + 5$      **d.** $y = 4(0.2)^x + 1$

**9. Error Analysis** A classmate says that the growth factor of the exponential function $y = 15(0.3)^x$ is 0.3. What is the student's mistake?

## Practice and Problem-Solving Exercises

**Ⓐ Practice**

Graph each function.      ◀ See Problem 1.

**10.** $y = 6^x$    **11.** $y = 3(10)^x$    **12.** $y = 1000(2)^x$    **13.** $y = 9(3)^x$

**14.** $f(x) = 2(3)^x$    **15.** $s(t) = 1.5^t$    **16.** $y = 8(5)^x$    **17.** $y = 2^{2x}$

Without graphing, determine whether the function represents exponential    ◀ See Problem 2.
growth or exponential decay. Then find the $y$-intercept.

**18.** $y = 129(1.63)^x$    **19.** $f(x) = 2(0.65)^x$    **20.** $y = 12\left(\frac{17}{10}\right)^x$    **21.** $y = 0.8\left(\frac{1}{8}\right)^x$

**22.** $f(x) = 4\left(\frac{5}{6}\right)^x$    **23.** $y = 0.45(3)^x$    **24.** $y = \frac{1}{100}\left(\frac{4}{3}\right)^x$    **25.** $f(x) = 2^{-x}$

**26. Interest** Suppose you deposit \$2000 in a savings account that pays    ◀ See Problems 3 and 4.
interest at an annual rate of 4%. If no money is added or withdrawn
from the account, answer the following questions.
 **a.** How much will be in the account after 3 years?
 **b.** How much will be in the account after 18 years?
 **c.** How many years will it take for the account to contain \$2500?
 **d.** How many years will it take for the account to contain \$3000?

Write an exponential function to model each situation. Find each amount after    ◀ See Problem 5.
the specified time.

**27.** A population of 120,000 grows 1.2% per year for 15 years.

**28.** A population of 1,860,000 decreases 1.5% each year for 12 years.

**29. a. Sports** Before a basketball game, a referee noticed that the ball seemed
 under-inflated. She dropped it from 6 feet and measured the first bounce
 as 36 inches and the second bounce as 18 inches. Write an exponential
 function to model the height of the ball.
 **b.** How high was the ball on its fifth bounce?

---

**14.**     **15.**

**16.**     **17.**

**18.** exponential growth; 129
**19.** exponential decay; 2
**20.** exponential growth; 12
**21.** exponential decay; 0.8
**22.** exponential decay; 4

**23.** exponential growth; 0.45
**24.** exponential growth; $\frac{1}{100}$
**25.** exponential decay; 1
**26. a.** \$2249.73
 **b.** \$4051.63
 **c.** 6 yrs
 **d.** 11 yrs
**27.** $y = 120{,}000(1.012)^x$; 143,512
**28.** $y = 1{,}860{,}000(0.985)^x$; 1,551,485
**29. a.** $y = 72\left(\frac{1}{2}\right)^x$
 **b.** 2.25 in.

---

# 3 Lesson Check

## Do you know HOW?    ERROR INTERVENTION

• For Exercises 1–4, students may need to be reminded that if there is no stated value of $a$, then $a = 1$.
• If the students are having difficulty seeing the graph on a calculator screen for Exercises 5 and 6, remind them that they may need to reset the window on their calculators to a standard viewing window from the window they likely used in Problem 5.

## Do you UNDERSTAND? ERROR INTERVENTION

• If students have trouble with the vocabulary in Exercise 7, remind them that the value of $b$ is the factor determining growth or decay; $r$ is the rate of growth or decay.
• If students have trouble identifying the function types for Exercise 8, have them determine whether $x$ is an exponent or a polynomial term. If a polynomial, have them determine the degree.

## Close

**Q** How can you determine the growth rate or decay rate for an exponential function given two consecutive $y$-values? **[Find the percentage increase or decrease.]**

**Q** Why does a rate of decay of 23% correspond to a $b$ value of 0.77? **[Since 23% decays, 77% remains.]**

### PowerAlgebra.com

## 3 Lesson Check

For a digital lesson check, use the Got It questions.

**Support in Algebra 2 Companion**
• Lesson Check

## 4 Practice

Assign homework to individual students or to an entire class.

# 4 Practice

**ASSIGNMENT GUIDE**

Basic: 10–29 all, 30–32, 34–40 even

Average: 11–29 odd, 30–41

Advanced: 11–29 odd, 30–45

Standardized Test Prep: 46–50

Mixed Review: 51–63

Reasoning exercises have blue headings.

Applications exercises have red headings.

EXERCISE 32: Use the Think About a Plan worksheet in the **Practice and Problem Solving Workbook** (also available in the Teaching Resources in print and online) to further support students' development in becoming independent learners.

**HOMEWORK QUICK CHECK**

To check students' understanding of key skills and concepts, go over Exercises 11, 19, 30, 31, and 32.

 **Apply**

**30.** **Think About a Plan** Your friend invested $1000 in an account that pays 6% annual interest. How much interest will your friend have after her college graduation in 4 years?
  • Is an exponential model reasonable for this situation?
  • What equation should you use to model this situation?
  • Is the solution of the equation the final answer to the problem?

**31.** **Oceanography** The function $y = 20(0.975)^x$ models the intensity of sunlight beneath the surface of the ocean. The output $y$ represents the percent of surface sunlight intensity that reaches a depth of $x$ feet. The model is accurate from about 20 feet to about 600 feet beneath the surface.
  **a.** Find the percent of sunlight 50 feet beneath the surface of the ocean.
  **b.** Find the percent of sunlight at a depth of 370 feet.

 **32.** **Population** The population of a certain animal species decreases at a rate of 3.5% per year. You have counted 80 of the animals in the habitat you are studying.
  **a.** Write a function that models the change in the animal population.
  **b.** **Graphing Calculator** Graph the function. Estimate the number of years until the population first drops below 15 animals.

**33.** **Sports** While you are waiting for your tennis partner to show up, you drop your tennis ball from 5 feet. Its rebound was approximately 35 inches on the first bounce and 21.5 inches on the second. What exponential function would be a good model for the bouncing ball?

**For each annual rate of change, find the corresponding growth or decay factor.**

| | | | |
|---|---|---|---|
| **34.** +70% | **35.** +500% | **36.** −75% | **37.** −55% |
| **38.** +12.5% | **39.** −0.1% | **40.** +0.1% | **41.** +100% |

 **Challenge**

**42.** **Manufacturing** The value of an industrial machine has a decay factor of 0.75 per year. After six years, the machine is worth $7500. What was the original value of the machine?

**43.** **Zoology** Determine which situation best matches the graph.
  Ⓐ A population of 120 cougars decreases 98.75% yearly.
  Ⓑ A population of 120 cougars increases 1.25% yearly.
  Ⓒ A population of 115 cougars decreases 1.25% yearly.
  Ⓓ A population of 115 cougars decreases 50% yearly.

**44.** **Open-Ended** Write a problem that could be modeled with $y = 20(1.1)^x$.

**45.** **Reasoning** Which function does the graph represent? Explain. (Each interval represents one unit.)
  Ⓐ $y = \left(\frac{1}{3}\right)2^x$
  Ⓑ $y = 2\left(\frac{1}{3}\right)^x$
  Ⓒ $y = -2\left(\frac{1}{3}\right)^x$

---

# Answers

## Practice and Problem-Solving Exercises
(continued)

**30.** $262.48; yes; $A(t) = 1000(1.06)^t$; No, when $t = 4$, $A(t) = $1262.48$ which represents the amount of money in the account after four yrs.

**31. a.** about 5.6%
  **b.** about 0.0017%

**32. a.** $y = 80(0.965)^x$
  **b.**

  about 47 yrs

**33.** Answers may vary. Sample: $y = 59.5(0.6)^x$

**34.** 1.70

**35.** 6

**36.** 0.25

**37.** 0.45

**38.** 1.125

**39.** 0.999

**40.** 1.001

**41.** 2

**42.** about $42,140

**43.** C

**44.** Check students' work.

**45.** B; The graph shows a decreasing function, which eliminates A. The $y$-values are all positive, which eliminates C.

**SAT/ACT**

**46.** Which function represents the value after $x$ years of a new delivery van that costs $25,000 and depreciates 15% each year?

   Ⓐ $y = -15(25{,}000)^x$      Ⓒ $y = 25{,}000(0.85)^x$

   Ⓑ $y = 25{,}000(0.15)^x$      Ⓓ $y = 25{,}000(1.15)^x$

**47.** What is $f(x) = 3x^{\frac{1}{3}}$ for $x = \frac{1}{125}$?

   Ⓕ 15      Ⓖ $\frac{3}{5}$      Ⓗ $\frac{\sqrt[3]{3}}{5}$      Ⓘ $5\sqrt[3]{3}$

**48.** What is the simplified form of $\frac{2+i}{2-i}$?

   Ⓐ $-1$      Ⓑ $\frac{3+4i}{3}$      Ⓒ $\frac{5+4i}{5}$      Ⓓ $\frac{3+4i}{5}$

**49.** Which graph represents the equation $y = x^2 - x - 2$?

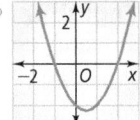

**Extended Response**

**50.** You are driving a car when a deer suddenly darts across the road in front of you. Your brain registers the emergency and sends a signal to your foot to hit the brake. The car travels a reaction distance $D$, in feet, during this time, where $D$ is a function of the speed $r$, in miles per hour, that the car is traveling when you see the deer, given by $D(r) = \frac{11r + 5}{10}$. Find the inverse and explain what it represents. Is the inverse a function?

## Mixed Review

Graph each function.     ◆ See Lesson 6-8.

**51.** $y = 3 - 2\sqrt{x + 2}$     **52.** $y = 3\sqrt[3]{2x - 1}$     **53.** $y = -2 + \sqrt{x}$

Factor the expression.     ◆ See Lesson 4-4.

**54.** $8 + 27x^3$     **55.** $3x^2 + 11x - 4$     **56.** $25 - 40x + 16x^2$

Solve the system of equations using a matrix.     ◆ See Lesson 3-6.

**57.** $\begin{cases} x + 5y = -4 \\ x + 6y = -5 \end{cases}$     **58.** $\begin{cases} 3a + 5b = 0 \\ a + b = 0 \end{cases}$     **59.** $\begin{cases} -x + 2y + z = 0 \\ y = -2x + 3 \\ z = 3x \end{cases}$

**Get Ready!** To prepare for Lesson 7-2, do Exercises 60–63.

Graph each function.     ◆ See Lesson 7-1.

**60.** $y = 3^x$     **61.** $y = 4(2)^x$     **62.** $y = 0.75^x$     **63.** $y = 0.5(4)^x$

---

**53.**

**54.** $(2 + 3x)(4 - 6x + 9x^2)$

**55.** $(3x - 1)(x + 4)$

**56.** $(4x - 5)(4x - 5)$

**57.** $(1, -1)$

**58.** $(0, 0)$

**59.** $(3, -3, 9)$

**60.**

**61.**

**62.**

**63.**

---

## Standardized Test Prep

**46.** C

**47.** G

**48.** D

**49.** G

**50.** [4]     $r = \frac{11D^{-1}(r) + 5}{10}$

     $10r - 5 = 11D^{-1}(r)$

     $\frac{10r - 5}{11} = D^{-1}(r)$; this function tells you the speed the car is traveling when you see the deer, given the number of ft the car travels during your reaction time. $D^{-1}(r)$ is a function.

     [3] appropriate method and explanation, but with one computational error

[2] incomplete explanation OR, inverse and explanation are correct, but inverse is not labeled a function

[1] correct inverse function, but without explanation of what the inverse represents

## Mixed Review

**51.**

**52.**

## Differentiated Remediation

Available in editable format online.

## Additional Instructional Support

### Algebra 2 Companion

Students can use the **Algebra 2 Companion** worktext (4 pages) as you teach the lesson. Use the Companion to support

- New Vocabulary
- Key Concepts
- Got It for each Problem
- Lesson Check

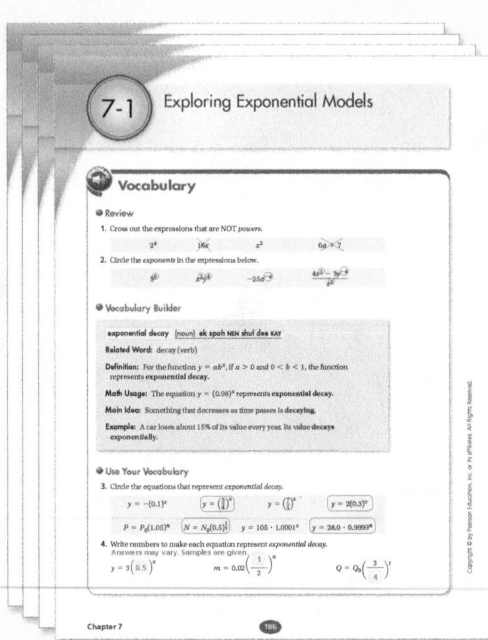

## 5  Assess & Remediate

### Lesson Quiz

1. What is the graph of $y = \left(\frac{1}{3}\right)^x$?

2. Identify $y = 3(1.2)^x$ as an example of exponential growth or decay. What is the $y$-intercept?

3. You deposit $3000 in an account that pays 5% annual interest. What is the balance after 2 years?

4. You invest $75 in a savings account that pays 2% annual interest. If you make no additional deposits or withdrawals, how many years will it take for the account to grow to at least $100?

5. **Do you UNDERSTAND?** There were 50,000 bacteria in a petri dish yesterday at noon, and 40,000 bacteria at noon today. If the trend continues, on what day at noon can you expect to find less than 5,000 bacteria?

### ANSWERS TO LESSON QUIZ

1.

2. growth; (0, 3)

3. $3307.50

4. 15 years

5. on the eleventh day

## Intervention

- **Reteaching** (2 pages) Provides reteaching and practice exercises for the key lesson concepts. Use with struggling students or absent students.

- **English Language Learner Support** Helps students develop and reinforce mathematical vocabulary and key concepts.

### All-in-One Resources/Online
#### Reteaching

**7-1**  **Reteaching**
Exploring Exponential Models

- The general form of an exponential function is $y = ab^x$, where $a$ is the initial amount and $b$ is the growth or decay factor.
- To find $b$, use the formula $b = 1 + r$, where $r$ is the constant rate of growth or decay. If $r$ is a rate of growth, it will be positive. If $r$ is a rate of decay, it will be negative. Therefore, if $b$ is greater than 1, the function models growth. If $b$ is between zero and 1, the function models decay. When you see words like *increase* or *appreciation*, think growth. When you see words like *decrease* or *depreciation*, think decay.
- For an exponential function, the $y$-intercept is always equal to the value of $a$.

**Problem**

Carl's weight at 12 yr is 82 lb. Assume that his weight increases at a rate of 16% each year. Write an exponential function to model the increase. What is his weight after 5 years?

**Step 1** Find $a$ and $b$.

$a = 82$  $a$ is the original amount.

$b = 1 + 0.16$  $b$ is the growth or decay factor. Since this problem models growth, $r$ will be positive. Make sure to rewrite the rate, $r$, as a decimal.

$= 1.16$

**Step 2** Write the exponential function.

$y = ab^x$  Use the formula.

$y = 82(1.16)^x$  Substitute.

**Step 3** Calculate.

$y = 82(1.16)^5$  Substitute 5 for $x$.

$y \approx 172.228$  Use a calculator.

Carl will weigh about 172 lb in 5 years.

**Exercises**

Determine whether the function represents exponential growth or exponential decay. Then find the $y$-intercept.

1. $y = 8000(1.15)^x$  growth; 8000

2. $y = 20(0.75)^x$  decay; 20

3. $y = 15\left(\frac{1}{2}\right)^x$  decay; 15

4. $f(x) = 6\left(\frac{5}{2}\right)^x$  growth; 6

---

### ELL Support

**Use Graphic Organizers** Have students make a two-column chart. Label the first column *growth* and the second column *decay*. In pairs, have students discuss and decide what words and symbols will help them decode the word problems. Have each pair exchange lists with another pair of students and review their classmates' work. If they disagree on a word in the list, ask them to explain why it should be changed or eliminated. Check the lists when they are finished, and make sure that they have at least the following terms and symbols for growth: *interest*, *appreciation*, *increase*, $+$, *returns*. For decay, they should have *depreciation*, *decrease*, $-$, *decline*. Then at the bottom of each column, have students sketch a basic shape of the corresponding graph with $a$ labeled and a description of valid values for $b$.

**PRESCRIPTION FOR REMEDIATION**

Use the student work on the Lesson Quiz to prescribe a differentiated review assignment:

| Points | Differentiated Remediation |
|--------|---------------------------|
| 0–2 | Intervention |
| 3–4 | On-level |
| 5 | Extension |

**PowerAlgebra.com**

## 5  Assess & Remediate

Assign the Lesson Quiz. Appropriate intervention, practice, or enrichment is automatically generated based on student performance.

### All-in-One Resources/Online
#### English Language Learner Support

**7-1**  **ELL Support**
Exploring Exponential Models

Choose the word or phrase from the list that best completes each sentence.

| exponential function | exponential growth | exponential decay |
|---|---|---|
| asymptote | growth factor | decay factor |

1. In the function $y = 12(2.3)^x$, the value 2.3 is the ___growth factor___.

2. An ___asymptote___ is a line that a graph approaches as $x$ or $y$ increases in absolute value.

3. For ___exponential decay___, as the value of $x$ increases, the value of $y$ decreases.

4. A function in the general form $y = ab^x$ is called an ___exponential function___.

5. For ___exponential growth___, as the value of $x$ increases, the value of $y$ increases.

6. In the function $y = 4(0.3)^x$, the value 0.3 is the ___decay factor___.

Identify whether each function represents exponential growth or exponential decay.

7. $y = 0.75(4)^x$  exponential growth

8. $y = 0.63(0.5)^x$  exponential decay

9. $y = 9(0.83)^x$  exponential decay

10. $y = 12(7)^x$  exponential growth

Identify the $y$-intercept for each function.

11. $y = 4.5(7)^x$  4.5

12. $y = 5(3.2)^x$  5

# Differentiated Remediation *continued*

Available in editable format online.

## On-Level

- **Practice** (2 pages) Provides extra practice for each lesson. For simpler practice exercises, use the Form K Practice pages found in the All-in-One Teaching Resources and online.

- **Think About a Plan** Helps students develop specific problem-solving skills and strategies by providing scaffolded guiding questions.

- **Standardized Test Prep** Focuses on all major exercises, all major question types, and helps students prepare for the high-stakes assessments.

## Extension

- **Enrichment** Provides students with interesting problems and activities that extend the concepts of the lesson.

- **Activities, Games, and Puzzles** Worksheets that can be used for concepts development, enrichment, and for fun!

---

### Practice and Problem Solving Wkbk/ All-in-One Resources/Online
**Practice page 1**

**7-1 Practice** *Form G*
Exploring Exponential Models

Graph each function.

1. $y = (0.3)^x$    2. $y = 3^x$    3. $y = 2\left(\frac{1}{3}\right)^x$

4. $y = \frac{2}{3}(3)^x$    5. $s(t) = 2.5^t$    6. $f(x) = \frac{1}{3}(5)^x$

Without graphing, determine whether the function represents exponential growth or exponential decay. Then find the *y*-intercept.

7. $y = 0.99\left(\frac{1}{3}\right)^x$ decay; 0.99    8. $y = 20(1.75)^x$ growth; 20

9. $y = 185\left(\frac{5}{3}\right)^x$ growth; 185    10. $f(x) = \frac{2}{3}\left(\frac{1}{2}\right)^x$ decay; $\frac{2}{3}$

11. $f(x) = 0.25(1.05)^x$ growth; 0.25    12. $y = \frac{1/6}{8}\left(\frac{3}{8}\right)^x$ growth; $\frac{1}{8}$

13. Suppose you deposit $1500 in a savings account that pays interest at an annual rate of 6%. No money is added or withdrawn from the account.
  a. How much will be in the account after 5 years? about $2007.34
  b. How much will be in the account after 20 years? $4810.70
  c. How many years will it take for the account to contain $2500? about 9 years
  d. How many years will it take for the account to contain $4000? about 17 years

Write an exponential function to model each situation. Find each amount after the specified time.

14. A population of 1,236,000 grows 1.3% per year for 10 years.
  $y = 1,236,000(1.013)^x$; about 1,406,413

15. A population of 752,000 decreases 1.4% per year for 18 years.
  $y = 752,000(0.986)^x$; about 583,448

16. A new car that sells for $18,000 depreciates 25% each year for 4 years.
  $y = 18,000(0.75)^x$; $5695.31

---

### Practice and Problem Solving Wkbk/ All-in-One Resources/Online
**Practice page 2**

**7-1 Practice** *(continued)* *Form G*
Exploring Exponential Models

For each annual rate of change, find the corresponding growth or decay factor.

17. +45% 1.45    18. −10% 0.9    19. −40% 0.6    20. +200% 3

21. +28% 1.28    22. +100% 2    23. −5% 0.95    24. +3% 1.03

25. In 2009, there were 1570 bears in a wildlife refuge. In 2010, the population had increased to approximately 1884 bears. If this trend continues and the bear population is increasing exponentially, how many bears will there be in 2018? ≈100 bears

26. The value of a piece of equipment has a decay factor of 0.80 per year. After 5 years, the equipment is worth $98,304. What was the original value of the equipment? $300,000

27. Your friend drops a rubber ball from 4 ft. You notice that its rebound is 32.5 in. on the first bounce and 22 in. on the second bounce.
  a. What exponential function would be a good model for the height of the ball? $y = 48(0.677)^x$
  b. How high will the ball bounce on the fourth bounce? about 10.08 in.

28. An investment of $75,000 increases at a rate of 12.5% per year. What is the value of the investment after 30 years? $2,568,247.87

29. A new truck that sells for $29,000 depreciates 12% each year. What is the value of the truck after 7 years? $11,851.59

30. The price of a new home is $350,000. The value of the home appreciates 2% each year. How much will the home be worth in 10 years? $426,648.05

31. The population of an endangered bird is decreasing at a rate of 0.75% per year. There are currently about 200,000 of these birds.
  a. What exponential function would be a good model for the population of these endangered birds? $y = 200,000(0.9925)^x$
  b. How many birds will there be in 100 years? almost 94,207 birds

---

### All-in-One Resources/Online
**Enrichment**

**7-1 Enrichment**
Exploring Exponential Models

**Determining Relationships Between Variables**

On the basis of data, scientists sometimes hypothesize that a quantity $z$ depends on two quantities $x$ and $y$ such that

$$z = Cx^r y^s$$

where $C$ is a constant and $r$ and $s$ are integers. By doing experiments in which the values of $x$ and $y$ are varied, they determine the values of integers $r$ and $s$.

For instance, suppose the momentum $M$ of a moving object seems to be related to the mass $m$ and velocity $v$ by the equation $M = Cm^r v^s$. Later, scientists find that doubling the mass and keeping the velocity constant doubles the momentum, so

$$2M = C(2m)^r v^s.$$

Using substitution and simplifying:    $2(Cm^r v^s) = C2^r m^r v^s$
Dividing each side by $Cm^r v^s$:    $2 = 2^r$
    $1 = r$

1. Suppose that doubling the velocity while holding the mass constant also doubles the momentum. Express this relationship in an equation. $2M = Cm^r(2v)^s$

2. Solve your equation for $s$. $s = 1$

3. Use the values of $r$ and $s$ to write an expression for momentum in terms of mass $m$, velocity $v$, and the constant $C$. $M = Cmv$

Use a similar method to solve the following problems.

4. The price $P$ of a diamond is related to both the weight $W$ of the diamond and its brilliance $B$. If both the weight and brilliance are simultaneously doubled, the price of the diamond increases by a factor of 32. If the weight is doubled and, at the same time, the brilliance is halved, the price increases by a factor of 2. Write a formula for $P$ in terms of $W$, $B$, and the constant $C$. $P = CW^3 B^2$

5. The price of wheat depends upon the weight and the water content. A particular wheat trader pays according to this pattern: the price $P$ increases by a factor of 2 when the weight is doubled and the water content is constant. If the weight is doubled and the water content is halved, the price is constant. Write a formula for $P$ in terms of weight $w$, water content $h$, and the constant $C$. $P = Cwh$

---

### Practice and Problem Solving Wkbk/ All-in-One Resources/Online
**Think About a Plan**

**7-1 Think About a Plan**
Exploring Exponential Models

**Population** The population of a certain animal species decreases at a rate of 3.5% per year. You have counted 80 of the animals in the habitat you are studying.
  a. Write a function that models the change in the animal population.
  b. **Graphing Calculator** Graph the function. Estimate the number of years until the population first drops below 15 animals.

1. Is an exponential model reasonable for this situation? Explain.
Yes; the population decreases at a fixed, constant rate of 3.5% per year.
An exponential model is reasonable.

2. Write the function that models exponential growth or decay. $A(t) = \boxed{a(1 + r)^t}$

3. The initial population is $\boxed{80 \text{ animals}}$.

4. Is the rate of change positive or negative? Explain.
The population is decreasing, so the rate of change is negative.

5. The rate of change is $\boxed{-0.035}$.

6. Write a function that models the change in the animal population. $P(t) = \boxed{80(0.965)^t}$

7. Graph your function on a graphing calculator. Sketch your graph.

8. How can you find the *x*-value that produces a given *y*-value?
Answers may vary. Sample: Use the TRACE function.

9. Use your graph to estimate the number of years until the population first drops below 15 animals. 47 years

---

### Practice and Problem Solving Wkbk/ All-in-One Resources/Online
**Standardized Test Prep**

**7-1 Standardized Test Prep**
Exploring Exponential Models

**Multiple Choice**

For Exercises 1 and 2, choose the correct letter.

1. Which of the following functions represents exponential decay and has a *y*-intercept of 2? D
  Ⓐ $y = 2\left(\frac{4}{3}\right)^x$    Ⓒ $y = \frac{1}{2}(2)^x$
  Ⓑ $y = \frac{1}{2}(0.95)^x$    Ⓓ $y = 2\left(\frac{2}{6}\right)^x$

2. Suppose you deposit $3000 in a savings account that pays interest at an annual rate of 4%. If no other money is added or withdrawn from the account, how much will be in the account after 10 years? H
  Ⓕ $3122.18    Ⓗ $4440.73
  Ⓖ $4994.50    Ⓘ $86,776.40

**Extended Response**

3. In 2009 there was an endangered population of 270 cranes in a western state. Due to wildlife efforts, the population is increasing at a rate of 5% per year.
  a. What exponential function would be a good model for this population of cranes? Explain in words or show work for how you determined the exponential function.
  b. If this trend continues, how many cranes will there be in this population in 2020? Show your work.
  [4] a. The general form of an exponential function is $y = a(b)^x$. $x$ represents time in years, $y$ represents the population of cranes, and $a$ is the initial value of 270 cranes. Because the crane population is increasing by 5%, $b = 1 + r = 1 + 0.05 = 1.05$. The exponential function that models the crane population is $y = 270(1.05)^x$ OR equivalent explanation.
  b. $y = 270(1.05)^{11} = 461.79$; almost 462 cranes
  [3] appropriate methods and correct function, but with one computational error in evaluating the function
  [2] incorrect function or multiple computational errors in evaluating the function
  [1] correct function and population, without work shown
  [0] incorrect answers and no work shown OR no answers given

---

### Online Teacher Resource Center
**Activities, Games, and Puzzles**

**7-1 Activity: Financial Considerations**
Exploring Exponential Models

You can work on your own or with a partner.

Suppose you received a gift of $10,000 and want to invest it. You visit two banks to see what they have to offer. Bank A is near your home and pays 5% interest compounded annually. Bank B is farther from your home and pays 6% interest compounded annually. You do not think a 1% difference in rates is that significant, but you want to check.

Calculate the amount of interest each plan will earn after one year. Record your answers on the lines provided.

**Bank A:** $10,000(1.05) − $10,000 = $500    **Bank B:** $10,000(1.06) − $10,000 = $600

You decide to calculate how long it will take each bank to pay $5000 interest.

Complete the table below. Round your answers to the nearest dollar. Then record the number of years below the table.

| Years | 1 | 2 | 3 | 4 | 5 | 6 | 7 | 8 | 9 |
|---|---|---|---|---|---|---|---|---|---|
| Bank A($) | 500 | 1025 | 1576 | 2155 | 2763 | 3401 | 4071 | 4775 | 5513 |
| Bank B($) | 600 | 1236 | 1910 | 2625 | 3382 | 4185 | 5036 | 5938 | 6895 |

**Bank A:** about __9__ years

**Bank B:** about __7__ years

Complete the bar graph to show the amount by which Bank B will outperform Bank A over nine years. Use estimation to determine the heights of the bars.

# 1 Interactive Learning

## Solve It!

**PURPOSE** To identify transformations of exponential functions

**PROCESS** Students may

- trace one function by hand and place the tracing on top of the other function to determine how it was transformed.
- make a table of plotted points for each function and compare values.

**FACILITATE**

**Q** What are the definitions of a compression, reflection, and translation? **[Answers may vary. Sample: compression: shrink; reflection: flip; translation: slide]**

**Q** Which transformation(s) can be eliminated? Why? **[Reflection. The orientation of the functions has not changed.]**

**Q** Could the transformation be a compression? A translation? Explain. **[The transformation could be either a compression or a translation. You can divide the function $f$ by 4 to get $g$, or translate $f$ 2 units to the right to get $g$.]**

**ANSWER** See Solve It in Answers on next page.

**CONNECT THE MATH** To complete the Solve It, students must identify compressions, reflections, and translations given the graphs of two exponential functions. In the lesson they will identify transformations of the families of exponential functions.

---

# 7-2 Properties of Exponential Functions

**Objectives** To explore the properties of functions of the form $y = ab^x$
To graph exponential functions that have base $e$

**Getting Ready!**

$f$ and $g$ are exponential functions with the same base. Is the graph of $g$

- a compression,
- a reflection, or
- a translation

of the graph of $f$? Or is it none of the above? Justify your reasoning.

You've already learned how to transform functions.

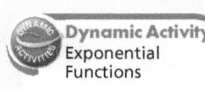

**Dynamic Activity** Exponential Functions

You can apply the four types of transformations—stretches, compressions, reflections, and translations—to exponential functions.

**Essential Understanding** The factor $a$ in $y = ab^x$ can stretch or compress, and possibly reflect the graph of the parent function $y = b^x$.

**Lesson Vocabulary**
- natural base exponential function
- continuously compounded interest

The graphs of $y = 2^x$ (in red) and $y = 3 \cdot 2^x$ (in blue) are shown. Each $y$-value of $y = 3 \cdot 2^x$ is 3 times the corresponding $y$-value of the parent function $y = 2^x$.

| x | $y = 2^x$ | $y = 3 \cdot 2^x$ |
|---|---|---|
| −2 | $\frac{1}{4}$ | $\frac{3}{4}$ |
| −1 | $\frac{1}{2}$ | $\frac{3}{2}$ |
| 0 | 1 | 3 |
| 1 | 2 | 6 |
| 2 | 4 | 12 |

$y = 3 \cdot 2^x$ stretches the graph of the parent function $y = 2^x$ by the factor 3.

---

# 7-2 Preparing to Teach

**BIG idea** Function  **UbD**

**ESSENTIAL UNDERSTANDINGS**

- The factor $a$ in $y = ab^x$ can stretch or compress, and possibly reflect the graph of the parent function $y = b^x$.
- The function $y = ab^x$, $a > 0$, $b > 1$, models exponential growth. $y = ab^x$ models exponential decay if $0 < b < 1$.

## Math Background

Like the other functions seen so far, the graphs of exponential functions can be transformed.

The graph of the parent function $y = b^x$ for $b > 1$ is a smooth curve through $(0, 1)$ and $(1, b)$. It approaches but never touches the $x$-axis toward the left and rises rapidly toward the right. For a parent function $y = b^x$ and its "offspring", the value of $b$ is constant. A different value of $b$ implies a different parent function.

Whether the graph of the parent function is stretched, compressed, or reflected depends on the factor $a$.

- $a > 1$: stretch
- $a < -1$: stretch and reflection in $x$-axis
- $0 < a < 1$: compression
- $0 > a > -1$: compression and reflection in $x$-axis

The graph of the parent function $y = b^x$ can also be translated. The general form is $y = ab^{(x-h)} + k$, where $h$ is a horizontal translation and $k$ is a vertical translation. Using the laws of exponents, the general form can also be written as $y = (ab^{-h})b^x + k$.

If a factor of $a$ is the constant $b^{-h}$, then $a$ also translates the parent function horizontally and stretches or compresses it by $\frac{a}{b^b}$.

## Support Student Learning

Use the **Algebra 2 Companion** to engage and support students during instruction. See Lesson Resources at the end of this lesson for details.

---

**PowerAlgebra.com**

## 1 Interactive Learning

**Solve It!**
Step out how to solve the Problem with helpful hints and an online question. Other questions are listed above in Interactive Learning.

**Dynamic Activity** This activity allows students to graph exponential functions in the form $y = a \cdot b^{kx}$ by adjusting sliders. The interactive graph also lets students set the value of $b$ to $e$.

**Problem 1** Graphing $y = ab^x$

How does the graph of $y = -\frac{1}{3} \cdot 3^x$ compare to the graph of the parent function?

**Think**

Which *x*-values should you use to make a table?
Use $x = 0$ and then choose both positive and negative values.

**Step 1** Make a table of values.

| $x$ | $y = 3^x$ | $y = -\frac{1}{3} \cdot 3^x$ |
|---|---|---|
| $-2$ | $\frac{1}{9}$ | $-\frac{1}{27}$ |
| $-1$ | $\frac{1}{3}$ | $-\frac{1}{9}$ |
| $0$ | $1$ | $-\frac{1}{3}$ |
| $1$ | $3$ | $-1$ |
| $2$ | $9$ | $-3$ |

Each value is $-\frac{1}{3}$ times the corresponding value of the parent function.

**Step 2** Graph the function.

The $-\frac{1}{3}$ in $y = -\frac{1}{3} \cdot 3^x$ reflects the graph of the parent function $y = 3^x$ across the $x$-axis and compresses it by the factor $\frac{1}{3}$. The domain and asymptote remain unchanged. The $y$-intercept becomes $-\frac{1}{3}$ and the range becomes $y < 0$.

**Got It?** **1.** How does the graph of $y = -0.5 \cdot 5^x$ compare to the graph of the parent function?

A horizontal shift $y = ab^{(x-h)}$ is the same as the vertical stretch or compression $y = (ab^{-h})b^x$. A vertical shift $y = ab^x + k$ also shifts the horizontal asymptote from $y = 0$ to $y = k$.

 **Problem 2** Translating the Parent Function $y = b^x$

How does the graph of each function compare to the graph of the parent function?

**A** $y = 2^{(x-4)}$

**Think**

How is the graph of $y = 2^{(x-4)}$ different from the graph of $y = 2^x$?
The graph of $y = 2^{(x-4)}$ is a horizontal translation of $y = 2^x$ to the right 4 units.

**Step 1** Make a table of values of the parent function $y = 2^x$.

| $x$ | $y = 2^x$ |
|---|---|
| $-2$ | $\frac{1}{4}$ |
| $-1$ | $\frac{1}{2}$ |
| $0$ | $1$ |

| $x$ | $y = 2^x$ |
|---|---|
| $1$ | $2$ |
| $2$ | $4$ |
| $3$ | $8$ |

**Step 2** Graph $y = 2^x$ then translate 4 units to the right.

4 units

The $(x - 4)$ in $y = 2^{(x-4)}$ translates the graph of $y = 2^x$ to the right 4 units. The asymptote remains $y = 0$. The $y$-intercept becomes $\frac{1}{16}$.

 PowerAlgebra.com | **Lesson 7-2** Properties of Exponential Functions | 443

---

# 2 Guided Instruction

## Problem 1 SYNTHESIZING

Students compare the transformation of an exponential function to its parent function. The transformation consists of a reflection and compression.

**Q** How does multiplying the parent function by $-1$ affect the graph of the parent function? **[The *y*-coordinates are opposites of those of the parent function, so the graph is reflected across the *x*-axis.]**

**Q** How does multiplying the parent function by $\frac{1}{3}$ affect its graph? **[Each *y*-coordinate is multiplied by $\frac{1}{3}$, so the graph is compressed.]**

**Q** Is it necessary to use the parent function when graphing this problem? Explain. **[Answers may vary. Sample: No, but constructing a table and graph of the parent function allows you to use transformations to graph the new function.]**

### Got It? ERROR PREVENTION

**Q** How is this function a transformation of the parent function $y = 5^x$? **[The graph of the parent function is reflected across the *x*-axis and compressed by a factor of 0.5.]**

## Problem 2 SYNTHESIZING

**Q** Will a horizontal shift ever change a horizontal asymptote? Explain. **[No; the *x*-coordinates are changed but the *y*-coordinates stay the same.]**

---

# 2 Guided Instruction

Each Problem is worked out and supported online.

**Problem 1**
Graphing $y = ab^x$

**Alternative Problem 1**
Graphing $y = ab^x$
*Animated*

**Problem 2**
Translating the Parent Function $y = b^x$
*Animated*

**Problem 3**
Using an Exponential Model

**Problem 4**
Evaluating $e^x$

**Problem 5**
Continuously Compounded Interest
*Animated*

**Support in Algebra 2 Companion**
• Vocabulary
• Key Concepts
• Got It?

---

# Answers

### Solve It!
compression or translation; for each $x$, $g(x) = f(x - 2)$ and $g(x) = \frac{f(x)}{4}$

### Got It?
**1.** reflects across the $x$-axis; compresses by a factor of 0.5

Students graph a vertical shift of a given parent function.

**Q** What is the parent function? What are the transformations of the parent function. **[$y = (\frac{1}{2})^x$. To obtain the new function, stretch the parent by a factor of 20, and move it up 10 units.]**

## Got It?                    ERROR PREVENTION

**Q** What indicates a horizontal shift in a given exponential equation? **[A value is added to or subtracted from the exponent.]**

**Q** What indicates a vertical shift in a given exponential equation? **[A value is added to or subtracted from the function.]**

**Q** What indicates a stretch or compression in a given exponential equation? **[A value is multiplied by the function.]**

## Take Note                    VISUAL LEARNERS

Write the equations for Problems 1 and 2 under each equation form. Identify $a$, $b$, $h$, and $k$, and discuss each transformation. For example, $y = -\frac{1}{3} \cdot 3^x$ is in the form $y = ab^x$ where $a = -\frac{1}{3}$ and $b = 3$. Since $a < 0$, this is a reflection in the $x$-axis.

---

**B** $y = 20(\frac{1}{2})^x + 10$

**Step 1** Make a table of values for $y = 20(\frac{1}{2})^x$.

| $x$ | $y = 20 \cdot (\frac{1}{2})^x$ |
|-----|-----|
| −1 | 40 |
| 0 | 20 |
| 1 | 10 |
| 2 | 5 |
| 3 | 2.5 |

**Step 2** Graph $y = 20(\frac{1}{2})^x$, then translate 10 units up.

**Think**
**Where have you seen this situation before?**
The graph of a function like $y = 20(\frac{1}{2})^x + 10$ is both a stretch and a vertical translation of its parent function.

The "+ 10" in $y = 20(\frac{1}{2})^x + 10$ translates the graph of $y = 20(\frac{1}{2})^x$ up 10 units. It also translates the asymptote, the $y$-intercept, and the range 10 units up. The asymptote becomes $y = 10$, the $y$-intercept becomes 30, and the range becomes $y > 10$. The domain is unchanged.

**Check** Use a graphing calculator to graph $y = 20(\frac{1}{2})^x + 10$.

**Got It? 2.** How does the graph of each function compare to the graph of the parent function?

**a.** $y = 4^{(x+2)}$                    **b.** $y = 5 \cdot 0.25^x + 5$

---

**take note**

### Concept Summary    Families of Exponential Functions

| | |
|---|---|
| Parent function | $y = b^x$ |
| Stretch ($\|a\| > 1$) Compression (Shrink) ($0 < \|a\| < 1$) Reflection ($a < 0$) in $x$-axis | $y = ab^x$ |
| Translations (horizontal by $h$; vertical by $k$) | $y = b^{(x-h)} + k$ |
| All transformations combined | $y = ab^{(x-h)} + k$ |

---

# Additional Problems

**1.** How does the graph of $y = -\frac{1}{5} \cdot 4^x$ compare to the graph of the parent function?

**ANSWER** it compresses the parent graph $y = 4^x$ by a factor of $\frac{1}{5}$ and reflects the graph in the $x$-axis.

**2.** How does the graph of $y = 3^{(x+1)}$ compare to the graph of the parent function?

**ANSWER** It shifts the parent graph $y = 3^x$ one unit to the left.

**3.** Some insects reproduce exponentially. The chart shows the population of roaches in a colony at 36-day intervals. On what day will the colony reach 50,000,000 roaches?

| Day | Number of Roaches |
|-----|-----|
| 1 | 50 |
| 37 | 1125 |
| 73 | 25,290 |
| 109 | 569,025 |
| 145 | 12,803,040 |

**ANSWER** The colony will reach 50,000,000 during the 161st day.

**4.** What is the value of $2e^6$? (Use a graphing calculator.)

**ANSWER** about 806.86

**5.** You have $1500 in a bank account that pays 4.5% annual interest compounded continuously. How much will you have in the account after 15 years? Round the answer to the nearest dollar.

**ANSWER** $2946

# Answers

**Got It?** (continued)

**2. a.** translate 2 units to the left; the $y$-intercept becomes 16

**b.** Stretch the graph of $y = (0.25)^x$ by a factor of 5 and translate the graph of $y = 5 \cdot 0.25^x$ up 5 units.

## Problem 3 — Using an Exponential Model

**Physics** The best temperature to brew coffee is between 195°F and 205°F. Coffee is cool enough to drink at 185°F. The table shows temperature readings from a sample cup of coffee. How long does it take for a cup of coffee to be cool enough to drink? Use an exponential model.

| Time (min) | Temp (°F) |
|---|---|
| 0 | 203 |
| 5 | 177 |
| 10 | 153 |
| 15 | 137 |
| 20 | 121 |
| 25 | 111 |
| 30 | 104 |

**Know**
- Set of values
- Best serving temperature

**Need**
Time it takes for a cup of coffee to become cool enough to drink

**Plan**
Use an exponential model to find the time it takes for coffee to reach 185°F.

**Think**

Why does it make sense that a graph of this data would have an asymptote?
The temperature of the hot coffee will get closer and closer to room temperature as it cools, but it cannot cool below room temperature.

**Step 1**
Plot the data to determine if an exponential model is realistic.

**Step 2**
The graphing calculator exponential model assumes the asymptote is $y = 0$. Since room temperature is about 68°F, subtract 68 from each temperature value. Calculate the third list by letting **L3 = L2 − 68**.

> The graphing calculator exponential model assumes the asymptote is $y = 0$.

**Step 3**
Use the **ExpReg L1**, **L3** function on the transformed data to find an exponential model.

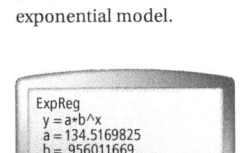

```
ExpReg
y = a*b^x
a = 134.5169825
b = .956011669
r² = .9981659939
r = ¯.9990825761
```

**Step 4**
Translate $y = 134.5(0.956)^x$ vertically by 68 units to model the original data. Use the model $y = 134.5 \cdot 0.956^x + 68$ to find how long it takes the coffee to cool to 185°F.

| X | Y1 |
|---|---|
| 2.6 | 187.65 |
| 2.7 | 187.11 |
| 2.8 | 186.58 |
| 2.9 | 186.05 |
| 3 | 185.52 |
| 3.1 | 184.99 |
| 3.2 | 184.46 |

X=3.1

The coffee takes about 3.1 min to cool to 185°F.

**Got It?**  **3. a.** Use the exponential model. How long does it take for the coffee to reach a temperature of 100 degrees?
  **b. Reasoning** In Problem 3, would the model of the exponential data be useful if you did not translate the data by 68 units? Explain.

---

## Problem 3 — SYNTHESIZING

**Q** What transformation does the calculator include in the exponential model? Explain. [In $y = ab^x$, **a** suggests a compression. Other transformations will have to be adjusted by you.]

**Q** What information that the calculator gives you indicates the exponential model is the best fit? Explain. [$r = -.9990$ is close to −1, which indicates that the exponential model is the best fit.]

**Q** What is the horizontal asymptote of your model? Why? [$y = 68$; 68° represents room temperature. In this model, as the coffee cools, its temperature approaches 68° but never equals 68°.]

## Got It? — ERROR PREVENTION

**Q** What is an approximation for your answer? Explain. [Since it takes coffee 3.1 min. to cool to 185°, the answer would be greater than 3.1 min.]

**Q** If the function was not translated by 68, would the calculated time to cool the coffee be less than or greater than 3.1 min? Would the result make sense? [The time would be less than 3.1 (2.7 min.) because room temperature would not be a factor. The answer would not make sense, since the original data are for a room-temperature environment, not one of 0°F.]

---

**3. a.** about 31.9 min
  **b.** No; a hot coffee cannot cool below room temperature. So, to use exponential data, it is important to translate the data by 68 units.

446   Chapter 7

## Problem 4

**Q** What is the approximate value of $e$? **[2.7182]**

**Q** How can you use a function to evaluate a power of $e$? Explain. **[Evaluate the function $y = e^x$ at the given value of $x$ by using the $e^x$ key on a graphing calculator or by finding the value on a graph or table.]**

**Q** Consider the graph of $y = e^x$. Why does the graphing calculator give an error message when $x$ is sufficiently large? **[The overflow error occurs because the calculator does not have enough memory to store sufficiently large values. $y = e^x$ does not have an upper bound.]**

## Got It?

**Q** How would you calculate $3e^2 + 1$? **[Answers may vary. Sample: Calculate $e^2$, multiply it by 3, and add 1.]**

**Q** Consider the function $y = 3e^2 + 1$. How does its graph compare to the graph of its parent function? **[The graph of the parent function is stretched by a factor of 3 and moved up 1 unit.]**

## Take Note

**Q** What does it mean to have interest compounding continuously? **[It means that the balance increases a small amount every instant, unlike compounding in other time frames such as annually, monthly, or quarterly.]**

---

Up to this point you have worked with rational bases. However, exponential functions can have irrational bases as well. One important irrational base is the number $e$. The graph of $y = \left(1 + \frac{1}{x}\right)^x$ has an asymptote at $y = e$ or $y \approx 2.71828$.

| $x$ | $y = \left(1 + \frac{1}{x}\right)^x$ |
|-----|------|
| 1 | $y = 2$ |
| 10 | $y \approx 2.594$ |
| 100 | $y \approx 2.70$ |
| 1000 | $y \approx 2.717$ |

As $x$ approaches infinity the graph approaches the value of e.

**Natural base exponential functions** are exponential functions with base $e$. These functions are useful for describing continuous growth or decay. Exponential functions with base $e$ have the same properties as other exponential functions.

### Problem 4  Evaluating $e^x$

How can you use a graphing calculator to evaluate $e^3$?

**Method 1**
Use the $e^x$ key.

**Method 2**
Use the graph of $y = e^x$.

**Method 3**
Use a table of values for $y = e^x$.

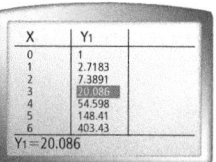

$e^3 \approx 20.086$

**Got It?  4.** How can you use a graphing calculator to calculate $e^8$?

In Lesson 7-1 you studied interest that was compounded annually. The formula for continuously compounded interest uses the number $e$.

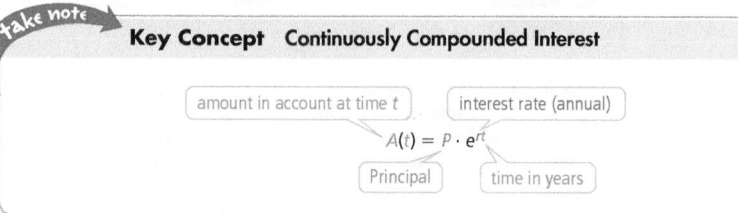

**take note**

**Key Concept   Continuously Compounded Interest**

amount in account at time $t$    interest rate (annual)

$$A(t) = P \cdot e^{rt}$$

Principal    time in years

---

# Answers

### Got It? (continued)
**4.** $e^8 \approx 2980.957987$; three methods: use the $e^x$ key, $x = 8$; graph $y = e^x$ and find $y$ for $x = 8$; or use the table of values for $y = e^x$ and find $y$ for $x = 8$

**5.** about \$4475

### Lesson Check
**1.** stretch by a factor of 2 and reflection across the $x$-axis

**2.** compress by a factor of $\frac{1}{2}$

**3.** translate 5 units to the right

**4.** translate 3 units up

**5.** yes

**6.** no; $2000e^{0.05t} \neq 1000(e^{0.04t} + e^{0.06t})$

### Practice and Problem-Solving Exercises

**7.**

**8.**

**9.**

**10.**

**11.**

**12.**

**13.**

**Problem 5** **Continuously Compounded Interest** GRIDDED RESPONSE

**Scholarships** Suppose you won a contest at the start of 5th grade that deposited $3000 in an account that pays 5% annual interest compounded continuously. How much will you have in the account when you enter high school 4 years later? Express the answer to the nearest dollar.

**Plan**

**What is the unknown?**
The amount $A$ in the account after 4 years.

$A = P \cdot e^{rt}$

$= 3000e^{(0.05)(4)}$    Substitute values for $P$, $r$, and $t$.

$= 3000e^{0.2}$    Simplify.

$\approx 3664$    Use a calculator. Round to the nearest dollar.

The amount in the account, to the nearest dollar, is $3664.
Write your answer, 3664 in the grid.

 **Got It? 5.** About how much will be in the account after 4 years of high school?

**Problem 5**                                    SYNTHESIZING

**Q** Which method of compounding will yield more money: compounding continuously or compounding annually? Assume all other values remain the same. Explain. **[Compounding continuously yields the greatest return, because compounding is performed more often, so you get more interest on your interest.]**

**Got It?**                                    ERROR PREVENTION

**Q** What is the variable whose value you want to find? What variable are you given the value of? **[You want to find the amount $A$ given the time $t$.]**

 **Lesson Check**

**Do you know HOW?**

For each function, identify the transformation from the parent function $y = b^x$.

**1.** $y = -2 \cdot 3^x$

**2.** $y = \frac{1}{2}(9)^x$

**3.** $y = 7^{(x-5)}$

**4.** $y = 5^x + 3$

**Do you UNDERSTAND?**

**5. Vocabulary** Is $y = e^{(x+7)}$ a natural base exponential function?

**6. Reasoning** Is investing $2000 in an account that pays 5% annual interest compounded continuously the same as investing $1000 at 4% and $1000 at 6%, each compounded continuously? Explain.

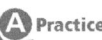 **Practice and Problem-Solving Exercises**

(A) **Practice**    Graph each function.    ◆ See Problem 1.

**7.** $y = -5^x$

**8.** $y = \left(\frac{1}{2}\right)^x$

**9.** $y = 2(4)^x$

**10.** $y = -9(3)^x$

**11.** $y = 3(2)^x$

**12.** $y = 24\left(\frac{1}{2}\right)^x$

**13.** $y = -4^x$

**14.** $y = -\left(\frac{1}{3}\right)^x$

**15.** $y = 2\left(\frac{3}{2}\right)^x$

Graph each function as a transformation of its parent function.    ◆ See Problem 2.

**16.** $y = 2^x + 5$

**17.** $y = 5\left(\frac{1}{3}\right)^x - 8$

**18.** $y = -(0.3)^{x-2}$

**19.** $y = -2(5)^{x+3}$

**20.** $y = 3(2)^{x-1} + 4$

**21.** $y = -2(3)^{x+1} - 5$

**3 Lesson Check**

**Do you know HOW?**

• For Exercises 1–4, students may get confused when identifying the transformations. Suggest they write the parent function and then identify which value represents the transformation.

**Do you UNDERSTAND?**

• For Exercise 5, make sure students understand the natural base exponential function definition.

**Close**

**Q** In the equation $y = ab^{(x-h)} + k$, what are the roles of $a$, $h$, and $k$? Consider both positive and negative values. **[If $|a| > 1$, the function is stretched by a factor of $a$. If $0 < |a| < 1$, the function is compressed by a factor of $a$. If $a < 0$, the function is reflected in the $x$-axis. Positive $h$ moves the function to the right $h$ units and negative $h$ moves the function to the left $h$ units. Positive $k$ moves the function up $k$ units and negative $k$ moves the function down $k$ units.]**

**14.**

**15.**

**16.**

**17.**

**18.**

**19.**

**20.**

**21.**

**PowerAlgebra.com**

**3 Lesson Check**

For a digital lesson check, use the Got It questions.

**Support in Algebra 2 Companion**
• Lesson Check

**4 Practice**

Assign homework to individual students or to an entire class.

# 4 Practice

## ASSIGNMENT GUIDE

Basic: 7–30 all, 31–33, 35, 38–42 even

Average: 7–29 odd, 31–42

Advanced: 7–29 odd, 31–44

Standardized Test Prep: 45–50

Mixed Review: 51–63

**Reasoning** exercises have blue headings.

**Applications** exercises have red headings.

**EXERCISE 32:** Use the Think About a Plan worksheet in the **Practice and Problem Solving Workbook** (also available in the Teaching Resources in print and online) to further support students' development in becoming independent learners.

## HOMEWORK QUICK CHECK

To check students' understanding of key skills and concepts, go over Exercises 7, 17, 31, 32, and 33.

---

**22. Baking** A cake recipe says to bake the cake until the center is 180°F, then let the cake cool to 120°F. The table shows temperature readings for the cake.

a. Given a room temperature of 70°F, what is an exponential model for this data set?

b. How long does it take the cake to cool to the desired temperature?

| Time (min) | Temp (°F) |
|---|---|
| 0 | 180 |
| 5 | 126 |
| 10 | 94 |
| 15 | 80 |
| 20 | 73 |

◄ *See Problem 3.*

 **Graphing Calculator** Use the graph of $y = e^x$ to evaluate each expression to four decimal places.

◄ *See Problem 4.*

**23.** $e^6$    **24.** $e^{-2}$    **25.** $e^0$    **26.** $e^{\frac{5}{2}}$    **27.** $e^e$

Find the amount in a continuously compounded account for the given conditions.

◄ *See Problem 5.*

**28.** principal: $2000
annual interest rate: 5.1%
time: 3 years

**29.** principal: $400
annual interest rate: 7.6%
time: 1.5 years

**30.** principal: $950
annual interest rate: 6.5%
time: 10 years

 **Apply**

**31. Think About a Plan** A student wants to save $8000 for college in five years. How much should be put into an account that pays 5.2% annual interest compounded continuously?
- What formula should you use?
- What information do you know?
- What do you need to find?

**32. Investment** How long would it take to double your principal in an account that pays 6.5% annual interest compounded continuously?

**33. Error Analysis** A student says that the graph of $f(x) = \left(\frac{1}{3}\right)^{x+2} + 1$ is a shift of the parent function 2 units up and 1 unit to the left. Describe and correct the student's error.

**34.** Assume that $a$ is positive and $b \geq 1$. Describe the effects of $c > 0$, $c = 0$, and $c < 0$ on the graph of the function $y = ab^{cx}$.

**35. Graphing Calculator** Using a graphing calculator, graph each of the functions below on the same coordinate grid. What do you notice? Explain why the definition of exponential functions has the constraint that $b \neq 1$.

$y = \left(\frac{1}{2}\right)^x$    $y = \left(\frac{8}{10}\right)^x$    $y = \left(\frac{9}{10}\right)^x$    $y = \left(\frac{99}{100}\right)^x$

**36. Botany** The half-life of a radioactive substance is the time it takes for half of the material to decay. Phosphorus-32 is used to study a plant's use of fertilizer. It has a half-life of 14.3 days. Write the exponential decay function for a 50-mg sample. Find the amount of phosphorus-32 remaining after 84 days.

**37. Archaeology** Archaeologists use carbon-14, which has a half-life of 5730 years, to determine the age of artifacts in carbon dating. Write the exponential decay function for a 24-mg sample. How much carbon-14 remains after 30 millennia? (*Hint:* 1 millennium = 1000 years)

---

# Answers

## Practice and Problem-Solving Exercises
(continued)

**22. a.** $y = 127.27(0.837)^x + 70$
   **b.** about 5.25 min

**23.** 403.4288

**24.** 0.1353

**25.** 1

**26.** 12.1825

**27.** 15.1543

**28.** $2330.65

**29.** $448.30

**30.** $1819.76

**31.** $6168.41

**32.** about 10.7 yrs

**33.** graph is a shift of the parent function 2 units to the left and 1 unit up

**34.** If $c < 0$, the graph models exponential decay. If $c = 0$, the graph is a horizontal line. If $c > 0$, the graph models exponential growth.

**35.** As the value of $b$ approaches 1, the graph comes closer to being a straight line.

**36.** $y = 50\left(\frac{1}{2}\right)^{\frac{1}{14.3}x}$; 0.85mg

**37.** $y = 24\left(\frac{1}{2}\right)^{\frac{1}{5730}x}$; 0.64 mg

The parent function for each graph below is of the form $y = ab^x$. Write the parent function. Then write a function for the translation indicated.

**38.**

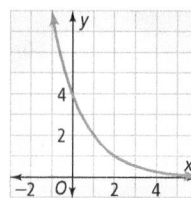

translation: left 4 units, up 3 units

**39.**

translation: right 8 units, up 2 units

**40.**

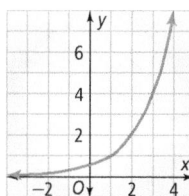

translation: right 6 units, down 7 units

**41.**

translation: left 15 units, down 1 unit

**42. Physics** At a constant temperature, the atmospheric pressure $p$ in pascals is given by the formula $p = 101.3e^{-0.001h}$, where $h$ is the altitude in meters. What is $p$ at an altitude of 500 m?

**Ⓒ Challenge**

**43. Psychology** Psychologists use an exponential model of the learning process, $f(t) = c(1 - e^{-kt})$, where $c$ is the total number of tasks to be learned, $k$ is the rate of learning, $t$ is time, and $f(t)$ is the number of tasks learned.

  **a.** Suppose you move to a new school, and you want to learn the names of 25 classmates in your homeroom. If your learning rate for new tasks is 20% per day, how many complete names will you know after 2 days? After 8 days?

  **b. Graphing Calculator** Graph the function on your graphing calculator. How many days will it take to learn everyone's name? Explain.

  **c. Open-Ended** Does this function seem to describe your own learning rate? If not, how could you adapt it to reflect your learning rate?

**44. Landscaping** A homeowner is planting hedges and begins to dig a 3-ft-deep trench around the perimeter of his property. After the first weekend, the homeowner recruits a friend to help. After every succeeding weekend, each digger recruits another friend. One person can dig 405 ft³ of dirt per weekend. The figure at the right shows the dimensions of the property and the width of the trench.

  **a. Geometry** Determine the volume of dirt that must be removed for the trench.

  **b.** Write an exponential function to model the volume of dirt remaining to be shoveled after $x$ weekends. Then, use the model to determine how many weekends it will take to complete the trench.

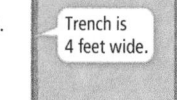

|←——180 ft——→|

Trench is 4 feet wide.

210 ft

**38.** $y = 4\left(\frac{1}{2}\right)^x$; $y = 4\left(\frac{1}{2}\right)^{x+4} + 3$

**39.** $y = -3^x$; $y = -3^{x-8} + 2$

**40.** $y = \frac{1}{2}(2)^x$; $y = \frac{1}{2}(2)^{x-6} - 7$

**41.** $y = -3\left(\frac{1}{3}\right)^x$; $y = -3\left(\frac{1}{3}\right)^{x+15} - 1$

**42.** ≈61.4 pascals

**43. a.** about 8 names; about 20 names

  **b.** Graphically, it will never happen; the graph has $y = 25$ as an asymptote. (In reality, you would be close to knowing all the names in about 21 days.)

  **c.** Answers may vary. Sample: My learning rate might be higher since I can learn names quickly.

**44. a.** 9,168 ft³

  **b.** $V = 9168 - 405(2^x - 1)$; about 5 weekends

# Answers

## Standardized Test Prep

**45.** C
**46.** G
**47.** A
**48.** H
**49.** C
**50.** [2] $A(t) = Pe^{rt}$
$8000 = Pe^{(0.06)(4)}$
$P = \dfrac{8000}{e^{(0.06)(4)}}$
$P = \$6293.02$
[1] correct amount, but without work shown

## Mixed Review

**51.** exponential growth; 23
**52.** exponential growth; 3
**53.** exponential decay; 2
**54.** exponential growth; 5
**55.** $6\sqrt{5}$
**56.** $-\sqrt[3]{4}$
**57.** $5(\sqrt{3} + \sqrt{5})$
**58.** $2(\sqrt[4]{2} + \sqrt[4]{8})$
**59.** $\sqrt{3}$
**60.** $11\sqrt{7}$
**61.** $f^{-1}(x) = \dfrac{x+1}{4}$; yes
**62.** $f^{-1}(x) = x^{\frac{1}{7}}$; yes
**63.** $f^{-1}(x) = \left(\dfrac{x-1}{5}\right)^{\frac{1}{3}}$; yes

---

## Standardized Test Prep

**SAT/ACT**

**45.** A savings account earns 4.62% annual interest, compounded continuously. After approximately how many years will a principal of $500 double?
Ⓐ 2 years　　Ⓑ 10 years　　Ⓒ 15 years　　Ⓓ 44 years

**46.** What is the inverse of the function $f(x) = \sqrt{x-4}$?
Ⓕ $f^{-1}(x) = x^2 - 4, x \geq 0$　　　Ⓗ $f^{-1}(x) = \sqrt{x+4}$
Ⓖ $f^{-1}(x) = x^2 + 4, x \geq 0$　　　Ⓘ $f^{-1}(x) = \dfrac{\sqrt{x-4}}{x-4}$

In Exercises 47 and 48, let $f(x) = x^2 - 4$ and $g(x) = \dfrac{1}{x+4}$.

**47.** What is $(g \circ f)(x)$?
Ⓐ $\dfrac{1}{x^2}$　　Ⓑ $\dfrac{1}{x^2 - 8x + 16} - 4$　　Ⓒ $\dfrac{x^2 - 4}{x+4}$　　Ⓓ $x - 4$

**48.** What is $(f \circ f)(3)$?
Ⓕ 1　　Ⓖ 5　　Ⓗ 21　　Ⓘ 77

**49.** What is the equation of the line shown at the right?
Ⓐ $y = -\dfrac{4}{5}x + 2$　　　Ⓒ $-4x + 5y = 7$
Ⓑ $y = \dfrac{5}{4}x - 2$　　　Ⓓ $4x - 5y = 15$

**Short Response**

**50.** How much should you invest in an account that pays 6% annual interest compounded continuously if you want exactly $8000 after four years? Show your work.

## Mixed Review

Without graphing, determine whether the function represents exponential growth or exponential decay. Then find the $y$-intercept.
　　　　　　　　　　　　　　　　　　　　　　◀ See Lesson 7-1.

**51.** $y = 23(3.03)^x$　　　　　**52.** $f(x) = 3(5)^x$

**53.** $y = 2\left(\dfrac{3}{4}\right)^x$　　　　　**54.** $y = 5\left(\dfrac{8}{3}\right)^x$

Simplify.　　　　　　　　　　　　　　　　　◀ See Lesson 6-3.

**55.** $5\sqrt{5} + \sqrt{5}$　　　**56.** $\sqrt[3]{4} - 2\sqrt[3]{4}$　　　**57.** $\sqrt{75} + \sqrt{125}$
**58.** $\sqrt[4]{32} + \sqrt[4]{128}$　　　**59.** $5\sqrt{3} - 2\sqrt{12}$　　　**60.** $3\sqrt{63} + \sqrt{28}$

**Get Ready!** To prepare for Lesson 7-3, do Exercises 61–63.

Find the inverse of each function. Is the inverse a function?　◀ See Lesson 6-7.

**61.** $f(x) = 4x - 1$　　　**62.** $f(x) = x^7$　　　**63.** $f(x) = 5x^3 + 1$

# Lesson Resources

## Additional Instructional Support

### Algebra 2 Companion

Students can use the **Algebra 2 Companion** worktext (4 pages) as you teach the lesson. Use the Companion to support

- New Vocabulary
- Key Concepts
- Got It for each Problem
- Lesson Check

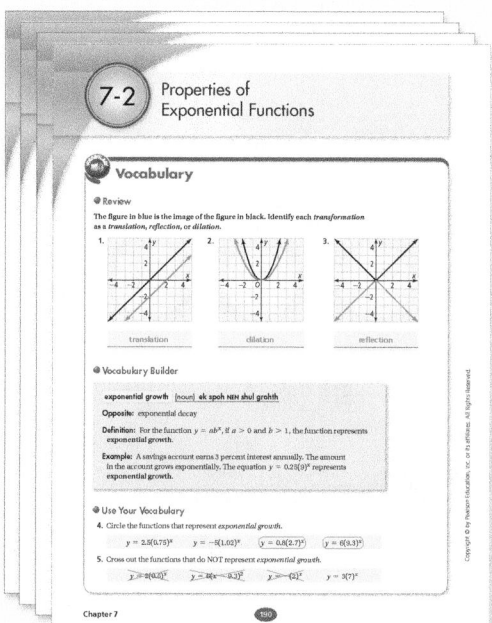

### ELL Support

**Use Graphic Organizers** Instruct students to make a six-column organizer titled "Families of Exponential Functions" with the following column heads: Stretch, Compression, Reflection, Horizontal Translation, Vertical Translation, and All.

Divide students in pairs. Assign Exercises 1–21. Each pair is required to place each exercise in one of the five columns. For each exercise, the pair should discuss what the parent function is and what transformation or transformations the problem represents. The pair should be ready to justify each decision. At the end of the activity, the pair of students should write an example for each column.

Each pair should present one exercise to the class explaining their conclusion and justification. They should field questions from the class if necessary.

## 5 Assess & Remediate

### Lesson Quiz

1. How does the graph of $y = 2 \cdot 2^x$ compare to the graph of the parent function?

2. How does the graph of $y = 4^{(x-6)}$ compare to the graph of the parent function?

3. **Do you UNDERSTAND?** A pot of water is heated to $200°$F. The table shows typical temperature readings for the pot. The room temperature is $70°$F. How long will it take the water to cool to $150°$F?

| Time (min) | Temp (°F) |
|---|---|
| 0 | 200 |
| 5 | 164 |
| 10 | 140 |
| 15 | 124 |
| 20 | 108 |
| 25 | 98 |

4. You have $10,000. You place it in an account that pays 6.1% annual interest compounded continuously. How much will you have in 20 years? Round the answer to the nearest dollar.

### ANSWERS TO LESSON QUIZ

1. $y = 2 \cdot 2^x$ stretches the parent graph $y = 2^x$ by a factor of 2.

2. $y = 4^{(x-6)}$ shifts the parent graph $y = 4^x$ six units to the right.

3. The water will reach $150°$F in about 7.9 min.

4. $33,871

### PRESCRIPTION FOR REMEDIATION

Use the student work on the Lesson Quiz to prescribe a differentiated review assignment:

| Points | Differentiated Remediation |
|---|---|
| 0–2 | Intervention |
| 3 | On-level |
| 4 | Extension |

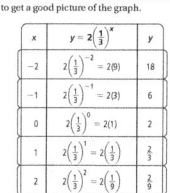

**PowerAlgebra.com**

## 5 Assess & Remediate

Assign the Lesson Quiz. Appropriate intervention, practice, or enrichment is automatically generated based on student performance.

## Differentiated Remediation

Available in editable format online.

### Intervention

- **Reteaching** (2 pages) Provides reteaching and practice exercises for the key lesson concepts. Use with struggling students or absent students.

- **English Language Learner Support** Helps students develop and reinforce mathematical vocabulary and key concepts.

#### All-in-One Resources/Online
**Reteaching**

**7-2 Reteaching**
Properties of Exponential Functions

There are four types of transformations that can change the graph of an exponential function.

**Stretches**
The factor $a$ in $y = ab^x$ can stretch the graph of an exponential function when
$$|a| > 1$$

**Compressions**
The factor $a$ in $y = ab^x$ can compress the graph of an exponential function when
$$0 < |a| < 1$$

**Reflections**
The factor $a$ in $y = ab^x$ can reflect the graph of an exponential function in the $x$-axis when
$$a < 0$$

**Translations**
The graph of an exponential function translates horizontally by $h$; vertically by $k$.
$$y = ab^{(x-h)} + k$$

**Problem**

How does the graph of $y = 2\left(\frac{1}{3}\right)^{x+1} - 4$ compare to the parent function $y = 2\left(\frac{1}{3}\right)^x$?

**Step 1** Determine the base of the function $y = 2\left(\frac{1}{3}\right)^x$. Because $b < 1$, the graph will represent exponential decay.

**Step 2** Make a table. Find more values if necessary to get a good picture of the graph.

| $x$ | $y = 2\left(\frac{1}{3}\right)^x$ | $y$ |
|---|---|---|
| $-2$ | $2\left(\frac{1}{3}\right)^{-2} = 2(9)$ | 18 |
| $-1$ | $2\left(\frac{1}{3}\right)^{-1} = 2(3)$ | 6 |
| 0 | $2\left(\frac{1}{3}\right)^0 = 2(1)$ | 2 |
| 1 | $2\left(\frac{1}{3}\right)^1 = 2\left(\frac{1}{3}\right)$ | $\frac{2}{3}$ |
| 2 | $2\left(\frac{1}{3}\right)^2 = 2\left(\frac{1}{9}\right)$ | $\frac{2}{9}$ |

**Step 3** Use the values for $x$ and $y$ from the table to graph the function.

**Step 4** For $y = 2\left(\frac{1}{3}\right)^x - 4$, $h = -1$ and $k = -4$. Shift the graph of the parent function above 1 unit left and 4 units down. The horizontal asymptote shifts down as well, from $y = 0$ to $y = -4$.

**Step 5** Use a graphing calculator to check your graph.

#### All-in-One Resources/Online
**English Language Learner Support**

**7-2 ELL Support**
Properties of Exponential Functions

**Concept List**

| compression | continuously compounded interest |
|---|---|
| horizontal translation 3 units to the right | natural base exponential function |
| parent function | reflection in $x$-axis |
| stretch | vertical translation 3 units upward |

Choose the concept from the list above that best represents the item in each box.

| 1. $y = 3 \cdot 5^x$ stretch | 2. $y = 0.6^x$ parent function |
|---|---|
| **3.** $y = 7^x + 3$ vertical translation 3 units upward | **4.** $A(t) = P \cdot e^{rt}$ continuously compounded interest |
| **5.** $y = -7^x$ reflection in $x$-axis | **6.** $y = 0.56(7)^x$ compression |
| **7.** $y = e^x$ natural base exponential function | **8.** $y = 11^{(x-3)}$ horizontal translation 3 units to the right |

# Differentiated Remediation *continued*

Available in editable format online.

## On-Level

- **Practice** (2 pages) Provides extra practice for each lesson. For simpler practice exercises, use the Form K Practice pages found in the All-in-One Teaching Resources and online.

- **Think About a Plan** Helps students develop specific problem-solving skills and strategies by providing scaffolded guiding questions.

- **Standardized Test Prep** Focuses on all major exercises, all major question types, and helps students prepare for the high-stakes assessments.

## Extension

- **Enrichment** Provides students with interesting problems and activities that extend the concepts of the lesson.

- **Activities, Games, and Puzzles** Worksheets that can be used for concepts development, enrichment, and for fun!

---

### Practice and Problem Solving Wkbk/ All-in-One Resources/Online
#### Practice page 1

### Practice and Problem Solving Wkbk/ All-in-One Resources/Online
#### Practice page 2

### All-in-One Resources/Online
#### Enrichment

### Practice and Problem Solving Wkbk/ All-in-One Resources/Online
#### Think About a Plan

### Practice and Problem Solving Wkbk/ All-in-One Resources/Online
#### Standardized Test Prep

### Online Teacher Resource Center
#### Activities, Games, and Puzzles

# 7-3 Logarithmic Functions as Inverses

**Objectives** To write and evaluate logarithmic expressions
To graph logarithmic functions

**Dynamic Activity**
Logarithmic Functions

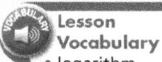

**Lesson Vocabulary**
• logarithm
• logarithmic function
• common logarithm
• logarithmic scale

**Getting Ready!**

The chart shows the different ways you can write 4 and 16 in the form $a^b$, in which $a$ and $b$ are positive integers and $a \neq 1$. What is the smallest number you can write in this $a^b$ form in four different ways? In five different ways? In seven different ways? Explain how you found your answers.

$4 = 4^1$     $16 = 16^1$
$\phantom{4} = 2^2$      $= 4^2$
          $= 2^4$

Many even numbers can be written as power functions with base 2. In this lesson you will find ways to express all numbers as powers of a common base.

**Essential Understanding** The exponential function $y = b^x$ is one-to-one, so its inverse $x = b^y$ is a function. To express "$y$ as a function of $x$" for the inverse, write $y = \log_b x$.

### Key Concept  Logarithm

A **logarithm** base $b$ of a positive number $x$ satisfies the following definition.

For $b > 0$, $b \neq 1$, $\log_b x = y$ if and only if $b^y = x$.

You can read $\log_b x$ as "log base $b$ of $x$." In other words, the logarithm $y$ is the exponent to which $b$ must be raised to get $x$.

The exponent $y$ in the expression $b^y$ is the logarithm in the equation $\log_b x = y$. The base $b$ in $b^y$ and the base $b$ in $\log_b x$ are the same. In both, $b \neq 1$ and $b > 0$.

Since $b \neq 1$ and $b > 0$, it follows that $b^y > 0$. Since $b^y = x$ then $x > 0$, so $\log_b x$ is defined only for $x > 0$.

Because $y = b^x$ and $y = \log_b x$ are inverse functions, their compositions map a number $a$ to itself. In other words, $b^{\log_b a} = a$ for $a > 0$ and $\log_b b^a = a$ for all $a$.

---

# 7-3 Preparing to Teach

**BIG idea Function**    UbD

**ESSENTIAL UNDERSTANDINGS**
• The exponential function $y = b^x$ is one-to-one, so its inverse $x = b^y$ is a function. To express "$y$ as a function of $x$" for the inverse, write $y = \log_b x$.
• An exponential function is a function with the general form $y = ab^x$, $a \neq 0$, with $b > 0$, and $b \neq 1$. In an exponential function, the base $b$ is a constant. The exponent $x$ is the independent variable with domain the set of real numbers.
• Logarithms are exponents. In fact, $\log_b a = c$ if and only if $b^c = a$.

## Math Background

The inverse of the exponential function is the logarithmic function. By definition, $y = b^x$ is equivalent to $\log_b y = x$.

Converting between exponential and logarithmic functions is useful for
• finding the value of a logarithm using properties of exponents,
• making a table of values when graphing a logarithmic function,
• solving exponential and logarithmic equations, as shown in Lesson 7-5.

As inverse functions, the domain of $y = \log_b x$ is the range of $y = b^x$, and the range of $y = \log_b x$ is the domain of $y = b^x$. Logarithms exist only for positive real numbers, which makes sense when you consider that the range of exponential functions is always positive.

### Support Student Learning

Use the **Algebra 2 Companion** to engage and support students during instruction. See Lesson Resources at the end of this lesson for details.

# 1 Interactive Learning

**Solve It!**

**PURPOSE** To find multiple ways to represent numbers as powers of other numbers
**PROCESS** Students may
• try to write $2^5$ as powers of other numbers and realize the power cannot be a prime such as 5.
• notice that $4^2 = 16$ and write $16^2 = 256$ as powers of numbers.

**FACILITATE**

**Q** What operation can you do to 4 to get 16? **[Answers may vary. Samples: You can multiply 4 by 4; you can square 4.]**

**Q** What is the pattern of smallest numbers? **[Each number must be a power of 2 whose exponent can be factored in the required number of ways. For example, $2^6 = (2^6)^1 = (2^3)^2 = (2^2)^3 = (2^1)^6$.]**

**Q** What must be the smallest base of each of the smallest numbers? Explain. **[Sample: 2; if the smallest base was 3, the first smallest number would be $9 = 9^1 = 3^2$, and the second smallest would be $81 = 81^1 = 9^2 = 3^4$; 9 and 81 are larger than 4 and 16.]**

**ANSWER** See Solve It in Answers on next page.
**CONNECT THE MATH** Students find numbers that can be written as a power function of base 2 to solve this problem. In the lesson they will express numbers as powers of a common base.

# 2 Guided Instruction

### Take Note

Each different base $b$ defines a different logarithmic parent function $y = \log_b x$, just as each base $b$ defines a different exponential parent function $y = b^x$.

**PowerAlgebra.com**

## 1 Interactive Learning

**Solve It!**
Step out how to solve the Problem with helpful hints and an online question. Other questions are listed above in Interactive Learning.

**Dynamic Activity** Students can graph logarithmic functions, as well as their related exponential functions. Use this feature with students who have difficulty understanding logarithms to help them visualize the relationship between logarithms and exponents.

## Problem 1

**Q** How does the logarithmic form of an exponential equation compare to the original equation? **[They are equivalent.]**

**ERROR PREVENTION**

Use these examples as a model for how students should solve this kind of problem. Make sure they write out the definition each time if: $x = b^y$ then $\log_b x = y$. This will help reduce errors when applying the definition.

### Got It?

**Q** For any $b > 0$, what is $\log_b 1$? Explain. **[$\log_b 1 = 0$, because $b^0 = 1$ for any $b > 0$.]**

## Problem 2    ERROR PREVENTION

Students can check the reasonableness of their answer when evaluating a logarithm by checking integer powers of the base close to the answer.

**Q** Between which two integers is $\frac{5}{3}$? **[1 and 2]**

**Q** What are $8^1$ and $8^2$? **[8 and 64]**

**Q** Is your answer reasonable? Explain. **[Yes; the function $y = 8^x$ is increasing, so $8^{\frac{5}{3}}$ should be greater than $8^1$ and less than $8^2$, and $8 < 32 < 64$.]**

### Got It?    ERROR INTERVENTION

To use the method shown in Problem 2 to evaluate logarithms both the value of the base, $b$, and the number, $x$, must be expressed as numbers of a common base.

---

You can use the definition of a logarithm to write exponential equations in logarithmic form.

 **Problem 1**  Writing Exponential Equations in Logarithmic Form

**What is the logarithmic form of each equation?**

**A** $100 = 10^2$

Use the definition of logarithm.

If $x = b^y$   then   $\log_b x = y$
If $100 = 10^2$   then   $\log_{10} 100 = 2$

**B** $81 = 3^4$

Use the definition of logarithm.

If $x = b^y$   then   $\log_b x = y$
If $81 = 3^4$   then   $\log_3 81 = 4$

**Think**
To what power do you raise 10 to get 100?
10 raised to the 2nd power equals 100.

✓ **Got It?**  **1.** What is the logarithmic form of each equation?

    **a.** $36 = 6^2$       **b.** $\frac{8}{27} = \left(\frac{2}{3}\right)^3$       **c.** $1 = 3^0$

---

You can use the exponential form to help you evaluate logarithms.

 **Problem 2**  Evaluating a Logarithm

**Multiple Choice**  What is the value of $\log_8 32$?

  Ⓐ $\frac{3}{5}$       Ⓑ $\frac{5}{3}$       Ⓒ 3       Ⓓ 5

$\log_8 32 = x$   Write a logarithmic equation.
$32 = 8^x$   Use the definition of a logarithm to write an exponential equation.
$2^5 = (2^3)^x$   Write each side using base 2.
$2^5 = 2^{3x}$   Power Property of Exponents
$5 = 3x$   Since the bases are the same, the exponents must be equal.
$\frac{5}{3} = x$   Solve for $x$.

**Plan**
How can you use the definition of logarithm to help you find the value of $\log_8 32$?
If $\log_b x = y$ then $x = b^y$, so to what power must you raise 8 to get 32?

Since $8^{\frac{5}{3}} = 32$, then $\log_8 32 = \frac{5}{3}$.
The correct answer is B.

✓ **Got It?**  **2.** What is the value of each logarithm?

    **a.** $\log_5 125$       **b.** $\log_4 32$       **c.** $\log_{64} \frac{1}{32}$

---

# Answers

### Solve It!
64; 4096; 16,777,216;
$64 = 2^6 = (2^2)^3 = (2^3)^2 = (2^6)^1$;
$4096 = 2^{12} = (2^2)^6 = (2^3)^4 = (2^4)^3 = (2^6)^2$;
$16{,}777{,}216 = 2^{24} = (2^2)^{12} = (2^3)^8 = (2^4)^6 = (2^6)^4 = (2^8)^3 = (2^{12})^2$

### Got It?
**1. a.** $\log_6 36 = 2$

  **b.** $\log_{\frac{2}{3}} \frac{8}{27} = 3$

  **c.** $\log_3 1 = 0$

**2. a.** 3

  **b.** $\frac{5}{2}$

  **c.** $-\frac{5}{6}$

---

 **PowerAlgebra.com**

## 2 Guided Instruction

Each Problem is worked out and supported online.

**Problem 1**
Writing Exponential Equations in Logarithmic Form
      *Animated*

**Problem 2**
Evaluating a Logarithm
      *Animated*

**Problem 3**
Using a Logarithmic Scale

**Problem 4**
Graphing a Logarithmic Function

**Problem 5**
Translating $y = \log_b x$

**Alternative Problem 5**
Translating $y = \log_b x$
      *Animated*

**Support in Algebra 2 Companion**
• Vocabulary
• Key Concepts
• Got It?

A **common logarithm** is a logarithm with base 10. You can write a common logarithm $\log_{10} x$ simply as log $x$, without showing the 10.

Many measurements of physical phenomena have such a wide range of values that the reported measurements are logarithms (exponents) of the values, not the values themselves. When you use the logarithm of a quantity instead of the quantity, you are using a **logarithmic scale**. The Richter scale is a logarithmic scale. It gives logarithmic measurements of earthquake magnitude.

**The Richter Scale**
magnitude: + 1

| 0 | 1 | 2 | 3 | 4 | 5 | 6 | 7 | 8 | 9 |
|---|---|---|---|---|---|---|---|---|---|
| E | E·30 | E·30² | E·30³ | E·30⁴ | E·30⁵ | E·30⁶ | E·30⁷ | E·30⁸ | E·30⁹ |

energy released: × 30

 **Problem 3** Using a Logarithmic Scale

In December 2004, an earthquake with magnitude 9.3 on the Richter scale hit off the northwest coast of Sumatra. The diagram shows the magnitude of an earthquake that hit Sumatra in March 2005. The formula $\log \frac{I_1}{I_2} = M_1 - M_2$ compares the intensity levels of earthquakes where $I$ is the intensity level determined by a seismograph, and $M$ is the magnitude on a Richter scale. How many times more intense was the December earthquake than the March earthquake?

$\log \dfrac{I_1}{I_2} = M_1 - M_2$    Use the formula.

$\log \dfrac{I_1}{I_2} = 9.3 - 8.7$    Substitute $M_1 = 9.3$ and $M_2 = 8.7$.

$\log \dfrac{I_1}{I_2} = 0.6$    Simplify.

$\dfrac{I_1}{I_2} = 10^{0.6}$    Apply the definition of common logarithm.

$\approx 4$    Use a calculator.

The December earthquake was about 4 times as strong as the one in March.

**Think**

What is the base of this logarithm?
This is the common logarithm. It has base 10.

**Got It? 3.** In 1995, an earthquake in Mexico registered 8.0 on the Richter scale. In 2001, an earthquake of magnitude 6.8 shook Washington state. How many times more intense was the 1995 earthquake than the 2001 earthquake?

THAILAND

Magnitude 8.7

MALAYSIA

Epicenter, March 2005

Sumatra

INDONESIA

---

**Q** Why is the Richter scale more convenient to use than the explicit measurements of the released energy? **[Answers may vary. Sample: Small changes in the Richter scale correspond to large changes in intensity. The numbers are small and easy to work with.]**

**Q** What is the difference in magnitude on the Richter scale of two earthquakes if the amount of energy released from one is 900 times as great as the amount of energy released from the other? Explain. **[2; because $30^2 = 900$]**

**Problem 3**
For an increase of 1 on the Richter scale, the amplitude of the ground motion recorded by a seismograph increases by a factor of ten.

**Q** What does $\log \frac{I_1}{I_2}$ represent? **[The difference in intensity level determined by a seismograph of two earthquakes]**

**Got It?**

**Q** How does the difference in magnitude on the Richter scale of the earthquakes in Problem 3 compare to the difference in magnitude of the earthquakes in the Got It? **[The difference in magnitude is twice as great in the Got It.]**

**Q** How will the difference in intensities of the earthquakes in the Problem and Got It compare to the difference in the magnitudes on the Richter scale? **[Answers may vary. Sample: The difference in intensity will be much greater than the difference in magnitude on the Richter scale.]**

---

# Additional Problems

**1.** What is the logarithmic form of each equation?

   **a.** $8^0 = 1$

   **b.** $4^3 = 64$

   **ANSWERS**

   **a.** $\log_8 1 = 0$    **b.** $\log_4 64 = 3$

**2.** What is the value of $\log_{16} 64$?

   **ANSWER** $\frac{3}{2}$

**3.** The loudness of a sound in decibels, dB, is defined as $10 \log \frac{I}{10^{-12}}$, where $I$ is the intensity of the sound. How loud is a whisper with an intensity of $10^{-10}$?

   **ANSWER** 20 dB

**4.** What is the graph of $y = \log_6 x$? Describe the domain and range and

identify the $y$-intercept and the asymptote.

**ANSWER**

domain: all nonnegative real numbers; range: all real numbers; $y$-intercept: does not exist; asymptote: $x = 0$

**5.** How does the graph of $y = \frac{3}{4} \log x - 2$ compare to the graph of the parent function?

   **ANSWER** The graph is compressed by a factor of $\frac{3}{4}$ and translated down 2 units.

# Answers

**Got It?** (continued)

   **3.** ≈16 times

**Q** If $y = \log_b x$ and $y = a^x$ are inverse functions, what must be true about $a$ and $b$? **[$a = b$; the bases must be the same.]**

**Q** How do the coordinates of the points on the graph of a function compare to the coordinates of the corresponding points on the graph of its inverse? **[The $x$-coordinates and $y$-coordinates are reversed.]**

## Problem 4

**Q** Does the graph of $y = \log_3 x$ have a horizontal asymptote? Explain. **[No; the graph increases as $x$ increases in the same way that the exponent decreases as $x$ decreases.]**

## Got It?

**Q** How does the graph of $y = \log_3 x$ compare to the graph of $y = \log_4 x$? **[The domain, range, $y$-intercept and asymptotes are the same. The graph of $y = \log_4 x$ is steeper and above the graph of $y = \log_3 x$ for $x > 1$, and $y = \log_3 x$ is steeper and above the graph of $y = \log_4 x$ for $x < 1$.]**

**Q** To make a table of values to graph $y = \log_4 x$, what are the best values of $x$ to use to make calculations easy? **[powers of 4, for example, $\frac{1}{16}$, $\frac{1}{4}$, 1, 4, and 16.]**

---

A **logarithmic function** is the inverse of an exponential function. The graph shows $y = 10^x$ and its inverse $y = \log x$. Note that $(0, 1)$ and $(1, 10)$ are on the graph of $y = 10^x$, and that $(1, 0)$ and $(10, 1)$ are on the graph of $y = \log x$.

Recall that the graphs of inverse functions are reflections of each other across the line $y = x$. You can graph $y = \log_b x$ as the inverse of $y = b^x$.

### Problem 4  Graphing a Logarithmic Function

**What is the graph of $y = \log_3 x$? Describe the domain and range and identify the $y$-intercept and the asymptote.**

$y = \log_3 x$ is the inverse of $y = 3^x$.

**Think**

How are the domain and range of $y = 3^x$ and $y = \log_3 x$ related?
Since they are inverse functions, the domain and range of $y = \log_3 x$ are the same as the range and domain of $y = 3^x$.

**Step 1** Graph $y = 3^x$.

**Step 2** Reflecting across the line $y = x$ produces the inverse of $y = 3^x$.

**Step 3** Choose a few points on $y = 3^x$ and reverse their coordinates. Plot these new points and graph $y = \log_3 x$.

The domain is $x > 0$. The range is all real numbers. There is no $y$-intercept. The vertical asymptote is $x = 0$.

**Got It? 4. a.** What is the graph of $y = \log_4 x$? Describe the domain, range, $y$-intercept and asymptotes.

   **b.** Reasoning Suppose you use the following table to help you graph $y = \log_2 x$. (Recall that if $y = \log_2 x$, then $2^y = x$.) Copy and complete the table. Explain your answers.

| x | $2^y = x$ | y |
|---|---|---|
| −1 | $2^y = -1$ | |
| 0 | $2^y = 0$ | |
| 1 | $2^y = 1$ | |
| 2 | $2^y = 2$ | |

---

# Answers

## Got It? (continued)

**4. a.** domain: $x > 0$; range: all real numbers; no $y$-intercept; vertical asymptote: $x = 0$

**b.**

| x | $2^y = x$ | y |
|---|---|---|
| −1 | $2^y = -1$ | undefined |
| 0 | $2^y = 0$ | undefined |
| 1 | $2^y = 1$ | 0 |
| 2 | $2^y = 2$ | 1 |

The function $y = \log_b x$ is the parent for a function family. You can graph $y = \log_b(x - h) + k$ by translating the graph of the parent function, $y = \log_b x$, horizontally by $h$ units and vertically by $k$ units. The $a$ in $y = a \log_b x$ indicates a stretch, a compression, and possibly a reflection.

### Concept Summary   Families of Logarithmic Functions

| | |
|---|---|
| Parent functions: | $y = \log_b x, b > 0, b \neq 1$ |
| Stretch $(\lvert a \rvert > 1)$ <br> Compression (Shrink) $(0 < \lvert a \rvert < 1)$ <br> Reflection $(a < 0)$ in $x$-axis | $y = a \log_b x$ |
| Translations (horizontal by $h$; vertical by $k$) | $y = \log_b(x - h) + k$ |
| All transformations together | $y = a \log_b(x - h) + k$ |

### Problem 5   Translating $y = \log_b x$

**How does the graph of $y = \log_4(x - 3) + 4$ compare to the graph of the parent function?**

**Think**

**How is the function $y = \log_4(x - 3) + 4$ similar to other functions you have seen?**
Recall that the graph of $y = f(x - h) + k$ is a vertical and horizontal translation of the parent function, $y = f(x)$.

**Step 1**

Make a table of values for the parent function. Use the definition of logarithm.

| $x$ | $\log_4 x = y \longrightarrow 4^y = x$ | $y$ |
|---|---|---|
| $\frac{1}{16}$ | $4^{-2} = \frac{1}{16}$ | $-2$ |
| $\frac{1}{4}$ | $4^{-1} = \frac{1}{4}$ | $-1$ |
| $1$ | $4^0 = 1$ | $0$ |
| $4$ | $4^1 = 4$ | $1$ |
| $16$ | $4^2 = 16$ | $2$ |

**Step 2**

Graph the parent function. Shift the graph to the right 3 units and up 4 units to graph $y = \log_4(x - 3) + 4$.

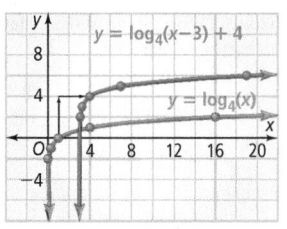

Because $y = \log_4(x - 3) + 4$ translates the graph of the parent function 3 units to the right, the asymptote changes from $x = 0$ to $x = 3$. The domain changes from $x > 0$ to $x > 3$. The range remains all real numbers.

**Got It?** **5.** How does the graph of each function compare to the graph of the parent function?
   **a.** $y = \log_2(x - 3) + 4$     **b.** $y = 5 \log_2 x$

PowerAlgebra.com   **Lesson 7-3**   Logarithmic Functions as Inverses       455

## Take Note   ERROR PREVENTION

Note that the base of the logarithm is one parameter that does not change within a family of logarithmic functions. Each base of a logarithm is formally a separate family of functions.

### Problem 5

**Q** How does the shape of the graph of the transformed function compare to the graph of the parent function? **[Answers may vary. Sample: There is no stretch or compression, so the shape is the same.]**

**Q** How does a horizontal translation by $h$ units affect the domain? **[It translates the domain by $h$ units.]**

**Q** Could you use the definition of logarithms to make a table of values for the given function and then graph it directly? Explain. **[No; the definition of logarithms only considers the base, $x$, and $y$ and does not allow for the translations.]**

### Got It?

**Q** What is the parent function of the logarithmic functions in 5a and 5b? **[$y = \log_2 x$]**

**Q** Does the stretch factor change the intercept or asymptote? Explain. **[No; multiplying the function by a stretch factor does not change the $x$-value for which $y = 0$ or change the domain of the function.]**

**5. a.** translates the graph of the parent function 3 units to the right and 4 units up; The asymptote changes from $x = 0$ to $x = 3$. The domain changes from $x > 0$ to $x > 3$. The range remains all real numbers.

**b.** stretch the graph of the parent function by a factor of 5; The asymptote, domain, and the range remain the same.

**Lesson 7-3**   **455**

# 3 Lesson Check

## Do you know HOW?

- For Exercises 1–8, if students have trouble converting between logarithmic form and exponential form, remind them to write out the definition of logarithms before beginning.

- For Exercises 5–8, if students have trouble relating the logarithmic *expressions* to the definition for logarithms, which is in the form of an *equation*, then remind them to set the logarithm equal to $x$ before proceeding to evaluate it.

## Do you UNDERSTAND?

- If students have difficulty with Exercise 10, remind them that $y = \log_b x$ and $y = b^x$ are inverses. Then remind them that inverses are reflections across the line $y = x$.

## Close

> **Q** How can you use the properties of exponents to evaluate a logarithm? **[Answers may vary. Sample: Rewrite the logarithm as a logarithmic function equal to $x$, convert it to an exponential function, and use the properties of exponents to solve for $x$.]**
>
> **Q** How can you use the graph of an exponential function to graph its inverse? **[Answers may vary. Samples: Reflect the graph over the line $y = x$; Choose several points on the graph, reverse the $x$- and $y$-coordinates, and plot them.]**

---

 **Lesson Check**

### Do you know HOW?

**Write each equation in logarithmic form.**

**1.** $25 = 5^2$    **2.** $64 = 4^3$

**3.** $243 = 3^5$    **4.** $25 = 5^2$

**Evaluate each logarithm.**

**5.** $\log_2 8$    **6.** $\log_9 9$

**7.** $\log_7 49$    **8.** $\log_2 \frac{1}{4}$

### Do you UNDERSTAND?

**9. Vocabulary** Determine whether each logarithm is a common logarithm.

  **a.** $\log_2 4$　**b.** $\log 64$　**c.** $\log_{10} 100$　**d.** $\log_5 5$

**10. Reasoning** Explain how you could use an inverse function to graph the logarithmic function $y = \log_6 x$.

**11. Compare and Contrast** Compare the graph of $y = \log_2(x + 4)$ to the graph of $y = \log_2 x$. How are the graphs alike? How are they different?

---

 ## Practice and Problem-Solving Exercises

**(A) Practice**

**Write each equation in logarithmic form.** ◆ **See Problem 1.**

**12.** $49 = 7^2$　　**13.** $10^3 = 1000$　　**14.** $625 = 5^4$　　**15.** $\frac{1}{10} = 10^{-1}$

**16.** $8^2 = 64$　　**17.** $4 = \left(\frac{1}{2}\right)^{-2}$　　**18.** $\left(\frac{1}{3}\right)^3 = \frac{1}{27}$　　**19.** $10^{-2} = 0.01$

**Evaluate each logarithm.** ◆ **See Problem 2.**

**20.** $\log_2 16$　　**21.** $\log_4 2$　　**22.** $\log_8 8$　　**23.** $\log_4 8$

**24.** $\log_2 8$　　**25.** $\log_{49} 7$　　**26.** $\log_5(-25)$　　**27.** $\log_3 9$

**28.** $\log_2 2^5$　　**29.** $\log_{\frac{1}{2}} \frac{1}{2}$　　**30.** $\log 10,000$　　**31.** $\log_5 125$

**Seismology** In 1812, an earthquake of magnitude 7.9 shook New Madrid, Missouri. Compare the intensity level of that earthquake to the intensity level of each earthquake below. ◆ **See Problem 3.**

**32.** magnitude 7.7 in San Francisco, California, in 1906

**33.** magnitude 9.5 in Valdivia, Chile, in 1960

**34.** magnitude 3.2 in Charlottesville, Virginia, in 2001

**35.** magnitude 6.9 in Kobe, Japan, in 1995

**Graph each function on the same set of axes.** ◆ **See Problem 4.**

**36.** $y = \log_2 x$　　**37.** $y = 2^x$　　**38.** $y = \log_{\frac{1}{2}} x$　　**39.** $y = \left(\frac{1}{2}\right)^x$

**Describe how the graph of each function compares with the graph of the parent function, $y = \log_b x$.** ◆ **See Problem 5.**

**40.** $y = \log_5 x + 1$　　　　　　**41.** $y = \log_7(x - 2)$

**42.** $y = \log_3(x - 5) + 3$　　　　**43.** $y = \log_4(x + 2) - 1$

---

## 3 Lesson Check

For a digital lesson check, use the Got It questions.

**Support in Algebra 2 Companion**
- Lesson Check

## 4 Practice

Assign homework to individual students or to an entire class.

---

# Answers

## Lesson Check

**1.** $\log_5 25 = 2$　**2.** $\log_4 64 = 3$

**3.** $\log_3 243 = 5$　**4.** $\log_5 25 = 2$

**5.** 3　　**6.** 1　　**7.** 2　　**8.** $-2$

**9. a.** no　**b.** yes　**c.** yes　**d.** no

**10.** Choose a few points on the graph of $y = 6^x$, reverse their coordinates, and plot them.

**11.** $y = \log_2(x + 4)$ translates the graph of $y = \log_2 x$ 4 units to the left. Asymptote changes from $x = 0$ to $x = -4$. Domain changes from $x > 0$ to $x > -4$. Range remains the same.

## Practice and Problem-Solving Exercises

**12.** $\log_7 49 = 2$　**13.** $\log 1000 = 3$

**14.** $\log_5 625 = 4$　**15.** $\log \frac{1}{10} = -1$

**16.** $\log_8 64 = 2$　**17.** $\log_{\frac{1}{2}} 4 = -2$

**18.** $\log_{\frac{1}{3}} \frac{1}{27} = 3$　**19.** $\log 0.01 = -2$

**20.** 4　　**21.** $\frac{1}{2}$　　**22.** 1

**23.** $\frac{3}{2}$　　**24.** 3　　**25.** $\frac{1}{2}$

**26.** undefined　　**27.** 2

**28.** 5　　**29.** 1　　**30.** 4　　**31.** 3

**32.** The earthquake in Missouri was about 1.58 times more intense.

**33.** The earthquake in Chile was about 39.81 times more intense.

**34.** The earthquake in Missouri was about 50,119 times more intense.

**35.** The earthquake in Missouri was about 10 times more intense.

**36–39.**

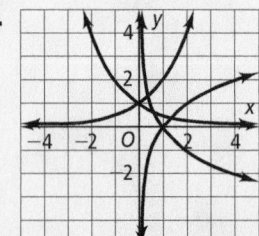

**40.** translate the graph 1 unit up

**41.** translate the graph 2 units to the right

**Apply**

**44. Think About a Plan** The pH of a substance equals $-\log[H^+]$, where $[H^+]$ is the concentration of hydrogen ions, and it ranges from 0 to 14. A pH level of 7 is neutral. A level greater than 7 is basic, and a level less than 7 is acidic. The table shows the hydrogen ion concentration $[H^+]$ for selected foods. Is each food basic or acidic?
- How can you find the pH value of each food?
- What rule can you use to determine if the food is basic or acidic?

**Approximate $[H^+]$ of Foods**

| Food | $[H^+]$ |
| --- | --- |
| Apple juice | $3.2 \times 10^{-4}$ |
| Buttermilk | $2.5 \times 10^{-5}$ |
| Cream | $2.5 \times 10^{-7}$ |
| Ketchup | $1.3 \times 10^{-4}$ |
| Shrimp sauce | $7.9 \times 10^{-8}$ |
| Strained peas | $1.0 \times 10^{-6}$ |

**45. Chemistry** Find the concentration of hydrogen ions in seawater, if the pH level of seawater is 8.5.

**Write each equation in exponential form.**

**46.** $\log_2 128 = 7$     **47.** $\log 0.0001 = -4$     **48.** $\log_6 6 = 1$     **49.** $\log_4 1 = 0$

**50.** $\log_7 16{,}807 = 5$     **51.** $\log_2 \frac{1}{2} = -1$     **52.** $\log_3 \frac{1}{9} = -2$     **53.** $\log 10 = 1$

**Find the greatest integer that is less than the value of the logarithm. Use your calculator to check your answers.**

**54.** $\log 5$     **55.** $\log 0.08$     **56.** $\log 17.52$     **57.** $\log(1.3 \times 10^7)$

**58. Error Analysis** Find the error in the following evaluation of $\log_{27} 3$. Then evaluate the logarithm correctly.

$x = \log_{27} 3$
$x^3 = 27$
$\sqrt[3]{x^3} = \sqrt[3]{27}$
$x = 3$
$\log_{27} 3 = 3$

**59. Writing** Explain why the base $b$ in $y = \log_b x$ cannot equal 1.

**60. Open-Ended** Write a logarithmic function of the form $y = \log_b x$. Find its inverse function. Graph both functions on one set of axes.

**Find the inverse of each function.**

**61.** $y = \log_4 x$     **62.** $y = \log_{0.5} x$     **63.** $y = \log_{10} x$     **64.** $y = \log_2 2x$

**65.** $y = \log(x + 1)$     **66.** $y = \log 10x$     **67.** $y = \log_2 4x$     **68.** $y = \log(x - 6)$

**Graph each logarithmic function.**

**69.** $y = \log 2x$     **70.** $y = 2\log_2 x$     **71.** $y = \log_4(2x + 3)$     **72.** $y = \log_3(x + 5)$

**Find the domain and the range of each function.**

**73.** $y = \log_5 x$     **74.** $y = 3\log x$     **75.** $y = \log_2(x - 3)$     **76.** $y = 2\log(x - 2)$

You can write $5^3 = 125$ in logarithmic form using the fact that $\log_b b^x = x$.

$\log_5(5^3) = \log_5(125)$    Apply the log base 5 to each side.
$3 = \log_5 125$    Use $\log_b b^x = x$ to simplify.

**Use this method to write each equation in logarithmic form. Show your work.**

**77.** $3^4 = 81$       **78.** $x^4 = y$       **79.** $6^8 = a + 1$

**4 Practice**

**ASSIGNMENT GUIDE**
Basic: 12–43 all, 44–47, 58–61, 72–76 even
Average: 13–43 odd, 44–79
Advanced: 13–43 odd, 44–84
Standardized Test Prep: 85–88
Mixed Review: 89–98

**Reasoning** exercises have blue headings.

**Applications** exercises have red headings.

**EXERCISE 45:** Use the Think About a Plan worksheet in the **Practice and Problem Solving Workbook** (also available in the Teaching Resources in print and online) to further support students' development in becoming independent learners.

**HOMEWORK QUICK CHECK**
To check students' understanding of key skills and concepts, go over Exercises 13, 21, 44, 45, and 59.

**42.** translate the graph 5 units to the right and 3 units up

**43.** translate the graph 2 units to the left and 1 unit down

**44.** apple juice: acidic; buttermilk: acidic; cream: acidic; ketchup: acidic; shrimp sauce: basic; strained peas: acidic

**45.** $\approx 3.16 \times 10^{-9}$

**46.** $2^7 = 128$

**47.** $10^{-4} = 0.0001$

**48.** $6^1 = 6$     **49.** $4^0 = 1$

**50.** $7^5 = 16{,}807$

**51.** $2^{-1} = \frac{1}{2}$     **52.** $3^{-2} = \frac{1}{9}$

**53.** $10^1 = 10$     **54.** 0

**55.** $-2$     **56.** 1     **57.** 7

**58.** error in the second line. It should read $27^x = 3$; the correct answer is $\frac{1}{3}$.

**59.** First rewrite $y = \log_1 x$ as $1^y = x$. For any real number $y$, $x = 1$.

**60.** Answers may vary. Sample:
$y = \log_3 x$; $y = 3^x$

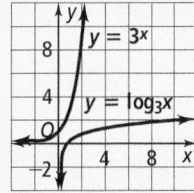

**61.** $y = 4^x$     **62.** $y = 0.5^x$

**63.** $y = 10^x$     **64.** $y = 2^{x-1}$

**65.** $y = 10^x - 1$     **66.** $y = 10^{x-1}$

**67.** $y = 2^{x-2}$     **68.** $y = 10^x + 6$

**69.**

**70.**

**71.**

**72.**

**73.** domain $x > 0$, range: all real numbers

**74.** domain $x > 0$, range: all real numbers

**75.** domain $x > 3$, range: all real numbers

**76.** domain $x > 2$, range: all real numbers

**77.** $4 = \log_3(81)$

**78.** $4 = \log_x(y)$

**79.** $8 = \log_6(a + 1)$

# Answers

## Practice and Problem-Solving Exercises
(continued)

**80.** 4

**81.** 3

**82.** 3

**83.** −2

**84. a.** II

   **b.** III

   **c.** I

## Standardized Test Prep

**85.** D

**86.** I

**87.** C

**88. [2]** $\sqrt[3]{(\sqrt{a})^7} = \left(\left(a^{\frac{1}{2}}\right)^7\right)^{\frac{1}{3}} = a^{\frac{7}{6}}$

   **[1]** correct answer, without work shown

## Mixed Review

**89.**

**90.**

**91.**

**92.** $(2x - 3)(2x - 1)$

**93.** $4(b - 5)(b + 5)$

**94.** $(5x - 2)(x + 3)$

**95.** 2

**96.** 256

**97.** $\frac{1}{4}$

**98.** 12

---

**Challenge**   Find the least integer greater than each number. Do not use a calculator.

**80.** $\log_3 38$     **81.** $\log_{1.5} 2.5$     **82.** $\log_{\sqrt{7}} \sqrt{50}$     **83.** $\log_5 \frac{1}{47}$

**84.** Match each function with the graph of its inverse.

  **a.** $y = \log_3 x$      **b.** $y = \log_2 4x$      **c.** $y = \log_{\frac{1}{2}} x$

  **I.**    **II.**    **III.**

## Standardized Test Prep

**SAT/ACT**

**85.** Which is the logarithmic form of the exponential equation $2^3 = 8$?

  Ⓐ $\log_8 2 = 3$     Ⓑ $\log_8 3 = 2$     Ⓒ $\log_3 8 = 2$     Ⓓ $\log_2 8 = 3$

**86.** Dan will begin advertising his video production business online using a pay-per-click method, which charges $30 as an initial fee, plus a fixed amount each time the ad is clicked. Dan estimates that with the cost of 8 cents per click, his ad will be clicked about 150 times per day. Which expression represents Dan's total estimated cost of advertising, in dollars, after $x$ days?

  Ⓕ $(30 + 0.08x)150$     Ⓖ $360x$     Ⓗ $30 + 1200x$     Ⓘ $30 + 12x$

**87.** Which translation takes $y = |x|$ to $y = |x + 3| - 1$?

  Ⓐ 3 units right, 1 unit down        Ⓒ 3 units left, 1 unit down

  Ⓑ 3 units right, 1 unit up         Ⓓ 3 units left, 1 unit up

**Short Response**

**88.** What is the expression $\sqrt[3]{(\sqrt{a})^7}$ written as a variable raised to a single rational exponent?

## Mixed Review

Graph each function.      ◀ **See Lesson 7-2.**

**89.** $y = 5^x - 100$      **90.** $y = -10(4)^{x+2}$      **91.** $y = -27(3)^{x-1} + 9$

Factor each expression.      ◀ **See Lesson 4-4.**

**92.** $4x^2 - 8x + 3$      **93.** $4b^2 - 100$      **94.** $5x^2 + 13x - 6$

**Get Ready!**  **To prepare for Lesson 7-4, do Exercises 95–98.**      ◀ **See Lesson 1-3.**

Evaluate each expression for the given value of the variable.

**95.** $x^2 - x; x = 2$     **96.** $x^3 \cdot x^5; x = 2$     **97.** $\frac{x^8}{x^{10}}; x = 2$     **98.** $x^3 + x^2; x = 2$

# Lesson Resources

## Additional Instructional Support

### Algebra 2 Companion
Students can use the **Algebra 2 Companion** worktext (4 pages) as you teach the lesson. Use the Companion to support

- New Vocabulary
- Key Concepts
- Got It for each Problem
- Lesson Check

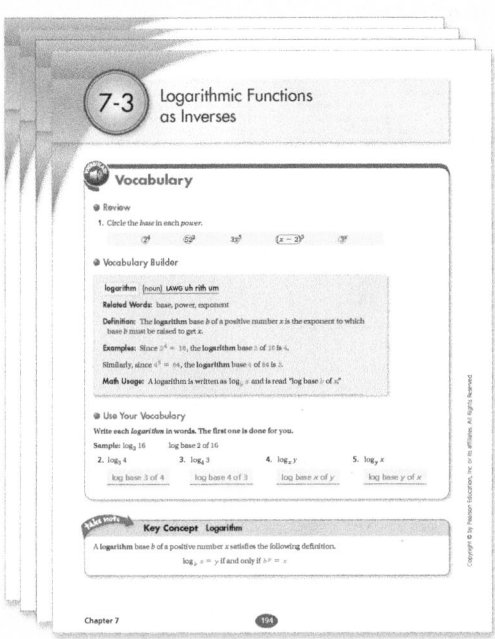

### ELL Support
**Connect to Prior Knowledge** Have a volunteer graph the exponential function $y = 5^x$ on the board. Have students name points that appear on the exponential graph to help the volunteer graph $y = \log_5 x$. Have the class explain how each property of the graph of $y = \log_5 x$ is related to the graph of $y = 5^x$, including the domain, range, intercepts, and asymptotes.

Have another volunteer graph the exponential function $y = 4^x$ and this time reflect the graph over the line $y = x$ to find the graph of $y = \log_4 x$. Ask how the graph of $y = \log_4 x$. compares to the graph of $y = \log_5 x$. Ask students to specifically identify why the graphs have the same intercepts and asymptotes and why $\log_4 x < \log_5 x$ when $x < 1$.

## 5 Assess & Remediate

### Lesson Quiz
1. What is the logarithmic form of $144 = 12^2$?
2. What is the value of $\log_9 27$?
3. **Do you UNDERSTAND?** The pH of a substance equals $-\log [\text{H}^+]$, where $[\text{H}^+]$ is the concentration of hydrogen ions. $[\text{H}^+]$ for tomato juice is $10^{-4}$. What is the pH of tomato juice?
4. What is the graph of $y = \log_5 x$? Describe the domain and range, and identify the $y$-intercept and the asymptote.
5. How does the graph of $y = 2\log (x + 5)$ compare to the graph of the parent function?

### ANSWERS TO LESSON QUIZ
1. $\log_{12}144 = 2$
2. $\frac{3}{2}$
3. 4
4.  domain: all positive real numbers; range: all real numbers; $y$-intercept: does not exist; asymptote: $x = 0$
5. The graph is stretched by a factor of 2 and translated to the left 5 units.

### PRESCRIPTION FOR REMEDIATION
Use the student work on the Lesson Quiz to prescribe a differentiated review assignment:

| Points | Differentiated Remediation |
|--------|---------------------------|
| 0–2 | Intervention |
| 3–4 | On-level |
| 5 | Extension |

**PowerAlgebra.com**

### 5 Assess & Remediate
Assign the Lesson Quiz. Appropriate intervention, practice, or enrichment is automatically generated based on student performance.

## Intervention

- **Reteaching** (2 pages) Provides reteaching and practice exercises for the key lesson concepts. Use with struggling students or absent students.
- **English Language Learner Support** Helps students develop and reinforce mathematical vocabulary and key concepts.

**All-in-One Resources/Online**
**Reteaching**

7-3 Reteaching
Logarithmic Functions as Inverses

A logarithmic function is the inverse of an exponential function.
To evaluate logarithmic expressions, use the fact that $x = \log_b y$ is the same as $y = b^x$. Keep in mind that $x = \log y$ is another way of writing $x = \log_{10} y$.

**Problem**
What is the logarithmic form of $6^3 = 216$?

**Step 1** Determine which equation to use.
The equation is in the form $b^x = y$.
**Step 2** Find $x$, $y$, and $b$.
$b = 6$, $x = 3$, and $y = 216$
**Step 3** Because $y = b^x$ is the same as $x = \log_b y$, rewrite the equation in logarithmic form by substituting for $x$, $y$, and $b$.
$3 = \log_6 216$

**Exercises**
Write each equation in logarithmic form.
1. $4^{-3} = \frac{1}{64}$  2. $5^{-2} = \frac{1}{25}$  3. $8^{-1} = \frac{1}{8}$  4. $11^0 = 1$
   $\log_4 \frac{1}{64} = -3$   $\log_5 \frac{1}{25} = -2$   $\log_8 \frac{1}{8} = -1$   $\log_{11} 1 = 0$
5. $6^1 = 6$  6. $6^{-3} = \frac{1}{216}$  7. $17^0 = 1$  8. $17^1 = 17$
   $\log_6 6 = 1$   $\log_6 \frac{1}{216} = -3$   $\log_{17} 1 = 0$   $\log_{17} 17 = 1$

**Problem**
What is the exponential form of $4 = \log_5 625$?

**Step 1** Determine which equation to use.
The equation is in the form $x = \log_b y$.
**Step 2** Find $x$, $y$, and $b$.
$x = 4$, $b = 5$, and $y = 625$
**Step 3** Because $x = \log_b y$ is the same as $y = b^x$, rewrite the equation in exponential form by substituting for $x$, $y$, and $b$.
$625 = 5^4$

**All-in-One Resources/Online**
**English Language Learner Support**

7-3 ELL Support
Logarithmic Functions as Inverses

For Exercises 1–3, draw a line from each word or phrase in Column A to the matching item in Column B.

Column A
1. logarithmic function
2. common logarithm
3. logarithmic scale

Column B
A. a logarithm with base 10
B. the inverse of an exponential function
C. uses the logarithm of a quantity instead of the quantity itself

For Exercises 4–9, draw a line from each word or phrase in Column A to the matching item in Column B.

Column A
4. parent function
5. stretch
6. compression
7. reflection in $x$-axis
8. translation 3 units to the right
9. translation 3 units downward

Column B
A. $y = 0.75\log_4 x$
B. $y = 5\log_4 x$
C. $y = \log_4 x - 3$
D. $y = \log_4 x$
E. $y = -\log_4 x$
F. $y = \log_4 (x - 3)$

# Differentiated Remediation *continued*

Available in editable format online.

## On-Level

- **Practice** (2 pages) Provides extra practice for each lesson. For simpler practice exercises, use the Form K Practice pages found in the All-in-One Teaching Resources and online.

- **Think About a Plan** Helps students develop specific problem-solving skills and strategies by providing scaffolded guiding questions.
- **Standardized Test Prep** Focuses on all major exercises, all major question types, and helps students prepare for the high-stakes assessments.

## Extension

- **Enrichment** Provides students with interesting problems and activities that extend the concepts of the lesson.
- **Activities, Games, and Puzzles** Worksheets that can be used for concepts development, enrichment, and for fun!

---

### Practice and Problem Solving Wkbk/ All-in-One Resources/Online
#### Practice page 1

**7-3 Practice** — Form G
Logarithmic Functions as Inverses

Write each equation in logarithmic form.

1. $9^2 = 81$  $\log_9 81 = 2$
2. $\frac{1}{64} = \left(\frac{1}{4}\right)^3$  $\log_{\frac{1}{4}}\left(\frac{1}{64}\right) = 3$
3. $8^3 = 512$  $\log_8 512 = 3$
4. $\left(\frac{1}{3}\right)^{-2} = 9$  $\log_{\frac{1}{3}} 9 = -2$

5. $2^9 = 512$  $\log_2 512 = 9$
6. $4^5 = 1024$  $\log_4 1024 = 5$
7. $5^4 = 625$  $\log_5 625 = 4$
8. $10^{23} = 0.001$  $\log_{10} 0.001 = -3$

Evaluate each logarithm.

9. $\log_2 128$  7
10. $\log_4 32$  $\frac{5}{2}$
11. $\log_9 (27)$  $\frac{3}{2}$
12. $\log_2 (-32)$  undefined

13. $\log_3 \frac{1}{9}$  -2
14. $\log 100{,}000$  5
15. $\log_7 7^6$  6
16. $\log_3 \frac{1}{81}$  -4

In 2004, an earthquake of magnitude 7.0 shook Papua, Indonesia. Compare the intensity level of that earthquake to the intensity level of each earthquake below.

17. magnitude 6.1 in Costa Rica, in 2009
The Papua earthquake was about 8 times as strong as the Costa Rica earthquake.

18. magnitude 5.1 in Greece, in 2008
The Papua earthquake was about 79 times as strong as the Greece earthquake.

19. magnitude 7.8 in the Fiji Islands, in 2007
The Fiji Islands earthquake was about 6 times as strong as the Papua earthquake.

20. magnitude 8.3 in the Kuril Islands, in 2006
The Kuril Islands earthquake was about 20 times as strong as the Papua earthquake.

Graph each logarithmic function.

21. $y = \log x$
22. $y = \log_3 x$
23. $y = \log_6 x$

---

### Practice and Problem Solving Wkbk/ All-in-One Resources/Online
#### Practice page 2

**7-3 Practice** (continued) — Form G
Logarithmic Functions as Inverses

Describe how the graph of each function compares with the graph of the parent function, $y = \log_b x$.

24. $y = \log_6 x - 2$  translates 2 units down

25. $y = \log_5 (x - 2)$  translates 2 units to the right

26. $y = \log_6 (x + 1) - 5$  translates 1 unit to the left and 5 units down

27. $y = \log_2 (x - 4) + 1$  translates 4 units to the right and 1 unit up

Write each equation in exponential form.

28. $\log_4 256 = 4$  $4^4 = 256$
29. $\log_7 1 = 0$  $7^0 = 1$
30. $\log_2 32 = 5$  $2^5 = 32$

31. $\log 10 = 1$  $10^1 = 10$
32. $\log_5 5 = 1$  $5^1 = 5$
33. $\log_8 \frac{1}{64} = -2$  $8^{-2} = \frac{1}{64}$

34. $\log_5 59{,}049 = 5$  $5^5 = 59{,}049$
35. $\log_{17} 289 = 2$  $17^2 = 289$
36. $\log_{60} 1 = 0$  $56^0 = 1$

37. $\log_{12} \frac{144}{144} = -2$  $12^{-2} = \frac{1}{144}$
38. $\log_2 \frac{1024}{2} = -10$  $2^{-10} = \frac{1}{1024}$
39. $\log_3 6561 = 8$  $3^8 = 6561$

40. A single-celled bacterium divides every hour. The number $N$ of bacteria after $t$ hours is given by the formula $\log_2 N = t$. After how many hours will there be 32 bacteria?  5 hours

For each pH given, find the concentration of hydrogen ions $[H^+]$. Use the formula $pH = -\log[H^+]$.

41. $7.2$  $6.3 \times 10^{-8}$
42. $7.3$  $5.0 \times 10^{-8}$
43. $8.2$  $6.3 \times 10^{-9}$
44. $6.2$  $6.3 \times 10^{-7}$

45. $5.6$  $2.5 \times 10^{-6}$
46. $4.6$  $2.5 \times 10^{-5}$
47. $7.0$  $1.0 \times 10^{-7}$
48. $2.9$  $1.3 \times 10^{-3}$

Find the inverse of each function.

49. $y = \log_2 x$  $y = 2^x$
50. $y = \log_{0.7} x$  $y = (0.7)^x$
51. $y = \log_{100} x$  $y = 10^{2x}$

52. $y = \log_8 x$  $y = 2^{3x}$
53. $y = \log_2 (4x)$  $y = 2^{x-2}$
54. $y = \log (x + 4)$  $y = 10^x - 4$

Find the domain and range of each function.

55. $y = \log_5 x - 2$
domain: $x > 0$; range: all real numbers
56. $y = 2\log_6 x$
domain: $x > 0$; range: all real numbers
57. $y = \log (x + 1)$
domain: $x > -1$; range: all real numbers

---

### All-in-One Resources/Online
#### Enrichment

**7-3 Enrichment**
Logarithmic Functions as Inverses

**Log Jams**

The logarithm is a tool originally developed and used to aid in calculations, yet this viewpoint of logarithms is not the only one of interest. Logarithms are also useful when thought of as real-valued functions, or as inverse functions of the corresponding exponential functions. The idea of a logarithm as an inverse function of an exponential function means that $\log_2 x$ is a question to be answered. For example, you can read the expression $\log_2 8$ as "what exponent on base 2 gives 8?" The answer is 3, because $2^3 = 8$.

Thinking of a logarithm as an exponent helps to order some logarithms without evaluating them. For example, the logarithms $\log_7 8$, $\log_7 7$, and $\log_7 6$ are in descending order since the exponent needed on base 7 that gives 8 would be greater than 1, and 1 is in turn greater than the exponent needed on base 7 that gives 6.

You can also compose logarithms as you would compose other functions, where their domain and ranges agree. Thus, you evaluate $\log_4 (\log_5 25)$ by evaluating $\log_5 25 = 2$, then evaluating $\log_4 2 = \frac{1}{2}$.

Rewrite each equation in exponential form to solve the equation.

1. Solve for $x$: $\log_3 81 = 4$  3
2. Solve for $x$: $\log_x 2 = 2$  $\sqrt{2}$
3. Which is greater, $\log_2 3$ or $\log_3 2$?  $\log_2 3$ is greater
4. Solve for $x$: $\log_x 3 = \frac{1}{3}$  3
5. Which is greater, $\frac{1}{3}\log_4 2$ or $\frac{1}{2}\log 10$?  $\frac{1}{2}\log 10$ is greater
6. Solve for $x$: $\log_2 (\log_2 x) = 2$  16
7. Which is greater, $\frac{1}{2}\log_2 (\log_3 8.5)$ or $\frac{1}{3}\log_3 (\log_2 8.5)$?  $\frac{1}{3}\log_3 (\log_2 8.5)$ is greater
8. Which of the following are equal? $\log \frac{1}{2}$ and $\log 1 - \log 2$ are equal
$\log\frac{1}{2}$     $\frac{\log 1}{\log 2}$     $\log 1 - \log 2$

Rewrite in exponential form and solve for $x$.

9. $\log_5 1 = x$  0
10. $\log_5 (2x^2 - 7) = 0$  $-2, 2$
11. $\log_7 7 = 1$  7
12. $\log_x 2^2 = 2$  $\sqrt{2}$
13. $\log_3 1 = x$  0
14. $\log_{17} 17 = x$  1
15. $\log_5 3^4 = 1$  81
16. $\log_x 5 = 0$  1
17. $\log_5 3^2 = x$  2
18. $\log_4 (x + 1) = 0$  0
19. $1 + \log_6 (x - 1) = 1$  2
20. $-1 + \log x = -1$  1

---

### Practice and Problem Solving Wkbk/ All-in-One Resources/Online
#### Think About a Plan

**7-3 Think About a Plan**
Logarithmic Functions as Inverses

**Chemistry** Find the concentration of hydrogen ions in seawater, if the pH level of seawater is 8.5.

**Understanding the Problem**

1. What is the pH of seawater?  8.5

2. How do you represent the concentration of hydrogen ions?  $H^+$

3. What is the problem asking you to determine?
the concentration of hydrogen ions in seawater

**Planning the Solution**

4. Write the formula for the pH of a substance.  $pH = -\log[H^+]$

5. Write an equation relating the pH of seawater to the concentration of hydrogen ions in seawater.  $8.5 = -\log[H^+]$

**Getting an Answer**

6. Solve your equation to find the concentration of hydrogen ions in seawater.
$8.5 = -\log[H^+]$
$-8.5 = \log[H^+]$
$10^{-8.5} = 10^{\log[H^+]}$
$10^{-8.5} = [H^+]$
$[H^+] = 10^{-8.5}$ or $3.16 \times 10^{-9}$

---

### Practice and Problem Solving Wkbk/ All-in-One Resources/Online
#### Standardized Test Prep

**7-3 Standardized Test Prep**
Logarithmic Functions as Inverses

**Multiple Choice**

For Exercises 1–4, choose the correct letter.

1. Which of the following is the logarithmic form of the equation $4^{-3} = \frac{1}{64}$?  C
  Ⓐ $\log_{-3}\left(\frac{1}{64}\right) = 4$
  Ⓒ $\log_4 \left(\frac{1}{64}\right) = -3$
  Ⓑ $\log_{-3} 4 = \frac{1}{64}$
  Ⓓ $\log_4 \frac{1}{64} = -3$

2. What is the value of $\log_2 8$?  I
  Ⓕ 64
  Ⓗ 16
  Ⓖ 8
  Ⓘ 3

3. How does the graph of $y = \log_6 (x - 3)$ compare with the graph of the parent function, $y = \log_6 x$?  C
  Ⓐ translated 3 units to the left
  Ⓒ translated 3 units to the right
  Ⓑ translated 3 units down
  Ⓓ translated 3 units up

4. In 2009, an earthquake of magnitude 6.7 shook the Kermadec Islands off the coast of New Zealand. Also in 2009, an earthquake of magnitude 5.1 occurred in the Alaska Peninsula. How many times stronger was the Kermadec earthquake than the Alaska earthquake?  F
  Ⓕ 39.811
  Ⓗ 5.77
  Ⓖ 20.593
  Ⓘ 0.025

**Short Response**

5. A single-celled bacterium divides every hour. The number $N$ of bacteria after $t$ hours is given by the formula $\log_2 N = t$.
a. After how many hours will there be 64 bacteria?
b. Explain in words or show work for how you determined the number of hours.

[2] a. 6 hours
b. $\log_2 N = t$ can be written in the exponential form $2^t = N$. Substituting 64 for N, the equation becomes $2^t = 64$. Rewriting 64 with base 2, the equation becomes $2^t = 2^6$. Since the bases are equal, $t = 6$.
[1] incorrect exponential form OR incorrect explanation
[0] incorrect answers and no explanation OR no answers given

---

### Online Teacher Resource Center
#### Activities, Games, and Puzzles

**7-3 Puzzle: Evaluating Logs**
Logarithmic Functions as Inverses

The puzzle at the bottom of the page has been separated into twelve sections. Each section contains three squares. In each section, there is a number in a circle. This tells you the sum of the two numbers in the section's empty squares. All missing numbers are natural numbers: 1, 2, 3, . . . Additional instructions (A–L) are given for each section of missing numbers.

For example, look at the section marked by Ⓐ. The sum of the two missing numbers in the empty squares is 11. Complete each equation with numbers that meet the requirements for each given section, and then place them in the puzzle.

A. $\log_3 \underline{8} = \underline{3}$
B. $\log_5 25 = \underline{2}$
C. $\log_3 \underline{27} = \underline{3}$
D. $\log_5 \underline{125} = \underline{3}$
E. $\log_{10} 10 = \underline{1}$
F. $\log_2 32 = \underline{5}$
G. $\log_7 \underline{49} = \underline{2}$
H. $\log_2 \underline{16} = \underline{8}$
I. $\log_4 \underline{64} = \underline{3}$
J. $\log_3 \underline{81} = 4$
K. $\log_2 \underline{32} = 5$
L. $\log_5 \underline{25} = 2$

**Final Question:** Use four letters from the puzzle to find the value of $\log_2 \sqrt{2}$.
"ONE-HALF"

---

# Fitting Curves to Data

## Example 1

**Which type of function models the data best—linear, logarithmic, or exponential?**

Connect the points with a smooth curve. Since the points do not fall along a line, the function is not linear. The graph appears to approach a horizontal asymptote, so an exponential function models the data best.

## Example 2

**Which type of function models the data best—quadratic, logarithmic, or cubic?**

**Step 1** Press (stat) (enter) to enter the data in lists.

**Step 2** Use the (stat plot) feature to draw a scatter plot.

**Step 3** If you connect the points with a smooth curve, the end behavior of the graph is up and up. The graph is not cubic or logarithmic, so the quadratic function best models the data.

| x | y |
|---|-----|
| 0 | 14 |
| 1 | 7.5 |
| 2 | 4 |
| 3 | 1.8 |
| 4 | 1.8 |
| 5 | 3.9 |

## Exercises

1. Which type of function models the data shown in the graphing calculator screen best—*linear, quadratic, logarithmic, cubic,* or *exponential*?

2. Which type of function models the data in the table best—*linear, quadratic, logarithmic, cubic,* or *exponential*?

| x | y |
|----|------|
| −1 | 0 |
| 1 | 1.4 |
| 3 | 2.09 |
| 5 | 2.53 |
| 7 | 2.81 |
| 9 | 3.12 |

3. **Reasoning** Could you use a different model for the data in Exercises 1 and 2? Explain.

# Guided Instruction

**PURPOSE** To fit data to a curve and extrapolate to find a new point that fits the data

**PROCESS** Students will

- connect data points to determine the type of function that models the data.
- use the **STAT PLOT** feature on a calculator to graph a table of data and regression features to find the best-fitting function.
- use the model to extrapolate a new point that fits the data.

**DISCUSS** The purpose of fitting a curve to data is to *approximate* a function that has the points on its graph. Sometimes not all of the points will lie exactly on the curve. Not all data will have a reasonable model of linear, quadratic, logarithmic, or exponential type.

> **Q** If a set of data is always increasing, could the best-fitting curve be a parabola? **[Yes; the curve that fits the data could be the increasing portion of an upward-facing parabola.]**

## Example 1

> **Q** Why is a linear function not a reasonable model? **[Answers may vary. Sample: The slope of the model is not constant because the ratio of the change in *x*-values to the change in *y*-values is not constant.]**

## Example 2                              VISUAL LEARNERS

> **Q** How can you tell by looking at the table that the function that models the graph is not logarithmic? **[The *y*-values decrease and then increase. A logarithmic function is always increasing or always decreasing.]**

# Answers

## Concept Byte

**1.** cubic

**2.** quadratic

**3.** Yes; problem 1 could also be linear with outliers; problem 2 could also be linear or cubic. They cannot be logarithmic due to negative values.

## Example 3

When the ExpReg feature on the calculator is used, the function that models the data is not given in explicit form. The feature reads the data listed in the table and returns the constants $a$ and $b$ that define the function $y = ab^x$.

**Q** Do you think you can make a reasonable prediction about the bacteria population 10 days from now? Explain. **[No; the data only covers the population growth over 10 hours. The model may not continue to be reasonable for the much larger time period of 10 days.]**

## Exercises SYNTHESIS

For Exercises 4–7, either a quadratic or an exponential function could be used to model the graph. The exponential model would consist of only half of the parabola. Choose which function to use based on which models the graph of the points most closely.

**Q** Why is the scale of the axes in the graph important? How can you choose an appropriate scale? **[To see the shape of the curve, the scale must be adjusted so that the points are not clustered too closely on the x- or y-axis. The range of each axis should be slightly larger than the range of the x- and y-values of the data points.]**

**Q** In Exercise 5, do you think that the quadratic or exponential function would predict a larger y-value for the model when x = 9? Why? **[The exponential model, because exponential functions increase more rapidly than quadratic functions.]**

---

## Example 3

The table shows the number of bacteria in a culture after the given number of hours. Find a good model for the data. Based on the model, how many bacteria will be in the culture after an additional ten hours?

| Hour | Bacteria |
| --- | --- |
| 1 | 2205 |
| 2 | 2270 |
| 3 | 2350 |
| 4 | 2653 |
| 5 | 3052 |
| 6 | 3417 |
| 7 | 3890 |
| 8 | 4522 |
| 9 | 5107 |
| 10 | 5724 |

**Step 1** Press **stat** **enter** to enter the data in lists. Use the **stat plot** feature to draw a scatter plot.

**Step 2** Notice from the scatter plot that the data appears exponential. Find the equations for the best-fitting exponential function. Press **stat** ▷ **0** to use the **ExpReg** feature.

$$y = 1779.404(1.121)^x$$

**Step 3** Graph the function. Press **y=** **clear** **vars** **5** ▷ ▷ **enter** to enter the **ExpReg** results. Press **graph** to display the function and the scatter plot together. Press **zoom** **9** to automatically adjust the window.

**Step 4** In 10 more hours, there will be approximately $y = 1779.404(1.121)^{20} \approx 17{,}474$ bacteria in the culture.

## Exercises

Use a graphing calculator to find the exponential or quadratic function that best fits each set of data. Graph each function.

**4.**

| x | y |
| --- | --- |
| −1 | 4.9 |
| 0 | 3.8 |
| 1 | 5.0 |
| 2 | 8.1 |
| 3 | 13.3 |
| 4 | 70.2 |

**5.**

| x | y |
| --- | --- |
| −3 | 0.1 |
| −1 | 0.4 |
| 1 | 1.6 |
| 3 | 6.4 |
| 5 | 25.6 |
| 7 | 102.4 |

**6.**

| x | y |
| --- | --- |
| 1 | 3.5 |
| 2 | 2.11 |
| 3 | 1.30 |
| 4 | 0.73 |
| 5 | 0.28 |
| 6 | 0.08 |

**7.**

| x | y |
| --- | --- |
| −1 | 0.04 |
| 0 | 0.1 |
| 1 | 0.5 |
| 2 | 2.5 |
| 3 | 12.5 |
| 4 | 62.5 |

**8. Writing** In Exercise 6 the function appears to level off. Explain why.

**9.** Find a quadratic model for the data in Exercise 6. Compare the graphs of the quadratic and exponential models for this data. Predict the y-values for both models when x = −2. Discuss the differences if any between the predictions.

---

# Answers

## Concept Byte (continued)

**4.** $y = 5.46x^2 - 6.16x - 1.44$

**5.** $y = 0.8(2)^x$

**6.** $y = 0.13x^2 - 1.59x + 4.88$

**7.** $y = 0.13(4.5)^x$

**8.** $x = 0$ is an asymptote.

**9.** quadratic model: $y \approx 2.03x^2 + 0.34x - 9.72$, $f(-2) = -2.28$; exponential model: $y = 0.8(2)^x$; $f(-2) = 0.2$; The exponential model is the best fit.

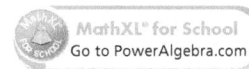
MathXL® for School
Go to PowerAlgebra.com

### Do you know HOW?

Determine whether each function is an example of exponential growth or decay. Then find the y-intercept.

**1.** $y = 100(0.25)^x$ **2.** $y = 0.6\left(\frac{1}{10}\right)^x$ **3.** $y = \frac{7}{8}(18)^x$

Graph each function. Then find the domain, range, and y-intercept.

**4.** $y = -4(2)^x$ **5.** $y = \frac{1}{4}(10)^x$ **6.** $y = 8(0.25)^x$

**7. Investment** Suppose you deposit $600 into a savings account that pays 3.9% annual interest. How much will you have in the account after 3 years if no money is added or withdrawn?

**8. Depreciation** The initial value of a car is $25,000. After one year, the value of the car is $21,250. Write an exponential function to model the expected value of the car. Estimate the value of the car after 5 years.

Graph each function as a transformation of its parent function. Write the parent function.

**9.** $y = 3^x - 2$ **10.** $y = \frac{1}{2}(5)^{x-1} + 4$

**11.** $y = -(0.5)^{x+3}$ **12.** $y = -6\left(\frac{3}{4}\right)^x - 10$

Evaluate each expression to four decimal places.

**13.** $e^5$ **14.** $e^{\frac{3}{2}}$ **15.** $e^{-4}$

Find the amount in a continuously compounded account for the given conditions.

**16.** principal: $500; annual interest rate: 4.9%; time: 2.5 years

**17.** principal: $6000; annual interest rate: 6.8%; time: 10 years

Write each equation in logarithmic form.

**18.** $10^4 = 10,000$ **19.** $\frac{1}{4} = 4^{-1}$ **20.** $8 = \left(\frac{1}{2}\right)^{-3}$

Evaluate each logarithm.

**21.** $\log_8 64$ **22.** $\log_4(256)$ **23.** $\log_{\frac{1}{5}} 625$

Graph each logarithmic function. Find the domain and range.

**24.** $y = \log_5(x - 1)$ **25.** $y = 4 \log x + 5$

**26. Crafts** For glass to be shaped, its temperature must stay above 1200°F. The temperature of a piece of glass is 2200°F when it comes out of the furnace. The table shows temperature readings for the glass. Write an exponential model for this data set and then find how long it takes for the piece of glass to cool to 1200°F.

| Time (min) | Temp (°F) |
|---|---|
| 0 | 2200 |
| 5 | 1700 |
| 10 | 1275 |
| 15 | 1000 |
| 20 | 850 |
| 25 | 650 |

### Do you UNDERSTAND?

**27. Error Analysis** A student claims the y-intercept of the graph of the function $y = ab^x$ is the point $(0, b)$. What is the student's mistake? What is the actual y-intercept?

**28. Writing** Without graphing, how can you tell whether an exponential function represents exponential growth or exponential decay?

**29. Compare and Contrast** Compare the graph of $y = \log_3(x + 1)$ to the graph of its inverse $y = 3^x - 1$. How are the graphs alike? How are they different?

**30. Vocabulary** Explain how the continuously compounded interest formula differs from the annually compounded interest formula.

**7.** $672.97

**8.** $y = 25000(0.85)^x$; $11,093

**9.** $y = 3^x - 2$

**10.** $y = 5^x$

**11.** $y = -(0.5)^x$

**12.** $y = \left(\frac{3}{4}\right)^x$

**13.** $\approx 148.4132$ **14.** $\approx 4.4817$

**15.** $\approx 0.0183$ **16.** $565.16

**17.** $11,843.27 **18.** $\log 10000 = 4$

**19.** $\log_4 \frac{1}{4} = -1$ **20.** $\log_{\frac{1}{2}} 8 = -3$

**21.** 2 **22.** 4 **23.** $-4$

**24–30.** See back of book.

## Answers

**1.** exponential decay; 100

**2.** exponential decay; 0.6

**3.** exponential growth; $\frac{7}{8}$

**4.** domain: all real numbers; range: $y < 0$; y-intercept: $(0, -4)$
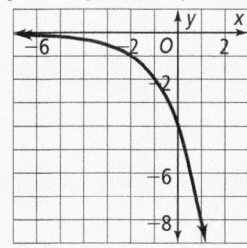

**5.** domain: all real numbers; range: $y > 0$; y-intercept: $\left(0, \frac{1}{4}\right)$

**6.** domain: all real numbers; range: $y > 0$; y-intercept: $(0, 8)$

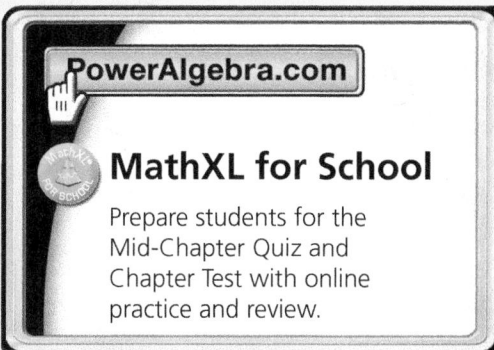
**PowerAlgebra.com**
**MathXL for School**
Prepare students for the Mid-Chapter Quiz and Chapter Test with online practice and review.

# 1 Interactive Learning

## Solve It!

**PURPOSE** To introduce the properties of logarithms by using the inverse relationship between exponential and logarithmic functions

**PROCESS** Students may use a calculator to perform the series of operations and to graph the series of operations as a single function: $y = \sqrt{\dfrac{10^{1+2\log x}}{10}}$.

### FACILITATE

**Q** The series of operations returns the starting number for all positive numbers. How is this possible? **[Each step is undone later by an inverse operation.]**

**Q** Which step undoes the common logarithm? Which step does taking the square root undo? **[the exponential function with base 10; the multiplication step and part of the addition step]**

**ANSWER** See Solve It in Answers on next page.

**CONNECT THE MATH** The Solve It uses the inverse relationship of exponents and logarithms. The lesson shows that the properties of logarithms correspond to the properties of exponents.

# 2 Guided Instruction

## Here's Why It Works

**Q** What property of exponents can be used to simplify $a^5 b^4$? $(a^3)^2$? $\dfrac{a^6}{a^2}$? **[Product Property; Power Property; Quotient Property]**

## Take Note

**Q** When do these properties apply? **[Sample: when all of the logarithms have a common base]**

---

**Objective** To use the properties of logarithms

Getting Ready!

Write a positive number on a piece of paper. Key this number into your calculator and press _enter_. Then perform the steps shown here. Press _enter_ after each line. Do you recognize the number that results? Explain why this result makes sense.

log (Ans)
2 * Ans
Ans + 4
10^Ans
√(Ans)
Ans/100

Press enter after each step.

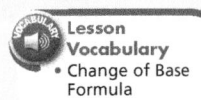

**Lesson Vocabulary**
• Change of Base Formula

You can derive the properties of logarithms from the properties of exponents.

**Essential Understanding** Logarithms and exponents have corresponding properties.

**Here's Why It Works** You can use a product property of exponents to derive a product property of logarithms.

Let $x = \log_b m$ and $y = \log_b n$.

| | |
|---|---|
| $m = b^x$ and $n = b^y$ | Definition of logarithm |
| $mn = b^x \cdot b^y$ | Write $mn$ as a product of powers. |
| $mn = b^{x+y}$ | Product Property of Exponents |
| $\log_b mn = x + y$ | Definition of logarithm |
| $\log_b mn = \log_b m + \log_b n$ | Substitute for $x$ and $y$. |

**take note**

**Properties** Properties of Logarithms

For any positive numbers $m$, $n$, and $b$ where $b \neq 1$, the following properties apply.

**Product Property** $\qquad \log_b mn = \log_b m + \log_b n$

**Quotient Property** $\qquad \log_b \dfrac{m}{n} = \log_b m - \log_b n$

**Power Property** $\qquad \log_b m^n = n \log_b m$

---

**BIG** ideas **Equivalence**
  **Function**
  **Modeling**

**UbD**

### ESSENTIAL UNDERSTANDINGS

• Logarithms and exponents have corresponding properties.

• An exponential function is a function with the general form $y = ab^x$, $a \neq 0$, with $b > 0$, and $b \neq 1$. In an exponential function, the base $b$ is a constant. The exponent $x$ is the independent variable with domain the set of real numbers.

### Math Background

The Product, Quotient, and Power Properties of Logarithms allow many expressions and equations to be simplified. For instance, the Power Property allows the equation $4 = 9^x$ to be solved for $x$:

$\log 4 = x \log 9$

$x = \dfrac{\log 4}{\log 9}$

Logarithmic expressions that you cannot simplify using the properties, however, are not always obvious to students.

• The logarithm function is not distributive over addition or subtraction. You cannot simplify the logarithm of a sum or difference using the Product or Quotient Properties.

$\log_b (x + y) \neq \log_b x + \log_b y$
$\log_b (x - y) \neq \log_b x - \log_b y$

• You cannot factor a quotient of logarithms.

$\dfrac{\log_b x}{\log_b y} \neq \log_b \dfrac{x}{y}$

• You cannot factor out a logarithm, except in the manner prescribed by the Product Property.

$\log_b 6 \neq 3 \log_b 2$
$\neq (\log_b 3)(\log_b 2)$

When a student makes one of these mistakes, show several examples with concrete numbers and a calculator.

### Support Student Learning

Use the **Algebra 2 Companion** to engage and support students during instruction. See Lesson Resources at the end of this lesson for details.

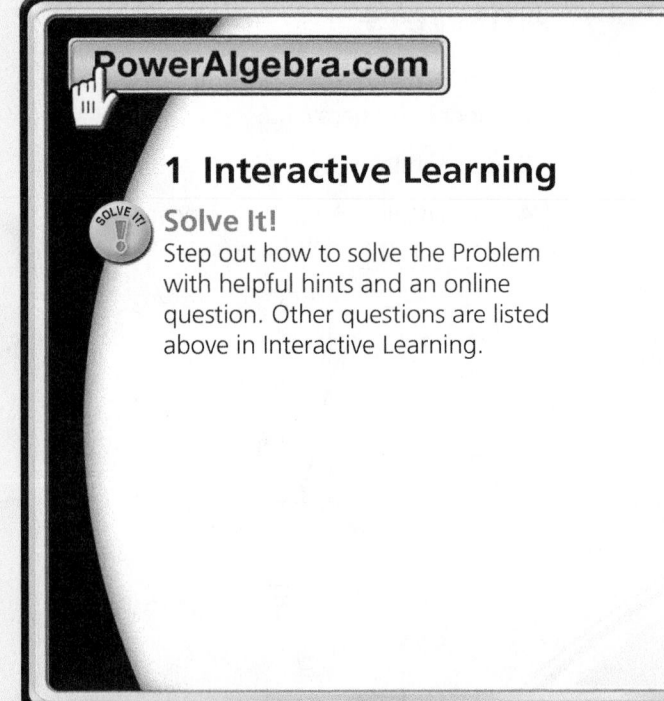

**PowerAlgebra.com**

# 1 Interactive Learning

## Solve It!

Step out how to solve the Problem with helpful hints and an online question. Other questions are listed above in Interactive Learning.

**Problem 1** Simplifying Logarithms

**What is each expression written as a single logarithm?**

**A** $\log_4 32 - \log_4 2$

$\log_4 32 - \log_4 2 = \log_4 \frac{32}{2}$     Quotient Property of Logarithms

$= \log_4 16$     Divide.

$= \log_4 4^2$     Write 16 as a power of 4.

$= 2$     Simplify.

**Think**

What must you do with the numbers that multiply the logarithms?
Apply the Power Property of Logarithms.

**B** $6 \log_2 x + 5 \log_2 y$

$6 \log_2 x + 5 \log_2 y = \log_2 x^6 + \log_2 y^5$     Power Property of Logarithms

$= \log_2 x^6 y^5$     Product Property of Logarithms

 **Got It?** 1. What is each expression written as a single logarithm?

    **a.** $\log_4 5x + \log_4 3x$            **b.** $2 \log_4 6 - \log_4 9$

You can expand a single logarithm to involve the sum or difference of two or more logarithms.

 **Problem 2** Expanding Logarithms

**What is each logarithm expanded?**

**A** $\log \frac{4x}{y}$

$\log \frac{4x}{y} = \log 4x - \log y$     Quotient Property of Logarithms

$= \log 4 + \log x - \log y$     Product Property of Logarithms

**Think**

Can you apply the Power Property of Logarithms first?
No; the fourth power applies only to $x$.

**B** $\log_9 \frac{x^4}{729}$

$\log_9 \frac{x^4}{729} = \log_9 x^4 - \log_9 729$     Quotient Property of Logarithms

$= 4 \log_9 x - \log_9 729$     Power Property of Logarithms

$= 4 \log_9 x - \log_9 9^3$     Write 729 as a power of 9.

$= 4 \log_9 x - 3$     Simplify.

 **Got It?** 2. What is each logarithm expanded?

    **a.** $\log_3 \frac{250}{37}$            **b.** $\log_3 9x^5$

---

## Problem 1

**Q** How can you use the Power Property to solve 1A? [Express 32 and 2 as powers of 4: $\log_4 4^{\frac{5}{2}} - \log_4 4^{\frac{1}{2}}$; use the Product Property: $\frac{5}{2} \log_4 4 - \frac{1}{2} \log_4 4$; Simplify: $\frac{5}{2} - \frac{1}{2} = 2$.]

### Got It?

**Q** What property of logarithms can be used to solve 1a? [**Product Property**]

## Problem 2

**Q** Is there a way to simplify $\log \frac{4x}{y}$ without using the Quotient Property? Explain. [**Yes;** answers may vary. Sample: Rewrite the expression with the $y$ term in the numerator: $\log 4xy^{-1}$. Use the Product Property: $\log 4 + \log x + \log y^{-1}$. Finally, use the Power Property and simplify: $\log 4 + \log x + (-1)\log y = \log 4 + \log x - \log y$.]

### Got It?     EXTENSION

**Q** How do you know that neither term in 2a will simplify to an integer? [**The number inside the logarithm must be a power of the base, so it must be divisible by the base. Neither 250 nor 37 is divisible by 3.**]

**Q** How many units and in what direction is the graph of $y = \log_3 9x$ translated compared with $y = \log_3 x$? [**two units up**]

---

## 2 Guided Instruction

 Each Problem is worked out and supported online.

**Problem 1**
Simplifying Logarithms
*Animated*

**Problem 2**
Expanding Logarithms
*Animated*

**Problem 3**
Using the Change of Base Formula
*Animated*

**Problem 4**
Using a Logarithmic Scale

**Support in Algebra 2 Companion**
• Vocabulary
• Key Concepts
• Got It?

---

# Answers

### Solve It!

You get the number that you wrote on paper;

$$\frac{10^{\frac{(2\log(x)) + 4}{2}}}{100} = \frac{10^{\log(x) + 2}}{100} = \frac{10^{\log(x)} \cdot 10^2}{100} = 10^{\log(x)} = x$$

### Got It?

**1. a.** $\log_4 15x^2$

    **b.** 1

**2. a.** $\log_3 2 + 3 \log_3 5 - \log_3 37$

    **b.** $2 + 5 \log_3 x$

## Take Note

**Q** How is this formula useful when you calculate a log with a calculator that only has keys for the common and natural logarithms? **[You can convert a logarithm with any base to a quotient of common or natural logarithms.]**

## Here's Why It Works

The Change of Base Formula can also be derived by setting $\log_b m = x$.

| | |
|---|---|
| $m = b^x$ | Definition of Logarithm |
| $\log_c m = \log_c b^x$ | Take logarithm base c of both sides. |
| $\log_c m = x\log_c b$ | Power Property of Logarithms |
| $x = \dfrac{\log_c m}{\log_c b}$ | Solve for x. |
| $\log_b m = \dfrac{\log_c m}{\log_c b}$ | Substitute $\log_b m$ for x. |

## Problem 3

**Q** Is 0.75 a reasonable answer for 3A? Explain. **[Yes; because $81^0 = 1$ and $81^1 = 81$, the answer should be between 0 and 1.]**

**Q** In 3B, how do you know that 36 and 5 have no common base? **[They have no common factor other than 1.]**

## Got It?

**Q** What base did you choose for 3a? **[Answers may vary. Sample: Base 2 because both 32 and 8 are powers of 2]**

---

You have seen logarithms with many bases. The **log** key on a calculator finds $\log_{10}$ of a number. To evaluate a logarithm with any base, use the **Change of Base Formula**.

**take note**

### Property  Change of Base Formula

For any positive numbers $m$, $b$, and $c$, with $b \neq 1$ and $c \neq 1$,

$$\log_b m = \frac{\log_c m}{\log_c b}.$$

### Here's Why It Works

$$\log_b m = \frac{(\log_b m)(\log_c b)}{\log_c b} \quad \text{Multiply } \log_b m \text{ by } \frac{\log_c b}{\log_c b} = 1.$$

$$= \frac{\log_c b^{\log_b m}}{\log_c b} \quad \text{Power Property of Logarithms}$$

$$= \frac{\log_c m}{\log_c b} \quad b^{\log_b m} = m$$

### Problem 3  Using the Change of Base Formula

**What is the value of each expression?**

**Think**
What common base has powers that equal 27 and 81?
3; $3^3 = 27$ and $3^4 = 81$.

**A** $\log_{81} 27$

**Method 1**  Use a common base.

$$\log_{81} 27 = \frac{\log_3 27}{\log_3 81} \quad \text{Change of Base Formula}$$

$$= \frac{3}{4} \quad \text{Simplify.}$$

**Method 2**  Use a calculator.

$$\log_{81} 27 = \frac{\log 27}{\log 81} \quad \text{Change of Base Formula}$$

$$= 0.75 \quad \text{Use a calculator.}$$

**Think**
What would be a reasonable result?
$5^2 = 25$ and $5^3 = 125$, so $\log_5 36$ should be between 2 and 3.

**B** $\log_5 36$

$$\log_5 36 = \frac{\log 36}{\log 5} \quad \text{Change of Base Formula}$$

$$\approx 2.23 \quad \text{Use a calculator to evaluate.}$$

**Got It?**  **3.** Use the Change of Base Formula. What is the value of each expression?

**a.** $\log_8 32$  **b.** $\log_4 18$

---

# Additional Problems

**1.** What is each expression written as a single logarithm? If possible, simplify the single logarithm.

**a.** $\log_3 x - 2 \log_3 7$

**b.** $\log_8 48 + \log_8 \frac{4}{3}$

**ANSWERS**

**a.** $\log_3 \frac{x}{49}$  **b.** 2

**2.** What is each logarithm expanded? Simplify your answer, if possible.

**a.** $\log_5 \frac{125}{xy}$

**b.** $\log x^2 y^2 z^{-1}$

**ANSWERS**

**a.** $3 - \log_5 x - \log_5 y$

**b.** $2 \log x + 2 \log y - \log z$

**3.** What is the value of each expression?

**a.** $\log_9 111$  **b.** $\log_{216} 36$

**ANSWERS**

**a.** about 2.14  **b.** $\frac{2}{3}$

**4.** The speed $s$ (in mi/h) of the wind near the center of a tornado is related to the distance $d$ (in miles) the tornado travels by $s = 93 \log d + 65$. What was the difference in speed between a tornado that traveled 16 mi and one that traveled 8 mi?

**ANSWER**  about 28 mi/h

---

# Answers

**Got It?** (continued)

**3. a.** $\frac{5}{3}$

**b.** $\approx 2.085$

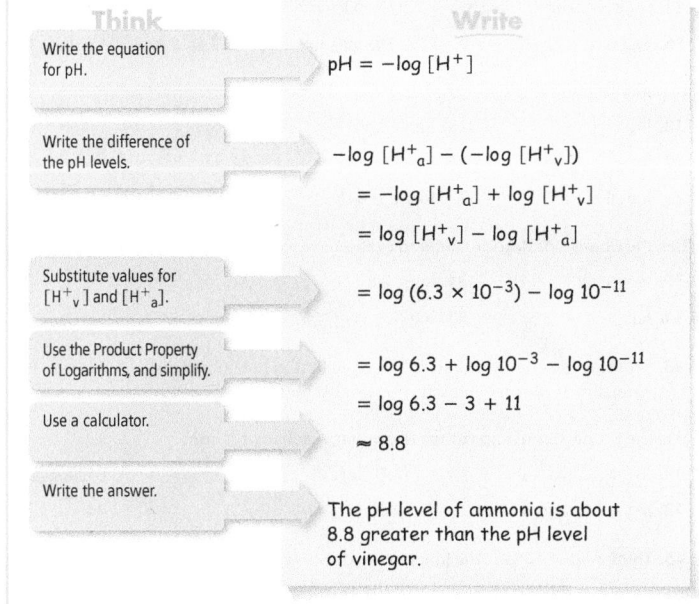

## Problem 4 Using a Logarithmic Scale

**Chemistry** The pH of a substance equals $-\log[H^+]$, where $[H^+]$ is the concentration of hydrogen ions. $[H^+_a]$ for household ammonia is $10^{-11}$. $[H^+_v]$ for vinegar is $6.3 \times 10^{-3}$. What is the difference of the pH levels of ammonia and vinegar?

**Think**

Write the equation for pH.

Write the difference of the pH levels.

Substitute values for $[H^+_v]$ and $[H^+_a]$.

Use the Product Property of Logarithms, and simplify.

Use a calculator.

Write the answer.

**Write**

$$pH = -\log[H^+]$$

$$-\log[H^+_a] - (-\log[H^+_v])$$
$$= -\log[H^+_a] + \log[H^+_v]$$
$$= \log[H^+_v] - \log[H^+_a]$$

$$= \log(6.3 \times 10^{-3}) - \log 10^{-11}$$

$$= \log 6.3 + \log 10^{-3} - \log 10^{-11}$$

$$= \log 6.3 - 3 + 11$$

$$\approx 8.8$$

The pH level of ammonia is about 8.8 greater than the pH level of vinegar.

**Got It?** **4. Reasoning** Suppose the hydrogen ion concentration for Substance A is twice that for Substance B. Which substance has the greater pH level? What is the greater pH level minus the lesser pH level? Explain.

## Lesson Check

**Do you know HOW?**

Write each expression as a single logarithm.

**1.** $\log_4 2 + \log_4 8$

**2.** $\log_6 24 - \log_6 4$

Expand each logarithm.

**3.** $\log_3 \frac{x}{y}$     **4.** $\log m^2 n^5$     **5.** $\log_2 \sqrt{x}$

**Do you UNDERSTAND?**

**6. Vocabulary** State which property or properties need to be used to write each expression as a single logarithm.

**a.** $\log_4 5 + \log_4 5$     **b.** $\log_5 4 - \log_5 6$

**7. Reasoning** If $\log x = 5$, what is the value of $\log \frac{1}{x}$?

**8. Open-Ended** Write log 150 as a sum or difference of two logarithms. Simplify if possible.

---

## Problem 4

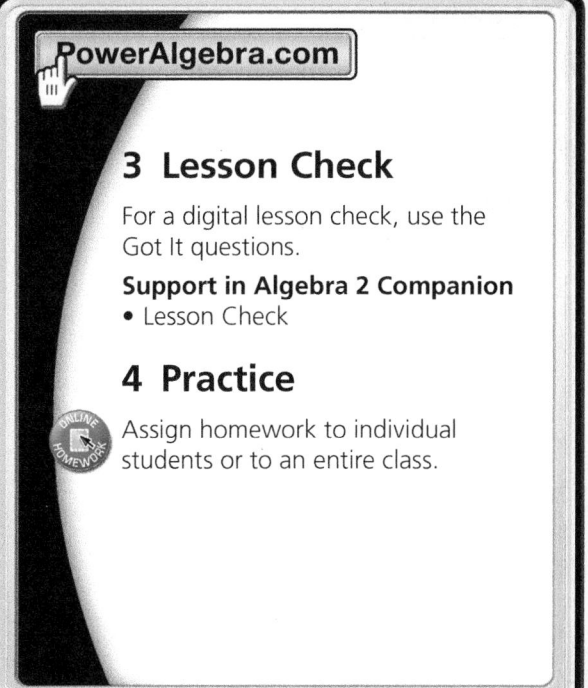

**Q** What does the 8.8 difference mean in terms of $[H^+]$ concentration? Why? **[Answers may vary. Sample: The 8.8 pH difference is on a logarithmic scale with base 10, so the concentration of $[H^+]$ in vinegar is $10^{8.8}$ (or 630,000,000) times that of the concentration of $[H^+]$ in ammonia.]**

**Q** The pH level of pure water is 7. What is the concentration of $[H^+]$ in pure water? Explain your method. **[Answers may vary. Sample: Write the formula: $pH = -\log[H^+]$; Substitute: $7 = -\log[H^+]$; Solve for $[H^+]$: $10^{-7} = [H^+]$.]**

### Got It?

Because the pH scale is a negative logarithmic scale, a smaller concentration of $[H^+]$ has a greater pH value than a larger concentration.

## 3 Lesson Check

### Do you know HOW?

- If students do not know how to proceed with Exercise 5, then remind them that $\sqrt{x} = x^{\frac{1}{2}}$.

### Do you UNDERSTAND?

- In Exercise 8, be sure that students separate out factors of 150 and not addends.

### Close

**Q** How can you derive the Power Property of Logarithms from the Power Property of Exponents? **[Sample: Let $x = \log_b m$; $m = b^x$ (Definition of Logarithm); $m^n = (b^x)^n$ (Raise each side to the $n$ power.); $m^n = b^{nx}$ (Power Property of Exponents); $\log_b m^n = nx$ (Definition of Logarithm); $\log_b m^n = n\log_b m$ (Substitute for $x$.)]**

---

---

**4.** Substance B; $\log 2$; $-\log[H^+_B] + \log[H^+_B] = \log 2$

### Lesson Check

**1.** $\log_4 16$

**2.** $\log_6 6$

**3.** $\log_3 x - \log_3 y$

**4.** $2\log m + 5\log n$

**5.** $\frac{1}{2}\log_2 x$

**6. a.** Product Prop. and Power Prop.
   **b.** Quotient Prop.

**7.** 0.00001

**8.** Answers may vary. Samples:
   $\log 150 = \log 25 + \log 6$

### PowerAlgebra.com

#### 3 Lesson Check

For a digital lesson check, use the Got It questions.

**Support in Algebra 2 Companion**
- Lesson Check

#### 4 Practice

Assign homework to individual students or to an entire class.

# 4 Practice

**ASSIGNMENT GUIDE**
Basic: 9–38 all, 43–47, 50–60 even
Average: 9–37 odd, 39–74
Advanced: 9–37 odd, 39–79
Standardized Test Prep: 80–83
Mixed Review: 84–95

Reasoning exercises have blue headings.

Applications exercises have red headings.

**EXERCISE 46:** Use the Think About a Plan worksheet in the **Practice and Problem Solving Workbook** (also available in the Teaching Resources in print and online) to further support students' development in becoming independent learners.

**HOMEWORK QUICK CHECK**
To check students' understanding of key skills and concepts, go over Exercises 9, 31, 45, 46, and 47.

---

## Practice and Problem-Solving Exercises

**A Practice**

Write each expression as a single logarithm. ◀ See Problem 1.

**9.** $\log 7 + \log 2$

**10.** $\log_2 9 - \log_2 3$

**11.** $5 \log 3 + \log 4$

**12.** $\log 8 - 2 \log 6 + \log 3$

**13.** $4 \log m - \log n$

**14.** $\log 5 - k \log 2$

**15.** $\log_6 5 + \log_6 x$

**16.** $\log_7 x + \log_7 y - \log_7 z$

**17.** $\log_3 4 + \log_3 y + \log_3 8x$

Expand each logarithm. ◀ See Problem 2.

**18.** $\log x^3 y^5$

**19.** $\log_7 49xyz$

**20.** $\log_b \frac{b}{x}$

**21.** $\log a^2$

**22.** $\log_5 \frac{r}{s}$

**23.** $\log_3 (2x)^2$

**24.** $\log_3 7(2x - 3)^2$

**25.** $\log \frac{a^2 b^3}{c^4}$

**26.** $\log_4 5\sqrt{x}$

**27.** $\log_8 8\sqrt{3a^5}$

**28.** $\log_5 \frac{25}{x}$

**29.** $\log 10m^4 n^{-2}$

Use the Change of Base Formula to evaluate each expression. ◀ See Problem 3.

**30.** $\log_2 9$

**31.** $\log_{12} 20$

**32.** $\log_7 30$

**33.** $\log_5 10$

**34.** $\log_4 7$

**35.** $\log_3 54$

**36.** $\log_5 62$

**37.** $\log_3 33$

**38. Science** The concentration of hydrogen ions in household dish detergent is $10^{-12}$. What is the pH level of household dish detergent? ◀ See Problem 4.

**B Apply**

Use the properties of logarithms to evaluate each expression.

**39.** $\log_2 4 - \log_2 16$

**40.** $\log_2 96 - \log_2 3$

**41.** $\log_3 27 - 2\log_3 3$

**42.** $\log_6 12 + \log_6 3$

**43.** $\log_4 48 - \frac{1}{2}\log_4 9$

**44.** $\frac{1}{2}\log_5 15 - \log_5 \sqrt{75}$

**45. Think About a Plan** The loudness in decibels (dB) of a sound is defined as $10 \log \frac{I}{I_0}$, where $I$ is the intensity of the sound in watts per square meter $(\text{W/m}^2)$. $I_0$, the intensity of a barely audible sound, is equal to $10^{-12} \text{ W/m}^2$. Town regulations require the loudness of construction work not to exceed 100 dB. Suppose a construction team is blasting rock for a roadway. One explosion has an intensity of $1.65 \times 10^{-2} \text{ W/m}^2$. Is this explosion in violation of town regulations?
- Which physical value do you need to calculate to answer the question?
- What values should you use for $I$ and $I_0$?

**46. Construction** The foreman of a construction team puts up a sound barrier that reduces the intensity of the noise by 50%. By how many decibels is the noise reduced? Use the formula $L = 10 \log \frac{I}{I_0}$ to measure loudness. (*Hint:* Find the difference between the expression for loudness for intensity $I$ and the expression for loudness for intensity $0.5I$.)

**47. Error Analysis** Explain why the expansion at the right of $\log_4 \sqrt{\frac{t}{s}}$ is incorrect. Then do the expansion correctly.

**48. Reasoning** Can you expand $\log_3 (2x + 1)$? Explain.

**49. Writing** Explain why $\log (5 \cdot 2) \neq \log 5 \cdot \log 2$.

---

# Answers

## Practice and Problem-Solving Exercises

**9.** $\log 14$

**10.** $\log_2 3$

**11.** $\log 972$

**12.** $\log \frac{2}{3}$

**13.** $\log \frac{m^4}{n}$

**14.** $\log \frac{5}{2^k}$

**15.** $\log_6 5x$

**16.** $\log_7 \frac{xy}{z}$

**17.** $\log_3 32xy$

**18.** $3 \log x + 5 \log y$

**19.** $2 + \log_7 x + \log_7 y + \log_7 z$

**20.** $1 - \log_b x$

**21.** $2 \log a$

**22.** $\log_5 r - \log_5 s$

**23.** $2 \log_3 2 + 2 \log_3 x$

**24.** $\log_3 7 + 2\log_3 (2x - 3)$

**25.** $2 \log a + 3 \log b - 4 \log c$

**26.** $\log_4 5 + \frac{1}{2}\log_4 x$

**27.** $1 + \frac{1}{2}\log_8 3 + \frac{5}{2}\log_8 a$

**28.** $2 - \log_5 x$

**29.** $1 + 4 \log m - 2 \log n$

**30.** $\approx 3.17$

**31.** $\approx 1.2$

**32.** $\approx 1.748$

**33.** $\approx 1.43$

**34.** $\approx 1.4$

**35.** $\approx 3.631$

**36.** $\approx 2.564$

**37.** $\approx 3.183$

**38.** 12

**39.** $-2$

**40.** 5

**41.** 1

**42.** 2

**43.** 2

**44.** $-\frac{1}{2}$

**45.** Yes, because the loudness of the sound is 102 dB.

**46.** about 3 dB

**47.** The coefficient $\frac{1}{2}$ is missing in $\log_4 s$;

$$\log_4 \sqrt{\frac{t}{s}} = \frac{1}{2}\log_4 \frac{t}{s}$$
$$= \frac{1}{2}(\log_4 t - \log_4 s)$$
$$= \frac{1}{2}\log_4 t - \frac{1}{2}\log_4 s$$

**48.** No; the expression $(2x + 1)$ is a sum, so it is not covered by the Product, Quotient, or Power Props.

**49.** The log of a product is equal to the sum of the logs. $\log(MN) = \log M + \log N$.

**Determine if each statement is *true* or *false*. Justify your answer.**

**50.** $\log_2 4 + \log_2 8 = 5$

**51.** $\log_3 \frac{3}{2} = \frac{1}{2}\log_3 3$

**52.** $\log(x-2) = \dfrac{\log x}{\log 2}$

**53.** $\dfrac{\log_b x}{\log_b y} = \log_b \frac{x}{y}$

**54.** $(\log x)^2 = \log x^2$

**55.** $\log_4 7 - \log_4 3 = \log_4 4$

**Write each logarithmic expression as a single logarithm.**

**56.** $\frac{1}{4}\log_3 2 + \frac{1}{4}\log_3 x$

**57.** $\frac{1}{2}(\log_x 4 + \log_x y) - 3\log_x z$

**58.** $x\log_4 m + \frac{1}{y}\log_4 n - \log_4 p$

**59.** $\left(\frac{2\log_b x}{3} + \frac{3\log_b y}{4}\right) - 5\log_b z$

**Expand each logarithm.**

**60.** $\log\sqrt{\frac{2x}{y}}$

**61.** $\log\frac{s\sqrt{7}}{t^2}$

**62.** $\log\left(\frac{2\sqrt{x}}{5}\right)^3$

**63.** $\log\frac{m^3}{n^4 p^{-2}}$

**64.** $\log 4\sqrt{\frac{4r}{s^2}}$

**65.** $\log_b \frac{\sqrt{x}\sqrt[3]{y^2}}{\sqrt[5]{z^2}}$

**66.** $\log_4 \frac{\sqrt{x^5 y^7}}{zw^4}$

**67.** $\log\frac{\sqrt{x^2-4}}{(x+3)^2}$

**Write each logarithm as the quotient of two common logarithms. Do not simplify the quotient.**

**68.** $\log_7 2$   **69.** $\log_3 8$   **70.** $\log_5 140$   **71.** $\log_9 3.3$   **72.** $\log_4 3x$

**Astronomy** The apparent brightness of stars is measured on a logarithmic scale called magnitude, in which lower numbers mean brighter stars. The relationship between the ratio of apparent brightness of two objects and the difference in their magnitudes is given by the formula $m_2 - m_1 = -2.5\log\frac{b_2}{b_1}$, where $m$ is the magnitude and $b$ is the apparent brightness.

**73.** How many times brighter is a magnitude 1.0 star than a magnitude 2.0 star?

**74.** The star Rigel has a magnitude of 0.12. How many times brighter is Capella than Rigel?

Capella ⊙
m = 0.1

 Challenge **Expand each logarithm.**

**75.** $\log\sqrt{\frac{x\sqrt{2}}{y^2}}$

**76.** $\log_3 [(xy^{\frac{1}{3}}) + z^2]^3$

**77.** $\log_7 \frac{\sqrt{r+9}}{s^2 t^{\frac{1}{3}}}$

**Simplify each expression.**

**78.** $\log_3(x+1) - \log_3(3x^2 - 3x - 6) + \log_3(x-2)$

**79.** $\log(a^2 - 10a + 25) + \frac{1}{2}\log\frac{1}{(a-5)^3} - \log(\sqrt{a-5})$

---

**71.** $\dfrac{\log 3.3}{\log 9}$

**72.** $\dfrac{\log 3x}{\log 4}$

**73.** A 1.0 magnitude star is about 2.5 times brighter than a 2.0 magnitude star.

**74.** Capella is about 1.02 times brighter than Rigel.

**75.** $\frac{1}{2}\log x + \frac{1}{4}\log 2 - \log y$

**76.** $3\log_3\left[xy^{\frac{1}{3}} + z^2\right]$

**77.** $\frac{1}{2}\log_7(r+9) - 2\log_7 s - \frac{1}{3}\log_7 t$

**78.** $-1$

**79.** 0

---

**50.** true; $\log_2 4 = 2$ and $\log_2 8 = 3$; $2 + 3 = 5$

**51.** false; $\frac{1}{2}\log_3 3 = \log_3 3^{\frac{1}{2}}$, not $\log_3 \frac{3}{2}$

**52.** False; this is not an example of the Quotient Prop. $\log(x-2) \neq \log x - \log 2$

**53.** false; $\log_b \frac{x}{y} = \log_b x - \log_b y$

**54.** false; $(\log x)^2 = (\log x) \times (\log x) \neq \log x^2$

**55.** false; $\log_4 7 - \log_4 3 = \log_4 \frac{7}{3}$ not $\log_4 4$.

**56.** $\log_3 \sqrt[4]{2x}$

**57.** $\log_x \frac{2\sqrt{y}}{z^3}$

**58.** $\log_4 \frac{m^x n^{\frac{1}{y}}}{p}$

**59.** $\log_b \frac{\sqrt[3]{x^2}\sqrt[4]{y^3}}{z^5}$

**60.** $\frac{1}{2}\log 2 + \frac{1}{2}\log x - \frac{1}{2}\log y$

**61.** $\log s + \frac{1}{2}\log 7 - 2\log t$

**62.** $3\log 2 + \frac{3}{2}\log x - 3\log 5$

**63.** $3\log m - 4\log n + 2\log p$

**64.** $3\log 2 + \frac{1}{2}\log r - \log s$

**65.** $\frac{1}{2}\log_b x + \frac{2}{3}\log_b y - \frac{2}{5}\log_b z$

**66.** $\frac{5}{2}\log_4 x + \frac{7}{2}\log_4 y - \log_4 z - 4\log_4 w$

**67.** $\frac{1}{2}\log(x+2) + \frac{1}{2}\log(x-2) - 2\log(x+3)$

**68.** $\dfrac{\log 2}{\log 7}$

**69.** $\dfrac{\log 8}{\log 3}$

**70.** $\dfrac{\log 140}{\log 5}$

# Answers

## Standardized Test Prep

**80.** B

**81.** I

**82.** C

**83.** [2] $\log 18 = \log \frac{36}{2} = \log 36 - \log 2$;
Quotient Prop.

$\quad = \log 2 \cdot 9 = \log 2 + \log 9$;
Product Prop.

$\quad = \log 324^{\frac{1}{2}} = \frac{1}{2}\log 324$;
Power Prop.

$\quad = \log 2 \cdot 3^2 = \log 2 + 2 \log 3$;
Product and Power Prop.

[1] $\log 18$ is written in only 2 ways with the properties named OR properties are not named

## Mixed Review

**84.** $\log_7 49 = 2$

**85.** $\log_8 \frac{1}{4} = -\frac{2}{3}$

**86.** $-3 = \log_5 \frac{1}{125}$

**87.** $\pm 8$

**88.** $\frac{64}{7}$

**89.** 2

**90.** $x^3 + 5x^2 - 3x - 15$

**91.** $x^4 + 17x^2 + 16$

**92.** $x^4 - 2x^3 - 2x^2 + 14x - 35$

**93.** 2

**94.** 3

**95.** $\frac{1}{3}$

---

## Standardized Test Prep

SAT/ACT

**80.** Which expression is NOT equivalent to $\sqrt[6]{16r^2}$?

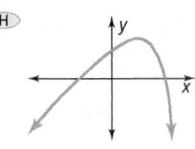

- Ⓐ $(16r^2)^{\frac{1}{6}}$
- Ⓑ $4r^{\frac{1}{3}}$
- Ⓒ $(4r)^{\frac{1}{3}}$
- Ⓓ $\sqrt[3]{4r}$

**81.** Assume that there are no more turning points beyond those shown. Which graph CANNOT be the graph of a fourth degree polynomial?

**82.** A florist is arranging a bouquet of daisies and tulips. He wants twice as many daisies as tulips in the bouquet. If the bouquet contains 24 flowers, how many daisies are in the bouquet?

- Ⓐ 8 daisies
- Ⓑ 12 daisies
- Ⓒ 16 daisies
- Ⓓ 24 daisies

Short Response

**83.** Use the properties of logarithms to write log 18 in four different ways. Name each property you use.

## Mixed Review

Write each equation in logarithmic form.  ◆ See Lesson 7-3.

**84.** $49 = 7^2$

**85.** $\frac{1}{4} = 8^{-\frac{2}{3}}$

**86.** $5^{-3} = \frac{1}{125}$

Solve. Check for extraneous solutions.  ◆ See Lesson 6-5.

**87.** $\sqrt[3]{y^4} = 16$

**88.** $\sqrt[3]{7x} - 4 = 0$

**89.** $2\sqrt{w - 1} = \sqrt{w + 2}$

Write a polynomial function with rational coefficients and the given roots.  ◆ See Lesson 5-5.

**90.** $\sqrt{3}, -5$

**91.** $-i, 4i$

**92.** $-\sqrt{7}, 1 + 2i$

**Get Ready!**  To prepare for Lesson 7-5, do Exercises 93–95.

Evaluate each logarithm.  ◆ See Lesson 7-3.

**93.** $\log_{12} 144$

**94.** $\log_4 64$

**95.** $\log_{64} 4$

# Additional Instructional Support

## Algebra 2 Companion

Students can use the **Algebra 2 Companion** worktext (4 pages) as you teach the lesson. Use the Companion to support

- New Vocabulary
- Key Concepts
- Got It for each Problem
- Lesson Check

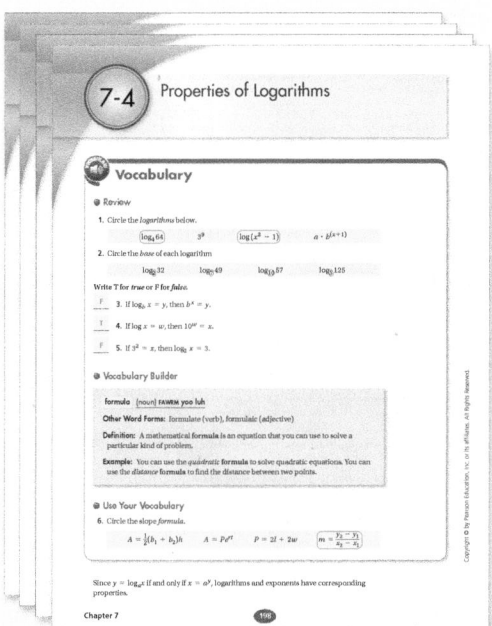

## ELL Support

**Connect to Prior Knowledge** Write the expressions "$m \cdot n$," "$m \times n$," and "$mn$." Have students work in pairs to brainstorm any words associated with the expression. Expected responses include *times, multiply, factor, product, of, variable,* etc.

After brainstorming has slowed down, have the group list responses as a whole. If a response does not apply (e.g., *addend*), ask the pair to describe their reasoning. Write "product" above the expressions.

Ask for a volunteer to say the Product Property of Exponents. (Students may use their textbooks.) Have students write the property and circle the multiplication, *mn*. Now ask for a volunteer to say the Product Property of Logarithms. Have students write the property and circle the multiplication.

Repeat this exercise for the Quotient and Power Properties of Exponents and Logarithms.

# 5 Assess & Remediate

## Lesson Quiz

1. What is $\log_5 4 + \log_5 3$ written as a single logarithm? If possible, simplify the single logarithm.

2. What is $\log \frac{10}{x^2}$ expanded? Simplify your answer, if possible.

3. What is the value of $\log_7 25$? Use the Change of Base Formula.

4. **Do you UNDERSTAND?** The magnitude of a city can be defined as the common logarithm of the population, *P*. In 2007, Tallahassee had a population of about $1.7 \times 10^5$ people. The town of Bascom, FL, had a population of about $1.1 \times 10^2$ people. What is the difference in magnitude between Tallahassee and Bascom?

### ANSWERS TO LESSON QUIZ

1. $\log_5 12$
2. $1 - 2 \log x$
3. about 1.65
4. about 3.19

**PRESCRIPTION FOR REMEDIATION**

Use the student work on the Lesson Quiz to prescribe a differentiated review assignment:

| Points | Differentiated Remediation |
|--------|---------------------------|
| 0–1 | Intervention |
| 2–3 | On-level |
| 4 | Extension |

**PowerAlgebra.com**

## 5 Assess & Remediate

Assign the Lesson Quiz. Appropriate intervention, practice, or enrichment is automatically generated based on student performance.

# Differentiated Remediation

Available in editable format online.

## Intervention

- **Reteaching** (2 pages) Provides reteaching and practice exercises for the key lesson concepts. Use with struggling students or absent students.

- **English Language Learner Support** Helps students develop and reinforce mathematical vocabulary and key concepts.

**All-in-One Resources/Online**
**Reteaching**

### 7-4 Reteaching
Properties of Logarithms

**All-in-One Resources/Online**
**English Language Learner Support**

### 7-4 ELL Support
Properties of Logarithms

# Differentiated Remediation *continued*

Available in editable format online.

## On-Level

- **Practice** (2 pages) Provides extra practice for each lesson. For simpler practice exercises, use the Form K Practice pages found in the All-in-One Teaching Resources and online.

- **Think About a Plan** Helps students develop specific problem-solving skills and strategies by providing scaffolded guiding questions.

- **Standardized Test Prep** Focuses on all major exercises, all major question types, and helps students prepare for the high-stakes assessments.

## Extension

- **Enrichment** Provides students with interesting problems and activities that extend the concepts of the lesson.

- **Activities, Games, and Puzzles** Worksheets that can be used for concepts development, enrichment, and for fun!

---

### Practice and Problem Solving Wkbk/All-in-One Resources/Online
#### Practice page 1

### Practice and Problem Solving Wkbk/All-in-One Resources/Online
#### Practice page 2

### All-in-One Resources/Online
#### Enrichment

---

### Practice and Problem Solving Wkbk/All-in-One Resources/Online
#### Think About a Plan

### Practice and Problem Solving Wkbk/All-in-One Resources/Online
#### Standardized Test Prep

### Online Teacher Resource Center
#### Activities, Games, and Puzzles

# 7-5 Exponential and Logarithmic Equations

**Objective** To solve exponential and logarithmic equations

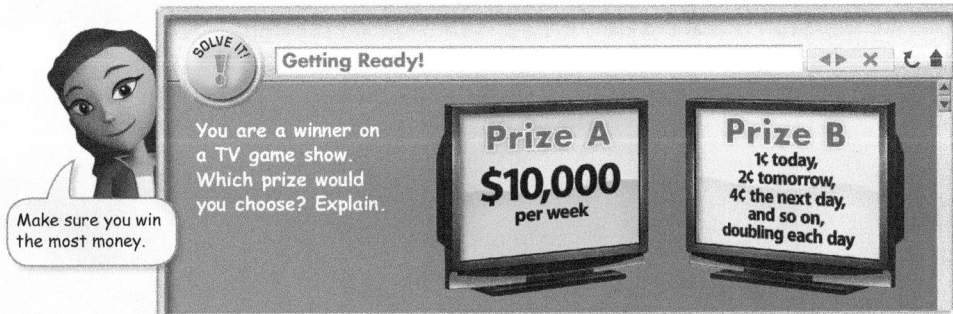

**Getting Ready!**

You are a winner on a TV game show. Which prize would you choose? Explain.

*Make sure you win the most money.*

**Prize A**
**$10,000**
per week

**Prize B**
1¢ today,
2¢ tomorrow,
4¢ the next day,
and so on,
doubling each day

**Lesson Vocabulary**
• exponential equation
• logarithmic equation

Any equation that contains the form $b^{cx}$, such as $a = b^{cx}$ where the exponent includes a variable, is an **exponential equation**.

**Essential Understanding** You can use logarithms to solve exponential equations. You can use exponents to solve logarithmic equations.

**Plan**

**What common base is appropriate?**
2 because 16 and 8 are both powers of 2.

**Problem 1** Solving an Exponential Equation—Common Base

**Multiple Choice** What is the solution of $16^{3x} = 8$?

Ⓐ $x = \frac{1}{4}$   Ⓑ $x = \frac{3}{7}$   Ⓒ $x = 1$   Ⓓ $x = 4$

$16^{3x} = 8$

$(2^4)^{3x} = 2^3$    Rewrite the terms with a common base.

$2^{12x} = 2^3$    Power Property of Exponents

$12x = 3$    If two numbers with the same base are equal, their exponents are equal.

$x = \frac{1}{4}$    Solve and simplify.

The correct answer is A.

**Got It?** **1.** What is the solution of $27^{3x} = 81$?

---

# 1 Interactive Learning

## Solve It!

**PURPOSE** To use equations with variable exponents to make a decision

**PROCESS** Students may

• estimate the total amount of money for either prize and draw a conclusion when the amount of one prize exceeds the other.

• calculate the total amount of money received in prize B by adding exponential terms.

**FACILITATE**

**Q** How can you find an expression to represent each day for Prize B? **[List the amounts for each day to determine a pattern. 1, 2, 4, 8, 16...; the pattern is exponential because the numbers are doubled, so $2^{n-1}$ where $n$ is the number of days.]**

**Q** How much additional money would you receive from prize B on day 10? 20? **[$5.12; $5,242.88]**

**ANSWER** See Solve It in Answers on next page.

**CONNECT THE MATH** Students use their knowledge of exponential growth to make a decision in the Solve It. In this lesson, students will write and solve exponential equations.

# 2 Guided Instruction

## Problem 1

**Q** How can you check your answer? **[If $x = \frac{1}{4}$, then $16^{\frac{3}{4}} = 8$. So $\sqrt[4]{16} = 2$ and $2^3 = 8$]**

## Got It?

**Q** What common base do you recognize? **[Both 27 and 81 are powers of 3.]**

---

# 7-5 Preparing to Teach

**BIG ideas** Equivalence   **UbD**
         Function

**ESSENTIAL UNDERSTANDINGS**

• Logarithms can be used to solve exponential equations. Exponents can be used to solve logarithmic equations.

• An exponential function is a function with the general form $y = ab^x$, $a \neq 0$, with $b > 0$, and $b \neq 1$. In an exponential function, the base $b$ is a constant. The exponent $x$ is the independent variable with domain the set of real numbers.

• The exponential function $y = b^x$ and the logarithmic function $y = \log_b x$ are inverse functions.

## Math Background

Exponential and logarithmic functions are inverse functions. This relationship allows you to use logarithms to simplify

exponential equations and exponents to simplify logarithmic equations.

• To solve an exponential equation that cannot be rewritten with a common base, take the logarithm of both sides, and use the properties of logs to simplify.

• To solve a logarithmic equation, rewrite both sides in exponential form to remove the log, and use the properties of exponents to simplify.

The common log or $\log_{10}$ is most often used due to the ease of calculations. Any other base could be used, but the Change of Base formula from Lesson 7-4 would need to be applied in order to find the log using a calculator.

## 1 Interactive Learning

**Solve It!**
Step out how to solve the Problem with helpful hints and an online question. Other questions are listed above in Interactive Learning.

## Problem 2

**Q** What logarithmic base is being used to solve this equation? Explain. **[When no base is shown, it is assumed that the logarithm is base 10. This is easier to calculate, because the log button on a calculator is $\log_{10}$.]**

**Q** Can the method used in this problem be used to solve exponential equations with common bases? Give an example. **[Yes; by taking the log of each side of the equation in Problem 1, you get $3x = \frac{\log 8}{\log 16}$. So $x = 0.25$]**

## Got It?                                    EXTENSION

**Q** How can you use the log of any base to solve an exponential equation with a calculator? **[Use the Change of Base Formula to convert to $\log_{10}$, and then solve the equation.]**

## Problem 3

An estimate of the solution is helpful to determine window or table parameters when solving by graphing or using a table.

**Q** If no parentheses are used to enter $y = 4^{3x}$, how does the calculator interpret what is entered? **[If no parentheses are used, $y = 4^{3x}$ is interpreted as $y = 4^3 x$ which is a linear equation.]**

## Got It?

**Q** How can you determine whether your solution is reasonable? **[For 3a, $7^3 = 343$ and $7^4 = 2401$. Because the exponent is $4x$, $x$ will be between 0.75 and 1.]**

---

When bases are not the same, you can solve an exponential equation by taking the logarithm of each side of the equation. If $m$ and $n$ are positive and $m = n$, then $\log m = \log n$.

 **Problem 2** Solving an Exponential Equation—Different Bases

**What is the solution of $15^{3x} = 285$?**

$$15^{3x} = 285$$

**Think**
**Which property of logarithms will help isolate $x$?**
The rule $\log a^x = x \log a$ moves $x$ out of the exponent position.

| | |
|---|---|
| $\log 15^{3x} = \log 285$ | Take the logarithm of each side. |
| $3x \log 15 = \log 285$ | Power Property of Logarithms. |
| $x = \dfrac{\log 285}{3 \log 15}$ | Divide each side by $3 \log 15$ to isolate $x$. |
| $x \approx 0.6958$ | Use a calculator. |

**Check** $15^{3x} = 285$
$$15^{3(0.6958)} \approx 285.0840331 \approx 285 \checkmark$$

 **Got It?** **2. a.** What is the solution of $5^{2x} = 130$?
**b. Reasoning** Why can't you use the same method you used in Problem 1 to solve Problem 2?

 **Problem 3** Solving an Exponential Equation With a Graph or Table

**What is the solution of $4^{3x} = 6000$?**

**Method 1** Solve using a graph.

Use a graphing calculator. Graph the equations.

$$Y_1 = 4^{3x}$$
$$Y_2 = 6000$$

Adjust the window to find the point of intersection. The solution is $x \approx 2.09$.

**Method 2** Solve using a table.

Use the table feature of a graphing calculator. Enter $Y_1 = 4^{3x}$.

Use the **TABLE SETUP** and **ΔTbl** features to locate the $x$-value that gives the $y$-value closest to 6000.

The solution is $x \approx 2.09$.

**Think**
**How do you choose TblStart and ΔTbl values?**
Start with 0 and 1, respectively. Adjust both values as you close in on the solution.

 **Got It?** **3.** What is the solution of each exponential equation? Check your answer.
**a.** $7^{4x} = 800$                      **b.** $5.2^{3x} = 400$

---

# Answers

## Solve It!

Prize B; compare the prizes over a year:
$2^{365} > 520{,}000$

## Got It?

**1.** $\frac{4}{9}$

**2. a.** $\approx 1.5122$

**b.** because the terms cannot be written with a common base

**3. a.** $\approx 0.8588$

**b.** $\approx 1.2114$

---

**PowerAlgebra.com**

## 2 Guided Instruction

Each Problem is worked out and supported online.

**Problem 1**
Solving an Exponential Equation—Common Base

**Problem 2**
Solving an Exponential Equation—Different Bases
*Animated*

**Problem 3**
Solving an Exponential Equation With a Graph or Table

**Problem 4**
Modeling With an Exponential Equation
*Animated*

**Problem 5**
Solving a Logarithmic Equation

**Problem 6**
Using Logarithmic Properties to Solve an Equation
*Animated*

**Support in Algebra 2 Companion**
• Vocabulary
• Key Concepts
• Got It?

**Problem 4** Modeling With an Exponential Equation

**Resource Management** Wood is a sustainable, renewable, natural resource when you manage forests properly. Your lumber company has 1,200,000 trees. You plan to harvest 7% of the trees each year. How many years will it take to harvest half of the trees?

| Know | Need | Plan |
|------|------|------|
| • Number of trees<br>• Rate of decay | Number of years it takes to harvest 600,000 trees | • Write an exponential equation.<br>• Use logarithms to solve the equation. |

**Think**

**What equation should you use to model this situation?** Since you are planning to harvest 7% of the trees each year, you should use $y = ab^x$, where $b$ is the decay factor.

**Step 1** Is an exponential model reasonable for this situation?

Yes, you are harvesting a fixed percentage each year.

**Step 2** Define the variables and determine the model.

Let $n$ = the number of years it takes to harvest half of the trees.

Let $T(n)$ = the number of trees remaining after $n$ years.

A reasonable model is $T(n) = a(b)^n$.

**Step 3** Use the model to write an exponential equation.

$T(n) = 600{,}000$

$a = 1{,}200{,}000$

$r = -7\% = -0.07$

$b = 1 + r = 1 + (-0.07) = 0.93$

So, $1{,}200{,}000(0.93)^n = 600{,}000$.

**Step 4** Solve the equation. Use logarithms.

$1{,}200{,}000(0.93)^n = 600{,}000$

$0.93^n = \dfrac{600{,}000}{1{,}200{,}000}$    Isolate the term with $n$.

$\log 0.93^n = \log 0.5$    Take the logarithm of each side.

$n \log 0.93 = \log 0.5$    Power Property of Logarithms.

$n = \dfrac{\log 0.5}{\log 0.93}$    Solve for $n$.

$n \approx 9.55$    Use a calculator.

It will take about 9.55 years to harvest half of the original trees.

 **Got It?** **4.** After how many years will you have harvested half of the trees if you harvest 5% instead of 7% yearly?

A **logarithmic equation** is an equation that includes one or more logarithms involving a variable.

---

## Problem 4

Suggest students look for key words in the situation to determine if the model represents an increase or decrease, and define the variable accordingly.

**Q** What does $b$ represent in $y = ab^x$? What does $r$ represent in $T(n) = a(1 + r)^n$? **[The variable $b$ represents the growth factor if $b > 1$, and it represents the decay factor if $b < 1$. The variable $r$ represents the rate of increase if $r > 0$, and it represents the rate of decrease if $r < 0$.]**

**Q** How can either model be used when writing this equation? Explain. **[The 7% harvest can be used to find the decay factor, or it can represent the rate of decrease. Because 93% of the harvest will remain after each year, a decay factor of $b = 0.93$ can be used. Using the 7% harvest as a rate of decrease, $r = -0.07$.]**

### Got It?    VISUAL LEARNERS

Students can use a recursive routine with a graphing calculator to check the reasonableness of their answer. Input the following:

1,200,000      press Enter
Ans * 0.95      press Enter

Count the number of times Enter is pressed to find the total number of years.

---

# Additional Problems

**1.** What is the solution of $256^{2x} = 64$?

**ANSWER** $\frac{3}{8}$

**2.** What is the solution of $6^{4x} = 512$?

**ANSWER** 0.8704

**3.** What is the solution of $5^{2x} = 3500$?

**ANSWER** 2.54

**4.** Your MP3 player has about 126,000,000 bytes of memory. Each month you plan to use 5% of the memory remaining. How many months will it take you to use $\frac{1}{4}$ of the memory?

**ANSWER** 5.61 months

**5.** What is the solution of $\log (5x + 2) = 2$?

**ANSWER** 19.6

**6.** What is the solution of $\log 2x^2 - \log 5 = 1$?

**ANSWER** 5, −5

---

# Answers

**Got It?** (continued)

**4.** $\approx 13.51$ yrs

## Problem 5

Converting a logarithmic equation to exponential form can be thought of as raising both sides to the power of 10. Note that $\log(4x - 3) = 2$ is the same as $10^{\log(4x-3)} = 10^2$.

**Q** What are the advantages and disadvantages of using a graph or table to solve a logarithmic equation? **[An advantage is that you can see how the exponential equation changes for values of $x$. A disadvantage is that you must either zoom in at the intersection or change the ΔTbl values to find more precise answers.]**

## Got It?

**Q** Which method would you choose to solve this problem? Explain. **[Sample: You would choose exponents, because it is simpler to rewrite the equation as $3 - 2x = 10^{-1}$ and solve for $x$. You need an estimate to set the window or the TblStart values in a calculator. Since you have to rewrite the equation in exponential form to estimate, it is easier to just solve for $x$.]**

## Problem 6

**Q** Why is it not possible to find $\log(-2)$? **[$\log(-2) = x$ means $10^x = -2$. Raising a positive base to any number, either positive or negative, will never result in a negative number.]**

## Got It?

**Q** How can you determine which property of logarithms to use when solving the equation? **[If logarithms are added, use the Product Property. If they are subtracted, use the Quotient Property. If a number is multiplied by a logarithm, use the Power Property.]**

---

**Plan**

**How do you convert between log form and exponential form?**
Use the rule: $\log a = b$ if and only if $a = 10^b$.

### Problem 5  Solving a Logarithmic Equation

**What is the solution of $\log(4x - 3) = 2$?**

**Method 1**  Solve using exponents.

$$\log(4x - 3) = 2$$
$$4x - 3 = 10^2 \qquad \text{Write in exponential form.}$$
$$4x = 103 \qquad \text{Simplify.}$$
$$x = \frac{103}{4} = 25.75 \qquad \text{Solve for } x.$$

**Method 2**  Solve using a graph.
Graph the equations $Y_1 = LOG (4x - 3)$ and $Y_2 = 2$. Find the point of intersection. The solution is $x = 25.75$.

**Method 3**  Solve using a table.
Enter $Y_1 = LOG (4x - 3)$.
Use the **TABLE SETUP** feature to find the $x$-value that corresponds to a $y$-value of 2 in the table.
The solution is $x = 25.75$.

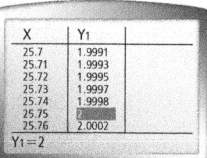

**Got It?  5.** What is the solution of $\log(3 - 2x) = -1$?

### Problem 6  Using Logarithmic Properties to Solve an Equation

**What is the solution of $\log(x - 3) + \log x = 1$?**

$$\log(x - 3) + \log x = 1$$
$$\log((x - 3)x) = 1 \qquad \text{Product Property of Logarithms}$$
$$(x - 3)x = 10^1 \qquad \text{Write in exponential form.}$$
$$x^2 - 3x - 10 = 0 \qquad \text{Simplify to a quadratic equation in standard form.}$$
$$(x - 5)(x + 2) = 0 \qquad \text{Factor the trinomial.}$$
$$x = 5 \quad \text{or} \quad x = -2 \qquad \text{Solve for } x.$$

**Think**

**What is the domain of the logarithm function?**
Logs are defined only for positive numbers. The log of a negative number is undefined.

**Check**

$$\log(x - 3) + \log(x) = 1 \qquad\qquad \log(x - 3) + \log(x) = 1$$
$$\log(-2 - 3) + \log(-2) \stackrel{?}{=} 1 \ \times \qquad \log(5 - 3) + \log(5) \stackrel{?}{=} 1$$
$$\log 2 + \log 5 \stackrel{?}{=} 1$$
$$0.3010 + 0.6990 = 1 \ \checkmark$$

If $\log(x - 3) + \log(x) = 1, x = 5$.

**Got It?  6.** What is the solution of $\log 6 - \log 3x = -2$?

---

# Answers

**Got It?** (continued)
5. 1.45
6. 200

**Lesson Check**

**Do you know HOW?**

Solve each equation.

**1.** $3^x = 9$

**2.** $2^{y+1} = 25$

**3.** $\log 4x = 2$

**4.** $\log x - \log 2 = 3$

**Do you UNDERSTAND?**

**5.** Error Analysis Describe and correct the error made in solving the equation.

$$\log_2 x = 2\log_3 9$$
$$\log_2 x = \log_3 9^2$$
$$x = 9^2$$
$$x = 81$$

**6.** Reasoning Is it possible for an exponential equation to have no solutions? If so, give an example. If not, explain why.

 **Practice and Problem-Solving Exercises**

 **Practice**

Solve each equation.

⬥ See Problem 1.

**7.** $2^x = 8$
**8.** $3^{2x} = 27$
**9.** $4^{3x} = 64$
**10.** $5^{3x} = \frac{1}{125}$

**11.** $2^{5x+1} = 32$
**12.** $3^{-2x+2} = 81$
**13.** $2^{3x} = 4^{x+1}$
**14.** $3^{x+2} = 27^{2x}$

Solve each equation. Round to the nearest ten-thousandth. Check your answers.

⬥ See Problem 2.

**15.** $2^x = 3$
**16.** $4^x = 19$
**17.** $8 + 10^x = 1008$
**18.** $5 - 3^x = -40$

**19.** $9^{2y} = 66$
**20.** $12^{y-2} = 20$
**21.** $25^{2x+1} = 144$
**22.** $2^{3x-4} = 5$

📱 Graphing Calculator Solve by graphing. Round to the nearest ten-thousandth.

⬥ See Problem 3.

**23.** $4^{7x} = 250$
**24.** $5^{3x} = 500$
**25.** $6^x = 4565$
**26.** $1.5^x = 356$

Use a table to solve each equation. Round to the nearest hundredth.

**27.** $2^{x+3} = 512$
**28.** $3^{x-1} = 72$
**29.** $6^{2x} = 10$
**30.** $5^{2x} = 56$

**31.** The equation $y = 6.72(1.014)^x$ models the world population $y$, in billions of people, $x$ years after the year 2000. Find the year in which the world population is about 8 billion.

⬥ See Problem 4.

Solve each equation. Check your answers.

⬥ See Problem 5.

**32.** $\log 2x = -1$
**33.** $2\log x = -1$
**34.** $\log(3x + 1) = 2$
**35.** $\log x + 4 = 8$

**36.** $\log 6x - 3 = -4$
**37.** $3\log x = 1.5$
**38.** $2\log(x + 1) = 5$
**39.** $\log(5 - 2x) = 0$

Solve each equation.

⬥ See Problem 6.

**40.** $\log x - \log 3 = 8$
**41.** $\log 2x + \log x = 11$
**42.** $2\log x + \log 4 = 2$

**43.** $\log 5 - \log 2x = 1$
**44.** $3\log x - \log 6 + \log 2.4 = 9$
**45.** $\log(7x + 1) = \log(x - 2) + 1$

# 3 Lesson Check

**Do you know HOW?**    ERROR INTERVENTION

- If students have difficulty with Exercises 1–2, remind them they can either search for a common base or take the logarithm of each side. Taking the logarithm of each side will work for both types of equations, while finding a common base may not be possible.
- For Exercise 2, students might mistakenly believe they can use a common base. Point out that the right side of the equation would have base 5.

**Do you UNDERSTAND?**

- For Exercise 6, if students cannot find an exponential equation that has no solutions, point out Problem 6. The logarithm of a negative number does not have a real solution.

## Close

**Q** How is the relationship between exponents and logarithms used to solve problems? Explain. **[Exponential and logarithmic functions are inverse functions. You can solve an exponential equation by taking logarithms of both sides. You can solve a logarithmic equation by rewriting it in exponential form.]**

**Q** What methods can be used to solve an exponential equation? **[Rewrite the terms with a common base, or take a logarithm of each side. You can also use a graphing calculator to graph or find a solution using a table.]**

**Q** What methods can be used to solve a logarithmic equation? **[Rewrite the problem using exponents, use a graph, use a table, or use logarithmic properties.]**

**Lesson Check**

**1.** 2

**2.** ≈3.6439

**3.** 25

**4.** 2000

**5.** The log bases are not equal.
$$\log_2 x = 2\log_3 9$$
$$\log_2 x = \log_3 9^2$$
$$\log_2 x = 4$$
$$x = 2^4$$
$$x = 16$$

**6.** Yes; $5^x = 0$ has no solution.

**Practice and Problem-Solving Exercises**

**7.** 3    **8.** $\frac{3}{2}$    **9.** 1

**10.** −1    **11.** $\frac{4}{5}$    **12.** −1

**13.** 2    **14.** $\frac{2}{5}$    **15.** 1.5850

**16.** 2.1240    **17.** 3    **18.** 3.4650

**19.** 0.9534    **20.** 3.2056    **21.** 0.2720

**22.** 2.1073    **23.** 0.5690    **24.** 1.2871

**25.** 4.7027    **26.** 14.4894    **27.** 6

**28.** 4.89    **29.** 0.64

**30.** 1.25

**31.** about the yr 2012

**32.** 0.05

**33.** $\frac{\sqrt{10}}{10}$ or about 0.3162

**34.** 33

**35.** 10,000

**36.** $\frac{1}{60}$ or ≈0.0167

**37.** $\sqrt{10}$ or ≈3.1623

**38.** $100\sqrt{10} - 1$ or ≈315.2

**39.** 2

**40.** $3 \times 10^8$

**41.** $100,000\sqrt{5}$ or ≈223,606.8

**42.** 5    **43.** $\frac{1}{4}$

**44.** 1357.2

**45.** 7

**PowerAlgebra.com**

## 3 Lesson Check

For a digital lesson check, use the Got It questions.

**Support in Algebra 2 Companion**
- Lesson Check

## 4 Practice

Assign homework to individual students or to an entire class.

# 4 Practice

## ASSIGNMENT GUIDE

Basic: 7–45 all, 46–54 even, 60, 61

Average: 7–45 odd, 46–78

Advanced: 7–45 odd, 46–83

Standardized Test Prep: 84–88

Mixed Review: 89–100

Reasoning exercises have blue headings.

Applications exercises have red headings.

EXERCISE 48: Use the Think About a Plan worksheet in the **Practice and Problem Solving Workbook** (also available in the Teaching Resources in print and online) to further support students' development in becoming independent learners.

## HOMEWORK QUICK CHECK

To check students' understanding of key skills and concepts, go over Exercises 9, 33, 46, 48, and 61.

---

 **Apply**

**46. Think About a Plan** An earthquake of magnitude 9.1 occurred in 2004 in the Indian Ocean near Indonesia. It was about 74,900 times as strong as the greatest earthquake ever to hit Texas. Find the magnitude of the Texas earthquake. (Remember that an increase of 1.0 on the Richter scale means an earthquake is 30 times stronger.)
- Can you write an exponential or logarithmic equation?
- How does the solution of your equation help you find the magnitude?

**47.** Consider the equation $2^{\frac{x}{3}} = 80$.
  **a.** Solve the equation by taking the logarithm base 10 of each side.
  **b.** Solve the equation by taking the logarithm base 2 of each side.
  **c. Writing** Compare your result in parts (a) and (b). What are the advantages of each method? Explain.

**48. Seismology** An earthquake of magnitude 7.7 occurred in 2001 in Gujarat, India. It was about 4900 times as strong as the greatest earthquake ever to hit Pennsylvania. What is the magnitude of the Pennsylvania earthquake? (*Hint*: Refer to the Richter scale on page 453.)

**49.** As a town gets smaller, the population of its high school decreases by 6% each year. The senior class has 160 students now. In how many years will it have about 100 students? Write an equation. Then solve the equation without graphing.

**Mental Math Solve each equation.**

**50.** $2^x = \frac{1}{2}$   **51.** $3^x = 27$   **52.** $\log_9 3 = x$   **53.** $\log_4 64 = x$

**54.** $\log_8 2 = x$   **55.** $10^x = \frac{1}{100}$   **56.** $\log_7 343 = x$   **57.** $25^x = \frac{1}{5}$

**58. Demography** The table below lists the states with the highest and with the lowest population growth rates. Determine in how many years each event can occur. Use the model $P = P_0(1 + r)^x$, where $P_0$ is population from the table, as of July, 2007; $x$ is the number of years after July, 2007, $P$ is the projected population and $r$ is the growth rate.
  **a.** Population of Idaho exceeds 2 million.
  **b.** Population of Michigan decreases by 1 million.
  **c.** Population of Nevada doubles.

| State | Growth rate (%) | Population (in thousands) | State | Growth rate (%) | Population (in thousands) |
|---|---|---|---|---|---|
| 1. Nevada | 2.93 | 2,565 | 46. New York | 0.08 | 19,298 |
| 2. Arizona | 2.81 | 6,339 | 47. Vermont | 0.08 | 621 |
| 3. Utah | 2.55 | 2,645 | 48. Ohio | 0.03 | 11,467 |
| 4. Idaho | 2.43 | 1,499 | 49. Michigan | −0.30 | 10,072 |
| 5. Georgia | 2.17 | 9,545 | 50. Rhode Island | −0.36 | 1,058 |

Source: U.S. Census Bureau

---

# Answers

## Practice and Problem-Solving Exercises
(continued)

**46.** 5.8

**47. a.** 18.9658
   **b.** 18.9658
   **c.** Answers may vary. Sample: You don't have to use the change of base formula with the base-10 method, but there are fewer steps with the base-2 method.

**48.** about 5.2

**49.** ≈7.6 yrs

**50.** −1

**51.** 3

**52.** $\frac{1}{2}$

**53.** 3

**54.** $\frac{1}{3}$

**55.** −2

**56.** 3

**57.** $-\frac{1}{2}$

**58. a.** 13 yrs after July 2007
   **b.** 35 yrs after July 2007
   **c.** 25 yrs after July 2007

**59. Open-Ended** Write and solve a logarithmic equation.

**60. Reasoning** The graphs of $y = 2^{3x}$ and $y = 3^{x+1}$ intersect at approximately (1.1201, 10.2692). What is the solution of $2^{3x} = 3^{x+1}$?

**61. Reasoning** If $\log 12^{0.5x} = \log 143.6$, then $12^{0.5x} = \underline{\ ?\ }$.

**Acoustics** In Exercises 62–63, the loudness measured in decibels (dB) is defined by loudness $= 10 \log \frac{I}{I_0}$, where $I$ is the intensity and $I_0 = 10^{-12}$ W/m².

**62.** The human threshold for pain is 120 dB. Instant perforation of the eardrum occurs at 160 dB.
  **a.** Find the intensity of each sound.
  **b.** How many times as intense is the noise that will perforate an eardrum as the noise that causes pain?

**63.** The noise level inside a convertible driving along the freeway with its top up is 70 dB. With the top down, the noise level is 95 dB.
  **a.** Find the intensity of the sound with the top up and with the top down.
  **b.** By what percent does leaving the top up reduce the intensity of the sound?

**Solve each equation. If necessary, round to the nearest ten-thousandth.**

**64.** $8^x = 444$

**65.** $\frac{1}{2}\log x + \log 4 = 2$

**66.** $4\log_3 2 - 2\log_3 x = 1$

**67.** $\log x^2 = 2$

**68.** $9^{2x} = 42$

**69.** $\log_8(2x - 1) = \frac{1}{3}$

**70.** $\log(5x - 4) = 3$

**71.** $12^{4-x} = 20$

**72.** $5^{3x} = 125$

**73.** $\log 4 + 2\log x = 6$

**74.** $4^{3x} = 77.2$

**75.** $\log_7 3x = 3$

**Use the properties of exponential and logarithmic functions to solve each system. Check your answers.**

**76.** $\begin{cases} y = 2^{x+4} \\ y - 4^{x-1} = 0 \end{cases}$

**77.** $\begin{cases} 2^{x+y} = 16 \\ 4^{x-y} = 1 \end{cases}$

**78.** $\begin{cases} \log(2x - y) = 1 \\ \log(x + y) = 3\log 2 \end{cases}$

 **Challenge**  **Solve each equation.**

**79.** $\log_7(2x - 3)^2 = 2$

**80.** $\log_2(x^2 + 2x) = 3$

**81.** $\frac{3}{2}\log_2 4 - \frac{1}{2}\log_2 x = 3$

**82. Meteorology** In the formula $P = P_0\left(\frac{1}{2}\right)^{\frac{h}{4795}}$, $P$ is the atmospheric pressure in millimeters of mercury at elevation $h$ meters above sea level. $P_0$ is the atmospheric pressure at sea level. If $P_0$ equals 760 mm, at what elevation is the pressure 42 mm?

**59.** Answers may vary. Sample: $\log x = 1.6$; $x \approx 39.81$

**60.** 1.1201

**61.** 143.6

**62. a.** 1 W/m²; $10^4$ W/m²
  **b.** 10,000 times as intense

**63. a.** top up: $10^{-5}$ W/m² top down: $10^{-2.5}$ W/m²
  **b.** 99.68%

**64.** 2.9315

**65.** 625

**66.** 2.3094

**67.** 10

**68.** 0.8505

**69.** 1.5

**70.** 200.8

**71.** 2.7944

**72.** 1

**73.** 500

**74.** 1.0451

**75.** $114.\overline{3}$

**76.** $x = 6, y = 1024$

**77.** $x = y = 2$

**78.** $x = 6, y = 2$

**79.** $-2, 5$

**80.** $-4, 2$

**81.** 1

**82.** $\approx 20{,}031$ m above sea level

# Answers

## Practice and Problem-Solving Exercises
(continued)

**83 a.** bassoon, guitar, harp, violin, viola, cello

   **b.** bassoon, guitar, harp, cello, bass

   **c.** harp, violin

   **d.** harp

## Standardized Test Prep

**84.** 4

**85.** 333

**86.** 25

**87.** 4

**88.** 18

## Mixed Review

**89.** $\log 2 + 3 \log x - 2 \log y$

**90.** $\log_3 x - \log_3 y$

**91.** $1 + \frac{1}{2}\log_3 x$

**92.** $x^2 - 3x - 1$

**93.** $3x^2 - 3$

**94.** $9x^2 - 1$

**95.** $1, \pm i$

**96.** $\pm 2, \pm 2i$

**97.** $\pm\sqrt{3}, \pm\sqrt{2}$

**98.** $\log_2 3$

**99.** $\log 3x^4$

**100.** $\log_7 \frac{32}{y^2}$

---

**83. Music** The pitch, or frequency, of a piano note is related to its position on the keyboard by the function $F(n) = 440 \cdot 2^{\frac{n}{12}}$, where $F$ is the frequency of the sound waves in cycles per second and $n$ is the number of piano keys above or below Concert A, as shown. If $n = 0$ at Concert A, which of the instruments shown in the diagram can sound notes at the given frequency?

   **a.** 590      **c.** 1440

   **b.** 120      **d.** 2093

## Standardized Test Prep

GRIDDED RESPONSE

**SAT/ACT**

**84.** The graph at the right shows the translation of the graph of the parent function $y = |x|$ down 2 units and 3 units to the right. What is the area of the shaded triangle in square units?

**85.** What does $x$ equal if $\log (1 + 3x) = 3$?

**86.** Using the change of base formula, what is the value of $x$ for which $\log_9 x = \log_3 5$?

**87.** The polynomial $x^4 + 3x^3 + 16x^2 - 19x + 8$ is divided by the binomial $x - 1$. What is the coefficient of $x^2$ in the quotient?

**88.** What positive value of $b$ makes $x^2 + bx + 81$ a perfect square trinomial?

## Mixed Review

Expand each logarithm.                                    ◀ See Lesson 7-4.

**89.** $\log 2x^3 y^{-2}$        **90.** $\log_3 \frac{x}{y}$        **91.** $\log_3 \sqrt{9x}$

Let $f(x) = 3x$ and $g(x) = x^2 - 1$. Perform each function operation.     ◀ See Lesson 6-6.

**92.** $(g - f)(x)$        **93.** $(f \circ g)(x)$        **94.** $(g \circ f)(x)$

Find all the zeros of each function.                          ◀ See Lesson 5-6.

**95.** $y = x^3 - x^2 + x - 1$        **96.** $f(x) = x^4 - 16$        **97.** $f(x) = x^4 - 5x^2 + 6$

**Get Ready!**   To prepare for Lesson 7-6, do Exercises 98–100.

Write each logarithmic expression as a single logarithm.          ◀ See Lesson 7-4.

**98.** $\log_2 15 - \log_2 5$        **99.** $\log 3 + 4 \log x$        **100.** $5 \log_7 2 - 2 \log_7 y$

## Additional Instructional Support

### Algebra 2 Companion

Students can use the **Algebra 2 Companion** worktext (4 pages) as you teach the lesson. Use the Companion to support

- New Vocabulary
- Key Concepts
- Got It for each Problem
- Lesson Check

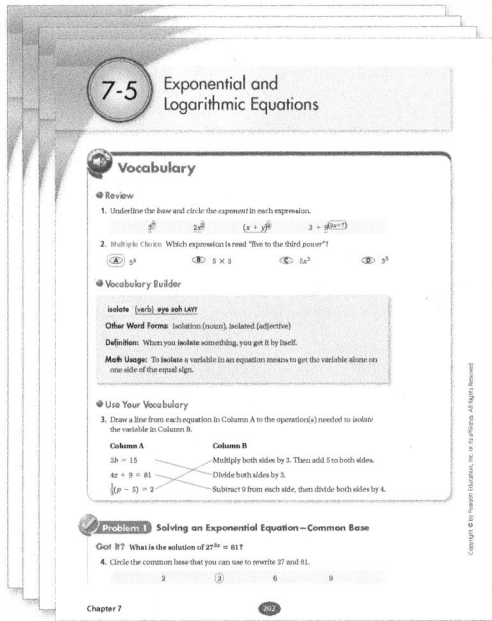

### ELL Support

**Focus on Communication** Have students write exponential or logarithmic properties used to solve equations on index cards and an example of the property on the back. For example, students can write the Power Property of Exponents, Power Property of Logarithms, Product Property of Logarithms, and Quotient Property of Logarithms. Divide students into pairs, and have one person solve the problem while the other asks a question. Have students ask, "How did you complete that step?" A student might respond by stating, "I used the Power Property of Logarithms," or the student may show the index card with the correct property. If the student uses the index card, encourage the student to read the words of the property to practice using the academic language. Next, have the students switch roles so that each has practice solving the problem and answering questions.

## 5 Assess & Remediate

### Lesson Quiz

1. What is the solution of $16^{-3n+2} = 64$?
2. What is the solution of $12^{4x} = 256$?
3. What is the solution of $36^{-3x} = 1500$?
4. **Do you UNDERSTAND?** A population of 12,000 fish has a growth rate of 4% each year. Write a model for the situation. How many years will it take for the population to reach 20,000?
5. What is the solution of log $5x - 3 = 2$?
6. Solve log $2x - $ log $8 = 3$.

**ANSWERS TO LESSON QUIZ**

1. $\frac{1}{6}$
2. 0.5579
3. −0.68
4. $12{,}000(1.04)^n = 20{,}000$; 13.02 years
5. 20,000
6. 4000

**PRESCRIPTION FOR REMEDIATION**

Use the student work on the Lesson Quiz to prescribe a differentiated review assignment:

| Points | Differentiated Remediation |
|--------|---------------------------|
| 0–2 | Intervention |
| 3–5 | On-level |
| 6 | Extension |

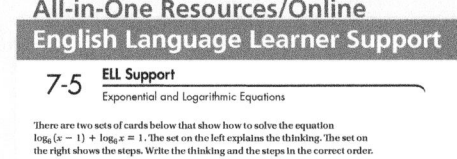

### 5 Assess & Remediate

Assign the Lesson Quiz. Appropriate intervention, practice, or enrichment is automatically generated based on student performance.

## Differentiated Remediation

Available in editable format online.

### Intervention

- **Reteaching** (2 pages) Provides reteaching and practice exercises for the key lesson concepts. Use with struggling students or absent students.
- **English Language Learner Support** Helps students develop and reinforce mathematical vocabulary and key concepts.

**All-in-One Resources/Online**
**Reteaching**

**All-in-One Resources/Online**
**English Language Learner Support**

# Differentiated Remediation *continued*

Available in editable format online.

## On-Level

- **Practice** (2 pages) Provides extra practice for each lesson. For simpler practice exercises, use the Form K Practice pages found in the All-in-One Teaching Resources and online.

- **Think About a Plan** Helps students develop specific problem-solving skills and strategies by providing scaffolded guiding questions.
- **Standardized Test Prep** Focuses on all major exercises, all major question types, and helps students prepare for the high-stakes assessments.

## Extension

- **Enrichment** Provides students with interesting problems and activities that extend the concepts of the lesson.
- **Activities, Games, and Puzzles** Worksheets that can be used for concepts development, enrichment, and for fun!

---

### Practice and Problem Solving Wkbk/All-in-One Resources/Online
**Practice page 1**

**7-5 Practice** — Form G
Exponential and Logarithmic Equations

Solve each equation.

1. $8^{2x} = 32$ $\frac{5}{6}$
2. $7^n = 343$ 3
3. $9^{2x} = 27$ $\frac{3}{4}$
4. $25^{2n+1} = 625$ $\frac{1}{2}$
5. $36^{-2x+1} = 216$ $-\frac{1}{4}$
6. $64^x = 4096$ 2

Solve each equation. Round answers to the nearest hundredth.

7. $5^{2x} = 20$ 0.93
8. $8^{n+1} = 3$ $-0.47$
9. $4^{n-2} = 3$ 2.79
10. $4^{3n} = 5$ 0.39
11. $15^{2n-3} = 245$ 2.52
12. $4^x - 5 = 12$ 2.04

Solve by graphing. Round to the nearest hundredth.

13. $2^n + 5 = 120$ 1.91
14. $5^{n+1} = 175$ 2.21
15. $8^x = 58$ 1.95
16. $10^n = 3$ 0.48
17. $10^{3y} = 5$ 0.23
18. $10^{k-2} = 20$ 3.30
19. $5^x = 4$ 0.86
20. $2^{4x} = 8$ 0.75
21. $3^{x+5} = 15$ $-2.54$

Use a table to solve each equation. Round to the nearest hundredth.

22. $8^{2n} = 3$ 0.26
23. $12^{2n-1} = 64$ 1.34
24. $12^{n-2} = 8$ 2.84
25. $10^x = 182$ 2.26
26. $8^n = 12$ 1.19
27. $12^n = 9$ 0.48
28. $5^{n+1} = 3$ $-0.32$
29. $10^{k-2} = 0.3$ 1.48
30. $3^{3n} = 50$ 1.19

31. The equation $y = 281(1.01)^x$ is a model for the population of the United States $y$, in millions of people, $x$ years after the year 2000. Estimate when the United States population will reach 400 million people. in the year 2035

Solve each equation. Check your answers.

32. $\log x = 2$ 100
33. $\log 4x = -1$ $\frac{1}{40}$
34. $\log 3x = 2$ $\frac{100}{3}$
35. $\log 4x = 2$ 25
36. $4 \log x = 4$ 10
37. $8 \log x = 16$ 100
38. $2 \log x = 2$ 10
39. $\log (2x + 5) = 3$ $\frac{995}{2}$
40. $\log (3x - 2) = 3$ 334
41. $\log (x - 25) = 2$ 125
42. $2 \log (2x + 5) = 4$ $\frac{95}{2}$
43. $3 \log (1 - 2x) = 6$ $-\frac{99}{2}$

---

### Practice and Problem Solving Wkbk/All-in-One Resources/Online
**Practice page 2**

**7-5 Practice** (continued) — Form G
Exponential and Logarithmic Equations

Solve each equation.

44. $\log x - \log 4 = 3$ 4000
45. $\log x - \log 4 = -2$ $\frac{1}{25}$
46. $2 \log x - \log 4 = 2$ 20
47. $\log 3x - \log 5 = 1$ $\frac{50}{3}$
48. $2 \log x - \log 3 = 1$ $\sqrt{30}$
49. $\log 8 - \log 2x = -1$ 40
50. $2 \log 3x - \log 9 = 1$ $\sqrt{10}$
51. $2 \log x - \log 5 = -2$ $\frac{\sqrt{20}}{20}$
52. $\log (x + 21) + \log x = 2$ 4

53. The function $y = 1000(1.005)^x$ models the value of $1000 deposited at an interest rate of 6% per year (0.005 per month) $x$ months after the money is deposited.
   a. Use a graph (on your graphing calculator) to predict how many months it will be until the account is worth $1100. about 19 months
   b. Predict how many years it will be until the account is worth $5000. about 27 years

54. Suppose the population of a country is currently 8,100,000. Studies show this country's population is increasing 2% each year.
   a. What exponential function would be a good model for this country's population? $y = 8,100,000(1.02)^x$
   b. Using the equation you found in part (a), how many years will it take for the country's population to reach 9 million? Round your answer to the nearest hundredth. 5.32 years

55. Suppose you deposit $2500 in a savings account that pays you 5% interest per year.
   a. How many years will it take for you to double your money? about 14 years
   b. How many years will it take for your account to reach $8,000? about 24 years

**Mental Math** Solve each equation.

56. $5^x = \frac{1}{25}$ $-2$
57. $4^x = 64$ 3
58. $10^x = 0.0001$ $-4$
59. $\log_3 81 = x$ 4
60. $\log_2 \frac{1}{32} = x$ $-5$
61. $\log 1,000,000 = x$ 6

Use the properties of exponential and logarithmic functions to solve each system. Check your answers.

62. $\begin{cases} -2^{10-x} + y = 0 \\ y = 8^{x+2} \end{cases}$ (1, 512)
63. $\begin{cases} 3^{2x-y} = 1 \\ 4^{x+y} - 8 = 0 \end{cases}$ $\left(\frac{1}{2}, 1\right)$
64. $\begin{cases} \log_2 (x - 2y) = 3 \\ \log_2 (x + y) = \log_2 8 \end{cases}$ (8, 0)

---

### All-in-One Resources/Online
**Enrichment**

**7-5 Enrichment**
Exponential and Logarithmic Equations

When solving logarithm equations, you primarily use the Product Property, Quotient Property, and Power Property to simplify the equation. Here's an interesting, lesser-known property of logarithms to explore.

1. Determine the value of each pair of expressions.
   $\log_4 2, \log_4 2$ $2, \frac{1}{2}$
   $\log_3 81, \log_{81} 3$ $4, \frac{1}{4}$
   $\log_{10} 1000, \log_{1000} 10$ $3, \frac{1}{3}$

2. How are the values of each pair of expressions related?
   Answers may vary. Sample: When the base and argument are switched, the expressions are reciprocals.

3. This reciprocal property states that $\log_a b = \frac{1}{\log_b a}$. To prove this property, assume $r = \log_a b$ and $s = \log_b a$. Rewrite each of these equations in exponential form. $a^r = b, b^s = a$

4. Next, use one equation to substitute an equivalent expression in for $a$. What is your new equation? $(b^s)^r = b$

5. Use the laws of exponents to simplify. $b^{sr} = b$

6. Because the bases are the same, what equation can you write for the exponents? $sr = 1$

7. What must be true about $s$ and $r$ if the product equals 1? $s$ and $r$ must be reciprocals.

8. Use this new property to solve the equation $\log_5 x + \frac{1}{\log_{x} 5} = 4$. 25

---

### Practice and Problem Solving Wkbk/All-in-One Resources/Online
**Think About a Plan**

**7-5 Think About a Plan**
Exponential and Logarithmic Equations

**Seismology** An earthquake of magnitude 7.6 occurred in 2001 in Gujarat, India. It was 251 times as strong as the greatest earthquake ever to hit Pennsylvania. What is the magnitude of the Pennsylvania earthquake? (*Hint:* Refer to the Richter scale on page 453.)

**Know**

1. The magnitude of the Gujarat earthquake is [ 7.6 ].

2. The ratio of the intensity of the Gujarat earthquake to the intensity of Pennsylvania's greatest earthquake is [ 251 ].

**Need**

3. To solve the problem I need to find:
   the magnitude of the greatest Pennsylvania earthquake

**Plan**

4. Let $I_1$ and $M_1$ be the intensity and magnitude of the Gujarat earthquake. Let $I_2$ and $M_2$ be the intensity and magnitude of Pennsylvania's greatest earthquake. What equation should you use to model this situation?
   $\log \frac{I_1}{I_2} = M_1 - M_2$

5. What does $\frac{I_1}{I_2}$ represent? the ratio of the intensity of the Gujarat earthquake to the intensity of Pennsylvania's greatest earthquake

6. What can you substitute for $\frac{I_1}{I_2}$ in your equation? 251

7. Solve your equation for the magnitude of Pennsylvania's greatest earthquake.
   $M_2 = M_1 - \log 251 = 7.6 - \log 251 \approx 5.2$

8. The magnitude of Pennsylvania's greatest earthquake is [ about 5.2 ].

---

### Practice and Problem Solving Wkbk/All-in-One Resources/Online
**Standardized Test Prep**

**7-5 Standardized Test Prep**
Exponential and Logarithmic Equations

**Multiple Choice**

For Exercises 1–5, choose the correct letter.

1. If $9^x = 243$, what is the value of $x$? C
   Ⓐ 2  Ⓑ 2.5  Ⓒ 2.5  Ⓓ 10

2. If $2^{3x+2} = 64$, what is the value of $x$? G
   Ⓕ $\frac{8}{3}$  Ⓖ $\frac{4}{3}$  Ⓗ 2  Ⓘ $\frac{3}{4}$

3. If $\log (3x + 25) = 2$, what is the value of $x$? A
   Ⓐ 25  Ⓑ 75  Ⓒ $41\frac{2}{3}$  Ⓓ 100

4. Which best approximates the solution of $16^{2x} = 124$? F
   Ⓕ 0.869  Ⓖ 1.150  Ⓗ 1.739  Ⓘ 3.477

5. Which equation represents the solution of $2^{3x+1} = 7$? D
   Ⓐ $x = 3\left(\frac{\log 7}{\log 2} - 1\right)$
   Ⓑ $x = \frac{\log 7}{3 \log 2} - 1$
   Ⓒ $x = \frac{1}{3}\left(\frac{\log 7}{\log 2} - 1\right)$
   Ⓓ $x = \frac{1}{3}\left(\frac{\log 7}{\log 2}\right)$

**Short Response**

6. In 2007, the population of Tallahassee, Florida was 168,979. Some researchers believe that the population of Tallahassee will increase at a rate of 1% each year for the 10 years following this.
   a. If the researchers are correct, how many years will it take for the population of Tallahassee to reach 180,000?
   b. Explain in words or show your work for how you determined the number of years found in part (a).
   [2] a. about 7 years
   b. Because the population grows at a constant rate each year, an exponential model of the situation is $y = 168,979(1.01)^x$. $180,000 = 168,979(1.01)^x \rightarrow \frac{180,000}{168,979} = 1.01^x \rightarrow 1.0652 = x \log 1.01 \rightarrow x = \frac{\log 1.0652}{\log 1.01} = 6.348$.
   [1] incorrect number of years OR incorrect explanation
   [0] incorrect answers and no work shown OR no answers given

---

### Online Teacher Resource Center
**Activities, Games, and Puzzles**

**7-5 Game: Analyzing Equations**
Exponential and Logarithmic Equations

This is a game for the entire class. You will work in teams of three students. Your teacher can serve as the host. Your teacher will decide the order in which the questions are chosen and he or she may also decide on a time limit for each question. No calculators allowed!

- Write your answer next to each question. A correct response is worth three points.
  - **Category 1:** Answer *none, one,* or *two.*
  - **Category 2:** Give two consecutive numbers such as 5 *and* 6.
  - **Category 3:** Write A or B.

| Category 1: How Many Solutions? | Score |
|---|---|
| 1. $2^x = x + 3$ two | |
| 2. $\log_2 x = x + 2$ none | |
| 3. $2^x = 5$ one | |
| 4. $\log_2 x = 2$ one | |
| 5. $2^x = -5$ none | |
| 6. $\log_2 x = x - 2$ two | |
| 7. $2^x + 2 = 0$ none | |
| 8. $\log_2 (x - 2) = 4x$ none | |

| Category 2: Between Which Two Whole Numbers is $x$? | Score |
|---|---|
| 1. $3 \times 2^x = 75$ 4 and 5 | |
| 2. $2 \times 2^x = 20$ 3 and 4 | |
| 3. $\log_2 x = 3.1$ 8 and 9 | |
| 4. $\log_2 x = 0.1$ 1 and 2 | |
| 5. $5 \times 2^x = 60$ 3 and 4 | |
| 6. $-3 \times 2^x = -9$ 1 and 2 | |

| Category 3: Which Equation Has the Greater Solution? | | | Score |
|---|---|---|---|
| 1. A. $2^x = 64$ | or | B. $3^x = 81$ A | |
| 2. A. $10^x = 1000$ | or | B. $5^x = 25$ A | |
| 3. A. $4^x = 1$ | or | B. $5^x = 125$ B | |
| 4. A. $3^x = 27$ | or | B. $2^x = 32$ B | |

# Using Logarithms for Exponential Models

You can transform an exponential function into a linear function by taking the logarithm of each side. Since linear models are easy to recognize, you can then determine whether an exponential function is a good model for a set of values.

$y = ab^x$ — Write the general form of an exponential function.

$\log y = \log ab^x$ — Take the logarithm of each side.

$\log y = \log a + x(\log b)$ — Use the Product Property and the Power Property.

If $\log b$ and $\log a$ are constants, then $\log y = (\log b)x + \log a$ is a linear equation in slope-intercept form when you plot the points as $(x, \log y)$.

## Activity

Determine whether an exponential function is a good model for the values in the table.

| x | 0 | 2 | 4 | 6 | 8 | 10 |
|---|---|---|---|---|---|---|
| y | 0.5 | 2 | 7.8 | 32 | 127.9 | 511.7 |

**Step 1** Enter the values into (stat) lists $L_1$ and $L_2$. To enter the values of $\log y$, place the cursor in the heading of $L_3$ and press (log) $L_2$ (enter).

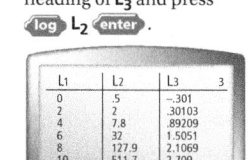

**Step 2** To graph $\log y$, access the (stat plot) feature and press **1**. Then enter $L_3$ next to **YLIST:**. Then press (zoom) **9**.

The points $(x, \log y)$ lie on a line, so an exponential model is appropriate.

**Step 3** Press (stat) ▷ **0** (enter) to find the exponential function $y = 0.5(2)^x$.

## Exercises

For each set of values, determine whether an exponential function is a good model. If so, find the exponential function.

**1.**

| x | 1 | 3 | 5 | 7 | 9 |
|---|---|---|---|---|---|
| y | 6 | 22 | 54 | 102 | 145 |

**2.**

| x | −1 | 0 | 1 | 2 | 3 |
|---|---|---|---|---|---|
| y | 40.2 | 19.8 | 9.9 | 5.1 | 2.5 |

**3. Writing** Explain how you could determine whether a logarithmic function is a good model for a set of data.

# Guided Instruction

**PURPOSE** To use logarithms to determine the appropriateness of an exponential model

**PROCESS** Students will
- take the logarithms of the y-values in a table.
- graph the new points (x, log y) to see if the new data is linear.

**DISCUSS** The Product Property of Logarithms is used to write an exponential equation in linear form.
- A linear function in slope-intercept form is $y = mx + b$.
- Visual inspection or a line of best fit can be used to determine if data are linear.

## Activity

An exponential model of the original data is appropriate if the points (x, log y) are linear.

**Q** What is the difference between using logarithms to solve an exponential equation and using logarithms to determine whether an exponential model is appropriate? **[When solving equations, logarithms of both sides must be taken. When determining appropriateness of an exponential model, use (x, log y) to see whether the data appears linear.]**

**Q** What happens if you try to find the logs of the values in a list that contains 0? Explain. **[The calculator gives the message ERR: DOMAIN because the domain contains 0 and log 0 is not defined.]**

# Answers

## Concept Byte

**1.** not a good model

**2.** $y = 20.0(0.50)^x$

**3.** Answers may vary. Sample: Use the Change of Base Formula to get $\log x = \frac{\log b}{a} y$. Let $L_1 = x$, $L_2 = y$, and $L_3 = \log x$. Graph $L_2$ and $L_3$. If it is linear, then the equation is logarithmic.

# 1 Interactive Learning

## Solve It!

**PURPOSE** To determine whether a bounding number exists for $y = \ln x$

**PROCESS** Students may

- use the asymptotes of $y = e^x$ to draw conclusions about a bounding number for $y = \ln x$.
- use graphs and tables to determine whether a bounding number exists.

### FACILITATE

**Q** How can you use $y = e^x$ to find the range of $y = \ln x$? **[The domain of $y = e^x$ is the range of $y = \ln x$, so the range of $y = \ln x$ is all real numbers.]**

**ANSWER** See Solve It in Answers on next page.

**CONNECT THE MATH** Students use asymptotes to draw conclusions about a bounding number for the natural logarithm function. In the lesson, students apply the same properties of regular logarithms to natural logarithms.

## 2 Guided Instruction

### Take Note

**Q** How can you write ln $5x$ using $\log_b$ notation? Explain. **[$\log_e 5x$; the natural log uses the number $e$ as its base.]**

### Problem 1                    EXTENSION

**Q** How are log 3 and ln 3 different? Explain. **[Log 3 means 10 raised to some number is 3. log 3 ≈ 0.477. ln 3 means $e$ raised to some number is 3. ln 3 ≈ 1.099]**

---

**Objectives** To evaluate and simplify natural logarithmic expressions
To solve equations using natural logarithms

**Getting Ready!**

A function f is <u>bounded above</u> if there is some number B that f(x) can never exceed. The exponential function base $e$ shown here is not bounded above. Is the logarithmic function base $e$ bounded above? If so, find a bounding number. If not, explain why.

> If you can find one number that bounds y = $\log_e$ x above, then you know there are many others.

**Lesson Vocabulary**
- natural logarithmic function

The function $y = e^x$ has an inverse, the **natural logarithmic function**, $y = \log_e x$, or $y = \ln x$.

**Essential Understanding** The functions $y = e^x$ and $y = \ln x$ are inverse functions. Just as before, this means that if $a = e^b$, then $b = \ln a$, and vice versa.

### take note

**Key Concept**   **Natural Logarithmic Function**

If $y = e^x$, then $x = \log_e y = \ln y$. The natural logarithmic function is the inverse of $x = \ln y$, so you can write it as $y = \ln x$.

① $y = e^x$
② $y = \ln x$

**Plan**

**Can you use properties of logarithms?**
Yes; the properties you studied in Lesson 7-4 apply to logarithms with any base.

**Problem 1** Simplifying a Natural Logarithmic Expression

What is $2 \ln 15 - \ln 75$ written as a single natural logarithm?

$2 \ln 15 - \ln 75 = \ln 15^2 - \ln 75$    Power Property of Logarithms

$= \ln \dfrac{15^2}{75}$    Quotient Property of Logarithms

$= \ln 3$    Simplify.

478    Chapter 7   Exponential and Logarithmic Functions

---

**BIG idea** Function                    **UbD**

**ESSENTIAL UNDERSTANDINGS**

- The function $y = e^x$ and $y = \ln x$ are inverse functions. Just as before, this means that if $a = e^b$, then $b = \ln a$, and vice versa.
- The exponential function $y = b^x$ and the logarithmic function $y = \log_b x$ are inverse functions.

### Math Background

Just as 10 is the base of common logarithms, the number $e$ is the base of natural logarithms. The natural logarithm function and the exponential functions with base $e$ are inverse functions. The rules and properties used for solving regular logarithms can also be used for solving natural logarithms. This is evident because the only restriction for logarithms of the form $\log_b y = x$ is that $y$ is positive and $b$ is greater than 0 but not equal to 1. Because $e \approx 2.71828$, it falls within the restrictions for $b$, and the properties can be used. In fact, ln $x$ is

equivalent to $\log_e x$. Convention dictates using ln for natural logarithms. Natural logarithms are introduced here because they arise in so many situations. Biology, banking, physics, and statistics are just a few of the areas that use natural logarithms.

### Support Student Learning

Use the **Algebra 2 Companion** to engage and support students during instruction. See Lesson Resources at the end of this lesson for details.

**PowerAlgebra.com**

## 1 Interactive Learning

### Solve It!

Step out how to solve the Problem with helpful hints and an online question. Other questions are listed above in Interactive Learning.

**Got It?** **1.** What is each expression written as a single natural logarithm?

**a.** $\ln 7 + 2 \ln 5$      **b.** $3 \ln x - 2 \ln 2x$      **c.** $3 \ln x + 2 \ln y + \ln 5$

You can use the inverse relationship between the functions $y = \ln x$ and $y = e^x$ to solve certain logarithmic and exponential equations.

**Think**

How do you go from logarithmic form to exponential form?
Use the definition of logarithm: $\ln x = y$ if and only if $x = e^y$.

**Problem 2** Solving a Natural Logarithmic Equation

What are the solutions of $\ln (x - 3)^2 = 4$?

$$\ln (x - 3)^2 = 4$$
$$(x - 3)^2 = e^4 \qquad \text{Rewrite in exponential form.}$$
$$x - 3 = \pm e^2 \qquad \text{Find the square root of each side.}$$
$$x = 3 \pm e^2 \qquad \text{Solve for } x.$$
$$x \approx 10.39 \text{ or } -4.39 \qquad \text{Use a calculator.}$$

**Check**

$$\ln (10.39 - 3)^2 \overset{?}{=} 4 \qquad \ln (-4.39 - 3)^2 \overset{?}{=} 4$$
$$4.0003 \approx 4 \; \checkmark \qquad\qquad 4.0003 \approx 4 \; \checkmark$$

 **Got It?** **2.** What are the solutions of each equation? Check your answers.

**a.** $\ln x = 2$      **b.** $\ln (3x + 5)^2 = 4$      **c.** $\ln 2x + \ln 3 = 2$

**Plan**

How can you solve this equation?
First get $e^x$ by itself on one side of the equation. Then rewrite the equation in logarithmic form and solve for $x$.

**Problem 3** Solving an Exponential Equation

What is the solution of $4e^{2x} + 2 = 16$?

$$4e^{2x} + 2 = 16$$
$$4e^{2x} = 14 \qquad \text{Subtract 2 from each side.}$$
$$e^{2x} = 3.5 \qquad \text{Divide each side by 4.}$$
$$2x = \ln 3.5 \qquad \text{Rewrite in logarithmic form.}$$
$$x = \frac{\ln 3.5}{2} \qquad \text{Divide each side by 2.}$$
$$x \approx 0.626 \qquad \text{Use a calculator.}$$

**Check**

$$4e^{2x} + 2 = 16$$
$$4e^{2(0.626)} + 2 \overset{?}{=} 16$$
$$15.99 \approx 16 \; \checkmark$$

 **Got It?** **3.** What is the solution of each equation? Check your answers.

**a.** $e^{x-2} = 12$      **b.** $2e^{-x} = 20$      **c.** $e^{3x} + 5 = 15$

---

**Q** What do you need to do first before applying the Quotient or Product Property? **[Apply the Power Property.]**

## Problem 2

**Q** What are all the steps when writing a natural logarithmic equation in exponential form? **[Rewrite in exponential form by raising each side to the power of $e$, simplify the equation algebraically, and then solve with a calculator.]**

### Got It?

**Q** How can you use a graph or table to solve 2b? **[Answers may vary. Sample: Enter $Y_1 = 2 \ln (3x + 5)$ and $Y_2 = 4$ in your graphing calculator. Set your window, and find the intersection.]**

## Problem 3     EXTENSION

**Q** Can $e$ be raised to a negative power? Explain. **[Yes; answers may vary. Sample: Negative exponents indicate division by the base. Because $e$ is the irrational number $2.718\ldots$, it is possible to write $e^{-x}$ as a fraction. So $e^{-x}$ is equal to $\frac{1}{e^x}$]**

### Got It?     EXTENSION

Logarithms to any base can be used to solve exponential equations. Therefore, natural logarithms can be used to solve exponential equations that do not include the number $e$. For example, $2^x = 8$ can be solved by finding $\ln 2^x = \ln 8$. Thus, $x = \frac{\ln 8}{\ln 2} = 3$.

---

## 2 Guided Instruction

Each Problem is worked out and supported online.

**Problem 1**
Simplifying a Natural Logarithmic Expression

**Problem 2**
Solving a Natural Logarithmic Equation
*Animated*

**Problem 3**
Solving an Exponential Equation
*Animated*

**Problem 4**
Using Natural Logarithms

**Support in Algebra 2 Companion**
• Vocabulary
• Key Concepts
• Got It?

## Answers

**Solve It!**
No; $y = \ln x$ is the inverse of $y = e^x$. Since the domain of $y = e^x$ is all real numbers, the range of $y = \ln x$ is all real numbers.

### Got It?
**1. a.** $\ln 175$

    **b.** $\ln \frac{x}{4}$

    **c.** $\ln 5x^3 y^2$

**2. a.** $e^2$, or about 7.39

    **b.** $\frac{-5 \pm e^2}{3}$, or about 0.8 or $-4.13$

    **c.** $\frac{e^2}{6}$, or about 1.23

**3. a.** $\ln 2 + 2$, or about 4.48

    **b.** $-\ln 10$, or about $-2.3$

    **c.** $\frac{\ln 10}{3}$, or about 0.77

## Problem 4

**Q** What is $v = -0.0098t + c \ln R$ solved for $R$? Describe your steps. [$R = e^{\frac{v + 0.0098t}{c}}$; answers may vary. Sample: First add $0.0098t$ to both sides, then divide both sides by $c$. Then rewrite in exponential form.]

## Got It?

Encourage students to experiment with the formula on a calculator to see how the velocity will change given changes in $t$, $c$, or $R$.

# 3 Lesson Check

### Do you know HOW?  ERROR INTERVENTION

- If students have difficulty with Exercises 1–4, remind them to use the same properties as regular logarithms.

### Do you UNDERSTAND?

- If students have trouble with Exercise 9, review that $\ln 4x = 5$ means $e$ raised to some number is equal to $4x$.

### Close

**Q** How can you use the relationship between $y = e^x$ and $y = \ln x$ to solve exponential and logarithmic equations? [**The functions are inverses, so use exponents with base e to solve natural logarithms and natural logarithms to solve equations with e.**]

---

Natural logarithms are useful because they help express many relationships in the physical world.

 **Problem 4** Using Natural Logarithms

**Space** A spacecraft can attain a stable orbit 300 km above Earth if it reaches a velocity of 7.7 km/s. The formula for a rocket's maximum velocity $v$ in kilometers per second is $v = -0.0098t + c \ln R$. The booster rocket fires for $t$ seconds and the velocity of the exhaust is $c$ km/s. The ratio of the mass of the rocket filled with fuel to its mass without fuel is $R$. Suppose the rocket shown in the photo has a mass ratio of 25, a firing time of 100 s and an exhaust velocity as shown. Can the spacecraft attain a stable orbit 300 km above Earth?

2.8 km/s

**Plan**

**How can you solve the problem?**
Use the given formula to find the maximum velocity $v$ of the spacecraft. If $v \geq 7.7$, the spacecraft can attain a stable orbit.

Let $R = 25$, $c = 2.8$, and $t = 100$. Find $v$.

| | |
|---|---|
| $v = -0.0098t + c \ln R$ | Use the formula. |
| $= -0.0098(100) + 2.8 \ln 25$ | Substitute. |
| $\approx -0.98 + 2.8(3.219)$ | Use a calculator. |
| $\approx 8.0$ | Simplify. |

The maximum velocity of 8.0 km/s is greater than the 7.7 km/s needed for a stable orbit. Therefore, the spacecraft can attain a stable orbit 300 km above Earth.

 **Got It?  4. a.** A booster rocket for a spacecraft has a mass ratio of about 15, an exhaust velocity of 2.1 km/s, and a firing time of 30 s. Can the spacecraft achieve a stable orbit 300 km above Earth?
  **b. Reasoning** Suppose a rocket, as designed, cannot provide enough velocity to achieve a stable orbit. Could alterations to the rocket make a stable orbit achievable? Explain.

 **Lesson Check**

**Do you know HOW?**

Write each expression as a single natural logarithm.

**1.** $4 \ln 3$   **2.** $\ln 18 - \ln 10$

**3.** $\ln 3 + \ln 4$   **4.** $-2 \ln 2$

Solve each equation.

**5.** $\ln 5x = 4$   **6.** $\ln (x - 7) = 2$

**7.** $2 \ln x = 4$   **8.** $\ln (2 - x) = 1$

**Do you UNDERSTAND?**

**9. Error Analysis** Describe the error made in solving the equation. Then find the correct solution.

$$\ln 4x = 5$$
$$e^{\ln 4x} = e^5$$
$$4x = 5$$
$$x = \frac{5}{4}$$
$$x = 1.25$$

**10. Reasoning** Can $\ln 5 + \log_2 10$ be written as a single logarithm? Explain your reasoning.

---

# Additional Problems

**1.** What is each expression written as a single natural logarithm?

**a.** $3 \ln 2 - 3 \ln x$
**b.** $2 \ln 3 + \ln 8$
**c.** $20 \ln x + 5 \ln y - 2 \ln z$

**ANSWER**

**a.** $\ln \frac{8}{x^3}$
**b.** $\ln 72$
**c.** $\ln \frac{x^{20}y^5}{z^2}$

**2.** What are the solutions of each equation?

**a.** $\ln x = 5$
**b.** $\ln (6x + 1) = 3$
**c.** $\ln (2x + 1)^2 = 6$

**ANSWER**
**a.** about 148.41
**b.** about 3.18
**c.** about 9.54 or $-10.54$

**3.** What is the solution of each equation?

**a.** $e^{x+3} = 24$
**b.** $5e^{-3x} = 45$
**c.** $2e^{5x} - 8 = 30$

**ANSWER**
**a.** about 0.18
**b.** about $-0.73$
**c.** about 0.59

**4.** Carbon dating is a method used to determine the age of organic material less than 50,000 years old. One of the formulas for carbon-14 dating is $t = \dfrac{\ln\left(\frac{N_f}{N_o}\right)}{-0.693} \times 5700$ where $\frac{N_f}{N_o}$ is the percent of carbon-14 remaining and $t$ is the time in years. A fossil is found to have 30% carbon-14 compared to a living sample. Using this formula, what is the age of the fossil?

**ANSWER** about 9903 years

# Answers

**Got It?** (continued)

**4. a.** No; the maximum velocity of 5.4 km/s is less than the 7.7 km/s needed for a stable orbit.

**b.** Yes; if, R could be changed so that $V > 7.7$.

## Practice and Problem-Solving Exercises

**A** Practice

Write each expression as a single natural logarithm.  See Problem 1.

**11.** $3 \ln 5$

**12.** $\ln 9 + \ln 2$

**13.** $\ln 24 - \ln 6$

**14.** $5 \ln m - 3 \ln n$

**15.** $\frac{1}{3}(\ln x + \ln y) - 4 \ln z$

**16.** $\ln a - 2 \ln b + \frac{1}{3}\ln c$

**17.** $4 \ln 8 + \ln 10$

**18.** $\ln 3 - 5 \ln 3$

**19.** $2 \ln 8 - 3 \ln 4$

Solve each equation. Check your answers.  See Problem 2.

**20.** $\ln 3x = 6$

**21.** $\ln x = -2$

**22.** $\ln(4x - 1) = 36$

**23.** $1.1 + \ln x^2 = 6$

**24.** $\ln \frac{x-1}{2} = 4$

**25.** $\ln 4r^2 = 3$

**26.** $2 \ln 2x^2 = 1$

**27.** $\ln(2m + 3) = 8$

**28.** $\ln(t - 1)^2 = 3$

Use natural logarithms to solve each equation.  See Problem 3.

**29.** $e^x = 18$

**30.** $e^{\frac{x}{5}} + 4 = 7$

**31.** $e^{2x} = 12$

**32.** $e^{\frac{x}{2}} = 5$

**33.** $e^{x+1} = 30$

**34.** $e^{2x} = 10$

**35.** $e^{3x} + 5 = 6$

**36.** $e^{\frac{x}{9}} - 8 = 6$

**37.** $7 - 2e^{\frac{x}{2}} = 1$

**Space** For Exercises 38 and 39, use $v = -0.0098t + c \ln R$, where $v$ is the velocity of the rocket, $t$ is the firing time, $c$ is the velocity of the exhaust, and $R$ is the ratio of the mass of the rocket filled with fuel to the mass of the rocket without fuel.  See Problem 4.

**38.** Find the velocity of a spacecraft whose booster rocket has a mass ratio of 20, an exhaust velocity of 2.7 km/s, and a firing time of 30 s. Can the spacecraft achieve a stable orbit 300 km above Earth?

**39.** A rocket has a mass ratio of 24 and an exhaust velocity of 2.5 km/s. Determine the minimum firing time for a stable orbit 300 km above Earth.

**B** Apply

**40. Think About a Plan** By measuring the amount of carbon-14 in an object, a paleontologist can determine its approximate age. The amount of carbon-14 in an object is given by $y = ae^{-0.00012t}$, where $a$ is the amount of carbon-14 originally in the object, and $t$ is the age of the object in years. In 2003, a bone believed to be from a dire wolf was found at the La Brea Tar Pits. The bone contains 14% of its original carbon-14. How old is the bone?
• What numbers should you substitute for $y$ and $t$?
• What properties of logarithms and exponents can you use to solve the equation?

**41. Archaeology** A fossil bone contains 25% of its original carbon-14. What is the approximate age of the bone?

Simplify each expression.

**42.** $\ln 1$

**43.** $\frac{\ln e}{4}$

**44.** $\frac{\ln e^2}{2}$

**45.** $\ln e^{83}$

**46.** $\ln e$

**47.** $\ln e^2$

**48.** $\ln e^{10}$

**49.** $10 \ln e$

**50.** $\ln e^3$

**51.** $\frac{\ln e^4}{8}$

## 4 Practice

**ASSIGNMENT GUIDE**

Basic: 11–39 all, 40–44 all, 52, 53

Average: 11–39 odd, 40–59

Advanced: 11–39 odd, 40–65

Standardized Test Prep: 66–71

Mixed Review: 72–84

**Reasoning** exercises have blue headings.

**Applications** exercises have red headings.

**EXERCISE 41:** Use the Think About a Plan worksheet in the **Practice and Problem Solving Workbook** (also available in the Teaching Resources in print and online) to further support students' development in becoming independent learners.

**HOMEWORK QUICK CHECK**

To check students' understanding of key skills and concepts, go over Exercises 13, 21, 40, 41, and 53.

## Answers

### Lesson Check

**1.** $\ln 81$  **2.** $\ln 1.8$  **3.** $\ln 12$

**4.** $-\ln 4$  **5.** $\approx 10.9$  **6.** $\approx 14.4$

**7.** $\approx 7.39$  **8.** $\approx -0.718$

**9.** error in 3rd line: $4x = 5$
should be: $4x = e^5$
$x = \frac{e^5}{4}; x \approx 37.1$

**10.** No; $\ln 5$ has base $e$ and $\log_2 10$ has base 2.

### Practice and Problem-Solving Exercises

**11.** $\ln 125$  **12.** $\ln 18$  **13.** $\ln 4$

**14.** $\ln \frac{m^5}{n^3}$  **15.** $\ln \frac{\sqrt[3]{xy}}{z^4}$  **16.** $\ln \frac{a\sqrt[3]{c}}{b^2}$

**17.** $\ln 40{,}960$  **18.** $\ln \frac{1}{81}$

**19.** $\ln 1$  **20.** $134.476$

**21.** $0.135$  **22.** $1.078 \times 10^{15}$

**23.** $\pm 11.588$  **24.** $110.196$

**25.** $\pm 2.241$  **26.** $\pm 0.908$

**27.** $1488.979$  **28.** $5.482, -3.482$

**29.** $\approx 2.890$  **30.** $\approx 5.493$

**31.** $\approx 1.242$  **32.** $\approx 3.219$

**33.** $\approx 2.401$  **34.** $\approx 1.151$

**35.** $0$  **36.** $\approx 23.752$

**37.** $\approx 2.2$  **38.** $7.79$ km/s; yes

**39.** at least 25 s  **40.** $\approx 16{,}384$ yrs

**41.** $\approx 11{,}552$ yrs  **42.** $0$

**43.** $\frac{1}{4}$  **44.** $1$

**45.** $83$  **46.** $1$

**47.** $2$  **48.** $10$

**49.** $10$  **50.** $3$

**51.** $\frac{1}{2}$

**PowerAlgebra.com**

## 3 Lesson Check

For a digital lesson check, use the Got It questions.

**Support in Algebra 2 Companion**
• Lesson Check

## 4 Practice

Assign homework to individual students or to an entire class.

# Answers

## Practice and Problem-Solving Exercises
(continued)

**52.** $\log e \neq 1$;

$$\ln 100 = \frac{\log 100}{\log e} = \frac{\log 10^2}{\log e} = \frac{2}{\log e} \approx 4.61$$

**53.** $\approx 301$ days

**54.** sometimes

**55.** never

**56.** always

**57.** 10.8

**58.** $\approx 5.8\%$ per h

**59.** $\approx 19.8$ h

**60.** 27,347.9

**61.** 78.342

**62.** no solution

**63.** Because the function is simplified in the beginning and the sq. root of the exponential function is not calculated.

**64. a.** $y = 1.5e^{0.12104t}$

    **b.** 2010

    **c.** 2018

    **d.** $t = \dfrac{\ln\left(\dfrac{y}{1.5}\right)}{0.12104}$

    **e.** Substitute the number of users found in (b) and (c) into the equation in (d). Determine whether your answers in years are the same as $t$.

---

**52. Error Analysis** A student has broken the natural logarithm key on his calculator, so he decides to use the Change of Base Formula to find ln 100. Explain his error and find the correct answer.

**53. Satellite** The battery power available to run a satellite is given by the formula $P = 50\,e^{-\frac{t}{250}}$, where $P$ is power in watts and $t$ is time in days. For how many days can the satellite run if it requires 15 watts of power?

Determine whether each statement is *always*, *sometimes*, or *never* true.

**54.** $\ln e^x \geq 1$        **55.** $\ln e^x = \ln e^x + 1$        **56.** $\ln t = \log_e t$

**57. Space** Use the formula for maximum velocity $v = -0.0098t + c \ln R$. Find the mass ratio of a rocket with an exhaust velocity of 3.1 km/s, a firing time of 50 s, and a maximum shuttle velocity of 6.9 km/s.

**Biology** The formula $H = \frac{1}{r}(\ln P - \ln A)$ models the number of hours it takes a bacteria culture to decline, where $H$ is the number of hours, $r$ is the rate of decline, $P$ is the initial bacteria population, and $A$ is the reduced bacteria population.

**58.** A scientist determines that an antibiotic reduces a population of 20,000 bacteria to 5000 in 24 hours. Find the rate of decline caused by the antibiotic.

**59.** A laboratory assistant tests an antibiotic that causes a rate of decline of 0.14. How long should it take for a population of 8000 bacteria to shrink to 500?

 **Challenge**    Solve each equation.

**60.** $\frac{1}{3}\ln x + \ln 2 - \ln 3 = 3$      **61.** $\ln(x + 2) - \ln 4 = 3$      **62.** $2e^{x-2} = e^x + 7$

**63. Error Analysis** Consider the solution to the equation $\ln(x - 3)^2 = 4$ at the right. In Problem 2 you saw that there are two solutions to this equation, $3 + e^2$ and $3 - e^2$. Why do you get only one solution using this method?

**64. Technology** In 2008, there were about 1.5 billion Internet users. That number is projected to grow to 3.5 billion in 2015.

    **a.** Let $t$ represent the time, in years, since 2008. Write a function of the form $y = ae^{ct}$ that models the expected growth in the population of Internet users.

    **b.** In what year are there 2 billion Internet users?

    **c.** In what year are there 5 billion Internet users?

    **d.** Solve your equation for $t$.

    **e. Writing** Explain how you can use your equation from part (d) to verify your answers to parts (b) and (c).

**65. Physics** The function $T(t) = T_r + (T_i - T_r)e^{kt}$ models Newton's Law of Cooling. $T(t)$ is the temperature of a heated substance $t$ minutes after it has been removed from a heat (or cooling) source. $T_i$ is the substance's initial temperature, $k$ is a constant for that substance, and $T_r$ is room temperature.

   **a.** The initial surface temperature of a beef roast is 236°F and room temperature is 72°F. If $k = -0.041$, how long will it take for this roast to cool to 100°F?

   **b. Graphing Calculator** Write and graph an equation that you can use to check your answer to part (a). Use your graph to complete the table below.

| Temperature (°F) | 225 | 200 | 175 | 150 | 125 | 100 | 75 |
|---|---|---|---|---|---|---|---|
| Minutes Later | | | | | | | |

---

## Standardized Test Prep

**66.** An investment of $750 will be worth $1500 after 12 years of continuous compounding at a fixed interest rate. What percent is the interest rate?

**67.** What is $\log 33{,}000 - \log 99 + \log 30$?

**68.** If $f(x) = 5 - x^2$ and $g(x) = x^2 - 3$, what is $(g \circ f)(6)$?

**69.** What is the positive root of $y = 2x^2 - 35x - 57$?

**70.** What is the real part of $3 + 2i$?

**71.** What is $\dfrac{\sqrt{36}}{\sqrt{4}}$?

---

## Mixed Review

**Solve each equation.**        **See Lesson 7-5.**

**72.** $3^{2x} = 6561$      **73.** $7^x - 2 = 252$      **74.** $25^{2x+1} = 144$

**75.** $\log 3x = 4$      **76.** $\log 5x + 3 = 3.7$      **77.** $\log 9 - \log x + 1 = 6$

**Find the inverse of each function. Is the inverse a function?**    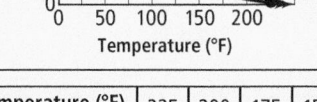 **See Lesson 6-7.**

**78.** $y = 5x + 7$     **79.** $y = 2x^3 + 10$     **80.** $y = -x^2 + 5$     **81.** $y = 3x + 2$

**Get Ready!**    **To prepare for Lesson 8-1, do Exercises 82–84.**

**For Exercises 82–84, $y$ varies directly with $x$.**      **See Lesson 2-2.**

**82.** If $x = 2$ when $y = 4$, find $y$ when $x = 5$.

**83.** If $x = 1$ when $y = 5$, find $y$ when $x = 3$.

**84.** If $x = 10$ when $y = 3$, find $y$ when $x = 4$.

PowerAlgebra.com     Lesson 7-6   Natural Logarithms     483

---

**65. a.** ≈43 min

  **b.** $t = -\dfrac{1}{0.041} \ln\left(\dfrac{T - 72}{164}\right)$

| Temperature (°F) | 225 | 200 | 175 | 150 | 125 | 100 | 75 |
|---|---|---|---|---|---|---|---|
| Minutes Later | 1.7 | 6.0 | 11.3 | 18.1 | 27.6 | 43.1 | 97.6 |

## Standardized Test Prep

**66.** 5.78

**67.** 4

**68.** 958

**69.** 0.2975

**70.** 3

**71.** 3

## Mixed Review

**72.** 4

**73.** 2.846

**74.** 0.272

**75.** $3333.\overline{3}$

**76.** 1.002

**77.** $9.0 \times 10^{-5}$

**78.** $y = \dfrac{x - 7}{5}$; yes

**79.** $y = \sqrt[3]{\dfrac{x - 10}{2}}$; yes

**80.** $y = \pm\sqrt{5 - x}$; no

**81.** $y = \dfrac{x - 2}{3}$; yes

**82.** 10

**83.** 15

**84.** $\dfrac{6}{5}$

Lesson 7-6   483

## Differentiated Remediation
Available in editable format online.

## Additional Instructional Support

### Algebra 2 Companion

Students can use the **Algebra 2 Companion** worktext (4 pages) as you teach the lesson. Use the Companion to support

- New Vocabulary
- Key Concepts
- Got It for each Problem
- Lesson Check

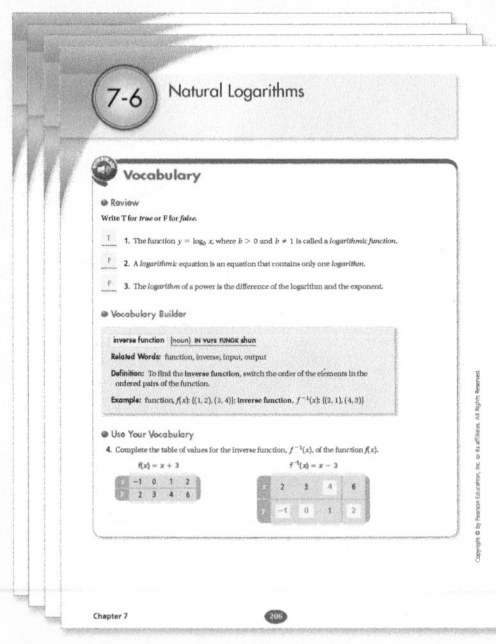

### ELL Support

**Connect to Prior Knowledge** Discuss the conventions for naming mathematical terms. First, explain to students that many Latin-based languages place the modifier after the noun. If students speak Spanish, Italian, French, Portuguese, or Romanian, ask them to give an example of a phrase in their language in which this convention is shown. Thus the term natural logarithms can be thought of as "logarithms, natural" which can be abbreviated as ln.

Continue the discussion by having students think of different mathematical terms that have been abbreviated. Examples might include $r$ for rate, $t$ for time, and $P$ for principal or probability. Examples of vocabulary terms that do not appear to be abbreviations include $m$ for slope and $b$ for $y$-intercept.

## 5 Assess & Remediate

### Lesson Quiz

1. What is $3 \ln 5 + \ln x$ written as a single natural logarithm?

2. What is the solution of $\ln (x + 2)^2 = 10$?

3. What is the solution of $3e^{-2x} + 5 = 23$?

4. **Do you UNDERSTAND?** The formula $t = \dfrac{\ln 2}{\ln(1 + r)}$, where $r$ is the interest rate and $t$ is the time in years, can be used to calculate the number of years it takes an investment to double in value. If an amount of money is invested at 3% interest, how many years will it take the investment to double?

### ANSWERS TO LESSON QUIZ

1. $\ln 125x$
2. about 146.41 or −150.41
3. about −0.896
4. about 23.4 years

### PRESCRIPTION FOR REMEDIATION

Use the student work on the Lesson Quiz to prescribe a differentiated review assignment:

| Points | Differentiated Remediation |
|--------|---------------------------|
| 0–1 | Intervention |
| 2–3 | On-level |
| 4 | Extension |

**PowerAlgebra.com**

### 5 Assess & Remediate

Assign the Lesson Quiz. Appropriate intervention, practice, or enrichment is automatically generated based on student performance.

## Intervention

- **Reteaching** (2 pages) Provides reteaching and practice exercises for the key lesson concepts. Use with struggling students or absent students.

- **English Language Learner Support** Helps students develop and reinforce mathematical vocabulary and key concepts.

**All-in-One Resources/Online**
**Reteaching**

**All-in-One Resources/Online**
**English Language Learner Support**

# Differentiated Remediation *continued*

Available in editable format online.

## On-Level

- **Practice** (2 pages) Provides extra practice for each lesson. For simpler practice exercises, use the Form K Practice pages found in the All-in-One Teaching Resources and online.

- **Think About a Plan** Helps students develop specific problem-solving skills and strategies by providing scaffolded guiding questions.

- **Standardized Test Prep** Focuses on all major exercises, all major question types, and helps students prepare for the high-stakes assessments.

## Extension

- **Enrichment** Provides students with interesting problems and activities that extend the concepts of the lesson.

- **Activities, Games, and Puzzles** Worksheets that can be used for concepts development, enrichment, and for fun!

### Practice and Problem Solving Wkbk/All-in-One Resources/Online
**Practice page 1**

### Practice and Problem Solving Wkbk/All-in-One Resources/Online
**Practice page 2**

### All-in-One Resources/Online
**Enrichment**

### Practice and Problem Solving Wkbk/All-in-One Resources/Online
**Think About a Plan**

### Practice and Problem Solving Wkbk/All-in-One Resources/Online
**Standardized Test Prep**

### Online Teacher Resource Center
**Activities, Games, and Puzzles**

# Guided Instruction

**PURPOSE** To show how to solve exponential and logarithmic inequalities using graphs or tables

**PROCESS** Students will

- find the point of intersection for two functions and use this information to solve the inequality.
- define the window and table start values to find all solutions of the inequalities.

**DISCUSS** Point out that you are using a system of equations to determine the solution to the inequality. Each side of the equation is written as a function, and then the intersection is found. Elicit that

- the intersection of two functions represents the solution to an equality. Use the trace function to find values that make the inequality true.
- it is not possible to find the logarithm of 0 or a negative number.

## Example 1

> **Q** Why are you not shading above and/or below the functions? **[Shading above and below functions indicates you are solving a system of inequalities. The inequality being solved contains 1 variable, so your solution is shown on a number line.]**

## Exercises

It is important to visualize a graph before using a graphing calculator to minimize mistakes in input.

> **Q** How would you describe the graph used to determine the solution for Exercise 2? **[The graph of $y = \log x + 3\log(x - 1)$ resides only in Quadrants I and IV. The domain is all positive real numbers greater than 1 and the range is all real numbers.]**

---

You can use the graphing and table capabilities of your calculator to solve problems involving exponential and logarithmic inequalities.

## Example 1

**Solve $2(3)^{x+4} > 10$ using a graph.**

**Step 1** Define **Y1** and **Y2**.

**Step 2** Make a graph and find the point of intersection.

**Step 3** Identify the $x$-values that make the inequality true.

$2(3)^{x+4} > 10$

The solution is $x > -2.535$.

## Exercises

**Solve each inequality using a graph.**

1. $4(3)^{x+1} > 6$
2. $\log x + 3\log(x - 1) < 4$
3. $3(2)^{x+2} \geq 5$
4. $x + 1 < 12\log x$
5. $2(3)^{x-4} > 7$
6. $\log x + 2\log(x - 1) < 1$
7. $4(2)^{x-1} \leq 5$
8. $2\log x + 4\log(x + 3) > 3$
9. $5(4)^{x-1} < 2$

10. **Bacteria Growth** Scientists are growing bacteria in a laboratory. They start with a known population of bacteria and measure how long it takes the population to double.
    a. Write an exponential function that models the population in Sample A as a function of time in hours.
    b. Write an exponential function that models the population in Sample B as a function of time in hours.
    c. Write an inequality that models the population in Sample B overtaking the population in Sample A.
    d. Use a graphing calculator to solve the inequality in part (c).

**Bacteria Population**

| Sample | Initial Population | Doubling Time (in hours) |
|---|---|---|
| Sample A | 200,000 | 1 |
| Sample B | 50,000 | 0.5 |

11. **Writing** Describe the solution sets to the inequality $x + c < \log x$ as $c$ varies over the real numbers.

---

# Answers

## Concept Byte

1. $x > -0.63093$
2. $1 < x < 10.7591$
3. $x \geq -1.26303$
4. $1.67 < x < 11.9$
5. $x > 5.14031$
6. $1 < x < 2.86746$
7. $x \leq 1.32193$
8. $x > 1.53655$
9. $x < 0.339036$
10. a. $A(t) = 200,000(2)^t$
    b. $B(t) = 50,000(2)^{2t}$
    c. $200,000(2)^t < 50,000(2)^{2t}$
    d. $t > 2$
11. $x > 0$ and $c < 0$

## Example 2

Solve $\log x + 2\log(x + 1) < 2$ using a table.

**Step 1** Define **Y1** and **Y2**.

**Step 2** Make a table and examine the values.

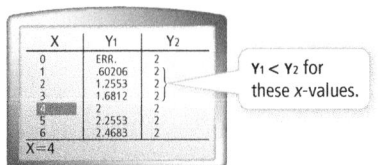

Y1 < Y2 for these *x*-values.

**Step 3** Identify the *x*-values that make the inequality true.

The solution is $0 < x < 4$.

## Exercises

Solve each inequality using a table.
(Hint: For more accurate results, set ΔTbl = 0.001.)

**12.** $\log x + \log(x + 1) < 3$

**13.** $3(2)^{x+1} > 5$

**14.** $\log x + 5\log(x - 1) \geq 3$

**15.** $5(3)^x \leq 2$

**16.** $3\log x + \log(x + 2) > 1$

**17.** $2(4)^{x+3} \leq 8$

**Barometric Pressure** Average barometric pressure varies with the altitude of a location. The greater the altitude is, the lower the pressure. The altitude $A$ is measured in feet above sea level. The barometric pressure $P$ is measured in inches of mercury (in. Hg). The altitude can be modeled by the function $A(P) = 90,000 - 26,500 \ln P$.

**18.** What is a reasonable domain of the function? What is the range of the function?

 **19. Graphing Calculator** Use a graphing calculator to make a table of function values. Use **TblStart** = 30 and **ΔTbl** = −1.

**20.** Write an equation to find what average pressure the model predicts at sea level, or $A = 0$. Use your table to solve the equation.

**21.** Kilimanjaro is a mountain in Tanzania that formed from three extinct volcanoes. The base of the mountain is at 3000 ft above sea level. The peak is at 19,340 ft above sea level. On Kilimanjaro, $3000 \leq A(P) \leq 19,340$ is true for the altitude. Write an inequality from which you can find minimum and maximum values of normal barometric pressure on Kilimanjaro. Use a table and solve the inequality for $P$.

**22.** Denver, Colorado, is nicknamed the "Mile High City" because its elevation is about 1 mile, or 5280 ft, above sea level. The lowest point in Phoenix, Arizona, is 1117 ft above sea level. Write an inequality that describes the range of $A(P)$ as you drive from Phoenix to Denver. Then solve the inequality for $P$. (Assume that you never go lower than 1117 ft and you never go higher than 5280 ft.)

**12.** $0 < x < 31.125$

**13.** $x > -0.263$

**14.** $x \geq 4.015$

**15.** $x \leq -0.835$

**16.** $x > 1.429$

**17.** $x \leq -2$

**18.** positive real numbers; real numbers

**19.**

**20.** $0 = 90,000 - 26,500 \ln P$; ≈29.85 in.

**21.** $3000 \leq 90,000 - 26,500 \ln P \leq 19,340$; $14.4 \leq P \leq 26.7$

**22.** $1117 \leq 90,000 - 26,500 \ln P \leq 5280$; $24.5 \leq P \leq 28.6$

# Performance Task

## Pull It All Together
The following questions are designed to:
- Help support students as they do the Tasks.
- Gauge the amount of support students need as they become independent problem solvers.

### Task 1
Solve problems involving exponential equations through algebraic, graphic, and numeric methods.
- For what variable in $A(t) = a(1 + r)^t$ will you substitute the expression $e^r - 1$ to answer part a?
- What portion of the graph of the exponential function would you look at to answer part b, remembering that $r$ is expressed as a decimal?
- To which equation should you add 1 so that the equations will have equal value and can be set equal to each other?

### Task 2
Model and solve a problem as a system of equations in two unknowns.
- How can you rewrite $b^{x-h}$ as $b^x$ times a constant value in terms of $b$ to answer part a?
- How can you write the inverse of $f_1(x) = b^{x-h}$?
- Is it easier to compare $h(x)$ to $g(x)$ in terms of common logarithms?

---

> To solve these problems, you will pull together concepts and skills related to exponential functions and logarithms.

**BIG** idea Modeling
You can represent many real-world mathematical problems algebraically. An algebraic model can lead to an algebraic solution.

### Task 1

**Suppose you invest $a$ dollars to earn an annual interest rate of $r$ percent (as a decimal). After $t$ years, the value of the investment with interest compounded yearly is $A(t) = a(1 + r)^t$. The value with interest compounded continuously is $A(t) = a \cdot e^{rt}$.**

**a.** Explain why you can call $e^r - 1$ the effective annual interest rate for the continuous compounding.

**b.** Suppose you can earn interest at some rate between 0% and 5%. Use your knowledge of the exponential function to explain why continuous compounding does not give you much of an investment advantage.

**c.** For each situation find the unknown quantity, such that continuous compounding gives you a $1 advantage over annually compounded interest.
- How much must you invest for 1 year at 2%?
- At what interest rate must you invest $1000 for 1 year?
- For how long must you invest $1000 at 2%?

**BIG** idea Function
You can use transformations such as translations, reflections, and dilations to understand relationships within a family of functions.

### Task 2

$f(x) = b^x$ and $g(x) = \log_b x$ **are inverse functions. Explain why each of the following is true.**

**a.** The translation $f_1(x) = b^{x-h}$ of $f$ is equivalent to a vertical stretch or compression of $f$.

**b.** The inverse of $f_1(x) = b^{x-h}$ is equivalent to a translation of $g$.

**c.** The inverse of $f_1(x) = b^{x-h}$ is not equivalent to a vertical stretch or compression of $g$.

**d.** The function $h(x) = \log_c x$ is a vertical stretch or compression of $g$ or of its reflection $-g$.

---

# Assess Performance

## Pull It All Together
See p. 49 for a holistic scoring rubric to gauge a student's progress on Understanding the Problem, Planning a Solution, Getting an Answer, and Assessing Autonomy.

### PARTIAL SOLUTION OUTLINES
**1. a.** Possible Plan: Set $a(1 + r)^t$ equal to $a \cdot e^{rt}$ and solve for $r$. (You will find that $r = e^r - 1$. Since $r$ is the annual interest rate, you can call $er - 1$ the effective annual interest rate for continuous compounding.)

**b.** Possible Plan: Calculate the interest earned for $1000 at 1%, 2%, 3%, 4%, and 5% interest compounded yearly for 1 year. Then calculate the interest earned for $1000 at 1%, 2%, 3%, 4%, and 5% interest compounded continuously for 1 year.

Compare the interest earned for each rate.

(You will see that the differences really don't give you that big an advantage. The differences are: 5 cents at 1%; 20 cents at 2%; 45 cents at 3%; 81 cents at 4%, and $1.27 at 5%.)

**c.** Possible Plan: Use the differences you found in part (b) to answer each question. For example, if the difference for 1 year at 2% is 20 cents then you would need 5 times that or 5 years worth of interest to make a $1 difference.
($5000; 5%; 5 years)

**2. a.** First step: Use the quotient of powers property to rewrite $b^{x-h}$ as $\frac{b^x}{b^h}$. (So, $f_1$ is now in the format $y = ab^x$. Thus, $f_1$ is a vertical stretch or compression of $f$.)

**b.** First step: Find the inverse of $f_1$. ($x = b^{y-h}$)

Second step: Write your result from Step 1 in logarithmic form to show that the inverse of $f_1$ is a translation of $g$. ($y = \log_b x + h$)

**c.** First step: Find the inverse of $f_1$. ($x = b^{y-h}$)

Second step: Write your result from Step 1 in logarithmic form. (A vertical stretch or compression of $g$ would be in the form $y = a \log_b x + h$ not $y = \log_b x + h$)

**d.** First step: Use the change of base formula to rewrite $\log_c x$ as $\frac{\log_b x}{\log_b c}$, or $\frac{1}{\log_b c} \log_b x$. ($h$ is now in the format $y = a \log_b x$. Therefore, $h$ is a vertical stretch or compression of $g$.)

# 7 Chapter Review

## Connecting **BIG** ideas to the Math You've Learned

**1 Modeling**
The function $y = ab^x$, $a > 0$, $b > 1$, models exponential growth. $y = ab^x$ models exponential decay if $0 < b < 1$.

**Exponential Models (Lesson 7-1)**
The population $P$ is 1000 at the start. In each time period,
• $P$ grows by 5%.
  $P = 1000(1.05)^t$
• $P$ shrinks by 5%.
  $P = 1000(0.95)^t$

**Properties of Logarithms (Lesson 7-4)**
$$b^a b^c = b^{a+c}$$
$$\log_b mn = \log_b m + \log_b n$$
$$\frac{b^a}{b^c} = b^{a-c}$$
$$\log_b \frac{m}{n} = \log_b m - \log_b n$$
$$\log_b m^n = n \log_b m$$
$$\log_n m = \frac{\log_b m}{\log_b n}$$

**2 Equivalence**
Logarithms are exponents. In fact, $\log_b a = c$ if and only if $b^c = a$.

**3 Function**
The exponential function $y = b^x$ and the logarithmic function $y = \log_b x$ are inverse functions.

**Logarithmic Functions as Inverses (Lesson 7-3)**
• $y = 2^x$
• $y = \log_2 x$
• $y = 2^{x-1}$
• $y = (\log_2 x) + 1$

**Exponential and Natural Logarithm Equations (Lessons 7-5 and 7-6)**
$$e^{x+3} = 4$$
$$e^x \cdot e^3 = 4 \quad \text{or} \quad x + 3 = \ln 4$$
$$e^x = \frac{4}{e^3}$$
$$x = \ln \frac{4}{e^3}$$
$$x = \ln 4 - \ln e^3 \quad x = (\ln 4) - 3$$

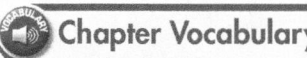

## Chapter Vocabulary

• asymptote (p. 435)
• Change of Base Formula (p. 464)
• common logarithm (p. 453)
• continuously compounded interest (p. 446)
• decay factor (p. 436)
• exponential decay (p. 435)
• exponential equation (p. 469)
• exponential function (p. 434)
• exponential growth (p. 435)
• growth factor (p. 436)
• logarithm (p. 451)
• logarithmic equation (p. 471)
• logarithmic function (p. 454)
• logarithmic scale (p. 453)
• natural base exponential functions (p. 446)
• natural logarithmic function (p. 478)

**Fill in the blanks.**

1. There are two types of exponential functions. For __?__, as the value of $x$ increases, the value of $y$ decreases, approaching zero. For __?__, as the value of $x$ increases, the value of $y$ increases.

2. As $x$ or $y$ increases in absolute value, the graph may approach a(n) __?__.

3. A(n) __?__ with a base $e$ is a __?__.

4. $A = Pe^{rt}$ is known as the __?__ formula.

5. The inverse of an exponential function with a base $e$ is the __?__.

**BIG** idea **Modeling**
**ESSENTIAL QUESTION** How do you model a quantity that changes regularly over time by the same percentage?
**ANSWER** The function $y = ab^x$, $a > 0$, $b > 1$, models exponential growth. $y = ab^x$ models exponential decay if $0 < b < 1$.

**BIG** idea **Equivalence**
**ESSENTIAL QUESTION** How are exponents and logarithms related?
**ANSWER** Logarithms are exponents. In fact, $\log_b a = c$ if and only if $b^c = a$.

**BIG** idea **Function**
**ESSENTIAL QUESTION** How are exponential functions and logarithmic functions related?
**ANSWER** The exponential function $y = b^x$ and the logarithmic function $y = \log_b x$ are inverse functions.

## Answers

### Chapter Review

1. exponential decay; exponential growth
2. asymptote
3. logarithm; natural logarithm function
4. continuously compounded interest
5. natural logarithmic function

## Summative Questions

Use the following prompts as you review this chapter with your students. The prompts are designed to help you assess your students' understanding of the BIG Ideas they have studied.

• How could you find the value of $\log_{16} 8$ without using a calculator?
• Compare continuously compounded interest to annual interest. Which method of compounding gives the most interest?
• How can you use exponents to solve a logarithmic equation? How can you use logarithms to solve an exponential equation?

# Answers

## Chapter Review (continued)

6. exponential growth; (0, 1)
7. exponential growth; (0, 2)
8. exponential growth; (0, 0.2)
9. exponential decay; (0, 3)
10. exponential growth; $\left(0, \frac{25}{7}\right)$
11. exponential growth; (0, 0.0015)
12. exponential decay; (0, 2.25)
13. exponential decay; (0, 0.5)
14. $y = 12{,}500(0.91)^x$; \$7800
15. $y = 50(1.03)^x$; \$58
16. The parent graph $y = 2^x$ is stretched by a factor of 5, translated 1 unit to the left, and 3 units up.
17. The parent graph $y = \left(\frac{1}{3}\right)^x$ is reflected across the $x$-axis, stretched by a factor of 2, and translated 2 units to the right.
18. \$1100.76
19. \$291.91
20. 0.0498
21. 0.3679
22. 148.4132
23. 0.6065

## 7-1 Exploring Exponential Models

### Quick Review

The general form of an **exponential function** is $y = ab^x$, where $x$ is a real number, $a \neq 0$, $b > 0$, and $b \neq 1$. When $b > 1$, the function models **exponential growth**, and $b$ is the **growth factor**. When $0 < b < 1$, the function models **exponential decay**, and $b$ is the **decay factor**. The $y$-intercept is $(0, a)$.

### Example

Determine whether $y = 2(1.4)^x$ is an example of exponential growth or decay. Then, find the $y$-intercept.

Since $b = 1.4 > 1$, the function represents exponential growth.

Since $a = 2$, the $y$-intercept is $(0, 2)$.

### Exercises

Determine whether each function is an example of exponential growth or decay. Then, find the $y$-intercept.

6. $y = 5^x$
7. $y = 2(4)^x$
8. $y = 0.2(3.8)^x$
9. $y = 3(0.25)^x$
10. $y = \frac{25}{7}\left(\frac{7}{5}\right)^x$
11. $y = 0.0015(10)^x$
12. $y = 2.25\left(\frac{1}{3}\right)^x$
13. $y = 0.5\left(\frac{1}{4}\right)^x$

Write a function for each situation. Then find the value of each function after five years. Round to the nearest dollar.

14. A \$12,500 car depreciates 9% each year.
15. A baseball card bought for \$50 increases 3% in value each year.

## 7-2 Properties of Exponential Functions

### Quick Review

Exponential functions can be translated, stretched, compressed, and reflected.

The graph of $y = ab^{x-h} + k$ is the graph of the parent function $y = b^x$ stretched or compressed by a factor $|a|$, reflected across the $x$-axis if $a < 0$, and translated $h$ units horizontally and $k$ units vertically.

The **continuously compounded interest** formula is $A = Pe^{rt}$, where $P$ is the principal, $r$ is the annual interest rate, and $t$ is time in years.

### Example

How does the graph of $y = -3^x + 1$ compare to the graph of the parent function?

The parent function is $y = 3^x$.

Since $a = -1$, the graph is reflected across the $x$-axis.

Since $k = 1$, it is translated up 1 unit.

### Exercises

How does the graph of each function compare to the graph of the parent function?

16. $y = 5(2)^{x+1} + 3$
17. $y = -2\left(\frac{1}{3}\right)^{x-2}$

Find the amount in a continuously compounded account for the given conditions.

18. principal: \$1000
    annual interest rate: 4.8%
    time: 2 years
19. principal: \$250
    annual interest rate: 6.2%
    time: 2.5 years

Evaluate each expression to four decimal places.

20. $e^{-3}$
21. $e^{-1}$
22. $e^5$
23. $e^{-\frac{1}{2}}$

## 7-3 Logarithmic Functions as Inverses

### Quick Review

If $x = b^y$, then $\log_b x = y$. The **logarithmic function** is the inverse of the exponential function, so the graphs of the functions are reflections of one another across the line $y = x$. Logarithmic functions can be translated, stretched, compressed, and reflected, as represented by $y = a \log_b(x - h) + k$, similarly to exponential functions.

When $b = 10$, the logarithm is called a **common logarithm**, which you can write as $\log x$.

### Example

Write $5^{-2} = 0.04$ in logarithmic form.

If $y = b^x$, then $\log_b y = x$.

$y = 0.04$, $b = 5$ and $x = -2$.

So, $\log_5 0.04 = -2$.

### Exercises

Write each equation in logarithmic form.

**24.** $6^2 = 36$  **25.** $2^{-3} = 0.125$

**26.** $3^3 = 27$  **27.** $10^{-3} = 0.001$

Evaluate each logarithm.

**28.** $\log_2 64$  **29.** $\log_3 \frac{1}{9}$

**30.** $\log 0.00001$  **31.** $\log_2 1$

Graph each logarithmic function.

**32.** $y = \log_3 x$  **33.** $y = \log x + 2$

**34.** $y = 3 \log_2(x)$  **35.** $y = \log_5(x + 1)$

How does the graph of each function compare to the graph of the parent function?

**36.** $y = 3 \log_4(x + 1)$  **37.** $y = -\ln x + 2$

## 7-4 Properties of Logarithms

### Quick Review

For any positive numbers, $m$, $n$, and $b$ where $b \neq 1$, each of the following statements is true. Each can be used to rewrite a logarithmic expression.

- $\log_b mn = \log_b m + \log_b n$, by the Product Property
- $\log_b \frac{m}{n} = \log_b m - \log_b n$, by the Quotient Property
- $\log_b m^n = n \log_b m$, by the Power Property

### Example

Write $2 \log_2 y + \log_2 x$ as a single logarithm. Identify any properties used.

$2 \log_2 y + \log_2 x$

$= \log_2 y^2 + \log_2 x$  Power Property

$= \log_2 xy^2$  Product Property

### Exercises

Write each expression as a single logarithm. Identify any properties used.

**38.** $\log 8 + \log 3$  **39.** $\log_2 5 - \log_2 3$

**40.** $4 \log_3 x + \log_3 7$  **41.** $\log x - \log y$

**42.** $\log 5 - 2 \log x$  **43.** $3 \log_4 x + 2 \log_4 x$

Expand each logarithm. State the properties of logarithms used.

**44.** $\log_4 x^2 y^3$  **45.** $\log 4s^4 t$

**46.** $\log_3 \frac{2}{x}$  **47.** $\log(x + 3)^2$

**48.** $\log_2(2y - 4)^3$  **49.** $\log \frac{z^2}{5}$

Use the Change of Base Formula to evaluate each expression.

**50.** $\log_2 7$  **51.** $\log_3 10$

---

**24.** $2 = \log_6 36$

**25.** $-3 = \log_2 0.125$

**26.** $3 = \log_3 27$

**27.** $-3 = \log 0.001$

**28.** 6  **29.** $-2$  **30.** $-5$  **31.** 0

**32.**

**33.**

**34.**

**35.**

**36.** The parent graph $y = \log_4 x$ is stretched by a factor of 3 and translated 1 unit to the left.

**37.** The parent graph $y = \ln x$ is reflected across the $x$-axis and translated 2 units up.

**38.** $\log 24$; Product Prop.

**39.** $\log_2 \frac{5}{3}$; Quotient Prop.

**40.** $\log_3 7x^4$; Power and Product Prop.

**41.** $\log \frac{x}{y}$; Quotient Prop.

**42.** $\log \frac{5}{x^2}$; Power and Quotient Prop.

**43.** $\log_4 x^5$; Power and Product Prop.

**44.** $2 \log_4 x + 3 \log_4 y$; Product and Power Prop.

**45.** $\log 4 + 4 \log s + \log t$; Product and Power Prop.

**46.** $\log_3 2 - \log_3 x$; Quotient Prop.

**47.** $2 \log(x + 3)$; Power Prop.

**48.** $3 \log_2 2 + 3 \log_2(y - 2)$; Power and Product Prop.

**49.** $2 \log z - \log 5$; Power and Quotient Prop.

**50.** $\approx 2.8$

**51.** $\approx 2.1$

# Answers

## Chapter Review (continued)

**52.** 0.75
**53.** 3.2619
**54.** 4.6542
**55.** 1.3652
**56.** 3.3333
**57.** 8
**58.** 50
**59.** $7.6256 \times 10^{12}$
**60.** 0.9307
**61.** 0.6599
**62.** 0.6658
**63.** 3.0589
**64.** $\approx 18.2\ h$
**65.** $\approx 0.83$
**66.** $\approx 2.26$
**67.** $\approx 4.31$
**68.** $\approx 0.54$
**69.** $\approx 3.77$
**70.** $\approx 6.03$
**71.** $\approx 3.4\%$

## 7-5 Exponential and Logarithmic Equations

### Quick Review

An equation in the form $b^{cx} = a$, where the exponent includes a variable, is called an **exponential equation**. You can solve exponential equations by taking the logarithm of each side of the equation. An equation that includes one or more logarithms involving a variable is called a **logarithmic equation**.

### Example

Solve and round to the nearest ten-thousandth.

$$6^{2x} = 75$$

| | |
|---|---|
| $\log 6^{2x} = \log 75$ | Take the logarithm of both sides. |
| $2x \log 6 = \log 75$ | Power Property of Logarithms |
| $x = \dfrac{\log 75}{2 \log 6}$ | Divide both sides by 2 log 6. |
| $x \approx 1.2048$ | Evaluate using a calculator. |

### Exercises

**Solve each equation. Round to the nearest ten-thousandth.**

**52.** $25^{2x} = 125$  **53.** $3^x = 36$

**54.** $7^{x-3} = 25$  **55.** $5^x + 3 = 12$

**56.** $\log 3x = 1$  **57.** $\log_2 4x = 5$

**58.** $\log x = \log 2x^2 - 2$  **59.** $2 \log_3 x = 54$

**Solve by graphing. Round to the nearest ten-thousandth.**

**60.** $5^{2x} = 20$  **61.** $3^{7x} = 160$

**62.** $6^{3x+1} = 215$  **63.** $0.5^x = 0.12$

**64.** A culture of 10 bacteria is started, and the number of bacteria will double every hour. In about how many hours will there be 3,000,000 bacteria?

## 7-6 Natural Logarithms

### Quick Review

The inverse of $y = e^x$ is the **natural logarithmic function** $y = \log_e x = \ln x$. You solve natural logarithmic equations in the same way as common logarithmic equations.

### Example

Use natural logarithms to solve $\ln x - \ln 2 = 3$.

| | |
|---|---|
| $\ln x - \ln 2 = 3$ | |
| $\ln \frac{x}{2} = 3$ | Quotient Property |
| $\frac{x}{2} = e^3$ | Rewrite in exponential form. |
| $\frac{x}{2} \approx 20.0855$ | Use a calculator to find $e^3$. |
| $x \approx 40.171$ | Simplify. |

### Exercises

**Solve each equation. Check your answers.**

**65.** $e^{3x} = 12$

**66.** $\ln x + \ln (x + 1) = 2$

**67.** $2 \ln x + 3 \ln 2 = 5$

**68.** $\ln 4 - \ln x = 2$

**69.** $4e^{(x-1)} = 64$

**70.** $3 \ln x + \ln 5 = 7$

**71.** An initial investment of $350 is worth $429.20 after six years of continuous compounding. Find the annual interest rate.

# 7 Chapter Test

**MathXL® for School**
Go to PowerAlgebra.com

## Do you know HOW?

Determine whether each function is an example of exponential growth or decay. Then find the *y*-intercept.

**1.** $y = 3(0.25)^x$

**2.** $y = 2(6)^{-x}$

**3.** $y = 0.1(10)^x$

**4.** $y = 3e^x$

Describe how the graph of each function is related to the graph of its parent function. Then find the domain, range, and asymptotes.

**5.** $y = 3^x + 2$

**6.** $y = \left(\frac{1}{2}\right)^{x+1}$

**7.** $y = -(2)^{x+2}$

Write each equation in logarithmic form.

**8.** $5^4 = 625$

**9.** $e^0 = 1$

Evaluate each logarithm.

**10.** $\log_2 8$

**11.** $\log_7 7$

**12.** $\log_5 \frac{1}{125}$

**13.** $\log_{11} 1$

Graph each logarithmic function. Compare each graph to the graph of its parent function. List each function's domain, range, *y*-intercept, and asymptotes.

**14.** $y = \log_3 (x - 1)$

**15.** $y = \frac{1}{2}\log_3 (x + 2)$

**16.** $y = 1 - \log_2 x$

Write each logarithmic expression as a single logarithm.

**17.** $\log_2 4 + 3 \log_2 9$

**18.** $3 \log a - 2 \log b$

Expand each logarithm.

**19.** $\log_7 \frac{a}{b}$

**20.** $\log 3x^3y^2$

Use the properties of logarithms to evaluate each expression.

**21.** $\log_9 27 - \log_9 9$

**22.** $2 \log 5 + \log 40$

Solve each equation.

**23.** $(27)^{3x} = 81$

**24.** $3^{x-1} = 24$

**25.** $2e^{3x} = 16$

**26.** $2 \log x = -4$

Use the Change of Base Formula to rewrite each expression using common logarithms.

**27.** $\log_3 16$

**28.** $\log_2 10$

**29.** $\log_7 8$

**30.** $\log_4 9$

Use the properties of logarithms to simplify and solve each equation. Round to the nearest thousandth.

**31.** $\ln 2 + \ln x = 1$

**32.** $\ln (x + 1) + \ln (x - 1) = 4$

**33.** $\ln (2x - 1)^2 = 7$

**34.** $3 \ln x - \ln 2 = 4$

## Do you UNDERSTAND?

**35. Writing** Show that solving the equation $3^{2x} = 4$ by taking the common logarithm of each side is equivalent to solving it by taking the logarithm with base 3 of each side.

**36. Open-Ended** Give an example of an exponential function that models exponential growth and an example of an exponential function that models exponential decay.

**37. Investment** You put $1500 into an account that pays 7% annual interest compounded continuously. How long will it be before you have $2000 in your account?

PowerAlgebra.com    Chapter 7  Chapter Test    491

**16.**

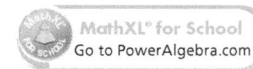

The parent graph $y = \log_2 x$ is reflected across the *x*-axis and translated 1 unit up; domain: $x > 0$, range: all real numbers; no *y*-intercept; asymptote: $x = 0$

**17.** $\log_2 2916$

**18.** $\log \dfrac{a^3}{b^2}$

**19.** $\log_7 a - \log_7 b$

**20.** $\log 3 + 3 \log x + 2 \log y$

**21.** $\dfrac{1}{2}$

**22.** 3

**23.** $0.\overline{44}$

**24.** $\approx 3.89$

**25.** $\approx 0.69$

**26.** 0.01

**27.** $\dfrac{\log 16}{\log 3}$

**28.** $\dfrac{1}{\log 2}$

**29.** $\dfrac{\log 8}{\log 7}$

**30.** $\dfrac{\log 9}{\log 4}$

**31.** 1.359

**32.** 7.456

**33.** 17.058, $-16.058$

**34.** 4.780

**35.**
$$3^{2x} = 4$$
$$\log 3^{2x} = \log 4$$
$$2x \log 3 = \log 4$$
$$x = \frac{\log 4}{2 \log 3}$$
$$x \approx 0.6309$$

and

$$3^{2x} = 4$$
$$\log_3 3^{2x} = \log_3 4$$
$$2x = \log_3 4$$
$$x = \frac{1}{2}\log_3 4$$
$$x \approx 0.6309$$

**36.** Answers may vary. Sample: exponential growth: $y = \frac{1}{3}(2)^x$; exponential decay: $y = 7\left(\frac{1}{5}\right)^x$

**37.** 4.11 yrs

# Answers

## Chapter Test

**1.** exponential decay, (0, 3)

**2.** exponential decay, (0, 2)

**3.** exponential growth, (0, 0.1)

**4.** exponential growth, (0, 3)

**5.** The parent graph $y = 3^x$ is translated 2 units up; domain: all real numbers, range: $y > 2$; asymptote: $y = 2$

**6.** The parent graph $y = \left(\frac{1}{2}\right)^x$ is translated 1 unit to the left; domain: all real numbers, range $y > 0$; asymptote: $y = 0$

**7.** The parent graph $y = 2^x$ is translated 2 units to the left and reflected across the *x*-axis; domain: all real numbers, range: $y > 0$; asymptote: $y = 0$

**8.** $\log_5 625 = 4$

**9.** $\log_e 1 = 0$

**10.** 3  **11.** 1  **12.** $-3$  **13.** 0

**14.**

The parent graph $y = \log_3 x$ is translated 1 unit to the right; domain: $x > 1$, range: all real numbers; no *y*-intercept; asymptote: $x = 1$

**15.**

The parent graph $y = \log_3 x$ is compressed by the factor $\frac{1}{2}$, then translated 2 units to the left; domain: $x > -2$, range: all real numbers; *y*-intercept: $\left(0, \frac{1}{2}\log_3 2\right) \approx (0, 0.3155)$; asymptote: $x = -2$

**PowerAlgebra.com**

**MathXL for School**

Prepare students for the Mid-Chapter Quiz and Chapter Test with online practice and review.

**Chapter Test    491**

| Item Number | Lesson |
|---|---|
| 1 | 7-1 |
| 2 | 4-8 |
| 3 | 7-4 |
| 4 | 5-3 |
| 5 | 7-5b |
| 6 | 7-6 |
| 7 | 6-4 |
| 8 | 1-4 |
| 9 | 5-4 |
| 10 | 3-2 |
| 11 | 5-2 |
| 12 | 5-3 |
| 13 | 6-3 |
| 14 | 5-2 |
| 15 | 6-8 |
| 16 | 5-1 |
| 17 | 7-5 |
| 18 | 7-1 |
| 19 | 5-5 |
| 20 | 7-4 |
| 21 | 7-5 |
| 22 | 4-7 |
| 23 | 5-6 |
| 24 | 2-2 |
| 25 | 2-4 |
| 26 | 6-5 |
| 27 | 6-4 |
| 28 | 5-3 |
| 29 | 4-1 |
| 30 | 3-3 |
| 31 | 4-6 |
| 32 | 5-5 |
| 33 | 7-2 |
| 34 | 2-7 |

# 7 Cumulative Test Prep

## TIPS FOR SUCCESS

Some problems ask you to find lengths of arcs or areas of sectors. Read the question at the right. Then follow the tips to answer the sample question.

### TIP 1

Draw a diagram

Let $f(x) = \pi x^2$ represent the area of a circle with radius $x$. Let $g(x) = \frac{60x}{360}$ represent the area of a 60° sector of a circle with area $x$. A circle with radius 6 centimeters has a sector measuring 60°. What is the area of this sector $(g \circ f)(x)$?

- (A) $6\pi$ cm$^2$
- (B) $12\pi$ cm$^2$
- (C) $24\pi$ cm$^2$
- (D) $36\pi$ cm$^2$

### TIP 2

Find $f(x)$ first.
$$f(x) = \pi x^2$$
$$= \pi \cdot 6^2$$
$$= 36\pi$$

### Think It Through

$$g(x) = \frac{60x}{360}$$

$$(g \circ f)(x) = \frac{60(36\pi)}{360}$$

$$= \frac{36\pi}{6}$$

$$= 6\pi$$

The correct answer is A.

## Vocabulary Builder

As you solve problems, you must understand the meanings of mathematical terms. Match each term with its mathematical meaning.

**A.** growth factor

**B.** asymptote

**C.** logarithmic function

**D.** exponential equation

**I.** the inverse of an exponential function

**II.** a line that a graph approaches as $x$ or $y$ increases in absolute value

**III.** the value of $b$ in $y = ab^x$, when $b > 1$

**IV.** an equation of the form $b^{cx} = a$, where the exponent includes a variable

## Multiple Choice

Read each question. Then write the letter of the correct answer on your page.

1. The population of a town is modeled by the equation $P = 16{,}581e^{0.02t}$ where $P$ represents the population $t$ years after 2000. According to the model, what will the population of the town be in 2020?
   - (A) 16,916
   - (B) 17,258
   - (C) 20,252
   - (D) 24,736

2. If $i = \sqrt{-1}$, then which expression is equal to $9i(13i)$?
   - (F) $-117$
   - (G) $117i$
   - (H) $117$
   - (I) $-117i$

3. Which expression is equivalent to $\log_5 32$?
   - (A) $\log 5 + \log 32$
   - (B) $\log 5 - \log 32$
   - (C) $(\log 5)(\log 32)$
   - (D) $\frac{\log 32}{\log 5}$

# Answers

## Vocabulary Builder
**A.** III
**B.** II
**C.** I
**D.** IV

## Multiple Choice
1. D
2. F
3. D

**4.** The table shows the height of a ball that was tossed into the air. Which equation best models the relationship between time $t$ and the height of the ball $h$?

| Time (seconds) | 0 | 0.25 | 0.5 | 0.75 |
|---|---|---|---|---|
| Height (feet) | 4 | 10.5 | 15 | 17.5 |

F) $h = 26t + 4$

G) $h = -16t^2 + 30t + 4$

H) $h = 4t^2$

I) $h = -16t^2 + 4$

**5.** Which is the graph of $y = 3^x$?

A)

C)

B)

D)

**6.** Which exponential function is equivalent to $y = \log_3 x$?

F) $y = 3^x$

G) $y = \frac{x}{3}$

H) $y = x^3$

I) $x = 3^y$

**7.** Simplify $\left(\dfrac{3x^{\frac{1}{2}}y^4}{x^2y^3}\right)^2$

A) $\dfrac{3y^2}{x^3}$

C) $\dfrac{9y^2}{x^3}$

B) $3x^3y^2$

D) $9x^3y^2$

**8.** Solve the mass energy equivalence formula $e = mc^2$ for $c$.

F) $c = e^2m$

H) $c = \sqrt{\dfrac{e}{m}}$

G) $c = \sqrt{\dfrac{m}{e}}$

I) $c = \sqrt{(e - m)}$

**9.** What is the quotient of $(x^3 + 2x^2 - x + 6) \div (x + 3)$?

A) $x^2 + 5x + 14$, R 42

C) $x^3 + 5x^2 + 14x + 42$

B) $x^2 - x + 2$

D) $x^2 + x - 2$

**10.** On a certain night, a restaurant employs $x$ servers at $25 per hour and $y$ bus persons at $8 per hour. The total hourly cost for the restaurant's 12 employees that night is $249. The following system of equations can be used to find the number of servers and the number of bus persons at work.

$$\begin{cases} 25x + 8y = 249 \\ x + y = 12 \end{cases}$$

Based on the solution of the system of equations, which of the following can you conclude?

F) Fewer than 2 bus persons were working.

G) More than ten servers were working.

H) 50% of the people working were bus persons.

I) 75% of the people working were servers.

**11.** Which polynomial equation has the real roots of $-3$, 1, 1, and $\frac{3}{2}$?

A) $x^4 - \frac{1}{2}x^3 - \frac{13}{2}x^2 + \frac{21}{2}x - \frac{9}{2} = 0$

B) $x^4 - \frac{1}{2}x^3 - \frac{17}{2}x^2 - 10x - \frac{9}{2} = 0$

C) $x^4 + x^3 - 5x^2 + 3x - \frac{3}{2} = 0$

D) $(x - 3)(x + 1)(x + 1)\left(x + \frac{3}{2}\right) = 0$

**12.** What is the factored form of $2x^3 + 5x^2 - 12x$?

F) $x(2x - 3)(x + 4)$

G) $(2x^2 - 3)(x + 4)$

H) $x(2x + 4)(x - 3)$

I) $(2x - 4)(x + 3)$

**13.** Simplify $5\sqrt[3]{x^2} + 3\sqrt[3]{x^2}$.

A) $8\sqrt[3]{x^2}$  B) $8\sqrt[6]{x^2}$  C) $8\sqrt[3]{x^4}$  D) $8\sqrt[6]{x^4}$

**14.** What is the equation of the function graphed below?

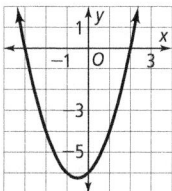

F) $y = (x + 2)(x - 3)$

H) $y = (x + 3)(x - 2)$

G) $y = (x - 6)^2$

I) $y = (x - 1)(x + 5)$

**4.** G
**5.** C
**6.** I
**7.** C
**8.** H
**9.** B
**10.** I
**11.** A
**12.** F
**13.** A
**14.** H

# Answers

## Multiple Choice (continued)
**15.** D
**16.** H

## Gridded Response
**17.** 1
**18.** 15
**19.** 3
**20.** $\frac{3}{2}$
**21.** 1.25
**22.** 0
**23.** 7
**24.** 52.5
**25.** 13
**26.** 2
**27.** 243
**28.** −0.75

## Short Response
**29.** **[2]** domain: all real numbers, range: $y \le 5$
**[1]** incorrect domain or range
**30.** **[2]** let $x$ = a child's weight, then $15 \le x \le 35$

**[1]** graph drawn with open circles

**31.** **[2]**
$$x^2 + 3x = 1$$
$$x^2 + 3x + 2.25 = 3.25$$
$$(x + 1.5)^2 = 3.25$$
$$x + 1.5 = \pm\sqrt{3.25}$$
$$x = -1.5 \pm \sqrt{3.25}$$
**[1]** one computational error

**32.** **[2]** No, imaginary roots are always in pairs with one positive and one negative root.
**[1]** incomplete explanation

**33.** **[2]**

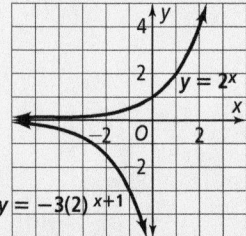

**[1]** graph is not labeled correctly

## Extended Response
**34.** **[4]** **a.** The graph of $y = -|x - 3| + 2$ is the graph of $y = |x|$ reflected across the $x$-axis and translated 3 units to the right and 2 units up.
**b.** $y = -|x + 3| - 2$

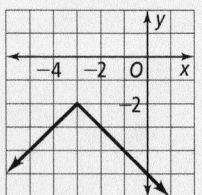

---

**15.** Which graph shows $y = -\sqrt{x + 3} + 2$, a transformation of the radical parent function $y = \sqrt{x}$?

**16.** Which function would have a graph whose end behavior is up and up?
**F** $f(x) = x^3 + 1$     **H** $f(x) = 5x^2 - 7$
**G** $f(x) = -2x^4$     **I** $f(x) = -3x$

### GRIDDED RESPONSE

**17.** What is the solution of the equation $\log_9 x = \log_6 x$?

**18.** A savings account pays 4.62% annual interest, compounded continuously. After approximately how many years will a principal of $500 double?

**19.** The graph of a polynomial has $x$-intercepts at $(-3, 0)$, $(-1, 0)$, and $(1, 0)$. What is the least possible degree of the polynomial?

**20.** Evaluate $\log_4 8$.

**21.** Solve $4^{2x} = 32$.

**22.** How many different real solutions are there for the equation $4x^2 = -4x - 4$?

**23.** Use the Fundamental Theorem of Algebra to determine the total number of complex zeros of $f(x) = x^2 - 3x^5 + 4x - x^7 - 44$.

**24.** $y$ varies directly with $x$ and $y = 30$ when $x = 4$. What is $y$ when $x = 7$?

**25.** What is the $y$-intercept of the line that passes through the point $(-2, 7)$ and is parallel to $y = 3x + 5$?

**26.** What is the solution of $\sqrt{x + 2} = x$?

**27.** Simplify $9^{\frac{5}{2}}$.

**28.** What is the $x$-intercept of $f(x) = x^3 - x^2 + 1$? Round the answer to the nearest hundredth.

### Short Response

**29.** What are the domain and range of the parabola?

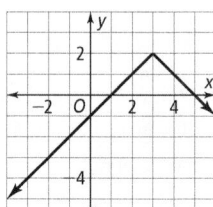

**30.** To use an outdoor toddler swing, a child must weigh at least 15 pounds, and can weigh no more than 35 pounds. Draw a graph to model this situation.

**31.** Solve the equation $0 = x^2 + 3x - 1$ by completing the square.

**32.** Can a quadratic equation with real coefficients have exactly one imaginary root? Explain your answer.

**33.** Graph the function $y = -3(2)^{x+1}$ as a translation of its parent function.

### Extended Response

**34.** A transformation of the parent absolute value function is shown in the graph.

**a.** What is the transformation from the parent function $y = |x|$?

**b.** Draw the graph of the transformed function after reflecting it across the $y$-axis and translating it 4 units down.

**[3]** graph is not labeled correctly
**[2]** only part (a) is correct OR only part (b) is correct
**[1]** part (a) is incorrect and the graph is not labeled correctly

# Skills Handbook Contents

Percents and Percent Applications . . . . . . . . . . . . . . . . . . . . . . . . . T496

Operations With Fractions . . . . . . . . . . . . . . . . . . . . . . . . . . . . . . T497

Ratios and Proportions . . . . . . . . . . . . . . . . . . . . . . . . . . . . . . . T498

Simplifying Expressions With Integers . . . . . . . . . . . . . . . . . . . T499

Area and Volume . . . . . . . . . . . . . . . . . . . . . . . . . . . . . . . . . . T500

The Coordinate Plane, Slope, and Midpoint . . . . . . . . . . . . . . . T501

Operations With Exponents . . . . . . . . . . . . . . . . . . . . . . . . . . . T502

Factoring and Operations With Polynomials . . . . . . . . . . . . . . . T503

Scientific Notation and Significant Digits . . . . . . . . . . . . . . . . . T504

The Pythagorean Theorem and the Distance Formula . . . . . . . . T505

Bar and Circle Graphs . . . . . . . . . . . . . . . . . . . . . . . . . . . . . . . T506

Descriptive Statistics and Histograms . . . . . . . . . . . . . . . . . . . . T507

Operations With Rational Expressions . . . . . . . . . . . . . . . . . . . T508

## Skills Handbook

### Percents and Percent Applications

*Percent* means "per hundred." Find fraction, decimal, and percent equivalents by replacing one symbol for *hundredths* with another.

#### Example 1

Write each number as a percent.

**a.** $0.082 = 8.2\%$

Move the decimal point two places to the right and write a percent sign.

**b.** $\frac{3}{5} = \frac{60}{100} = 60\%$

Write the fraction as hundredths. Then replace the hundredths with a percent sign.

**c.** $1\frac{1}{6} = \frac{7}{6} = 1.166\overline{6} = 116.\overline{6}\%$

First, use $7 \div 6$ to write $1\frac{1}{6}$ as a decimal.

#### Example 2

Write each percent as a decimal.

**a.** $50\% = 0.50 = 0.5$

Move the decimal point two places to the left and drop the percent sign.

**b.** $\frac{1}{2}\% = 0.5\% = 00.5\% = 0.005$

#### Example 3

Use an equation to solve each percent problem.

**a.** What is 30% of 12?

$n = 0.3 \times 12$

$n = 3.6$

**b.** 18 is 0.3% of what?

$18 = 0.003 \times n$

$\frac{18}{0.003} = \frac{0.003n}{0.003}$

$6000 = n$

**c.** What percent of 60 is 9?

$n \times 60 = 9$

$60n = 9$

$n = \frac{9}{60} = 0.15 = 15\%$

#### Exercises

Write each decimal as a percent and each percent as a decimal.

**1.** 0.46  **2.** 1.506  **3.** 0.007  **4.** 8%  **5.** 103.5%  **6.** 3.3%

Write each fraction or mixed number as a percent.

**7.** $\frac{1}{4}$  **8.** $\frac{3}{8}$  **9.** $\frac{2}{3}$  **10.** $\frac{4}{9}$  **11.** $1\frac{3}{20}$  **12.** $\frac{1}{200}$

Use an equation to solve each percent problem. Round your answer to the nearest tenth, if necessary.

**13.** What is 25% of 50?  **14.** What percent of 58 is 37?  **15.** 120% of what is 90?

**16.** 8 is what percent of 40?  **17.** 15 is 75% of what?  **18.** 80% of 58 is what?

964

## Answers

### Percents and Percent Applications

**1.** 46%  **2.** 1150.6%

**3.** 0.7%  **4.** 0.08

**5.** 1.035  **6.** 0.033

**7.** 25%  **8.** 37.5%

**9.** $66.\overline{6}\%$  **10.** $44.\overline{4}\%$

**11.** 115%  **12.** 0.5%

**13.** 12.5  **14.** 63.8%

**15.** 75  **16.** 20%

**17.** 20%  **18.** 46.4

## Operations With Fractions

To add or subtract fractions, use a common denominator. The common denominator is the least common multiple of the denominators.

### Example 1

Simplify $\frac{2}{3} + \frac{3}{5}$.

$$\frac{2}{3} + \frac{3}{5} = \frac{2}{3} \cdot \frac{5}{5} + \frac{3}{5} \cdot \frac{3}{3} \qquad \text{For 3 and 5, the least common multiple is 15.}$$
$$= \frac{10}{15} + \frac{9}{15} \qquad \text{Write } \frac{2}{3} \text{ and } \frac{3}{5} \text{ as equivalent fractions with denominators of 15.}$$
$$= \frac{19}{15} \text{ or } 1\frac{4}{15} \qquad \text{Add the numerators.}$$

### Example 2

Simplify $5\frac{1}{4} - 3\frac{2}{3}$.

$$5\frac{1}{4} - 3\frac{2}{3} = 5\frac{3}{12} - 3\frac{8}{12} \qquad \text{Write equivalent fractions.}$$
$$= 4\frac{15}{12} - 3\frac{8}{12} \qquad \text{Write } 5\frac{3}{12} \text{ as } 4\frac{15}{12} \text{ so you can subtract the fractions.}$$
$$= 1\frac{7}{12} \qquad \text{Subtract the fractions. Then subtract the whole numbers.}$$

To multiply fractions, multiply the numerators and multiply the denominators. You can simplify by using a greatest common factor.

### Example 3

Simplify $\frac{3}{4} \cdot \frac{8}{11}$

**Method 1** $\frac{3}{4} \cdot \frac{8}{11} = \frac{24}{44} = \frac{24 \div 4}{44 \div 4} = \frac{6}{11}$
Divide 24 and 44 by 4, their greatest common factor.

**Method 2** $\frac{3}{\cancel{4}} \cdot \frac{\cancel{8}^2}{11} = \frac{6}{11}$
Divide 4 and 8 by 4, their greatest common factor.

To divide fractions, use a reciprocal to change the problem to multiplication.

### Example 4

Simplify $3\frac{1}{5} \div 1\frac{1}{2}$

$$3\frac{1}{5} \div 1\frac{1}{2} = \frac{16}{5} \div \frac{3}{2} \qquad \text{Write mixed numbers as improper fractions.}$$
$$= \frac{16}{5} \cdot \frac{2}{3} \qquad \text{Multiply by the reciprocal of the divisor.}$$
$$= \frac{32}{15} \text{ or } 2\frac{2}{15} \qquad \text{Simplify.}$$

### Exercises

**Perform the indicated operation.**

1. $\frac{3}{5} + \frac{4}{5}$    2. $\frac{1}{2} + \frac{2}{3}$    3. $4\frac{1}{2} + 2\frac{1}{3}$    4. $5\frac{3}{4} + 4\frac{2}{5}$    5. $\frac{2}{3} - \frac{3}{7}$

6. $5\frac{1}{2} - 3\frac{2}{5}$    7. $7\frac{3}{4} - 4\frac{4}{5}$    8. $3\frac{3}{4} \cdot 10$    9. $2\frac{1}{2} \cdot 3\frac{1}{5}$    10. $6\frac{3}{4} \cdot 5\frac{2}{3}$

11. $\frac{1}{2} \div \frac{1}{3}$    12. $\frac{6}{5} \div \frac{3}{5}$    13. $8\frac{1}{2} \div 4\frac{1}{4}$    14. $\frac{8}{9} - \frac{2}{3}$    15. $5\frac{1}{4} \cdot 8$

## Operations With Fractions

1. $1\frac{2}{5}$    2. $1\frac{1}{6}$
3. $6\frac{5}{6}$    4. $10\frac{3}{20}$
5. $\frac{5}{21}$    6. $2\frac{1}{10}$
7. $2\frac{19}{20}$    8. 38
9. 8    10. $38\frac{1}{4}$
11. $1\frac{1}{2}$    12. 2
13. 2    14. $\frac{2}{9}$
15. 42

## Ratios and Proportions

A *ratio* is a comparison of two quantities by division. You can write *equal ratios* by multiplying or dividing each quantity by the same nonzero number.

**Ways to Write a Ratio**
$a:b \quad a \text{ to } b \quad \frac{a}{b} \ (b \neq 0)$

### Example 1

Write $3\frac{1}{3} : \frac{1}{2}$ as a ratio in simplest form.

$$3\frac{1}{3} : \frac{1}{2} \rightarrow \frac{3\frac{1}{3}}{\frac{1}{2}} = \frac{20}{3} \text{ or } 20:3$$

In simplest form, both terms should be integers.
Multiply by the common denominator, 6.

A rate is a ratio that compares different types of quantities. In simplest form for a rate, the second quantity is one unit.

### Example 2

Write 247 mi in 5.2 h as a rate in simplest form.

$$\frac{247 \text{ mi}}{5.2 \text{ h}} = \frac{47.5 \text{ mi}}{1 \text{ h}} \text{ or } 47.5 \text{ mi/h}$$

Divide by 5.2 to make the second quantity one unit.

A proportion is a statement that two ratios are equal. You can find a missing term in a proportion by using the cross products.

**Cross Products of a Proportion**
$\frac{a}{b} = \frac{c}{d} \ \rightarrow \ ad = bc$

### Example 3

The Copy Center charges \$2.52 for 63 copies. At that rate, how much will the Copy Center charge for 140 copies?

$$\begin{array}{l} \text{cost} \rightarrow \\ \text{copies} \rightarrow \end{array} \quad \frac{2.52}{63} = \frac{c}{140} \qquad \text{Set up a proportion.}$$

$$2.52 \cdot 140 = 63c \qquad \text{Use cross products.}$$

$$c = \frac{2.52 \cdot 140}{63} \qquad \text{Solve for } c.$$

$$= 5.6 \text{ or } \$5.60$$

### Exercises

Write each ratio or rate in simplest form.

**1.** 15 to 20  **2.** 85 : 34  **3.** 38 g in 4 oz  **4.** 375 mi in 4.3 h  **5.** $\frac{84}{30}$

Solve each proportion. Round your answer to the nearest tenth, if necessary.

**6.** $\frac{a}{5} = \frac{12}{15}$  **7.** $\frac{21}{12} = \frac{14}{x}$  **8.** $8 : 15 = n : 25$  **9.** $2.4 : c = 4 : 3$  **10.** $\frac{17}{8} = \frac{n}{20}$

**11.** $\frac{13}{n} = \frac{20}{3}$  **12.** $5 : 7 = y : 5$  **13.** $\frac{0.4}{3.5} = \frac{5.2}{x}$  **14.** $\frac{4}{x} = \frac{7}{6}$  **15.** $4 : n = n : 9$

**16.** A canary's heart beats 130 times in 12 s. Use a proportion to find about how many times its heart beats in 50 s.

## Answers

### Ratios and Proportions

**1.** 3 to 4  **2.** 5 : 2

**3.** 19 g in 2 oz

**4.** approximately 87.2 mi in 1 h

**5.** $\frac{14}{5}$  **6.** 4

**7.** 8  **8.** $13.\overline{3}$

**9.** 1.8  **10.** 42.5

**11.** 1.95  **12.** 3.6

**13.** 45.5  **14.** 3.4

**15.** $\pm 6$  **16.** about 542 times

# Simplifying Expressions With Integers

To add two numbers with the same sign, *add* their absolute values. The sum has the same sign as the numbers. To add two numbers with different signs, find the *difference* between their absolute values. The sum has the same sign as the number with the greater absolute value.

### Example 1

**Add.**

**a.** $-8 + (-5) = -13$      **b.** $-8 + 5 = -3$      **c.** $8 + (-5) = 3$

To subtract a number, add its opposite.

### Example 2

**Subtract.**

**a.** $4 - 7 = 4 + (-7)$      **b.** $-4 - (-7) = -4 + 7$      **c.** $-4 - 7 = -4 + (-7)$
        $= -3$                       $= 3$                        $= -11$

The product or quotient of two numbers with the same sign is positive. The product or quotient of two numbers with different signs is negative.

### Example 3

**Multiply or divide.**

**a.** $(-3)(-5) = 15$      **b.** $-35 \div 7 = -5$      **c.** $24 \div (-6) = -4$

### Example 4

**Simplify $2^2 - 3(4 - 6) - 12$.**          **Order of Operations**

$2^2 - 3(4 - 6) - 12 = 2^2 - 3(-2) - 12$      **1.** Perform any operation(s) inside grouping symbols.
$\phantom{2^2 - 3(4 - 6) - 12} = 4 - 3(-2) - 12$      **2.** Simplify any terms with exponents.
$\phantom{2^2 - 3(4 - 6) - 12} = 4 - (-6) - 12$      **3.** Multiply and divide in order from left to right.
$\phantom{2^2 - 3(4 - 6) - 12} = 4 + 6 - 12 = -2$      **4.** Add and subtract in order from left to right.

## Exercises

**Simplify each expression.**

**1.** $-4 + 5$      **2.** $12 - 12$      **3.** $-15 + (-23)$      **4.** $4 - 17$      **5.** $-5 - 12$

**6.** $3 - (-5)$      **7.** $-8 - (-12)$      **8.** $-19 + 5$      **9.** $(-7)(-4)$      **10.** $-120 \div 30$

**11.** $(-3)(4)$      **12.** $75 \div (-3)$      **13.** $(-6)(15)$      **14.** $(18)(-4)$      **15.** $-84 \div (-7)$

**16.** $-2(1 + 5) + (-3)(2)$      **17.** $-4(-2 - 5) + 3(1 - 4)$      **18.** $20 - (3)(12) + 4^2$

**19.** $\frac{-15}{-5} - \frac{36}{-12} + \frac{-12}{-4}$      **20.** $5^2 - 6(5 - 9)$      **21.** $(-3 + 2^3)(4 + \frac{-42}{7})$

## Simplifying Expressions With Integers

**1.** 1      **2.** 0
**3.** $-38$      **4.** $-13$
**5.** $-17$      **6.** 8
**7.** 4      **8.** $-14$
**9.** 28      **10.** $-4$
**11.** $-12$      **12.** $-25$
**13.** $-90$      **14.** $-72$
**15.** 12      **16.** $-18$
**17.** 19      **18.** 0
**19.** 9      **20.** 49
**21.** $-10$

## Area and Volume

The *area* of a plane figure is the number of square units contained in the figure.
The *volume* of a space figure is the number of cubic units contained in the figure.
Formulas for area and volume are listed on page 693.

### Example 1

Find the area of each figure.

**a.**

$$A = \pi r^2$$
$$\approx \frac{22}{7} \cdot \left(\frac{21}{10}\right)^2$$
$$= \frac{693}{50} = 13\frac{43}{50} \text{ in.}^2$$

**b.**

$$A = \frac{1}{2}(b_1 + b_2)h$$
$$= \frac{1}{2}(19 + 23) \cdot 8.5$$
$$= 178.5 \text{ mm}^2$$

### Example 2

Find the volume of each figure.

**a.**

$$V = \frac{4}{3}\pi r^3$$
$$\approx \frac{4}{3} \cdot 3.14 \cdot 2.7^3$$
$$= 82.40616 \approx 82.4 m^3$$

**b.**

$$V = \frac{1}{3}Bh$$
$$= \frac{1}{3}(37^2) \cdot 24$$
$$= 10{,}952 \text{ ft}^3$$

### Exercises

Find the exact area of each figure.

**1.**

**2.**

**3.**

**4.**

Find the exact volume of each figure.

**5.**

**6.**

**7.** 12 in. — 5 in.

**8.** 50 ft — 60 ft — 80 ft

**9.** Find the area of a triangle with a base of 17 in. and a height of 13 in.

**10.** Find the volume of a rectangular box 64 cm long, 48 cm wide, and 58 cm high.

**11.** Find the surface area of the cube in Exercise 5.

## Answers

### Area and Volume

**1.** $14 \text{ m}^2$

**2.** $14\frac{1}{16} \text{ ft}^2$

**3.** $30 \text{ cm}^2$

**4.** $25\pi \text{ in.}^2$

**5.** $91\frac{1}{8} \text{ ft}^3$

**6.** $\frac{2048}{3}\pi \text{ m}^3$

**7.** $100\pi \text{ in.}^3$

**8.** $80{,}000 \text{ ft}^3$

**9.** $110.5 \text{ in.}^2$

**10.** $178{,}176 \text{ cm}^3$

**11.** $121\frac{1}{2} \text{ ft}^2$

# The Coordinate Plane, Slope, and Midpoint

The *coordinate plane* is formed when two perpendicular number lines intersect at a point called the origin, forming four quadrants.

## Example 1

**In which quadrant would you find each point?**

**a.** $(3, -4)$   Move 3 units right and 4 units down. The point is in Quadrant IV.

**b.** $(-2, -5)$   Move 2 units left and 5 units down. The point is in Quadrant III.

To find the slope of a line on the coordinate plane, choose two points on the line and use the slope formula.

## Example 2

**Find the slope of each line.**

**a.**

$$m = \frac{y_2 - y_1}{x_2 - x_1}$$
$$= \frac{2 - (-2)}{-2 - 3}$$
$$= \frac{4}{-5} \text{ or } -\frac{4}{5}$$

**b.**

$$m = \frac{y_2 - y_1}{x_2 - x_1}$$
$$= \frac{2 - 0}{-1 - (-1)} = \frac{2}{0}$$

Since you cannot divide by zero, this line has an undefined slope.

If $(x_m, y_m)$ is the midpoint of the segment joining $(x_1, y_1)$ and $(x_2, y_2)$, then $x_m = \frac{x_1 + x_2}{2}$ and $y_m = \frac{y_1 + y_2}{2}$.

## Example 3

**Find the coordinates of the midpoint of the segment with endpoints $(-2, 5)$ and $(6, -3)$.**

$\frac{-2 + 6}{2} = 2$ and $\frac{5 + (-3)}{2} = 1$ so the midpoint is $(2, 1)$.

## Exercises

**In which quadrant would you find each point? Graph each point on a coordinate plane.**

**1.** $(3, 2)$   **2.** $(-4, 3)$   **3.** $(2, -3)$   **4.** $(4, -2)$   **5.** $(-4, -5)$   **6.** $(-1, -3)$

**Find the slope of each line.**

**7.**

**8.**

**9.**

**10.** the line containing $(-3, 4)$ and $(2, -6)$

**11.** the line containing $(25, 40)$ and $(100, 55)$

**Find the midpoint of the segment with the given endpoints.**

**12.** $(-4, 4), (2, -5)$   **13.** $(3, 3), (7, -6)$   **14.** $(-1, -8), (0, -3)$   **15.** $(3, 4), (2, -6)$

---

# The Coordinate Plane, Slope, and Midpoint

**1.** I

**2.** II

**3.** IV

**4.** IV

**5.** III

**6.** III

**7.** $\frac{4}{5}$

**8.** $-1$

**9.** 0

**10.** $-2$

**11.** $\frac{1}{5}$

**12.** $\left(-1, -\frac{1}{2}\right)$

**13.** $\left(5, -\frac{3}{2}\right)$

**14.** $\left(-\frac{1}{2}, -\frac{11}{2}\right)$

**15.** $\left(\frac{5}{2}, -1\right)$

## Operations With Exponents

An exponent indicates how many times a number is used as a factor.

| $2^n = \blacksquare$ | $10^n = \blacksquare$ |
|---|---|
| $2^2 = 4$ | $10^2 = 100$ |
| $2^1 = 2$ | $10^1 = 10$ |
| $2^0 = 1$ | $10^0 = 1$ |
| $2^{-1} = \frac{1}{2}$ | $10^{-1} = \frac{1}{10}$ |
| $2^{-2} = \frac{1}{4}$ | $10^{-2} = \frac{1}{100}$ |

### Example 1

Write using exponents.

**a.** $3 \cdot 3 \cdot 3 \cdot 3 \cdot 3 = 3^5$  **b.** $a \cdot a \cdot b \cdot b \cdot b \cdot b = a^2 b^4$

The patterns shown at the right indicate that $a^0 = 1$ and that $a^{-n} = \frac{1}{a^n}$.

### Example 2

Write each expression so that all exponents are positive.

**a.** $a^{-2}b^3 = \frac{1}{a^2} \cdot b^3 = \frac{b^3}{a^2}$  **b.** $x^3 y^0 z^{-1} = x^3 \cdot 1 \cdot \frac{1}{z} = \frac{x^3}{z}$

You can simplify expressions that contain powers with the same base.

### Example 3

Simplify each expression.

**a.** $b^5 \cdot b^3 = b^{5+3}$  Add exponents to multiply
$= b^8$  powers with the same base.

**b.** $\frac{x^5}{x^7} = x^{5-7}$  Subtract exponents to divide
$= x^{-2} = \frac{1}{x^2}$  powers with the same base.

You can simplify expressions that contain parentheses and exponents.

### Example 4

Simplify each expression.

**a.** $\left(\frac{ab}{n}\right)^3 = \frac{a^3 b^3}{n^3}$  Raise each factor in the
parentheses to the third power.

**b.** $(c^2)^4 = c^{2 \cdot 4} = c^8$  Multiply exponents to raise a
power to a power.

### Exercises

Write each expression using exponents.

**1.** $x \cdot x \cdot x$  **2.** $x \cdot x \cdot x \cdot y \cdot y$  **3.** $a \cdot a \cdot a \cdot a \cdot b$  **4.** $\frac{a \cdot a \cdot a \cdot a}{b \cdot b}$

Write each expression so that all exponents are positive.

**5.** $c^{-4}$  **6.** $m^{-2}n^0$  **7.** $x^5 y^{-7} z^{-3}$  **8.** $ab^{-1}c^2$

Simplify each expression. Use positive exponents.

**9.** $d^2 d^6$  **10.** $\frac{a^5}{a^2}$  **11.** $\frac{c^7}{c}$  **12.** $\frac{n^3}{n^6}$  **13.** $\frac{a^5 b^3}{ab^8}$  **14.** $(3x)^2$

**15.** $\left(\frac{a}{b}\right)^4$  **16.** $\left(\frac{xz}{y}\right)^6$  **17.** $(c^3)^4$  **18.** $\left(\frac{x^2}{y^5}\right)^3$  **19.** $(u^4 v^2)^3$  **20.** $(p^5)^{-2}$

**21.** $\frac{(2a^4)(3a^2)}{6a^3}$  **22.** $(x^{-2})^3$  **23.** $(mg^3)^{-1}$  **24.** $g^{-3}g^{-1}$  **25.** $\frac{(3a^3)^2}{18a}$  **26.** $\frac{c^3 d^7}{c^{-3}d^{-1}}$

# Answers

## Operations With Exponents

**1.** $x^3$  **2.** $x^3 y^2$

**3.** $a^4 b$  **4.** $\frac{a^4}{b^2}$

**5.** $\frac{1}{c^4}$  **6.** $\frac{1}{m^2}$

**7.** $\frac{x^5}{y^7 z^3}$  **8.** $\frac{ac^2}{b}$

**9.** $d^8$  **10.** $a^3$

**11.** $c^6$  **12.** $\frac{1}{n^3}$

**13.** $\frac{a^4}{b^5}$  **14.** $9x^2$

**15.** $\frac{a^4}{b^4}$  **16.** $\frac{x^6 z^6}{y^6}$

**17.** $c^{12}$  **18.** $\frac{x^6}{y^{15}}$

**19.** $u^{12} v^6$  **20.** $\frac{1}{p^{10}}$

**21.** $a^3$  **22.** $\frac{1}{x^6}$

**23.** $\frac{1}{mg^3}$  **24.** $\frac{1}{g^4}$

**25.** $\frac{a^5}{2}$  **26.** $c^6 d^8$

# Factoring and Operations With Polynomials

## Example 1

**Perform each operation.**

**a.** $(3y^2 - 4y + 5) + (y^2 + 9y)$

$= (3y^2 + y^2) + (-4y + 9y) + 5$    To add, group like terms.

$= 4y^2 + 5y + 5$

**b.** $(n + 4)(n - 3)$

$= n(n) + n(-3) + 4(n) + 4(-3)$   Distribute $n$ and 4.

$= n^2 - 3n + 4n - 12$          Combine like terms.

$= n^2 + n - 12$

---

To factor a polynomial, first find the greatest common factor (GCF) of the terms.
Then use the distributive property to factor out the GCF.

## Example 2

**Factor $6x^3 - 12x^2 + 18x$.**

$6x^3 = 6 \cdot x \cdot x \cdot x; -12x^2 = 6 \cdot (-2) \cdot x \cdot x; 18x = 6 \cdot 3 \cdot x$    List the factors of each term. The GCF is 6x.

$6x^3 - 12x^2 + 18x = 6x(x^2) + 6x(-2x) + 6x(3)$    Use the distributive property to factor out 6x.

$\qquad\qquad = 6x(x^2 - 2x + 3)$

---

When a polynomial is the product
of two binomials, you can work
backward to find the factors.

$x^2 + bx + c = (x + \blacksquare)(x + \blacksquare)$

The *sum* of these numbers must equal $b$.

The *product* of these numbers must equal $c$.

## Example 3

**Factor $x^2 - 13x + 36$.**

Choose numbers that are factors of 36. Look for a pair with the sum $-13$.

The numbers $-4$ and $-9$ have a product of 36 and a sum of $-13$. The
factors are $(x - 4)$ and $(x - 9)$. So, $x^2 - 13x + 36 = (x - 4)(x - 9)$.

| Factors | Sum |
|---|---|
| $-6 \cdot (-6)$ | $-12$ |
| $-4 \cdot (-9)$ | $-13$ |

---

## Exercises

**Perform the indicated operations.**

**1.** $(x^2 + 3x - 1) + (7x - 4)$    **2.** $(5y^2 + 7y) - (3y^2 + 9y - 8)$    **3.** $4x^2(3x^2 - 5x + 9)$

**4.** $-5d(13d^2 + 7d + 8)$          **5.** $(x - 5)(x + 3)$                **6.** $(n - 7)(n - 2)$

**Factor each polynomial.**

**7.** $a^2 - 8a + 12$    **8.** $n^2 - 2n - 8$    **9.** $x^2 + 5x + 4$    **10.** $3m^2 - 9$

**11.** $y^2 + 5y - 24$    **12.** $s^3 + 6s^2 + 11s$    **13.** $2x^3 + 4x^2 - 8x$    **14.** $y^2 - 10y + 25$

## Factoring and Operations With Polynomials

**1.** $x^2 + 10x - 5$

**2.** $2y^2 - 2y + 8$

**3.** $12x^4 - 20x^3 + 36x^2$

**4.** $-65d^3 - 35d^2 - 40d$

**5.** $x^2 - 2x - 15$

**6.** $n^2 - 9n + 14$

**7.** $(a - 6)(a - 2)$

**8.** $(n - 4)(n + 2)$

**9.** $(x + 4)(x + 1)$

**10.** $3(m^2 - 3)$

**11.** $(y + 8)(y - 3)$

**12.** $s(s^2 + 6s + 11)$

**13.** $2x(x^2 + 2x - 4)$

**14.** $(y - 5)^2$

## Scientific Notation and Significant Digits

In *scientific notation*, a number has the form $a \times 10^n$, where $n$ is an integer and $1 \le a < 10$.

### Example 1

**Write $5.59 \times 10^6$ in standard form.**

$5.59 \times 10^6 = 5\,590\,000 = 5,590,000$      A positive exponent indicates a value greater than 1.
Move the decimal point six places to the right.

### Example 2

**Write 0.0000318 in scientific notation.**

$0.0000318 = 3.18 \times 10^{-5}$      Move the decimal point to create a number between 1 and 10.
Since the original number is less than 1, use a negative exponent.

When a measurement is in scientific notation, all the digits of the number between 1 and 10 are *significant digits*. When you multiply or divide measurements, your answer should have as many significant digits as the least number of significant digits in any of the numbers involved.

### Example 3

**Multiply $(6.71 \times 10^8 \text{ mi/h})$ and $(3.8 \times 10^4 \text{ h})$.**

$(6.71 \times 10^8 \text{ mi/h})(3.8 \times 10^4 \text{ h}) = (6.71 \cdot 3.8)(10^8 \cdot 10^4)$    Rearrange factors.

three significant digits    two significant digits

$= 25.498 \times 10^{12}$      Add exponents when multiplying powers of 10.
$= 2.5498 \times 10^{13}$      Write in scientific notation.
$\approx 2.5 \times 10^{13} \text{mi}$      Round to two significant digits.

### Exercises

**Change each number to scientific notation or to standard form.**

**1.** 1,340,000    **2.** $6.88 \times 10^{-2}$    **3.** 0.000775    **4.** 0.0072    **5.** $1.113 \times 10^5$

**6.** $8.0 \times 10^{-4}$    **7.** 1895    **8.** $2.3 \times 10^3$    **9.** 123,400    **10.** $7.985 \times 10^4$

**Write each product or quotient in scientific notation. Round to the appropriate number of significant digits.**

**11.** $(1.6 \times 10^2)(4.0 \times 10^3)$    **12.** $(2.5 \times 10^{-3})(1.2 \times 10^4)$    **13.** $(4.237 \times 10^4)(2.01 \times 10^{-2})$

**14.** $\dfrac{7.0 \times 10^5}{2.89 \times 10^3}$    **15.** $\dfrac{1.4 \times 10^4}{8.0 \times 10^2}$    **16.** $\dfrac{6.48 \times 10^6}{3.2 \times 10^5}$

**17.** $(1.78 \times 10^{-7})(5.03 \times 10^{-5})$    **18.** $(7.2 \times 10^{11})(5 \times 10^6)$    **19.** $(8.90 \times 10^8) \div (2.36 \times 10^{-2})$

**20.** $(3.95 \times 10^4) \div (6.8 \times 10^8)$    **21.** $(4.9 \times 10^{-8}) \div (2.7 \times 10^{-2})$    **22.** $(3.972 \times 10^{-5})(4.7 \times 10^{-4})$

## Answers

### Scientific Notation and Significant Digits

**1.** $1.34 \times 10^6$    **2.** 0.0688

**3.** $7.75 \times 10^{-4}$    **4.** $7.2 \times 10^{-3}$

**5.** 111,300    **6.** 0.0008

**7.** $1.895 \times 10^3$    **8.** 2300

**9.** $1.234 \times 10^5$    **10.** 79,850

**11.** $6.4 \times 10^5$    **12.** 30

**13.** $8.52 \times 10^2$    **14.** $2.4 \times 10^2$

**15.** 17.5    **16.** 20

**17.** $8.95 \times 10^{-12}$    **18.** $3.6 \times 10^{18}$

**19.** $3.77 \times 10^{10}$    **20.** $5.8 \times 10^{-5}$

**21.** $1.8 \times 10^{-6}$    **22.** $1.9 \times 10^{-8}$

# The Pythagorean Theorem and the Distance Formula

In a right triangle, the sum of the squares of the lengths of the legs is equal to the square of the length of the hypotenuse. Use this relationship, known as the Pythagorean Theorem, to find the length of a side of a right triangle.

**The Pythagorean Theorem**

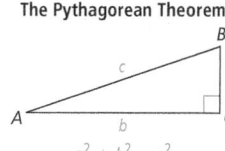

$$a^2 + b^2 = c^2$$

## Example 1

Find $m$ in the triangle below, to the nearest tenth.

$$m^2 + n^2 = k^2$$
$$m^2 + 7.8^2 = 9.6^2$$
$$m^2 = 9.6^2 - 7.8^2 = 31.32$$
$$m = \sqrt{31.32} \approx 5.6$$

To find the distance between two points on the coordinate plane, use the distance formula.

The distance $d$ between any two points $(x_1, y_1)$ and $(x_2, y_2)$ is

$$d = \sqrt{(x_2 - x_1)^2 + (y_2 - y_1)^2}$$

## Example 2

Find the distance between $(-3, 2)$ and $(6, -4)$.

$$d = \sqrt{(6 - (-3))^2 + (-4 - 2)^2}$$
$$= \sqrt{9^2 + (-6)^2}$$
$$= \sqrt{81 + 36}$$
$$= \sqrt{117}$$
$$\approx 10.8$$

Thus, $d$ is about 10.8 units.

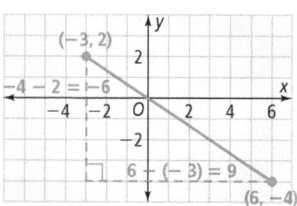

## Exercises

In each problem, $a$ and $b$ are the lengths of the legs of a right triangle and $c$ is the length of the hypotenuse. Find each missing length. Round your answer to the nearest tenth.

**1.** $c$ if $a = 6$ and $b = 8$
**2.** $a$ if $b = 12$ and $c = 13$
**3.** $b$ if $a = 8$ and $c = 17$
**4.** $c$ if $a = 10$ and $b = 3$
**5.** $a$ if $b = 100$ and $c = 114$
**6.** $b$ if $a = 12.0$ and $c = 30.1$

Find the distance between each pair of points, to the nearest tenth.

**7.** $(0, 0), (4, -3)$
**8.** $(-5, -5), (1, 3)$
**9.** $(-1, 0), (4, 12)$
**10.** $(-4, 2), (4, -2)$
**11.** $(0, 15), (17, 0)$
**12.** $(-8, 8), (8, 8)$
**13.** $(-1, 1), (1, -1)$
**14.** $(-2, 9), (0, 0)$
**15.** $(-5, 3), (4, 3)$
**16.** $(2, 1), (3, 4)$
**17.** $(3, -2), (3, 5)$
**18.** $(5, 4), (-3, 1)$

# The Pythagorean Theorem and the Distance Formula

**1.** 10
**2.** 5
**3.** 15
**4.** 10.4
**5.** 54.7
**6.** 27.6
**7.** 5
**8.** 10
**9.** 13
**10.** 8.9
**11.** 22.7
**12.** 16
**13.** 2.8
**14.** 9.2
**15.** 9
**16.** 3.2
**17.** 7
**18.** 8.5

# Bar and Circle Graphs

Sometimes you can draw different graphs to represent the same data, depending on the information you want to share. A *bar graph* is useful for comparing amounts; a *circle graph* is useful for comparing percents.

## Example

Display the 2007 data on immigration to the United States in a bar graph and a circle graph.

**To make a circle graph,** first find the *percent* of the data in each category. Then express each percent as a decimal and multiply by 360° to find the size of each *central angle*.

$$\text{Africa} \rightarrow \frac{89.3}{\text{Total}} \rightarrow \frac{89.3}{1003.7} \approx 0.09 \text{ or } 9\%$$

$$0.09 \times 360° \approx 32°$$

Draw a circle and use a protractor to draw each central angle.

**Immigration to the United States, 2007**

| Place of Origin | Immigrants (1000's) |
|---|---|
| Africa | 89.2 |
| Asia | 359.4 |
| Europe | 120.8 |
| North America | 331.7 |
| South America | 102.6 |

Source: Department of Homeland Security

**To make a bar graph,** place the categories along the bottom axis. Decide on a scale for the side axis. An appropriate scale would be 0–300, marked in intervals of 50. For each data item, draw a bar whose height is equal to the data value.

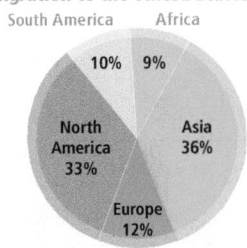

Immigration to the United States, 2007

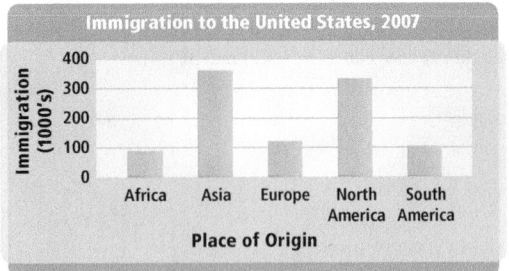

## Exercises

Display the data from each table in a bar graph and a circle graph.

**1.** NASA Space Shuttle Expenses, 2000

| Operation | Millions of Dollars |
|---|---|
| Orbiter, integration | 698.8 |
| Propulsion | 1,053.1 |
| Mission, launch operations | 738.8 |
| Flight operations | 244.6 |
| Ground operations | 510.3 |

Source: U.S. National Aeronautics and Space Administration

**2.** Cable TV Revenue, 2006

| | Millions of Dollars |
|---|---|
| Airtime | 4,566 |
| Basic service | 42,918 |
| Pay-per-view, premium services | 13,322 |
| Installation | 729 |
| Other | 27,188 |

Source: U.S. Census Bureau

974

# Answers

## Bar and Circle Graphs

**1.**

NASA Space Shuttle Expenses, 2000

# Descriptive Statistics and Histograms

For numerical data, you can find the *mean,* the *median,* and the *mode.*

| | |
|---|---|
| **Mean** | The sum of the data values in a data set divided by the number of data values |
| **Median** | The middle value of a data set that has been arranged in increasing or decreasing order. If the data set has an even number of values, the median is the mean of the middle two values. |
| **Mode** | The most frequently occurring value in a data set |

## Example 1

**Find the mean, median, and mode for the following data set.**     5  7  6  3  1  7  9  5  10  7

Mean     $\dfrac{5 + 7 + 6 + 3 + 1 + 7 + 9 + 5 + 10 + 7}{10} = 6$

Median     5, 7, 6, 3, 1, 7, 9, 5, 10, 7     Rearrange the numbers from least to greatest.

1, 3, 5, 5, 6, 7, 7, 7, 9, 10     The median is the mean of the two middle numbers, 6 and 7.

The median is $\dfrac{6 + 7}{2} = 6.5$.

Mode     The most frequently occurring data value is 7.

The frequency of a data value is the number of times it occurs in a data set.
A *histogram* is a bar graph that shows the frequency of each data value.

## Example 2

Use the survey results to make a histogram for the cost of a movie ticket at various theaters.

Movie Ticket Prices

## Exercises

**Find the mean, the median, and the mode of each data set.**

**1.** $-3\ 4\ 5\ 5\ -2\ 7\ 1\ 8\ 9$

**2.** $0\ 0\ 1\ 1\ 2\ 3\ 3\ 5\ 3\ 8\ 7$

**3.** $2.4\ 2.4\ 2.3\ 2.3\ 2.4\ 12.0$

**4.** $1\ 1\ 1\ 1\ 2\ 2\ 2\ 3\ 3\ 4$

**5.** $1.2\ 1.3\ 1.4\ 1.5\ 1.6\ 1.7\ 1.8$

**6.** $-4\ -3\ -2\ -1\ 0\ 1\ 2\ 3\ 4$

**Make a histogram for each data set.**

**7.** $7\ 4\ 8\ 6\ 6\ 8\ 7\ 7\ 5\ 7$

**8.** $73\ 75\ 76\ 75\ 74\ 75\ 76\ 74\ 76\ 75$

**2.**

Cable TV Revenue, 2006

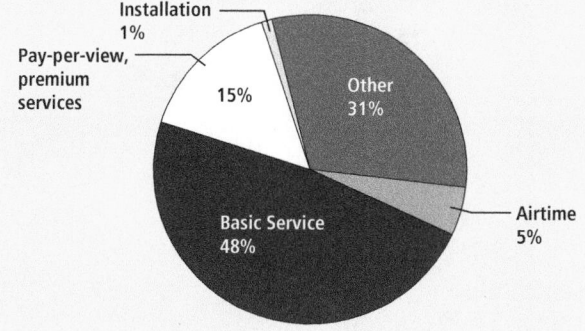

Cable TV Revenue, 2006

## Descriptive Statistics and Histograms

**1.** $3.\overline{7}$; 5; 5     **2.** 3; 3; 3

**3.** $3.9\overline{6}$; 2.4; 2.4     **4.** 2; 2; 1

**5.** 1.5; 1.5; no mode

**6.** 0; 0; no mode

**7.**

**8.**

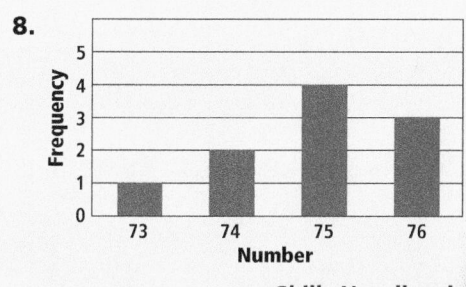

# Operations With Rational Expressions

A *rational expression* is an expression that can be written in the form $\frac{polynominal}{polynominal}$, where the denominator is not zero. A rational expression is in simplest form if the numerator and denominator have no common factors except 1.

## Example 1

**Write the expression $\frac{4x+8}{x+2}$ in simplest form.**

$\frac{4x+8}{x+2} = \frac{4(x+2)}{x+2}$      Factor the numerator.

      $= 4$      Divide out the common factor $x + 2$.

To add or subtract two rational expressions, use a common denominator.

## Example 2

**Simplify $\frac{x}{2y} + \frac{x}{3y}$.**

$\frac{x}{2y} + \frac{x}{3y} = \frac{x}{2y} \cdot \frac{3}{3} + \frac{x}{3y} \cdot \frac{2}{2}$      The common denominator of 3y and 2y is 6y.

      $= \frac{3x}{6y} + \frac{2x}{6y}$

      $= \frac{5x}{6y}$      Add the numerators.

To multiply rational expressions, first find and divide out any common factors in the numerators and the denominators. Then multiply the remaining numerators and denominators. To divide rational expressions, first use a reciprocal to change the problem to multiplication.

## Example 3

**Simplify $\frac{40x^2}{21} \div \frac{5x}{14}$.**

$\frac{40x^2}{21} \div \frac{5x}{14} = \frac{40x^2}{21} \cdot \frac{14}{5x}$      Change dividing by $\frac{5x}{14}$ to multiplying by the reciprocal, $\frac{14}{5x}$.

      $= \frac{8\,\cancel{40x^2}^{\,1}}{3\,\cancel{21}} \times \frac{\cancel{14}^{\,2}}{\cancel{5x}_{\,1}}$      Divide out the common factors 5, $x$, and 7.

      $= \frac{16x}{3}$      Multiply the numerators ($8x \cdot 2$). Multiply the denominators ($3 \cdot 1$).

## Exercises

**Write each expression in simplest form.**

1. $\frac{4a^2b}{12ab^3}$      2. $\frac{5n+15}{n+3}$      3. $\frac{x-7}{2x-14}$      4. $\frac{28c^2(d-3)}{35c(d-3)}$

**Perform the indicated operation.**

5. $\frac{3x}{2} + \frac{5x}{2}$    6. $\frac{3x}{8} + \frac{5x}{8}$    7. $\frac{5}{h} - \frac{3}{h}$    8. $\frac{6}{11p} - \frac{9}{11p}$    9. $\frac{3x}{5} - \frac{x}{2}$

10. $\frac{13}{2x} - \frac{13}{3x}$    11. $\frac{7x}{5} + \frac{5x}{7}$    12. $\frac{5a}{b} + \frac{3a}{5b}$    13. $\frac{7x}{8} \cdot \frac{32x}{35}$    14. $\frac{3x^2}{2} \cdot \frac{6}{x}$

15. $\frac{8x^2}{5} \cdot \frac{10}{x^3}$    16. $\frac{7x}{8} \cdot \frac{64}{14x}$    17. $\frac{16}{3x} \div \frac{5}{3x}$    18. $\frac{4x}{5} \div \frac{16}{15x}$    19. $\frac{x^3}{8} \div \frac{x^2}{16}$

# Answers

## Operations With Rational Expressions

1. $\frac{a}{3b^2}$      2. 5

3. $\frac{1}{2}$      4. $\frac{4c}{5}$

5. $4x$      6. $x$

7. $\frac{2}{h}$      8. $\frac{-3}{11p}$

9. $\frac{x}{10}$      10. $\frac{13}{6x}$

11. $\frac{74x}{35}$      12. $\frac{28a}{5b}$

13. $\frac{4x^2}{5}$      14. $9x$

15. $\frac{16}{x}$      16. $4$

17. $\frac{16}{5}$      18. $\frac{3x^2}{4}$

19. $2x$

# Reference

## Table 1 Measures

| | United States Customary | Metric |
|---|---|---|
| Length | 12 inches (in.) = 1 foot (ft)<br>36 in. = 1 yard (yd)<br>3 ft = 1 yard<br>5280 ft = 1 mile (mi)<br>1760 yd = 1 mile | 10 millimeters (mm) = 1 centimeter (cm)<br>100 cm = 1 meter (m)<br>1000 mm = 1 meter<br>1000 m = 1 kilometer (km) |
| Area | 144 square inches (in.²) = 1 square foot (ft²)<br>9 ft² = 1 square yard (yd²)<br>43,560 ft² = 1 acre (a)<br>4840 yd² = 1 acre | 100 square millimeters (mm²) = 1 square centimeter (cm²)<br>10,000 cm² = 1 square meter (m²)<br>10,000 m² = 1 hectare (ha) |
| Volume | 1728 cubic inches (in.³) = 1 cubic foot (ft³)<br>27 ft³ = 1 cubic yard (yd³) | 1000 cubic millimeters (mm³) = 1 cubic centimeter (cm³)<br>1,000,000 cm³ = 1 cubic meter (m³) |
| Liquid Capacity | 8 fluid ounces (fl oz) = 1 cup (c)<br>2 c = 1 pint (pt)<br>2 pt = 1 quart (qt)<br>4 qt = 1 gallon (gal) | 1000 milliliters (mL) = 1 liter (L)<br>1000 L = 1 kiloliter (kL) |
| Weight or Mass | 16 ounces (oz) = 1 pound (lb)<br>2000 pounds = 1 ton (t) | 1000 milligrams (mg) = 1 gram (g)<br>1000 g = 1 kilogram (kg)<br>1000 kg = 1 metric ton |
| Temperature | 32°F = freezing point of water<br>98.6°F = normal human body temperature<br>212°F = boiling point of water | 0°C = freezing point of water<br>37°C = normal human body temperature<br>100°C = boiling point of water |

| | Customary Units and Metric Units | |
|---|---|---|
| Length | 1 in. ≈ 2.54 cm<br>1 ft ≈ 0.305 m<br>1 mi ≈ 1.61 km | 1 cm ≈ 0.39 in.<br>1 m ≈ 3.28 ft<br>1 km ≈ 0.62 mi |
| Area | 1 acre ≈ 0.40 ha | 1 ha ≈ 2.47 acres |
| Capacity | 1 qt ≈ 0.95 L | 1 L ≈ 1.06 qt |
| Weight and Mass | 1 oz ≈ 28.4 g<br>1 lb ≈ 0.45 kg | 1 oz ≈ 0.035 oz<br>1 kg ≈ 2.205 lb |

| Time | | |
|---|---|---|
| 60 seconds (s) = 1 minute (min)<br>60 minutes = 1 hour (h)<br>24 hours = 1 day (d)<br>7 days = 1 week (wk) | 4 weeks (approx.) = 1 month (mo)<br>365 days = 1 year (yr)<br>52 weeks (approx.) = 1 year | 12 months = 1 year<br>10 years = 1 decade<br>100 years = 1 century |

## Table 2 Reading Math Symbols

| Symbols | Words |
|---|---|
| · , × | multiplication sign, times |
| ± | plus or minus<br>positive or negative |
| = | equals |
| ≟ | equals? |
| ≈ | is approximately equal to |
| ≠ | is not equal to |
| < | is less than |
| > | is greater than |
| ≤ | is less than or equal to |
| ≥ | is greater than or equal to |
| ≅ | is congruent to |
| ~ | is similar to |
| ( ) | parentheses for grouping |
| [ ] | brackets for grouping |
| { } | braces for a set |
| % | percent |
| $|a|$ | absolute value of a |
| $-a$ | opposite of a |
| $a : b; \frac{a}{b}$ | ratio of a to b |
| $\frac{1}{a}, a^{-1}, a \neq 0$ | reciprocal of a |
| $a^n$ | nth power of a |
| $a^{-n}$ | $\frac{1}{a^n}, a \neq 0$ |
| $\sqrt{a}$ | nonnegative square root of a |
| $\sqrt[n]{a}$ | nth root of a (nonnegative if n even) |
| ° as in a° | degree(s) |
| ∘ as in f ∘ g | composition of functions |
| π | pi, an irrational number, approximately equal to 3.14 |
| e | an irrational number approximately equal to 2.72 |
| i | the imaginary number $\sqrt{-1}$ |
| $a + bi, b \neq 0$ | a complex number |
| ∞ | infinity |
| Σ | sigma, summation |
| σ | sigma, standard deviation |
| σ² | variance |
| $\overleftrightarrow{AB}$ | line through points A and B |
| $\overrightarrow{AB}$ | vector AB |

| Symbols | Words |
|---|---|
| $\overline{AB}$ | segment with endpoints A and B |
| AB | length of $\overline{AB}$; distance between points A and B |
| ∠A | angle A |
| m∠A | measure of angle A |
| △ABC | triangle ABC |
| (x, y) | ordered pair |
| $x_1, x_2, \ldots$ | specific values of the variable x |
| $y_1, y_2, \ldots$ | specific values of the variable y |
| $\bar{x}$ | mean of data values $x_i$ |
| f(x) | f of x, the function value at x |
| $f^{-1}$ | function inverse |
| log | logarithm |
| ln | natural logarithm |
| $\begin{bmatrix} a & b \\ c & d \end{bmatrix}$ | matrix |
| $a_{mn}$ | element in mth row, nth column of matrix A |
| $A^{-1}$ | inverse of matrix A |
| $\begin{vmatrix} a & b \\ c & d \end{vmatrix}$ | determinant of a matrix |
| det A | determinant of matrix A |
| n! | n factorial |
| $_nC_r$ | combinations of n things chosen r at a time |
| $_nP_r$ | permutations of n things arranged r at a time |
| P(event) | probability of the event |
| P(A|B) | probability of event A, given event B |
| sin A | sine of ∠A |
| cos A | cosine of ∠A |
| tan A | tangent of ∠A |
| csc A | cosecant of ∠A |
| sec A | secant of ∠A |
| cot A | cotangent of ∠A |
| ^ | raised to a power (in a spreadsheet formula) |
| * | multiply (in a spreadsheet formula) |
| / | divide (in a spreadsheet formula) |
| … | and so on |

## Properties and Formulas

### Order of Operations
1. Perform any operation(s) inside grouping symbols.
2. Simplify any terms with exponents.
3. Multiply and divide in order from left to right.
4. Add and subtract in order from left to right.

### The Pythagorean Theorem
In a right triangle, the sum of the squares of the lengths of the legs is equal to the square of the length of the hypotenuse.
$$a^2 + b^2 = c^2$$

### The Distance Formula
The distance d between any two points $(x_1, y_1)$ and $(x_2, y_2)$ is $d = \sqrt{(x_2 - x_1)^2 + (y_2 - y_1)^2}$.

### The Midpoint Formula
The midpoint M of a line segment with endpoints $A(x_1, y_1)$ and $B(x_2, y_2)$ is $\left(\frac{x_1 + x_2}{2}, \frac{y_1 + y_2}{2}\right)$.

### Chapter 1 Expressions, Equations, and Inequalities

**Closure**
For all real numbers a and b, a + b and a · b are real numbers.

**The Associative Properties**
For all real numbers a, b, and c:
$(a + b) + c = a + (b + c)$
$(a \cdot b) \cdot c = a \cdot (b \cdot c)$

**The Commutative Properties**
For all real numbers a and b:
$a + b = b + a$ and $a \cdot b = b \cdot a$

**The Identity Properties**
For every real number a:
$a + 0 = a$ and $0 + a = a$ · $a \cdot 1 = a$ and $1 \cdot a = a$
0 is the additive identity.  1 is the multiplicative identity.

**The Inverse Properties**
For every real number a:
$a + (-a) = 0$ and $a \cdot \frac{1}{a} = 1$ $(a \neq 0)$

**The Distributive Properties**
For all real numbers a, b, and c:
$a(b + c) = ab + ac$  $(b + c)a = ba + ca$
$a(b - c) = ab - ac$  $(b - c)a = ba - ca$

### Multiplication
Let a represent a real number.
Multiplication by 0:  $0 \cdot a = 0$.
Multiplication by -1:  $-1 \cdot a = -a$

### Opposites
Let a and b represent real numbers.
Opposite of a Sum:  $-(a + b) = -a + (-b) = -a - b$
Opposite of a Difference:  $-(a - b) = -a + b = b - a$
Opposite of a Product:  $-(ab) = -a \cdot b = a \cdot (-b)$
Opposite of an Opposite:  $-(-a) = a$

### Properties of Equality
Assume a, b, and c represent real numbers.

| | |
|---|---|
| Reflexive: | $a = a$ |
| Symmetric: | If $a = b$, then $b = a$. |
| Transitive: | If $a = b$ and $b = c$, then $a = c$. |
| Substitution: | If $a = b$, then you can replace a with b and vice versa. |
| Addition: | If $a = b$, then $a + c = b + c$. |
| Subtraction: | If $a = b$, then $a - c = b - c$. |
| Multiplication: | If $a = b$, then $ac = bc$. |
| Division: | If $a = b$ and $c \neq 0$, then $\frac{a}{c} = \frac{b}{c}$. |

### Properties of Inequality
Let a, b, and c represent real numbers.

| | |
|---|---|
| Transitive: | If $a > b$ and $b > c$, then $a > c$. |
| Addition: | If $a > b$, then $a + c > b + c$. |
| Subtraction: | If $a > b$, then $a - c > b - c$. |
| Multiplication: | If $a > b$ and $c > 0$, then $ac > bc$.<br>If $a > b$ and $c < 0$, then $ac < bc$. |
| Division: | If $a > b$ and $c > 0$, then $\frac{a}{c} > \frac{b}{c}$.<br>If $a > b$ and $c < 0$, then $\frac{a}{c} < \frac{b}{c}$. |

### Chapter 2 Functions, Equations, and Graphs

**Direct Variation**
$y = kx$ or $\frac{y}{x} = k$, where $k \neq 0$.

**Slope of a Line Containing $(x_1, y_1)$ and $(x_2, y_2)$**
$slope = \frac{vertical\ change\ (rise)}{horizontal\ change\ (run)} = \frac{y_2 - y_1}{x_2 - x_1}$,
where $x_2 - x_1 \neq 0$

**Point-Slope Equation of a Line**
The equation of the line through point $(x_1, y_1)$ with slope m is $y - y_1 = m(x - x_1)$.

## Function Families

Assume $a$, $k$, and $h$ are positive numbers.
Parent $\quad\quad\quad\quad\quad\quad y = f(x)$
Reflection across x-axis $\quad y = -f(x)$
Vertical stretch $(a > 1)$
Vertical shrink $(0 < a < 1)$ $\quad y = af(x)$

Translation
horizontal to left by $h$ $\quad y = f(x + h)$
horizontal to right by $h$ $\quad y = f(x - h)$
vertical up by $k$ $\quad\quad\quad y = f(x) + k$
vertical down by $k$ $\quad\quad y = f(x) - k$

## Chapter 4 Quadratic Functions and Equations

### Quadratic Functions
Parent $\quad\quad\quad\quad\quad\quad y = x^2$
Reflection across x-axis $\quad y = -x^2$

Stretch $(a > 1)$
Shrink $(0 < a < 1)$ $\quad y = ax^2$

Translation
horizontal by $h$
vertical by $k$ $\quad\quad\quad y = (x - h)^2 + k$

Vertex Form $\quad\quad\quad y = a(x - h)^2 + k$
Standard Form $\quad\quad y = f(x) = ax^2 + bx + c$
The graph is a parabola that opens up
if $a > 0$ and down if $a < 0$.
The vertex is $(h, k)$ (Vertex Form) and
$\left(-\frac{b}{2a}, f\left(-\frac{b}{2a}\right)\right)$ (Standard Form).
The axis of symmetry is $x = h$ (Vertex Form)
and $x = -\frac{b}{2a}$ (Standard Form).

### Factoring Perfect-Square Trinomials
$a^2 + 2ab + b^2 = (a + b)^2$
$a^2 - 2ab + b^2 = (a - b)^2$

### Factoring a Difference of Two Squares
$a^2 - b^2 = (a + b)(a - b)$

### Multiplication Property of Square Roots
For any numbers $a \geq 0$ and $b \geq 0$, $\sqrt{ab} = \sqrt{a} \cdot \sqrt{b}$.

### Division Property of Square Roots
For any numbers $a \geq 0$ and $b > 0$, $\sqrt{\frac{a}{b}} = \frac{\sqrt{a}}{\sqrt{b}}$.

### Zero-Product Property
If $ab = 0$, then $a = 0$ or $b = 0$.

### The Quadratic Formula
If $ax^2 + bx + c = 0$, then $x = \frac{-b \pm \sqrt{b^2 - 4ac}}{2a}$

### Discriminant
The discriminant of a quadratic equation in the form
$ax^2 + bx + c = 0$ is $b^2 - 4ac$.
$b^2 - 4ac > 0 \Rightarrow$ two real solutions
$b^2 - 4ac = 0 \Rightarrow$ one real solution
$b^2 - 4ac < 0 \Rightarrow$ two complex solutions

### Square Root of a Negative Real Number
For any positive number $a$,
$\sqrt{-a} = \sqrt{-1 \cdot a} = \sqrt{-1} \cdot \sqrt{a} = i\sqrt{a}$.
Example: $\sqrt{-5} = i\sqrt{5}$
Note that
$(\sqrt{-5})^2 = (i\sqrt{5})^2 = i^2(\sqrt{5})^2 = -1 \cdot 5 = -5$ (not 5).

## Chapter 5 Polynomials and Polynomial Functions

### End Behavior of a Polynomial Function
The end behavior of a polynomial function of degree $n$ with leading term $ax^n$:

| $a$ | $n$ | end behavior |
|-----|-----|-----|
| positive | even | up and up |
| positive | odd | down and up |
| negative | even | down and down |
| negative | odd | up and down |

### Factor Theorem
The expression $x - a$ is a linear factor of a polynomial if and only if the value $a$ is a zero of the related polynomial function.

### Remainder Theorem
If you divide a polynomial $P(x)$ of degree $n \geq 1$ by $x - a$, then the remainder is $P(a)$.

### Factoring a Sum or Difference of Cubes
$a^3 + b^3 = (a + b)(a^2 - ab + b^2)$
$a^3 - b^3 = (a - b)(a^2 + ab + b^2)$

### Rational Root Theorem
Let $P(x) = a_n x^n + a_{n-1} x^{n-1} + \cdots + a_1 x + a_0$ be a polynomial with integer coefficients.
Integer roots of $P(x) = 0$ must be factors of $a_0$.
Rational roots have reduced form $\frac{p}{q}$ where $p$ is an integer factor of $a_0$ and $q$ is an integer factor of $a_n$.

### Conjugate Root Theorems
Suppose $P(x)$ is a polynomial with *rational* coefficients.
If $a + \sqrt{b}$ is an irrational root with $a$ and $b$ rational, then $a - \sqrt{b}$ is also a root.

Suppose $P(x)$ is a polynomial with *real* coefficients.
If $a + bi$ is a complex root with $a$ and $b$ real, then $a - bi$ is also a root.

---

### Fundamental Theorem of Algebra
If $P(x)$ is a polynomial of degree $n \geq 1$, then $P(x) = 0$ has exactly $n$ roots, including multiple and complex roots.

### Binomial Theorem
For every positive integer $n$, $(a + b)^n =$
$P_0 a^n + P_1 a^{n-1}b + P_2 a^{n-2}b^2 + \cdots + P_{n-1}ab^{n-1} + P_n b^n$
where $P_0, P_1, \ldots, P_n$ are the numbers in the $n$th row of Pascal's Triangle.

## Chapter 6 Radical Functions and Rational Exponents

### Properties of Exponents
For any nonzero number $a$ and any integers $m$ and $n$,
$a^0 = 1$ $\quad\quad\quad\quad (ab)^n = a^n b^n$
$\frac{a^m}{a^n} = a^{m-n}$ $\quad\quad a^m \cdot a^n = a^{m+n}$
$a^{-n} = \frac{1}{a^n}$ $\quad\quad\quad (a^m)^n = a^{mn}$
$\left(\frac{a}{b}\right)^n = \frac{a^n}{b^n}$

### $n$th Roots of $n$th Powers
For any real number $a$,
$\sqrt[n]{a^n} = \begin{cases} a \text{ if } n \text{ is odd} \\ |a| \text{ if } n \text{ is even} \end{cases}$

### Combining Radical Expressions: Products
If $\sqrt[n]{a}$ and $\sqrt[n]{b}$ are real numbers, then $\sqrt[n]{a} \cdot \sqrt[n]{b} = \sqrt[n]{ab}$.

### Combining Radical Expressions: Quotients
If $\sqrt[n]{a}$ and $\sqrt[n]{b}$ are real numbers and $b \neq 0$,
then $\frac{\sqrt[n]{a}}{\sqrt[n]{b}} = \sqrt[n]{\frac{a}{b}}$.

### Properties of Rational Exponents
If the $n$th root of $a$ is a real number and $m$ is an integer, then
$a^{\frac{m}{n}} = \sqrt[n]{a^m}$ and $a^{\frac{m}{n}} = \sqrt[n]{a^m} = \left(\sqrt[n]{a}\right)^m$. If $m$ is negative, $a \neq 0$.

### Composition of Inverse Functions
If $f$ and $f^{-1}$ are inverse functions, then
$(f^{-1} \circ f)(x) = x$ and $(f \circ f^{-1})(x) = x$ for $x$ in the domains of $f$ and $f^{-1}$, respectively.

### Radical Functions

| | Square Root | $n$th Root |
|---|---|---|
| Parent | $y = \sqrt{x}$ | $y = \sqrt[n]{x}$ |
| Reflection across x-axis | $y = -\sqrt{x}$ | $y = -\sqrt[n]{x}$ |
| Stretch $(a > 1)$ Shrink $(0 < a < 1)$ | $y = a\sqrt{x}$ | $y = a\sqrt[n]{x}$ |

Translation
horizontal by $h$
vertical by $k$ $\quad y = \sqrt{x - h} + k \quad y = \sqrt[n]{x - h} + k$

## Chapter 7 Exponential and Logarithmic Functions

### Exponential Functions
Parent, $b > 0, b \neq 1$ $\quad y = b^x$
Reflection across x-axis $\quad y = -b^x$
Stretch $(a > 1)$ $\quad\quad\quad y = ab^x$
Shrink $(0 < a < 1)$

Translation
horizontal by $h$
vertical by $k$ $\quad y = b^{x-h} + k$

### Continuously Compounded Interest
$A(t) = P \cdot e^{rt}$, where $A(t)$ represents the total, $P$ represents the principal, $r$ represents the interest rate, and $t$ represents time in years.

### Logarithmic Functions

| | Base $b$ | Base $e$ |
|---|---|---|
| Parents, $b > 0, b \neq 1$ | $y = \log_b x$ | $y = \ln x$ |
| Reflection across x-axis | $y = -\log_b x$ | $y = -\ln x$ |
| Stretch $(a > 1)$ Shrink $(0 < a < 1)$ | $y = a \log_b x$ | $y = a \ln x$ |

Translation
horizontal by $h$
vertical by $k$ $\quad y = \log_b(x - h) + k \quad y = \ln(x - h) + k$

### Properties of Logarithms
For any positive numbers $m$, $n$, and $b$ where $b \neq 1$
Product Property: $\log_b mn = \log_b m + \log_b n$
Quotient Property: $\log_b \frac{m}{n} = \log_b m - \log_b n$
Power Property: $\log_b m^n = n\log_b m$

### Change of Base Formula
For any positive numbers $m$, $b$, and $c$, with
$b \neq 1$ and $c \neq 1$, $\log_b m = \frac{\log_c m}{\log_c b}$.

## Chapter 8 Rational Functions

### Inverse Variation
$xy = k$, $y = \frac{k}{x}$, or $x = \frac{k}{y}$, where $k \neq 0$.

### Combined Variation
$z$ varies jointly with $x$ and $y$: $z = kxy$
$z$ varies jointly with $x$ and $y$ and inversely with $w$: $z = \frac{kxy}{w}$
$z$ varies directly with $x$ and inversely with the product $wy$: $z = \frac{kx}{wy}$

### Reciprocal Functions
Parent $\quad\quad\quad\quad\quad\quad\quad y = \frac{1}{x}, x \neq 0$
Reflection across x-axis $\quad\quad y = -\frac{1}{x}, x \neq 0$
Stretch $(a > 1)$ $\quad\quad\quad\quad\quad y = \frac{a}{x}, x \neq 0$
Shrink $(0 < a < 1)$

Translation
horizontal by $h$
vertical by $k$ $\quad\quad\quad\quad y = \frac{a}{x-h} + k, x \neq h$
Asymptotes $\quad\quad\quad\quad\quad y = k$ (horiz.), $x = h$ (vert.)

---

## Chapter 9 Sequences and Series

### Arithmetic Mean of Two Numbers
$\frac{x + y}{2}$

### Arithmetic Sequence
A recursive definition for an arithmetic sequence with a starting value $a$ and a common difference $d$ has two parts:
$a_1 = a$: initial condition
$a_{n+1} = a_n + d$, for $n \geq 1$: recursive formula
An explicit definition for this sequence is the formula:
$a_n = a + (n - 1)d$ for $n \geq 1$.

### Geometric Sequence
A recursive definition for a geometric sequence with a starting value $a$ and a common ratio $r$ has two parts:
$a_1 = a$: initial condition
$a_{n+1} = a_n \cdot r$, for $n \geq 1$: recursive formula
An explicit definition for this sequence is the formula:
$a_n = ar^{n-1}$, for $n \geq 1$.

### Sum of a Finite Arithmetic Series
The sum $S_n$ of a finite arithmetic series
$a_1 + a_2 + a_3 + \cdots + a_n$ is $S_n = \frac{n}{2}(a_1 + a_n)$
where $a_1$ is the first term, $a_n$ is the $n$th term, and $n$ is the number of terms.

### Sum of a Finite Geometric Series
The sum $S_n$ of a finite geometric series
$a_1 + a_2 + a_3 r^2 + \cdots + a_1 r^{n-1}$ is $S_n = \frac{a_1(1 - r^n)}{1 - r}$
where $a_1$ is the first term, $r$ is the common ratio, and $n$ is the number of terms.

### Sum of an Infinite Geometric Series
An infinite geometric series with $|r| < 1$ converges to the sum $S$ given by the following formula:
$S = \frac{a_1}{1 - r}$

## Chapter 10 Quadratic Relations and Conic Sections

### Parabolas

| | Vertex (0, 0) | Vertex $(h, k)$ |
|---|---|---|
| Vertical | | |
| Equation | $y = \frac{1}{4c}x^2$ | $y = \frac{1}{4c}(x - h)^2 + k$ |
| Focus | $(0, c)$ | $(h, c + k)$ |
| Directrix | $y = -c$ | $y = -c + k$ |
| Horizontal | Vertex (0, 0) | Vertex $(h, k)$ |
| Equation | $x = \frac{1}{4c}y^2$ | $x = \frac{1}{4c}(y - k)^2 + h$ |
| Focus | $(c, 0)$ | $(c + h, k)$ |
| Directrix | $x = -c$ | $x = -c + h$ |

### Circles, radius = $r$

| | Center (0, 0) | Center $(h, k)$ |
|---|---|---|
| Equation | $x^2 + y^2 = r^2$ | $(x - h)^2 + (y - k)^2 = r^2$ |

### Ellipses

| Horizontal, $a > b$ | Center (0, 0) | Center $(h, k)$ |
|---|---|---|
| Equation | $\frac{x^2}{a^2} + \frac{y^2}{b^2} = 1$ | $\frac{(x - h)^2}{a^2} + \frac{(y - k)^2}{b^2} = 1$ |
| Vertices | $(\pm a, 0)$ | $(\pm a + h, k)$ |
| Co-Vertices | $(0, \pm b)$ | $(h, \pm b + k)$ |
| Foci, $c^2 = a^2 - b^2$ | $(\pm c, 0)$ | $(\pm c + h, k)$ |
| Major axis | $y = 0$ | $y = k$ |
| Minor axis | $x = 0$ | $x = h$ |

| Vertical, $a > b$ | Center (0, 0) | Center $(h, k)$ |
|---|---|---|
| Equation | $\frac{x^2}{b^2} + \frac{y^2}{a^2} = 1$ | $\frac{(x - h)^2}{b^2} + \frac{(y - k)^2}{a^2} = 1$ |
| Vertices | $(0, \pm a)$ | $(h, \pm a + k)$ |
| Co-Vertices | $(\pm b, 0)$ | $(\pm b + h, k)$ |
| Foci, $c^2 = a^2 - b^2$ | $(0, \pm c)$ | $(h, \pm c + k)$ |
| Major axis | $x = 0$ | $x = h$ |
| Minor axis | $y = 0$ | $y = k$ |

### Hyperbolas

| Horizontal, $a > b$ | Center (0, 0) | Center $(h, k)$ |
|---|---|---|
| Equation | $\frac{x^2}{a^2} - \frac{y^2}{b^2} = 1$ | $\frac{(x - h)^2}{a^2} - \frac{(y - k)^2}{b^2} = 1$ |
| Vertices | $(\pm a, 0)$ | $(\pm a + h, k)$ |
| Foci, $c^2 = a^2 + b^2$ | $(\pm c, 0)$ | $(\pm c + h, k)$ |
| Transverse axis | $y = 0$ | $y = k$ |
| Asymptotes | $y = \pm\frac{b}{a}x$ | $y = \pm\frac{b}{a}(x - h) + k$ |

| Vertical, $a > b$ | Center (0, 0) | Center $(h, k)$ |
|---|---|---|
| Equation | $\frac{y^2}{a^2} - \frac{x^2}{b^2} = 1$ | $\frac{(y - k)^2}{a^2} - \frac{(x - h)^2}{b^2} = 1$ |
| Vertices | $(0, \pm a)$ | $(h, \pm a + k)$ |
| Foci, $c^2 = a^2 + b^2$ | $(0, \pm c)$ | $(h, \pm c + k)$ |
| Transverse axis | $x = 0$ | $x = h$ |
| Asymptotes | $y = \pm\frac{a}{b}x$ | $y = \pm\frac{a}{b}(x - h) + k$ |

---

## Chapter 11 Probability and Statistics

### Fundamental Counting Principle
If event $M$ can occur in $m$ ways and is followed by event $N$ that can occur in $n$ ways, then event $M$ followed by event $N$ can occur in $m \cdot n$ ways.

### Number of Permutations
The number of permutations of $n$ items of a set arranged $r$ items at a time is
$_nP_r = \frac{n!}{(n - r)!}$ for $0 \leq r \leq n$.

### Number of Combinations
The number of combinations of $n$ items of a set chosen $r$ items at a time is
$_nC_r = \frac{n!}{r!(n-r)!}$ for $0 \leq r \leq n$.

### Probability of $A$ and $B$
If $A$ and $B$ are independent events, then
$P(A \text{ and } B) = P(A) \cdot P(B)$.

### Probability of $A$ or $B$
$P(A \text{ or } B) = P(A) + P(B) - P(A \text{ and } B)$
If $A$ and $B$ are mutually exclusive events, then
$P(A \text{ or } B) = P(A) + P(B)$.

### Conditional Probability
For any two events $A$ and $B$ with $P(A) \neq 0$, the probability of event $B$, given event $A$, is:
$P(B | A) = \frac{P(A \text{ and } B)}{P(A)}$

### Mean, Variance, and Standard Deviation
Mean: $\bar{x} = \frac{x_1 + x_2 + x_3 + \cdots + x_n}{n}$
Variance: $\sigma^2 = \frac{\Sigma(x - \bar{x})^2}{n}$
Standard deviation: $\sigma = \sqrt{\frac{\Sigma(x - \bar{x})^2}{n}}$

### Binomial Probability
For repeated independent trials, each with a probability of success $p$ and a probability of failure $q$ (with $p + q = 1$), the probability of $x$ successes in $n$ trials is
$P(x) = {}_nC_x p^x q^{n-x}$.

### Binomial Theorem Using Combinations
For every positive integer $n$, use the combinations formula $_nC_r$ to expand $(a + b)^n$:
$(a + b)^n = {}_nC_0 a^n + {}_nC_1 a^{n-1}b + {}_nC_2 a^{n-2}b^2 + \cdots + {}_nC_{n-1}ab^{n-1} + {}_nC_n b^n$

## Chapter 12 Matrices

### Properties of Matrix Addition
If $A$, $B$, and $C$ are $m \times n$ matrices, then
Closure Property: $A + B$ is an $m \times n$ matrix
Commutative Property: $A + B = B + A$
Associative Property: $(A + B) + C = A + (B + C)$
Identity Property: There is a unique $m \times n$ matrix $O$ such that $O + A = A + O = A$
Inverse Property: For each $A$, there is a unique opposite, $-A$, such that $A + (-A) = O$

### Properties of Scalar Multiplication
If $A$ and $B$ are $m \times n$ matrices, $c$ and $d$ are scalars, and $O$ is the $m \times n$ zero matrix, then
Closure Property: $cA$ is an $m \times n$ matrix
Associative Property: $(cd)A = c(dA)$
Distributive Property: $c(A + B) = cA + cB$
$(c + d)A = cA + dA$
Identity Property: $1 \cdot A = A$
Property of Zero: $0 \cdot A = O$ and $cO = O$

### Properties of Matrix Multiplication
If $A$, $B$, and $C$ are $n \times n$ matrices and $O$ is the $n \times n$ zero matrix, then
Closure Property: $AB$ is an $n \times n$ matrix
Associative Property: $(AB)C = A(BC)$
Distributive Property: $A(B + C) = AB + AC$
$(B + C)A = BA + CA$
Property of Zero: $OA = AO = O$

### Determinants of $2 \times 2$ and $3 \times 3$ Matrices
The determinant of a $2 \times 2$ matrix $\begin{bmatrix} a & b \\ c & d \end{bmatrix}$ is $ad - bc$.

The determinant of a $3 \times 3$ matrix $\begin{bmatrix} a_1 & b_1 & c_1 \\ a_2 & b_2 & c_2 \\ a_3 & b_3 & c_3 \end{bmatrix}$ is
$a_1 b_2 c_3 + b_1 c_2 a_3 + c_1 a_2 b_3 - (a_3 b_2 c_1 + b_3 c_2 a_1 + c_3 a_2 b_1)$

### Inverse of a $2 \times 2$ Matrix
If $A = \begin{bmatrix} a & b \\ c & d \end{bmatrix}$ and $\det A \neq 0$,
then the inverse of $A$ is
$A^{-1} = \frac{1}{\det A}\begin{bmatrix} d & -b \\ -c & a \end{bmatrix} = \frac{1}{ad - bc}\begin{bmatrix} d & -b \\ -c & a \end{bmatrix}$

## Chapter 13 Periodic Functions and Trigonometry

### Convert Between Radians and Degrees
Use the proportion $\frac{d}{180°} = \frac{t \text{ radians}}{\pi \text{ radians}}$ to convert between radians and degrees.

To convert degrees to radians, multiply by $\frac{\pi \text{ radians}}{180°}$.

To convert radians to degrees, multiply by $\frac{180°}{\pi \text{ radians}}$.

### Length of an Intercepted Arc
For a circle of radius $r$ and a central angle of measure $\theta$ (in radians), the length $s$ of the intercepted arc is $s = r\theta$.

### Sine and Cosine Functions

| | Sine | Cosine |
|---|---|---|
| Parents | $y = \sin x$ | $y = \cos x$ |
| Reflection across $x$-axis | $y = -\sin x$ | $y = -\cos x$ |
| Amplitude $\lvert a \rvert$ | $y = a \sin x$ | $y = a \cos x$ |
| Period $\frac{2\pi}{b}$, $b > 0$ | $y = \sin bx$ | $y = \cos bx$ |
| Translation horizontal by $h$ vertical by $k$ | $y = \sin (x - h) + k$ | $y = \cos (x - h) + k$ |

### Tangent Function

| | |
|---|---|
| Parent | $y = \tan x$ |
| Reflection across $x$-axis | $y = -\tan x$ |
| Period $\frac{\pi}{b}$ | $y = \tan bx$ |
| Translation horizontal by $h$ vertical by $k$ | $y = \tan (x - h) + k$ |
| Asymptotes ($\tan bx$) | $x = n\frac{\pi}{2b}$, $n$ odd |

## Chapter 14 Trigonometric Identities and Equations

### Basic Identities
Reciprocal Identities:
$$\csc \theta = \frac{1}{\sin \theta} \qquad \sec \theta = \frac{1}{\cos \theta} \qquad \tan \theta = \frac{1}{\cot \theta}$$
$$\sin \theta = \frac{1}{\csc \theta} \qquad \cos \theta = \frac{1}{\sec \theta} \qquad \cot \theta = \frac{1}{\tan \theta}$$

Tangent Identity:
$$\tan \theta = \frac{\sin \theta}{\cos \theta}$$
Cotangent Identity:
$$\cot \theta = \frac{\cos \theta}{\sin \theta}$$

### Pythagorean Identities
$$\cos^2 \theta + \sin^2 \theta = 1 \quad 1 + \tan^2 \theta = \sec^2 \theta \quad \cot^2 \theta + 1 = \csc^2 \theta$$

### Area of a Triangle
In $\triangle ABC$ with $a$, $b$, and $c$ the lengths of the sides opposite $\angle A$, $\angle B$, and $\angle C$, respectively,
$$\text{Area } \triangle ABC = \tfrac{1}{2}bc \sin A = \tfrac{1}{2}ac \sin B = \tfrac{1}{2}ab \sin C.$$

### Law of Sines
In $\triangle ABC$ with $a$, $b$, and $c$ the lengths of the sides opposite $\angle A$, $\angle B$, and $\angle C$, respectively,
$$\frac{\sin A}{a} = \frac{\sin B}{b} = \frac{\sin C}{c}$$

### Law of Cosines
In $\triangle ABC$ with $a$, $b$, and $c$ the lengths of the sides opposite $\angle A$, $\angle B$, and $\angle C$, respectively,
$$a^2 = b^2 + c^2 - 2bc \cdot \cos A$$
$$b^2 = a^2 + c^2 - 2ac \cdot \cos B$$
$$c^2 = a^2 + b^2 - 2ab \cdot \cos C$$

### Negative Angle Identities
$$\sin (-\theta) = -\sin \theta \quad \cos (-\theta) = \cos \theta \quad \tan (-\theta) = -\tan \theta$$

### Cofunction Angle Identities
$$\sin \left(\tfrac{\pi}{2} - \theta\right) = \cos \theta \quad \cos \left(\tfrac{\pi}{2} - \theta\right) = \sin \theta \quad \tan \left(\tfrac{\pi}{2} - \theta\right) = \cot \theta$$

### Angle Difference Identities
$$\sin (A - B) = \sin A \cos B - \cos A \sin B$$
$$\cos (A - B) = \cos A \cos B + \sin A \sin B$$
$$\tan (A - B) = \frac{\tan A - \tan B}{1 + \tan A \tan B}$$

### Angle Sum Identities
$$\sin (A + B) = \sin A \cos B + \cos A \sin B$$
$$\cos (A + B) = \cos A \cos B - \sin A \sin B$$
$$\tan (A + B) = \frac{\tan A + \tan B}{1 - \tan A \tan B}$$

### Double-Angle Identities
$$\cos 2\theta = \cos^2 \theta - \sin^2 \theta \qquad \sin 2\theta = 2 \sin \theta \cos \theta$$
$$\cos 2\theta = 2 \cos^2 \theta - 1 \qquad \tan 2\theta = \frac{2 \tan \theta}{1 - \tan^2 \theta}$$
$$\cos 2\theta = 1 - 2 \sin^2 \theta$$

### Half-Angle Identities
$$\sin \tfrac{A}{2} = \pm \sqrt{\frac{1 - \cos A}{2}}$$
$$\cos \tfrac{A}{2} = \pm \sqrt{\frac{1 + \cos A}{2}}$$
$$\tan \tfrac{A}{2} = \pm \sqrt{\frac{1 - \cos A}{1 + \cos A}}$$

## Formulas of **Geometry**

You will use a number of geometric formulas as you work through your algebra book. Here are some perimeter, area, and volume formulas.

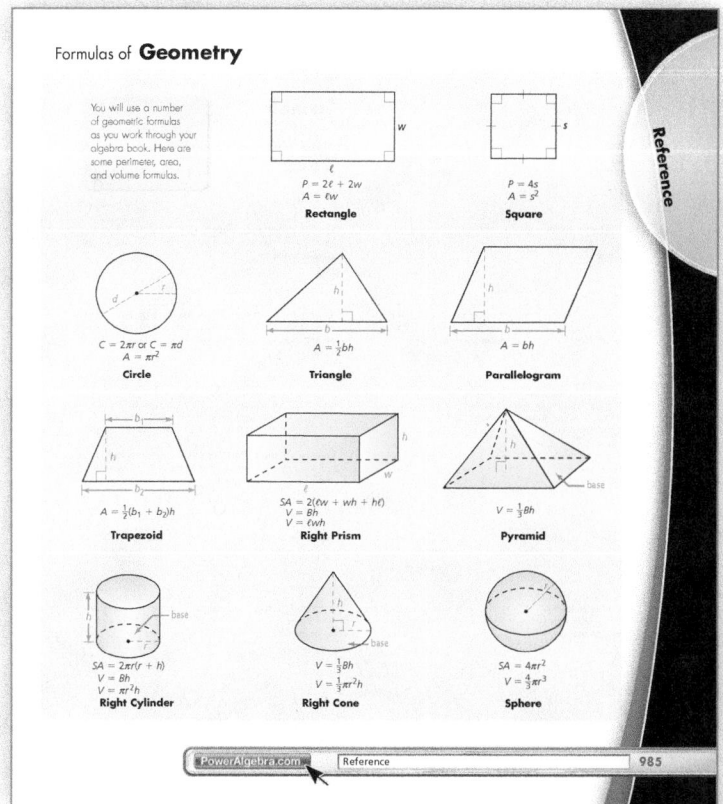

**Rectangle**
$$P = 2\ell + 2w$$
$$A = \ell w$$

**Square**
$$P = 4s$$
$$A = s^2$$

**Circle**
$$C = 2\pi r \text{ or } C = \pi d$$
$$A = \pi r^2$$

**Triangle**
$$A = \tfrac{1}{2}bh$$

**Parallelogram**
$$A = bh$$

**Trapezoid**
$$A = \tfrac{1}{2}(b_1 + b_2)h$$

**Right Prism**
$$SA = 2(\ell w + wh + h\ell)$$
$$V = Bh$$
$$V = \ell wh$$

**Pyramid**
$$V = \tfrac{1}{3}Bh$$

**Right Cylinder**
$$SA = 2\pi r(r + h)$$
$$V = Bh$$
$$V = \pi r^2 h$$

**Right Cone**
$$V = \tfrac{1}{3}Bh$$
$$V = \tfrac{1}{3}\pi r^2 h$$

**Sphere**
$$SA = 4\pi r^2$$
$$V = \tfrac{4}{3}\pi r^3$$

# English/Spanish Illustrated **Glossary**

## English    A    Spanish

**Absolute value (p. 41)** The absolute value of a real number, $x$, written $|x|$, is its distance from zero on the number line.

Example $|3| = 3$
$|-4| = 4$

**Valor absoluto de un número real (p. 41)** El valor absoluto de un número real, $x$, escrito como $|x|$, es su distancia desde cero en la recta numérica.

**Absolute value function (p. 107)** A function of the form $f(x) = |mx + b| + c$, where $m \neq 0$, is an absolute value function.

Example $f(x) = |3x - 2| + 3$
$f(x) = |2x|$

**Función de valor absoluto (p. 107)** Una función de la forma $f(x) = |mx + b| + c$, donde $m \neq 0$, es una función de valor absoluto.

**Absolute value of a complex number (p. 249)** The absolute value of a complex number is its distance from the origin on the complex number plane. In general, $|a + bi| = \sqrt{a^2 + b^2}$.

Example $|3 - 4i| = \sqrt{3^2 + (-4)^2} = 5$

**Valor absoluto de un número complejo (p. 249)** El valor absoluto de un número complejo es la distancia a la que está del origen en el plano de números complejo. Generalmente, $|a + bi| = \sqrt{a^2 + b^2}$.

**Additive identity (p. 14)** The additive identity is 0. The sum of 0 and any number is that number. The sum of opposites is 0.

**Identidad aditiva (p. 14)** La identidad aditiva es 0. La suma de 0 y cualquier número es ese mismo número. La suma de opuestos es 0.

**Additive inverse (p. 14)** The opposite or additive inverse of any number $a$ is $-a$. The sum of opposites is 0, the additive identity.

Example $3 + (-3) = 0$
$5.2 + (-5.2) = 0$

**Inverso aditivo (p. 14)** El opuesto o inverso aditivo de un número $a$ es $-a$. La suma de opuestos es 0, la identidad aditiva.

**Algebraic expression (p. 5)** An algebraic expression is a mathematical phrase that contains one or more variables.

Example $2x + 3$
$z - y$

**Expresión algebraica (p. 5)** Una expresión algebraica es una frase matemática que contiene una o más variables.

**Amplitude (p. 822)** The amplitude of a periodic function is half the difference between the maximum and minimum values of the function.

Example The maximum and minimum values of $y = 4 \sin x$ are 4 and $-4$, respectively.
amplitude $= \frac{4 - (-4)}{2} = 4$

**Amplitud (p. 822)** La amplitud de una función periódica es la mitad de la diferencia entre los valores máximo y mínimo de la función.

---

## English      Spanish

**Arithmetic mean (p. 574)** The arithmetic mean, or average, of two numbers is their sum divided by two.

Example The arithmetic mean of 12 and 15 is $\frac{12 + 15}{2} = 13.5$.

**Media aritmética (p. 574)** La media aritmética, o promedio, de dos números es su suma dividida por dos.

**Arithmetic sequence (p. 572)** An arithmetic sequence is a sequence with a constant difference between consecutive terms.

Example The arithmetic sequence 1, 5, 9, 13, . . . has a common difference of 4.

**Secuencia aritmética (p. 572)** Una secuencia aritmética es una secuencia de números en la que la diferencia entre dos números consecutivos es constante.

**Arithmetic series (p. 587)** An arithmetic series is a series whose terms form an arithmetic sequence.

Example $1 + 5 + 9 + 13 + 17 + 21$ is an arithmetic series with six terms.

**Serie aritmética (p. 587)** Una serie aritmética es una serie cuyos términos forman una progresión aritmética.

**Asymptote (p. 435)** An asymptote is a line that a graph approaches as $x$ or $y$ increases in absolute value.

Example The function $y = \frac{x + 2}{x - 2}$ has $x = 2$ as a vertical asymptote and $y = 1$ as a horizontal asymptote.

**Asíntota (p. 435)** Una asíntota es una recta a la cual se acerca una gráfica a medida que $x$ o $y$ aumentan de valor absoluto.

**Axis of symmetry (pp. 107, 194)** The axis of symmetry is the line that divides a figure into two parts that are mirror images.

Example

$y = x^2 + 2x - 1$

**Eje de simetría (p. 107, 194)** El eje de simetría es la recta que divide una figura en dos partes que son imágenes una de la otra.

### B

**Bias (p. 719)** A bias is a systematic error introduced by the sampling method.

**Sesgo (p. 719)** El sesgo es un error sistemático introducido por medio del método de muestreo.

**Bimodal (p. 705)** A bimodal data set has two modes.

Example $\{1, 2, 3, 3, 4, 5, 6, 6\}$
mode = 3 and 6

**Bimodal (p. 705)** Un conjunto bimodal de datos tiene dos modas.

---

## English      Spanish

**Binomial experiment (p. 725)** A binomial experiment is one in which the situation involves repeated trials. Each trial has two possible outcomes (success or failure), and the probability of success is constant throughout the trials.

**Experimento binomial (p. 725)** Un experimento binomial es un experimento que requiere varios ensayos. Cada ensayo tiene dos resultados posibles (éxito o fracaso), y la probabilidad de éxito es constante durante todos los ensayos.

**Binomial probability (p. 726)** In a binomial experiment with probability of success $p$ and probability of failure $q$, the probability of $x$ successes in $n$ trials is given by $_nC_xp^xq^{n-x}$.

Example Suppose you roll a standard number cube and that you call rolling a 1 a success. Then $p = \frac{1}{6}$ and $q = \frac{5}{6}$. The probability of rolling nine 1's in twenty rolls is $_{20}C_9\left(\frac{1}{6}\right)^9\left(\frac{5}{6}\right)^{11} \approx 0.0022$.

**Probabilidad binomial (p. 726)** En un experimento binomial con una probabilidad de éxito $p$ y una probabilidad de fracaso $q$, la probabilidad de $x$ éxitos en $n$ ensayos se expresa con $_nC_xp^xq^{n-x}$.

**Binomial Theorem (pp. 327, 727)** For every positive integer $n$, $(a + b)^n = P_0a^n + P_1a^{n-1}b + \cdots + P_{n-1}ab^{n-1} + P_nb^n$ where $P_0, P_1, \ldots, P_n$ are the numbers in the row of Pascal's Triangle that has $n$ as its second number.

Example $(x + 1)^3 = {}_3C_0(x)^3 + {}_3C_1(x)^2(1) + {}_3C_2(x)(1)^2 + {}_3C_3(1)^3 = x^3 + 3x^2 + 3x + 1$

**Teorema binomial (pp. 327, 727)** Para cada número entero positivo $n$, $(a + b)^n = P_0a^n + P_1a^{n-1}b + P_2a^{n-2}b^2 + \cdots + P_{n-1}ab^{n-1} + P_nb^n$, donde $P_0, P_1, \ldots, P_n$ son los números de la fila del Triángulo de Pascal cuyo segundo número es $n$.

**Boundary (p. 114)** A boundary of the graph of a linear inequality is a line in the coordinate plane. It separates the solutions of the inequality from the nonsolutions. Points of the line itself may or may not be solutions.

**Límite (p. 114)** Un límite de la gráfica de una desigualdad lineal es una línea en el plano de coordenadas. Ésta separa las soluciones de la desigualdad de las no soluciones. Los puntos de la línea pueden ser o no puntos de la línea.

**Box-and-whisker plot (p. 707)** A box-and-whisker plot is a method of displaying data that uses quartiles to form the center box and the maximum and minimum values to form the whiskers.

Example

**Gráfica de cajas (p. 707)** Una gráfica de cajas es un método para mostrar datos que utiliza cuartiles para formar una casilla central y los valores máximos y mínimos para formar los conectores.

---

## English      Spanish

**Branch (p. 508)** Each piece of a discontinuous graph is called a branch.

Example

**Rama (p. 508)** Cada segmento de una gráfica discontinua se llama rama.

### C

**Center of a circle (p. 630)** The center of a circle is the point that is the same distance from every point on the circle.

Example circle

**Centro de un círculo (p. 630)** El centro de un círculo es el punto que está situado a la misma distancia de cada punto del círculo.

**Center of an ellipse (p. 639)** The center of an ellipse is the midpoint of the major axis.

**Centro de una elipse (p. 639)** El centro de una elipse es el punto medio entre los dos ejes mayores.

**Center of rotation (p. 796)** A center of rotation is the fixed point of a rotation.

Example center of rotation

**Centro de rotación (p. 796)** Un centro de rotación es el punto fijo de una rotación.

**Central angle (p. 836)** A central angle of a circle is an angle whose vertex is at the center of a circle.

Example central angle, intercepted arc

**Ángulo central (p. 836)** El ángulo central de un círculo es un ángulo cuyo vértice está situado en el centro del círculo.

**Change of Base Formula (p. 464)** $\log_b M = \frac{\log_c M}{\log_c b}$, where $M$, $b$, and $c$ are positive numbers, and $b \neq 1$ and $c \neq 1$.

Example $\log_3 8 = \frac{\log 8}{\log 3} \approx 1.8928$

**Fórmula de cambio de base (p. 464)** $\log_b M = \frac{\log_c M}{\log_c b}$, donde $M$, $b$ y $c$ son números positivos y $b \neq 1$ y $c \neq 1$.

## Page 990

| English | Spanish |
|---|---|

**Circle (p. 630)** A circle is the set of all points in a plane at a distance $r$ from a given point. The standard form of the equation of a circle with center $(h, k)$ and radius $r$ is $(x - h)^2 + (y - k)^2 = r^2$.

**Círculo (p. 630)** Un círculo es el conjunto de todos los puntos situados en un plano a una distancia $r$ de un punto dado. La forma normal de la ecuación cuyo centro es $(h, k)$ y cuyo radio es $r$ es $(x - h)^2 + (y - k)^2 = r^2$.

Example

**Coefficient (p. 20)** The numerical factor in a term.

**Coeficiente (p. 20)** El factor numérico de un término.

Example The coefficient of $-3k$ is $-3$.

**Coefficient matrix (p. 785)** When representing a system of equations with a matrix equation, the matrix containing the coefficients of the system is the coefficient matrix.

**Matriz de coeficientes (p. 785)** Al representar un sistema de ecuaciones con una ecuación de matriz, la matriz que contiene los coeficientes del sistema es la matriz de coeficientes.

Example $\begin{cases} x + 2y = 5 \\ 3x + 5y = 14 \end{cases}$

coefficient matrix $\begin{bmatrix} 1 & 2 \\ 3 & 5 \end{bmatrix}$

**Combination (p. 676)** Any unordered selection of $r$ objects from a set of $n$ objects is a combination. The number of combinations of $n$ objects taken $r$ at a time is $_nC_r = \frac{n!}{r!(n-r)!}$ for $0 \le r \le n$.

**Combinación (p. 676)** Cualquier selección no ordenada de $r$ objetos tomados de un conjunto de $n$ objetos es una combinación. El número de combinaciones de $n$ objetos, cuando se toman $r$ objetos cada vez, es $_nC_r = \frac{n!}{r!(n-r)!}$ para $0 \le r \le n$.

Example The number of combinations of seven items taken four at a time is $_7C_4 = \frac{7!}{4!(7-4)!} = 35$.
There are 35 ways to choose four items from seven items without regard to order.

**Combined variation (p. 501)** A combined variation is a relation in which one variable varies with respect to each of two or more variables.

**Variación combinada (p. 501)** Una variación combinada es una relación en la que una variable varía con respecto a cada una de dos o más variables.

Example $y = kx^2\sqrt{z}$
$z = \frac{kx}{y}$

## Page 991

| English | Spanish |
|---|---|

**Common difference (p. 572)** A common difference is the difference between consecutive terms of an arithmetic sequence.

**Diferencia común (p. 572)** La diferencia común es la diferencia entre los términos consecutivos de una progresión aritmética.

Example The arithmetic sequence 1, 5, 9, 13, . . . has a common difference of 4.

**Common logarithm (p. 453)** A common logarithm is a logarithm that uses base 10. You can write the common logarithm $\log_{10} y$ as $\log y$.

**Logaritmo común (p. 453)** El logaritmo común es un logaritmo de base 10. El logaritmo común $\log_{10} y$ se expresa como $\log y$.

Example $\log 1 = 0$
$\log 10 = 1$
$\log 50 = 1.698970004 . . .$

**Common ratio (p. 580)** A common ratio is the ratio of consecutive terms of a geometric sequence.

**Razón común (p. 580)** Una razón común es la razón de términos consecutivos en una secuencia geométrica.

Example The geometric sequence 2.5, 5, 10, 20, . . . has a common ratio of 2.

**Completing the square (p. 235)** Completing the square is the process of finding a constant $c$ to add to $x^2 + bx$ so that $x^2 + bx + c$ is the square of a binomial.

**Completar el cuadrado (p. 235)** Completar un cuadrado es el proceso mediante el cual se halla una constante $c$ que se le pueda sumar a $x^2 + bx$, de manera que $x^2 + bx + c$ sea el cuadrado de un binomio.

Example $x^2 - 12x + \blacksquare$
$x^2 - 12x + \left(\frac{-12}{2}\right)^2$
$x^2 - 12x + 36$

**Complex conjugates (p. 251)** Number pairs of the form $a + bi$ and $a - bi$ are complex conjugates.

**Conjugados complejos (p. 251)** Los pares de números de la forma $a + bi$ y $a - bi$ son conjugados complejos.

Example The complex numbers $2 - 3i$ and $2 + 3i$ are complex conjugates.

**Complex fraction (p. 536)** A complex fraction is a rational expression that has a fraction in its numerator or denominator, or in both its numerator and denominator.

**Fracción compleja (p. 536)** Una fracción compleja es una expresión racional en la que el numerador, el denominador o ambos son una fracción.

Example $\frac{\frac{2}{5}}{\frac{7}{3}}$

**Complex number (p. 249)** Complex numbers are the real numbers and the imaginary numbers.

**Número complejo (p. 249)** Los números complejos son los números reales y los números imaginarios.

Example $6 + i$
$7, 2i$

## Page 992

| English | Spanish |
|---|---|

**Complex number plane (p. 249)** The complex number plane is identical to the coordinate plane except each ordered pair $(a, b)$ represents the complex number $a + bi$. The horizontal axis is the Real axis. The vertical axis is the Imaginary axis.

**Plano de números complejos (p. 249)** El plano de los números complejos es idéntico al plano de coordenadas, a excepción de que cada par ordenado $(a, b)$ representa el número complejo $a + bi$. El eje horizontal es el eje real. El eje vertical es el eje imaginario.

Example

**Composite function (p. 399)** A composite function is a combination of two functions such that the output from the first function becomes the input for the second function.

**Función compuesta (p. 399)** Una función compuesta es la combinación de dos funciones. La cantidad de salida de la primera función es la cantidad de entrada de la segunda función.

Example $f(x) = 2x + 1$   $g(x) = x^2 - 1$
$(g \circ f)(5) = g(f(5)) = g(2(5) + 1)$
$= g(11)$
$= 11^2 - 1 = 120$
$(f \circ g)(5) = f(g(5)) = f(5^2 - 1)$
$= f(24)$
$= 2(24) + 1 = 49$

**Compound inequality (p. 36)** You can join two inequalities with the word and or the word or to form a compound inequality.

**Desigualdad compuesta (p. 36)** Puedes unir dos desigualdades por medio de la palabra y o la palabra o para formar una desigualdad compuesta.

Example $-1 < x$ and $x \le 3$
$x < -1$ or $x \ge 3$

**Conditional probability (p. 696)** A conditional probability contains a condition that may limit the sample space for an event. The notation $P(B|A)$ is read "the probability of event $B$, given event $A$." For any two events $A$ and $B$ in the sample space, $P(B|A) = \frac{P(A \text{ and } B)}{P(A)}$.

**Probabilidad condicional (p. 696)** Una probabilidad condicional contiene una condición que puede limitar el espacio muestral de un suceso. La notación $P(B|A)$ se lee "la probabilidad del suceso $B$, dado el suceso $A$". Para dos sucesos cualesquiera $A$ y $B$ en el espacio muestral, $P(B|A) = \frac{P(A \text{ y } B)}{P(A)}$.

Example $= \frac{P(\text{departs and arrives on time})}{P(\text{departs on time})}$
$= \frac{0.75}{0.83}$
$\approx 0.9$

## Page 993

| English | Spanish |
|---|---|

**Conic section (p. 614)** A conic section is a curve formed by the intersection of a plane and a double cone.

**Sección cónica (p. 614)** Una sección cónica es una curva que se forma por la intersección de un plano con un cono doble.

Example

ellipse    hyperbola

**Conjugate axis (p. 646)** The conjugate axis for the hyperbola $\frac{x^2}{a^2} - \frac{y^2}{b^2} = 1$, $a > b > 0$, is the segment from $(0, -b)$ to $(0, b)$. For $\frac{y^2}{a^2} - \frac{x^2}{b^2} = 1$, the conjugate axis is the segment from $(-b, 0)$ to $(b, 0)$.

**Eje conjugado (p. 646)** El eje conjugado de la hipérbola $\frac{x^2}{a^2} - \frac{y^2}{b^2} = 1$, $a > b > 0$, es el segmento desde el punto $(0, -b)$ hasta el punto $(0, b)$. Para $\frac{y^2}{a^2} - \frac{x^2}{b^2} = 1$, el eje conjugado es el segmento desde el punto $(-b, 0)$ hasta el punto $(b, 0)$.

**Conjugate Root Theorem (p. 314)** If $P(x)$ is a polynomial with rational coefficients, then the irrational roots of $P(x) = 0$ occur in conjugate pairs. That is, if $a + \sqrt{b}$ is an irrational root with $a$ and $b$ rational, then $a - \sqrt{b}$ is also a root. If $P(x)$ is a polynomial with real coefficients, then the complex roots of $P(x) = 0$ occur in conjugate pairs. That is, if $a + bi$ is a complex root with $a$ and $b$ real, then $a - bi$ is also a root.

**Teorema de raíces conjugadas (p. 314)** Si $P(x)$ es un polinomio con coeficientes racionales, entonces las raíces irracionales de $P(x) = 0$ ocurren en pares conjugados. Es decir, si $a + \sqrt{b}$ es una raíz irracional donde $a$ y $b$ son racionales, entonces $a - \sqrt{b}$ también es una raíz. Si $P(x)$ es un polinomio con coeficientes reales, entonces las raíces complejas de $P(x) = 0$ ocurren en los pares conjugados. Es decir, si $a + bi$ es una raíz compleja donde $a$ y $b$ son reales, entonces $a - bi$ también es una raíz.

**Conjugates (p. 314)** Number pairs of the form $a + \sqrt{b}$ and $a - \sqrt{b}$ are conjugates.

**Conjugados (p. 314)** Los pares de números con la forma $a + \sqrt{b}$ y $a - \sqrt{b}$ son conjugados.

Example $5 + \sqrt{3}$ and $5 - \sqrt{3}$ are conjugates.

**Consistent system (p. 137)** A system of linear equations is consistent if it has at least one solution.

**Sistema consistente (p. 137)** Un sistema de ecuaciones lineales es consistente si tiene por lo menos una solución.

**Constant (p. 5)** A constant is a quantity whose value does not change.

**Constante (p. 5)** Una constante es una cantidad cuyo valor no cambia.

**Constant matrix (p. 785)** When representing a system of equations with a matrix equation, the matrix containing the constants of the system is the constant matrix.

**Matriz de constantes (p. 785)** Al representar un sistema de ecuaciones con una ecuación matricial, la matriz que contiene las constantes del sistema es la matriz de constantes.

Example $\begin{cases} x + 2y = 5 \\ 3x + 5y = 14 \end{cases}$

constant matrix $\begin{bmatrix} 5 \\ 14 \end{bmatrix}$

## English | Spanish

**Constant of proportionality (p. 341)** If $y = ax^b$ describes $y$ as a power function of $x$, then $y$ varies directly with, or is proportional to, the $b^{th}$ power of $x$. The constant $a$ is the constant of proportionality.

**Constante de proporcionalidad (p. 341)** Si $y = ax^b$ describe a $y$ como una potencia de la función de $x$, entonces $y$ varía directamente con, o es proporcional a, la $b^{ma}$ potencia de $x$. La constante $a$ es la constante de proporcionalidad.

**Constant of variation (p. 68)** The constant of variation is the ratio of the two variables in a direct variation and the product of the two variables in an inverse variation.

**Constante de variación (p. 68)** La constante de variación es la razón de dos variables en una variación directa y el producto de las dos variables en una variación inversa.

Example In $y = 3.5x$, the constant of variation $k$ is 3.5. In $xy = 5$, the constant of variation $k$ is 5.

**Constant term (p. 20)** A constant term is a term with no variables.

**Término constante (p. 20)** Un término constante es un término que no tiene variables.

**Constraint (p. 157)** Constraints are restrictions on the variables of the objective function in a linear programming problem. See **Linear programming**.

**Restricción (p. 157)** Las restricciones son limitaciones a las variables de una función objetiva en un problema de programación lineal. *Ver* **Linear programming**.

**Continuous graph (p. 516)** A graph is continuous if it has no jumps, breaks, or holes.

**Gráfica continua (p. 516)** Una gráfica es continua si no tiene saltos, interrupciones o huecos.

**Continuous probability distribution (p. 733)** A continuous probability distribution has as its events any of the infinitely many values in an interval of real numbers.

**Distribución de probabilidad continua (p. 733)** Una distribución de probabilidad continua tiene como sucesos a cualquiera del número infinito de valores en un intervalo de números reales.

**Continuously compounded interest (p. 446)** When interest is compounded continuously on principal $P$, the value $A$ of an account is $A = Pe^{rt}$.

**Interés compuesto continuo (p. 446)** En un sistema donde el interés es compuesto continuamente sobre el capital $P$, el valor de $A$ de una cuenta es $A = Pe^{rt}$.

Example Suppose that $P = \$1200$, $r = 0.05$, and $t = 3$. Then
$$A = 1200e^{0.05 \cdot 3}$$
$$= 1200(2.718\ldots)^{0.15}$$
$$\approx 1394.20$$

**Controlled experiment (p. 719)** In a controlled experiment, you divide the sample into two groups. You impose a treatment on one group but not the other "control" group. Then you compare the effect on the treated group to the control group.

**Experimento controlado (p. 719)** En un experimento controlado, se divide la muestra en dos grupos. Uno de los grupos se manipula y el otro grupo "controlado" se mantiene en su estado original. Luego se comparan el estado del grupo manipulado y el estado del grupo controlado.

**Convenience sample (p. 718)** In a convenience sample you select any members of the population who are conveniently and readily available.

**Muestra de conveniencia (p. 718)** En una muestra de conveniencia se selecciona a cualquier miembro de la población que está convenientemente disponible.

---

## English | Spanish

**Converge (p. 598)** An infinite series $a_1 + a_2 + \cdots + a_n + \cdots$ converges if the sum $a_1 + a_2 + \cdots + a_n$ get closer and closer to a real number as $n$ increases.

**Convergir (p. 598)** Una serie infinita $a_1 + a_2 + \cdots + a_n + \cdots$ es convergente si la suma $a_1 + a_2 + \cdots + a_n$ se aproxima cada vez más a un número real a medida que el valor de $n$ incrementa.

Example $1 + \frac{1}{2} + \frac{1}{4} + \frac{1}{8} + \cdots$ converges.

**Coordinate space (p. 164)** Coordinate space is a three-dimensional space where each point is described uniquely using an ordered triple of numbers.

**Espacio de coordenadas (p. 164)** Un espacio de coordenadas es un espacio tridimensional en el cual cada punto es definido de manera única por una tripleta ordenada de números.

Example

$A (2, -1, 3)$

**Correlation (p. 92)** A correlation indicates the strength of a relationship between two data sets.

**Correlación (p. 92)** Una correlación indica la fuerza de una relación entre dos conjuntos de datos.

**Correlation coefficient (p. 94)** The correlation coefficient, $r$, indicates the strength of the correlation. The closer $r$ is to 1 or $-1$, the more closely the data resembles a line and the more accurate your model is likely to be.

**Coeficiente de correlación (p. 94)** El coeficiente de correlación, $r$, indica la fuerza de la correlación. Mientras más cerca está $r$ de 1 ó $-1$, más se parecen los datos a una línea y será más probable que tu modelo sea preciso.

**Corresponding elements (p. 756)** Corresponding elements are elements in the same position in each matrix.

**Elementos correspondientes (p. 756)** Los elementos correspondientes son elementos que se encuentran en la misma posición de cada matriz.

**Cosecant function (p. 875)** The cosecant (csc) function is the reciprocal of the sine function. For all real numbers $\theta$ except those that make sin $\theta = 0$, csc $\theta = \frac{1}{\sin \theta}$.

**Función cosecante (p. 875)** La función cosecante (csc) se define como el recíproco de la función seno. Para todos los números reales $\theta$, excepto aquéllos para los que sin $\theta = 0$, csc $\theta = \frac{1}{\sin \theta}$.

Example If sin $\theta = \frac{5}{13}$, then csc $\theta = \frac{13}{5}$.

---

## English | Spanish

**Cosine function, Cosine of $\theta$ (p. 853)** The cosine function, $y = \cos \theta$, matches the measure $\theta$ of an angle in standard position with the $x$-coordinate of a point on the unit circle. This point is where the terminal side of the angle intersects the unit circle. The $x$-coordinate is the cosine of $\theta$.

**Función coseno, Coseno de $\theta$ (p. 853)** La función coseno, $y = \cos \theta$, empareja la medida $\theta$ de un ángulo en posición estándar con la coordenada $x$ de un punto en el círculo unitario. Este es el punto en el que el lado terminal del ángulo interseca al círculo unitario. La coordenada $x$ es el coseno de $\theta$.

Example

$P(\cos \theta, \sin \theta)$

**Cotangent function (p. 875)** The cotangent (cot) function is the reciprocal of the tangent function. For all real numbers $\theta$ except those that make tan $\theta = 0$, cot $\theta = \frac{1}{\tan \theta}$.

**Función cotangente (p. 875)** La función cotangente (cot) es el recíproco de la función tangente. Para todos los números reales $\theta$, excepto aquéllos para los que tan $\theta = 0$, cot $\theta = \frac{1}{\tan \theta}$.

Example If tan $\theta = \frac{5}{12}$, then cot $\theta = \frac{12}{5}$.

**Coterminal angle (p. 829)** Two angles in standard position are coterminal if they have the same terminal side.

**Ángulo coterminal (p. 829)** Dos ángulos que están en posición normal son coterminales si tienen el mismo lado terminal.

Example

coterminal angles

Angles that have measures 135° and $-225°$ are coterminal.

**Co-vertices (p. 639)** The endpoints of the minor axis of an ellipse are the co-vertices of the ellipse.

**Covértices (p. 639)** Los puntos de intersección entre la elipse y los ejes menores son los covértices de la elipse.

Example

co-vertices

**Cumulative probability (p. 695)** Probability over a continuous range of events is cumulative probability.

**Probabilidad acumulativa (p. 695)** La probabilidad que existe a lo largo de una serie continua de sucesos es la probabilidad acumulativa.

---

## English | Spanish

**Cycle (p. 820)** A cycle of a periodic function is an interval of $x$-values over which the function provides one complete pattern of $y$-values.

**Ciclo (p. 820)** El ciclo de una función periódica es un intervalo de valores de $x$ de los cuales la función produce un patrón completo de valores de $y$.

Example

a cycle

**D**

**Decay factor (p. 436)** In an exponential function of the form $y = ab^x$, $b$ is the decay factor if $0 < b < 1$.

**Factor de decremento (p. 436)** En una función exponencial de la forma $y = ab^x$, $b$ es el factor de decremento si, $0 < b < 1$.

Example In the equation $y = 0.3^x$, 0.7 is the decay factor.

**Degree of a monomial (p. 280)** The degree of a monomial in one variable is the exponent of the variable.

**Grado de un monomio (p. 280)** El grado de un monomio en una variable es el exponente de la variable.

**Degree of a polynomial (p. 280)** The degree of a polynomial is the greatest degree among its monomial terms.

**Grado de un polinomio (p. 280)** El grado de un polinomio es el grado mayor entre los términos de monomios.

Example $P(x) = x^6 + 2x^3 - 3$ degree 6

**Dependent events (p. 688)** Two events are dependent if the occurrence of one event affects the probability of the second event.

**Sucesos dependientes (p. 688)** Cuando el resultado de un suceso influye en la probabilidad de que ocurra el segundo suceso, los dos sucesos son dependientes.

Example You have a bag with red and blue marbles. You draw one marble at random and then another without replacing the first. The colors drawn are dependent events. A red marble on the first draw changes the probability for each color on the second draw.

**Dependent system (p. 137)** A system of equations that does not have a unique solution is a dependent system.

**Sistema dependiente (p. 137)** Un sistema de ecuaciones es dependiente cuando no tiene una solución única.

Example $\begin{cases} y = 2x + 3 \\ -4x + 2y = 6 \end{cases}$ represents two equations for the same line, so it has many solutions. It is a dependent system.

---

# English / Spanish

## Page 998

**Dependent variable (p. 63)** If a function is defined by an equation using the variables $x$ and $y$, where $y$ represents output values, then $y$ is the dependent variable.

Example $y = 2x + 1$
$y$ is the dependent variable.

**Variable dependiente (p. 63)** Si una función es definida por una ecuación que usa las variables $x$ e $y$, donde $y$ representa valores de salida, entonces $y$ es la variable dependiente.

**Descartes' Rule of Signs (p. 315)** Let $P(x)$ be a polynomial with real coefficients written in standard form.
– The number of positive real roots of $P(x) = 0$ is either equal to the number of sign changes between consecutive coefficients of $P(x)$ or is less than that by an even number;
– The number of negative real roots of $P(x) = 0$ is either equal to the number of sign changes between consecutive coefficients of $P(-x)$ or is less than that by an even number. (Count multiple roots according to their multiplicity.)

**Regla de los signos de Descartes (p. 315)** Sea $P(x)$ un polinomio con coeficientes reales escritos en forma normal.
– El número de raíces positivas reales de $P(x) = 0$ es igual al número de cambios de signos entre coeficientes consecutivos de $P(-x)$ o es menor que ese en un número par;
– El número de raíces negativas reales de $P(x) = 0$ es igual al número de cambios de signos entre coeficientes consecutivos de $P(-x)$ o es menor que ese en un número par. (Cuenta las raíces múltiples según su multiplicidad.)

**Determinant (p. 776)** The determinant of a square matrix is a real number that can be computed from its elements according to a specific formula.

Example The determinant of $\begin{bmatrix} 3 & -2 \\ 5 & 6 \end{bmatrix}$ is
$3(6) - 5(-2) = 28.$

**Determinante (p. 776)** El determinante de una matriz cuadrada es un número real que se puede calcular a partir de sus elementos por medio de una fórmula específica.

**Difference of cubes (p. 297)** A difference of cubes is an expression of the form $a^3 - b^3$. It can be factored as $(a - b)(a^2 + ab + b^2)$.

Example $x^3 - 27 = (x - 3)(x^2 + 3x + 9)$

**Diferencia de dos cubos (p. 297)** La diferencia de dos cubos es una expresión de la forma $a^3 - b^3$. Se puede factorizar como $(a - b)(a^2 + ab + b^2)$.

**Difference of two squares (p. 220)** A difference of two squares is an expression of the form $a^2 - b^2$. It can be factored as $(a + b)(a - b)$.

Example $25a^2 - 1 = (5a + 2)(5a - 2)$
$m^6 - 1 = (m^3 + 1)(m^3 - 1)$

**Diferencia de dos cuadrados (p. 220)** La diferencia de dos cuadrados es una expresión de la forma $a^2 - b^2$. Se puede factorizar como $(a + b)(a - b)$.

**Dilation (p. 794)** A dilation is a transformation that can change the size of a figure. When the center of the dilation is the origin, you can use scalar multiplication to find the coordinates of an image.

Example

**Dilatación (p. 794)** Una dilatación es una transformación que puede cambiar el tamaño de una figura. Cuando el centro de dilatación está en el origen, se hallan las coordenadas de los vértices de la imagen por medio de la multiplicación de escalar.

## Page 999

**Direct variation (p. 68)** A linear function defined by an equation of the form $y = kx$, where $k \neq 0$, represents direct variation.

Example $y = 3.5x, y = 7x, y = -\frac{1}{2}x$

**Variación directa (p. 68)** Una función lineal definida por una ecuación de la forma $y = kx$, donde $k \neq 0$, representa una variación directa.

**Directrix (p. 622)** The directrix of a parabola is the fixed line used to define a parabola. Each point of the parabola is the same distance from the focus and the directrix.

Example

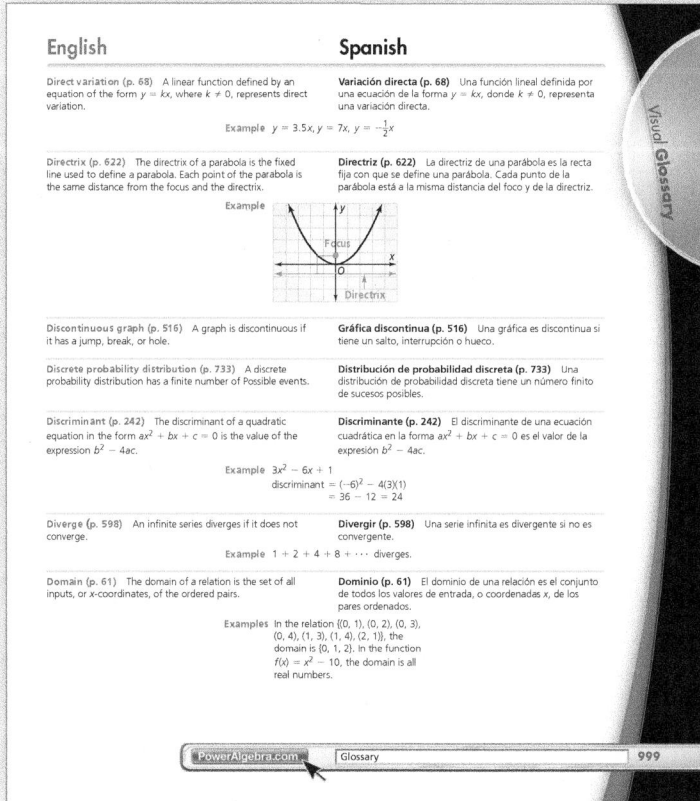

**Directriz (p. 622)** La directriz de una parábola es la recta fija con que se define una parábola. Cada punto de la parábola está a la misma distancia del foco y de la directriz.

**Discontinuous graph (p. 516)** A graph is discontinuous if it has a jump, break, or hole.

**Gráfica discontinua (p. 516)** Una gráfica es discontinua si tiene un salto, interrupción o hueco.

**Discrete probability distribution (p. 733)** A discrete probability distribution has a finite number of Possible events.

**Distribución de probabilidad discreta (p. 733)** Una distribución de probabilidad discreta tiene un número finito de sucesos posibles.

**Discriminant (p. 242)** The discriminant of a quadratic equation in the form $ax^2 + bx + c = 0$ is the value of the expression $b^2 - 4ac$.

Example $3x^2 - 6x + 1$
discriminant $= (-6)^2 - 4(3)(1)$
$= 36 - 12 = 24$

**Discriminante (p. 242)** El discriminante de una ecuación cuadrática en la forma $ax^2 + bx + c = 0$ es el valor de la expresión $b^2 - 4ac$.

**Diverge (p. 598)** An infinite series diverges if it does not converge.

Example $1 + 2 + 4 + 8 + \cdots$ diverges.

**Divergir (p. 598)** Una serie infinita es divergente si no es convergente.

**Domain (p. 61)** The domain of a relation is the set of all inputs, or $x$-coordinates, of the ordered pairs.

Examples In the relation $\{(0, 1), (0, 2), (0, 3), (0, 4), (1, 3), (1, 4), (2, 1)\}$, the domain is $\{0, 1, 2\}$. In the function $f(x) = x^2 - 10$, the domain is all real numbers.

**Dominio (p. 61)** El dominio de una relación es el conjunto de todos los valores de entrada, o coordenadas $x$, de los pares ordenados.

## Page 1000

**Dot product (p. 804)** Given vectors $\mathbf{v} = \langle v_1, v_2 \rangle$ and $\mathbf{w} = \langle w_1, w_2 \rangle$, the dot product $\mathbf{v} \cdot \mathbf{w}$ is the quantity $v_1w_1 + v_2w_2$.

**Producto escalar (p. 804)** Dados los vectores $\mathbf{v} = \langle v_1, v_2 \rangle$ y $\mathbf{w} = \langle w_1, w_2 \rangle$, el producto escalar $\mathbf{v} \cdot \mathbf{w}$ es la suma $v_1w_1 + v_2w_2$.

### E

**Ellipse (p. 638)** An ellipse is the set of points $P$ in a plane such that the sum of the distances from $P$ to two fixed points $F1$ and $F2$ is a given constant $k$. The standard form of the equation of an ellipse with its center at the origin is $\frac{x^2}{a^2} + \frac{y^2}{b^2} = 1$ if the major axis is horizontal and $\frac{x^2}{b^2} + \frac{y^2}{a^2} = 1$ if the major axis is vertical, where $a > b$.

Example

$\frac{x^2}{36} + \frac{y^2}{9} = 1$
$F_1 = (-3\sqrt{3}, 0), F_2 = (3\sqrt{3}, 0)$

**Elipse (p. 638)** Una elipse es el conjunto de puntos $P$ situados en un plano tal que la suma de las distancias entre $P$ y dos puntos fijos $F_1$ y $F_2$ es una constante dada $k$. La forma normal de la ecuación de una elipse con su centro en el origen es $\frac{x^2}{a^2} + \frac{y^2}{b^2} = 1$ si el eje mayor es horizontal y $\frac{x^2}{b^2} + \frac{y^2}{a^2} = 1$ si el eje mayor es vertical, donde $a > b$.

**End behavior (p. 282)** End behavior of the graph of a function describes the directions of the graph as you move to the left and to the right, away from the origin.

**Comportamiento extremo (p. 282)** El comportamiento extremo de la gráfica de una función describe las direcciones de la gráfica al moverse a la izquierda y a la derecha, apartándose del origen.

**Equal matrices (p. 759)** Equal matrices are matrices with the same dimensions and equal corresponding elements.

Example Matrices $A$ and $B$ are equal.
$A = \begin{bmatrix} 2 & 6 \\ \frac{9}{3} & 1 \end{bmatrix} \quad B = \begin{bmatrix} \frac{9}{9} & 6 \\ 3 & \frac{-13}{13} \end{bmatrix}$

**Matrices equivalentes (p. 759)** Dos matrices son equivalentes si y sólo si tienen las mismas dimensiones y sus elementos correspondientes son iguales.

**Equally likely outcomes (p. 682)** Equally likely outcomes are events in a sample space that have the same chance of occurring.

**Resultados igualmente probables (p. 682)** Resultados igualmente probables son sucesos en un espacio muestral con la misma probabilidad de ocurrir.

**Equation (p. 26)** An equation is a statement that two algebraic expressions are equal.

**Ecuación (p. 26)** Una ecuación es un enunciado que describe dos expresiones algebraicas iguales.

**Equivalent systems (p. 144)** Equivalent systems are systems that have the same solution(s).

**Sistemas equivalentes (p. 144)** Sistemas equivalentes son sistemas que tienen la misma solución o las mismas soluciones.

## Page 1001

**Evaluate (p. 19)** To evaluate an algebraic expression, substitute a number for each variable in the expression. Then simplify using the order of operations.

Example When $x = 2$ and $y = -1$, $2x + 3y$ evaluates to 1.

**Evaluar (p. 19)** Para evaluar una expresión algebraica, sustituye cada variable de la expresión con un número. Luego, simplifica usando el orden de operaciones.

**Expand (p. 326)** To expand the power of a binomial, multiply as needed, then write the polynomial in standard form.

Example $(x + 4)^3 = (x + 4)(x + 4)^2$
$= (x + 4)(x^2 + 8x + 16)$
$= x^3 + 8x^2 + 16x + 4x^2 + 32x + 64$
$= x^3 + 12x^2 + 48x + 64$

**Expandir (p. 326)** Para expandir la potencia de un binomio, multiplica como sea necesario. Luego, escribe el polinomio en forma normal.

**Experimental probability (p. 681)** The experimental probability of an event is the ratio $\frac{\text{number of times the event occurs}}{\text{number of trials}}$.

Example Suppose a basketball player has scored 19 times in 28 attempts at a basket. The experimental probability of the player's scoring is $P(\text{score}) = \frac{19}{28} \approx 0.68$, or 68%.

**Probabilidad experimental (p. 681)** La probabilidad experimental de un suceso es la razón $\frac{\text{number of times the event occurs}}{\text{number of trials}}$.

**Explicit formula (p. 565)** An explicit formula expresses the $n$th term of a sequence in terms of $n$.

Example Let $a_n = 2n + 5$ for positive integers $n$. If $n = 7$, then $a_7 = 2(7) + 5 = 19$.

**Fórmula explícita (p. 565)** Una fórmula explícita expresa el $n$-ésimo término de una progresión en función de $n$.

**Exponential decay (p. 435)** Exponential decay is modeled by a function of the form $y = ab^x$ with $0 < b < 1$.

**Decaimiento exponencial (p. 435)** El decaimiento exponencial se expresa con una función $y = ab^x$ donde $0 < b < 1$.

**Exponential equation (p. 469)** An exponential equation contains the form $b^{cx}$, with the exponent including a variable.

Example $5^{2x} = 270$
$\log 5^{2x} = \log 270$
$2x \log 5 = \log 270$
$2x = \frac{\log 270}{\log 5}$
$2x \approx 3.4785$
$x \approx 1.7392$

**Ecuación exponencial (p. 469)** Una ecuación exponencial tiene la forma $b^{cx}$, y su exponente incluye una variable.

## English | Spanish

**Exponential function (p. 434)** The general form of an exponential function is $y = ab^x$, where $x$ is a real number, $a \neq 0$, $b > 0$, and $b \neq 1$. When $b > 1$, the function models exponential growth with growth factor $b$. When $0 < b < 1$, the function models exponential decay with decay factor $b$.

**Función exponencial (p. 434)** La forma general de una función exponencial es $y = ab^x$, donde $x$ es un número real, $a \neq 0$, $b > 0$ y $b \neq 1$. Cuando $b > 1$, la función representa un incremento exponencial con factor de incremento $b$. Cuando $0 < b < 1$, la función representa el decremento exponencial con factor de decremento $b$.

Example

**Exponential growth (p. 435)** Exponential growth is modeled by a function of the form $y = ab^x$ with $b > 1$.

**Crecimiento exponencial (p. 435)** El crecimiento exponencial se expresa con una función de la forma $y = ab^x$ donde $b > 1$.

**Extraneous solution (p. 42)** An extraneous solution is a solution of an equation derived from an original equation but it is not a solution of the original equation.

**Solución extraña (p. 42)** Una solución extraña es una solución de una ecuación derivada de una ecuación dada, pero que no satisface la ecuación dada.

Example $\sqrt{x - 3} = x - 5$
$x - 3 = x^2 - 10x + 25$
$0 = x^2 - 11x + 28$
$0 = (x - 4)(x - 7)$
$x = 4$ or $7$
The number 7 is a solution, but 4 is not, since $\sqrt{4 - 3} \neq 4 - 5$.

**F**

**Factor Theorem (p. 289)** The expression $x - a$ is a linear factor of a polynomial if and only if the value of $a$ is a root of the related polynomial function.

**Teorema de factores (p. 289)** La expresión $x - a$ es un factor lineal de un polinomio si y sólo si el valor de $a$ es una raíz de la función polinomial con la que se relaciona.

Example The value 2 makes the polynomial
$x^2 + 2x - 8$ equal to zero. So,
$x - 2$ is a factor of $x^2 + 2x - 8$.

**Factoring (p. 216)** Factoring is rewriting an expression as the product of its factors.

**Descomposición factorial (p. 216)** Descomponer en factores es el proceso de escribir de nuevo una expresión como el producto de sus factores.

Example expanded form      factored form
$x^2 + x - 56$          $(x + 8)(x - 7)$

**Feasible region (p. 157)** In a linear programming problem, the feasible region contains all the values that satisfy the constraints on the objective function.

**Región factible (p. 157)** En un problema de programación lineal, la región factible contiene todos los valores que satisfacen las restricciones de la función objetiva.

---

## English | Spanish

**Finite Series (p. 587)** A finite series is a series with a finite number of terms.

**Serie finita (p. 587)** Una serie finita es una serie con un número finito de términos.

**Focal length (p. 622)** The focal length of a parabola is the distance between the vertex and the focus.

**Distancia focal (p. 622)** La distancia focal de una parábola es la distancia entre el vértice y el foco.

**Focus (plural: foci) of a hyperbola (p. 645)** A hyperbola is the set of all points $P$ in a plane such that the difference of the distances from $P$ to two fixed points is constant. Each of the fixed points is a focus of the hyperbola.

**Foco de una hipérbola (p. 645)** Una hipérbola es el conjunto de puntos $P$ en un plano tal que la diferencia de las distancias desde $P$ hasta dos puntos fijos es constante. Cada uno de los puntos fijos es el foco de la hipérbola.

**Focus (plural: foci) of a parabola (p. 622)** A parabola is the set of all points in a plane that are the same distance from a fixed line and a fixed point not on the line. The fixed point is the focus of the parabola.

**Foco de una parábola (p. 622)** Una parábola es el conjunto de todos los puntos en un plano con la misma distancia desde una línea fija y un punto fijo que no permanece en la línea. El punto fijo es el foco de la parábola.

**Focus (plural: foci) of an ellipse (p. 638)** An ellipse is the set of all points $P$ in a plane such that the sum of the distances from $P$ to two fixed points is constant. Each of the fixed points is a focus of the ellipse.

**Foco de una elipse (p. 638)** Una elipse es el conjunto de todos los puntos $P$ en un plano en el cual la suma de las distancias desde $P$ hasta dos puntos fijos es constante. Cada uno de estos puntos fijos es un foco de la elipsis.

**Frequency table (p. 694)** A frequency table is a list of the outcomes in a sample space and the number of times each outcome occurs.

**Tabla de frecuencias (p. 694)** Una tabla de frecuencias es una lista de los resultados de un espacio muestral y el número de veces que cada resultado ocurre.

**Function (p. 62)** A function is a relation in which each element of the domain corresponds with exactly one element in the range.

**Función (p. 62)** Una función es una relación en la que cada elemento del dominio corresponde exactamente con un elemento del rango.

Example The relation $y = 3x^3 - 2x + 3$ is a function. $f(x) = 3x^3 - 2x + 3$ is the same relation written in function notation.

**Function notation (p. 63)** If $f$ is the name of a function, the function notation $f(x)$ shows the function name $f$ and also represents the range value $f(x)$ for the domain value $x$. You read the function notation $f(x)$ as "$f$ of $x$" or "a function of $x$." Note that $f(x)$ does not mean "$f$ times $x$."

**Notación de una función (p. 63)** Si $f$ es el nombre de una función, la notación de la función $f(x)$ indica el nombre de la función y también representa el valor del rango $f(x)$ para el valor del dominio $x$. La función de la notación $f(x)$ se lee "$f$ de $x$" o "una función de $x$." Observa que $f(x)$ no significa "$f$ por $x$."

Example When the value of $x$ is 3, $f(3)$, read "$f$ of 3," represents the value of the function at 3.

**Function rule (p. 63)** A function rule represents an output value in terms of an input value.

**Regla de función (p. 63)** Una regla de función representa un valor de salida en función a un valor de entrada.

**Fundamental Counting Principle (p. 674)** The Fundamental Counting Principle is a tool that you can use to quickly count the number of ways certain things can happen.

**Principio básico de conteo (p. 674)** El principio básico de conteo es una herramienta que se puede utilizar para hacer un conteo rápido del número de formas en que pueden ocurrir ciertas cosas.

---

## English | Spanish

**Fundamental Theorem of Algebra (p. 320)** If $P(x)$ is a polynomial of degree $n \geq 1$ with complex coefficients, then $P(x) = 0$ has at least one complex root.

**Teorema fundamental de álgebra (p. 320)** Si $P(x)$ es un polinomio de grado $n \geq 1$ con coeficientes complejos, entonces $P(x) = 0$ tiene por lo menos una raíz compleja.

Example $P(x) = 3x^3 - 2x + 3$ is of degree 3, so $P(x) = 0$ has at least one complex root.

**G**

**Geometric mean (p. 583)** The geometric mean of any two positive numbers is the positive square root of the product of the two numbers.

**Media geométrica (p. 583)** La media geométrica de dos números positivos es la raíz cuadrada positiva del producto de los dos números.

Example The geometric mean of 12 and 18 is $\sqrt{12 \cdot 18} \approx 14.6969$.

**Geometric sequence (p. 580)** A geometric sequence is a sequence with a constant ratio between consecutive terms.

**Secuencia geométrica (p. 580)** Una secuencia geométrica es una secuencia con una razón constante entre términos consecutivos.

Example The geometric sequence 2.5, 5, 10, 20, 40 . . . , has a common ratio of 2.

**Geometric series (p. 595)** A geometric series is the sum of the terms in a geometric sequence.

**Serie geométrica (p. 595)** Una serie geométrica es la suma de términos en una progresión geométrica.

Example One geometric series with five terms is $2.5 + 5 + 10 + 20 + 40$.

**Greatest common factor (p. 218)** The greatest common factor (GCF) of an expression is the common factor of each term of the expression that has the greatest coefficient and the greatest exponent.

**Máximo factor común (p. 218)** El máximo factor común de una expresión es el factor común de cada término de la expresión que tiene el mayor coeficiente y el mayor exponente.

Example The GCF of $4x^2 + 20x - 12$ is 4.

**Greatest integer function (p. 90)** The greatest integer function corresponds each input $x$ to the greatest integer less than or equal to $x$.

**Función del entero mayor (p. 90)** La función del entero mayor relaciona cada entrada $x$ con el entero mayor que es menor o igual a $x$.

**Growth factor (p. 436)** In an exponential function of the form $y = ab^x$, $b$ is the growth factor if $b > 1$.

**Factor de incremento (p. 436)** En una función exponencial de la forma $y = ab^x$, $b$ es el factor de incremento si $b > 1$.

Example In the exponential equation $y = 2^x$, 2 is the growth factor.

**H**

**Half-plane (p. 114)** A half-plane is the set of points in a coordinate plane that are on one side of the boundary of the graph of a linear inequality.

**Semiplano (p. 114)** Un semiplano es el conjunto de puntos de un plano de coordenadas que están a un lado del límite de la gráfica de desigualdad lineal.

---

## English | Spanish

**Hyperbola (p. 645)** A hyperbola is a set of points $P$ in a plane such that the difference between the distances from $P$ to the foci $F_1$ and $F_2$ is a given constant $k$. $|PF_1 - PF_2| = k$ The standard form of an equation of a hyperbola centered at $(0, 0)$ is $\frac{x^2}{a^2} - \frac{y^2}{b^2} = 1$ if the transverse axis is horizontal and $\frac{y^2}{a^2} - \frac{x^2}{b^2} = 1$ if the transverse axis is vertical.

**Hipérbola (p. 645)** Una hipérbola es un conjunto de puntos $P$ en un plano tal que la diferencia entre las distancias de $P$ a los focos $F_1$ y $F_2$ es una constante $k$ dada. $|PF_1 - PF_2| = k$ La forma normal de la ecuación de una hipérbola centrada en $(0, 0)$ es $\frac{x^2}{a^2} - \frac{y^2}{b^2} = 1$, si el eje transversal es horizontal, y $\frac{y^2}{a^2} - \frac{x^2}{b^2} = 1$, si el eje transversal es vertical.

Example

$\frac{x^2}{5^2} - \frac{y^2}{3^2} = 1$

**I**

**$i$ (p. 248)** The imaginary number $i$ is the principal square root of $-1$.

**$i$ (p. 248)** El número imaginario $i$ es la raíz cuadrada principal de $-1$.

Example $i = \sqrt{-1}$ and $i^2 = -1$.

**Identity (p. 28)** An equation that is true for every value of the variable is an identity.

**Identidad (p. 28)** Una ecuación que es verdadera para cada valor de la variable es una identidad.

**Image (p. 793)** An image is a figure obtained by a transformation of a preimage.

**Imagen (p. 793)** Una imagen es la figura que resulta después de que la preimagen sufre una transformación.

Example

**Imaginary number (p. 249)** An imaginary number is any number of the form $a + bi$, where $a$ and $b$ are real numbers and $b \neq 0$.

**Número imaginario (p. 249)** Un número imaginario es cualquier número de la forma $a + bi$, donde $a$ y $b$ son números reales y $b \neq 0$.

Example $2 + 3i$
$7i$
$i$

**Imaginary unit (p. 248)** The imaginary unit $i$ is the complex number whose square is $-1$.

**Unidad imaginaria (p. 248)** La unidad imaginaria $i$ es el número complejo cuyo cuadrado es $-1$.

## English / Spanish

### Page 1006

| English | Spanish |
|---|---|

**Inconsistent system (p. 137)** A system of equations that has no solution is an inconsistent system.

**Sistema incompatible (p. 137)** Un sistema incompatible es un sistema de ecuaciones para el cual no hay solución.

Example $\begin{cases} y = 2x + 3 \\ -2x + y = 1 \end{cases}$ is a system of

parallel lines, so it has no solution.
It is an inconsistent system.

**Independent events (p. 688)** When the outcome of one event does not affect the probability of a second event, the two events are independent.

**Sucesos independientes (p. 688)** Cuando el resultado de un suceso no altera la probabilidad de otro, los dos sucesos son independientes.

Example The results of two rolls of a number cube are independent. Getting a 5 on the first roll does not change the probability of getting a 5 on the second roll.

**Independent system (p. 137)** A system of linear equations that has a unique solution is an independent system.

**Sistema independiente (p. 137)** Un sistema de ecuaciones lineales que tenga una sola solución es un sistema independiente.

Example $\begin{cases} x + 2y = -7 \\ 2x - 3y = 0 \end{cases}$

has the unique solution $(-3, -2)$.
It is an independent system.

**Independent variable (p. 63)** If a function is defined by an equation using the variables $x$ and $y$, where $x$ represents input values, then $x$ is the independent variable.

**Variable independiente (p. 63)** Si una función es definida por una ecuación con las variables $x$ e $y$, donde $x$ representa los valores de entrada, entonces $x$ es la variable independiente.

Example $y = 2x + 1$
$x$ is the independent variable.

**Index (p. 362)** With a radical sign, the index indicates the degree of the root.

**Índice (p. 362)** Con un signo de radical, el índice indica el grado de la raíz.

Example  index 2   index 3   index 4
$\sqrt{16}$   $\sqrt[3]{16}$   $\sqrt[4]{16}$

**Infinite series (p. 587)** An infinite series is a series with infinitely many terms.

**Serie infinita (p. 587)** Una serie infinita es una serie con un número infinito de términos.

**Initial point (p. 801)** The initial point of a vector is the endpoint (not the tip) of a vector arrow.

**Punto de inicio (p. 801)** El punto de inicio de un vector es el extremo (no la punta) de una flecha vectorial.

### Page 1007

| English | Spanish |
|---|---|

**Initial side (p. 828)** When an angle is in standard position, the initial side of the angle is given to be on the positive $x$-axis. The other ray is the terminal side of the angle.

**Lado inicial (p. 828)** Cuando un ángulo está en posición normal, el lado inicial del ángulo se ubica en el eje positivo de las $x$. El otro rayo, o semirrecta, forma el lado terminal del ángulo.

Example
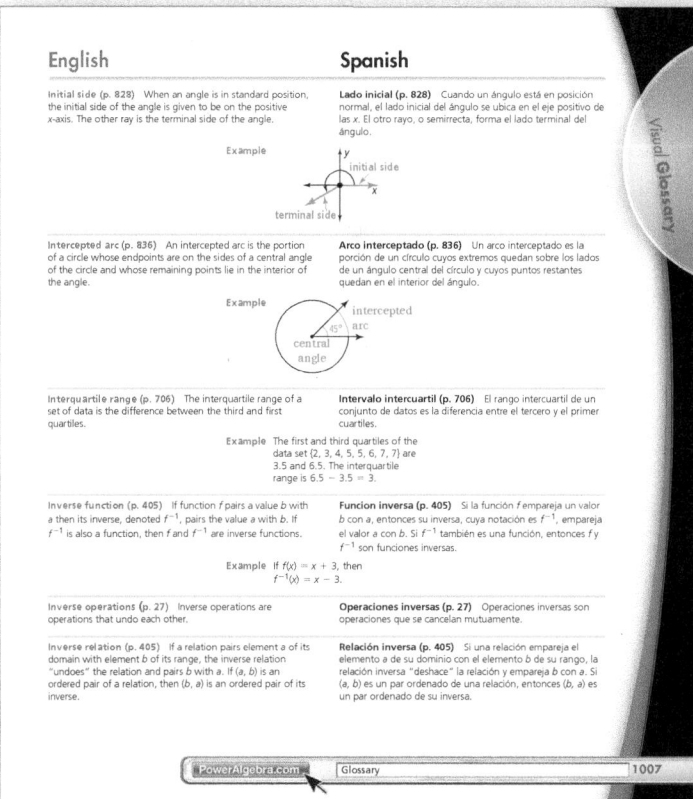

**Intercepted arc (p. 836)** An intercepted arc is the portion of a circle whose endpoints are on the sides of a central angle of the circle and whose remaining points lie in the interior of the angle.

**Arco interceptado (p. 836)** Un arco interceptado es la porción de un círculo cuyos extremos quedan sobre los lados de un ángulo central del círculo y cuyos puntos restantes quedan en el interior del ángulo.

Example

**Interquartile range (p. 706)** The interquartile range of a set of data is the difference between the third and first quartiles.

**Intervalo intercuartil (p. 706)** El rango intercuartil de un conjunto de datos es la diferencia entre el tercero y el primer cuartiles.

Example The first and third quartiles of the data set {2, 3, 4, 5, 5, 6, 7, 7} are 3.5 and 6.5. The interquartile range is $6.5 - 3.5 = 3$.

**Inverse function (p. 405)** If function $f$ pairs a value $b$ with $a$ then its inverse, denoted $f^{-1}$, pairs the value $a$ with $b$. If $f^{-1}$ is also a function, then $f$ and $f^{-1}$ are inverse functions.

**Función inversa (p. 405)** Si la función $f$ empareja un valor $b$ con $a$, entonces su inversa, cuya notación es $f^{-1}$, empareja el valor $a$ con $b$. Si $f^{-1}$ también es una función, entonces $f$ y $f^{-1}$ son funciones inversas.

Example If $f(x) = x + 3$, then $f^{-1}(x) = x - 3$.

**Inverse operations (p. 27)** Inverse operations are operations that undo each other.

**Operaciones inversas (p. 27)** Operaciones inversas son operaciones que se cancelan mutuamente.

**Inverse relation (p. 405)** If a relation pairs element $a$ of its domain with element $b$ of its range, the inverse relation "undoes" the relation and pairs $b$ with $a$. If $(a, b)$ is an ordered pair of a relation, then $(b, a)$ is an ordered pair of its inverse.

**Relación inversa (p. 405)** Si una relación empareja el elemento $a$ de su dominio con el elemento $b$ de su rango, la relación inversa "deshace" la relación y empareja $b$ con $a$. Si $(a, b)$ es un par ordenado de una relación, entonces $(b, a)$ es un par ordenado de su inversa.

### Page 1008

| English | Spanish |
|---|---|

**Inverse variation (p. 498)** An inverse variation is a relation represented by an equation of the form $xy = k$, $y = \frac{k}{x}$, or $x = \frac{k}{y}$, where $k \neq 0$.

**Variación inversa (p. 498)** Una variación inversa es una relación representada por la ecuación $xy = k$, $y = \frac{k}{x}$, ó $x = \frac{k}{y}$, donde $k \neq 0$.

Example

$xy = 5$, or $y = \frac{5}{x}$

**— J —**

**Joint variation (p. 501)** A joint variation is a relation in which one variable varies directly with respect to each of two or more variables.

**Variación conjunta (p. 501)** Una variación conjunta es una relación en la cual el valor de una variable varía directamente con respecto a cada una de dos o más variables.

Example $z = 8xy$
$T = kPV$

**— L —**

**Law of Cosines (p. 928)** In $\triangle ABC$, let $a$, $b$, and $c$ represent the lengths of the sides opposite $\angle A$, $\angle B$, and $\angle C$, respectively. Then
$a^2 = b^2 + c^2 - 2bc \cos A$,
$b^2 = a^2 + c^2 - 2ac \cos B$, and
$c^2 = a^2 + b^2 - 2ab \cos C$

**Ley de cosenos (p. 928)** En $\triangle ABC$, sean $a$, $b$ y $c$ las longitudes de los lados opuestos a $\angle A$, $\angle B$ y $\angle C$. respectivamente. Entonces
$a^2 = b^2 + c^2 - 2bc \cos A$,
$b^2 = a^2 + c^2 - 2ac \cos B$ y
$c^2 = a^2 + b^2 - 2ab \cos C$

Example

$LM^2 = 11.41^2 + 8.72^2 - 2(11.42)(8.72) \cos 18°$
$LM^2 = 16.9754$
$LM = 4.12$

**Law of Sines (p. 921)** In $\triangle ABC$, let $a$, $b$, and $c$ represent the lengths of the sides opposite $\angle A$, $\angle B$, and $\angle C$, respectively. Then $\frac{\sin A}{a} = \frac{\sin B}{b} = \frac{\sin C}{c}$.

**Ley de senos (p. 921)** En $\triangle ABC$, sean $a$, $b$ y $c$ las longitudes de los lados opuestos a $\angle A$, $\angle B$ y $\angle C$, respectivamente. Entonces $\frac{\sin A}{a} = \frac{\sin B}{b} = \frac{\sin C}{c}$.

$m\angle L = 180 - (120 + 18) = 42°$
$\frac{KL}{\sin 120°} = \frac{872}{\sin 42°}$
$KL = \frac{872 \sin 120°}{\sin 42°}$
$KL = 11.26$

### Page 1009

| English | Spanish |
|---|---|

**Like radicals (p. 374)** Like radicals are radical expressions that have the same index and the same radicand.

**Radicales semejantes (p. 374)** Los radicales semejantes son expresiones radicales que tienen el mismo índice y el mismo radicando.

Example $4\sqrt[3]{7}$ and $\sqrt[3]{7}$ are like radicals.

**Like terms (p. 21)** Like terms have the same variables raised to the same powers.

**Términos semejantes (p. 21)** Los términos semejantes tienen las mismas variables elevadas a las mismas potencias.

**Limits (p. 589)** Limits in summation notation are the least and greatest integer values of the index $n$.

**Límites (p. 589)** Los límites en notación de sumatoria son el menor y el mayor valor del índice $n$ en números enteros.

Example
$$\text{limits} \quad \sum_{n=1}^{3} (3n + 5)$$

**Line of best fit (p. 94)** The trend line that gives the most accurate model of related data is the line of best fit.

**Recta de mayor aproximación (p. 94)** La línea de tendencia que representa con mayor precisión los datos relacionado es la recta de mayor aproximación.

**Linear equation (p. 75)** A linear equation in two variables is an equation that can be written in the form $ax + by = c$. See also **Standard form of a linear equation.**

**Ecuación lineal (p. 75)** Una ecuación lineal de dos variables es una ecuación que se puede escribir de la forma $ax + by = c$. Ver también **Standard form of a linear equation.**

Example $y = 2x + 1$ can be written as $-2x - y = 1$.

**Linear function (p. 75)** A function whose graph is a line is a linear function. You can represent a linear function with a linear equation.

**Función lineal (p. 75)** Una función cuya gráfica es una recta es una función lineal. La función lineal se representa con una ecuación lineal.

Example

**Linear inequality (p. 114)** A linear inequality is an inequality in two variables whose graph is a region of the coordinate plane that is bounded by a line.

**Desigualdad lineal (p. 114)** Una desigualdad lineal es una desigualdad de dos variables cuya gráfica es una región del plano de coordenadas delimitada por una recta.

Example
$y > x + 1$

## English / Spanish

**Linear programming (p. 157)** Linear programming is a method for finding a minimum or maximum value of some quantity, given a set of constraints.

**Programación lineal (p. 157)** Programación lineal es un método para hallar el valor mínimo y máximo de una cantidad que se expresa como un conjunto de limitaciones.

Example Restrictions $x \ge 0$, $y \ge 0$, $x + y \le 7$, and $y \le -2x + 8$
Objective function: $B = 2x + 4y$
Evaluate $B = 2x + 4y$ at each vertex. The minimum value of $B$ occurs when $x = 0$ and $y = 0$. The maximum value of $B$ occurs when $x = 0$ and $y = 7$.

**Linear system (p. 134)** A linear system is a set of two or more linear equations that use the same variables.

**Sistema lineal (p. 134)** Un sistema lineal es un conjunto de dos o más ecuaciones lineales con las mismas variables.

Example

$4x + 5y = 7$    $2x - 3y = -13$

**Literal equation (p. 29)** A literal equation is an equation that uses more than one letter as a variable.

**Ecuación literal (p. 29)** Una ecuación literal es una ecuación en la cual más de una letra expresa una variable.

**Logarithm (p. 451)** The logarithm base $b$ of a positive number $x$ is defined as follows: $\log_b x = y$, if and only if $x = b^y$.

**Logaritmo (p. 451)** La base del logaritmo $b$ de un número positivo $x$ se define como $\log_b x = y$, si y sólo si $x = b^y$.

Example $\log_2 8 = 3$
$\log_{10} 100 = \log 100 = 2$
$\log_5 5^7 = 7$

**Logarithmic equation (p. 471)** A logarithmic equation is an equation that includes a logarithm involving a variable.

**Ecuación logarítmica (p. 471)** Una ecuación logarítmica es una ecuación que incluye un logaritmo con una variable.

Example $\log_3 x = 4$

---

**Logarithmic function (p. 454)** A logarithmic function is the inverse of an exponential function.

**Función logarítmica (p. 454)** Una función logarítmica es la inversa de una función exponencial.

Example

$y = 10^x$    $y = \log x$

**Logarithmic scale (p. 453)** A logarithmic scale is a scale that uses the logarithm of a quantity instead of the quantity itself.

**Escala logarítmica (p. 453)** Una escala logarítmica es una escala que usa el logaritmo de una cantidad en vez de la cantidad misma.

— M —

**Magnitude (p. 801)** The magnitude of a vector **v** is the length of the arrow.

**Magnitud (p. 801)** La magnitud de un vector **v** es la longitud de la flecha.

**Major axis (p. 639)** The major axis of an ellipse is the segment that contains the foci of the ellipse and has endpoints on the ellipse.

**Eje mayor (p. 639)** En una elipsis, el eje mayor es el segmento que contiene los focos de la elipsis y tiene puntos extremos sobre la elipsis.

Example

major axis

**Mapping diagram (p. 60)** A mapping diagram describes a relation by linking elements of the domain with elements of the range.

**Mapa (p. 60)** Un mapa describe una relación al unir los elementos del dominio con los elementos del rango.

Example   Domain   Range

$-5 \to -10$
$-1 \to -2$
$3 \to 2$
$\to 6$

**Matrix (p. 174)** A matrix is a rectangular array of numbers written within brackets.

**Matriz (p. 174)** Una matriz es un conjunto de números encerrados en corchetes y dispuestos en forma de rectángulo.

Example $A = \begin{bmatrix} 1 & -2 & 0 & 10 \\ 9 & 7 & -3 & 8 \\ 2 & -10 & 1 & -6 \end{bmatrix}$

The number 2 is the element in the third row and first column. $A$ is a $3 \times 4$ matrix.

---

**Matrix element (p. 174)** Every item listed in a matrix is an element of the matrix. An element is identified by its position in the matrix.

**Elemento matricial (p. 174)** Cada cifra de una matriz es un elemento de la matriz. El elemento se identifica según la posición que ocupa en la matriz.

Example $A = \begin{bmatrix} 1 & -2 & 0 & 10 \\ 9 & 7 & -3 & 8 \\ 2 & -10 & 1 & -6 \end{bmatrix}$

Element $a_{21}$ is 9, the element in the second row and first column.

**Matrix equation (p. 757)** A matrix equation is an equation in which the variable is a matrix.

**Ecuación matricial (p. 757)** Una ecuación matricial es una ecuación en que la variable es una matriz.

Example

Solve $X + \begin{bmatrix} 3 & -2 \\ 5 & 1 \end{bmatrix} = \begin{bmatrix} 4 & 0 \\ 0 & 3 \end{bmatrix}$

$X + \begin{bmatrix} 3 & -2 \\ 5 & 1 \end{bmatrix} = \begin{bmatrix} 4 & 0 \\ 0 & 3 \end{bmatrix}$

$X = \begin{bmatrix} 4 & 0 \\ 0 & 3 \end{bmatrix} - \begin{bmatrix} 3 & -2 \\ 5 & 1 \end{bmatrix} = \begin{bmatrix} 1 & 2 \\ -5 & 2 \end{bmatrix}$

**Maximum value (p. 195)** The maximum value of a function $y = f(x)$ is the greatest $y$-value of the function. It is the $y$-coordinate of the highest point on the graph of $f$.

**Valor máximo (p. 195)** El valor máximo de una función $y = f(x)$ es el valor más alto de $y$ de la función. Es la coordenada $y$ del punto más alto de la gráfica de $f$.

**Mean (p. 704)** The sum of the data values divided by the number of data values is the mean. See also **Arithmetic mean.**

**Media (p. 704)** La suma de los valores de datos dividida por el número de valores de datos sumados es la media. Ver también **Arithmetic mean.**

Example {1, 2, 3, 3, 6, 6}
$\text{mean} = \dfrac{1 + 2 + 3 + 3 + 6 + 6}{6}$
$= \dfrac{21}{6} = 3.5$

**Measures of central tendency (p. 704)** The mean, median, and the mode are each central values that help describe a set of data. They are called measures of central tendency.

**Medidas de tendencia central (p. 704)** La media, la mediana y la moda son los valores centrales que facilitan la descripción de un conjunto de datos. A estos valores se les llama medidas de tendencia central.

Example {1, 2, 3, 3, 4, 5, 6, 6}
$\text{mean} = 3.75$
$\text{median} = 3.5$
$\text{modes} = 3$ and $6$

**Measure of variation (p. 712)** Measures of variation, such as the range, the interquartile range, and the standard deviation, describe how the data in a data set are spread out.

**Medida de dispersión (p. 712)** Las medidas de dispersión, tal como el rango, el intervalo intercuartil y la desviación típica, describen cómo se dispersan los datos en un conjunto de datos.

---

**Median (p. 704)** The median is the middle value in a data set. If the data set contains an even number of values, the median is the mean of the two middle values.

**Mediana (p. 704)** La mediana es el valor situado en el medio en un conjunto de datos. Si el conjunto de datos contiene un número par de valores, la mediana es la media de los dos valores del medio.

Example {1, 2, 3, 3, 4, 5, 6, 6}
$\text{median} = \dfrac{3 + 4}{2} = \dfrac{7}{2} = 3.5$

**Minor axis (p. 639)** The minor axis of an ellipse is the segment that is perpendicular to the major axis at its midpoint and has endpoints on the ellipse.

**Eje menor (p. 639)** En una elipsis, el eje menor es el segmento perpendicular al eje mayor en su punto medio y que tiene puntos extremos sobre la elipsis.

Example

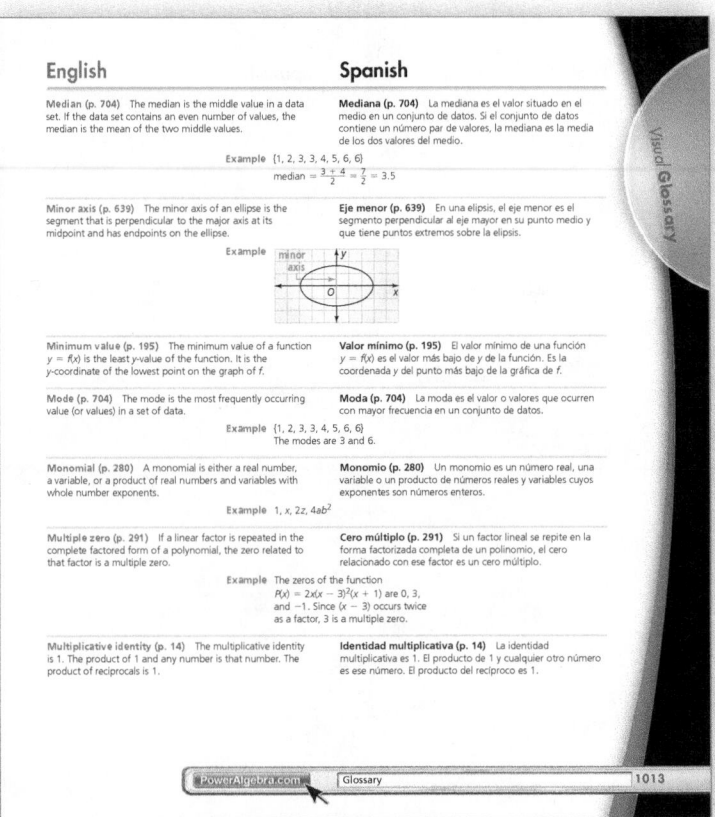

minor axis

**Minimum value (p. 195)** The minimum value of a function $y = f(x)$ is the least $y$-value of the function. It is the $y$-coordinate of the lowest point on the graph of $f$.

**Valor mínimo (p. 195)** El valor mínimo de una función $y = f(x)$ es el valor más bajo de $y$ de la función. Es la coordenada $y$ del punto más bajo de la gráfica de $f$.

**Mode (p. 704)** The mode is the most frequently occurring value (or values) in a set of data.

**Moda (p. 704)** La moda es el valor o valores que ocurren con mayor frecuencia en un conjunto de datos.

Example {1, 2, 3, 3, 6, 6}
The modes are 3 and 6.

**Monomial (p. 280)** A monomial is either a real number, a variable, or a product of real numbers and variables with whole number exponents.

**Monomio (p. 280)** Un monomio es un número real, una variable o un producto de números reales y variables cuyos exponentes son números enteros.

Example $1$, $x$, $2z$, $4ab^2$

**Multiple zero (p. 291)** If a linear factor is repeated in the complete factored form of a polynomial, the zero related to that factor is a multiple zero.

**Cero múltiplo (p. 291)** Si un factor lineal se repite en la forma factorizada completa de un polinomio, el cero relacionado con ese factor es un cero múltiplo.

Example The zeros of the function
$P(x) = 2x(x - 3)^2(x + 1)$ are 0, 3, and $-1$. Since $(x - 3)$ occurs twice as a factor, 3 is a multiple zero.

**Multiplicative identity (p. 14)** The multiplicative identity is 1. The product of 1 and any number is that number. The product of reciprocals is 1.

**Identidad multiplicativa (p. 14)** La identidad multiplicativa es 1. El producto de 1 y cualquier otro número es ese número. El producto del recíproco es 1.

## Page 1014

| English | Spanish |
|---|---|

**Multiplicative identity matrix (p. 774)** For an $n \times n$ square matrix, the multiplicative identity matrix is an $n \times n$ square matrix $I$, or $I_{n \times n}$, with 1's along the main diagonal and 0's elsewhere.

**Matriz de identidad multiplicativa (p. 774)** Para una matriz cuadrada $n \times n$, la matriz de identidad multiplicativa es la matriz cuadrada $I$ de $n \times n$, o $I_{n \times n}$, con unos por la diagonal principal y ceros en los demás lugares.

Example $I_{2 \times 2} = \begin{bmatrix} 1 & 0 \\ 0 & 1 \end{bmatrix}$

$I_{3 \times 3} = \begin{bmatrix} 1 & 0 & 0 \\ 0 & 1 & 0 \\ 0 & 0 & 1 \end{bmatrix}$

**Multiplicative inverse (p. 14)** The reciprocal or multiplicative inverse of any nonzero number $a$ is $\frac{1}{a}$. The product of reciprocals is 1, the multiplicative identity.

**Inverso multiplicativo (p. 14)** El recíproco o inverso multiplicativo de cualquier número $a$, que no sea cero, es $\frac{1}{a}$. El producto de recíprocos es 1, la identidad multiplicativa.

Example $5 \times \frac{1}{5} = 1$

**Multiplicative inverse of a matrix (p. 774)** If $A$ and $X$ are $n \times n$ matrices, and $AX = XA = I$, then $X$ is the multiplicative inverse of $A$, written $A^{-1}$.

**Inverso multiplicativo de una matriz (p. 774)** Si $A$ y $X$ son matrices $n \times n$, y $AX = XA = I$, entonces $X$ es el inverso multiplicativo de $A$, expresado como $A^{-1}$.

Example $A = \begin{bmatrix} 2 & 1 \\ 4 & 0 \end{bmatrix}$

$X = \begin{bmatrix} 0 & \frac{1}{4} \\ 1 & \frac{1}{2} \end{bmatrix}$

$AX = \begin{bmatrix} 1 & 0 \\ 0 & 1 \end{bmatrix} = I$, so $X = A^{-1}$

**Multiplicity (p. 291)** The multiplicity of a zero of a polynomial function is the number of times the related linear factor is repeated in the factored form of the polynomial.

**Multiplicidad (p. 291)** La multiplicidad de un cero de una función polinomial es el número de veces que el factor lineal relacionado se repite en la forma factorizada del polinomio.

Example The zeros of the function
$P(x) = 2x(x - 3)^2(x + 1)$ are 0, 3, and $-1$. Since $(x - 3)$ occurs twice as a factor, the zero 3 has multiplicity 2.

**Mutually exclusive events (p. 689)** When two events cannot happen at the same time, the events are mutually exclusive. If $A$ and $B$ are mutually exclusive events, then $P(A \text{ or } B) = P(A) + P(B)$.

**Sucesos mutuamente excluyentes (p. 689)** Cuando dos sucesos no pueden ocurrir al mismo tiempo, son mutuamente excluyentes. Si $A$ y $B$ son sucesos mutuamente excluyentes, entonces $P(A \text{ or } B) = P(A) + P(B)$.

Example Rolling an even number $E$ and rolling a multiple of five $M$ on a standard number cube are mutually exclusive events.
$P(E \text{ or } M) = P(E) + P(M)$
$= \frac{3}{6} + \frac{1}{6}$
$= \frac{4}{6}$, or $\frac{2}{3}$

## Page 1015

**n factorial (n!) (p. 675)** For any positive integer $n$, $n$ factorial is $n(n - 1) \cdot \cdots \cdot 3 \cdot 2 \cdot 1$. Zero factorial (0!) = 1.

**n factorial (n!) (p. 675)** Para cualquier entero $n$, $n$ factorial es $n(n - 1) \cdot \cdots \cdot 3 \cdot 2 \cdot 1$. El cero factorial (0!) = 1.

Example $4! = 4 \times 3 \times 2 \times 1 = 24$

**nth root (p. 361)** For any real numbers $a$ and $b$, and any positive integer $n$, if $a^n = b$, then $a$ is an $n$th root of $b$.

**raíz n-ésima (p. 361)** Para todos los números reales $a$ y $b$, y todo número entero positivo $n$, si $a^n = b$, entonces $a$ es la $n$-ésima raíz de $b$.

Example $\sqrt[5]{32} = 2$ because $2^5 = 32$.
$\sqrt[4]{81} = 3$ because $3^4 = 81$.

**Natural base exponential function (p. 446)** A natural base exponential function is an exponential function with base $e$.

**Función exponencial con base natural (p. 446)** Una función exponencial con base natural es una función exponencial con base $e$.

**Natural logarithmic function (p. 478)** A natural logarithmic function is a logarithmic function with base $e$. The natural logarithmic function, $y = \ln x$, is $y = \log_e x$. It is the inverse of $y = e^x$.

**Función logarítmica natural (p. 478)** Una función logarítmica natural es una función logarítmica con base $e$. La función logarítmica natural, $y = \ln x$, es $y = \log_e x$. Ésta es la función inversa de $y = e^x$.

Example

$\ln e^3 = 3$
$\ln 10 = 2.3026$
$\ln 36 = 3.5835$

**Non-removable discontinuity (p. 516)** A non-removable discontinuity is a point of discontinuity that is not removable. It represents a break in the graph of $f$ where you cannot redefine $f$ to make the graph continuous.

**Discontinuidad irremovible (p. 516)** Una discontinuidad irremovible es un punto de discontinuidad que no se puede remover. Representa una interrupción en la gráfica $f$ donde no se puede redefinir $f$ para volverla una gráfica continua.

## Page 1016

| English | Spanish |
|---|---|

**Normal distribution (p. 733)** A normal distribution shows data that vary randomly from the mean in the pattern of a bell-shaped curve.

**Distribución normal (p. 733)** Una distribución normal muestra, con una curva en forma de campana, datos que varían aleatoriamente respecto de la media.

Example

**Distribution of Test Scores**

In a class of 200 students, the scores on a test were normally distributed. The mean score was 66.5 and the standard deviation was 6.5. The number of students who scored greater than 73 percent was about 13.5% + 2.5% of those who took the test.
16% of 200 = 32
About 32 students scored 73 or higher on the test.

**Normal vectors (p. 804)** Normal vectors are perpendicular vectors. Their dot product is 0.

**Vectores normales (p. 804)** Los vectores normales son vectores perpendiculares. El producto escalar es 0.

**Numerical expression (p. 5)** A numerical expression is a mathematical phrase that contains numbers and operation symbols.

**Expresión numérica (p. 5)** Una expresión numérica es una expresión matemática compuesta de números y símbolos de operación.

**Objective function (p. 157)** In a linear programming model, the objective function is a model of the quantity that you want to make as large or as small as possible. See **Linear programming**.

**Función objetiva (p. 157)** En un modelo de programación lineal, la función objetiva es un modelo de la cantidad que se quiere aumentar o disminuir cuanto sea posible. Ver **Linear programming**.

**Observational study (p. 719)** In an observational study, you measure or observe members of a sample in such a way that they are not affected by the study.

**Estudio de observación (p. 719)** En un estudio de observación, se miden u observan a los miembros de una muestra de tal manera que no les afecte el estudio.

**One-to-one function (p. 408)** A one-to-one function is a function for which each $y$-value in the range corresponds to exactly one $x$-value in the domain. A one-to-one function $f$ has an inverse $f^{-1}$ that is also a function.

**Función uno a uno (p. 408)** Una función uno a uno es una función donde cada valor $y$ que se encuentra en el rango corresponde exactamente a un valor $x$ en el dominio. Una función uno a uno $f$ tiene un inverso $f^{-1}$ que también es una función.

## Page 1017

| English | Spanish |
|---|---|

**Opposite (p. 14)** The opposite or additive inverse of any number $a$ is $-a$. The sum of opposites is zero, the additive identity.

**Opuesto (p. 14)** El opuesto o inverso aditivo de cualquier número $a$ es $-a$. La suma de opuestos es cero, la identidad aditiva.

Example $3 + (-3) = 0$
$5.2 + (-5.2) = 0$

**Ordered triples (p. 164)** Ordered triples of the form $(x, y, z)$ represent the location of a point in coordinate space.

**Tripletas ordenadas (p. 164)** Las tripletas ordenadas de la forma $(x, y, z)$ representan la ubicación de un punto en el espacio de coordenadas.

Example $(2, 4, 5)$
$(0, 1, 2)$
$(0, 0, 0)$

**Outlier (p. 705)** An outlier is a value substantially different from the rest of the data in a set.

**Valor extremo (p. 705)** Un valor extremo es un valor considerablemente diferente al resto de los datos de un conjunto.

Example The outlier in the data set
$\{56, 64, 73, 59, 98, 65, 59\}$ is 98.

**P**

**Parabola (p. 194)** A parabola is the graph of a quadratic function. It is the set of all points $P$ in a plane that are the same distance from a fixed point $F$, the focus, as they are from a line $d$, the directrix.

**Parábola (p. 194)** La parábola es la gráfica de una función cuadrática. Es el conjunto de todos los puntos $P$ situados en un plano a la misma distancia de un punto fijo $F$, o foco, y de la recta $d$, o directriz.

Example

**Parallel lines (p. 85)** Parallel lines are coplanar lines that do not intersect. In the coordinate plane, parallel lines have the same slope.

**Rectas paralelas (p. 85)** Rectas paralelas son líneas coplanares que no se intersecan. En un plano de coordenadas, las rectas paralelas tienen la misma pendiente.

**Parent function (p. 99)** A parent function is the simplest form of a set of functions that form a family.

**Función elemental (p. 99)** Una función madre es la mínima expresión de un conjunto de funciones que forma una familia.

Example $y = x$ is the parent function for the functions of the form
$y = x + k$.

## English / Spanish

### Page 1018

| English | Spanish |
|---|---|

**Pascal's Triangle (p. 327)** Pascal's Triangle is a triangular array of numbers in which the first and last number is 1. Each of the other numbers in the row is the sum of the two numbers above it.

**Triángulo de Pascal (p. 327)** El Triángulo de Pascal es una distribución triangular de números en la cual el primer número y el último número son 1. Cada uno de los otros números en la fila es la suma de los dos números de encima.

Example  Pascal's Triangle

```
        1
       1 1
      1 2 1
     1 3 3 1
    1 4 6 4 1
   1 5 10 10 5 1
```

**Percentiles (p. 707)** A percentile is a number from 0 to 100 that you can associate with a value $x$ from a data set. It shows the percent of the data that are less than or equal to $x$.

**Percentiles (p. 707)** Un percentil es un número de 0 a 100 que se puede asociar con un valor $x$ de un conjunto de datos. Éste muestra el porcentaje de los datos que son menores o iguales a $x$.

**Perfect square trinomial (p. 219)** A perfect square trinomial is a trinomial that is the square of a binomial.

**Trinomio cuadrado perfecto (p. 219)** Un trinomio cuadrado perfecto es un trinomio que es el cuadrado de un binomio.

Example
```
 perfect square        binominal
   trinomial             square
16x² − 24x + 9 = (4x − 3)²
```

**Period (p. 820)** The period of a periodic function is the horizontal length of one cycle.

**Período (p. 820)** El período de una función periódica es el intervalo horizontal de un ciclo.

Example

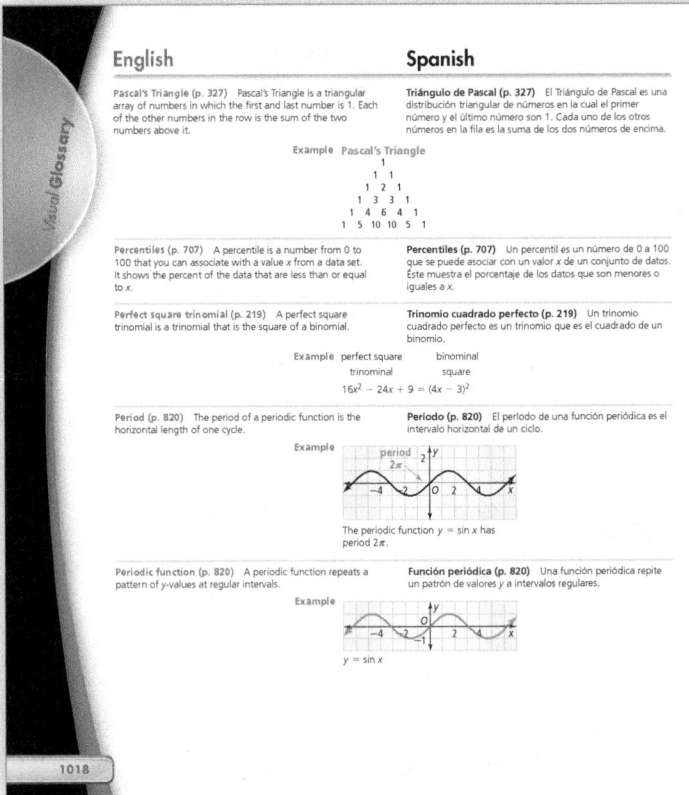

The periodic function $y = \sin x$ has period $2\pi$.

**Periodic function (p. 820)** A periodic function repeats a pattern of $y$-values at regular intervals.

**Función periódica (p. 820)** Una función periódica repite un patrón de valores $y$ a intervalos regulares.

Example

$y = \sin x$

---

### Page 1019

| English | Spanish |
|---|---|

**Permutation (p. 675)** A permutation is an arrangement of items in a particular order. The number of permutations of $n$ objects taken $r$ at a time is $_nP_r = \frac{n!}{(n-r)!}$ for $1 \le r \le n$.

**Permutación (p. 675)** Una permutación es la disposición de objetos en un orden determinado. El número de permutaciones de $n$ objetos seleccionados $r$ veces es $_nP_r = \frac{n!}{(n-r)!}$ para $1 \le r \le n$.

Example
$$_8P_5 = \frac{8!}{(8-5)!}$$
$$= \frac{8 \cdot 7 \cdot 6 \cdot 5 \cdot 4 \cdot 3!}{3!}$$
$$= 8 \times 7 \times 6 \times 5 \times 4$$
$$= 6720$$

**Perpendicular lines (p. 85)** Perpendicular lines are lines that intersect to form right angles. In the coordinate plane, perpendicular lines have slopes with product $-1$.

**Rectas perpendiculares (p. 85)** Rectas perpendiculares son rectas que se intersecan y forman ángulos rectos. En un plano de coordenadas, las rectas perpendiculares tienen pendientes cuyo producto es $-1$.

**Phase shift (p. 867)** A horizontal translation of a periodic function is a phase shift.

**Cambio de fase (p. 867)** Una traslación horizontal de una función periódica es un cambio de fase.

Example

$g(x)$ horizontal translation of $f(x)$
$$g(x) = f(x - h)$$

**Piecewise function (p. 90)** A piecewise function has different rules for different parts of its domain.

**Función de fragmentos (p. 90)** Una función de fragmentos tiene reglas diferentes para diferentes partes de su dominio.

**Point of discontinuity (p. 516)** A point of discontinuity is the $x$-coordinate of a point where the graph of $f(x)$ is not continuous.

**Punto de discontinuidad (p. 516)** Un punto de discontinuidad es la coordenada $x$ de un punto donde la gráfica de $f(x)$ no es continua.

Example  $f(x) = \frac{-2}{x-2}$ has a point of discontinuity at $x = 2$.

**Point-slope form (p. 81)** The point-slope form of an equation of a line is $y - y_1 = m(x - x_1)$, where $m$ is the slope of the line and $(x_1, y_1)$ is a point on the line.

**Forma punto-pendiente (p. 81)** La forma punto-pendiente de una ecuación lineal es $y - y_1 = m(x - x_1)$, donde $m$ es la pendiente de la recta y $(x_1, y_1)$ es un punto de la recta.

Example
$$y - 3 = 2(x - 1)$$
$$y + 4 = 5(x - 2)$$
$$y - 2 = 3(x + 2)$$

---

### Page 1020

| English | Spanish |
|---|---|

**Polynomial (p. 280)** A polynomial is a monomial or the sum of monomials.

**Polinomio (p. 280)** Un polinomio es un monomio o la suma de dos o más monomios.

Example
$$3x^3 + 4x^2 - 2x + 5$$
$$8x$$
$$x^2 + 4x + 2$$

**Polynomial function (p. 280)** A polynomial in the variable $x$ defines a polynomial function of $x$.

**Función polinomial (p. 280)** Un polinomio en la variable $x$ define una función polinomial de $x$.

Example  $P(x) = a_n x^n + a_{n-1} x^{n-1} + \cdots + a_1 x + a_0$ is a polynomial function, where $n$ is a nonnegative integer and the coefficients $a_n, \ldots, a_0$ are real numbers.

**Population (p. 718)** A population is the members of a set.

**Población (p. 718)** Una población está compuesta por los miembros de un conjunto.

**Power function (p. 341)** A power function is a function of the form $y = a \cdot x^b$, where $a$ and $b$ are nonzero real numbers.

**Función de potencia (p. 341)** Una función de potencia es una función de la forma $y = a \cdot x^b$, donde $a$ y $b$ son números reales diferentes de cero.

**Preimage (p. 793)** The preimage is the original figure before a transformation.

**Preimagen (p. 793)** La preimagen es la figura original antes de sufrir una transformación.

Example

**Principal root (p. 361)** When a number has two real roots, the positive root is called the principal root. A radical sign indicates the principal root. The principal root of a negative number $a$ is $i\sqrt{|a|}$.

**Raíz principal (p. 361)** Cuando un número tiene dos raíces reales, la raíz positiva es la raíz principal. El signo del radical indica la raíz principal. La raíz principal de un número negativo $a$ es $i\sqrt{|a|}$.

Example  The number 25 has two square roots, 5 and $-5$. The principal square root, 5, is indicated by $\sqrt{25}$ or $25^{\frac{1}{2}}$.

---

### Page 1021

| English | Spanish |
|---|---|

**Probability distribution (p. 694)** A probability distribution is a function that tells the probability of each outcome in a sample space.

**Distribución de probabilidades (p. 694)** Una distribución de probabilidades es una función que señala la probabilidad de que cada resultado ocurra en un espacio muestral.

Example

| Roll | Fr. | Prob. |
|---|---|---|
| 1 | 5 | 0.125 |
| 2 | 9 | 0.225 |
| 3 | 7 | 0.175 |
| 4 | 8 | 0.2 |
| 5 | 8 | 0.2 |
| 6 | 3 | 0.075 |

The table and graph both show the experimental probability distribution for the outcomes of 40 rolls of a standard number cube.

**Pure imaginary number (p. 249)** If $a = 0$ and $b \ne 0$, the number $a + bi$ is a pure imaginary number.

**Número imaginario puro (p. 249)** Si $a = 0$ y $b \ne 0$, el número $a + bi$ es un número imaginario puro.

**Quadratic equation (p. 226)** A quadratic equation is one that can be written in the standard form $ax^2 + bx + c = 0$, where $a \ne 0$.

**Ecuación cuadrática (p. 226)** Una ecuación cuadrática es una ecuación que se puede expresar en forma normal como $ax^2 + bx + c = 0$, donde $a \ne 0$.

Example  $2x^2 + 3x + 1 = 0$

**Quadratic Formula (p. 240)** The Quadratic Formula is $x = \frac{-b \pm \sqrt{b^2 - 4ac}}{2a}$. It gives the solutions to the quadratic equation $ax^2 + bx + c = 0$.

**Fórmula cuadrática (p. 240)** La fórmula cuadrática es $x = \frac{-b \pm \sqrt{b^2 - 4ac}}{2a}$. Ésta da las soluciones a la ecuación cuadrática $ax^2 + bx + c = 0$.

Example  If $-x^2 + 3x + 2 = 0$, then
$$x = \frac{-3 \pm \sqrt{(3)^2 - 4(-1)(2)}}{2(-1)}$$
$$= \frac{-3 \pm \sqrt{17}}{-2}$$

**Quadratic function (p. 194)** A quadratic function is a function that you can write in the form $f(x) = ax^2 + bx + c$ with $a \ne 0$.

**Función cuadrática (p. 194)** Una función cuadrática es una función que puedes escribir como $f(x) = ax^2 + bx + c$ con $a \ne 0$.

Example

$y = x^2 + 2x - 2$

## Page 1022

| English | Spanish |
|---|---|

**Quantity (p. 5)** A mathematical quantity is anything that can be measured or counted.

**Cantidad (p. 5)** Una cantidad matemática es cualquier cosa que se puede medir o contar.

**Quartile (p. 706)** Quartiles are values that separate a finite data set into four equal parts. The second quartile ($Q_2$) is the median of the data. The first and third quartiles ($Q_1$ and $Q_3$) are the medians of the lower half and upper half of the data, respectively.

**Cuartil (p. 706)** Los cuartiles son valores que separan un conjunto finito de datos en cuatro partes iguales. El segundo cuartil ($Q_2$) es la mediana de los datos. Los cuartiles primero y tercero ($Q_1$ y $Q_3$) son las medianas de la mitad superior e inferior de los datos, respectivamente.

Example $\{2, 3, 4, 5, 5, 6, 7, 7\}$
$Q_1 = 3.5$
$Q_2 \text{ (median)} = 5$
$Q_3 = 6.5$

### R

**Radian (p. 836)** $\frac{d^\circ}{180} = \frac{r \text{ radians}}{\pi \text{ radians}}$

**Radián (p. 836)** $\frac{d^\circ}{180} = \frac{r \text{ radianes}}{\pi \text{ radianes}}$

Example $60^\circ \rightarrow \frac{60}{180} = \frac{x}{\pi}$
$x = \frac{60\pi}{180}$
$= \frac{\pi}{3}$
Thus, $60^\circ = \frac{\pi}{3}$ radians.

**Radical equation (p. 390)** A radical equation is an equation that has a variable in a radicand or has a variable with a rational exponent.

**Ecuación radical (p. 390)** La ecuación radical es una ecuación que contiene una variable en el radicando o una variable con un exponente racional.

Example $(\sqrt{x})^3 + 1 = 65$
$x^{\frac{3}{2}} + 1 = 65$

**Radical function (p. 415)** A radical function is a function that can be written in the form $f(x) = a\sqrt[n]{x - h} + k$, where $a \neq 0$. For even values of $n$, the domain of a radical function is the real numbers $x \geq h$. See also **Square root function**.

**Función radical (p. 415)** Una función radical es una función quepuede expresarse como $f(x) = a\sqrt[n]{x - h} + k$, donde $a \neq 0$. Para $n$ par, el dominio de la función radical son los números reales tales que $x \geq h$. Ver también **Square root function**.

Example $f(x) = \sqrt{x - 2}$

**Radicand (p. 362)** The number under a radical sign is the radicand.

**Radicando (p. 362)** La expresión que aparece debajo del signo radical es el radicando.

Example The radicand in $3\sqrt[3]{7}$ is 7.

## Page 1023

| English | Spanish |
|---|---|

**Radius (p. 630)** The radius $r$ of a circle is the distance between the center of the circle and any point on the circumference.

**Radio (p. 630)** El radio $r$ de un círculo es la distancia entre el centro del círculo y cualquier punto de la circunferencia.

Example

**Random sample (p. 718)** In a random sample, all members of the population are equally likely to be chosen as every other member.

**Muestra aleatoria (p. 718)** En una muestra aleatoria, la probabilidad de ser seleccionado es igual para todos los miembros.

Example Let the set of all females between the ages of 19 and 34 be the population. A random selection of 900 females between those ages would be a sample of the population.

**Range (p. 61)** The range of a relation is the set of all outputs or $y$-coordinates of the ordered pairs.

**Rango (p. 61)** El rango de una relación es el conjunto de todas las salidas posibles, o coordenadas $y$, de los pares ordenados.

Example In the relation $\{(0, 1), (0, 2), (0, 3), (0, 4), (1, 3), (1, 4), (2, 1)\}$, the range is $\{1, 2, 3, 4\}$.
In the function $f(x) = |x - 3|$, the range is the set of real numbers greater than or equal to 0.

**Range of a set of data (p. 706)** The range of a set of data is the difference between the greatest and least values.

**Rango de un conjunto de datos (p. 706)** El rango de un conjunto de datos es la diferencia entre el valor máximo y el valor mínimo de los datos.

Example The range of the set $\{3.2, 4.1, 2.2, 3.4, 3.8, 4.0, 4.2, 2.8\}$ is $4.2 - 2.2 = 2$.

**Rational equation (p. 542)** A rational equation is an equation that contains a rational expression.

**Ecuación racional (p. 542)** Una ecuación racional es una ecuación que contiene una expresión racional.

**Rational exponent (p. 382)** If the $n$th root of $a$ is a real number and $m$ is an integer, then $a^{\frac{1}{n}} = \sqrt[n]{a}$ and $a^{\frac{m}{n}} = \sqrt[n]{a^m} = (\sqrt[n]{a})^m$. If $m$ is negative, $a \neq 0$.

**Exponente racional (p. 382)** Si la raíz $n$-ésima de $a$ es un número real y $m$ es un número entero, entonces $a^{\frac{1}{n}} = \sqrt[n]{a}$ y $a^{\frac{m}{n}} = \sqrt[n]{a^m} = (\sqrt[n]{a})^m$. Si $m$ es negativo, $a \neq 0$.

Example $4^{\frac{1}{3}} = \sqrt[3]{4}$
$5^{\frac{3}{2}} = \sqrt{5^3} = (\sqrt{5})^3$

**Rational expression (p. 527)** A rational expression is the quotient of two polynomials.

**Expresión racional (p. 527)** Una expresión racional es el cociente de dos polinomios.

## Page 1024

| English | Spanish |
|---|---|

**Rational function (p. 515)** A rational function $f(x)$ can be written as $f(x) = \frac{P(x)}{Q(x)}$, where $P(x)$ and $Q(x)$ are polynomial functions. The domain of a rational function is all real numbers except those for which $Q(x) = 0$.

**Función racional (p. 515)** Una función racional $f(x)$ se puede expresar como $f(x) = \frac{P(x)}{Q(x)}$, donde $P(x)$ y $Q(x)$ son funciones de polinomios. El dominio de una función racional son todos los números reales excepto aquéllos para los cuales $Q(x) = 0$.

Example

The function $y = \frac{x - 2}{x^2 - 9}$ is a rational function with three branches separated by asymptotes $x = -3$ and $x = 3$.

**Rational Root Theorem (p. 312)** Let $P(x) = a_nx^n + a_{n-1}x^{n-1} + \cdots + a_1x + a_0$ be a polynomial with integer coefficients.
Then there are a limited number of possible roots of $P(x) = 0$:
–Integer roots must be factors of $a_0$;
–Rational roots must have reduced form $p/q$ where $p$ is an integer factor of $a_0$ and $q$ is an integer factor of $a_n$.

**Teorema de la Raíz Racional (p. 312)** Sea $P(x) = a_nx^n + a_{n-1}x^{n-1} + \cdots + a_1x + a_0$ un polinomio con enteros como coeficientes.
Entonces hay un número limitado de raíces posibles para $P(x) = 0$:
–Las raíces enteras deben ser factores de $a_0$;
–Las raíces racionales deben ser de forma simplificada $p/q$, donde $p$ es un factor entero de $a_0$ y $q$ es un factor entero de $a_n$.

Example The polynomial equation
$10x^3 + 6x^2 - 11x - 2 = 0$ has
leading coefficient 10 (with factors
$\pm 1, \pm 2, \pm 5, \pm 10$) and constant
term $-2$ (with factors $\pm 1$ and $\pm 2$).
Its only possible rational roots are
$\pm 1, \pm 2, \pm\frac{1}{2}, \pm\frac{1}{5},$
$\pm\frac{2}{5}, \pm\frac{1}{10}.$

**Rationalize the denominator (p. 369)** To rationalize the denominator of an expression, rewrite it so there are no radicals in any denominator and no denominators in any radical.

**Racionalizar el denominador (p. 369)** Para racionalizar el denominador de una expresión, ésta se escribe de modo que no haya radicales en ningún denominador y no haya denominadores en ningún radical.

Example $\frac{1}{\sqrt{2}} = \frac{1}{\sqrt{2}} \times \frac{\sqrt{2}}{\sqrt{2}} = \frac{\sqrt{2}}{2}$

**Reciprocal (p. 14)** The reciprocal or multiplicative inverse of any nonzero number $a$ is $\frac{1}{a}$. The product of reciprocals is 1, the multiplicative identity.

**Recíproco (p. 14)** El recíproco o inverso multiplicativo de un número distinto de cero $a$ es $\frac{1}{a}$. El producto de recíprocos es 1, la identidad multiplicativa.

Example $5 \times \frac{1}{5} = 1$

## Page 1025

| English | Spanish |
|---|---|

**Reciprocal function (p. 507)** A reciprocal function belongs to the family whose parent function is $f(x) = \frac{1}{x}$ where $x \neq 0$. You can write a reciprocal function in the form $f(x) = (\frac{a}{x} - h) + k$, where $a \neq 0$ and $x \neq h$.

**Función recíproca (p. 507)** Una función recíproca pertenece a la familia cuya función madre es $f(x) = \frac{1}{x}$ donde $x \neq 0$. Se puede escribir una función recíproca como $f(x) = (\frac{a}{x} - h) + k$, donde $a \neq 0$ y $x \neq h$.

Example $f(x) = \frac{1}{2x + 5}$
$p(v) = \frac{3}{v} + 5$

**Recursive formula (p. 565)** A recursive formula defines the terms in a sequence by relating each term to the ones before it.

**Fórmula recursiva (p. 565)** Una fórmula recursiva define los términos de una secuencia al relacionar cada término con los términos que lo anteceden.

Example Let $a_n = 2.5a_{n-1} + 3a_{n-2}$.
if $a_5 = 3$ and $a_4 = 7.5$, then
$a_6 = 2.5(3) + 3(7.5) = 30.$

**Reduced row echelon form (p. 177)** A matrix that represents the solution of a system is in reduced row echelon form. The leading 1 in each row has 0's elsewhere in its column.

**Forma reducida fila-escalón (p. 177)** Una matriz que representa la solución de un sistema está en forma reducida fila-escalón. El 1 principal en cada fila tiene ceros en otras partes de la columna.

**Reflection (p. 101)** A reflection flips the graph of a function across a line, such as the $x$- or $y$-axis. Each point on the graph of the reflected function is the same distance from the line of reflection as the corresponding point on the graph of the original function.

**Reflexión (p. 101)** Una reflexión voltea la gráfica de una función sobre una línea, como el eje de las $x$ o el eje de las $y$. Cada punto de la gráfica de la función reflejada está a la misma distancia del eje de reflexión que el punto correspondiente en la gráfica de la función original.

Example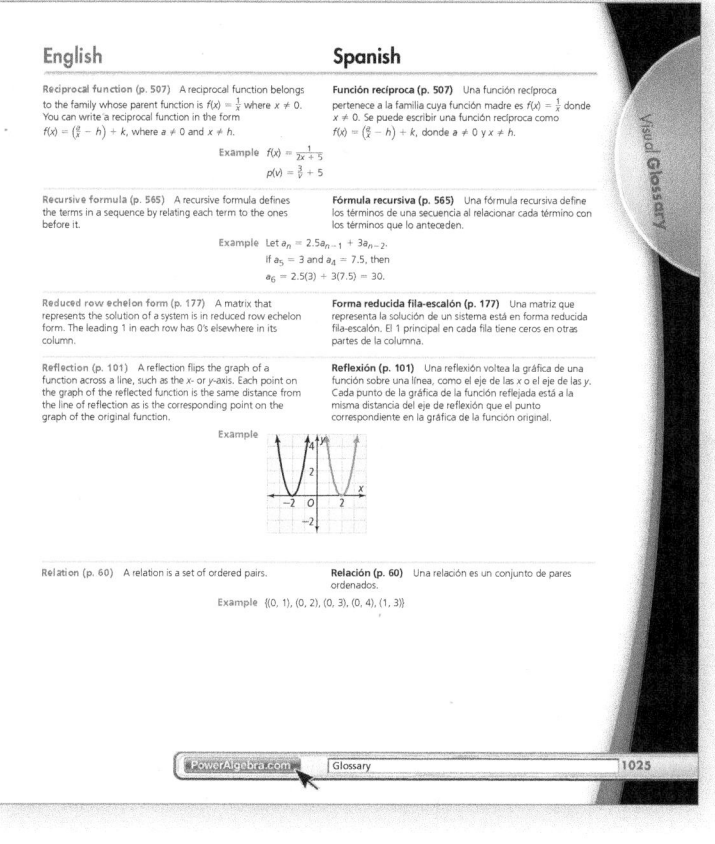

**Relation (p. 60)** A relation is a set of ordered pairs.

**Relación (p. 60)** Una relación es un conjunto de pares ordenados.

Example $\{(0, 1), (0, 2), (0, 3), (0, 4), (1, 3)\}$

## English | Spanish

**Relative maximum (minimum) (p. 291)** A relative maximum (minimum) is the value of the function at an up-to-down (down-to-up) turning point.

**Máximo (mínimo) relativo (p. 291)** El máximo (mínimo) relativo es el valor de la función en un punto de giro de arriba hacia abajo (de abajo hacia arriba).

Example

relative maximum $\left(-\frac{1}{3}, \frac{22}{27}\right)$

relative minimum $(1, -2)$

**Remainder Theorem (p. 307)** If you divide a polynomial $P(x)$ of degree $n > 1$ by $x - a$, then the remainder is $P(a)$.

**Teorema del residuo (p. 307)** Si divides un polinomio $P(x)$ con un grado $n > 1$ por $x - a$, el residuo es $P(a)$.

Example If $P(x) = x^3 - 4x^2 + x + 6$ is divided by $x - 3$, then the remainder is $P(3) = 3^3 - 4(3)^2 + 3 + 6 = 0$ (which means that $x - 3$ is a factor of $P(x)$).

**Removable discontinuity (p. 516)** A removable discontinuity is a point of discontinuity, $a$, of function $f$ that you can remove by redefining $f$ at $x = a$. Doing so fills in a hole in the graph of $f$ with the point $(a, f(a))$.

**Discontinuidad removible (p. 516)** Una discontinuidad removible es un punto de discontinuidad $a$ en una función $f$ que se puede remover al redefinir $f$ en $x = a$. Al hacer esto, se llena un hueco en la gráfica $f$ con el punto $(a, f(a))$.

**Root (p. 232)** A root of a function is the input value for which the value of the function is zero. A root of an equation is a value that makes the equation true. *See also* **Zero of a function.**

**Raíz (p. 232)** La raíz de una función es el valor de entrada para el cual el valor de la función es cero. La raíz de una ecuación es un valor que hace verdadera la ecuación. Ver *también* **Zero of a function.**

Example $-2$ and 3 are roots of the function $f(x) = (x + 2)(x - 3)$ and the equation $(x + 2)(x - 3) = 0$.

**Rotation (p. 796)** A rotation is a transformation that turns a figure about a fixed point called the center of rotation.

**Rotación (p. 796)** Rotación es una transformación que hace girar una figura alrededor de un punto fijo llamado centro de rotación.

Example

**Row operation (p. 176)** A row operation on an augmented matrix is any of the following: switch two rows, multiply a row by a constant, add one row to another.

**Operación de fila (p. 176)** Una operación de fila en una matriz ampliada es cualquiera de las siguientes opciones: el intercambio de dos filas, la multiplicación de una fila por una constante o la suma de dos filas.

---

## English | Spanish

**Sample (p. 718)** A sample from a population is some of the population.

**Muestra (p. 718)** Una muestra de una población es una parte de la población.

Example Let the set of all males between the ages of 19 and 34 be the population. A random selection of 900 males between those ages would be a sample of the population.

**Sample space (p. 682)** The set of all possible outcomes of an experiment is called the sample space.

**Espacio muestral (p. 682)** El espacio muestral es el conjunto de todos los resultados posibles de un suceso.

Example When you roll a number cube, the sample space is {1, 2, 3, 4, 5, 6}.

**Scalar (p. 764)** A scalar is a real number factor in a special product, such as the 3 in the vector product 3**v**.

**Escalar (p. 764)** Un escalar es un factor que es un número real en un producto especial, como el 3 en el producto vectorial 3**v**.

Example $2.5\begin{bmatrix} 1 & 0 \\ -2 & 3 \end{bmatrix} = \begin{bmatrix} 2.5(1) & 2.5(0) \\ 2.5(-2) & 2.5(3) \end{bmatrix}$

$= \begin{bmatrix} 2.5 & 0 \\ -5 & 7.5 \end{bmatrix}$

**Scalar multiplication (p. 764)** Scalar multiplication is an operation that multiplies a matrix $A$ by a scalar $c$. To find the resulting matrix $cA$, multiply each element of $A$ by $c$.

**Multiplicación escalar (p. 764)** La multiplicación escalar es la que multiplica una matriz $A$ por un número escalar $c$. Para hallar la matriz $cA$ resultante, multiplica cada elemento de $A$ por $c$.

Example $2.5\begin{bmatrix} 1 & 0 \\ -2 & 3 \end{bmatrix} = \begin{bmatrix} 2.5(1) & 2.5(0) \\ 2.5(-2) & 2.5(3) \end{bmatrix}$

$= \begin{bmatrix} 2.5 & 0 \\ -5 & 7.5 \end{bmatrix}$

**Scatter plot (p. 92)** A scatter plot is a graph that relates two different sets of data by plotting the data as ordered pairs. You can use a scatter plot to determine a relationship between the data sets.

**Diagrama de puntos (p. 92)** Un diagrama de puntos es una gráfica que relaciona dos conjuntos de datos presentando los datos como pares ordenados. El diagrama de puntos sirve para definir la relación entre conjuntos de datos.

Example

**Dollars Spent Per Capita on Entertainment**

Source: U.S. Bureau of Labor Statistics

---

## English | Spanish

**Secant function (p. 875)** The secant (sec) function is the reciprocal of the cosine function. For all real numbers $\theta$ except those that make $\cos \theta = 0$, $\sec \theta = \frac{1}{\cos \theta}$.

**Función secante (p. 875)** La función secante (sec) es el recíproco de la función coseno. Para todos los números reales $\theta$, excepto aquéllos para los que $\cos \theta = 0$, $\sec \theta = \frac{1}{\cos \theta}$.

Example If $\cos \theta = \frac{5}{13}$, then $\sec \theta = \frac{13}{5}$.

**Self-selected sample (p. 718)** In a self-selected sample you select only members of the population who volunteered for the sample.

**Muestra de voluntarios (p. 718)** En una muestra de voluntarios se seleccionan sólo a los miembros de la población que se ofrecen voluntariamente para ser parte de la muestra.

**Sequence (p. 564)** A sequence is an ordered list of numbers.

**Progresión (p. 564)** Una progresión es una sucesión de números.

Example 1, 4, 7, 10, . . .

**Series (p. 587)** A series is the sum of the terms of a sequence.

**Serie (p. 587)** Una serie es la suma de los términos de una secuencia.

Example The series $3 + 6 + 9 + 12 + 15$ corresponds to the sequence 3, 6, 9, 12, 15. The sum of the series is 45.

**Simplest form of a radical expression (p. 368)** A radical expression with index $n$ is in simplest form if there are no radicals in any denominator, no denominators in any radical, and any radicand has no $n$th power factors.

**Mínima expresión de una expresión radical (p. 368)** Una expresión radical con índice $n$ está en su mínima expresión si no tiene radicales en ningún denominador ni denominadores en ningún radical y los radicandos no tienen factores de potencia.

**Simplest form of a rational expression (p. 527)** A rational expression is in simplest form if its numerator and denominator are polynomials that have no common divisor other than 1.

**Forma simplificada de una expresión racional (p. 527)** Una expresión racional se encuentra en su mínima expresión si su numerador y su denominador son polinomios que no tienen otro divisor aparte de 1.

Example $\frac{x^2 - 7x + 12}{x^2 - 9} = \frac{(x - 4)(x - 3)}{(x + 3)(x - 3)} = \frac{x - 4}{x + 3}$, where $x \neq -3$

**Simulation (p. 682)** A simulation is a model that imitates one or more events.

**Simulación (p. 682)** Una simulación es un modelo que imita uno o más sucesos.

Example Suppose a weather forecaster predicts a 50% chance of rain for the next three days. You can use three coins landing heads up to simulate three days in a row of rain.

---

## English | Spanish

**Sine curve (p. 844)** A sine curve is the graph of a sine function.

**Sinusoide (p. 844)** Sinusoide es la gráfica de la función seno.

Example

**Sine function, Sine of $\theta$ (p. 843)** The sine function, $y = \sin \theta$, matches the measure $\theta$ of an angle in standard position with the $y$-coordinate of a point on the unit circle. This point is where the terminal side of the angle intersects the unit circle. The $y$-coordinate is the sine of $\theta$.

**Función seno, Seno de $\theta$ (p. 843)** La función seno, $y = \sin \theta$, empareja la medida $\theta$ de un ángulo en posición estándar con la coordenada $y$ de un punto en el círculo unitario. Éste es el punto en el que el lado terminal del ángulo interseca al círculo unitario. La coordenada $y$ es el seno de $\theta$.

Example

$P(\cos \theta, \sin \theta)$

**Singular matrix (p. 777)** A singular matrix is a square matrix with no inverse. Its determinant is 0.

**Matriz singular (p. 777)** Una matriz singular es una matriz al cuadrado que no tiene inverso. El determinante de la matriz es 0.

**Slope (p. 74)** The slope of a non-vertical line is the ratio of the vertical change to the horizontal change between points. You can calculate slope by finding the ratio of the difference in the $y$-coordinates to the difference in the $x$-coordinates for any two points on the line. The slope of a vertical line is undefined.

**Pendiente (p. 74)** La pendiente de una línea no vertical es la razón del cambio vertical al cambio horizontal entre puntos. Puedes calcular la pendiente al hallar la razón de la diferencia de la coordenada $y$ y la diferencia de la coordenada $x$ para dos puntos cualesquiera de la línea. La pendiente de una línea vertical es indefinida.

Example The slope of the line through points $(-1, -1)$ and $(1, -2)$ is $\frac{-2 - (-1)}{1 - (-1)} = \frac{-1}{2} = -\frac{1}{2}$.

**Slope-intercept form (p. 76)** The slope-intercept form of an equation of a line is $y = mx + b$, where $m$ is the slope and $b$ is the $y$-intercept.

**Forma pendiente-intercepto (p. 76)** La forma pendiente-intercepto de una ecuación lineal es $y = mx + b$, donde $m$ es la pendiente y $b$ es el intercepto en $y$.

Example $y = 8x + 2$
$y = -x + 1$
$y = -\frac{1}{2}x - 14$

**Solution of a system (p. 134)** A solution of a system is a set of values for the variables that makes all the equations true.

**Solución de un sistema (p. 134)** Una solución de un sistema es un conjunto de valores para las variables que hace que todas las ecuaciones sean verdaderas.

---

## English — Spanish

**Solution of an equation (p. 27)** A solution of an equation is a number that makes the equation true.

Example The solution of $2x - 7 = -12$ is $x = -2.5$.

**Solución de una ecuación (p. 27)** Una solución de una ecuación es cualquier número que haga verdadera la ecuación.

---

**Square matrix (p. 774)** A square matrix is a matrix with the same number of columns as rows.

Example Matrix $A$ is a square matrix.

$$A = \begin{bmatrix} 1 & 2 & 0 \\ -1 & 0 & -2 \\ 1 & 2 & 3 \end{bmatrix}$$

**Matriz cuadrada (p. 774)** Una matriz cuadrada es la que tiene la misma cantidad de columnas y filas.

---

**Square root equation (p. 390)** A square root equation is a radical equation in which the radical has index 2.

Example $\sqrt{x} = 4$

**Ecuación de raíz cuadrada (p. 390)** Una ecuación de raíz cuadrada es una ecuación radical en la cual el radical tiene índice 2.

---

**Square root function (p. 415)** A square root function that can be written in the form $f(x) = a\sqrt{x - h} + k$, where $a \neq 0$. The domain of a square root function is all real numbers $x \geq h$.

Example $f(x) = 2\sqrt{x - 3} + 4$

**Función de raíz cuadrada (p. 415)** Una función de raíz cuadrada es una función que puede ser expresada como $f(x) = a\sqrt{x - h} + k$, donde $a \neq 0$. El dominio de una función de raíz cuadrada son todos los números reales tales que $x \geq h$.

---

**Standard deviation (p. 712)** Standard deviation is a measure of how much the values in a data set vary, or deviate, from the mean, $\bar{x}$. To find the standard deviation, follow five steps:
· Find the mean of the data set.
· Find the difference between each data value and the mean.
· Square each difference.
· Find the mean of the squares.
· Take the square root of the mean of the squares. This is the standard deviation.

Example $\{0, 2, 3, 4, 6, 7, 8, 9, 10, 11\}$
$\bar{x} = 6$
standard deviation $= \sqrt{12} \approx 3.46$

**Desviación típica (p. 712)** La desviación típica denota cuánto los valores de un conjunto de datos varían, o se desvían, de la media, $\bar{x}$. Para hallar la desviación típica, se siguen cinco pasos:
· Se halla la media del conjunto de datos.
· Se calcula la diferencia entre cada valor de datos y la media.
· Se eleva al cuadrado cada diferencia.
· Se halla la media de los cuadrados.
· Se calcula la raíz cuadrada de la media de los cuadrados. Ésa es la desviación típica.

---

**Standard form of a circle (p. 630)** See **Circle**.

Example $(x - 3)^2 + (y - 4)^2 = 4$

**Forma normal de un círculo (p. 630)** Ver **Circle**.

---

## English — Spanish

**Standard form of a linear equation (p. 82)** The standard form of a linear equation is $Ax + By = C$, where $A$, $B$, and $C$ are real numbers, and $A$ and $B$ are not both zero.

Example In standard form, the equation
$y = \frac{4}{3}x - 1$ is
$4x + (-3)y = 3$.

**Forma normal de una ecuación lineal (p. 82)** La forma normal de una ecuación lineal es $Ax + By = C$, donde $A$, $B$ y $C$ son números reales, y $A$ y $B$ no son cero ambos.

---

**Standard form of a polynomial function (p. 281)** The standard form of a polynomial function arranges the terms by degree in descending numerical order. A polynomial function, $P(x)$, in standard form is $P(x) = a_n x^n + a_{n-1} x^{n-1} + \cdots + a_1 x + a_0$, where $n$ is a nonnegative integer and $a_n, \ldots, a_0$ are real numbers.

Example $2x^3 - 5x^2 - 2x + 5$

**Forma normal de una función polinomial (p. 281)** La forma normal de una función polinomial organiza los términos por grado en orden numérico descendente. Una función polinomial, $P(x)$, en forma normal es $P(x) = a_n x^n + a_{n-1} x^{n-1} + \cdots + a_1 x + a_0$, donde $n$ es un número entero no negativo y $a_n, \ldots, a_0$ son números reales.

---

**Standard form of a quadratic function (p. 202)** The standard form of a quadratic function is $f(x) = ax^2 + bx + c$ with $a \neq 0$.

Example $f(x) = 2x^2 + 5x + 2$

**Forma normal de una función cuadrática (p. 202)** La forma normal de una función cuadrática es $f(x) = ax^2 + bx + c$ con $a \neq 0$.

---

**Standard normal curve (p. 733)** The standard normal curve is a normal distribution centered on the $y$-axis. The mean of the standard normal curve is 0. The standard deviation is 1.

Example

**Curva normal en posición normal (p. 733)** La curva normal es la distribución normal centrada en el eje $y$. La media de la curva normal es 0. La desviación normal es 1.

---

**Standard position (p. 828)** An angle in the coordinate plane is in **standard position** when the vertex is at the origin and one ray is on the positive $x$-axis.

Example

**Posición estándar (p. 828)** Un ángulo en el plano de coordenadas se encuentra en **posición estándar** si el vértice se encuentra en el origen y una semirrecta se encuentra en el eje $x$ positivo.

---

**Step function (p. 90)** A step function pairs every number in an interval with a single value. The graph of a step function can look like the steps of a staircase.

**Función escalón (p. 90)** Una función escalón empareja cada número de un intervalo con un solo valor. La gráfica de una función escalón se puede parecer a los peldaños de una escalera.

---

## English — Spanish

**Sum of cubes (p. 297)** The sum of cubes is an expression of the form $a^3 + b^3$. It can be factored as $(a + b)(a^2 - ab + b^2)$.

Example $x^3 + 27 = (x + 3)(x^2 - 3x + 9)$

**Suma de dos cubos (p. 297)** La suma de dos cubos es una expresión de la forma $a^3 + b^3$. Se puede factorizar como $(a + b)(a^2 - ab + b^2)$.

---

**Survey (p. 719)** In a survey, you ask every member of a sample the same set of questions.

**Encuesta (p. 719)** En una encuesta, se le hace a cada miembro de una muestra la misma serie de preguntas.

---

**Synthetic division (p. 306)** Synthetic division is a process for dividing a polynomial by a linear expression $x - a$. You list the standard-form coefficients (including zeros) of the polynomial, omitting all variables and exponents. You use $a$ for the "divisor" and add instead of subtract throughout the process.

Example

Divide $2x^4 + 5x^3 - 2x - 8$ by
$x + 3$. $2x^4 + 5x^3 - 2x - 8$
divided by $x + 3$ gives
$2x^3 - x^2 + 3x - 11$ as quotient
and 25 as remainder.

**División sintética (p. 306)** La división sintética es un proceso para dividir un polinomio por una expresión lineal $x - a$. En este proceso, escribes los coeficientes de forma normal (incluyendo los ceros) del polinomio, omitiendo todas las variables y todos los exponentes. Usas $a$ como "divisor" y sumas, en vez de restar, a lo largo del proceso.

---

**System of equations (p. 134)** A system of equations is a set of two or more equations using the same variables.

Example $\begin{cases} 2x - 3y = -13 \\ 4x + 5y = 7 \end{cases}$

**Sistema de ecuaciones (p. 134)** Un sistema de ecuaciones es un conjunto de dos o más ecuaciones que contienen las mismas variables.

---

**Systematic sample (p. 718)** In a systematic sample you order the population in some way, and then select from it at regular intervals.

**Muestra sistemática (p. 718)** En una muestra sistemática se ordena la población de cierta manera y luego se selecciona una muestra de esa población a intervalos regulares.

## T

**Tangent function, Tangent of $\theta$ (p. 860)** The tangent function, $y = \tan\theta$, matches the measure $\theta$, of an angle in standard position with the $y/x$ ratio of the $(x, y)$ coordinates of a point on the unit circle. This point is where the terminal side of the angle intersects the unit circle. $y/x$ is the tangent of $\theta$.

Example

**Función tangente, Tangente de $\theta$ (p. 860)** La función tangente, $y = \tan\theta$, empareja la medida $\theta$, de un ángulo en posición estándar con la razón $y/x$ de las coordenadas $(x, y)$ de un punto en el círculo unitario. Éste es el punto en el que el lado terminal del ángulo interseca al círculo unitario. $y/x$ es la tangente de $\theta$.

---

## English — Spanish

**Term of a sequence (p. 564)** Each number in a sequence is a term.

Example 1, 4, 7, 10, …
The second term is 4.

**Término de una progresión (p. 564)** Cada número de una progresión es un término.

---

**Term of an expression (p. 20)** A term is a number, a variable, or the product of a number and one or more variables.

Example The expression $4x^2 - 3y + 7.3$
has 3 terms.

**Término de una expresión (p. 20)** Un término es un número, una variable o el producto de un número y una o más variables.

---

**Terminal point (p. 801)** The terminal point of a vector is the tip (not the endpoint) of a vector arrow.

**Punto terminal (p. 801)** El punto terminal de un vector es la punta (no el extremo) de una flecha vectorial.

---

**Terminal side (p. 828)** See **Initial side**.

**Lado terminal (p. 828)** Ver **Initial side**.

---

**Test point (p. 115)** A test point is a point that you pick on one side of the boundary of the graph of a linear inequality. If the test point makes the inequality true, then all points on that side of the boundary are solutions of the inequality. If the test point makes the inequality false, then all points on the other side are solutions.

**Punto de prueba (p. 115)** Un punto de prueba es un punto que escoges a un lado del límite de la gráfica de una desigualdad lineal. Si el punto de prueba hace que la desigualdad sea verdadera, entonces todos los puntos en ese límite son soluciones de la desigualdad. Si el punto de prueba hace que la desigualdad sea falsa, entonces todos los puntos del otro lado del límite son soluciones.

---

**Theoretical probability (p. 683)** If a sample space has $n$ equally likely outcomes, and an event $A$ occurs in $m$ of these outcomes, then the theoretical probability of event $A$ is $P(A) = \frac{m}{n}$.

Example Use the set $\{1, 4, 9, 16, 25, 36, 49, 64, 81, 100\}$. The probability that a number selected at random is greater than 50 is $P(A) = \frac{3}{10} = 0.3$.

**Probabilidad teórica (p. 683)** Si un espacio muestral tiene $n$ resultados con la misma probabilidad de ocurrir, y ocurre un suceso $A$ en $m$ de estos resultados, entonces la probabilidad teórica del suceso $A$ es $P(A) = \frac{m}{n}$.

---

**Tolerance (p. 44)** The difference between a desired measurement and its maximum and minimum allowable values is the tolerance. The tolerance equals one half the difference between the maximum and minimum values.

Example A manufacturing specification calls for a dimension $d$ of 10 cm with a tolerance of 0.1 cm. The allowable difference between $d$ and 10 is less than or equal to 0.1.

**Tolerancia (p. 44)** La diferencia entre una medida deseada y sus valores máximo y mínimo permitidos es la tolerancia. La tolerancia equivale a la mitad de la diferencia entre los valores máximo y mínimo.

---

**Transformation (p. 99)** A transformation of a function $y = af(x - h) + k$ is a change made to at least one of the values $a$, $h$, and $k$. The four types of transformations are dilations, reflections, rotations, and translations.

Example $g(x) = 2(x - 3)^2$ is a transformation of $f(x) = x^2$.

**Transformación (p. 99)** Una transformación de una función $y = af(x - h) + k$ es un cambio que se le hace a por lo menos uno de los valores $a$, $h$ y $k$. Hay cuatro tipos de transformaciones: dilataciones, reflexiones, rotaciones y traslaciones.

# English — Spanish

**Translation (p. 99)** A translation shifts the graph of the parent function horizontally, vertically, or both without changing its shape or orientation.

**Traslación (p. 99)** Una traslación desplaza la gráfica de la función madre horizontalmente, verticalmente o en ambas direcciones, sin cambiar su forma u orientación.

Example

**Transverse axis (p. 646)** The transverse axis of a hyperbola is the segment that is on the line containing the foci and has endpoints on the hyperbola.

**Eje transversal (p. 646)** El eje transversal de una hipérbola es el segmento que se encuentra sobre la línea que contiene los focos y tiene sus puntos extremos sobre la hipérbola.

Example

**Trend line (p. 93)** A trend line is a line that approximates the relationship between two variables, or data sets, of a scatter plot.

**Línea de tendencia (p. 93)** Una línea de tendencia es una línea que aproxima la relación entre dos variables o conjuntos de datos de un diagrama de dispersión.

Example

Used Car Prices

**Trigonometric identity (p. 896)** A trigonometric identity in one variable is a trigonometric equation that is true for all values of the variable for which both sides of the equation are defined.

**Identidad trigonométrica (p. 896)** Una identidad trigonométrica en una variable es una ecuación trigonométrica que es verdadera para todos los valores de la variable para los cuales se definen los dos lados de la ecuación.

Example $\tan \theta = \frac{\sin \theta}{\cos \theta}$

---

**Trigonometric ratios (p. 912)** If $\theta$ is an acute angle of a right triangle, $x$ is the length of the adjacent leg (ADJ), $y$ is the length of the opposite leg (OPP), and $r$ is the length of the hypotenuse (HYP), then the trigonometric ratios of $\theta$ are

$\sin \theta = \frac{y}{r} = \frac{OPP}{HYP}$   $\csc \theta = \frac{r}{y} = \frac{HYP}{OPP}$

$\cos \theta = \frac{x}{r} = \frac{ADJ}{HYP}$   $\sec \theta = \frac{r}{x} = \frac{HYP}{ADJ}$

$\tan \theta = \frac{y}{x} = \frac{OPP}{ADJ}$   $\cot \theta = \frac{x}{y} = \frac{ADJ}{HYP}$

**Razones trigonométricas (p. 912)** Si $\theta$ es un ángulo agudo de un triángulo, $x$ es la longitud del cateto adyacente (ADJ), $y$ es la longitud del cateto opuesto (OPP) y $r$ es la longitud de la hipotenusa (HYP), entonces las razones trigonométricas son:

$\sin \theta = \frac{y}{r} = \frac{OPP}{HYP}$   $\csc \theta = \frac{r}{y} = \frac{HYP}{OPP}$

$\cos \theta = \frac{x}{r} = \frac{ADJ}{HYP}$   $\sec \theta = \frac{r}{x} = \frac{HYP}{ADJ}$

$\tan \theta = \frac{y}{x} = \frac{OPP}{ADJ}$   $\cot \theta = \frac{x}{y} = \frac{ADJ}{HYP}$

Example

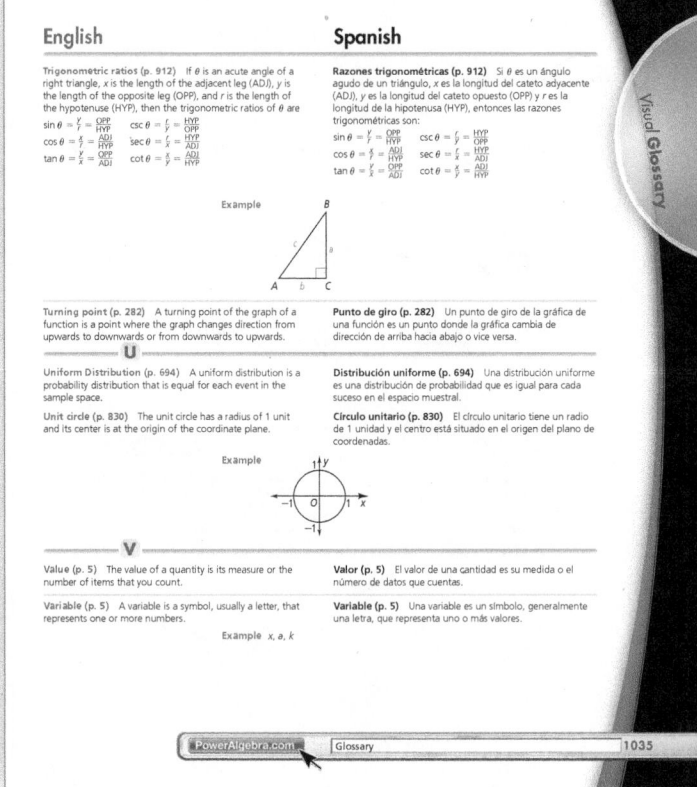

**Turning point (p. 282)** A turning point of the graph of a function is a point where the graph changes direction from upwards to downwards or from downwards to upwards.

**Punto de giro (p. 282)** Un punto de giro de la gráfica de una función es un punto donde la gráfica cambia de dirección de arriba hacia abajo o vice versa.

**Uniform Distribution (p. 694)** A uniform distribution is a probability distribution that is equal for each event in the sample space.

**Distribución uniforme (p. 694)** Una distribución uniforme es una distribución de probabilidad que es igual para cada suceso en el espacio muestral.

**Unit circle (p. 830)** The unit circle has a radius of 1 unit and its center is at the origin of the coordinate plane.

**Círculo unitario (p. 830)** El círculo unitario tiene un radio de 1 unidad y el centro está situado en el origen del plano de coordenadas.

Example

**V**

**Value (p. 5)** The value of a quantity is its measure or the number of items that you count.

**Valor (p. 5)** El valor de una cantidad es su medida o el número de datos que cuentas.

**Variable (p. 5)** A variable is a symbol, usually a letter, that represents one or more numbers.

**Variable (p. 5)** Una variable es un símbolo, generalmente una letra, que representa uno o más valores.

Example $x, a, k$

---

**Variable matrix (p. 785)** When representing a system of equations with a matrix equation, the matrix containing the variables of the system is the variable matrix.

**Matriz variable (p. 785)** Al representar un sistema de ecuaciones con una ecuación de matricial, la matriz que contenga las variables del sistema es la matriz variable.

Example $\begin{cases} x + 2y = 5 \\ 3x + 5y = 14 \end{cases}$

variable matrix $\begin{bmatrix} X \\ Y \end{bmatrix}$

**Variable quantity (p. 5)** A variable quantity can have values that vary.

**Cantidad variable (p. 5)** Una cantidad variable puede tener valores que varían.

**Variance (p. 712)** Variance is the square of the standard deviation. $\sigma^2 = \frac{\Sigma(x - \bar{x})^2}{n}$

**Varianza (p. 712)** La varianza es el cuadrado de la desviación estándar. $\sigma^2 = \frac{\Sigma(x - \bar{x})^2}{n}$

**Vector (p. 801)** A vector is a mathematical object that has both magnitude and direction.

**Vector (p. 801)** Un vector es un objeto matemático que tiene tanto magnitud como dirección.

**Vertex (p. 107)** A vertex of a function is a point where the function reaches a maximum or a minimum value.

**Vértice (p. 107)** El vértice de una función es el punto donde la función alcanza un valor máximo o mínimo.

**Vertex form of a quadratic function (p. 194)** The vertex form of a quadratic function is $f(x) = a(x - h)^2 + k$, where $a \neq 0$ and $(h, k)$ is the coordinate of the vertex of the function.

**Forma del vértice de una función cuadrática (p. 194)** La forma vértice de una función cuadrática es $f(x) = a(x - h)^2 + k$, donde $a \neq 0$ y $(h, k)$ es la coordenada del vértice de la función.

Example $f(x) = x^2 + 2x - 1 = (x + 1)^2 - 2$
The vertex is $(-1, -2)$.

**Vertex of a parabola (p. 194)** The vertex of a parabola is the point where the function for the parabola reaches a maximum or a minimum value. The parabola intersects its axis of symmetry at the vertex.

**Vértice de una parábola (p. 194)** El vértice de una parábola es el punto donde la función de la parábola alcanza un valor máximo o mínimo. La parábola y su eje de simetría se intersecan en el vértice.

Example

The vertex of the quadratic function $y = x^2 + 2x - 1$ is $(-1, -2)$.

**Vertical compression (p. 102)** A vertical compression reduces all $y$-values of a function by the same factor between 0 and 1.

**Compresión vertical (p. 102)** Una compresión vertical reduce todos los valores de $y$ de una función por el mismo factor entre 0 y 1.

**Vertical stretch (p. 102)** A vertical stretch multiplies all $y$-values of a function by the same factor greater than 1.

**Estiramiento vertical (p. 102)** Un estiramiento vertical multiplica todos los valores de $y$ por el mismo factor mayor que 1.

---

**Vertical-line test (p. 62)** You can use the vertical-line test on the graph of a relation to tell whether the relation is a function. If a vertical line passes through more than one point on the graph of a relation, then the relation is *not* a function.

**Prueba de la recta vertical (p. 62)** Puedes usar la prueba de la línea vertical en la gráfica de una relación para saber si la relación es una función. Si una línea vertical pasa por más de un punto de la gráfica de la relación, entonces la relación no es una función.

Example

This relation is not a function.

**Vertices of a hyperbola (p. 646)** The endpoints of the transverse axis of a hyperbola are the vertices of the hyperbola.

**Vértices de una hipérbola (p. 646)** Los dos puntos de intersección de la hipérbola y su eje mayor son los vértices de la hipérbola.

Example

**Vertices of an ellipse (p. 639)** The endpoints of the major axis of an ellipse are the vertices of the ellipse.

**Vértices de una elipse (p. 639)** Los dos puntos de intersección de la elipse y su eje mayor son los vértices de la elipse.

Example

**X**

**$x$-intercept, $y$-intercept (p. 76)** The point at which a line crosses the $x$-axis (or the $x$-coordinate of that point) is an $x$-intercept. The point at which a line crosses the $y$-axis (or the $y$-coordinate of that point) is a $y$-intercept.

**Intercepto en $x$, intercepto en $y$ (p. 76)** El punto donde una recta corta el eje $x$ (o la coordenada $x$ de ese punto) es el intercepto en $x$. El punto donde una recta cruza el eje $y$ (o la coordenada $y$ de ese punto) es el intercepto en $y$.

Example

The $x$-intercept of $y = 2x + 1$ is $\left(-\frac{1}{2}, 0\right)$ or $-\frac{1}{2}$.

The $y$-intercept of $y = 2x + 1$ is $(0, 1)$ or 1.

**Zero matrix (p. 758)**   The zero matrix $O$, or $O_{m \times n}$, is the $m \times n$ matrix whose elements are all zeros. It is the additive identity matrix for the set of all $m \times n$ matrices.

Example $\begin{bmatrix} 1 & 4 \\ 2 & -3 \end{bmatrix} + O = \begin{bmatrix} 1 & 4 \\ 2 & -3 \end{bmatrix}$

**Matriz cero (p. 758)**   La matriz cero, $O$, o $O_{m \times n}$, es la matriz $m \times n$ cuyos elementos son todos ceros. Es la matriz de identidad aditiva para el conjunto de todas las matrices $m \times n$.

**Zero of a function (p. 226)**   A zero of a function $f(x)$ is any value of $x$ for which $f(x) = 0$.

Example

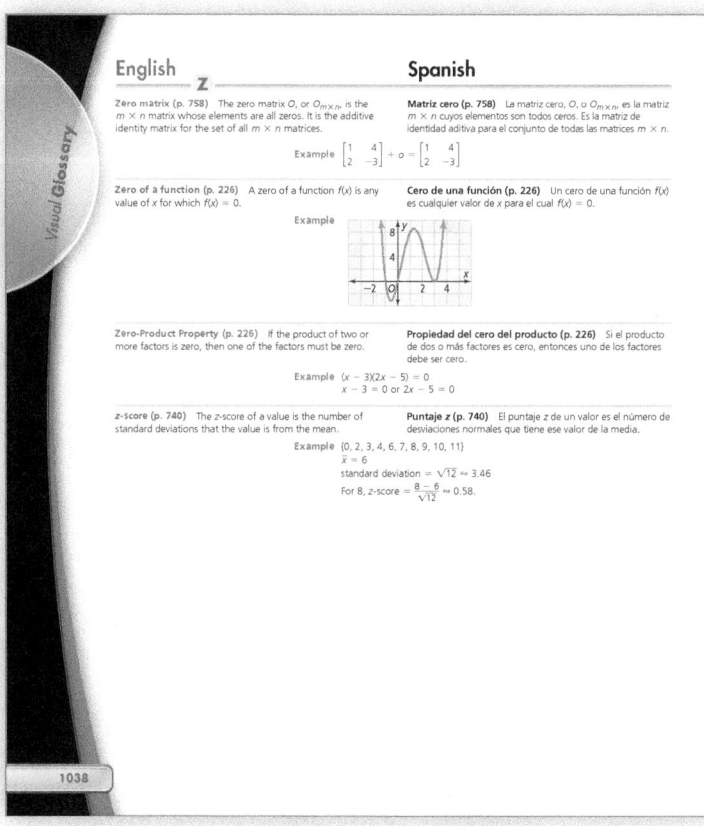

**Cero de una función (p. 226)**   Un cero de una función $f(x)$ es cualquier valor de $x$ para el cual $f(x) = 0$.

**Zero-Product Property (p. 226)**   If the product of two or more factors is zero, then one of the factors must be zero.

Example $(x - 3)(2x - 5) = 0$
$x - 3 = 0$ or $2x - 5 = 0$

**Propiedad del cero del producto (p. 226)**   Si el producto de dos o más factores es cero, entonces uno de los factores debe ser cero.

**z-score (p. 740)**   The z-score of a value is the number of standard deviations that the value is from the mean.

Example $\{0, 2, 3, 4, 6, 7, 8, 9, 10, 11\}$
$\bar{x} = 6$
standard deviation $= \sqrt{12} \approx 3.46$
For 8, z-score $= \frac{8 - 6}{\sqrt{12}} \approx 0.58$.

**Puntaje z (p. 740)**   El puntaje z de un valor es el número de desviaciones normales que tiene ese valor de la media.

## *Selected* **Answers**

### Chapter 1

**Get Ready! pp. 1** **1.** 0 **2.** −2 **3.** −2.09 **4.** 8.05
**5.** −$\frac{3}{4}$ **6.** $\frac{11}{12}$ **7.** 10$\frac{7}{12}$ **8.** 3$\frac{1}{2}$ **9.** −42 **10.** 72 **11.** 9
**12.** −9.8 **13.** −3$\frac{1}{4}$ **14.** −5$\frac{1}{2}$ **15.** −4$\frac{2}{3}$ **16.** −$\frac{3}{4}$
**17.** −21 **18.** 7.35 **19.** −$\frac{1}{6}$ **20.** −$\frac{3}{8}$ **21.** −20 **22.** 8
**23.** 0.97 **24.** −5 **25.** 55 **26.** 3 **27.** because the
placement of the parentheses changes the order of
operations **28.** 3 **29.** 3 terms **30.** Calculate the answer
numerically. **31.** $\frac{3}{n-3}$

### Lesson 1-1      pp. 4–10

**Got It? 1.** The pattern shows a center
square and a yellow square added to
each side with the number of squares
per side increasing by one.

**2.** 52 tiles **3. a.** $12 **b.** $20 **c.** The
number of platys must be a whole number whereas the
length of fish can be a fraction or a decimal.
**Lesson Check 1.** add 35 **2.** rotate 90° clockwise
**3.**

| Input | Process Column | Output |
|---|---|---|
| 1 | 2(1) | 2 |
| 2 | 2(2) | 4 |
| 3 | 2(3) | 6 |
| 4 | 2(4) | 8 |
| n | 2(n) | 2n |

**4.**

| Input | Process Column | Output |
|---|---|---|
| 1 | 3(1) | 3 |
| 2 | 3(2) | 6 |
| 3 | 3(3) | 9 |
| 4 | 3(4) | 12 |
| n | 3(n) | 3n |

**5.** Answers may vary. Sample: Look for the same type of
change between consecutive figures.
**6.** Answers may vary. Sample: Tables of values and
pictorial representations are both convenient ways to
organize data and discover patterns. Tables give more

detail. Pictorial representations are visual. **7.** No; the
output is $\frac{1}{2}$ the input for all values except the first (Input:
3; Output: 2).
**Exercises 9.** Base of 3 squares with the number
of squares increasing vertically by one on each of
the outer squares of the base.

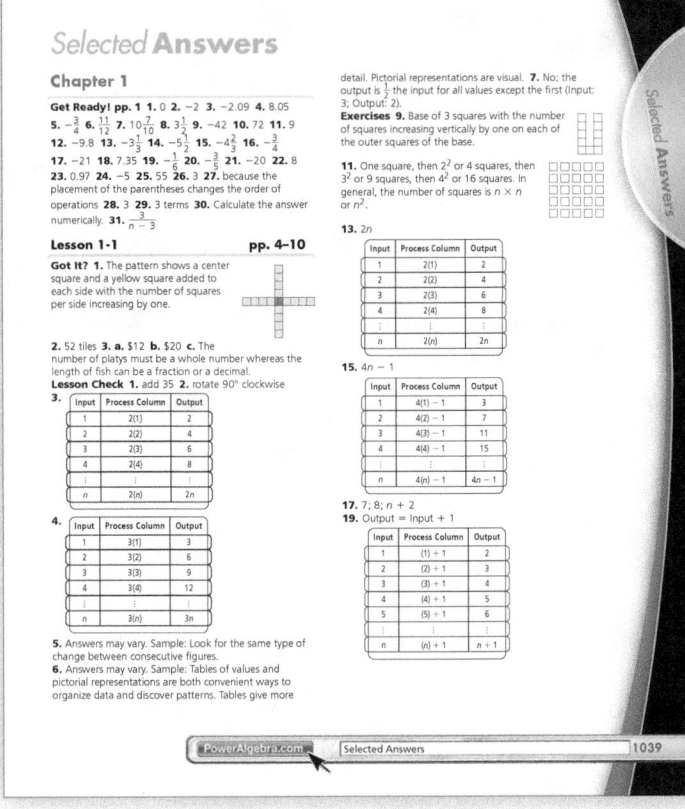

**11.** One square, then $2^2$ or 4 squares, then
$3^2$ or 9 squares, then $4^2$ or 16 squares. In
general, the number of squares is $n \times n$
or $n^2$.

**13.** 2n

| Input | Process Column | Output |
|---|---|---|
| 1 | 2(1) | 2 |
| 2 | 2(2) | 4 |
| 3 | 2(3) | 6 |
| 4 | 2(4) | 8 |
| n | 2(n) | 2n |

**15.** 4n − 1

| Input | Process Column | Output |
|---|---|---|
| 1 | 4(1) − 1 | 3 |
| 2 | 4(2) − 1 | 7 |
| 3 | 4(3) − 1 | 11 |
| 4 | 4(4) − 1 | 15 |
| n | 4(n) − 1 | 4n − 1 |

**17.** 7; 8; n + 2
**19.** Output = Input + 1

| Input | Process Column | Output |
|---|---|---|
| 1 | (1) + 1 | 2 |
| 2 | (2) + 1 | 3 |
| 3 | (3) + 1 | 4 |
| 4 | (4) + 1 | 5 |
| 5 | (5) + 1 | 6 |
| n | (n) + 1 | n + 1 |

---

**21.** Output = Input − 1

| Input | Process Column | Output |
|---|---|---|
| 1 | (1) − 1 | 0 |
| 2 | (2) − 1 | 1 |
| 3 | (3) − 1 | 2 |
| 4 | (4) − 1 | 3 |
| 5 | (5) − 1 | 4 |
| n | (n) − 1 | n − 1 |

**23.** 40 **25.** add 6 or 6n; 30, 36, 42 **27.** add 3, then add
4, then add 5, and so on; 21, 28, 36 **29.** multiply by 3;
243, 729, 2187 **31.** The black square and dot each move
clockwise one block
**33.** 9216 in.³ **35.** n + 10, where n is the number of
months **37.** 21; 4n + 1 **39.** −1; 3; −4n; or −4n + 1
**46.** 1.9 **47.** −3.8 **48.** 27 **49.** 0 **50.** −0.4 **51.** 7
**52.** 50% **53.** 25% **54.** 33.33% **55.** 140% **56.** 172%
**57.** 123%

### Lesson 1-2      pp. 11–17

**Got It? 1.** rational numbers
**2.**

**3. a.** $\sqrt{26}$ < 6.25 or 6.25 > $\sqrt{26}$ **b.** a < c; a will be
to the left of c on the number line.
**4. a.** Distr. Prop.
  **b.** a + [3 + (−a)]
    = a + [(−a) + 3]    Comm.
    = [a + (−a)] + 3    Assoc.
    = 0 + 3    Inverse
    = 3    Identity
**Lesson Check 1.** Answers may vary. Sample: the
number of times a cricket chirps **2.** Answers may vary.
Sample: the change in number of people on a bus after
a stop **3.** Answers may vary. Sample: the outdoor
temperature in tenths of a degree **4.** Inv. Prop. of Add.
**5.** Assoc. Prop. of Mult. **6.** multiplicative inverse **7.** Both
properties result in the original term; 0 is the additive
identity, whereas 1 is the multiplicative identity. **8.** The
equation illustrates the Comm. Prop. of Add. **9.** Answers
may vary. Sample: $\sqrt{2}$ is not a rational number because it
cannot be written as a quotient of integers.
**Exercises 11.** y, natural numbers; p, rational numbers
**13.**

**15.**

**17.**

**19.**

**21.**

**23.** > **25.** < **27.** > **29.** > **31.** > **33.** <
**35.** Distr. Prop. **37.** Assoc. Prop. of Mult. **39.** Ident.
Prop. of Add. **41–48.** Answers may vary. Samples are
given. **41.** −5 **43.** −1$\frac{1}{4}$ **45.** 1$\frac{2}{3}$ **47.** 4 **49.** $\sqrt{50}$ in. ×
$\sqrt{50}$ in. × $\sqrt{50}$ in. **51.** natural numbers **53.** irrational
numbers **55.** irrational numbers **57.** 8, 1, $\frac{1}{3}$, −$\sqrt{2}$, −3
**59.** 5.73, $\frac{1}{4}$, −0.06, −3$\sqrt{3}$, −17 **61.** Answers may vary.
Sample: 7 **63.** Answers may vary. Sample: $\sqrt{2}$ and
$\sqrt{2}$ **75.** add 4; 20, 24, 28 **76.** add 1; 12, 13, 14
**77.** add 1; 0, 1, 2 **78.** 2$\frac{1}{4}$ **79.** 11$\frac{5}{6}$ **80.** 1$\frac{1}{2}$
**81.** 5 **82.** 38 **83.** 15

### Lesson 1-3      pp. 18–24

**Got It? 1.** H **2.** 150 − 2d, with d = the number of
days **3. a.** 18 **b.** Yes; the numerator will become
$2x^2 − y^2$, not $2x^2 − 2y^2$. **4.** Let x = the number of
two-point shots, y = the number of three-point shots,
z = the number of one-point free throws,
2x + 3y + 1z; 42 points **5. a.** −3$j^2$ − 7k + 5j
**b.** 12a − 53b
**Lesson Check 1.** $\frac{2+b}{3}$ **2.** 4k + m **3.** 12 **4.** 13
**5.** −5 **6.** −5 **7.** The student did not distribute the −1.
$3p^2q + 2p − (5q + p − 2p^2q) = 3p^2q + 2p −$
$5q − p + 2p^2q = 5p^2q + p − 5q$ **8.** A constant is a
term with no variables, whereas a coefficient is the
numerical factor in a term. **9.** Answers may vary. Sample:
Both algebraic expressions and numerical expressions
represent a quantity using numbers, operations and
grouping symbols. An algebraic expression includes
variables when representing a quantity. Examples:
numerical expression: 3 + 6(5 − 2); algebraic expression:
2z + 3z(6 + 5z).
**Exercises 11.** 8(x + 3) **13.** 130 − 10w, with w =
number of weeks **15.** 250 − 60w, with w = number of
weeks **17.** −16 **19.** −12 **21.** 4 ft **23.** 1600 ft
**25.** $1331 **27.** $1610.51 **29.** Let x = the number of
3-run home runs and y = the number of 2-run hits;
3x + 2y; 14 **31.** 2s + 5 **33.** 6a + 3b **35.** −0.5x
**37.** 4g − 2 **39.** 3 **41.** 37 **43.** 10 **45.** $\frac{$84}{m}$ **47.** $\frac{5x^2}{2}$
**49.** y **51.** −2$x^3$ + 2$y^2$ **53.** 8.5x − 15 **55.** No; John
did not use the opposite of a sum correctly; −(x + y) +
3(x − 4y); −x − y + 3x − 12y; 2x − 13y **57.** Distr.
Prop. **59.** Opposite of a Difference **67.** −1.5, −$\sqrt{2}$,
−1.4, −0.5 **68.** −$\frac{5}{6}$, −$\frac{3}{4}$, −$\frac{3}{8}$, $\frac{1}{2}$ **69.** −20, 0.2, $\frac{1}{2}$, $\sqrt{2}$
**70.** −3, −0.5, −$\frac{1}{4}$, $\frac{3}{4}$ **71.** 7x − 4 **72.** −p − $\frac{2q}{3}$
**73.** 2b − 28 **74.** 2k − 2m

---

### Lesson 1-4      pp. 26–32

**Got It? 1.** $\frac{3}{2}$ **2.** −1 **3.** 40 m × 120 m **4. a.** never
**b.** always **5. a.** C = K − 273 **b.** always
**Lesson Check 1.** 23.2 **2.** −90 **3.** 12
**4.** k = $\frac{1}{2}$(r − 15) **5.** k = $\frac{1}{3}$(z + 6)
**6.** k = −$\frac{1}{6}$(h + 14) **7.** To find a solution of an
equation means to find the value of the variable that
makes the equation true. **8.** Four buses are not enough.
The number of buses must be a whole number, so round
the number of buses to 5. **9.** The 2nd line is incorrect;
subtract 10 from both sides: 12x = −12 x = −1
**Exercises 11.** −81 **13.** 14 **15.** 8 **17.** −5
**19.** −$\frac{1}{3}$ **21.** $\frac{3}{2}$ **23.** −5 **27.** 300 mi/h; 600 mi/h
**29.** sometimes **31.** sometimes **33.** h = $\frac{2A}{b}$ **35.** w = $\frac{V}{\ell h}$
**37.** x = $\frac{c}{a-b}$, a ≠ b **39.** x = 2(m + n) + 2 **41.** 1.5
**43.** $\frac{23}{4}$, or 7$\frac{5}{8}$ **45.** 34° and 56° **47.** $b_2$ = $\frac{2A}{h}$ − $b_1$
**49.** x = $\frac{h + 5t^2}{t}$ **51.** $r_2$ = $\frac{Rr_1}{r_1 - R}$ **53.** 40°, 140°
**55.** x = $\frac{3b + 2c - 5}{b - c}$, $\frac{b^2}{c}$ ≠ a **57.** x = $\frac{4a - 3bc}{aq - 5bp}$, 5bp ≠ aq
**59.** x = $\frac{10c}{a}$, a ≠ 0 **61.** Let c = number of swim days;
3c = 82 + c; 41 days **63.** No; n = $\frac{1}{n-5}$, not $\frac{1}{n-5}$
**70.** −7 **71.** −$\frac{16}{5}$ **72.** −20 **73.** −1 **74.** x + 5
**75.** 16x **76.** 3(12 − x) **77.** true **78.** false **79.** true

### Lesson 1-5      pp. 33–40

**Got It? 1.** $\frac{x}{8}$ ≤ 15
**2.** x ≤ −8

**3.** more than 32 songs **4.** always
**5. a.** x ≥ 2 and x < 6

**b.** sometimes; The compound inequality is true when
x = 5 and not true when x = 7.
**6. a.** w < −3 or w > $\frac{9}{7}$

**b.** x < −1 or x > 3

**Lesson Check 1.** R ≥ J **2.** w ≥ 40 and w < 74
**3.** x ≤ −2

**4.** 1 < x < $\frac{9}{2}$

**5.** x ≤ 0 or x > 3

**6.** Answers may vary. Sample: 5 < 6, but −5 > −6.
**7.** The transitive, addition and subtraction properties of
inequality are similar to the properties of equality. The
multiplication and division properties differ. Multiplying or
dividing each side of an inequality by a negative number
reverses the direction of the inequality symbol.
**8.** Answers may vary. Sample: 3x + 5 < 3(x + 5)
**9.** No; Answers may vary. Sample: 2x < x + 1 and
x + 1 > 3
**Exercises 11.** 8x ≥ 25 **13.** $\frac{x}{12}$ ≤ 6
**15.** k > −9

**17.** t ≤ 11

**19.** x ≤ −6

**21.** m < 10

**23.** w > 6

**25.** The longest side is less than 21 cm. **27.** at most 40
students **29.** always **31.** never **33.** sometimes
**35.** sometimes
**37.** −4 ≤ x ≤ 2

**39.** −5 < x ≤ 6

**41.** all real numbers

**43.** x ≤ −3 or x ≥ 9

**45.** z ≥ 6

**47.** x ≥ −48

**49.** no solution **51.** 98 **53.** 2 < AB < 6 **55.** The
classmate reversed the direction of the ≥ symbol to ≤
incorrectly. The correct answer is y ≤ −20. **57.** Distr.
Prop.; arithmetic; Subtr. Prop. of Inequality; Mult. Prop. of
Inequality

**59.** $-1 < x < 8$

**61.** $x < -2$ or $x > 2$

**71.** $7a + 5$ **72.** $-2x + 14y$ **73.** $\frac{b}{3} + 1$ **74.** $1.61 - 0.1k$ **75.** 4 **76.** no solution **77.** $\frac{9}{10}$ **78.** $-20$

### Lesson 1-6    pp. 41–48
**Got It?**
**1.** $\frac{2}{3}$, $-2$

**2.** $-7$, $-11$

**3.** $-1$ **4.** $-\frac{4}{3} \le x \le 4$

**5. a.** $x < -5$ or $x > 1$

**b.** The graph will have two closed circles with an arrow extending to the left of one and to the right of the other. **6.** $|h - 52.5| \le 0.5$
**Lesson Check 1.** $-4, 4$ **2.** $-12, 4$ **3.** $-\frac{6}{5}$
**4.** $-11 < x < 9$

**5.** $x \le -1$ or $x \ge 4$

**6.** A solution of an eq. is extraneous if it is a solution to a derived eq., but is not a solution to the original eq. **7.** when the number is positive or 0 **8.** Answers may vary. Sample: $d < -5$ and $5d > 25$ **9.** Answers may vary. Sample: An absolute value equation or inequality represents two equations or inequalities; each equation or inequality is solved in the same manner as a linear equation or inequality.
**Exercises 11.** $-8, 8$ **13.** $-\frac{5}{3}$ **15.** no solution
**17.** $-7, 17$ **19.** $-\frac{3}{2}, \frac{3}{2}$ **21.** $\frac{3}{2}, -1$ **23.** $-1, \frac{1}{2}$
**25.** $0 < y < 18$

**27.** $-2 < x < 6$

**29.** $-3\frac{1}{2} \le w \le \frac{1}{2}$

**31.** $x < -12$ or $x > 6$

**33.** $y \le -9$ or $y \ge 15$

**35.** $x \le -3$ or $x \ge 4$

**37.** $|h - 1.4| \le 0.1$ **39.** $|C - 27.5| \le 0.25$
**41.** $|m - 1250| \le 50$ **43.** no solution **45.** $-\frac{14}{3}, \frac{16}{3}$
**47.** no solution **49.** $-\frac{1}{3}, 1$ **51.** $-\frac{71}{36}$ **53.** $|c - 28.75| \le 0.25$; 0.25; $28.50 \le c \le 29.00$ **55.** $|x| < 4$
**57.** $-6 \le x \le 8\frac{2}{3}$

**59.** all real numbers

**61.** all real numbers

**63.** $x \le -8.4$ or $x \ge 9.6$

**65.** $-5 < x < 11$

**67.** The graph of $|x| < a$ is the set of all points on the number line that lie between $a$ and $-a$. The graph of $|x| > a$ has two parts; the left part consists of the points to the left of $-a$, and the right part consists of the points to the right of $a$. **69.** $|t - 350| \le 5$ **71.** $|t - 15| \le 30$ **73.** $|x - 9.55| \le 0.02$; $9.53 \le x \le 9.57$ **75.** never; absolute value is nonnegative **77.** sometimes; $|5| = 5$ but $|-5| \ne -5$ **79.** sometimes; $|-4 + 2| \ne -4 + 2$ **81.** The "3" in the second set of equations should be "$-3$."
$-4x + 1 < -3$
$-4x < -4$
$x > 1$ not $x > -\frac{1}{2}$
**94.** $y < 6$

**95.** $s < \frac{2}{15}$

**96.** $a > 4$

**97.** Each figure has 4 more squares than the previous figure.

**98.** Each figure $n$ has $n$ more circles than the previous figure.

**99.** **100.** **101.** **102.**

### Chapter Review    pp. 50–52
**1.** solution of the equation **2.** absolute value **3.** reciprocal **4.** compound inequality **5.** add 5; 25, 30, 35 **6.** add 1; 7, 8, 9 **7.** 1; $n + 8$ **8.** 76; 19n **9.** \$20n **10.** irrational numbers **11.** rational numbers, integers **12.** rational numbers, integers, whole numbers, natural number **13.** real numbers, rational numbers **14.** $-\sqrt{60} > -8$ or $-8 < -\sqrt{60}$ **15.** $5 < \sqrt{32}$ or $\sqrt{32} > 5$ **16.** Inv. Prop. of Mult. **17.** Assoc. Prop. of Mult. **18.** 114 **19.** 5b **20.** 11 **21.** 6
**22.** $z \le \frac{5}{2}$

**23.** $x > 2$

**24.** no solution
**25.** $x \le \frac{3}{2}$ or $x > 6$

**26.** 10 cm, 6 cm **27.** 1 **28.** no solution **29.** $x = -8$ or $x = -12$ **30.** no solution
**31.** $-\frac{1}{3} \le x \le \frac{5}{3}$

**32.** $y < 0$ or $y > 18$

**33.** $-\frac{18}{7} \le x \le \frac{18}{7}$

**34.** $x < -14$ or $x > 10$

**35.** $|x - 43.6| \le 0.1$

### Chapter 2
**Get Ready! p. 57 1.** 6s **2.** $4a + b$ **3.** $xy - y + x$ **4.** 1.5g **5.** 0 **6.** $3b - 2c - 2$ **7.** $6f - 5d$ **8.** $3h + 3g$ **9.** $-2z + 5$ **10.** $2g - 4dg - 12d$ **11.** $8v - 6$ **12.** $7t - 3st - 5s$ **13.** $-56$ **14.** 80 **15.** $-10$ **16.** $-24$ **17.** 1075 **18.** 5 **19.** $-1.75$ **20.** 1.5 **21.** 20 **22.** 2 **23.** 5 **24.** 4 **25.** $-2 < x < 8$
**26.** $a \le 0$

**27.** $x > -1$

**28.** $x < -4$ or $x > \frac{10}{3}$

**29.** $-\frac{1}{3} \le d \le \frac{25}{4}$

**30.** $-24 \le f \le 18$

**31.** Answers may vary. Sample: the Civil War, the Great Depression, the Louisiana Purchase **32.** Answers may vary. Sample: From 1 to 2 years of age, a person has usually stopped growing by age 30, but a baby is still growing at age 1. **33.** Answers may vary. Sample: The image is a reflection, left to right, of what other people see; the size is the same. **34.** Answers may vary. Sample: An inequality determines the limit of a value, or a boundary, for the solution on the number line.

### Lesson 2-1    pp. 60–67
**Got It?**
**1.** Let Jan = 1, Feb = 2, Mar = 3, and Apr = 4.

Input → Output
1 → 69
2 → 70
3 → 75
4 → 78

{(1, 69), (2, 70), (3, 75), (4, 78)}

| Month | Temperature (°F) |
| --- | --- |
| 1 | 69 |
| 2 | 70 |
| 3 | 75 |
| 4 | 78 |

**2.** domain: {−3, 0, 2, 9, 23}, range: {−99, −18, 0, 7, 14} **3. a.** no **b.** yes **c.** In a mapping diagram for a relation that is not a function, there is at least one element in the domain that has more than one arrow originating from it. In a mapping diagram for a function, each element in the domain has at most one arrow originating from it. **4.** b and c **5. a.** 9 **b.** 1 **c.** −19 **6.** Let $x$ = number of bottles purchased and $C$ = total cost; $C(x) = 1.19x$; \$17.85
**Lesson Check 1.** domain: {0, 3, 4}, range: {−2, 1, 2, 4} **2.** domain: {−4, −3, 0, 4}, range: {−4, −3, 0, 4} **3.** no **4.** yes **5.** Yes; a relation is any set of pairs of input and output values. No; a function is a relation in which each element of the domain is paired with exactly one element of the range. **6.** Every vertical line does not need to intersect a function. Rewrite as: "In a function, every vertical line must intersect the graph in at most one point." **7.** A horizontal-line test checks the pairing of one element of the range with one or more elements of the domain. A function can have a pairing of one element of the range with one or more elements of the domain. A horizontal-line test cannot determine whether a relation is a function.
**Exercises 9.** domain: {1, 2, 3, 4, 5, 6}, range: {6, 7, 8, 9, 11} **11.** yes **13.** yes **15.** yes **17.** 71; (4, 71) **19.** −15; (9, −15) **21.** −2; (3, −2) **23.** −132; (−11, −132) **25.** $C(m) = 4.52 + 0.12m$; \$34.52 **27.** 13.5 cm² **29.** domain: all numbers, range: $y \ge 0$; yes **31.** ≈4849 cm³ **33. a.** 109.4 **b.** 10.4 **c.** −11.1 **d.** −7.2 **44.** $-\frac{2}{3}, -\frac{21}{2}$ **45.** −13, 15
**46.** $x > -3$ **47.** $x \le \frac{3}{4}$ **48.** $-\frac{4}{3} < x < \frac{3}{2}$ **49.** $x \ge -3$
**50.** $\frac{1}{8}x$ **51.** $-\frac{1}{3}x$ **52.** 20x

### Lesson 2-2    pp. 68–73
**Got It? 1. a.** yes; $-7, y = -7x$ **b.** no **2. a.** yes; $-\frac{5}{3}$
**b.** yes; $\frac{1}{9}$ **3.** 60 **4. a.** 280 **b.** No; if $y^2 = kx^2$, then $y = \pm\sqrt{kx}$. So, $\frac{y}{x}$ could be $+\sqrt{k}$ for one pair of values and $-\sqrt{k}$ for another pair. Then $y$ would not vary directly with $x$.

**5. a.** **b.**
**Lesson Check 1.** $y = -\frac{1}{2}x$ **2.** $\frac{2}{3}$ **3.** $\frac{5}{2}$ **4.** Answers may vary. Sample: Two variables are directly related when the ratio of the output to the input is a constant value. **5.** For a direct variation, $y = kx$ where $k$ is the constant of variation. If $x = 0$, then $y = 0$ and the graph of $y = kx$ passes through the origin. **6.** Answers may vary. Sample: $y = -8x$.
**Exercises 7.** yes; 7, $y = 7x$ **9.** no **11.** yes; 12 **13.** yes; −15 **17.** yes; 6 **19.** −3 **21.** $\frac{7}{9}$ **23.** 21
**25.** 4 min **27.** [table]
**29.** [table and graph]
**31.** yes; $k = \frac{2}{3}$; $y = \frac{2}{3}x$ **33.** no
**35.** $y = 2x$ **37.** $y = -4.5x$
**39.** $y = \frac{2}{3}x$ **41.** $y = \frac{2}{7}x$
**43.** 0.625 **45.** 0.225 **47.** First, it does not say that $y$ varies directly with $x$. Second, every direct variation includes the point (0, 0), so $x$ cannot be determined because $k$ could be any value.
**49.** Answers may vary. Sample: $y = 3.2x$
**51.** Answers may vary. Sample: If $y$ varies directly with $x^2$, and $y = 2$ when $x = 4$, then $y = \frac{81}{8}$ when $x = 9$. **53.** $c = 0$, $a \ne 0$, $b \ne 0$

**62.** domain: {−2, 0, 1, 3}; range: {−3, 1}
**63.** domain: {4, 7}; range: {−1, 0}
**64.** domain: {1, 2, 4, 5}; range: {−2, −1, 1, 2}
**65.** domain: {1, 2, 3, 4}; range: {7, 8, 9, 10}

**66.** 8n; 40, 48, 56 **67.** $7 - 2n$; −3, −5, −7 **68.** $12(13 - n)$; 96, 84, 72 **69.** $15(n + 1)$; 90, 105, 120 **70.** $\frac{3}{2}$; 7; $\frac{1}{2}$ **71.** −2; −2; −1.4; 0.4 **72.** −5; 1; 4; 13 **73.** −9; −8; −7.5; −6

### Lesson 2-3    pp. 74–80
**Got It? 1. a.** −1 **b.** 1 **c.** undefined **d.** $\frac{1 - 4}{8 - 5} = \frac{-3}{3} = -1$ **e.** $\frac{4 - 1}{5 - 8} = \frac{3}{-3} = -1$ **2. a.** $y = 6x + 5$
**b.** $y = -\frac{1}{2}x - 3$ **c.** No; any two points on a line can be used to calculate the slope. **3. a.** $y = -\frac{3}{2}x + 9$; $-\frac{3}{2}$; (0, 9)
**b.** $y = -\frac{7}{5}x - 7$; $-\frac{7}{5}$; (0, −7)
**4.** $y = \frac{4}{3}x - 2$

**Lesson Check 1.** $y = \frac{1}{3}x + 1$ **2.** $y = \frac{4}{3}x + \frac{1}{3}$ **3.** −1 **4.** 1 **5.** The y-intercept of a line is the point at which the line crosses the y-axis. The x-intercept is the point at which the line crosses the x-axis. **6.** Since division by zero is undefined, the slope of a vertical line that passes through $(a, b)$ and $(a, c)$, $\frac{c - b}{0}$, is undefined. **7.** She subtracted the x-coordinates in the wrong order. The x- and y-coordinates of each point must be subtracted consistently.
**Exercises 9.** −2 **11.** $\frac{4}{11}$ **13.** 1 **15.** 0 **17.** $y = 3x + 2$ **19.** $y = \frac{5}{4}x + 12$ **21.** $y = -5x - 7$ **23.** $y = \frac{3}{2}x + \frac{3}{2}$, $\left(0, \frac{3}{2}\right)$ **25.** $y = -\frac{4}{3}x + \frac{5}{6}$, $\left(0, \frac{5}{6}\right)$ **27.** $y = 7$; 0, (0, 7)

**29.** **31.** **33.** **35.** **37.** **39.** **41.** **43.** **45.**

**47.** 0; (0, 3) **49.** $-\frac{1}{4}$; (0, 3) **51.** undefined slope; no y-intercept **53.** $-\frac{1}{2}$; $\left(0, -\frac{5}{2}\right)$ **55.** $-\frac{1}{8}$; $\left(0, \frac{5}{6}\right)$ **57. a.** 1 **b.** 1 **c.** 1 **d.** 1 **e.** Any two points on a line can be used to find the slope of the line. **59.** $-\frac{5}{3}$ **61.** $\frac{15}{2}$
**67.** domain: {−2, 1, 2, 3, 4}; range: {−2, −1, 2, 3}; no **68.** domain: all real numbers, range: $y \ge -2$; no **69.** domain: {−5, 0, 2, 9}, range: {−3, −1, 5, 15}; no **70.** 2 **71.** 8 **72.** 13

### Lesson 2-4    pp. 81–88
**Got It? 1.** $y + 1 = -3(x - 7)$ **2. a.** $y - 7 = \frac{7}{6}x$
**b.** $y = \frac{1}{6}(x + 5)$. Either point can be used to put the equation of the line in point-slope form. **3.** $-91x + 10y = 36$

**4.** $(0, -2), (4, 0)$;

**5. a.**

Packs of Paper Left

**b.** $7x + 4y = 560$ **c.** 87.5 **6. a.** $y = -2x + 6$
**b.** $y = -\frac{3}{2}x + 6$
**Lesson Check 1.** $y = -3x - 1$ **2.** $y = \frac{1}{2}x + 2$
**3.** $(0, 6), (2, 0)$

**4.** $3x + y = -1$ **5.** $3x + 2y = -9$ **6. a.** point-slope
**b.** slope-intercept **c.** standard **d.** point-slope
**7.** Point-slope form; since the $x$-intercept is the point
where $y$ is zero, you know the point on the line, $(x, 0)$,
and you know the slope. **8.** $-\frac{5}{9}$ **9.** No; one line has a
slope of $-2$ and the other line has a slope of $-\frac{1}{2}$. $-\frac{1}{2}$ is
the reciprocal of $-2$, not the *negative* reciprocal.
**Exercises 11.** $y - 12 = \frac{2}{5}(x - 22)$ **13.** $y + 2 = 0$
**15.** $y - 2 = 5x$ **17.** Answers may vary. Sample:
$y = \frac{5}{3}(x - 1)$ or $y - 5 = \frac{5}{3}(x - 5)$ **19.** Answers may
vary. Sample: $y + 1 = -\frac{4}{3}x$ or $y + 5 = -\frac{4}{3}(x - 3)$
**21.** Answers may vary. Sample: $y - 9 = -\frac{1}{5}(x - 1)$
or $y - 2 = -\frac{1}{5}(x - 6)$ **23.** $7x + y = -9$
**25.** $-42x + 10y = 79$
**27.** $(0, -2), (-5, 0)$ **29.** $(0, 2), \left(\frac{14}{5}, 0\right)$

**31.** $y = -2.5x + 20$

Meal Cards

**33.** $y = \frac{5}{2}x + \frac{17}{2}$ **35.** $y = \frac{1}{3}x + \frac{5}{10}$

**37.** **39.** **41.**

**43.** $y + 4 = \frac{7}{5}(x + 3)$ or $y + 1 = \frac{7}{5}\left(x + \frac{1}{2}\right)$
**45.** $y = \frac{3}{4}x + 3$ **47.** $y = -\frac{3}{2}x - \frac{1}{2}$
**49.** $-1; (0, 1000), (1000, 0)$ **51.** $54; (0, -1), \left(\frac{1}{54}, 0\right)$
**53.** $0; (0, 0)$, all points on $x$-axis
**55.** $y = -1$ **57.** $y = -\frac{3}{4}x - 1$

**66.** domain: $\{-3, -1, 0, 1, 2\}$, range: $\{-2, 0, 2, 4\}$;
yes **67.** domain: all real numbers, range: $\{-2\}$;
yes **68.** domain: $\{-18, -2, 0, 3, 39\}$, range:
$\{-1, 3, 17, 28, 32\}$; yes **69.** Multiplicative Inv. **70.** Distr.
Prop. **71.** Add. Inv., Add. Ident. **72.** $y = 3x - 5$
**73.** $y = \frac{1}{2}x$ **74.** $y = \frac{4}{5}x + 7$ **75.** $y = -\frac{3}{8}x + 12$

**Lesson 2-5** pp. 92–98

**Got It?**
**1. a.** strong negative correlation

Computer Use and Test Scores

**b.** about $170 **2.** Answers may vary. Sample:
$y = 3575x + 19354$
**3.** $y = 0.09x + 2.44$, where 1997 is year 0; $4.96
**Lesson Check**
**1.** strong positive correlation **2.** no correlation

1046

**3.** strong positive correlation

**4.** Plot the data points in a scatter plot to determine the
correlation. The closer the data points fall along a line
with a positive or negative slope, the stronger the
correlation. **5.** No; answers may vary. Sample: A trend
line is determined by using two pts. close to the line
drawn through the data sets of the scatter plot. The line
of best fit is the most accurate of the trend lines because
it uses all the data pts. **6.** The slope of the trend line or
line of best fit is positive for data pts. with positive
correlation and negative for data pts. with negative
correlation. The constant of variation for a direct variation
is positive for data pts. with positive correlation.
**Exercises**
**7.** strong negative correlation

**9.** Answers may vary. Sample: $y = -0.7x - 4$
**11.** Answers may vary. Sample: $y = 4.47x + 33.31$
**13.** 6,055,359 tonnes **15.** positive correlation; no
**17.** positive correlation; yes

**24.** **25.**

**26.**

**27.** $-2x + y = 2$ **28.** $x + y = 0$ **29.** $y = 2$

**30.** **31.**

**32.**

**Lesson 2-6** pp. 99–106

**Got It? 1. a.** Each output for $y = 2x - 3$ is three less
than the corresponding output for $y = 2x$. The graph of
$y = 2x - 3$ is the graph of $y = 2x$ translated down
three units.
**b.**

**2.** $f\left(x + \frac{1}{2}\right)$ **3.** $h(x) = -3x - 3$
**4. a.**

| x | y |
|---|---|
| $-5$ | $\frac{3}{2}$ |
| $-2$ | $\frac{3}{2}$ |
| $0$ | $-1$ |
| $3$ | $\frac{3}{2}$ |
| $5$ | $-\frac{3}{2}$ |

**b.** Sometimes; Answers may vary. Sample: switching the
order of a horizontal translation and a reflection in the
$y$-axis will change the resulting graph, but switching the
order of a horizontal and vert. translation will not.
**5. a.** $g(x) = 2x - 3$ **b.** $g(x) = f(x + 4) - 2$; translated
left 4 units and translated down 2 units
**Lesson Check 1.** translated 6 units up **2.** compressed
vertically by a factor of 0.25 **3.** translated 4 units to the rt.
**4.** reflected over $y$-axis

**5.** translated 1 unit to the left and 2 units down

**6.** stretched vertically by a factor of 2
and translated 1 unit up
**7.** $g(x)$ is the graph of $h(x)$ translated 2 units up

**8.** Answers may vary. Sample: $f(x) = x$, $f(x - 2) =
f(x) - 2$ **9.** $f(x) = -x - 2$; $g(x) = f(-x) = x - 2$
**Exercises**
**11.** The function is $y = x$ translated 4.5 units up.

**13.**

| x | $f(x) + 3$ |
|---|---|
| $-2$ | 6 |
| 0 | 4 |
| 1 | 1 |
| 3 | 2 |

**15.**

| x | $f(x) + 4$ |
|---|---|
| $-3$ | 5 |
| $-1$ | 2 |
| 4 | 1 |
| 4 | 7 |

**17.** $y = f(x) + 4$
**19.** translated rt. 4 units **21.** translated left 3 units

**23.** $g(x) = -x - 1$ **25.** $g(x) = -2x + 4$
**27.** $y = 2x$ **29.** $y = \frac{1}{4}x$ **31.** $g(x) = -0.5x$ **33.** vertically
compressed by a factor of $\frac{1}{3}$ and translated down 2 units
**35.** translate to the right 10 s

**37.** $f(x) = -\frac{1}{3}x - 1$; $g(x) = \frac{1}{3}x + 1$; $g(x) = -f(x)$
**41.** translated 6 units down **43.** translated 4 units up

**45.** The first two steps are incorrect; the transformations
should be: shift 1 unit left, vertically stretch by a factor of 2,
and shift 3 units down. **55.** $y = -15.82x + 914.59$
**56.** $-2, 8$ **57.** $-12, 11$ **58.** $-3, \frac{21}{5}$

**Lesson 2-7** pp. 107–113

**Got It?**
**1. a.**

vertex at $(0, 2)$; translated up 2 units
from the parent function
**b.** No; transformations of this form move the vertex up or
down along the axis of symmetry, so the axis stays the
same.
**2.**

**3. a.** **b.**

**4.** $(1, -3)$; $x = 1$; translated 1 unit to the rt., vertically
stretched by a factor of 2, then reflected over the $x$-axis
and translated down 3 units **5.** $y = \frac{1}{4}|x - 2| - 1$
**Lesson Check 1.** $(-4, -3)$; $x = -4$ **2.** $(-3, 9)$; $x = -3$
**3.** vert. stretch **4.** vert. stretch **5.** Yes; you can determine
the position of a graph of an absolute value function by
identifying the vertex, axis of symmetry, and the
transformation of the absolute value parent function.
Answers may vary. Sample: $y = -\frac{1}{2}|x + 3| - 5$; vertex

1048

$(-3, -5)$; axis of symmetry, $x = -3$; translated 3 units to
the left, vertically compressed by a factor of $\frac{1}{2}$, then
reflected over the $x$-axis and translated down 5 units.
**6.** Answers may vary. Sample: $y = |x + 1| - 2$ and
$y = -|x + 1| - 2$ **7.** $y = |x|$ is the same as $y = x$
when $x \geq 0$ and is the reflection of $y = x$ across the
$x$-axis when $x < 0$.
**Exercises**
**9.**

| x | y |
|---|---|
| $-2$ | 2 |
| $-1$ | 1 |
| 0 | 0 |
| 1 | 1 |
| 2 | 2 |

**11.**

| x | y |
|---|---|
| $-4$ | 2 |
| $-3$ | 1 |
| $-2$ | 0 |
| $-1$ | 1 |
| 0 | 2 |

**13.**

| x | y |
|---|---|
| $-7$ | 2 |
| $-6$ | 1 |
| $-5$ | 0 |
| $-4$ | 1 |
| $-3$ | 2 |

**15.**

| x | y |
|---|---|
| $-8$ | 1 |
| $-7$ | 0 |
| $-6$ | 0 |
| $-5$ | 0 |
| $-4$ | 1 |

**17.**

vertically stretched
by a factor of 3

**19.**

vertically stretched by a
factor of 2 and reflected
across the $x$-axis

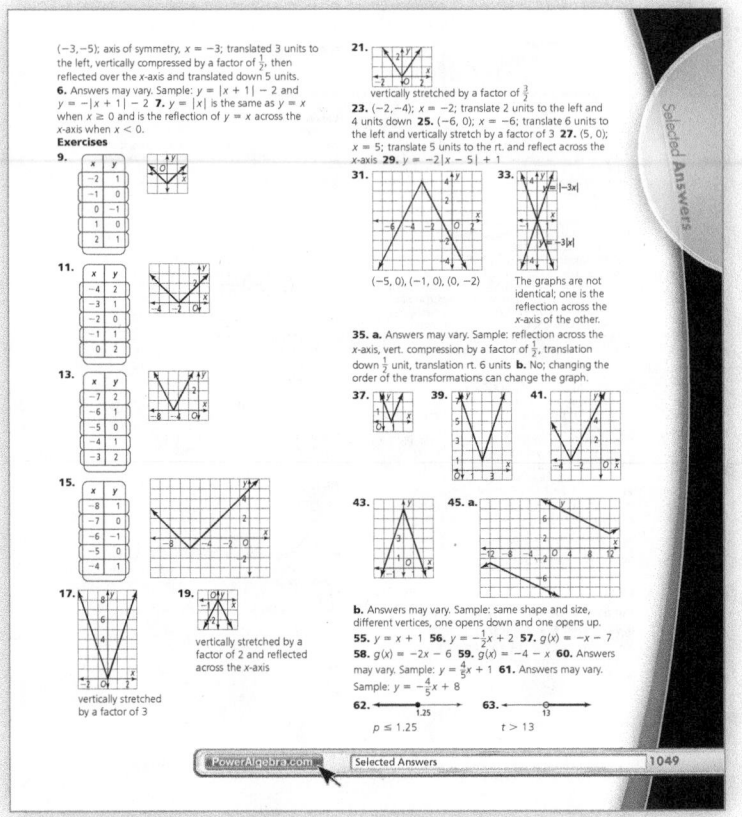

**21.**

vertically stretched by a factor of $\frac{3}{2}$
**23.** $(-2, -4)$; $x = -2$; translate 2 units to the left and
4 units down **25.** $(-6, 0)$; $x = -6$; translate 6 units to
the left and vertically stretch by a factor of 3 **27.** $(5, 0)$;
$x = 5$; translate 5 units to the rt. and reflect across the
$x$-axis **29.** $y = -2|x - 5| + 1$

**31.** **33.**

$(-5, 0), (-1, 0), (0, -2)$   The graphs are not
identical; one is the
reflection across the
$x$-axis of the other.

**35. a.** Answers may vary. Sample: reflection across the
$x$-axis, vert. compression by a factor of $\frac{1}{2}$, translation
down $\frac{1}{2}$ unit, translation rt. 6 units **b.** No; changing the
order of the transformations can change the graph.

**37.** **39.** **41.**

**43.** **45. a.**

**b.** Answers may vary. Sample: same shape and size,
different vertices, one opens down and one opens up.
**55.** $y = x + 1$ **56.** $y = -\frac{1}{2}x + 2$ **57.** $g(x) = -x - 7$
**58.** $g(x) = -2x - 6$ **59.** $g(x) = -4 - x$ **60.** Answers
may vary. Sample: $y = -\frac{4}{5}x + 1$ **61.** Answers may vary.
Sample: $y = -\frac{4}{5}x + 8$
**62.** $p \leq 1.25$ **63.** $t > 13$

**64.**

$t \le -3$

**Lesson 2-8**      pp. 114–120

**Got It?**

**1. a.** **b.**

**2. a.** Rides at the Fair

**b.** The number of rides cannot be neg.

**3.**

**4. a.** $y > -|x + 4| + 3$ **b.** No; when you solve the ineq. for $y$, you multiply both sides by $-1$. This changes the ineq. sign from $>$ to $<$.

**Lesson Check**

**1.** **2.**

**3.** **4.**

**5.** No; the boundary consists of points where equality holds, while the shaded region consists of points where the inequality holds. **6.** Graphing a linear inequality in two variables includes first graphing the boundary line, which is a linear eq. in two variables, and then shading the half-plane. **7.** No; $\left(\frac{3}{4}, 0\right)$ does not satisfy the inequality because $2.25 > 3$ is false.

**Exercises**

**9.** **11.**

**13.** **15.**

**17. a.** $y \ge 20x$ if $x \le 6$; $y \ge 15x$ if $x > 6$

**b.**

**19.** **21.**

**23.** **25.**

**27.** $y < -x - 2$ **29.** $2y \ge |2x + 6|$

**31.** **33.**

**35.** **37.**

**39.** $x > -3$ **41.** $y \ge -2x + 4$
**43.** $y < -|x - 4|$ **45.** C

**56.** **57.**

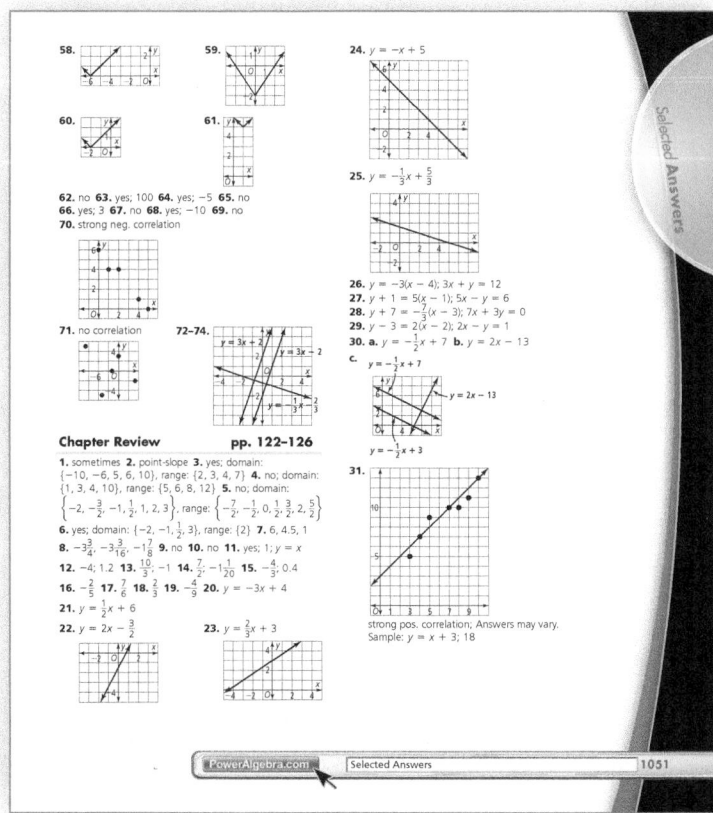

**58.** **59.** **24.** $y = -x + 5$

**60.** **61.**

**62.** no **63.** yes; 100 **64.** yes; $-5$ **65.** no
**66.** yes; 3 **67.** no **68.** yes; $-10$ **69.** no
**70.** strong neg. correlation

**25.** $y = -\frac{1}{3}x + \frac{5}{3}$

**71.** no correlation **72–74.**

**26.** $y = -3(x - 4)$; $3x + y = 12$
**27.** $y + 1 = 5(x - 1)$; $5x - y = 6$
**28.** $y + 7 = -\frac{2}{3}(x - 3)$; $7x + 3y = 0$
**29.** $y - 3 = 2(x - 2)$; $2x - y = 1$
**30. a.** $y = -\frac{1}{2}x + 7$ **b.** $y = 2x - 13$
**c.**

**Chapter Review**      pp. 122–126

**1.** sometimes **2.** point-slope **3.** yes; domain: $\{-10, -6, 5, 6, 10\}$, range: $\{2, 3, 4, 7\}$ **4.** no; domain: $\{1, 3, 4, 10\}$, range: $\{5, 6, 8, 12\}$ **5.** no; domain: $\left\{-2, -\frac{3}{2}, -1, \frac{1}{2}, 1, 2, 3\right\}$, range: $\left\{-\frac{7}{2}, -\frac{1}{2}, 0, \frac{1}{2}, \frac{3}{2}, 2, \frac{5}{2}\right\}$ **6.** yes; domain: $\{-2, -1, \frac{1}{3}\}$; range: $\{2\}$ **7.** 6, 4.5, 1 **8.** $-3\frac{3}{4}$, $-3\frac{3}{16}$, $-1\frac{1}{2}$ **9.** no **10.** no **11.** yes; 1; $y = x$ **12.** $-4$; 1.2 **13.** $\frac{10}{3}$; $-1$ **14.** $\frac{7}{5}$; $-1\frac{1}{20}$ **15.** $-\frac{4}{9}$; 0.4 **16.** $-\frac{2}{5}$ **17.** $\frac{7}{8}$ **18.** $\frac{7}{3}$ **19.** $-\frac{4}{9}$ **20.** $y = -3x + 4$ **21.** $y = \frac{1}{2}x + 6$ **22.** $y = 2x - \frac{3}{2}$ **23.** $y = \frac{2}{3}x + 3$

**31.**

strong pos. correlation; Answers may vary. Sample: $y = x + 3$; 18

**32.**

strong neg. correlation; Answers may vary. Sample: $y = -0.9x + 21$; 7.5

**33.**

strong pos. correlation; Answers may vary. Sample: $y = 4x + 22$; 82
**34.** $y = f(x + 2) - 7$ **35.** $y = -f(x - 5)$
**36.** $y = f(-x) + 3$ **37.** translated 4 units down
**38.** vertically stretched by a factor of 12, translated 2 units up **39.** vertically stretched by a factor of 2, reflected across the $y$-axis, reflected across the $x$-axis
**40.** $y = |x - 2| + 4$ **41.** $y = |x + 3|$
**42.** $y = |x - 5| + 2$ **43.** $y = |x - 4| + 1$
**44.**

**45.**

**46.** **47.**

**48.** $(4, 0)$; $x = 4$ **49.** $(0, 2)$; $x = 0$
**50.** **51.**

**52.**

**53.**

**54. a.** Answers may vary. Sample: $x + 3y \le 15$
**b.** Answers may vary. Sample: domain: $\{0, 1, 2, 3, 4, 5, 6, 7, 8, 9, 10, 11, 12, 13, 14, 15\}$, range: $\{0, 1, 2, 3, 4, 5\}$
**c.**

**55.** Answers may vary. Sample: $y \le -|x| - 1$

## Chapter 3

**Get Ready! p. 131 1.** 28 **2.** 33 **3.** $-\frac{15}{2}$ **4.** 15
**5.** $y = \frac{1}{3}x - \frac{5}{3}$ **6.** $y = -2x + 3$ **7.** $y = 5x + 16$
**8.** $y = 3x - 7$ **9.** $y = \frac{2}{3}x - \frac{3}{4}$ **10.** $y = 4x + 11$
**11.** $y = -6x - 8$ **12.** $y = -3x + 18$
**13.** **14.**

**15.** **16.**

**17.** **18.**

**19.** **20.**

**21.** Answers may vary. Samples: Rocky Mountains, Appalachian Mountains **22.** Answers may vary. Sample: Your actions are consistent with your words when your

actions show what you are saying. For example, if you say you are happy and you are laughing or smiling. **23.** 15 books or more; 15 books or more but less than 19, i.e., 15, 16, 17, or 18 books

**Lesson 3-1**      pp. 134–141
**Got It? 1.** $(2, -1)$ **2. a.** Spiny Dogfish: 59.5 cm; Greenland: 55.75 cm **b.** Each species of shark has a maximum total length; growth rates decrease with increase in age. **3.** In the yr 1990; about 1,100,000 **4. a.** inconsistent **b.** independent **c.** dependent
**Lesson Check**
**1.** $(2, 1)$ **2.** $(2, 0)$

**3.** 2 pens; 4 pencils **4.** No; an independent system has a unique solution whereas an inconsistent system has no solution.
**5.** Answers may vary. Sample: $\begin{cases} y = 2x + 1 \\ y = 2x - 3 \end{cases}$
**6.** Independent; if the slope of one equation is the negative reciprocal of the slope of the other equation, the lines are perpendicular and intersect at a unique point.
**Exercises 7–11.** How solutions are determined may vary (graphing or using a table).
**7.** $(3, 1)$ **9.** $(-2, 4)$

**11.** no solution

**13.** 2 small; 4 large
**15.** Models may vary. Sample: Use 0 for 1970. $\begin{cases} y = 0.22x + 67.5 \\ y = 0.15x + 75.507 \end{cases}$
Around 2085, the quantities will be equal.
**17.** dependent **19.** inconsistent **21.** independent
**23.** dependent **25.** independent **27.** dependent

**29.** infinitely many solutions **31.** no solution

**33.** $\left(-\frac{1}{33}, \frac{9}{11}\right)$ **35.** $(6, 4)$

**37.** $\left(\frac{12}{7}, \frac{18}{7}\right)$

**39.** dependent
**41.**

After 20 min you and your friend will have read the same number of pages.
**43.** My friend did not extend the table of values far enough. Scrolling down will show that when $x = 4$, then $Y1 = Y2 = -2$. So, the system has a solution, $(4, -2)$.
**45.** An independent system has one solution. The slopes are different, but the $y$-intercepts could be the same. An inconsistent system has no solution. The slopes are the same and the $y$-intercepts are different. A dependent system has an infinite number of solutions. The slopes and $y$-intercepts are the same. **47.** sometimes **49.** never
**59.** **60.**

**61.**

**62.** $n < -\frac{9}{5}$ **63.** $x \geq -\frac{29}{2}$ or $-14.5$ **64.** $x > \frac{5}{6}$
**65.** 2 **66.** $-\frac{2}{3}$ **67.** 2 **68.** 10 **69. a.** $-3$ **b.** 8 **c.** $-10$

**Lesson 3-2**  pp. 142–148
**Got It? 1.** $(-2.5, 2.5)$ **2.** $.95 per download; $5.50 one-time registration fee **3.** $(4, 0)$ **4. a.** $(-2, 3)$ **b.** Yes; the solution $(-5, 2)$ is a solution to both eqs. in the system, so substituting $y = 2$ into either equation will result in $x = -5$. **5. a.** no solution; The eq. is always false. **b.** infinite number of solutions; The eq. is always true.
**Lesson Check 1.** $(1, 2)$ **2.** $(-6, -6)$ **3.** $(2, 1)$ **4.** $(5, -3)$ **5.** $\left(-\frac{1}{5}, \frac{19}{5}\right)$ **6.** $(2, 1)$
**7.** Answers may vary. Sample:
$\begin{cases} 4x - 3y = -2 \\ 3x - 2y = -1 \end{cases}$
$\begin{cases} -8x + 6y = 4 \\ 9x - 6y = -3 \end{cases}$
**8.** In the substitution method of solving a system of equations, you first solve one equation for one of the variables. Then substitute for this variable in the other equation and solve for the other variable. In the elimination method, you create an equivalent system of equations that contain a pair of additive inverses so that you can eliminate one variable and solve for the remaining variable.
**9.** Let $r$ = number of regular cups of coffee and $c$ = number of large cups of coffee. First, $r + c = 5$: because a total of 5 cups of coffee were purchased. Second, $r + 1.5c = 6$: because each regular cup of coffee is $1, each large cup is $1.50, and the total spent is $6. Then, solve the system of equations using elimination by subtracting the first equation from the second to eliminate $r$ and solve for $c$. $c = 2$; 2 large cups
**Exercises 11.** $(-2, 4)$ **13.** $(0.75, 2.5)$ **15.** $(8, -1)$ **17.** $(-2, -5)$ **19.** seven $1-bills; eight $5-bills **21.** 3 vans and 2 sedans **23.** $(2, 4)$ **25.** $(2, -2)$ **27.** $(4, 1)$ **29.** $(1, 1)$ **31.** infinite number of solutions; $\{(x, y) | -2x + 3y = 13\}$ **33.** $(3, 2)$ **35.** $(5, 4)$ **37.** $\left(\frac{20}{17}, \frac{19}{17}\right)$ **39.** $(4, 1)$ **41.** no solution
**43.** 10 deliveries **45.** $(-4, -3)$ **47.** $(-3, 4)$ **49.** $(300, 150)$ **51.** $(0.5, 0.25)$
**53.** Error in 5th line: $-4(-7 - x) = 28 + 4x$ not $-28 - 4x$; Lines 5–9 should be: $3x + 28 + 4x = 14$; $7x = -14$; $x = -2$; $y = -7 - (-2)$; $y = -5$
**55.** Answers may vary. Sample:
$\begin{cases} -3x + 4y = 12 \\ 5x - 3y = 13 \end{cases}, (8, 9)$

**57.** In determining whether to use substitution or elimination to solve an equation, look at the equations to determine if one is solved or can be easily solved for a particular variable. If that is the case, substitution can easily be used. Otherwise, elimination might be easier.
**59.** Substitution; the second equation is solved for $y$: $(-7, -26)$ **61.** Elimination; substitution would be difficult since no coefficient is 1 in the original system. Dividing the first equation by 3 and dividing the second equation by 5 results in an equivalent system where $y$ would be eliminated from the system if the equations were subtracted; $(-1, -3)$
**72.** no solution

**73.** infinite number of solutions, $\{(x, y) | -9x - 3y = 1\}$

**74.** no solution

**75.** function **76.** function **77.** not a function
**78.** $x < -1$

**79.** $x > -\frac{1}{2}$

**80.** $y < 1$

**Lesson 3-3**  pp. 149–155
**Got It? 1.** $(4, 1), (5, 0), (6, 0), (7, 0)$
**2.**

**3.** 5 meats and no vegetables; 4 meats and 1 or 2 vegetables; 3 meats and 2, 3, or 4 vegetables; 2 meats and 3, 4, 5, or 6 vegetables; 1 meat and 4 – 8 vegetables; no meat 5 – 10 vegetables
**4.** $y > 2|x - 1|$

---

**Lesson Check**
**1.**

**2.**

**3.**

**4.** 0 h TV and 1, 2, or 3 h football; 1 h TV and 1 or 2 h football; or 2 h TV and 1 h football **5.** Intersection; the solution of two inequalities is the overlap or the intersection of the graphs of the individual inequalities.
**6.** The graphical solution of a system of inequalities consists of the overlap or intersection of the individual half-planes and corresponding boundary lines (either dotted or solid). The graphical solution of a system of equations includes only the intersection of the lines, not the half-planes. **7.** For each inequality, the wrong half-plane has been shaded. The half-plane below $y = \frac{1}{2}x - 1$ should be shaded and the half-plane above $y = -3x + 3$ should be shaded. Also, both boundary lines should be dashed because the inequalities are $<$ and $>$.
**Exercises 9.** $(0, 0), (0, 1), (0, 2), (0, 3), (0, 4), (0, 5), (0, 6), (0, 7), (1, 1), (1, 2), (1, 3), (1, 4), (1, 5), (1, 6), (2, 0), (2, 1), (2, 2), (2, 3), (2, 4), (2, 5), (3, 3), (3, 4)$
**11.**

**13.**

**15.**

**17.** $y > -2|x - 1| + y \leq -2$ **19.** no solution

**21.** Let $r$ = number of rose plants and $t$ = number of tulip plants.
$t + r \leq 50$
$r \leq 80$
Because the number of plants must be a whole number, only the points in the overlap that represent whole numbers are solutions of the problem.

**23.**

**25.**

**27.** $y \leq -|x - 3|$

**29.**

**31.** $(0, 4), (0, 5), (0, 6), (1, 3), (1, 4), (1, 5), (2, 3), (2, 4)$; the sum of the servings must be greater than or equal to 4 and less than or equal to 6.

**33.** Answers may vary. Sample: $\begin{cases} x < 5 \\ y \geq 1 \end{cases}$

**35.** Use test pts. that are not on either of the boundary lines and that make the calculations as easy as possible (e.g., the origin). **37.** A, B **39.** A, B, C **41.** B, C **43.** A **45.** A
**47.**

**49.**

**51.**

**53.** $y > |x - 1| + 1$

**63.** $(-9, -26)$ **64.** $\left(\frac{23}{14}, -\frac{13}{14}\right)$ **65.** no solution

---

**66.** $(-2, -1)$ **67.** $(-1, 2)$ **68.** $\left(-\frac{4}{7}, \frac{1}{14}\right)$
**69–72.** Answers may vary. Samples are given for each exercise. **69.** $(0, 3)$ **70.** $(0, 3)$ **71.** $(2, -1)$ **72.** $(1, -1)$

**Lesson 3-4**  pp. 157–162
**Got It? 1. a.** $P$ has a maximum value of 7.5 at $(0, 2.5)$. **b.** Yes; Answers may vary. Sample: $P = 5$ has the same (maximum) value at all four vertex points. $P = x + 2y$ has maximum 5 at $R$ and $S$. **2.** 100 T-shirts and 10 sweatshirts.
**Lesson Check**
**1.**

**2.**

**3.**

**4.**

**5.** $(0, 0), (0, 4), (5, 0), (5, 4)$ **6.** $(0, 8), (3, 5), (0, 5)$

**7.** Constraints are limits or restrictions on the variables in the objective function in a linear programming problem. These constraints are written as linear inequalities.
**8.** Linear programming is an extension of solving linear inequalities. For each, you are given constraints represented by linear inequalities that are graphed. All the points in the overlapping region are solutions, but linear programming problems are usually looking for maximum or minimum values of some quantity modeled with an objective function.
**9.** Answers may vary. Sample: $\begin{cases} y \leq x \\ y \leq -x + 4 \\ 0 \leq y \leq 1 \end{cases}$
$P = 2x + 3y$, $P(0, 0) = 0$, $P(1, 1) = 5$, $P(3, 1) = 9$, $P(4, 0) = 8$; maximum value of $P$ is 9 at $(3, 1)$

**Exercises**
**11.**

vertices: $(8, 0), (2, 3)$; minimized at $(8, 0)$
**13.** Let $s$ = number of Spruce trees and $m$ = number of Maple trees.
$\begin{cases} 30s + 40m \leq 2100 \\ 600s + 900m \leq 45,000 \\ s \geq 0, m \geq 0 \end{cases}$
**a.** as above
**b.** $P = 650s + 300m$
**c.**

vertices: $(0, 0), (0, 50), (30, 30), (70, 0)$
**d.** 70 spruce trees and 0 maple trees
**15.** He is not considering the constraint $y \leq x + 3$; maximize when $P = 11$ at $(1, 4)$

**17.**

vertices: $(0, 0), (1, 4), (0, 4.5), \left(\frac{7}{3}, 0\right)$; maximized when $P = 6$ at $(1, 4)$

**19.**

vertices: $(0, 0), \left(7\frac{1}{3}, 3\frac{2}{3}\right), (0, 11)$; maximized when $P = 29\frac{1}{3}$ at $\left(7\frac{1}{3}, 3\frac{2}{3}\right)$.

**21.**

vertices: $\left(\frac{28}{19}, \frac{50}{19}\right), (4, 2), (1, 5)$; minimized when $C = 67,370$ at $\left(\frac{28}{19}, \frac{50}{19}\right)$

---

**28.** $y < -2x + 8$

**29.**

**30.**

**31.** 1 **32.** $-34$ **33.** 24 **34.** 65 **35.** $(0, 6), (-3, 0)$ **36.** $(0, 4), (18, 0)$ **37.** $(0, -1), (1, 0)$

**Lesson 3-5**  pp. 166–173
**Got It? 1.** $(4, 2, -3)$ **2. a.** $(4, -1, 2)$ **b.** Answers may vary. Sample: Yes; you can choose to eliminate either $x$, $y$, or $z$ resulting in a system of equations in 2 variables.
**3. a.** $(2, 1, -4)$ **b.** No; in Step 1 we solved for $x$ in terms of $y$ only. Therefore, once we found the value of $y$ we could have substituted that value into the equation we wrote in Step 1 and solved for $x$ without ever finding the $z$-value. **4.** 50 T-shirts, 50 polo shirts, and 100 rugby shirts
**Lesson Check 1.** $(5, -3, -2)$ **2.** $(6, 0, -2)$
**3.** $(0, 3, 4)$ **4.** $(2, 1, -5)$ **5.** Answers may vary. Sample: Substitution is the best method to use when one of the equations can be solved easily for one variable.
**6.** Answers may vary. Sample: (1) A unique solution to a system of three variables. The planes intersect at one common point. When a system has no solution, no point lies in all three planes. **7.** No solution since no point lies in all three planes. The three planes are parallel. **8.** infinitely many solutions
**Exercises 9.** $(4, 2, -3)$ **11.** $(2, 1, -5)$ **13.** $\left(\frac{1}{2}, -3, 1\right)$
**15.** $(1, -4, 3)$ **17.** $(4, -1, 2)$ **19.** $\left(-\frac{10}{13}, -\frac{12}{13}, \frac{17}{13}\right)$
**21.** $(8, -4, 2)$ **23.** $(-2, -1, -3)$ **25.** $(0, 1, 7)$
**27.** $(5, -2, 0)$ **29.** $(1, 3, 2)$ **31.** $m\angle P = 32°$; $m\angle Q = 96°$; $m\angle R = 52°$ **33.** $(8, 1, 3)$
**35.** $\left(\frac{1}{2}, 2, -2\right)$ **37.** no solution **39.** $(2, 4, 6)$
**41.** $(3, -2, -3)$ **50.** $P = 12$ is maximized at $(0, 4)$.
**51.** $x \geq -\frac{3}{2}$

**52.** $x \leq -18$;

**53.** $x < -1$;

**54.** $\left(7, \frac{5}{4}\right)$

**55.** dependent system; infinite number of solutions, $\left\{(x, y) \mid y = -\frac{1}{2}x - \frac{3}{4}\right\}$
**56.** inconsistent system; no solution

**Lesson 3-6**  pp. 174–181
**Got It? 1.** 17
**2. a.** $\begin{bmatrix} -4 & -2 \\ 3 & 7 \\ -5 \end{bmatrix}$ **b.** $\begin{bmatrix} 4 & -1 & 2 & 1 \\ 0 & 1 & 5 & 20 \\ 2 & 1 & 0 & 9 \end{bmatrix}$
**3.** $\begin{cases} 2x = 6 \\ 5x - 2y = 1 \end{cases}$
**4. a.** $(1, 2)$ **b.** elimination; you use the same steps to solve **5.** $\left(1, \frac{1}{3}, 3\right)$
**Lesson Check 1.** $2 \times 1$ **2.** $2 \times 4$
**3.** $\begin{bmatrix} 3 & 5 & 0 \\ 1 & 1 & 2 \end{bmatrix}$  $\begin{bmatrix} 1 & 3 & -1 & 2 \\ 1 & 0 & 2 & 8 \\ 0 & 2 & -1 & 4 \end{bmatrix}$
**5.** 16 **6.** $a_{21}$ is 0, the element in row 2, column 1. $a_{12}$ is $-9$, the element in row 1 and column 2. **7.** Answers may vary. Sample: The entry fee to a school play is $2 for adults. Jamie paid a total of $8 for 4 student entry fees and 2 adult entry fees. What is the student entry fee?
**Exercises 9.** $(1, 1)$ **11.** 8
**13.** $\begin{bmatrix} 3 & 2 & 16 \\ 0 & 1 & 5 \end{bmatrix}$ **15.** $\begin{bmatrix} 1 & -1 & 150 \\ 2 & 0 & 1 & 425 \\ 0 & 1 & 1 \end{bmatrix}$
**17.** $\begin{bmatrix} 1 & -1 & 1 \\ 1 & -2 & -1 \\ 2 & -1 & 2 \end{bmatrix}$ **19.** $\begin{cases} 5x + y = -3 \\ -2x + y = 4 \end{cases}$
**21.** $\begin{cases} 2x + y + z = 1 \\ x + y + z = 2 \\ x - y - z = -2 \end{cases}$ **23.** $\begin{cases} 5x + 2y + z = 5 \\ 4x + y + z = 8 \\ x + 3y - 6z = 2 \end{cases}$
**25.** $(-1, 0)$ **27.** $(4, 6)$ **29.** $(2, 3)$
**31.** $10,000 at 4% and $15,000 at 6%; Let $x$ = amount invested at 4% and $y$ = amount invested at 6%.
$\begin{cases} x + y = 25,000 \\ 0.04x + 0.06y = 1300 \end{cases}$
$\begin{bmatrix} 1 & 1 & 25000 \\ 0.04 & 0.06 & 1300 \end{bmatrix} = \begin{bmatrix} 1 & 0 & 10000 \\ 0 & 1 & 15000 \end{bmatrix}$
**33.** $(3, 1, 1)$ **35.** $(35, -22, -16)$ **37.** $(1, 1, 1, 1)$
**39.** $(2, 3)$ **41.** 1 qt. of red paint: $7.75; 1 qt. of yellow paint: $5.75
**51.** $x \leq -\frac{3}{2}$;

**52.** $x \geq -35$;

**53.** $x \geq 4$;

**54.** $\frac{15}{2}, -\frac{5}{2}$ **55.** 10, −10 **56.** 10, −6 **57.** $y = 2x$
**58.** $y = \frac{1}{3}x$

## Chapter Review    pp. 183–186

**1.** independent system **2.** Linear programming; constraints
**3.**

independent; (−1, −4)

**4.** dependent **5.** inconsistent **6.** dependent
**7.** independent; (−4, 6)    **8.** independent; (1, 0)

**9.** 3 pens **10.** (−1, −2) **11.** (0, −5) **12.** (−2, 3)
**13.** inconsistent; no solution **14.** 1 serving of roast beef and 2 servings of mashed potatoes
**15.**                **16.**

**17.**                **18.**

**19.** Let $r$ = amount of regular coffee and $d$ = amount of decaffeinated coffee
$\begin{cases} r + d \le 10 \\ r \ge 3d, r \ge 0, d \ge 0 \end{cases}$

**20.** vertices: (4, 0) and (2, 3); $C = 4$ is minimized at (4, 0).

**21.** vertices: (0, 0), (4, 0), (2, 3), (0, 5); $P = 25$ is maximized at (0, 5).

**22.** 50 chef's salads and 50 Caesar salads **23.** (1, 3, −2)
**24.** (−4, 1, −5) **25.** (6, 0, −2) **26.** no solution
**27.** $\left(\frac{1}{2}, \frac{1}{4}\right)$ **28.** (1, −1) **29.** (2, −4, 6) **30.** (5, 2, −3)

## Chapter 4

### Get Ready! p. 191 **1.** 6 **2.** 4
**3.** −2 < x < 6
**4.** $y \le -\frac{5}{4}$ or $y \ge \frac{9}{4}$
**5.** $y = 9x - 10$ **6.** $y = \frac{1}{3}x + 8$

**7.** translated 4 units to the right and 2 units up
**8.** translated 10 units to the left and 3 units down
**9.** (10, −1) **10.** (−6, −6) **11.** Answers may vary. Sample: application forms, registration forms, tests
**12.** Answers may vary. Sample: monsters, ghosts, tooth fairy **13.** writing

### Lesson 4-1    pp. 194–201

**Got It?**
**1. a.**
**b.** If a is a negative number, the parabola will open downward. There will be a maximum value for y at the vertex of the parabola.

**2. a.** translated 3 units up
**b.** translated 1 unit to the left

**3.** vertex: (−1, 4); axis of symmetry: x = −1; maximum: 4; domain: all real numbers, range: $y \le 4$ **4.** stretch by the factor 2, translate 2 units to the left and 5 units down.
**5.** $f(x) = -\frac{2}{9}(x - 2)^2 + 7$

**Lesson Check**
**1.**
**2.** minimum **3.** $y = -2(x - 0)^2 + 35$ **4.** when a > 0
**5.** No; a must be > 0 or < 0. **6.** $y = (x + 6)^2$ is the graph of $y = x^2$ translated 6 units to the left and has a minimum at (−6, 0); $y = (x - 6)^2 + 7$ is the graph of $y = x^2$ translated 6 units to the right and 7 units up, with a minimum at (6, 7).
**Exercises**
**7.**                **9.**

**11.**               **13.**

**15.** translated 3 units up    **17.** translated 6 units down

**19.** translated 9 units down    **21.** translated 1.5 units up

**23.** vertex: (−20, 0); axis of symmetry: x = −20; maximum: 0; domain: all real numbers, range: $y \ge 0$
**25.** vertex: (−5.5, 0); axis of symmetry: x = −5.5; minimum: 0; domain: all real numbers, range: $y \ge 0$
**27.** vertex: (4, −25); axis of symmetry: x = 4; maximum: −25; domain: all real numbers, range: $y \le -25$
**29.** x = 1    **31.** x = 2    **33.** x = 1

**35.** $y = (x - 2)^2 + 5$ **37.** $y = -\frac{1}{2}(x + 4)^2 + 2$
**39.** 1000 chips; $20 **41.** stretch vertically by a factor of 2, reflect across the x-axis, translate 1 unit to the left and 1 unit up

**43.** reflect across the x-axis, translate 4 units to the left and 5 units up

**45.** stretch vertically by a factor of 0.2, translate 12 units to the right and 3 units down

**47.** parabola $y = a(x - 3)^2 + 4$ with vertex (3, 4) and a > 0 or a < 0 **49.** $y = -7(x - 1)^2 + 2$
**51.** $y = -7x^2 + 5$ **53.** similar: same vertex (2, 1) and open downward, same domain (all real numbers), same range ($y \le 1$), same x-intercepts, (1, 0), (3, 0); different: $y = -|x - 2| + 1$ is an absolute value function with y-intercept (0, −1) and $y = -(x - 2)^2 + 1$ is a quadratic function with y-intercept of (0, −3).

**55.** similar: same vertex (0, 4) and open downward, same domain (all real numbers), same range ($y \le 4$), same y-intercept, (0, 4); different: $y = -2|x| + 4$ is an absolute value function with x-intercepts ($\pm 2$, 0) and

---

$y = -2(x)^2 + 4$ is a quadratic function with x-intercepts ($\pm \sqrt{2}$, 0)

**57.** Answers may vary. Sample: $y = (x + 10)^2 - 4$
**74.** (3, 2) **75.** (−10, 6) **76.** (1, 0, 3)
**77.**            **78.**            **79.**

**80.** yes **81.** no **82.** no **83.** (0, 0) **84.** (−1, 0) **85.** (5, 0)

### Lesson 4-2    pp. 202–208

**Got It?** **1.** vertex: $\left(-\frac{2}{3}, 7\frac{1}{3}\right)$; axis of symmetry: $x = -\frac{2}{3}$; maximum: $7\frac{1}{3}$; range: $y \le 7\frac{1}{3}$
**2.**
**3.** $y = -(x - 2)^2 - 1$ **4. a.** 4 ft **b.** because the y-intercept is (0, 0)
**Lesson Check** **1.** vertex: (0, −4); axis of symmetry: x = 0; minimum: −4
**2.**               **3.**

**4.** $y = (x - 1)^2 + 8$ **5.** $y = -\left(x - \frac{3}{2}\right)^2 + \frac{5}{4}$
**6.** Error in calculation of x. The correct calculation is:
$x = \frac{-(-4)}{2(2)} = 1$
$y = 2(1) - 4(1) - 3 = 2 - 4 - 3 = -5$
Vertex: (1, −5)

**7.** The vertex of a function written in vertex form can easily be determined. It is (h, k) where $f(x) = a(x - h)^2 + k$. The vertex of a function in standard form is $\left(\frac{-b}{2a}, f\left(\frac{-b}{2a}\right)\right)$ where $f(x) = ax^2 + bx + c$.
**Exercises 9.** vertex: (1, 2); axis of symmetry: x = 1; maximum: 2; range: $y \ge 2$ **11.** vertex: (1, 6); axis of symmetry: x = 1; maximum: 6; range: $y \le 6$
**13.** vertex: $\left(-\frac{1}{4}, 5\frac{3}{8}\right)$; axis of symmetry: $x = -\frac{1}{4}$; maximum: $5\frac{3}{8}$; range: $y \le 5\frac{3}{8}$ **15.** vertex: $\left(-\frac{1}{2}, \frac{1}{4}\right)$; axis of symmetry: $x = -\frac{1}{2}$; maximum: $\frac{1}{4}$; range: $y \le \frac{1}{4}$
**17.**                **19.**

**21.**                **23.**

**25.**                **27.** $y = (x + 1)^2 + 4$ **29.** $y = 2\left(x - \frac{5}{4}\right)^2 + \frac{7.1}{8}$
**31.** $y = \frac{9}{4}\left(x + \frac{2}{3}\right)^2 - 2$
**33.**                **35.**

**37.** 4 cm × 9 cm × 9 cm **39.** $b = -6$; c = 5
**41.** a = 1; c = −2 **43.** 2s; 64 ft **45.** (0, 3)
**47.** (0, −54) **57.** $\frac{1}{4}$ **58.** −2.5 **59–61.** Explanations may vary. Samples are given. **59.** Elimination because the x-terms have opposite signs; (7, −1) **60.** Substitution because the first equation is already solved for y; (27, 15)
**61.** Elimination because you can multiply the second equation by −3 to eliminate n; (3, 2) **62.** vertex: (−2, −1); axis of symmetry: x = −2; minimum: −1; domain: all real numbers, range: $y \ge -1$ **63.** vertex: (1, 3); axis of symmetry: x = 1; maximum: 3; domain: all real numbers, range: $y \le 3$ **64.** vertex: (3, −2); axis of symmetry: x = 3; minimum: −2; domain: all real numbers, range: $y \ge -2$ **65.** vertex: (−3, 5); axis of symmetry: x = −3; maximum: 5; domain: all real numbers, range: $y \le 5$ **66.** vertex: (−4, 0); axis of symmetry: x = −4; minimum: 0; domain:

all real numbers, range: $y \ge 0$ **67.** vertex: (4, 6); axis of symmetry: x = 4; maximum: 6; domain: all real numbers, range: $y \le 6$ **68.** $y = -(x - 1)^2 + 5$ **69.** $y = x^2 - 4$
**70.** $y = (x + 1)^2 - 2$

### Lesson 4-3    pp. 209–214

**Got It? 1.** $y = -3x^2 + x$ **2. a.** No; the ball will only reach a height of 5 when x = 5, which is lower than the top of the wall at (5, 6). The ball will hit the wall on its way down. **b.** domain: $0 \le x \le 7$, range: $0 \le y \le 6\frac{1}{8}$
**3.** $y = -0.329x^2 + 9.798x + 15.571$; 88.5°F at 2:53 P.M. (although the meteorologist's prediction is 89° at 3 P.M.)
**Lesson Check 1.** $y = -2x^2 - 1$
**2.** $y = 2x^2 + 6x + 7.5$ **3.** $y = -2x^2 + 10x - 13.5$
**4.** Answers may vary. Sample: A rough plot of the data will indicate whether the data are collinear (linear regression) or non-collinear where the data follows a curve (quadratic regression). **5.** Answers may vary. Sample: A rough plot will show that the four points do not lie on a single parabola. **6.** y is not a function of x since for one value of x, "3," there are 2 values of y, "4" and "0."
**Exercises 7.** $y = -x^2 + 3x - 4$ **9.** $y = 2x^2 - x + 3$
**11.** $y = -6x + 3$ **13.** $y = x^2 + 2x$
**15.** $y = -x^2 + x - 2$ **17. a.** $y = -16x^2 + 33x + 46$, where x is the number of seconds after release and y is the height in ft **b.** 28.5 ft **c.** about 63 ft **19.** yes; $y = -2x^2 + 3x + 5$ **21.** yes; $y = 0.625x^2 - 1.75x + 1$
**23.** $y = 0.005x^2 - 1.95x + 120$; 66 mm
**25. a.** $y = -0.004x^2 + 0.859x + 27.53$ **b.** Answers may vary. Sample: domain: integers from −10 to 17; range: whole numbers from 18 to 42 **c.** the year 2003 **d.** The year 2022; the year is outside the domain of the data pts. **27.** Answers may vary. Sample: $y = \frac{7}{25}x^2$, $y = \frac{1}{25}x^2 - \frac{2}{5}x$, $y = \frac{1}{5}x^2 - \frac{6}{5}x$
**35.**               **36.**               **37.**

**38.** (2, 5) **39.** (5, 8) **40.** (−1, −1) **41.** $\frac{4}{5}$ **42.** $-\frac{7}{2}$
**43.** $x^2 + 5x - 1$ **44.** $6x^2 - 10x - 3$ **45.** $4x^2 - x - 10$

### Lesson 4-4    pp. 216–223

**Got It? 1. a.** (x + 10)(x + 4) **b.** (x − 5)(x − 6)
**c.** −(x + 2)(x − 16) **2. a.** 7(n² − 3) **b.** 9(x + 2)(x − 1)
**c.** 4(x² + 2x + 3) **3. a.** (x + 1)(4x + 3)
**b.** (x − 2)(2x − 3) **c.** No; $2x^2 + 2x + 2 = 2(x^2 + x + 1)$, there are no real factors of a and c whose

product is 1 and whose sum is 1. **4.** (8x − 1)²
**5.** (4x − 9)(4x + 9)
**Lesson Check 1.** (x + 4)(x + 2) **2.** (x − 12)(x − 1)
**3.** (x − 9)(x + 9) **4.** (5y − 6)(5y + 6) **5.** (x − 3)²
**6.** (2x − 1)² **7.** 5x **8.** 6 **9.** 6x **10.** 7h **11.** No; the middle term is not twice the product of the square root of the end terms. **12.** For a ≠ 1, look for two factors whose sum is b and whose product is ac. For a = 1, look for two factors whose sum is b and whose product is c.
**13.** $a^2 - 2ab + b^2 - 25$    Group the first 3 terms.
$= (a^2 - 2ab + b^2) - 25$
$= (a - b)^2 - 5^2$
$= (a - b - 5)(a - b + 5)$
**Exercises 15.** (x + 2)(x + 3) **17.** (x + 2)(x + 8)
**19.** (x + 2)(x + 20) **21.** −(x − 1)(x − 12)
**23.** (x − 9)(x + 9) **25.** (x − 4)(x − 9)
**27.** −(x − 4)(x + 6) **29.** (c − 7)(c + 9)
**31.** −(t − 11)(t + 4) **33.** 5b(5b − 4)
**35.** 5(t + 1)(t − 2) **37.** 9(3p² − p + 2)
**39.** (x − 8)(2x − 3) **41.** (m − 3)(2m − 5)
**43.** −(x − 12)(2x − 3) **45.** (y + 4)(5y − 8)
**47.** (x + 4)(2x − 7) **49.** (4x + 3)(7x − 2)
**51.** (t − 7)² **53.** (2z − 5)² **55.** (9z + 2)²
**57.** (x − 8)(c + 8) **59.** The rectangle would have one side equal to x and one side equal to x + 2y.
**61.** 9(x + 2)(x − 2) **63.** 3(2y + 5)(2y − 5)
**65.** 3(2x + 3)² **67.** 2(a − 4)² **69.** 2(3b + 5)(3b − 1)
**71.** 3(y + 3)(y + 5) **73.** 2(x − 5)(x + y)
**75.** −6(2z + 100) **77.** (x − y)(x + y) **79.** The third line should be x(2x − 5) − (2x − 5), and the final line should be (x − 1)(2x − 5). **81.** y; (y − 1)
**83.** 10(x − 3)(x + 3) **85.** 2(x² − 37x + 6) **87.** D
**106.** −y² − 3(x + 3) **107.** penny: 2.5g, nickel: 5g, dime: 2.3g
**108.**               **109.**

**110.**

### Algebra Review p. 225 **1.** $3\sqrt{2}$ **3.** $-4\sqrt{2}$ **5.** $-\frac{\sqrt{91}}{13}$
**7.** $-10\sqrt{2}$ **9.** 108 **11.** $|xy|$ **13.** $-\frac{|x|\sqrt{35}}{5}$ **15.** $\frac{5\sqrt{14}}{7}$

## Lesson 4-5 pp. 226–231

**Got It? 1.** 3, 4 **2.** 3, $\frac{1}{4}$ **3.** −6, 4 **4. a.** $53\frac{1}{3}$ ft; $21\frac{1}{3}$ ft; answers may vary. Sample: domain: $0 \le x \le 60$, range: $0 \le y \le 30$ **b.** No; domains and ranges are constrained by real-world limits.
**Lesson Check 1.** 3, −3 **2.** −4, −9 **3.** $-\frac{2}{3}$, 1
**4.** 4.372, −1.372 **5.** 2.608, −2.108 **6.** −1; since $y = 0$ when $x = 5$, substitute these values into the equation to find $b$. **7.** when the coefficients are integers and a recognizable pattern of factoring is evident **8.** One solution: when the table's range consists of zero and all positive numbers or zero and all negative numbers. No solution: when the table does not include zero and the $y$-values are either all positive or all negative numbers.
**Exercises 9.** −4, −2 **11.** −1, $\frac{3}{2}$ **13.** −2, −1 **15.** 0, 4
**17.** 0, 4 **19.** 3, 8 **21.** −0.78, 1.28 **23.** 4, −10
**25.** 0.8, −1 **27.** −1.67, −1.5 **29.** −0.94, 2.34
**31.** −1, 0.25 **33.** −1.46, 5.46 **35.** −1.16, 2.16
**37.** 3 in. **39.** about 3.6 ft **41.** Answers may vary. Samples are given: **a.** $x^2 - 8x + 15 = 0$
**b.** $x^2 + x - 6 = 0$ **c.** $x^2 + 7x + 6 = 0$ **43.** $-\frac{3}{2}, -\frac{2}{3}$
**45.** −4, $\frac{2}{5}$ **47.** −1, 4 **49.** −4, 0 **51.** 4.37, −1.37
**53.** −1, $\frac{10}{3}$ **55.** (0, −2), (2, 2) **64.** $(4x - 1)(4x + 1)$
**65.** $(5x − 1)(x − 5)$ **66.** $(2x − 1)(x + 7)$
**67.** (2, 0, −2) **68.** (−2, 1, 5) **69.** (7, 1, −1) **70.** vertex: (−9, 4); axis of symmetry: $x = −9$; translation 9 units to the left and 4 units up **71.** vertex: $\left(\frac{7}{2}, 0\right)$; axis of symmetry: $x = \frac{7}{2}$; stretch by a factor of 2, translation $3\frac{1}{2}$ units to the right **72.** vertex: (0, −1); axis of symmetry: $x = 0$; vert. compression by a factor of $\frac{3}{4}$, translation 1 unit down
**73.** $x^2 + 8x + 13$ **74.** $4x^2 − 4x + 1$ **75.** $x^2 − 6x + 9$

## Lesson 4-6 pp. 233–239

**Got It? 1. a.** $\sqrt{5}$, $-\sqrt{5}$ **b.** $\sqrt{2}$, $-\sqrt{2}$
**2.** 42 in. × 67.2 in. **3.** 2, 12 **4. a.** 9 **b.** No; $\left(\frac{b}{2}\right)^2 = \frac{b^2}{4}$, which is a function of $b$. **5.** $\frac{1}{2} \pm \frac{\sqrt{13}}{2}$
**6.** $y = \left(x + \frac{3}{4}\right)^2 - \frac{33}{4}$; vertex: $\left(-\frac{3}{4}, -\frac{33}{4}\right)$; $y$-intercept: (0, −6)
**Lesson Check 1.** 6, −6 **2.** 3, −3 **3.** 1, 4 **25.** 5, 4
**6.** 36 **7.** 2500 **8.** 256 **9.** First, you rewrite the eq. to get all terms with $x$ on one side. Then, you find $\left(\frac{b}{2}\right)^2$ and add it to both sides of the eq. Then, you factor the resulting trinomial.
**10.** $x^2 + 12x + 5 = 3$
$x^2 + 12x = -2$    Rewrite to get all terms with $x$ on one side of the eq.

$\left(\frac{12}{2}\right)^2 = 6^2 = 36$    Find $\left(\frac{b}{2}\right)^2 = 36$.
$x^2 + 12x + 36 = -2 + 36$   Add 36 to each side.
$(x + 6)^2 = 34$     Factor the trinomial.
**11.** Your friend should also have subtracted 49;
$(x^2 − 14x + 49) + 36 − 49$
$= (x − 7)^2 − 13$
**Exercises 13.** 2, −2 **15.** $\frac{5}{3}, -\frac{5}{3}$ **17.** $2\sqrt{2}, -2\sqrt{2}$
**19.** −4, −2 **21.** −1, 3 **23.** −4, 3 **25.** $-\frac{4}{5}, \frac{4}{5}$
**27.** $-\frac{10}{3}, \frac{2}{3}$ **29.** $\frac{1}{3}$, 100 **33.** 4 **35.** $6 \pm \sqrt{29}$
**41.** $1 \pm \sqrt{6}$ **39.** $5 \pm \sqrt{13}$ **41.** $3 \pm \sqrt{11}$
**43.** $-\frac{5}{4} \pm \frac{1}{4}\sqrt{17}$ **45.** $-\frac{3}{5} \pm \frac{\sqrt{21}}{5}$
**47.** $y = 2(x − 2)^2 − 7$ **49.** $y = (x + 2)^2 − 11$
**51.** $y = -(x − 2)^2 + 3$ **53.** 10, −10 **55.** 22, −22
**57.** 18, −18 **59.** 1, −1 **61.** 84, −84
**65.** $\frac{-5 \pm \sqrt{37}}{4}$ **67.** $\frac{2 \pm \sqrt{10}}{3}$
**69.** $\frac{-3 \pm \sqrt{41}}{8}$ **71.** $-\frac{1}{3}, -\frac{2}{3}$ **73.** $-3 \pm \sqrt{9}$
**75. a.** $-.01(x − 59)^2 + 36.81$; 36.81 **b.** 7.65 ft
**c.** about 120 ft **90.** $\frac{1}{2}$, 1 **91.** −4, 1 **92.** 8, $-\frac{2}{3}$
**93.** yes; $y = \frac{1}{2}x^2 + \frac{7}{2}x + 9$ **94.** yes; $y = -\frac{7}{2}x^2 + x + 2$ **95.** yes; $y = 3x^2 − 5x + 2$
**96.** (2, 0) **97.** (3, 1) **98.** (3, 1) **99.** 24 **100.** 84

## Lesson 4-7 pp. 240–247

**Got It? 1. a.** −2 **b.** −2 ± $\sqrt{7}$ **2. a.** $10.74 **b.** Yes; a neg. profit means more money was spent than earned.
**3. a.** no real solutions **b.** two real solutions **4.** Yes; $b^2 − 4ac = (85)^2 − 4(−16)\left(−109\frac{11}{12}\right) = 190\frac{3}{4}$. The discriminant is pos. So the eq. has two real solutions.
**Lesson Check 1.** $\frac{5 \pm \sqrt{53}}{2}$ **2.** $\frac{-3 \pm \sqrt{61}}{4}$ **3.** 3, $-\frac{1}{2}$
**4.** no real solutions **5.** −32; no real solutions **6.** 273; two real solutions **7.** 0; one real solution **8.** $k = \pm 6$ for real solution; $k > 6$ or $k < −6$ for two real solutions **9.** Answers may vary. Sample: The discriminants of eqs. with one real solution are all zero and thus equal, but the solutions may or may not be equal. An example is $x^2 − 8x + 16$ and $x^2 − 4x + 4$. Each has a discriminant of zero, but the solutions are 4 and 2. **10.** Yes; the eqs. can share common factors such as for $x^2 + 2x − 8$ where the discriminant is 36 and the solutions are 2 and −4, and $x^2 − 4x + 4$ where the discriminant is zero and the solution is 2.
**Exercises 11.** 1, 3 **13.** $-\frac{7}{2}$, 1 **15.** −5 **17.** $\frac{3 \pm \sqrt{5}}{2}$
**19.** $\frac{2 \pm \sqrt{10}}{3}$ **21.** 1, 4 **23.** $16.34 **25.** −4; no real solutions **27.** 0; one **29.** 169; two **31.** 1; two **33.** 0; one **35.** −23; no real solutions **37.** no

---

**39.** 2.29 in. × 15.71 in. **41.** $-\frac{1}{3}, 1$ **43.** −2.49, 0.89
**45.** −0.19, 2.69 **47.** 1, 10 **49.** $-\frac{3}{2}, \frac{1}{2}$ **51.** −1.70, 4.70
**53.** −8.47, 0.47 **55.** 1.47, −7.47 **57.** about 1.89 s
**59.** one **61.** two **63.** two **65.** two **67. a.** $k$ such that $|k| < 12$ **b.** 12 or −12 **c.** $k$ such that $|k| > 12$
**69. a.** $x^2 = 100\pi$ **b.** 17.72 cm **82.** −2, 10
**83.** $\frac{3 \pm \sqrt{2}}{2}$ **84.** $\frac{3 \pm \sqrt{41}}{8}$ **85.** $9x^2 + 3z$ **86.** $4x + k$
**87.** $2y − 8x$ **88.** $2\sqrt{17}$ **89.** 5 **90.** 13

## Lesson 4-8 pp. 248–255

**Got It? 1. a.** $2/\sqrt{3}$ **b.** $5/c$. $i\sqrt{7}$ **d.** $8i \ne -8$
**2. a.**  ; $\sqrt{26}$
**b.** ; $\sqrt{13}$   **c.** ; $\sqrt{17}$

**3. a.** $4 − i$ **b.** $−2 + 7i$ **c.** $12i$ **d.** $18i$ **4. a.** −21
**b.** 23 − 2$i$ **c.** 41 **5. a.** $-\frac{7}{25} - \frac{26}{25}i$ **b.** $-\frac{1}{6} - \frac{5}{6}i$
**c.** $\frac{15}{113} - \frac{112}{113}i$ **6. a.** ±2$i$ **b.** ±$i\sqrt{15}$ **7. a.** $\frac{1 \pm i\sqrt{23}}{6}$
**b.** 2 ± $i$
**Lesson Check 1.** $5i/\sqrt{3}$ **2.** 5 **3.** ±4$i$ **4.** 7 − 3$i$
**5.** 13 − 6$i$ **6.** The add. inv. of a complex number, $a + bi$, is the opposite of the complex number, or $−a − bi$. The complex conjugate of a complex number, $a + bi$, is the real part plus the opposite of the imaginary part of the complex number, or $a − bi$. **7.** error in the sign of the last term of the first line, which carries through to the end of the calculation; the line should be: "...
$= 16 + 28i − 28i − 49i^2$
$= 16 + 49$
$= 65.$"
**Exercises 9.** $i$ **11.** 9$i$
**13.** ; 2 **15.** ; $2\sqrt{2}$
**17.** ; $3\sqrt{5}$ **19.** 1 − 7$i$ **21.** 10 + 6$i$
**23.** 9 + 2$i$ **25.** −36 **27.** $-\frac{2}{5} - \frac{3}{5}i$ **29.** $\frac{5}{17} + \frac{19}{17}i$
**31.** $\frac{8}{13} + \frac{12}{13}i$ **33.** ±5$i$ **35.** ±8$i\frac{\sqrt{3}}{3}$ **37.** ±6$i$
**39.** −1 ± $i\sqrt{2}$ **41.** $1 \pm i\frac{\sqrt{10}}{2}$ **43.** 2 ± $i$

---

**45. a.** A: −5; B: 3 + 2$i$; C: 2 − $i$; D: 3$i$; E: −6 − 4$i$; F: −1 + 5$i$ **b.** A: 5; B: −3 − 2$i$; C: −2 + $i$; D: −3$i$; E: 6 + 4$i$; F: 1 − 5$i$ **c.** A: −5; B: 3 − 2$i$; C: 2 + $i$; D: −3$i$; E: −6 + 4$i$; F: −1 − 5$i$ **d.** A: 5; B: $\sqrt{3}$; C: $\sqrt{5}$; D: 3; E: $2\sqrt{13}$; F: $\sqrt{26}$ **47.** −5, 5 **49.** −1 + 5$i$
**51.** 8 − 2$i$ **53.** 6 + 10$i$ **55.** 10 + 11$i$ **57.** trapezoid
**59.** $\frac{3}{25} + \frac{4}{25}i$ **61.** sum: 2, product: 3 **63.** sum: $\frac{2}{3}$, product: $\frac{2}{3}$ **65.** Answers may vary. Sample: $x^2 − 4x + 29 = 0$ **67.** $x = −7$, $y = 3$
**69.** $x = −7$, $y = −3$ **77.** $\frac{3 \pm \sqrt{41}}{4}$ **78.** $\frac{-1 \pm \sqrt{41}}{8}$
**80.**  ; axis of symmetry: $x = −1$
**81.** ; axis of symmetry: $x = 4$
**82.** ; axis of symmetry: $x = 1$
**83.** $y = 3x − 4$ **84.** $y = −0.5x − 2$
**85.** $y = −7x + 10$ **86.** $y = 2x + 8$
**87.**    **88.**
       no solution
**89.**

## Lesson 4-9 pp. 258–264

**Got It? 1.** (−3, 0), (−2, 1) **2.** (−5, 0), (1, 6)
**3. a.** (0, 5), (2, 1) **b.** no solution

---

**4. a.**     **b.** infinite, one, or none

**Lesson Check 1.** (1, 2), (2, 3) **2.** (1, −1), (2, 0)
**3.** (2, −5), $\left(-\frac{4}{3}, \frac{25}{9}\right)$
**4.**    **5.**

**6.** For each system of eqs., linear or quadratic, to solve the system you need to find the pt. (or pts.) of intersection or, in the case of inequalities, the regions of intersection. A linear system of eqs. can have one, infinite, or no solutions, whereas a quadratic systems of eqs. can have one, two, infinite, or no solutions.
**7. a.** two, one, or zero

**b.** two, one, or zero
$y = x^2$
$y = x^2 + 2$
$y = x^2$
$y = -x^2$
$y = x^2 + 1$
$y = -x^2$

**c.** four, three, two, one, or zero
$y = x^2 − 1$
$y = -|x|$

**Exercises**
**9.** (0, 1), (4, 9); **11.** (0, 1), $\left(-\frac{5}{2}, 6\right)$;

**13.** $\left(\frac{-3 + \sqrt{17}}{2}, \frac{-11 + \sqrt{17}}{2}\right), \left(\frac{-3 - \sqrt{17}}{2}, \frac{-11 - \sqrt{17}}{2}\right)$
≈ (0.56, −3.44), (−3.56, −7.56)

**15.** (3, 7), (−2, 2) **17.** (1, −2) **19.** (−3 + $\sqrt{6}$, −1 + $\sqrt{6}$), (−3 − $\sqrt{6}$, −1 − $\sqrt{6}$) **21.** (0, −1) ·
**23.** (0, −3), $\left(\frac{1}{3}, -\frac{31}{9}\right)$ **25.** no solution
**27.**

**29.** width = 20.45 in. and length = 21.45 in.; or width = 6.55 in. and length = 7.55 in.
**31.** (8.42, −5.42), (−1.42, 4.42) **33.** $\left(-1, -\frac{3}{2}\right)$
**35.** (0, −4), (2, −2)
**37.**    **39.**

**41.** (0, −1), (1, 0) **43.** (10, 68), (−3, 16)
**45.** (−8, −16), $\left(-\frac{4}{3}, 4\right)$ **47. a.** $0 < p < 25$
**b.** 13 **49.** no solution **51.** $\left(\frac{1}{2}, \frac{7}{2}\right)$
**53.** ; (0, −2)

---

**55.**  ; $\left(3, \frac{9}{2}\right)$
$y = (x − 3)^2 + 4$
$y = (x − 3)^2 + 5$

**66.** −4 ± 4$i$ **67.** 7 + 7$i$ **68.** 3 + 3$i$ **69.** −1, $-\frac{3}{2}$
**70.** −1, 3 **71.** $\frac{3}{2}, 2$ **72.** −$(k − 2)^2 + 10$
**73.** $y = (x + 3)^2 − 8$ **74.** $y = 2(n − 2)^2 − 11$
**75.** 11$q$ **76.** $2a^2b + ab^2$ **77.** $-ry^2 + 2y$

## Chapter Review pp. 267–272

**1.** standard **2.** discriminant **3.** complex **4.** vertex: (−2, −4); axis of symmetry: $x = −2$; minimum: −6; domain: all real numbers; range: $y \ge −6$ **5.** vertex: (3, 2); axis of symmetry: $x = 3$; maximum: 2; domain: all real numbers; range: $y \le 2$ **6.** vertex: (1, 5); axis of symmetry: $x = 1$; minimum: 5; domain: all real numbers; range: $y \ge 5$ **7.** vertex: (−9, −4); axis of symmetry: $x = −9$; minimum: −4 domain: all real numbers; range: $y \ge −4$
**8.**    translation 4 units up

**9.**    translation 9 units to the right and 2 units up

**10.**    vert. compression by a factor of $\frac{1}{3}$, translation 1 unit to the left and 5 units down

**11.** $y = 2(x − 2)^2 + 1$ **12.** $y = \left(-\frac{1}{3}\right)(x + 5)^2 + 4$
**13.**    **14.**

---

**15.**    **16.**

**17.** $f(x) = 4(x − 1)^2 − 2$ **18.** $f(x) = (x − 4)^2 − 4$
**19.** $f(x) = 8\left(x + \frac{1}{2}\right)^2 − 14$ **20.** $f(x) = -2\left(x + \frac{3}{2}\right)^2 + \frac{29}{2}$
**21.** 1s; 25 ft **22.** $y = x^2 − 6x + 5$
**23.** $y = -2x^2 + 8x − 8$ **24.** $y = x^2 + 3x − 18$
**25.** $y = -0.5x^2 + 2.5x − 7$
**27.** $y = -0.0043x^2 + 0.3521x + 0.3691$
**28.** (3x − 4)(x + 5) **29.** −2(2x − 1)(x − 3) **30.** (x + 10)(x + 4)
**31.** (x − 7)^2 **32.** (3x + 5)^2 **33.** 4(3x − 2)(3x + 2)
**34.** (5x − 2)(5x + 2) **35.** 6x; 6x(x − 4)
**36.** 7; −7(2x^2 + 7) **37.** −2, 6 **38.** −2, $\frac{7}{3}$
**39.** −4, 2 **40.** −9, 2
**41.** 1, −2.6;    **42.** 1.345, −3.345;

**43.** 1.618, −0.618;    **44.** 3.236, −1.236;

**45.** 2, 4 **46.** no real solutions **47.** 4.56, 0.44 **48.** 2, 4
**49.** ±4 **50.** ±$\sqrt{5}$ **51.** ±3 **52.** ±$2\sqrt{3}$ **53.** 9 **54.** $\frac{5}{4}$
**55.** −4 ± $\sqrt{10}$ **56.** 5 ± $\sqrt{38}$ **57.** −1, $\frac{1}{5}$ **58.** 1 ± $i\sqrt{3}$
**59.** $\frac{-3 \pm \sqrt{91}}{10}$ **60.** −1, $\frac{3}{4}$ **61.** −1, $\frac{8}{5}$ **62.** 3 **63.** 4, −1
**64.** 1.744, −0.344 **65.** 164; two **66.** −3; none
**67.** 0; one **68.** 233; two **69.** 10.2736 ft × 16.5472 ft
**70.** 2$i\sqrt{6}$ **71.** −3 + $i\sqrt{2}$ **72.** −50 + 40$i$
**73.** 6 + 4$i\sqrt{6}$ **74.** 3 + 9$i$ **75.** 13 + 20$i$ **76.** 21 − 25$i$
**77.** −12 − 15$i$ **78.** −3 − 2$i$ **79.** $-\frac{1}{2} - \frac{1}{2}i$ **80.** ±3$i$
**81.** $\frac{1}{5} \pm \frac{2}{5}i$ **82.** 2 ± $i\sqrt{6}$ **83.** $\frac{-4 \pm i\sqrt{2}}{7}$
**84.** (7, −6), (−2, 12) **85.** (5, −27), (−2, 8)

**86.** (−5, 37), (3, −27);
(graph) $y = x^2 - 6x$ ; $y = -x^2 - 10x + 12$

**87.** (6.32, 15.64), (−3.32, −3.64);
(graph) $y = 2x + \dots$ ; $y = \dots x - 18$

**88.** (graph) **89.** (graph)

## Chapter 5

### Get Ready! p. 277

**1.** (graph) **2.** (graph) **3.** (graph)

**4.** $y = x^2 + 3x - 4$ **5.** $y = x^2 - 2x + 1$
**6.** $y = -x^2 - x + 12$ **7.** 0.25, −1 **8.** −6.39, 4.39
**9.** −6.38, 0.38 **10.** −4, 5 **11.** −9, 3 **12.** 1, 2
**13.** 24; two real solutions **14.** 0; one real solution
**15.** 0; one real solution **16.** south **17.** The highest pt. in Maine may be lower than the highest pt. in the United States. The relative maximum of a graph for a given region is the maximum for that region only, whereas the maximum of the graph may be greater than or equal to the relative maximum for the region.
**18.** $4x^2 + 4x + 1$

### Lesson 5-1  pp. 280–287

**Got It? 1. a.** $5x^4 + 3x^3 - x$; quartic trinomial
**b.** $-4x^5 + 2x^2 + 13$; quintic trinomial **2.** up and down
**3. a.** end behavior: up and down; two turning points
**b.** end behavior: down and up; no turning points (graphs)
**4. a.** degree: 4 **b.** Answers may vary. Sample: $y = x^5$
**Lesson Check 1.** cubic monomial **2.** quadratic trinomial **3.** $5x^2 + 7x + 3$ **4.** $9x - 3$; up and down
**6.** Yes; the graph of a linear binomial or linear monomial is a straight line; $f(x) = 2x$ **7.** The graph of $y = 4x^3 + 4$ has no turning points, *not* one turning point.
**Exercises 9.** $-3x + 5$; linear binomial
**11.** $x^4 - x^3 + x$; quartic trinomial **13.** $3a^3 + 5a^2 + 1$; cubic trinomial **15.** $12x^4 + 3$; quartic binomial
**17.** $-2x^3$; cubic monomial **19.** $-x^4 + 3x^2$; quartic binomial **21.** up and up **23.** down and up **25.** down and down **27.** up and down **29.** up and down
**31.** up and up **33.** end behavior: up and down; two turning pts. **35.** end behavior: down and up; no turning pts. **37.** end behavior: down and up; no turning pts.
**39.** 3 **41.** $-4a^5 + a^3 + a^2$; quartic trinomial **43.** $6x^2$; quadratic monomial **45.** $-9d^3 - 13$; cubic binomial
**47.** negative; 3 **49.** positive; 4
**51.** For $f(x) = x^3 - 3x^2 - 2x - 6$,

| x | f(x) | 1ˢᵗ diff | 2ⁿᵈ diff | 3ʳᵈ diff |
|---|---|---|---|---|
| 0 | −6 | | | |
| 1 | −10 | −4 | | |
| 2 | −14 | −4 | 0 | |
| 3 | −12 | 2 | 6 | 6 |
| 4 | 2 | 14 | 12 | 6 |
| 5 | 34 | 32 | 18 | 6 |

For $f(x) = ax^3 + bx^2 + cx + d$,

| x | f(x) | 1ˢᵗ diff | 2ⁿᵈ diff | 3ʳᵈ diff |
|---|---|---|---|---|
| 0 | $d$ | | | |
| 1 | $a + b + c + d$ | $a + b + c$ | | |
| 2 | $8a + 4b + 2c + d$ | $7a + 3b + c$ | $6a + 2b$ | |
| 3 | $27a + 9b + 3c + d$ | $19a + 5b + c$ | $12a + 2b$ | $6a$ |
| 4 | $64a + 16b + 4c + d$ | $37a + 7b + c$ | $18a + 2b$ | $6a$ |
| 5 | $125a + 25b + 5c + d$ | $61a + 9b + c$ | $24a + 2b$ | $6a$ |

---

**53. a.**

| x | y | 1ˢᵗ diff | 2ⁿᵈ diff |
|---|---|---|---|
| −2 | 8 | | |
| −1 | 2 | −6 | |
| 0 | 0 | −2 | 4 |
| 1 | 2 | 2 | 4 |
| 2 | 8 | 6 | 4 |

**b.**

| x | y | 1ˢᵗ diff | 2ⁿᵈ diff |
|---|---|---|---|
| −2 | 20 | | |
| −1 | 5 | −15 | |
| 0 | 0 | −5 | 10 |
| 1 | 5 | 5 | 10 |
| 2 | 20 | 15 | 10 |

**c.**

| x | y | 1ˢᵗ diff | 2ⁿᵈ diff |
|---|---|---|---|
| −2 | 18 | | |
| −1 | 3 | −15 | |
| 0 | −2 | −5 | 10 |
| 1 | 3 | 5 | 10 |
| 2 | 18 | 15 | 10 |

**d.**

| x | y | 1ˢᵗ diff | 2ⁿᵈ diff |
|---|---|---|---|
| −2 | 28 | | |
| −1 | 7 | −21 | |
| 0 | 0 | −7 | 14 |
| 1 | 7 | 7 | 14 |
| 2 | 28 | 21 | 14 |

**e.**

| x | y | 1ˢᵗ diff | 2ⁿᵈ diff |
|---|---|---|---|
| −2 | 29 | | |
| −1 | 8 | −21 | |
| 0 | 1 | −7 | 14 |
| 1 | 8 | 7 | 14 |
| 2 | 29 | 21 | 14 |

**f.**

| x | y | 1ˢᵗ diff | 2ⁿᵈ diff |
|---|---|---|---|
| −2 | 23 | | |
| −1 | 5 | −18 | |
| 0 | 1 | −4 | 14 |
| 1 | 11 | 10 | 14 |
| 2 | 35 | 24 | 14 |

Second differences of quadratic functions are constant.

**61.** (3.7, −4.4), (−2.7, 8.4) **62.** (−20, 360)
**63.** (−3, 0), (−1, −8) **64.** $35x - 5y = -2$
**65.** $6x + 2y = -5$ **66.** $2x + 7y = 28$
**67.** $12x - 10y = 5$ **68.** $(x + 4)(x + 3)$
**69.** $(x + 10)(x - 2)$ **70.** $(x - 12)(x - 2)$

### Lesson 5-2  pp. 288–295

**Got It? 1.** $x(x - 4)(x + 3)$
**2.** 0, 3, −5; (graph)
**3. a.** $f(x) = x^2 - 9$ **b.** $P(x) = x^3 - 3x^2 - 9x + 27$
**c.** (graphs) $y = x^2 - 9$ and $y = x^3 - 3x^2 - 9x + 27$
Both graphs have x-intercepts of 3 and −3. The quadratic has up and up end behavior and one turning pt., and the cubic has down and up end behavior and two turning pts.
**4.** 0 is a zero of multiplicity 1, the graph looks close to linear at x = 0; 2 is a zero of multiplicity 2, the graph looks close to quadratic at x = 2. **5.** relative maximum: (−0.86, 3.13); relative minimum: (0.64, −2) **6.** 2.28 in.³
**Lesson Check 1.** 0, 6 **2.** −4, 5 **3.** −12, 7, 9
**4.** $f(x) = x^3 - x$ **5.** $h(x) = x^4 + 4x^3 - 26x^2 - 60x + 225$
**6.** Error in writing the factors: a function that has zeros at 3 and −1 has factors of $x - 3$ and $x + 1$ *not* $x + 3$ and $-1$; so $f(x) = x^2 - 2x - 3$ *not* $x^2 + 2x - 3$.
**Exercises 7.** $x(x + 5)(x + 2)$ **9.** $x(x - 7)(x + 3)$
**11.** $x(x + 4)^2$
**13.** 1, −2; (graph)
**15.** 0, −5, 8; (graph)

---

Selected Answers

**17.** −1, 1, 2; (graph)

**19.** $y = x^3 - 18x^2 + 107x - 210$ **21.** $y = x^3 + 9x^2 + 15x - 25$ **23.** $y = x^3 + 2x^2 - x - 2$
**25.** $y = x^4 - 5x^3 + 6x^2$ **27.** −3 (multiplicity 3)
**29.** −1, 0, ½ **31.** 4 (multiplicity 2) **33.** −3/2, 1 (multiplicity 2) **35.** relative maximum: (−3.19, 24.19); relative minimum: (0.52, −1.38) **37.** relative maximum: (2.15, 12.32); relative minimum: (−0.15, −12.32)
**39. a.** $\ell = 16 - 2x$; $w = 12 - 2x$; $h = x$
**b.** $V = x(16 - 2x)(12 - 2x)$
(calculator: Maximum X=2.2629072 Y=194.04736) 194 in.³, 2.26 in.
**41.** $y = -2x(x + 5)(x - 4)$ **43.** 1 ft increase in each dimension **45.** $V = 12x^3 - 27x^2$ **47.** relative maximum: (2.53, 10.51); relative minimum: (5.14, −7.14); ¾, 4, 6
**49.** no relative maximum; relative minimum: (−1, −1); −2, 0 **51.** Answers may vary. Sample: The linear factors can be determined by examining the x-intercepts of the graph. **53.** −1, 4, ¾ **61.** $-3x^5 + 3x^2 - 1$; quintic trinomial **62.** $-7x^4 - x^3$; quartic binomial **63.** $x^3 - 2$; cubic binomial **64.** $(x + 4)(x + 1)$ **65.** $(x - 5)(x + 3)$
**66.** $(x - 6)^2$ **67.** −3, 2 **68.** ½, 3 **69.** ±5/2

### Lesson 5-3  pp. 296–302

**Got It? 1. a.** ±1, ±2i **b.** 0, 2, 3 **2. a.** ±2, ±2i
**b.** 0, −4, 2 **c.** $-1 \pm i\sqrt{3}$ **3. a.** −1.84
**b.** The second method seems to be a more reliable way to find the solutions because you do not risk missing a pt. of intersection. **4.** 7, 8, 9
**Lesson Check 1.** $(x - 6)(x + 3)$
**2.** $(x - 3)(x^2 + 3x + 9)$ **3.** $(x^2 + 4)(x + 3)$
**4.** $(x - 2)(x + 2)(x^2 + 2)$ **5.** −4, ¼ **6.** −2, 0, 1
**7. a.** difference of squares **b.** sum of cubes **c.** difference of cubes **d.** difference of squares **8.** Graphing; imaginary numbers don't exist on the x-axis. **9.** Method 1: Graph $y = x^6 - x^2$. Find the zeros for the real solutions.

Method 2: Factor and solve x for $x^6 - x^2 = 0$.
$x^2(x^4 - 1) = x^2(x^2 - 1)(x^2 + 1) =$
$x^2(x - 1)(x + 1)(x^2 + 1) = 0$
$x = 0, \pm 1$
**Exercises 11.** 10, $-5 \pm 5i\sqrt{3}$ **13.** ¼, $\dfrac{-1 \pm i\sqrt{3}}{8}$
**15.** ⅓, −⅚ **17.** 4, $-2 \pm 2i\sqrt{3}$ **19.** −½, $\dfrac{-1 \pm i\sqrt{3}}{2}$
**21.** ±2 ± 2√2, ±3i **25.** 1, 5, **27.** 0, 1
**29.** 0, −1, −2 **31.** 0, −0.5, 1.5 **33.** 1, 7 **35.** −2, 5
**37.** 16 yrs old; $x^2(x + 2) = 3x + 4560$; (graph)
**39.** 0, $5 \pm 2\sqrt{3}$ **41.** 0, $\dfrac{5 \pm 5\sqrt{2}}{2}$ **43.** 4/3, $\dfrac{-2 \pm 2\sqrt{3}}{3}$
**45.** $1.9(1 \pm i)$, $-1.9(1 \pm i)$ **47.** 0, ±1, ±2 **49.** −1, ±i
**51.** 2 ft × 3 ft × 6 ft **53.** 5 m
**55.** ±3, ±1; $y = (x - 1)(x + 1)(x - 3)(x + 3)$; (graph)
**65.** $3(x - 4)(x - 2)$ **66.** $2x(x + 3)^2(x - 1)$
**67.** $x^2(x - 5)(x + 1)$ **68.** −2, 6 **69.** ±6
**70.** −½, 3 **71.** 12 **72.** −5/4

### Lesson 5-4  pp. 303–310

**Got It? 1.** 3x − 8, R 0 **2. a.** yes; $P(x) = (x + 5)(x^4 - 1)$
**b.** $(x + 2)(3x + 1)$ in.; height: (x + 2) in.; length: (x + 3) in. **5.** 0
**Lesson Check 1.** 2x + 3, R 5 **2.** $x^2 + 2x + 5$
**3.** $x^2 + x - 2$ **4.** $4x^2 + x - 6$, R 6
**5.** $9x^2 + 12x + 40$, R 120 **6.** $x - a$ is a factor of $P(x)$.
**7.** The polynomials need to be written in standard form since the leading coefficient of both polynomials determines the leading term of the quotient.
**8.** Answers may vary. Check student's work.
**Exercises 9.** x − 8 **11.** $x^2 + 4x + 3$, R 5
**13.** $3x^2 + 3x + 2$ **15.** x − 10, R 40 **17.** no
**19.** yes **21.** R 4 **25.** x + 1, R 4 **27.** $x^2 - 3x + 9$
**29.** $y = (x + 1)(x + 3)(x - 2)$
**31.** width = x; length = x + 3; height = x − 2
**33.** 0 **35.** 12 **37.** 10 **39.** 0 **41.** The constant term of the dividend is missing and the divisor is −1 *not* 1: $x^3 - x^2 - 2x = x(x + 1)(x - 2)$

---

Selected Answers

**43.** x + 2 **45.** $x^3 - 3x^2 + 12x - 35$, R 109
**47.** x + 4 **49.** no **51.** yes **53.** yes **55.** no
**57.** $x^3 - x^2 + 1$ **59.** $x^3 + 7x + 5$
**61.** $x^3 - 2x^2 - x + 6$ **71.** 0, −1 **72.** 0, 1
**73.** −5, 0, 5 **74.** $\dfrac{-3 \pm \sqrt{17}}{2}$ **75.** $-1 \pm \sqrt{3}$
**76.** −5/7 **77.** $\dfrac{5 \pm \sqrt{5}}{2}$ **78.** ±√2 **79.** $\dfrac{-7 \pm \sqrt{5}}{2}$
**80.** (graph) **81.** (graph)
**82.** (graph) **83.** 24 **84.** 5 **85.** 23 − 11i

### Lesson 5-5  pp. 312–317

**Got It? 1.** ⅔ **2.** 2, −1, −3/2 **3.** 3 + 2i
**4.** $P(x) = x^4 - 14x^3 + 69x^2 - 194x + 208$ **5. a.** There are three or one positive real roots and one negative real root. **b.** Real roots can be confirmed graphically because they are x-intercepts. Complex roots cannot be confirmed graphically because they have an imaginary component.
**Lesson Check 1.** ±1, ±2 **2.** ±1, ±2, ±3, ±6, ±½, ±3/2 **3.** ±1, ±2, ±3, ±4, ±6, ±12, ±½, ±¾, ±3/2, ±⅔, ±4/3, ±⅓ **4.** $P(x) = x^3 - 2x^2 + 4x + 16$ **5.** $P(x) = x^3 + 4x^2 + 4x + 16$
**6.** Answers may vary. Samples: 1 + 2i, 1 − 2i; $1 + \sqrt{2}$, $1 - \sqrt{2}$ **7. a.** never; 5 does not divide 8 evenly **b.** always; −2 divides 8 evenly **8.** Complex number roots come in pairs; if −4i is a root, so is 4i.
**Exercises 9.** ±1; no rational roots **11.** ±1, ±2, ±4, ±½; no rational roots **13.** ±1, ±2, ±3, ±4, ±6, ±12, ±½, ±3/2; no rational roots **15.** ±1, ±3, ±½, ±⅓, ±⅙; no rational roots **17.** 3, ±1 **19.** 2, ±√3 **21.** ±2, ±i
**23.** $P(x) = x^3 + 24x + 135$ **25.** $P(x) = x^2 - 18x + 90$
**27.** $P(x) = x^4 - 10x^3 + 294x^2 - 1690x + 21{,}125$
**29.** $P(x) = x^4 - 58x^3 + 1290x^2 - 13{,}066x + 51{,}545$
**31.** two or no positive real roots; one negative real root **33.** no rational roots **35.** no rational roots **37.** no rational

**roots 39.** $P(x) = x^4 + 3x^3 + 207x^2 + 675x - 4050$
**41.** $P(x) = x^4 + 6x^3 + 27x^2 - 366x - 518$ **43.** Error in second line, sign of second term; the line should be: $P(-1) = -x^3 + x^2 - x + 1$. Since there are three sign changes in $P(-x)$, there are three or one negative real roots. **45.** height: 5 ft; bases: 10 ft, 14 ft **55.** $x^2 + 6x + 6$, R 3 **56.** $8x^2 - 36x + 216$, R −1289 **57.** 7x − 3, R 2
**58.** ±3i **59.** ±9i **60.** ±12i **61.** $-5x^4 + 6x^2 + 9x + 11$; quartic polynomial of four terms
**62.** $-4x^5 + 7x^3 + 13x + 2$; quintic polynomial of four terms

### Lesson 5-6  pp. 319–324

**Got It? 1.** 0, 1, −5, 2 **2. a.** −1, 2, $\dfrac{1 \pm \sqrt{23}}{4}$
**b. i.** A 5th degree polynomial function has four, two, or no turning pts. Three turning pts. are visible, so there must be a fourth one. This will turn the graph back across the x-axis. **ii.** The Fundamental Thm. of Algebra states there will be five roots, and the Conjugate Root Thm. requires pairs of irrational or complex roots. Only two zeros appear in the graph, so there are three zeros remaining. Of the remaining roots, either there are three real roots, or one real and two complex roots. Either way, there is at least one real root that does not appear in the graph.
**Lesson Check 1.** four roots **2.** fourteen roots
**3.** 5, ±4i **4.** 0, 2, ±i **5.** By the Fundamental Thm. of Algebra, polynomial equation of degree n has exactly n roots. **6.** Answers may vary. Sample: $y = x^4 + 8x^2 + 16$ **7.** Use synthetic division to test for and factor out linear factors until a quadratic factor is obtained. Then use the Quadratic Formula if the quadratic factor cannot be factored further.
**Exercises 9.** −1, ±2i **11.** −1, 2, 4 **13.** 2, ±√3
**15.** 0, ±3, ±i **17.** 3, ±i **19.** 2, ±√3 **21.** ±2, ±i
**23.** −6, ±i **25.** ±4, ±5, ±9, ±18 **27.** five complex roots; one, three, or five real roots; possible rational roots: ±1, ±2, ±3, ±6, ±9, ±18 **29.** six complex roots; zero, two, four, or six real roots; possible rational roots: ±¼, ±½, ±¾, ±1, ±3/2, ±2, ±3, ±4, ±6, ±8, ±12, ±24 **31.** −2, ±√5 **33.** −2, ⅔, 3
**35.** 3, $-1 \pm i\sqrt{2}$ **37.** −½, −1, 2 **39.** 3 bridges
**41.** sometimes **43.** always **45.** Answers may vary. Sample: $y = x^4 + 3x^2 + 2$ **54.** $x^4 + 6x^3 + 14x^2 + 24x + 40$ **55.** $3 \pm 2\sqrt{3}$ **56.** $\dfrac{-5 \pm i\sqrt{47}}{4}$
**57.** $\dfrac{3 \pm \sqrt{23}}{4}$ **58.** $f(x) = -x^2 + 2x + 3$
**59.** $f(x) = 2x^2 + 24x + 75$ **60.** $x^3 + 3x^2 + 3x + 1$
**61.** $x^3 - 9x^2 + 27x - 27$ **62.** $x^5 - 8x^4 + 6x^3 + 14x^2 - 32x + 16$ **63.** $x^2 - 2x + 1$ **64.** $x^4 + 15x^2 + 75x + 125$
**65.** $-x^3 + 12x^2 + 48x + 64$

## Lesson 5-7 — pp. 326–330

**Got It? 1.** $a^8 + 8a^7b + 28a^6b^2 + 56a^5b^3 + 70a^4b^4 + 56a^3b^5 + 28a^2b^6 + 8ab^7 + b^8$ **2. a.** $16x^4 - 96x^3 + 216x^2 - 216x + 81$ **b.** If you express 11 as $(10 + 1)$ and calculate the powers using Pascal's triangle, it will be the coefficients.

**Lesson Check 1.** $x^3 + 3x^2a + 3xa^2 + a^3$
**2.** $x^3 - 10x^4 + 40x^3 - 80x^2 + 80x - 32$
**3.** $4x^2 + 16x + 16$ **4.** $27a^3 - 54a^2 + 36a - 8$
**5. a.** yes **b.** yes **c.** no **6.** The coefficients for the expansion of $(a + b)^n$ are equal to the numbers in the $n$th row of Pascal's Triangle, respectively. **7.** 13; $n + 1$

**Exercises 9.** $a^4 + 8a^3 + 24a^2 + 32a + 16$
**11.** $x^5 - 15x^4 + 75x - 125$ **13.** $x^{10} + 20x^9 + 180x^8 + 960x^7 + 3360x^6 + 8064x^5 + 13,440x^4 + 15,360x^3 + 11,520x^2 + 5120x + 1024$ **15.** $b^9 + 27b^8 + 324b^7 + 2268b^6 + 10,206b^5 + 30,618b^4 + 61,236b^3 + 78,732b^2 + 59,049b + 19,683$
**17.** $a^4 + 12a^3b + 54a^2b^2 + 108ab^3 + 81b^4$
**19.** $65,536 - 131,072x + 114,688x^2 - 57,344x^3 + 17,920x^4 - 3584x^5 + 448x^6 - 32x^7 + x^8$
**21.** $27a^3 - 1188a^2 + 441a - 343$
**23.** $81j^4 - 1188j^3 + 6534j^2 - 15,972j + 14,641$
**25. a. 6 b.** $489,888$ **27.** $135x^4$ **29.** $625b^8$ **31.** The challenge of the Binomial Theorem occurs when there is a coefficient with the $x$. However, it is much more efficient to use the Binomial Theorem than FOIL when expanding a binomial that is raised to a high power. **33.** $x^{20} + 40x^{18} + 720x^{16} + 7680x^{14} + 53,760x^{12} + 258,048x^{10} + 860,160x^8 + 1,966,080x^6 + 2,949,120x^4 + 2,621,440x^2 + 1,048,576$ **35.** $a^5 - 5a^4b + 10a^3b^4 - 10a^2b^6 + 5ab^8 - b^{10}$ **37.** $256x^{15} - 1792x^3y + 4704x^2y^2 - 5488xy^3 + 2401y^4$ **39.** $4096x^{18} + 12,288x^{15}y^2 + 15,360x^{12}y^4 + 10,240x^9y^6 + 3840x^6y^8 + 768x^3y^{10} + 64y^{12}$ **41.** $125a^3 + 150a^2b + 60ab^2 + 8b^3$ **43.** $-32y^{10} + 80y^8x - 80y^6x^2 + 40y^4x^3 - 10y^2x^4 + x^5$ **45.** Answers may vary. Sample: Since one of the terms is negative $(-y)$ and it is alternately raised to odd and even powers, the term is negative when raised to an odd power and positive when raised to an even power. **58.** $-3, -1, \dfrac{-3 \pm i\sqrt{11}}{2}$
**59.** $1, \pm1; \pm3i$ **60.** $-4, \dfrac{-3 \pm i\sqrt{7}}{4}$ **61.** $-1, 1, 2, 7$
**62.** $-18 + 43i$ **63.** $600i$ **64.** $-2$ **65.** $\dfrac{7}{8} + \dfrac{3}{4}i$
**66.** $2x^3 + 5x^2 - x + 9$; cubic polynomial of 4 terms
**67.** $-7x^2 + 4x + 1$; quadratic trinomial
**68.** $12x^4 - 3x^3 - 9x^2 + x - 8$; quartic polynomial of 5 terms

## Lesson 5-8 — pp. 331–338

**Got It? 1.** $y = 1.667x^3 + 1.3 \times 10^{-12} x^2 - 4.667x + 5$ **2.** 15.58 billion lbs **2.** Answers may vary. Sample: The cubic model would fit the data better than the linear model because of the $(n + 1)$ Pt. Principle. Both models have down and up end behavior and increasing growth. The cubic shows slowing growth followed by rapidly increasing growth.
**4. a.** $y = 0.269867411x - 3.919692952$

Years (after 1900)

**b.** 1980: 17.7 lbs; 2000: 23.07 lbs; 2012: 26.31 lbs; most confident for the yrs 1980 and 2000, since they are within the domain of the data set; least confident for the yr 2012, since it is outside the domain of the data set
**Lesson Check 1.** linear **2.** quadratic **3.** cubic
**4.** quartic **5.** interpolation since the data point is within the domain of the data set **6.** yes, since the four pts. pass the vertical-line test, a cubic function will fit the pts.; $y = -x^3 - 3x^2 - 3x$ **7.** cubic model; the closer $R^2$ is to 1, the better the fit

**Exercises 9.** $y = \frac{1}{3}x - 3$ **11.** $y = -0.929x^2 + 7.786x + 4$ **13.** $y = x^2 - 6x + 1$ **15.** $y = 2x^3 + x^2 - 6x + 4$ **17.** (where $x = $ yrs after 1900) quadratic: $y = -1.25 \times 10^{-4}x^2 - 0.003x + 2.804$, cubic: $y = -8.33 \times 10^{-6}x^3 + 0.002x^2 - 0.190x + 8.142$; cubic; cubic **19.** linear: $y = -0.057x + 19.93$, quadratic: $y = -0.025x^2 + 0.14x + 19.595$; quadratic; quadratic **21.** 1950: 2.60%; 1988: 1.23%; 2010: 0.35% **23.** January: 19.714 millions of barrels/day; March: 19.8 millions of barrels/day; October: 18.535 millions of barrels/day **25.** cubic: $y = 10.25x^3 + 5x^2 - 2.25x - 8.2$; quartic: $y = 2.042x^4 + 10.25x^3 - 4.042x^2 - 2.25x - 4$; quartic, $(R^2 = )$ **27.** $y = -0.275x^4 + 0.85x^3 - 4.025x^2 - 8.15x + 7$ **29.** $y = 0.0611511911x^3 - 0.9276466231x^2 + 6.184642324x + 1.750778723$; $R^2 = 0.9994739763$; good fit **31.** $y = 0.111x^4 - 45.618x^3 + 6997.73x^2 - 476,931.355x + 12,185,696.59$ **33.** A quadratic model would be more appropriate, given the real world context. According to the cubic model, there would be a negative number of students enrolled in the course in the year 2024.

**35. a.**

A cubic model seems to be most appropriate.
**b.** The model is $y = 0.0002268842 3x^3 - 0.0525547786x^2 + 3.505260295x - 38.64568765$.
**c.** 17.3% **d.** yes; $R^2 = 0.99288$ **43.** $32x^5 + 240x^4 + 720x^3 + 1080x^2 + 810x + 243$ **44.** $1331x^3 - 363x^2y + 33x - 1$ **45.** $4096 - 6144x + 3456x^2 - 864x^3 + 81x^4$ **46.** $64 + 432x + 972x^2 + 729x^3$ **47.** $|x - 8| < 1$ **48.** $|x - \frac{8}{3}| \le \frac{1}{3}$
**49.** $|y - 2.8| < 1.1$ **50.** $|t - 750| < 250$
**51.** $s = \sqrt{A}$ **52.** $t = \frac{F}{2\pi} - \frac{5}{2}$ **53.** $r = \frac{5}{2\pi}$ **54.** $b = \frac{A}{h}$
**55.** **56.** **57.** **58.**

## Lesson 5-9 — pp. 339–345

**Got It? 1.** $y = 2(x + 3)^3 - 4$ **2.** $1 - \sqrt[3]{2}$
**3. a.** Answers may vary. Sample: $y = ax^3$, where $y$ varies directly with the $b$th power of $x$. So $y = x^3$ has end behavior of down and up with no turning pt. Thus, at most, there is one real root. **b.** Both $y = x^3$ and $y = 4x^3$ pass through the origin, have the same end behavior of down and up, and no turning pts. So $y = 4x^3$ is $y = x^3$ stretched vertically by a factor of 4. **4.** 972 kW
**Lesson Check 1.** $-2$ **2.** 3 **3.** $\frac{1}{5}$ **4.** No; a power function is of the form $y = ax^b$, where $y$ varies directly with the $b$th power of $x$.

**Exercises 7.** $y = 3(x - 1)^3 + 2$
**9.** $y = -(x + 5)^3 - 1$ **11.** $y = -3(x + \frac{1}{3})^3 + \frac{3}{4}$
**13.** $\frac{8}{9}$ **15.** $-\frac{2}{15}$ **17.** $1 - \frac{1}{2}\sqrt[3]{20}$ **For Exercises 19–24, answers may vary. Samples: 19.** $x^4 - x^3 - x^2 - x - 2$ **21.** $x^4 - 2x^3 - 2x^2 - 2x - 3$

## Chapter Review — pp. 347–352

**1.** D **2.** B **3.** C **4.** A **5.** $y = -x^4 + 12$; quartic binomial; down and down **6.** $y = -x^2 - x + 7$; quadratic trinomial; up and up **7.** $y = -x^4 + 2x^3 + 3x^2 - 6x + 12$; quartic polynomial of five terms; down and down **8.** $y = x^3 + 2x^2 - 4x + 8$; cubic polynomial of four terms; down and up **9.** $y = x^4 - 3x^3 + 3x^2 + 10$; quartic polynomial of four terms; up and up **10.** 3 **11.** If $n$ is even there are an odd number of turning points; if $n$ is odd there are an even number of turning points.
**12.** $f(x) = x^3 - 4x^2 - 11x + 6$ **13.** $f(x) = x^3 - 2x$ **14.** $f(x) = x^3 + 6x^2 + 11x - 6$
**15.** $f(x) = x^3 - 3x^2 - 6x + 8$ **16.** $0, -2$ (multiplicity 3) **17.** 2 (multiplicity 2), $-2$ (multiplicity 2) **18.** $0, -\frac{1}{2}, 1$ **19.** 5, $-2$ (multiplicity 2) **20.** relative maximum: $(0.8672, -1.9351)$; relative minimums: $(0, -3)$, $(2.8828, -12.1704)$; zeros: $x = -0.5992$, $x = 3.7115$ **21.** relative maximum: $(-0.8441, 9.3023)$; relative minimum: $(0.7108, -0.0964)$; zeros: $x = -1.6180$, $x = 0.6180$, $x = 0.8$ **22.** relative minimum: $(1, -4)$; zeros: $x = -0.2491$, $x = 1.6633$ **23.** relative maximum: $(-0.4142, -3.3432)$; relative minimum: $(2.4142, -14.6569)$; zero: $x = 4$ **24.** 3, 8
**25.** $-\frac{3}{2}$ **26.** $0, \dfrac{-1 \pm \sqrt{37}}{2}$ **27.** $2\frac{1}{2}, \dfrac{1 \pm \sqrt{2}}{2}$
**28.** no real roots; **29.** 2.3949;

**23.** $x^4 + 5x^3 + 5x^2 + 5x + 4$ **25.** 38.4 ≈ 38 slices **27.** 90 lb·ft²/s² **29.** Yes; using parent function $y = x^2$, stretch vertically by a factor of 2, then translate 5 units up and 3 units to the right. **31.** Yes; using parent function $y = x^2$, translate 9 units down and 4 units to the right. **33.** Yes; using parent function $y = x^3$, stretch vertically by a factor of 4 and reflect across the $x$-axis. **35.** reflection across the $x$-axis, vert. stretch by a factor of 2, translation 1 unit up and 1 unit to the right **37.** vert. stretch by a factor of 3, translation 2 units down and 1 unit to the right **39.** reflection across the $x$-axis, translation 2 units up and 4 units to the right **41.** The parent function, $y = x^3$, has only one $x$-intercept. **43.** Error in (2) "a transformation of $y = x^2$." Some polynomials do not contain an $x^2$ term.
**50.** $y = -2x^3 + 3x^2 - x - 2$ **51.** $y = 3x^3 - 5x - 3$ **52.** $y = -\frac{1}{6}x + \frac{1}{2}$ **53.** $y = -3x + 5$ **54.** yes **55.** no **56.** $x^2(x^6 + 1)$ **57.** $(x - y)(x + y)(x^2 + y^2)$ **58.** $13x^3y^5(13x^3y^6 - 1)$

---

**30.** 4.87 in. × 2.87 in. × 2.87 in. **31.** $x^2 + 6x + 9$ **32.** $2x^2 + x - 3$, R 1 **33.** yes **34.** no **35.** $x^2 - 1$ **36.** $2x^2 - 6x + 2$, R $-20$ **37.** $5x^2 + 18x + 36$, R 12 **38.** $-14$ **39.** 2 **40.** $\pm1, \pm2, \pm3, \pm6$
**41.** $\pm1, \pm2, \pm\frac{1}{3}, \pm\frac{2}{3}$ **42.** $\pm1, \pm2, \pm3, \pm4, \pm6, \pm12, \pm\frac{1}{4}, \pm\frac{1}{2}, \pm\frac{3}{4}, \pm\frac{3}{2}$ **43.** $\pm1, \pm7, \pm\frac{1}{3}, \pm\frac{7}{3}$ **44.** $-3$
**45.** $-5$ **46.** 1, $-4, -\frac{1}{2}$ **47.** 1, $-2, -\frac{4}{3}$ **48.** $1 + i$
**49.** $5 - \sqrt{3}$, $\sqrt{2}$ **50.** $3i, -7i$ **51.** $-2 - \sqrt{11}, -4 + 6i$ **52.** $y = x^2 - 17x + 72$ **53.** $y = x^3 + 3x^2 + 25x + 75$ **54.** $y = x^3 - 12x + 37$ **55.** $y = x^4 - 4x^3 - 10x^2 + 68x - 80$ **56.** one positive real zero; two or no negative real zeros **57.** two or no positive real zeros; one negative real zero **58.** two, or no positive real zeros; no negative real zeros **59.** two, or no positive real zeros; two or no negative real zeros **60.** 3 **61.** 4 **62.** 5 **63.** 6
**64.** 1, $-3 \pm \sqrt{7}$ **65.** 2, $\pm\sqrt{5}$ **66.** 1, $\dfrac{1 \pm \sqrt{15}}{2}$
**67.** $-3, 6, \dfrac{1 \pm \sqrt{3}}{2}$ **68.** 9 **69.** 1, 8, 28, 56, 70, 56, 28, 8, 1 **70.** 16 **71.** 105 **72.** $x^3 + 27x^2 + 243x + 729$
**73.** $b^4 + 8b^3 + 24b^2 + 32b + 16$
**74.** $27a^3 + 27a^2 + 9a + 1$ **75.** $x^2 - 15x^2 + 75x - 125$ **76.** $x^3 - 6x^2y + 12xy^2 - 8y^3$
**77.** $243a^5 + 1620a^4b + 4320a^3b^2 + 5760a^2b^3 + 3840ab^4 + 1024b^5$ **78.** $x^6 + 6x^5 + 15x^4 + 20x^3 + 15x^2 + 6x + 1$ **79.** $64x^6 - 192x^5 + 240x^4 - 160x^3 + 60x^2 - 12x + 1$ **80.** 108 **81.** $6a^2c^2$
**82.** $y = 3.5x^2 - 4.5x + 5$
**83.** $y = 2.082999x - 2.475234$;
$y = 0.086232x^2 + 0.008929x + 5.963724$;
$y = -0.002554x^3 + 0.178307x^2 - 0.913645x + 8.205128$; cubic is best fit since $R^2 = 1$.
**84.** $y = -5.8667x^3 + 120.5333x^2 - 629.2667x + 1421$; $1097.2 \approx 1097$ **85.** $y = -(x - 2)^3 + 1$
**86.** $y = 6(x + 3)^3$ **87.** Answers may vary. Sample: $y = x^4 - 10x^3 + 25x^2 - 10x + 24$

## Chapter 6

**Get Ready! p. 357 1.** domain: {1, 2, 3, 4}, range: {2, 3, 4, 5} **2.** domain: {1, 2, 3, 4}, range: {2} **3.** domain: all real numbers, range: $y = -8$ **4.** domain: all real numbers, range: $y \ge 3$
**5.** **6.**

**7.**

**8.** $3y^2 - 14y + 8$ **9.** $49a^2 - 100$
**10.** $x^3 + 4x^2 - 15x - 18$ **11.** $-7, 2$ **12.** $\frac{5}{2}, 3$
**13.** $-4, \frac{2}{5}$ **14.** $\frac{1}{2}$ **15.** $\pm\frac{2}{3}$ **16.** $\pm\sqrt{7}$ **17.** Yes; it is a better deal to first take 50% off the shirt then take the $10 coupon. **18.** A "one-to-one function" is a function where there is exact correspondence of every element of the domain with exactly one element of the range.
**19.** the non-negative root

## Lesson 6-1 — pp. 361–367

**Got It? 1. a.** 0; $-1$; 2 **b.** $\pm0.1$; no real square root; $\pm\frac{6}{11}$ **c.** Any negative number multiplied by itself an even number of times will always be positive. Therefore, there can be no real $n$th roots (where $n$ is even) for a negative number **b. 2. a.** $-3$ **b.** no real root **c.** 7 **d.** no real root **3. a.** $9x^2$ **b.** $a^4b^5$ **c.** $|x|y^4$ **4.** 0; 100
**Lesson Check 1.** $\pm5$ **2.** $\pm0.4$ **3.** no real root **4.** $3|b|$ **5.** $5a^4|b^9|$ **6.** $-5a$ **7.** 16 has two real fourth roots, $\pm2$. **8.** The real roots of a number are the positive and negative (but not imaginary) roots of the number; the principal root of a number is the nonnegative root of the number. **9.** $n$ is odd.
**Exercises 11.** $\pm0.07$ **13.** $\pm\frac{8}{13}$ **15.** 0.5 **17.** 0.07
**19.** none **21.** $\pm\frac{19}{3}$ **23.** 0.5 **25.** $-3$ **27.** $3y^2$ **29.** $2y^2$ **31.** $\pm10$ **33.** $\pm0.5$ **35.** about 0.8 in. **37. a.** about 79.01 ft **b.** about 44.44 ft **39.** $\frac{1}{4}$ **41.** $\frac{1}{4}$ **43.** Answers may vary. Sample: $\sqrt[4]{-8}a^4$, $-\sqrt[4]{16}a^8$, $\sqrt[6]{-32}x^{10}$ **45.** all; $x^2$ is always nonnegative **47.** some; they are equal for $x = -1, 0, 1$ **49.** $y = (x + 2)^3 + 3$ **51.** $y = -(x - 3)^3 - 2$
**61.** $y = -(x - 2)^3 + 1$ **63.** $\dfrac{5 \pm \sqrt{11}}{2}$ **64.** $\frac{11}{6}, \frac{3}{2}$ **65.** $2x^3y^3$ **66.** $\dfrac{6c}{2}$
**67.** $-\frac{4}{9}$

## Lesson 6-2 — pp. 367–373

**Got It? 1. a.** No; the indexes are different. **b.** Yes; $\sqrt[3]{10}$
**2.** $4x^3\sqrt[3]{2x}$ **3.** $15x^3y^3\sqrt[3]{y}$ **4. a.** $5|x|$ **b.** yes; $\dfrac{3x^2\sqrt[3]{2x}}{x\sqrt{2x}} = 3x$ **5. a.** $\dfrac{\sqrt[3]{175xy}}{5y}$ **b.** D; there is no $y$ in the expression.
**Lesson Check 1.** $\sqrt[3]{10}$ **2.** $-3\sqrt[4]{4}$ **3.** Not possible, the indexes are different. **4.** not possible; $\sqrt{-4}$ is not a real number. **5.** $\sqrt[3]{3x}$ **6.** $x^2\sqrt[3]{3x}$ **7.** $2x\sqrt[4]{4x}$ **8.** $x \le 0$; for $x \le 0, -4x^3 \ge 0$ and $\sqrt{-4x^3}$ is real. **9.** error in line 1: $\dfrac{\sqrt[3]{x^3}}{\sqrt[4]{x^2}} \ne \dfrac{7 - 4\sqrt[4]{x}}{\sqrt{2}}$

---

**Exercises 11.** 4 **13.** not possible **15.** 5 **17.** 6
**19.** $2x\sqrt{5x}$ **21.** 5 **23.** not possible **25.** $-5x^2y\sqrt{2}\sqrt{2y^2}$ **27.** $-2xy\sqrt{y}$ **29.** $8y^3\sqrt{5y}$ **31.** $40x|y|\sqrt{3}$ **33.** $\dfrac{2\sqrt[3]{y}}{x}$ **35.** $4xy^2\sqrt{3y}$ **37.** 10 **39.** $2x^2y^2\sqrt{2}$ **41.** $\dfrac{x^2}{y}$ **47.** $4\sqrt{3}$ **49.** $\dfrac{\sqrt{15y}}{5y}$ **51.** $\dfrac{\sqrt[3]{150ab^2}}{5b}$ **53.** 6 cm **55.** about 212 mi/h **57.** $5\sqrt{10}$ **59.** $3x^2\sqrt{3}xy$ **61.** $10 + 7\sqrt{2}\sqrt{6}$ **63.** $\dfrac{|x|\sqrt{10y}}{2y^2}$
**65.** $\dfrac{\sqrt[3]{3x}}{3x}$ **67.** $\dfrac{\sqrt[3]{2y^2}}{xy}$ **69.** 4 g/cm³ **71.** Check students' work. **73.** always **75.** sometimes **85.** $11|a^{45}|$
**86.** $9c^{24}d^{32}$ **87.** $4a^{27}$ **88.** $2y^5$ **89.** $y^2 - 4y + 16$, R $-128$ **90.** $4a^2 - 8a + 13$ **91.** $y^3 - 3y + 2$ **92.** 25 **93.** $\dfrac{121}{4}$
**94.** $\dfrac{121}{36}$ **95.** $\dfrac{3}{4}j + \dfrac{1}{2}j$ **96.** $10 - \dfrac{15}{2}j$ **97.** $\dfrac{16}{25} - \dfrac{4}{5}j$
**98.** $-\dfrac{7}{74} - \dfrac{5}{74}j$

## Lesson 6-3 — pp. 374–380

**Got It? 1. a.** The indexes are different. You cannot combine the expressions. **b.** $7x\sqrt{xy}$ **c.** $2\sqrt[3]{3x}$
**2. a.** about 84.9 in. **b.** The length of the diagonal of a square of side 6 can be found using the Pythagorean Thm. to be $\sqrt{6^2 + 6^2} = \sqrt{72}$. Using this information you can calculate the perimeter at the end. **3.** $6\sqrt{2}$
**4.** $46 + 16\sqrt{5}$ **5. a.** $\sqrt{21} - \sqrt{35}$
**b.** $\frac{1}{2}(12x + 4x\sqrt{6})$ **c.** after rationalizing; When the numerator is multiplied by the conjugate of the denominator it is more convenient if $\sqrt{8}$ is not yet simplified.
**Lesson Check 1.** can combine **2.** cannot combine **3.** $\sqrt{3x}\sqrt{3x}$ **4.** $7\sqrt{3}$ **5.** 13 **6.** $75 + 34\sqrt{5}$ **7.** $-16 - 3\sqrt{2}$ **8. a.** not like radicals **b.** like radicals; $9xy\sqrt{3xy}$ **c.** not like radicals **9.** They are alike in that you can also use the FOIL method and Distr. Prop. to multiply binomial radical expressions; they are different in that you cannot multiply like radicals together if they do not have the same index.
**Exercises 11.** $4\sqrt{3}$ **13.** $-2\sqrt{4}$ **15.** $5\sqrt[3]{y^2}$
**17.** $\sqrt{3x}$ **19.** $7\sqrt{2}$ **21.** $5\sqrt{3} - 6\sqrt{2}$ **23.** $8 + 4\sqrt{5}$ **25.** $63 - 38\sqrt{2}$ **27.** $49 + 12\sqrt{13}$ **29.** 14 **31.** $-40$ **33.** $\sqrt{3}\sqrt{2} + 1$ **35.** $7 + 7\sqrt{3}$ **37.** 140.3 in.² **39.** $8\sqrt{13}$ **41.** $5\sqrt{3} - 4\sqrt{3}$ **43.** $2\sqrt{13}$
**45.** $-11 + \sqrt{21}$ **47.** $84 + 24\sqrt{6}$ **49.** 2 **51.** $4x\sqrt{3}$ **53.** Answers may vary. Sample: Without simplifying first, you must estimate three square roots and then add the estimates. If they are first simplified, then they can be combined as $13\sqrt{2}$. Then only one square root need be estimated. **55.** Answers may vary. Sample: $(\sqrt{7} + 2)(\sqrt{7} - 2)$, $(2\sqrt{2} + \sqrt{5})(2\sqrt{2} - \sqrt{5})$

## Lesson 6-4 — pp. 381–388

**Got It? 1. a.** 8 **b.** 11 **c.** 6 **2. a.** $\dfrac{\sqrt[5]{y}}{\sqrt[7]{w^2}} \cdot \sqrt[3]{w}$ **b.** $\dfrac{1}{x^2}$
**c.** If $m$ is negative, $a$ is in the denominator and $a$ is undefined when $a = 0$. **3. a.** The length of a Venusian year is about 0.61 Earth years. **b.** The length of a Jovian year is about 12.76 Earth years. **4. a.** $\sqrt[6]{27}$ **b.** $\dfrac{1}{\sqrt[5]{x^4}}$ **c.** $\sqrt[10]{16,807}$ **d.** $\dfrac{1}{8}$ **e.** $\dfrac{5}{2187}$ **f.** $\dfrac{1}{2x^5}$
**b.** $27x\sqrt[6]{x^3y^3}$
**Lesson Check 1.** 5 **2.** 5 **3.** $\frac{1}{125}$ **4.** $\frac{1}{125}$ **5.** $\sqrt[8]{11^3}$
**6.** $\dfrac{\sqrt[4]{x}}{x}$ **7.** $(1 + \sqrt{2})$ or any nonzero number times $(1 + \sqrt{2})$ **8.** error in third line, second term; $5(5^{\frac{2}{5}}) = 5^{\frac{7}{5}}$. The third and fourth lines should be: $\dfrac{20 - 5^{\frac{2}{5}}}{20 - 5\sqrt{5}}$.
**9.** $(-64)^{\frac{2}{3}} = \sqrt[3]{-64}^2 = -4$ and $-64^{\frac{1}{3}} = \sqrt[3]{-64} = -4$; $(-64)^{\frac{2}{3}} = \sqrt[3]{-64}^2$, is not a real number, but $-64^{\frac{2}{3}} = -\sqrt[3]{64}^2$ is a real number.
**Exercises 11.** 3 **13.** 10 **15.** $7\sqrt{3}$ **17.** 3 **19.** $\sqrt[9]{x}$
**21.** $\sqrt[6]{x^2}$ or $(\sqrt[3]{x})^2$ **23.** $\dfrac{1}{\sqrt[9]{y}}$ or $\dfrac{1}{(\sqrt[9]{y})^4}$ **25.** $\sqrt[4]{x}$ or $(\sqrt{x})^3$ **27.** $(-10)^2$ **29.** $7\sqrt{x}$ **31.** $a^{\frac{1}{2}}$ **33.** $c^{\frac{2}{5}}$ **35.** ≈72.8 m **37.** ≈7.9 m **39.** $\dfrac{12^{\frac{2}{3}}}{6}$ **41.** $\sqrt[3]{2}\sqrt[6]{2}$ **43.** $\dfrac{\sqrt[4]{45}}{6}$ **45.** $\dfrac{1}{6}$ **47.** 4 **49.** 4 **51.** $\frac{1}{16}$ **53.** 64 **55.** $\frac{1}{2}$ **57.** $\dfrac{x^{\frac{3}{4}}}{y^2}$ **59.** $-\frac{3}{2}$ **61.** $\dfrac{x^{\frac{4}{5}}}{y^{\frac{3}{2}}}$ **63.** $\frac{1}{8}$ **65.** $x^3y^{10}$ **67.** about 78%; 61%; 37% **69.** $\dfrac{1}{9b^{\frac{2}{3}}}$ **71.** 64 **73.** 2,097,152 **75.** $\frac{1}{2}$ **77.** 125 **79.** $x^{\frac{7}{2}}$ **81.** $x^{\frac{2}{3}}$ **83.** $\dfrac{4x^2}{9a^8}$ **85.** $\dfrac{2c^{\frac{5}{2}}}{a^3}$ **89. a.** $(\sqrt[3]{x})^4 = \sqrt[3]{x} \cdot \sqrt[3]{x} \cdot \sqrt[3]{x} \cdot \sqrt[3]{x} = x \cdot x = x^2$, so $\sqrt[3]{x^4} = (\sqrt[3]{x})^4$ **b.** $\sqrt[6]{x^4} = x^{\frac{4}{6}} = x^{\frac{2}{3}} = \sqrt[3]{x^2}$ **102.** $4\sqrt{3}$ **103.** $21\sqrt{2}$ **104.** $1 + 3\sqrt{5}$ **105.** $-7$ **106.** $-3\sqrt{5}$ **107.** $9\sqrt{2}$ **108.** $4ax^2 - 2x + 4$ **109.** $(x + 2)^2$ **110.** $(x - 9)^2$ **111.** $(4a - 3b)(4a + 3b)$

**112.** $(5x - 4y)^2$ **113.** $(3x + 8)^2$ **114.** $-3, 2$
**115.** $7, -2$ **116.** $-\frac{3}{2}, 1$ **117.** $-\frac{1}{3}, 2$ **118.** $-\frac{5}{2}, \frac{1}{2}$
**119.** $-\frac{2}{3}, \frac{1}{2}$

### Lesson 6-5     pp. 390–397

**Got It? 1.** 6 **2.** 5, −11 **3.** $\frac{1}{3}$, 37,500,000 m³
**4. a.** 10 **b.** when you raise each side of an equation to a power **5.** 9
**Lesson Check 1.** 12 **2.** 27 **3.** $\frac{1}{16}$ **4.** 4 **5.** 1 **6.** 512
**7.** 3; The solution of 3 yields a negative value for $x - 6$, but the right side of the equation ($\sqrt{3(3)}$) cannot be negative. **8.** Solving square root equations is different from solving absolute value equations in that you use a different technique to isolate the variable. In square root equations, you square each side. In absolute value equations, you write two new equations and solve both. Solving square root equations is similar to solving absolute value equations in that both can introduce extraneous solutions.
**Exercises 9.** 16 **11.** 22 **13.** 5 **15.** 4 **17.** $\frac{2}{5}$
**19.** −29, 25 **21.** 78 **23.** 0 **25.** about 4 in. **27.** 1
**29.** 3 **31.** −3, −4 **33.** 1 **35.** 3 **37.** 1 **39.** −2 **41.** 1
**43.** 5 **45.** $10\sqrt[3]{3}$ cm or about 13.16 cm **47.** 5 **49.** 8
**51.** 5 **53.** 1 **55.** 9, −7 **57.** 59. $x = 4$ is a solution, but $x = 1$ is an extraneous solution. **61.** Answers may vary. Sample: $\sqrt{x - 3} = \sqrt{3x + 5}$ **63.** C **65.** 0, 2
**67.** 0 **77.** 3 **78.** 2 **79.** 625 **80.** 512 **81.** $\frac{1}{1000}$
**82.** 16 **83.** 125 **84.** $6\sqrt{2}$ **85.** 3, 4 **86.** 3, 5
**87.** −5, −4 **88.** −2, −$\frac{2}{5}$ **89.** −$\frac{1}{3}$, −$\frac{4}{3}$ **90.** −2, −$\frac{3}{4}$
**91.** domain: {0, 2, 4}, range: {−5, −3, −1}; yes
**92.** domain: {−1, 0, 1}, range: {2, 0, 1}; yes
**93.** domain: {−2, 0, 1}, range: {−2, 0, 1}; yes
**94.** domain: {3, 4, 5}, range: {−1}; yes
**95.** domain: {0, 1, 2}, range: {0, 1, 2}; no
**96.** domain: {0}, range: {−2, 0, 2}; no

### Lesson 6-6     pp. 398–404

**Got It? 1.** $(f + g)(x) = 2x^2 + x + 5$, domain: all real numbers; $(f - g)(x) = 2x^2 - x + 11$, domain: all real numbers **2.** $(f \cdot g)(x) = 9x^3 - 30x^2 - 23x - 4$, domain: all real numbers; $(\frac{f}{g})(x) = x - 4$, domain: all real numbers except $x = -\frac{1}{3}$ **3, 4.** Let $D(x) = $ cost after applying the 15% store discount, $E(x) = $ cost after applying the 20% employee discount, and $x = $ cost of items. Then $D(x) = 0.85x$ and $E(x) = 0.80x$.
**a.** $(E \circ D)(x) = 0.68x$ **b.** $(D \circ E)(x) = 0.68x$
**c.** The total discounts are the same.
**Lesson Check 1.** $3x^3 - 2x^2 + 3x - 2$
**2.** $-x^2 + 3x - 3$ **3.** $3x^2 + 1$ **4.** $x^2 + 3x - 1$
**5.** $x^2 - 3x + 3$ **6.** $-x^2 + 3x - 3$ **7.** Answers may vary.

Sample: $f(x) = 3x^2 + 1$, $g(x) = 2x + 1$; $(f \circ g)(x) = 12x^2 + 12x + 4$; $(g \circ f)(x) = 6x^2 + 3$ **8.** Answers may vary. Sample: $f(x) = 2x$, $g(x) = 0.5x$; $f(g(x)) = x$
**Exercises 9.** $x^2 + 7x + 5$; domain: all real numbers
**11.** $x^2 - 7x - 5$; domain: all real numbers
**13.** $\frac{7x + 5}{x^2}$; domain: all real numbers except $x = 0$
**15.** $2 - x + \frac{1}{x}$; domain: all real numbers except $x = 0$
**17.** $\frac{1}{x} + x - 2$; domain: all real numbers except $x = 0$
**19.** $2x - x^2$; domain: all real numbers except $x = 0$
**21.** $2x^2 + 2x - 4$; domain: all real numbers
**23.** $-2x^2 + 2$; domain: all real numbers
**25.** $2x + 3$; domain: all real numbers except $x = 1$
**27, 28 29.** 20 **31.** 8 **33.** 4a **35.** $4a^2 + 4$ **37.** 25
**39.** 41. 0.25 **43.** $a^2 - 3$ **45. a.** $f(x) = 0.95x$
**b.** $g(x) = x - 200$ **c.** $\$1225$ **d.** $\$1235$
**47.** $x^2 - x + 7$; domain: all real numbers
**49.** $x^2 - 5x - 3$; domain: all real numbers
**51.** $-x^2 + 5x + 13$; domain: all real numbers
**53.** $4x^2 - 14x + 3$; domain: all real numbers
**55.** $2x^3 - x^2 - 11x + 10$; domain: all real numbers
**57.** $\frac{2x - 5}{3x - 2}$; domain: all real numbers except $x = 1$ and 2 **59.** Substitute 5995x for y; $\$79,850$ **61. a.** $g(x)$ is the bonus earned when $x$ is the amount of sales over $\$5000$. $h(x)$ is the excess sales over $\$5000$. **b.** $(g \circ h)(x)$; you first need to find the excess sales over $\$5000$ to calculate the bonus. **63.** 1 **65.** 0 **67.** 8 **69.** −2
**71. a.** ≈1963; The area after 2 seconds is about 1963 in.²
**b.** ≈7854 in.² **73.** $x - 2$; $x - 2$ **75.** $x - 3$; $x - 6$
**94.** 2 **95.** 3 **96.** $4x^6 + 32x^5 + 448x^6 + 3584x^5 + 17,920x^4 + 57,344x^3 + 114,688x^2 + 131,072x + 65,536$ **97.** $x^6 + 6x^5y + 15x^4y^2 + 20x^3y^3 + 15x^2y^4 + 6xy^5 + y^6$ **98.** $16x^4 - 32x^3y + 24x^2y^2 - 8xy^3 + y^4$
**99.** $128x^7 - 1344x^6y + 6048x^5y^2 - 15,120x^4y^3 + 22,680x^3y^4 - 20,412x^2y^5 + 10,206xy^6 - 2187y^7$
**100.** $59,049 - 65,610x + 29,160x^2 - 6480x^3 + 720x^4 - 32x^5$ **101.** $1024x^5 - 1280x^4y + 640x^3y^2 - 160x^2y^3 + 20xy^4 - y^5$ **102.** $x^8 + 4x^7y + 6x^6 + 4x^5 + x^4$ **103.** $x^{12} + 12x^{10}y^3 + 60x^8y^6 + 160x^6y^9 + 240x^4y^{12} + 192x^2y^{15} + 64y^{18}$
**104.** no solution **105.** (2, 2)

### Lesson 6-7     pp. 405–412

**Got It?**
**1. a.**

**b.** $t$ is a function; the inverse of $t$ is not a function; there are 2 $y$-values for one $x$-value. **2.** $y = \frac{x}{2} - 4$
**3.**
**4. a.** domain: all real numbers; range: all real numbers
**b.** $g^{-1}(x) = -\frac{1}{2}x + \frac{3}{2}$ **c.** domain: all real numbers; all real numbers **d.** Yes; for each $x$ in the domain of $g^{-1}$, there is only one value of $y$ in the range. **5.** $v = \sqrt{19.6d}$; 21.7 m/s **6. a.** $g^{-1}(x) = \frac{4 - 2x}{5}$ **b.** 0 is not in the domain of $g^{-1}$ so $(g \circ g^{-1})(0)$ does not exist **c.** 0
**Lesson Check 1.** $f^{-1}(x) = \frac{x - 3}{4}$; yes
**2.** $f^{-1}(x) = \pm\sqrt{x + 1}$; no **3.** $f^{-1}(x) = -1 \pm \sqrt{x}$; no
**4. a.** $h^{-1}(x) = -\frac{1}{3}x - 2$ **b.** −2.25 **c.** 0 **5.** no; yes
**6.** 2, 5 **7.** Answers may vary. Samples: $f(x) = 2x + 1$ and $g(x) = x - 2$; $f(x) = x^2$ and $g(x) = x + 1$
**Exercises**
**9.** **11.**
**13.** $y = \frac{1}{2}x + \frac{1}{2}$; yes **15.** $y = \pm\sqrt{\frac{5 - x}{2}}$; no
**17.** $y = \pm\sqrt{\frac{x + 5}{3}}$; no **19.** $y = \frac{4 \pm \sqrt{x}}{3}$; no
**21. 23. 25. 27. 29.**
**31.** $f^{-1}(x) = x^2 + 5$, $x \geq 0$, domain of $f$: $x \leq 5$, range of $f$: $y \geq 0$, domain of $f^{-1}$: $x \geq 0$, range of $f^{-1}$: $y \geq 5$; $f^{-1}$ is a function **33.** $f^{-1}(x) = \frac{3 - x}{2}$, $x \geq 0$, domain of $f$: $x \leq \frac{3}{2}$, range of $f$: $y \geq 0$, domain of $f^{-1}$: $x \geq 0$, range of $f^{-1}$: $y \leq \frac{3}{2}$; $f^{-1}$ is a function **35.** $f^{-1}(x) = \pm\sqrt{1 - x}$, domain of $f$: all real numbers, range of $f^{-1}$: $x \leq 1$, range of $f^{-1}$: all real numbers; $f^{-1}$ is not a function **37. a.** $r = \frac{\sqrt{3V}}{4\pi}$; yes **b.** 20.29 ft **39.** −10
**41. d 43.** $f^{-1}(x) = \pm\sqrt{x}$; no **45.** $f^{-1}(x) = \sqrt{\frac{3x + 8}{2}}$; no
**47.** $f^{-1}(x) = \frac{x^2 - 6x + 10}{2}$, $x \geq 3$, yes **49.** −1
**51.** $f^{-1}(x) = x^2$, $x \leq 0$, domain of $f$: $x \geq 0$, range of $f$: $y \leq 0$, domain of $f^{-1}$: $x \leq 0$, range of $f^{-1}$: $y \geq 0$; $f^{-1}$ is a function **53.** $f^{-1}(x) = x^2 - 3$, $x \geq 0$, domain of $f$: $x \leq 3$, range of $f$: $y \geq 0$, domain of $f^{-1}$: $x \geq 0$, range of $f^{-1}$: $y \leq 3$; $f^{-1}$ is a function **55.** $f^{-1}(x) = \pm\sqrt{x}$, domain of $f$: $x \geq 0$, range of $f^{-1}$: all real numbers; $f^{-1}$ is not a function **57.** $f^{-1}(x) = \sqrt{x} + 4$, domain of $f$: all real numbers, range of $f$: $y \geq 0$, domain of $f^{-1}$: $x \geq 0$, range of $f^{-1}$: all real numbers; $f^{-1}$ is not a function **59.** $f^{-1}(x) = \pm\frac{1}{\sqrt{x}} - 1$, domain of $f$: $x \neq -1$, range of $f$: $y > 0$, domain of $f^{-1}$: $x > 0$, range of $f^{-1}$: $y \neq -1$; $f^{-1}$ is not a function **61.** $f^{-1}(x) = (\frac{2}{3})^x$, $x \geq 0$, domain of

$f$: $x > 0$, range of $f$: $y > 0$, domain of $f^{-1}$: $x > 0$, range of $f^{-1}$: $y > 0$; $f^{-1}$ is a function
**63.** a–b. Answers may vary. Samples are given.
**a.** **b.**
**65.** $h = s\sqrt{2}$; $s = \frac{h\sqrt{2}}{2} = 3\sqrt{2} \approx 4.2$ in. **67. a.** The horizontal line test tells you if there is more than one $x$-value for every $y$-value. Since the graph of $f^{-1}$ interchanges the $x$ and $y$ values of $f$, if $f$ passes the horizontal line test, $f^{-1}$ will pass the vertical line test and it will be a function. **b.** no **79.** $2x + 7$ **80.** $-x - 10$
**81.** $-\frac{3}{2}x + 11$ **82.** $2x^2 + 28x$ **83.** 32 **84.** $2x + 28$
**85.** −2 **86.** no real root **87.** 3 **88.** −3 **89.** −3
**90.** 0.4 **91.** 30 **92.** 0.05
**93.** **94.** **95.**

### Lesson 6-8     pp. 414–420

**Got It?**
**1.** $y = \sqrt{x + 2}$
**2.** $y = \sqrt{x + 2}$    $y = \sqrt{x - 3}$
**3.** **4.** 1999 **5.**

**6. a.** $y = \sqrt[3]{8x + 32} - 2$ is the graph of $y = 2\sqrt[3]{x}$ translated 4 units to the left and 2 units down.
**b.** $y = 9|x + 2|$; the graph of $y = 9|x + 2|$ is the graph of $y = 9|x|$ translated 2 units to the left; You are rewriting the function so that $x$ has a coefficient of 1.

**Lesson Check**
**1.** **2.**
**3.** $y = 2\sqrt{x} - 1$; the graph of $y = 2\sqrt{x}$ translated 1 unit to the right **4.** $y = 2\sqrt[3]{x} + 2$; the graph of $y = 2\sqrt[3]{x}$ translated 2 units to the left **5.** When $|a| < 1$, $a$ will vertically compress $y = a\sqrt{x}$ and when $|a| > 1$, $a$ will vertically stretch $y = a\sqrt{x}$; this is similar to its effect on other functions. **6.** $g(x)$ is the reflection of $f(x)$ across the $x$-axis and again across $x = -1$.
**Exercises**
**7.** **9.**
**11.** **13.**
**15.** **17.**
**19.** **21.** 147 **23.** −1
**25.** **27.**
**29.**
**31.** $y = 3\sqrt{x - 1}$; the graph of $y = 3\sqrt{x}$ translated 1 unit to the right **33.** $y = -4\sqrt{x + 4}$; the graph of $y = -4\sqrt{x}$ translated 4 units to the left
**35.** $y = 5\sqrt{x + 5} - 3$; the graph of $y = 5\sqrt{x}$ translated 5 units to the left and 3 units down
**37.** ≈16.44 ft; ≈29.22 ft

**39.**     domain: $x \geq 1$, range: $y \geq 3$
**41. a.** $y = \sqrt{x - 2} - 2$ **b.** domain: $x \geq 2$, range: $y \geq -2$ **c.** No; the function pairs the number 3 with the number −1, which is not a non-negative real number. **43. a.** $y = 5\sqrt{x - 4} - 1$; the graph of $y = 5\sqrt{x}$, translated 4 units to the right and 1 unit down
**45.** $y = -2\sqrt[3]{x} - \frac{1}{4}$; the graph of $y = -2\sqrt[3]{x}$, translated $\frac{1}{4}$ unit to the right **47.** $y = 10 - \frac{1}{3}\sqrt[3]{x + 3}$; the graph of $y = -\frac{1}{3}\sqrt[3]{x}$, translated 3 units to the left and 10 units up
**49.** $\frac{3}{2}$ **51.** 0, 1, 9
**53. a.** **b.** $15\sqrt{2}$ in. ≈ 21.2 in.
**64.** $f^{-1}(x) = \frac{3(x + 3)}{2}$; yes
**65.** $f^{-1}(x) = (x + 4)^2 - 3$, $x \geq -4$; yes
**66.** $f^{-1}(x) = \frac{-1 \pm \sqrt{x}}{2}$; no **67.** $\frac{x\sqrt{3xy}}{y}$ **68.** $\frac{\sqrt{6xy}}{2y}$
**69.** $\frac{\sqrt[3]{9xy^2}}{3y}$ **70.** $\frac{\sqrt[4]{48x^3y^3}}{10z^2}$ **71.** $\frac{9 \pm \sqrt{21}}{2}$
**72.** $\frac{-3 \pm 3\sqrt{5}}{2}$ **73.** $\frac{-1 \pm \sqrt{61}}{2}$ **74.** 8 **75.** 16 **76.** 2

### Chapter Review     pp. 422–426

**1.** radicand **2.** radical functions **3.** rational exponent
**4.** composite function **5.** 6 **6.** 0.7 **7.** −2 **8.** −2
**9.** $9|x|$ **10.** $4x^2$ **11.** $2|x^3|$ **12.** $0.2x$ **13.** $\frac{x^2}{2y}$ **14.** $5x^2y^3$
**15.** 3 **16.** −7 **17.** 4 **18.** $4x^2$ **19.** $30y$ **20.** 4 **21.** $3xy$
**22.** $\frac{3|x|}{2}$ **23.** $\frac{2\sqrt{3}}{3}$ **24.** $\frac{\sqrt{3x}}{8}$ **25.** $\frac{x\sqrt[3]{150x}}{8}$ **26.** $22\sqrt{3}$
**27.** $26\sqrt[3]{5x}$ **28.** $x\sqrt{2}$ **29.** 14 + $7\sqrt{2}$ **30.** −6
**31.** $100 + 10\sqrt{6} - 10\sqrt{3} - 3\sqrt{2}$ **32.** $\frac{5 + 2\sqrt{5}}{5}$
**33.** $\frac{9 + 3\sqrt{2}}{2}$ **34.** 5 **35.** 3 **36.** 4 **37.** 25 **38.** $x$
**39.** $-2y^3$ **40.** $81x^2y^4$ **41.** $\frac{1}{\sqrt[3]{p}}$ **42.** $\frac{1}{x}$ **43.** $x^3y^6$ **44.** −1
**45.** 15 **46.** 5 **47.** 10, −8 **48.** 2, −1 **49.** −2 **50.** 0, 16
**51.** 0, 36 **52.** 9.05 W **53.** 2 **54.** $x^2 - x - 20$; domain: all real numbers **54.** $x^2 - x - 12$; domain: all real numbers **55.** $x^3 - 4x^2 - 16x + 64$; domain: all real numbers
**56.** $x + 4$; domain: all real numbers except $x = 4$ **57.** 50

**58.** 5 **59.** 23 **60.** $5a^2 + 3$ **61.** $D(C(x)) = 0.5x - 0.5$, $C(D(x)) = 0.5x - 1$; use the coupon after the store discount.
**62.** $f^{-1}(x) = \pm\sqrt{\frac{x + 8}{2}}$; no **63.** $f^{-1}(x) = 5 - \frac{1}{3}x$; yes
**64.** $f^{-1}(x) = x^2 - 6$, $x \geq 0$; yes **65.** $f^{-1}(x) = \frac{3 \pm \sqrt{x}}{2}$; no
**66.**     domain of $f$: all real numbers, domain of $f^{-1}$: all real numbers, range of $f$ and $f^{-1}$: all real numbers

$y = (x + 3)^2$

**67.** domain of $f$: all real numbers, range of $f$: $y \geq 0$; domain of $f^{-1}$: $x \geq 0$, range of $f^{-1}$: all real numbers

$y = (x + 3)^2$    $y = -3 \pm \sqrt{x}$

**68.** domain of $f$: $x \geq 3$, range of $f$: $y \geq 0$, domain of $f^{-1}$: $x \geq 0$, range of $f^{-1}$: $y \geq 3$

$y = x^2 + 3$    $y = \sqrt{x - 3}$

**69.** domain of $f$: all real numbers, range of $f$: $y \leq 6$, domain of $f^{-1}$: $x \leq 6$, range of $f^{-1}$: all real numbers

$y = 6 - 5x^2$

**70.** $s = \sqrt[3]{V}$; 4 ft
**71.** domain: $x \geq 0$, range: $y \geq -5$
**72.** domain: $x \geq -8$, range: $y \geq 0$

**73.** domain: $x \geq 0$, range: $y \geq 9$

**74.** domain: $x \geq 4$, range: $y \leq 0$

**75.** domain: all real numbers, range: all real numbers

**76.** domain: all real numbers, range: all real numbers

**77.** $y = 3\sqrt{x-3} + 4$; the graph of $y = 3\sqrt{x}$ translated 3 units to the right and 4 units up **78.** $y = -6\sqrt{x-4}$; the graph of $y = -6\sqrt{x}$ translated 4 units to the right **79.** $y = 2\sqrt{x+3}$; the graph of $y = 2\sqrt{x}$ translated 3 units to the left **80.** $y = \frac{1}{2}\sqrt{x-4} + 6$; the graph of $y = \frac{1}{2}\sqrt{x}$ translated 4 units to the right and 6 units up **81.** no solution **82.** 6

### Chapter 7

**Get Ready! p. 431 1.** 0.1; 10; 1000 **2.** $\frac{4}{9}$; $\frac{9}{4}$ **3.** $-\frac{1}{625}$; $-\frac{1}{25}$; 1 **4.** $-\frac{1}{3}$; $-1$; $-3$

**5.** ; $y = 2x + 2$

**6.** ; $y = 25x + 25$

**7.** $y = x^2$

**8.** $y = x^3$

**9.** $x^2$ **10.** $16x^4$ **11.** $y = \pm\sqrt{\frac{10-x}{2}}$; no **12.** $y = -4 + \sqrt[3]{x+1}$; yes **13.** decrease **14.** exponential **15.** no

### Lesson 7-1 pp. 434–441

**Got It?**
**1. a.** **b.** **c.** **d.** domain: all real numbers, range: $y > 0$; $y$-intercept: $(0, a)$ where $y = ab^x$

**2. a.** exponential growth; 3 **b.** exponential decay; 11 **c.** exponential growth; 2000 **3.** $593.84 **4. a.** after 8 yrs **b.** after 11 yrs; then the account contains $1710.34 **5. a.** $\approx 3$ **b.** No; the function is asymptotic to the $x$-axis. **Lesson Check 1.** decay; 10 **2.** decay; 0.75 **3.** growth; 1 **4.** decay; 1

**5.** **6.**

**7.** If $a > 0$ and $b > 1$, then the function represents exponential growth; if $a > 0$ and $0 < b < 1$, then the function represents exponential decay. **8. a.** quadratic; degree 2 with $3x^2$ as the leading term **b.** exponential; the equation is of the form $y = ab^x$ **c.** linear; degree 1 with $x$ as the leading term **d.** exponential; the equation is of the form $y = ab^x$ **9.** $0.3 < 1$, so 0.3 is the decay factor

**Exercises**
**11.** **13.**

**15.** **17.**

**19.** exponential decay; 2 **21.** exponential decay; 0.8 **23.** exponential growth; 0.45 **25.** exponential decay; 1 **27.** $y = 120,000(1.012)^x$; 143,512 **29. a.** $y = 72(\frac{1}{2})^x$ **b.** 2.25 in. **31. a.** about 5.6% **b.** about 0.001? % **33.** Answers may vary. Sample: $y = 59.5(0.6)^x$ **35.** 6 **37.** 0.45 **39.** 0.999 **41.** 2

**51.** **52.**

**53.**

**54.** $(2 + 3x)(4 - 6x + 9x^2)$ **55.** $(3x - 1)(x + 4)$ **56.** $(4x - 5)(4x - 5)$ **57.** $(1, -1)$ **58.** $(0, 0)$ **59.** $(3, -3, 9)$

**60.** **61.**

**62.**

**63.**

### Lesson 7-2 pp. 442–450

**Got It?**
**1.** reflects across the $x$-axis; compresses by a factor of 0.5

**2. a.** translate 2 units to the left; the $y$-intercept becomes 16 **b.** Stretch the graph of $y = (0.25)^x$ by a factor of 5 and translate the graph of $y = 5 \cdot 0.25^x$ 5 units up **3. a.** about 31.9 min **b.** No; a hot coffee cannot cool below room temperature. So, to use exponential data, it is important to translate the data by 68 units. **4.** $e^8 \approx 2980.957987$; three methods: use the $e^x$ key, $x = 8$; graph $y = e^x$ and find $y$ for $x = 8$; or use the table of values for $y = e^x$ and find $y$ for $x = 8$ **5.** about $4475 **Lesson Check 1.** stretch by a factor of 2 and reflection across the $x$-axis **2.** compress by a factor of $\frac{1}{3}$ **3.** translate 5 units to the right **4.** translate 3 units up **5.** yes **6.** no; $2000e^{0.05t} \neq 1000(e^{0.04t} + e^{0.06t})$

**Exercises**
**7.** **9.**

**11.** **13.**

**15.** **17.**

**19.** **21.**

**23.** 403.4288 **25.** 1 **27.** 15.1543 **29.** $448.30 **31.** $6168.41 **33.** graph is a shift of the parent function 2 units to the left and 1 unit up

**35.** As the value of $b$ approaches 1, the graph comes closer to being a straight line.

**37.** $y = 24(\frac{1}{2})^{t/30}$; 0.64 mg **39.** $y = -3^x$; $y = -3^{x-8} + 2$ **41.** $y = -3(\frac{1}{3})^x$; $y = -3(\frac{1}{3})^{x+15} - 1$ **51.** exponential growth; 23 **52.** exponential growth; 3 **53.** exponential decay; 2 **54.** exponential growth; 5 **55.** $6\sqrt{5}$ **56.** $-\sqrt[3]{4}$ **57.** $5(\sqrt{3} + \sqrt{5})$ **58.** $2(\sqrt[3]{2} + \sqrt[3]{8})$ **59.** $\sqrt[3]{3}$ **60.** $11\sqrt{7}$ **61.** $f^{-1}(x) = \frac{x+1}{4}$; yes **62.** $f^{-1}(x) = x^{\frac{1}{7}}$; yes **63.** $f^{-1}(x) = (\frac{x-1}{3})$; yes

### Lesson 7-3 pp. 451–458

**Got It? 1. a.** $\log_6 36 = 2$ **b.** $\log_9 \frac{8}{27} = 3$ **c.** $\log_1 0 = 0$ **2. a.** 3 **b.** $\frac{5}{2}$ **c.** $-\frac{5}{6}$ **3.** $\approx 16$ times **4. a.** domain: $x > 0$; range: all real numbers; no $y$-intercept; vertical asymptote: $x = 0$

**b.**

| $x$ | $2^y = x$ | $y$ |
|---|---|---|
| $-1$ | $2^y = -1$ | undefined |
| 0 | $2^y = 0$ | undefined |
| 1 | $2^y = 1$ | 0 |
| 2 | $2^y = 2$ | 1 |

**5. a.** translates the graph of the parent function 3 units to the right and 4 units up; The asymptote changes from $x = 0$ to $x = 3$. The domain changes from $x > 0$ to $x > 3$. The range remains all real numbers. **b.** stretch the graph of the parent function by a factor of 5; The asymptote, domain, and the range remain the same. **Lesson Check 1.** $\log_5 25 = 2$ **2.** $\log_4 64 = 3$ **3.** $\log_3 243 = 5$ **4.** $\log_5 25 = 2$ **5.** 3 **6.** 1 **7.** 2 **8.** $-2$ **9. a.** no **b.** yes **c.** yes **d.** no **10.** Choose a few points on the graph of $y = 6^x$, reverse their coordinates, and plot them. **11.** $y = \log_2 (x + 4)$ translates the graph of $y = \log_2 x$ 4 units to the left. Asymptote changes from $x = 0$ to $x = -4$. Domain changes from $x > 0$ to $x > -4$. Range remains the same.

**Exercises 13.** $\log 1000 = 3$ **15.** $\log \frac{1}{10} = -1$ **17.** $\log_7 4 = -2$ **19.** $\log 0.01 = -2$ **21.** $\frac{1}{2}$ **23.** $\frac{3}{2}$ **25.** $\frac{1}{2}$ **27.** 2 **29.** 1 **31.** 3 **33.** The earthquake in Chile was about 39.81 times more intense. **35.** The earthquake in Missouri was about 10 times more intense.

**36–39.**

**41.** translate the graph 2 units to the right **43.** translate the graph 2 units to the left and 1 unit down **45.** $\approx 3.16 \times 10^{-9}$ **47.** $10^{-4} = 0.0001$ **49.** $4^0 = 1$ **51.** $2^{-1} = \frac{1}{2}$ **53.** $10^1 = 10$ **55.** $-2$ **57.** 59. First rewrite $y = \log_1 x$ as $1^y = x$. For any real number $y$, $4 = 1$, yes **61.** $y = 4^x$ **63.** $y = 10^x$ **65.** $y = 10^x - 1$ **67.** $y = 2^{x-2}$

**69.** **71.**

**73.** domain: $x > 0$, range: all real numbers **75.** domain: $x > 3$, range: all real numbers **77.** $4 = \log_3 (81)$ **79.** $8 = \log_6 (a + 1)$

**89.** **90.**

**91.**

**92.** $(2x - 3)(2x - 1)$ **93.** $4(b - 5)(b + 5)$ **94.** $(5x - 2)(x + 3)$ **95.** 2 **96.** 256 **97.** $\frac{1}{4}$ **98.** 12

### Lesson 7-4 pp. 462–468

**Got It? 1. a.** $\log_4 15x^2$ **b.** $\log_2 \frac{x^2}{y}$ **c.** $\log_2 2 + 3\log_2 5 - \log_2 37$ **b.** $2 + 5\log_3 x$ **3. a.** $\frac{5}{2} \approx 2.085$ **4.** Substance B; $\log 2$; $-\log([H^+_A]) + \log([H^+_B]) = \log 2$ **Lesson Check 1.** $\log_4 16$ **2.** $\log_6 6$ **3.** $\log_3 x - \log_3 y$ **4.** $2\log m + 5\log n$ **5.** $\frac{1}{3}\log_2 x$ **6. a.** Product Prop. and Power Prop. **b.** Quotient Prop. **7.** 0.00001 **8.** Answers may vary. Samples: $\log 150 = \log 25 + \log 6$ **Exercises 9.** $\log 14$ **11.** $\log 972$ **13.** $\log \frac{m^4}{n}$ **15.** $\log_6 5x$ **17.** $\log_3 32xy$ **19.** $2 + \log_2 x + \log_2 y + \log_2 z$ **21.** $2\log a$ **23.** $2\log_3 2 + 2\log_3 x$ **25.** $2\log a + 3\log b - 4\log c$ **27.** $1 + \frac{1}{2}\log_3 3 + \frac{1}{2}\log_3 a$ **29.** $1 + 3\log m - 2\log n$ **31.** $\approx 1.2$ **33.** $\approx 1.43$ **35.** $\approx 3.631$ **37.** $\approx 3.183$ **39.** $-2$ **41.** 1 **43.** 2 **45.** Yes, because the loudness of the sound is 102 dB. **47.** The coefficient $\frac{1}{2}$ is missing in $\log_4 s$;
$$\log_4 \sqrt{\frac{t}{s}} = \frac{1}{2}(\log_4 t - \log_4 s) = \frac{1}{2}\log_4 t - \frac{1}{2}\log_4 s$$
**49.** The log of a product is equal to the sum of the logs. $\log(MN) = \log M + \log N$ **51.** false; $\frac{1}{3}\log_3 3 = \log_3 3^{1/3}$, not $\log_3 3$ **53.** false; $\log_3 \frac{y}{x} = \log_3 y - \log_3 y$ **55.** false; $\log_4 7 - \log_4 3 = \log_4 \frac{7}{3}$ not $\log_4 4$. **57.** $\log_4 \frac{2\sqrt{y}}{z}$ **59.** $\log_2 \frac{\sqrt{x} \cdot \sqrt[3]{y^2}}{z^3}$ **61.** $\log s + \frac{1}{3}\log 7 - 2\log t$ **63.** $3\log m - 4\log n + 2\log p$ **65.** $\frac{1}{3}\log_6 x + \frac{2}{3}\log_6 y - \frac{2}{3}\log_6 z$ **67.** $\frac{1}{2}\log(x + 2) + \frac{1}{2}\log(x - 2) - 2\log(x + 3)$ **69.** $\frac{\log 8}{\log 3}$ **71.** $\frac{\log 3.3}{\log 9}$ **73.** A 1.0 magnitude star is about 2.5 times brighter than a 2.0 magnitude star. **84.** $\log_7 49 = 2$ **85.** $\log_6 \frac{1}{6} = -\frac{2}{3}$ **86.** $-3 = \log_5 \frac{1}{125}$ **87.** $\pm 8$ **88.** $\frac{64}{9}$ **89.** 2 **90.** $x^3 + 5x^2 - 15$ **91.** $x^4 + 17x^2 + 16$ **92.** $x^4 - 2x^3 - 2x^2 + 14x - 35$ **93.** 2 **94.** 5 **95.** $\frac{1}{3}$

### Lesson 7-5 pp. 469–476

**Got It? 1.** $\frac{4}{9}$ **2. a.** $\approx -1.5122$ **b.** because the terms cannot be written with a common base **3. a.** $\approx 0.8588$ **b.** $\approx 1.2114$ **4.** $\approx 13.51$ yrs **5.** 1.45 **6.** 200 **Lesson Check 1.** 2 **2.** $\approx 3.6439$ **3.** 25 **4.** 2000 **5.** The log bases are not equal.
$$\log_3 x = 2\log_3 9$$
$$\log_3 x = \log_3 9^2$$
$$\log_3 x = 4$$
$$x = 2^4$$
$$x = 16$$
**6.** Yes; $5^x = 0$ has no solution.

**Exercises 7.** 3 **9.** 1 **11.** $\frac{4}{9}$ **13.** 2 **15.** 1.5850 **17.** 3 **19.** 0.9534 **21.** 0.2720 **23.** 0.5690 **25.** 4.7027 **27.** 6 **29.** 0.64 **31.** about the yr 2012 **33.** $\frac{\sqrt{10}}{10}$ or about 0.3162 **35.** 10,000 **37.** $\sqrt{10} \approx 3.1623$ **39.** 2 **41.** $100,000\sqrt{5}$ or $\approx 223,606.8$ **43.** $\frac{1}{4}$ **45.** 7 **47. a.** 18.9658 **b.** 18.9658 **c.** Answers may vary. Sample: You don't have to use the Change of Base Formula with the base-10 method, but there are fewer steps with the base-2 method. **49.** $\approx 7.6$ yrs **51.** 3 **53.** 3 **55.** $-2$ **57.** $-\frac{1}{3}$ **59.** Answers may vary. Sample: $x = 1.6$; $x \approx 39.81$ **61.** 143.6 **63. a.** top up: $10^{-5}$ W/m²; top down: $10^{-2.5}$ W/m² **b.** 99.68% **65.** 625 **67.** 10 **69.** 1.5 **71.** 2.7944 **73.** 500 **75.** 114.3 **77.** $x = y = 2$ **89.** $\log 2 + 3\log x - 2\log y$ **90.** $\log_5 x - \log_5 y$ **91.** $1 + \frac{1}{2}\log_3 y$ **92.** $x^2 - 3x - 1$ **93.** $3x^2 - 3$ **94.** $9x^2 - 1$ **95.** 1, $\pm i$ **96.** $\pm 2$, $\pm 2i$ **97.** $\pm\sqrt{3}$, $\pm\sqrt{2}$ **98.** $\log_2 3$ **99.** $\log 3x^4$ **100.** $\log \frac{32}{y^2}$

### Lesson 7-6 pp. 478–483

**Got It? 1. a.** $\ln 175$ **b.** $\ln \frac{x}{4}$ **c.** $\ln 5x^3y^2$ **2. a.** $e^2$, or about 7.39 **b.** $\frac{-5}{2}$, $e^2$, or about 0.8 or $-4.13$ **c.** $\frac{e^2}{6}$, or about 1.23 **3. a.** $\ln 2 + 2$, or about 4.48 **b.** $-\ln 10$, or about $-2.3$ **c.** $\frac{\ln 10}{3}$, or about 0.77 **4. a.** No; the maximum velocity of 5.4 km/s is less than the 7.7 km/s needed for a stable orbit. **b.** Yes; if, R could be changed so that $V > 7.7$. **Lesson Check 1.** $\ln 81$ **2.** $\ln 1.8$ **3.** $\ln 12$ **4.** $-\ln 4$ **5.** $\approx 10.9$ **6.** $\approx 14.4$ **7.** $\approx 7.39$ **8.** $\approx -0.718$ **9.** error in 3rd line: $4x = 5$ should be: $4x = e^5$
$$x = \frac{e^5}{4}; x \approx 37.1$$
**10.** No; in 5 has base $e$ and $\log_2 10$ has base 2.

**Exercises 11.** $\ln 125$ **13.** $\ln 4$ **15.** $\ln \frac{\sqrt[3]{xy}}{z^4}$ **17.** $\ln 40,960$ **19.** $\ln 1$ **21.** 0.135 **23.** $\pm 11.588$ **25.** $\pm 2.241$

PowerAlgebra.com Selected Answers

**27.** 1488.979 **29.** ≈2.890 **31.** ≈1.242 **33.** ≈2.401
**35.** 0 **37.** ≈2.2 **39.** at least 25 s **41.** ≈11,552 yrs
**43.** $\frac{4}{5}$ **45.** 83 **47.** 2 **49.** 10 **51.** $\frac{1}{2}$ **53.** ≈301 days
**55.** never **57.** 10.8 **59.** ≈19.8 h **72.** 4 **73.** 2.846
**74.** 0.272 **75.** 3333.$\overline{3}$ **76.** 1.002 **77.** 9.0 × 10⁻⁵
**78.** $y = \frac{x}{5} - \frac{7}{5}$; yes **79.** $y = \frac{\sqrt[3]{x-10}}{2}$; yes
**80.** $y = \pm\sqrt{5 - x}$; no **81.** $y = \frac{x}{5} - \frac{2}{5}$; yes **82.** 10
**83.** 15 **84.** $\frac{6}{5}$

## Chapter Review    pp. 487–490

**1.** exponential decay; exponential growth **2.** asymptote
**3.** logarithm; natural logarithm function **4.** continuously
compounded interest **5.** natural logarithmic function
**6.** exponential growth; (0, 1) **7.** exponential growth;
(0, 2) **8.** exponential growth; (0, 0.2) **9.** exponential
decay; (0, 3) **10.** exponential growth; $\left(0, \frac{25}{7}\right)$
**11.** exponential growth; (0, 0.0015) **12.** exponential
decay; (0, 2.25) **13.** exponential decay; (0, 0.5)
**14.** $y = 12{,}500(0.91)^x$; $7800$ **15.** $y = 50(1.03)^t$; $58$
**16.** The parent graph $y = 2^x$ is stretched by a factor of 5,
translated 1 unit to the left, and 3 units up. **17.** The
parent graph $y = \left(\frac{1}{3}\right)^x$ is reflected across the x-axis,
stretched by a factor of 2, and translated 2 units to the
right. **18.** $1100.76$ **19.** $291.91 **20.** 0.0498
**21.** 0.3679 **22.** 148.4132 **23.** 0.6065 **24.** 2 = log₆ 36
**25.** −3 = log₅ 0.125 **26.** 3 = log₃ 27
**27.** −3 = log 0.001 **28.** 6 **29.** −2 **30.** −5 **31.** 0

**32.**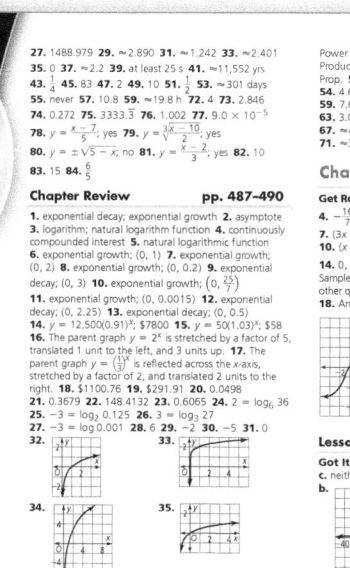
**33.**
**34.**
**35.**

**36.** The parent graph $y = \log_4 x$ is stretched by a factor
of 3 and translated 1 unit to the left. **37.** The parent
graph $y = \ln x$ is reflected across the x-axis and translated
2 units up. **38.** log 24; Product Prop. **39.** $\log_2 \frac{5}{3}$;
Quotient Prop. **40.** log₃ 7x⁴; Power and Product Prop.
**41.** $\log_6 \frac{6}{x}$; Quotient Prop. **42.** $\log \frac{5}{2}$; Power and
Quotient Prop. **43.** log₄ x⁵; Power and Power Prop.
**44.** 2 log₄ x + 3 log₄ y; Product and Power Prop.
**45.** log 4 + 4 log s + log t; Product and Power Prop.
**46.** log₃ 2 − log₃ x; Quotient Prop. **47.** 2 log(x + 3);

Power Prop. **48.** 3 log₂ 2 + 3 log₂ (y − 2); Power and
Product Prop. **49.** 2 log₂ − log 5; Power and Quotient
Prop. **50.** ≈2.8 **51.** ≈2.1 **52.** 0.75 **53.** 3.2619
**54.** 4.6542 **55.** 1.3652 **56.** 3.3333 **57.** 8 **58.** 50
**59.** 7.6256 × 10¹² **60.** 0.9307 **61.** 0.6599 **62.** 0.6658
**63.** 3.0589 **64.** ≈18.2 h **65.** ≈0.83 **66.** ≈2.26
**67.** ≈4.31 **68.** ≈0.54 **69.** ≈3.77 **70.** ≈6.03
**71.** ≈3.4%

## Chapter 8

**Get Ready!** p. 495 **1.** $\frac{4}{3}$; −4 **2.** −$\frac{2}{3}$; 2 **3.** −$\frac{10}{3}$; 10
**4.** −$\frac{16}{7}$; $\frac{48}{7}$ **5.** $(x + 3)(x − 2)$ **6.** $(4x + 5)(x + 3)$
**7.** $(3x − 5)(3x + 5)$ **8.** $(x − 6)^2$ **9.** $(3x + 4)(x + 2)$
**10.** $(x − 3)(x − 2)$ **11.** 1, −8 **12.** −6, −8 **13.** 4, 2
**14.** 0, −$\frac{2}{3}$ **15.** 8, $\frac{1}{3}$ **16.** 15, −2 **17.** Answers may vary.
Sample: Inverse is used when one quantity increases as the
other quantity decreases.
**18.** Answers may vary. Sample:

## Lesson 8-1    pp. 498–505

**Got It? 1. a.** direct; $y = 40x$ **b.** inverse; $y = \frac{8}{x}$
**c.** neither **2. a.** $y = \frac{56}{x}$
**b.**
**c.** −28

**3. a.** $t = \frac{225}{d}$ **b.** 9 students **4.** 23 bags
**5. a.** 4018 joules **b.** 12 m; No, you need not calculate PE
to find the height. Substitute the mass and height of the
first diver, and the mass of the second diver in PE = mgh
and set the two expressions equal. Solve the equation for h
to calculate the height of the second diver.
**Lesson Check 1.** inverse; $y = \frac{9}{x}$ **2.** direct; $y = 5x$
**3.** In direct variation, two positive quantities either
increase together or decrease together. In an inverse
variation, as one quantity increases, the other quantity
decreases and vice versa. **4.** p varies directly with q, r, and

---

t and inversely with s. **5.** d varies directly with the cube
root of r and inversely with the square of t.
**Exercises 7.** neither **9.** inverse; $y = \frac{0.3}{x}$
**11.** $y = -\frac{1300}{x}$; −130 **13.** $y = \frac{5}{x^2}$
**15.** $y = \frac{250}{x}$; 25 **17.** $y = -\frac{5}{3x} - \frac{1}{6}$

**19. a.** $s = 2.5m$ **b.** 100 muffins **21.** $PE = 2gh$
**23.** $F = \frac{km}{d^2}$ **25. a.** ≈76.58 L **b.** ≈20 moles
**27.** $z = 10xy$; 360 **29.** 10 **31.** 18$\frac{2}{3}$ **33.** 18 **35.** $\frac{1}{2}$
**37.** 2.5 **39.** 2.625 **49.** $\frac{e^5}{4}$ ≈ 37.1 **50.** 3e⁴ ≈ 163.79
**51.** $\frac{e^3}{8}$ ≈ 0.92 **52.** −90x² **53.** 84x² **54.** 10x²y²√2y
**55.** |x⁵|y⁵⁰ **56.** −4ab² **57.** 2m²|n|⁴√4 **58.** x, if n is
odd; |x| if n is even
**59.** $y = |x|$ translated 2 units up

**60.** $y = |x|$ translated 2 units to the left

**61.** $y = |x|$ translated 3 units down

**62.** $y = |x|$ translated 3 units to the rt.

**63.** $y = |x|$ translated 4 units to the left and 5 units down

**64.** $y = |x|$ translated 10 units to the rt. and 7 units up

## Lesson 8-2    pp. 507–514

**Got It?**
**1. a.**
no x- or y-intercept; horizontal
asymptote: $y = 0$; vertical
asymptote: $x = 0$; domain: all
real numbers except $x = 0$,
range: all real numbers except
$y = 0$

**b.** Yes; because all the functions have similar graphs.
**2. a.** $y = \frac{1}{2x}$ is a shrink of the graph of $y = \frac{1}{x}$ by a factor
of $\frac{1}{2}$. **b.** $y = \frac{5}{x}$ is a stretch of the graph of $y = \frac{1}{x}$ by a
factor of 2. **c.** $y = -\frac{1}{2x}$ is a reflection across the x-axis and
a shrink of the graph of $y = \frac{1}{x}$ by a factor of $\frac{1}{2}$.
**3.**
domain: all real numbers except
$x = 4$, range: all real numbers except
$y = 6$

**4.** $y = \frac{2}{x} - 4$ **5. a.** $C = \frac{1200}{n}$; domain: whole
numbers from 1 to 312; 160 students **b.** $C = \frac{1200}{n - 30}$;
Domain: whole numbers from 1 to 282; 190 students
**Lesson Check**
**1.**

**2.** $y = \frac{1}{x}$ translated 5 units up **3.** $y = \frac{1}{x}$ reflected across
the x-axis and stretched by a factor of 4 **4.** horizontal
asymptote: $y = -7$, vertical asymptote: $x = -2$
**5.** shrink of the graph of $y = \frac{1}{x}$ by a factor of $\frac{1}{2}$

---

**6.** Answers may vary. Sample: $y = -\frac{2}{x}$. For $y = \frac{2}{x}$:
stretch if $|a| > 1$ and shrink if $0 < |a| < 1$
**Exercises**
**9.**
no x- or y-intercept; horizontal
asymptote: $y = 0$; vertical
asymptote: $x = 0$; domain: all real
numbers except $x = 0$, range: all
real numbers except $y = 0$

**11.**
no x- or y-intercept; horizontal
asymptote: $y = 0$; vertical
asymptote: $x = 0$; domain: all
real numbers except $x = 0$,
range: all real numbers except
$y = 0$

**13.**    **15.**

stretch by a factor of 2    compression by a
factor of 0.5

**17.**    compression by a factor
of 0.75

**19.**
domain: all real numbers
except $x = 0$, range: all
numbers except $y = -3$

**21.**
domain: all real numbers except
$x = 3$, range: all real numbers except
$y = 4$

**23.**
domain: all real numbers except
$x = -1$, range: all real numbers
except $y = -8$

**25.**
domain: all real numbers except
$x = -5$, range: all real numbers
except $y = -6$

**27.** $y = -\frac{2}{x} + 3$ **29.** 7.67 ft
**33.**    **35.**

**37.** Answers may vary. Sample: The graph of the
translation looks similar to the graph of $y = \frac{1}{x}$, so
knowing the asymptotes helps to position the translation;
check students' work.
**39.**    : (3, 6)

**41.**    : (−1.75, −4)

**43. a.** $m = \frac{10{,}000}{g}$

Mileage (mi/gal) vs Gasoline Used (gal)

**b.** $m = \frac{10{,}000}{g - 50}$    **c.** 25 mi/gal; 28.57 mi/gal

Mileage (mi/gal) vs Gasoline Used Originally (gal)

**54.** $y = \frac{2^4}{x}$; −$\frac{2^4}{5}$ **55.** $y = \frac{50}{x}$; −10 **56.** $y = \frac{48}{x}$; −$\frac{48}{5}$
**57.** exponential growth; 3 **58.** exponential growth; 0.1

---

**59.** exponential decay; 5 **60.** exponential decay; 3
**61.** 79 − 20√3 **62.** 6 **63.** −2 **64.** $(x − 4)(x − 2)$
**65.** $(x + 9)(x − 3)$ **66.** $(2x − 7)(x + 4)$
**67.** $(2x − 3)(x − 7)$

## Lesson 8-3    pp. 515–523

**Got It? 1. a.** domain: all real numbers except $x = 4$
and $x = -4$; points of discontinuity: non-removable at
$x = 4$ and $x = -4$; no x-intercept, y-intercept: $\left(0, -\frac{1}{16}\right)$
**b.** domain: all real numbers; no points of discontinuity;
x-intercepts: (1, 0) and (−1, 0), y-intercept: $\left(0, -\frac{1}{3}\right)$
**c.** domain: all real numbers except $x = -2$ and $x = -1$;
points of discontinuity: non-removable at $x = -2$, removable
at $x = -1$; no x-intercept, y-intercept: $\left(0, \frac{1}{2}\right)$ **2. a.** $x = 1$
and $x = -3$ **b.** −3 **c.** no vertical asymptotes
**3. a.** $y = -2$ **b.** $y = 0$ **c.** no horizontal asymptote
**4.**

**5. a.** 4 gal **b.** No, because the graph changes when
$y_1 = 0.8$ and intersects the graph of $y_2 = \frac{2 + 0.1x}{2 + x}$ at
$x ≈ 0.6$. So, to have 80% orange juice, about 0.6 gal
should be added.
**Lesson Check 1.** $x = -5$ and $x = -4$ **2.** $x = 9$ and
$x = -2$ **3.** $x = -1$ **4.** $x = \frac{1}{3}$ **5.** $x = -5$
**6.** $x = -2$ and $x = -3$ **7.** $x = 1$
**8.** $x = 1$ and $x = -3$
**9.**    **10.**

**11.** the function is undefined at $x = 1$ and $x = -3$
**12.** degree 2; function is discontinuous at 2 values of x
**Exercises 13.** domain: all real numbers except $x = 0$
and $x = 2$; points of discontinuity: non-removable at
$x = 0$ and $x = 2$; no x- or y-intercept **15.** domain: all
real numbers except $x = \pm 1$; pts. of discontinuity: non-
removable at $x = -1$, removable at $x = 1$; no x-intercept;
y-intercept: (0, 3) **17.** vertical asymptote at $x = -2$
**19.** vertical asymptotes at $x = -\frac{3}{2}$ and $x = 1$
**21.** hole at $x = -2$ **23.** $y = 0$ **25.** $y = 1$ **27.** $y = 0$

**29.**    **31.**

**33.**

**35.** 900 ml **37.** vertical asymptote at $x = -2$
**39.** 6 free throws
**41.** correct answer: vertical asymptotes: $x = -5$ and
$x = -1$, horizontal asymptote: $y = 1$
**43.**    **45.**

**47.** Answers may vary. Sample: There is no value of x for
which the denominator equals 0.
**55.**
domain: all real numbers
except $x = 0$, range: all real
numbers except $y = 4$

**56.**
domain: all real numbers
except $x = -3$, range: all
real numbers except $y = 0$

**57.**
domain: all real numbers
except $x = -1$, range: all
real numbers except $y = 1$

**58.**  domain: all real numbers except $x = 7$, range: all real numbers except $y = -3$

**59.** domain: all real numbers except $x = 0$, range: all real numbers except $y = 0$

**60.** domain: all real numbers except $x = 1$, range: all real numbers except $y = 2$

**61.** $y = \frac{x+3}{x}$; yes **62.** $y = 6 - \frac{4}{x}$; yes **63.** $y = \pm\sqrt{\frac{x}{2}}$; no **64.** $y = \pm\sqrt{5x}$; no **65.** $y = \frac{2}{x} - 2$; yes **66.** $y = (x - 1)^2 + 2$; yes

**67.** $a < 10\frac{2}{3}$

**68.** $x \ge 36$

**69.** $x \ge 17\frac{4}{5}$

**70.** $y > 4$

**71.** $x < 3$

**72.** $b < 5$

**73.** $(2x - 1)(x - 1)$ **74.** $(x - 3)(2x + 3)$ **75.** $(5x + 1)(x + 1)$ **76.** $10(x - 1)(x + 1)$

## Lesson 8-4    pp. 527–533

**Got It? 1. a.** $-\frac{4x}{y}$; $x \ne 0$, $y \ne 0$ **b.** $\frac{x+4}{x-3}$; $x \ne 2$ or 3 **c.** $-\frac{4}{x-5}$; $x \ne \pm 3$ **2.** $\frac{2(x+1)}{(x+4)^2}$; $x \ne \pm 4$ **3. a.** $\frac{2x}{x-1}$; $x \ne 1, -1, -4, 0,$ or 3 **b.** 6 restrictions; 2 in each of the original denominators, and 2 in the denominator of the reciprocal of the second rational expression. **4.** a square

**Lesson Check 1.** $\frac{z-7}{z+2}$; $z \ne -3$ **2.** $\frac{3}{x}$; $x \ne 0$ or 1 **3.** $\frac{3(x+5)}{x+3}$; $x \ne -3, -6,$ or 2 **4.** $\frac{x+6}{x-5}$; $x \ne -6, -2, 2, 3,$ or 5 **5.** Yes; the numerator and denominator are polynomials with no common factor. **6.** No; $x = 2$ will make the denominator of the $\frac{x}{x-2}$ 0, so $x = 2$ is not a solution. There is no solution to the equation.

**7.** Length $= \frac{2(a+8)}{a+5}$, $-10 < a < -5$, $a \ne -8$

**Exercises 9.** $\frac{1}{2x-1}$; $x \ne 0$ or $\frac{1}{2}$ **11.** $7 - z$; $z \ne -7$ **13.** $\frac{xy^2}{x-5}$; $x \ne 0$, $y \ne 0$ **17.** $-\frac{4(x+6)}{3(3x+8)}$; $x \ne 3$ or $-\frac{8}{3}$ **19.** $1$; $x \ne 2, -1, 2,$ or 3 **21.** $\frac{7y}{x}$; $x \ne 0$, $y \ne 0$ **23.** $1$; $y \ne -2$ or 4 **25.** $\frac{4(y-3)}{(y+5)}$; $y \ne 2, -5,$ or 0 **27.** $\frac{3}{x}$; $x \ne -3$ or 10 **29.** $\frac{y(y+3)}{2(y-1)}$; $x \ne 0$, $y \ne -4$ or 3

**31.** $R_{cylinder} = \frac{V_{cylinder}}{SA_{cylinder}} = \frac{rh}{2(r+h)}$, $R_{cube} = \frac{V_{cube}}{SA_{cube}} = \frac{s}{6}$; if $r = h = s$, then $R_{cylinder} = \frac{s}{4}$ and $R_{cube} = \frac{s}{6}$; $R_{cylinder} > R_{cube}$. The cylindrical shaped box is more efficient. If $s = h = 2r$ (diameter), then $R_{cylindrical} = R_{cube}$. The boxes are equally efficient. **33.** $\frac{18x}{(x+9)(x+3)}$; $x \ne -9, -3,$ or 3 **35.** $\frac{x+1}{x-1}$; $x \ne -\frac{1}{2}, \frac{1}{2}, 1,$ or $-2$ **37.** They are equally efficient. **39.** never **41.** never **43.** $\frac{2}{x}$; $x \ne -3$ or 1 **54.** hole at $x = 3$ **55.** vertical asymptotes at $x = -1$ and $x = -1$ hole at $x = 4$, vertical asymptote at $x = -3$ **57.** 3 **58.** $-5$ **59.** $\frac{7}{8}$ **60.** $\frac{1}{4}$ **61.** 49 **62.** 168 **63.** 2 **64.** $\frac{17}{38}$ **65.** $\frac{19}{75}$ **66.** $\frac{11}{72}$ **67.** $\frac{137}{180}$

## Lesson 8-5    pp. 534–541

**Got It? 1. a.** $2(x + 2)(x - 3)$ **b.** $(x - 1)(x - 2)^2(x + 4)$ **2. a.** $\frac{x+2}{x}$, $x \ne 1$ or 0

**b.** $\frac{2(x-1)}{x^2 - 4}$; $x \ne \pm 2$ **c.** Yes, however the denominator could have to be factored more and there would be additional, incorrect limitations on $x$. **3. a.** $\frac{x-2}{x+1}$, $x \ne 1$ or 2 **b.** $\frac{x^2 - x - 4}{x^2 + 6x + 5}$; $x \ne -5$ or $-1$ **4. a.** $\frac{x^3y}{x+y}$ **b.** $\frac{(x-1)^2}{2x}$, $x \ne 0, -2,$ or $\pm 1$ **5.** Option 1 still gives the better combined mpg since Option 3 gives 18.46 mpg.

**Lesson Check 1.** $\frac{2a-10}{3a-5}$; $a \ne \frac{5}{3}$ **2.** $\frac{6x - 11}{x^2 - 4}$; $x \ne \pm 2$ **3.** $\frac{-11m}{3m + 6}$; $m \ne -2$ **4.** $\frac{-4(2b - 5)}{(b - 4)(b + 4)(b - 2)}$; $b \ne 2$ or $\pm 4$ **5.** error in finding a common denominator:

$$\frac{1 + \frac{1}{x}}{\frac{3}{x}} = \frac{\frac{x+1}{x}}{\frac{3}{x}}$$
$$= \frac{x+1}{x} \cdot \frac{x}{3}$$
$$= \frac{x+1}{3}$$

**6.** Answers may vary. Sample: $\frac{x^2 - 1}{x^2 - 6x + 5}$; $\frac{x^2 + 6x + 5}{x^2 - 25}$

**Exercises 7.** $9(x + 2)(2x - 1)$ **9.** $5(y + 4)(y - 4)$ **11.** $\frac{1}{2x}$, $x \ne 0$ **13.** $\frac{-3}{x}$; $x \ne 0$ **15.** $\frac{xy + 8y + 4}{2xy}$; $x \ne 0$, $y \ne 0$ **17.** $\frac{2}{(y + 2)}$; $y \ne -2$ **19.** $\frac{-x + 6}{(x - 3)(x + 3)}$; $x \ne \pm 1$ or 2 **21.** $\frac{-2x(x + 3)}{(x - 2)(x - 1)(x + 1)}$; $x \ne \pm 1$ or $-16$ **23.** $\frac{15}{28}$ **25.** $\frac{b}{4}$ **27.** $\frac{3x}{x^2 + xy}$; $x \ne -\frac{3}{5}$ or $\frac{3}{x - 6}$ **31.** $\frac{3x - 8}{4x^2}$; $x \ne 0$ **33.** $\frac{7x - 17}{(x - 3)(x + 3)}$; $x \ne \pm 3$ **35.** $\frac{x(3x^2 + x - 1)}{x^2 - 2}$; $x \ne \pm\sqrt{2}$ **37.** 3.84 in.

**41.** $\frac{3x + 2y}{7x - 5y}$ **43.** 4 **45.** a. $\frac{2}{5}$ b. $\frac{c}{2}$ c. $\frac{2}{3}$ d. $\frac{1}{5}$ **53.** $\frac{x + 1}{x + 3}$; $x \ne 2$ or $\pm 3$ **55.** $\frac{3(x + 1)}{2(x + 3)}$; $x \ne 1$ or $-3$ **57.** $\log p^7 q^2$

**58.** $\log \frac{x}{\sqrt[3]{y}}$ **59.** 30 **60.** 82 **61.** $\frac{13}{4}$ **62.** 101 **63.** $-\frac{4}{3}$ **64.** 21 **65.** 18

## Lesson 8-6    pp. 542–548

**Got It? 1. a.** 1 **b.** 0 **2. a.** $\approx 4.47$ m/h **b.** The direction of wind affects the speed (rate) of the bike. Since the speed is inversely related to time, change in speed will lead to change in time. Since there is no wind, the speed of the bike will remain same to and from the store, hence the time to and from the store will remain the same. **3.** $0.\overline{27}$

**Lesson Check 1.** 5 **2.** −1 **3.** −2 **4.** 310 m/h **5.** LCD was not found. The correct answer is
$$\frac{35 + 9x}{7x} = \frac{28(7)}{7x}; x \ne 0$$
$$9x = 161$$
$$x = \frac{161}{9} = 17.\overline{8}$$
**6.** Answers may vary. Sample: $\frac{2}{x - 3} + \frac{1}{x + 3} = \frac{5x}{x^2 - 9}$ **7.** Answers may vary. Sample: (1) Substitute the solution into the original equation. (2) Check to see if the solution is in the domain of the graph of the original equation. **Exercises 9.** 10 **11.** 2 **13.** −1, 12 **15.** ≈−1.45, ≈1.65 **17.** −3, −2 **19.** 1 **21.** 0.6 **23.** 1.5 **25.** 1.75 **27.** ±2 **29.** ≈1.69, ≈−0.44 **31.** $E = mc^2$ **33.** $c = \pm\sqrt{a^2 - b^2}$ **35.** $B = \pm\sqrt{\frac{r^2 (2h)}{r^2 q}}$ **37.** $1\frac{5}{7}$ h **39.** 4 test scores **41. a.** $2250$ **b.** $\frac{15,000}{24} + \frac{x}{24}$ (3.60) **c.** $2250 - \frac{15,000}{24} + \frac{x}{24}$ (3.60) **d.** ≈32.7 mpg **43.** 3 **45.** no solution **47.** no solution **49.** no solution **51.** $1, -\frac{2}{3}$ **61.** $\frac{y - 1}{(x + 3)}$ **62.** $\frac{5xy - 1}{2y(y + 2)}$ **63.** $\frac{x^3 + 3}{2(x - 1)(x + 3)}$ **64.** $x = -3$ **65.** $x = -1$ **66.** $x = -0.875$ **67.** $y = \frac{5 - x}{2}$; yes **68.** $y = 3 + \sqrt{x - 1}$; no **69.** $y = \sqrt[3]{x + 4}$; yes **70.** add 2; 9, 11, 13 **71.** subtract 2; −10, −12, −14 **72.** multiply by 5; 625, 3125, 15625 **73.** subtract 5; 30, 25, 20 **74.** multiply by 2; 128, 256, 512 **75.** subtract 4; −19, −23, −27

## Chapter Review    pp. 553–556

**1.** simplest form **2.** combined variation **3.** complex fraction **4.** point of discontinuity **5.** branch **6.** 12 **7.** $y = \frac{7.5}{x}$ **8.** $y = 6x$ **9.** $z = \frac{7}{4}xy$; 56 **10.** $z = \frac{4x}{y}$; 2 **11.**  no $x$- or $y$-intercept; vert. asymptote: $x = 0$, horizontal asymptote: $y = 0$

**12.** no $x$- or $y$-intercept; vert. asymptote: $x = 0$, horizontal asymptote: $y = 0$

**13.** $x$-intercept: $(-0.25, 0)$, no $y$-intercept; vert. asymptote: $x = 0$, horizontal asymptote: $y = -4$

**14.** $x$-intercept: $(-1, 0)$, $y$-intercept: $(0, -\frac{1}{3})$; vert. asymptote: $x = -3$, horizontal asymptote: $y = -1$

**15.** $y = \frac{4}{x} + 3$ **16.** $y = \frac{4}{x - 2} + 2$ **17.** $y = \frac{4}{x + 3} - 4$ **18.** $y = \frac{4}{x - 4} - 3$ **19.** pts. of discontinuity: $x = -2, 1$;

vert. asymptote: $x = -2$, horizontal asymptote: $y = 0$; hole at $x = 1$ **20.** 1, −1

vert. asymptote: $x = -1$; hole at $x = 1$

**21.** no pts. of discontinuity

horizontal asymptote: $y = 2$

**22.** ≈31,056 headsets

Number of Headsets (thousands)

**23.** $\frac{x+5}{4x}$; $x \ne 4$ or −5 **24.** $\frac{(x-1)(x+1)}{x+3}$; $x \ne -4, -3,$ or 6 **25.** $\frac{(2x-1)(x+1)}{x+4}$; $x \ne -4, -1,$ or 0

**26.** $\frac{r}{3}$, where $r$ is the radius **27.** $\frac{3(3x - 4)}{(x - 2)(x + 2)}$; $x \ne \pm 2$ **28.** $\frac{-x^2 + 3x + 2}{x(x + 1)}$; $x \ne \pm 1, 0,$ or −3 **29.** $\frac{2(x - 1)}{x}$ **30.** $\frac{1}{4(x - 1)}$ **31.** −1 **32.** no solution **33.** −12, 9 **34.** you: 10 mi/h friend: 8 mi/h

## Chapter 9

**Get Ready! p. 561 1.** 9, 11, 13, 15 **2.** 1, 6, 11, 16 **3.** 0.9, 1.1, 1.3, 1.5 **4.** −2, −7, −12, −17 **5.** $3\frac{1}{2}, 7\frac{1}{2}, 11\frac{1}{2}, 15\frac{1}{2}$ **6.** subtract 5; −11, −16, −21 **7.** mult. by 2; 16, 32, 64 **8.** mult. by 2; 16, 32, 64 **9.** alternate subtract 9 and add 1; −7, −6, −15 **10.** add 3; 19, 22, 25 **11.** $\frac{4}{9}$ **12.** $\frac{1}{8}$ **13.** $\frac{5}{3}$ **14.** $\frac{5}{18}$ **15.** Answers may vary. Sample: $f(x) = 2x - 1$; 1, 3, 5, 7, 9 **16.** Answers may vary. Sample: $g(x) = 1 - 2x$; −1, −3, −5, −7, −9; yes; common difference: −2 **17.** Answers may vary. Sample: $h(x) = 5(2)^x$; 10, 20, 40, 80, 160; yes; common ratio: 2

## Lesson 9-1    pp. 564–571

**Got It? 1.** 147 **2. a.** $a_1 = 1$ and $a_n = na_{n-1}$ **b.** $a_1 = 1$ and $a_n = a_{n-1} + n^2$ **3. a.** $a_n = n^2 - 1$; 399 **b.** To find the $n$th term using an explicit formula, you simply substitute for $n$ in the formula. To find the $n$th term using a recursive definition may require many iterations. **4.** 18 months

**Lesson Check 1.** 2, 7, 12, 17, 22 **2.** −1, 0, 3, 8, 15 **3.** $a_1 = 3$ and $a_n = 2a_{n-1}$ **4.** $a_n = 2 + 3n$ **5.** A recursive formula defines the terms in a sequence by relating each term after the first term to the one before it and requires that the previous term be known to find a given term. An example of a recursive formula for the sequence 8, 4, 2, 1, ... is $a_1 = 8$ and $a_n = \frac{1}{2}a_{n-1}$. An explicit formula describes the $n$th term of a sequence using the variable $n$ and only requires the number of the term to be known. An example of an explicit formula for the sequence 1, 3, 5, 7, ... is $a_n = 2n - 1$. **6.** The "+1" in the explicit formula $a_n = 3n + 1$ is incorrect for the sequence 1, 4, 7, 10, .... The correct explicit formula is $a_n = 3n - 2$.

**Exercises 7.** 5, 8, 11, 14, 17, 20 **9.** $\frac{1}{2}, 1, \frac{3}{2}, 2, \frac{5}{2}, 3$ **11.** 2, 10, 24, 44, 70, 102 **13.** $-\frac{1}{3}, 3, \frac{25}{3}, 31, \frac{123}{3}, 107$ **15.** $a_1 = 80$ and $a_n = a_{n-1} - 3$ **17.** $a_1 = 0$ and $a_n = a_{n-1} + (n + 1)$ **19.** $a_1 = 100$ and $a_n = \frac{1}{10}a_{n-1}$ **21.** $a_1 = 4$ and $a_n = a_{n-1}$ **23.** $a_1 = 1$ and $a_n = a_{n-1} + n$ **25.** $a_1 = \frac{n-2}{2}$; 2 **29.** $a_n = n^2 + 1$; 101 **31.** $a_n = 3^{n-1}$; 19,683 **33.** 3, 9, 21, 45, 93 **35.** $\frac{15}{7}$ **37.** $\frac{-3}{1024}$ **39.** −47 **41.** $-\frac{8}{5}$ **43.** recursive; 9, 11, 13, 15 **45.** explicit; −24, −21, −16, −9, 0

**47.** explicit; −6, −18, −38, −66, −102 **49.** 25, 36, 49, 64 **51.** $\frac{16}{5}, \frac{25}{6}, \frac{36}{7}, \frac{49}{8}$ **53.** $140 **55.** 20, 23; $a_n = 3n + 2$, explicit OR $a_n = a_{n-1} + 3$, 5, recursive **57.** 216, 343; $a_n = n^3$, explicit **59.** 144, 169; $a_n = (n + 6)^2$, explicit OR $a_n = a_{n-1} + 2n + 11$, $a_1 = 49$, recursive **61.** −1, −$\frac{1}{2}$; $a_n = \frac{a_{n-1}}{2}$, $a_1 = -16$, recursive **63.** −11, −19; $a_n = 29 - 8n$, explicit OR $a_n = a_{n-1} - 8$, $a_1 = 21$, recursive **65. a.** 25 boxes **b.** 110 boxes **c.** 9 levels **76.** 277.4 **78.** −5 **79.** −1 **80.** 1 **81.** 2 **82.** subtract 2; −2, −4, −6 **83.** add 17; 185, 202, 219 **84.** add $\frac{3}{7}$; $\frac{17}{7}, \frac{20}{7}, \frac{23}{7}$

## Lesson 9-2    pp. 572–577

**Got It? 1. a.** not arithmetic **b.** arithmetic **2. a.** 93 **b.** 95, 112, 129 **3. a.** 115 **b.** yes, use the formula for arithmetic mean and solve for $a_2$; $a_2 = 2a_0$ **c.** $a_3$ **4.** 65 seats **Lesson Check 1.** 56 **2.** 87 **3.** 13 **4.** 39 **5.** In an arithmetic sequence, the diff. between any two consecutive terms is always the same number. **6.** Answers may vary. 2, 4, 8, 16, 32, ...

**Exercises 7.** yes; 10 **9.** yes; 3 **11.** yes; 4 **13.** 127 **15.** 240 **17.** 12.5 **19.** 7 **21.** 13 **23.** 7.5 **25.** $135 **27.** 18 **29.** 36 **31.** 2 **33.** The student multiplied the third term by 2 instead of adding 2. The correct answer is 6. **35.** 120 **37.** 1.1 **39.** 0 **41.** $a_n = 2 + (2n - 1)$; $a_n = a_{n-1} + 2$, $a_1 = 2$ **43.** $a_n = -5 + 1(n - 1)$; $a_n = a_{n-1} + 1$, $a_1 = -5$ **45.** $a_n = -5 + 1.5(n - 1)$; $a_n = a_{n-1} + 1.5$, $a_1 = -5$ **47.** $a_n = 1 + \frac{1}{3}(n - 1)$; $a_n = a_{n-1} + \frac{1}{3}$, $a_1 = 1$ **49.** $a_n = 27 - 12(n - 1)$; $a_n = a_{n-1} - 12$, $a_1 = 27$ **51.** Answers may vary. Sample: An advantage of a recursive formula is that only the preceding term must be known to find the next term; a disadvantage is that many calculations may be required to find a term. An advantage of an explicit formula is that it is easy to find any term. Use the recursive formula when the previous term and common diff. are known. Use the explicit formula when the term number and common diff. are known. **53.** −4, −10, −16 **55.** −8, −17, −26 **57.** 17, 17, 17 **59.** −12.5, −8, −3.5 **61.** $5055 **78.** recursive; −2, −7, −12, −17, −22 **79.** explicit; 6, 18, 36, 60, 90 **80.** explicit; 0, 3, 8, 15, 24 **81.** recursive; −121, −108, −95, −82, −69 **82.** $y - 3 = \frac{5}{3}(y - 11 = \frac{3}{5}(x - 3)$ **83.** $y - 6 = 4(x - 4)$ or $y - 30 = 4(x - 16)$ **84.** $y - 10 = 8(x - 1)$ or $y - 42 = 8(x - 5)$ **85.** $r = \frac{\sqrt[7]{6x^7 V}}{2\pi}$ **86.** 32 **87.** 625 **88.** −81

## Lesson 9-3    pp. 580–586

**Got It? 1. a.** yes; $a_1 = 2$, $r = 2$ **b.** no **c.** yes; $a_1 = 2^3$, $r = 2^4$ **2.** 6 or −6 **3. a.** explicit; it is easier to use because only one calculation is needed. **b.** about 16.8 cm, about 4 cm **4.** ±60 **Lesson Check 1.** no **2.** yes; 2 **3.** 729 **4.** 0.0064 **5.** The third term would be the geometric mean of 5 and 80 which is 20. Since $a$ is pos. and $r^2$ is always pos., the third term, $ar^2$, cannot be neg. **6.** For both the arithmetic mean and the geometric mean, the middle term of any three consecutive terms can be determined using the first and last of the three terms. The arithmetic mean is the sum of the first and last terms divided by 2, whereas the geometric mean is the square root (or its opposite) of the product of the first and the last terms.

**Exercises 7.** yes; 2 **9.** yes; −2 **11.** yes; 0.4 **13.** yes; $\frac{1}{3}$ **15.** yes; 1.5 **17.** yes; 6 **19.** 6561 **21.** 0.078125 **23.** $-\frac{3}{2048}$ **25.** about 656.1 g; about 182.5 g; about 96.2 g **27.** ±1530 **29.** ±1.5 **31.** ±6 **33.** $a_n = 100(-20)^{n-1}$; {100, −2000, 40,000, −800,000, 16,000,000} **35.** $a_n = 1024(0.5)^{n-1}$; 1024, 512, 256, 128, 64 **37.** $a_n = 10(-1)^{n-1}$; 10, −10, 10, −10, 10 **39.** arithmetic; 125, 150 **41.** geometric; −80, 160 **43.** neither; 25, 36 **45.** 7.5, 22.5, 67.5 or −7.5, 22.5, −67.5 **47.** −6.64, −11.02, −18.30 or 6.64, −11.02, 18.30 **49.** about 74.3 mi **51.** 768 **53.** $3 \times 4^{19}$ or 824,633,720,832 **54.** 57 **59.** 10 **59.** Both the common diff. and the common ratio are used to find the next term in a sequence, but a common diff. is added and a common ratio is multiplied. **67.** $a_n = -3 + 3(n - 1)$; $a_n = a_{n-1} + 3$, $a_1 = -3$ **69.** $a_n = 17 - 9(n - 1)$; $a_n = a_{n-1} - 9$, $a_1 = 17$ **70.** $a_n = -2 - 11(n - 1)$; $a_n = a_{n-1} - 11$, $a_1 = -2$ **71.** $7\sqrt{14}$ **72.** $\frac{3\sqrt{3}\sqrt{x}}{7x}$ **73.** $\sqrt[3]{\frac{y}{x}}$ **74.** $5\sqrt[3]{6}$ **75.** vert. asymptote: $x = -3$ **76.** vert. asymptote: $x = -1$ **77.** vert. asymptotes: $x = 0, 1$ **78.** vert. asymptote: $x = 3$; hole at $x = -3$ **79.** $a_n = a_{n-1} + n$, $a_1 = 1$ **80.** $a_n = a_{n-1} + (2n - 1)$, $a_1 = 1$ **81.** $a_n = a_{n-1} + n^2$, $a_1 = 1$

## Lesson 9-4    pp. 587–593

**Got It? 1. a.** 1030 **b.** Yes; no; the sum of any number of even numbers is always even. The sum of an odd number of odd numbers is odd, but the sum of an even number of odd numbers is even. **2.** 59 sales; 1725 sales **3. a.** $\sum_{n=1}^{6}(-12 + 7n)$ **b.** $\sum_{n=1}^{4}(510 - 10n)$ **4. a.** 2140 **b.** 100 **c.** 1 **5.** 41,650

**Lesson Check 1.** 91 **2.** 780 **3.** $\sum_{n=1}^{15} 3n$

**4.** $\sum_{n=1}^{32}(-3 + 4n)$ **5.** An arithmetic sequence is a list of numbers for which successive numbers have a common difference. **6.** The lower limit should not be 3, it should be one and the expression $5n - 2$ should be in parentheses. The correct summation notation is $\sum_{n=1}^{5}(3 + 5n)$. **7.** Yes; $44 = 2(a_1 + a_4)$, so any combination of $a_1$ and $a_4$ with a sum of 22 is a possible series.

**Exercises 9.** 92 **11.** 176 **13.** −165 **15.** $\sum_{n=1}^{20} 4n$

**17.** $\sum_{n=1}^{20}(2 + 3n)$ **19.** $\sum_{n=1}^{15}(-3n)$ **21.** 25 **23.** 20

**25.** −2 **27.** 2400 **29.** 682 **31.** −8556 **33.** 432 seats **35.** sequence; finite **37.** series; infinite **39.** series; finite **41.** −48 **43.** 35 **45.** −146 **47. a.** $a_n = n + 1$

**b.** $\frac{n}{2}(n + 1)$ **c.** 18 cans **d.** No; no; 13 rows have 104 cans, 14 rows have 119 cans, 15 rows have 135 cans, and 16 rows have 152 cans. The number of rows would not be an integer for 110 cans or 140 cans. **49.** −765

**62.** $a_n = 2^{n-1}$; 1, 2, 4 **63.** $a_n = -1(-1)^{n-1}$; −1, 1, −1

**64.** $a_n = 3\left(\frac{2}{3}\right)^{n-1}$; 3, $\frac{9}{2}$, $\frac{27}{4}$ **65.** $\frac{x-3}{4}$; $x \neq 4$, $x \neq -1$

**66.** $\frac{c-2}{c-5}$; $c \neq 5$, $c \neq 6$ **67.** $\frac{z^2 + 12z + 20}{z - 1}$, $z \neq 1$, $z \neq 0$ **68.** $-\frac{1}{8}$ **69.** $\frac{3}{4}$ **70.** $-\frac{1}{2}$

**Lesson 9-5** pp. 595–601

**Got It? 1. a.** 315 **b.** −1705 **2.** about $2138.43 **3. a.** diverges **b.** converges; $\frac{1}{4}$ **c.** converges; 2 **d.** Yes; if $|r| < 1$, the series converges. If $|r| \geq 1$, the series diverges.

**Lesson Check 1.** $\frac{31}{80}$ **2.** $\frac{55}{9}$ **3.** converges **4.** diverges **5.** Since $r = 1.1 > 1$, the series diverges and does not have a sum. **6.** An infinite geometric series has a sum only when the series converges, which is when $|r| < 1$. **7.** The sum of a finite arithmetic series is $S_n = \frac{n}{2}(a_1 + a_n)$. The sum of finite geometric series is $S_n = \frac{a_1(1 - r^n)}{1 - r}$. The formulas are similar in that each sum requires the first term and the number of terms. The formulas are different in that the sum of a finite arithmetic series needs the last term, while the sum of a finite geometric series needs the common ratio.

**Exercises 9.** 1456 **11.** −5115 **13.** $\frac{15}{32}$ **15.** $\frac{121}{81}$

**17.** converges; $\frac{4}{3}$ **19.** converges; 8 **21.** diverges; no sum **23.** diverges; no sum **25.** diverges; no sum **27.** 1 **29.** $\frac{7}{2}$ **31.** $\frac{9}{5}$ **33.** arithmetic; 420 **35.** geometric; about 96.47

**37.** geometric; about 121.5
**39. a.**

Stage 1 — 4 calls  Stage 2 — 16 calls  Stage 3 — 64 calls

**b.** $4 + 16 + 64 + 256 + 1024 + 4096$ **c.** 5460 employees **41.** $\frac{5}{4}$ **43.** $\frac{3}{4}$ **45.** $0.8\overline{3}$ **47. a.** $\frac{7}{8}$ **b.** 10 **49. a.** Answers may vary. Sample: The student used $r - 1$ instead of $1 - r$ in the formula for the sum of an infinite geometric series. **b.** $\frac{1}{2}$

**51. a.** $rS_n = r(a_1 + a_1r + \cdots + a_1r^{n-1}) = a_1r + a_1r^2 + \cdots + a_1r^n$

**b.** $S_n - rS_n = a_1 + a_1r + a_1r^2 + \cdots + a_1r^{n-1} - a_1r - a_1r^2 - \cdots - a_1r^{n-1} - a_1r^n$
$= a_1 - a_1r^n$

**c.** $S_n - rS_n = a_1 - a_1r^n$
$S_n(1 - r) = a_1 - a_1r^n$
$S_n = \frac{a_1 - a_1r^n}{1 - r} = \frac{a_1(1 - r^n)}{1 - r}$

**59.** 140 **60.** −825 **61.** $\frac{7c - 4}{2c^2}$ **62.** $\frac{10(2y + 3)}{(y + 3)(y - 3)}$

**63.** $\frac{x^2 + 6x + 4}{(x + 6)(x - 6)}$ **64.** 0 **65.** 2 **66.** 1

**67.**  **68.** **69.**

**Chapter Review** pp. 603–606

**1.** limits **2.** sequence **3.** converges **4.** common ratio **5.** explicit formula **6.** 1, −1, −3, −5, −7 **7.** 1, 0, −3, −8, −15 **8.** 2, 3, 5, 9, 17 **9.** 20, 10, 5, 2.5, 1.25 **10.** $a_n = a_{n-1} + 17$, $a_1 = 5$ **11.** $a_n = a_{n-1} + 9$, $a_1 = -2$ **12.** $a_n = 3n - 2$ **13.** $a_n = 6.5 - 2.5n$ **14.** no **15.** yes; $d = 15$, $a_{32} = 468$ **16.** yes; $d = 3$, $a_{32} = 100$ **17.** no **18.** 5 **19.** 101.5 **20.** 5 **21.** −4.9 **22.** −10.5, −8, −5.5 **23.** 1.4, 0.8, 0.2 **24.** $a_n = -2 + 9(n - 1)$ **25.** $a_n = 62 - 3(n - 1)$ **26.** yes; $r = \frac{1}{2}$; $\frac{1}{16}$, $\frac{1}{32}$ **27.** no **28.** yes; $r = 1.2$; 6.2208, 7.46496 **29.** ±6 **30.** ±0.04

**31.** ±10, −5, ±2.5 **32.** $a_n = 2^{n-1}$
**33.** $a_n = 25\left(\frac{1}{5}\right)^{n-1}$ **34.** 2560 **35.** 1536

**36.** $\sum_{n=1}^{5}(13 - 3n)$; 20 **37.** $\sum_{n=1}^{5}(45 + 5n)$; 455

**38.** $\sum_{n=1}^{5}(4.6 + 1.4n)$; 143 **39.** $\sum_{n=1}^{4}(23 - 2n)$; 112

**40.** 3; −8, 26; 27 **41.** $\frac{5}{4}$; 4; 8; 54 **42.** 31 **43.** $53\frac{1}{8}$ **44.** $14\frac{1}{18}$ **45.** converges; $S = 187.5$ **46.** diverges **47.** diverges **48.** converges; $S = 2$

## Chapter 10

**Get Ready! p. 611**

**1.**  **2.**

**3.** **4.**

**5.** quadratic; $-x^2$, 6x, 1 **6.** linear; none, $-12x$, $-18$ **7.** linear; none, $x$, $-\frac{13}{2}$ **8.** quadratic; $-8x^2$, 28x, none **9.** quadratic; $-2x^2$, $-3x$, 6 **10.** linear; none, $-x$, $-10$ **11.** 16 **12.** $\frac{25}{4}$ **13.** 49 **14.** $y = (x + 3)^2 - 2$ **15.** $y = 2(x - 1)^2 + 8$ **16.** $y = -3\left(x - \frac{1}{2}\right)^2 + \frac{1}{12}$

**17.** **18.** **19.** **20.**

**21.** The radius of a circle is the distance from the center of the circle to any pt. on the circle. The radius extends in every direction from the center and ends on the circle. All radii of the same circle are equal. **22.** The vertex of a parabola is the lowest or highest pt. of a parabola; it is the pt. where the parabola changes direction.

**Lesson 10-1** pp. 614–621

**Got It?**
**1. a.** circle: center (0,0), radius 3; lines of sym.: every line through the origin; domain: $-3 \leq x \leq 3$, range: $-3 \leq y \leq 3$
**b.** 6 is outside the domain of x.
**2.** ellipse: center (0,0); lines of sym.: x-axis and y-axis; domain: $-3 \leq x \leq 3$, range: $-3\sqrt{2} \leq y \leq 3\sqrt{2}$
**3.** hyperbola: center (0,0); lines of sym.: x-axis and y-axis; domain: $x \leq -4$ or $x \geq 4$, range: all real numbers

**4.** center of hyperbola: (0, 0); no x-intercepts, y-intercepts: (0, 1), (0, −1); domain: all real numbers, range: $y \leq -1$ or $y \geq 1$ **5. a.** Ellipse; the eq. $9x^2 + 25y^2 = 225$ represents a conic section with two sets of intercepts, $(\pm 3, 0)$ and $(0, \pm 5)$. Since the intercepts are not equidistant from the center, the eq. models an ellipse. **b.** Hyperbola; the eq. $x^2 - y^2 = 1$ represents a conic section with one set of intercepts, $(\pm 1, 0)$, so the eq. must model a hyperbola.

**Lesson Check**
**1.**  lines of sym.: x-axis and y-axis; domain: $-6 \leq x \leq 6$, range: $-3 \leq y \leq 3$

**2.** lines of sym.: x-axis and y-axis; domain: $x \leq -3$ or $x \geq 3$, range: all real numbers

**3.** domain: $x \leq -2.5$ or $x \geq 2.5$, range: all real numbers **4.** domain: $-6 \leq x \leq 6$, range: $-1.5 \leq y \leq 1.5$ **5. a.** hyperbola **b.** circle **6.** Answers may vary. Sample answer: The domain of an ellipse is an interval between two real numbers, such as $-a \leq x \leq a$. The domain of a hyperbola is two intervals, such as $x \leq -a$ or $x \geq a$, if there are x-intercepts, or all real numbers if there are no x-intercepts.

**Exercises**
**7.** hyperbola; center: (0, 0); no x-intercepts, y-intercepts: $\left(0, \pm\frac{5\sqrt{3}}{3}\right)$; lines of sym.: x-axis and y-axis; domain: all real numbers, range: $y \leq -\frac{5\sqrt{3}}{3}$ or $y \geq \frac{5\sqrt{3}}{3}$

**9.** circle; center: (0, 0); radius: 4; x-intercepts: ($\pm4$, 0), y-intercepts: (0, $\pm4$); infinitely many lines of sym.; domain: $-4 \leq x \leq 4$, range: $-4 \leq y \leq 4$

**11.** ellipse; center: (0, 0); x-intercepts: ($\pm5$, 0); y-intercepts: (0, $\pm2$); lines of sym.: x-axis and y-axis; $-5 \leq x \leq 5$, range: $-2 \leq y \leq 2$

**13.** hyperbola; center: (0, 0); no x-intercepts, y-intercepts: (0, $\pm1$); lines of sym.: x-axis and y-axis; domain: all real numbers, range: $y \leq -1$ or $y \geq 1$

**15.** circle; center: (0, 0); radius: 10; x-intercepts: ($\pm10$, 0), y-intercepts: (0, $\pm10$); infinitely many lines of sym.; domain: $-10 \leq x \leq 10$, range: $-10 \leq y \leq 10$

**17.** ellipse; center: (0, 0); x-intercepts: ($\pm4$, 0), y-intercepts: (0, $\pm2$); lines of sym.: x-axis and y-axis; domain: $-4 \leq x \leq 4$, range: $-2 \leq y \leq 2$

**19.** ellipse; center: (0, 0); x-intercepts: ($\pm1$, 0), y-intercepts: (0, $\pm\frac{1}{3}$); lines of sym.: x-axis and y-axis; domain: $-1 \leq x \leq 1$, range: $-\frac{1}{3} \leq y \leq \frac{1}{3}$

**21.** hyperbola; center: (0, 0); no x-intercepts, y-intercepts: $\left(0, \pm\frac{1}{3}\right)$; lines of sym.: x-axis and y-axis; domain: all real numbers; range: $y \leq -\frac{1}{3}$ or $y \geq \frac{1}{3}$

**23.** hyperbola; center: (0, 0); no x-intercepts, y-intercepts: (0, $\pm2$); domain: all real numbers, range: $y \leq -2$ or $y \geq 2$ **25.** hyperbola; center: (0, 0); x-intercepts: ($\pm3$, 0), no y-intercepts; domain: $x \leq -3$ or $x \geq 3$, range: all real numbers **27.** hyperbola; center: (0, 0); no x-intercepts, y-intercepts: (0, $\pm3$); domain: all real numbers; range: $y \leq -3$ or $y \geq 3$ **29.** 22 **31.** 24 **33.** 27

**35.** circle; center: (0, 0); radius: 2; x-intercepts: ($\pm2$, 0), y-intercepts: (0, $\pm2$); infinitely many lines of sym.; domain: $-2 \leq x \leq 2$, range: $-2 \leq y \leq 2$

**37.**  ellipse; center: (0, 0); x-intercepts: $\left(\pm\frac{8\sqrt{5}}{5}, 0\right)$, y-intercepts: (0, $\pm2\sqrt{5}$); lines of sym.: x-axis and y-axis; domain: $-\frac{8\sqrt{5}}{5} \leq x \leq \frac{8\sqrt{5}}{5}$, range: $-2\sqrt{5} \leq y \leq 2\sqrt{5}$

**39. a.** All lines in the plane that pass through the center of a circle are axes of sym. of the circle. **b.** The axes of sym. of an ellipse intersect at the center of the ellipse. The same is true for a hyperbola. This can be confirmed using, for example, $4x^2 + 9y^2 = 36$ and $4x^2 - 9y^2 = 36$.

**41.** **43.**

$x^2 + y^2 = \frac{1}{4}$   $x^2 + y^2 = 1.5625$

**45.** Sample: ($\sqrt{2}$, 1) **47.** Sample: (2, 0) **49.** (0, $-\sqrt{7}$) **59.** diverges **60.** diverges **61.** converges **62.** $x^3 - 3x^2y + 3xy^2 - y^3$ **63.** $p^6 + 6p^5q + 15p^4q^2 + 20p^3q^3 + 15p^2q^4 + 6pq^5 + q^6$ **64.** $x^4 - 8x^3 + 24x^2 - 32x + 16$ **65.** $243 - 405x + 270x^2 - 90x^3 + 15x^4 - x^5$

**66.**

| x | −2 | −1 | 0 | 1 | 2 |
|---|---|---|---|---|---|
| y | 2 | 1 | 0 | 1 | 2 |

**67.**

| x | −2 | −1 | 0 | 1 | 2 |
|---|---|---|---|---|---|
| y | 5 | 3 | 4 | 3 | 5 |

**68.**

| x | 0 | 1 | 2 | 3 | 4 |
|---|---|---|---|---|---|
| y | | | | | |

**69.**

| x | −3 | −2 | −1 | 0 | 1 |
|---|---|---|---|---|---|
| y | −3 | −2 | −3 | −4 | −3 |

**Lesson 10-2** pp. 622–629

**Got It? 1. a.** $y = -\frac{1}{8}x^2$ **b.** vertex: (0, 0); focus: (0, 1); directrix: $y = -1$ **c.** As the distance between the vertex and focus increases, the width of the parabola increases.
**2. a.** $x = \frac{1}{16}y^2$ **b.** vertex: (0, 0); focus: $\left(-\frac{1}{16}, 0\right)$; directrix: $x = \frac{1}{16}$. 1 cm **4.** vertex: (−4, 2); focus: $\left(-4, 2\frac{1}{4}\right)$; directrix: $y = 1\frac{3}{4}$ **5.** $y = \frac{1}{8}(x - 2)^2 + 4$

**Lesson Check 1.** $y = \frac{1}{4}x^2$ **2.** $x = \frac{1}{8}(y - 2)^2 + 3$ **3.** vertex: (0, 0); focus: (4, 0); directrix: $x = -4$ **4.** vertex: (−3, −4); focus: (−3, −3.75); directrix: $y = -4.25$ **5.** 6 units **6.** With the focus one unit away from the vertex of a parabola at the origin, $c = \pm1$. Given this information, the student cannot tell whether the parabola opens in the vert. direction, with one of the eqs. $y = \frac{1}{4}x^2$ or $y = -\frac{1}{4}x^2$, or whether the parabola opens in the horizontal direction, with one of the eqs. of $x = \frac{1}{4}y^2$ or $x = -\frac{1}{4}y^2$.

**Exercises 7.** $x = \frac{1}{24}y^2$ **9.** $y = \frac{1}{28}x^2$ **11.** $x = \frac{1}{8}y^2$ **13.** vertex: (0, 0); focus: $\left(0, \frac{1}{16}\right)$; directrix: $y = -\frac{1}{16}$ **15.** vertex: (0, 0); focus: $\left(\frac{1}{4}, 0\right)$; directrix: $x = -\frac{1}{4}$

**17.** $x = \frac{1}{12}y^2$ **19.** $y = \frac{3}{4}x^2$ **21.** $y = -\frac{1}{56}x^2$ **23.** Answers may vary. Sample: $y = x^2$. The light produced by the bulb will reflect off the parabolic mirror in parallel rays. **25.** vertex: (3, 2); focus: $\left(3, \frac{9}{4}\right)$; directrix: $y = \frac{7}{4}$ **27.** vertex: (1, −5); focus: $\left(1, -4\frac{3}{4}\right)$; directrix: $y = -5\frac{1}{4}$

**29.** vertex: $(-1, -4)$;
focus: $\left(-1, -3\frac{7}{8}\right)$;
directrix: $y = -4\frac{1}{8}$

**31.** $x = -\frac{1}{32}(y - 3)^2$ **33.** $y = -\frac{1}{16}(x - 7)^2 + 2$
**35.** vertex: $(0, 0)$; focus: $(0, -1)$; directrix: $y = 1$

**37.** vertex: $(0, 0)$;
focus: $(-2, 0)$;
directrix: $x = 2$

**39.** vertex: $(4, 0)$;
focus: $(4, -6)$;
directrix: $y = 6$

**41.**

**43.** $y = \frac{1}{4}x^2$ **45.** 3.5 in.

**47.**

**49.**

**51.**

**53.** $x = -\frac{1}{2}(y - 1)^2 + 1$

**55.** Answers may vary. Sample: Write the eq. in the form $x = \frac{1}{4\left(\frac{1}{8}\right)}y^2$. The distance from the focus to the directrix is $2\left(\frac{1}{8}\right)$, or $\frac{1}{4}$.

**63.**

circle: center $(0, 0)$, radius 8; x-intercepts: $(\pm 8, 0)$, y-intercepts: $(0, \pm 8)$; infinitely many lines of sym.; domain: $-8 \le x \le 8$, range: $-8 \le y \le 8$

**64.**

ellipse: center $(0, 0)$; x-intercepts: $(\pm 3, 0)$, y-intercepts: $(0, \pm 1)$; lines of sym.: x-axis and y-axis; domain: $-3 \le x \le 3$, range: $-1 \le y \le 1$

**65.**

hyperbola: center $(0, 0)$; x-intercepts $(\pm 3, 0)$, no y-intercept; lines of sym.: x-axis and y-axis; domain: $x \le -3$ or $x \ge 3$, range: all real numbers

**66.** 1 **67.** 4 **68.** 25 **69.** 9

## Lesson 10-3     pp. 630–636

**Got It? 1.** $(x - 5)^2 + (y + 2)^2 = 64$ **2. a.** $(x + 5)^2 + (y + 3)^2 = 1$ **b.** $(x - 2)^2 + (y - 3)^2 = 9$
**3. a.** $(x - 7)^2 + (y + 10)^2 = 144$ **b.** Yes; the values $h$ and $k$ determine the position of the circle and $r$ determines the size. **4. a.** center $(-8, -3)$, radius 11
**b.** center $(3, -7)$, radius $\sqrt{66}$
**5.**

**Lesson Check 1.** $(x + 1)^2 + (y + 5)^2 = 4$
**2.** $x^2 + y^2 = 36$ **3.** $x^2 + (y - 3)^2 = 121$
**4.** $(x + 5)^2 + (y + 3)^2 = 16$ **5.** The circle with equation $(x + 7)^2 + (y - 7)^2 = 8$ is a translation of the circle with equation $x^2 + y^2 = 8$ as 7 units left and 7 units up, not right and down. **6.** If $P(x, y)$ is one of the pts. $(r, 0)$, $(-r, 0)$, $(0, r)$, or $(0, -r)$, subst. shows that $x^2 + y^2 = r^2$. If $P(x, y)$ is any other pt. on the circle, drop a perpendicular $\overline{PK}$ from $P$ to $K$ on the x-axis. $\triangle OPK$ is a rt. triangle with legs of lengths $|x|$ and $|y|$ and with hypotenuse of length $r$. By the Pythagorean Thm., $|x|^2 + |y|^2 = r^2$, so $x^2 + y^2 = r^2$.

**Exercises 7.** $x^2 + y^2 = 100$ **9.** $(x - 2)^2 + (y - 3)^2 = 20.25$ **11.** $(x - 1)^2 + (y + 3)^2 = 100$
**13.** $x^2 + (y + 1)^2 = 9$ **15.** $(x - 2)^2 + (y + 4)^2 = 25$
**17.** $x^2 + (y + 5)^2 = 100$
**19.**

$x^2 + y^2 = 144$,
$x^2 + y^2 = 576$,
$x^2 + y^2 = 1296$,
$x^2 + y^2 = 2304$,
$x^2 + y^2 = 3600$

**21.** $(x - 2)^2 + (y + 6)^2 = 16$ **23.** center $(-2, 10)$, radius 2 **25.** center $(-3, 5)$, radius 9 **27.** center $(-6, 0)$, radius 11
**29.**

**31.**

**33.**

**35.** $x^2 + y^2 = 9$ **37.** $x^2 + y^2 = 3$ **39.** $x^2 + y^2 = 169$
**41.** $x^2 + y^2 = 26$ **43.** $x^2 + y^2 = 36$, $(x - 8)^2 + (y - 6)^2 = 16$, $(x - 8)^2 + (y)^2 = 4$ **45.** $(x + 6)^2 + (y - 13)^2 = 49$ **47.** $(x + 2)^2 + (y - 7.5)^2 = 2.25$
**49.** $(x - 2)^2 + (y - 1)^2 = 25$ **51.** $(x + 1)^2 + (y + 7)^2 = 36$ **53.** center $(0, 0)$, radius $\sqrt{2}$ **55.** center $(0, 0)$, radius $\sqrt{14}$ **57.** center $(-5, 0)$, radius $3\sqrt{2}$
**59.** center $(-3, 5)$, radius $\sqrt{38}$ **61.** center $(3, 1)$, radius $\sqrt{6}$ **72.** $x = -\frac{1}{12}y^2$ **73.** at $x = -1$ **74.** at $x = 2$, and at $x = 3$ **75.** no points of discontinuity **76.** 4
**77.** 2 **78.** $-3$ **79.** 4 **80.** $\frac{1}{2}$ **81.** 1 **82.** $-2, -9$
**83.** 0, $\pm 4$, $\pm 4i$ **84.** $\pm 2, \pm 2\sqrt{2}$

## Lesson 10-4     pp. 638–644

**Got It? 1.** $\frac{x^2}{4} + \frac{y^2}{25} = 1$

**2. a.** $(\pm 8, 0)$

**b.** The vertex and co-vertex approach the same distance from the center of the ellipse; a circle

**3.** 24 ft **4.** $\frac{x^2}{36} + \frac{y^2}{53} = 1$

**Lesson Check 1.** $\frac{x^2}{64} + \frac{y^2}{36} = 1$ **2.** $(\pm \sqrt{21}, 0)$
**3.** $\frac{x^2}{169} + \frac{y^2}{25} = 1$ **4.** $6\sqrt{23}$ ft $\approx 28.77$ ft **5.** The student used $a$ and $b$ instead of $a^2$ and $b^2$; $\frac{x^2}{1681} + \frac{y^2}{841} = 1$
**6.** The eq. of an ellipse with center at the origin is $\frac{x^2}{a^2} + \frac{y^2}{b^2} = 1$. For a circle, the major axis and the minor axis are of equal length such that $a = b = r$. Thus, by subst., $\frac{x^2}{r^2} + \frac{y^2}{r^2} = 1$ or $x^2 + y^2 = r^2$.

**Exercises 7.** $\frac{x^2}{16} + \frac{y^2}{1} = 1$ **9.** $\frac{x^2}{4} + y^2 = 1$
**11.** $\frac{x^2}{16} + \frac{y^2}{49} = 1$ **13.** $\frac{x^2}{81} + \frac{y^2}{4} = 1$
**15.** $(0, \pm \sqrt{5})$ **17.** $(\pm 4\sqrt{2}, 0)$

**19.** $(0, \pm 6)$ **21.** $(\pm 2\sqrt{3}, 0)$

**23.** 32 **25.** 6 **27.** 12 **29.** $24\sqrt{2}$ **31.** $\frac{x^2}{100} + \frac{y^2}{64} = 1$
**33.** $\frac{x^2}{89} + \frac{y^2}{64} = 1$ **35. a.** about 22.25 ft **b.** Due to the reflective prop. of an ellipse, you can aim your putt at any part of the border. The ball will reflect off the border and go directly into the hole. **37.** $(0, \pm 2\sqrt{3})$ **39.** $(0, \pm \sqrt{21})$
**41.** $(0, \pm 6)$ **43. a.** 0.9 **b.** 0.1 **c.** The shape is close to a circle. **d.** The shape is close to a line segment.
**45.** $\frac{x^2}{16} + y^2 = 1$ **49.** $\frac{x^2}{25} + \frac{y^2}{4} = 1$
**51.** $\frac{x^2}{702.25} + \frac{y^2}{210.25} = 1$ **53.** $\frac{x^2}{256} + \frac{y^2}{324} = 1$
**55.** $\frac{x^2}{16} + \frac{y^2}{1} = 1$ **57.** $\frac{x^2}{36} + \frac{y^2}{27} = 1$ **59.** $\frac{x^2}{20} + \frac{y^2}{18} = 1$
**67.** $(x - 1)^2 + (y + 5)^2 = 9$ **68.** $(x + 2)^2 + (y - 4)^2 = 81$ **69.** $\frac{x^2}{12 - 3x^2} x \ne 0, x \ne \sqrt[3]{\frac{4}{9}}$ **70.** $\frac{x - 6}{x - 1}$; $x \ne 1, x \ne -6$ **71.** $\frac{x - 5}{x + 1}$; $x \ne -2$ **72.** log 15
**73.** $\log_5 6$ **74.** log 2 **75.** $y = 2x + 4$ **76.** $y = \frac{1}{3}x$

## Lesson 10-5     pp. 645–652

**Got It? 1. a.** $\frac{y^2}{16} - \frac{x^2}{9} = 1$

**b.**

**c.** when $a = b$
**2.** vertices: $(\pm 2, 0)$; foci: $(\pm \sqrt{13}, 0)$; asymptotes: $y = \pm \frac{3}{2}x$

**3.** $\frac{x^2}{49} - \frac{y^2}{72} = 1$

**Lesson Check**
**1.** vertices: $(\pm 6, 0)$; foci: $(\pm \sqrt{61}, 0)$; slopes of asymptotes: $\pm \frac{5}{6}$

**2.** vertices: $(0, \pm 4)$; foci: $(0, \pm \sqrt{41})$; slopes of asymptotes: $\pm \frac{4}{5}$

**3.** vertices: $(0, \pm 2)$; foci: $(0, \pm 2\sqrt{5})$; slopes of asymptotes: $\pm \frac{1}{2}$

**4.** vertices: $(\pm 5, 0)$; foci: $(\pm \sqrt{41}, 0)$; slopes of asymptotes: $\pm \frac{4}{5}$

**5.** $\frac{x^2}{25} - \frac{y^2}{24} = 1$ **6.** Answers may vary. Sample: Similarities—Both have two axes of sym. that intersect at the center of the figure and two foci that lie on the same line as the two "principal" vertices. Differences—An ellipse consists of pts. whose distances from the foci have a constant sum, whereas a hyperbola consists of pts. whose distances from the foci have a constant diff.
**7.** Answers may vary. Sample: A hyperbola is vert. or horizontal depending on whether it has a positive coefficient with the larger denominator is under the $y^2$ term.

**Exercises 9.** $\frac{x^2}{144} - \frac{y^2}{25} = 1$ **11.** $\frac{x^2}{49} - \frac{y^2}{121} = 1$
**13.** $\frac{x^2}{3} - \frac{y^2}{5} = 1$
**15.** vertices: $(0, \pm 7)$; foci: $(0, \pm \sqrt{113})$; asymptotes: $y = \pm \frac{7}{8}x$
**17.** vertices: $(\pm 8, 0)$; foci: $(\pm 10, 0)$; asymptotes: $y = \pm \frac{3}{4}x$

**19.** vertices: $(0, \pm 3)$; foci: $(0, \pm 3\sqrt{10})$; asymptotes: $y = \pm \frac{1}{3}x$
**21.** vertices: $(\pm 2\sqrt{2}, 0)$; foci $(\pm 2\sqrt{11}, 0)$; asymptotes: $y = \pm \frac{3\sqrt{2}}{2}x$

**23.** $x^2 - \frac{y^2}{6} = 1$ **25.** $\frac{y^2}{9} - \frac{x^2}{16} = 1$
**27.** $y^2 - \frac{x^2}{3} = 1$ **29.** $\frac{x^2}{20.25} - \frac{y^2}{4} = 1$
**31.** $\frac{x^2}{32} - \frac{y^2}{64} = 1$
**33.** $y = \pm \sqrt{x^2 - 1}$; $(\pm 1, 0)$ **35.**

**37.**

**47.** foci: $(\pm 3, 0)$

**48.** foci: $(0, \pm 1)$

**49.** foci: $(0, \pm 6)$

**50.** $\frac{1}{3}$ **51.** 125 **52.** 6 **53.** $y = (x - 3)^2 - 8$
**54.** $y = 2(x + 3)^2 - 18$ **55.** $y = 3(x + 4)^2 - 50$

## Lesson 10-6     pp. 653–660

**Got It?**
**1.** $\frac{(x - 12)^2}{100} + \frac{(y - 3)^2}{64} = 1$;

**2.** center $(2, -2)$; vertices: $(-4, -2)$, $(8, -2)$; $(-8, -2)$, $(12, -2)$; asymptotes: $y + 2 = \pm \frac{4}{3}(x - 2)$

**3. a.** circle with center $(6, -2)$ and radius $4\sqrt{3}$

**b.** Replace $+y^2$ with $-y^2$ to get a new eq., $4x^2 - y^2 - 24x + 6y + 9 = 0$. The standard eq. of the hyperbola is $\frac{(x - 3)^2}{4.5} - \frac{(y - 3)^2}{18} = 1$.
**4.** $\frac{(x + 1)^2}{9} + \frac{y^2}{8} = 1$

**Lesson Check 1.** center $(-7, -1)$; vertices: $(-22, -1)$, $(8, -1)$; foci: $(-16, -1)$, $(2, -1)$ **2.** center $(1, 3)$; vertices: $(4, 3)$, $(-2, 3)$; foci: $(1 \pm \sqrt{13}, 3)$ **3.** $\frac{x^2}{48} + \frac{(y - 4)^2}{61} = 1$
**4.** $\frac{(y + 1)^2}{7} - \frac{(x + 3)^2}{51} = 1$ **5.** ellipse and hyperbola
**6.** Your friend used the center $(-2, 1)$ instead of $(2, -1)$. The vertices are $(-10, -1)$ and $(14, -1)$. **7.** The student didn't write the standard-form equation correctly. The standard-form equation is $(x + 4)^2 + (y - 5)^2 = 0$. This is an equation of a circle with center at $(-4, 5)$ and radius 0. Since the radius is 0, the graph is a single point, $(-4, 5)$.

**Exercises**
**9.** $\frac{(x - 3)^2}{21} + \frac{(y + 6)^2}{25} = 1$ **11.** $\frac{(x - 1.5)^2}{42.25} + \frac{(y - 4)^2}{12} = 1$

**13.** center $(3, 4)$; vertices: $(3, 1)$, $(3, 7)$; foci: $(3, 4 \pm \sqrt{13})$
**15.** $y = (x - 4)^2 + 3$; parabola; vertex: $(4, 3)$ **17.** $y = (y - 2)^2 - (x - 3)^2 = 1$; hyperbola; center: $(3, 2)$, foci: $(3, 2 \pm \sqrt{2})$;

**19.** $x = \frac{1}{4}(y - 2)^2 + 3$; parabola; vertex: $(3, 2)$

**21. a.** hyperbola **b.** one focus; the other focus **c.** with the center at the origin, $x^2 - \frac{y^2}{5} = 1$ **23. a.** hyperbola **b.** horizontal line
**25.**

$\frac{(y + 3)^2}{4} - \frac{(x - 6)^2}{5} = 1$

**27.** $\frac{(x-1)^2}{9} + \frac{(y+1)^2}{16} = 1$ **29.** $x^2 + y^2 = 16$
**31.** $y = 2(x+2)^2 + 4$
**33.** **35.**

ellipse; $\frac{x^2}{9} + \frac{y^2}{36} = 1$  ellipse; $\frac{x^2}{36} + \frac{y^2}{9} = 1$

**42.** foci: $(\pm\sqrt{85}, 0)$ **43.** foci: $(0, \pm\sqrt{21})$

**44.** foci: $(0, \pm 2\sqrt{26})$

**45.** $\frac{3\pm\sqrt{17}}{2}$ **46.** 5 **47.** $\frac{9+\sqrt{201}}{12}$ **48.** 1 **49.** 2 **50.** 3
**51.** 8 **52.** −19 **53.** 6

**Chapter Review** pp. 663–666

**1.** directrix **2.** major axis **3.** standard form of an eq. of a circle **4.** radius **5.** transverse axis
**6.**
ellipse; lines of sym.: x-axis and y-axis; domain: $-7 \le x \le 7$, range: $-11 \le y \le 11$

**7.**
circle; lines of sym.: every line through the center; domain: $-2 \le x \le 2$, range: $-2 \le y \le 2$

**8.**
hyperbola; lines of sym.: x-axis and y-axis; domain: $x \le -5$ or $x \ge 5$, range: all real numbers
**9.**
parabola; line of sym.: x-axis; domain: $x \ge 5$, range: all real numbers
**10.** center (0, 0); domain: $x \le -4$ or $x \ge 4$, range: all real numbers **11.** center (0, 0); domain: $-3 \le x \le 3$, range: $-2 \le y \le 2$ **12.** $x = \frac{1}{20}y^2$ **13.** $y = -\frac{1}{20}x^2$
**14.** $y = \frac{1}{24}x^2$ **15.** $y = \frac{1}{10}x^2$ **16.** $y = 3x^2$
**17.** $y = \frac{1}{8}x^2$ **18.** $x = -\frac{1}{12}y^2 + 1$
**19.** focus: $\left(0, \frac{1}{20}\right)$, directrix: $y = -\frac{1}{20}$ **20.** focus: $\left(\frac{1}{8}, 0\right)$, directrix: $x = -\frac{1}{8}$
**21.** focus: (−2, 0), directrix: $x = 2$
**22.** $x^2 + y^2 = 16$ **23.** $(x-8)^2 + (y-1)^2 = 25$ **24.** $(x+3)^2 + (y-2)^2 = 100$
**25.** $(x-5)^2 + (y+3)^2 = 64$ **26.** center (1, 0), radius 8

circle with radius 8 translated 1 unit to the rt.

**27.** center (−7, −3), radius 7

circle with radius 7 translated 7 units to the left and 3 units down
**28.** $\frac{x^2}{17} + \frac{y^2}{16} = 1$ **29.** $\frac{x^2}{25} + \frac{y^2}{29} = 1$ **30.** $\frac{x^2}{9} + \frac{y^2}{10} = 1$
**31.** $\frac{x^2}{40} + \frac{y^2}{16} = 1$ **32.** $\frac{x^2}{64} + \frac{y^2}{19} = 1$
**33.** foci: $(0, \pm\sqrt{5})$ **34.** foci: $(\pm3\sqrt{29}, 0)$

**35.** foci: $(0, \pm\sqrt{569})$ **36.** foci: $(\pm\sqrt{202}, 0)$

**37.** $\frac{x^2}{64} - \frac{y^2}{225} = 1$ **38.** $\frac{y^2}{49} - \frac{x^2}{576} = 1$
**39.** $\frac{x^2}{1.148 \times 10^{20}} - \frac{y^2}{3.395 \times 10^{10}} = 1$
**40.** $(x-1)^2 + (y-1)^2 = 25$
**41.** $\frac{(x-3)^2}{4} + \frac{(y+2)^2}{9} = 1$
**42.** $\frac{(x-6)^2}{16} - \frac{(y-3)^2}{9} = 1$
**43.** hyperbola; center (0, −2), foci: $(0, -2 \pm 2\sqrt{10})$ **44.** circle; center $\left(-\frac{3}{2}, 2\right)$, radius $\frac{\sqrt{61}}{2}$

**45.** parabola; vertex: $\left(-\frac{1}{2}, -\frac{169}{4}\right)$

**Chapter 11**

**Get Ready!** p. 671

**1.** $83.\overline{3}\%$ **2.** $19.\overline{4}\%$ **3.** $\approx 92.308\%$ **4.** 30.56%
**5.** 6720 **6.** 22,100 **7.** 10 **8.** $a^5 + 5a^4b + 10a^3b^2 + 10a^2b^3 + 5ab^4 + b^5$ **9.** $j^3 + 9j^2k + 27jk^2 + 27k^3$
**10.** $m^2 + 1.4m + 0.49$ **11.** $16 + 32t + 24t^2 + 8t^3 + t^4$ **12.** $m^2 + 2mn + n^2$ **13.** $x^4 + 12x^3y + 54x^2y^2 + 108xy^3 + 81y^4$ **14.** $\pm\frac{1}{10}$ **15.** $\pm\frac{1}{20}$
**16.** $\pm\frac{1}{14}$ **17.** $\pm\frac{1}{2}$ **18.** $\pm\frac{1}{3}$ **19.** $\pm\frac{1}{24}$ **20.** In a math class, when actual trials are difficult to conduct, you can find experimental probability by using a simulation which is a model of one or more events. **21.** It rained today.
**22.** The mean, $12.\overline{6}$; the data are fairly evenly distributed around the mean which makes the mean the best representation of the data given.

**Lesson 11-1** pp. 674–680

**Got It? 1.** 6,760,000 **2.** 40,320 **3a.** 2730 **b.** Yes; because $n = 10$ and $r = 3$ in the formula $_nP_r$ for both cases. **4a.** 56 **b.** 36 **c.** 3003 **5.** 1680
**Lesson Check 1.** 120 **2.** 3024 **3.** 10 **4.** 21
**5.** 4,151,347,200 **6.** A permutation is an arrangement of items in a particular order; order is important. An arrangement in which order does not matter is a combination. **7.** $_nP_r = \frac{n!}{(n-r)!}$; substituting $n = r$, we get $_nP_n = \frac{n!}{(n-n)!} = \frac{n!}{0!}$, but $_nP_n = n! = n!$; substituting values again, we get $\frac{n!}{0!} = \frac{n!}{(n-n)!}$, and so $0! = 1$.
**Exercises 9.** 20 **11.** 13 **13.** 3,628,800 **15.** 720
**17.** 120 **19.** 3003 **21.** 8 **23.** 336 **25.** 6 **27.** 60,480
**29.** 10,897,286,400 **31.** 56 **33.** 4 **35.** 15 **37.** $\frac{5}{18}$
**39.** combination; 4368 **41.** combination; 70
**43.** True because of the Assoc. Prop. of Mult.
**45.** False; answers may vary. Sample: $(3 \cdot 2)! = 6! = 720$ and $3! \cdot 2! = 6 \cdot 2 = 12$
**47.** False; answers may vary. Sample: $(3!)^2 = 6^2 = 36$ and $3^{(2!)} = 3^2 = 9$ **49.** C **51.** Two ways, because order matters. **53a.** 2 **b.** 6

**c.** $(n-1)!$ **61.** center: (2, 1); vertices: (2, 6), (2, −4); co-vertices: (5, 1), (−1, 1); foci: (2, 5), (2, −3)
**62.** $(x-1)^2 + (y-1)^2 = 36$ is a circle (not an ellipse) with center (1, 1) and radius 6. **63.** $4(x-1)^2$
**64.** $-(x+3)^2$ **65.** $3(x-5)(x+5)$ **66.** 30,240
**67.** $\frac{x^2}{25}$ **68.** 210

**Lesson 11-2** pp. 681–687

**Got It? 1.** 0.40 or 40% **2.** 0.20 or 20% **3a.** $\frac{1}{2}$. The likelihood of getting an even or odd is the same, i.e. $\frac{1}{2}$.
**4.** $\frac{48}{2,598,960}$ or 0.0000184689 or $\approx 0.00185\%$
**5.** 0.05 or 5%
**Lesson Check 1.** 0.75 or 75% **2.** 0.80 or 80%
**3.** $\frac{4}{5}$ **4.** $\frac{1}{3}$ **5.** Experimental probabilities are calculated on the basis of data from an experiment, actual or simulated. Given equally likely outcomes, the basis for calculating theoretical probability is being able to determine the no. of ways that an event can occur within these outcomes. Comparisons of measures such as length and area are the basis of geometric probability. **6.** Answers may vary. Samples: Flip a coin; generate random numbers on a calculator; roll a die with odd numbers as true and even numbers as false. **7.** Because you are averaging over more samples, you are getting a more accurate average.
**Exercises 9.** the number 1: $\frac{11}{70} \approx 15.7\%$; the number 2: $\frac{11}{67} \approx 16.4\%$; the number 3: $\frac{50}{298} \approx 16.8\%$; the number 4: $\frac{11}{67} \approx 16.4\%$; the number 5: $\frac{42}{240} \approx 17.5\%$; the number 6: $\frac{73}{424} \approx 17.2\%$ **11.** Answers may vary. Sample: Toss 5 coins. Keep a tally of the times three or more heads are tossed. (A head represents a correct answer.) Do this 100 times. The total number of tally marks, as a percent, gives the experimental probability. The simulated probability should be about 50%. **13.** $\frac{3}{10}$ or 30%
**15.** $\frac{4}{5}$, or 80% **17.** $\frac{48}{125}$, or 38.4% **19.** $\frac{103}{125}$, or 82.4%
**21.** $\frac{77}{125}$, or 61.6% **23.** $\frac{30(_5C_3 \cdot 1)0_6C_6}{150C_9} \approx 0.17879 \approx 17.9\%$
**25.** $\frac{5}{8}$, or 62.5% **27.** $\frac{3}{4}$, or 75% **29.** $\frac{116}{147} \approx 78.9\%$
**31.** $\frac{43}{147} \approx 29.3\%$ **33.** 1 chance in 2,869,685 or $\approx 0.00003485\%$ **35.** if there are any restrictions on the last digit of a ZIP code **42.** 20 **43.** 840 **44.** 10
**45.** 45 **46.** $\frac{25b-7a^3}{5a^2b^2}$ **47.** $\frac{3q+7p}{pq}$ **48.** 0
**49.** $\frac{7}{36} \approx 19.\overline{4}\%$ **50.** $\frac{25}{36} \approx 69.\overline{4}\%$ **51.** $\frac{1}{2}$, or 50%

**Lesson 11-3** pp. 688–693

**Got It? 1.** Independent; the number of coins is the same after the coin is replaced. **2.** 0.20, or 20% **3a.** Not mutually exclusive; 2 is a prime number and an even number. **b.** Mutually exclusive; there is no even number less than 2 in the roll of a number cube. **4a.** 0.61, or 61% **b.** Yes; the percentage of students tells which language is chosen by more students. **5a.** $\frac{5}{9}$ **b.** $\frac{5}{9}$
**3.** 1, or 100% **4.** $\frac{5}{8}$ or 87.5% **5.** $\frac{5}{8}$, or 62.5%
**6.** Events A and B are independent if the outcomes of A do not affect the outcomes of B. The events are mutually exclusive if A and B cannot occur at the same time. For independent events, $P(A \text{ and } B) = P(A) \cdot P(B)$. For mutually exclusive events, $P(A \text{ and } B) = 0$. For any events, $P(A \text{ or } B) = P(A) + P(B) - P(A \text{ and } B)$. **7.** Since these are not mutually exclusive events, the student should have multiplied to get the correct answer, which is 0.21 or 21%.
**Exercises 9.** independent **11.** dependent **13.** $\frac{1}{6}$
**15.** 0.54 **17.** $\frac{7}{8}$ **19.** mutually exclusive; if the numbers are equal, then the sum is even **21.** $\frac{1}{3}$ **23.** 39% **25.** $\frac{1}{2}$
**27.** $\frac{5}{9}$ **29.** $\frac{3}{8}$ **31.** $\frac{1}{64}$; independent; $\frac{1}{4}$ **33.** 14.5%
**35.** 87.4% **37.** $\frac{16}{81}$ **39.** $\frac{41}{68}$; not mutually exclusive
**51.** $\frac{5}{6}$ **52.** $\frac{1}{2}$ **53.** $\frac{1}{3}$ **54.** $\frac{5}{7}$ **55.** $-\frac{2}{3}$ **56.** $\frac{5}{12}$
**57.** $\frac{159}{12} \approx 10.04$ **58.** $\frac{1}{3}6^6 \approx 201.71$ **59.** $\pm e^2 \approx \pm 7.39$
**60.** $\frac{1}{16}$ **61.** $\frac{1}{16}$ **62.** $\frac{1}{48}$

**Lesson 11-4** pp. 696–702

**Got It? 1a.** $\approx 0.57355$ or $\approx 57.355\%$ **b.** Female; there are more females enrolled. **2a.** $\approx 0.026448$ or $\approx 2.64\%$
**b.** $\approx 0.040302$ or $\approx 4.03\%$ **3.** 0.2 **4.** 9%
**Lesson Check 1.** $\frac{1}{2}$ **2.** $\frac{1}{13}$ **3.** $\frac{1}{12}$ **4.** 0.5 **5.** 50%
**5.** The sum of the probability of an event happening and the probability of an event not happening is 1. Each branch represents either the event happening or the event not happening. **7.** Answers may vary. Sample: Tree diagrams apply to cases in which more than one event occurs in a sequence. The Fundamental Counting Principle applies to situations in which there are multiple outcomes of a single event. With a tree diagram, but not with the Fundamental Counting Principle, you can determine probabilities of dependent events, or conditional probabilities.
**Exercises 9.** 0.6 **11.** $\approx 0.085$ **13.** $\approx 0.682$
**15.** $\approx 0.709$ **17.** $\approx 23\%$

**19.**

M = male
F = female
R = right-handed
L = left-handed

$P(L | F) = 10\%$, $P(M \text{ and } R) \approx 11.4\%$
**21.** 75% **23.** $P(S \text{ and } W)$ **25.** $\frac{2}{3}$, or 66.67%
**27.** 0.08, or 8% **29.** 0.84 **31.** 0.16 **38.** $\frac{1}{3} \approx 33.\overline{3}\%$
**39.** $\frac{17}{76} \approx 0.22368 \approx 22.37\%$ **40.** $x = \frac{1}{4}(y-2)^2 + 5$
**41.** $y = \frac{1}{12}(x+2)^2 + 3$ **42.** $\pm 3$ **43.** 0.830 **44.** 1.404
**45.** 3.465 **46.** 0.2, 0.3, 0.6, 0.7, 0.8, 0.9, 1.2; 0.7
**47.** 11, 15, 17, 18, 21, 21, 23; 18

**Lesson 11-5** pp. 704–711

**Got It? 1.** mean: 5.25, median: 5, mode: 5 **2a.** Yes; it is unlikely that the water temperature of a lake would change by 25 degrees. **b.** No; 98 would represent the busiest night of the week and it may relate to a weekly event. **3.** Dauphin Island: mean: 69.083, mode: 84, range: 33, $Q_1 = 58$, median: 71, $Q_3 = 81$, interquartile range: 23; Grand Isle: mean: 73.416, modes: 61, 70, 77, 83, 85, range: 24, $Q_1 = 64.5$, median: 73.5, $Q_3 = 83$, interquartile range: 18.5; The range and the interquartile range show the temperatures varying less at Grand Isle than at Dauphin Island. Also, the temperatures at Grand Isle are generally higher. **4a.** Use STAT PLOT, select a box-and-whisker plot. Enter data for the three remaining Gulf Coast sites. Enter the window values. Draw the box-and-whisker plots. Use TRACE on the plot to find quartiles $Q_1$, $Q_2$ and $Q_3$.

**b.** Yes, a box-and-whisker plot uses minimum and maximum values, the median, and the first and third quartiles to display the variability in a data set. **5a.** at or below 79 **b.** at or below 98
**Lesson Check 1.** outlier: 54; outlier included: mean: 22.8, median: 19.5, mode: 18; outlier not included: mean: $19.\overline{3}$, median: 19, mode: 18 **2.** outlier: 40; outlier included: mean: 92.6, median: 98, mode: 90; outlier not included: mean: 99.25, median: 99, mode: 90 **3.** the mean because the sum of the data values is affected and the mean depends on the sum **4.** 40%: 49 and below; 80%: 58 and below **5.** the mean; when data are somewhat sym. the best representation is the mean. **6.** The error is in how to calculate the median. The median is the middle value or the 11th value which is 90.
**Exercises 7.** mean: $112.\overline{3}$, median: 95, mode: none
**9.** 8 **11.** Jacksonville: mean: 67.9916, mode: none, range: 29.2, $Q_1 = 58.15$, median: 68.4, $Q_3 = 78.6$, interquartile range: 20.45; Austin: mean: 68.583, mode: none, range: 36, $Q_1 = 56.85$, median: 70.5, $Q_3 = 80.75$, interquartile range: 23.9; the range and the interquartile range show the temperatures varying less at Jacksonville than at Austin.
**13.**

**15.** 5; 17 **17.** outlier: 381; outlier included: mean: $\approx 161.214$, median: 158, mode: none; outlier not included: mean: $\approx 144.308$, median: 142, mode: none
**19.**

**21.** 30th **23.** 89 is at the 100th percentile, since 100% of the values are less than or equal to 89. **25.** the median; a few outliers can heavily influence the mean without drastically affecting the median. **27.** 83.9
**34.** 0.20 **35.** 0.56 **36.** yes; −9 **37.** yes; 17 **38.** no **39.** yes; 0 **40.** $\pm 16$ **41.** $\pm 0.09$ **42.** $\pm\frac{11}{4}$ **43.** $\pm\frac{19}{3}$

**Lesson 11-6** pp. 712–717

**Got It? 1.** $\bar{x} = 69.8\overline{3}$, $\sigma^2 = 115.1389$, $\sigma = 10.7303$
**2.** $\bar{x} = 7.26$, $\sigma = 3.316$ **3a.** within 3 standard deviations of the mean **b.** FEMA can expect that the no. of hurricanes for a 15-year period will fall within 3 standard deviations of the mean.
**Lesson Check 1.** $\bar{x} = 10$, $\sigma^2 = 19.8$, $\sigma = 4.45$
**2.** within 2 standard deviations of the mean **3.** Measures of central tendency are specific data pts. which give a summary of the middle of the data set, whereas the measures of variation give a summary of the variation of the data set within the range of distribution. **4.** Standard deviation measures how widely spread the data values are. If the data pts. are close to the mean, the standard deviation is small; if the data pts. are far from the mean, the standard deviation is large. The data pts. of Set B are closer to the mean of 70 than the data pts. of Sets A and C; likewise, the data pts. of Set A are closer to 70 than the data pts. of Set C. **5.** The effect of an outlier on the standard deviation is to increase the standard deviation.

## Page 1102

**Exercises 7.** $\bar{x} \approx 15.1, \sigma^2 \approx 12.4, \sigma \approx 3.5$
**9.** $\bar{x} \approx 43.8, \sigma^2 \approx 75.76, \sigma \approx 8.7$ **11.** $\bar{x} \approx 12320.00$, $\sigma \approx 273.71$ **13.** 3 standard deviations **15.** $\bar{x} = 53.8$, $\sigma \approx 3.4$; $1\sigma$; 7; $2\sigma$; 9; $3\sigma$; 10 **17.** Overall farm income increased slightly, but there was less variability among the states in 2002. The income in 2001 clustered more tightly around the mean. (2001: $\sigma_x \approx 2679$, 2002: $\sigma_x \approx 2758$) **21.** Your first friend; one standard deviation encompasses all values within one standard deviation above and below the mean. The graph shows that all values are within 3 standard deviations of the mean.

**28.**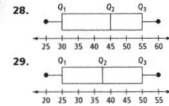

**29.**

**30.** center $(2, -1)$; radius 6 **31.** center $(1, 1)$; radius 2
**32.** $\frac{1}{2}$ **33.** $-\frac{1}{3}$ **34.** $\frac{1}{6}$ **35.** $-\frac{1}{11}$ **36.** $-\frac{1}{9}$ **37.** $\frac{1}{7}$

### Lesson 11-7     pp. 718–723

**Got It? 1a.** convenience sample; yes; since the location is at the food court in the mall, the sample may over represent food court or fast food supporters. **b.** Answers may vary. Sample: population data for the US census
**2a.** Yes; the question asks about two issues, nutrition and taste. **b.** Yes; the question is "loaded", suggesting the student council is "highly effective" and that you want a particular answer. **3.** Answers may vary. Sample: Have pictures of five well-known figures, the governor and four others who are not politicians, such as an actor, a sports figure, etc. Ask a member in every fifth house in your neighborhood to identify the five figures.
**Lesson Check 1a.** convenience sample **b.** Yes; since the location is near the exit of a history museum, the sample may over represent people who enjoy learning history and the results will have a bias. **2.** Yes; the question is leading and loaded. It suggests the person wants a particular answer. **3.** All members of the set are the population. A sample is a subset of the population. Answers may vary. Sample: population: students in a high school; sample: students who like to snowboard **4.** It is important to have as little error as poss. in a sample, thus giving an unbiased sample. An unbiased sample is more representative of an entire population. **5.** A large sample size would give a better estimate. The size of the sample is important to the reliability of the sample.
**Exercises 7.** systematic sampling; no **9.** The question asks about two issues, academic homework and household chores. **11.** The question is leading. It suggests you want a certain answer, that the wrestling team doesn't get enough coverage in the school newspaper. **13.** Answers may vary. Sample: Convenience sampling; interview students at a local high school. **15.** Answers may vary. Sample: Self-selected sampling; a newspaper article invites females over the age of 21 to call the paper and express their opinions. **17.** self-selected sampling; biased because only those who spend time online will respond. **19.** Answers may vary. Sample: Do you think career opportunities will decrease if Congress considers additional unemployment control laws? **21.** Answers may vary. Sample: Do you think opening more colleges and encouraging students to complete their education will help provide careers to financially challenged people? **23.** Systematic and self-selected sampling; people with no strong interest in any leisure-time activity may choose not to respond. **25.** $\approx 0.01988$ or $\pm 1.988\%$ **27.** 37% to 47% **29.** 38.5% to 45.5% **31.** Doubling the sample size decreases the margin of error by a factor of $\frac{1}{\sqrt{2}}$.
**38.** $\bar{x} \approx 2.83, \sigma \approx 2.54$ **39.** $\bar{x} \approx 5.62, \sigma \approx 3.67$
**40.** $y = \frac{1}{2}(x - 5)$; yes **41.** $y = \pm\sqrt{x}$; no **42.** $y = \pm\sqrt{\frac{9x}{5}}$; no **43.** $y = \frac{x^2}{5}$, $x \ge 0$; yes **44.** $\le 45$ **45.** 10 **46.** 10 **47.** 792

### Lesson 11-8     pp. 725–732

**Got It?**
**1.** $P(0) = 0.07776; P(1) = 0.2592; P(2) = 0.3456;$ $P(3) = 0.2304; P(5) = 0.01024$
**2.** $81x^4 + 108x^3y + 54x^2y^2 + 12xy^3 + y^4$
**3.** $\approx 0.1035$, or about 10.4%
**Lesson Check 1.** $\approx 0.3110$, or $\approx 31.10\%$.
**3.** 0.1641, or 16.41% **3.** $20c^3d^3$ **4.** $-10x^4y$
**5.** 0.2646, or 26.46% **6.** Answers may vary. Sample: A binomial experiment has three important features: **a.** The situation involves repeated trials; flipping a coin 10 times has 10 trials. **b.** Each trial has two possible outcomes; in this case, heads or tails. **c.** The probability of success is constant throughout the trials; the trials of flipping a coin, are independent. **7.** The student wrote "5" instead of "4". It should be: $_{n}C_{(5-1)}n^{(n-4)}b^4 = {}_{7}C_4 3^3(-k)^4 = 35\,j^3k^4$
**Exercises 9.** $\approx 0.1361$, or $\approx 13.61\%$
**11.** $\approx 0.0015$, or $\approx 0.15\%$
**13.** $a^4 + 4a^3b + 6a^2b^2 + 4ab^3 + b^4$
**15.** $243x^5 + 810x^4y + 1080x^3y^2 + 720x^2y^3 + 240xy^4 + 32y^5$ **17.** $896g^6h$ **19.** $e^6$
**21.** $P(0) \approx 0.1176, P(1) \approx 0.3025, P(2) \approx 0.3241, P(3) \approx 0.1852, P(4) \approx 0.0595, P(5) \approx 0.0102, P(6) \approx 0.0007$
**23.** $P(0) \approx 0.000001, P(1) \approx 0.000054, P(2) \approx 0.0012, P(3) \approx 0.0146, P(4) \approx 0.0984, P(5) \approx 0.3543, P(6) \approx 0.5314$

## Page 1103

**25.** 0.99328 **27.** $\approx 0.2824$ **29.** $\approx 0.1109$
**31.** $\approx 0.2461$ **33.** $\approx 0.6230$ **35a.** 0.0914 **b.** The probability that three boxes would be underweight is 0.0001. You can conclude that there might be a malfunction in the machinery or that the company's claim may be false. **37.** The probability of a group of 30 students having 4 or fewer left-handed students is about 77.05%. This means that more than three quarters of the classes will have enough left-handed desks; 4 is an adequate no.
**39a.** $P(0) = 0.001, P(1) = 0.027,$ $P(2) = 0.243, P(3) = 0.729$

**b.** $P(0) = 0.166375, P(1) = 0.408375,$ $P(2) = 0.334125, P(3) = 0.091125$

**c.** The probabilities of each graph sum to 1; $P(0) + P(1) + P(2) + P(3) = 1$. The probabilities of part (a) increase with increasing success numbers; the maximum probability occurring at $P(3)$. The probabilities of part (b) peak with a maximum at $P(1)$ and then decrease with increasing success numbers. **49.** loaded and leading question by the use of the word "beautiful" and the phrase "Do you agree." **50.** does not provide enough information about the amendments to make a decision **51.** vertices: $(0, \pm 7)$; foci: $(0, \pm\sqrt{74})$; asymptotes: $y = \pm\frac{7}{5}x$ **52.** vertices: $(0, \pm 3)$; foci: $(0, \pm\sqrt{13})$; asymptotes: $y = \pm\frac{3}{2}x$ **53.** vertices: $(0, \pm 3)$; foci: $(0, \pm 5)$; asymptotes: $y = \pm\frac{3}{4}x$ **54.** $\frac{7}{2}$ **55.** $\frac{1}{2}$
**56.** $\frac{2}{3}$ **57.** $\bar{x} = 24.4, \sigma \approx 5.04$ **58.** $\bar{x} = 81.8, \sigma \approx 4.77$
**59.** $\bar{x} = 8.6, \sigma \approx 0.47$ **60.** $\bar{x} = 24.74, \sigma \approx 2.046$

### Lesson 11-9     pp. 733–739

**Got It? 1a.** 71% **b.** 88%
**2.**

**Distribution of Female European Eels**

**3a.** 2.5% **b.** 210 students **c.** The students that received a 3 had scores between 165 and 180.
**Lesson Check 1.** 94%
**2.**

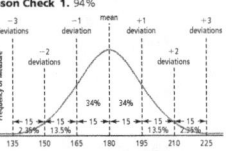

**3.** 47.5% **4.** Normal distribution means that most of the examples in a data set are close to the mean; the distribution of the data is within 1, 2, or 3 standard deviations of the mean. **5.** The mean and median are equivalent in a normal distribution. **6.** mean increases by 10: the bell curve is translated 10 units to the r.; standard deviation increases by 10: the bell curve is stretched out by a factor of 10; the bell curve will be less steep due to the larger standard deviation.
**Exercises 7.** $\approx 43\%$ **9.** $\approx 43$ men
**11.** **13.**

**15.** 68% **17.** 50% **19a.** Set 2
**b. and c.**

**21.** 59 min **23.** 47.5% **25.** 81.5% **27.** 84%

## Page 1104

**29a.**

**b.** Yes; the curve is skewed to the left. **31.** Yes; Elena scored within the top 10% of her group. Her score is 2.75 standard deviations above the mean, which places her in the top 1%. Jake did not score in the top 10%. His score is 1.16 standard deviations above the mean, or at the 88th percentile. **38.** 0.02867 **39.** 0.1612 **40.** 0.03676
**41.** circle; center: $(0, 0)$; radius: 8; lines of sym.: all lines through the center; domain: $-8 \le x \le 8$, range: $-8 \le y \le 8$

**42.** hyperbola; center: $(0, 0)$, foci: $(\pm 3\sqrt{2}, 0)$; lines of sym.: $x = 0, y = 0$; domain: $x \le -3$ or $x \ge 3$; range: all real numbers

**43.** ellipse; center: $(0, 0)$, foci: $(\pm 4, 0)$; lines of sym.: $x = 0, y = 0$; domain: $-5 \le x \le 5$, range: $-3 \le y \le 3$

**44.** $y = x - 3$; **45.** $y = x$;

**46.** $y = x - \frac{1}{3}$;

### Chapter Review     pp. 743–748

**1.** sample **2.** outlier **3.** probability distribution **4.** range of a set of data **5.** 6 **6.** 362,880 **7.** 12 **8.** 30 **9.** 21 **10.** 10 **11.** 30 **12.** 744 **13.** 220; 84; 20; 1
**14.** $3.315312 \times 10^9$ **15.** 216 **16.** $\frac{42}{70}$ **17.** 0 **18.** $\frac{2}{5}$
**19.** Not necessarily; you may pick a 5 zero times, one time, or more than once. Each time you pick, the prob.
that it will be a 5 is $\frac{1}{10}$. **20.** dependent **21.** independent
**22.** 0.21 **23.** 0.79 **24.** 0.3 **25.** 0.7 **26.** $\frac{1}{4}$ **27.** $\frac{4}{5}$ **28.** $\frac{1}{8}$
**29.** 9 **30.** mean: 6, median: 6, mode: 9 **31.** mean: 10.6, median: 7, modes: 3 and 7 **32.** mean: 15, median: 15, mode: 18 **33.** mean: 9.5, median: 9.5, mode: none **34.** range: 30; $Q_1 = 30$; $Q_3 = 55$ **35.** range: 35; $Q_1 = 25$; $Q_3 = 50$ **36.** range: 65; $Q_1 = 47$; $Q_3 = 87$ **37.** heights of 3 ppl. **38.** ages of thirty college students **39.** gas mileage of 18 automobiles of various types **40.** $\bar{x} \approx 6.64, \sigma \approx 5.12$ **41.** $\bar{x} \approx 17.14, \sigma \approx 3.52$ **42.** $\bar{x} \approx 7.5, \sigma \approx 2.67$ **43.** not a random sample; they will all begin with the letter "a" **44.** not a random sample; the lawyers will choose jurors that are likely to support their side **45.** random sample; all students have an equal chance to be chosen **46.** not a random sample; the five with the largest (or smallest) circulation size will be picked **47.** Ppl. at the bus station may be less likely to own a car and therefore less likely to be in favor of a new garage.
**48.** $\frac{4}{35}$ **49.** $\frac{1}{3}$ **50.** $\approx 0.14$ **51.** $\approx 0.0710$ **52.** $\approx 0.2066$
**53.** $\approx 0.1766$ **54.** $21a^5b^7$ **55.** $56a^3b^5$ **56.** continuous **57.** discrete **58.** discrete **59.** continuous **60.** 16%; 2.5%

### Chapter 12

### Get Ready!     p. 753

**1.** 6 **2.** $\frac{1}{3}$ **3.** $-\frac{3}{4}$ **4.** $\frac{7}{12}$ **5.** $-9$ **6.** 11 **7.** 3 **8.** $(\frac{1}{2}, -4)$
**9.** $(-\frac{2}{3}, -\frac{2}{3})$ **10.** $(\frac{3}{4}, \frac{11}{4})$ **11.** $(7, 9, -6)$ **12.** $(0, 0, 8)$
**13.** $(7, 5, 0)$

### Lesson 12-1     pp. 756–762

**Got It?**
**1a.** $\begin{bmatrix} -15 & 25 \\ -1 & 1 \\ -2 & 15 \end{bmatrix}$ **b.** $\begin{bmatrix} -9 & 23 \\ -5 & 9 \\ 0 & 5 \end{bmatrix}$
**c.** Yes; it does not matter in which order you add matrices.
**2.** $A = \begin{bmatrix} 3 & 6 \\ 1 & 3 \\ 1 & 1 \end{bmatrix}$ **3a.** $\begin{bmatrix} 0 & 0 \\ 0 & 0 \\ 0 & 0 \end{bmatrix}$ **b.** $\begin{bmatrix} -1 & 10 & -5 \\ 2 & -3 \end{bmatrix}$
**4a.** $x = 6, y = -6$ **b.** $x = 4, y = -3, z = 2$
**Lesson Check**
**1.** $\begin{bmatrix} 1 & 1 \\ -2 & 8 \end{bmatrix}$ **2.** $\begin{bmatrix} 1 & -9 \\ -3 & 1 \end{bmatrix}$ **3.** $\begin{bmatrix} -3 & 4 \\ -5 & 11 \end{bmatrix}$ **4.** $\begin{bmatrix} 6 & 10 \\ 13 & -4 \end{bmatrix}$
**5.** Yes; the elements in each of the corresponding positions are equal.
**6.** The elements were not subtracted. The correct answer is $\begin{bmatrix} 6 \\ 5 \end{bmatrix} - \begin{bmatrix} 3 \\ 7 \end{bmatrix} = \begin{bmatrix} 3 \\ -2 \end{bmatrix}$
**Exercises**
**7.** $\begin{bmatrix} 6 & 5 \\ 2 & -1 \end{bmatrix}$ **9.** $\begin{bmatrix} 3.9 & -2.3 \\ -0.6 & 9.1 \end{bmatrix}$ **11.** $\begin{bmatrix} 4 & -8 \\ -1 & -1 \\ 11 & 1 \end{bmatrix}$

## Page 1105

**13.** $\begin{bmatrix} 6 & 2 \\ -1 & 3 \end{bmatrix}$ **15.** $\begin{bmatrix} 2 & -3 & 4 \\ 5 & 6 & -7 \end{bmatrix}$
**17.** $x = -2, y = 3, z = 1$ **19.** $\begin{bmatrix} 0 & 5 \\ 8 & -6 \\ 3 & 9 \end{bmatrix}$ **21.** $\begin{bmatrix} 6 & 3 \\ -3 & 3 \end{bmatrix}$
**23.** $\begin{bmatrix} -4 \\ -3 \end{bmatrix}$ **25a.** $\begin{bmatrix} 952 & 760 \\ 720 & 832 \\ 1108 & 1252 \\ 1172 & 1144 \\ 1044 & 1064 \end{bmatrix}$
**b.** Allen: 4996; Iagorashvili: 5052 **27.** Matrix B would have the same dimensions as A. Its elements would be the opposites of the corresponding elements in A.
**29.** $c = \frac{2}{3}, d = \frac{5}{2}, f = 7, g = 5, h = -1$ **37.** 68%
**38.** 97.5% **39.** 47.5% **40.** 2, $-6$ **41.** $\frac{2}{3}, 2$ **42.** $-\frac{1}{2}, -6$
**43.** 5, 0 **44.** $\begin{bmatrix} 9 & 15 \\ 6 & 24 \end{bmatrix}$ **45.** $\begin{bmatrix} -20 \\ 35 \end{bmatrix}$

### Lesson 12-2     pp. 764–771

**Got It?**
**1.** $\begin{bmatrix} 8 & 24 & -19 \\ -3 & 9 & 10 \end{bmatrix}$ **2.** $\begin{bmatrix} 5 & -1 \\ 2 & 9 \end{bmatrix}$ **3a.** $\begin{bmatrix} -6 & 0 \\ 0 & -6 \end{bmatrix}$
**b.** $\begin{bmatrix} -3 & 7 \\ 6 & 8 \end{bmatrix}$ **c.** No; explanations may vary. Sample: For the matrices in parts (a) and (b), $AB = \begin{bmatrix} -6 & 0 \\ -9 & 11 \end{bmatrix}$ and $BA = \begin{bmatrix} -3 & 7 \\ 6 & 8 \end{bmatrix}$, so $AB \ne BA$. **4.** player from 1994: 100 pts., player from 2006: 81 pts. **5a.** no **b.** yes
**c.** yes **d.** no **e.** yes
**Lesson Check**
**1.** $\begin{bmatrix} 6 & -1 \\ 4 & 0 \end{bmatrix}$ **2.** $\begin{bmatrix} -3 & 11 \\ -10 & 46 \end{bmatrix}$ **3.** $\begin{bmatrix} 5 & 7 \\ 2 & 6 \end{bmatrix}$ **4.** $\begin{bmatrix} 4 & -1 \\ -2 & 1 \end{bmatrix}$
**5.** Scalar; repeated matrix addition is repeated addition of each element of the matrix, which is the same as scalar multiplication of the matrix. **6.** The product of two matrices A and B exists only if the number of columns of A is equal to the number of rows of B. Since A is a $2 \times 4$ matrix with 4 columns and B is a $3 \times 6$ matrix with 3 rows and $4 \ne 3$, the product AB does not exist. Likewise, since $6 \ne 2$, the product BA does not exist.
**Exercises**
**7.** $\begin{bmatrix} 3 & 1 \\ -18 & -6 \\ 3 & 0 \end{bmatrix}$ **9.** $\begin{bmatrix} -3 & 6 \\ 9 & -3 \end{bmatrix}$ **11.** $\begin{bmatrix} 9 & 2 \\ 2 & 6 \\ 3 & -10 \end{bmatrix}$
**13.** $\begin{bmatrix} 19 & 11 \\ -12 & 16 \end{bmatrix}$ **15.** $\begin{bmatrix} 8 & -2.5 \\ -1.5 & -1 \end{bmatrix}$ **17.** $\begin{bmatrix} -4 & 8 \\ -22 & 2 \end{bmatrix}$
**19.** $\begin{bmatrix} 5 & -12 \\ 9 & -6 \end{bmatrix}$ **21.** $\begin{bmatrix} -8 & 0 \\ 0 & -45 \end{bmatrix}$ **23.** $[34 \; 0]$

**25.** $\begin{bmatrix} -15 & 0 \\ 25 & 0 \end{bmatrix}$ **27.** $\begin{bmatrix} -2 \\ 5 \end{bmatrix}$ **29.** yes **31.** yes **33.** yes
**35a.** River's Edge: 99 pts.; West River: 97 pts. **b.** West River
**37.** $\begin{bmatrix} 9 & -6 \\ 15 & -39 \\ -6 & -12 \end{bmatrix}$ **39.** $\begin{bmatrix} 17 & -24 \\ -33 & -47 \\ 69 & -18 \end{bmatrix}$ **41.** $\begin{bmatrix} 34 & -1 \\ 6 & -13 \\ 7 & -16 \end{bmatrix}$
**43.** $\begin{bmatrix} -90 & 0 \\ -78 & 42 \\ -30 & 30 \end{bmatrix}$ **54.** $\begin{bmatrix} -33 & -12 \\ -6 & 27 \end{bmatrix}$ **55.** $\begin{bmatrix} 9 & -6 \\ 2 & 12 \end{bmatrix}$ **56a.** 12 **b.** 12 **c.** 0 **57a.** $-12$ **b.** $-12$ **c.** 0

### Lesson 12-3     pp. 774–782

**Got It? 1a.** yes **b.** yes **c.** No; no matrix that is multiplied by the zero matrix will give an identity matrix.
**2a.** 3 **b.** c. $-48$ **3a.** 12 units² **b.** 28 units²
**4a.** yes; $\begin{bmatrix} 1 & -1 \\ -2 & 3 \end{bmatrix}$ **b.** no **c.** yes; $\begin{bmatrix} 3 & -4 \\ -5 & 7 \end{bmatrix}$
**5a.** 88, 68, 84, 60, 12, 32, 52, 72, 28, 30, 14, 18, 2, 8, 14, 20 **b.** Multiply the coded information by the inverse of the coding matrix: $\begin{bmatrix} 4 & 1 & 7 \\ 1 & 3 & 1 \\ 9 & 8 & 7 \end{bmatrix}^{-1} \begin{bmatrix} 3 & 2 \\ 1 & 4 \\ 6 & 1 & 3 & 5 & 7 \end{bmatrix}$
**Lesson Check 1.** 16 **2.** 7 **3.** does not exist
**4.** yes; $\begin{bmatrix} 3 & -2 \\ -7 & 5 \end{bmatrix}$
**5.** The student did not subtract correctly. $\det\begin{bmatrix} 2 & 5 \\ -3 & 1 \end{bmatrix} = (2)(1) - (-3)(5) = 2 - (-15)$ $= 2 + 15 = 17$
**6.** A $2 \times 3$ matrix does not have a multiplicative inverse because it is not a square matrix. The number of rows must equal the number of columns for a multiplicative inverse to be possible.
**Exercises 7.** yes **9.** yes **11.** no **13.** $-15$ **15.** $-\frac{11}{40}$
**17.** 11 **19.** $-6$ **21.** $-5$ **23.** 106 **25.** 4 **27.** 466,250 mi²
**29.** yes; $\begin{bmatrix} -1 & 1 \\ 2 & 1 \end{bmatrix}$ **31.** yes; $\begin{bmatrix} 1 & 0 \\ \frac{1}{3} & \frac{1}{6} \end{bmatrix}$
**33.** yes; $\begin{bmatrix} \frac{1}{3} & -\frac{1}{3} \\ -\frac{3}{16} & \frac{1}{16} \end{bmatrix}$ **35.** yes; $\begin{bmatrix} 0 & \frac{1}{3} \\ 1 & -\frac{1}{6} \end{bmatrix}$
**37.** 2, 10, 10, 6, 9, 55, 15, 9, 20 **39.** $-120$ **41.** 9
**43.** $-3$ **45.** 47. Answers may vary. Sample: Form a new matrix by switching the element in row 1, column 1 with the element in row 2, column 2. Then replace the other two elements with their opposites. Finally, divide each element by the determinant of the original matrix. **49.** 38 units²
**51.** yes; $\begin{bmatrix} -5 & 7 \\ 2 & -3 \end{bmatrix}$ **53.** yes; $\begin{bmatrix} 0.5 & 0 \\ 0 & 0.5 \end{bmatrix}$

**55.** yes; $\begin{bmatrix} 0.4 & 0.4 & 0.2 \\ -0.6 & -0.6 & 0.2 \\ -0.2 & 0.8 & 0.4 \end{bmatrix}$

**57.** no inverse because the determinant equals zero

**59.** 6 **67.** $\begin{bmatrix} 2 & 5 \\ 1 & 1 \end{bmatrix}$ **68.** $\begin{bmatrix} -10 & 19 \\ -20 & 7 \end{bmatrix}$ **69.** 720

**70.** 362,880 **71.** $1.08972864 \times 10^{10}$ **72.** 110,880
**73.** no solution **74.** (6, 0, −3) **75.** (3, −3, 9)
**76.** (−2, −1, −3)

### Lesson 12-4    pp. 784–792

**Got It?**
**1a.** $\begin{bmatrix} -8 \\ 9 \end{bmatrix}$ **b.** $\begin{bmatrix} -14 & -20 \\ 19 & 28 \end{bmatrix}$

**c.** Since matrix A has no inverse, the eq. has no solution.

**2a.** $\begin{bmatrix} 3 & -7 \\ 5 & 1 \end{bmatrix}\begin{bmatrix} x \\ y \end{bmatrix} = \begin{bmatrix} 8 \\ -2 \end{bmatrix}$

**b.** $\begin{bmatrix} 1 & 3 & 5 \\ -2 & 1 & 4 \\ 7 & -2 & 0 \end{bmatrix}\begin{bmatrix} x \\ y \\ z \end{bmatrix} = \begin{bmatrix} 12 \\ -2 \\ 8 \end{bmatrix}$

**c.** $\begin{bmatrix} 2 & -8 \\ -1 & 1 \end{bmatrix}\begin{bmatrix} x \\ y \end{bmatrix} = \begin{bmatrix} -3 \\ -4 \end{bmatrix}$

**3a.** (5, −21) **b.** no solution **4.** run: 32 min; jog: 8 min
**Lesson Check**

**1.** $\begin{bmatrix} -6 & 3 \\ 4 & -1 \end{bmatrix}\begin{bmatrix} x \\ y \end{bmatrix} = \begin{bmatrix} 8 \\ 10 \end{bmatrix}$ **2.** $\begin{bmatrix} 1 & 3 \\ -1 & 2 \\ 0 & 6 \end{bmatrix}\begin{bmatrix} x \\ y \\ z \end{bmatrix} = \begin{bmatrix} 12 \\ 9 \\ -4 \end{bmatrix}$

**3.** (5, 3) **4.** (−6, −6) **5.** The student did not separate the coefficient matrix and the variable matrix. The matrix eq. should be written as $\begin{bmatrix} 2 & 3 \\ -4 & 5 \end{bmatrix}\begin{bmatrix} x \\ y \end{bmatrix} = \begin{bmatrix} 5 \\ -1 \end{bmatrix}$

**6.** Use matrix multiplication to combine the coefficient matrix and the variable matrix into a product matrix. Then set the first element in the product matrix equal to the first element in the constant matrix and set the second element in the product matrix equal to the second element in the constant matrix. The result will be a system of equations.; $-2p + 3q = 2$ $4p + q = -5$

**Exercises**

**7.** $\begin{bmatrix} -15 & -17 \\ 26 & 34 \end{bmatrix}$ **9.** $\begin{bmatrix} \frac{29}{31} \\ -\frac{66}{217} \\ \frac{34}{217} \end{bmatrix}$ **11.** $\begin{bmatrix} 1 & 1 \\ 1 & -2 \end{bmatrix}\begin{bmatrix} x \\ y \end{bmatrix} = \begin{bmatrix} 5 \\ -4 \end{bmatrix}$;

coefficient matrix: $\begin{bmatrix} 1 & 1 \\ 1 & -2 \end{bmatrix}$; variable matrix: $\begin{bmatrix} x \\ y \end{bmatrix}$;

constant matrix: $\begin{bmatrix} 5 \\ -4 \end{bmatrix}$ **13.** $\begin{bmatrix} 3 & 5 \\ 1 & 1 \end{bmatrix}\begin{bmatrix} a \\ b \end{bmatrix} = \begin{bmatrix} 0 \\ 2 \end{bmatrix}$; coefficient

matrix: $\begin{bmatrix} 3 & 5 \\ 1 & 1 \end{bmatrix}$; variable matrix: $\begin{bmatrix} a \\ b \end{bmatrix}$; constant matrix: $\begin{bmatrix} 0 \\ 2 \end{bmatrix}$

**15.** $\begin{bmatrix} 1 & -1 & 1 \\ 2 & 0 & 1 \\ 0 & 1 & 3 \end{bmatrix}\begin{bmatrix} r \\ s \\ t \end{bmatrix} = \begin{bmatrix} 150 \\ 425 \\ 0 \end{bmatrix}$; coefficient

matrix: $\begin{bmatrix} 1 & -1 & 1 \\ 2 & 0 & 1 \\ 0 & 1 & 3 \end{bmatrix}$; variable matrix: $\begin{bmatrix} r \\ s \\ t \end{bmatrix}$;

constant matrix: $\begin{bmatrix} 150 \\ 425 \\ 0 \end{bmatrix}$

**17.** (2, 1) **19.** $(\frac{1}{2}, 20)$ **21.** (3, 2) **23.** (2, −1, 3)
**25.** (1, 2, −2) **27.** 2.5 lb of almonds, 3.5 lb of peanuts, and 3 lb of raisins **29.** (−2, −1) **31.** (−1, 0) **33.** (5, 0, 1)
**35.** (1, 0, 3) **37.** (1, 1, 1, 1) **39.** (6, 2) **41.** (16, −22)
**43.** (5.4, 7.4) **45.** (6, 1) **47.** (2, −1, 4) **49.** length = 280 ft, width = 140 ft **63.** −44 **64.** 4913 **65.** −218
**66.** 34.$\overline{4}$; 30.9; 5.56 **67.** 4.17; 1.32; 1.15 **68.** 19.$\overline{6}$ m;
22.$\overline{2}$ m; 4.7 m **69.** 57.4 mi; 345.44 mi²; 18.6 mi

**70.**  translation 4 units to the left

**71.** translation 3 units down

**72.** translation 5 units to the right and 3 units up

### Lesson 12-5    pp. 793–800

**Got It? 1a.** Subtract 8 from each $x$-coordinate and add 5 to each $y$-coordinate.

**b.** $\begin{bmatrix} 0 & -1 & -5 & 1 \\ -5 & 1 & 0 & 3 \end{bmatrix} + \begin{bmatrix} -3 & -3 & -3 & -3 \\ 2 & 2 & 2 & 2 \end{bmatrix}$
$= \begin{bmatrix} -3 & -4 & -8 & -2 \\ -3 & 1 & 2 & 5 \end{bmatrix}$; (−3, −3), (−4, 1), (−8, 2), (−2, 5), (1, 2)

**2.** Answers may vary. Samples:
**a.** $\begin{bmatrix} 0 & 5 & 5 & 0 \\ 0 & 0 & 3 & 3 \end{bmatrix}$
**b.** $\begin{bmatrix} 0 & 5 & 5 & 0 \\ 0 & 0 & 6 & 6 \end{bmatrix} = \begin{bmatrix} 0 & 10 & 10 & 0 \\ 0 & 0 & 6 & 6 \end{bmatrix}$; (0, 0), (10, 0), (10, 6), (0, 6)
**c.** 4

---

**3a.** (0, 3), (4, 4), (1, −1); **b.** (−3, 0), (−4, 4), (1, 1);

**4a.** (1, −1), (3, −1), (6, −4), (1, −3);

**b.** (1, 1), (1, 3), (4, 6), (3, 1);

**Lesson Check 1.** $A'(\frac{1}{2}, \frac{1}{2})$, $B'(1, 2)$, $C'(2, -\frac{1}{2})$
**2.** $A'(1, -1)$, $B'(4, -2)$, $C'(-1, 4)$ **3.** $A'(1, 1)$, $B'(4, 2)$, $C'(-1, 4)$ **4.** Translations, rotations and reflections leave the size of the figure unchanged. Translation moves the figure to a new location. Rotation turns the figure about a fixed pt. Reflection maps a figure in the coordinate plane to its mirror image using a specific line as its mirror. **5.** Answers may vary. Sample: reflection across $y = x$; translation 4 units to the right and 4 units down
**6.** They are equal.
$\begin{bmatrix} -3 & 0 \\ 0 & -3 \end{bmatrix}\begin{bmatrix} 1 & 3 \\ 1 & -2 \end{bmatrix} = -3\begin{bmatrix} 1 & 0 \\ 0 & 1 \end{bmatrix}\begin{bmatrix} 1 & 3 \\ 1 & -2 \end{bmatrix}$
$= -3\begin{bmatrix} 1 & 3 \\ 1 & -2 \end{bmatrix}$

**Exercises 7.** (−2, 2), (−2, 6), (2, 6), (2, 2);

**9.** (−13, 7), (−19, 6), (9, 0);

**11.** (0, 0), (4, 8), (10, 10), (16, 2) **13.** (−12, 9), (3, 6), (4.5, 0), (1.5, −6), (−3, 0)

**15.**

**17.** (−3, 3), (3, −6), (3, −3), (−3, −6)
**19.** (−1, −3), (−2, −2), (−3, −2), (−4, −3), (−2.5, −5)

**21.**

**23.** (3, −3), (−3, −6), (−3, −3), (3, −3)
**25.** (3, 1), (2, 2), (2, 3), (3, 4), (5, 2.5)
**27.** $\begin{bmatrix} -8 & -5 & -2 & -5 \\ -8 & -5 & -8 & -11 \end{bmatrix}$ **29.** $\begin{bmatrix} -5 & -1 & -3 \\ 2 & -4 & 7 \end{bmatrix}$

**31.** $\begin{bmatrix} 3 & -1 & 1 \\ -1 & -2 & -4 \end{bmatrix}$ **33.** Apply a 90° rotation matrix $\begin{bmatrix} 0 & -1 \\ 1 & 0 \end{bmatrix}$ three times to determine the image matrix for each frame. The fourth application of the 90° rotation matrix would show the gymnast at the starting position of Frame 1.

**37.** $f$. $\begin{bmatrix} -5 & -2 & 1 \\ 3 & 0 & 3 \end{bmatrix}$, $g$. $\begin{bmatrix} -1 & 2 & 5 \\ 1 & 1 & 1 \end{bmatrix}$ translation
**47.** (3, −2) **48.** (−1, 2) **49.** (0, 1, −2)
**50.** $\begin{bmatrix} 16 \\ 12 \end{bmatrix}$ **51.** [12] **52.** [22]

### Lesson 12-6    pp. 801–807

**Got It? 1. u** = (3, 4); **v** = (−1, −6) **2a.** (5, 3)
**b.** translation, reflection and dilation **3.** $\sqrt{74} \approx 8.60$
**4a.**

**5a.** not normal **b.** normal
**Lesson Check 1.** (5, 2) **2.** (9, −11) **3.** (−1, −12)
**4.** (0, −15) **5.** The magnitudes of vectors **a, b,** and **c** are the same; 5. **6.** Although the $x$-component of (8, 3) is 4 times the $x$-component of (2, 1), the $y$-component and

---

the magnitude of (8, 3) are not 4 times those of (2, 1), $3 \neq 4 \times 1$ and $\sqrt{73} \neq 4 \times \sqrt{5}$.
**Exercises 7.** (4, 1) **9.** (4, −2) **11.** (0, 2) **13.** (−1, 5)
**15.** (2, 0) **17.** (3, 0) **19.** (3, −4) **21.** (4, −1)
**23.** (−3, 8) **25.** (−8, 20) **27.** (−6, −12) **29.** not normal **31.** normal **33.** (0, −14) **35.** (18, −13)
**37.** about 304 mi/h **39.** $\overline{AB}$ = (3, 1), $\overline{BC}$ = (−2, 3), $\overline{CA}$ = (−1, −4) **41.** (6, −3) **43.** (−4, −2)
**45.** v − v = (0, 0); (0, 0), the zero vector, is the additive identity for the set of all vectors and −v is the additive inverse of any given vector **v**; so **v** + (0, 0) = **v** and **v** + (−**v**) = (0, 0).
**47.** yes; Distributive Prop.

**49.** yes; Assoc. Prop. of Add.

**60.** $\begin{bmatrix} 1 & -2 & 3 \\ 1 & 5 & 3 \end{bmatrix}$

**61.** $\begin{bmatrix} -3 & 0 & 2 & -1 \\ -2 & -3 & 0 & 2 \end{bmatrix}$

**62.** **63.**

**64.**

**65.** $y - 1 = -3x$ OR $y + 5 = -3(x - 2)$
**66.** $y + 4 = \frac{7}{5}(x + 4)$ OR $y - 3 = -\frac{2}{5}(x + 9)$
**67.** $y - 2 = -(x - 7)$ OR $y - 8 = -(x - 1)$ **68.** yes
**69.** no **70.** yes **71.** no

### Chapter Review    pp. 809–812

**1.** equal matrices **2.** zero matrix **3.** matrix equation
**4.** square matrix

**5.** $\begin{bmatrix} -1 & 9 & -8 \\ 4 & 0 & 6 \end{bmatrix}$ **6.** $\begin{bmatrix} -4 & 5 \\ 5 & -4 \end{bmatrix}$ **7.** [1  −8  12]

**8.** $\begin{bmatrix} -3 & 10 \\ 3 & 3 \end{bmatrix}$ **9.** $x = -2, w = 8, r = 4, t = -1$
**10.** $t = -4, y = \frac{11}{3}, r = 4, w = 4$

**11.** $\begin{bmatrix} 18 & 3 & 0 & 24 \\ -12 & 9 & 21 & 33 \end{bmatrix}$ **12.** undefined **13.** undefined

**14.** $\begin{bmatrix} -6 & 10 & 21 & 41 \\ -28 & 10 & 28 & 28 \end{bmatrix}$ **15.** $\begin{bmatrix} -14 & -2 \\ 43 & -7 \end{bmatrix}$

**16.** $\begin{bmatrix} -11 & 18 \\ -17 & -2 \end{bmatrix}$ **17.** 24; $\begin{bmatrix} \frac{1}{6} & -\frac{1}{24} \\ \frac{1}{4} & \frac{1}{12} \end{bmatrix}$ **18.** 0; does not exist

**19.** 42; $\begin{bmatrix} \frac{5}{42} & -\frac{1}{42} \\ -\frac{4}{21} & \frac{5}{21} \end{bmatrix}$ **20.** 6; $\begin{bmatrix} -\frac{2}{3} & 0 \\ -\frac{1}{6} & -\frac{1}{3} \\ \frac{1}{3} & 0 \end{bmatrix}$

**21.** $\begin{bmatrix} 1 & 2 \\ 3 & 4 \end{bmatrix}$ **22.** (−4, −7) **23.** $\begin{bmatrix} 2 & 4 \\ 3 & 2 \end{bmatrix}$ **24.** $\begin{bmatrix} 2 & 1 \\ 3 & 2 \end{bmatrix}$

**25.** no unique solution **26.** no unique solution
**27.** $\begin{bmatrix} 0 & -5 \\ 5 & 4 \end{bmatrix}$ **28.** $\begin{bmatrix} -3 & 2 & -1 \\ 1 & 0 & 5 \end{bmatrix}$ **29.** $\begin{bmatrix} 1 & 0 & 5 \\ 3 & -2 & 1 \end{bmatrix}$

**30.** $\begin{bmatrix} 1.5 & -1 & 0.5 \\ 0.5 & 0 & 2 \end{bmatrix}$ **31.** $\begin{bmatrix} 6 & -4 & 2 \\ 4 & 3 & -1 \end{bmatrix}$ **32.** $\begin{bmatrix} 1 & 0.5 \\ -3 & 2 \end{bmatrix}$

**33.** (−1, 8); about 8.1 **34.** (7, −5); about 8.6
**35.** (−9, 12); 15 **36.** (−2, 14); about 14.1
**37.** (−8, 14); about 16.1 **38.** (−4, 21); about 21.4
**39.** 0; normal **40.** 0; normal

---

## Chapter 13

### Get Ready!    p. 817

**1.** vert. asymptote: $x = 3$ **2.** vert. asymptotes:
$x = -\frac{1}{2}$ and $x = 4$ **3.** $\frac{2b}{a}$ **4.** $\frac{55}{18}$ **5.** $\frac{5}{2(c + d)}$ **6.** $\frac{c}{16}$
**7.** $\frac{c - 4}{9}$ **8.** $\frac{16}{9}$ **9.** $\frac{15}{2}$ **10.** 6 **11.** 4; 1; $a_n = 19 - 3n$, explicit or $a_1 = 16$, $a_n = a_{n-1} - 3$, recursive
**12.** −216, −343; $a_n = -n^3$, explicit
**13.** $(x - 1)^2 + (y + 4)^2 = 16$;

**14.** $\frac{(x - 2)^2}{9} + \frac{(y - 5)^2}{4} = 1$;

**15.** $y = \frac{1}{33}x^2 - 3$; **16.** $\frac{(y - 1)^2}{9} - \frac{(x - 6)^2}{16} = 1$;

**17.** Answers may vary. Sample: Similar data tends to recur after a certain period has lapsed. In this case, 12 months.

### Lesson 13-1    pp. 820–826

**Got It? 1a.** from $x = -3$ to $x = 1$ or from $x = 0$ to $x = 4$; **b.** from $x = -4$ to $x = -1$ or from $x = 0$ to $x = 3$; **2a.** no **b.** yes; 4 **c.** 15 cycles; $\frac{1}{3}$ s; $\frac{1}{440}$ s **3a.** 1.5 **b.** 1.5 **4.** period: 0.006; amplitude: $\frac{1}{4}$
**Lesson Check 1.** periodic; 5 **2.** no **3.** Answers may vary. Sample: hands of a clock, phases of the moon
**4.** The amplitude is not 2, but $\frac{1}{2} = 1$. **5.** $f(6) = f(11) = 2$; for any $x$, $f(x + 5)$ will always equal $f(x)$ because the period is 5
**Exercises 7.** Answers may vary. Sample: $x = 0$ to $x = 4$, $x = 5$ to $x = 9$; 4 **9.** not periodic
**11.** not periodic **13.** periodic; 8 **15.** 4 **17.** 1

**19.**

1 unit on the $x$-axis is 0.001 s.

**21a–c.** Answers may vary. Samples: **a.** This could be; average monthly temperatures for three years should be cyclical due to the variation of the seasons. **b.** Probably not; population usually increases or decreases, but is usually not cyclical. **c.** This could be; traffic that passes through an intersection should be at similar levels at the same times of day on each of the two consecutive work days.
**23.** 60 beats per minute
**27.** 5, 0, 8;

**29.** 1 yr **31.** 3 months **33.** 1 day **41.** about 302 mph
**42.**

| | | | | | | |
|---|---|---|---|---|---|---|
| 21 | 33 | 45 | 57 | 69 | 81 | 93 |
| −3 | −2 | −1 | m | +1 | +2 | +3 |
| std | std | std | | std | std | std |
| dev | dev | dev | | dev | dev | dev |

**43.** $x^2 + y^2 = 1$ **44.** $x^2 + y^2 = 13$ **45.** $x^2 + y^2 = 25$
**46.** $x^2 + y^2 = 2$ **47.** $x^2 + y^2 = 1$ **48.** $x^2 + y^2 = 1$

### Geometry Review    p. 827

**1.** $\frac{\sqrt{2}}{2}$ in. **3.** $\frac{\sqrt{6}}{2}$ ft **5.** hypotenuse: 6 in., longer leg: $3\sqrt{3}$ in. **7.** shorter leg: $\frac{1}{2}$ ft, longer leg: $\frac{\sqrt{3}}{2}$ ft

### Lesson 13-2    pp. 828–834

**Got It? 1.** 225°
**2a.** **b.** **c.**

**3.** −315°, 45°, 405°
**4.** $\cos(-90°) = 0$, $\sin(-90°) = -1$; $\cos(360°) = 1$, $\sin(360°) = 0$; $\cos(540°) = -1$, $\sin(540°) = 0$
**5a.** $\frac{\sqrt{2}}{2}, -\frac{\sqrt{2}}{2}$ **b.** $-\frac{\sqrt{3}}{2}$ **c.** Yes; for example, when $\theta = 45°$, $\sin\theta = \cos\theta$.

**Lesson Check 1.** 135° **2.** 240°
**3.** ; −332° **4.** ; −35°

**5.** Answers may vary. Sample: 45° and −315° **6.** The measure of the coterminal angle is not 310°; the measure of the coterminal angle is 50° − 360° = −310°.
**Exercises 7.** −315° **9.** 240° **11.** −30°
**13. 15.**

**17.**

**19.** 215° **21.** 4° **23.** 150° **25.** 180° **27.** $-\frac{\sqrt{2}}{2}, \frac{\sqrt{2}}{2}$, −0.71, 0.71 **29.** $-\frac{1}{2}, \frac{\sqrt{3}}{2}$, −0.50, 0.87 **31.** $\frac{\sqrt{2}}{2}, -\frac{\sqrt{2}}{2}$, 0.71, −0.71 **33.** $-\frac{\sqrt{2}}{2}, \frac{\sqrt{2}}{2}$, −0.71, 0.71 **35.** 0.98, −0.17 **37.** 0.00, 1.00 **39.** 5 **41–43.** Answers may vary. Samples: **41.** 370°, −350° **43.** 40°, −320° **45.** II **47.** negative x-axis **49.** positive x-axis
**51a.**

Quadrant II: cos θ is −, sin θ is +
Quadrant I: cos θ is +, sin θ is +
Quadrant III: cos θ is −, sin θ is −
Quadrant IV: cos θ is +, sin θ is −

**b.** II **c.** If the terminal side of an angle is in Quadrants I or II, then the sine of the angle is positive. If the terminal side of an angle is in Quadrants I or IV, then the cosine of the angle is positive. **64.** periodic; 3 **65.** not periodic **66.** periodic; 6 **67.** (0, 2√5), (0, −2√5); **68.** (0, 5√5), (0, −5√5);

**69.** (√85, 0), (−√85, 0);

**70.** (√145, 0), (−√145, 0);

**71.** 50.24 in.² **72.** 3846.5 m² **73.** 200.96 mi²
**74.** 9.0746 ft²

**Lesson 13-3** pp. 836–842

**Got It? 1a.** 90° **b.** $\frac{5\pi}{4}$ radians **c.** $\frac{360°}{\pi} \approx 114.59°$
**d.** $\frac{5\pi}{6}$ radians **2.** $-\frac{\sqrt{3}}{2}, -\frac{1}{2}$ **3a.** 6.3 in. Arc length would also double. **4.** ≈15,708 km
**Lesson Check 1.** $\frac{5\pi}{8}$ radians ≈ 5.24 radians **2.** 135°
**3.** $\frac{20\pi}{3} \approx 20.94$ in. **4.** 1 radian **5.** 6 "perfect" slices
**Exercises 7.** $\frac{5\pi}{6}$, 2.62 **9.** $-\frac{\pi}{3}$, −1.05 **11.** $\frac{\pi}{9}$, 0.35 **13.** 198° **15.** −172° **17.** 270° **19.** $\frac{1}{2}, \frac{\sqrt{3}}{2}$ **21.** $\frac{\sqrt{2}}{2}, -\frac{\sqrt{2}}{2}$ **23.** 0, −1 **25.** $-\frac{\sqrt{3}}{2}, -\frac{1}{2}$ **27.** 10.5 m **29.** 25.1 in. **31.** 43.2 cm **33.** ≈31.9 ft **35.** ≈42.2 in. **37.** III **39.** negative x-axis
**41.**

0.71, −0.71

**43.**

0.00, 1.00

**45.** If two angles measured in radians are coterminal, the difference of their measures will be evenly divisible by 2π. **47.** ≈11 radians **49.** ≈6.3 cm
**58.** **59.**

**60.** **61.**

**62.**

**63.** mean ≈ 12.9, s.d. ≈ 3.53 **64.** mean = 30, s.d. ≈ 8.09 **65.** 2 **66.** all real numbers **67.** 1

**Lesson 13-4** pp. 843–850

**Got It? 1a.** ≈0.1411; estimates may vary. **b.** −1
**2a.** 2; 2π **b.** 3; $\frac{4\pi}{3}$ **3.** −3 **b.** 0.6; 0.6
**4.**

$y = 3 \sin \frac{1}{3}\theta$

**5a.** **b.**

**6.** $y = \sin \frac{\pi}{320}\theta$
**Lesson Check 1a.** 2 **b.** 3; π **c.** $y = 3 \sin 2\theta$
**2.**

**3.** One cycle of a sine function is an interval on the x-axis with length equal to the period. The period is the length of one cycle. **4.** Answers may vary. Sample: $y = 5 \sin \frac{\theta}{3}$

**5.** The amplitude is 3, but since a < 0, the graph is reflected across the x-axis. Also, the period is 2, not π.

**Exercises 7.** ≈0.1 **9.** ≈−1 **11.** ≈−0.7 **13.** $\frac{1}{2}$; 1, 4π
**15.**

$y = 2 \sin 3\theta$

**17.**

$y = 4 \sin \frac{1}{3}\theta$

**19.** **21.**

$y = \sin \pi\theta$

**23.** **25.**

**27.** 2π; $y = 2 \sin \frac{\pi}{3}\theta$ **29.** π; $y = \frac{5}{2} \sin 2\theta$ **31.** 1; 1, 2π **33.** π; 1, 2 **35.** 1; 5, 2π
**37.**

They are reflections of each other across the x-axis. When a is replaced by its opposite, the graph is a reflection of the original graph across the x-axis.

**39.**

**41.** π; $\frac{5}{2}$;

**43.** $\frac{2\pi}{3}$, 0.4;

**45.** $\frac{12}{5}$; 1.2;

**47.**

**60.** $-\frac{4\pi}{9}$ radians, −1.40 radians **61.** $\frac{5\pi}{6}$ radians, 2.62 radians **62.** $-\frac{4\pi}{3}$ radians, −4.19 radians **63.** $\frac{16\pi}{9}$ radians, 5.59 radians **64.** $-\frac{5\pi}{2}$ radians, −7.85 radians **65.** ≈49% **66.** 1 **67.** 0 **68.** −1 **69.** 0

**Lesson 13-5** pp. 853–860

**Got It? 1.** domain: all real numbers; period: 2π; range: −1 ≤ y ≤ 1; amplitude: 1 sine: max at $\frac{\pi}{2}$; min at $\frac{3\pi}{2}$; zeros at 0, π, 2π
**2.**

**3.** $f(t) = -35 \cos\left(\frac{4\pi}{25}t\right)$ **4a.** 1.15, 1.99, 4.29, 5.13 **b.** 2.21, 4.06 **c.** 0 ≤ θ < 2.21 and 4.06 ≤ θ ≤ 2π; 2.21 < θ < 4.06
**Lesson Check**
**1.** **2.**

**3.** $y = 3 \cos \theta$ **4.** $y = 1.5 \cos 2\theta$ **5.** Answers may vary. Sample: $y = 5 \cos\left(\frac{\pi}{3}\theta\right)$ **6a.** 0 ≤ θ ≤ $\frac{\pi}{2}$, $\frac{3\pi}{2}$ ≤ θ ≤ 2π **b.** π < θ < 2π **c.** $y = 3 \sin\left(\frac{2\pi}{5}x - \frac{\pi}{5}\right)$
**Exercises 7.** 2π; 3; max: 0, 2π; min: π; zeros: $\frac{\pi}{2}, \frac{3\pi}{2}$
**9.** π; 1; max: 0, π, 2π; min: $\frac{\pi}{2}, \frac{3\pi}{2}$; zeros: $\frac{\pi}{4}, \frac{3\pi}{4}, \frac{5\pi}{4}, \frac{7\pi}{4}$
**11.** **13.**

**15.**

**17.** $y = \frac{\pi}{2} \cos \frac{2\pi}{3}\theta$ **19.** $y = -3 \cos 3\theta$ **21.** 0.52, 2.62, 3.67, 5.76 **23.** 0.55, 1.45, 2.55, 3.45, 4.55, 5.45 **25.** 0.00 **27.** 2π, −3 ≤ y ≤ 3, 3 **29.** 4π, −2 ≤ y ≤ 2, 2 **31.** 6π, −3 ≤ y ≤ 3, 3 **33.** $\frac{4}{3}$, −16 ≤ y ≤ 16, 16 **35.** y = 70 + 13 cos $\frac{\pi}{6}$(x − 1) where x represents the months of the year with January as 1, February as 2, March as 3, etc. **37.** 0.64, 2.50 **39.** 0.50, 4.50
**41a.**

**b.** 4:40 P.M.; 5:00 A.M. (next day); 5:20 P.M. (next day); 5:40 A.M. (2 days after time 0) **c.** 6 h 10 min; 6 h 10 min
**51.**

$y = \sin 6\theta$

**53.**

$y = 4 \sin 2\pi x$

**54.** about 1111 **55.** about 204 **56.** about 83 **57.** $a_n = 10 \cdot 3^{n-1}$; 10, 30, 90, 270, 810 **58.** $a_n = 12(-0.3)^{n-1}$; 12, −3.6, 1.08, −0.324, 0.0972 **59.** $a_n = 900\left(-\frac{1}{3}\right)^{n-1}$; 900, −300, 100, $-\frac{100}{3}, \frac{100}{9}$ **60.** 0.866, 0.5, 1.732 **61.** 0.5, 0.866, 0.577 **62.** 1, 0, undefined **63.** 0.5, −0.866, −0.577 **64.** 1, 0, undefined **65.** 0, 1, 0

**Lesson 13-6** pp. 860–866

**Got It? 1a.** not defined **b.** √3 **c.** −1
**2a.** **b.**

**3a.** ≈46.6 ft **b.** ≈8°
**Lesson Check 1. 1. 2.** $\frac{\sqrt{3}}{3}$ **3.** −1 **4.** 0 **5.** $\frac{2\pi}{3}$ **6.** The student found 3θ instead of θ. Divide each side of the equation 3θ = −1.33 by 3 to get θ ≈ −0.44.
**7.** y = tan 2θ; the period of the function y = sin 4θ is $\frac{\pi}{2}$. For a tangent function to have the same period, $\frac{\pi}{b}$, b must equal 2.
**Exercises 9.** 0 **11.** undefined **13.** 0 **15.** undefined **17.** $\frac{\pi}{2}$ **19.** $\frac{2\pi}{3}$; θ = −$\frac{\pi}{3}$ and θ = $\frac{\pi}{3}$ **21.** $\frac{3\pi}{2}$; θ = −$\frac{3\pi}{4}$ and θ = $\frac{3\pi}{4}$
**23.** **25.**

**27.**

−100, undefined, 100

**29a.**

**b.** ≈14.3 ft **c.** ≈20.2 ft

**31.** $\frac{2\pi}{5}$;

**33.** 1.11, 4.25 **35.** 0.08, 1.65, 3.22, 4.79
**37.**

150√3 in.² ≈ 260 in.²

**39.** 200 **41.** 135 **43.** 70 **45.** y = −tan($\frac{1}{2}x$)
**47a.**

≈6.9 ft

**b.** ≈27.7 ft²
**c.** ≈166.3 ft²

**57.** 1.32, 4.97 **58.** 1.77, 4.51 **59.** 6.15 **60.** 0.44, 1.56, 2.44, 3.56, 4.44, 5.56 **61.** mean ≈ 5.9, median = 6, modes = 4 and 6 **62.** 83 **63.** −227 **64.** 145 **65.** −332 **66.** 2 units to the right and up 5 units **67.** 5 units to the left and down 4 units **68.** 2 units to the left and up 1 unit

**Lesson 13-7** pp. 867–874

**Got It? 1a.** 5; 5 units to the right **b.** −3; 3 units to the left
**2a.** **b.**

**c.** y = sin(x − 2) is a phase shift.
**3a.** **b.**

**4a.**

**5a.** y = cos x + $\frac{\pi}{5}$ **b.** y = 2 sin(x − $\frac{\pi}{4}$) **6a.** 69.9°F **b.** Yes; data can be extrapolated to calculate for next year.
**Lesson Check**
**1.**

**2.** phase shift: 2 units to the right; vertical shift: 9 units up **3.** y = cos(x − $\frac{\pi}{3}$) + 3 **4.** Answers may vary. Sample: y = 4 sin $\frac{\pi}{2}$(x − π) − 5 **5.** Scott is correct; y = a sin b(x − h) + k = cos 3(x + $\frac{\pi}{6}$) where h = −$\frac{\pi}{6}$. The phase shift is $\frac{\pi}{6}$ units to the left of y = cos 3x.
**Exercises 7.** −2; 2 units to the left **9.** 3; 3 units to the right **11.** $\frac{5\pi}{2}$; $\frac{5\pi}{2}$ units to the right
**13.**

## Top-left region

**15.** **17.**

**19.** **21.**

**23.** 1 unit to the left and 2 units down **25.** 3 units to the right and 2 units up

**27.** **29.**

**31.** **33.**

**35.**

**37.** $y = \cos x - \frac{\pi}{3}$ **39.** $y = \cos(x - 1.5)$ **41.** $y = \cos(x + 3) + \pi$ **43.** $y = 1.5 \cos\left[\frac{\pi}{6}(x - 6) - \frac{\pi}{2}\right] + 2$

**45.** $y = -10 \cos\frac{\pi}{15}x;\ y = 10 \sin\left(\frac{\pi}{15}x - \frac{\pi}{2}\right)$ **59.** $\frac{\pi}{6};\ \theta = -\frac{\pi}{12},\ \frac{\pi}{12}$ **60.** $4\pi;\ \theta = -2\pi,\ 2\pi$
**61.** $\frac{2\pi}{3};\ \theta = -\frac{\pi}{3},\ \frac{\pi}{3}$ **62.** $6\pi;\ \theta = -3\pi,\ 3\pi$ **63.** 0.0064
**64.** 0.3456 **65.** $\approx 0.136$ **66.** $\approx 0.198$ **67.** $\frac{13}{9}$ **68.** $-\frac{8}{5}$
**69.** $2\pi$ **70.** $\frac{15}{4\pi}$ **71.** $-\frac{1}{14}$

### Lesson 13-8 pp. 875–882

**Got It? 1a.** $\frac{2\sqrt{3}}{3}$ **b.** $-1$ **c.** $-1$ **d.** $\frac{3}{4},\ \frac{5}{4},\ \frac{5}{3}$ by the definition of a unit circle, the length of the hypotenuse of the right triangle is 1; by the Pythag. Thm., the length of the unlabeled leg is $\frac{4}{5}$. So the triangle is similar to a 3-4-5 right triangle. **2a.** $\approx 2.16$ **b.** $\approx 4.649$ **c.** $\approx 1.035$
**d.** undefined **e.** use $\frac{\cos x}{\sin x}$
**3.**

## Top-middle region

**4.** $\approx 1.4142$ **5.** about 860 ft away and 3185 ft away
**Lesson Check 1.** 1 **2.** $\frac{2\sqrt{3}}{3}$ **3.** $\approx 1.003$ **4.** $\approx 1.346$
**5.** 29.4 ft **6.** $y = 5 \sec \theta = \frac{5}{\cos \theta}$; there is no value of $\theta$ that will make $\frac{5}{\cos \theta}$ equal to zero. **7.** The student found the reciprocal of $(1 + \cos 20°) = \frac{1}{1 + \cos 20°} \approx 0.5155$. The answer should be: $\sec 20° + 1 = \frac{1}{\cos 20°} + 1 \approx 1.0642 + 1 = 2.0642$. **8.** The graphs have the same period and range. The domain of $y = \sec x$ is all real numbers except $n\pi + \frac{\pi}{2}$ (where $n$ is an integer), which are its asymptotes. The domain of $y = \csc x$ is all real numbers except $n\pi$ (where $n$ is an integer), which are its asymptotes. The graph of $y = \csc x$ can be obtained as a translation of $y = \sec\left(x - \frac{\pi}{4}\right)$ of the parent function $y = \sec x$.

**Exercises 9.** $-1$ **11.** $\frac{-\sqrt{3}}{\sqrt{3}}$ **13.** 0 **15.** $-\sqrt{2}$
**17.** $\approx -1.248$ **19.** $\approx 0.675$ **21.** $\approx -1.6$ **23.** undefined
**25.** **27.**

**29.** 1.1547 **31.** $-2.9238$ **33.** 1.0642 **35.** 1.7321
**37.** $\approx 104$ ft and $\approx 164$ ft **39.** Answers may vary. Sample:
$y = \csc\left(\theta + \frac{\pi}{3}\right)$ **41.** C
**43.** **45.**

**47a.** domain: all real numbers except multiples of $\pi$, range: $y \geq 1$ or $y \leq -1$; period: $2\pi$ **b.** 1 **c.** $-1$
**49.** $\csc 180°$ is undefined because $\sin 180° = 0$ and $\csc \theta = \frac{1}{\sin \theta}$. **51.** $\cot 0°$ is undefined because $\sin 0° = 0$ and $\cot \theta = \frac{\cos \theta}{\sin \theta}$.
**53a.**

**b.** The domain of $y = \tan x$ is all real numbers except odd multiples of $\frac{\pi}{2}$, where its asymptotes occur. The domain of $y = \cot x$ is all real numbers except multiples of $\pi$, where its asymptotes occur. The range of both functions is all real numbers. **c.** The graphs have the same period and range. Their asymptotes are shifted $\frac{\pi}{2}$ units. **d.** Answers may vary. Sample: $x = \frac{\pi}{4},\ x = \frac{3\pi}{4}$

## Top-right region

**55.** $\frac{\pi}{2}$ units to the left

**57.** 2 units to the left and 1 unit down

**59.** $\frac{\pi}{6}$ units to the right and 2 units down

**61a.** 1 **b.** 1 **71.** 2, $2\pi$; 5 units down **72.** 1, $2\pi$; 4 units left, 7 units down **73.** 3, $2\pi$; $\frac{\pi}{2}$ units to the left, 4 units up
**74.** 5, 2; 1.5 units to the right, 8 units down
**75.**

**76.**

**77.** true; Distr. Prop. **78.** true; Distr. Prop. and Comm. Prop. of Add. **79.** not true

### Chapter Review pp. 884–888

**1.** period **2.** unit circle **3.** tangent function **4.** phase shift **5.** secant function **6.** periodic; from 0 to 4 or from 4 to 6; 4; 2
**7.** Answers may vary. Sample:

**8.**

**9.** $-225°$

**10.**

**11.** 240° **12.** $\sin (315°) = -\frac{\sqrt{2}}{2} \approx -0.71$, $\cos (315°) = \frac{\sqrt{2}}{2} \approx 0.71$; $\sin (-315°) = \frac{\sqrt{2}}{2} \approx 0.71$, $\cos (-315°) = \frac{\sqrt{2}}{2} \approx 0.71$ **13a.** $\frac{\pi}{6},\ \frac{1}{2}$ **14a.** $-\frac{\pi}{4}$
**b.** $\frac{\sqrt{2}}{2},\ \frac{\sqrt{2}}{2}$ **15a.** $\pi$ **b.** $-1$, 0 **16a.** 360° **b.** 1, 0
**17a.** 150° **b.** $-\frac{\sqrt{3}}{2},\ \frac{1}{2}$ **18a.** $-135°$ **b.** $-\frac{\sqrt{2}}{2},\ -\frac{\sqrt{2}}{2}$
**19.** 26.2 ft
**20.** **21.**

**22.** **23.** $y = 4 \sin 4\theta$

**23.** **24.**

**25.** $y = 3 \cos 2\theta$ **26.** 0.58, 1.00, 2.15, 2.57, 3.72, 4.14, 5.29, 5.71 **27.** 0.70, 1.30, 2.70, 3.30, 4.70, 5.30
**28.** **29.**

0.41, 1 $-1$, undefined

**30.** **31.**

2, undefined undefined, 0

**32.** **33.**

**34.** **35.**

**36.** $y = \sin\left(x - \frac{\pi}{4}\right)$ **37.** $y = \cos x - 2$ **38.** $\sqrt{2}$

## Bottom-left region

**39.** $-\frac{\sqrt{3}}{3}$ **40.** 2 **41.** $\sqrt{3}$

**42.**

**43.**

**44.**

**45.**

### Chapter 14

#### Get Ready! p. 893

**1.** $x = \pm\frac{5}{2}$ **2.** $x = \pm\sqrt{23}$ **3.** $x = \pm 4\sqrt{\frac{5}{2}}$ **4.** $x = \pm\sqrt{\frac{11}{2}}$
**5.** $x = \pm\sqrt{30}$ **6.** $x = \pm 2$ **7.** $f^{-1}(x) = \frac{x}{5} - 2$; domain of $f$ and range of $f^{-1}$: all real numbers, range of $f$ and domain of $f^{-1}$: all real numbers; yes **8.** $f^{-1}(x) = x^2 - 3$; domain of $f$ and range of $f^{-1}$: all real numbers $\geq -3$, domain of $f^{-1}$ and range of $f$: all real numbers $\geq 0$; yes **9.** $f^{-1}(x) = \frac{x^2 + 4}{3}$; domain of $f$ and range of $f^{-1}$: all real numbers $\geq \frac{4}{3}$; domain of $f^{-1}$ and range of $f$: all real numbers $\geq 0$; yes
**10.** $f^{-1}(x) = \frac{5}{x}$; domain of $f$ and range of $f^{-1}$: all real numbers except 0, domain of $f^{-1}$ and range of $f$: all real numbers except 0; yes **11.** $f^{-1}(x) = \frac{10}{x} + 1$; domain of $f$ and range of $f^{-1}$: all real numbers except 1, domain of $f^{-1}$ and range of $f$: all real numbers except 0; yes
**12.** $f^{-1}(x) = \frac{10}{x + 1}$; domain of $f$ and range of $f^{-1}$: all real numbers except 0, domain of $f^{-1}$ and range of $f$: all real numbers except $-1$; yes **13.** $x = -\frac{3}{2}$ **14.** $x = 0.002$
**15.** $x = 1.0646$ **16.** $x = 18257.4$ **17.** $x = 0.00003$
**18.** $x = 5$ **19.** 0.67; 0.74; 1.11 **20.** $-0.26$; $-0.97$; 3.73 **21.** 0.96; 0.28; 0.29 **22.** $-0.87$; 0.50; $-0.58$

## Bottom-middle region

**23.** Answers may vary. Sample: The eq. is true for all values of $\theta$ for which $\tan^2 \theta$ and $\sec^2 \theta$ are defined.
**24.** Answers may vary. Sample: the lengths of the sides of rt. triangles.

### Lesson 14-1 pp. 896–902

**Got It? 1.** all real numbers except multiples of $\pi$
**2.** $\frac{\csc \theta}{\sec \theta} = \frac{\left(\frac{1}{\sin \theta}\right)}{\left(\frac{1}{\cos \theta}\right)} = \frac{\cos \theta}{\sin \theta} = \cot \theta$; all real numbers except multiples of $\frac{\pi}{2}$
**3a.** $1 + \cot^2 \theta = 1 + \left(\frac{\cos \theta}{\sin \theta}\right)^2$
$= 1 + \frac{\cos^2 \theta}{\sin^2 \theta}$
$= 1 + \frac{1 - \sin^2 \theta}{\sin^2 \theta}$
$= 1 + \frac{1}{\sin^2 \theta} - \frac{\sin^2 \theta}{\sin^2 \theta}$
$= 1 + \csc^2 \theta - 1$
$= \csc^2 \theta$
**b.** No; the domains of $\sin \theta$ and $\cos \theta$ are all real numbers, but the domains of $\tan \theta$, $\cot \theta$, $\sec \theta$, and $\csc \theta$ have restrictions.
**4.** $\sec^2 \theta - \sec^2 \theta \cos^2 \theta$
$= \left(\frac{1}{\cos \theta}\right)^2 - \left(\frac{1}{\cos \theta}\right)^2 \cos^2 \theta$
$= \frac{1}{\cos^2 \theta} - \frac{1}{\cos^2 \theta} \cdot \cos^2 \theta$
$= \frac{1}{\cos^2 \theta} - \frac{\cos^2 \theta}{\cos^2 \theta}$
$= \frac{1}{\cos^2 \theta} - 1$
$= \frac{\sin^2 \theta}{\cos^2 \theta}$
$= \tan^2 \theta$
**5.** $\csc \theta$

### Lesson Check
**1.** $\tan \theta \csc \theta$
$= \frac{\sin \theta}{\cos \theta} \cdot \frac{1}{\sin \theta}$
$= \frac{1}{\cos \theta}$
$= \sec \theta$
**2.** $\csc^2 \theta - \cot^2 \theta$
$= \left(\frac{1}{\sin \theta}\right)^2 - \left(\frac{\cos \theta}{\sin \theta}\right)^2$
$= \frac{1}{\sin^2 \theta} - \frac{\cos^2 \theta}{\sin^2 \theta}$
$= \frac{1 - \cos^2 \theta}{\sin^2 \theta}$
$= \frac{\sin^2 \theta}{\sin^2 \theta}$
$= 1$

## Bottom-right region

**3.** $\sin \theta \tan \theta$
$= \sin \theta + \frac{\sin \theta}{\cos \theta}$
$= \frac{\sin^2 \theta}{\cos \theta}$
$= \frac{1 - \cos^2 \theta}{\cos \theta}$
$= \frac{1}{\cos \theta} - \frac{\cos^2 \theta}{\cos \theta}$
$= \sec \theta - \cos \theta$
**4.** $\tan \theta \cot \theta - \sin^2 \theta$
$= \tan \theta \frac{1}{\tan \theta} - \sin^2 \theta$
$= \frac{\tan \theta}{\tan \theta} - \sin^2 \theta$
$= 1 - \sin^2 \theta$
$= \cos^2 \theta$
**5.** Answers may vary. Sample: Letting $a$ and $b$ be the legs, and $c$ the hypotenuse of a right triangle, the Pythagorean Theorem states that $a^2 + b^2 = c^2$. Dividing both sides by $c^2$, then $\frac{a^2}{c^2} + \frac{b^2}{c^2} = \left(\frac{a}{c}\right)^2 + \left(\frac{b}{c}\right)^2 = 1$. Calling the angle between $a$ and $c$ $\theta$, then $\sin \theta = \frac{a}{c}$ and $\cos \theta = \frac{b}{c}$. By substitution, $\cos^2 \theta + \sin^2 \theta = 1$. **6.** wrong calculation: $2 - \cos^2 \theta = 2 - (1 - \sin^2 \theta) = 2 - 1 + \sin^2 \theta = 1 + \sin^2 \theta$
### Exercises
**7.** $\cos \theta \cot \theta$
$= \cos \theta \left(\frac{\cos \theta}{\sin \theta}\right)$
$= \frac{\cos^2 \theta}{\sin \theta}$
$= \frac{1 - \sin^2 \theta}{\sin \theta}$
$= \frac{1}{\sin \theta} - \sin \theta$; all real numbers except multiples of $\pi$
**9.** $\cos \theta \tan \theta$
$= \cos \theta \left(\frac{\sin \theta}{\cos \theta}\right) = \sin \theta$; all real numbers except odd multiples of $\frac{\pi}{2}$
**11.** $\cos \theta \sec \theta$
$= \cos \theta \left(\frac{1}{\cos \theta}\right) = 1$; all real numbers except odd multiples of $\frac{\pi}{2}$
**13.** $\sin \theta \csc \theta$
$= \sin \theta \left(\frac{1}{\sin \theta}\right) = \frac{\sin \theta}{\sin \theta} = 1$; all real numbers except multiples of $\pi$
**15.** $\cos \theta - \sec \theta$
$= \frac{1}{\sin \theta} - \sin \theta$
$= \frac{1 - \sin^2 \theta}{\sin \theta}$
$= \frac{\cos^2 \theta}{\sin \theta}$
$= \cot \theta \cos \theta$; all real numbers except odd multiples of $\frac{\pi}{2}$

**17.** $\sin^2 \theta$ **19.** $-\cot^2 \theta$ **21.** $\sin \theta$ **23.** 1 **25.** 1 **27.** 1
**29.** $\sec \theta$ **31.** $\sec^2 \theta$ **33.** $\csc \theta$ **35.** $\sec \theta$ **37.** 1 **39.** 1
**41.** $\pm\sqrt{1 - \cos^2 \theta}$ **43.** $\frac{\pm\sqrt{1 - \sin^2 \theta}}{\sin \theta}$
**45.** $\pm\sqrt{\csc^2 \theta - 1}$

**47.** $\sin^2 \theta \tan \theta = \sin^2 \theta \left(\frac{\sin \theta}{\cos \theta}\right)$
$= (1 - \cos^2 \theta)\left(\frac{\sin \theta}{\cos \theta}\right)$
$= \frac{\sin \theta - \sin \theta \cos^2 \theta}{\cos \theta}$
$= \frac{\sin \theta}{\cos \theta} - \frac{\sin \theta \cos^2 \theta}{\cos \theta}$
$= \tan^2 \theta - \cos \theta$
**49.** $\sin \theta \cos \theta(\tan \theta + \cot \theta)$
$= \sin \theta \cos \theta\left(\frac{\sin \theta}{\cos \theta} + \frac{\cos \theta}{\sin \theta}\right)$
$= \frac{\sin^2 \theta \cos \theta}{\cos \theta} + \frac{\cos^2 \theta \sin \theta}{\sin \theta}$
$= \sin^2 \theta + \cos^2 \theta = 1$
**51.** $\frac{\sec \theta}{\csc \theta + \tan \theta}$
$= \frac{\frac{1}{\cos \theta}}{\frac{\sin \theta}{\cos \theta} + \frac{\cos \theta}{\sin \theta}} \cdot \frac{\sin \theta \cos \theta}{\sin \theta \cos \theta}$
$= \frac{\sin \theta}{\sin^2 \theta + \cos^2 \theta} = \frac{\sin \theta}{1} = \sin \theta$
**53.** $\frac{1 - \sin^2 \theta}{\sin^2 \theta}$
**55.** Errors are in the first line and the last 2 lines: first line, incorrect cancellation of $\tan^2 \theta$; last 2 lines, $\frac{\sin^2 \theta}{\cos^2 \theta} = \tan^2 \theta$, not $\cot^2 \theta$. The correct identity verification is:
$$\frac{\sec^2 \theta - \tan^2 \theta}{\tan^2 \theta} = \frac{\frac{1}{\cos^2 \theta} - \frac{\sin^2 \theta}{\cos^2 \theta}}{\frac{\sin^2 \theta}{\cos^2 \theta}}$$
$$= \frac{1 - \sin^2 \theta}{\cos^2 \theta} \cdot \frac{\cos^2 \theta}{\sin^2 \theta} = \frac{1 - \sin^2 \theta}{\sin^2 \theta} = \frac{\cos^2 \theta}{\sin^2 \theta} = \cot^2 \theta$$
**57.** $(x - 1)^2 - 1 = x(x - 2)$ is an identity since: $(x - 1)^2 - 1 = x^2 - 2x + 1 - 1 = x^2 - 2x = x(x - 2)$. $(x - 1)^2 = x(x - 1)$ is not an identity since it has a unique solution:
$(x - 1)^2 = x(x - 1)$
$x^2 - 2x + 1 = x^2 - x$
$-x = -1$
$x = 1$

**70.** **71.**

**72.** **73.**

**74.** 35° **75.** 45° **76.** 135° **77.** 211°
**78.** $f^{-1}(x) = x - 1$ **79.** $f^{-1}(x) = \frac{x+1}{3}$
**80.** $f^{-1}(x) = \pm\sqrt{x-4}$

### Lesson 14-2     pp. 903–910

**Got It? 1a.** 120° **b.** 30° **c.** 45° **2a.** 0.46 + 2πn and 2.69 + 2πn **b.** −0.82 + 2πn and 3.96 + 2πn
**3a.** 0.41 + 2πn and 3.56 + 2πn, or just 0.41 + πn
**b.** −0.63 + 2πn and 2.51 + 2πn, or just −0.63 + πn
**c.** $\tan(\theta + \pi) = \tan \theta$ **4.** $\frac{11\pi}{6}$, $\frac{7\pi}{6}$ **5.** $\frac{\pi}{2}$, $\frac{3\pi}{2}$
**6.** The air conditioner comes on about 7 hours after midnight, 7 A.M., and goes off about 7 hours before midnight, 5 P.M.

**Lesson Check 1.** −30° + 360° · n and 210° + 360° · n **2.** 60° + 360° · n and 120° + 360° · n **3.** 2.30, 3.98 **4.** 0 **5.** Answers may vary. Sample: To find the inverse of y = 3x − 4, you interchange x and y and solve for y: x = 3y − 4, y = $\frac{x+4}{3}$. Replace y with $f^{-1}(x)$ to find $f^{-1}(x) = \frac{x+4}{3}$. To find the inverse of y = 3 sin θ − 4, you interchange θ and y and solve for sin y and then solve for y: θ = 3 sin y − 4, sin y = $\frac{\theta + 4}{3}$ and y = $\sin^{-1}\left(\frac{\theta + 4}{3}\right)$.
Replace y with $f^{-1}(\theta)$ to find $f^{-1}(\theta) = \sin^{-1}\left(\frac{\theta + 4}{3}\right)$. The procedure for finding the inverse is the same; for y = 3 sin θ − 4 you will also use the inverse sine function. **6.** The student divided both sides of the equation by sin θ, which in the given interval can be equal to zero. There is an error in that the student failed to take into account the fact that division by zero is not possible. **Exercises 7.** 90° + n · 360° **9.** 240° + n · 360° and 300° + n · 360° **11.** 90° + n · 360° and 270° + n · 360°, or just 90° + n · 180° **13.** 0.79 + πn, or just $\frac{\pi}{4} + \pi n$ **15.** −0.89 + 2πn and 4.04 + 2πn
**17.** 2.67 + 2πn and 3.62 + 2πn **19.** $\frac{5\pi}{6}$, $\frac{5\pi}{6}$ **21.** $\frac{\pi}{4}$, $\frac{3\pi}{4}$
**23.** 0.46, 3.61 **25.** no solution **27.** $\frac{\pi}{3}$, $\frac{\pi}{6}$
**29.** $\frac{\pi}{4}$, $\frac{3\pi}{4}$, $\frac{5\pi}{4}$, $\frac{7\pi}{4}$ **31.** 0, π **33.** $\frac{7\pi}{6}$, $\frac{11\pi}{6}$ **35.** 30° + n · 360° and 150° + n · 360° **37.** 210° + n · 360° and 330° + n · 360° **39.** $\frac{\pi}{4}$ **41.** 3.04, 6.18 **43.** 0.0028 s; 0.019 s **45.** 0 + 2πn, $\frac{2}{3}\pi$ + 2πn, $\frac{4}{3}\pi$ + 2πn

**47.** $\frac{\pi}{6}$ + 2πn, $\frac{5\pi}{6}$ + 2πn, $\frac{3\pi}{2}$ + 2πn
**49.** $\frac{\pi}{6}$ + 2πn, $\frac{5\pi}{6}$ + 2πn, $\frac{\pi}{2}$ + πn
**51.** $\frac{\pi}{6}$ + πn, $\frac{7\pi}{6}$ + πn **53.** $\frac{\pi}{6}$ + 2πn, $\frac{5\pi}{6}$ + 2πn **55.** $\frac{\pi}{6}$ + $\frac{\pi n}{2}$ **57.** $\frac{\pi}{6}$ + $\frac{\pi n}{2}$
**59.** $\frac{2\pi}{3}$ + 2πn, $\frac{4\pi}{3}$ + 2πn **61a.** Answers may vary. Sample: cos θ = −1, 2 cos θ = −2, 3 cos θ = −3 **b.** Start with cos θ = −1, and then multiply both sides of the eq. by any nonzero number. **73.** cot θ **74.** $\tan^2 \theta$
**75.** 1 **76.** 1 **77.** sin θ **78.** tan θ **79.** $\frac{\pi}{4}$ = 4 cos $\frac{\pi}{8}\theta$
**80.** y = 3 cos θ **81.** y = $\frac{\pi}{4}$ cos $\frac{\pi}{8}\theta$ **82.** 4 **83.** 21
**84.** 52$\frac{1}{2}$

### Lesson 14-3     pp. 911–918

**Got It? 1.** sin θ = $\frac{12}{13}$, cos θ = $-\frac{5}{13}$, tan θ = $-\frac{12}{5}$, csc θ = $\frac{13}{12}$, sec θ = $-\frac{13}{5}$, cot θ = $-\frac{5}{12}$ **2a.** 27.1 m **b.** 32.3 m **3.** sin E = $\frac{3}{5}$, sec F = $\frac{5}{3}$ **4.** ≈76,430 ft ≈ 14.5 mi **5a.** 23.58° **b.** 56.25° **6a.** 72 ft **b.** Answers may vary. Sample: Build the ramp in 3 sections, each of which is 24 ft, and with landings between sections.

**Lesson Check 1.** sin 57° = $\frac{b}{c}$, cos 57° = $\frac{a}{c}$, tan 57° = $\frac{b}{a}$ **2.** 15.4 **3.** sin 33° = $\frac{a}{5}$ = 0.5, cos 33° = $\frac{b}{5}$ = 0.8, tan 33° = $\frac{a}{b}$ = 0.6 **4.** 36.9° **5.** Answers may vary. Sample: Using the inverse of cosine, you can find the acute angle between the shortest side and the hypotenuse, θ = $\cos^{-1}\left(\frac{8.4}{12.9}\right)$ ≈ 49.4°. Because the triangle is a right triangle, the remaining acute angle is ≈90° − 49.4° ≈ 40.6°. **6.** The student confuses $\sin^{-1}\theta$ with $\frac{1}{\sin\theta}$. He or she should have divided by sin 0.45. x = $\frac{4}{\sin 0.45}$ ≈ 9.20 cm

**Exercises**
**7.** sin θ = $\frac{4}{5}$, cos θ = $-\frac{4}{5}$, tan θ = $-\frac{3}{4}$, csc θ = $\frac{5}{3}$, sec θ = $-\frac{5}{4}$, cot θ = $-\frac{4}{3}$
**9.** sin θ = $\frac{5\sqrt{26}}{26}$, cos θ = $-\frac{\sqrt{26}}{26}$, tan θ = −5, csc θ = $\frac{\sqrt{26}}{5}$, sec θ = $-\sqrt{26}$, cot θ = $-\frac{1}{5}$
**11.** sin θ = $\frac{\sqrt{7}}{4}$, cos θ = $-\frac{3}{4}$, tan θ = $-\frac{\sqrt{7}}{3}$, csc θ = $\frac{4\sqrt{7}}{7}$, sec θ = $-\frac{4}{3}$, cot θ = $-\frac{3\sqrt{7}}{7}$
**13a.** $\frac{8}{17}$ ≈ 0.88 **b.** $\frac{8}{15}$ ≈ 2.13 **c.** $\frac{15}{17}$ ≈ 0.53 **d.** $\frac{17}{8}$ ≈ 2.13 **e.** $\frac{17}{15}$ ≈ 1.13 **f.** $\frac{8}{15}$ ≈ 0.53 **15.** 41.8 **17.** 25.2 **19.** a ≈ 8.7, m∠A ≈ 60.0°, m∠B ≈ 30.0° **21.** a = 9.0, m∠A ≈ 36.9°, m∠B ≈ 53.1° **23.** a = 8.0, m∠A ≈ 61.8°, m∠B ≈ 28.2° **25a.** m∠A = $\cos^{-1}\left(\frac{1200}{d}\right)$ **b.** 37° **c.** 53°

**27.**

sin θ = $\frac{3\sqrt{39}}{20}$, tan θ = $\frac{3\sqrt{39}}{7}$, csc θ = $\frac{20\sqrt{39}}{117}$, sec θ = $\frac{20}{7}$, cot θ = $\frac{7\sqrt{39}}{117}$

**29.**

sin θ = $\frac{24}{25}$, cos θ = $\frac{7}{25}$, tan θ = $\frac{25}{24}$, sec θ = $\frac{25}{7}$, cot θ = $\frac{7}{24}$

**31.**

sin θ = $\frac{4\sqrt{41}}{41}$, cos θ = $\frac{5\sqrt{41}}{41}$, tan θ = $\frac{4}{5}$, csc θ = $\frac{\sqrt{41}}{4}$, sec θ = $\frac{\sqrt{41}}{5}$

**33.**

sin θ = $\frac{5}{26}$, cos θ = $\frac{\sqrt{651}}{26}$, tan θ = $\frac{5\sqrt{651}}{651}$, sec θ = $\frac{26\sqrt{651}}{651}$, csc θ = $\frac{\sqrt{651}}{5}$

**35.** 33.4 ft **37.** 20.3 m² **39.** c ≈ 12.2, m∠A = 35.0°, m∠B ≈ 55.0° **41.** a ≈ 3.9, c ≈ 6.9, m∠B ≈ 55.8° **43.** a ≈ 19.8, b ≈ 2.9, m∠A ≈ 81.7° **45.** Using inverse sine, you can find that A ≈ 30°. Since sine is positive in the first and second quadrants, another solution is 150°. All the solutions would be 30° + n · 360° and 150° + n · 360°. **57.** 180° + n · 360° **58.** 45° + n · 180° and 90° + n · 180° **59.** 0° + n · 180°

**60.** **61.**

**62.**

**63.** 6 cm² **64.** 45 in.² **65.** 32.76 mm²

### Lesson 14-4     pp. 920–926

**Got It? 1.** 36.6 in.² **2.** 31.0 yd **3a.** 68.4° **b.** yes; $\frac{\sin T}{height} = \frac{\sin 90°}{9}$; height ≈ 9 sin 47° ≈ 6.6
**4.** 104.7 ft

**Lesson Check 1.** ≈10.7 square units **2.** ≈19.8 **3.** ≈26.3° or ≈153.7° **4.** AAS, ASA **5.** No; For $\frac{\sin 22°}{\sin 45°}$ you find the sine of each numerator and denominator, sin 22° and sin 45°; for $\sin\left(\frac{22°}{45°}\right)$ you find the sine of the quotient of $\left(\frac{22°}{45°}\right)$. **Exercises 7.** 9.1 in.² **9.** 10.9 **11.** 7.4 **13.** 33.5° **15.** 31.7° **17.** 32 cm **19.** 66° **21.** m∠E ≈ 40.3°, m∠F ≈ 85.7°, f ≈ 12.3 m **25.** 44.4 **27.** 49.4 **29.** 28.0 ft **31.** 4.0 cm **33a.** 56.4°, 93.6°, 26.4° **b.** No; △EFG could be congruent to △ABC instead of △ABD.
**40.** **41.**

**42.**

**43.** (−1, 7) **44.** (5, 3) **45.** (−3, −1) **46.** (−6, 4) **47.** 53.1° **48.** 24.6° **49.** 38.7° **50.** 54.7°

### Lesson 14-5     pp. 928–934

**Got It? 1a.** 6.4
**b.** 1 mi to 6 mi;
$a^2 = 2.5^2 + 3.5^2 - 2(2.5)(3.5) \cos A$
$a^2 = 18.5 - 17.5 \cos A$;
if A = 0°, then cos A = 1 and a = 1; if A = 180°, then cos A = −1 and a = 6. **2.** 75.3° **3.** 30.7°
**Lesson Check 1.** ≈11.85 in. **2.** ≈52.4° **3.** ≈34.1° **4.** ≈60.3° **5.** Use the Law of Sines when you have two sides and a non-included angle or two angles and a side; use the Law of Cosines when you have two sides and an

---

included angle or three sides. **6.** The denominator should be negative. The answer should be:
$\cos C = \frac{15^2 - 11^2 - 17^2}{2(11)(17)} \approx 0.495$
$C = \cos^{-1}(0.495) \approx 60.3°$
**Exercises 7.** 37.1 **9.** 13.7 **11.** 27.0 **13.** 33.7° **15.** 47.2° **17.** 50.8 **19.** 27.0 **21.** $b^2 = a^2 + c^2 - 2ac \cos B$
**23.** $\frac{\sin B}{b} = \frac{\sin C}{c}$ **25.** $\frac{\sin C}{c} = \frac{\sin A}{a}$ **27.** ≈59.1 nautical miles **29.** b = 34.7, m∠A = 26.7°, m∠C ≈ 53.9° **31.** m∠A ≈ 56.1°, m∠B ≈ 70.0°, m∠C ≈ 53.9°
**33.** For any two side lengths a and b, the ratio $\frac{a}{b}$ is equal to the ratio $\frac{\sin A}{\sin B}$, which can be found since A and B are given.
**35a.** ≈ 45.4 mi **b.** 14.4° left; 4.4° west of north **37.** 11.0 cm **39.** 27.0° **41.** 13.0 cm **43.** 21.5°
**45.** 8.3 ft **47.** 79.6° **49.** 18 cm **60.** 17.1 in. **61.** 8.9 m **62.** 26.3 in. **63.** 54.0° **64.** 2π, x = ±π **65.** $\frac{\pi}{3}$, x = ±$\frac{1}{3}$
**66.** $\frac{\pi}{3}$, x = ±$\frac{\pi}{6}$ **67.** 1, x = ±$\frac{1}{2}$ **68.** sin θ **69.** cos θ
**70.** 1 **71.** $\csc^2 \theta$

### Lesson 14-6     pp. 935–942

**Got It?**
**1.** $\cos\left(\theta - \frac{\pi}{2}\right) = \cos\left(-\left(\frac{\pi}{2} - \theta\right)\right)$
$= \cos\left(\frac{\pi}{2} - \theta\right)$
$= \sin \theta$
**2.** sec(90° − A) = $\frac{1}{\cos(90° - A)} = \frac{1}{\sin A}$ = csc A
sec(90° − A) = csc A
**3a.** 0, π **b.** yes; πn
**4.** $\frac{\sqrt{6} - \sqrt{2}}{4}$
**5.** sin(A + B) = sin(A − (−B))
= sin A cos(−B) − cos A sin(−B)
= sin A cos B − cos A(−sin B)
= sin A cos B + cos A sin B
**6.** −2 − $\sqrt{3}$
**Lesson Check**
**1.** $\sin\left(\frac{\pi}{2} + \theta\right) + \sin\left(\frac{\pi}{2} - \theta\right)$
= $\sin\left(\frac{\pi}{2} - (-\theta)\right) + \sin\left(\frac{\pi}{2} - \theta\right)$
= $\cos(-\theta) + \cos \theta$
= cos θ + cos θ
= 2 cos θ
**2.** $\frac{\pi}{4}$, $\frac{5\pi}{4}$ **3.** $\frac{\sqrt{2} - \sqrt{6}}{4}$, $-\frac{\sqrt{2} + \sqrt{6}}{4}$
**5.** There are 2 solutions, $\frac{\pi}{4}$ and $\frac{3\pi}{4}$, between 0 and 2π because: −cos θ = cos θ
2 cos θ = 0
cos θ = 0; θ = $\frac{\pi}{2}$, $\frac{3\pi}{2}$
**6.** $\sin\left(\frac{\pi}{2} - \theta\right)$ = sin $\frac{\pi}{2}$ cos θ − cos $\frac{\pi}{2}$ sin θ
= (1) cos θ − (0) sin θ
= cos θ

**Exercises**
**7.** $\csc\left(\theta - \frac{\pi}{2}\right) = \frac{1}{\sin\left(\theta - \frac{\pi}{2}\right)}$
$= \frac{1}{\sin\left(-\left(\frac{\pi}{2} - \theta\right)\right)}$
$= \frac{1}{-\sin\left(\frac{\pi}{2} - \theta\right)}$
$= \frac{1}{-\cos \theta}$
$= -\sec \theta$
**9.** $\cot\left(\frac{\pi}{2} - \theta\right) = \frac{\cos\left(\frac{\pi}{2} - \theta\right)}{\sin\left(\frac{\pi}{2} - \theta\right)}$
$= \frac{\sin \theta}{\cos \theta}$
= tan θ
**11.** $\tan\left(\theta - \frac{\pi}{2}\right) = \tan\left(-\left(\frac{\pi}{2} - \theta\right)\right)$
$= -\tan\left(\frac{\pi}{2} - \theta\right)$
= −cot θ
**13.** tan (90° − A) = cot A **15.** cot (90° − A) = tan A
**17.** $\frac{\pi}{2}$, $\frac{3\pi}{2}$ **19.** π **21.** $\frac{\pi}{2}$, $\frac{3\pi}{2}$ **23.** $\frac{\sqrt{2}}{2}$ **25.** 0
**27.** $-\sqrt{3}$ **29.** $\frac{\sqrt{2 + \sqrt{3}}}{2}$
**31.** −2 + $\sqrt{3}$ **33.** −$\frac{1}{2}$ **35.** $\frac{1}{2}$
**37.** sin(A − B) = $\cos\left[\frac{\pi}{2} - (A - B)\right]$
$= \cos\left[\left(\frac{\pi}{2} - A\right) + B\right]$
$= \cos\left(\frac{\pi}{2} - A\right)\cos B - \sin\left(\frac{\pi}{2} - A\right)\sin B$
= sin A cos B − cos A sin B
**39.** tan(A + B) = $\frac{\sin(A + B)}{\cos(A + B)}$
$= \frac{\sin A \cos B + \cos A \sin B}{\cos A \cos B - \sin A \sin B}$
$= \frac{\frac{\sin A \cos B + \cos A \sin B}{\cos A \cos B}}{\frac{\cos A \cos B - \sin A \sin B}{\cos A \cos B}}$
$= \frac{\frac{\sin A \cos B}{\cos A \cos B} + \frac{\cos A \sin B}{\cos A \cos B}}{\frac{\cos A \cos B}{\cos A \cos B} - \frac{\sin A \sin B}{\cos A \cos B}}$
$= \frac{\tan A + \tan B}{1 - \tan A \tan B}$
**41.** (5 cos A − 5$\sqrt{3}$ sin A, 5 sin A + 5$\sqrt{3}$ cos A)
**43.** sin 5θ **45.** cos 5θ **47.** tan 2θ **60.** ≈16.34 ft
**61.** −10.0 cm **62.** $\frac{4\pi}{18}$ and 1.40 **63.** −$\frac{5\pi}{18}$ and −0.87
**64.** −$\frac{\pi}{18}$ and −0.26 **65.** $\frac{7\pi}{18}$ and 1.22 **66.** $\frac{19\pi}{18}$ and 3.32
**67.** cos A cos B − sin A sin B **68.** sin A cos B + cos A sin B **69.** $\frac{\tan A + \tan B}{1 - \tan A \tan B}$

### Lesson 14-7     pp. 943–949

**Got It?**
**1.** cos 2θ = $\cos^2 \theta - \sin^2 \theta$
$= \cos^2 \theta - (1 - \cos^2 \theta)$
$= \cos^2 \theta - 1 + \cos^2 \theta$
$= 2\cos^2 \theta - 1$
**2.** $\frac{\sqrt{3}}{2}$ **3.** cos 2θ = 2(2 $\cos^2 \theta$ − 1) = 4 $\cos^2 \theta$ − 3
**4a.** $\frac{1}{2}$ **b.** −$\frac{4}{5}$ **c.** If 270° < θ < 360°, 135° < $\frac{\theta}{2}$ < 180° and $\frac{\theta}{2}$ is also in Quadrant II. The answers will remain the same.
**Lesson Check 1.** $\frac{\sqrt{3}}{2}$ **2.** 1 **3a.** −$\frac{5}{13}$ **b.** $\frac{13 + 2\sqrt{13}}{26}$
**c.** −$\frac{\sqrt{13 - 2\sqrt{13}}}{26}$ **4.** The student did not correctly determine in which quadrant $\frac{\theta}{2}$ will be. If 180° < θ < 270°, 90° < $\frac{\theta}{2}$ < 135°, then $\frac{\theta}{2}$ is in Quadrant II and the tangent will be negative. **5.** sin 4A **6.** $\sin^2\frac{5A}{2} = -\frac{\sqrt{1 - \cos 5A}}{2}$ if 360° < 5A < 450°, 180° < $\frac{5A}{2}$ < 225° and the sine is negative in Quadrant III.
**Exercises**
**7.** sin 2θ = sin(θ + θ)
= sin θ cos θ + cos θ sin θ
= 2 sin θ cos θ
**9.** −$\frac{\sqrt{3}}{2}$ **11.** −$\sqrt{3}$ **13.** −$\frac{1}{2}$ **15.** 1 **17.** $\frac{\sqrt{2 + \sqrt{3}}}{2}$
**19.** $\frac{\sqrt{2 - \sqrt{3}}}{2}$ **21.** $\frac{\sqrt{2 + \sqrt{3}}}{2}$ **23.** 0 **25.** $\frac{\sqrt{10}}{10}$ **27.** 3
**29.** $\frac{4\sqrt{17}}{17}$ **31.** −4
**33.** cos B = 2 $\cos^2 \frac{B}{2}$ − 1
2 $\cos^2 \frac{B}{2}$ = cos B + 1
$\cos^2 \frac{B}{2} = \frac{\cos B + 1}{2}$
Since cos B = $\frac{c}{r}$,
$\cos^2 \frac{B}{2} = \frac{\frac{c}{r} + 1}{2} = \frac{\frac{c}{r} + \frac{r}{r}}{2} = \frac{\frac{r + c}{r}}{2} = \frac{r + c}{2r}$
**35.** cos 2R = $\cos^2 R$ − $\sin^2 R$
$= \left(\frac{t}{r}\right)^2 - \left(\frac{s}{r}\right)^2$
$= \frac{t^2}{r^2} - \frac{s^2}{r^2}$
$= \frac{t^2 - s^2}{r^2}$

**37.** $\sin^2 \frac{s}{2} = \left(\sin \frac{s}{2}\right)^2$
$= \left(\pm\sqrt{\frac{1 - \cos s}{2}}\right)^2$
$= \frac{1 - \cos s}{2} = \frac{1 - \frac{t}{r}}{2}$
$= \frac{1}{2} - \frac{t}{2r} = \frac{r - t}{2r}$
**39.** $\tan^2 \frac{s}{2} = \left(\tan \frac{s}{2}\right)^2$
$= \left(\pm\sqrt{\frac{1 - \cos s}{1 + \cos s}}\right)^2 = \frac{1 - \cos s}{1 + \cos s} = \frac{1 - \frac{t}{r}}{1 + \frac{t}{r}}$
$= \frac{r - t}{r + r}$
**41.** −$\frac{24}{25}$ **43.** $\frac{24}{25}$ **45.** $\frac{\sqrt{6}}{3}$ **47.** −$\frac{1}{7}$
**49.** cos θ(8 sin θ − 3) = 0; $\frac{\pi}{2}$, $\frac{3\pi}{2}$, 0.384, 2.757
**51.** cos θ(2 sin θ − 1) = 0; $\frac{\pi}{6}$, $\frac{3\pi}{2}$, $\frac{5\pi}{6}$, $\frac{3\pi}{2}$, $\frac{7\pi}{6}$ **53.** 1 **55.** cos θ **57.** Answers may vary. Sample: **a.** sin $\frac{1}{2}$ $\sqrt{3}$ **b.** sin 120° = $\frac{\sqrt{3}}{2}$
**c.** cos 30° = $\frac{\sqrt{3}}{2}$ **71.** $\frac{\sqrt{3}}{2}$ **72.** $\frac{\sqrt{2}}{2}$ **73.** $\sqrt{3}$ **74.** about 4.1; 12 **75.** 2; 4 **76.** 4.2 **77.** 26.6 **78.** 57.6

### Chapter Review     pp. 951–954

**1.** Law of Sines **2.** trig. ratios **3.** Law of Cosines **4.** trig. ident. **5.** Law of Sines **6.** sin θ tan θ = sin θ $\frac{\sin \theta}{\cos \theta}$ = $\frac{\sin^2 \theta}{\cos \theta}$ = $\frac{1 - \cos^2 \theta}{\cos \theta}$ = $\frac{1}{\cos \theta}$ − cos θ; domain of validity: all real numbers except odd multiples of $\frac{\pi}{2}$

**7.** $\cos^2 \theta \cot^2 \theta = \cos^2 \theta \frac{\cos^2 \theta}{\sin^2 \theta} = \frac{\cos^2 \theta(1 - \sin^2 \theta)}{\sin^2 \theta}$ = $\frac{\cos^2 \theta - \cos^2 \theta \sin^2 \theta}{\sin^2 \theta}$ = $\cot^2 \theta - \cos^2 \theta$; domain of validity: all real numbers except 0 and multiples of π **8.** cos² θ **9.** 1 **10.** 1 **11.** −$\sin^2 \theta$ **12.** cos² θ **13.** 1 **14.** −60° **15.** 60° **16.** −30° **17.** 30° **18.** 0.34 **19.** −1.11 **20.** 2.27 **21.** 0.20 **22.** $\frac{\pi}{4}$, $\frac{3\pi}{4}$, $\frac{5\pi}{4}$, $\frac{7\pi}{4}$ **23.** $\frac{\pi}{3}$, $\frac{5\pi}{3}$ **24.** 0, $\frac{\pi}{2}$, π **25.** $\frac{\pi}{6}$, $\frac{\pi}{2}$, $\frac{5\pi}{6}$ **26.** sin θ = $\frac{4}{5}$, cos θ = $\frac{3}{5}$, tan θ = −$\frac{4}{3}$, csc θ = $\frac{5}{4}$, sec θ = −$\frac{5}{3}$, cot θ = −$\frac{3}{4}$ **27.** sin θ = −$\frac{15}{17}$, cos θ = $\frac{8}{17}$, tan θ = −$\frac{15}{8}$, sec θ = $\frac{17}{8}$, cot θ = −$\frac{8}{15}$ **28.** $\frac{5}{3}$, 0.6 **29.** $\frac{4}{3}$, 0.8 **30.** $\frac{3}{2}$, 0.75 **31.** $\frac{5}{3}$, 1.6 **32.** g ≈ 9.5, ∠F ≈ 18.4, ∠H ≈ 71.6 **33.** h = 16, ∠F ≈ 36.9, ∠H ≈ 53.1 **34.** f ≈ 37.7, ∠F ≈ 43.3, ∠H ≈ 46.7 **35.** g ≈ 6.4, ∠F ≈ 51.3, ∠H ≈ 38.7 **36.** 13.7 **37.** 29.4 **38.** 13.14 m² **39.** 92.12 ft² **40.** 7.1 in. **41.** 43.9° **42.** 52.2°

**43.** $\cos\left(\theta + \frac{\pi}{2}\right) = \cos\theta\cos\frac{\pi}{2} - \sin\theta\sin\frac{\pi}{2}$

$= \cos\theta \times 0 - \sin\theta \times 1 = -\sin\theta$

**44.** $\sin^2\left(\theta - \frac{\pi}{2}\right) = \left[\sin\left(\theta - \frac{\pi}{2}\right)\right]^2$

$= \left[\sin\theta\cos\frac{\pi}{2} - \cos\theta\sin\frac{\pi}{2}\right]^2$

$= [\sin\theta \times 0 - \cos\theta \times 1]^2$

$= (-\cos\theta)^2 = \cos^2\theta$

**45.** $2 - \sqrt{3}$ **46.** $-\frac{\sqrt{3}}{2}$ **47.** $\frac{\sqrt{2} - \sqrt{6}}{4}$ **48.** $-2 - \sqrt{3}$

**49.** $\frac{\sqrt{3}}{2}$ **50.** $\frac{\sqrt{3}}{2}$ **51.** $-\sqrt{3}$ **52.** $-\frac{\sqrt{3}}{2}$

### Skills Handbook

**p. 964 1.** 46% **3.** 0.7% **5.** 1.035 **7.** 25%
**9.** 66.6% **11.** 115% **13.** 12.5 **15.** 75 **17.** 20%
**p. 965 1.** $1\frac{2}{3}$ **3.** $6\frac{5}{6}$ **5.** $\frac{5}{21}$ **7.** $2\frac{19}{20}$ **9.** 8 **11.** $1\frac{1}{2}$
**13.** 2 **15.** $42$
**p. 966 1.** 3 to 4 **3.** 19 g in 2 oz **5.** $\frac{14}{5}$ **7.** 8 **9.** 1.8
**11.** 1.95 **13.** 45.5 **15.** $\pm6$
**p. 967 1.** 1 **3.** $-38$ **5.** $-17$ **7.** 4 **9.** 28 **11.** $-12$
**13.** $-90$ **15.** 12 **17.** 19 **19.** 9 **21.** $-10$
**p. 968 1.** 14 m$^2$ **3.** 30 cm$^2$ **5.** $91\frac{1}{8}$ ft$^2$ **7.** $100\pi$ in.$^3$
**9.** 110.5 in.$^2$ **11.** $121\frac{1}{2}$ ft$^2$
**p. 969 1.** I **3.** IV **5.** III **7.** $\frac{4}{5}$ **9.** 0 **11.** $\frac{5}{6}$ **13.** $\left(5, -\frac{3}{2}\right)$
**15.** $\left(\frac{5}{2}, -1\right)$
**p. 970 1.** $x^3$ **3.** $a^4b$ **5.** $\frac{1}{c^2}$ **7.** $\frac{x^5}{7^2z^3}$ **9.** $a^8$ **11.** $c^6$
**13.** $\frac{a^4}{b^2}$ **15.** $\frac{a^4}{b^4}$ **17.** $c^{12}$ **19.** $u^{12}v^6$ **21.** $a^3$ **23.** $\frac{1}{mg^3}$
**25.** $\frac{a^5}{7}$
**p. 971 1.** $x^2 + 10x - 5$ **3.** $12x^4 - 20x^3 + 36x^2$
**5.** $x^2 - 2x - 15$ **7.** $(a-6)(a-2)$ **9.** $(x+4)(x+1)$
**11.** $(y+8)(y-3)$ **13.** $2x(x^2 + 2x - 4)$
**p. 972 1.** $1.34 \times 10^6$ **3.** $7.75 \times 10^{-4}$ **5.** 111,300
**7.** $1.895 \times 10^3$ **9.** $1.234 \times 10^5$ **11.** $6.4 \times 10^5$
**13.** $8.52 \times 10^2$ **15.** 17.5 **17.** $8.95 \times 10^{-12}$
**19.** $3.77 \times 10^{10}$ **21.** $1.8 \times 10^{-6}$
**p. 973 1.** 10 **3.** 15 **5.** 54.7 **7.** 5 **9.** 13 **11.** 22.7
**13.** 2.8 **15.** 9 **17.** 7

**p. 974**
**1.**

**p. 975 1.** $3.\overline{7}$; 5; 5 **3.** $3.9\overline{6}$; 2.4; 2.4 **5.** 1.5; 1.5;
no mode

**7.**

**p. 976 1.** $\frac{a}{3b^2}$ **3.** $\frac{1}{2}$ **5.** $4x$ **7.** $\frac{2}{h}$ **9.** $\frac{x}{10}$ **11.** $\frac{74x}{35}$
**13.** $\frac{4a^2}{5}$ **15.** $\frac{16}{x}$ **17.** $\frac{16}{5}$ **19.** $2x$

1122

**Selected Answers    T547**

# Additional Answers

## Chapter 2

### Lesson 2-7

**Practice and Problem page 112 Solving Exercises**

**45. a.**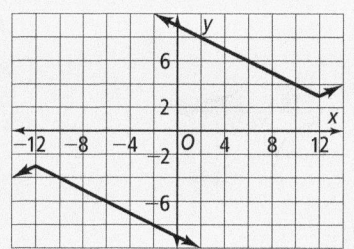

**b.** Answers may vary. Sample: same shape and size, different vertices, one opens down and one opens up.

**46.**

**47.**

**48.**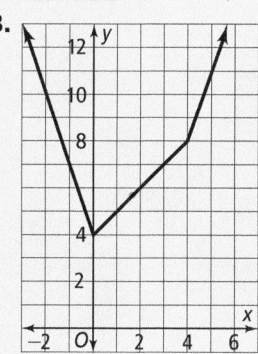

**49.** B

**50.** Answers may vary. Sample:
  **a.** $y = |x|, y = -|x|$
  **b.** $y = |x|, y = |x - 1| + 1$

**Sunshine State page 113 Standards Practice**

**51.** C

**52.** G

**53.** A

**54.** **[2]** No; both $(1, -1)$ and $(1, 1)$ are pts. on the graph of $|y| = x$. Since there is more than one $y$-value ($-1$ and $1$) for a given $x$-value (1), $|y| = x$ is not a function. (OR equivalent explanation)

  **[1]** incomplete explanation

---

### page 113 Mixed Review

**55.** $y = x + 1$

**56.** $y = -\frac{1}{2}x + 2$

**57.** $g(x) = -x - 7$

**58.** $g(x) = -2x - 6$

**59.** $g(x) = -4 - x$

**60.** Answers may vary. Sample: $y = \frac{4}{5}x + 1$

**61.** Answers may vary. Sample: $y = -\frac{4}{5}x + 8$

**62.**
━━━━━●━━━━━
         1.25

$p \leq 1.25$

**63.**
━━━━━○━━━━━
         13

$t > 13$

**64.**
━━━━━●━━━━━
      −3

## Chapter 5

### Lesson 5-7

**page 325 Concept Byte**

**8. b.**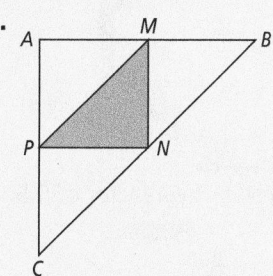

Begin with a large isosc. rt. triangle, $\triangle ABC$. Connect midpts. of all sides to form four congruent triangles. Shade $\triangle MNP$ (the "middle" triangle). Now repeat the process in each unshaded triangle by connecting midpts. and shading the "middle" triangles. After two repetitions of the process, the pattern resembles the shaded grid.

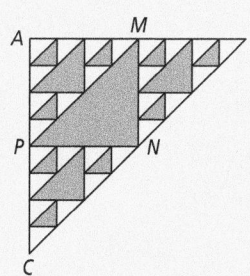

**9.** Answers may vary. Sample: The numbers in the grid form a triangular shape.

**10.** 1, 2, 4, 8, 16, 32, 64, 128, 256; the sum of each row is double the sum of the previous row.

## Chapter 7

### Mid-Chapter Quiz

**page 461 Mid-Chapter Quiz**

**24.** domain: $x > 1$, range: all real numbers

**25.** domain: all real numbers, range: all real numbers

**26.** $y = 2144.23(0.95)^x$; about 6 minutes

**27.** The $y$-intercept is when $x = 0$ i.e. $(0, a)$.

**28.** If $a > 0$ and $b > 1$, the function represents exponential growth; if $a > 0$ and $0 < b < 1$, the function represents exponential decay.

**29.** The graphs are a reflection of each other over the line $y = x$. The domain of one is the range of the other, and vice-versa. They both share a common $y$-intercept, $(0, 0)$.

**30.** The annually compounded interest formula is $A = P(1 + r)^t$. The continuously compounded interest formula is $A = Pe^{rt}$.

## Chapter 8

### Lesson 8-2

**page 506 Concept Byte**

**5.**

**6.**

**7.**

**8.**

**9.**

**10.**

**11.**

**Practice and Problem**
**page 512   Solving Exercises**

**10.**

no x- or y-intercept; horizontal asymptote: $y = 0$, vertical asymptote: $x = 0$; domain: all real numbers except $x = 0$, range: all real numbers except $y = 0$

**11.**

no x- or y-intercept; horizontal asymptote: $y = 0$, vertical asymptote: $x = 0$; domain: all real numbers except $x = 0$, range: all real numbers except $y = 0$

**12.**

no x- or y-intercept; horizontal asymptote: $y = 0$, vertical asymptote: $x = 0$; domain: all real numbers except $x = 0$, range: all real numbers except $y = 0$

**13.**

stretch by a factor of 2

**14.**

reflection across the x-axis and a stretch by a factor of 4

**15.**

compression by a factor of 0.5

**16.**

stretch by a factor of 12

**17.**

compression by a factor of 0.75

**18.**

domain: all real numbers except $x = 0$, range: all real numbers except $y = -3$

**19.**

domain: all real numbers except $x = 0$, range: all real numbers except $y = -3$

**20.**

domain: all real numbers except $x = 2$, range: all real numbers except $y = 5$

**21.**

domain: all real numbers except $x = 3$, range: all real numbers except $y = 4$

**22.**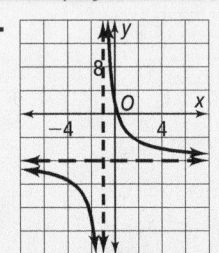

domain: all real numbers except $x = -6$, range: all real numbers except $y = -1$

**23.**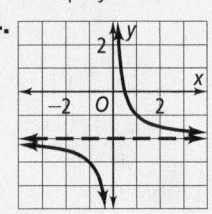

domain: all real numbers except $x = -1$, range: all real numbers except $y = -8$

**24.**

domain: all real numbers except $x = 0$, range: all real numbers except $y = -2$

**25.**

domain: all real numbers except $x = -5$, range: all real numbers except $y = -6$

**26.** $y = \dfrac{2}{x} + 4$

**27.** $y = \dfrac{2}{x + 2} + 3$

**28.** $y = \dfrac{2}{x - 4} - 8$

**29.** 7.67 ft

**30.**

$c = \dfrac{750}{a}$; domain: whole numbers from 5 to 15, range: $50 \le c \le 750$

# Chapter 10

## Get Ready

### page 611   Get Ready!

**15.** $y = 2(x - 1)^2 + 8$

**16.** $y = -3\left(x - \dfrac{1}{6}\right)^2 + \dfrac{1}{12}$

**17.**

**18.**

**19.**

**20.**

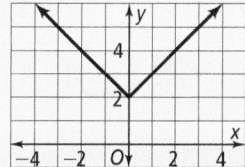

**21.** The radius of a circle is the distance from the center of the circle to any pt. on the circle. The radius extends in every direction from the center and ends on the circle. All radii of the same circle are equal.

**22.** The vertex of a parabola is the lowest or highest pt. of a parabola; it is the pt. where the parabola changes direction.

## Lesson 10-1

### Practice and Problem Solving Exercises

### page 619

**38.** parabola: Hold the lamp so that the edge of the shade furthest from the wall is parallel to the plane of the wall.

circle: Hold the lamp so that the circular top rim of the shade is parallel to the wall.

hyperbola: Let the lamp sit in a normal, upright position, but close enough to the wall for the bottom rim of the shade to almost touch the wall.

ellipse: Hold the lamp at an angle so that the light from the top of the shade gives a closed, curved oblong area of light on the wall.

**39. a.** All lines in the plane that pass through the center of a circle are axes of sym. of the circle.

**b.** The axes of sym. of an ellipse intersect at the center of the ellipse. The same is true for a hyperbola. This can be confirmed using, for example, $4x^2 + 9y^2 = 36$ and $4x^2 - 9y^2 = 36$.

**40.**

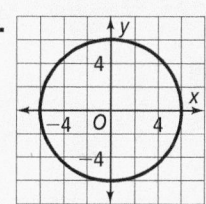

$x^2 + y^2 = 36$

**41.**

$x^2 + y^2 = \dfrac{1}{4}$

**42.**

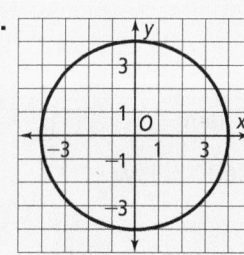

$x^2 + y^2 = 16$

**43.**

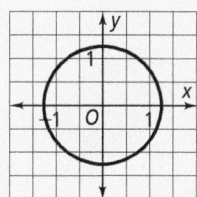

$x^2 + y^2 = 1.5625$

**44–49.** Answers may vary. Samples are given.

**44.** $(2, 4)$

**45.** $(\sqrt{2}, 1)$

**46.** $(-2, 2\sqrt{2})$

**47.** $(2, 0)$

**48.** $(3, \sqrt{51})$

**49.** $(0, -\sqrt{7})$

**50.** one branch of a hyperbola

**51.** Check students' work.

**52. a.**

**b.** hyperbola

**c.** no intercepts; lines of symmetry: $y = x$ and $y = -x$

**d.** yes; $f(x) = \dfrac{16}{x}$

**53. a.**

**b.**

**Standardized Test Prep**
**page 620**

**54.** D
**55.** I
**56.** D
**57.** H
**58.** [2]

$a_n = (n + 1)^2; a_9 = (9 + 1)^2 = 100$

[1] correct explicit formula, incorrect ninth term

**page 620   Mixed Review**

**59.** diverges
**60.** diverges
**61.** converges
**62.** $x^3 - 3x^2y + 3xy^2 - y^3$
**63.** $p^6 + 6p^5q + 15p^4q^2 + 20p^3q^3 + 15p^2q^4 + 6pq^5 + q^6$
**64.** $x^4 - 8x^3 + 24x^2 - 32x + 16$
**65.** $243 - 405x + 270x^2 - 90x^3 + 15x^4 - x^5$

**66.**

| x | −2 | −1 | 0 | 1 | 2 |
|---|----|----|---|---|---|
| y | 2  | 1  | 0 | 1 | 2 |

**67.**

| x | −2 | −1 | 0 | 1 | 2 |
|---|----|----|---|---|---|
| y | 5  | 4  | 3 | 4 | 5 |

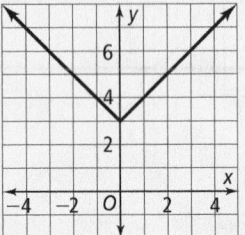

**68.**

| x | 0 | 1 | 2 | 3 | 4 |
|---|---|---|---|---|---|
| y | 2 | 1 | 0 | 1 | 2 |

**69.**

| x | −3 | −2 | −1 | 0  | 1  |
|---|----|----|----|----|----|
| y | −2 | −3 | −4 | −3 | −2 |

**Concept Byte   p. 621**

**7. a.**

**b.** x-intercepts: (±4.5, 0), y-intercepts: (0, ±4.5)

**c.** Check students' work.

**d.** circle with center at the origin and radius 4.5

**8.**

x-intercepts: (±2.5, 0), y-intercepts: (0, ±5)

**9.**

x-intercepts: (± $\sqrt{30}$, 0), y-intercepts: (0, ± $\sqrt{30}$)

**10.**

x-intercepts: (±2$\sqrt{2}$, 0), no y-intercepts

**11.** Answers may vary. Sample: Graph on the same screen: $y = 3 - x$ where $x \geq 0$ and $y = 3 + x$ where $x \geq 0$.

**12.** Parabolas with a vert. axis of sym.; other conic sections have the x-axis as a line of sym., so they fail the vert. line test.

# Chapter 11

**Concept Byte   pp. 694–695**

**10.**

| Event: Number of Days in a Month | 28 | 29 | 30 | 31 |
|---|---|---|---|---|
| Frequency | 3 | 1 | 16 | 28 |
| Probability | $\frac{1}{16}$ | $\frac{1}{48}$ | $\frac{1}{3}$ | $\frac{7}{12}$ |

# Chapter 14

## Mid-Chapter Quiz    p. 919

**40.**

$$\sin \theta = \frac{11\sqrt{137}}{137}, \cos \theta = \frac{4\sqrt{137}}{137},$$

$$\csc \theta = \frac{\sqrt{137}}{11},$$

$$\sec \theta = \frac{\sqrt{137}}{4}, \cot \theta = \frac{4}{11}$$

**41.**

$$\sin \theta = \frac{\sqrt{26}}{26}, \cos \theta = \frac{5\sqrt{26}}{26},$$

$$\tan \theta = \frac{1}{5},$$

$$\csc \theta = \sqrt{26}, \sec \theta = \frac{\sqrt{26}}{5}$$

**42.** Answers may vary. Sample: In the eq. $x^2 - 3x + 2 = 0$, you isolate the variable $x$ to get the solution. In the eq. $\tan^2 \theta - 3 \tan \theta + 2 = 0$, you first isolate the tangent function, but then you must continue to find the inverse tangent to solve for $\theta$:

$x^2 - 3x + 2 = 0$
$\tan^2 \theta - 3 \tan \theta + 2 = 0$
$(x - 2)(x - 1) = 0$
$(\tan \theta - 2)(\tan \theta - 1) = 0$
$x - 2 = 0; x - 1 = 0$
$\tan \theta = 2; \tan \theta = 1$
$x = 2; x = 1$
$\theta \approx 63° + 180° \cdot n;$
$\theta = 45° + 180° \cdot n$

**43.** Answers may vary. Sample: Use the Pythagorean Theorem, $c^2 = a^2 + b^2$. Check students' work.

**44.**    $\sin^2 \theta - \sin \theta - 6 = 0$
$(\sin \theta - 3)(\sin \theta + 2) = 0$
       $\sin \theta = 3; \sin \theta = -2$
There is no solution because the zeros of the eq. are 3 and −2, but the range of sine is between 1 and −1.

**45.** 76 in.

## Pull It All Together    p. 950

**3.** First, use the Law of Cosines to write an expression to represent the length of one side of the regular $n$-gon.

$$\left( \sqrt{r^2 + r^2 - 2r^2 \cos\left(\frac{2\pi}{n}\right)} \right)$$

Second, write an expression for the perimeter of the regular $n$-gon using your expression from the first step. Remember that in a unit circle $r = 1$ and the $n$-gon has $n$ sides.

$$\left( \text{perimeter} = \sqrt{2 - 2 \cos\left(\frac{2\pi}{n}\right)} \right)$$

Third, enter your expression from Step 2 into a graphing calculator and check the table of values beginning with $n = 3$. Scrolling down the table shows that the value of the expression converges to $2\pi$ fairly quickly (the answer to part (h)).

**4.** $d_1 = r\sqrt{2}; d_2 = 2r; d_3 = r(\csc 15)$

# Index

## A

**absolute value**
  of algebraic expressions, 41, 52
  of complex numbers, 249
  defined, 41
  equations, 41–48
  inequalities, 41–48, 117
  of real numbers, 41
  symbols, 36, 44

**absolute value function(s)**
  defined, 107
  family of, 108, 126
  graphing, 107–113, 126
  piecewise function, 90
  reflection, 125
  simplest form of, 107
  writing, 110

**Absolute Value Parent Function,** 107

**act it out,** 675

*Activities, Games, and Puzzles*
    *worksheets* 10B, 17B, 24B, 32B, 40B,
    48B, 67B, 73B, 80B, 88B, 98B, 106B,
    113B, 120B, 141B, 148B, 155B, 162B,
    165B, 173B, 181B, 201B, 208B, 214B,
    223B, 231B, 239B, 247B, 255B, 264B,
    287B, 295B, 302B, 310B, 317B, 324B,
    330B, 338B, 345B, 366B, 373B, 380B,
    388B, 397B, 404B, 412B, 420B, 441B,
    450B, 458B, 468B, 476B, 483B, 505B,
    514B, 523B, 533B, 541B, 548B, 571B,
    577B, 586B, 593B, 601B, 620B, 629B,
    636B, 644B, 652B, 660B, 680B, 687B,
    693B, 702B, 711B, 717B, 723B, 732B,
    739B, 762B, 771B, 782B, 792B, 800B,
    807B, 826B, 834B, 842B, 850B, 859B,
    866B, 874B, 882B, 902B, 910B, 918B,
    926B, 934B, 942B

**Activity**
  Describing Data, 724
  Dynamic. *See* Dynamic Activities
  Graphing Inverses, 413
  Graphs in Three Dimensions, 164–165
  Linear Programming, 163
  Measuring Radians, 835
  Probability Distributions, 694–695
  Quadratic Inequalities, 256–257
  Systems with Rational Equations, 549
  Using Logarithms for Exponential Models,
    477
  Writing Equations From Roots, 232

**addition.** *See also* summation
  of complex numbers, 250
  of function, 398
  inverse operation to, 27
  of matrices, 756–762, 794, 810
  properties of, 759
  of radical expressions, 374–380
  of rational expressions, 534, 535,
    556
  of vectors, 803

*Additional Problems* 6, 13, 20, 28, 35, 43,
    62, 70, 76, 83, 94, 101, 109, 116, 136,
    144, 151, 159, 168, 176, 196, 204, 211,
    218, 228, 235, 242, 250, 260, 282,
    290, 298, 305, 314,    328, 333, 340,
    363, 369, 376, 383, 393, 400, 407,
    416, 436, 444, 453, 464, 471, 480,
    500, 509, 517, 529, 536, 544, 566,
    574, 582, 589, 597, 616, 624, 632,
    647, 655, 676, 683, 690, 698, 706,
    714, 720, 727, 735, 759, 766, 776,
    786, 795, 803, 822, 830, 838, 845,
    855, 862, 869, 877, 898, 905, 913,
    922, 930, 937, 945

**Addition Property**
  of Equality, 27, 143
  of Inequality, 34

**additive identity,** 13, 14

**additive identity matrix,** 759

**Additive Identity Property,** 759

**additive inverse**
  of complex number, 250
  defined, 14
  of a matrix, 759
  opposites, 14

**Additive Inverse Property,** 759

**additive trigonometric identities,** 935

**agriculture,** 222, 738

**algebraic expressions,** 18–24
  defined, 5
  dividing, 21
  evaluating, 19, 52
  modeling words with, 18–19
  representing patterns using, 5, 51
  simplifying, 21, 52
  subtracting, 21

**The Ambiguous Case,** 927

**amplitude,** 822, 845, 886

**angle(s)**
  acute, 914
  central, 836, 887
  in a circle, 836
  in a coordinate plane, 828
  cosine of, 830, 831, 837, 886
  coterminal, 829, 830
  identities of, 935–948
  initial side of, 828, 886
  of inverse trigonometric functions, 904
  measuring, 828
  radian measure, 836–842, 887
  sine of, 830, 831, 837, 886
  in standard position, 828, 829, 886
  tangent of, 860, 888
  terminal side of, 828, 886
  of triangles, 920–924, 927, 928–931
  in unit circle, 828–834, 886

**angle difference identities,** 938, 939, 954

**angle sum identities,** 939, 940, 943, 954

**applications**
  academics, 364
  acoustics, 475
  activities, 726
  advertising, 710, 744
  aerodynamics, 643
  aircraft, 544
  airline ticket pricing, 749
  air quality, 160, 246
  air traffic control, 652
  animation, 799
  aquarium, 6
  athletics, 585
  auto maintenance, 748
  automobiles, 45, 66, 213, 513, 538, 547,
    675, 678, 729
  aviation, 30, 806, 914
  awards, 678
  bacteria growth, 484
  baking, 245, 448
  banking, 19, 53, 585
  barometric pressure, 485
  basketball, 210, 731
  battery life, 729
  board games, 597
  boat building, 365
  bonus, 588
  break-even point, 147
  bridges, 204, 323
  bus travel, 30
  calendar, 825
  camping, 744
  career, 705
  carpentry, 294·
  car racing, 45
  car rental, 66
  ceramics, 865
  class project, 23
  climate, 47
  clubs, 511
  coins, 223
  collecting, 9
  college enrollment, 153
  comets, 651
  communications, 212, 600, 741
  competition, 228
  construction, 39, 466, 512, 530, 865, 915
  consumer issues, 679
  cooking, 47, 118, 161, 245, 343, 448
  coordinate geometry, 791
  crafts, 461
  critical thinking, 40
  data analysis, 97, 680
  data collection, 716, 722
  demographics, 136, 440
  depreciation, 461
  digital media, 795
  discounts, 425
  distance, 71, 880
  elections, 723
  electricity, 365, 425, 540, 909
  electronics, 419
  endangered species, 438
  education, 696, 699
  energy, 716, 721
  energy conservation, 907, 908
  entertainment, 30, 35, 116, 148, 570, 722
  environment, 160, 246, 438, 440, 628,
    907, 908
  estimation, 849
  exercise, 569
  financial planning, 19, 23, 53, 187, 448,
    461, 491, 576, 579, 599
  firefighter, 229
  fitness, 31, 237, 269, 569, 790
  flight, 544, 652
  food, 16, 95, 180, 592
  food production, 96, 323, 333
  forestry, 925
  fuel economy, 513, 538, 547
  fundraising, 151, 245, 503, 504
  games, 686
  gardening, 271, 317
  gears, 941
  genetics, 731
  geometry, 17, 30, 31, 39, 52, 66, 73, 88,
    154, 173, 180, 213, 222, 238, 246, 294,
    301, 308, 309, 329, 366, 379, 410, 411,

426, 449, 570, 577, 684, 686, 781, 791, 799, 800, 866, 881, 917, 925, 933
golf, 238, 585, 642
grades, 39, 365, 522, 547, 591, 710
grocery, 592
harmony, 540
health, 825
hydraulics, 395
income, 576, 716
indirect measurement, 881, 916, 917, 919
investing/investment, 23, 187, 448, 461, 491, 579
landscaping, 207, 230, 418, 449
languages, 690
lottery, 686
machinery, 635
manufacturing, 96, 172, 199, 440, 532, 728, 739, 741
margin of error, 722
margin of error interval, 722
marketing, 730
market researcher, 698
measurement, 294, 427, 925
media postage, 91
metalwork, 294
money, 19, 23, 53, 146, 187, 448, 461, 491, 576, 579, 585, 588, 599
motor vehicles, 675
movie rentals, 30, 35
musical, 53
nature, 198, 578
navigation, 544, 657, 658, 806, 933
nutrition, 97, 790, 791
optics, 540
optimal height, 386
paint/painting, 180, 503
Pascal's Triangle, 731
pets, 741
picnic, 689
planetary motion, 383
population, 136, 440, 692
postage/postal rates, 91, 213
potential energy, 503
projectile motion, 244
public opinion, 719
quality control, 730
reading, 691
recreation, 127
restaurant, 16
road safety, 213
rocket, 31
rocket science, 916
sailing, 926
sales, 187, 402, 403, 783
sample size, 722
satellite dish, 649, 650
satellites, 372, 482
savings, 19, 53
scheduling, 678
science, 484, 916
security, 679
shopping, 813
sky diving, 61
snacks, 180
solar reflector, 625
sound, 619, 628, 850
sound waves, 823
space, 480, 481, 482, 841
sports, 20, 31, 72, 139, 172, 238, 246, 269, 439, 440, 511, 548, 579, 585, 642, 676, 678, 686, 700, 731, 738, 757, 761, 767, 770, 932
sports arena, 574

statistics, 692, 731
storage, 546
summer job, 23
surveying, 923, 924
swimming, 31
teamwork, 547
technology, 200, 292, 482
television, 212
temperature, 66, 84, 410, 706, 873
temperature cycles, 871
testing, 682, 708
ticket price, 64
tides, 858, 910
time, 47, 833
track and field, 269, 676, 711
traffic signs, 395
transportation, 126, 146, 546, 576, 701, 841
travel, 30, 544, 773
utilities, 93
volume, 343, 395
weather, 148, 388, 485, 701, 709, 730, 738
weather satellite, 839
wind generated power, 342
woodworking, 547

**Approximating a Binomial Distribution,** 740

**arc, intercepted,** 836, 837, 887

**archaeology,** 448, 481

**architecture,** 234, 375, 592, 863

**area**
of circles, 310, 407, 414
Law of Sines and, 920–926
of polygons, 776, 777
of triangles, 776, 920–921

**arithmetic mean,** 574, 604

**arithmetic sequences,** 572–577
defined, 572
formulas for, 572
geometric vs., 583
identifying and generating, 573, 604

**arithmetic series,** 587–593
defined, 587, 605
sum of, 588, 589

**assessment**
Chapter Review, 50–52, 122–126, 183–185, 267–272, 347–352, 422–426, 487–490, 553–556, 603–606, 663–666, 743–748, 809–812, 885–889
Chapter Test, 53, 127, 187, 273, 353, 427, 491, 557, 607, 667, 749, 813, 889, 955
End-of-Course, 956–963
Got It? 4, 5, 6, 12, 13, 14, 18, 19, 20, 21, 27, 28, 29, 30, 34, 35, 36, 37, 42, 43, 44, 45, 61, 62, 63, 64, 69, 70, 75, 76, 77, 82, 83, 84, 85, 93, 94, 95, 100, 101, 102, 103, 108, 109, 110, 115, 116, 117, 135, 136, 137, 143, 144, 145, 150, 151, 152, 158, 159, 167, 168, 169, 170, 175, 176, 177, 178, 195, 196, 197, 198, 203, 204, 205, 209, 210, 211, 217, 218, 219, 220, 227, 228, 233, 234, 235, 236, 237, 241, 242, 243, 244, 249, 250, 251, 252, 253, 259, 260, 261, 281, 283, 284, 288, 289, 290, 291, 292, 297, 298, 299, 304, 305, 306, 307, 313, 314, 315, 320, 321, 327, 328, 332, 333, 334, 340, 341, 362, 363, 367, 368, 369, 370, 375, 376, 377, 382, 383, 384, 385, 391, 392, 393, 394, 399, 400, 401, 406, 407, 408, 409, 415, 416, 417, 426, 435, 436, 437, 438, 443,

444, 445, 446, 447, 452, 453, 454, 455, 463, 464, 465, 469, 470, 471, 472, 479, 480, 499, 500, 501, 502, 508, 509, 510, 511, 517, 518, 519, 520, 528, 529, 530, 535, 536, 537, 538, 543, 544, 545, 565, 566, 567, 568, 573, 574, 580, 581, 582, 583, 588, 589, 590, 596, 597, 598, 615, 616, 617, 624, 625, 626, 631, 632, 633, 639, 640, 641, 647, 648, 649, 654, 655, 656, 657, 675, 676, 677, 681, 682, 683, 684, 688, 689, 690, 697, 698, 699, 705, 707, 714, 719, 720, 727, 728, 734, 735, 736, 757, 758, 759, 765, 766, 767, 768, 775, 776, 777, 778, 779, 785, 786, 787, 789, 794, 795, 797, 802, 803, 804, 821, 822, 823, 829, 830, 831, 837, 838, 839, 844, 845, 846, 847, 854, 855, 856, 861, 863, 868, 869, 870, 871, 876, 877, 878, 879, 897, 898, 899, 905, 906, 907, 912, 913, 914, 915, 921, 922, 923, 929, 930, 931, 936, 937, 939, 944, 945, 946
Mid-Chapter Quiz, 25, 89, 156, 224, 311, 389, 461, 526, 579, 637, 703, 783, 851, 919
Mixed Review, 10, 17, 24, 32, 40, 44, 67, 73, 80, 88, 98, 106, 113, 120, 141, 148, 155, 162, 165, 173, 181, 201, 208, 214, 223, 231, 239, 247, 255, 264, 287, 295, 302, 310, 317, 324, 330, 338, 345, 366, 373, 380, 388, 397, 404, 412, 420, 441, 450, 458, 468, 476, 483, 505, 514, 523, 533, 541, 548, 571, 577, 586, 593, 601, 620, 629, 636, 644, 652, 660, 680, 687, 693, 702, 711, 717, 723, 732, 739, 762, 771, 782, 792, 800, 807, 826, 834, 842, 850, 859, 866, 874, 882, 902, 910, 926, 934, 942, 949
Open-Ended exercises, 8, 9, 24, 40, 47, 72, 105, 112, 126, 127, 138, 140, 147, 154, 160, 173, 179, 181, 187, 200, 213, 222, 224, 230, 254, 262, 273, 286, 294, 302, 311, 317, 323, 365, 372, 379, 385, 387, 396, 403, 411, 427, 440, 449, 457, 475, 491, 505, 512, 513, 525, 526, 531, 539, 540, 545, 548, 557, 570, 578, 579, 585, 592, 600, 607, 619, 635, 643, 651, 660, 667, 678, 691, 700, 701, 703, 730, 731, 749, 783, 791, 813, 825, 832, 833, 834, 841, 847, 849, 851, 856, 864, 873, 890, 901, 909, 919, 925, 933, 948, 955
Quick Review, 51–52, 121–126, 182–185, 266–272, 346–352, 421–426, 486–490, 552–556, 602–606, 662–666, 744–748, 810–812, 886–889, 952–954
Standardized Test Prep, 10, 17, 24, 32, 40, 48, 54–56, 67, 73, 80, 88, 98, 106, 113, 120, 127–129, 141, 148, 155, 162, 165, 173, 181, 188–190, 201, 208, 214, 223, 231, 239, 247, 255, 264, 274–276, 287, 295, 302, 310, 317, 324, 330, 338, 345, 354–356, 366, 373, 380, 388, 397, 404, 412, 420, 428–430, 441, 450, 458, 468, 476, 483, 492–494, 505, 514, 523, 533, 541, 548, 558–560, 571, 577, 586, 593, 601, 608–610, 620, 629, 636, 644, 652, 660, 668–670, 680, 693, 702, 711, 717, 723, 732, 739, 750, 762, 771, 782, 792, 800, 807, 814, 826, 834, 842, 850, 859, 866, 874, 882, 891, 902, 910, 918, 926, 934, 942, 949

*Assignment Guides*
chapter Pacing and Assignment Guides 3C, 59C, 133C, 193C, 279C, 359C,

433C, 496C, 563C, 613C, 673C, 755C, 819C, 895C

lesson Assignment Guides 8, 16, 23, 31, 38, 46, 65, 72, 79, 87, 97, 104, 112, 119, 139, 146, 153, 161, 172, 180, 199, 207, 213, 222, 230, 238, 245, 254, 262, 286, 293, 301, 309, 316, 323, 329, 336, 343, 365, 371, 379, 386, 395, 402, 410, 419, 440, 448, 457, 466, 474, 481, 504, 513, 522, 531, 540, 546, 569, 576, 584, 592, 599, 635, 643, 651, 659, 679, 692, 701, 709, 716, 722, 730, 738, 761, 770, 780, 790, 799, 806, 824, 833, 840, 848, 857, 864, 873, 880, 901, 907, 916, 925, 932, 941, 948

**Associative Property**
of Addition, 759
of Multiplication, 765, 768
of Real Numbers, 14, 51

**astronomy,** 467, 636, 644, 849

**asymptotes**
defined, 435, 487
oblique, 524–525
of rational functions, 517–518

**average.** *See* mean

**axis**
of ellipse, 639, 665
of hyperbola, 645, 646
imaginary, 249, 250
major, 639, 665
minor, 639, 665
real, 249, 250
of symmetry, 107, 194, 622, 646
of systems of inequalities, 194
transverse, 645
*x* and *y*, 101, 102, 164, 195, 197, 226, 256, 435

# B

**base e, exponential function,** 442–444, 446

**base ten logarithms,** 453, 463

**Basic Identities,** 896

**best fit line,** 94, 95, 125

**bias,** 743, 747

**Big Ideas,** 3, 59, 133, 193, 279, 359, 433, 497, 563, 613, 673, 755, 819, 895
Connecting, 50, 122, 183, 267, 347, 422, 487, 553, 603, 663, 743, 809, 885, 951
coordinate geometry, 662, 663
data collection and analysis, 743
data representation, 742, 808, 809
equations, 182
equivalence, 121, 122, 133, 183, 266, 267, 346, 347, 422, 487, 552, 553, 602, 603, 662, 663, 950, 951
functions, 122, 133, 182, 183, 266, 267, 346, 347, 422, 486, 487, 552, 553, 884, 950, 951
geometry, 950, 951
modeling, 121, 122, 421, 486, 487, 602, 603, 662, 663, 808, 809, 884, 885
probability, 742, 743
properties, 49, 50, 346
proportionality, 552, 553
Pull It All Together, 49, 121, 182, 266, 346, 421, 486, 552, 602, 662, 742, 808, 884, 950
related expressions, functions, and equations, 346
solving equations, 266, 267, 347, 422

solving equations and inequalities, 49, 50, 133, 182, 183, 421
transformations, 808, 809
variable, 49, 50, 346, 602, 603

*Big Ideas* 2, 3A, 50, 58, 59A, 122, 132, 133A, 183, 192, 193A, 267, 278, 279A, 347, 358, 359A, 422, 432, 433A, 487, 495, 496A, 553, 562, 563A, 603, 612, 613A, 663, 672, 673A, 674, 681, 688, 696, 704, 712, 718, 725, 733, 743, 754, 755A, 756, 764, 774, 793, 801, 809, 818, 819A, 820, 828, 836, 860, 867, 875, 884, 894, 895A, 896, 911, 920, 928, 943, 951

**bimodal, defined,** 704

**binomial(s)**
defined, 281
distributions, 725–732, 740, 741
expanding, 326–330, 727–728
experiment, 725, 728, 747
multiplying, 376
probability, 726, 728
radical expressions, 374–380, 424

**Binomial Theorem,** 326–330, 351, 727, 728, 747

**biology,** 83, 84, 135, 482, 737, 858

**botany,** 448

**boundary line,** 107, 114, 115, 126

**box-and-whisker plots,** 707, 746

**branches**
defined, 508
of hyperbola, 616, 646, 649
of reciprocal function graph, 508, 554

**business,** 159, 170, 180, 245, 263, 522, 769

# C

**CALC feature,** 163, 202, 227

**calculator.** *See also* graphing calculator
Change of Base Formula, 464
degree mode, 912
EDIT option, 763
exercises, 96, 180
inverses of trigonometric functions, 905
linear regression modeling, 136
linear systems, 178
log key, 464
matrix equation, 785
matrix feature, 763
quadratic equations, 227
reciprocal trigonometric functions, 877
right-triangle trigonometry, 912
RREF function, 177, 178
standard deviation using, 713
STAT CALC feature, 713
STAT EDIT feature, 713
TABLE feature, 227

*The Celebrated Jumping Frog of Calaveras County* (Twain), 228

**center**
of a circle, 630, 633, 665
of an ellipse, 639
of hyperbola, 646, 666
of rotation, 796

**central angle,** 836, 887

**central tendency, measures of,** 704, 705, 746

**Challenge exercises,** 9–10, 17, 24, 32, 40, 48, 66–67, 71, 73, 80, 88, 98, 106, 112, 120, 140, 148, 154, 162, 173, 181, 200–201, 207, 214, 223–224, 230–231, 239, 247, 255, 256, 263–264, 287, 296, 302, 310, 317, 324, 330, 337–338, 345, 366, 372, 380, 397, 404, 412, 420, 440, 449, 458, 467, 475–476, 482–483, 505, 513, 523–524, 532, 540–541, 546–548, 570–571, 576, 585, 592–593, 601, 619, 629, 636, 644, 651–652, 660, 680, 687, 693, 701, 710–711, 717, 723, 731, 739, 762, 771, 782, 791, 800, 806–807, 825, 834, 842, 849–850, 858, 866, 874, 882, 901, 909–910, 917–918, 926, 933–934, 942, 948

**Change of Base Formula,** 464

**Chapter Review.** *See* assessment, Chapter Review

**Chapter Test.** *See* assessment, Chapter Test

**check for reasonableness,** 236, 624, 777

**check your answers,** 608

**chemistry,** 39, 67, 147, 379, 457, 504

**circle,** 630–636
angles in, 836, 887
area of, 310, 407, 414
center of, 630, 633, 665
circumference of, 15, 17, 831
conic sections, 614
defined, 630, 665
equations of, 630, 631–632, 665
graphing, 615, 632, 633
intercepted arc, 836, 837, 887
Moiré pattern, 617
radius of, 414, 633, 665
transformations, 632
translations, 631

**circumference,** 831

**classification of events,** 688

*Close* 7, 15, 22, 30, 37, 45, 64, 71, 78, 86, 96, 103, 111, 118, 145, 152, 160, 171, 179, 198, 206, 212, 221, 229, 237, 244, 253, 261, 285, 293, 300, 308, 315, 322, 328, 335, 342, 364, 370, 378, 385, 394, 401, 409, 418, 439, 447, 456, 465, 473, 480, 503, 512, 521, 530, 539, 545, 568, 575, 583, 591, 598, 627, 634, 642, 650, 658, 678, 685, 691, 700, 708, 715, 721, 729, 737, 759, 769, 779, 789, 798, 805, 823, 832, 839, 847, 856, 863, 872, 879, 900, 907, 915, 931, 940, 947

**Closure Property,** 54
of Addition, 759
of Matrix Multiplication, 768
of Real Numbers, 14
of Scalar Multiplication, 765

**coefficient,** 20, 94

**coefficient matrix,** 175, 786, 811

**cofunction identities,** 936, 937, 954

**combinations,** 674–680
defined, 676, 696
finding the number in *n* items, 676, 677
importance of order in, 677
numbers of, 676

**combinatorics,** 683

**combined**
transformations, 103
translations, 109, 509
variation, 500, 501, 502

**common**
   difference, 572, 589, 604
   factors, 218
   logarithm, 453, 489
   ratio, 580, 605

*Common Errors. See* **Math Background,**
   for chapters

**communication.** *See* Reasoning; Writing

**Commutative Property**
   of Addition, 759
   of Real Numbers, 14, 51

*Companion* 10A, 17A, 24A, 32A, 40A,
   48A, 67A, 73A, 80A, 88A, 98A, 106A,
   113A, 120A, 141A, 148A, 155A,
   162A, 165A, 173A, 181A, 201A,
   208A, 214A, 223A, 231A, 239A,
   247A, 255A, 264A, 287A, 295A,
   302A, 310A, 317A, 324A, 330A,
   338A, 345A, 366A, 373A, 380A,
   388A, 397A, 404A, 412A, 420A,
   441A, 450A, 458A, 468A, 476A,
   483A, 505A, 514A, 523A, 533A,
   541A, 548A, 571A, 577A, 586A,
   593A, 601A, 620A, 629A, 636A,
   644A, 652A, 660A, 680A, 687A,
   693A, 702A, 711A, 717A, 723A,
   732A, 739A, 762A, 771A, 782A,
   792A, 800A, 807A, 826A, 834A,
   842A, 850A, 859A, 866A, 874A,
   882A, 902A, 910A, 918A, 924, 926A,
   934A, 942A

**Compare and Contrast exercises,** 7, 15, 22,
   37, 45, 96, 103, 111, 118, 145, 152,
   160, 198, 206, 212, 221, 229, 261, 329,
   342, 378, 394, 456, 461, 503, 557, 583,
   598, 617, 650, 700, 715, 724, 737, 879,
   881

**completing the square**
   defined, 235
   solving equations by, 233–239, 240,
   271

**complex conjugates,** 251, 314

**complex fractions**
   defined, 536
   simplifying, 537

**complex number(s),** 249–256
   absolute value of, 249
   adding, 250
   additive inverse of, 250
   conjugates, 251, 314
   defined, 249, 272
   dividing, 251
   factoring polynomials using, 319–322
   identifying, 249
   multiplying, 251
   operations with, 250
   powers of, 265
   simplifying, 249
   simplifying quotients of, 251
   solutions to quadratic equations,
   248–255
   subsets of, 248
   subtracting, 250
   writing using imaginary numbers,272

**complex number plane,** 249, 250, 272

**composition**
   of functions, 399, 400–401
   of inverse functions, 408, 409

**compound interest,** 446, 488

**compression**
   absolute value functions, 108, 109
   defined, 102, 125

exponential functions, 434, 444
logarithmic functions, 455
quadratic functions, 195

**Concept Byte**
   The Ambiguous Case, 927
   Approximating a Binomial Distribution, 740
   Describing Data, 724
   Exponential and Logarithmic Inequalities,
   484–485
   The Fibonacci Sequence, 578
   Fitting Curves to Data, 459–460
   Geometry and Infinite Series, 594
   Graphing Conic Sections, 621
   Graphing Inverses, 413
   Graphing Rational Functions, 506
   Graphing Trigonometric Functions,
   852
   Graphs in Three Dimensions,
   164–165
   Identifying Quadratic Data, 215
   Linear Programming, 163
   Measuring Radians, 835
   Networks, 772–773
   Oblique Asymptotes, 524–525
   Pascal's Triangle, 325
   Piecewise Function, 90–91
   Powers of Complex Numbers, 265
   Probability Distributions, 694–695
   Properties of Exponents, 360
   Quadratic Inequalities, 256–257
   Rational Inequalities, 550–551
   Solving Polynomial Inequalities, 318
   Special Right Triangles, 827
   Systems with Rational Equations,
   549
   Using Logarithms for Exponential Models,
   477
   Working with Matrices, 763
   Writing Equations From Roots, 232

**conditional probability,** 696–702
   defined, 696
   finding using tables, 696–697
   finding using tree diagrams, 699
   formula for, 697, 698, 745
   in statistics, 697

**conic sections,** 614–620
   circle, 614, 630–636
   defined, 614, 664
   ellipse, 638–644
   family of, 614
   graphing, 616, 621
   hyperbola, 614, 645–652
   identifying, 616
   modeling with, 617, 657
   Moiré pattern, 617
   parabola, 614, 622–629
   translations, 653–660, 666
   types of, 664

**conjecture,** 295, 317, 420, 578, 594, 651,
   882

**conjugate axis,** 640, 646

**Conjugate Root Theorem,** 314, 350

**conjugates**
   complex, 251, 314
   constructing polynomials using, 314
   defined, 377
   multiplying, 377
   radical, 377

**Connecting Big Ideas,** 50, 122, 183, 267,
   347, 422, 487, 553, 603, 663, 743, 809,
   885, 951

**conservation,** 71

**consistent system,** 127, 137, 184

**constant,** 5
   matrix, 785, 811
   ratio, 74
   term, 20

**constant of proportionality,** 341

**constant of variation,** 68, 554

**constraint(s),** 157, 185

**continuous function,** 516

**continuously compounded interest,** 446,
   488

**continuous probability distribution,** 733,
   748

**controlled experiment,** 720

**convenience sample,** 718

**convergence of a series,** 598, 606

**Coordinate Geometry, as Big Idea,** 662,
   663

**coordinate plane**
   angles in, 828
   boundary line, 114, 126
   movement in, 74
   points on, 164
   reflection matrices for, 796
   rotation matrices for, 796

**coordinate space,** 164

**coordinate system**
   three-dimensional, 164–165
   two-dimensional, 164

**correlation,** 92, 125

**correlation coefficient,** 94

**cosecant,** 879

**cosecant function,** 875, 889

**cosine**
   of an angle, 830, 831, 837, 886
   curve, 936
   equation, 856–857

**cosine function,** 853–859
   families of, 869
   graphing, 853–855
   modeling with a, 855
   properties of, 854, 887
   translations, 867–874, 888, 936

**cotangent**
   curve, 936
   function, 875, 889
   identity, 896, 952

**coterminal angles,** 829, 830

**counting, fundamental principle of,** 674, 675

**co-vertices of ellipse,** 639, 665

**cricket chirps per minute,** 84

**cube root function,** 417

**cubes, sum or difference of,** 297

**cubic functions,** 283–284, 339–340

**cubic polynomial,** 281, 331

**CUBICREG feature,** 331, 332, 334

**cumulative**
   frequency, 695
   probability, 695

**curves**
   conic sections. *See* conic sections
   cosine, 936
   cotangent, 936
   fitting to data, 459–460
   sine, 844, 887, 936
   standard normal, 740

tangent, 936

**cycles**
identifying, 820
of periodic functions, 820–821
tangent function, 861

**cylinder,** 831

# D

**data, describing,** 722

**data analysis,** 704–711
binomial distributions, 725–732, 740, 741
binomial experiment, 725, 728, 747
box-and-whisker plots, 707, 746
exercises, 761
interquartile range, 706
mean, 704, 746
measures of central tendency, 704, 712, 746
measures of variation, 712, 746
median, 704, 746
mode, 704, 746
normal distribution, 733–739, 740, 748
outliers, 705, 746
percentiles, 708
probability distributions, 694, 728, 733, 748
quartile, 706, 746
random sample, 718, 747
range, 706, 746
sample, 718–723, 743, 747
standard deviation, 704, 712–717
variance, 712, 713, 746
z-score, 740

**data collection and analysis, as Big Idea,** 743

**data modeling,** 209–213, 269, 331–334, 352

**data representation, as Big Idea,** 742, 808, 809

**data sets**
bimodal, 705
comparing, 706
range of, 706
of scatter plots, 92, 93, 125

**decay factor,** 436, 488

**decoding matrix,** 779

**degrees**
converting to and from radians, 836, 837
of polynomials, 280–284

**ΔTbl feature,** 470

**demography,** 474

**denominator**
least common (LCD), 535, 537
rationalizing the, 369, 370, 377, 423

**dependent**
events, 688, 698, 745
system, 137, 184
variable, 63

**Descartes' Rule of Signs,** 315, 350

**Describing Data,** 724

**design,** 863

**determinants,** 774–782
defined, 775
of matrices, 776, 811

**diagrams**
drawing and using for problem solving, 39, 53, 54, 55, 56, 60, 62, 65, 238, 294, 302, 316, 355, 375, 378, 379, 395, 421, 449, 453, 492, 532, 570, 594, 617, 628,

629, 631, 657, 806, 833, 913, 925, 930, 932
mapping, 60
tree, 699, 726

**difference**
common, 572, 589, 604
of cubes, factoring, 297
opposite of a, 21
of squares, factoring, 220, 297
using to determine degree, 284

*Differentiated Remediation* 10A–B, 17A–B, 24A–B, 32A–B, 40A–B, 48A–B, 67A–B, 73A–B, 80A–B, 88A–B, 98A–B, 106A–B, 113A–B, 120A–B, 141A–B, 148A–B, 155A–B, 162A–B, 165A–B, 173A–B, 181A–B, 201A–B, 208A–B, 214A–B, 223A–B, 231A–B, 239A–B, 247A–B, 255A–B, 264A–B, 287A–B, 295A–B, 302A–B, 310A–B, 317A–B, 324A–B, 330A–B, 338A–B, 345A–B, 366A–B, 373A–B, 380A–B, 388A–B, 397A–B, 404A–B, 412A–B, 420A–B, 441A–B, 450A–B, 458A–B, 468A–B, 476A–B, 483A–B, 505A–B, 514A–B, 523A–B, 533A–B, 541A–B, 548A–B, 571A–B, 577A–B, 586A–B, 593A–B, 601A–B, 620A–B, 629A–B, 636A–B, 644A–B, 652A–B, 660A–B, 680A–B, 687A–B, 693A–B, 702A–B, 711A–B, 717A–B, 723A–B, 732A–B, 739A–B, 762A–B, 771A–B, 782A–B, 792A–B, 800A–B, 807A–B, 826A–B, 834A–B, 842A–B, 850A–B, 859A–B, 866A–B, 874A–B, 882A–B, 902A–B, 910A–B, 918A–B, 926A–B, 934A–B, 942A–B

*Digital Resources. See* **PowerAlgebra.com**

**dilation,** 793, 794, 795, 812

**dimensional analysis,** 837

**dimensions, determining,** 234

**directrix of parabola,** 622, 664

**direct variation,** 68–73, 123, 498–499

**discontinuity**
non-removable, 516
point of, 516–517, 555
removable, 516

**discontinuous function,** 516

**discrete**
function, 437
probability distribution, 733, 748

**discriminant,** 242, 243, 244, 271

**distribution**
binomial, 725–732, 740, 741
continuous probability, 733, 748
discrete probability, 733, 748
normal, 733–739, 740, 748
probability, 694
skewed, 734
uniform, 694

**Distributive Property**
of Matrix Multiplication, 768
of Real Numbers, 14, 51
of Scalar Multiplication, 765
for Subtraction, 21

**divergence of a series,** 598, 606

**division**
of algebraic expressions, 21
of complex numbers, 251
definition of, 21
of functions, 398, 399
inverse operation to, 27
of logarithms, 462

of polynomials, 302–310, 349
of radical expressions, 367–373, 423
of rational expressions, 529
of square roots, 225
synthetic, 303, 306–307, 349

**Division Property**
of Equality, 27
of Inequality, 34
of Square Roots, 225

**domain**
extrapolating, 334
of functions, 62, 398, 399, 408, 414, 425, 434, 435, 515, 516
predicting, 334
of rational expressions, 527
of relations, 61, 62, 123
of validity, 896, 897

**dot product,** 804, 812

**double-angle identities,** 943–949, 954

**drawing**
a diagram for problem solving, 806, 833, 913, 925, 930, 932
a graph for problem solving, 36, 849, 854, 856, 857, 861, 865, 870, 873
sketch angles in standard position, 829
sketch sine curves, 846
sketch solutions in a plane, 164, 184

**DrawInv feature,** 413

**Dynamic Activities**
Absolute Value, 107
Box-and-Whisker Plots, 705
Circles, 630
Cosine Function, 853
Dilations, 793
Ellipse, 639
Factored-form, 226
Geometric Probability, 682
Growth/Decay, 435
Hyperbola, 645
Independent and Dependent Events, 689
Inequality Systems, 149
Linear Factors, 289
Linear Programming, 158
Log Functions, 451, 478
Matrix Addition, 756
Parabolas, 622
Probability Binomial, 725
Quadratic Functions, 203
Radical Functions, 415
Rational Functions, 515
Real Number Line, 11
Roots, 240
Sequences, 572
Simplifying, 361
Sine Function, 843
Special Solutions, 143
Sum and Difference Identities for Sine and Cosine, 935
Synthetic Division, 303
Systems of Linear Equations, 135
Tangent Function, 860
Translation, 99, 507
Trigonometric Functions, 867
Trigonometric Identities, 896
Variation, 499
Vertex Form, 194

# E

*e*
base of exponential function, 442–444, 446
natural logarithmic function, 478

Index

**earthquakes,** 456, 474, 543

**earth science,** 392, 628

**eccentricity,** 643

**economics,** 140, 206, 402

**EDIT option,** 763

**elimination,** 144, 148, 166–173, 186

**ellipse,** 638–644
  center of, 639
  conic sections, 614
  co-vertices of, 639, 665
  defined, 638, 665
  eccentricity of, 643
  endpoints of, 639, 665
  equation of, 639–640, 653–654
  foci of, 638, 640–641, 665
  graphing, 615
  horizontal, 639, 653–654
  major and minor axis, 639, 665
  reflection property, 640
  translations, 653–654
  vertical, 639, 653–654
  vertices of, 639, 665

**ellipsoid,** 641

**encoding matrix,** 779

**end behavior,** 282–283

**endpoints,** 91, 639, 665

*English Language Learner (ELL) Support*
  10A, 17A, 24A, 32A, 40A, 44, 48A,
  67A, 73A, 80A, 88A, 98A, 106A,
  113A, 120A, 141A, 148A, 155A,
  162A, 165A, 170, 173A, 178, 181A,
  195, 201A, 203, 208A, 214A, 217,
  223A, 231A, 235, 239A, 243, 247A,
  255A, 264A, 283, 287A, 295A, 302A,
  310A, 317A, 324A, 330A, 334, 338A,
  345A, 366A, 373A, 380A, 388A,
  397A, 404A, 412A, 420A, 441A,
  450A, 458A, 468A, 476A, 483A,
  505A, 514A, 523A, 533A, 541A,
  548A, 571A, 577A, 586A, 593A,
  601A, 620A, 629A, 636A, 644A,
  652A, 660A, 680A, 687A, 693A,
  702A, 704, 711A, 713, 714, 717A,
  723A, 726, 728, 732A, 739A, 762A,
  771A, 782A, 792A, 795, 800A, 807A,
  826A, 834A, 842A, 850A, 859A,
  866A, 874A, 882A, 902A, 910A,
  918A, 926A, 934A, 942A

  Assess Understanding 98A, 141A,
    155A, 330A, 412A, 514A, 571A,
    723A, 739A, 792A, 826A, 874A,
    918A, 926A, 942A

  Connect to Prior Knowledge 48A,
    148A, 181A, 255A, 388A, 404A,
    458A, 468A, 483A, 800A, 842A,
    910A, 918A, 934A

  Focus on Communication 80A, 148A,
    162A, 173A, 338A, 476A, 533A,
    702A, 739A, 762A, 902A

  Focus on Language 98A, 120A, 162A,
    208A, 214A, 223A, 295A, 345A,
    373A, 397A, 420A, 505A, 523A,
    541A, 577A, 586A, 593A, 620A,
    629A, 636A, 644A, 652A, 679A,
    693A, 717A, 834A

  Guided Instruction 4, 11, 18, 26, 33, 41,
    60, 68, 74, 81, 90–91, 92, 99, 107,
    114, 134, 142, 149, 157, 163, 164–165,
    166, 174, 194, 202, 209, 215, 216,
    226, 232, 234, 241, 249, 256–257,
    259, 265, 280, 288, 296, 303, 312,
    318, 319, 325, 326, 331, 339, 360,

    361, 367, 374, 381, 390, 398, 405,
    413, 414, 434, 442, 451, 459–460,
    462, 469, 477, 478, 484–485, 498,
    506, 507, 515, 524–525, 527, 534,
    542, 549, 550–551, 564, 572, 578,
    580, 587, 594, 595, 614, 621, 622,
    630, 638, 645, 653, 663, 674, 681,
    688, 696, 704, 712, 718, 725, 733,
    756, 764, 774, 793, 801, 820, 828,
    836, 860, 867, 875, 896, 911, 920,
    928, 943

  Use Graphic Organizers 10A, 16A, 40A,
    67A, 88A, 106A, 155A, 231A, 302A,
    324A, 380A, 441A, 450A, 586A,
    601A, 711A, 771A, 782A, 859A,
    866A, 949A

  Use Manipulatives 10A, 201A, 239A,
    247A, 264A, 366A, 687A, 850A, 882A

  Use Multiple Representation 141A

  Use Role Playing 24A, 32A, 113A,
    287A, 317A, 420A, 548A, 732A, 807A

  *Enrichment worksheets* 10B, 17B, 24B,
    32B, 40B, 48B, 67B, 73B, 80B, 88B,
    98B, 106B, 113B, 120B, 141B, 148B,
    155B, 162B, 165B, 173B, 181B, 201B,
    208B, 214B, 223B, 231B, 239B, 247B,
    255B, 264B, 287B, 295B, 302B, 310B,
    317B, 324B, 330B, 338B, 345B, 366B,
    373B, 380B, 388B, 397B, 404B, 412B,
    420B, 441B, 450B, 458B, 468B, 476B,
    483B, 505B, 514B, 523B, 533B, 541B,
    548B, 571B, 577B, 586B, 593B, 601B,
    620B, 629B, 636B, 644B, 652B, 660B,
    680B, 687B, 693B, 702B, 711B, 717B,
    723B, 732B, 739B, 762B, 771B, 782B,
    792B, 800B, 807B, 826B, 834B, 842B,
    850B, 859B, 866B, 874B, 882B, 902B,
    910B, 918B, 926B, 934B, 942B

**equality, properties of,** 26–27, 34, 143, 938

**equally likely sample space,** 682, 744

**equal matrices,** 759, 810

**equation(s).** *See also* function(s)
  absolute value, 41–48
  as Big Idea, 182
  of a circle, 630, 631–632
  cosine, 856–857
  defined, 26
  direct variation, 68–73
  of ellipse, 639–640, 653–654
  exponential. *See* exponential equations
  of hyperbola, 647, 648, 655–656
  as an identity, 28, 29, 52
  for the inverse, 406
  of a line. *See* linear equations
  literal, 29
  logarithmic, 469–476
  matrix, 757, 784–785, 810
  with no solution, 28, 29, 52
  of parabola, 209, 623–624, 627
  parametric, 413
  polynomial. *See* polynomial equations
  quadratic. *See* quadratic equations
  radical, 390–397, 416, 425
  rational, 542–548, 549, 556
  solving, as Big Idea, 266, 267, 347,
    422
  solving by completing the square, 233–
    239, 240, 271
  solving by finding square roots, 233, 235,
    271
  solving multi-step, 27
  solving one-step, 27
  solving using inverses, 903–910
  solving using properties, 26–27, 52

  solving with logarithmic properties, 472
  square root, 390–397, 425
  systems of. *See* systems of equations
  of transformations, 510
  of a trend line, 94
  trigonometric, 871, 903–910, 937, 952
  writing from roots, 232
  writing in slope-intercept form, 74–80, 83,
    124
  writing to describe a translation, 871

**Equations and Inequalities, solving as Big
  Idea,** 49, 50, 133, 182, 183, 421, 422

**Equivalence, as Big Idea,** 121, 122, 133,
  183, 266, 267, 346, 347, 422, 487, 552,
  553, 602, 603, 662, 663, 950, 951

**equivalent**
  compound inequalities, 36
  equations, 142, 144, 168
  expressions, 381

**Error Analysis exercises,** 7, 16, 22, 24, 30,
  31, 37, 39, 47, 64, 72, 78, 79, 86, 87,
  97, 105, 112, 140, 147, 152, 161, 171,
  180, 200, 206, 207, 212, 222, 230, 237,
  244, 253, 263, 285, 293, 301, 309, 315,
  316, 323, 329, 337, 342, 344, 364, 370,
  372, 379, 385, 389, 396, 401, 409, 418,
  439, 448, 457, 461, 466, 473, 480, 482,
  503, 522, 530, 539, 545, 547, 568, 575,
  583, 591, 598, 600, 627, 634, 642, 650,
  651, 658, 691, 703, 708, 710, 716, 729,
  738, 760, 769, 779, 780, 789, 805, 823,
  832, 841, 847, 863, 872, 879, 900, 901,
  907, 915, 924, 931, 940, 942, 947

*Error Intervention* 15, 22, 30, 45, 86, 103,
  118, 138, 152, 160, 179, 225, 244,
  253, 261, 315, 342, 364, 378, 439,
  452, 473, 480, 503, 530, 539, 545,
  568, 575, 598, 617, 642, 678, 685,
  691, 773, 805, 832, 839, 847, 856,
  872, 947

*Error Prevention* 3, 3A, 14, 19, 21, 27, 34,
  43, 59, 59A, 61, 62, 63, 64, 69, 77, 82,
  83, 85, 90, 91, 101, 110, 115, 117, 133,
  133A, 134, 135, 136, 143, 152, 158,
  163, 175, 176, 193, 193A, 195, 196,
  198, 202, 204, 210, 215, 218, 227,
  232, 234, 236, 241, 242, 243, 250,
  261, 279A, 281, 283, 290, 292, 297,
  298, 300, 305, 312, 313, 314, 320,
  321, 359A, 363, 375, 376, 377, 382,
  383, 385, 394, 400, 408, 416, 417,
  433A, 436, 443, 444, 445, 447, 452,
  455, 479, 496A, 499, 502, 509, 517,
  519, 525, 536, 538, 544, 563A, 573,
  574, 589, 590, 596, 597, 613A, 624,
  640, 653, 673A, 677, 682, 714, 727,
  755A, 757, 773, 778, 786, 789, 797,
  819A, 821, 844, 856, 869, 870, 875,
  877, 895A, 899, 905, 906, 914, 922

**Essential Questions,** 3, 59, 133, 193, 279,
  359, 433, 497, 563, 613, 673, 755, 819,
  894
  answering Essential Questions, 50, 122,
    267, 347, 422, 553, 603, 663, 743, 809,
    950

**estimation using line of best fit,** 94, 95,
  125

**evaluating**
  algebraic expressions, 19, 20, 52
  $e^x$, 446
  logarithmic expressions, 451–458
  sequences, 573, 581
  series, 598

**events**
dependent, 688, 745
independent, 688, 689, 745
multiple, 688
mutually exclusive, 689, 745
theoretical probability of, 683

**expanding**
binomial(s), 326–330, 727–728
logarithms, 463

**experimental probability,** 681–682, 744

**experiments**
binomial, 725, 728, 747
controlled, 719, 720

**Explicit Formulas,** 565, 567, 604, 605

**exponential**
growth and decay, 434–441, 488
inequalities, 484–485
models, 434–441, 445, 477, 488

**exponential equation(s)**
base $e$, 446
common base, 469
defined, 469, 490
different base, 470
exponential growth, 488
general form of, 438
modeling, 471
solving by graphing, 470
solving using logarithms, 479
solving using tables, 470
writing, 452

**exponential function(s)**
base $e$, 442–444, 446
defined, 434
discrete, 437
families of, 444
general form of, 488
graphing, 434–435, 437
graphing base $e$, 442–450
inverses of, 454, 489
natural base, 446
properties of, 442–450, 488
transformations, 443–444

**exponents**
properties of, 360, 462
rational, 381–388, 424

**ExpReg feature,** 445, 460

**expression(s)**
algebraic. *See* algebraic expressions
as Big Idea, 346
equivalent, 381
greatest common factor (GCF), 218
logarithmic, 451, 478–479
numerical, 5
quadratic. *See* quadratic expressions
radical. *See* radical expressions
rational. *See* rational expressions
representing patterns using, 6
writing, 20

**Extended Response exercises**
end of chapter problems, 130, 190, 276,
356, 430, 494, 560, 610, 670, 752, 816,
892, 958
end of lesson problems, 40, 120, 141, 214,
223, 239, 295, 310, 330, 366, 412, 441,
548, 577, 629, 732, 826, 910

**Extension**
Exponential and Logarithmic Inequalities,
484–485
The Fibonacci Sequence, 578
Linear and Exponential, 477
Solving Polynomial Inequalities, 318

*Extension* 3, 10B, 16B, 18, 24B, 32B, 40B,
48B, 59, 67B, 69, 73B, 76, 77, 80B,
88B, 98B, 101, 106B, 113B, 115, 120B,
136, 137, 141B, 148B, 149, 150, 155B,
162B, 167, 173B, 175, 178, 181B, 193,
195, 196, 201B, 208B, 214B, 217, 218,
219, 220, 223B, 227, 231B, 233, 239B,
247B, 255B, 260, 264B, 282, 284,
287B, 290, 291, 295B, 302B, 305, 307,
310B, 315, 317B, 324B, 330B, 338B,
345B, 359, 360, 366B, 368, 373B,
380B, 388B, 397B, 404B, 412B, 420B,
433, 436, 437, 438, 441B, 446, 450B,
454, 458B, 463, 468B, 470, 476B, 478,
479, 483B, 497, 501, 505B, 508, 509,
510, 514B, 518, 519, 523B, 524, 529,
533B, 538, 541B, 545, 548B, 563, 565,
566, 571B, 574, 577B, 582, 583, 586B,
589, 590, 593B, 597, 601B, 613, 615,
616, 620B, 623, 629B, 631, 632, 636B,
640, 644B, 648, 652B, 654, 655, 656,
660B, 673, 680B, 682, 687B, 689,
693B, 695, 702B, 706, 707, 711B, 713,
717B, 719, 723B, 727, 732B, 735, 736,
739B, 755, 757, 762B, 765, 766, 771B,
776, 778, 782B, 792B, 796, 800B, 804,
807B, 819, 823, 826B, 834B, 838,
842B, 845, 850B, 855, 859B, 866B,
871, 874B, 877, 878, 882B, 895, 898,
902B, 907, 910B, 912, 914, 918B, 923,
926B, 931, 934B, 939, 942B, 949B

**extraneous solutions,** 42, 43, 393

**extrapolation,** 334

# F

**factor(s)**
common, 218
greatest common (GCF), 218, 297
growth and decay, 435, 436, 488

**factorial notation,** 675

**factoring**
defined, 216
difference of cubes, 297
difference of squares, 220, 297
to find discontinuities, 516–517
the GCF out, 297
by grouping, 297
perfect square trinomials, 219, 220, 234–
235, 297
polynomials, 288–295, 297, 349
quadratic expressions, 216–223, 270
quadratic trinomial, 297
rational expressions, 527
solving polynomial equations by,
296–302
solving quadratic equations by,
218–219, 226–231, 270, 271
sum or difference of cubes, 297

**Factor Theorem,** 290

**Family(ies)**
of absolute value functions, 108,
126
of conic sections, 614
of cosine function, 869
of exponential functions, 444
of functions, 99–106, 125
of logarithmic functions, 455
of radical functions, 415
of reciprocal functions, 507–514,
554
of sine function, 869

**feasible region,** 157, 185

**Fibonacci Sequence,** 578

**finance,** 51, 94, 172, 568, 571

**find needed information,** 128, 274, 558,
608, 668

**finite geometric series,** 595, 596

**finite sequences,** 587

**finite series,** 587, 595, 596

**flips.** *See* reflections

**FLOAT feature,** 568

**flower carpets,** 28

**focus (foci)**
of ellipse, 638, 640–641, 665
of hyperbola, 645, 666
of parabola, 622, 664

**FOIL,** 376

**formulas**
for area, 310, 407, 414, 558, 920
arithmetic sequences, 572, 604
atmospheric pressure, 475, 513
for binomial probability, 726, 728
brightness of stars, 467
for centripetal force, 372
Change of Base, 464
circumference of a circle, 15, 17
for conditional probability, 697, 745
converting between radians and degrees,
836
for density, 372
direct variation function, 68
for distance, 408
earthquake intensity, 453
electric current, 16
error of margin for drilling a hole, 48
for expanding a binomial, 327
experimental probability of an event, 681
explicit, 565, 567, 604, 605
generating mathematical patterns, 564,
565, 567
for geometric sequences, 565, 566, 567
for geometric series, 597, 606
harmonic mean, 540
for height as a function of time, 344
hourly wage, 548
Ideal Gas Law, 504
independent events, 745
interest, 446, 488
inverses of, 408
for kinetic energy, 343, 344
mass energy equivalence, 493
maximum flow of water in a pipe, 395
mean, 704, 746
measuring bacteria populations, 482
median, 704
mode, 704
mutually exclusive events, 689, 745
number of combinations, 676
number of permutations, 676
perimeter of a rectangle, 28
for planetary motion, 383
point-slope form, 81
potential energy, 502
probability of $A$ and $B$, 688, 745
probability of $A$ or $B$, 689, 745
quadratic, 240–248
radioactive to nonradioactive carbon, 387
radius of a circle, 414
radius of a sphere, 365
recursive, 565, 566, 604, 605
resistance, 540
slope, 81, 84
solving for one variable, 142, 184
sound, measuring, 466, 475

standard deviation, 704, 712
sum of arithmetic series, 587, 605
sum of geometric series, 595, 606
surface area, 66, 276, 531
surface area of a cylinder, 53
tapered cylinders, 547
temperature conversions, 29, 410
for time as a function of acceleration, 371
variance, 712
for velocity, 372, 404, 480
for volume, 67, 292, 309, 365, 392, 410, 421, 426, 531
wind chill, 387
wind power, 327

**fractions, complex,** 536, 537

**frequency, cumulative,** 695

**frog-jumping competition,** 228

**function(s).** *See also* equation(s)
absolute value, 90, 107–113, 125, 126
adding, 398, 399
as Big Idea, 122, 133, 182, 183, 266, 267, 346, 347, 422, 486, 487, 552, 553, 884, 950, 951
composition of, 399, 400–401, 408, 409
continuous, 516
cosecant, 875
cosine, 867–874, 887
cotangent, 875
cube root, 417
cubic, 283–284, 339–340
defined, 62
dependent variable in, 63
discontinuous, 516
discrete, 437
dividing, 398, 399
domain of, 62, 398, 399, 408, 414, 425, 434, 435, 515, 516
exponential. *See* exponential functions
family of, 99–106, 125
graphing quadratic, 194–201
graphing trigonometric, 852, 878
greatest integer, 90
identifying, 60–65
independent variables in, 63
input of the, 63
inverse. *See* inverse functions
linear. *See* linear functions
logarithmic. *See* logarithmic functions
maximum and minimum values, 158, 185, 195, 291, 292
monomial, 352
multiplying, 398, 399
natural logarithmic, 478–483
objective, 157, 185
one-to-one, 408
operations with, 398–404, 425
parent. *See* Parent Function
periodic. *See* periodic function
piecewise, 90–91
polynomial. *See* polynomial functions
power, 341
quadratic. *See* quadratic functions
quartic, 341
radical, 414–420
rational. *See* rational functions
reciprocal. *See* reciprocal functions
reciprocal trigonometric, 875–882, 888
rewriting by completing the square, 233–239
secant, 875
simplest form of, 99, 125
sine, 843–850, 867–874, 886
square root, 414–420, 426
step, 90

subtracting, 398, 399
transformations. *See* transformations
translations. *See* translations
trigonometric, 852, 878
vertical-line test, 62–63
zeros of. *See* zero(s)

**function notation,** 62, 63, 407

**function rule,** 63

**Fundamental Counting Principle,** 674, 675

**Fundamental Theorem of Algebra,** 319–324, 351

# G

**Galton box,** 725

**GCF (greatest common factor),** 218, 297

**geography,** 841

**geometric**
mean, 583, 605
probability, 684
series, 595–601, 606
transformations, 793–800, 812

**geometric sequences,** 580–586
analyzing, 581
arithmetic vs., 583
defined, 580
formula for, 565, 566, 567, 605
geometric series, 595–601, 606
identifying, 580–581

**Geometry as Big Idea,** 950, 951

**Geometry exercises,** 17, 30, 31, 39, 52, 66, 73, 88, 154, 173, 180, 213, 222, 238, 246, 294, 301, 308, 309, 329, 366, 379, 410, 411, 426, 449, 570, 577, 684, 686, 781, 791, 799, 800, 866, 881, 917, 925, 933

**Geometry Review**
Special Right Triangles, 827

**Get Ready!**
for chapters, 1, 57, 131, 191, 277, 431, 495, 561, 611, 671, 753, 817, 893
for lessons, 10, 17, 24, 32, 40, 48, 67, 73, 80, 88, 98, 106, 113, 120, 141, 148, 155, 162, 165, 173, 181, 201, 208, 214, 223, 231, 239, 247, 255, 264, 287, 295, 302, 310, 317, 324, 330, 338, 345, 366, 373, 380, 388, 397, 404, 412, 420, 441, 450, 458, 468, 476, 483, 505, 514, 523, 533, 541, 548, 571, 577, 586, 593, 601, 620, 629, 636, 644, 652, 660, 680, 687, 693, 702, 711, 717, 723, 732, 739, 762, 771, 782, 792, 800, 807, 826, 834, 842, 850, 859, 866, 874, 882, 902, 910, 918, 926, 934, 942

**Glossary,** 986

**Got It?** *See* assessment, Got It?

**graph(s)**
of absolute value functions, 107–113
of absolute value inequalities, 117
boundary lines, 107, 114, 115, 126
of circles, 615, 632, 633
complex number plane, 250
of conic sections, 616, 621
of cosine function, 853–855
of cube root function, 417
of cubic functions, 283–284
of direct variation equations, 70
drawing for problem solving, 849, 854, 856, 857, 861, 865, 870, 873
of ellipse, 615

end behavior of, 282–283
of exponential functions, 434–435, 437
of exponential functions with base *e*, 442–450
feasible region, 157, 185
of hyperbola, 616, 647
of inequalities, 33, 35, 114–120, 126
of inverse functions, 413, 508, 904
of linear equations, 77, 83, 84, 124
of linear inequalities, 115, 117, 150–151
line of best fit, 94, 95, 125
of logarithmic functions, 454–455
multiple zeros effect on, 291
numbers on a number line, 13
ordered pairs, 60, 110, 121–122, 123, 164
of parabola, 194, 197, 268
piecewise function, 90–91
points on a coordinate plane, 164
of polynomial functions, 283–284, 291, 339–345
of quadratic functions, 194–201
of quadratic functions in standard form, 202–208
of radical functions, 414–420, 426
of rational functions, 506, 515–523
of real numbers, 11, 13
of reciprocal functions, 507–511, 554
of reciprocal trigonometric functions, 878
of relations, 60–61, 406–407
scatter plot, 92–93, 125
of sine function, 843, 844–846
solving exponential equations using, 470
solving linear-quadratic system using, 259
solving linear systems using, 134–141, 166, 168
solving polynomial equations using, 296–302
solving quadratic equations using, 226–231
solving radical equations using, 416
solving systems of inequalities using, 115, 117, 150–151, 185
of square root function, 416
of tangent function, 862
in three-dimensions, 164–165, 166
transformations. *See* transformations
translations. *See* translations
of trigonometric functions, 852
turning point, 291
using for problem solving, 6, 9, 13, 16, 60, 61, 65, 70, 77, 78, 79, 83, 84, 87, 93, 94, 100, 105, 106, 109, 110, 111, 115, 116, 117, 118, 119, 121, 127, 129, 134, 141, 150, 152, 153, 154, 155, 156, 158, 159, 161, 162, 189, 190, 195, 196, 197, 199, 200, 205, 210, 227, 229, 230, 246, 250, 254, 257, 268, 275, 276, 286, 289, 291, 319, 333, 337, 338, 340, 341, 344, 345, 346, 352, 355, 356, 373, 406, 414, 415, 416, 418, 419, 429, 430, 434, 437, 440, 441, 442, 443, 444, 449, 450, 454, 455, 468, 484, 493, 494, 499, 508, 509, 510, 514, 515, 519, 533, 541, 554, 559, 593, 608, 609, 615, 616, 618, 623, 624, 632, 633, 635, 640, 641, 642, 644, 647, 649, 655, 656, 657, 659, 664, 668, 669, 670, 709, 714, 716, 734, 735, 736, 738, 781, 799, 803, 825, 844, 863, 904
vertical-line test, 62–63, 414

**graphing calculator.** *See also* calculator
activity, 163
area of a polygon, 777
box-and-whisker plots, 707
CALC feature, 163, 202, 227
conic sections, 621

CONNECTED mode, 506
cosine equation, 856–857
CubicReg feature, 331, 332, 334
ΔTbl feature, 470
determinant of a matrix, 776
direct and inverse variation, 498–499, 500
DOT plotting mode, 506
DrawInv feature, 413
encoding and decoding with matrices, 779
exercises, 87, 88, 90; 97, 120, 121, 138,
    139, 140, 151, 180, 213, 229, 265, 300,
    318, 337, 413, 418, 419, 420, 440, 448,
    449, 458, 460, 473, 483, 485, 512, 513,
    514, 522, 545, 546, 600, 619, 634, 651,
    685, 715, 731, 763, 780, 789, 790, 791,
    833, 849, 856–857, 858, 859, 864, 865,
    874, 880, 881, 909
exponential and logarithmic inequalities,
    484–485
exponential equations, 470
exponential functions, 437, 444, 445, 446,
    477
ExpReg feature, 445, 460
extraneous solutions, 393
FLOAT feature, 568
hyperbola, 647, 648
INTERSECT feature, 136, 137, 163, 260,
    299, 416, 511, 550, 856
INTERSECT option, 163
inverse of a matrix, 778
linear regression, 136
linear systems, 178
line of best fit, 94, 95
LINREG function, 94, 95, 136, 137, 331,
    334
LIST feature, 590
logarithmic equations, 472
matrices, 763
MAXIMUM feature, 292
MODE feature, 506, 568
natural logarithmic function, 478
oblique asymptotes, 524–525
parametric mode, 413
piecewise function, 90
polynomial equations, 298
polynomial functions, 282, 290, 332
polynomial inequalities, 317
polynomial models, 331, 333–334
quadratic equations, 227, 228
quadratic formula, 241
quadratic functions, 195, 202
quadratic regression, 211
quadratic systems, 260, 661
QuadReg feature, 211, 331
rational functions, 506, 521
rational inequalities, 549, 550
real roots, 299
reciprocal function, 509, 511
relative maximums or minimums, 292
roots of polynomial equations, 315
RREF function, 177–178, 332
sequences, 568
sine curves, 844, 845
STAT EDIT feature, 707
STAT feature, 95, 459, 460, 477
STAT PLOT feature, 459, 460, 477, 707
sum of a series, 590
systems of equations, 788
TABLE feature, 140, 202, 227, 437, 863
tangent function, 863
TBLSET feature, 470, 472
Tmax feature, 413
Tmin feature, 413
TRACE feature, 506
transformations, 110

trigonometric functions, 852, 878
VALUE option, 163
VARS feature, 413, 460
vertex form, 236
Xmax feature, 413
Xmin feature, 413
YLIST feature, 477
ZERO option, 163, 227, 299
zeros of polynomial function, 321
ZOOM feature, 460

**Graphing Conic Sections,** 621

**Graphing Trigonometric functions,**
    852

**Greatest Common Factor (GCF),** 218, 297

**Greatest Integer Function,** 90

**Gridded Response**
    exercises, 32, 48, 56, 73, 130, 148, 173,
        190, 208, 247, 276, 317, 338, 356, 380,
        388, 430, 476, 483, 494, 523, 560, 571,
        601, 610, 636, 670, 681, 693, 717, 803,
        807, 921, 934
    problems, 27, 175, 242, 307, 400, 447,
        520, 574, 752, 782, 816,
        892

**growth, exponential,** 434–441, 488

**growth factor,** 435, 436, 488

**guess and check,** 286, 312

*Guided Instruction* **4, 11, 18, 26, 33, 41,
    60, 68, 74, 81, 90–91, 92, 99, 107,
    114, 134, 142, 149, 157, 163, 164–165,
    166, 174, 194, 202, 209, 215, 216,
    226, 232, 234, 241, 249, 256–257,
    259, 265, 280, 288, 295, 303, 312,
    318, 319, 325, 326, 331, 339, 360,
    361, 367, 374, 381, 390, 398, 405,
    413, 414, 434, 442, 451, 459–460,
    462, 469, 477, 478, 484–485, 498,
    506, 507, 515, 524–525, 527, 534,
    542, 549, 550–551, 564, 572, 578,
    580, 587, 594, 595, 614, 621, 622,
    630, 638, 645, 653, 663, 674, 681,
    688, 696, 704, 712, 718, 725, 733,
    756, 764, 774, 793, 801, 820, 828,
    836, 860, 867, 875, 896, 911, 920,
    928, 943**
*Concept Byte* **90–91, 163, 164–165,
    215, 232, 256–257, 265, 318, 325,
    360, 413, 459–460, 477, 484–485,
    506, 524–525, 549, 550–551, 578,
    594, 621, 694–695, 724, 740, 763,
    772–773, 827, 835, 852, 927**

# H

*Haitian-Creole Support* **3D, 59D, 133D,
    193D, 279D, 359D, 433D, 496D, 563D,
    613D, 673D, 755D, 819D, 895D**

**half-angle identities,** 943–949, 954

**half-plane,** 114

**Here's Why It Works,** 674, 920
    angle difference identities, 938
    area of a triangle, 920
    Change of Base Formula, 464
    cofunction identities, 936
    double-angle identities, 943
    Fundamental Counting Principle,
        674
    half-angle identities, 945
    inequalities, 34
    Law of Cosines, 929
    length of an intercepted arc, 838

logarithms, 462
negative angle identities, 935
parabolas, 623
point-slope form, 81
quadratic function, 203
relating radians and degrees, 837
Remainder Theorem, 307
sum and differences of cubes, 298
vertical in-line test, 62

**Homework Online,** 7–10, 15–17, 22–24,
    30–32, 38–40, 46–48, 65–67, 71–73,
    78–80, 86–88, 96–98, 104–106, 111–
    113,
    118–120, 138–140, 146–148,
    153–154, 160–162, 171–173,
    179–181, 199–201, 206–207,
    212–214, 217–220, 221–223,
    229–231, 237–239, 245–247,
    253–255, 262–264, 293–295,
    301–302, 308–309, 316–317,
    322–324, 329–330, 335–337,
    343–345, 364–366, 371–373,
    378–380, 386–388, 395–397,
    402–404, 410–412, 418–420,
    439–440, 447–449, 456–458,
    466–467, 473–476, 481–483,
    503–505, 512–513, 521–523,
    531–532, 539–540, 546–548,
    569–571, 575–576, 584–585,
    591–593, 599–601, 618–619,
    627–629, 634–636, 642–644,
    658–660, 678, 685–686, 691–692,
    700–701, 708–709, 715, 721, 729, 737,
    760, 769–770, 780–781,
    789–790, 798, 805, 824, 832–833,
    840–841, 848, 856–857, 864,
    872–873, 880, 900, 908, 916, 924,
    931–932, 940–941, 947

*Homework Quick Check* **8, 16, 23, 31, 38,
    46, 65, 72, 79, 87, 97, 104, 112, 119,
    139, 146, 153, 161, 172, 180, 199, 207,
    213, 222, 230, 238, 245, 254, 262,
    286, 293, 301, 309, 316, 323, 329,
    336, 343, 365, 371, 379, 386, 395,
    402, 410, 419, 440, 448, 457, 466,
    474, 481, 504, 513, 522, 531, 540,
    546, 569, 576, 584, 592, 599, 635,
    643, 651, 659, 679, 692, 701, 709,
    716, 722, 730, 738, 761, 770, 780,
    790, 799, 806, 824, 833, 840, 848,
    857, 864, 873, 880, 901, 907, 916,
    925, 932, 941, 948**

**horizontal**
    asymptotes, 518, 554
    ellipse, 639
    line, 75, 414
    translation, 100–101, 102, 108, 415

**Horse Hollow Wind Energy Center,** 342

**hyperbola,** 645–652
    analyzing, 648
    axes of, 646
    branches of, 616, 646, 649
    center of, 646, 666
    conic sections, 614
    defined, 645, 666
    equation of, 647, 648, 655–656
    foci of, 645, 666
    graphing, 616, 647
    horizontal, 655
    reflection property, 649
    translations, 655
    vertical, 655
    vertices of, 645, 646

# I

*i*, **imaginary number,** 248, 249, 272

**Iberian lynx,** 438

**identity(ies)**
    additive, 14, 759
    of angles, 935–948, 954
    cofunction, 936, 937, 954
    cotangent, 896, 952
    domain of validity, 896
    equations as, 28, 29, 52
    multiplicative, 14, 774, 811
    Pythagorean, 898, 952
    reciprocal, 896, 952
    tangent, 896, 939, 952
    trigonometric, 896–902, 952
    verifying, 897, 898, 944–945
    writing without parentheses, 898

**image,** 793, 812

**imaginary**
    axis, 249, 250
    numbers, 248, 249, 272
    solutions to quadratic equations, 252, 272
    unit, 248, 249

**inconsistent system,** 137

**independent**
    events, 688, 689, 745
    system, 137, 184
    variable, 63

**index of the radical expression,** 362, 423

**industrial design,** 531

**industry,** 548

**inequality(ies)**
    absolute-value, 41–48, 117, 152
    compound, 36–37, 43, 52
    exponential, 484–485
    graphing, 33, 35, 114–120, 126
    linear, 114, 115, 117, 149–155, 166, 185
    logarithmic, 484–485
    polynomial. *See* polynomial equations
    properties of, 34
    quadratic, 256–257, 261, 272
    rational, 550–551
    real numbers as a solution, 36, 52
    solving, 33–40
    solving, as Big Idea, 49, 50, 133, 182, 183, 421, 422
    systems of, 157, 166, 184, 185
    writing, 33, 34, 117

**infinite**
    geometric series, 594, 598
    series, 587

**initial**
    point, 801, 812
    side of angles, 828, 886

**integers,** 12

**intercepted arc,** 836, 837, 887

**interdisciplinary**
    agriculture, 222, 738
    archaeology, 448, 481
    architecture, 234, 375, 592, 863
    astronomy, 467, 636, 644, 849
    biology, 83, 84, 135, 482, 737, 740, 858
    botany, 448
    business, 159, 170, 180, 245, 263, 522, 769
    chemistry, 39, 67, 147, 379, 457, 504
    conservation, 71
    demography, 474
    design, 863

    earth science, 392, 628
    economics, 140, 206, 402
    finance, 51, 94, 172, 568, 571
    geography, 841
    industrial design, 531
    industry, 548
    language arts, 825
    meteorology, 475, 710, 713, 714
    music, 143, 476, 841, 849
    oceanography, 440, 855
    packaging design, 286
    physics, 22, 212, 231, 245, 269, 273, 344, 345, 372, 387, 396, 419, 449, 483, 502, 504, 581, 600, 807, 890, 933
    psychology, 449
    science, 466, 584
    seismology, 474
    social studies, 98
    sociology, 730
    zoology, 440, 734, 735

**interest, continuously compounded,** 446, 488

**interpolation,** 334

**interquartile range,** 706

**INTERSECT feature,** 136, 137, 163, 260, 299, 416, 511, 550, 856

**inverse**
    additive, 14
    of matrices, 774–782, 784–792, 811
    multiplicative, 13, 14
    operations, 27
    relations, 405–413, 426
    solving trigonometric equations, 903–910, 952
    variation, 498–505, 554

**inverse functions,** 405–413
    composition of, 408, 409
    domain and range, 426
    exponential, 454
    graphing, 413, 508, 904
    logarithmic, 451–458, 489
    representative part, 903
    sine, 905, 923
    tangent, 905
    trigonometric, 903–910

**Inverse Property of Real Numbers,** 14

**inverse variation Function,** 508

**irrational**
    numbers, 12
    roots, 314, 350

# J

**joint variation,** 501, 554

**justifying steps,** 39

**justify your reasoning,** 54

# K

**Kepler's Third Law of Orbital Motion,** 383

**Key Concepts**
    Absolute Value, 41
    Absolute Value Functions, 107
    Approximating a Binomial Distribution, 741
    Area of a Triangle, 776
    Arithmetic Sequence, 572
    Basic Identities, 896
    Binomial Experiment, 725
    Binomial Probability, 726
    Binomial Theorem, 727
    Box-and-whisker plots, 707

    Combined Variations, 501
    Completing The Square, 235
    Complex Numbers, 249
    Composition of Functions, 400
    Composition of Inverse Functions, 408
    Compression, 195
    Conditional Probability, 697
    Conic Sections, 614
    Continuously Compounded Interest, 446
    Converting Between Radians and Degrees, 837
    Cosecant, Secant, and Cotangent Functions, 875
    Cosine and Sine of an Angle, 830
    Determinants of $2 \times 2$ and $3 \times 3$ Matrices, 776
    Discriminant, 242
    Division Algorithm for Polynomials, 304
    Ellipse, 638
    Experimental Probability, 681
    Exponential Growth and Decay, 436
    Factoring a Difference of Two Squares, 220
    Factoring Perfect Square Trinomials, 219
    Families of Radical Functions, 415
    Family of Absolute Value Functions, 108
    Four Ways To Represent Relations, 60
    Function Operations, 398
    Fundamental Counting Principle, 674
    General Form of Absolute Value Function, 110
    General Form of the Reciprocal Family Function, 507
    Geometric Sequences, 580
    Horizontal Asymptote of a Rational Function, 518
    How Multiple Zeros Affect a Graph, 291
    Identity and Multiplicative Inverse Matrices, 774
    Infinite geometric series, 598
    Inverse of a $2 \times 2$ Matrix, 777
    Inverses of Three Trigonometric Functions, 903
    Length of an Intercepted Arc, 838
    Logarithm, 451
    Matrix Addition and Subtraction, 756
    Matrix Multiplication, 766
    Measures of Central Tendency, 704
    The $(n + 1)$ Point Principle, 332
    Natural Logarithmic Function, 478
    Normal Distribution, 733
    The *n*th Root, 361
    Number of Combinations, 676
    Number of Permutations, 676
    Parabolas, 622
    Parallel Lines, 85
    Perpendicular Lines, 85
    Point of Discontinuity, 516
    Point-slope Form, 81
    Power Functions, 341
    Probability of $A$ and $B$, 688
    Probability of $A$ or $B$, 689
    Properties of Ellipses with Center (0, 0), 639
    Properties of Hyperbolas with Centers (0, 0), 645
    Properties of Rational Exponents, 383
    Pythagorean Identities, 898
    The Quadratic Formula, 241
    Rational Exponent, 382
    Reciprocal Family Function, 509
    Reflection, 195
    Roots, Zeros, and *x*-intercepts, 289
    Row Operations, 176
    Sampling Types and Methods, 718
    Scalar Multiplication, 764
    Slope, 74

Index

Slope-intercept Form, 76
Solutions of a Linear-quadratic System, 258
Solving an Equation by Completing the Square, 235
Square Root of a Negative Real Number, 248
Standard Form of a Linear Equation, 82
Standard Form of an Equation of a Circle, 630
Standard Form of a Polynomial Function, 281
Stretch, 195
Study Methods, 719
Summation Notation and Linear Functions, 589
Sum of a Finite Arithmetic Series, 595
Tangent of an Angle, 860
Theoretical Probability, 683
Transformations of a Parabola, 626
Transforming a Circle, 632
Translation of the Parabola, 197
Trigonometric Ratios for a Circle, 911
Trigonometric Ratios for a Right Triangle, 912
Variables and Expressions, 5
Variance and Standard Deviation, 712
Vectors in Two Dimensions, 801
Vertex Principle of Linear Programming, 158
Vertical Asymptotes of Rational Functions, 517
Writing and Graphing Inequalities, 33

**Know/Need/Plan problems,** 20, 69, 77, 82, 94, 117, 136, 151, 205, 284, 289, 313, 320, 391, 400, 445, 471, 502, 511, 597, 615, 626, 631, 640, 690, 706, 714, 726, 758, 795, 831, 839, 846, 855, 914, 946

# L

**language arts,** 825

**Law**
of Cosines, 928–934, 953
of Sines, 920–926, 953

**Least Common Denominator (LCD),** 535, 537

**Least Common Multiple (LCM),** 534–535

**length**
of an intercepted arc, 837, 838
sides of triangles, 920–924, 927, 928–931

**Lesson Check,** 7, 15, 22, 30, 37, 45, 64, 71, 78, 86, 96, 103, 111, 118, 138, 145, 152, 160, 171, 179, 198, 206, 212, 221, 229, 237, 244, 253, 261, 285, 293, 300, 308, 315, 322, 328, 335, 342, 364, 370, 378, 385, 394, 401, 409, 418, 439, 447, 456, 465, 473, 480, 503, 512, 521, 530, 539, 545, 568, 575, 583, 591, 598, 617, 627, 634, 642, 650, 658, 678, 691, 700, 715, 721, 729, 737, 760, 769, 779, 789, 798, 805, 823, 832, 838, 847, 856, 863, 872, 879, 900, 907, 915, 924, 931, 940, 947

*Lesson Quiz* 10A, 17A, 24A, 32A, 40A, 48A, 67A, 73A, 80A, 88A, 98A, 106A, 113A, 120A, 141A, 148A, 155A, 162A, 165A, 173A, 181A, 201A, 208A, 214A, 223A, 231A, 239A, 247A, 255A, 264A, 287A, 295A, 302A, 310A, 317A, 324A, 330A, 338A, 345A, 366A, 373A, 380A,

388A, 397A, 404A, 412A, 420A, 441A, 450A, 458A, 468A, 476A, 483A, 505A, 514A, 523A, 533A, 541A, 548A, 571A, 577A, 586A, 593A, 601A, 620A, 629A, 636A, 644A, 652A, 660A, 680A, 687A, 693A, 702A, 711A, 717A, 723A, 732A, 739A, 762A, 771A, 782A, 792A, 800A, 807A, 826A, 834A, 842A, 850A, 859A, 866A, 874A, 882A, 902A, 910A, 918A, 926A, 934A, 942A

*Lesson Resources. See* **Resources**

*Lesson Vocabulary. See* **vocabulary, Lesson Vocabulary**

*Leveled Courses with Pacing. See* **Pacing and Assignment Guides**

**like radicals,** 374, 424

**like terms,** 21, 52

**limits,** 589, 605

**line(s).** *See also* linear equations
boundary, 107, 114, 115, 126
horizontal, 75, 414
intercept of, 76
parallel, 81, 85, 124
perpendicular, 81, 85, 124
slope of, 74, 75, 124
vertical, 75, 107, 414
writing equations of, 83
*x*-intercept, 76, 289
*y*-intercept, 76

**linear data,** 215

**linear equation(s)**
defined, 75
direct variation, 68–73, 123
graphing, 77, 83, 84, 124
line of best fit, 94–95
matrix representation of, 174–178
modeling, 92–98
for parallel lines, 85
for perpendicular lines, 85
Piecewise Function, 90–91
point-slope form, 81–82, 83, 124
slope formula, 74
slope-intercept form, 77, 83, 124
solving using calculators, 178
solving using matrices, 174–178, 186
standard form, 82–83, 124
systems of. *See* linear systems
for a trend line, 94
writing, 76

**linear factors,** 288, 289

**linear functions,** 74–80
defined, 75
graphs of, 124
slope-intercept form of, 76

**linear inequality(ies),** 149–155
defined, 114
solving by graphing, 115, 117, 150–151, 185
solving using tables, 149–150
systems of, 166, 185

**linear polynomial,** 281

**linear programming,** 157–162
activity, 163
constraints in, 157, 185
defined, 157
vertex principle of, 158

**linear-quadratic system,** 258–264
solving by graphing, 259
solving by substitution, 259

**linear regression,** 94, 136, 352

**linear regression (LinReg),** 94

**linear system(s)**
absolute-value, 152
classifying, 137
consistent, 137, 184
defined, 134, 184
dependent, 137, 184
equivalent, 142, 144, 168
inconsistent, 137, 184
independent, 137, 184
of inequalities, 157, 184
linear term, 281
with no unique solution, 145, 166, 184
solving algebraically, 142–155, 184
solving by elimination, 144, 184
solving by graphing, 134–141, 150, 166, 168
solving by substitution, 142–143, 169, 184
solving with calculators, 178
solving with matrix equations, 174–178
solving with tables, 134–141, 149–150

**line of best fit,** 94, 95, 125

**LIST feature,** 590

**literal equation,** 29

**logarithm(s)**
base ten, 453, 463
Change of Base Formula, 464
common, 453, 489
defined, 451
evaluating, 452
expanding, 463
natural, 478–483, 490
properties of, 462–468, 472, 489
simplifying, 463
using for exponential models, 477

**logarithmic**
expressions, 451, 478–479
inequalities, 484–485
scale, 453, 465

**logarithmic equation(s)**
defined, 490
natural, 479
solving, 469–476

**logarithmic function(s)**
define, 454
families of, 455
graphing, 454–455
as inverses, 451–458, 489
natural, 478, 490
translations, 455

**long division of polynomials,** 302–304

**look for a pattern,** 325, 522

**look for key words,** 34, 72

**Looking Ahead Vocabulary,** 1, 57, 131, 191, 277, 357, 431, 495, 561, 611, 671, 753, 817, 893

# M

**magnitude,** 801, 812

**major axis of an ellipse,** 639, 665

**make a drawing,** 188

**manipulatives**
number cubes, 694–695
protractor, 831

**mapping diagram,** 60

*Math Background*
for chapters 3A–B, 59A–B, 133A–B, 193A–B, 279A–B, 359A–B, 433A–B,

496A–B, 563A–B, 613A–B, 673A–B, 755A–B, 819A–B, 895A–B
for lessons 4, 11, 18, 26, 33, 41, 60, 68, 74, 81, 92, 99, 107, 114, 134, 142, 149, 157, 166, 174, 194, 202, 209, 216, 226, 234, 241, 249, 259, 280, 288, 296, 303, 312, 319, 326, 331, 339, 361, 367, 374, 381, 390, 398, 405, 414, 434, 442, 451, 462, 469, 478, 498, 507, 515, 527, 534, 542, 564, 572, 580, 587, 595, 614, 622, 630, 638, 645, 653, 674, 681, 688, 696, 704, 712, 718, 725, 733, 756, 764, 774, 793, 801, 820, 828, 836, 860, 867, 875, 896, 911, 920, 928, 943

**Math Behind the Scenes,** 3, 59, 133, 193, 279, 359, 433, 497, 563, 613, 755, 895

**mathematical modeling**
exponential equations, 472
exponential functions, 445, 477
exponential growth and decay, 434–441, 488
infinite series, 594
inverse variation, 499
linear equations, 92–98
logarithmic equations, 472
polynomial functions, 331–334, 352
quadratic functions, 209–213, 269
trend line, 94

**mathematical patterns,** 564–571, 604. *See also* patterns

**mathematical quantity,** 5

**MathXL for School,** 25, 53, 89, 127, 156, 187, 224, 273, 311, 353, 389, 427, 461, 491, 526, 557, 570, 579, 607, 637, 667, 703, 749, 783, 851, 919, 955

**matrices**
adding, 756–762, 794, 810
additive identity, 759
additive inverse, 759
coefficients, 175, 811
constant, 176, 785, 811
defined, 134, 174
determinants, 776, 811
dilation, 793, 794, 795
dimensions of, 756
elements of, 174, 175
encoding with, 779
equal, 759, 810
inverse of, 758, 774–782, 784–792, 811
multiplicative identity, 774, 811
multiplying, 764–771, 810, 812
properties of, 768
reflection, 793, 796, 797
rotation, 793, 796
row operations, 176
scalar multiplication, 764–765, 794, 810
solving systems of equations using, 174–178, 186, 787, 788
solving using scalars, 765–766
square, 768, 774, 811
subtracting, 756–762, 810
translations of geometric, 793–800, 812
variable, 785, 811
writing vectors as, 802
writing vertices as, 793

**matrix**
element, 174, 175, 759
equation, 757, 784–785, 810

**MAXIMUM feature,** 292

**maximums or minimums**
amplitude of periodic functions, 822
defined, 195
of functions, 158, 185, 195, 268, 291, 292
linear programming for finding, 157, 158
relative, 291
of tolerance, 44

**max-zero-min-zero-max pattern,** 854

**mean**
arithmetic, 574, 604
average, 574
defined, 704
formula for finding, 704, 746
geometric, 583, 605

**measurement**
of angles, 828, 836–842
in radians, 835, 836–842, 887

**measures**
of central tendency, 704, 746
of variation, 712, 746

**median,** 704, 746

**Mental Math,** 232, 396, 474, 619, 941

**Meteor Crater,** 392

**meteorology,** 475, 710, 713, 714

**Mid-Chapter Quiz.** *See* assessment, Mid-Chapter Quiz

**minor axis of an ellipse,** 639, 665

**Mixed Review.** *See* assessment, Mixed Review

**mode,** 704, 746

**MODE feature,** 506, 568

**modeling**
algebraic expressions with words, 18–19
as Big Idea, 121, 122, 421, 486, 487, 602, 603, 662, 663, 808, 809, 884, 885
with a cosine function, 855
light waves with sine function, 847
mathematical. *See* Mathematical modeling
trigonometric equations, 871
word problems, 274

**Moiré pattern,** 617

**monomial,** 280, 281

**monomial function,** 352

**Multiple Choice**
exercises, 54–56, 128–130, 188–190, 274–276, 354–356, 428–430, 492–494, 608, 668–670, 750–752, 814–816, 891–892
problems, 12, 18, 109, 112, 119, 146, 158, 169, 197, 222, 259, 314, 323, 340, 370, 387, 396, 416, 452, 469, 501, 510, 513, 583, 589, 627, 632, 656, 690, 697, 705, 788, 830, 847, 904, 927, 929

**multiple events,** 688–693

**multiple representations**
with diagrams, 249, 683, 684, 690, 694, 695, 699, 705, 726, 735, 772, 827, 835, 839, 858, 912, 913, 914, 915, 920, 921, 922, 923, 927, 928, 929, 930, 935, 936, 937, 938
with examples, 5, 26, 34, 41, 74, 176, 242, 248, 249, 341, 383
exercises, 880, 917
with graphs, 33, 44, 60, 85, 107, 194, 195, 197, 258, 291, 434, 478, 507, 622, 632, 638, 639, 645, 646, 707, 714, 728, 733, 734, 735, 736, 793, 794, 797, 801, 802, 803, 804, 820, 821, 822, 829, 830, 843, 844, 846, 847, 853, 854, 855, 856, 857, 867, 868, 869, 870, 878, 897, 904, 905, 906, 907, 911, 912, 935, 936, 938

with photographs, 84, 777, 795
with tables, 60, 107, 694, 695, 696, 697, 698, 705, 706, 713, 714, 724, 757, 767, 788, 808, 871

**multiplication**
of binomials, 376
of complex numbers, 251
of conjugates, 377
counting using, 674
of exponents, 360
of functions, 398, 399
inverse operation to, 27
of logarithms, 462
of matrices, 764–771, 810, 812
by minus one, 21
properties of exponents, 360
of radical expressions, 367–373, 423
of rational expressions, 528
scalar, 764–765, 794, 803, 804
of square roots, 225
by zero, 21

**Multiplication Property,** 21
of Equality, 27
of Inequality, 34
of Square Roots, 225

**multiplicative identity,** 14
matrix, 774, 811
property, 765

**multiplicative inverse**
of any nonzero number, 14
defined, 13, 14
matrix, 774
zero and the, 13

**Multiplicative Property of Zero,** 765, 768

**multiplicity of a zero,** 291

**multi-step equations,** 27

**music,** 143, 476, 841, 849

**mutually exclusive events,** 689, 690, 745

**My Math Video,** 3, 59, 133, 196, 279, 359, 433, 497, 563, 613, 673, 755, 819, 895

# N

**The (*n* + 1) Point Principle,** 332, 333, 352

**natural**
logarithmic equation, 478–479
logarithms, 478–483, 490
numbers, 12

**natural base exponential functions,** 446

**natural logarithmic function,** 478

**negative**
angle identities, 935, 954
numbers, 21
square root, 248

**Networks,** 772–773

**Newton's Law of Cooling,** 483

***n* factorial (*n!*),** 675, 744

**non-mutually exclusive events,** 690

**non-removable discontinuity,** 516

**normal**
curve, 735
vectors, 804

**normal distribution,** 733–739
analyzing, 736
defined, 738, 748
sketching a normal curve, 735
standard, 740

**notation**
    alternative for radicals, 381
    factorial, 675
    function, 62, 63, 407
    summation, 589, 590, 605

*n*th root, 361–366, 423

*n*th term of a sequence, 565

**number(s)**
    of combinations, 676
    complex. *See* complex number(s)
    imaginary, 249, 272
    integers, 12
    irrational, 12
    natural, 12
    of permutations, 676
    rational, 12, 377
    real. *See* real numbers
    roots of. *See* roots of numbers
    simplifying, 249
    whole, 12

**number cubes,** 694–695

**number line,** 13

**numerical expression,** 5

# O

**objective function,** 157, 185

**oblique asymptotes,** 524–525

**observational study,** 720

**oceanography,** 440, 855

**one-step equations,** 27

**one-to-one function,** 408

**online activities.** *See* Dynamic Activities;
    Homework Online; MathXL for School;
    My Math Video; PowerAlgebra.com;
    Problems Online; Solve It!; vocabulary,
    Vocabulary Audio Online

**Open-Ended exercises,** 8, 9, 24, 40, 47, 72,
    105, 112, 126, 127, 138, 140, 147, 154,
    160, 173, 179, 181, 187, 200, 213, 222,
    224, 230, 254, 262, 273, 286, 294, 302,
    311, 317, 323, 365, 372, 379, 385, 387,
    396, 403, 411, 427, 440, 449, 457, 475,
    491, 505, 512, 513, 526, 531, 539, 540,
    545, 548, 557, 570, 579, 585, 592, 600,
    607, 619, 635, 643, 651, 660, 667, 678,
    691, 700, 701, 703, 730, 731, 749, 783,
    791, 813, 825, 832, 833, 834, 841, 847,
    849, 851, 856, 864, 873, 890, 901, 909,
    919, 925, 933, 948, 955

**operations**
    with complex numbers, 250
    with functions, 398–404, 425
    inverse, 27
    with rational expressions, 528, 534, 535,
       536
    row, 176, 185

**opposites**
    additive inverse, 14
    defined, 14
    of a difference, 21
    of an opposite, 21
    of a product, 21
    of real numbers, 14
    simplifying algebraic expressions, 21
    of a sum, 21

**ordered**
    pairs, 60, 110, 121–122, 123, 164
    triples, 164, 167

**outliers,** 705, 746

# P

*Pacing and Assignment Guides* 3C, 59C,
    **133C, 193C, 279C, 359C, 433C, 496C,**
    **563C, 613C, 673C, 755C, 819C, 895C**

**packaging design,** 286

**parabola(s),** 622–629
    axis of symmetry, 194, 624
    conic sections and, 614
    defined, 194, 622, 664
    directrix, 622, 664
    equation of, 209, 623–624, 627
    focal length, 622, 664
    graphing, 194, 197, 268
    maximums and minimums, 195
    points on, 622–623
    properties of, 194, 268
    transformations, 195, 626
    translations, 197
    vertex form, 194, 196, 198

**parallel lines,** 81, 85, 124

**parameters,** 266

**parametric equations,** 413

**Parent Function**
    absolute value, 107, 108
    defined, 99, 125
    exponential functions, 444
    logarithmic functions, 455
    quadratic, 194
    radical functions, 415
    reciprocal functions, 509

**Pascal, Blaise,** 327

**Pascal's Triangle,** 325, 326–330

**patterns,** 4–9. *See also* sequences
    expressing with algebra, 5–6, 51
    formulas to generate, 564, 565,
       567
    identifying, 4, 51
    look for, 325
    mathematical, 564–571, 604
    Moiré, 617

**percentile**
    defined, 708
    finding, 708

**perfect square trinomial**
    defined, 220
    factoring, 219, 220, 234–235, 297

*Performance Task* 49, 121, 182, 266, 346,
    **421, 486, 552, 602, 662, 742, 808,**
    **884, 894, 950**

**period**
    defined, 820
    of functions, 820, 885
    of sine curve, 844
    of tangent function, 861

**periodic**
    cycle, 820–821
    data, 820–826, 886

**periodic function(s)**
    amplitude of, 822
    cycles of, 820–821
    defined, 820, 885
    identifying, 821

**permutations,** 674–680
    defined, 675
    finding the number in *n* items, 675, 676
    importance of order in, 677
    *n* factorial (*n*!), 675, 744

**perpendicular lines,** 81, 85, 124, 804

**phase shift,** 868

**physics,** 22, 212, 231, 245, 269, 273, 344,
    345, 372, 387, 396, 419, 449, 483, 502,
    504, 581, 600, 807, 890, 933

**Piecewise Function,** 90–91

**plane**
    complex number, 249, 250, 272
    coordinate, 74, 114, 126, 164
    sketching solutions in a, 164, 185
    solutions as the intersection of, 166

**point(s)**
    on a coordinate plane, 164
    on parabolas, 622–623
    terminal, 801, 812
    test, 115
    turning, 282, 348

**point of discontinuity,** 516–517, 555, 860

**point-slope form,** 81–82, 83, 124

**polygons, area of,** 776, 777

**polynomial(s),** 312–317
    classifying, 281
    constructing using conjugates, 314
    defined, 280
    degree of, 280–284
    dividing, 302–310, 349
    equivalent, 289
    expansion, 326
    factoring, 288, 297
    inequalities, 318
    standard form of, 281, 348

**polynomial equation(s)**
    with complex solutions, 319–322, 351
    roots of. *See* roots of polynomial equations
    solving by factoring, 296–302, 349
    solving by graphing, 296–302
    writing, 232

**polynomial function(s),** 280–287
    behaviors of, 280
    defined, 280
    degree of, 280–284
    end behavior, 282–283
    graphing, 283–284, 291, 339–345
    modeling, 331–334, 352
    relative maximums or minimums, 291, 292,
       348
    standard form of, 281, 348
    transformations, 339–345, 352
    zeros of, 288, 289, 348

**positive (principal) root,** 361, 369, 381, 423

**PowerAlgebra.com,** 2, 25, 53, 58, 89, 127,
    132, 135, 156, 187, 192, 224, 273, 278,
    311, 353, 358, 389, 427, 432, 461, 491,
    495, 526, 557, 562, 570, 579, 607, 612,
    637, 667, 671, 703, 749, 754, 783, 818,
    851, 894, 919, 955

*PowerAlgebra.com* 2, 4, 7, 10A, 11, 12, 14,
    **15, 16A, 18, 21, 22, 24A, 25, 26, 29,**
    **32A, 33, 34, 36, 37, 40A, 41, 42, 44,**
    **45, 48A, 53, 60, 64, 67A, 68, 71, 73A,**
    **74, 78, 80A, 81, 82, 86, 88A, 89, 92,**
    **96, 98A, 99, 100, 103, 106A, 107, 108,**
    **111, 113A, 114, 118, 120A, 133, 134,**
    **138, 141A, 142, 145, 148A, 149, 150,**
    **152, 155A, 156, 157, 158, 160, 162A,**
    **166, 171, 173A, 173B, 179, 181A, 187,**
    **192, 194, 198, 201A, 202, 206, 208A,**
    **209, 210, 212, 214A, 216, 221, 223A,**
    **224, 226, 229, 231A, 233, 234, 237,**
    **239A, 240, 244, 247A, 248, 253,**
    **255A, 258, 261, 264A, 278, 280, 285,**
    **287A, 288, 293, 295A, 296, 300,**
    **302A, 303, 304, 308, 310A, 311, 312,**
    **315, 317A, 319, 320, 322, 324A, 326,**

328, 330A, 331, 332, 335, 338A, 339, 340, 342, 345A, 353, 358, 361, 362, 364, 366A, 367, 368, 370, 373A, 374, 378, 380A, 381, 382, 386, 388A, 389, 390, 394, 397A, 398, 401, 404A, 405, 406, 409, 412A, 414, 418, 420A, 427, 432, 434, 439, 441A, 442, 447, 450A, 451, 452, 456, 458A, 461, 462, 465, 468A, 469, 470, 473, 476A, 478, 481, 483A, 491, 496, 498, 503, 505A, 507, 508, 512, 514A, 515, 516, 521, 523A, 526, 527, 528, 530, 533A, 534, 539, 541A, 542, 545, 548A, 557, 562, 564, 568, 571A, 572, 575, 577A, 579, 583, 586A, 587, 588, 591, 593A, 595, 596, 598, 601A, 607, 612, 614, 617, 620A, 622, 627, 629A, 630, 634, 636A, 637, 638, 640, 642, 644A, 645, 646, 650, 652A, 653, 654, 658, 660A, 667, 672, 674, 678, 679A, 681, 682, 685, 687A, 688, 691, 693A, 696, 700, 702A, 703, 704, 708, 711A, 712, 715, 717A, 718, 721, 723A, 725, 726, 729, 732A, 733, 734, 737, 739A, 749, 754, 756, 759, 762A, 764, 769, 771A, 774, 779, 782A, 783, 784, 789, 792A, 793, 794, 798, 800A, 801, 802, 805, 807A, 813, 818, 820, 823, 826A, 828, 832, 834A, 836, 839, 842A, 843, 844, 847, 850A, 851, 854, 856, 859A, 860, 863, 866A, 867, 868, 872, 874A, 875, 876, 879, 882A, 889, 894, 896, 900, 902A, 903, 904, 907, 910A, 911, 912, 915, 918A, 919, 920, 924, 926A, 928, 931, 934A, 935, 936, 940, 942A, 943, 944, 947, 949A, 955

**power function,** 341, 352, 415

**Power Property of Logarithms,** 462

**powers of complex numbers,** 265

*Practice worksheets* 10B, 17B, 24B, 32B, 40B, 48B, 67B, 73B, 80B, 88B, 98B, 106B, 113B, 120B, 141B, 148B, 155B, 162B, 165B, 173B, 181B, 201B, 208B, 214B, 223B, 231B, 239B, 247B, 255B, 264B, 287B, 295B, 302B, 310B, 317B, 324B, 330B, 338B, 345B, 366B, 373B, 380B, 388B, 397B, 404B, 412B, 420B, 441B, 450B, 458B, 468B, 476B, 483B, 505B, 514B, 523B, 533B, 541B, 548B, 571B, 577B, 586B, 593B, 601B, 620B, 629B, 636B, 644B, 652B, 660B, 680B, 687B, 693B, 702B, 711B, 717B, 723B, 732B, 739B, 762B, 771B, 782B, 792B, 800B, 807B, 826B, 834B, 842B, 850B, 859B, 866B, 874B, 882B, 902B, 910B, 918B, 926B, 934B, 942B

**prediction,** 334

**preimage,** 793, 812

**principal (positive) root,** 361, 369, 381, 423

**Principles**
  Fundamental Counting Principle, 674, 675
  The $(n + 1)$ Point Principle, 332, 333, 352
  Vertex principle of linear programming, 158, 185

**probability,** 681–688
  of $A$ and $B$, 688, 745
  of $A$ or $B$, 689, 745
  as Big Idea, 742, 743
  binomial, 726, 727, 728
  conditional, 696–702, 745
  cumulative, 695
  of dependent events, 698, 745
  distributions, 694–695

experimental, 681–682, 744
geometric, 684
of independent events, 745
of multiple events, 688–693
of mutually exclusive events, 745
normal distribution, 733–739, 748
sample space, 744
standard normal curve, 740
theoretical, 682, 683, 744
using combinatorics, 683

**probability distribution(s)**
  for binomial experiments, 728
  continuous, 733, 748
  defined, 694
  discrete, 733, 748

**problem solving**
  exercises, 7–10, 15–17, 22–24, 30–32, 38–40, 46–48, 65–67, 71–73, 78–80, 86–88, 96–98, 104–106, 111–113, 118–120, 138–140, 146–148, 153–154, 160–162, 171–173, 179–181, 199–201, 206–207, 212–214, 217–220, 221–223, 229–231, 237–239, 245–247, 253–255, 262–264, 293–295, 301–302, 308–309, 316–317, 322–324, 329–330, 335–337, 343–345, 364–366, 371–373, 378–380, 386–388, 395–397, 402–404, 410–412, 418–420, 439–440, 447–449, 456–458, 466–467, 473–476, 481–483, 503–505, 512–513, 521–523, 531–532, 539–540, 546–548, 569–571, 575–576, 584–585, 591–593, 599–601, 618–619, 627–629, 634–636, 642–644, 658–660
  Pull It All Together, 49, 121, 182, 266, 346, 421, 486, 552, 602, 662, 742, 808, 950
  Solve It! 4, 11, 18, 26, 33, 41, 60, 68, 74, 81, 92, 99, 107, 114, 134, 142, 149, 157, 166, 174, 194, 202, 209, 216, 226, 234, 241, 249, 259, 280, 288, 296, 303, 312, 319, 326, 331, 339, 361, 367, 374, 381, 390, 398, 405, 414, 434, 442, 451, 462, 469, 478, 498, 507, 515, 527, 534, 542, 564, 572, 580, 587, 595, 614, 622, 630, 638, 645, 653, 674, 681, 688, 696, 704, 712, 718, 725, 733, 756, 764, 774, 793, 801, 820, 828, 836, 860, 867, 875, 896, 911, 920, 928, 935, 943
  Think About a Plan, 9, 16, 17, 23, 31, 39, 46, 66, 72, 79, 87, 105, 112, 119, 139, 147, 153, 161, 172, 180, 199, 207, 213, 222, 230, 238, 245, 254, 262, 286, 294, 301, 309, 316, 323, 329, 336, 343, 365, 371, 379, 387, 395, 403, 411, 419, 440, 448, 457, 466, 474, 481, 504, 512, 522, 532, 540, 546, 569, 575, 585, 592, 599, 618, 628, 635, 643, 650, 659

**problem solving strategies**
  act it out, 675
  check for reasonableness, 236, 624, 777
  draw a diagram, 492, 657, 806, 833, 913, 925, 930, 932
  draw a graph, 36, 849, 854, 856, 857, 861, 865, 870, 873
  guess and check, 286, 312
  look for a pattern, 325, 522
  look for key words, 34, 72
  make a conjecture, 295, 317, 420, 578, 594, 651, 882
  solve a simpler problem, 12, 18, 19, 21, 23, 24, 25, 26, 28, 35, 36, 42, 49, 51,

52, 53, 63, 64, 69, 70, 76, 82, 84, 101, 124, 128, 167, 169, 170, 176, 177, 182, 204, 225, 236, 240, 241, 242, 244, 249, 250, 251, 252, 254, 256, 271, 272, 286, 290, 297, 300, 304, 321, 328, 330, 342, 349, 354, 360, 365, 366, 367, 368, 369, 370, 371, 372, 375, 376, 377, 378, 379, 382, 384, 385, 386, 387, 388, 389, 391, 392, 393, 394, 403, 404, 417, 422, 423, 424, 425, 426, 430, 436, 441, 447, 453, 463, 465, 466, 469, 472, 478, 480, 481, 490, 493, 494, 501, 502, 505, 510, 516, 517, 527, 528, 531, 532, 534, 536, 537, 538, 539, 540, 542, 543, 555, 556, 565, 573, 574, 577, 581, 588, 596, 597, 631, 633, 640, 647, 648, 649, 652, 656, 657, 899, 900
  use a diagram, 39, 53, 54, 55, 56, 60, 62, 65, 238, 294, 302, 316, 355, 375, 378, 379, 395, 421, 449, 453, 532, 570, 594, 617, 628, 629, 631
  use a graph, 6, 9, 13, 16, 60, 61, 65, 70, 77, 78, 79, 83, 84, 87, 93, 94, 100, 105, 106, 109, 110, 111, 115, 116, 117, 118, 119, 121, 127, 129, 134, 141, 150, 152, 153, 154, 155, 156, 158, 159, 161, 162, 189, 190, 195, 196, 197, 199, 200, 205, 210, 227, 229, 230, 246, 250, 254, 257, 268, 275, 276, 286, 289, 291, 319, 333, 337, 338, 340, 341, 344, 345, 346, 352, 355, 356, 373, 406, 414, 415, 416, 418, 419, 429, 430, 434, 437, 440, 441, 442, 443, 444, 449, 450, 454, 455, 468, 484, 493, 494, 499, 508, 509, 510, 514, 515, 519, 533, 541, 554, 559, 593, 608, 609, 615, 616, 618, 623, 624, 632, 633, 635, 640, 641, 642, 644, 647, 649, 655, 656, 657, 659, 664, 668, 669, 670, 709, 714, 716, 734, 735, 736, 738, 781, 799, 803, 825, 844, 863, 904
  use a matrix, 174, 175, 176, 177, 179, 180, 181, 186
  use a spreadsheet, 200, 504, 524
  use a table, 5, 6, 8, 9, 51, 54, 60, 61, 65, 67, 68, 69, 72, 92, 93, 94, 95, 96, 97, 98, 100, 102, 104, 106, 121, 123, 125, 127, 130, 135, 136, 138, 149, 150, 153, 159, 160, 211, 212, 213, 215, 229, 230, 232, 256, 257, 259, 261, 262, 263, 266, 269, 270, 283, 286, 287, 335, 336, 337, 338, 352, 405, 406, 410, 434, 437, 442, 443, 444, 448, 454, 455, 458, 460, 473, 474, 477, 485, 493, 499, 503, 508, 526, 533, 544, 551, 554, 565, 570, 584, 585, 609, 615, 616, 636, 644, 660, 669, 713, 716, 761, 770
  use substitution, 142, 143, 144, 231, 259
  work backwards, 362

**Problems Online,** 4–7, 12–14, 18–22, 27–30, 34–37, 42–46, 61–64, 69–70, 71, 75–77, 82–85, 93–95, 100–103, 108–110, 115–117, 135–137, 142–145, 150–152, 158–159, 167–170, 175–178, 195–198, 204–205, 209–211, 217–220, 226–228, 233–236, 241–244, 249–252, 259–261, 285–287, 293–295, 301–307, 313–315, 320–321, 332–334, 339–342, 367–370, 375–377, 381–385, 390–394, 399–401, 405–409, 415–417, 434–438, 443–447, 452–455, 463–466, 469–472, 478–479, 498–502, 508–511, 516–520, 527–530,

534–538, 543–545, 565–568,
573–574, 580–583, 588–590,
596–598, 615–617, 623–625,
631–633, 639–641, 647–649,
654–657, 675–677, 681–685,
688–691, 696–699, 705–708,
713–714, 720, 726–728, 734–736,
775–779, 784–789, 802–804,
820–823, 829–831, 837–839,
844–847, 854–856, 861–863,
868–871, 876–879, 897–899,
904–907, 912–915, 921–923,
936–940, 944–946

**product matrix,** 766, 768

**Product Property**
of Exponents, 462
of Logarithms, 462

*Professional Development. See* **Math
Background**

*Program Resources. See* **Resources**

**proof,** 32, 629

**properties**
of addition, 27, 34, 143, 374, 759
additive identity, 13, 759
additive inverse, 759
angles, 935, 938, 939, 943
asymptotes, 518
as Big Idea, 49, 50, 346
change of base formula, 464
cofunction identities, 936
combining radicals, 367, 369, 374
of cosine function, 854, 887
of division, 27, 34, 225, 369
of ellipse, 639
of equality, 26–27, 34, 143, 938
of exponential functions, 442–450, 488
of exponents, 360
factoring differences of squares, 220, 297
of hyperbola, 645
of inequalities, 34
of inequality, 34
of logarithms, 462–468, 472, 489
of matrices, 759, 765, 768, 796
of multiplication, 13, 27, 34, 225, 367,
765
multiplicative identity, 765
$n$th Roots of $n$th Powers, 363
operations with vectors, 803
of parabolas, 194, 268
of a product matrix, 768
of quadratic functions, 203
of rational exponents, 383
of real numbers, 11–17, 51
reflexive, 26
relating radians and degrees, 836
for simplifying, 21
of sine function, 845, 886
square roots, 225
of subtraction, 21, 27, 34, 369
of summation, 587, 588
of symmetry, 26, 34
of tangent function, 862, 887
Zero-Product, 226, 270, 289, 349
of zeros, 13, 226, 270, 289, 349,
765

**proportionality**
as Big Idea, 552, 553
constant of, 341

**psychology,** 449

**Pull It All Together,** 49, 121, 182, 266, 346,
421, 486, 552, 602, 662, 742, 808, 884,
894, 950

**Pythagorean identities,** 898, 952

**Pythagorean Theorem,** 640, 666, 801, 898

## Q

**quadratic**
data, 215
formula, 240–248, 271
inequalities, 256–257
polynomial, 281, 314
regression, 211
systems, 258–264, 271
trinomials, 196–197, 198, 218–219, 297

**quadratic equation(s)**
complex number solutions, 248–255, 271
discriminant, 242, 243, 244, 271
imaginary solutions, 272
parabola, 623
perfect square trinomials, 219, 220, 234–
235, 271
solving by completing the square, 233–
239, 271
solving by factoring, 218–219,
226–231, 270, 271
solving by graphing, 226–231
solving using imaginary numbers, 252, 272
solving using tables, 227
solving using the quadratic formula, 240–
248, 271
standard form of, 270
Zero-Product Property, 226, 270, 288, 289,
349

**quadratic expressions**
factoring, 216–223, 270
perfect square trinomials, 219, 220

**quadratic function(s)**
defined, 194
graphing, 194–201
graphing standard form of, 202–208
maximum and minimum values, 268
modeling, 209–213, 269
standard form of, 202–208, 268, 269
transformations, 194–201
vertex form, 194, 196–197, 198, 203, 204,
268

**Quadratic Parent Function,** 194

**quadratic-quadratic systems,** 260

**QuadReg feature,** 211, 331

**quantity,** 5

**quartic polynomial,** 281, 341

**quartic regression,** 352

**quartile,** 706, 746

**Quick Review,** 51–52, 121–126,
182–185, 266–272, 346–352,
421–426, 486–490, 552–556,
602–606, 662–666, 744–748,
810–812, 886–889, 952–954

**quintic polynomial,** 281

**Quotient Property of Logarithms,** 462

**quotients,** 251, 369, 462

## R

**radian(s)**
converting to and from degrees, 836, 837
cosine, 837
defined, 836
measuring in, 836–842, 887
reciprocal trigonometric functions, 875–
877

**radical conjugates,** 377

**radical equations**
defined, 390
solving, 390–397, 416, 425

**radical expression(s)**
binomial, adding and subtracting, 374–380
binomial, multiplying and dividing, 376
combining, 374
conjugates, 377
dividing, 367–373, 423
equivalent form of, 381
index of, 362, 423
like radicals, 374, 424
multiplying, 367–373, 423
principal root, 361, 423
radicand, 362, 423
rational exponents and, 381–388
rationalizing the denominator, 369, 370,
377, 423
simplifying, 363, 368–370, 376, 423
square roots, 361–368, 377

**radical function(s),** 414–420, 426

**radical(s)**
combining, 367, 369, 374, 384
like, 374, 424
simplest form of, 368

**radical symbol,** 225

**radicand,** 362, 423

**radius**
circle, 630, 633, 665
unit circle, 830, 886

**random sample,** 718, 747

**range**
of a data set, 706, 746
interquartile, 706
of relations, 61, 62, 123, 124

**rate of change,** 437

**ratio(s)**
common, 581, 605
constant, 74
of outcomes, 682
trigonometric, 860, 911–918, 953

**rational**
inequalities, 550–551
numbers, 12, 377

**rational equation(s)**
solving, 542–548, 556
systems with, 549

**rational exponent(s)**
converting to radical form, 381–382, 424
simplifying expressions with, 381–388

**rational expression(s)**
adding, 534, 535, 556
complex fractions, 537
defined, 527
dividing, 529
Least Common Denominator, 535, 537
Least Common Multiple, 534–535
multiplying, 528
operations with, 528, 534, 535, 536
simplifying, 527–533, 535, 536, 555
subtracting, 536, 556

**rational function(s)**
asymptotes, 517–518
defined, 515
graphing, 506, 515–523
point of discontinuity, 516–517, 555

**rationalizing the denominator,** 369, 370,
377, 423

**Rational Root Theorem,** 312, 313, 350

Index

**real-number roots,** 362–363

**real number(s)**
absolute value of, 41
graphing, 11, 13
negative, 248
ordering, 13
properties of, 11–17, 51
square root of a negative, 248, 249
subsets of, 12

**Reasoning**
exercises, 6, 9, 13, 14, 15, 16, 19, 23, 25,
29, 30, 36, 37, 40, 44, 45, 48, 53, 62,
64, 66, 70, 71, 72, 73, 75, 76, 79, 82,
87, 89, 93, 97, 102, 103, 105, 108, 112,
116, 117, 118, 119, 135, 138, 139, 140,
145, 152, 157, 158, 162, 167, 168, 169,
171, 176, 177, 195, 205, 210, 212, 214,
215, 219, 221, 223, 224, 228, 229, 230,
235, 242, 244, 246, 249, 255, 261, 263,
284, 285, 286, 287, 290, 299, 300, 305,
308, 309, 310, 311, 315, 316, 318, 321,
323, 324, 325, 328, 329, 334, 335, 337,
341, 344, 345, 353, 360, 362, 364, 365,
366, 369, 370, 372, 375, 377, 379, 382,
385, 387, 389, 393, 396, 397, 401, 403,
406, 409, 411, 417, 435, 437, 438, 439,
440, 445, 447, 454, 456, 459, 465, 466,
470, 473, 475, 480, 502, 505, 506, 508,
513, 520, 521, 522, 525, 526, 529, 530,
532, 535, 544, 545, 549, 557, 567, 571,
574, 576, 582, 588, 591, 592, 598, 600,
607, 615, 621, 624, 629, 632, 634, 637,
640, 642, 647, 651, 656, 659, 660, 667,
676, 678, 679, 683, 685, 686, 690, 693,
695, 697, 700, 701, 703, 707, 710, 714,
715, 717, 719, 721, 723, 724, 730, 736,
737, 738, 739, 757, 761, 766, 775, 779,
782, 783, 789, 791, 794, 795, 798, 802,
821, 823, 825, 831, 833, 834, 835, 839,
840, 841, 851, 856, 858, 863, 866, 871,
873, 876, 877, 879, 881, 882, 889, 897,
905, 909, 915, 917, 919, 925, 929, 933,
934, 937, 940, 942, 946, 948
Here's Why It Works, 34, 62, 81, 203, 298,
307, 464, 623, 674, 837, 838, 920, 929,
935, 936, 938, 943, 945
Think / Write problems, 6, 35, 101, 108, 144,
168, 176, 198, 220, 234, 243, 252, 259,
300, 328, 364, 368, 376, 384, 417, 437,
465, 519, 529, 538, 543, 566, 582, 588,
648, 654, 677, 682, 698, 778, 787, 822,
862, 871, 876, 899, 906, 922, 930, 940

**reciprocal,** 14
identities, 896, 952

**reciprocal function(s)**
defined, 507
family of, 507–514, 554
graphing, 507–511, 554, 878
transformations, 508
translations, 509, 510
trigonometric, 875–882, 889

**recursive formula,** 565, 566, 604, 605

**reduced row echelon form,** 177

**Reference**
Formulas of Geometry, 985
Glossary, 986
Math Symbols, 978
Measures, 977
Properties and Formulas, 979–984

**reflection matrix,** 796

**reflection(s)**
absolute value functions, 108
defined, 101, 125

of ellipse, 640
exponential functions, 434, 444
geometric, 793, 797, 812
of hyperbola, 649
logarithmic functions, 455
quadratic functions, 195
reciprocal function, 509

**Reflexive Property of Equality,** 26

**regression**
cubic, 331–334
exponential, 459
linear, 94–95, 333
logarithmic, 459
polynomial, 331–334
quadratic, 211, 331

**relation(s),** 60–65
defined, 60, 123
domain of, 61, 62, 123
graphing, 60–61, 406–407
inverse, 405–413
mapping diagram, 60–61
range of, 61, 62, 123
table of values, 60–61

**Remainder Theorem,** 307, 349

**removable discontinuity,** 516

*Resources* 3D, 10A–B, 17A–B, 24A–B,
32A–B, 40A–B, 48A–B, 59D, 67A–B,
73A–B, 80A–B, 88A–B, 98A–B,
106A–B, 113A–B, 120A–B, 133D,
141A–B, 148A–B, 155A–B, 162A–B,
165A–B, 173A–B, 181A–B, 193D,
201A–B, 208A–B, 214A–B, 223A–B,
231A–B, 239A–B, 247A–B, 255A–B,
264A–B, 279D, 287A–B, 295A–B,
302A–B, 310A–B, 317A–B, 324A–B,
330A–B, 338A–B, 345A–B, 359D,
366A–B, 373A–B, 380A–B, 388A–B,
397A–B, 404A–B, 412A–B, 420A–B,
433D, 441A–B, 450A–B, 458A–B,
468A–B, 476A–B, 483A–B, 496D,
505A–B, 514A–B, 523A–B, 533A–B,
541A–B, 548A–B, 563D, 571A–B,
577A–B, 586A–B, 593A–B, 601A–B,
613D, 620A–B, 629A–B, 636A–B,
644A–B, 652A–B, 660A–B, 673D,
680A–B, 687A–B, 693A–B, 702A–B,
711A–B, 717A–B, 723A–B, 732A–B,
739A–B, 755D, 762A–B, 771A–B,
782A–B, 792A–B, 800A–B, 807A–B,
819D, 826A–B, 834A–B, 842A–B,
850A–B, 859A–B, 866A–B, 874A–B,
882A–B, 895D, 902A–B, 910A–B,
918A–B, 926A–B, 934A–B, 942A–B

*Reteaching worksheets* 10A, 17A, 24A,
32A, 40A, 48A, 67A, 73A, 80A, 88A,
98A, 106A, 113A, 120A, 141A, 148A,
155A, 162A, 165A, 173A, 181A,
201A, 208A, 214A, 223A, 231A,
239A, 247A, 255A, 264A, 287A,
295A, 302A, 310A, 317A, 324A,
330A, 338A, 345A, 366A, 373A,
380A, 388A, 397A, 404A, 412A,
420A, 441A, 450A, 458A, 468A,
476A, 483A, 505A, 514A, 523A,
533A, 541A, 548A, 571A, 577A,
586A, 593A, 601A, 620A, 629A,
636A, 644A, 652A, 660A, 680A,
687A, 693A, 702A, 711A, 717A, 723A,
732A, 739A, 762A, 771A, 782A,
792A, 800A, 807A, 826A, 834A,
842A, 850A, 859A, 866A, 874A,
882A, 902A, 910A, 918A, 926A,
934A, 942A

**Review**
Square Roots and Radicals, 225
Properties of Exponents, 360
Special Right Triangles, 827

**right triangles**
side lengths of, 912, 914
special, 827
trigonometric ratios for, 911–918

**roots of numbers**
cube, 361, 362, 417
*n*th, 361–366, 423
principal, 361, 381, 423
real, 362–363
square. *See* Square root(s)
writing equations from, 232

**roots of polynomial equations**
Conjugate Root Theorem, 350
Descartes' Rule of Signs, 315, 350
determining the number of, 319–322
finding by graphing, 299
identifying, 314
irrational, 314, 350
theorems of, 312, 313, 350
writing equations from, 232

**rotation**
center of, 796
of matrices, 793, 796, 812
measures of angles, 828
of vectors, 802

**row operation,** 176, 185

# S

**sample(s),** 718–723
bias in, 743, 747
convenience, 718
defined, 718, 747
random, 718, 747
self-selected, 718
systematic, 718

**sample space**
defined, 682
equally likely, 682, 744

**scalar multiplication,** 764–765, 794, 803,
804, 810

**scalars,** 764, 765–766

**scatter plots,** 92–93, 125

**science,** 466, 584

**secant function,** 875, 889

**seismology,** 474

**self-selected sample,** 718

**sequences**
arithmetic, 572–577, 604
defined, 564, 604
explicit formulas, 565, 567, 604, 605
Fibonacci Sequence, 578
finite, 587
geometric, 580–586, 605
infinite, 587
*n*th term, 565
recursive formula, 565, 566, 604, 605
terms of, 564, 568

**series**
analyzing, 598
arithmetic, 587–595, 605
defined, 587, 604, 605
finite, 587, 595, 596
geometric, 594, 595–601, 606

infinite, 587, 594, 598
sum of a, 589, 590

**Short Response exercises,**
    end of chapter problems, 56, 130, 190,
       276, 356, 430, 494, 560, 610, 670, 752,
       816, 892, 958
    end of lesson problems, 10, 17, 24, 67, 80,
       88, 98, 106, 113, 155, 162, 181, 201,
       231, 255, 264, 287, 302, 324, 345, 373,
       397, 404, 420, 450, 458, 468, 505, 514,
       533, 541, 586, 593, 620, 644, 652, 660,
       680, 687, 702, 711, 723, 739, 762, 771,
       792, 800, 834, 842, 850, 859, 866, 874,
       902, 918, 926, 942, 949

**show your work,** 54

**shrink.** *See* compression

**sigma**
    standard deviation, 712
    summation, 589

**simplest form**
    absolute value functions, 107
    defined, 527
    of functions, 99, 125
    of radical expressions, 368
    of rational expressions, 527, 535, 536, 555
    writing expressions in, 385

**simplifying**
    expressions, 21, 52
    imaginary numbers, 249
    logarithms, 463
    numbers, 249
    problem solving strategy, 12, 18, 19, 21,
       23, 24, 25, 26, 28, 35, 36, 42, 49, 51,
       52, 53, 63, 64, 69, 70, 76, 82, 84, 101,
       124, 128, 167, 169, 170, 176, 177, 182,
       204, 225, 236, 240, 241, 242, 244, 249,
       250, 251, 252, 254, 256, 271, 272, 286,
       290, 297, 300, 304, 321, 328, 330, 342,
       349, 354, 360, 365, 366, 367, 368, 369,
       370, 371, 372, 373, 375, 376, 377, 378,
       379, 382, 384, 385, 386, 387, 388, 389,
       391, 392, 393, 394, 403, 404, 417, 422,
       423, 424, 425, 426, 430, 436, 441, 447,
       453, 463, 465, 466, 469, 472, 478, 480,
       481, 490, 493, 494, 501, 502, 505, 510,
       516, 517, 527, 528, 531, 532, 534, 536,
       537, 538, 539, 540, 542, 543, 555, 556,
       565, 573, 574, 577, 581, 588, 596, 597,
       631, 633, 640, 647, 648, 649, 652, 656,
       657, 899, 900
    radical expressions, 363, 368–370, 376,
       423
    rational exponents, 381–388
    rational expressions, 528

**simulations,** 682, 725, 744

**sine, of angles,** 830, 831, 837, 886

**sine curve,** 844, 887, 936

**sine function,** 843–850
    families of, 869
    graphing, 843, 844–846
    inverse, 905
    modeling light waves, 847
    properties of, 845, 886
    radian measures, 843
    translations, 867–874, 888, 936
    unit circles and, 843

**Skills Handbook**
    Area and Volume, 964
    Bar and Circle Graphs, 965
    Descriptive Statistics and Histograms, 966
    Factoring and Operations With
       Polynomials, 967

Operations With Exponents, 968
Operations With Fractions, 969
Operations With Rational Expressions, 970
Percent and Percent Applications,
    971
Ratios and Proportions, 972
Scientific Notation and Significant Digits,
    973
Simplifying Expressions With Integers, 974
The Coordinate Plane, Slope, and
    Midpoint, 975
The Pythagorean Theorem and the
    Distance Formula, 976

**slope**
    defined, 74, 124
    formula for, 74, 124
    horizontal lines, 75
    negative, 75
    of parallel lines, 85
    of perpendicular lines, 85
    positive, 75
    undefined, 75
    vertical lines, 75
    zero, 75

**slope-intercept form,** 74–80
    defined, 76
    writing equations in, 74–80, 83, 124

**social studies,** 98

**sociology,** 730

**The Soldier's Reasonable Request,** 596,
    597

**solution(s)**
    of absolute value statements, 44
    complex, 248–255, 319–322, 351
    extraneous, 42, 43, 393
    imaginary, 252, 272
    as the intersection of planes, 166
    to polynomial equations. *See* polynomial
       equations
    to quadratic equations. *See* quadratic
       equations
    real numbers as, 36, 52
    to systems of equations. *See* systems of
       equations

**Solve It!** 4, 11, 18, 26, 33, 41, 60, 68, 74, 81,
    92, 99, 107, 114, 134, 142, 149, 157,
    166, 174, 194, 202, 209, 216, 226, 233,
    240, 248, 258, 280, 288, 296, 303, 312,
    319, 326, 331, 339, 361, 367, 374, 381,
    390, 398, 405, 414, 434, 442, 451, 462,
    469, 478, 498, 507, 515, 527, 534, 542,
    564, 572, 580, 587, 595, 614, 622, 630,
    638, 645, 653, 674, 681, 688, 696, 704,
    712, 718, 725, 733, 756, 764, 774, 784,
    793, 801, 820, 828, 836, 843, 853, 860,
    867, 875, 896, 903, 911, 920, 928, 935,
    943

**Solving Equations, as Big Idea,** 266, 267,
    346, 347, 421, 422

**Solving Equations and Inequalities, as Big
    Idea,** 49, 50, 133, 182, 183, 421, 422

**space, graphing points in,** 164

*Spanish Support. See* **Resources**

**special right triangles,** 827

**spreadsheets, using for problem solving,**
    200, 504, 524

**square(s)**
    completing the, 233–239
    difference of, factoring, 220, 297
    perfect square trinomial, 219, 220, 297

**square matrix,** 768, 774, 811

**square root(s)**
    of a negative real number, 248, 249
    principal root, 361
    properties of, 225
    radical expressions, 361–368, 377
    solving equations using, 233, 271, 390–
       397, 425

**square root function,** 414–420, 426

**standard deviation,** 712–717
    defined, 712
    formula for, 704, 712
    using to describe data, 714
    z-score, 740

**standard form**
    defined, 202
    of equation of circle, 630, 665
    of equation of ellipse, 639
    of equation of hyperbola, 647
    of equation of parabola, 209
    of linear equations, 82–83, 124
    of polynomial functions, 281, 348
    of quadratic equation, 270
    of quadratic functions, 202–208, 268, 269

**Standardized Test Prep.** *See* assessment,
    Standardized Test Prep

*Standardized Test Prep worksheets* 10B,
    17B, 24B, 32B, 40B, 48B, 67B, 73B,
    80B, 88B, 98B, 106B, 113B, 120B,
    141B, 148B, 155B, 162B, 165B, 173B,
    181B, 201B, 208B, 214B, 223B, 231B,
    239B, 247B, 255B, 264B, 287B, 295B,
    302B, 310B, 317B, 324B, 330B, 338B,
    345B, 366B, 373B, 380B, 388B, 397B,
    404B, 412B, 420B, 441B, 450B, 458B,
    468B, 476B, 483B, 505B, 514B, 523B,
    533B, 541B, 548B, 571B, 577B, 586B,
    593B, 601B, 620B, 629B, 636B, 644B,
    652B, 660B, 680B, 687B, 693B, 702B,
    711B, 717B, 723B, 732B, 739B, 762B,
    771B, 782B, 792B, 800B, 807B, 826B,
    834B, 842B, 850B, 859B, 866B, 874B,
    882B, 902B, 910B, 918B, 926B, 934B,
    942B

**standard normal curve,** 740

**standard normal distribution,** 740

**standard position of angle,** 828, 829, 886

**STAT CALC feature,** 713

**STAT EDIT feature,** 707, 713

**STAT feature,** 95, 459, 460, 477

**STAT PLOT feature,** 459, 460, 477,
    707

**step function,** 90

**stretch**
    absolute value functions, 108, 109
    exponential functions, 434, 444
    logarithmic functions, 455
    quadratic functions, 195
    reciprocal function, 509
    vertical defined, 102, 125

**study methods**
    controlled experiment, 719
    observational study, 719
    survey, 719

**substitution**
    solving linear-quadratic system using, 259
    solving linear systems using, 144
    solving systems of equations using, 142–
       143, 166–173
    solving three-variable systems, 186

**Substitution Property of Equality,** 26

*Index* (vertical sidebar text)

**subtraction**
of algebraic expressions, 21
of complex numbers, 250
definition of, 21
of functions, 398, 399
inverse operation to, 27
of matrices, 756–762, 810
of radical expressions, 374–380
of rational expressions, 536, 556
of vectors, 803

**Subtraction Property,** 21
of Equality, 27
of Inequality, 34

**Sumatra, earthquake in,** 453

**summation.** *See also* addition
of cubes, 297
notation, 589, 590, 605
opposite of a, 21
of a series, 588, 589, 590, 596, 598, 605, 606

**Sum of a Finite Arithmetic Series,** 587

**surveys,** 718–723
analyzing questions in, 720
defined, 720
designing, 720

**symbols**
absolute value, 36, 44
inequality, 13
radical, 225
sigma, for standard deviation, 712
sigma, for summation, 589
square root, 225
summation, 505, 589, 590

**Symmetric Property of Equality,** 26

**symmetry, axis of,** 107, 194, 622, 646

*Synthesizing* 83, 100, 109, 115, 144, 169, 175, 176, 177, 178, 197, 203, 204, 205, 227, 236, 240, 241, 248, 260, 282, 283, 284, 313, 314, 315, 318, 320, 321, 377, 393, 443, 445, 446, 447, 460, 498, 499, 501, 543, 572, 573, 597, 647, 682, 785, 787, 794

**synthetic division,** 303, 306–307, 349

**systematic sample,** 718

**systems of equations**
defined, 134, 184
linear. *See* linear systems
linear-quadratic, 258–264
with no unique solution, 145, 166, 184, 787
quadratic, 258–264, 272
solving by elimination, 144, 166–173, 184, 186
solving by substitution, 166–173, 186
solving using matrices, 174–178, 186, 787, 788
in three-variables, 166–173, 186
writing as a matrix equation, 785, 786

**systems of linear inequalities,**
149–155, 157, 166, 184, 185

**systems with rational equations,** 549

# T

**table(s)**
finding conditional probability using, 696–697
identifying direct variation from, 68–69

for problem solving, 5, 6, 8, 9, 51, 54, 60, 61, 65, 67, 68, 69, 72, 92, 93, 94, 95, 96, 97, 98, 100, 102, 104, 106, 121, 123, 125, 127, 130, 135, 136, 138, 149, 150, 153, 159, 160, 211, 212, 213, 215, 229, 230, 232, 256, 257, 259, 261, 262, 263, 266, 269, 270, 283, 286, 287, 335, 336, 337, 338, 352, 405, 406, 410, 434, 437, 442, 443, 444, 448, 454, 455, 458, 460, 473, 474, 477, 485, 493, 499, 503, 508, 526, 533, 544, 551, 554, 565, 570, 584, 585, 609, 615, 616, 636, 644, 660, 669, 713, 716, 761, 770
representing relations, 60
solving exponential equations using, 470
solving quadratic equations with, 227
solving systems of equations using, 134–141, 149–150
using to find patterns, 6

**TABLE feature,** 140, 202, 227, 437, 863

**Table of Values,** 60

*Tactile Learners* 83, 100, 101, 261, 623

**Take Note**
Concept Summary, 21, 44, 83, 102, 297, 322, 435, 444, 455, 653–654, 655, 869
Family(ies). *See* Family(ies)
Key Concepts. *See* Key Concepts
Polynomial Factoring Techniques, 297
Properties. *See* Properties
Solutions of Absolute Value Statements, 44
Theorems. *See* Theorems
Transformations of *f(x)*, 102
Translating Horizontal and Vertical Ellipses, 653–654
Translating Horizontal and Vertical Hyperbolas, 655
Writing Equations of Lines, 83

**tangent**
of angle, 860, 888
curve, 936
identity, 896, 939, 952

**tangent function,** 860–866
graphing, 862
inverse, 905
properties of, 862, 886
translations, 936

**TBLSET feature,** 470, 472

**technical writing,** 525

**Technology**
Fitting Curves to Data, 459–460
Graphic Conic Sections, 621
Graphing Inverses, 413
Graphing Rational Functions, 506
Graphing Trigonometric Functions, 852
Linear Programming, 163
Oblique Asymptotes, 524–525
Rational Inequalities, 550–551
Using Logarithms for Exponential Models, 477

**term(s)**
in algebraic expressions, 20
in arithmetic sequences, 604
constant, 20
defined, 20, 564
degree of, 281
in geometric sequences, 580
like, 21, 52
in polynomials, 281
in sequences, 568, 604

**terminal**
point, 801, 812
side of angles, 828, 886

**test point,** 115

**Test-Taking Strategies**
Answering Word Problems, 274
Check Your Answers, 608
Draw a Diagram, 492
Find Needed Information, 128, 274, 558, 608, 668
Justify Your Reasoning, 54
Make a Drawing, 188
Model Word Problems, 274
Show Your Work, 54
Simplify, 354
tips for success, 54, 128, 188, 274, 354, 428, 492, 558, 608, 668, 750, 814, 891
Use a Formula, 558
Use What You Know, 274, 558

**Test-Taking Tips,** 54, 128, 188, 274, 354, 428, 492, 558, 608, 668, 750, 814, 891

*Texas Instrument*™ *Activities. See* Resources

**Theorems**
Binomial Theorem, 326–330, 351
Conjugate Root Theorem, 314, 350
Descartes' Rule of Signs, 315, 350
Factor Theorem, 290
Fundamental Theorem of Algebra, 319–324, 351
Law of Cosines, 928–934, 953
Law of Sines, 921, 953
Pythagorean Theorem, 640, 666, 801, 898
Rational Root Theorem, 312, 313, 350
Remainder Theorem, 307, 349

**theoretical probability,** 682, 683, 744

**Think About a Plan exercises,** 9, 16, 17, 23, 31, 39, 46, 66, 72, 79, 87, 105, 112, 119, 139, 147, 153, 161, 172, 180, 199, 207, 213, 222, 230, 238, 245, 254, 262, 286, 294, 301, 309, 316, 323, 329, 336, 343, 365, 371, 379, 387, 395, 403, 411, 419, 440, 448, 457, 466, 474, 481, 504, 512, 522, 532, 540, 546, 570, 575, 585, 592, 599, 619, 628, 635, 643, 650, 659, 679, 686, 692, 701, 709, 716, 722, 730, 738, 761, 770, 781, 790, 799, 806, 833, 841, 849, 857, 865, 873, 880, 900, 909, 917, 925, 932, 941, 947

*Think About a Plan worksheets* 10B, 17B, 24B, 32B, 40B, 48B, 67B, 73B, 80B, 88B, 98B, 106B, 113B, 120B, 141B, 148B, 155B, 162B, 165B, 173B, 181B, 201B, 208B, 214B, 223B, 231B, 239B, 247B, 255B, 264B, 287B, 295B, 302B, 310B, 317B, 324B, 330B, 338B, 345B, 366B, 373B, 380B, 388B, 397B, 404B, 412B, 420B, 441B, 450B, 458B, 468B, 476B, 483B, 505B, 514B, 523B, 533B, 541B, 548B, 571B, 577B, 586B, 593B, 601B, 620B, 629B, 636B, 644B, 652B, 660B, 680B, 687B, 693B, 702B, 711B, 717B, 723B, 732B, 739B, 762B, 771B, 782B, 792B, 800B, 807B, 826B, 834B, 842B, 850B, 859B, 866B, 874B, 882B, 902B, 910B, 918B, 926B, 934B, 942B

**Think/Write problems,** 6, 35, 101, 108, 144, 168, 176, 198, 220, 234, 243, 252, 259, 300, 328, 364, 368, 376, 384, 417, 437, 465, 519, 529, 538, 543, 566, 582, 588, 648, 654, 677, 682, 698, 778, 787, 822, 862, 871, 876, 899, 906, 922, 930, 940

**three-dimensional coordinate space,**
164–165

**three-variable system of equations,** 166–173, 186

**Tips for Success,** 54, 127, 188, 274, 354, 428, 492, 558, 608, 668, 750, 814, 891

**tip-to-tail method,** 803

**Tmax feature,** 413

**Tmin feature,** 413

**tolerance,** 44

**TRACE feature,** 506

**transformation(s)**
  as Big Idea, 808, 809
  of circles, 632
  combining, 103
  compressions, 102, 108, 109, 125, 195, 434, 444, 455
  defined, 99
  dilation, 793, 794, 795, 812
  of exponential functions, 443–444
  of functions, 99–106
  geometric, 793–800, 812
  identifying, 110
  image, 793
  of parabolas, 195, 626
  of polynomial functions, 339–341, 352
  preimage, 793, 812
  of quadratic functions, 194–201
  of reciprocal functions, 508
  reflection, 101, 108, 125, 195, 434, 444, 455, 509, 793, 797, 812, 936
  rotation, 793, 796, 802, 812, 828
  stretches, 102, 108, 109, 125, 195, 434, 444, 455, 509
  translations. *See* translations
  types of, 125, 793

**Transitive Property**
  of Equality, 26, 938
  of Inequality, 34

**translations.** *See also* transformations
  of circles, 631
  compressions, 102, 108
  of conic sections, 653–660, 666
  cosine function, 867–874, 888, 936
  defined, 99
  dilations, 793, 794, 795, 812
  of ellipses, 653–654
  equations of, 631
  of exponential functions, 444
  geometric, 793–800, 812
  graphing, 108, 125, 126, 196, 510, 853, 868–870
  horizontal, 100–101, 102, 108, 125, 415
  of hyperbola, 655
  image, 812
  of logarithmic functions, 455
  of parabola, 197
  phase shifts, 868
  of quadratic functions, 195, 196
  of reciprocal functions, 509, 510
  rotation, 793, 796, 802, 812, 828
  sine and cosine graphs, 853
  sine function, 867–874, 888, 936
  square root function, 415
  tangent function, 936
  types of, 108
  using matrix addition, 794
  vertical, 100, 102, 108, 109, 125, 415, 639
  writing, 869, 871

**transverse axis,** 645, 646

**tree diagrams,** 699, 726

**trend line,** 93–94, 125

**triangles**
  angles of, 920–924, 927, 928–931
  area of, 776, 920–921
  congruent, 927
  finding height of, 913
  finding sides of, 920–924, 927, 928–931
  Law of Cosines, 928–934
  Law of Sines, 920–926
  right, 911–918
  special right, 827

**trigonometric**
  expressions, 896, 899
  ratios, 911–918, 953

**trigonometric equations**
  modeling with, 871
  solving by factoring, 906
  solving using angle identities, 937
  solving using inverses, 903–910, 952
  trigonometric identities vs., 906

**trigonometric functions**
  graphing, 852, 878
  inverse, 903–910
  non-additive, 938
  reciprocal, 875–882, 888

**trigonometric identities,** 896–902
  additive, 935
  angles of, 935
  cotangent, 896
  defined, 896, 952
  domain of validity, 896
  reciprocal, 896
  tangent, 896
  trigonometric equations vs., 906
  verifying, 899

**trinomial**
  defined, 281
  perfect square, 219, 220, 234–235, 271, 297
  quadratic, 196–197, 198, 218–219, 297

**turning point,** 282, 348

**Twain, Mark,** 228

## U

*Understanding by Design* 2, 4, 11, 18, 26, 33, 41, 49, 50, 58, 60, 68, 74, 81, 92, 99, 107, 114, 121, 122, 132, 134, 142, 149, 157, 166, 174, 182, 183, 192, 194, 202, 209, 216, 226, 234, 241, 249, 259, 266, 267, 278, 280, 288, 296, 303, 312, 319, 326, 331, 339, 346, 347, 358, 361, 367, 374, 381, 390, 398, 405, 414, 421, 422, 432, 434, 442, 451, 462, 469, 478, 486, 487, 495, 498, 507, 515, 527, 534, 542, 552, 553, 562, 564, 572, 580, 587, 595, 602, 603, 612, 614, 622, 630, 638, 645, 653, 662, 663, 672, 674, 681, 688, 696, 704, 712, 718, 725, 733, 742, 743, 754, 756, 764, 774, 793, 801, 808, 809, 818, 820, 828, 836, 860, 867, 875, 884, 894, 896, 911, 920, 928, 943, 950, 951

**uniform distribution,** 694

**unit circle**
  angles in, 828–834, 886
  cosine of angle, 853
  defined, 830
  inverse trigonometric functions, 904–905
  sine of angle, 843

  tangent of angle, 860
  to verify identity, 898

## V

**variable(s)**
  as Big Idea, 49, 50, 346, 602, 603
  clarifying, 12
  classifying, 12
  dependent, 63
  independent, 63

**variable**
  matrix, 785, 811
  quantity, 5

**variance,** 712, 713, 746

**variation**
  combined, 500, 501, 502
  constant of, 68, 123, 554
  direct, 68–73, 123, 498–499
  inverse, 498–505, 554
  joint, 501, 554
  measure of, 712, 746

**VARS feature,** 413, 460

**vectors,** 801–807
  adding, 803
  defined, 801
  direction of, 801, 812
  dot product, 804
  initial point, 801, 812
  magnitude of, 801, 812
  normal, 804
  operations with, 803
  representing, 802
  rotating, 802
  scalar multiplication of, 803
  size and direction, 801
  subtracting, 803
  terminal point, 801, 812
  in two dimensions, 801
  writing in matrix form, 802

**vertex(ices)**
  of absolute value functions, 107, 126
  defined, 107
  of ellipse, 639, 665
  of feasible region, 158, 185
  of hyperbola, 645, 646
  matrix representation of, 793
  of parabolas, 194, 196

**vertex form of quadratic functions,** 194, 195, 196–197, 198, 203, 204, 236, 268

**Vertex Principle of Linear Programming,** 158, 185

**vertical**
  asymptotes, 518, 554
  ellipse, 639
  line, 75, 107, 414
  translation, 102, 108, 109, 125, 195, 415

**Vertical-line test,** 62–63, 414

*Visual Learners* 4, 20, 33, 43, 61, 82, 91, 108, 150, 158, 215, 217, 219, 235, 243, 250, 258, 264B, 291, 304, 340, 375, 416, 444, 446, 459, 471, 524, 616, 617, 661, 674, 675, 684, 689, 690, 714, 772, 805, 822, 831, 854, 869, 897, 906

**vocabulary**
  Chapter Vocabulary, 50, 122, 183, 267, 347, 422, 487, 553, 743, 809, 885
  exercises, 15, 22, 30, 45, 64, 71, 78, 86, 138, 145, 152, 160, 171, 179, 198, 221, 229, 235, 237, 285, 293, 300, 315, 322, 328, 335, 342, 370, 378, 394, 409, 439,

456, 461, 465, 512, 530, 557, 568, 591, 617, 627, 658, 678, 685, 691, 703, 708, 715, 721, 729, 737, 760, 769, 805, 840, 847, 863, 872, 900, 924

Lesson Vocabulary, 4, 11, 18, 26, 33, 41, 60, 68, 74, 81, 91, 99, 107, 114, 125, 134, 142, 157, 166, 174, 194, 202, 209, 216, 226, 234, 241, 249, 259, 280, 288, 296, 303, 312, 319, 326, 331, 339, 361, 367, 374, 390, 398, 405, 414, 434, 442, 451, 462, 469, 478, 498, 515, 527, 534, 542, 564, 572, 580, 587, 595, 614, 622, 630, 638, 645, 674, 681, 688, 696, 704, 712, 718, 725, 733, 756, 764, 774, 784, 793, 801, 820, 828, 836, 843, 853, 860, 867, 875, 896, 911, 920, 928

Looking Ahead Vocabulary, 57, 131, 191, 277, 431, 495, 561, 611, 671, 753, 817, 893

Vocabulary Audio Online, 2, 58, 132, 192, 278, 358, 432, 495, 562, 612, 672, 754, 818, 894

Vocabulary Builder, 54, 128, 188, 274, 750, 814, 891, 951

# W

**Whispering Gallery,** 641

**whole numbers,** 12

**words modeling algebraic expressions,** 18–19

**work backwards,** 362

**writing**
    equations, 74–80, 83, 124, 232, 452
    exercises, 16, 17, 24, 25, 31, 32, 39, 47, 48, 53, 72, 89, 96, 97, 105, 112, 120, 127, 140, 145, 147, 154, 171, 179, 180,

187, 200, 207, 213, 222, 224, 245, 273, 294, 302, 310, 311, 317, 325, 329, 336, 345, 353, 372, 379, 411, 413, 418, 427, 457, 460, 461, 466, 474, 477, 482, 484, 491, 503, 505, 512, 513, 522, 540, 547, 557, 576, 585, 598, 600, 607, 621, 629, 636, 644, 661, 667, 679, 680, 685, 686, 701, 703, 710, 716, 721, 722, 730, 738, 744, 749, 761, 770, 773, 781, 782, 783, 798, 799, 806, 813, 823, 825, 833, 841, 851, 852, 857, 863, 866, 881, 890, 901, 907, 909, 915, 919, 926, 931, 933, 942, 948, 955

    expressions, 20, 385
    functions, 110, 451–458
    inequalities, 33, 34, 117
    technical writing, 525
    Think/Write problems, 6, 35, 101, 108, 144, 168, 176, 198, 220, 234, 243, 252, 259, 300, 328, 364, 368, 376, 384, 417, 437, 465, 519, 529, 538, 543, 566, 582, 588, 648, 654, 677, 682, 698, 778, 787, 822, 862, 871, 876, 899, 906, 922, 930, 940
    translations, 869

# X

**$x$-axis,** 101, 102, 164, 195, 197, 226, 256, 435

**$x$-coefficient,** 175

**$x$-coordinate,** 61, 62, 74, 123, 124, 203, 416

**$x$-intercept,** 76, 243, 289, 291, 319, 348

**Xmax feature,** 413

**Xmin feature,** 413

**$xy$-coordinate plane,** 164

# Y

**$y$-axis,** 101, 102, 164

**$y$-coefficient,** 175

**$y$-coordinate,** 61, 62, 74, 123, 124, 203

**$y$-intercept,** 76

**YLIST feature,** 477

# Z

**$z$-axis,** 164

**zero(s)**
    additive identity, 13
    multiplication by, 21
    multiplicative inverse and, 13
    multiplicative property of, 765, 768
    multiplicity of, 291
    of polynomial functions, 288, 289, 348
    properties of, 13, 226, 270, 289, 765
    of quadratic equation, 226, 270
    of quadratic function, 226
    of quartic functions, 341
    as a real number, 13
    of transformed cubic function, 339–340

**ZERO option,** 163, 227, 299

**Zero-Product Property,** 226, 270, 288, 289, 349

**zoology,** 440, 734, 735

**ZOOM feature,** 460

**$z$-score,** 740

Index

# Acknowledgments

## Staff Credits

The people who made up the High School Mathematics team—representing composition services, core design digital and multimedia production services, digital product development, editorial, editorial services, manufacturing, marketing, and production management—are listed below.

Dan Anderson, Scott Andrews, Christopher Anton, Carolyn Artin, Michael Avidon, Margaret Banker, Charlie Bink, Niki Birbilis, Suzanne Biron, Beth Blumberg, Kyla Brown, Rebekah Brown, Judith Buice, Sylvia Bullock, Stacie Cartwright, Carolyn Chappo, Christia Clarke, Tom Columbus, Andrew Coppola, AnnMarie Coyne, Bob Craton, Nicholas Cronin, Patrick Culleton, Damaris Curran, Steven Cushing, Sheila DeFazio, Cathie Dillender, Emily Dumas, Patty Fagan, Frederick Fellows, Jorgensen Fernandez, Mandy Figueroa, Suzanne Finn, Sara Freund, Matt Frueh, Jon Fuhrer, Andy Gaus, Mark Geyer, Mircea Goia, Andrew Gorlin, Shelby Gragg, Ellen Granter, Jay Grasso, Lisa Gustafson, Toni Haluga, Greg Ham, Marc Hamilton, Chris Handorf, Angie Hanks, Scott Harris, Cynthia Harvey, Phil Hazur, Thane Heninger, Aun Holland, Amanda House, Chuck Jann, Linda Johnson, Blair Jones, Marian Jones, Tim Jones, Gillian Kahn, Brian Keegan, Jonathan Kier, Jennifer King, Tamara King, Elizabeth Krieble, Meytal Kotik, Brian Kubota, Roshni Kutty, Mary Landry, Christopher Langley, Christine Lee, Sara Levendusky, Lisa Lin, Wendy Marberry, Dominique Mariano, Clay Martin, Rich McMahon, Eve Melnechuk, Cynthia Metallides, Hope Morley, Christine Nevola, Michael O'Donnell, Michael Oster, Ameer Padshah, Jeffrey Paulhus, Jonathan Penyack, Valerie Perkins, Brian Reardon, Wendy Rock, Marcy Rose, Carol Roy, Irene Rubin, Hugh Rutledge, Vicky Shen, Jewel Simmons, Ted Smykal, Emily Soltanoff, William Speiser, Jayne Stevenson, Richard Sullivan, Dan Tanguay, Dennis Tarwood, Susan Tauer, Tiffany Taylor-Sullivan, Catherine Terwilliger, Mark Tricca, Maria Torti, Leonid Tunik, Ilana Van Veen, Lauren Van Wart, John Vaughan, Laura Vivenzio, Samuel Voigt, Kathy Warfel, Don Weide, Laura Wheel, Eric Whitfield, Sequoia Wild, Joseph Will, Kristin Winters, Allison Wyss, Dina Zolotusky

**Additional Credits:** Michele Cardin, Robert Carlson, Kate Dalton-Hoffman, Dana Guterman, Narae Maybeth, Carolyn McGuire, Manjula Nair, Rachel Terino, Steve Thomas

## Illustration

**Stephen Durke:** 574; **Phil Guzy:** 596, 597; **Rob Schuster:** 4, 5, 11, 18, 26, 33, 39, 41, 48, 60, 68, 74, 81, 84, 99, 107, 114, 116, 134, 142, 143, 149, 157, 165, 166, 168, 171, 174, 194, 202, 207, 216, 226, 233, 240, 258, 280, 288, 294, 296, 303, 308, 312, 325, 326, 331, 367, 374, 375, 381, 390, 395, 398, 405, 414, 429, 434, 449, 451, 469, 498, 515, 522, 527, 534, 542, 547, 564, 566, 567, 570, 571, 572, 580, 587, 595, 609, 614, 617, 619, 630, 638, 641, 653, 855 4, 5, 11, 18, 26, 33, 39, 41, 48, 60, 68, 74, 81, 84, 99, 107, 114, 116, 134, 142, 143, 149, 157, 165, 166, 168, 171, 174, 194, 202, 207, 216, 226, 233, 240, 258, 280, 288, 294, 296, 303, 308, 312, 325, 326, 331, 367, 374, 375, 381, 390, 395, 398, 405, 414, 429, 434, 449, 451, 469, 498, 515, 522, 527, 534, 542, 547, 564, 566, 567, 570, 571, 572, 580, 587, 595, 609, 614, 617, 619, 630, 638, 641, 653, 855; **Ted Smykel:** 209; **Pearson Education:** 596, 597; **Judi Pinkham:** 230; **Pronk&Associates:** 12, 362, 399, 462, 589; **XNR Productions:** 780

## Technical Illustration

GGS Book Services

## Photographs

Every effort has been made to secure permission and provide appropriate credit for photographic material. The publisher deeply regrets any omission and pledges to correct errors called to its attention in subsequent editions.

Unless otherwise acknowledged, all photographs are the property of Pearson Education, Inc.

Photo locators denoted as follows: Top (T), Center (C), Bottom (B), Left (L), Right (R), Background (Bkgd)

### Cover

JL Klein & ML Hubert/Biosphoto

### Front Matter

**ix, x, xviii** Peter Mason/Getty Images; **xii** Jeff Greenberg/PhotoEdit, Inc. **3** (T) Franck Seguin/Corbis; **28** (T) BL Images Ltd/Alamy Images; **39** (TR) Richard Wahlstrom/Workbook/Jupiter Images/Getty Images; **45** (TR) UPI Photo/Roger Williams/NewsCom; **59** (T) Joe McBride/Getty Images; **61** (TR, TCR, CR, CC) Jupiter Images/Brand X/Alamy, (TC) Roberto Mettifogo/Getty Images; **84** (BCR) William Harader, (BR) Zen Shui/SuperStock; **133** (T) Hisham Ibrahim/Getty Images; **135** (CR) Doug Perrine/Peter Arnold Inc./PhotoLibrary Group, Inc./Getty Images, (TCR) Paul Nicklen/National Geographic Image Collection; **159** (TCR) Andy Crawford/©DK Images, (TCR) Getty Images, (TC) Steve Gorton/©DK Images; **164** (BR) Image Source/Getty Images; **193** (T) Massimo Borchi/Corbis; **198** (T) Design Pics Inc/Alamy; **205** (TR) Jeff Greenberg/PhotoEdit, Inc.; **210** (TR) Thomas Barwick/Getty Images; **228** (TR) ©Harvey Lloyd/Getty Images, (TCR) Andy Harmer/Photo Researchers, Inc.; **234** (TR) Rolf Hicker Photography/Alamy Images; **279** (T) Claudius/zefa/Corbis; **306** (BR) James Baigrie/Botanica/Jupiter Images/Getty Images; **333** (T) Andre Gallant/Getty Images, (TC) D. Hurst/Alamy, (TCR) Mark Sytes/Alamy, (TR) Peter Cade/Getty Images; **342** AF/Fotolia; **359** (T) Jake Norton/Getty Images; **375** Wave Royalty Free/Alamy; **383** (TR) Detlev van Ravenswaay/Photo Researchers, Inc.; **392** (BC) Bob Llewellyn **408** (T) Bob Krist/Corbis; **433** (T) Peter Mason/Getty Images; **438** (TR) John Cancalosi/Alamy Images; **453** (CR) Earth Imaging/Getty Images; **467** (BR) Jerry Lodriguss/Science Photo Library/Photo Researchers, Inc.; **476** (TR) Dave King/©DK Images; **480** (TR) JPL/NASA; **497** (T) Brian Bevan/Alamy Images; **502** (TR) Chase Jarvis (R) Corbis Super RF/Alamy; **513** (TCR) NASA; **544** (TR) JPL/NASA; **563** (T) Yu Xiangquan/Corbis; **578** (CR) ©DK Images, (L) Bob Gibbons/Alamy Images, (R) John Glover/Alamy Images, (CL) Peter Anderson/©DK Images; **582** (T) Thomas J. Peterson/Alamy Images; **613** (T) Iain Masterton/Alamy Images; **625** (B) Hank Morgan/Photo Researchers, Inc.; **632** (B) George Steinmetz/Corbis; **641** (C) Museum of Science and Industry; **673** (T) Photolibrary Group, Inc.; **675** (T) Ron Chapple Stock; **684** (C) Koji Aoki/Aflo/Getty Images; **755** (T) Jim Sanborn; **767** (TR, TL) iStockphoto; **795** (TC) Wolfgang Spunbarg/PhotoEdit, Inc.; **819** (T) Ron Watts/Getty Images; **839** (CR) European Space Agency/Science Photo Library/Photo Researchers, Inc., (TCR) Steve Gorton/©DK Images; **840** (BL) David Zimmerman/Getty Images, (BR) Fnalphotos/Dreamstime LLC; **879** (TR) ART on FILE/Corbis; **881** (CR) Demetrio Carrasco/©DK Images; **895** (T) AFP PHOTO/Fabrice Coffrini/NewsCom; **913** (TR) age fotostock/SuperStock; **923** (C) mediacolor's/Alamy Images.